COMPREHENSIVE RENEWABLE ENERGY

COMPREHENSIVE RENEWABLE ENERGY

EDITOR-IN-CHIEF
Ali Sayigh
*Chairman of WREC, Director General of WREN, and
Chairman of IEI, Brighton, UK*

VOLUME 1
PHOTOVOLTAIC SOLAR ENERGY

VOLUME EDITOR
Wilfried G.J.H.M. van Sark
Utrecht University, Copernicus Institute, Utrecht, The Netherlands

ELSEVIER

AMSTERDAM BOSTON HEIDELBERG LONDON NEW YORK OXFORD
PARIS SAN DIEGO SAN FRANCISCO SINGAPORE SYDNEY TOKYO

Elsevier
Radarweg 29, PO Box 211, 1000 AE Amsterdam, The Netherlands
The Boulevard, Langford Lane, Kidlington, Oxford OX5 1GB, UK
225 Wyman Street, Waltham, MA 02451, USA

Copyright © 2012 Elsevier Ltd. All rights reserved.

4.04 Hydrogen Safety Engineering: The State-of-the-Art and Future Progress
Copyright © 2012 V Molkov

5.16 Renewable Fuels: An Automotive Perspective
Copyright © 2012 Lotus Cars Limited

The following articles are US Government works in the public domain and not subject to copyright:
1.19 Cadmium Telluride Photovoltaic Thin Film: CdTe
1.37 Solar Power Satellites
4.02 Current Perspective on Hydrogen and Fuel Cells
5.02 Historical Perspectives on Biofuels

No part of this publication may be reproduced, stored in a retrieval system or transmitted in any form or by any means electronic, mechanical, photocopying, recording or otherwise without the prior written permission of the publisher

Permissions may be sought directly from Elsevier's Science & Technology Rights Department in Oxford, UK: phone (+44) (0) 1865 843830; fax (+44) (0) 1865 853333; email: permissions@elsevier.com. Alternatively you can submit your request online by visiting the Elsevier web site at http://elsevier.com/locate/permissions, and selecting *Obtaining permission to use Elsevier material*

Notice
No responsibility is assumed by the publisher for any injury and/or damage to persons or property as a matter of products liability, negligence or otherwise, or from any use or operation of any methods, products, instructions or ideas contained in the material herein. Because of rapid advances in the medical sciences, in particular, independent verfication of diagnoses and drug dosages should be made.

British Library Cataloguing in Publication Data
A catalogue record for this book is available from the British Library

The Library of Congress Control Number: 2012934547

ISBN: 978-0-08-087872-0

For information on all Elsevier publications
visit our website at books.elsevier.com

Printed and bound in Italy

11 12 13 14 10 9 8 7 6 5 4 3 2 1

Working together to grow
libraries in developing countries

www.elsevier.com | www.bookaid.org | www.sabre.org

ELSEVIER   BOOK AID International   Sabre Foundation

Editorial: Gemma Mattingley, Joanne Williams
Production: Edward Taylor, Maggie Johnson

EDITOR-IN-CHIEF

Professor Ali Sayigh, BSc, DIC, PhD, CEng, a British citizen, graduated from Imperial College London and the University of London in 1966. He is a fellow of the Institute of Energy, a fellow of the Institution of Electrical Engineers, and is a chartered engineer.

From 1966 to 1985, Prof. Sayigh taught in the College of Engineering at the University of Baghdad and at King Saud University, Saudi Arabia, as a full-time professor, and also at Kuwait University as a part-time professor. From 1981 to 1985, he was Head of the Energy Department at the Kuwait Institute for Scientific Research (KISR) and expert in renewable energy at the Arab Organization of Petroleum Exporting Countries (AOPEC), Kuwait.

He started working in solar energy in September 1969. In 1984, he established links with Pergamon Press and became Editor-in-Chief of his first international journal, *Solar & Wind Technology*. Since 1990 he has been Editor-in-Chief of *Comprehensive Renewable Energy* incorporating *Solar & Wind Technology*, published by Elsevier Science Ltd., Oxford, UK. He is the editor of several international journals published in Morocco, Iran, Bangladesh, and Nigeria.

He has been a member of the International Society for Equitation Science (ISES) since 1973, founder and chairman of the ARAB Section of ISES since 1979, chairman of the UK Solar Energy Society for 3 years, and consultant to many national and international organizations, among them, the British Council, the Islamic Educational, Scientific and Cultural Organization (ISESCO), the United Nations Educational, Scientific and Cultural Organization (UNESCO), the United Nations Development Programme (UNDP), the Economic and Social Commission for Western Asia (ESCWA), and the United Nations Industrial Development Organization (UNIDO).

Since 1977 Prof. Sayigh has founded and directed several renewable energy conferences and workshops in the International Centre for Theoretical Physics (ICTP) – Trieste, Italy, Canada, Colombia, Algeria, Kuwait, Bahrain, Malaysia, Zambia, Malawi, India, the West Indies, Tunisia, Indonesia, Libya, Taiwan, UAE, Oman, the Czech Republic, Germany, Australia, Poland, the Netherlands, Thailand, Korea, Iran, Syria, Saudi Arabia, Singapore, China, the United States, and the United Kingdom.

In 1990 he established the World Renewable Energy Congress (WREC) and, in 1992, the World Renewable Energy Network (WREN), which hold their Congresses every 2 years, attracting more than 100 countries each time. In 2000, he and others in UAE, Sharjah, founded the Arab Science and Technology Foundation (ASTF) and regional conferences have been held in Sweden, Malaysia, Korea, Indonesia, Australia, UAE, and Libya, to name but a few. Prof. Sayigh has been running an annual international seminar on all aspects of renewable energy since 1990 in the United Kingdom and abroad. In total, 85 seminars have been held.

Prof. Sayigh supervised and graduated more than 34 PhD students and 64 MSc students at Reading University and the University of Hertfordshire when he was a professor from 1986 to 2004.

He has edited, contributed, and written more than 32 books and published more than 500 papers in various international journals and conferences.

In 2000–09, he initiated and worked closely with Sovereign Publication Company to produce the most popular magazine at annual bases called *Renewable Energy*, which was distributed freely to more than 6000 readers around the world. Presently, he is the editor-in-chief of *Comprehensive Renewable Energy*, coordinating 154 top scientists', engineers', and researchers' contributions in eight volumes published by Elsevier Publishing Company, Oxford, UK.

VOLUME EDITORS

Dr. Wilfried G. J. H. M. van Sark graduated from Utrecht University, the Netherlands, with an MSc in experimental physics in 1985, and with an MSc thesis on measurement and analysis of I–V characteristics of c-Si cells. He received his PhD from Nijmegen University, the Netherlands; the topic of his PhD thesis was III–V solar cell development, modeling, and processing. He then spent 7 years as a postdoc/senior researcher at Utrecht University and specialized in a-Si:H cell deposition and analysis. He is an expert in plasma chemical vapor deposition, both radio frequency and very high frequency. After an assistant professor position at Nijmegen University, where he worked on III–V solar cells, he returned to Utrecht University, with a focus on (single-molecule) confocal fluorescence microscopy of nanocrystals. In 2002, he moved to his present position as assistant professor at the research group Science, Technology and Society of the Copernicus Institute at Utrecht University, the Netherlands, where he performed and coordinated research on next-generation photovoltaic devices incorporating nanocrystals; for example, luminescent solar concentrators, as well as photovoltaic performance, life cycle analysis, socioeconomics, and policy development. He is member of the editorial board of Elsevier's scientific journal *Renewable Energy*, and member of various organizing committees of the European Union, the Institute of Electrical and Electronics Engineers (IEEE), and the SPIE PV conferences. He is author or coauthor of over 200 peer-reviewed journal and conference paper publications and book chapters. He has (co-)edited three books, including the present one.

Professor John K. Kaldellis holds a mechanical engineering degree from the National Technical University of Athens (NTUA) and a business administration diploma from the University of Piraeus. He obtained his PhD from NTUA (Fluid Sector) sponsored by Snecma–Dassault, France, and Bodossakis Foundation, Greece. He is currently the head of the Mechanical Engineering Department and since 1991 the director of the Soft Energy Applications and Environmental Protection Laboratory of the Technological Education Institute (TEI) of Piraeus. Prof. Kaldellis is also the scientific director (for TEI of Piraeus) of the MSc in Energy program organized by Heriot-Watt University and TEI of Piraeus. His scientific expertise is in the fields of energy and the environment. His research interests include feasibility analysis of energy sector applications; technological progress in wind, hydro, and solar energy markets; hybrid energy systems; energy storage issues; social attitudes toward renewable energy applications; and environmental technology–atmospheric pollution. He has participated in numerous research projects, funded by the European Union, European/Greek Industries, and the Greek State. Prof. Kaldellis has published six books concerning renewable energy applications and environmental protection. He is also the author of more than 100 scientific/research papers in international peer-reviewed journals and more than 300 papers for international scientific conferences. During the last decade, he was also a member of the Scientific Committee of the Hellenic Society of Mechanical–Electrical Engineers as well as a member of the organizing and scientific committee of several national and international conferences. He is currently a member of the editorial board of the *Renewable Energy International* journal and reviewer in more than 40 international journals in the energy and environment sector. He is the editor of the book *Stand-Alone and Hybrid Wind Energy Systems: Technology, Energy Storage and Applications* that has recently been published.

Dr. Soteris A. Kalogirou is a senior lecturer at the Department of Mechanical Engineering and Materials Science and Engineering at the Cyprus University of Technology, Limassol, Cyprus. He received his Higher Technical Institute (HTI) degree in mechanical engineering in 1982, his MPhil in mechanical engineering from the Polytechnic of Wales in 1991, and his PhD in mechanical engineering from the University of Glamorgan in 1995. In June 2011, he received the title of DSc from the University of Glamorgan.

For more than 25 years, he has been actively involved in research in the area of solar energy and particularly in flat-plate and concentrating collectors, solar water heating, solar steam generating systems, desalination, and absorption cooling. Additionally, since 1995, he has been involved in pioneering research dealing with the use of artificial intelligence methods, such as artificial neural networks, genetic algorithms, and fuzzy logic, for the modeling and performance prediction of energy and solar energy systems.

He has 29 books and book contributions and published 225 papers, 97 in international scientific journals and 128 in refereed conference proceedings. To date he has received more than 2550 citations on this work. He is Executive Editor of *Energy*, Associate Editor of *Renewable Energy*, and Editorial Board Member of another 11 journals. He is the editor of the book *Artificial Intelligence in Energy and Renewable Energy Systems*, published by Nova Science Inc.; coeditor of the book *Soft Computing in Green and Renewable Energy Systems*, published by Springer; and author of the book *Solar Energy Engineering: Processes and Systems*, published by Academic Press of Elsevier.

He has been a member of the World Renewable Energy Network (WREN) since 1992 and is a member of the Chartered Institution of Building Services Engineers (CIBSE), the American Society of Heating Refrigeration and Air-Conditioning Engineers (ASHRAE), the Institute of Refrigeration (IoR), and the International Solar Energy Society (ISES).

Dr. Andrew Cruden, a British citizen, was born in 1968. He obtained his BEng, MSc, and PhD in electrical engineering from the University of Strathclyde and CEng, MIEE Dr. Cruden is a past member of BSI GEL/105 Committee on Fuel Cells and Committee member of the IET Scotland Power Section. He is Director of the Scottish Hydrogen and Fuel Cell Association (SHFCA; www.shfca.org.uk) and Director of Argyll, Lomond and the Islands Energy Agency (www.alienergy.org.uk).

Dr. Cruden has been active in the field of hydrogen and fuel cells since 1995, when he acted as a consultant for Zevco Ltd., providing assistance with power electronic interfaces for early fuel cell systems. Later in 1998, he helped found the Scottish Fuel Cell Consortium (SFCC), supported by the Scottish Enterprise Energy Team, which ultimately developed a battery/fuel cell hybrid electric vehicle based on an AC Cobra kit car. The experience and contacts from the SFCC eventually gave rise to the formation of the Scottish Hydrogen and Fuel Cell Association (SHFCA), a trade body for the industry to promote and commercialize Scottish expertise in this field. Dr. Cruden was the founding chairman of the SHFCA.

Dr. Cruden is currently investigating alkaline electrolyzers in terms of improving their part load efficiency and lifetime when powered by variable renewable power sources, for example, wind turbines, as part of a £5 million EPSRC Supergen project on the 'Delivery of Sustainable Hydrogen' (EP/G01244X/1). He is also working with a colleague within Electronic and Electrical Engineering (EEE) at Strathclyde, studying the concept of vehicle-to-grid energy storage, as a mechanism not only to allow controlled load leveling on the power system, but also to potentially 'firm' up renewable energy generation. This work is supported by two research grants, an international E.On Research Initiative 2007 award and an ESPRC grant (EP/F062133/1).

Dr. Cruden is a senior lecturer within the Department of Electronic and Electrical Engineering at the University of Strathclyde. His current fields of research are modeling fuel cell and electrolyzer systems, fuel cell combined heat and power (CHP) systems, power electronic devices for interfacing both vehicular and stationary fuel cell systems, condition monitoring systems for renewable energy sources (i.e., wind turbines as part of EPSRC Supergen on Wind Energy Technologies, EP/D034566/1), and energy management systems for hybrid electric vehicles.

His areas of expertise include hydrogen-powered fuel cells and electrolyzers, energy storage for electric vehicles, and renewable energy generation.

Professor Dermot J. Roddy, BSc, PhD, CEng, FIET, joined Newcastle University as Science City Professor of Energy in 2008 after a period of some 20 years in the energy industry and petrochemical sectors. He is also Director of the Sir Joseph Swan Centre for Energy Research, which integrates energy research across Newcastle University and links with a powerful external industrial base in the energy sector. Outside of the university he is Chairman of Northeast Biofuels, Finance Director of the UK Hydrogen Association, and Vice-President of the Northern England Electricity Supply Companies Association. Prior to coming to Newcastle University, he was Chief Executive of Renew Tees Valley Ltd. – a company which he set up in 2003 to create a viable and vibrant economy in the Tees Valley based on renewable energy and recycling – where he was instrumental in a wide range of major renewable energy and low-carbon projects relating to biomass, biofuels, hydrogen, carbon capture and storage, wind, and advanced waste processing technologies. From 1998 to 2002, he ran the crude oil refinery on Teesside as a site director for a $5 billion turnover facility before moving to the Netherlands to work on Petroplus' international growth plans. Roddy's experience in the petrochemical industry began in 1985, involving a variety of UK and international roles in operations, engineering, and technology with ICI and others. Prior to that he developed leading-edge technology at Queen's University, Belfast, for optimization and control in aerospace applications.

André G. H. Lejeune was born on 2 August 1942 in Belgium. He was graduated in 1967 as a civil engineer, in 1972 as doctor in applied sciences (PhD), and in 1973 as master in oceanography in the University of Liège in Belgium. He was appointed full-time professor in the same university in 1976, and was visitor professor at the UNESCO–IHE Institute for Water Education in the Netherlands and Ecole Polytechnique Fédérale de Lausanne (EPFL) in Switzerland. Within the framework of his activities of professor, director of the Hydraulic Constructions and Hydraulic Research Laboratory, and expert, he took part in studies of dams and hydraulic structures and went on site in more than 90 countries of the world. In particular, he was for the last 6 years the chairman of the Technical Committee on Hydraulics for Dams in ICOLD (International Commission of Large Dams). He is a member of the Belgian Royal Academy of Sciences. He made his PhD thesis in hydraulic numerical modelization. This thesis received the Lorenz G. Straub Award in Minneapolis, USA (H. Einstein Jr. was a member of the Jury), and was used in particular by Chinese colleagues in the Three Gorges Project. Due to his practice and experience, he has a very complete knowledge of the hydraulic phenomena modelizations through both numerical and physical means.

With his wife, he has 3 children and 11 grandchildren. He likes books, tennis, and diving.

Thorsteinn I. Sigfusson is an internationally recognised physicist, educated in Copenhagen, Denmark, and Cambridge, UK. He is Director-General of the Innovation Center, Iceland and Professor of physics at the University of Iceland. He has been a visiting professor at Columbia University, New York, and he is currently the lead scientist in a prize-winning energy technology project performed at Tomsk Polytechnic University in Tomsk, Russia.

He has been a key figure in the introduction of new ideas and opportunities in the further greening of Icelandic society through the energy industry, and instrumental in the challenge of saving imported hydrocarbons by focusing on hydrogen from renewable energy.

He has started over a dozen start-up companies from research in Iceland and chaired various international societies in alternative energy. Among his achievements in geothermal energy is the construction of the world's largest solid-state thermoelectric generator powered with geothermal steam in southern Iceland. At the Innovation Center, Iceland, efforts are made to develop materials to withstand erosion in geothermal environments.

Volume Editors

AbuBakr S. Bahaj is Professor of Sustainable Energy at the University of Southampton. After completing his PhD, he was employed by the University, progressing from a researcher to a personnel chair of Sustainable Energy. Over the past 20 years, Prof. Bahaj has established the energy theme within the University and directed his Sustainable Energy Research Group (SERG, www.energy.soton.ac.uk), which is now considered to be one of the United Kingdoms's leading university-based research groups in renewable energy and energy in buildings. He initiated and managed research in ocean energy conversion (resources, technologies, and impacts), photovoltaics, energy in buildings, and impacts of climate change on the built environment in the University. This work has resulted in over 230 articles published in academic refereed journals and conference series of international standing (see www.energy.soton.ac.uk).

Prof. Bahaj is the head of the Energy and Climate Change Division (ECCD) within the highly rated Faculty of Engineering and the Environment – Civil Engineering and the Environment – (www.civil.soton.ac.uk/research/divisions/divlist.asp?ResearchGroupID=1) (second in the United Kingdom, Research Assessment Exercise in 2008, with 80% of research judged to be either 'World Leading' or 'Internationally Excellent'). The aims of the Division and SERG are to promote and execute fundamental and applied research and preindustrial development in the areas of energy resources, technologies, energy efficiency, and the impact of climate change.

Prof. Bahaj is an experienced research team director and has many internationally focused research projects including collaborative projects in China, the European Union, the Middle East, and Africa. He also coordinated (2006–10) the United Kingdom's Engineering and Physical Sciences Research Council (EPSRC), Ecoregion Research Networks that aim to develop research themes and projects to study eco-city development encompassing resource assessment, technology pathways for the production and conservation of energy, planning, and social and economic studies required in establishing eco-regions in China and elsewhere (http://www.eco-networks.org). He is a founding member of the Sino-UK Low Carbon City Development Cooperation (LCCD) which aims to promote and undertake research into pathways for low-carbon development in Chinese cities. His work also encompasses an ongoing multimillion pound program in Africa, 'Energy for Development' for promoting and implementing village electrification systems, addressing villager's needs, and establishing coherent approaches to the commercial sustainability of the projects. This program is funded by the Research Councils and the UK Department for International Development (DFID; www.energyfordevelopment.net).

Prof. Bahaj is the editor-in-chief of the *International Journal of Sustainable Energy* and associate Editor of the *Renewable & Sustainable Energy Review*. He was on the editorial boards of the journals *Sustainable Cities and Society* and *Renewable Energy* (2005–11), and the United Kingdom's Institute of Civil Engineering journal *Energy* (2006–09). He was a member of the Tyndall Centre for Climate Change Research Supervisory Board (2005–10), and from 2001 to 2007 he was a member of the UK Government Department of Business, Enterprise and Regulatory Reform (now Department for Business Innovations and Skills, BIS), Technology Programmes Panels on Water (including ocean energy) and Solar Energy, now being administered by the Technology Strategy Board (TSB). Prof. Bahaj was the chair of the Technical Committees of the World Renewable Energy Congress – held in Glasgow (July 2008) and in Abu Dhabi (September 2010). He was a member of the Technical Committee of the 27th International Conference on Offshore Mechanics and Arctic Engineering (OMAE, 2008), a member of the management and technical committees of the European Wave and Tidal Energy Conferences (EWTEC, Porto, Portugal, September 2007; and Uppsala, Sweden, September 2009). He is also a member of the British Standards Institution (BSI) Committee GEL/82 on PV Energy Systems. Recently, at the invitation of the International Energy Agency, he has completed the 2008 status report on tidal stream energy conversion and in September 2009 was elected to chair the next EWTEC conference in the series – EWTEC2011 which was held in Southampton, 5–9 September 2011, and attended by around 500 participants.

To address training in the areas of energy and climate change Prof. Bahaj has coordinated and developed a set of MSc programs under the banner 'Energy and Sustainability' that address Energy Resources and Climate Change and Energy, Environment and Buildings.

CONTRIBUTORS FOR ALL VOLUMES

P Agnolucci
Imperial College London, London, UK

EO Ahlgren
Chalmers University of Technology, Gothenburg, Sweden

D Aklil
Pure Energy Center, Unst, Shetland Isles, UK

D-C Alarcón Padilla
Centro de Investigaciones Energéticas Medioambientales y Tecnológicas (CIEMAT), Plataforma Solar de Almeria, Almeria, Spain

K Alexander
University of Canterbury, Christchurch, New Zealand

S Alexopoulos
Aachen University of Applied Sciences, Jülich, Germany

A Altieri
UNICA – Brazilian Sugarcane Industry Association, São Paulo, Brazil

A Anthrakidis
Aachen University of Applied Sciences, Jülich, Germany

E Antolín
Universidad Politécnica de Madrid, Madrid, Spain

P Archambeau
University of Liège, Liège, Belgium

H Ármannsson
Iceland GeoSurvey (ISOR), Reykjavík, Iceland

MF Askew
Wolverhampton, UK

A Athienitis
Concordia University, Montreal, QC, Canada

G Axelsson
University of Iceland, Reykjavik, Iceland

V Badescu
Polytechnic University of Bucharest, Bucharest, Romania

AS Bahaj
The University of Southampton, Southampton, UK

P Banda
Instituto de Sistema Fotovoltaicos de Concentración (ISFOC), Puertollano, Spain

VG Belessiotis
'DEMOKRITOS' National Center for Scientific Research, Athens, Greece

P Berry
ADAS High Mowthorpe, Malton, UK

F Bidault
Imperial College London, London, UK

D Biro
Fraunhofer Institute for Solar Energy Systems, Freiburg, Germany

G Boschloo
Uppsala University, Uppsala, Sweden

C Boura
Aachen University of Applied Sciences, Jülich, Germany

E Bozorgzadeh
Iran Water and Power Resources Development Company (IWPCO), Tehran, Iran

CE Brewer
Iowa State University, Ames, IA, USA

M Börjesson
Chalmers University of Technology, Gothenburg, Sweden

RC Brown
Iowa State University, Ames, IA, USA

F Bueno
University of Burgos, Burgos, Spain

K Burke
NASA Glenn Research Center, Cleveland, OH, USA

LF Cabeza
GREA Innovació Concurrent, Universitat de Lleida, Lleida, Spain

L Candanedo
Dublin Institute of Technology, Dublin, Ireland

YG Caouris
University of Patras, Patras, Greece

UB Cappel
Uppsala University, Uppsala, Sweden

JA Carta
Universidad de Las Palmas de Gran Canaria, Las Palmas de Gran Canaria, Spain

P Chen
Dalian Institute of Chemical Physics, Dalian, China

DG Christakis
Wind Energy Laboratory, Technological Educational Institute of Crete, Crete, Greece

DA Chwieduk
Warsaw University of Technology, Warsaw, Poland

J Clark
University of York, York, UK

G Conibeer
University of New South Wales, Sydney, NSW, Australia

AJ Cruden
University of Strathclyde, Glasgow, UK

MC da Silva

B Davidsdottir
University of Iceland, Reykjavík, Iceland

O de la Rubia
Instituto de Sistema Fotovoltaicos de Concentración (ISFOC), Puertollano, Spain

E Despotou
Formerly of the European Photovoltaic Industry Association, Brussels, Belgium

BJ Dewals
University of Liège, Liège, Belgium

AL Dicks
The University of Queensland, Brisbane, QLD, Australia

R DiPippo
University of Massachusetts Dartmouth, Dartmouth, MA, USA

E Dunlop
European Commission DG Joint Research Centre, Ispra, Italy

NM Duteanu
Newcastle University, Newcastle upon Tyne, UK;
University 'POLITEHNICA' Timisoara, Timisoara, Romania

LM Eaton
Oak Ridge National Laboratory, Oak Ridge, TN, USA

H-J Egelhaaf
Konarka Technologies GmbH, Nürnberg, Germany

T Ehara
Mizuho Information & Research Institute, Tokyo, Japan

B Erable
Newcastle University, Newcastle upon Tyne, UK;
CNRS-Université de Toulouse, Toulouse, France

S Erpicum
University of Liège, Liège, Belgium

G Evans
NNFCC, Biocentre, Innovation Way, Heslington, York, UK

AFO Falcão
Instituto Superior Técnico, Technical University of Lisbon, Lisbon, Portugal

G Faninger
University of Klagenfurt, Klagenfurt, Austria; Vienna University of Technology, Vienna, Austria

GA Florides
Cyprus University of Technology, Limassol, Cyprus

ÓG Flóvenz
Iceland GeoSurvey (ISOR), Reykjavík, Iceland

RN Frese
VU University Amsterdam, Amsterdam, The Netherlands

Þ Friðriksson
Iceland GeoSurvey (ISOR), Reykjavík, Iceland

VM Fthenakis
Columbia University, New York, NY, USA; Brookhaven National Laboratory, Upton, NY, USA

M Fuamba
École Polytechnique de Montréal, Montreal, QC, Canada

A Fuller
University of Canterbury, Christchurch, New Zealand

LMC Gato
Instituto Superior Técnico, Technical University of Lisbon, Lisbon, Portugal

R Gazey
Pure Energy Center, Unst, Shetland Isles, UK

TA Gessert
National Renewable Energy Laboratory (NREL), Golden, CO, USA

MM Ghangrekar
*Newcastle University, Newcastle upon Tyne, UK;
Indian Institute of Technology, Kharagpur, India*

M Giannouli
University of Patras, Patras, Greece

EA Gibson
University of Nottingham, Nottingham UK

A Gil
Hydropower Generation Division of Iberdrola, Salamanca, Spain

SW Glunz
Fraunhofer Institute for Solar Energy Systems, Freiburg, Germany

JC Goldschmidt
Fraunhofer Institute for Solar Energy Systems ISE, Freiburg, Germany

R Gottschalg
Loughborough University, Leicestershire, UK

MA Green
The University of New South Wales, Sydney, NSW, Australia

J Göttsche
Aachen University of Applied Sciences, Jülich, Germany

J Guo
China Institute of Water Resources and Hydropower Research (IWHR), Beijing, China

A Hagfeldt
Uppsala University, Uppsala, Sweden

B Hagin
Ingénieur-Conseil, Lutry, Switzerland

K Hall
Technology Transition Corporation, Ltd., Tyne and Wear, UK

O Hamandjoda
University of Yaounde, Yaounde, Republic of Cameroon

AP Harvey
Newcastle University, Newcastle upon Tyne, UK

JA Hauch
Konarka Technologies GmbH, Nürnberg, Germany

D Heinemann
University of Oldenburg, Oldenburg, Germany

V Heller
Imperial College London, London, UK

GP Hersir
Iceland GeoSurvey (ISOR), Reykjavík, Iceland

T Heyer
Technical University of Dresden, Dresden, Germany

P Hilger
Aachen University of Applied Sciences, Jülich, Germany

B Hillring
Swedish University of Agricultural Sciences, Skinnskatteberg, Sweden

T Hino
CTI Engineering International Co., Ltd., Chu-o-Ku, Japan

LC Hirst
Imperial College London, London, UK

B Hoffschmidt
Aachen University of Applied Sciences, Jülich, Germany

H Horlacher
Technical University of Dresden, Dresden, Germany

N Hughes
Imperial College London, London, UK

SL Hui
Bechtel Civil Company, San Francisco, CA, USA

D Husmann
University of Wisconsin–Madison, Madison, WI, USA

JTS Irvine
University of St Andrews, St Andrews, UK

D Jacobs
Freie Universität Berlin, Berlin, Germany

Y Jestin
Advanced Photonics and Photovoltaics Group, Bruno Kessler Foundation, Trento, Italy

A Jäger-Waldau
Institution for Energy Transport, Ispra, Italy

S Jianxia
Design and Research Institute, Yangzhou City, Jiangsu Province, China

E Johnson
Pure Energy Center, Unst, Shetland Isles, UK

HF Kaan
TNO Energy, Comfort and Indoor Quality, Delft, The Netherlands

JK Kaldellis
Technological Education Institute of Piraeus, Athens, Greece

SA Kalogirou
Cyprus University of Technology, Limassol, Cyprus

HD Kambezidis
Institute of Environmental Research and Sustainable Development, Athens, Greece

M Kapsali
Technological Education Institute of Piraeus, Athens, Greece

M Karimirad
Norwegian University of Science and Technology, Trondheim, Norway

T Karlessi
National and Kapodistrian University of Athens, Athens, Greece

SN Karlsdóttir
Innovation Center Iceland, Iceland

D Al Katsaprakakis
Wind Energy Laboratory, Technological Educational Institute of Crete, Crete, Greece

O Kaufhold
Aachen University of Applied Sciences, Jülich, Germany

CA Kaufmann
Helmholtz Zentrum für Materialien und Energie GmbH, Berlin, Germany

KA Kavadias
Technological Education Institute of Piraeus, Athens, Greece

LL Kazmerski
National Renewable Energy Laboratory, Golden, CO, USA

A Kazmi
University of York, York, UK

K Kendall
University of Birmingham, Birmingham, UK

J Kenfack
University of Yaounde, Yaounde, Republic of Cameroon

R Kenny
European Commission DG Joint Research Centre, Ispra, Italy

HC Kim
Brookhaven National Laboratory, Upton, NY, USA

L Kloo
KTH—Royal Institute of Technology, Stockholm, Sweden

G Knothe
USDA Agricultural Research Service, Peoria, IL, USA

FR Kogler
Konarka Technologies GmbH, Nürnberg, Germany

D Kolokotsa
Technical University of Crete, Crete, Greece

K Komoto
Mizuho Information & Research Institute, Tokyo, Japan

E Kondili
Technological Education Institute of Piraeus, Athens, Greece

H Kristjánsdóttir
University of Iceland, Reykjavík, Iceland

LA Lamont
Petroleum Institute, Abu Dhabi, UAE

GA Landis
NASA Glenn Research Center, Cleveland, OH, USA

JGM Lee
Newcastle University, Newcastle upon Tyne, UK

G Leftheriotis
University of Patras, Patras, Greece

A Lejeune
University of Liège, Liège, Belgium

T Leo
FuelCell Energy Inc., Danbury, CT, USA

E Lester
The University of Nottingham, Nottingham, UK

E Lorenz
University of Oldenburg, Oldenburg, Germany

JW Lund
Geo-Heat Center, Oregon Institute of Technology, Klamath Falls, OR, USA

A Luque
Universidad Politécnica de Madrid, Madrid, Spain

BP Machado
Intertechne, Curitiba, PR, Brazil

EBL Mackay
GL Garrad Hassan, Bristol, UK

T-F Mahdi
École Polytechnique de Montréal, Montreal, QC, Canada

GG Maidment
London South Bank University, London, UK

A Malmgren
BioC Ltd, Cirencester, UK

C Manson-Whitton
Progressive Energy Ltd., Stonehouse, UK

Á Margeirsson
Magma Energy Iceland, Reykjanesbaer, Iceland

A Martí
Universidad Politécnica de Madrid, Madrid, Spain

M Martinez
Instituto de Sistema Fotovoltaicos de Concentración (ISFOC), Puertollano, Spain

S Mathew
University of Brunei Darussalam, Gadong, Brunei Darussalam

PH Middleton
University of Agder, Grimstad, Norway

R Mikalsen
Newcastle University, Newcastle upon Tyne, UK

D Milborrow
Lewes, East Sussex, UK

H Müllejans
European Commission DG Joint Research Centre, Ispra, Italy

V Molkov
University of Ulster, Newtownabbey, Northern Ireland, UK

M Moner-Girona
Joint Research Centre, European Commission, Institute for Energy and Transport, Ispra, Italy

PE Morthorst
Technical University of Denmark, Roskilde, Denmark

N Mortimer
North Energy Associates Ltd, Sheffield, UK

E Mullins
Teagasc, Oak Park Crops Research Centre, Carlow, Republic of Ireland

P Mulvihill
Pioneer Generation Ltd., Alexandra, New Zealand

DR Myers
National Renewable Energy Laboratory, USA

D Nash
University of Strathclyde, Glasgow, UK

GF Nemet
University of Wisconsin–Madison, Madison, WI, USA

H Nfaoui
Mohammed V University, Rabat, Morocco

T Nikolakakis
Columbia University, New York, NY, USA

X Niu
Changjiang Institute of Survey, Planning, Design and Research, Wuhan, China

B Norton
Dublin Institute of Technology, Dublin, Ireland

A Nuamah
The University of Nottingham, Nottingham, UK; RWE npower, Swindon, UK

B O'Connor
Aachen University of Applied Sciences, Jülich, Germany

O Olsson
Swedish University of Agricultural Sciences, Skinnskatteberg, Sweden

V Ortisi
Pure Energy Center, Unst, Shetland Isles, UK

H Ossenbrink
European Commission DG Joint Research Centre, Ispra, Italy

AG Paliatsos
Technological Education Institute of Piraeus, Athens, Greece

A Pandit
VU University Amsterdam, Amsterdam, The Netherlands

E Papanicolaou
'DEMOKRITOS' National Center for Scientific Research, Athens, Greece

A Paurine
London South Bank University, London, UK

N Pearsall
Northumbria University, Newcastle, UK

RJ Pearson
Lotus Engineering, Norwich, UK

RD Perlack
Oak Ridge National Laboratory, Oak Ridge, TN, USA

H Pettersson
Swerea IVF AB, Mölndal, Sweden

GS Philip
KCAET, Malapuram, Kerala, India

S Pillai
The University of New South Wales, Sydney, NSW, Australia

M Pirotton
University of Liège, Liège, Belgium

BG Pollet
University of Birmingham, Birmingham, UK

D Porter
Association of Electricity Producers, London, UK

A Pouliezos
Technical University of Crete, Hania, Greece

R Preu
Fraunhofer Institute for Solar Energy Systems, Freiburg, Germany

CM Ramos

C Rau
Aachen University of Applied Sciences, Jülich, Germany

AA Refaat
Cairo University, Giza, Egypt

TH Reijenga
BEARiD Architecten, Rotterdam, The Netherlands

AHME Reinders
Delft University of Technology, Delft, The Netherlands; University of Twente, Enschede, The Netherlands

G Riley
RWE npower, Swindon, UK

DJ Roddy
Newcastle University, Newcastle upon Tyne, UK

S Rolland
Alliance for Rural Electrification, Brussels, Belgium

A Roskilly
Newcastle University, Newcastle upon Tyne, UK

F Rubio
Instituto de Sistema Fotovoltaicos de Concentración (ISFOC), Puertollano, Spain

F Rulot
University of Liège, Liège, Belgium

L Rybach
GEOWATT AG, Zurich, Switzerland

M Santamouris
National and Kapodistrian University of Athens, Athens, Greece

J Sattler
Aachen University of Applied Sciences, Jülich, Germany

M Sauerborn
Aachen University of Applied Sciences, Jülich, Germany

TW Schmidt
The University of Sydney, Sydney, NSW, Australia

N Schofield
University of Manchester, Manchester, UK

REI Schropp
Utrecht University, Utrecht, The Netherlands

K Scott
Newcastle University, Newcastle upon Tyne, UK

SP Sen
NHPC Ltd., New Delhi, India

TI Sigfusson
Innovation Center, Reykjavik, Iceland

L Sims
Konarka Technologies GmbH, Nürnberg, Germany; Universität Augsburg, Augsburg, Germany

C Smith
NNFCC, Biocentre, Innovation Way, Heslington, York, UK

K Sæmundsson
Iceland GeoSurvey (ISOR), Reykjavík, Iceland

BK Sovacool
Vermont Law School, South Royalton, VT, USA

J Spink
Teagasc, Oak Park Crops Research Centre, Carlow, Republic of Ireland

JN Sørensen
Technical University of Denmark, Lyngby, Denmark

T Stallard
The University of Manchester, Manchester, UK

GS Stavrakakis
Technical University of Crete, Chania, Greece

R Steim
Konarka Technologies GmbH, Nürnberg, Germany

BJ Stokes
CNJV LLC, Washington, DC, USA

L Sun
KTH—Royal Institute of Technology, Stockholm, Sweden; Dalian University of Technology (DUT), Dalian, China

L Suo
Science and Technology Committee of the Ministry of Water Resources, Beijing, China

DT Swift-Hook
Kingston University, London, UK; World Renewable Energy Network, Brighton, UK

A Synnefa
National and Kapodistrian University of Athens, Athens, Greece

S Szabo
Joint Research Centre, European Commission, Institute for Energy and Transport, Ispra, Italy

MJY Tayebjee
The University of Sydney, Sydney, NSW, Australia

A Tesfai
University of St Andrews, St Andrews, UK

P Thornley
The University of Manchester, Manchester, UK

Y Tripanagnostopoulos
University of Patras, Patras, Greece

L Tsakalakos
General Electric – Global Research Center, New York, NY, USA

JWG Turner
Lotus Engineering, Norwich, UK

E Tzen
Centre for Renewable Energy Sources and Saving (CRES), Pikermi, Attica, Greece

T Unold
Helmholtz Zentrum für Materialien und Energie GmbH, Berlin, Germany

J van der Heide
imec vzw, Leuven, Belgium

P van der Vleuten
Free Energy Consulting, Eindhoven, The Netherlands

F Van Hulle
XP Wind Consultancy, Leuven, Belgium

GC van Kooten
University of Victoria, Victoria, BC, Canada

WGJHM van Sark
Utrecht University, Utrecht, The Netherlands

I Waller
FiveBarGate Consultants Ltd, Cleveland, UK

I Walsh
Opus International Consultants Ltd., New Zealand

Y Wang
Newcastle University, Newcastle upon Tyne, UK

T Wizelius
Gotland University, Visby, Sweden; Lund University, Lund, Sweden

LL Wright
University of Tennessee, Knoxville, TN, USA

H Xie
Changjiang Institute of Survey, Planning, Design and Research, Wuhan, China

M Yamaguchi
Toyota Technological Institute, Tempaku, Nagoya, Japan

P Yianoulis
University of Patras, Patras, Greece

EH Yu
Newcastle University, Newcastle upon Tyne, UK

H Yu
Newcastle University, Newcastle upon Tyne, UK

DP Zafirakis
Technological Education Institute of Piraeus, Athens, Greece

G Zaragoza
Centro de Investigaciones Energéticas Medioambientales y Tecnológicas (CIEMAT), Plataforma Solar de Almeria, Almeria, Spain

M Zeman
Delft University of Technology, Delft, The Netherlands

PREFACE

Comprehensive Renewable Energy is the only multivolume reference work of its type at a time when renewable energy sources are increasingly in demand and realistically sustainable, clean, and helping to combat climate change and global warming. Renewable energy investment has exceeded US$10 billion per year during the past 5 years. The World Renewable Energy Network (WREN) predicts that this figure is set to increase to US$20 billion per year by 2015.

As Editor-in-Chief, I have assembled an impressive world-class team of 154 volume editors and contributing authors for the eight volumes. They represent policy makers, researchers, industrialists, financiers, and heads of organizations from more than 80 countries to produce this definitive complete work in renewable energy covering the past, explaining the present, and giving the ideas and prospects of development for the future. There are more than 1000 references from books, journals, and the Internet within the eight volumes. *Comprehensive Renewable Energy* is full of color charts, illustrations, and photographs of real projects and research results from around the world. Each chapter has been painstakingly reviewed and checked for consistent high quality. The result is an authoritative overview that ties the literature together and provides the user with reliable background information and a citation resource.

The field of renewable energy research and development is represented by many journals that are directly and indirectly concerned with the field. But no reference work encompasses the entire field and unites the different areas of research through in-depth foundational reviews. *Comprehensive Renewable Energy* fills this vacuum, and is the definitive work for this subject area. It will help users apply context to diverse journal literature, aiding them in identifying areas for further research and development.

Research into renewable energy is spread across a number of different disciplines and subject areas. These areas do not always share a unique identifying factor or subject themselves to clear and concise definitions. This work unites the different areas of research and allows users, regardless of their background, to navigate through the most essential concepts with ease, saving them time and vastly improving their understanding so that they can move forward, whether in their research, development, manufacturing, or purchase of renewable energy.

The first volume is devoted to Photovoltaic Technology and is edited by Mr. Wilfried G. J. H. M. van Sark from the Netherlands. It consists of 38 chapters, written by 41 authors from Europe, the United States, Japan, China, India, Africa, and the Middle East. The topics covered range from the smallest applications to MW projects. A brief introduction and history is followed by chapters on finance and economics, solar resources, up- and downconversion, crystalline photovoltaic (PV) cells, luminescent concentrators, thin-film and multiple-junction plastic solar cells, dye-sensitized solar cells, bio-inspired converters, application of micro- and nanotechnology, building integrated photovoltaics (BIPV) application in architecture, and very large-scale PV systems. Without doubt, this is an impressive tour of an immense field.

Volume 2 is devoted to Wind Energy and is edited by Professor John K. Kaldellis from Greece. It consists of 22 chapters written by 22 authors, again from various parts of the world, covering all aspects of wind energy from small wind mills to very large wind farms. The volume includes chapters on the history of wind power, the potential of wind power, wind turbine development, aerodynamic analysis, mechanical and electrical loads, control systems, noise and testing, onshore and offshore wind systems, policy, industry, and special wind power applications.

Volume 3 is devoted to Solar Thermal Applications and the editor is Professor Soteris A. Kalogirou from Cyprus. It consists of 19 chapters written by 17 authors. All aspects of solar thermal energy and its applications are covered. The volume begins with solar energy as a source of heat and goes on to describe the history of thermal applications, low-temperature and high-temperature storage systems, selective coating, glazing, modeling and simulation, hot water systems, space heating and cooling, water desalination, industrial and agricultural applications, concentration power, heat pumps, and passive solar architecture. The authors have looked at the Sun from the thermal energy aspect and put together a very informative and up-to-date volume from which every interested person, no matter what their level of knowledge, can benefit.

Volume 4 is on Fuel Cells and Hydrogen Technology and is edited by Dr. Andrew Cruden from the United Kingdom. It consists of 14 chapters covering the following topics: introduction and perspectives on hydrogen and fuel cells; theory and application of alkaline fuel cells; application of proton exchange membrane (PEM) fuel cells; molten carbonate fuel cells; solid oxide fuel cells; microbial and biological fuel cells; storage of compressed gas and hydrogen; the economy and policy of hydrogen technology; hydrogen safety engineering and future progress; the use of hydrogen for transport; and hydrogen and fuel cell power electronics. The 14 chapters were written by 16 authors. All aspects of practice, innovative technology, and future guidelines for researchers and industry have been addressed in this definitive volume.

Volume 5 deals with the huge field of Biomass and Biofuels and is edited by Professor Dermot J. Roddy from the United Kingdom. This work consists of 21 chapters written by 23 authors, again covering all aspects of biomass and biofuels, including their past, present, and future. The volume explains the history and prospective future of biofuels; bioethanol development in Brazil; power generation from biomass; biomass co-firing stations; biomass world market; a critical assessment of biomass – combined heat and power (CHP) energy systems; the ethics of biofuel production – issues, constraints, and limitations; greenhouse gases life cycle analysis; six different solutions from gasification and pyrolysis; new processes in biomass-to-liquid technology; new processes in biofuel production; biofuels from waste materials; novel feedstocks and woody biomass; feedstocks with the potential of yield improvement; renewable fuels – an automotive prospective; and novel use of biofuels in a range of engine configurations. Under Expanding the Envelope, there are chapters on biochar, extracting additional value from biomass, and biomass to chemicals. Finally, the chapter on bioenergy policy development concludes the volume.

Volume 6 is concerned with Hydro Power and is edited by Professor André G. H. Lejeune from Belgium. This is the oldest of all the renewable energy applications and has progressed over the ages from pico-hydro of a few hundred watts to large- and mega-scale dams generating more than 3000 MW with innovative civil engineering capability. This volume consists of 18 chapters prepared by 21 authors. It contains introduction – benefits and constraints of hydropower, recent developments and achievements in hydraulic research in China, and the management of hydropower and its impacts through construction and operation. The volume then assesses nine hydropower schemes around the world: the Three Gorges Project in China; large hydropower plants of Brazil; hydropower in Iran – vision and strategy; the recent trend in developing hydropower in India; the evolution of hydropower in Spain; hydropower in Japan; hydropower in Canada; an overview of institutional structure reform of the Cameroon power sector and assessment; and hydropower reliability in Switzerland. Other important issues are covered: pumped storage power plants; simplified generic axial-flow microhydro turbines; the development of a small hydroelectric scheme at Horseshoe Bend, Teviot River, New Zealand; concrete durability in dam design structure; and long-term sediment management for sustainable hydropower.

Volume 7 deals with Geothermal Energy. The editor of this volume is Professor Thorsteinn I. Sigfusson from Iceland. The volume consists of 10 chapters, which are written by 15 different authors. It covers the following areas: introduction and the physics of geothermal resources and management during utilization; geothermal shallow systems – heat pumps; geothermal exploration techniques; corrosion, scaling, and material selection in geothermal power production; direct heat utilization of geothermal energy; geothermal power plants; geochemical aspects of geothermal utilization; geothermal cost and investment factors; and the role of sustainable geothermal development.

Volume 8 is devoted to Generating Electricity from the Oceans, edited by Professor AbuBakr S. Bahaj from the United Kingdom. It consists of six chapters written by five authors. The volume covers the historical aspects of wave energy conversion, resource assessment for wave energy, development of wave devices from initial conception to commercial demonstration, air turbines, and the economics of ocean energy.

One chapter is totally devoted to Renewable Energy Policy and Incentives. It is included in the first volume only. The author of this chapter is Mr. David Porter, Chief Executive of the Association of Electricity Producers in the United Kingdom, an author who has had vast experience of dealing with electricity generation in the United Kingdom over many years. He has advised the British Government on how to meet supply and demand of electricity and coordinate with all electricity producers regarding their sources and supply. The chapter outlines the types of mechanisms used to promote renewable energy and their use, the impact on their deployment, ensuring investor certainty, the potential for harmonizing support schemes, and the conclusion.

In short, my advice to anyone who wants to acquire comprehensive knowledge concerning renewable energy, no matter which subject or application, is that they should acquire this invaluable resource for their home, research center and laboratory, company, or library.

Professor Ali Sayigh BSc, DIC, PhD, FIE, FIEE, CEng
Chairman of WREC (World Renewable Energy Congress)
Director General of WREN (World Renewable Energy Network)
Chairman of IEI (The Institution of Engineers (India))
Editor-in-Chief of *Renewable Energy*
Editor-in-Chief of *Renewable Energy Magazine*

CONTENTS

Editor-in-Chief	v
Volume Editors	vii
Contributors for All Volumes	xi
Preface	xix

Volume 1 Photovoltaic Solar Energy

Renewable Energy

1.01	Renewable Energy Policy and Incentives D Porter	1

Photovoltaic Solar Energy

1.02	Introduction to Photovoltaic Technology WGJHM van Sark	5
1.03	Solar Photovoltaics Technology: No Longer an Outlier LL Kazmerski	13
1.04	History of Photovoltaics LA Lamont	31

Economics and Environment

1.05	Historical and Future Cost Dynamics of Photovoltaic Technology GF Nemet and D Husmann	47
1.06	Feed-In Tariffs and Other Support Mechanisms for Solar PV Promotion D Jacobs and BK Sovacool	73
1.07	Finance Mechanisms and Incentives for Photovoltaic Technologies in Developing Countries M Moner-Girona, S Szabo, and S Rolland	111
1.08	Environmental Impacts of Photovoltaic Life Cycles VM Fthenakis and HC Kim	143
1.09	Overview of the Global PV Industry A Jäger-Waldau	161
1.10	Vision for Photovoltaics in the Future E Despotou	179

1.11	Storage Options for Photovoltaics *VM Fthenakis and T Nikolakakis*	199

Resource and Potential

1.12	Solar Radiation Resource Assessment for Renewable Energy Conversion *DR Myers*	213
1.13	Prediction of Solar Irradiance and Photovoltaic Power *E Lorenz and D Heinemann*	239

Basics

1.14	Principles of Solar Energy Conversion *LC Hirst*	293
1.15	Thermodynamics of Photovoltaics *V Badescu*	315

Technology

1.16	Crystalline Silicon Solar Cells: State-of-the-Art and Future Developments *SW Glunz, R Preu, and D Biro*	353
1.17	Thin-Film Silicon PV Technology *M Zeman and REI Schropp*	389
1.18	Chalcopyrite Thin-Film Materials and Solar Cells *T Unold and CA Kaufmann*	399
1.19	Cadmium Telluride Photovoltaic Thin Film: CdTe *TA Gessert*	423
1.20	Plastic Solar Cells *L Sims, H-J Egelhaaf, JA Hauch, FR Kogler, and R Steim*	439
1.21	Mesoporous Dye-Sensitized Solar Cells *A Hagfeldt, UB Cappel, G Boschloo, L Sun, L Kloo, H Pettersson, and EA Gibson*	481
1.22	Multiple Junction Solar Cells *M Yamaguchi*	497
1.23	Application of Micro- and Nanotechnology in Photovoltaics *L Tsakalakos*	515
1.24	Upconversion *TW Schmidt and MJY Tayebjee*	533
1.25	Downconversion *MJY Tayebjee, TW Schmidt, and G Conibeer*	549
1.26	Down-Shifting of the Incident Light for Photovoltaic Applications *Y Jestin*	563
1.27	Luminescent Solar Concentrators *JC Goldschmidt*	587
1.28	Thermophotovoltaics *J van der Heide*	603
1.29	Intermediate Band Solar Cells *E Antolín, A Martí, and A Luque*	619
1.30	Plasmonics for Photovoltaics *S Pillai and MA Green*	641
1.31	Artificial Leaves: Towards Bio-Inspired Solar Energy Converters *A Pandit and RN Frese*	657

Applications

1.32	Design and Components of Photovoltaic Systems WGJHM van Sark	679
1.33	BIPV in Architecture and Urban Planning TH Reijenga and HF Kaan	697
1.34	Product-Integrated Photovoltaics AHME Reinders and WGJHM van Sark	709
1.35	Very Large-Scale Photovoltaic Systems T Ehara, K Komoto, and P van der Vleuten	733
1.36	Concentration Photovoltaics M Martinez, O de la Rubia, F Rubio, and P Banda	745
1.37	Solar Power Satellites GA Landis	767
1.38	Performance Monitoring N Pearsall and R Gottschalg	775
1.39	Standards in Photovoltaic Technology H Ossenbrink, H Müllejans, R Kenny, and E Dunlop	787

Volume 2 Wind Energy

2.01	Wind Energy – Introduction JK Kaldellis	1
2.02	Wind Energy Contribution in the Planet Energy Balance and Future Prospects JK Kaldellis and M Kapsali	11
2.03	History of Wind Power DT Swift-Hook	41
2.04	Wind Energy Potential H Nfaoui	73
2.05	Wind Turbines: Evolution, Basic Principles, and Classifications S Mathew and GS Philip	93
2.06	Energy Yield of Contemporary Wind Turbines DP Zafirakis, AG Paliatsos, and JK Kaldellis	113
2.07	Wind Parks Design, Including Representative Case Studies D Al Katsaprakakis and DG Christakis	169
2.08	Aerodynamic Analysis of Wind Turbines JN Sørensen	225
2.09	Mechanical-Dynamic Loads M Karimirad	243
2.10	Electrical Parts of Wind Turbines GS Stavrakakis	269
2.11	Wind Turbine Control Systems and Power Electronics A Pouliezos	329
2.12	Testing, Standardization, Certification in Wind Energy F Van Hulle	371
2.13	Design and Implementation of a Wind Power Project T Wizelius	391
2.14	Offshore Wind Power Basics M Kapsali and JK Kaldellis	431

2.15	Wind Energy Economics *D Milborrow*	469
2.16	Environmental-Social Benefits/Impacts of Wind Power *E Kondili and JK Kaldellis*	503
2.17	Wind Energy Policy *GC van Kooten*	541
2.18	Wind Power Integration *JA Carta*	569
2.19	Stand-Alone, Hybrid Systems *KA Kavadias*	623
2.20	Wind Power Industry and Markets *PE Morthorst*	657
2.21	Trends, Prospects, and R&D Directions in Wind Turbine Technology *JK Kaldellis and DP Zafirakis*	671
2.22	Special Wind Power Applications *E Kondili*	725

Volume 3 Solar Thermal Systems: Components and Applications

Solar Thermal Systems

3.01	Solar Thermal Systems: Components and Applications – Introduction *SA Kalogirou*	1
3.02	Solar Resource *HD Kambezidis*	27
3.03	History of Solar Energy *VG Belessiotis and E Papanicolaou*	85

Components

3.04	Low Temperature Stationary Collectors *YG Caouris*	103
3.05	Low Concentration Ratio Solar Collectors *SA Kalogirou*	149
3.06	High Concentration Solar Collectors *B Hoffschmidt, S Alexopoulos, J Göttsche, M Sauerborn, and O Kaufhold*	165
3.07	Thermal Energy Storage *LF Cabeza*	211
3.08	Photovoltaic/Thermal Solar Collectors *Y Tripanagnostopoulos*	255
3.09	Solar Selective Coatings *P Yianoulis, M Giannouli, and SA Kalogirou*	301
3.10	Glazings and Coatings *G Leftheriotis and P Yianoulis*	313
3.11	Modeling and Simulation of Passive and Active Solar Thermal Systems *A Athienitis, SA Kalogirou, and L Candanedo*	357

Applications

3.12	Solar Hot Water Heating Systems G Faninger	419
3.13	Solar Space Heating and Cooling Systems SA Kalogirou and GA Florides	449
3.14	Solar Cooling and Refrigeration Systems GG Maidment and A Paurine	481
3.15	Solar-Assisted Heat Pumps DA Chwieduk	495
3.16	Solar Desalination E Tzen, G Zaragoza, and D-C Alarcón Padilla	529
3.17	Industrial and Agricultural Applications of Solar Heat B Norton	567
3.18	Concentrating Solar Power B Hoffschmidt, S Alexopoulos, C Rau, J Sattler, A Anthrakidis, C Boura, B O'Connor, and P Hilger	595
3.19	Passive Solar Architecture D Kolokotsa, M Santamouris, A Synnefa, and T Karlessi	637

Volume 4   Fuel Cells and Hydrogen Technology

4.01	Fuel Cells and Hydrogen Technology – Introduction AJ Cruden	1
4.02	Current Perspective on Hydrogen and Fuel Cells K Burke	13
4.03	Hydrogen Economics and Policy N Hughes and P Agnolucci	45
4.04	Hydrogen Safety Engineering: The State-of-the-Art and Future Progress V Molkov	77
4.05	Hydrogen Storage: Compressed Gas D Nash, D Aklil, E Johnson, R Gazey, and V Ortisi	111
4.06	Hydrogen Storage: Liquid and Chemical P Chen	137
4.07	Alkaline Fuel Cells: Theory and Application F Bidault and PH Middleton	159
4.08	PEM Fuel Cells: Applications AL Dicks	183
4.09	Molten Carbonate Fuel Cells: Theory and Application T Leo	227
4.10	Solid Oxide Fuel Cells: Theory and Materials A Tesfai and JTS Irvine	241
4.11	Biological and Microbial Fuel Cells K Scott, EH Yu, MM Ghangrekar, B Erable, and NM Duteanu	257
4.12	Hydrogen and Fuel Cells in Transport K Kendall and BG Pollet	281
4.13	H_2 and Fuel Cells as Controlled Renewables: FC Power Electronics N Schofield	295
4.14	Future Perspective on Hydrogen and Fuel Cells K Hall	331

Volume 5 Biomass and Biofuel Production

Biomass and Biofuels

5.01	Biomass and Biofuels – Introduction DJ Roddy	1
5.02	Historical Perspectives on Biofuels G Knothe	11

Case Studies

5.03	Bioethanol Development in Brazil A Altieri	15
5.04	Biomass Power Generation A Malmgren and G Riley	27
5.05	Biomass Co-Firing A Nuamah, A Malmgren, G Riley, and E Lester	55

Issues, Constraints & Limitations

5.06	A Global Bioenergy Market O Olsson and B Hillring	75
5.07	Biomass CHP Energy Systems: A Critical Assessment M Börjesson and EO Ahlgren	87
5.08	Ethics of Biofuel Production I Waller	99
5.09	Life Cycle Analysis Perspective on Greenhouse Gas Savings N Mortimer	109

Technology Solutions – New Processes

5.10	Biomass Gasification and Pyrolysis DJ Roddy and C Manson-Whitton	133
5.11	Biomass to Liquids Technology G Evans and C Smith	155
5.12	Intensification of Biofuel Production AP Harvey and JGM Lee	205
5.13	Biofuels from Waste Materials AA Refaat	217

Technology Solutions – Novel Feedstocks

5.14	Woody Biomass LL Wright, LM Eaton, RD Perlack, and BJ Stokes	263
5.15	Potential for Yield Improvement J Spink, E Mullins, and P Berry	293

Technology Solutions – Novel End Uses

5.16	Renewable Fuels: An Automotive Perspective RJ Pearson and JWG Turner	305
5.17	Use of Biofuels in a Range of Engine Configurations A Roskilly, Y Wang, R Mikalsen, and H Yu	343

Expanding the Envelope

5.18	Biochar CE Brewer and RC Brown	357
5.19	Extracting Additional Value from Biomass MF Askew	385
5.20	Biomass to Chemicals A Kazmi and J Clark	395
5.21	Bioenergy Policy Development P Thornley	411

Volume 6 Hydro Power

Hydro Power

6.01	Hydro Power – Introduction A Lejeune	1

Constraints of Hydropower Development

6.02	Hydro Power: A Multi Benefit Solution for Renewable Energy A Lejeune and SL Hui	15
6.03	Management of Hydropower Impacts through Construction and Operation H Horlacher, T Heyer, CM Ramos, and MC da Silva	49

Hydropower Schemes Around the World

6.04	Large Hydropower Plants of Brazil BP Machado	93
6.05	Overview of Institutional Structure Reform of the Cameroon Power Sector and Assessments J Kenfack and O Hamandjoda	129
6.06	Recent Hydropower Solutions in Canada M Fuamba and TF Mahdi	153
6.07	The Three Gorges Project in China L Suo, X Niu, and H Xie	179
6.08	The Recent Trend in Development of Hydro Plants in India SP Sen	227
6.09	Hydropower Development in Iran: Vision and Strategy E Bozorgzadeh	253
6.10	Hydropower Development in Japan T Hino	265
6.11	Evolution of Hydropower in Spain A Gil and F Bueno	309
6.12	Hydropower in Switzerland B Hagin	343

Design Concepts

6.13	Long-Term Sediment Management for Sustainable Hydropower F Rulot, BJ Dewals, S Erpicum, P Archambeau, and M Pirotton	355
6.14	Durability Design of Concrete Hydropower Structures S Jianxia	377
6.15	Pumped Storage Hydropower Developments T Hino and A Lejeune	405

6.16	Simplified Generic Axial-Flow Microhydro Turbines *A Fuller and K Alexander*	435
6.17	Development of a Small Hydroelectric Scheme at Horseshoe Bend, Teviot River, Central Otago, New Zealand *P Mulvihill and I Walsh*	467
6.18	Recent Achievements in Hydraulic Research in China *J Guo*	485

Volume 7 Geothermal Energy

7.01	Geothermal Energy – Introduction *TI Sigfusson*	1
7.02	The Physics of Geothermal Energy *G Axelsson*	3
7.03	Geothermal Energy Exploration Techniques *ÓG Flóvenz, GP Hersir, K Sæmundsson, H Ármannsson, and Þ Friðriksson*	51
7.04	Geochemical Aspects of Geothermal Utilization *H Ármannsson*	95
7.05	Direct Heat Utilization of Geothermal Energy *JW Lund*	169
7.06	Shallow Systems: Geothermal Heat Pumps *L Rybach*	187
7.07	Geothermal Power Plants *R DiPippo*	207
7.08	Corrosion, Scaling, and Material Selection in Geothermal Power Production *SN Karlsdóttir*	239
7.09	Geothermal Cost and Investment Factors *H Kristjánsdóttir and Á Margeirsson*	259
7.10	Sustainable Energy Development: The Role of Geothermal Power *B Davidsdottir*	271

Volume 8 Ocean Energy

8.01	Generating Electrical Power from Ocean Resources *AS Bahaj*	1
8.02	Historical Aspects of Wave Energy Conversion *AFO Falcão*	7
8.03	Resource Assessment for Wave Energy *EBL Mackay*	11
8.04	Development of Wave Devices from Initial Conception to Commercial Demonstration *V Heller*	79
8.05	Air Turbines *AFO Falcão and LMC Gato*	111
8.06	Economics of Ocean Energy *T Stallard*	151
Index		171

1.01 Renewable Energy Policy and Incentives

D Porter, Association of Electricity Producers, London, UK

© 2012 Elsevier Ltd. All rights reserved.

1.01.1	Types of Mechanism and Their Use	1
1.01.2	Impact on Deployment	3
1.01.3	Ensuring Investor Certainty	3
1.01.4	Potential for Harmonizing Support Schemes	4
1.01.5	Conclusion	4

The world's scarce resources are allocated mostly according to supply and demand and priced accordingly. We tend to use the cheapest first and economists approve of this because of the efficiency that it delivers. But in many different electricity supply industries, there are examples where particular technologies enjoy the protection of subsidy for an energy source. There can be different reasons for this – more rapid development of technologies that are not yet competitive, but are expected to become so in the future, or the protection of indigenous fuels, for example, through support for a coal mining industry. In the United Kingdom, before the liberalization of the economy in the 1980s, a state-controlled electricity industry was heavily dependent on a state-controlled coal industry and even the development and operation of the state-owned railway network, which transported most of the fuel, was influenced by this. Privatization of the electricity industry in 1990–91 and the liberalization of the electricity market led to the development of gas-fired power stations, which began, eventually, to undermine coal-fired electricity production.

But, the world's fossil fuels are finite and on the timescales that historians use, their deployment is no more than temporary – a passing phase. Dependence on them, however, is huge and the transition to alternatives could become urgent, so interest in support schemes for renewable energy has never been greater.

While schemes for supporting the use of renewable energy in heating and transport are developing, mechanisms to support the generation of renewable electricity are commonplace. This chapter reviews a range of such support schemes.

1.01.1 Types of Mechanism and Their Use

Renewable energy brings many benefits, and governments and society therefore wish to see it being widely used. However, renewable energy-generating technologies have high upfront costs compared with some conventional forms of electricity generation. Although schemes imposing emission limits (and trading) and fossil fuel taxes should make renewables more attractive investments, these are usually insufficient to make renewable technologies commercially viable. To ensure that renewables are produced in the quantities desired, governments therefore put in place support mechanisms that transfer some of the additional costs of renewable energy schemes to society at large or, at least, to those who buy electricity.

A common form of support mechanism is the production incentive, which rewards electricity producers using renewables with a payment for each unit of electricity they produce, thus encouraging the most efficient operation of the plant on an ongoing basis. These incentives take two forms: quantity- and price-based instruments.

For price-based instruments, the government specifies the price to be paid for output from renewable technologies, which is higher than the electricity price. This system of 'feed-in tariffs' can specify either a fixed price or a premium to be paid on top of the market price for electricity. Feed-in tariffs are used extensively around the world, including Germany, Spain, China, India, and several states in the United States.

For quantity-based instruments, the government sets the amount of renewable electricity that it would like to see provided and the market determines the price at which it will be delivered. This often takes the form of an obligation on a certain market participant (especially suppliers or 'retailers') to source a certain amount of renewable electricity, coupled with a system of tradable green certificates to demonstrate compliance. Certificate schemes are used in the United Kingdom, Australia, and states in the United States, which have a renewable portfolio standard.

Tender systems are also used, although such schemes have been abandoned in several countries (e.g., the United Kingdom and Ireland) and now seem to be used mainly for large-scale renewable projects, such as offshore wind in China.

Various forms of tax incentives and grant supports are widely used, often in conjunction with other methods of support. Tax incentives take the form of exemptions or credits for the investment made or electricity produced or accelerated depreciation of assets. In the United States, these have proven to be very effective, with the production tax credit helping to drive a significant uptake of wind generation over much of the past decade. In India, accelerated depreciation has been a key tool for encouraging investment in wind generation and will remain an option for wind projects alongside the new generation-based incentive.

A review of support schemes internationally reveals that it is not unusual for countries to use a mixture of different mechanisms targeted at particular investors and intended to achieve particular policy outcomes, with different schemes applying in different regions and for different technologies. In particular, separate mechanisms are often used to encourage investment in small-scale renewables, such as photovoltaics (PVs), by nonenergy professionals. For example, both the United Kingdom and Italy maintain certificate schemes as their primary support mechanism, but have feed-in tariffs to encourage the deployment of small-scale solar power (Table 1).

Governments are, of course, keen to ensure that public money is being used most efficiently and that it maximizes the deployment of renewables. Various methods are employed to keep costs down, including limiting eligibility to particular technologies that best exploit the available resource in that country or meet policy aims, reducing feed-in tariffs paid to new projects year on year (known as 'degression'), or differentiation of support by technology, resource, or location. Differentiation by technology is common across support schemes, including some certificate schemes, which award different multiples of certificates to particular technologies, such as in the United Kingdom. Differentiation by location or resource has been introduced in China, which provides different levels of support to wind projects across four resource areas.

Table 1 Financial incentives for renewables: four international case studies in summary

Country	Current financial assistance	Support scheme specifics
Australia	Financial support for renewables is primarily channeled through a quantity-based instrument – the renewable energy target. Australian states also provide state-level support through price-based instruments, grants, and tax incentives. There is no carbon emissions trading scheme or carbon tax.	The renewable energy target recently underwent an ambitious 'upgrade', increasing its target to 45 000 GWh (20%) from 9500 GWh, share for renewable electricity supply, by 2020. From 2011, small-scale renewables will be supported and subsidized separately (from large-scale renewables), using the same instrument albeit with different rules. Small generators will receive a fixed rate for certificates submitted and therefore (1) mitigate the price fluctuations small generators make on the renewable energy certificate (REC) market, and (2) will be protected from the market in general. State support mostly arrives in the form of localized grants and 'feed-in tariff' production incentives. For example, generators in New South Wales receive AUS$0.60 per kWh for all the electricity that their eligible solar photovoltaic (PV) system or wind turbine generates. In Queensland, the Solar Homes and Communities Plan provides cash rebates for the installation of solar PV systems on homes and community use buildings.
China	China outlines its ambitions in five-year plans – the next being the 12th plan covering the period 2011–15. Current Chinese policy targets state renewable energy to account for up to 10% of the total energy supply in 2010 and 16% in 2020.	China's Renewable Energy Law 2009 stipulates that grid companies are obliged to purchase the full amount of the electricity produced from renewable sources. Amendments to the Renewable Energy Law in 2009 require grid operators to purchase a certain fixed amount of renewable energy, and penalties for noncompliance are foreseen. There is a subsidy available to grid companies, the newly established 'Renewable Energy Fund', to cover the extra cost for integrating renewables if necessary. The Renewable Energy Premium formed part of the instruments laid out in the Renewable Energy Law and stipulates that the price difference between the electricity from renewable energy and that from coal-fired power plants should be shared across the whole electricity system. The current rate is set at 0.004 RMB kWh^{-1} (€0.000 4). The Chinese government introduced a feed-in tariff in 2009 for wind power, which applies for the entire operational period of a wind farm (20 years). There are four categories of tariff depending on a region's wind resources, ranging from 0.51 RMB kWh^{-1} (€0.054) to 0.61 RMB kWh^{-1} (€0.065)
India	India maintains several financial incentive schemes for development of a renewable electricity generation sector. Wind power, hydropower, and solar power remain India's key priorities.	Wind expansion is supported by a 'generation-based incentive' – essentially a feed-in tariff – for what the Government terms 'Grid Interactive Wind Power Projects', based on the following: ₹0.50 per unit of electricity fed into the grid for a period of no less than 4 years and no more than 10 years, with a cap of ₹62 lakhs[a] per MW. A maximum installed capacity limit is applied (4000 MW). Small hydro (>25 MW) is supported by financial contributions toward construction of the project. The Indian government usually awards 50% of the grant to help finance payments toward electromechanical equipment with a further 50% awarded on successful commissioning of the plant. The Solar Mission is an important policy in India, aimed at increasing India's security of supply. The government wish to have 20 000 MW of installed solar electricity equipment by 2022. One aim of the 'Mission' will be introducing a mandate on the state electricity regulators to fix a percentage for a purchase obligation on suppliers, to purchase solar electricity. The solar power purchase obligation will start at a low level and increase up to 3% by 2022. A power purchase obligation aims to achieve a 'Mission' target of grid cost parity (solar electricity vs. grid average) by 2022, and parity with coal-based thermal power generation by 2030.

(Continued)

Table 1	(Continued)	
Country	Current financial assistance	Support scheme specifics
USA	Federal financial assistance is managed and distributed by the US Department of Energy's Office of Energy Efficiency and Renewable Energy (EERE). Last year, EERE awarded $2.2 billion in financial assistance. Federal tax breaks are also employed. There are also state and local support schemes. Financial support is channeled through a variety of methods. The most frequently used methods are rebates, preferential loans, production incentives, and grants.	The federal department administers 'production incentive' funds for renewable power generators. Qualifying facilities are eligible for annual incentive payments of $0.015 per KWh (in 1993 dollars, and indexed for inflation) for the first 10-year period of their operation, subject to the availability of annual appropriations in each Federal fiscal year of operation. There are literally hundreds of support schemes across all of the US states. As an example, in California, there are 58 types of financial support (although many are very small or meant for niche markets), e.g., there are 48 types of rebate available. The California feed-in tariff allows eligible customer-generators to enter into 10-, 15-, or 20-year standard contracts with their utilities to sell the electricity produced by small renewable energy systems – up to 3 MW – at time-differentiated market-based prices. In Florida, a corporate tax break means renewable electricity generators receive the equivalent of $0.01 per kWh for electricity produced from 1 January 2007 to 30 June 2010. Qualifying renewable electricity is defined as "electrical, mechanical, or thermal energy produced from a method that uses one or more of the following fuels or energy sources: hydrogen, biomass, solar energy, geothermal energy, wind energy, ocean energy, waste heat, or hydroelectric power."

[a]1 lakh = 100 000.

1.01.2 Impact on Deployment

Various claims are made about the impact of different support mechanisms on levels of deployment. In the European Union, commentators often point to the German feed-in tariff as being a highly successful model, encouraging a massive expansion in wind (from 48 MW in 1990 to 6 GW in 2000 and more than 25 GW by 2010) and PV capacity (from 62 MW in 2000 to approximately 6 GW by 2010).

However, in reality, it is difficult to draw any clear correlation between the type of support scheme offered in a particular country and levels of deployment. Factors such as the availability of natural resources, public and political attitudes to and ambitions for renewables, long-term stability of support schemes, planning and network connection barriers, and the actual level of support offered will all affect how many projects get built. The massive expansion of PVs in Germany, for example, may have been built on an unsustainably high level of public support.

1.01.3 Ensuring Investor Certainty

Energy companies need a stable policy and regulatory framework to make the long-term, capital-intensive investments that electricity generation projects entail. They therefore place significant value on stability in renewable energy support schemes. However, governments' priorities and ambitions with respect to renewable energy are constantly evolving. This appears to have led to a lack of stability in support schemes globally, with changes being regularly implemented to encourage particular outcomes or reduce costs. A review of the evolution of support mechanisms across the European Union shows that of the 16 Member States that had a support mechanism in place in the year 2000, only a quarter did not change or significantly adapt their support schemes in the following 7 years.

The United Kingdom is a case in point, where the Non-Fossil Fuel Obligation (NFFO), a tender system that had only limited impact, gave way to the Renewables Obligation (RO), a certificate scheme, in 2002. Following criticism that the RO, which rewarded all technologies equally, was encouraging only a handful of cheaper technologies, differentiation of support was introduced to the mechanism by awarding different multiples of certificates to different technologies from 2009. In 2010, the system for small-scale renewables was changed again as a feed-in tariff was introduced for projects up to 5 MW in the light of concerns that a certificate scheme was too complicated and inaccessible for small-scale generators. The recent change of government in the United Kingdom has led to further uncertainty with an as yet undefined commitment to introduce a full system of feed-in tariffs while retaining the RO.

Without a long-term commitment to providing support for renewable energy, a 'start–stop' environment can develop for renewable energy. In the United States, a clear correlation can be seen between the occasions earlier in the decade when the production tax credit was allowed to expire and a dramatic reduction in levels of wind deployment. This sort of approach to support can discourage the development of supply chains and create a negative impression of the overall investment environment in a country. In the United Kingdom, the NFFO has put some developers' businesses under great strain, by inviting tenders at unpredictable intervals – staff had to be retained for an unknown period, with the developer having neither a contract nor, necessarily, the prospect of one, until the next call for tenders.

A serious concern for investors must be that governments will weaken their financial commitment to renewables in response to the current economic situation. Germany and Spain, for example, have both recently decided to cut the levels of support offered to PV dramatically as they are no longer considered affordable. Germany has agreed to cut its feed-in tariff by approximately 15%, while Spain is considering cuts even for existing installations.

1.01.4 Potential for Harmonizing Support Schemes

Support schemes tend to operate on a national or subnational basis. While many of the benefits of renewables may also be national – security of supply, economic development – some, such as reductions in carbon emissions, are supranational. Furthermore, natural resources, renewable energy targets, and even energy markets do not necessarily correspond with national boundaries. For example, Ireland now has a single electricity market, but separate support schemes operate in the Republic of Ireland (a feed-in tariff) and Northern Ireland (certificate scheme), with fears that this may be causing market distortions.

The European Union has a target for 20% of its energy to come from renewable sources by 2020, which is subdivided into 27 national targets. Although the majority of Member States seem confident that they will be able to meet their targets domestically, it would clearly be more cost-effective to exploit the lowest-cost potential across the European Union. Analysis carried out for the European electricity trade association, EURELECTRIC, suggests that implementing a full system of renewable Guarantee of Origin trading across the European Union could lead to a saving of €17 billion in the year 2020 compared with meeting the targets domestically. Even allowing only 20% of the target to be traded could lead to savings of €14 billion in the year 2020.

Theoretically, it would therefore seem desirable to harmonize or integrate support schemes across the European Union to allow for the most cost-effective deployment of renewables. Similar considerations about harmonization of state support schemes occur when considering the possible implementation of a federal Renewable Energy Standard in the United States. However, in practice, the multitude of different support schemes that have been implemented, each with their own features, and political sensitivities make such harmonization or integration challenging. Norway and Sweden have been discussing the possible implementation of a joint support scheme for several years without result. Furthermore, proposals to integrate support schemes or, as is being considered in the United Kingdom, to open them up to overseas projects face the underlying political question of whether citizens of one country are willing to pay for a project in another without seeing many of the direct benefits (e.g., job creation) that they bring.

1.01.5 Conclusion

Across the globe, financial support mechanisms are clearly seen as a key tool for encouraging the deployment of renewable energy. However, the cost of such schemes must ultimately be borne by society at large and there will be tensions, especially in economically straitened times, over how much we are willing to pay to achieve our renewable energy ambitions. Maximizing efficiency in support schemes will therefore be a priority for politicians, but this will need to be balanced against the needs of investors in terms of certainty and level of reward as, ultimately, a support scheme that does not work for them will be ineffective.

Renewable energy will play a central role in the world's decarbonized energy future – a study by EURELECTRIC suggests that 38% of the European Union's electricity (and approximately 50% of its generating capacity) will be renewable by 2050. It is highly unlikely that public subsidies for renewable energy will be sustainable in the long term, given the large volumes that would need to be supported. The renewable energy industry will therefore need to prepare for a transition to a world without subsidy, in which renewable energy projects are able to stand on their merits alone. In December 2010, the UK government proposed changes to its renewable energy support regime, to favor low-carbon technologies generally, via either a feed-in tariff with a contract for differences, or a premium feed-in tariff. Draft legislation is expected in 2011.

1.02 Introduction to Photovoltaic Technology

WGJHM van Sark, Utrecht University, Utrecht, The Netherlands

© 2012 Elsevier Ltd.

1.02.1	Introduction	5
1.02.2	Guide to the Reader	6
1.02.2.1	Quick Guide	6
1.02.2.2	Detailed Guide	7
1.02.2.2.1	Part 1: Introduction	7
1.02.2.2.2	Part 2: Economics and environment	7
1.02.2.2.3	Part 3: Resource and potential	8
1.02.2.2.4	Part 4: Basics of PV	8
1.02.2.2.5	Part 5: Technology	8
1.02.2.2.6	Part 6: Applications	10
1.02.3	Conclusion	11
References		11

Glossary

Balance of system All components of a PV energy system except the photovoltaics (PV) modules.
Grid parity The situation when the electricity generation cost of solar PV in dollar or Euro per kilowatt-hour equals the price a consumer is charged by the utility for power from the grid. Note, grid parity for retail markets is different from wholesale electricity markets.
Inverter Electronic device that converts direct electricity to alternating current electricity.
Photovoltaic energy system A combination of a PV system to generate direct current electricity, the necessary support and cabling structure, and an inverter system to convert direct electricity to alternating current electricity.
Photovoltaic module A number of solar cells together form a solar 'module' or 'panel'.

Photovoltaic system A number of PV modules combined in a system in arrays, ranging from a few watts capacity to multimegawatts capacity.
Photovoltaic technology generations PV technologies can be classified as first-, second-, and third-generation technologies. First-generation technologies are commercially available silicon wafer-based technologies, second-generation technologies are commercially available thin-film technologies, and third-generation technologies are those based on new concepts and materials that are not (yet) commercialized.
Photovoltaics (PV) It is a method of generating electrical power by converting solar radiation into direct current electricity using predominantly semiconductors or other materials that exhibit the PV effect.
Solar cell The device in which solar irradiation is converted into direct current electricity.

1.02.1 Introduction

The discovery of the photoelectric effect by Edmund Becquerel as reported in 1839 [1] has led to a multibillion solar photovoltaics (PVs) business today. The scientific discoveries by Max Planck [2] and Albert Einstein [3] in the early 1900s led to the first silicon solar cell made by Daryl Chapin, Calvin Fuller, and Gerald Pearson in 1954 [4]. Now, nearly 60 years later, this same solar cell design, in essence, is responsible for over 40 GW of installed solar power systems worldwide.

Figure 1 shows the development of annual PV production for the past 20 years [5]. Clearly, a nearly 1000-fold increase has occurred in these two decades, while the relative annual growth has also increased steadily, averaging over 50% over the past 10 years. Popular policy measures, such as the feed-in-tariff scheme pioneered in Germany, have pushed these developments forward [6]. The growth figures have to be sustained for the coming decades to reach global installed capacity, such that PV technology will be one of the major renewable electricity suppliers in a future sustainable society [7].

PV has become better and cheaper over the past decades. Starting with an efficiency of 7% in 1954, due to considerable amounts of public and private R&D funding, crystalline silicon wafer-based solar cells now have reached an efficiency of 25%, while cells that use other materials have reached an absolute record efficiency of 43.5% (two-terminal triple-junction GaInP/GaAs/GaInNAs, at an intensity of 418 suns) [8]. The magic 50% limit now becomes within reach, as recently reviewed by Antonio Luque [9]: intermediate band cell is considered to be as one of the best candidates.

From some $100 W_p^{-1} in the mid-1970s, present-day PV module prices have decreased to between $1 and $2 W_p^{-1} today. Price development seems to follow a so-called experience curve, meaning that for every doubling of the produced amount of PV modules,

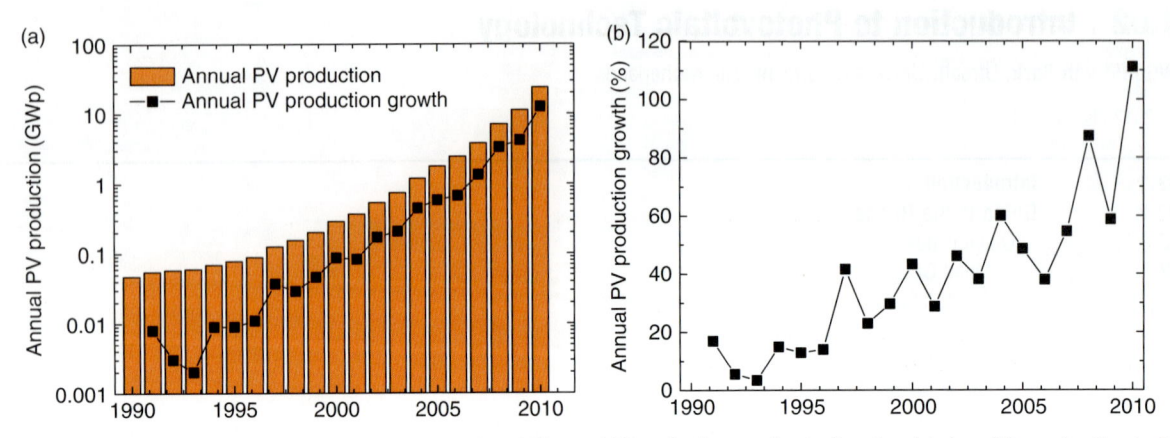

Figure 1 Twenty years of (a) annual PV production and growth and (b) annual PV production growth rate. Based on data from [5]; see also Chapter **1.03**.

the price is lowered by some 20% [10]. As modules constitute the main part of a PV system, also system prices have decreased considerably in the past decades. For example, current (2011) system prices in Europe are estimated to be in the range of €1.85–€5 W_p^{-1} [11].

In order to facilitate comparison with other electricity generation technologies, it is more useful to calculate the generation cost of PV electricity in terms of dollars or Euro per generated kilowatt-hour. The turnkey cost of a PV system is used as input to a levelized energy cost (LEC) calculation method, which requires assumptions regarding the operation and maintenance (O&M) cost, the lifetime of the system, the discount rate, and the specific energy yield (kWh W_p^{-1}). The latter mostly depends on the amount of solar irradiation (geographical location of the system, orientation), but also on specific system design (PV module technology, integration type). Typically, O&M cost are taken as 1% of the investment cost; lifetime is between 20 and 30 years, and discount rate is between 3% and 10%. The specific energy yield varies from 0.8 to 1.6 kWh W_p^{-1} over Europe [12]. With present turnkey system prices, the LEC is reported to range from €0.15 to €0.35 kWh^{-1} for Europe [11].

This LEC range brings the so-called 'grid parity' within reach for certain countries, especially those with high annual irradiation and high electricity prices. Grid parity is reached when the generation cost of solar PV in dollar or Euro per kilowatt-hour equals the price a consumer is charged by the utility for power from the grid. With LEC values between 0.15 and 0.35, PV electricity is cheaper for some retail electricity markets. With expected further reduction of turnkey system prices, in wholesale electricity markets also grid parity is forecast to be reached within 1–2 decades.

The emphasis of this volume is on PV cells and modules, which form an essential part of a complete PV system. A well-performing PV system cannot do without a well-designed direct current–alternative current (DC–AC) converter (inverter), which is to be carefully matched to the DC power output of the PV module. Their performance is important for the performance of the whole PV system. Present-day inverters show very high conversion efficiencies of 95–98% [13], thus inverter-associated power losses are small. Although inverters have seen substantial development in the past decades, they are not treated in this volume.

1.02.2 Guide to the Reader

1.02.2.1 Quick Guide

This volume is subdivided into six parts: (1) introduction; (2) economics and environment; (3) resource and potential; (4) basics of PV technology; (5) technological developments; and (6) applications. In the introduction part with three chapters, a quick overview of PV technology is presented as well as the history of PV. The second part provides seven chapters on historical and future economical developments and strategies for PV deployment such as the famous feed-in-tariff schemes in developed and developing countries. This part ends with a chapter on environmental aspects and chapters on industrial activity, a future vision for PV and storage options for PV. Part 3 contains three chapters detailing the solar irradiance resource, the application potential, and forecasting methods, which are of importance for actual PV power predictions. Part 4 then follows with two chapters, one treating the principles of PV conversion and the other on thermodynamics.

The largest part of the volume is part 5, with 16 chapters covering the so-called first-, second-, and third-generation PV technologies [14]. Commercially available solar cells based on wafer and thin-film silicon are treated as well as those based on copper indium selenide (CIS), cadmium telluride, plastic and 'dye-sensitized' solar cells, and multiple-junction III–V-based ones. New concepts, materials, and cell developments such as down- and upconversion and downshifting, intermediate band solar cells, the luminescent solar concentrator, thermophotovoltaics (TPVs), and plasmonics then are described. Nanotechnology plays a very important role in these new developments, which are summarized in Chapter **1.23**. An intriguing new concept is treated in a chapter on bio-inspired solar converters.

In the final and sixth part, PV applications are detailed in nine chapters; here building-integrated applications are described as well as product-integrated PV, concentrated PV, solar power satellites, and very large-scale PV plants. Also, aspects of PV performance of these applications are treated, as well as the developments in the field of standards, which is indispensable for successful deployment of massive scale PV.

1.02.2.2 Detailed Guide

1.02.2.2.1 Part 1: Introduction

Directly following the present chapter, Chapter **1.03** in this volume is contributed by Larry Kazmerski, who discusses the status and future technology, market, and industry opportunities for solar PVs. He stresses that both 'policy' and 'technology' investments are important for the future markets and competitiveness of PV. Furthermore, this chapter describes the requirement for PV to move from short-term and evolutionary developments to disruptive and revolutionary pathways in order for PV to fulfill society's renewable needs in the coming two to three decades.

Lisa Lamont then describes in Chapter **1.04** a brief history of PV development, starting from solar use in ancient civilizations to the discovery of the photoelectric effect, which marks the start of the historic PV timeline. She further discusses the reasons behind PV development in the early years, and provides an outlook for the future. She closes with the statement that "Mankind should aim for this (PV technology) to be the primary fuel of the future and not an alternative", which links back to Chapter **1.03**.

1.02.2.2.2 Part 2: Economics and environment

In Chapter **1.05**, authored by Gregory Nemet and Diana Husmann, an analysis is presented of the historical and future cost dynamics of PV. Their argue that the 700-fold reduction in PV cost, which occurred in the past 60 years, is caused by a combination of R&D, economies of scale, learning-by-doing, and knowledge spillovers from other technologies. Also, the importance of these factors varied in time. The so-called experience curves are usually employed to depict cost reductions, and benefits and limitations of this approach are discussed. For PV, both incremental and nonincremental technical improvements have led to cost reductions. Especially, nonincremental improvements are irregular and, therefore, are complicating cost projections that inform policy. A method is presented to model these incremental improvements for PV.

David Jacobs and Benjamin Sovacool describe financial support mechanisms in Chapter **1.06**. They present several case studies to corroborate their findings that the level of market development is decisive in the proper selection of support mechanisms. Besides R&D funding, and tax and investment incentives, they show that the only proven support mechanisms for large-scale GW markets are feed-in-tariffs. When PV has reached grid parity, other supporting schemes should be developed that create conditions for investors that minimize their investment risks.

Magda Moner-Girona, Simon Rolland, and Sandor Szabo continue to discuss on this topic in Chapter **1.07**, where they focus on off-grid PV technologies in developing countries. Renewable technologies offer the option to provide access to sustainable energy services and foster economic development, thereby contributing to the Millennium Development Goals. However, many barriers exist for their widespread diffusion, in particular of PV, of which the main barrier is a financial one. Therefore, schemes for financing off-grid PV are very important, and this chapter analyzes existing support mechanisms and incentives, particularly combining market, energy use, and socioeconomic elements. Based on lessons from the past, new solutions and adapted support mechanism are suggested for promoting sustainable energy options for remote rural areas in developing countries.

In Chapter **1.08**, Vasilis Fthenakis and Hyung Chul Kim present their findings on environmental aspects of some of today's PV technologies by using life-cycle assessment as their tool. Such an assessment describes material and energy flows as well as emissions to the environment for each stage in the life cycle. It is discussed that the lower the so-called energy payback time (EPBT), that is, the time it takes for a PV system to generate energy equal to the amount used in its production, the lower the life-cycle emissions. Comparing three commercial PV technologies, mounted on flat, fixed ground-mount systems, it is shown that the EPBT of multicrystalline Si, monocrystalline Si, and CdTe systems were estimated to be 1.7, 1.7, and 0.8 years, respectively, for average US and Southern Europe conditions. The chapter ends with a quantification of life-cycle risk indicators from which it is concluded that the PV fuel cycle is much safer than conventional sources of energy.

An overview of the PV industry is given by Arnulf Jäger-Waldau in Chapter **1.09**, who provides a regional breakdown of production growth over the past decade. Both China and Taiwan show the largest annual production growth in the past 5 years, and together account for more than 50% of the worldwide production. The present market is dominated by wafer-based silicon (80%), but thin-film technology is gaining market share. The top 20 solar cell producers are listed and described as well as the top 10 polysilicon manufacturers. Finally, a brief outlook is given in which several growth scenarios are compared.

The subsequent Chapter **1.10** by Eleni Despotou, Alexandre Roesch, Gaetan Masson, Giorgia Concas, Marie Latour, and Pieterjan Vanbuggenhout presents the industry vision for the future development of the PV market. The impressive market growth and the decrease of price bring PV toward full competitiveness on the electricity markets. PV will enter new markets and provide electricity to a growing number of consumers. The shift from households consuming electricity to households producing electricity will revolutionize the way power grids will operate and how market will deal with electricity. Electricity markets with double-digit PV market penetration are envisaged, for which the grid should be restructured to include an increased level of intelligence: smart grids.

As essential part of such a grid system with intermittent energy sources such as PV (and wind), electricity storage may play an important role. This is described in Chapter **1.11** authored by Vasilis Fthenakis and Thomas Nikolakakis. Storage technologies can smoothen the variability of PV. A number of technologies are discerned, based on their power quality, bridging power, and energy management. The main difference between them is the timescales over which they operate, and the extent to which power and energy are needed.

1.02.2.2.3 Part 3: Resource and potential

In Chapter **1.12**, Daryl Myers addresses measurements, modeling, and databases of solar energy potential. These are essential for identifying, locating, and prospecting for the appropriate quantity and quality of solar resources for PV systems, and are critical to system designers, investors, financial backers, utilities, governments, and owner/operators in assessing the performance, return-on-investments, and investment risks of planned or existing PV projects. This chapter addresses the fundamentals and state of the art for measuring, modeling, and applying solar radiation resource data to meet decision-making needs.

In Chapter **1.13**, the operation of installed PV systems, in particular their expected performance, is treated by Elke Lorenz and Detlev Heinemann. Depending on meteorological conditions, the generated power is variable; therefore reliable forecast information for management and operation strategies is required. This chapter provides an overview on different applications and state-of-the art models for solar irradiance and PV power prediction, including time series models based on on-site measured data, models based on the detection of cloud motion in satellite images, and numerical weather prediction-based models. The chapter further shows evaluation results for selected irradiance and power prediction schemes.

1.02.2.2.4 Part 4: Basics of PV

The conversion of sunlight into electricity is governed by the photoelectric effect, but it will only occur in a device that exhibits charge generation by photon absorption and charge separation. In Chapter **1.14**, Louise Hirst describes the principles of the PV action in a semiconductor single *p-n* junction in detail. The maximum efficiency of such a device under 1 sun irradiation is 31%, which is denoted as the Shockley–Queisser limit, named after William Shockley and Hans Queisser, who were the first to derive this detailed balance limit [15]. It is possible to exceed this limit by addressing the various loss factors; several examples are described in various chapters in Part 5 on specific third-generation-type solar cells.

Subsequently, Viorel Badescu discusses various thermodynamic aspects of photovoltaics in Chapter **1.15**. In this chapter, first elementary concepts about thermodynamics of undiluted and diluted thermal radiation are presented. Then, the mathematical description of reversible solar radiation concentration is developed by using a simple formalism based on the Lagrange invariant, the étendue. The basic thermodynamics necessary to describe the operation of PV devices is presented, followed by the principle of building the detailed balance equation models. Examples are given for single-gap solar cells and for omnicolor PV converters.

1.02.2.2.5 Part 5: Technology

This part starts off with a chapter on the workhorse of the PV industry: wafer-based crystalline silicon solar cells. To extend its success story, it is important to further bring down the costs of these cells. The cost distribution of a crystalline silicon PV module is clearly dominated by material costs, especially by the costs of the silicon wafer. Stefan Glunz, Ralf Preu, and Daniel Biro argue in Chapter **1.16** that besides improved production technology, the efficiency of the cells and modules is the main leverage to bring down the costs even more. They describe the state-of-the-art process for silicon solar cells and give insight into new advanced processes and cell designs.

Miro Zeman and Ruud Schropp treat thin-film silicon solar cell technology in Chapter **1.17**. It is one of the promising PV technologies for delivering low-cost solar electricity. Single-junction amorphous and microcrystalline silicon cells are responsible for most thin-film silicon modules presently on the market; tandem amorphous/microcrystalline silicon modules will take over in near future. Both cell designs are presented. In order to increase the absorption in thin absorber layers, novel approaches for tandem solar cells and for photon management are developed. Finally, also module production and application areas are briefly described.

In Chapter **1.18**, chalcopyrite-type thin-film materials and solar cell devices are reviewed by Thomas Unold and Christian Kaufmann. These types of polycrystalline materials are versatile and multinary with excellent optical and electronic properties and a high degree of chemical flexibility, and thus are naturally suited for high-efficiency thin-film solar cells. A thorough understanding of the material physics and device properties of the heterojunction solar cells is required to reach high efficiencies. A wide variety of deposition techniques are used, each having its own advantages and disadvantages regarding cost, scalability, and throughput. Recently, commercialization of chalcopyrite thin film has been scaled up to the gigawatt range, proving the competitiveness of this technology with regard to crystalline silicon solar technology.

Chapter **1.19** by Tim Gessert reviews the history, development, and present processes used to fabricate thin-film CdTe-based solar cells. It shows why certain processes may have commercial production advantages, and how the various process steps can interact with each other to affect device performance and reliability. The chapter concludes with a discussion of considerations of large-area CdTe PV deployment including issues related to material availability and EPBT.

In Chapter **1.20**, plastic or organic solar cells are described by Lothar Sims, Hans Egelhaaf, Jens Hauch, René Kogler, and Roland Steim. Organic solar cells are also considered a great promise to reduce costs as well as energy consumption during production compared with wafer-based silicon PV technologies. Properties such as transparency, flexibility, and various colors also make them attractive from an aesthetic point of view. This chapter describes the working principles of these cells, important materials, such as

P3HT:PCBM (poly(3-hexylthiophene):phenyl-C_{61}-butyric-acid-methyl ester), ways for improving the efficiency and stability, production methods, and ends with a short outlook on the future development of organic solar cells.

Anders Hagfeldt, Ute Cappel, Gerrit Boschloo, Licheng Sun, Lars Kloo, Henrik Pettersson, and Elizabeth Gibson discuss the developments in mesoporous dye-sensitized solar cells (DSCs, also called Grätzel cells) in Chapter **1.21**. In these cells, a dye is distributed over a porous material with a large surface area, and electrons which are excited upon absorption of photons are transferred from the dye to the porous substrate and collected via external contacts. It is shown in this chapter that the chemical complexity of DSCs has become clear, and the main challenge for future research is to understand and master this complexity, in particular at the oxide–dye–electrolyte interface. A challenging but realistic goal for the present DSC technology is to achieve efficiencies above 15% that are also stable. As DSCs perform relatively better compared with other solar cell technologies under diffuse light conditions, an overall goal for future research will be to collect data and develop models to make fair judgments of the DSC technology with regard to energy costs. Possible introduction of niche applications such as consumer electronics and successful development of manufacturing processes are expected.

Multiple-junction solar cells based on III–V materials are described in Chapter **1.22** by Masafumi Yamaguchi. These types of solar cells are capable of reaching efficiencies of up to 50% and are used for space and terrestrial applications, in particular in concentrator solar cell modules, as the cell cost is high. This chapter presents principles and key issues for realizing high-efficiency multiple-junction solar cells, as well as issues related to development and manufacturing, and applications for space and terrestrial uses.

New concepts, materials, and cells are developed, denoted as third-generation PVs. The application of micro- and nanotechnologies are becoming more and more important to solar PVs, as Loucas Tsakaloukos shows in Chapter **1.23**. In conventional thin-film solar cells, the use of nanoparticle inks are evidenced, as well as improving performance by using novel optical films. There are also efforts to develop novel micro/nanoarchitectures such as nanowire or nanocomposite-based devices. Finally, various quantum-based concepts are considered and progress toward demonstration of devices is discussed. The chapter ends with a perspective on the future of micro/nanosolar technologies in PVs and the potential manufacturing issues that are anticipated as these new technologies develop.

Chapter **1.24** deals with upconversion. Upconversion is defined as the conversion of a low-energy photon, which cannot be absorbed in a solar cell, into a higher-energy photon, which can be absorbed. In this chapter, Timothy Schmidt and Murad Tayebjee present the theory of upconversion as applied to PV devices using an equivalent circuit formalism. They analyze three circuits, corresponding to symmetric intermediate band and upconverting solar cells. The leading approaches to upconversion, rare earths and organic molecules, are described. Upconversion efficiencies are defined, and achieved efficiencies of both rare earth and photochemical upconversion are compared. The future prospects of photochemical upconversion are discussed in the light of a kinetic model, which reveals the parameters which currently limit the efficiency.

In Chapter **1.25**, downconversion is described by Gavin Conibeer, Murad Tayebjee, and Timothy Schmidt. Downconversion is defined as the conversion of a high-energy photon into a lower-energy photon. The theory of downconversion as applied to PV devices is revised from a thermodynamical standpoint, and downconverting as well as carrier-multiplication scenarios are analyzed. State-of-the-art technology is described comprising of downconversion using rare-earth ions and so-called singlet fission in organic molecules and semiconductor nanostructures.

Yoann Jestin describes in Chapter **1.26** the use of downshifting to enhancing the performance of solar cells. In this chapter, after a brief description of the downshifting process, a review of the most common downshifting elements and their use in solar cells will be presented. To conclude, an overview of patent filing and commercial applications will be given.

The luminescent solar concentrator is described in Chapter **1.27** by Jan Christoph Goldschmidt. These concentrators have the ability to concentrate direct and diffuse radiation, which is directly related to the Stokes shift that occurs between absorption of incoming light and subsequent emission. To achieve efficiency potential in the range of 10%, further progress in the development of luminescent materials that cover the visible and the near-infrared range of the solar spectrum, showing high luminescent quantum efficiencies and low reabsorption, is necessary. Furthermore, current progress in the research on photonic structures needs to be exploited for its application in luminescent concentrator systems.

Chapter **1.28** by Johan van der Heide gives an overview of TPV energy conversion, including a historical introduction. After a description of all elements present in a typical TPV system, a detailed overview of the different TPV cell concepts is given. Subsequently, some examples are given of TPV systems built in the world followed by an estimation of the TPV market potential.

The intermediate band gap solar cell is described by Elisa Antolin, Antonio Marti, and Antonio Luque in Chapter **1.29**. This cell was proposed to increase the current, while at the same time preserving the output voltage of solar cells, leading ideally to efficiencies above the Shockley–Queisser limit. In this chapter the concept is described, as well as the use of quantum dots. Present efficiencies are still low, and possible ways to overcome the issues involved are discussed. It is foreseen that these types of solar cells will be able to operate in tandem in concentrators with very high efficiencies or as thin cells at low cost with efficiencies above the present ones.

In Chapter **1.30**, the use of plasmonics for PVs is treated by Supriya Pillai and Martin Green. This light-trapping approach based on scattering by metal nanoparticles allows amplifying the interaction between light and matter. The rapid advancement in fabrication and characterization techniques for nanoscale particles and the increased understanding of mechanisms behind the enhancement process is leading the way to the realization of a mature technology. The ability of light to interact with particles that are much smaller than the wavelength of light opens ways to modify and manipulate local light fields to suit various applications. This is particularly interesting as the trend is toward high-performance miniature devices.

The final chapter in this part is on a very challenging concept: the artificial leaf. Anjali Pandit and Raoul Frese describe in Chapter 1.31 how bio-inspired solar energy converters could be designed. The term 'artificial leaves' is used to describe artificial photosynthetic devices assembled from interacting bio-based or bio-inspired components. After a brief description of natural photosynthesis and how its design principles have inspired artificial photosynthesis, the integration of biological components in artificial devices is discussed as well as recent developments in the design of biomimetic light-harvesting and charge-separation systems. The chapter ends with an outlook for the design of a fuel-producing solar cell.

1.02.2.2.6 Part 6: Applications

Chapter 1.32 by Wilfried van Sark provides an overview of PV system design aspects, such as the various components used and their interplay in the system. Basics of PV cell and module performance are described, briefly touching upon the loss factors in PV systems. Two case studies are shown exemplifying PV system design issues.

In Chapter 1.33, Tjerk Reijenga and Henk Kaan focus on building integration photovoltaics (BIPVs) in architecture and urban planning. They argue that to increase market acceptance for PV, it is important to show architecturally elegant, well-integrated systems. The main factors for successful integration are suitable buildings, and a reason for building integration. For newly constructed sustainable buildings, BIPV will be part of the energy strategy. For existing buildings there must be a valid reason for integrating PV systems. Building renovation, including the roof and façade, often provides an opportune time for selecting BIPV. In this chapter, criteria have been formulated for judging building integration of PV. These criteria are useful for manufacturers and technicians who are involved with building integration from the engineering and technical aspects of the building process. However, it is the task and responsibility of the individual architect to adapt the criteria to his or her own aesthetic standards.

In Chapter 1.34, Angèle Reinders and Wilfried van Sark present experiences with product-integrated photovoltaics (PIPVs) for various product categories: consumer products, lighting products, business-to-business products, recreational products, vehicles, and transportation and arts. The term PIPV indicates that PV technology is integrated in a product by positioning of PV cells on the surfaces of a product. An overview is given of existing solar-powered products and the design of PIPV will be presented from the context of design processes. This chapter demonstrates that many relevant issues regarding PIPV have not been explored thoroughly so far, in particular energy-efficient management of PIPV-battery systems, environmental aspects of PV technology in products, manufacturing of integrated PV in products, and user experiences with PIPV in different product categories. As PIPV can offer energy to products with a wide range of power demand, it is expected in future to become common, for instance, in public lighting products, sensors, boats, cars, and in urban furniture.

Very large-scale photovoltaic (VLS-PV) applications are addressed in Chapter 1.35 by Tomoki Ehara, Keiichi Komoto, and Peter van der Vleuten. VLS-PV was presented over a decade ago by the International Energy Agency-Photovoltaic Power Systems Programme (IEA-PVPS) Task 8 group [16]. This concept is to generate electricity in a desert region where solar irradiation is abundant. It also aims to achieve socioeconomic development in the region. A wide range of feasibility studies of the VLS-PV concept performed in the past 12 years is presented; these include not only technical perspectives, but also economic and environmental point of views. Further, current trends and actual projects are described.

Concentration photovoltaics (CPV) is one of the PV applications with highest efficiency in the field. Chapter 1.36 by Maria Martinez, Oscar de la Rubia, Francisco Rubio, and Pedro Banda state that since 2005, CPV systems are becoming commercially available and are experiencing a technological and industrial development momentum, complementing the growth of the global renewable energy market. Standardization and evaluation of demonstration systems are helping to establish reliability and quality standards for the CPV industry. CPV is sensitive only to direct radiation, which is collected by optical components and concentrated onto very high-efficiency solar cells. Systems are mounted on high-accuracy dual-axis trackers for their operation in the high solar resource areas of the world. Finally, this chapter presents operational results, showing that CPV technology is capable of performing optimally in regions with very high radiation and temperatures, but it also performs reasonably well in medium radiation regions like Spain.

Chapter 1.37 by Geoffrey Landis presents an old idea that is recently revitalized: solar power satellites. These collect solar irradiation and transfer the electrical energy using microwaves to large earth-based antennae. It is shown that the fundamental physics are feasible, but economical feasibility is as yet an open question. Although a space location for the solar panels gets more sun than a ground location, the bottom line numbers show that it is not that much more solar energy than the best ground locations. The added power mostly comes from 24 h sunlight, but much of the power may thus be produced when the need is low.

In Chapter 1.38, Nicola Pearsall and Ralph Gottschalg address performance monitoring of PV systems. Monitoring allows the determination of its energy output and any operational issues over its lifetime. As PV systems have moved from demonstration of the technology to commercial energy generation, the main purpose of the monitoring has also changed. This has resulted in new approaches and services meeting the requirements of the system owners. This chapter describes the principles of PV system monitoring and how it is now achieved in practice.

The last chapter in the volume deals with standards of PV technology: Chapter 1.39 by Heinz Ossenbrink, Harald Müllejans, Robert Kenny, Nigel Taylor, and Ewan Dunlop. The international standards relevant for PV devices and their measurement are developed within technical committee 82 (TC82) of the International Electrotechnical Committee (IEC). The way to new standards is normally paved by scientific research, first by single institutions and then applied by others of the international community. This might lead to some national standards. Eventually, however, once agreement in the international scientific community has been reached, an IEC standard is prepared. This chapter describes the international standards relevant for the determination of the electrical performance of PV devices.

1.02.3 Conclusion

It has been a long road to reach the present competitiveness for PV in predominantly retail electricity, and clearly still further developments are needed to ensure further deployment and increased competitiveness of PV in wholesale electricity in the coming decades. This volume on PV technology, as part of the *Comprehensive Renewable Energy* volume-set, presents a 39-chapter overview of the status in PV technology and its applications, its economic and technological development over the past decades, and future directions in PV technology R&D and applications. It is intended to provide a wealth of information for the fast growing and diverse group of professionals globally active in R&D and deployment, as all are needed together to join forces in reaching the ambitious targets set to help mitigate climate change by the middle of this century.

References

[1] Becquerel E (1839) Mémoire sur les effets électriques produits sous l'influence des rayons solaires. *Comptes Rendus de L´Academie des Sciences* 9: 561–567.
[2] Planck M (1901) Ueber die elementarquanta der materie und der elektricität. *Annalen der Physik* 309(3): 564–566.
[3] Einstein A (1905) Über einen die erzeugung und verwandlung des lichtes betreffenden heuristischen gesichtspunkt. *Annalen der Physik* 322(6): 132–148.
[4] Chapin DM, Fuller CS, and Pearson GL (1954) A new silicon p-n junction photocell for converting solar radiation into electrical power. *Journal of Applied Physics* 25: 676.
[5] Data from various issues of *Photon International* (February, 2009, 2010, and 2011), and PV News (June, 2011) see also Chapter 2.
[6] Lipp J (2007) Lessons for effective renewable electricity policy from Denmark, Germany and the United Kingdom. *Energy Policy* 5: 5481–5495.
[7] European Climate Foundation, Roadmap 2050: A practical guide to a prosperous, low-carbon Europe, 2010. http://www.roadmap2050.eu/(accessed 21 February 2012).
[8] Green MA, Emery K, Hishikawa Y, *et al.* (2011) Solar cell efficiency tables (version 38). *Progress in Photovoltaics: Research and Applications* 19: 565–572.
[9] Luque A (2011) Will we exceed 50% efficiency in photovoltaics? *Journal of Applied Physics* 110: 031301.
[10] van Sark WGJHM, Alsema EA, Junginger HM, *et al.* (2008) Accuracy of progress ratios determined from experience curves: The case of photovoltaic technology development. *Progress in Photovoltaics: Research and Applications* 16: 441–453.
[11] European Photovoltaic Industry Association (EPIA) (2011) Solar photovoltaics competing in the energy sector – On the road to competitiveness. Brussels: EPIA.
[12] Sinke WC (2009) Grid parity: Holy Grail or hype? – Photovoltaic solar electricity on its way to competitiveness. *Sustainable Energy Review* 3(1): 34–37.
[13] Reich NH, Mueller B, Armbruster A, *et al.* (2012) Performance ratio revisited: Are PR >90% realistic? *Progress in Photovoltaics* 20 (in press).
[14] Green MA (2003) *Third Generation Photovoltaic: Advanced Solar Energy Conversion.* Springer Series in Photonics, Vol. 12. New York: Springer.
[15] Shockley W and Queisser HJ (1961) Detailed balance limit of efficiency of p-n junction solar cells. *Journal of Applied Physics* 32(3): 510–519.
[16] International Energy Agency-Photovoltaic Power Systems Programme (IEA-PVPS), Task 8. http://www.iea-pvps.org/index.php?id=35 (accessed 27 October 2011).

1.03 Solar Photovoltaics Technology: No Longer an Outlier

LL Kazmerski, National Renewable Energy Laboratory, Golden, CO, USA

© 2012 Elsevier Ltd. All rights reserved.

1.03.1	**A Look at Policies, Progress, and Prognosis**	13
1.03.2	**A Glimpse at the Industry, the World, and the Markets**	16
1.03.3	**The Technologies**	18
1.03.3.1	Evolutionary Technologies	19
1.03.3.1.1	Crystalline Si (the base case)	20
1.03.3.1.2	Accelerating evolution (Si and first thin films)	20
1.03.3.2	Disruptive Technologies	21
1.03.3.2.1	Disruptive crystalline Si approaches	21
1.03.3.2.2	Thin films: amorphous, nano-, micro-, and polycrystalline Si	21
1.03.3.2.3	Thin-film copper indium diselenide, its alloys, and related chalcopyrites	22
1.03.3.2.4	Cadmium telluride	23
1.03.3.2.5	Very high-efficiency and concentrator devices	24
1.03.3.3	Revolutionary Photovoltaics: The Chase Toward the Next Generations	25
1.03.3.3.1	Fooling mother nature	26
1.03.3.3.2	Just one word – 'plastics'	26
1.03.3.3.3	Using more sun, less real estate	26
1.03.3.3.4	Hot flashes	26
1.03.3.3.5	Retro-voltaics	26
1.03.3.3.6	The far side	26
1.03.4	**Conclusions**	27
Acknowledgments		28
References		28
Further Reading		30

Glossary

Amorphous material One having no definite form or structure; random in character; a material with short-range order.

Bankability The term is used to describe the likelihood of success of a given photovoltaic (PV) technology. For example, if a PV technology is just too expensive to manufacture (e.g., more expensive than the selling price), it lacks 'bankability'.

Disruptive technology An innovation that helps create a new market or value network (changes an existing technology or market or value network in a beneficial sense that is not expected).

Organic A class of compounds whose molecules or structures are based upon carbon (although some carbon-containing materials, such as diamond and graphite, are considered inorganic). Organic PV materials are growing in interest, sometimes referred to 'plastic solar cells'.

Inorganic A class of compounds or materials considered to be nonbiological in nature. Most of PVs has been based upon inorganic semiconductors (silicon, gallium arsenide, copper indium selenide, cadmium telluride, etc.)

Metamorphic Usually refers to a change in form. In the case of PVs, the major reference is to layers in multijunction solar cells that are mismatched in their lattice parameters.

Microcrystalline material A material that has small grains or crystallites that are visible only through microscopic examination. Sometimes, it refers to materials having grains or crystallines in the micrometer-size range.

Nanocrystalline material A polycrystalline material with crystallite or grain size of only a few nanometers.

Polycrystalline A class of solids that are composed of many crystallites of varying size and orientation. For PV materials, the degree of 'polycrystallinity' can range from that visible to the eye (such as multicrystalline Si usually from casting) to those of sizes to the 10^{-6}–10^{-9} cm range, only detectable through microscopic observation.

1.03.1 A Look at Policies, Progress, and Prognosis

Almost 60 years ago, solar electricity technology marked a significant modern tipping point [1] at Bell Telephone Laboratories when Daryl Chapin, Gerald Pearson, and Calvin Fuller abruptly turned a research curiosity into a viable electricity producer [2]. This accomplishment was made more significant with the coming of a second turning point, this one marked by the opening of the first real photovoltaics (PV) market – space. On 17 March 1958, Vanguard, the first solar PV-powered satellite, reached orbit [3, 4], leading to a revolution in wireless communication that underlies all our modern information transfer – from cell phones and ATM machines to our huge current obsession in social networking.

In these formative years for this technology, Bell Labs and others showed that technology could be transferred rapidly from the laboratory bench to the consumer – something we have lost the ability to do effectively and an attribute desperately needed today for our continuing energy challenges. For renewable energy technologies, a return to this model of accelerated development and deployment (without neglecting either component!) is mandatory. This is especially true with the overlying energy concerns such as expanding business, particularly in the developing world; making our energy sources secure; and improving our environment to prevent a possible undesirable 'point of no return' in a critical global warming scenario. Certainly, this critical focus on renewable energy sources is sharpened by the recent rash of unfortunate man-made and natural disasters, from Hurricane Katrina to the Japan earthquake and nuclear catastrophe at Fukushima – involving loss of life, property, environment, and economy [5–11].

PV as a technology and a world industry had annual production of more than 20 GW in 2010 and is an approximately $70 billion business at the beginning of 2011. Production growth has exceeded 30% annually over the last 12 years – highlighted by a greater than 100% growth in 2010 [12, 13]; **Figure 1** presents one set of historical PV production data. This growth is despite the world economic problems that have been lingering since 2009. But this exceptional growth of the technology despite the sagging world economy bolsters the facts that PV is truly a 'real' business now, is proving itself as a competitor in the electricity sector, and is expected to exhibit substantial annual increase in capacity, production, and installations for some time to come.

Much of this growth has been the result of government incentives, mainly pioneered in Japan and Germany [12–17] and now reaching into the rest of the world [14]. Governments are showing that policies make a difference. Certainly, the incentives have spurred markets, but Germany and Japan have also received more substantial economic benefits, namely, industry growth and substantial creation of high-value jobs [15, 16]. These benefits were quickly grasped by the largest-growing economy and the biggest exporter in the world, 'China'. China supplied about one-third of the world's PV product in 2008, more than 40% in 2009, and nearly 50% in 2010 [17]. This is occurring because markets are growing, installations are booming, and acceptance of PV as an authentic electricity source is expanding among developed and developing populations. PV has advanced beyond the tipping point and is no longer an outlier [18] in our energy portfolios.

The successes of these policies sometimes overshadow equally important technology advancements. The solar energy cost of 16–23 US cents kWh^{-1} that has been reached today in the US grid-connected markets also required a progression of substantial and creative R&D improvement in materials, devices, fabrication, characterization, and processing. And all of this has led to better device performance and reliability, and lowered systems costs that the 'policies' have leveraged. Although these electricity prices have been decreasing steadily, they still remain far too high for the next wave of grid-tied applications by almost a factor of 2 (for prices on the consumer side of the meter) and about 4 times too high for wholesale (central utility) generation. The goals is for PV to achieve 'grid parity' by the start of the next decade. It has likely achieved grid parity already in the United States, for example, for peak-serving markets and more broadly, if it is fairly measured against 'unsubsidized' existing electricity sources using nuclear, coal, and natural gas [19–21].

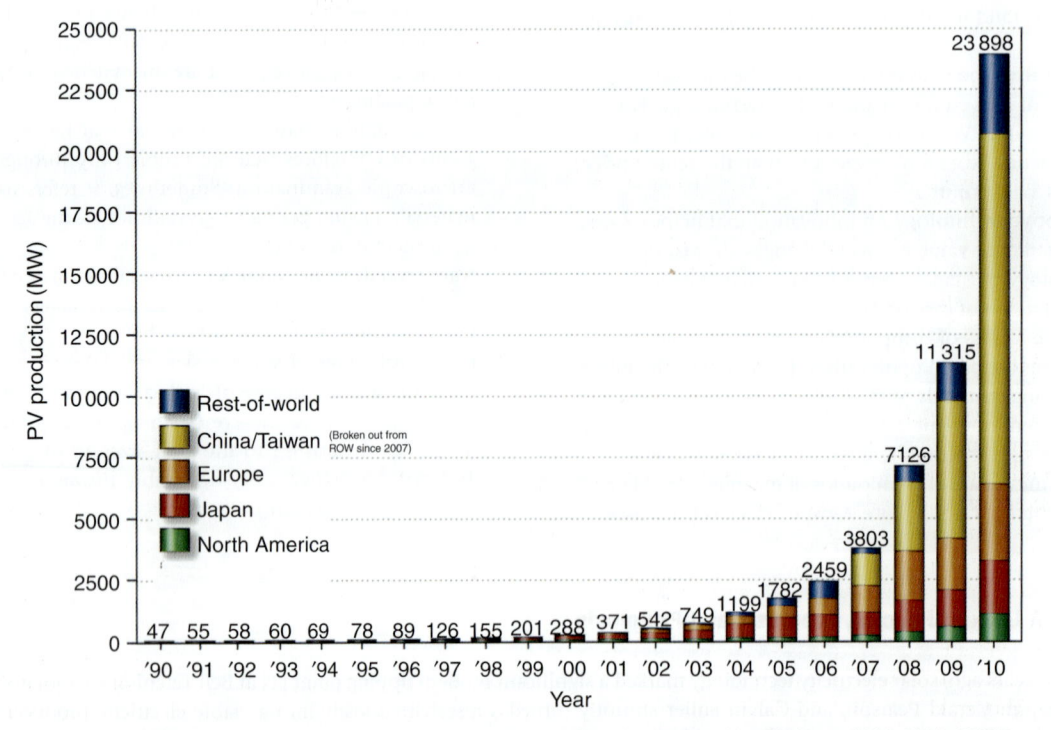

Figure 1 PV production 1990–2010, showing distribution by geographical area (Based on reports from PV News, 1980–2011, GTM Research, San Francisco).

Solar Photovoltaics Technology: No Longer an Outlier

Basic research driven

Technology investment pathways

'Closing the Gaps'

Time
Research bench discovery to consumer use

Performance
Research cells to predicted values
Commercial cells to research cells
Prototypes to commercial
Manufacturing cells to modules

Revolutionary (15 years and beyond)

Fundamental science
Third Generation PV
- Quantum dots
- Multiple excition generation (MEG)
- Nanotechnology
- Multi–multijunctions
- Thermophotonics
- Intermediate band
- Bio-inspired

Industry driven

Accelerated evolutionary (3–5 years)

Disruptive (5–15 years)

Technology driven

Applied science and technology
First and second Generation PV
- Lower Si feedstock prices
- Thinner Si wafer technology
- Thin films
- Improved processing
- Improved performance
- Advanced integration, packaging

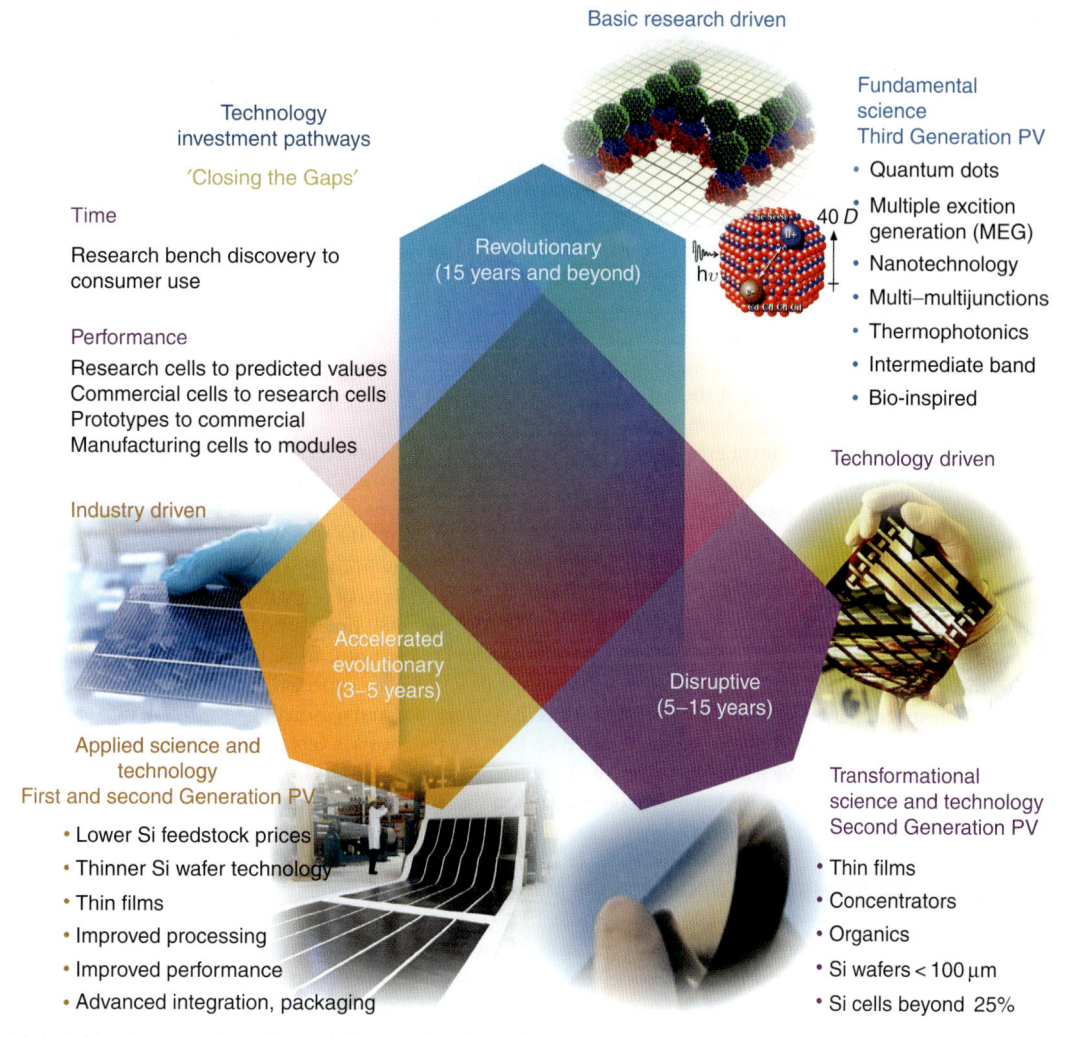

Transformational science and technology
Second Generation PV
- Thin films
- Concentrators
- Organics
- Si wafers < 100 μm
- Si cells beyond 25%

Figure 2 Technical investment pathways for evolutionary, disruptive, and revolutionary technologies.

What will it take to tip this technology to its next level – from these first multi-GW markets toward the terawatt echelons, and manufacturing plants from the current GW annual productions to 10s or 100s of GW? PV technology requires even 'more' innovation, science, and engineering to meet the growing and diverse technical and consumer demands. Neither policy nor technology advancement is sufficient 'on its own' to ensure a competitive PV future – both are essential elements for a sustainable pathway.

This chapter now looks at current PV technology status, the reasons underlying recent improvements, comparisons of approaches, with an emphasis on R&D needs and directions, and a brief look forward to what future-generation PV might encompass. **Figure 2** depicts technology investments. The 'now' PV markets are dominated by 'evolutionary technologies' (primarily crystalline Si), which need to be expanded and accelerated to meet near-term (2012–15) expectations. This evolutionary path has been experienced over the past 30 years, with a near classical 80% experience (or learning) characteristic (i.e., with the price of PV falling 20% for every doubling of manufacturing capacities [22, 23]). In fact, over the 1997–2007 period, this has been closer to a 90% experience curve – because of technology complications such as Si feedstock supply problems, capacity limitations at a time of growing product demands, and increased margins – and only now has returned to the 80% characteristic [22, 23].

These recent issues have also led to the realization that something more is needed, and that the major evolutionary paths are not those to position us for the 2020 and beyond technology demands and targets. The needed scenario calls for 'disruptive technologies', a very positive term in this context, representing improvement and innovation that we have experienced in our consumer lives many times. These push us off current learning curves, much like how the introduction of the integrated circuit significantly redirected us from discrete component electronics in the 1960s and how hard drives replaced our computers' floppy drives in the 1990s. Flat-screen displays have almost made us forget about cathode ray tubes in the 2000s, and the digital camera is the distractive accessory of almost every tourist. Disruptive technologies are accepted and sustained in a market because they have advantages. They offer price and/or performance value, as well as increases in manufacturing volume which bring about distinct consumer benefits – the ability to produce more product, to produce the product better, and the ability to produce better product. These disruptive choices are needed to meet mid-term targets (2015–25) and they include advanced thin films, organics, and concentrators, as well as progressive crystalline Si approaches. The shorter-term focus of the recently concluded Solar American Initiative (SAI) [24] included accelerating the evolutionary and making the disruptive real, with the goal of bringing the nation competitive solar electricity by 2015. (With the change in administrations in the United States, the 'Solar America Initiative' begun under the Bush Administration has been concluded [24]. The Initiative was largely an attempt to get the US manufacturing competitive in the short term and was a program more oriented in short vision, non-R&D investments. The US PV program is currently being restructured to make it more in line with the current goals of job creation, innovation, and economic recovery for the United States.) However, this US venture was too focused on the next year, rather than the more visionary and disruptive plans for a sustained effort. The US 'Sunspot' Initiative [25] has extended the timeframe to the end of this decade, but has imposed more aggressive targets that certainly will require R&D investment and the rapid realization of disruptive PV. This is expected to include Si, current thin films, concentrators, and the development of earth-abundant materials, new and refined solar-cell architectures, and performance improvements that quickly significantly reduce the gaps between 'best-in-class' research efficiencies and commercial product performances and the times between research discovery and use by the consumer.

Certainly among the previously ignored or discounted areas are the high-potential, high-risk 'revolutionary technologies' – those based on nanotechnology and 'innovation at the extreme', leading to cost and performance territories well beyond the limits of conventional approaches. These technologies have enormous payback potential, but are inherently wedded to that immense risk. They need a longer time to incubate, because most exist only as concepts and may need the discovery of technology and science not yet in our textbooks. They may not prove themselves until 2030 or beyond, but they are the 'PV' that can have efficiencies of 60% or more and/or prices an order of magnitude lower than now, serving the next generations of consumers with extraordinary clean energy technology. They include the quantum dot, the intermediate-band approach, the bioinspired, the nanophotonic, and the multi-multijunctions [26–28]. There is also a genuine concern for PV sustainability from the consideration of using readily available and safe materials throughout the system. The focus on 'earth-abundant' materials has even led to the renaissance of R&D on 'retro-voltaics', that is, those technologies that were evaluated during the 1950–early 1980 timeframe, but just did not make it because of performance failures [29]. With the 30–50 years of improved understanding of electronic materials and the sizeable improvement in both processing and characterization techniques (down to the nanoscales), there are expectations that these resurrected approaches can again become mainstream players. The key point of **Figure 2** is that a balanced and reasonable investment into each of these areas is needed for a sustained solar PV energy future for the world. With that, the prognosis is very good; but it shifts to excellent when we realize that we can create our future. "We learn from where we have been, and can take satisfaction from getting to where we are – but our future depends on taking us to where we know we should be. And the best way to protect our future is to create it … ."

1.03.2 A Glimpse at the Industry, the World, and the Markets

A PV-industry annual growth of 30%, reflected in vast portions of the production data of **Figure 1**, closely mirrors that for the semiconductor or some electronic product industry (e.g., flat-panel displays), rather than for the slower ('2%' level) traditional electricity power sector [30]. The recent growths of 50% to beyond 100% would bring solar electricity to hoped for levels before mid-century [31–33]. The industry growth and projections, based on input from the industry itself, are shown in **Figure 3**, and

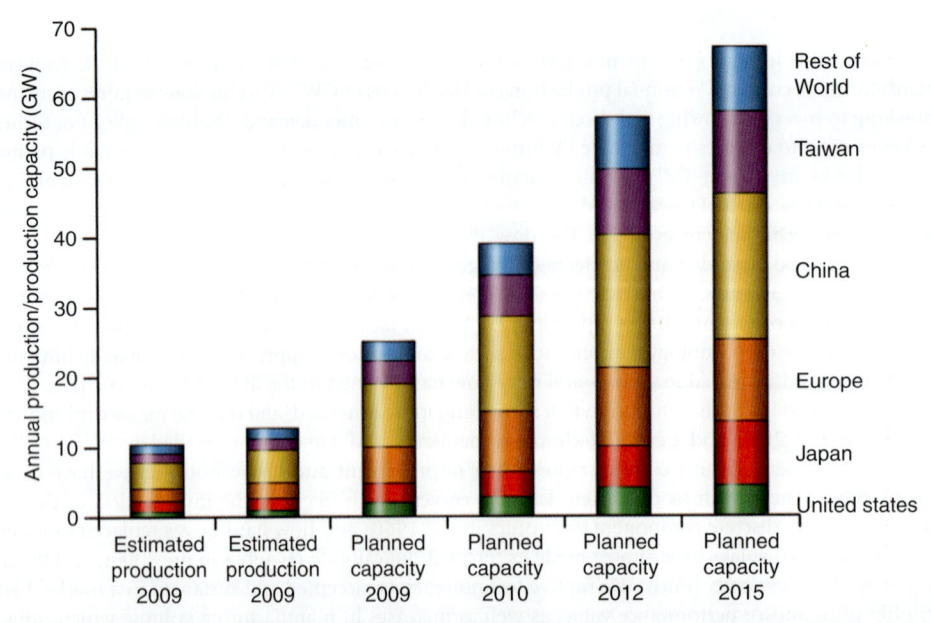

Figure 3 Current and planned production and capacity for 2009, 2010, 2012, and 2015. Intergovernmental Panel on Climate Change (IPCC) (in press) *Special Report on Renewable Energy Sources and Climate Change Mitigation (SRREN)* (United Nations, ipcc-wg3, 2010); Jäger-Waldau A (2010) Status and perspectives of thin film photovoltaics. In: *Thin Film Solar Cells: Current Status and Future Trends.* New York, NY: Nova Publishers [30, 34].

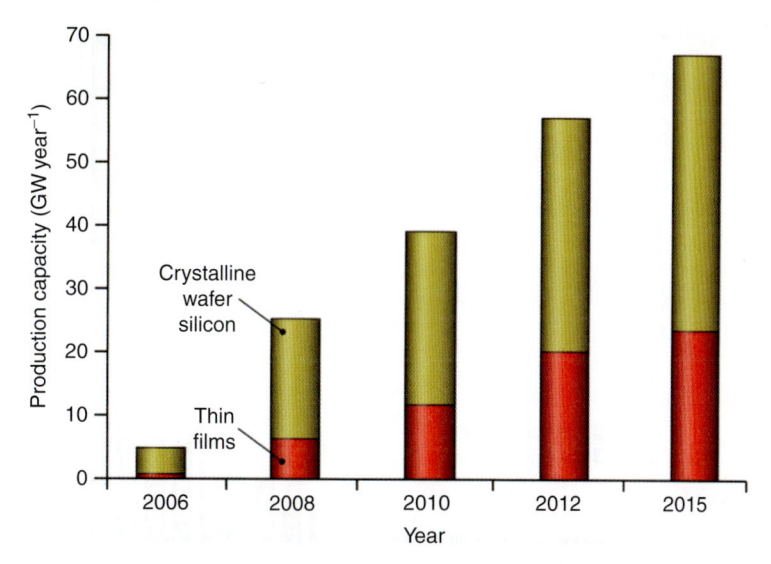

Figure 4 Comparison of crystalline Si and thin-film technology production, 2006–15. Jäger-Waldau A (2010) Status and perspectives of thin film photovoltaics. In: *Thin Film Solar Cells: Current Status and Future Trends*. New York, NY: Nova Publishers [34].

report conservative expectations of production of nearly 70 GW by 2015 [30, 34]. A continued trend toward production dominance from Asia (China, Taiwan, and Japan) is evident. Another interesting trend from this reporting source is the growth in the contribution from the thin-film PV technologies presented in **Figure 4** [35]. The 15–17% share of the production in 2009 and 2010 for these technologies can possibly increase to 34% of an expected 67.5 GW of capacity in 2015. The current population of up to 160 thin-film companies will certainly diminish [36], but the thin-film industry itself will expand through consolidation, amalgamation, technology choice, and market specification. However, this does not mean that crystalline Si is declining – but rather, that the incredible anticipated market growths will require added capacities and a diversity of technological approaches.

The reader should be alerted to some differences in terminology when speaking about PV 'growth'. In general, 'production' is the most-commonly cited value and is perhaps the easiest to measure, but prone to interpretation. It represents the number of watts of PV that come off the production line in a given year. However, as pointed out very correctly by Navigant Consulting, it is very easy to double or triple count [37], that is, a Si cell can be manufactured (counted in the total) and shipped to a module manufacturer (then recounted in the total). This is one reason that various sources differ on their numbers. 'Capacity' represents the manufacturing 'boiler specification' on what the factories could put out if at full production. Finally, 'installations' represent the actual number of these 'watts' that are actually fitted into the wide number of applications (roughly the number sold or shipped into our markets). Not all cells or modules that are produced in a given year are used to generate watts in that year, but may be stockpiled as inventory.

Where does this PV go? First, let us look at applications. A dozen years ago, the major use was for off-grid applications such as water pumping, communications, and water pumping/irrigation. With policy changes, this has changed dramatically, as indicated in **Figure 5** [38]. In 2009 and 2010, less than 1% of what was installed was off-grid, and the cumulative total is about 5%. PV has started to stake its presence as a reliable component of the electricity in the developed rather than developing world. The complementary nature of solar PV is striking – often producing power at a time when electricity is most in demand (and most expensive) – serving the peaking markets for electricity. One argument supporting the value of PV is that utilities can use the Sun to provide that 5–6 h demand in a market instead of having to commission a gas- or coal-fired plant that has to produce this same electricity for a 24-h period. For the consumer or the commercial supplier, the grid serves as their storage – selling during the daylight hours and buying back at night.

Because this technology is still expensive compared to 'conventional' electricity supplies, the installations correlate with those countries that have the policies to stimulate and support the markets. **Figure 6** illustrates this, where Germany, which has pioneered the feed-in tariff, remains the largest market in the world. (In fact, the sum of cumulative installations through 2009 from the next 99 ranked markets are less than those for Germany.) What is noteworthy is the sustained growth in those German markets over all others.

The concentrating PV (CPV) market has been emerging, with about a cumulative 25–30 MW installed through 2010. These markets are twofold: low-to-medium concentration (2× to 250×) and high concentration (greater than 250×). The high-concentration PV markets are finding a home in the 25–100 MW installation range, that is, those below the solar thermal electric or concentration solar power (CSP) utility scales, which have been considered to be economical only in larger (100–200 MW or greater) size. Low-concentration PV applications include commercial buildings and other distributed power applications.

The solar markets certainly are awaiting the opening of new horizons. These include India with their progressing 'Nehru Solar Mission' of having 20 GW installed by 2022 [39] and China's National Development and Reform Commission plan for 15% of total energy by renewables by 2020 [40] (and the recent inception of the feed-in tariff for China). Of course, Europe continues to be the foundation of the markets, and the United States has started to show some commitment and movement, though the economy and political changes continue to deprive PV and other renewable energy sources of a much better position in the electricity portfolio [40].

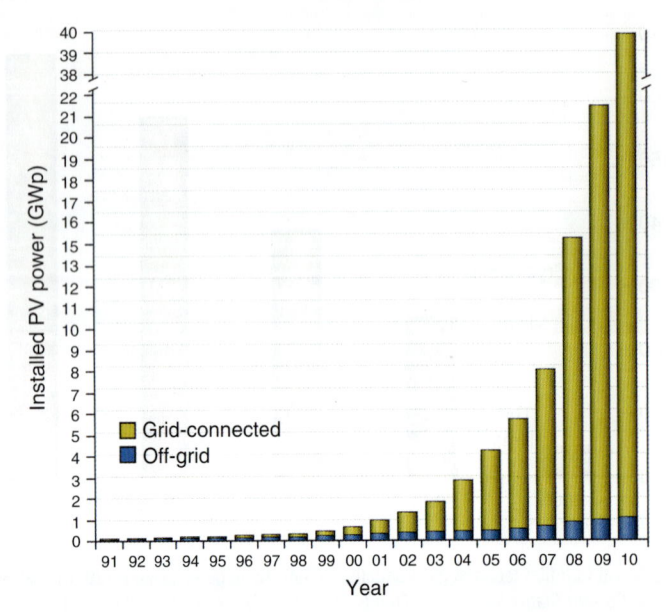

Figure 5 Comparisons of grid-connected and off-grid installations from 1992–2008, showing growing dominance of grid-connected PV applications since 1996. These data were updated for years 2009 and 2010 by the author. International Energy Agency (IEA) (2009) *Trends in Photovoltaic Applications: Survey Report of Selected IEA Countries Between 1992 and 2008*, IEA Photovoltaic Power Systems Program (PVPS) Task 1, p. 44 [38].

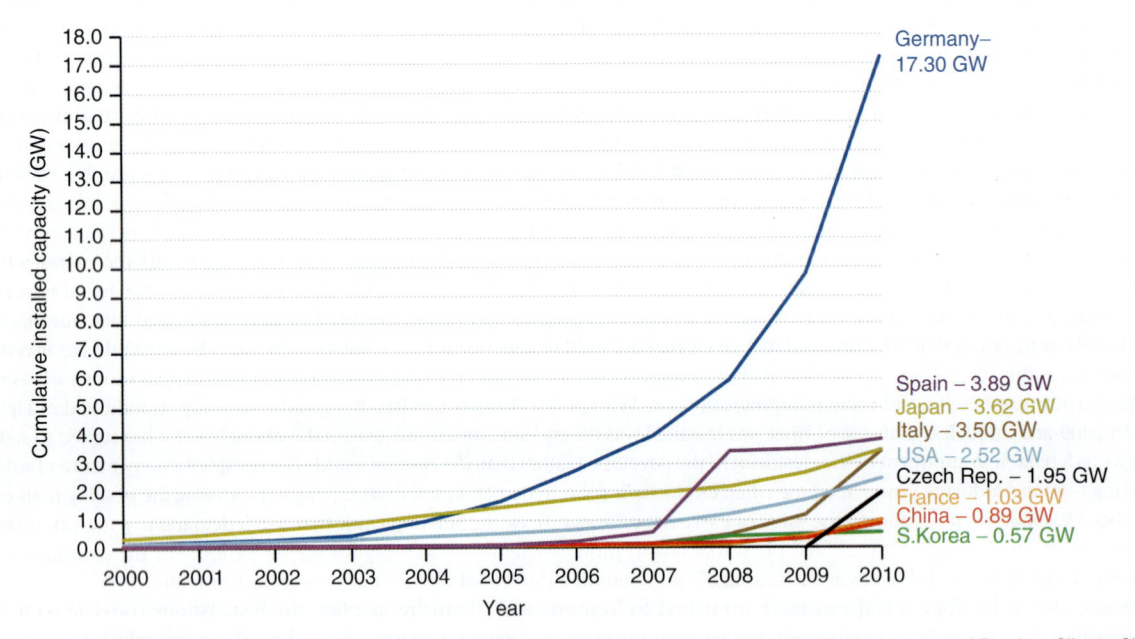

Figure 6 Installed PV capacity in leading country markets. These data were updated for 2011 by the author. Intergovernmental Panel on Climate Change (IPCC) (in press) *Special Report on Renewable Energy Sources and Climate Change Mitigation (SRREN)* (United Nations, ipcc-wg3, 2010); Jäger-Waldau A (2010) Status and perspectives of thin film photovoltaics. In: *Thin Film Solar Cells: Current Status and Future Trends*. New York, NY: Nova Publishers [30, 34].

1.03.3 The Technologies

Photovoltaic technologies still include a number of significant component-performance 'gaps' for various crystalline, polycrystalline, and amorphous technologies – both bulk and thin-film technologies. The 'first gap' is the breach between the theoretical limits (the attainable levels) and what has been demonstrated under the best conditions in the laboratory (the headline or record cells). These limits range from ~90% of attainable efficiency for crystalline Si to 50% for some thin films, to less than 25% for organic cells. **Figure 7** presents a summary representation of these gaps. Underlying these differences are losses that are inherent to the conversion process (theoretical to attainable), and the ability to fabricate the cell with the ensemble of optimal, interrelated properties and parameters. The gap between what can be attained and what has been reached is a major focus for researchers – a process of identifying,

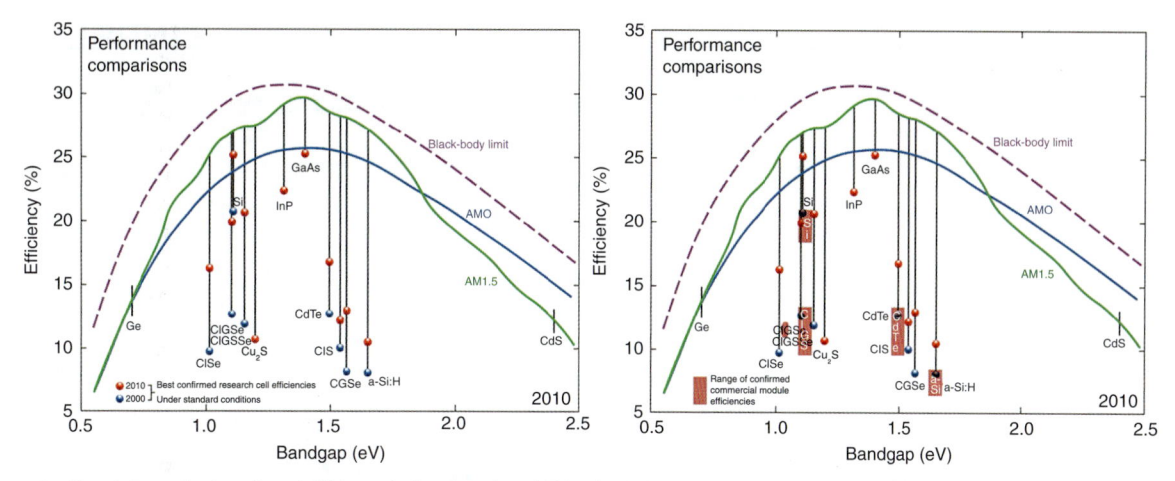

Figure 7 Gaps between best-confirmed efficiency devices for selected PV technologies and the black-body limit, the attainable AM0 and AM1.5 efficiencies. (a) 2010 status (compared to where these technologies were 10 years ago (dimmed dots)) and (b) Comparison to range of reported commercial modules currently for each technology (showing module efficiencies lag best cells by about 10 years). Modified with permission from Birkmire RW and Kazmerski LL (1999) In: Kapur VK, McConnell RD, Carlson D, et al. (eds.) *Photovoltaics for the 21st Century*, pp. 24–32. Electrochemical Society [42].

understanding, and minimizing losses – collecting every incident photon, allowing these to create the maximum number of electron-hole pairs, and then making these charge carriers live long enough to contribute to the process of generating electrical current.

The 'second gap' is the disparity between the laboratory efficiency of cells and those produced in commercial manufacturing lines. This has to do with scaling up the processing to larger areas, variations of materials (e.g., starting wafers, substrates, and coatings), less-controlled conditions, and higher required throughputs. The 'third gap' is that between the cell efficiencies and those of the modules. This depends on the ability to minimize the losses when wiring the cells into circuits, bringing the active area of the module to be closer to the cell area, and maximizing the optical transmission of the protective or support layers that are positioned between the cells and the incident sunlight. These gaps are ones that can and must be addressed and minimized, and they are active areas of R&D for all PV technologies [42–44]. Progress has been made – with current commercial module efficiencies about the same values as the best (one-of-a-kind) research cells 15–20 years ago. However, this progress in 'gap shrinking' has to be accelerated radically to bring make this clean power more acceptable in consumer markets.

Progress in PV technology can be measured in several ways. Researchers use their understanding of known device parameters (e.g., open-circuit voltage, short-circuit current, fill factor, dark current, junction capacitance, defect density of states, and band alignments) to help guide device improvements. Certainly, the cell efficiency is a benchmark of technology potential. **Figure 8** presents a snapshot of technology change over the past three decades for various materials-based cells – in this case, for research devices that have been measured under standard conditions in various laboratories around the world. (This efficiency graph has been maintained by L. L. Kazmerski at the National Renewable Energy Laboratory since 1984, and it represents the best *research-device* efficiencies confirmed in each of the cell technologies at one of the standard cell measurement laboratories around the world. It can be found on the NREL website and on Wikipedia [45].) Sometimes, these data are dismissed as 'incremental' improvements in technology, which is an attempt to diminish the contributions or the importance of such an ensemble of information.

First, such trends and improvements provide a demonstration of technology and indication of potential. Second, many lesser informed individuals do not appreciate that a 'materials line', such as single crystal Si, is a mosaic of many different technologies and device configurations – some of which are completely different than a recent predecessor, but all of which have been built on the understanding developed in the past. Third, some not so experienced in technology do not appreciate that improvements in research technologies can overcome problems that have stagnated commercial product. Thus, the improvement in the open-circuit voltage of a CdTe or CIGS thin-film cell can provide the pathway for improving a commercial module by several percentage points. Materials design can potentially replace more expensive, less available, or environmentally worrisome elements with alternatives – alternatives that might also improve performance. Insight from such fundamental and applied research can tip a technology from being merely 'interesting' to having real commercial readiness.

1.03.3.1 Evolutionary Technologies

Of the about 20 GW of PV commercial production in 2010 and 2011, about 84–87% were single-crystal, multicrystalline, ribbon, and sheet silicon [46]. Although these capacities might even triple in the next 3 years (with the experience in 2010), this 'over' demand for the 'semiconductor foundation' of the PV industry will likely lag behind the marketplace – as long as the incentives in Europe grow – and even more so if those starting to flourish in the United States are expanded by the change in political climate and growing public preference and acceptance. The plummeting of Si module prices over the past 2 years has been driven by the dominating Chinese manufacturers. There is considerable speculation on why this has happened, ranging from their 'superior manufacturing approaches' to allegations of 'illegitimate government assistance'. In any case, China has driven the price down for all PV module technologies to ranges that are more appealing to us as consumers.

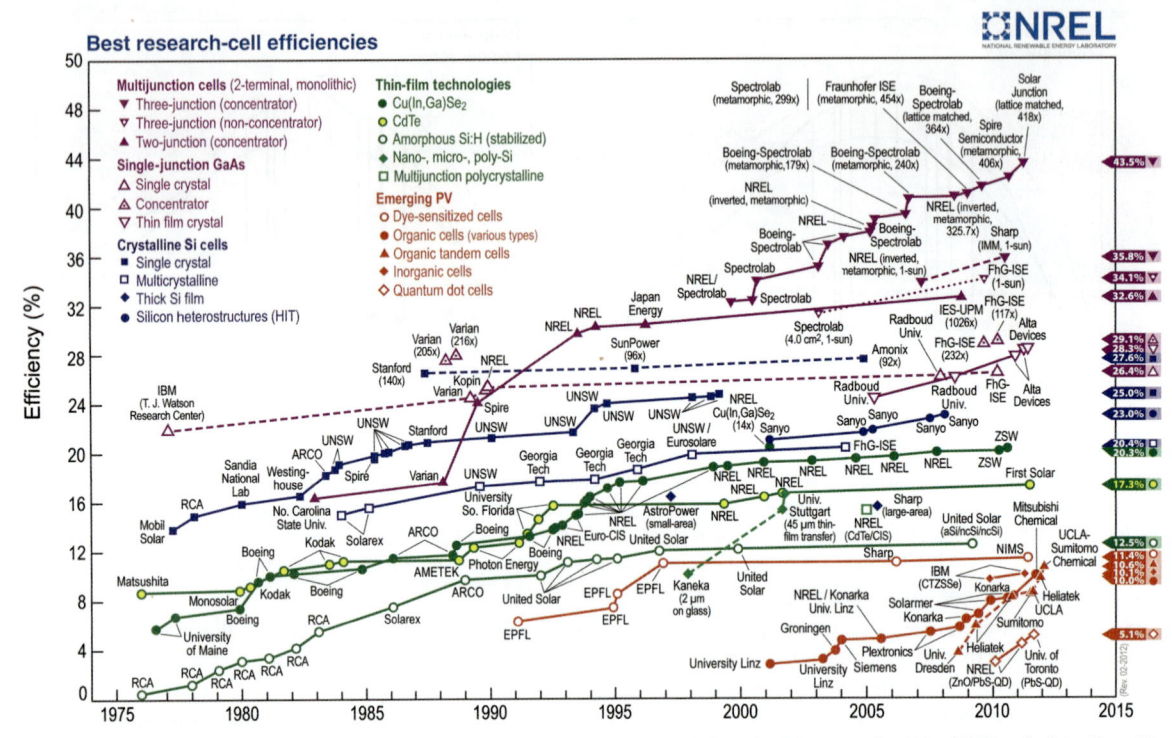

Figure 8 Best research-cell efficiencies as a function of time for various technologies. NREL website (www.nrel.gov) and Wikipedia (http://en.wikipedia.org/wiki/Solar_cell_efficiency) [45]. This is a snapshot of the status of these technologies taken in February 2012. The records change – and the reader is asked to check the latest version of this chart as referenced.

1.03.3.1.1 Crystalline Si (the base case)

We know more about Si than any other material – with a new paper published every 4 min in the literature about this leading electronic material! The relatively simple, conventional p–n junctions of the early 1980s have evolved toward more intelligent designs and complicated structures – all aimed at capturing every incident photon, maximizing electron-hole generation, and prolonging the lifetime of those carriers to be collected for maximizing current generation. The evolution of these designs has included metal/insulator/n-type/p-type (MINP), passivated emitter solar cells (PESCs), single-sided and doubled-sided buried contacts (SSBCs and DSBCs), point contact, and bifacial cells [47, 48]. It would appear that the single-crystal research phase plateaued some 10 years ago (**Figure 8**), leaving the impression that other technologies can only gain on this frontrunner. This limited viewpoint has not clouded the research thinking and strategies of some parts of the world, particularly in Europe and Japan, where it has been recognized that there are significant improvements for both current commercial approaches and especially potential next generation of Si solar technologies. The experience has been that every time Si technology has been judged to be 'ill' or 'on its deathbed', the technology innovators have continued to surprise us with new and creative approaches.

1.03.3.1.2 Accelerating evolution (Si and first thin films)

The Si industry has been reinstating previous market trends through material economy (e.g., thinner wafers, lowering kerf losses, adopting sheet and alternative thinner Si production, lowering processing costs and improving manufacturing, and improving performance). This is aimed at accelerating this technology to meet cost and price targets. Commercial cells have already been demonstrated at 23% or more on today's manufacturing lines (and modules above 20% efficiency). The best of the commercial designs are shown in **Figure 9**, although the Saturn cell was taken out of production last year, a victim of 'bankability'. Additionally, the shortage of adequate Si feedstock over the past few years has had another effect – bringing what have been termed 'second-generation' technologies to the market much sooner. These technologies have included the veteran a-Si:H thin films, the mercurial thin-film CdTe, and some newer Cu(In,Ga)Se$_2$ (or CIGS)-based technologies. Although it can be argued that these are advanced evolutionary technologies, they still represent a small, though growing, market share. The capabilities of these manufacturing operations have been expanding in response to market opportunities, with several manufactures more than tripling their production capacities, including the expansion to strategic locations around the world. These technologies continue to be extremely important, as indicated in the next sections.

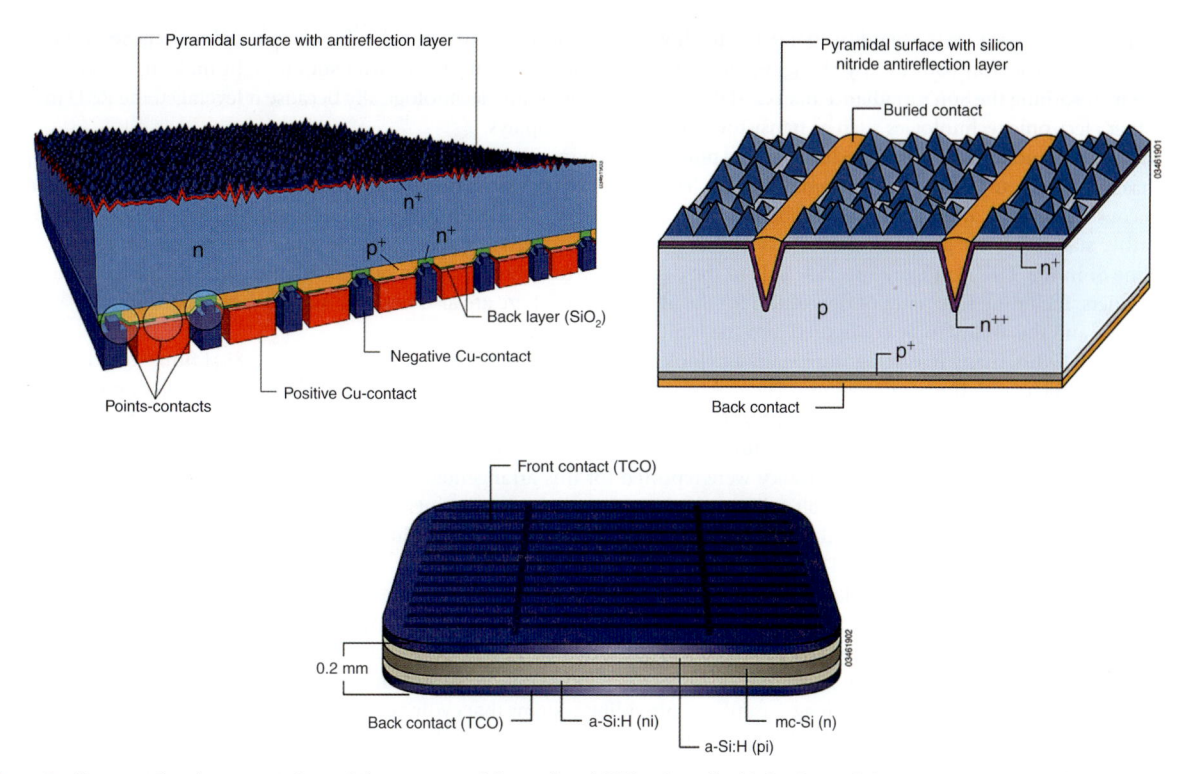

Figure 9 Cross-sectional representations of three commercially produced 20% solar cells: (a) SunPower Point-contact cell; (b) BP Saturn cell; and (c) Sanyo heterojunction or 'HIT' cell.

1.03.3.2 Disruptive Technologies

Again, 'disruptive' is a 'positive' description in this context, as it describes the case in which a new technology starts to take over because of its beneficial attributes compared to past approaches. In the context of our 'learning curve' discussions, it can be viewed as departing abruptly from the evolutionary 80–90% characteristic – with perhaps a 40–60% characteristic for some condensed period – giving the impression that the technology has 'jumped' for a while from the expected one. The disruptive technologies use here thinner layers, other materials, and other approaches than the traditional single-junction, 1-sun converter.

1.03.3.2.1 Disruptive crystalline Si approaches

Some have a misconception that there is little left to do in crystalline Si research. After all, since the Si technology 'tipping point' at Bell Telephone Labs nearly 60 years ago, cells have reached laboratory performances converting nearly one-fourth of the incident photons into electrical power – reaching about 90% of its reported 'theoretical limit'. There are approaches now being pursued to use even less material (thin and thinned wafers with thicknesses of 100 µm or less), extremely high efficiencies (targeted in the range 25–29%), and innovative processing and device engineering that can lower costs and increase yields/throughputs considerably. Another approach is to use extremely thin layers (sub-30 µm) that are initially grown on inexpensive foreign substrates at relatively low temperatures. With enhanced grain growth in these Si films, high efficiencies can be realized using light engineering techniques [49]. Such improvements are disruptive and can recast the thinking whether silicon can compete at the substantially sub-$1 per watt system price that other emerging technologies have taken as their exclusive real estate value in the longer term.

Alternatively, crystalline Si devices can be enhanced by manipulating and localizing the available light radiation [50, 51]. Recently, specially designed metallic and metallodielectric nanoparticle arrays have been used to exploit 'plasmonic effects', in particular to use the high reflection and absorption coefficients of these metallic structure to guide, focus, and switch light at visible and infrared wavelengths. This is based upon the phenomenon that the real part of the dielectric constant changes near the plasmon frequency where optical extinction is resonantly enhanced. This intricate and innovative nanoengineering of the Si devices (or other PV technologies) can enhance the light capture and related device parameters for increasing device performance.

1.03.3.2.2 Thin films: amorphous, nano-, micro-, and polycrystalline Si

Thin-film PV is always looked at as the much younger sibling of the silicon technology – poised to take over the energy production responsibilities of its mature relative, but never quite fulfilling its expectations or potential. Thin-film PV is not new – in fact, they made a visible appearance at the same time as the Bell Lab discovery, with Cu_2S/CdS devices that were actually considered to be the power sources in the first Vanguard satellite [52]. The introduction of a new class of semiconductors in the mid-1970s seemed to have positioned the ideal PV candidate absorber. Having no long-range and perhaps only limited short-range order, its physics was completely different than the crystalline Si model. Because of the defects associated with the 'dangling Si bonds', the amorphous Si was hydrogenated to reduce the bandgap states and to allow the development of open-circuit voltages. Its bandgap could be varied over tenths of an electron volt (eV) by changing the hydrogen content. Its optical characteristics in light make it 100 times more effective in absorbing the Sun's irradiance than crystalline Si. It also benefited technologically because it leveraged the R&D interests from other electronic technologies such as transistors and flat-panel displays.

The universal adoption of this PV technology has primarily been impaired by a single, important issue – 'stability'. The complete 'cure' has not been found, but cells and modules with less than 10% change in output characteristics are now attainable. Research groups continue to give attention to this problem – with several recent new paths toward understanding, depositing the material, and further stabilizing the semiconductor. This includes combining or using nanocrystalline and/or microcrystalline Si (or with crystalline Si in the 'HIT' configuration [53, 54]) in the device structure. From a viewpoint of manufacturing, this technology has some barriers, including slow rates of deposition for the absorber. But there are also benefits, such as better performance at higher temperature and the ability to be configured into the built environment.

In the mid-1990s, many research groups started to look at the first stages of crystallization of their a-Si:H films into nanocrystalline (nc) and microcrystalline (μc) regimes. The use of these longer-range order films 'at the edge' of the ordering process were deemed to provide the path toward devices with greater stability and higher performance. Some tagged this as the evolution of the amorphous technology toward thin-film crystalline silicon. The first advance was the introduction of the 'micromorph' solar cell [55]. Initial cells with 7.7% stabilized efficiency were reported for this arrangement, as well as an a-SiH/μc-SiH tandem cell with 10% stabilized efficiency. The micromorph cell was further improved with the introduction of a ZnO layer as an intermediate reflector. A major research effort exists today on microcrystalline and nanocrystalline films. The micromorph concept has progressed to commercial reality, with cells in the 13% range and modules near 12% efficiencies.

The large-scale deployment potential of these amorphous or micromorph technologies has been buoyed not from the device technologies, but rather, from the equipment suppliers. The introduction of large-scale turnkey systems has provided new directions for technology, markets, and applications. Certainly, the production equipment manufacturing companies have taken the industry in new directions. These directions are not only in producing larger modules and in new module handling and installation techniques, but also in providing technology versatility – providing systems that evolve performance improvements and technology changes to keep at the leading edge of thin-film advancements. This has perhaps reshaped how manufacturing has developed for PV in the past, where it is now the case of manufacturing shaping the technology rather than vice versa – although 'bankability' has also willowed some more visible approaches [56].

From the consideration of improving materials utilization, 'thin-film' Si was always the logical progression toward the ideal solar cell, and it has remained the holy grail of PV. Early work in this area was limited to cells having efficiencies in the 5% regime, much below expectations. These were mainly grown on foreign substrates, such as glass and graphite, using vacuum deposition and chemical vapor deposition – but always producing films with small grain sizes and high defect densities that limited carrier lifetimes. To learn more about the processes in thin-film Si, there has been some progress in both thinned and epitaxial layers of Si on Si. In addition, there has been some progress in polycrystalline thin-film Si on foreign substrates, including some recent commercial ventures [57–59].

Several demonstrations of thin Si cell performances have appeared in the literature over the past 10 years, mostly to demonstrate the viability of 'thin-Si' technology from the performance and device engineering perspectives. These demonstrations have ranged from thin epitaxial-Si films on Si substrates to Si on glass or ceramics, with the goal of being able to use inexpensive support structures in the latter case. A commercial entry that has attracted some attention and interest recently has been the 'crystalline silicon on glass' (CSG) technology. This approach had been under development by Pacific Solar in Australia since the mid-1990s, growing out of their analysis of the highest payoff paths to thin-film solar cell market penetration. Prototype modules into the 8–9% efficiency regime have been reached, and the expectation is to reach 10–12% levels in bringing this into consideration as a commercial product [57–59]. This concept has progressed rapidly from demonstration to prototyping and certainly has advantages if the performance levels, manufacturing cost, energy payback, and reliability parameters are realized in its first-time manufacturing phase (bankability again [56]). However, barriers still exist, and the 'DaVinci Code' for unraveling the complexities of this approach has not yet been solved.

1.03.3.2.3 Thin-film copper indium diselenide, its alloys, and related chalcopyrites

Interest in the Cu-ternary semiconductors began in the early 1970s; first for nonlinear optics and then for PV [60–62]. The bandgaps of several members (including $CuInX_2$, with X = S, Se, and Te) of this chalcopyrite family exhibited properties well suited for PV consideration. The device evolved into an alloy cousin, $Cu(In,Ga)Se_2$ and $Cu(In,Ga)(Se,S)_2$, which have slightly higher bandgaps (to about 1.2 eV for usual cell compositions compared to 1.04 eV for copper indium diselenide (CIS)) for better voltage output from this 'heterojunction' solar cell. The goal to increase the bandgap with the addition of Ga has been suppressed because of the nonlinearity of the V_{oc} versus Ga-content characteristics. Recently, however, a thin-film cell has been reported with an efficiency of 19.3% and a V_{oc} of xxx V, the highest for each of these combined parameters giving indication that this limitation can be overcome [63].

The best research cells have been validated at a remarkable 20.3% efficiency for thin-film CIGS devices (ZSW, **Figure 10(a)** [64]). This device technology had earlier provided the first polycrystalline cell with a better than 20% efficiency – at 21.1% under 14.3× concentration. Certainly, the positive and perhaps unique factors that favor this thin-film technology are stability and large-area production potential – with performance characteristics for smaller-area cells similar to the module performances. The best commercial modules have reached 13% with 4 ft^2 (0.37 m^2) areas, and manufacturers in the United States and Europe report 10–11.5% average efficiencies from their manufacturing lines. Submodules have been validated above 16% [51]. Research centers on the effects of alloying (with materials such as Ga and S), replacing the CdS window layers with Cd-free layers (including ZnS and

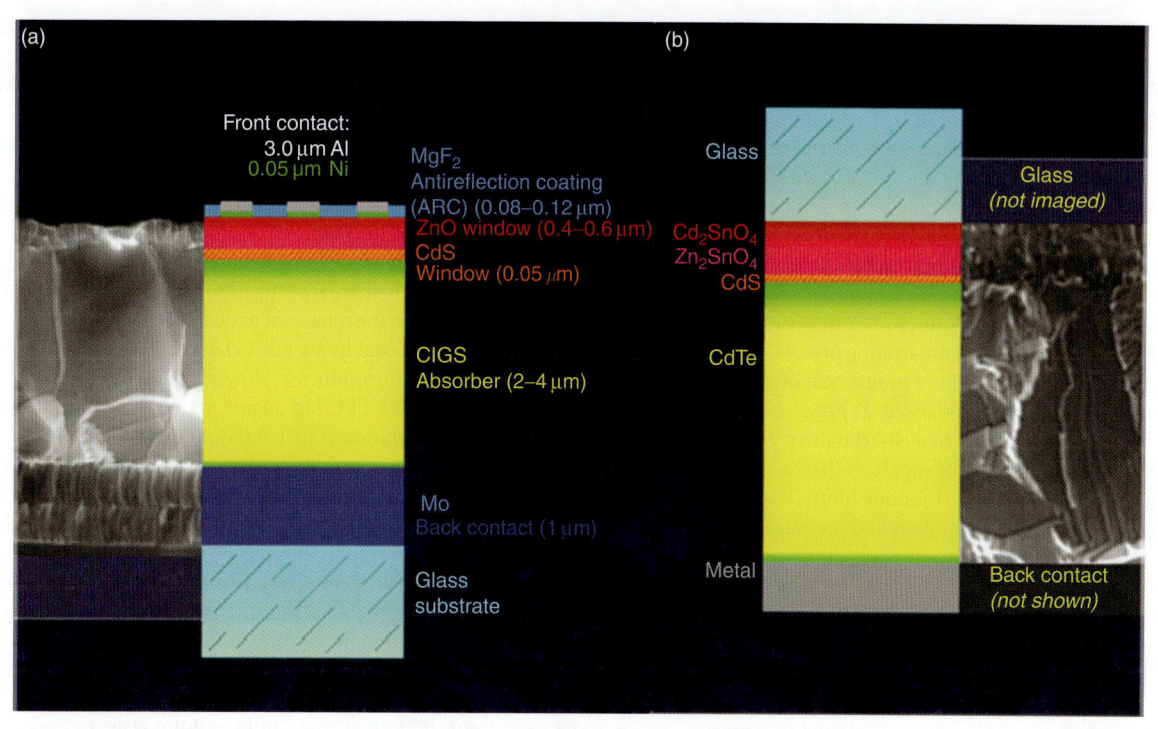

Figure 10 Cross-sections two major polycrystalline solar cells: (a) ZnO/CdS/CIGS cell and (b) CdS/CTe cell.

ZnO, with the best such cell ZnO/CIGS at 16.5% [65, 66]), and the use of nonglass substrates. The most successful of the nonglass approaches has been the use of flexible stainless steel, and commercial products for battery charging for military and recreational applications have efficiencies in the 8–11% range. Recently, commercial modules of this technology were verified with these better than 10% efficiency, providing both light weight and flexibility for the 'power roofing' applications – using both metallic (Global Solar, Tucson, USA) and plastic (Ascent Solar, Thornton, USA) substrates. Although this commercial activity is impressive, the number of these players is expected to decrease by consolidation or competition. Bankability issues have recently been raised within this technology with the departure of one visible and well-funded commercial venture [67, 68].

Work on other Cu-ternaries continues, with periodic reports of research progress on $CuGaSe_2$, $CuGaS_2$, and $CuInS_2$. This progress has some additional importance for new polycrystalline device directions – multijunction solar cells (or if this much thinner cell eventually is successful, as part of a multiple-junction approach). The United States had pioneered work in these polycrystalline multijunction technologies, but these efforts were cut from its national portfolio when the decision was made to focus on current or near-term technologies. Of course, others now have envisioned the worth of these approaches from both a performance and cost perspective, and the recent Japan roadmap provides the more far-sighted and innovative leadership to make this a reality.

Finally, a recent spin off brings back interest in the earth-abundant cousin of these chalcopyrite-related PV absorbers: $Cu_2(Zn,Sn)(S,Se)_4$ or CZTS. It is at the forefront of the bevy of new semiconductors under development. IBM brought this to the attention of the PV R&D community with thin-film devices validated at the 10% efficiency level. Numerous groups are pursuing this promising approach [69] – although the control of the material during deposition seems to be the most pressing problem [70, 71]. Vacuum co-deposition (Cu, Sn, Zn, and ZnS sources) and three-source sputtering of the metals followed for sulfurization (selenization) have been used (as well as spraying and electrodeposition), but the IBM atmospheric ink-based processing (which seems to less prone to the phase separation), is responsible for the best devices to date (10.1% in **Figure 8**). The Zn-compound solubility and contacting are key issues. The relatively sudden report of respectable devices and the IBM partnering with a leading thin-film manufacturer (Solar Frontier, Tokyo, Japan) gives this cell credibility and the kind of research demonstration to commercialization acceleration that is needed by PV.

1.03.3.2.4 Cadmium telluride

Since the 1960s, CdTe has been a candidate PV material – first for space, then as the 'next-in-line' among the polycrystalline thin films, and now, the 'leading' terrestrial thin-film product, with production exceeding 1.4 GW this past year [11, 12]. Having a nearly ideal bandgap for a single-junction solar cell, efficient CdTe cells have been fabricated by a variety of potentially scalable and low-cost processes, including physical deposition, spraying, screen printing/sintering, and electrodeposition. The best-confirmed, research-cell efficiency is 17.3% (**Figure 8**) [72]; the CdTe film was produced using close-spaced vapor transport, and a typical cross-section is shown in **Figure 10(b)**. The champion commercial module has reached 13.4% efficiency [72], with commercial off-the-shelf products in the 9–11% range. Like all PV technologies, higher V_{oc}'s are the key toward higher performance and lower cost. Areas of concern for devices relate to contacting, contact stability, ability to control the CdTe conductivity with oxygen and other extrinsic dopants, chemical and heat treatments, the transparent conducting oxides at the top surface of the cell, and the packaging critical for long-term life of the module. In fact, this initially caused some concern for the product operating in outdoor conditions, but attention to new packaging techniques and processes have successfully overcome most of the problems.

The commercial segment is growing, with the major producer, First Solar Corporation, reaching production capacities of about 1.5 GW yr^{-1} by the start of 2011. Their current module manufacturing costs dipped below $0.75 W^{-1}, significantly lower than any other commercial technology. They are the largest PV producer in the United States and rank among the top three in the world. This market growth is partially due to the issues with Si feedstock supply and costs, but the success of this thin-film technology has certainly grabbed the attention of investors and the major PV companies. Thin films have continued to penetrate the growing PV market – representing about 12–15% of production in 2010, compared to about 5% in 2006.

These particular thin-film materials pose some problems. The first is the perception of environmental harmful or toxic materials, primarily in the use of Cd. Several studies have addressed this issue, including comprehensive investigations reported by Brookhaven National Laboratory, the European Commission, the French government, and others on the release of toxic materials as a result of fire, leaching, or during the manufacturing process. It should be pointed out that these components are not 'Cd solar cells', but are based on materials in which the Cd is a component of a high-temperature, stable compound semiconductor. However, the concerns for use of such elements must be addressed, as previously indicated. Some have proposed that use of Cd in a large, stable CdTe module is not only far safer than its use in a Ni-Cd battery, but also that it might be considered an approach to 'Cd sequestration'!

A second issue is that of supply: Is there enough indium (In) or tellurium (Te) in our Earth's supply to make a real impact on the multiterawatt scale needed for our future? Can In ever be inexpensive enough to meet such a large terawatt production? Most of those working in the technology and investigating the supplies are convinced that both In and Te supplies are sufficient, especially if the design of the active layer reaches a thickness of less than the targeted 1 μm, or if this much thinner cell eventually is successful as part of a multiple-junction approach. Also, recent large start-ups of Bi_2Te_3 mining in China give some added optimism for Te supply, where this element is about 30% of the mining output. However, many others are skeptical – and these issues have to be addressed. It needs to be acknowledged that a single-material approach is not envisioned for PV, and either thin-film CIGS or CdTe can have market impacts. Whether these are at the 1 TW level or at the 10 TW level is now a matter of study and more careful evaluation. Some well-founded authorities think that the 'jury is still out'; other equally respected experts believe the 'hanging' has already taken place! (Readers are referred to a special session at the recent 35th IEEE PVSC held in Honolulu, Hawaii, June 2010, dealing with this topic [73]).

1.03.3.2.5 Very high-efficiency and concentrator devices

Higher-cost semiconductors, such as GaAs, GaAlAs, GaInAsP, InSb, and InP, have been receiving attention as PV converters because they have exceptional performance with potential to convert more than a third of the Sun's terrestrial power into electricity. Cost is the overriding consideration for terrestrial applications in conventional flat-plate technologies. One means for improving the PV efficiency, reducing the high-value converter area, and significantly reducing the systems cost is too use concentrators – lenses, reflectors, or other optics that focus the sunlight onto the collection area of the solar cell. Concentrators have been used successfully with crystalline silicon technology, with concentrations up to 400×, efficiencies to 27%, and larger-scale modules at 20% using 25%-efficient commercial cells. Single-junction GaAs cells have been measured at 28% at 1000× concentration. The economics of these approaches have been argued for decades, but it has been the leveraging of the multiple-junction III–V cell technologies for space applications that has brought renewed interest and investment into the terrestrial concentrator system. Many would classify these as third-generation technologies – but the fact is that they are here, work, have demonstrated the highest 1-sun and concentrator cell performances, and are starting to be deployed around the world.

The best terrestrial triple-junction monolithic cells have been confirmed at 43.5% under 416× concentration (Solar Junction, GaInP/GaAs/InGaAs,lattice-matched design [74]). This cell significantly was still over 43% efficient at 1000 ×. The best GaInP/GaAs/Ge lattice-matched cell is 41.1% by Boeing-Spectrolab, shown in **Figure 11(a)** [75]. Also, two metamorphic (lattice mismatched, also shown in **Figure 11b**)) devices have been confirmed at 41.1% [76]. An entirely different approach is an inverted, lattice-mismatched cell design (**Figure 12**) – grown on, then separated from, a reusable GaAs substrate. The cell is ultrathin [77], and significantly, this cell held its efficiency of greater than 39% to the 800× concentration regime and is currently being commercialized.

These concentrator technologies are primarily aimed at large, utility-scale applications for high solar-insolation regions such as the southwestern United States, southern Europe, northern Africa, and parts of the Middle East and Asia. However, a number of organizations have also been pursuing potential 'rooftop' systems, which can certainly be projected for commercial buildings and perhaps for some residences, as well, in the future. In any case, the 'concentrator' has developed a new life, thanks to the investment in space technology and to the persistence of this R&D community for terrestrial solar power service. This technology, which has always been dubbed the 'application of the future', may have made its first viable footprint in the nearer-term markets with high efficiency and high electricity value. 'Roadmaps' predict significant markets for such utility-scale PV in the 2020–25 timeframe, and CPV is positioning to serve those 10–100 MW markets not considered to be economical by the related and quickly advancing CSP (solar thermal-electric) approaches at the multi-100 MW size.

There is also a revived interest in the GaAs crystalline and 'thin-film' devices, both for concentrators and for crystalline thin films. These efforts have been led by Fraunhaufer ISE and Radboud University (The Netherlands) and Alta Devices (USA). The GaAs single-junction best crystalline cell is FhG-ISE (26.4%), with a concentrator cell at 29.1% (117× concentration). The best thin-film (crystalline) is Alta Devices 28.3% device. This device uses some interesting engineering that is currently being developed at CalTech for other technologies as well, discussed previously in the crystalline Si section [49–51].

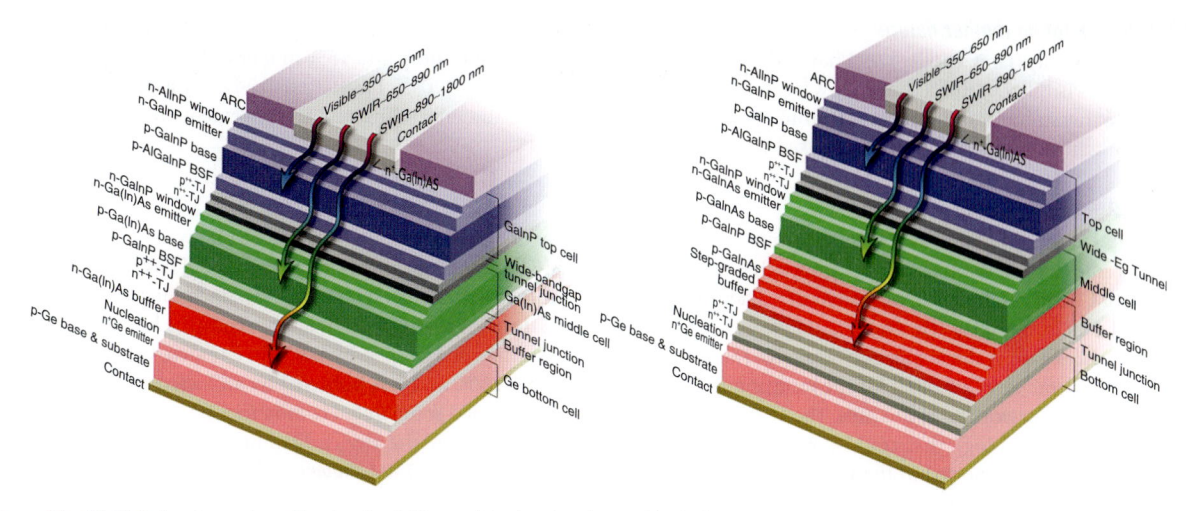

Figure 11 Multiple-junction solar cells, showing lattice-matched and metamorphic designs.

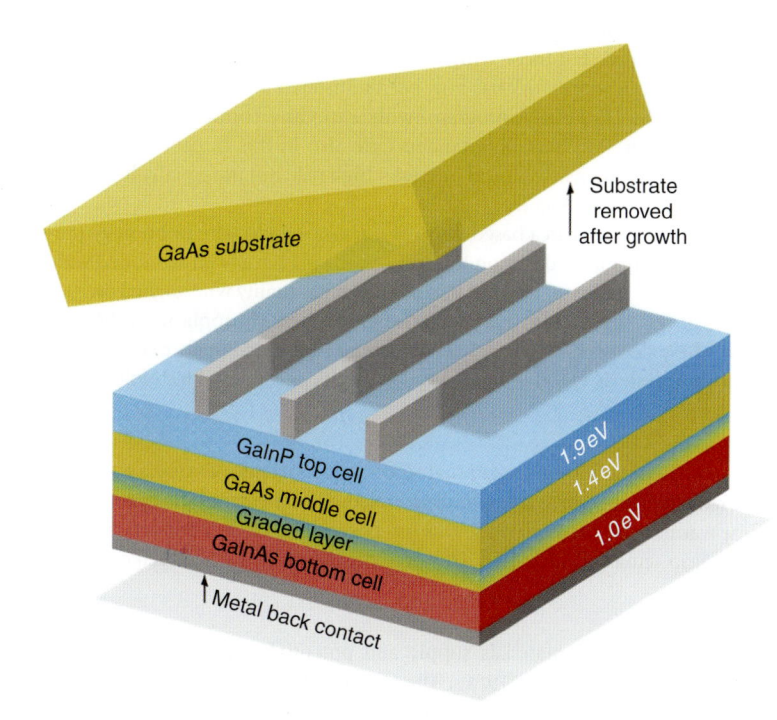

Figure 12 Inverted metamorphic multijunction (IMM) concentrator solar cell. Wanlass M (2008) Proceedings of the 32nd IEEE photovoltaic specialists conference (IEEE, New York, 2006). *Applied Physics Letters* [77].

1.03.3.3 Revolutionary Photovoltaics: The Chase Toward the Next Generations

Some of the possible contenders for the next PV generations have started their journeys in the laboratory. Martin Green [78] brought attention to this future when he classified first-generation PV as crystalline Si, second generation as the thin films, and third generation as a host of evolving devices, upstarts, and wild ideas that have lined up in the race to meet the performance and cost goals needed to deliver those 15–30 TW by mid-century. Whereas the second generations might be competing in the analogue of the 100 m dash to surpass Si in the current to near-term technologies, the third generations are in a marathon struggle that must not only bring them to commercialization, but also demonstrate their abilities to generate voltage and current for the very first time.

This is the PV researcher's field of dreams. It is also the parking lot of nightmares for the near-term real business of PV – with worries about delaying or inhibiting the adoption of real and working technologies that will serve for the next 20–30 years to wait for one that might not have even been demonstrated to generate electricity yet, but that theoretically promises performance beyond Olympic levels. (This is something many of us have experienced awaiting the next, then the next, speed bump up in computer microprocessors – and we may never purchase a computer!) There must be understanding and patience, knowing that the investment in these research areas is important for both future technology ownership and readying the next generation(s) of solar electricity for many generations of consumers to come. These third-generation contenders include the following.

1.03.3.3.1 Fooling mother nature

Dye-sensitized cells (Grätzel cells [79]) have efficiencies that are 11% in the laboratory and 15% in tandem with an inorganic cell. Although the visibility of this technology was lowered from its high point in the 1990s, it has started to advance again, largely due to technology investments and innovation from the Asian sectors. Increased understanding and improvements in processing have helped the status of this truly nanoscale-based technology.

1.03.3.3.2 Just one word – 'plastics'

Organic PV (or OPV) [80–82] also operate through excitonic processes, with small molecule ($<10^4$ molecular weight) to polymer or large molecule ($>10^6$ molecular weight) approaches under development. The best single-junction confirmed cell has 10.0% efficiency (Mitsubishi Chemical), followed by Konarka (8.3%). Several tandem approaches have been reported now, including the record 9.8% cell by Heliatek in Germany (December 2011) followed by UCLA's 8.6% device. These OPV cells are currently the hotbed of progress in the efficiency chase. A single-junction large-area (almost 2 cm^2) cell was confirmed at 5.9% by OSOL in Dresden, Germany. Overall, the progress is now exceeding that for the inorganic thin films in the early 1980s, and it is bolstered by an incredible population of scientific researchers working in this area. The organic solar technology has reached some initial commercial stage (really qualifying it as a disruptive technology that could have some impact in the mid-term), and the device lifetimes have started to improve substantially in work reported in the past year. "Dustin Hoffman, stay tuned ... ." (*The Graduate*, 1967). Recently the first greater than 10% organic tandem was verified at 10.6% for a UCLA-Sumitomo Chemical.

1.03.3.3.3 Using more sun, less real estate

Multiple-junction cells have been developed, but those with 'multi-multijunctions' – four to six such devices – are in the research stage. Europe is leading the efforts [83], but some work has now been reinstated in this area in the United States. Others include the recent split-spectrum reported under the US DARPA program, with a module confirmed at 37.5% [84]. There are also several metamorphic designs under investigation. Polycrystalline tandems are also in this category, with the first reported devices using CIGS and CdTe thin films. This area is of immense technical interest – high risk, but potentially high payoff with the dual promise of high performance and low cost. Again, look to Asia ... .

Silicon also has been evolving quickly in this area based upon Si micro- or nano-wire technology [85–89]. 'Single-wire cells' with excellent electrical properties (e.g., minority carrier diffusion length $L_n \gg 30\,\mu m$) have been fabricated with unconfirmed efficiencies in the 17% range (under low concentration). However, the goal is to use this high-quality wire aligned on a substrate, leading to large-area cell with similar or greater performances. Aligned micro- and nanowires for these PV applications have been reported with enhanced absorption and carrier collection. These devices have not only demonstrated enhanced performance, but also are coming with positive material utilization – perhaps using as little as 1/100 of the Si needed using conventional technology at the same efficiency level.

1.03.3.3.4 Hot flashes

Both thermophotovoltaics (TPV) and thermophotonics incorporate the infrared in their conversion schemes. The latter uses two thermally isolated diodes operating at the radiative limit which are optically coupled. The efficiency can approach the Carnot limit for conversion between the temperatures of the warmer and cooler devices. This has been modeled, but not yet confirmed. The TPV device has been confirmed, and uses very low-bandgap semiconductors [90]. However, the terrestrial use has been confined to niche applications.

1.03.3.3.5 Retro-voltaics

In the quest for solar cells that are devoid of materials supply and potential toxicity problems, a host of materials are being resurrected that initially evolved in the 1950s to the 1980s. These materials have optimal bandgap properties in addition to be fabricated from earth-abundant and/or nontoxic elements. These include Cu_xS, Cu_2O, Zn_3P_2, CdSe, Cu_2Se, SnSe2(S2), and FeS_2 [91, 92]. The most advanced of these was the Cu_2S/CdS cell, confirmed above 10% efficiency in the early 1980s [93] – and was actually first reported as a thin-film solar cell in 1955 [94]. Despite many groups representing six continents and being commercialized, stability issues surrounded its further development. The 30 or more years that separate these approaches from those 1970s–1980s rapture with new materials (and funding!) have brought about an expanded understanding of materials and device engineering, improvements in processing and deposition control, and an incredible new arsenal of characterization techniques that will provide new insights and guidance toward better performance (efficiency and stability). The Center for Inverse Design, a Department of Energy (DOE) Office of Science Energy Frontier Research Center (EFRC), has recently reported an example of implanting improved science, techniques, and methodologies that were not possible when one of these 'retro' materials was first considered. Using their inverse design approach (www.centerforinversedesign.org) to design materials according to specified target functionalities, they have recently reported new results by incorporating Si and Ge in the FeS_2 to control the defect density at the surface (device interface) that promises to provide gains in open-circuit voltage needed to continue with this earth-abundant semiconductor. It may well be time for 'something old and something borrowed'.

1.03.3.3.6 The far side

PV science and technology have always included higher-risk approaches in their R&D portfolio: alternatives to the conventional that are near or at the outer fringes of science and engineering and that might provide breakthroughs, significant progress leaps, or even new technologies. These alternatives center on nanotechnology and hot-carrier approaches resulting in multiple-exciton generation

Table 1 Predicted efficiencies for ideal revolutionary: second- and third-generation solar cells compared to limits (Carnot, Landsberg, and Shockley-Queisser)

Converter or limit ($T_{source} = 6000\,K$, $T_{device} = 300\,K$, isotropic illumination)	Efficiency (%)
Carnot limit	95.0
Landsberg	93.3
Multijunction (infinite number of junctions)	86.8
Impact ionization (best Q)	86.8
Hot electron	85.4
Solar thermal	85.4
Thermophotovoltaic	85.4
Thermophotonic	85.5
Intermediate band (quantum dot or alloy)	63.2
Multiple quantum well (second photon pumped)	63.2
Shockley-Queisser limit	40.3

Based on Honsberg CB and Barnett AM (2004) *20th European Photovoltaic Solar Energy Conference, Valencia, Spain.* Germany, WIP-Energies [96]; Honsberg CB (2004) *U.S. DOE Solar Energy Technologies Program Review.* Denver[98].

from a single photon, including quantum dot solar cells and intermediate-band solar cells [95–98]. Multiple-exciton generation (MEG) has been demonstrated in several materials; however, no solar cell has yet been confirmed. There is some question relating to the MEG results [99], but these approaches are new and need time to develop – patience is needed to let these quantum dots provide watts. Just when some skeptics were ready to write off these 'more for the price of one', two events occurred. First, the the first 'quantum dot' solar cells have been reported (**Figure 8**); PbSSe cells (reaching 5.1%, reported by the University of Toronto [100]). And more spectacularly, the first confirmed report of the multiple-exciton generation (MEG) process occurring in a PV quantum dot device [101]. Photocurrent enhancement was reported in lead selenide quantum dot solar cells, with a peak external quantum efficiency (QE) of 114% and a corrected internal QE of 130%. Ready for the manufacturing world? Not yet, but this does provide the proof of concept needed for continuing R&D investment in this approach. And, like all nascent technologies, stability is an issue. Of course, the payoff for these technologies is a conversion efficiency that, at least on paper, can exceed 60% and perhaps even approach 80%; a summary is shown in **Table 1** [96, 98]. They are the cells for our next–next generations of consumers, and they need the investment now to establish the R&D for realizing these very high-value technologies. These are at the most radical fringe in the PV technology revolution.

1.03.4 Conclusions

Currently, PV as a technology and a business comprises a complex network of co-dependent and intimately related tipping points [1]. First, it is a real business reached to $30–40 billion levels: clearly a fastest-growing electricity source over the past year, as well as in the past 5 years. But solar PV needs the attention of government policy and consumer awareness and acceptance to take it to its next levels – those pushes will make it 'spread like wildfire' [1] in markets around the world, growing into the bonfires that have been lit in Japan and Germany. These have shown technology value, as well as economic and employment value. Policy is important, but the wildfire needs additional and new fuels to make it endure.

Second, it is unfortunate that PVs and the renewable energy technologies continue to be pushed into political arguments and theater. Such political forces unnecessarily try to downgrade the renewables through a series of historical myths [104] – and unnecessarily pit these technologies against competing fossil and nuclear energies. There are even efforts to impose 'fights' among the different renewable energy technologies themselves to denigrate one over the other in our own renewable energy community. All this just slows our world's ability to meet energy needs. These energy technologies should be allowed to compete on a level playing field. What will make sense technically, economically, environmentally, and safety- and health-wise will succeed.

And third, solar PV has tipped into its next stages of technology development – this is actually the need for R&D to improve current and near-term technologies in crystalline Si and thin films and to develop the next generations that will fuel the wildfire of business and deployment. This investment in R&D is essential to bringing down costs and ensuring that our next generations of consumers have technologies ready to meet the mounting demands for energy in this century. PV has advanced incredibly from Bell Telephone Laboratories began in 1954 and the Vanguard satellite market initiation in 1958. The next two decades will likely produce 2 orders of magnitude more technically than that first half century of PV development. It has the potential to grow 100-fold as an energy resource. However, there is still need for 'intelligent design'. We have to provide the technical expertise, resources, creativity and innovation, and the belief – and solar PV 'will' be significant, no longer an 'outlier' [18] in our clean energy future.

Acknowledgments

The author expresses sincere gratitude and appreciation to colleagues within the National Center for Photovoltaics at the National Renewable Energy Laboratory, who helped in reviewing this material – especially Don Gwinner. Special thanks goes to my colleague and friend Keith Emery of NREL for his counsel and sharing his warehouse of knowledge on PV performance and characterization. This chapter represents primarily the thoughts, insights, and observations of the author, based on his some 40 years in PV R&D. Many of the opinions are those of the author – based on his experiences, his own research, and his observation of the political and other external influences on this PV technology's development. This was prepared partially through the support of the US Department of Energy under Contract No. DE-AC36-08GO28308.

References

[1] Gladwell M (2000) *The Tipping Point.* New York, NY: Little, Brown and Company, Inc.
[2] Chapin DM, Fuller CS, and Pearson GL (1954) A new silicon p-n junction photocell for converting solar radiation into electrical power. *Journal of Applied Physics* 25: 676.
[3] Vanguard the Satellite: Description of Project (2002). http://en.wikipedia.org/wiki/Project_Vanguard (accessed 10 January 2012).
[4] Vanguard the Satellite: 50th Anniversary (2008). http://www.msnbc.msn.com/id/23639980 (accessed 10 January 2012).
[5] West Virginia Coal Mine Explosion: 25 Dead After Massey Blast. http://www.huffingtonpost.com/2010/04/05/west-virginia-coal-mine-e_n_526151.html (accessed 10 January 2012).
[6] Poll: BP Oil Spill Response Rated Worse than Katrina. http://abcnews.go.com/PollingUnit/Media/poll-bp-oil-spill-rated-worse-katrina-criminal-charges/story?id=10846473 (accessed 10 January 2012).
[7] Gulf of Mexico Restoration. http://www.bp.com/bodycopyarticle.do?categoryId=1&contentId=7052055 (accessed 10 January 2012).
[8] Fukishima Nuclear Accident (2011) www.iaea.org/newscenter/news/tsunamiupdata01.html (accessed 10 January 2012).
[9] Nobel winner urges Japan to abandon nuclear power. www.contracostatimes.com/california/ci_18834103 (accessed 10 January 2012).
[10] Hurricane Katrina (2011). www.katrina.com (accessed 19 August 2005).
[11] Hurricane Irene (2011). www.bloomberg.com/news/2011-09-06/hurricane-irene-cost-taxpayers-1-5-billion-white-house-says.html (accessed 27 August 2011).
[12] *Photon International* (February, 2009, 2010, and 2011). PV News (June 2011).
[13] Paula M (2011) *European PV Solar Energy Conference.* Hamburg, Germany. http://www.electroiq.com/articles/pvw/2011/09/solar-and-the-law-of-unintended-consequences.html (accessed 10 January 2012).
[14] Solar Electricity Handbook (2011 Edition). http://solarelectricityhandbook.com/solar-incentives.html (accessed 10 January 2012).
[15] Lehr U Renewable Energy Employment in Germany. http://www.gws-os.de/downloads/tagungen/IEAA08.pdf (German Aerospace Center, Stuttgart, Germany) (accessed 10 January 2012).
[16] Bezdek RH ASES Green Collar Jobs in the U.S. and Colorado: Economic Drivers for the 21st Century. http://www.ases.org/images/stories/ASES/pdfs/CO_Jobs_Final_Report_December2008.pdf (accessed 10 January 2012).
[17] Mints P (2011) Navigant consulting. In: Singer P (ed.), *Photovoltaics World* (June 2010 through January 2011) Tulsa, OK: PennWell's Electronics Group, Penwell Corporation.
[18] Gladwell M (2009) *Outliers.* New York: Little, Brown and Company, Inc.
[19] Scheer H (2006) *Energy Autonomy.* London: Earthscan/James & James.
[20] Scheer H (2004) *The Solar Economy.* London: Earthscan/James & James.
[21] Scheer H (2005) *A Solar Manifesto.* London: Earthscan/James & James.
[22] International Technology Roadmap for Photovoltaics by SEMI and CTM Group. http://www.pvgroup.org/node/1271 (accessed 10 January 2012).
[23] Nemet G (2007) Learning Curves for Photovoltaics (IEA) www.iea.org/work/2007/learning/Nemet_PV.pdf (accessed 10 January 2012).
[24] SunShot Initiative. http://www1.eere.energy.gov/solar/solar_america (accessed 10 January 2012).
[25] Solar America Initiative. http://www1.eere.energy.gov/solar/solar_america/ (accessed 10 January 2012).
[26] Green MA (2003) *Third Generation Photovoltaics.* Germany: Springer.
[27] Luque A and Hegedus S (eds.) (2011) *Photovoltaic Science and Engineering.* New York: Wiley.
[28] Marti A and Luque A (2003) *Next Generation Photovoltaics.* New York: CRC Press.
[29] Kazmerski LL (1980) Introduction to Photovoltaics: Physics, Materials and Technology and Research and Device Problems in Photovoltaics. In: Murr L (ed.) *Solar Materials Science*, pp. 489–584. New York: Academic. (Ch. 15 and 16).
[30] Intergovernmental Panel on Climate Change (IPCC) (in press) *Special Report on Renewable Energy Sources and Climate Change Mitigation (SRREN)* (United Nations, ipcc-wg3, 2010).
[31] Hamri J, Hummel H, and Canapa R (2007) *Review of the Role of Renewable Energy / Global Energy Scenarios, CRS-06.05.07.* Paris: IEA.
[32] World Energy Outlook, IEA. http://www.worldenergyoutlook.org/docs/weo2009/World_Energy_Model.pdf (accessed 10 January 2012).
[33] Shell Energy Scienarios to 2050: Signals and Signposts. http://www-static.shell.com/static/aboutshell/downloads/aboutshell/signals_signposts.pdf (accessed 10 January 2012).
[34] Jäger-Waldau A (2010) Status and perspectives of thin film photovoltaics. In: Bosio A and Romeo A (eds.) *Thin Film Solar Cells: Current Status and Future Trends.*, ch. 1, pp. 1–24 New York: Nova Publishers.
[35] International Energy Agency (IEA) (2010) Technology Roadmap. In: Frankl P and Nowak S (eds.) *Solar Photovoltaic Energy*, pp. 48–52. Paris, France: International Energy Agency.
[36] Photon International. http://www.photon-magazine.com/ (accessed 10 January 2012).
[37] Mints P (2010) *Photovoltaics World*, 18 March 2010. (Also, April 2010 through September 2011).
[38] International Energy Agency (IEA) (2009) *Trends in Photovoltaic Applications: Survey Report of Selected IEA Countries Between 1992 and 2008*, IEA Photovoltaic Power Systems Program (PVPS) Task 1, p. 44.
[39] India's Solar Mission Projects 22 GW by 2020. http://www.medindia.net/news/Indias-Solar-Mission-Projects-20-GW-Of-Power-By-2020-56064-1.htm (accessed 10 January 2012).
[40] National Development and Reform Commission People's Republic of China, 11th Five-Year Plan (2011). http://en.ndrc.gov.cn/ (accessed 10 January 2012).
[41] http://www.whitehouse.gov/issues/energy-and-environment.
[42] Birkmire RW and Kazmerski LL (1999) In: Kapur VK, McConnell RD, Carlson D, et al. (eds.) *Photovoltaics for the 21st Century*, pp. 24–32. Pennington, NJ: Electrochemical Society.
[43] Kazmerski LL (1997) Photovoltaics: a review of cell and module technologies. *Renewable & Sustainable Energy Reviews* 1: 71.
[44] Kazmerski LL (2004) Solar photovoltaics R&D at the tipping point: A 2005 technology overview. *Journal of Electron Spectroscopy* 150: 105.

[45] PV Research Cell Efficiency Chart (http://en.wikipedia.org/wiki/Solar_cell_efficiency) (accessed 10 January 2012).
[46] Mints P (2011) *Solar Outlook*. Chicago, IL: Navigant Consulting. (Also presented at 26th European Photovoltaic Solar Energy Conference, Hamburg, 2011).
[47] Green M (2000) *Solar Cells: Operating principles, Technology, and System Applications*. New York: Prentice-Hall.
[48] Nelson J (2003) *The Physics of Solar Cells*. London: Imperial College Press.
[49] Atwater HA (2011) Paths to high-efficiency, low-cost photovoltaics. In: *Proceedings of the 37th IEEE PVSC*. New York: IEEE.
[50] Briggs RM, Grandidier J, Burgos SP, et al. (2010) Efficient coupling between dielectric-loaded plasmonic and silicon photonic waveguides. *Nano Letters* 10: 4851.
[51] Munday JN, Callahan DM, Chen C, and Atwater HA (2011) Three efficiency benefits from thin film plasmonic solar cells. In: *Proceedings of the 37th IEEE Photovoltaic Specialists Conference, Seattle*. New York, NY: IEEE.
[52] Brandhorst HW Jr. and Flood DJ (2006) *Proceedings of the 4th World Conference on Photovoltaic Energy Conversion, Hawaii*, pp. 1744–1749. New York, NY: IEEE. sri.auburn.edu/wcpec_past_present_and_future_v2.pdf.
[53] Sanyo Heterojunction with Intrinsic Thin layer Solar Cell (HIT). http://solar.sanyo.com/hit.html (accessed 10 January 2012).
[54] Tsunomura Y, Yoshimine Y, Taguchi M, et al. 22% Efficiency HIT Solar Cell (White Paper) http://us.sanyo.com/Dynamic/customPages/docs/solarPower_22_3_Cell_Efficiency_White_Paper_Dec_07.pdf (accessed 10 January 2012).
[55] Fischer D, Dubail S, Anna Selvan JA, et al. (1996) The 'micromorph' solar cell: Extending A-Si:H technology towards thin film crystalline silicon. In: *Proceedings of the 25th IEEE Photovoltaic Specialists Conference, Washington, DC*, pp. 1053–1056. New York, NY: IEEE.
[56] Bankability is defined as "Guaranteed to bring a profit; Acceptable to a bank or investor; Capable of being manufactured with a profit". Bankability examples: Applied Materials SunFab (thin-film amorphous Si, large-area modules), Solyndra CIGS (cylindrical thin-film design for module), BP Saturn (crystalline Si), and Suntech (CSG thin film polycrystalline Si).
[57] Green MA (2007) Thin film solar cells: Review of materials, technologies and commercial status. *Journal of Materials Science* 18: S15.
[58] AstroPower, Inc. Silicon Film PV Manufacturing Technology (1997). www.nrel.gov/docs/legosti/fy97/21588.pdf (accessed 10 January 2012).
[59] Barnett A (2011) *Proceedings of the 26th European Photovoltaic Solar Energy Conference, Hamburg*. München, Germany: WIP.
[60] Shay JL and Wernick JH (1975) *Ternary Chalcopyrite Semiconductors: Growth, Electronic Properties and Applications*. Oxford: Pergamon Press.
[61] Shay JL, Wagner S, and Kasper HM (1975) Efficient CuInSe$_2$/CdS solar cells. *Applied Physics Letters* 27: 89.
[62] Kazmerski LL, White FR, and Morgan GK (1976) Thin-film CuInSe$_2$/CdS heterojunction solar cells. *Applied Physics Letters* 29: 268.
[63] Contreras MA, Masfield L, Egaas B, et al. (2011) Improved energy conversion efficiency in wide Bandgap Cu(In,Ga)Se$_2$ solar cells. In: *Proceedings of the IEEE Photovoltaic Specialists Conference, Seattle*. New York, NY: IEEE.
[64] Powalla M, Wischmann W, and Kessler F (2011) CIGS solar cells with efficiencies >20%: Current status and new developments. In: *Proceedings of the 26th European Photovoltaics Solar Energy Conference, Hamburg*. München, Germany: WIP.
[65] Sugimoto H, Kawaghuchi Y, Yasaki Y, et al. (2011) Challenge to 18% efficiency with 30 × 30 cm-sized Cu(InGa)(SeS)$_2$ submodules in solar frontier. In: *Proceedings of the European Photovoltaics Solar Energy Conference, Hamburg*. München, Germany: WIP.
[66] Dalibor T, Jost S, Vogt H, et al. (2011) *Towards Module Efficiencies of 16% with an Improved CIGSSe Device*. München, Germany: WIP.
[67] Primack D (2011) http://finance.fortune.cnn.com/2011/09/19/solyndras-red-herring/ (accessed 10 January 2012).
[68] Infographic: What's Really Happening At Solyndra. http://www.businessbrokerjournal.com/blog/technology-blog/infographic-whats-really-happening-at-solyndra/ (accessed 10 January 2012).
[69] Todorov T, Reuter K, and Mitz D (2010) High-efficiency solar cell with earth-abundant liquid-processed absorber. *Advanced Materials*. 22: E156–E159 DOI: 10.1002/adma.200904155.
[70] Edoff M (2011) Thin film solar cells based on Cu(In,Ga)(S,Se)$_2$ and Cu$_2$ZnSnS$_4$: Recent progress in research and industry. In: *Proceedings of the 37th IEEE Photovoltaic Specialists Conference, Seattle*. New York, NY: IEEE.
[71] Redinger A, Berg DM, Dale, PJ, and Valle N (2011) Route towards high efficiency single phase Cu$_2$ZnS(S,Se)$_4$ thin film solar cells: Model experiments and literature review. In: *Proceedings of the 37th IEEE Photovoltaic Specialists Conference, Seattle*. New York, NY: IEEE.
[72] First Solar Sets World Record for CdTe Solar PV Efficiency, News Release by First Solar http://investor.firstsolar.com/releases.cfm?Year=&ReleasesType=PageNum=2 (accessed 26 July 2001).
[73] IEEE (2010) *Proceedings of the 36th IEEE Photovoltaic Specialists Conference, Hawaii*. New York, NY: IEEE (Special Session on Materials Availability).
[74] IEEE (2011) *Proceedings of the 37th IEEE Photovoltaic Specialists Conference, Seattle*. New York, NY: IEEE.
[75] King RR, Boca A, Hong W, et al. (2009) Band-Gap-Engineered Architectures For High-Efficiency Multijunction Concentrator Solar Cells. *Proceedings 24th European Photovoltaic Solar Energy Conference*, pp 55–61, Hamburg, Germany, 21–25 September 2009.
[76] King RR (2008) Multijunction cells: record breakers. *Nature Photonics* 2: 284.
[77] Geisz JF, Kurtz S, Wanlass MW, et al. (2007) High-efficiency GaInP/GaAs/InGaAs triple-junction solar cells grown inverted with a metamorphic bottom junction. *Applied Physics Letters* 91: 023502.
[78] Green M (2003) *Third Generation Photovoltaics: Advanced Solar Conversion*. Berlin: Springer.
[79] Graetzel M (2003) Dye-sensitized solar cells. *Journal of Photochemistry and Photobiology C: Photochemistry Reviews* 4: 145.
[80] Segura JL, Martin N, and Guldi DM (2005) Materials for organic solar cells: The C$_{60}$/pi-conjugated oligomer approach. *Chemical Society Reviews* 34: 31.
[81] Li G, Nguyen T-Q, Olson DC, and Riede M (2011) Organic Photovoltaic Devices and Processing, *2011 Fall MRS Meeting*, Boston, MA.
[82] Heeger A (2011) Progress in organic PV. In: *Proceedings of the 26th European Photovoltaic Solar Energy Conference, Hamburg*. München, Germany: WIP.
[83] Bett AW, Dimroth F, Guter W, et al. (2009) Highest Efficiency Multi-Junction Solar Cell for Terrestrial and Space Applications. *Proceedings 24th European Photovoltaic Solar Energy Conference*, pp. 1–6, Hamburg, Germany.
[84] Barnett A, Kirkpatrick D, Honsberg C, et al. (2009) Very high efficiency solar cell modules. *Progress in Photovoltaics* 16: 1.
[85] Kelzenberg MD, Boettcher SW, Petykiewicz JA, et al. (2010) Enhanced absorption and carrier collection in Si wire arrays for photovoltaic applications. *Nature Materials* 9: 239.
[86] Kelzenberg MD, Turner-Evans DB, Putnam MC, et al. (2011) High performance Si microwire photovoltaics. *Energy & Environmental Science* 4: 866. DOI: 10.1039/c0ee00549e.
[87] Jia G, Steglich M, Eisenhawer B, et al. (2011) Silicon nanowire heterojunction solar cells. In: *Proceedings of the European Photovoltaic Solar Energy Conference, Hamburg*. München, Germany: WIP.
[88] Turner-Evans DB, Kelzenberg MD, Tamboli, AC, and Atwater HA (2011) Optoelectronic design of multijunction wire-array solar cells. In: *Proceedings of the 37th IEEE PVSC, Seattle*. New York, NY: IEEE.
[89] van Lare C, Verschuuren, MA, and Polman A (2011) Light trapping in Ultra-Thin a-Si: Plasmonic solar cells. In: *Proceedings of the 26th European Photovoltaic Solar Energy Conference, Hamburg*. München, Germany: WIP.
[90] Gopinath A, Luther J, and Coutts TJ (eds.) (2004) *Proceedings of the 6th International Conference on Thermophotovoltaic Generation of Electricity*, Freiburg, Germany, 14–16 June 2004.
[91] Wadia C, Wu Y, and Gul S, et al. (2009) Surfactant-assisted hydrothermal synthesis of single phase pyrite FeS$_2$ nanocrystals. *Chemistry of Materials* 21: 2568.
[92] DOE Solar Technologies Program Peer Review (2009) www1.eere.energy.gov/solar/review_meeting/pdfs/prm2009_atwater_earth.pdf (accessed 10 January 2012).
[93] Hall RB, Birkmire RW, Phillips JE, and Meakin JD (1981) Thin-film polycrystalline Cu$_2$S/Cd$_{1-x}$Zn$_x$ S solar cells of 10% efficiency. *Applied Physics Letters* 38: 925.
[94] Reynolds DC, Leies G, Antes LL, and Marburger RE (1954) Photovoltaic effect in cadmium sulfide. *Physical Review* 96: 533.
[95] Hanna MC, Ellingson RJ, Beard M, et al. (2004) *Proceedings of 2004 DOE Solar Energy Technol*. Denver, CO, October 25–28 (NREL/C)-590-37036.
[96] Honsberg CB and Barnett AM (2004) *20th European Photovoltaic Solar Energy Conference, Valencia, Spain*. Germany, WIP-Energies.

[97] Luque A, Martí A, Antolín E, et al. (2004) New Approaches To The Intermediate Band Solar Cell Concept. *Proceedings 24 European Photovoltaic Solar Energy Conference*, pp. 7–14. Hamburg, Germany.
[98] Honsberg CB (2004) *U.S. DOE Solar Energy Technologies Program Review*. Denver.
[99] Services RF (2008) Shortfalls in Electron Production Dim Hopes for MEG Solar Cells. *Science* 322 (5909): 1784.
[100] Tang J, Kep KW, Hoogland S, et al. (2011) *Nature Materials* 10: 765–771.
[101] Semonin OE, Luther JM, Choi S, et al. (2011) Peak External Photocurrent Quantum Efficiency Exceeding 100% via MEG in a Quantum Dot Solar Cell. *Science* 334(6062): 1540–1533.
[102] EPIA Roadmap (2004) www2.epia.org/documents/Roadmap_EPIA.pdf (accessed 10 January 2012).
[103] NEDO (2009) PV Roadmap Toward 2030. www.nedo.go.jp/content/100116421.pdf (accessed 10 January 2012).
[104] Kazmerski LL (2002) Photovoltaics – exploding the myths. *Renewable Energy World* 5(4): 174–183.

Further Reading

IEEE (1960–2012) *Proceedings of the IEEE Photovoltaic Specialists Conferences*. New York: IEEE.
WIP (1977–2012) *Proceedings of the European Photovoltaic Solar Energy Conferences*. Dordrecht, The Netherlands: D. Reidel Publication; Dordrecht, The Netherlands: Kluwer Publication; London, UK: James and James Ltd.; Munich, Germany: WIP.
WIP (1984–2012) *Proceedings of the Photovoltaic Solar Energy Conferences*. Munich, Germany: WIP.
Willeke G and Weber ER (2013) *Advances in Photovoltaics Part II*. Manufacturing Issues, Semiconductors and Semimetals Series. New York: Elsevier.
Archer MD and Nozik AJ (eds.) (2011) *Nanostructured and Photoelectrochemical Systems for Solar Photon Conversion*. London, UK: Imperial College Press.
Bauer T (2011) *Thermophotovoltaics*. London, UK: Springer.
Fonash SJ (2011) *Solar Cell Device Physics*. New York: Academic Press.
Krebs F (ed.) (2010) *Polymeric Solar Cells – Materials, Design, Manufacture*. Lancashire, UK: Destech Publication Inc.
Wenham SR, Green MA, Watt ME, and Corkish R (eds.) (2007) *Applied Photovoltaics*. Oxford, UK: Earthscan.
Poortmans J (ed.) (2006) *Thin Film Solar Cells Fabrication, Characterization, and Applications*. Hoboken, NJ: Wiley.
Marti A and Luque A (eds.) (2005) *Next-Generation Photovoltaics: High Efficiency through Full Spectrum Utilization*. London, UK: CRC Press.
Sun S-S and Sariciftci NS (2005) *Organic Photovoltaics: Mechanisms, Materials, Devices*. Boca Raton, FL: CRC Press.
Markvart T and Castaner L (2004) *Solar Cells – Materials, Manufacture and Operation*. Oxford, UK: Elsevier.
Green MA (2003) *Third Generation Photovoltaics: Advanced Energy Conversion*. New York: Springer.
Luque A and Hegedus S (eds.) (2003) *Handbook of Photovoltaics Science and Engineering*. New York: Springer.
Marshall JM and Dimova-Maliovska D (2002) *Photovoltaic and Photoactive Materials – Properties, Technology and Applications*. New York: Springer.
Archer MD and Hill R (eds.) (2001) *Clean Electricity from Photovoltaics*. London, UK: Imperial College Press.
Bube R (1998) *Photovoltaic Materials*. London, UK: Imperial College Press.

1.04 History of Photovoltaics

LA Lamont, Petroleum Institute, Abu Dhabi, UAE

© 2012 Elsevier Ltd. All rights reserved.

1.04.1	Harnessing Solar Energy – A New Invention?	31
1.04.2	What Was the Catalyst for Photovoltaic Development?	33
1.04.3	A Photovoltaic Modern Historical Timeline	37
1.04.4	Current Photovoltaic Technologies	41
1.04.5	Photovoltaics – Where We Are Now?	43
References		44

1.04.1 Harnessing Solar Energy – A New Invention?

Many may think that the use of solar energy is a modern time phenomenon being a repercussion of the 1970s' oil embargo; however, this is not the case. The use of solar energy in different forms to support the growth and development of civilization has been around as long as mankind existed. When modern society considers energy sources, normally what would come to mind first would be traditional energy sources such as coal, oil, and gas; however, our current biomass of wood, dried animal dung, and peat has traditionally been the choice of fuel of ancient cultures. Obviously, the traditional and modern biofuels, as with other renewable energy forms, are all originally created from the sun with the biofuels acting like an early storage device of solar energy which was useful only during daylight hours. Early humans did not have the scientific capability and knowledge that we have today, but they had a basic understanding of the power of the sun and they understood that from this 'bright yellow star' different forms of energy came to enhance their standard of living. This is the reason why many ancient civilizations, such as the Native Americans, both north and south, the Babylonians, the Persians, ancient Hindus, and the Egyptians, had a great respect for the sun, even going to the extent of worshipping it. The Greeks, well known for their gods, were devoted to the sun gods Helios and Apollo, and with their traditions built temples to show their devotion. This was also seen in the ancient Egyptian Civilization and their dedication to Ra, who was normally depicted with the sun disk of Wadjet placed on top of his falcon head. However, it was really the Greeks and Romans who fully embraced the potential of the sun in the first instance as a free energy source [1].

The first known invention that captured the solar rays was in 600 BC (before Christ) when fire was initiated by focusing the solar rays onto wood via a magnifying material (**Figure 1**).

This principle was not abandoned but rather it was further used for light applications, specifically torch lighting in the third and second century BC. However, as with many innovations, developments in solar energy are often not only used to improve human comfort but also developed and used by the military. An ancient example of this was introduced by Archimedes in 212 BC when the Greeks used the magnifying principle of solar radiation to burn the sails on Roman ships that were attacking Syracuse (**Figure 2**), thus diversifying the potential of solar to include war as well as daily life [3].

Very rarely does any civilization move forward with a new idea or technology unless there is a growing need for advancement: Greece experienced a fuel shortage in the fourth century BC, and therefore the need to be innovative and initiate an idea that would provide heat and light for its communities was vitally important for their survival. From as early as 400 BC, the Greeks implemented passive solar designs into their accommodations, thus being the first community to fully integrate solar energy into their society for reasons other than religious worship.

The basic principle of passive solar design (**Figure 3**) was to protect the north side of the building from the elements (wind, rain, etc.) and ensure that the south was open to solar radiation in the winter but shaded in the summer.

This simple principle was accepted widely and was implemented not only in private homes but also in public buildings and the world famous Roman bathhouses (**Figure 4**).

This ensured that the civilization captured the optimum amount of energy from the sun; even with a limited understanding of why this worked, the cultures constructed cities based on this principle. Greeks and Romans were not the only two societies that embraced this abundant energy source, but also the Pueblo, Anasazi, and Chinese also used the idea for the same purposes of light and heat. Although many societies had similar ideas, they were not generated together or the knowledge transferred, rather they were developed separately, as the sharing of knowledge was not as readily available as it is in today's modern society. Societies did however advance their designs and a good example of this was the improvement by the Romans to use glass to enclose the heat in the building, hence storing it and ensuring maximum warmth [1]. The Roman Government went further by declaring the first law highlighting that it was illegal to block your neighbor's sunlight, supporting the embracement of solar heating and lighting at both government and community level. The Romans developed and embraced the greenhouse idea we depend on now to grow fruits and vegetables that they brought back from different countries as they were expanding their empire. This idea is still used in much the same form today as it was in Roman times to ensure that we have sufficient supplies and varieties of food to feed the world, ensuring self-survival.

After the turn of history into the *anno Domini* (AD) period, very little changes or developments occurred with solar energy until during the Industrial Revolution. In the different centuries from the beginning of this era, acts by certain people/communities to use

32 **Photovoltaic Solar Energy**

Figure 1 Creating fire from the sun [2].

Figure 2 Archimedes mirror burning Roman military ships [4].

Figure 3 Passive solar design in Anasazi cliff [5].

the heat and light of the sun were noted but no improvements or breakthroughs were highlighted or noted. In 100 AD, Pliny the Younger (**Figure 5**), who was a lawyer, author, and Roman magistrate, was documented as having a summer house in Italy with what we would consider today a conservatory, but as mentioned before this use of the sun was common in Greek and Roman times so was not a new idea [7].

Furthermore, it was recorded that the North American Pueblo people in 1200 AD discovered and embraced the benefits of passive solar. By the eighteenth century, it was accepted as normal for the upper classes to have greenhouses, and this was further expanded in the nineteenth century when people with wealth constructed conservatories (**Figure 6**) for people to relax, walk, and enjoy warmth in very pleasant surroundings.

However, the next step proved to be the most complicated period with the move from the sun as the provider of light and heat to a supplier of much more. The mystery of energy from the sun truly eluded societies until the nineteenth century when one discovery opened many possibilities for the sun to be a future energy-supplying giant.

History of Photovoltaics 33

Figure 4 Roman bathhouses [6].

Figure 5 Pliny the Younger [8].

Figure 6 Conservatories first initiated by Romans [9].

1.04.2 What Was the Catalyst for Photovoltaic Development?

As discussed previously, for centuries we have been using the power of the sun in a number of basic ways. However, it was not until the 1800s that the scientific breakthrough happened to enable us to fully harness all the potential of this free, largely abundant fuel source. The credit of this turnaround in the use of solar energy is due to a publication in 1839 by a physicist Edmund Becquerel (**Figure 7**) from France, who discussed an experiment he had undertaken with a wet cell battery [10].

Figure 7 Edmund Becquerel [11].

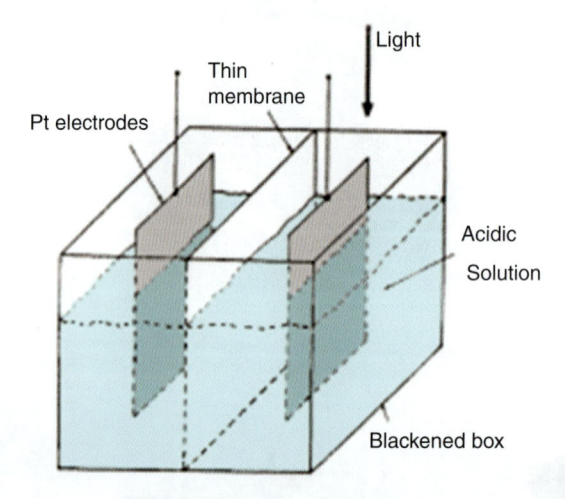

Figure 8 Photoelectric effect [14].

During his investigation, Becquerel discovered that when sunlight is made available to the silver plates, the output voltage of the battery increased (**Figure 8**). This discovery paved the way for other researches [12, 13]; however, it was not a priority at the time as fossil fuel was reasonably priced and in abundant supply.

Some other support of this original discovery was undertaken during the 1800s, but progression to prove was slow until the mid-twentieth century. Adams (**Figure 9**) and Day discussed in a publication the effect of sunlight on selenium, and later in 1883, an electrician Charles Edgar Fritts from New York designed a very inefficient (1–2%) prototype cell that is similar to the typical cells used today [15].

The efficiency of this and all other cells is calculated by measuring the electricity produced from the total of possible energy that hits the photovoltaic (PV) surface. The prototype held many of the characteristics of today's solar cells – it had a glass cover beneath which was a mass of fine gold wires sandwiched between glass and a thin layer of selenium. This was the first model for scientists to improve further, but it would take many decades before an increased efficiency was achieved and a true understanding of the reasons of the earlier low output was reached.

Little development had occurred over the half century since the initial discovery and whether this was due to lack of knowledge, lack of interest, or the constant low price of fossil fuels is not clear. The first half of the twentieth century was to follow much the same trend with the only real notable occurrences being Planck's (**Figure 10**) new idea regarding his light quantum hypothesis [17] which supported Albert Einstein's (**Figure 11**) 1905 paper [18] on the photoelectric effect that won him the Nobel Prize in 1921.

Figure 9 William Grylls Adams [16].

Figure 10 Max Planck [19].

Figure 11 Albert Einstein [20].

Figure 12 Bell Labs scientists Daryl Chaplin, Calvin Fuller, and Gerald Pearson. Courtesy of John Perlin Bell Labs silicon solar cell [24].

The second half of the twentieth century was to see faster progression, some of which was just natural scientific progression but also some historical occurrences helped to speed up the growth of PV cells. Bell Labs researchers in America were responsible for one of the largest discoveries that turned the solar industry into what we see today and unbeknownst to them it was their work in semiconductors that would actually support the development of solar cells [21, 22]. Semiconductors are the middle ground between conductors and insulators and are made from silicon that is doped and the researchers at Bell Labs had seen silicon reaching better results than the previously tested selenium [23]. They, for the first time, foresaw the possibility for solar cells with efficiencies of more than 20% compared with current levels of 1–2%. The team (**Figure 12**), however, realized that they could not make this significant step with only the transition to a different material and they continued to undertake research to find an optimal p–n junction.

Bell researchers discovered that they could achieve 6% (US$250 per watt versus approximately $3 per watt for coal) cell efficiency by mixing arsenic with silicon and placing a thin coat of boron on the cell [25]. Probably unknown to the scientists they had started a revolution in energy supply that in less than 20 years would be needed worldwide even if their discovery was a spin off from their transistor technology and expertise. Even with the advancement, the current product was too expensive for terrestrial use; however, for space power applications, it was the perfect solution as there was no other alternative, so despite its negative points it was still the best solution [16].

The first of many solar cells for powering space machines was placed on the Vanguard I space satellite in 1958 and this worked until it was decommissioned in 1964 [26]. The huge success of PV cells as an endless and nonpolluting power supply has ensured a place for these cells in the space industry (**Figure 13**) independent of cost and efficiency [27].

As more improvements and developments have been made to cells so has the option of where they can be incorporated. As the efficiency continues to improve, the efficiency of PV cells improved to 14% by Hoffman Electronics (1960) [29], so does the

Figure 13 Solar-powered space satellite [28].

transition between using these cells only in space and a future of installing them in terrestrial applications. However, in the early 1970s, there were still limitations with only the powering of systems in remote locations with no grid excess being considered a possibility.

From a sustainability point of view, it is a shame that such a major source of energy as solar technology took so long to develop and expand due to the continuing popularity of fossil fuels. This would probably still have been the situation if the oil crises in 1973 and 1979 with the OPEC oil embargo had not occurred [16, 30]. This substantial rise in oil prices and huge shortages of oil specifically in America forced the government to realize that this dependency on foreign fossil fuel was a risky business and highlighted the volatility of the traditional energy market, especially when there was free access to the sun, the most powerful fuel source. At this point, more interest was initiated in 'alternative' energy through research and development (R&D) as well as government incentives that helped to support the acceptance of renewable energy [31, 32].

During the 15-year period from 1970 onward, PV cells saw a huge growth, which culminated in a breakthrough in the price of PV cells per watt to under one-tenth of its previous cost in this short period (1970 – $100 per watt to 1985 – $7 per watt). This could have continued if the oil price had not dropped again, which meant people quickly forgot about the issues of the decade before and went directly back to their old habits, meaning that for another extended period progress was limited and the world went back to embracing fossil fuels. Even the government's support during this period was somewhat focused in the wrong direction as it did not see the importance of supporting the PV companies to develop the systems that would have speeded the progression of solar technology; rather it directed its efforts to universities for large-scale R&D making the public's access to this technology more difficult. Another factor that played an important part in the slow development of this technology was the attitude of the fossil fuel providers which traditionally most communities and governments depend on for energy. This industry did not support the development of alternative energy initially providing it with a challenging path; however, this has changed as nowadays most people widely accept the idea of renewable energy as a supporting source to the traditional source.

The United States very much took the lead in solar cell development after the initial nineteenth century French discovery, and until 1990 they were the leaders in the market, R&D, and implementation. Nevertheless, this changed at the end of the twentieth century with this domination moving and splitting between Europe and Japan. In this decade, the world reached a huge milestone with one million homes integrating some type of solar power. During this period, both Japan and Europe, particularly Germany, introduced government subsidies, increased public awareness, and invested in R&D. In the 1990s, Japan had seen its market increasing 10-fold with Germany floundering initially but modifications to its subsidies had seen its output rise by a multiple of 40 even topping Japan's success. Other European countries such as Spain have followed their lead and achieved much the same growth.

The PV market has completed an exciting part in its history with R&D still ongoing together with product development for tasks such as lighting, desalination, and pumping, and hence making it interesting not only to scientists and engineers but also to the general public (**Figures 14** and **15**).

Solar energy is now not only a more accessible power supply to satisfy the ever-growing demands but it also has lower costs, has higher efficiency, and is a clean alternative to fossil fuels.

1.04.3 A Photovoltaic Modern Historical Timeline

The previous section discussed the major events that happened to develop solar energy to what it is today; however, many other smaller events played their part in the growth of this technology. **Table 1** outlines the year of the event, the person/company/country responsible, if available, together with a summary of the discovery outlining the modern history of PV technology.

Figure 14 PV on homes [33].

Figure 15 Large-scale PV plants [34].

Table 1 Glimpse of the modern PV history

Year	Person/company/country	Summary of discovery
1839	Alexandre Edmond Becquerel	The photoelectric effect (light to electricity conversion) which saw both the conductance and illuminance rise during an experiment he was undertaking with metal electrodes and electrolyte
1873	Willoughby Smith	Selenium sensitivity to light was discovered during another experiment he was undertaking promoting branching into selenium solar cell experiments
1876	Richard Day, William Adams	Smith's discovery of the photoelectric effect on selenium was further verified and advanced by testing it with a platinum intersection which experiences the same phenomenon
1877	William Adams	Constructed an initial solar cell from selenium
1883	Charles Fritts	Explained the selenium wafer solar cell with his version having approximately 1–2% efficiency
1887	Heinrich Hertz	The effect of ultraviolet light on reducing the minimum value of voltage capable of inducing sparking between a pair of metal electrodes was tested
1888	Edward Weston	'Solar Cell' obtained first US patent [35]
1901	Nikola Tesla	US Patent 'Method of Utilizing and Apparatus for the Utilization of Radiant Energy' [36, 37]
1904	Wilhelm Hallwachs	Further discoveries continued with regard to photosensitive material mixing specifically cuprous oxide and copper
1905	Albert Einstein	Published on the photoelectric effect – 'On a Heuristic Viewpoint Concerning the Production and Transformation of Light' [18]
1914	Goldman and Brodsky	PV barrier layer was discovered
1916	Robert Milliken	Proved Albert Einstein's 1904 photoelectric effect theory
1918	Jan Czochralski	Discovered a method to nurture single-crystal silicon, hence supporting the development and future production of solar cells using monocrystalline silicon based material
1921	Albert Einstein	Nobel Prize for 1904 paper on photoelectric effect
1932	Many scientists	More material combinations were being observed to react to the photoelectric effect, specifically cadmium selenide
1941		Development of the initial monocrystalline solar cell made from silicon was completed
1951		Primary solar cells using germanium were built as advancements enabling a p–n junction of a single-crystal cell of this material to be grown
1953	Dan Trivich	Completed research on theoretical solar cell material efficiency and the wavelength of the solar spectrum [38]
1954	Reynolds, Leiess, Antes, and Marburger	Published on the photoelectric effect of cadmium sulfide [39]
1954	AT & T	Solar cell operations were widely exposed to the American public
1954	Pearson, Chapin, and Fuller – Bell Laboratory	Solar cells produced using silicon with 4.5% efficiency. This work was developed from a discovery that researchers made on the photoelectric effect on silicon when conducting another project on semiconductors [23]
1954	Mort Prince and team	Bell Labs broke its own efficiency record by 1.5%, raising the new level to 6% in a short time frame
1955		Initial research into powering satellites using solar cells commenced
1955	Western Electric	Silicon solar cell production commercial license
1955	Hoffman Electronics – semiconductor division	Produced a PV with the following specification per cell: 14 mW peak power with 2% efficiency for US$25
1955		In Chicago, a car powered by solar energy was unveiled
1957	Hoffman Electronics	Efficiency of PV improved to 8%
1957	Chapin, Fuller, and Pearson AT & T	Patent issued – 'solar energy converting apparatus' [40]
1958	Hoffman Electronics	Efficiency of PV improved to 9%
1958		Solar cell was designed to withstand the radiation in space

(Continued)

Table 1   (*Continued*)

Year	Person/company/country	Summary of discovery
1958	US Signal Corps	First space satellite which was PV powered named Vanguard I was designed and operated for 8 years
1958	USA	Explorer III and Vanguard II – other solar-powered satellites launched
1958	Russia	Sputnik III solar-powered satellite launched
1959	Hoffman Electronics	Efficiency of their PV improved to 10%
1959	USA	Explorer VI and VII launched with the previous having 9600 cells
1960	Hoffman Electronics	Efficiency of their PV improved further to 14%
1961	United Nations	Conference was held on solar energy applications in the developing world
1961	Defence Studies Institute	First PV specialist conference
1962	Bell Labs	Telstar telecommunications commercial satellite with 14 W peak power
1962		Second PV conference
1963	Sharp Corporation	First viable silicon PV module
1963	Japan	World's largest 242 W PV array for powering a lighthouse was installed
1964	USA	New largest 470 W PV array for powering a space project (Nimbus) was designed
1965	Tyco Labs	Designed the edge-defined film-fed growth (EFG) process. Tyco Labs were the first to create crystal sapphire ribbons after the silicon version
1966	NASA	1 kW PV power astronomical observatory was launched and went into earthly orbit
1968	Peter Glaser	The idea of a solar power satellite system was announced [41]
1968		Another satellite (OVI-13) was launched, but this time with two cadmium selenide panels as power supplies
1969	Roger Little	Founding of Spire Corporation, which was a company that aimed to continue to be important in solar cell manufacturing
1970		All the historical developments to date and the high interest in research has ensured the constant reduction of PV technology to approximately 80% of the original cost, hence making it more readily available for common low-power applications
1972	France	Used a cadmium selenide PV to power a TV, which was used for educational purposes in Africa (Niger)
1972	Solar Power Corporation	Company founded
1973	Solar Power Corporation	Beginning of commercial operation and opening of sales division
1973	Solarex Corporation	Two NASA experts with experience in PV satellites founded this company
1973	Delaware University	Development of initial domestic PV cells and thermal combined appliances
1973		A $30 per watt cell was developed
1974	Project Sunshine	An initiative by the Japanese to further enhance, develop, and research in this area
1974	Tyco Labs	One-inch EFG ribbon using the endless belt process
1975	Bill Yerkes	Established Solar Technology International
1975	Jet Propulsion Laboratory	Research and development for earth-based PV systems at this lab was supported by the US Government. This occurred from an industrial conference recommendation
1975	Exxon	Established Solar Power Corporation
1976	Kyocera Corp	Produces silicon ribbon crystal modules
1976	NASA	From 1976 to 1985 and also from 1992 to 1995, the NASA Lewis Research Centre (LeRC) worked on integrating PV cells into small power systems that could be used in many areas especially rural places with limited power
1976	RCA Lab	Amorphous silicon cell was introduced
1976	Solec International	Established
1977	US Department of Energy	Established the National Renewable Energy Lab (NREL) in Colorado initially known as the Solar Energy Research Institute (SERI)
1977		This year the sum of all the PV modules produced topped 500 kW
1977	NASA (LeRC)	Six strategically placed meteorological stations in the United States were introduced for recording data
1977	NASA (LeRC)	Placed in a Papago Indian community the first PV system which supplied the power requirements for the entire village. The system was 3.5 kW and supplied power and pump water for 15 homes
1979	Solenergy	Established
1979	ARCO Solar	This company based in California built the largest PV production facility to date
1979	NASA (LeRC)	Installed a pumping station of 1.8 kW which was then upgraded to 3.6 kW in Burkina Faso
1979		60 kW diesel–PV hybrid system for powering a radar station was installed in Mount Laguna in sun-drenched California
1980	ARCO	1 MW per year peak power PV module produced
1980	BP	New company BP Solar
1980	Luz Co.	For just more than 10 years they produced 95% of the world's solar-based electricity. However, when the price of fossil fuels reduced, they closed due to lack of investor support
1980	Wasatch Electric	105.6 kW system built by a Utah company. The system integrated modules produced by Spectrolab, ARCO Solar, and Motorola. An interesting fact is that this system is still operational

(*Continued*)

Table 1 (*Continued*)

Year	Person/company/country	Summary of discovery
1981	NASA LeRC	For 3 years they worked on powering remotely located refrigerators for vaccine which was tested in 30 worldwide locations
1981	Solar Challenger	Maiden voyage of the first solar-powered plane
1981	USA	Solar projects
		90.4 kW – Square Shopping Centre, Lovington, New Mexico, powered by Solar Power Corporation modules
		97.6 kW – Beverly High School, Beverly, Massachusetts, powered by Solar Power Corporation modules
1981	Saudi Arabia	10.8 kW peak power desalination system in Jeddah, Saudi Arabia, powered by Mobil Solar
1981	Helios Technology	First European PV manufacturer was established
1982		Above 9.3 MW PV power produced worldwide
1982	ARCO	1 MW dual tracking PV plant called Solar's Hisperia in California was grid connected
1982	NASA LeRC	Unveiled two PV-powered systems for testing a power supply for public lighting and for terrestrial satellite reception stations
1982	Volkswagen	A system used to start a car by placing 160 W peak power PV on the car roof top was tested
1982	Solarex Production	Solar rooftop project of peak power 200 kW
1983		21.3 MW peak power produced worldwide
1983	Solar Trek	1 kW powered vehicle which participated in the Australia Race driving for 20 days and 4000 km with an average speed of 24 km h^{-1} and a maximum speed of 72 km h^{-1}. However, later in the same year, the car outperformed itself by traveling further than 4000 km in 18 days on its journey between Long Beach and Daytona Beach
1983	ARCO Solar	6 MW power plant grid subsystem for Pacific Gas and Electric Company which was enough to supply 2000/2500 homes
1983	Solar Power Corporation	A Tunisian village was supplied with four systems with a combined power of 124 kW
1983	NASA LeRC and Solarex	Built a system of 1.8 kW in Guyana to maintain power for basic hospital power requirements such as lighting, radios, and medical refrigerators. Other places were also provided with similar systems such as 4 kW in Ecuador and 1.8 kW in Zimbabwe
1983	Solaria Corporation	Merged with Amoco Solar, which was owned by Standard Oil
1984	David Carlson and Christopher Wronski	They were presented the IEEE Morris N Liebmann Award for their work in "use of amorphous silicon in low cost, high performance photovoltaic solar cells"
1984		Sacramento in California has a 1 MW PV power plant
1984	ARCO	Amorphous modules first shown
1984	NASA LeRC	Remote medical and school basic power supplies in Gabon by 17 separate systems
1984	BP Solar Systems and EGS	Grid-connected 30 kW system in Southampton, UK
1984	BP Solar	BP Solar expanded by purchasing Monosolar thin-film division
1985	University of New South Wales	20% solar cell efficiency obtained
1985	Urs Muntwyler	The Tour de Sol which ran from 1985 to 1993 based in Switzerland was another race for solar-powered vehicles. As the years progressed, different classes opened providing not only direct solar-powered cars the right to participate but also other solar-powered vehicles
1986	ARCO Solar	Unveiled the first thin-film PV
1989	Solarex	Provided a PV system of 50 kW in Pakistan for projects the United Nations was undertaking
1989	ARCO Solar	7 MW per year thin-film production possible. In addition to production in California, the company expanded its production to Germany and Japan
1989	BP Solar	Thin-film technology patent
1990	United Solar Systems Corporation	Company created out of the amalgamation of Energy Conversion Devices Inc. (ECD) and Canon Inc.
1990	ARCO Solar	Bought by Siemens and renamed Siemens Solar Industries
1990	Germany	First country to launch a program that aimed to get community embracement of solar energy – $500 million '100 000 solar roofs' program. This program focused not only on homes but any building including churches with the Cathedral in East Germany embracing this initiative
1991	BP Solar Systems	Name changed to BP Solar International as well as being a new division in the BP company
1992	Antarctica	New location for remote power application
1992		Patent of a 20% efficiency silicon cell
1994	Japan	Japan is the next country to follow Germany's subsidy lead with its '70 000 Solar Roofs' program
1994	National Renewable Energy Lab	Launched its website providing more access to information on renewable energy
1994	ASE Americas Inc.	German company ASE GmbH took over Mobil Solar Energy Corporation creating ASE Americas Inc.
1995	World Bank and Indian Renewable Energy Source Agency	The two groups along with Siemens Solar collaborated to support renewable energy projects which enhanced system commercialization in India
1996	BP Solar	Expanded their business by taking over APS's California production premises. In the same year, they further expanded their product line to include the production of CIS
1996	Icar	The Icar plane, which was powered by solar cells, had a total surface area of 21 m^2 covered by 3000 cells

(*Continued*)

Table 1 (*Continued*)

Year	Person/company/country	Summary of discovery
1997	General Motors Sunracer vehicle	This vehicle won the race through Australia called the Pentax World Solar Challenge with 71 km h^{-1} average speed
1998	California	$112 million program called 'Emerging Renewable Program' to support residential and commercial PV systems
1999	First Solar LLC	Created through the combination of True North Partners, Solar Cells Inc., and Phoenix LLC
2000	Japan	During these 2 years the output of Japanese products grew with Kyocera and Sharp, each producing enough peak power for a country like Germany
2001	NASA and Aero Vironment Inc.	HELIOS, another solar-powered plane, achieved a record height of 30 000 m
2002	California Public Utilities Commission	An incentive program of $100 million for PV systems less than 30 kW was initiated
2003	Germany	Continued to expand their acceptance of PV systems by building many more projects such as the example at Hemau, which was connected to the grid and considered the largest of its time (4 MW)
2004	Germany	Solarparks of up to 5 MWp were built in Leipzig, Geiseltalsee, Gottelborn, and other locations due to energy laws from the German Government
2004		60% of PV market is held by BP Solar, Kyocera, Sharp, Shell Solar, and RWE SCHOTT Solar
2004	GE	Purchased Astropower, the final American independent PV producer
2005	Worldwide	55 countries have embraced solar energy
2006	California Solar Initiative	A three billion dollar 10-year funded solar initiative was announced which commenced the following year with great interest and acceptance
2006	Worldwide	7 GW of PV modules installed
2006	California Public Utilities Commission	$2.8 billion toward incentives
2006		40% efficiency achieved on a PV cell
2007	Worldwide	9.5 GW of PV modules installed
2007	Google	Solar panel project initiated
2007	University of Delaware	42.8% efficiency achieved
2007	Nellis Solar Power Plant	15 MW installation
2008	NREL	Reached 40.8% efficiency
2008	Worldwide	16 GW of PV modules installed
2008	Worldwide	6.9 GW of PV cells are produced worldwide
2008	Siemens	20 MWp, which was at the time the world's largest plant
2008	California Governor	Initiated a requirement for utilities to have at least 33% of renewable energy portfolio
2009	Worldwide	23 GW of PV installed, with annual production of 11 GW
2009		Typical commercial efficiency is now 15%
2010	BP	Moved production from the United States to China
2010	US President	Installed more solar panels for hot water at his home
2010	Worldwide	From 2006, worldwide there has been an addition of approximately 16 000 MW of solar power
2010	Worldwide	40 GW of PV capacity
2010	Europe	Accounts for approximately 80% of the worldwide PV market
2010	Czech Republic	In 2 years, PV capacity is 2 GW
2010	Australia	70% of its PV systems are off-grid
2010	Worldwide	Current top five solar PV countries in order are Germany (17.3 GW), Spain (3.8 GW), Japan (3.5 GW), Italy (3.5 GW), and the United States (2.5 GW)
2010	Worldwide	Annual production of PV modules is currently at 24 GW, which is a doubling from the previous year
2010	Worldwide	The top three countries that added the most solar are Germany, Italy, and Czech Republic
2010	Worldwide	PV systems are implemented in more than 100 countries
2010	Worldwide	25% of PV systems are utility-scale PV plants
2010	Asia	From the top 15 PV-manufacturing companies 10 are located in Asia
2010	Germany	Purchased more than half the PV modules produced
2011	Germany	Increased the amount of electricity produced by PV systems by 87% over the previous year
2011	Worldwide	119 countries have embraced solar energy
2011	Worldwide	New countries that have utility-scale PV systems include Bulgaria, China, Egypt, India, Mali, Thailand, and United Arab Emirates
2011	Suntech Power Holdings – China	World's largest PV manufacturer
2011	China	Produces two-thirds of the PV modules manufactured

1.04.4 Current Photovoltaic Technologies

In the previous sections, we have discussed the history behind the development of PV technology, where it started, and why it developed quicker during certain periods of history. We did not investigate how the technology has branched out with relation to the combination of material used or the production methods selected. It is not only important where the technologies are now but rather how they got to this point and what are the historical steps to arrive at today's technology.

Photovoltaic Solar Energy

The efficiency and cost of the panels have been the two major issues in the development of PV technology, and still are today. There is an interlinking generally between the increase in efficiency and the cost, as normally they both rise and fall together. For example, the increase in cost due to more expensive materials could lead to identical $/W when the efficiency is increased at the same rate; or scale effects in manufacturing generally lead to cost reductions provided the efficiency remains at least the same. However, depending on the commercial use and market development, cost will be a major issue rather than efficiency as every manufacturer is trying to develop the 'super cell', which has high efficiency and low cost. In reality, a variety of cells and modules in terms of cost and efficiency are needed to provide an optimal solution for varying power system requirements.

Currently, there are two main areas in R&D: one is in the material being used and the other is in the construction of the cells. Let us first consider the latter by showing the effect of the number of junctions in a cell on cell efficiency. **Figure 16** shows the development of efficiency over three decades; it illustrates how much it has improved from the single-crystal single-junction gallium arsenide cell in 1980 of 22% to today's three-junction concentrators with 42.5% efficiency [42].

Within specific materials, there are advancements trying to further develop them, but sometimes the first prototype model provides the best results as with crystalline silicon cells the first developed single crystal has the highest efficiency of this family even if other attempts of improvements are ongoing (**Figure 17**).

One of the new second-generation technologies that is proving interesting is thin-film technology, and the many material-based variations. The development of this technology started in 1976 with cadmium telluride (CdTe) and amorphous silicon (a-Si), with the development of copper indium diselenide or copper indium gallium diselenide (Cu(In,Ga)Se$_2$) starting a year later in 1976. Although CdTe started with the highest efficiency, it was not long before Cu(In,Ga)Se$_2$ caught up and even overtook it with fast development in output efficiency. However, a-Si was initially lower than the first thin-film technologies and never managed to catch up or overtake the leaders. Over two decades later for about 4 years researchers started to look at nano-, micro-, and poly-Si thin

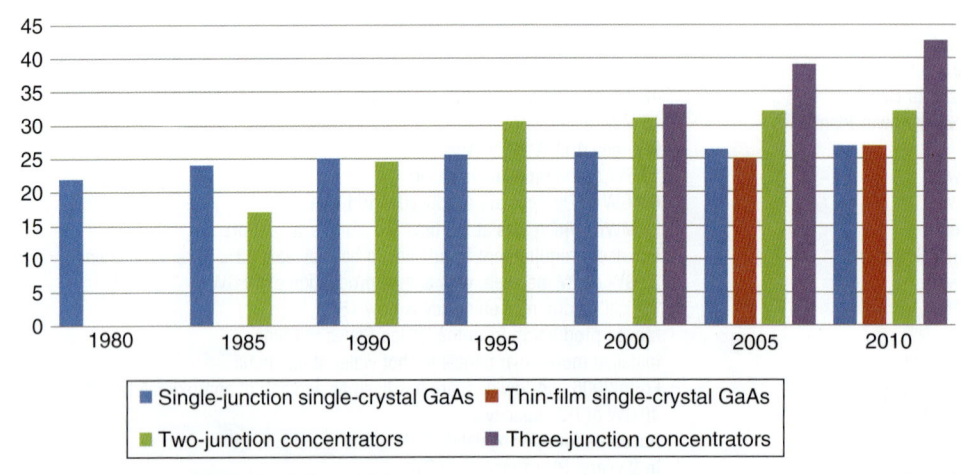

Figure 16 Effect of the number of junctions on efficiency [42].

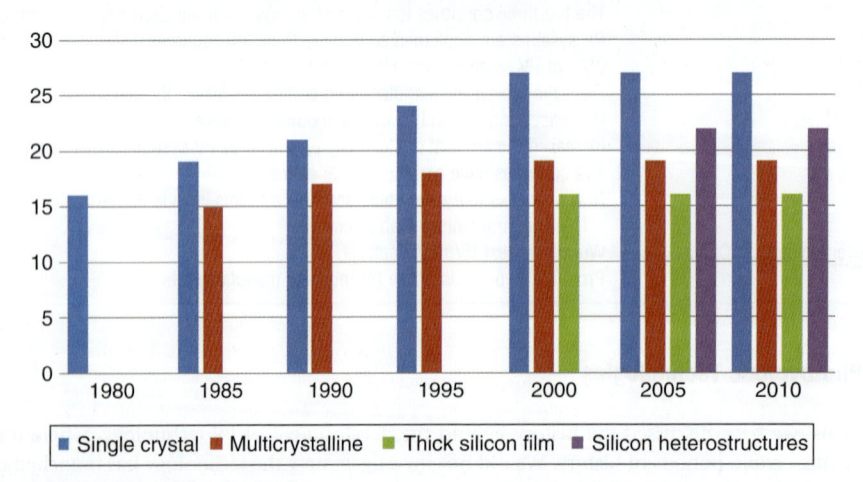

Figure 17 Efficiency development of the silicon family [42].

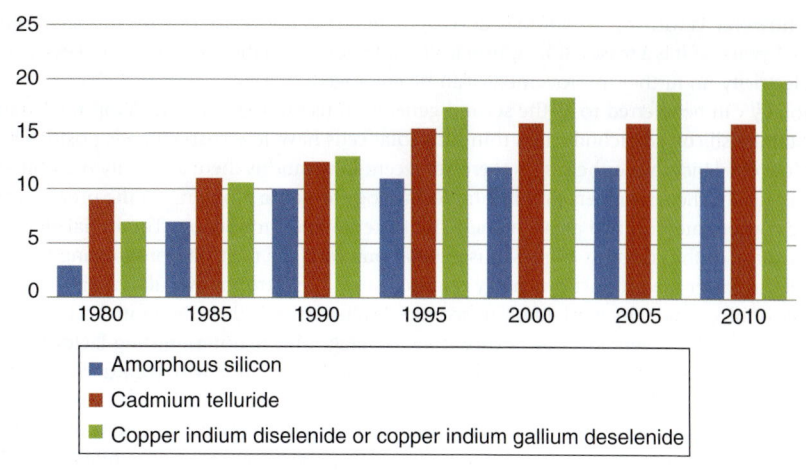

Figure 18 Efficiency development of some thin-film technologies [42].

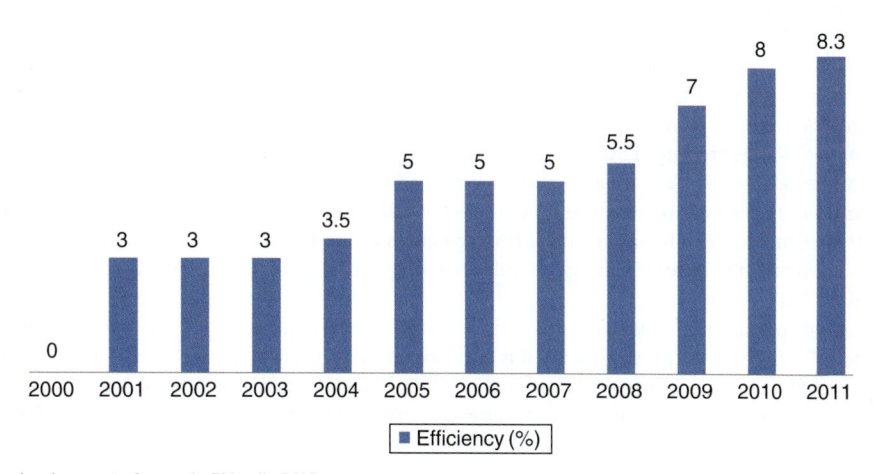

Figure 19 Efficiency development of organic PV cells [42].

films, and in this short period the efficiency grew by 6.7% from its 10% starting point but no further development was made after this point.

Figure 18 shows how the efficiency of the main thin-film players has changed from the 1980s to today.

As with every technology that strives to achieve the best, many inventions are tested some of which lead to a fruitful outcome whereas others do not. The PV market has some interesting emerging technologies that could further change the future of the power output. Some such as dye-sensitized cells have been researched since the early 1990s with minimum improvement (7–11%), so it seems that progress has stopped. Other developments such as organic cells are twenty-first century cells which are improving slowly but steadily (**Figure 19**).

Probably the two newest technologies being considered are inorganic (10%) and quantum-dot cells (3%) and their future has many possibilities but as with any technology the future will tell the tale of its success or failure.

1.04.5 Photovoltaics – Where We Are Now?

This chapter has discussed how solar energy has benefited the world for centuries and how after no breakthrough for years one scientific discovery and a lot of issues with the previously predominate fossil fuels enabled the development of PV technology to speed up. The earth has moved from a fossil fuel-dependent world to having other options such as PV solar energy. The current development of PV technology can basically be divided into three generations [43]. The first-generation technology focuses on silicon semiconductor devices, the second on the thin film, and the third is the further development of these two areas of interest.

The first generation offered a good innovative product with a reasonable future. The current single-junction silicon semiconductor is used in about 90% of the cells produced because of its high efficiency at unfortunately high cost which comes from the production costs of energy and labor input. To date, first-generation solar cells have nearly reached their previously assumed efficiency limit of 30%; however as with any technology development is ongoing. Currently for this technology the energy payback time is approximately 2–4 years, so it is a reasonable option to consider for installation and, currently even though it is nearly at cost parity with consumer electricity no further improvements can be envisaged.

The thin-film technology can be referred to as the second-generation technology as its development started later in the 1990s, but opposed to the crystalline silicon semiconductors thin-film solar cells have low cost which is positive but unfortunately along with this they also had low efficiency. Nevertheless, as there are recent innovations there are many possible improvements that can be introduced to them. Basically, the researchers in thin-film technology took the problems of the previous technology and tried to improve it, so they have concentrated on two areas, namely the material and production. The initial step was to look at different materials which address some of the concerns of previous generations with the next step progressing to considering the different manufacturing techniques to lower the production energy required such as electroplating, ultrasonic nozzles, or vapor depositing. A good example of this technology and why it might be an acceptable alternative is that the printed cells which have a low efficiency of 12% are fast to produce and have a very low cost, hence if the coverage area is not a limiting factor then they are definitively a good option. It is noted that this second generation, such as CdTe, is bypassing the first with regard to cost and in the future possibly may also become lower in cost than fossil fuels.

The third generation of PV technology is aiming at achieving such things as greater than 60% efficiency in thin-film or other devices, in addition to working on combining the better factors from the previous generations while embracing the low production cost of the second. In addition, from ideas now on the table, it is expected that there will be novel results from this R&D in the first quarter of this century [44]. Currently, scientists are looking at multijunction devices, the use of nanotechnology, spectral modification, enhanced light management using photonics and plasmonics, and much more, and it will be interesting to see how these develop in the future.

The currently available PV modules that are produced in 2010 normally cost approximately $1.80 per watt, which is expected to drop to $1.50 per watt in 2011 with the economic payback period of a full system being approximately 8–12 years [45]. This payback period is further effected by which country you live in and which, if any, government subsidies are available. One of the major positive sides of the PV is its lifetime of 30–35 years with a (manufacturers') warranty of 25 years, hence leaving the consumer a lot of time to earn money after the initial outlay is paid back. One of the main reasons for this extended lifetime is due to the fact that many PV systems do not have moving parts, hence they do not wear out and there is less maintenance making it a very useful electricity supplier. This estimation of lifetime is only a reserved guess as the technology is not old enough to have a guaranteed number; nevertheless, currently, the oldest PV system is still operating after almost half a century, so in the future the time frame might need to be revised [25].

One of the main factors to bear in mind is that a PV cell is not what operates practically, as this is only the first step of building a fully operational system. The production cost as of 2010 is approximately $1 per watt for a PV cell, which doubles when sold in a module to $2 per watt, and by the time the system is installed and fully commissioned the full cost is $5 per watt. It should be noted that the numbers are rapidly changing; for example, as of September 2011, in the Netherlands market, a complete roof-mounted PV system is quoted at a price of 2 Euro per Wp. A lot of investigation is needed to improve the cost effectiveness in all areas of the PV system, including cell and module cost, but also inverter and installation.

In conclusion, it is vitally important that modern society aims to optimize the harnessing of this abundant free source that provides nonpollutant energy and is silent in operation and therefore easier to get the public to accept than other renewable energies. Mankind should aim for this to be the primary fuel of the future and not an 'alternative' [44].

References

[1] Naff CF (2007) *Solar Power*, 1st edn. Farmington Hills, MI: Thomson Gale.
[2] http://survival-guy.blogspot.com/2010/09/creating-plan-food-part-4.html.
[3] Stanley T (2004) *Going Solar: Understanding and Using the Warmth in Sunlight*, 1st edn. Christchurch, New Zealand: Stonefield Publishing.
[4] Wikipedia. http://en.wikipedia.org/wiki/File:Archimedes_Heat_Ray_conceptual_diagram.svg.
[5] Nrel. http://www.nrel.gov/data/pix/searchpix.php?getrec=03544&display_type=verbose&search_reverse=1.
[6] Wikipedia. http://en.wikipedia.org/wiki/File:Roman_Bath_in_Spa,_England_-_July_2006.jpg (photo bt David Iliff. License: CC-BY-SA 3.0).
[7] Sklar S and Sheinkopf K (2002) *Consumer Guide to Solar Energy: New Ways to Lower Utility Costs, Cut Taxes, and Take Control of Your Energy Needs*, 3rd edn. Chicago, IL: Bonus Books.
[8] Wikipedia. http://en.wikipedia.org/wiki/File:Como_-_Dom_-_Fassade_-_Plinius_der_J%C3%BCngere.jpg.
[9] Wikipedia. http://en-wikipedia.org/wiki/File:Syon_House_Conservatory,_London.jpg.
[10] Becquerel AE (1839) Recherches sur les effets de la radiation chimique de la lumiere solaire au moyen des courants electriques. *Comptes Rendus de L´Academie des Sciences* 9: 145–149.
[11] Wikipedia. http://org/wiki/File:Alexandre_Edmond_Becquerel,_by_Pierre_Petit.jpg.
[12] Goetzberger A, Knobloch J, and Voss B (1998) *Crystalline Silicon Solar Cells*, 1st edn. New York: Wiley.
[13] Green MA (1995) *Silicon Solar Cells: Advanced Principles and Practice*, 1st edn. Sydney, NSW: Bridge Printery.
[14] Wikipedia. http://en.wikipedia.org/wiki/File:Photoelectric_effect.svg.
[15] McCrea A (2008) *Renewable Energy: A User's Guide*, 1st edn. Marlborough, UK: Crowood Press.
[16] National Centre for Photovoltaic Research and Education (NCPRE). http://www.ncpre.iitb.ac.in/page.php?pageid=1&pgtitle=about ncpre.
[17] Planck M (1901) Ueber die Elementarquanta der Materie und der Elektricität. *Annalen der Physik* 309(3): 564–566.
[18] Einstein A (1905) Über einen die Erzeugung und Verwandlung des Lichtes betreffenden heuristischen Gesichtspunkt. *Annalen der Physik* 322(6): 132–148.
[19] Wikipedia. http://en.wikipedia.org/wiki/File:Max_Planck.png.

[20] Wikipedia. http://en.wikipedia.org/wiki/File:Einstein_1921_portrait2.jpg.
[21] Tsokos KA (2008) *Physics for the IB Diploma*, 5th edn. Cambridge: Cambridge University Press.
[22] Perlin J (2004) *The Silicon Solar Cell Turns 50*. Golden, CO: National Renewable Energy Laboratory.
[23] Chapin DM, Fuller CS, and Pearson GLA (1954) New silicon p–n junction photocell for converting solar radiation into electrical power. *Journal of Applied Physics* 25: 676.
[24] Courtesy of John Perlin Bell Labs silicon solar cell.
[25] Schaeffer J (2008) *Solar Living Source Book*, 30th anniversary edn. Hopland, CA: Gaiam Real Goods.
[26] Boyle G (2004) *Renewable Energy: Power for a Sustainable Future*, 2nd edn. Oxford: Oxford University Press.
[27] Wolf M (1972) Historical development of solar cells. *Proceedings of the 25th Power Sources Symposium*, Fort Monmouth, NJ. Redbank, NJ: PSC Publications.
[28] Wikipedia. http://en.wikipedia.org/wiki/File:ROSSA.jpg.
[29] Gevorkian P (2006) *Sustainable Energy System Engineering: The Complete Green Building Design Resource*. New York: McGraw-Hill.
[30] (1973) Solar cell prices dropping, but broad terrestrial use awaits mass production. *Electronics* 40–41.
[31] Magid L (1976) The current status of the U.S. photovoltaic conversion program. *Proceedings of the 12th IEEE Photovoltaic Specialists Conference*. Baton Rouge, LA, USA. New York: IEEE.
[32] Borowitz S (1999) *Farewell Fossil Fuels: Reviewing America's Energy Policy*, 1st edn. New York: Plenum Press.
[33] Solarpowerportal. http://www.solarpowerportal.co.uk/news/kingdom_housing_association_wins_green_apple_environmental_award_5478/.
[34] Solarpowerportal. http://www.solarpowerportal.co.uk/news/uks_first_large-scale_power_plant_leaves_planning_stage548/.
[35] Weston E (1888) Solar Cell. US Patent 389,124, 4 September.
[36] Tesla NA (1901) Apparatus for the Utilization of Radiant Energy. US Patent 685,957, 5 November.
[37] Tesla NA (1901) Method of Utilizing Radiant Energy. US Patent 685,958. 5 November.
[38] Trivich D and Flinn PA (1955) Maximum efficiency of solar energy conversion by quantum processes. In: Daniels F and Duf EJ (eds.) *Solar Energy Research*. London: Thames and Hudson.
[39] Reynolds PC, Leiess G, Antes LL, and Marburger RE (1954) Photovoltaic effect in CdS. *Physical Review* 96: 533–534.
[40] Chapin DM, Fuller CS, and Pearson GL (1957) Solar Energy Converting Apparatus. US Patent 2,780,765, 5 February.
[41] Glaser PE (1968) Power from the sun. *Science* 162: 857–886.
[42] Wikipedia. http://en.wikipedia.org/wiki/File:PVeff(rev100414).png.
[43] Green MA (2003) *Third Generation Photovoltaics: Advanced Solar Energy Conversion*. Berlin, Germany: Springer Verlag.
[44] Kazmerski LL (2000) Photovoltaics R&D: Tour through the 21st Century. *Proceedings of the 16th European Photovoltaic Solar Energy Conference and Exhibition*, Glasgow, UK. James & James Ltd, UK.
[45] 3rd International Conference on Solar Photovoltaic Investments, Pvinvestmentconference.org. http://www.pvinvestmentconference.org.

1.05 Historical and Future Cost Dynamics of Photovoltaic Technology

GF Nemet and D Husmann, University of Wisconsin–Madison, Madison, WI, USA

© 2012 Elsevier Ltd. All rights reserved.

1.05.1	Introduction: Observed Reductions in the Cost of Photovoltaics	47
1.05.2	What Caused the 700× Reduction in the Cost of PV?	48
1.05.2.1	Identifying Drivers of Change	49
1.05.2.2	R&D and Efficiency Improvements	49
1.05.2.3	Sequential Niche Markets	49
1.05.2.4	Expectations about Future Demand	50
1.05.2.5	Learning by Doing	51
1.05.2.6	Intertechnology Spillovers	51
1.05.2.7	Materials	51
1.05.2.8	Drivers Related to Supply and Demand	52
1.05.2.8.1	Industry structure	52
1.05.2.8.2	Demand shocks and rising elasticity	52
1.05.2.9	Quality and Product Attributes	53
1.05.2.10	Interactions between R&D and Experience in Production	54
1.05.3	Using Learning Curves to Predict Costs	54
1.05.3.1	Use of Experience Curves in Modeling and Policy	54
1.05.3.1.1	Modeling	55
1.05.3.1.2	Policy	55
1.05.3.2	Problems with Using Experience Curves	55
1.05.3.3	How Reliable Are Experience Curve Predictions?	57
1.05.3.3.1	Assessing the significance of recent deviations	58
1.05.4	Nonincremental Cost-Reducing Developments	61
1.05.4.1	Identifying Breakthroughs	61
1.05.4.1.1	Defining breakthrough	61
1.05.4.1.2	First pass: Expert opinion	62
1.05.4.1.3	Why patent analysis?	62
1.05.4.1.4	Backward citation analysis	62
1.05.4.1.5	Implementing backward citation analysis for PV	63
1.05.4.2	Results: Combining Expert Opinion and Patent Analysis	65
1.05.5	Modeling Nonincremental Changes in PV	67
1.05.5.1	An Approach to Modeling Nonincremental Technological Change	67
1.05.5.2	Results for Nonincremental Technological Change	68
1.05.5.3	Summary of Nonincremental Modeling	69
1.05.6	Future Progress and Development	69
References		70

1.05.1 Introduction: Observed Reductions in the Cost of Photovoltaics

The cost of photovoltaics (PV) has declined by a factor of nearly 700 since the 1950s, which is more than that for any other energy technology in that period. At present, however, PV remains a niche electricity source and in the overwhelming majority of situations does not compete economically with conventional sources, such as coal and gas, or even with other renewable sources, such as wind and biomass. The extent to which the technology improves over the next few decades will determine whether PV reaches terawatt scale and makes a meaningful contribution to reducing greenhouse gas emissions or remains limited to niche applications.

In this chapter, we discuss the observed cost reductions in PV and the factors affecting them. We discuss the use of learning curves for forecasting PV costs and the nonincremental changes to technology that complicate such models. We include a discussion of an alternate forecasting methodology that incorporates R&D impacts and conclude with implications for policy and items for future progress.

Reductions have occurred across a wide variety of components within PV systems. Foremost, the cost of PV modules have declined from about $2700 W^{-1} in the 1950s to around $3 W^{-1} in 2006 (**Figure 1**) [1]. Although difficult to verify, claims that the marginal cost of manufacturing modules is as low as $1 W^{-1} are now widespread [2].

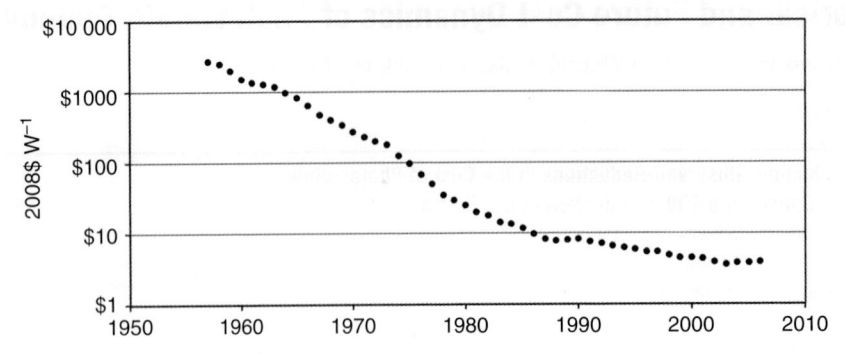

Figure 1 Cost of PV modules, 1957–2006 (2008$ W^{-1}) [1].

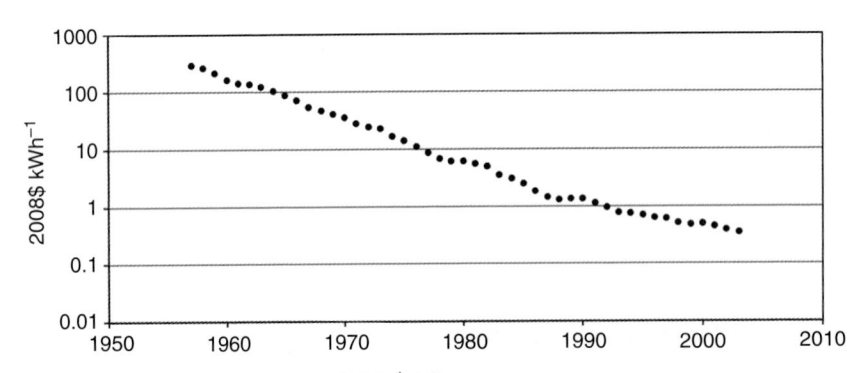

Figure 2 Levelized cost of electricity generated from PV (2008$ kWh^{-1}) [1].

Most assessment of PV has focused on the evolution of the core technology, the modules that convert sunlight to electricity. As the prices of modules have fallen, the rest of the components that comprise a PV system have accounted for an increasing share of the overall costs. A study of balance-of-system (BOS) prices in the 1990s found that the rate of technology improvement in BOS components has been quite similar to that of modules [3], which is rather surprising given the heterogeneous set of components and activities that fall under the rubric of BOS. Inverters, the largest hardware component of BOS, improved more slowly than modules; it was the noninverter costs – installation, wiring, mounting systems – that improved even more quickly. Dispersion in the data for BOS components is higher than that for modules.

Ultimately, because technology adoption decisions are based on the cost of electricity produced, the cost of fully installed systems is what matters most. Recent work at Lawrence Berkeley National Laboratory has documented the cost of installed systems in the 2000s [4]. Costs have fallen from over $10 W^{-1} in 1998 to under $8 W^{-1} in 2007. **Figure 2** shows the long-term decline in the cost of electricity from PV, a factor of 800 reduction.

1.05.2 What Caused the 700× Reduction in the Cost of PV?

A variety of factors, including government activities, have enabled the nearly 3 orders of magnitude reduction in the cost of PV over the past six decades. Despite this achievement, the technology still remains expensive, such that widespread deployment depends on substantial future improvement. No single determinant predominantly explains the improvement to date; R&D, economies of scale, learning by doing, and knowledge spillovers from other technologies have all played a role in reducing system costs. Moreover, interactions among factors that enable knowledge feedbacks – for example, between demand subsidies and R&D – have also proven important.

But not all of the factors were important for the entire sequence of the technology's development. Certain factors dominated for periods. These stages have been correlated with shifts in the geographic foci of effort, both by the private sector and by the government: in the 1970–85, R&D to improve efficiencies and manufacturing techniques; in the 1990s to early 2000s, long-term demand programs to enable economies of scale; and in the 2000s, efforts to stimulate local learning by doing to reduce installation costs in addition to continuous improvements through manufacturing scale [5]. As alternatives to crystallized silicon PV emerge, efforts to improve them follow a similar cycle.

1.05.2.1 Identifying Drivers of Change

Nemet [6] sought to understand the drivers behind technical change in PV by disaggregating historical cost reductions into observable technical factors. That study spanned the period of nascent commercialization in the mid-1970s through the early 2000s. During the 26-year period studied, there was a factor of 20 reduction in the cost of PV modules.

The results of that study point to two factors that stand out as most important: plant size accounts for 43% of the change in PV cost and efficiency accounts for 30% of the change. Of the remaining factors, the declining cost of silicon accounts for 12%. Yield, silicon consumption, wafer size, and polycrystalline share each have impacts of 3% or less. These observed changes are summarized in **Figure 3**. The following sections discuss the sources of these observed changes. **Table 1** summarizes this discussion.

1.05.2.2 R&D and Efficiency Improvements

The doubling of the average electrical conversion efficiency of PV systems since the 1970s has been important to cost reductions, accounting for about a third of the decline in cost over time. R&D, especially public sector R&D, has been central to this change (**Figure 4**). Data on the highest laboratory cell efficiencies over time show that of the 16 advances in efficiency since 1980 [7], only 6 were accomplished by firms that manufacture commercial cells. Most of the improvements were accomplished by universities, none of which would have learned from experience with large-scale production; government and university R&D programs produced 10 of the 16 breakthroughs in cell efficiency. Almost every one of the 20 most important improvements in PV occurred during a 10-year period between the mid-1970s and the mid-1980s [8], most of them in the United States where over a billion was invested in PV R&D during that period [9]. Section 1.05.4 discusses a novel methodology for identifying these types of nonincremental improvements.

1.05.2.3 Sequential Niche Markets

Deployment of PV has benefited from a sequence of niche markets where users of the technology were less price-sensitive and had strong preferences for characteristics such as reliability and performance that allowed product differentiation. Governments have played a large role in creating or enhancing some of these niche markets. In the 1960s and 1970s, the US space program and the

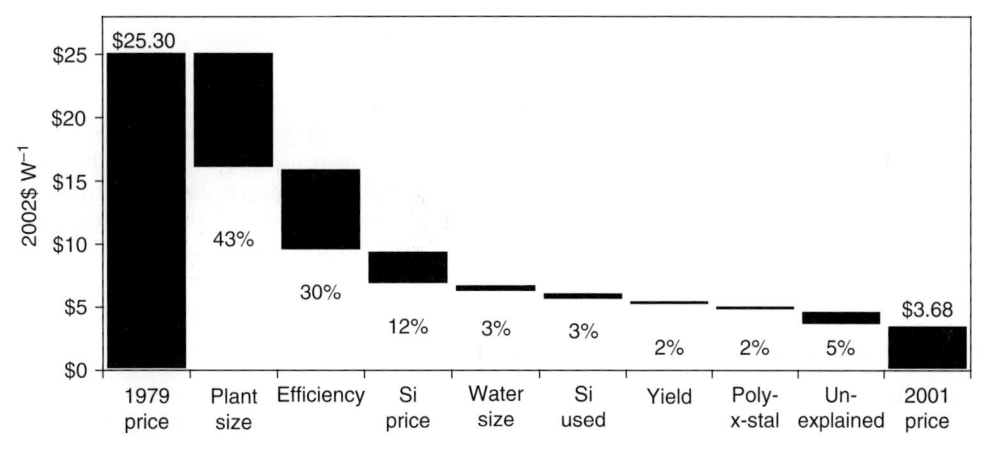

Figure 3 Portion of cost reduction in PV modules accounted for by each factor [1].

Table 1 Summary of effects of items on the cost of PV (1980–2001) and reasons for the change in each factor

Item	Share change in PV module costs attributable (%)	Main drivers of change in each factor
Plant size	43	Expected future demand and risk management
Efficiency	30	R&D, some LBD for lab-to-market
Silicon cost	12	Spillover benefit from information technology industry
Wafer size	3	Strong LBD
Si used	3	LBD and technology spillover
Yield	2	Strong LBD
Polycrystalline share	2	New process, LBD possible
Other factors	5	Not examined

LBD, learning by doing.

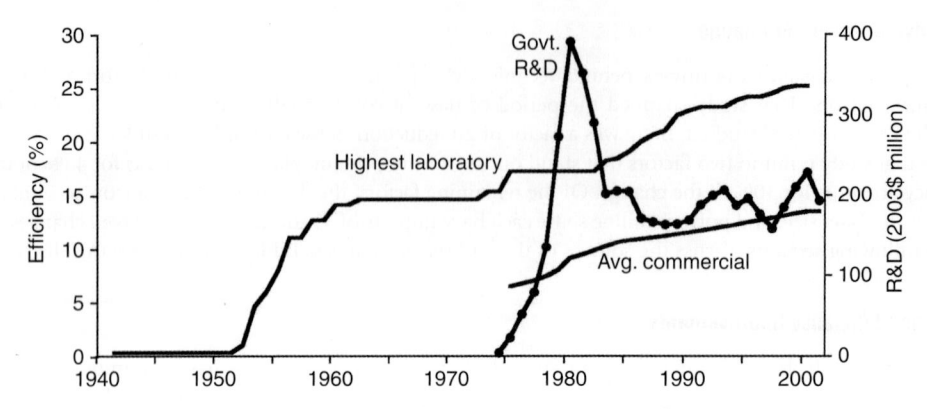

Figure 4 Improvements in energy conversion efficiency of PV and US public investment in PV R&D [1].

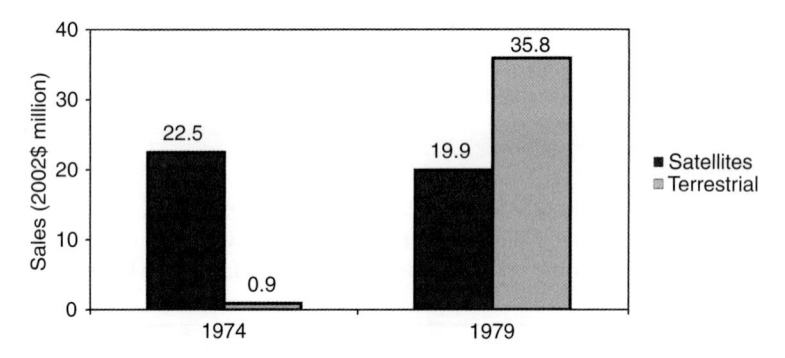

Figure 5 Shift in market from space to terrestrial applications from 1974 to 1979 [10].

Department of Defense accounted for more than half of the global market for PV (**Figure 5**). The high cost of electricity in space allowed PV to be competitive even at an early stage. Subsequent markets – telecom repeater stations, off-grid homes, and especially consumer electronics such as toys, calculators, and watches – were, importantly, independent of government decisions, and allowed the industry to expand from the mid-1980s until the late 1990s when energy prices, and thus alternative energy, were low social priorities. From the 1990s onward, households that had strong preferences for environmental protection, especially conspicuously, created larger markets.

1.05.2.4 Expectations about Future Demand

Increasing demand for PV has reduced costs by enabling opportunities for economies of scale in manufacturing. Nemet [6] assembled empirical data to populate a simple engineering-based model identifying the most important factors affecting the cost of PV over the past three decades. The study found that three factors account for almost all of the observed cost reductions: (1) a 2 orders of magnitude increase in the size of manufacturing facilities, which provided opportunities for economies of scale (**Figure 6**); (2) a doubling in the electrical conversion efficiency of commercial modules; and (3) a fall in the price of the primary input

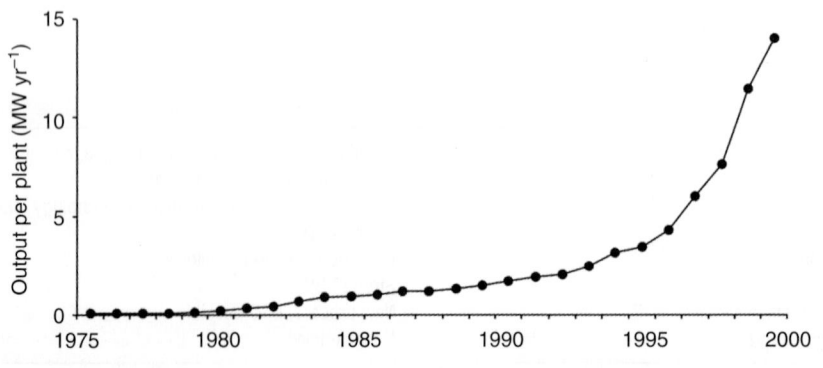

Figure 6 Size of PV manufacturing facilities [1].

material, purified silicon. Because investments in larger facilities take time to pay off, economies of scale depend on expectations of future demand. As a result, public programs that reduce uncertainty by setting clear long-term expectations, such as Japan's Sunshine Program in the 1990s [11], are more effective at enabling scale economies than generous subsidies that can suddenly disappear, such as California's incentives for wind and solar in the early 1980s. Government programs with longer time horizons such as Germany's in the 2000s and the recently launched California Solar Initiative create similar opportunities [1, 12]. Japan's program was especially innovative in that it not only took a long time horizon but also set a declining subsidy such that it fell to zero after 10 years of the program. This provided not only expectations of demand but also clear expectations of future levels of subsidy.

Germany's program is especially notable in that production there has become sufficient to create external economies of scale – the emergence of machine tool manufacturers that now produce equipment specifically for the PV industry [13]. Similarly, production of lower purity, thus cheaper, solar-grade silicon is now profitable because plants can be built at large scale. We also have begun to observe some economies of scale in unit size, where large installations show much lower per-watt costs [4]. Increasing installation size is likely to become more important as economies of scale reduce module-manufacturing costs, leaving installation costs as an increasingly large share of system costs.

The main drivers of the change in plant size over the period were growth in expected future demand and the ability to manage investment risk. Whether experience plays a role in enabling the shift to large facilities depends on new manufacturing problems at larger scales and how experience may help in overcoming these problems. Examples from three PV firms indicate that limited manufacturing experience did not preclude rapid increases in production. Mitsubishi Electric expanded from essentially zero production in 1997 to 12 MW and as of 2000 planned to expand to 600 MW by 2012 [14]. While the firm had decades of experience in research and satellite PV applications, its cumulative production was minimal. It began substantial manufacturing activity only with the opening of its Iida plant and its entry into the Japanese residential PV market in 1998. Similarly, Q-Cells, a German firm, began producing cells only in 2001 with a 12 MW line and increased production to 50 MW in only 2 years [15]. Sharp considered construction of a 500 MW yr^{-1} plant in 2006, which would amount to a 10-fold expansion in the firm's capacity in only 5 years. By 2011, it had increased capacity to 2.8 GW yr^{-1}. Note that by mid-2011, six firms had manufacturing capacities above 2 GW yr^{-1}. In the rapid expansions of the past 10 years, the ability to raise capital and to take on the risk of large investments that enable construction of large manufacturing facilities appears to have played more important roles than learning by experience in enabling cost reductions. These results support the claim that "sometimes much of what is attributed to experience is due to scale" [16].

1.05.2.5 Learning by Doing

Learning from experience in production has played a role, albeit not a dominant one, in reducing module costs. These changes occurred in several different processes. Experience in manufacturing led to lower defect rates and the utilization of the entire wafer area, which increased yields. Experience was probably important in enabling the growth of larger crystals and the formation of longer conductors from cell edges to electrical junctions; savings accrued from the ensuing larger wafer sizes. Less silicon was consumed as experience helped improve sawing techniques so that less crystal was lost as sawdust and thinner cells could be produced. The development of wire saws, a spillover technology from the radial tire industry, is less clearly related to experience. Learning by doing helped the gradual shift to polycrystalline ingots. Casting of rectangular multicrystalline ingots was a new technology that partially derives from experience with the Czochralski process for growing individual crystals. While learning by doing and experience play more important roles in these factors, together they account for only 10% of the overall change in module cost [6].

Learning by doing plays a much more important role in reducing installation costs [17]. An important aspect of this learning is that it is a local phenomenon, whereas module production is truly global [18]. As installation costs become a large portion of costs, the extent of this learning by doing will be important. Whether or not the benefits of this learning are appropriable will determine whether governments need to play a role in promoting learning investments. More generally, the global aspect of module manufacturing suggests that interfirm and international technology spillovers are likely to be more important in module production than in installation. Finally, learning by doing may be important in the translation of laboratory breakthroughs to commercial products, as observed in **Figure 4**.

1.05.2.6 Intertechnology Spillovers

Like many technologies, PV has benefited from the adoption of innovations that originated in other industries. These include the use of excess purified silicon from the chip-making industry, the use of wire saws from radial tires to slice multiple silicon wafers, electronic connectors to ease installation, screen-printing techniques from lithography, as well as an array of manufacturing techniques taken from microprocessors (for crystallized silicon) and liquid crystal displays (LCDs; for thin film).

1.05.2.7 Materials

Reductions in the cost of purified silicon were a spillover benefit from manufacturing improvements in the microprocessor industry. Until the 2000s, the PV industry accounted for less than 15% of the world market for purified silicon [19]. Through that time, the PV industry did not purify its own silicon but instead purchased silicon from producers whose main customers were in the much larger microprocessor industry, where purity standards were higher. Therefore, experience in the PV industry was irrelevant to silicon cost reductions. More recently, input costs, especially of purified silicon, increased in the mid-2000s in line with other commodity prices

[20]. This change has had the beneficial effect of creating strong incentives to reduce wafer thickness and find ways to conserve materials. Global recession in 2008–09 has seen commodity prices drop. However, the benefits of lower silicon utilization remain. Moreover, the shift to PV-specific silicon production has increased the potential for scale economies at lower levels of purity. If lifetimes and efficiencies can be maintained at these lower levels of purity, there is strong potential for materials costs to fall beyond the short-term business cycle effects.

1.05.2.8 Drivers Related to Supply and Demand

Changes in demand and in market structure have affected prices as well, even if they do not directly affect the technical characteristics of the technology.

1.05.2.8.1 Industry structure

Changes in industry concentration have affected market power and have led to a changing relationship between prices and costs over time. Market share data indicate a decline in industry concentration during this period. This change typically produces an increase in competitiveness, a decrease in market power, and lower profit margins. For example, there were only two US firms shipping terrestrial PV from 1970 to 1975 [21, 22]. In 1978, about 20 firms were selling modules and the top 3 firms made up 77% of the industry [23]. By 1983, there were dozens of firms in the industry, with the largest three firms accounting for only 50% of the megawatts sold [24].

One way to quantify this change is to use the Herfindahl–Hirschman index (HHI), which provides a way of measuring industry concentration [25, 26]. The HHI is calculated by summing the squares of the market shares of all firms in an industry. The maximum possible HHI is 10 000. The data show a trend to a less concentrated US market during the 1970s (**Figure 7**). Concentration in the global market remained stable in the 1990s, the period for which comprehensive worldwide data are available. The increase in international trade in PV over the last three decades indicates that the relevant scale of analysis shifted from a national market in the earlier years to an international market today.

1.05.2.8.2 Demand shocks and rising elasticity

Demand dynamics have shifted prices in opposite directions. Foremost, the surge in subsidy programs for PV in the 2000s resembles a demand shock, as observed in other sectors. The industry has had a difficult time adjusting quickly. The very high levels of demand in the 2005–07 period are in part to blame for the high prices during that period. This led to a reversal in the multidecade downward cost trajectory that can be observed in **Figure 9**. Some of this cost increase was due to higher materials costs [20] and the rest likely due to higher willingness to pay as aggressive subsidy programs brought new consumers to the market for PV.

In contrast, historically, the shift from satellites to terrestrial applications affected prices because of a difference in the demand elasticity of the two types of customers. Price data from that period provide some supporting evidence. In 1974–79, the price per watt of PV modules for satellites was 2.5 times higher than that for terrestrial modules [10]. The impact of this price difference on average PV prices is calculated by taking into account the change in market share mentioned below. In this period, the combination of these price and market shifts accounts for $22 of the $28 price decline not explained by the model. Satellite customers, with their hundreds of millions of dollars of related investments, almost certainly had a higher willingness to pay for PV panels than early terrestrial applications such as telecom repeater sites or buoys for marine navigation. The difference in quality must account for some of the price difference. But the difference in willingness to pay may also have led to higher differences between cost and price for satellite than for terrestrial applications.

Another historical explanation for the change in cost is that changes in production methods occurred due to an increase in the number of customers and the types of products they demanded. There was a shift away from a near-monopsony market in the early 1970s. Originally a single customer, the US space program, accounted for almost all sales. Conversely, in 1976, the US government

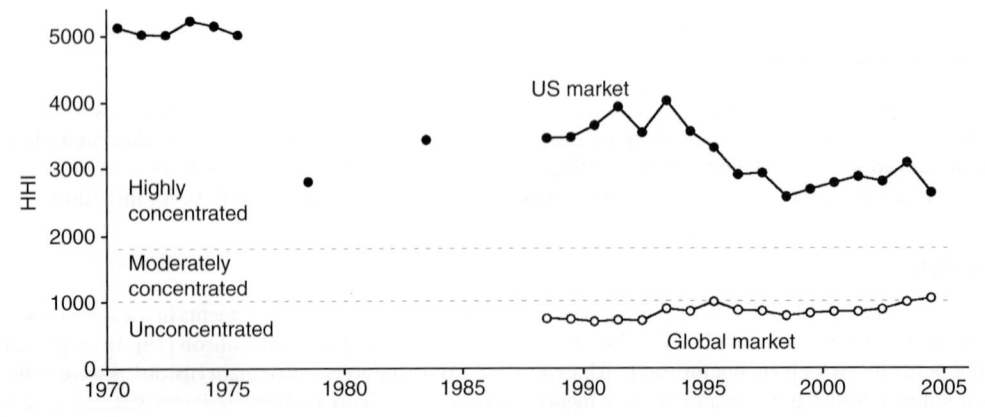

Figure 7 Concentration in the PV industry (HHI) [1].

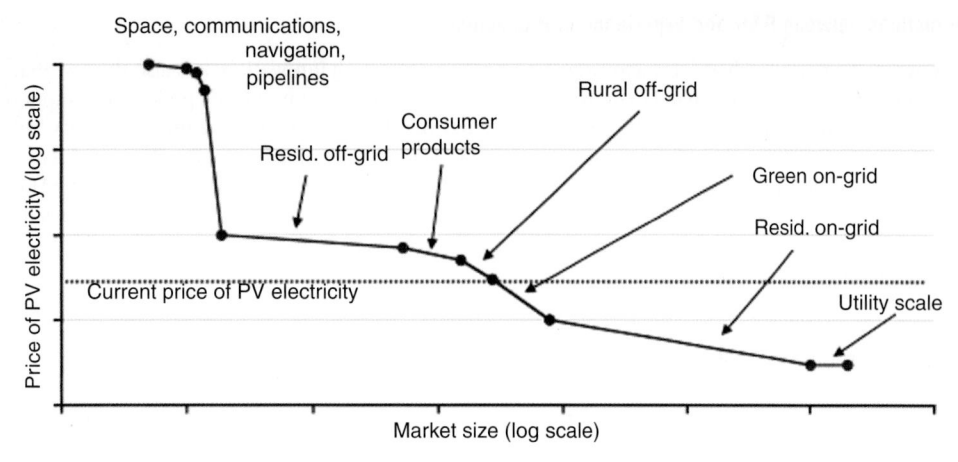

Figure 8 Illustrative demand curve for PV electricity. Reproduced from Nemet GF (2009) Interim monitoring of cost dynamics for publicly supported energy technologies. *Energy Policy* 37(3): 825–835 [28].

accounted for only one-third of terrestrial PV purchases [27]. With the rise of the terrestrial industry, a larger set of customers emerged over the course of the decade. When this change in the structure of demand occurred, one result was the shift away from producing customized modules, such as the 20 kW panels on Skylab, to producing increasingly standard products at much higher volumes. **Figure 8** provides a schematic example of what a demand curve for PV electricity might look like considering both historical data and projections of the future opportunity. The *x*-axis shows the size of each market segment. The *y*-axis shows that the price customers are willing to pay for PV electricity in each segment. Note the use of log–log axes. For example, in the upper left region, the cost of electricity is very high in off-grid and remote locations, although markets are relatively small. At the other end of the curve, markets for wholesale electricity are very large, but require PV to compete with large central station sources of electricity.

1.05.2.9 Quality and Product Attributes

Changes in quality and product attributes also affected costs. During the 1970s, the market for PV modules shifted toward terrestrial applications. Whereas in 1974, 94% of PV systems were manufactured for applications in space, by 1979, the market share for space had fallen to 36%. The shift led to a reduction in the quality of modules, which rendered certain characteristics nonessential, allowing manufacturers to switch to less costly processes.

First, space and weight constraints on rockets required high-efficiency panels to maximize watts delivered per square meter. The relaxation of this requirement for terrestrial applications enabled manufacturers to employ two important cost-saving processes [10]. Cheaper materials were now tolerable. Modules could use the entire area of the silicon wafer – even the portions near the edges, which tend to suffer from defects and high electrical resistivity. Also, the final assembly process could use a chemical polish to enhance light transmission through the glass cover, rather than the more expensive ground optical finish that was required for satellites. Second, reliability targets fell. Satellite programs, such as Vanguard and Skylab, needed satellite PV modules that would operate reliably without maintenance, perhaps for 20 years. Terrestrial applications, on the other hand, could still be useful with much shorter lifetimes. The rapid growth in the terrestrial market was the main driver of this change.

There are three assumptions that are commonly made when applying the experience curve model using prices rather than costs: that margins are constant over time, that margins are close to zero with only minor perturbations, and that margins are often negative due to forward pricing. Yet changes in demand and industry structure are important in that they erode support for these three assumptions. Indeed, earlier work pointed out that firms' recognition of the value of market domination, particularly during incipient commercialization, leads to unstable pricing behavior [29]. An implication of the variation in the price–cost margin is that industry structure affects the learning rate. In the case of an industry that becomes more competitive over time, such as PV, a price-based experience curve overestimates the rate of technical progress.

One solution for addressing this problem would be for future work to obtain real cost data where possible. An alternative would be to use an approach in which costs can be derived from prices and market shares using the assumptions in Cournot competition that a firm's profit margins decrease as the number of firms in the market increases and that a single firm's profit margins increase with that firm's market share [30]. However, comparisons of competing technologies are best made on the basis of prices, not costs, since prices reflect what a consumer faces in deciding whether to adopt a technology and which to adopt. A more general approach would be to incorporate market dynamics into predictions of technological change: industry concentration, market power, and changes in elasticity of demand affect prices. The HHI analysis described above shows that concentration is not stable over time, especially if international trade is taken into account. The assumptions of perfect competition and prices equal marginal cost are too strong in the early stages of the product life cycle when the technology is improving rapidly, industry structure is unstable, and new types of customers are entering the market.

1.05.2.10 Interactions between R&D and Experience in Production

While there do appear to be periods when one factor was dominant in supporting innovation, it is also the case that the interaction of various factors was important. In particular, Japan in the 1990s had both strong demand-side policies and support for R&D [31]. In this case, it was not so much efficiency breakthroughs and alternative cell designs that drove improvements, but rather support from the Japanese government, via the Ministry of International Trade and Industry (MITI). This enabled coordination of expectations and sharing of best practices, which enabled manufacturing improvements. The influence of the US federal government may have played a similar role in enabling the 1970s breakthroughs, not just through providing resources from R&D but by creating a sense of commitment that convinced many to work on the technical and market challenges associated with commercializing this nascent technology [32].

1.05.3 Using Learning Curves to Predict Costs

The potential for future cost reductions, combined with the magnitude of the potential impact of very inexpensive PV, has created a strong demand for tools that enable prediction of future costs. The experience curve has emerged as the most important of these tools. The following section surveys the use of experience curves in policy and modeling, caveats in their application, assessment of their reliability, and the implications for policy makers [33]. While this section focuses on the historically dominant design in the industry, crystalline silicon PV, more recent work has looked at other approaches, such as thin films [34] and organics (discussed below). Also, note here that we use the terminology experience curve (defined above), rather than the more specific concept of the learning curve, which, strictly defined, focuses on labor costs and within-firm knowledge accumulation.

Characterizations of technological change have identified patterns in the ways that technologies are invented, improve, and diffuse into society [35]. Studies have described the complex nature of an innovation process in which uncertainty is inherent [36], knowledge flows across sectors are important [37], and lags can be long [38]. Perhaps because of characteristics such as these, theoretical work on innovation provides only a limited set of methods with which to predict changes in technology. The learning curve model offers an exception.

Experience curves have been assembled for a wide range of technologies. While there is broad variation in the observed rates of 'learning', studies do provide evidence that costs almost always decline as cumulative production increases [16, 39–42]. The roots of these microlevel observations can be traced back to early economic theories about the importance of the relationship between specialization and trade, which were based in part on individuals developing expertise over time [41]. The notion of the experience curve varies from the more specific formulation behind the learning curve in that it aggregates from individuals to entire industries and from labor costs to all manufacturing costs. In the literature on experience curves, the technological 'learning' refers to a broad set of improvements in the cost and performance of technologies, not strictly to the more precise notion of learning by doing [43]. An experience curve for PV modules is shown in **Figure 9**, that is, a double-logarithmic graph of PV module price as a function of cumulative capacity.

1.05.3.1 Use of Experience Curves in Modeling and Policy

Experience curves have become a widely used tool both for models of future energy supply and to inform the design of public policies related to PV. For example, they provide a method for evaluating the cost-effectiveness of public policies to support new technologies [44] and for weighing public technology investment against environmental damage costs [45]. Energy supply models now also use learning curves to implement endogenous improvements in technology. Prior to the 1990s, technological change was typically included as an exogenous increase in energy conversion efficiency or ignored [46]. Studies in the 1990s began to use the learning curve to treat technology dynamically [47, 48], and since then, it has become a powerful and widely used model for

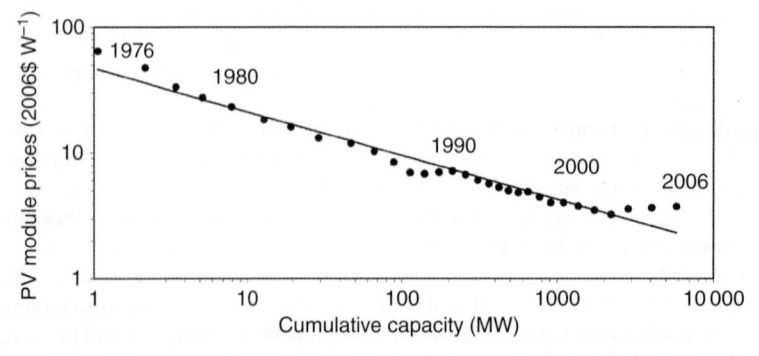

Figure 9 Experience curve for PV modules, 1976–2006. Reproduced from Nemet GF (2009) Interim monitoring of cost dynamics for publicly supported energy technologies. *Energy Policy* 37(3): 825–835 [28].

projecting technological change. Recent work, however, has cautioned that uncertainties in key parameters may be significant [49], making application of the learning curve to evaluate public policies inappropriate in some cases [50].

1.05.3.1.1 Modeling

The rate and direction of future technological change in energy technologies are important sources of uncertainty in models that assess the costs of stabilizing the climate [51]. Treatment of technology dynamics in integrated assessment models has become increasingly sophisticated [52] as models have incorporated lessons from the economics of innovation and as increased processing power and improved algorithms have enabled optimization of phenomena such as increasing returns, which in the past had made computation unwieldy [53]. Yet the representation of technological change in large energy-economic models remains highly stylized relative to the state of the art of understanding about the economics of innovation [54]. Perhaps one reason for the lag between the research frontier for the economics of innovation and the modeling of it has to do with incompatibilities in the methodological approaches of the two fields. On the one hand, research on the economics of innovation has tended to emphasize uncertainty [55], cumulativeness [38], and nonergodicity [56]. The outcomes of this line of inquiry, which dates back to Schumpeter [35], and even Marx [57], have often been characterized by richness of description, a case study approach, and, arguably, more progress with rigorous empirical observation than with strong theoretical claims. On the other hand, optimization and simulation models require compact quantitative estimation of parameters, with uncertainties that do not become infinite once propagated through the model. One of the few concepts that have bridged the epistemological gap between the economics of innovation and the integrated assessment of climate change is the experience curve. Experience curves provide a way to project future costs conditional on the cumulative quantity of capacity produced. The resulting cost predictions are less deterministic than those generated by temporal-based rates of technological change, but they are also not simply scenarios, internally consistent descriptions of one possible future state of technology; they are conditional predictions.

1.05.3.1.2 Policy

Large programs and deviations from trends in cost reductions are challenging policy makers to make decisions about whether, when, and how much to stimulate the development of energy technologies that have high external benefits. The net benefits of subsidies and other incentives programs depend heavily on the extent to which technologies improve over time. Experience curves provide a way for policy makers to incorporate technology dynamics into decisions that involve the future costs of technologies. They are now used widely to inform decisions that involve billions, and even trillions, of dollars in public funding. The general notion that learning from experience leads to cost reductions and performance improvements is well supported by a large array of empirical studies across a variety of technologies. But the appropriateness of using experience curves to guide policy is less uniformly acknowledged. Despite caveats in previous work, the cost projections that result from experience curves are typically used without characterizing uncertainty in those estimates. As a result, experience curves are now employed widely to inform decisions that involve billions of dollars in public funds. They have been used both directly – as graphical exhibits to inform debates – and indirectly – as inputs to energy-economic models that simulate the cost of achieving environmental goals. Much of the early work to translate the insights from experience curve studies to energy policy decisions is included in a study for the International Energy Agency [49]. Other studies have used the tool directly to make claims about policy implications [44, 45, 58].

As mentioned above, energy-economic models that minimize the cost of energy supply now also include experience curve relationships to include technology dynamics. Model comparison studies have found that models' estimates of the social costs of policy are sensitive to how technological change is characterized [51]. Working Group III of the Intergovernmental Panel on Climate Change (IPCC) used results from a variety of energy-economic models to estimate the magnitude of economically available greenhouse gas emissions in its Fourth Assessment Report [59]. The results of this assessment are widely used to inform national climate change policies, as well as the architecture for the next international climate policy regime. In the 17 models they review, some form of experience curve is used to characterize technological change in at least 10 of those models. See Table 11.15 of IPCC [59]. Another influential report in 2006, the *Stern Review on the Economics of Climate Change* [60], relied heavily on experience curves to model technological change. This report has been central to the formation of climate policy in the United Kingdom and has played a role in debates in the United States as well, both at the federal level and in California. The International Energy Agency relies on experience curves in its assessment of the least cost method for meeting greenhouse gas reduction targets and energy demand for 2050 [61]. Note that the 'learning investments' that result from the analyses in this report are estimated in a range of $5–8 trillion. Debates about subsidies and production requirements for ethanol also use historical experience curves as a justification for public support of the production of biofuels [62]. At the state level, experience curves have provided one of the most influential justifications for a $3 billion subsidy program for PV [12]. Experience curves have also been used in economic models of the cost of meeting California's ambitious greenhouse gas reduction targets [63]. Finally, in decisions by the 24 states that have passed renewable portfolio standards, debates include discussions of how mandatory renewables deployment will bring down its cost [64, 65].

1.05.3.2 Problems with Using Experience Curves

Demand among policy makers for rigorous, transparent, and reliable tools with which to predict future costs continues to be high. Yet an array of studies, which are cited below, warn about the limitations of experience curves.

The learning curve model operationalizes the explanatory variable experience using a cumulative measure of production or use. Change in cost typically represents the dependent variable and provides a measure of learning and technological improvement. Learning curve studies have experimented with a variety of functional forms to describe the relationship between cumulative capacity and cost [66]. The log-linear function is most common perhaps for its simplicity and generally high goodness-of-fit to observed data. The central parameter in this learning curve model is the exponent, defining the slope of a power function, which appears as a linear function when plotted on a log–log scale. This parameter is known as the learning coefficient (b) and can be used to calculate the progress ratio (PR) and learning ratio (LR) as shown below. C_0 and C_t are unit costs at time $t = 0$ and time t, respectively, and Q_0 and Q_t represent cumulative outputs at time $t = 0$ and time t, respectively.

$$C_t = C_0 \left(\frac{Q_t}{Q_0}\right)^{-b}$$

$$PR = 2^{-b}$$

$$LR = (1 - PR)$$

Wene [67] has developed a cybernetic theory that predicts an LR of 20%. Several studies have criticized the learning curve model, especially in its more general form as the experience curve. Dutton and Thomas [16] surveyed 108 learning curve studies and showed a wide variation in learning rates, leading them to question the explanatory power of experience. **Figure 10** combines their learning rate data with those in a more recent survey of learning rates by McDonald and Schrattenholzer [68]. The learning rate for PV, 0.23, lies near the mode of the distribution. Argote and Epple [69] explored this variation further and proposed four alternative hypotheses for the observed technical improvements: economies of scale, knowledge spillovers, and two opposing factors, organizational forgetting and employee turnover. Despite such critiques, the application of the learning curve model has persisted, without major modifications, as a basis for predicting technical change, informing public policy, and guiding firm strategy. Below, the advantages and limitations of using the more general version of the learning curve for such applications are outlined.

The experience curve provides an appealing model for several reasons:

1. Availability of the two empirical time series required to build an experience curve – cost and production data – facilitates testing of the model. As a result, a rather large body of empirical studies has emerged to support the model. Compare the simplicity of obtaining cost and production data with the difficulty of quantifying related concepts such as knowledge stocks [70] and inventive output [71]. Still, data quality and uncertainty are infrequently explicitly addressed and as shown below can have a large impact on results.
2. Earlier studies of the origin of technical improvements, such as in the aircraft industry [39] and shipbuilding [40], provide narratives consistent with the theory that firms learn from past experience.
3. Studies cite the generally high goodness-of-fit of power functions to empirical data over several years, or even decades, as validation of the model.
4. The dynamic aspect of the model – the rate of improvement adjusts to changes in the growth of production – makes the model superior to forecasts that treat change purely as a function of time.
5. The reduction of the complex process of innovation to a single parameter, the learning rate, facilitates its inclusion in large optimization and simulation models.

The combination of a rich body of empirical literature and the more recent applications of learning curves in predictive models has revealed weaknesses that echo earlier critiques.

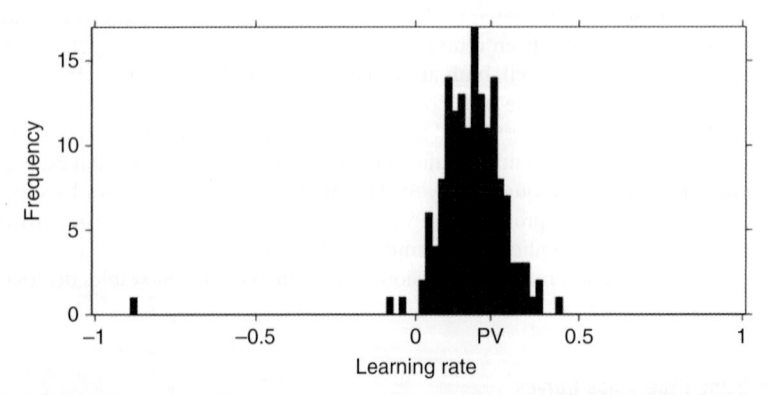

Figure 10 Frequency distribution of learning rates calculated in 156 learning curve studies. The learning rate for PV, 0.23, lies slightly above the mode of the distribution. Reproduced from Nemet GF (2009) Interim monitoring of cost dynamics for publicly supported energy technologies. *Energy Policy* 37(3): 825–835 [28].

1. The timing of future cost reductions is highly sensitive not only to changes in the market growth rate but also to small changes in the learning rate. Although a coefficient of determination for an experience curve of >0.95 is considered a strong validation of the experience curve model, variation in the underlying data can lead to uncertainty about the timing of cost reductions on the scale of decades. Two world surveys of PV prices [72, 73] produce learning rates of 0.26 and 0.17. What may appear as a minor difference has a large effect. For example, assuming a steady industry growth rate of 15% per year, consider how long it will take for PV costs to reach a threshold of $0.30 W^{-1}, an estimate for competitiveness with conventional alternatives. Just the difference in the choice of data set used produces a crossover point of 2039 for the 0.26 learning rate and 2067 for the 0.17 rate, a difference of 28 years. McDonald and Schrattenholzer [68] show that the range of learning rates for energy technologies in general is even larger. Neij et al. [50] find that calculations of the cost-effectiveness of public policies are sensitive to such variation. Wene [49] observes this sensitivity as well and recommends an ongoing process of policy evaluation that continuously incorporates recent data.

2. The experience curve model gives no way to predict discontinuities in the learning rate. In the case of PV, the experience curve switched to a lower trajectory around 1980. As a result, experience curve-based forecasts of PV in the 1970s predicted faster technological progress than actually occurred [3]. Discontinuities present special difficulties at early stages in the life of a technology. Early on, only a few data points define the experience curve, while at such times decisions about public support may be most critical. Early work in economics is skeptical about the assumption that historically observed rates of learning can be expected to continue in the future. Arrow [43] argued that that learning is subject to "sharply diminishing returns". Looking at studies within single plants, Hall and Howell [74] and Baloff [75] find that learning rates become essentially flat after a relatively short amount of time – approximately 2 years in these studies. Some have suggested that as a result a cubic or logistic function offers a more realistic functional form than a power function [76].

3. Studies that address uncertainty typically calculate uncertainties in the learning rate using the historical level of variance in the relationship between cost and cumulative capacity. This approach ignores uncertainties and limitations in the progress of the specific technical factors that are important in driving cost reductions [49]. For example, constraints on individual factors, such as theoretical efficiency limits, might affect our confidence in the likelihood of future cost reductions.

4. Due to their application in planning and forecasting, emphasis has shifted away from learning curves based on employee productivity and plant-level analysis toward experience curves aggregating industries and including all components of operating cost. While the statistical relationships generally remain strong, the conceptual story begins to look stretched, as one must make assumptions about the extent to which experience is shared across firms. In the strictest interpretation of the learning-by-doing model applied to entire industries, one must assume that each firm benefits from the collective experience of all. The model assumes homogeneous knowledge spillovers among firms.

5. The assumption that cost reductions are only determined by experience, as represented by cumulative capacity, ignores the effect of knowledge acquired from other sources, such as from R&D or from other industries. Earlier, Sheshinski [77] wrestled with the separation of the impact of two competing factors, investment and output. Others have addressed this limitation by incorporating additional factors such as workforce training [78], R&D [79, 80], and the interactions between R&D and diffusion [31]. Colinearity among the explanatory variables requires large and detailed data sets, the scarcity of which has so far limited widespread application of these more sophisticated models.

6. Experience curves ignore changes in quality beyond the single dimension being analyzed [81]. The dependent variable is limited to cost normalized by a single measure of performance – for example, hours of labor per aircraft, dollars per watt, or cents per megabyte. Performance measures like these ignore changes in quality such as aircraft speed, reliability of power generation, and the compactness of computer memory.

1.05.3.3 How Reliable Are Experience Curve Predictions?

Given these issues, how well do experience curves perform? Throughout the critiques, a primary concern is the issue of unacknowledged uncertainty. Although studies have cautioned that policy makers must contend with discontinuities and uncertainties in future learning rates, few do; the cost projections that result from experience curves are typically estimated without acknowledging uncertainty. Yet a wide array of studies now have pointed to serious reservations about using experience curve projections to inform policy decisions. Wene [49] emphasized the ways that experience curves could be used to design subsidy programs, but cautioned about the key uncertainties in parameters because "small changes in progress ratios will change learning investments considerably". Concerned about the scale of this uncertainty problem, one study concluded "we do not recommend the use of experience curves to analyze the cost effectiveness of policy measures" and recommended using multiple methods instead [82]. More recently, Neij [83] compared experience curve projections to those based on bottom-up models, as well as expert predictions, and found that they "agree in most cases". However, in some cases, large uncertainties that emerge from the bottom-up analyses are "not revealed" by experience curve studies. Rubin et al. [84] indicate that early prototypes often underestimate the costs of commercially viable applications so that costs rise. Koomey and Hultman [85] have documented a more persistent form of this cost inflation effect for nuclear reactors. Addressing PV specifically, Borenstein [86] argues that experience curve-based analyses do not justify government programs because they conflate multiple effects and ignore appropriability concerns.

Three sources of uncertainty complicate experience curve predictions. First, there is the typical dispersion in learning rates caused by imperfect correlations between cumulative capacity and cost. Sark [87] explores the effects of this 'r-squared' variation to calculate an error around the learning rate. Inconsistencies in the chosen system boundaries, for example, geographic scope, may introduce some of this variation. The second source has to do with whether historically observed learning rates can be expected to continue in the future. Even in his seminal work on learning by doing, Arrow [43] argued that that learning is subject to "sharply diminishing returns". Looking at studies within single manufacturing facilities, Hall and Howell [74] and Baloff [75] find that learning rates become essentially flat after a relatively short amount of time – approximately 2 years in these studies. As a result, some have suggested that a cubic or logistic function offers a more realistic functional form than a power function [76]. The third source of uncertainty derives from the choice of historical time period used to calculate learning rates. The timing issue captures variation in the source data, as well as changes in the slope over time.

Studies have characterized the effects of uncertainty. A prominent study showed that calculating the error in the PR could be used to develop a range of learning rates to use for sensitivity analysis in policy modeling [88]. Nemet [28] assessed these sources of uncertainty using a simple and transparent model of the costs of subsidizing technologies until they are competitive with alternatives. Those calculations include (1) the learning rate, (2) the year at which the cost of a subsidized technology approaches a target level, and (3) the discounted cost of government subsidies needed to achieve that level. The first result from that study is that there is a wide dispersion in learning rates depending on what time period was used. That study estimated the learning rate for PV in each of the 253 time periods of 10 years or greater between 1976 and 2006. **Figure 11** plots these learning rates by the year at which each time series ends. For example, the values shown for 1995 include all 11 time series that end in 1995. This set of values indicates the range of learning rates that would have been available to an analyst using experience curves to project costs in 1995. The data begin in 1985 because that is the first year for which 10 years of historical data (1976–85) are available. The data reveal two features about the trend in calculated learning rates: (1) there is a negative time trend, the mean of the learning rate values has decreased over time by approximately 0.005 per year, and (2) the dispersion in learning rate values around the annual mean has increased over time. The dispersion includes an oscillation with maxima in 1995 and 2006.

The second result from that study was estimation of the break-even year using the dispersion in learning rates described above. The target cost for PV modules used in this example is $P_a = \$1\ W^{-1}$ [89]. A 73% subsidy on actual 2006 prices is needed for consumers' costs to equal this target. **Figure 12(b)** shows distributions of the estimated years at which the price of PV will equal that of this competing technology. Descriptive statistics for these distributions are shown in **Table 2** for all time series and for all series that end in 2006. The median crossover year for all series, $t_a = 2034$, occurs 14 years earlier than the estimates using only data through 2006, $t_a = 2048$. Note that the dispersion has also increased with the more recent data set.

The third result from that study was to calculate the learning investment required to subsidize PV to the crossover point. The median cost to subsidize PV is $62 billion when using all time series and $163 billion when using only the time series that end in 2006. Note that a difference in median learning rate of 40% leads to a difference in median program costs of between a factor of 2 and 3. The dispersion in costs has also become large; the range from the 5th percentile to the 95th percentile spans an order of magnitude. Furthermore, notice that costs around the 95th percentile become very large, rising to the tens of trillions. Slow learning has nonlinear effects on cost and leads to very expensive subsidy programs – even when these future costs are discounted to present values.

Figure 12 summarizes these results. **Figure 12(a)** shows the distribution of learning rates for all 253 periods (black columns). The white columns show the distribution of rates using only those series that end in 2006. The latter is the data set one would expect a contemporary planner to use. The median of the distribution of learning rates from all 253 time series (LR = 0.21) is substantially higher than the median of the series ending in 2006 (LR = 0.15), although this difference is not significant.

1.05.3.3.1 *Assessing the significance of recent deviations*

One immediate policy implication of these results is that the possibility of very expensive subsidy programs makes early identification of such a scenario important. The price escalation in the mid-2000s prompts the question, "do recently observed costs represent a

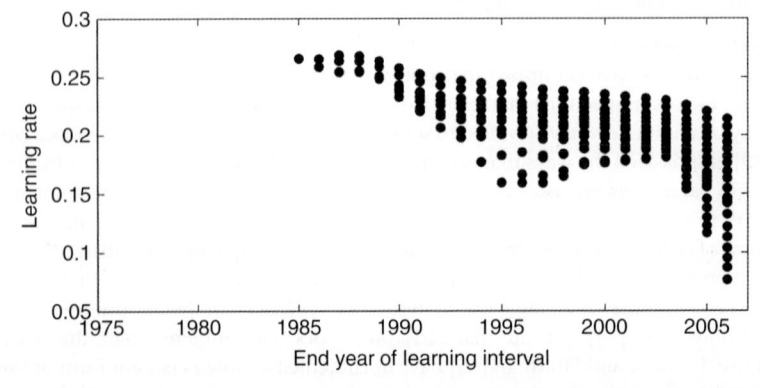

Figure 11 Learning rates for PV (1976–2006) calculated for all periods ≥10 years (*n* = 253). Reproduced from Nemet GF (2009) Interim monitoring of cost dynamics for publicly supported energy technologies. *Energy Policy* 37(3): 825–835 [28].

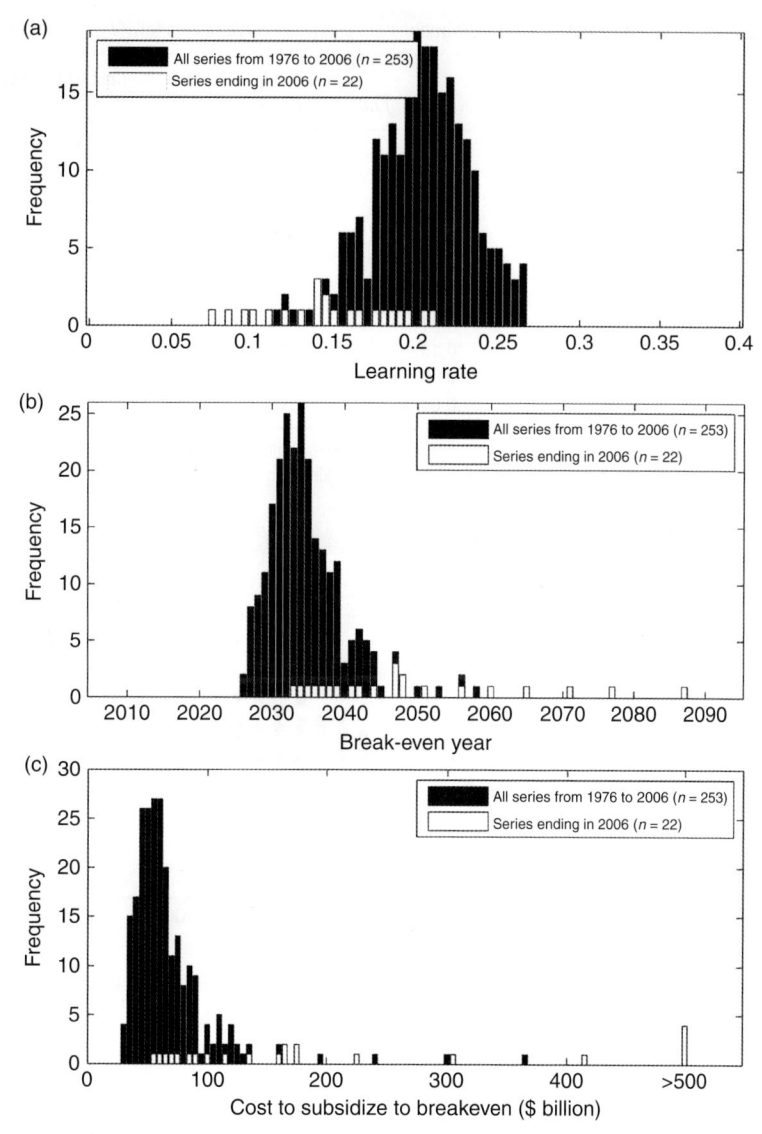

Figure 12 (a) Calculated learning rates for PV; (b) year at which the price of PV equals that of competing technology; (c) present value of cost to subsidize PV until it equals the cost of competing technology. Reproduced from Nemet GF (2009) Interim monitoring of cost dynamics for publicly supported energy technologies. *Energy Policy* 37(3): 825–835 [28].

significant deviation from the historical trend or does historical variation explain them?" Nemet [28] introduces two methods for addressing this question. First, recent costs are compared to the confidence interval for the power function resulting from the dispersion in past observations. Second, these costs are compared to the set of all possible experience curve forecasts made over time. The first method uses straightforward statistics to examine whether recent variation fits within the confidence interval for observations around the power function. This variation is caused by the imperfect fit of the power function to the experience curve data [87]. Here a confidence interval is constructed for the data through 2003. This range is compared to the most recent 3 years of data, 2004, 2005, and 2006, to determine whether they fit within the range defined by projecting the experience curve for 3 years. The data from 1976 to 2003 have $r^2 = 0.98$ and LR = 0.22. The variation around the experience curve power function using least squares yields a 95% confidence interval around the LR of 0.22 ± 0.01. Projecting the experience curve to the capacity reached in 2006 (E_{2006}) yields a 95% confidence interval of expected costs in 2006 of $1.58–$2.51. The actual value for 2006, $3.74, lies outside this range.

The second approach assumes the perspective of a policy analyst making *ex ante* forecasts each year, incorporating new data as they become available. This approach assesses whether recent observations could have been projected by the set of all possible historical forecasts. To illustrate, **Figure 13** shows the predictions, over time, of the price of PV for the cumulative capacity that was reached in 2006, E_{2006}. The first result is that none of the 231 possible projections for 2006 would have predicted a level at or above the actual 2006 price. Next, this method is used to project prices for the cumulative capacities reached in all years from 1986 to 2006. In **Figure 14**, the range in gray represents the full range of forecasts for the capacity that was reached each year. For example, the gray range for 2006 includes all of the 231 data points portrayed in **Figure 13**. Actual prices each year are shown as a line with

Table 2 Descriptive statistics for distributions of experience curve results for PV

	Learning rate	Break-even year	Cost to breakeven ($ billion)
For all time series (n = 253)			
5th percentile	0.25	2028	38
Median	0.21	2034	62
95th percentile	0.14	2049	175
σ	0.03	8	229
For all time series ending in 2006 (n = 22)			
5th percentile	0.21	2034	59
Median	0.15	2048	163
95th percentile	0.08	2082	2172
σ	0.04	15	713

Reproduced from Nemet GF (2006) Beyond the learning curve: Factors influencing cost reductions in photovoltaics. *Energy Policy* 34(17): 3218–3232 [6]; Nemet GF (2009) Interim monitoring of cost dynamics for publicly supported energy technologies. *Energy Policy* 37(3): 825–835 [28].

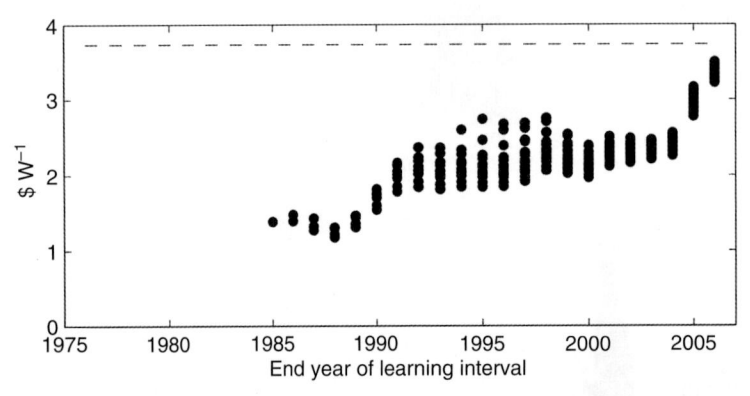

Figure 13 Trend in predictions of PV prices for the capacity levels reached in 2006. The dashed line shows the actual value in 2006. Reproduced from Nemet GF (2009) Interim monitoring of cost dynamics for publicly supported energy technologies. *Energy Policy* 37(3): 825–835 [28].

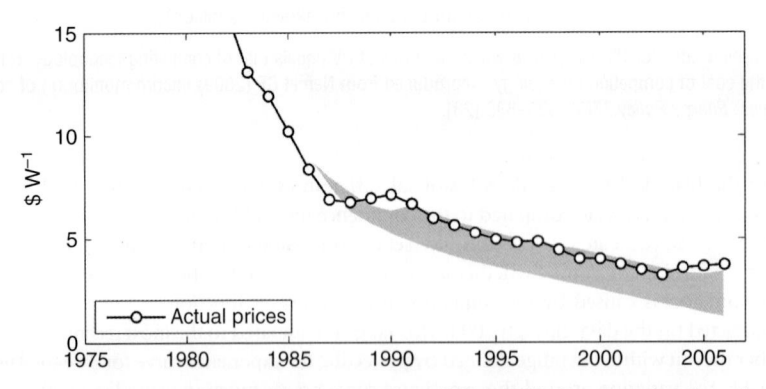

Figure 14 Price projections for the cumulative capacities reached in all years from 1986 to 2006. The gray region shows the range of all forecasts for the price of PV at the cumulative capacity reached each year. Actual prices are shown as a line with white circles [28].

white circles. The second result is that, other than two individual occurrences, the only time the actual prices have consistently fallen outside the range of all possible learning rate-derived price forecasts was in 2004–06.

The outcome of this analysis concurs with that of the confidence interval analysis: the recent deviations in PV fall outside the range of historical precedent. While further analysis is certainly needed to characterize the sources and persistence of these deviations, these methods may be useful as a preliminary screen to identify near-term deviations that merit further investigation. An important aspect to account for – given the prominent role described earlier in this chapter – is the role of niche markets. In particular, empirical analysis of the level of willingness to pay in niche markets and the size of these markets will add insight into the extent to which they reduce the cost of subsidy programs.

These results indicate (1) a need for policy makers to more explicitly consider uncertainty in cost projections and (2) the importance of the development of better tools to identify the significance of near-term deviations from projections. These results suggest that projected subsidy costs are highly sensitive to timing of the data used: both 'when' the forecast was made and the 'duration' of the historical data set used. The high dispersion in costs – and especially the skewness of the distribution toward high values – emphasizes the importance of interim monitoring of technological improvement. These results should not be surprising given the results above show that learning derived from experience is only one of several explanations for the cost reductions in PV. Its role in enabling changes in the two most important factors identified in this study – plant size and module efficiency – is small compared to those of expected future demand, risk management, R&D, and knowledge spillovers. This weak relationship suggests careful consideration of the conditions under which one should rely on experience curves to predict technical change.

The results have two normative conclusions for policy makers. First, if policy makers are to rely on future cost projections derived from experience curves, they need to be explicit about the reliability of predictions. Policy decisions should be made acknowledging the observed variation in the rates of technological improvement over time. Given the current state of knowledge about what actually causes variation in learning rates, policy makers would do well to consider learning as a stochastic process – that is, that some aspects of the process remain unpredictable [90]. In this respect, learning is similar to the outcomes of R&D investments; they are inherently uncertain despite improvements in understanding about R&D productivity [91]. Important further work on this topic involves assessment of whether this uncertainty is likely to diminish over time as more observations are obtained, as suggested by the central limit theorem. It is unclear whether the results in this study so far support such a notion. In **Figure 11**, it appears that the dispersion in learning rates has increased over time. Even if such a convergence were to occur, a practical issue for policy makers would be whether it will occur quickly enough to inform decision making and whether the cumulative capacity required for convergence is small relative to the size of the world energy demand.

Second, devising *ex ante* methods to identify the significance of near-term deviations in technology cost and performance trends is essential. How should policy makers respond to situations such as those in **Figure 14** in which recent prices appear to be deviating from the experience curve path? Are these short-term deviations driven by supply bottlenecks, or are they representations of the lower limits on cost? Deviations make policy difficult; policy makers need to be vigilant against encountering the extremely expensive outcomes found above. For example, debate over subsidies amounting to several billion dollars in the 2007 Independence and Security Act in the US Energy Information Administration (EIA) suggests that programs involving hundreds of billions will be subject to scrutiny [92]. The social value that these technologies have the potential to deliver is substantial, but may take many years to realize. As a result, policy makers may also need to defend technology support against competing social priorities when deviations are actually short-term aberrations. How can near-term data be used to assess confidence in longer-term projections? The methods developed in this section offer some avenues for analysis, but ultimately better tools will be required.

The inclusion of experience curves in models that optimize and simulate the costs of climate policy has enhanced their realism. Given the vast set of results showing that energy technologies improve over time, incorporating experience curves represents a substantial improvement over omitting them and implicitly assuming a learning rate of zero. But the results summarized here indicate that a broader set of influences than experience alone contributed to the rapid cost reductions in the past; one implication is that experience curves overestimate the technical improvements that should be expected to accrue from deployment alone. As a result, these findings support the efforts by modelers to explore ways of incorporating explanatory variables other than cumulative capacity, especially when nonincremental changes occur. The following sections describe some attempts to deepen our understanding of the impact of other factors on PV, both historically and prospectively.

1.05.4 Nonincremental Cost-Reducing Developments

The irregular occurrence of nonincremental technological improvement accounts for much of the concern about using experience curve cost projections to inform policy. Projecting the future costs of PV depends on a much better characterization of these changes – including when they are likely to occur, how big an impact they will have on costs, and conversely the consequences on costs of a sustained period without such changes. To achieve greater understanding of nonincremental changes in PV, in a recent master's thesis, Husmann [93] studied historical silicon PV breakthroughs under the expectation that past breakthroughs can illustrate the causes and effects of nonincremental changes on a still-developing technology. This section describes a novel methodology for identifying nonincremental changes ('breakthroughs') and provides some preliminary results. Ultimately, the identification and evaluation of specific technical improvements will be useful for informing the type of modeling described in Section 1.05.5.

1.05.4.1 Identifying Breakthroughs

Nonincremental changes can be identified using a combination of expert opinion and patent analysis.

1.05.4.1.1 *Defining breakthrough*
There is no widely accepted definition of breakthrough, even among researchers who study innovations in products and technology [94]. Among PV researchers, important achievements in the field are called many things; technical developments [8], major results

[95], and advances [7] are just a few of the names used in the PV literature. For the sake of simplicity, we will use breakthrough, since it is a word recognized in both research and colloquial literature. We define breakthrough as a technical achievement that represents a new combination of technologies. A breakthrough must either open up a new area of technology for exploration and use, or be a specific improvement that has spread to become industry standard. Although innovation researchers often require both technical and economic achievements in order to identify their breakthroughs, the truth is that technical achievement will not necessarily result in economic achievement [96]. Our goal was to first identify technological breakthroughs and then determine their economic value. However, we recognize that our methods for identifying breakthroughs contain a (sometimes strong) bias for economic success. That bias will be discussed later in this chapter.

1.05.4.1.2 First pass: Expert opinion

Silicon solar cells have been around since the early 1950s [97], which means that some researchers today have been studying crystalline silicon PV for their entire lives. Their extensive knowledge and experience represents a great resource, if it can only be tapped and distilled. Fortunately, that potential has been recognized, which has led to a profusion of recent papers describing the history of PV and, importantly, listing the most important PV breakthroughs in the authors' opinions.

Although none of the papers was written with the specific goal of identifying breakthroughs, they all mentioned various discoveries and technologies that have played important roles in crystalline silicon PV history. We read through six of the papers that seemed most relevant to crystalline silicon PV [8, 95, 96, 98–100] and compiled a list of breakthroughs mentioned by the experts. In the end, we had a list of 79 breakthroughs spanning from 1951 to 2000. We left out more recent developments, since identification of true breakthroughs requires several years of postbreakthrough observation.

An initial problem was that the original list of breakthroughs was too long. Not only would it have been prohibitively time-consuming to research all 79, but it also implied that a breakthrough took place every 8 months, which was not a reasonable assumption. Though the list was thorough, if we had tried to shorten it, we would have run into problems with the implicit biases found in expert opinion. Not only are experts more familiar with breakthroughs in their own areas of research – and thus more likely to list them as breakthroughs – but they can also suffer from success bias, in which experts tend to associate commercial success with technical value [101]. The combination of the six papers helped to reduce possible bias in any one researcher, but if we had asked an expert to pick just a few breakthroughs from our list of 79, it would have immediately suffered from that researcher's bias – and there were not enough researchers with enough time to look through the list. Instead, we chose to use another method of breakthrough identification to reduce the list of breakthroughs.

1.05.4.1.3 Why patent analysis?

Our second method of breakthrough identification is patent citation analysis. We decided to look at patents, because citation frequency of a patent can serve as a proxy for a possible breakthrough. Each patent is meant to represent a novel, useful, and nonobvious invention [102]. Not every invention is a breakthrough, but some may be – and our goal is to identify the patented inventions that are breakthroughs. It is also true that not all inventions are patented [103], but if they become common knowledge, then they may be incorporated into other patents. Thus, the breakthroughs that are incorporated into other patents become discoverable. The only problem is if the breakthrough is a trade secret, because by definition it cannot be identified by someone who does not know the secret.

Aside from trade secrets, it is likely that all the breakthroughs we are looking for can be found in at least one patent. Previous patent studies have shown that the semiconductor industry produces a large number of patents. Since key semiconductor breakthroughs have been patented, it makes sense that many key PV breakthroughs have also been patented. Even though trade secrets are an acknowledged intellectual property (IP) protection tool used by the industry, important patents appear to outweigh important secrets.

We are also focusing on patents because they can help us avoid expert bias – the tendency of experts to consider their own areas of expertise as important – and success bias – the tendency to equate commercial success with technical value. Any form of patent analysis precludes the possibility of expert bias, because patent citations are typically created by several experts: the inventors and their attorneys suggest the citations, while the patent examiner selects the citations from the list of suggestions and his or her own knowledge of prior art [104]. This process, combined with the fact that almost every patent represents a unique combination of inventors, attorneys, and examiners, ensures that no one expert has undue influence over the patents being analyzed – especially for such a large group of patents as the one we analyzed.

Patent analysis can also be constructed to limit success bias. One way to do this is to differentiate between backward and forward citations. Backward citations represent the prior art that the patent is either building off of or surpassing. It cannot be influenced by commercial success, because it is created before an invention is even patented. Forward citations represent the number of times that the patent serves as prior art to another patent. Not only can forward citations be heavily influenced by the commercial success of the patent, but they can also be influenced by the prior commercial success of the inventor. Because of the success bias present in forward citations, we have chosen a method of patent analysis that relies primarily on backward citations in identifying breakthroughs.

1.05.4.1.4 Backward citation analysis

A full explanation and derivation of backward citation analysis is presented by Dahlin and Behrens [101], but here we give a short overview. While forward citations represent a patent's commercial and technological impact, backward citations represent its technological roots. If each backward citation represents a piece of technology that was either used to create the patent or served as a source of inspiration, then the collection of all the backward citations in one patent can represent the specific combination of technologies that the new patent represents. And if each patent can be technologically represented by its backward citations, then a breakthrough technology can be identified by its backward citations alone – if the right definition of breakthrough can be found.

This method creates a mathematical definition of radicalness – which we usurp as our definition of breakthrough – that can be applied to a list of patents and used to identify specific patents. The three components of the definition are (1) novelty – the patent differs from previous inventions; (2) uniqueness – the patent differs from current inventions; and (3) influence – the patent needs to have affected future inventions. Although the third component can suffer from success bias, technological success will play a bigger role than commercial success; that is, if a particular invention works well enough to be somehow adopted by other patents, the backward citation analysis will notice this even if the authors of the other patents were not aware of the original patent. We considered ignoring influence, but that resulted in the identification of both successful breakthroughs and very unique failures with no obvious way to differentiate between the two.

In order to determine if a patent fulfills these three components, the backward citation analysis compares a patent's collection of backward citations to another patent's collection. If the two collections have any backward citations in common, then they are assumed to have similar technological roots. The similarity between patents i and j can be presented mathematically as overlap score os_{ij}, in which os_{ij} equals the number of backward citations shared by patents i and j divided by the total number of backward citations held by patents i and j. If this overlap score is computed for all the patents being analyzed, it can reveal the similarity between any one patent i and all of its peers j for any year t, where t can be any year before or after the patent was published. Thus, the average annual overlap score, os_{ti}/n_t, is the sum of all of the overlap scores for a patent and its peers during a particular year divided by the number of peers: $os_{ti}/n_t = (\Sigma_j os_{tij})/n_t$. This average annual overlap score is a measure of the similarity between a patent and all the analyzed patents in the chosen year.

This average annual overlap score is what determines whether a patent is novel, unique, or influential. For a patent to be novel, it cannot be similar to patents that have been published before it: for $t < t_i$, os_{ti}/n_t must be small. For a patent to be unique, it cannot be similar to patents that were published at the same time it was published: for $t = t_i$, os_{ti}/n_t must be small. And for a patent to be influential, it must be similar to patents that were published after it: for $t > t_i$, os_{ti}/n_t must be big. A breakthrough will satisfy all three requirements, while an incremental invention will not. However, these are all relative measures that will depend on the total number of patents being analyzed and the variation between patents. It is important to recognize that a breakthrough identified when looking at only PV patents may not appear to be a breakthrough when compared to patents covering, say, the World Wide Web or the steam engine.

Backward citation analysis can also be prone to biases of its own. If a patent does not have any backward citations, it shares no backward citations with any other patents and fails the influence component. This can happen occasionally if an inventor is trying to be strategic, but it is discouraged by patent examiners and therefore uncommon. Another problem can result if two patents had the same inventor (e.g., patents 4510674 and 4510675), because that inventor is much more likely to list the exact same backward citations, making the two patents appear very similar. However, this can be mitigated if a large number of patents are used in the analysis, because the greater number of patents tends to reduce the impact of any one overlap score. Lastly, the backward citation analysis tends to recognize early breakthroughs more easily than later breakthroughs, because early breakthroughs necessarily have a smaller overlap score for the few years of patents listed before them, while later patents have a smaller overlap score for the few years of patents listed after them. This is a problem specific to our use of backward citation analysis (not backward citation analysis in general) and will be addressed at length later in this chapter.

1.05.4.1.5 Implementing backward citation analysis for PV

In order to accurately identify crystalline silicon PV breakthroughs using backward citation analysis, we needed a list of every crystalline silicon PV patent. In all practicality, compiling such a list is impossible. If patents are given cryptic description – such as labeling a PV patent as a semiconductor improvement – they can evade common search terms. Furthermore, not every PV patent is relevant, since many relate to amorphous silicon, cadmium telluride, or some other form of PV. The only way to know if a patent is relevant to crystalline silicon PV is if a PV expert reads through the entire patent, which would require hundreds of man-hours.

Instead, we relied on a source that identified the crystalline silicon PV patents for us: NREL's (National Renewable Energy Laboratory) publication of *U.S. Photovoltaic Patents* from 1951 to 1993. This is a list of 1651 PV patents that was compiled by searching for patents in the subclasses 'Photoelectric', 'Testing', and 'Applications' under 'Batteries, Thermoelectric and Photoelectric' or containing the word 'photovoltaic(s)' or 'solar cell(s)' [105]. Since the search probably relied on specific patent classes [106], chances are that it missed most 'solar cell' patents outside of those classes; one omission (patent 4661200) has already been identified.

Despite the likelihood of other missed PV patents, the benefits of using NREL [105] outweigh the costs, because the patents are listed by category. It appears that at least one PV expert (Thomas Basso of NREL) read through the patents and was able to identify the single-crystal silicon cells, amorphous silicon cells, III–V cells, and so on [106], thus providing the lists of crystalline silicon PV patents that we require. Out of 17 categories of patents, we used 6: single-crystal silicon cells, polycrystalline and ribbon silicon cells, cell components, cell enhancement techniques, materials production and processes, and flat-plate collectors. Our goal was to look at the patents that have affected module design as well as silicon-specific developments, because even generic module changes have had an important effect on the steady improvement of crystalline silicon PV.

The 1993 cutoff date was imposed on our analysis by NREL [105], since the list was never updated after that year. This necessarily implies that our analysis will be historical, since the breakthroughs that we select for study are likely either no longer in use or considered 'common knowledge' in the PV field.

While going through the list of patents in NREL [105], we selectively removed or changed some of the patents to be analyzed. Design patents, which can be identified by the 'D' in front of the patent number, were considered irrelevant. They cover ornamental appearances and thus do not represent a technological advance. Defensive publications or technical disclosures, which can be identified by the 'T' in front of the patent number, were not considered patents and were not included. And reissued patents, which can be identified by the 'RE' in front of the patent number, were changed to the original patent number. This prevented a reissued patent from being compared to its original patent, since the two would necessarily have a high overlap score.

After changing or removing all of the design, defensive, and reissued patents, we ended up with a list of 1651 patents that were ready to be analyzed, not including repeated patents. The NREL source included the same patent on multiple lists if it counted for multiple categories. As we mentioned earlier, the composition of the list makes a difference in the breakthrough identification. If each list were analyzed separately, it would guarantee that we would find breakthroughs for each category of module design, because we can systematically take the top 10% of the results from each category. On the other hand, one complete list of all the patents could discover if one category somehow contained more breakthroughs – perhaps through more intensive study or greater innovation – but on the other hand, smaller lists by category could result in greater differentiation in scores, making it easier to separate out breakthroughs. Furthermore, it would guarantee that we would have results from every category of module design. In the end, we tried to balance these concerns by analyzing the categories both separately and combined in one list.

To conduct such a computation-intensive analysis, we used a very basic unpublished software program written by Dr. Harlan Husmann. The inputs to the program were lists of patents, the years when each patent was published, and the list of backward citations for each patent. The program calculated the average annual overlap score for each patent each year. The default level of the patent then calculates two scores for each patent: the 'before' score and the 'after' score. The 'before' score is the sum of each average annual overlap score from the first year to the year when the patent was published – that is, it represents the novelty and uniqueness of each patent (lower 'before' scores represent higher novelty and uniqueness). The 'after' score is the sum of each average annual overlap score from the year after the patent was published to the last year – that is, it represents the influence of each patent (higher 'after' scores represent higher influence). The advanced level does the same, but also lists the patents that overlap each other.

These two scores are where our analysis diverges from the backward citation analysis described above. That analysis only looks at the 5 years before the patent is published and the 5 years after publication, which is how they avoid biasing their results in favor of early patents. We cannot do this, because PV patents can lie around for years before being incorporated in the field's body of knowledge.

Once the 'before' and 'after' scores are calculated, we can eliminate the incremental patents by taking the ratio of 'after' scores to 'before' scores. The higher the ratio, the less likely the patent is to be incremental. However, this does not remove the failed patents, because if a failure has no overlaps before publication and a tiny overlap after publication, its ratio is still infinity. Therefore, to remove the failures, we then go through the high ratios and select for the high ratios that also have high 'after' scores.

There are no specific numbers that count as high ratios and 'after' scores, because the backward citation analysis is relative. Instead, our goal was to look at approximately the top 10% of high-scoring patents, since that would reduce the 1651 patents to a more manageable group of about 160 patents that could actually be read in a reasonable amount of time. Therefore, we went through the results for each list, first selecting the top ~50% of high ratios, then reducing it to the top ~10% with high ratios and high 'after' scores. Then we read through the abstracts of the top 10%, checking that each patent is actually relevant to crystalline silicon PV and not some other type of PV. This entire process is summarized in **Table 3**.

Although we analyzed a total of 1651 patents, the sum for the category lists is 1986 patents because many of the patents qualified for multiple categories. The ratio cutoff and 'after' cutoff values emphasize the relativity of the overlap scores. For example, a ratio cutoff of 2 resulted in the selection of 55% of the patents in the 'all patents' list, while a ratio cutoff of 5 resulted in a 55% selection in the 'cell enhancements' list. While the main goal of each ratio cutoff choice was in trying to end up with ~50% of the patents in the first round of selections and ~10% in the second round, the cutoff values were heavily influenced by our need to pick values that did not result in too high percentages of qualifying patents and to keep both values relatively high (i.e., a ratio of at least 2 and an 'after' value of at least 0.01). Once the cutoff values are applied and the ~10% point is reached, we checked that each patent was relevant – that it applied to silicon PV cells and was not purely decorative or similarly inconsequential. After removing the irrelevant and repeated patents in the multiple lists, we had a list of 113 patents culled from the multiple categories. The list of 103 relevant patents selected from the list of 'all patents' had 35 patents in common with the list of 113 patents, so our approach resulted in a total of 181 patents that qualified as breakthroughs under the backward citation analysis.

As mentioned earlier, our backward citation analysis is prone to its own biases – most importantly, the fact that the overlap score favors early breakthroughs over later breakthroughs. This can be seen in **Figure 15**, which shows, respectively, the percent and number of silicon cell patents selected by the backward citation analysis versus the year in which the patents were issued. It is possible that the first few years may have high percentages because the technology was new and each patent truly represented a breakthrough. However, the last year certainly had no selected patents because the 'after' values were zero, and it is more than likely

Table 3 Summary of the patent selection process in backward citation analysis

Patent list from U.S. Photovoltaic Patents	Number of patents in the list	Ratio cutoff	Percent making the cutoff	'After' cutoff	Percent making the cutoff	Number of remaining relevant patents
All patents	1651	2	55	0.02	6	103
Silicon cells	251	5	32	0.01	16	26
Polycrystalline silicon and ribbon silicon cells	99	3	43	0.07	11	10
Cell components	420	2	56	0.03	10	32
Cell enhancements	75	5	55	0.06	12	4
Material processes	713	2	59	0.03	7	19
Flat-plate collectors	428	2	32	0.03	10	34

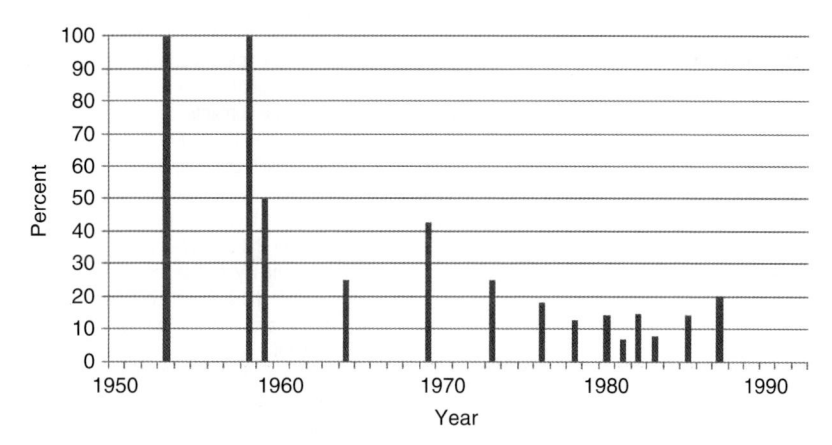

Figure 15 Percent of silicon cell patents selected by the backward citation analysis in the year in which the patents were issued [93].

that the last few years of patent selections also suffered from artificially low 'after' values. For the purposes of our study, this means that the range of years we are studying is slightly less than the range of years presented in the NREL document.

1.05.4.2 Results: Combining Expert Opinion and Patent Analysis

An ideal breakthrough selection process would combine an expert's proficiency born of years of practice with a computer's strict impartiality – and that is what we aim to do by combining the expert's list of breakthroughs with the patent list of breakthroughs. These two lists are not particularly well matched: the expert's list contains the names of breakthroughs, while the patent list contains the patent numbers of breakthroughs. Furthermore, the expert's list can be unclear in its meanings, especially if different researchers use different names for the same breakthrough or the same name for different breakthroughs. Likewise, an inventor often describes a new process or invention using names and terms that do not become standard in the literature – not to mention the fact that a patent number alone contains no indication of what technology the patent represents.

In order to combine these two very different lists, we have become interpreters of sorts by comparing experts' descriptions of breakthroughs and inventors' summaries of their inventions. There was no strict methodology – we simply read through each patent on the list, looking for processes or technologies that matched any of the breakthroughs described in the experts' papers. In general, we relied more heavily on the patents identified in the various categories of module design, because they had already been examined and sorted by experienced PV researcher Tom Basso [106]. While reading through patents, we looked for keywords (e.g., 'boron' in the case of boron diffusion), and while reading through research papers, we looked for references to previous research that could help elucidate the author's meaning behind a breakthrough name. For the most part, matching patents to breakthroughs was an iterative process that could always be improved with more time and expertise. However, we felt confident with our results after we had identified 39 patents that were connected to 23 breakthroughs (see **Table 4**).

The lists of patents and breakthroughs were not a one-to-one match. Most of the experts' breakthroughs had no patents that appeared related to them, whereas a few breakthroughs had multiple connected patents – up to six patents in one case. This is not surprising; although we call breakthroughs nonincremental, the truth is that most breakthroughs were developed over time, even if that interval of time was shorter than most breakthroughs. Furthermore, patents tend to emphasize incremental changes, since each change can earn the inventor intellectual property and money. We accommodate this reality by underscoring the fact that the 23 breakthroughs from the experts' list are the final breakthroughs that we select – not the patents. This way, our final list of

Table 4 List of selected breakthroughs and the patents that connect to them

Breakthrough	Patent (year)	Breakthrough description
Boron diffusion	2794846 (1957) 3015590 (1962)	P–N junctions created out of boron rather than lithium increase cell efficiency from 4% to 6%.
Contacts (grid and fingers)	2862160 (1958) 2919299 (1959) 3040416 (1962) 3046324 (1962) 3450568 (1969) 3493437 (1970)	Many thin contact fingers reduce the losses experienced by the current as it travels through the cell.
Antireflective coatings	3533850 (1970)	Transparent layer of antireflective material on top of the cell reduces reflection and increases the amount of sunlight that is absorbed by the cell.
Better, thinner top junctions	3811954 (1974)	Shallower P–N junctions increase the cell response to shorter wavelengths and thus the amount of sunlight the cell could convert.
Tunneling metal–insulator–semiconductor contact	3928073 (1975) 4104084 (1978)	A thin insulator placed between the semiconductor layer and the metal contacts reduces recombination losses and allows more electrons to reach the contacts.
Oxide surface passivation	3990100 (1976) 4086102 (1978) 4171997 (1979)	Silicon dioxide attached to broken silicon bonds on the surface of the cell increases cell efficiency.
Laminating cells to glass with polyvinyl butyral (PVB)	4009054 (1977)	Replacing the layer of exposed silicone with glass allows PV modules to weather the elements better.
Unexposed silicone rubber	4057439 (1977)	Replacing the layer of exposed silicone with glass allows PV modules to weather the elements better.
Aluminum-based pastes	4086102 (1978)	Al-based pastes used at the rear of the cell helped remove impurities and give the modules better weatherization.
Screen printing	4105471 (1978)	By printing contacts on the top and bottom of the cells, PV modules can be made more easily, reducing costs.
Hydrogen plasma passivation	4113514 (1978) 4321420 (1982) 4322253 (1982) 4557037 (1985)	Hydrogen atoms attach to broken silicon bonds throughout the cell and increase cell efficiency.
Pulse annealing	4154625 (1979)	Pulse annealing creates larger silicon crystals, improving the quality of the silicon at a lower cost.
Metallization	4235644 (1980) 4348546 (1982) 4361718 (1982)	Metallization uses thin films of metal to create contacts, reducing the amount of metal used and thus the cost.
Quasi-square wafers	4356141 (1982)	Square wafers use space and silicon more efficiently than circular wafers.
Reduced metallization resistance	4395583 (1983) 4694115 (1987)	Reduced resistance between the metal contacts and silicon decreases losses and allows more electrons to reach the contacts.
Metal–insulator N–P (MINP) cell	4404422 (1983)	Combining metal–insulator–semiconductor contacts with shallow N–P junctions, increasing efficiency.
Ribbon on sacrificial growth plate	4478880 (1984)	Thin ribbons of silicon are continuously produced with less waste silicon, reducing costs.
Ethylene–vinyl acetate (EVA) laminate	4499658 (1985)	EVA doesn't yellow with exposure to sunlight as quickly as PVB, allowing the PV module to last longer.
Plasma deposition of SiN passivation	4640001 (1987)	Thin films of silicon can be made by heating silicon nitride until the nitrogen escapes, reducing the cost and amount of silicon used.
Low-contact resistance with anti-reflective films	4643913 (1987)	Silver pastes lowered the contact resistance, reducing recombination losses and increasing efficiency.
Reactive-ion etching	4664748 (1987) 4667058 (1987)	Highly reactive ions texture the surface of the cell, reducing reflective losses.
Passivated emitter solar cell (PESC)	4589191 (1986)	Contacts are made through slits in the top oxide layer, increasing contact passivation and thus efficiency.
Microgrooving	4626613 (1986)	Selective surface etching of microgrooves reduces reflectivity, reduces resistance losses, and is easier to work with than etched pyramids.

breakthroughs is not beholden to the single point of time represented by a patent; it is associated more with idea behind the patent. Although we cannot prove that this is true in our backward citation analysis, we assume it is true for the purposes of our analysis.

One example that is illustrative of the usefulness of backward citation analysis is the case of patent number 4165241, which we had identified because its name included the words 'printed contact'. The backward citation analysis had not identified the patent as a possible breakthrough because its ratio value was 0.1429 – far below the cutoff. This was suspect because one of its inventors, John Yerkes, was a recognized PV researcher and the patent summary seemed perfect for the 'screen-printing' breakthrough. However, after further investigation, we discovered that this patent was a forward citation for patent 4105471 by the same inventor. The backward citation analysis had not only identified this patent as a breakthrough, but identified the patent 3 times – in the list of 'all patents' and two different categories of module design. This example does not mean that backward citation analysis will always lead to a breakthrough or the origin of a breakthrough, but it does give us confidence that it has some proficiency in tracing research developments in patents.

These results show the promise of a rigorous, transparent, and replicable methodology for identifying nonincremental cost reductions in PV. The identification of a specific list of the most important technical improvement provides an avenue for determining the factors that enabled these breakthroughs to occur – as well as to assess the impact they have had. Ultimately, this much more specific characterization of technological change will be helpful for structuring and populating models that predict future changes, such as the one described next.

1.05.5 Modeling Nonincremental Changes in PV

Given the importance of this array of nonincremental changes, how can modeling take them into account? The previous section shows a set of nonincremental technical advances within crystalline silicon PV. The transition to new technological generations in PV is likely to have greater impacts, limiting the reliability of learning curve projections in describing them. PV based on crystalline silicon has remained the overwhelmingly dominant technology for three decades, despite the advantages of thin-film technologies that use less raw material and are more amenable to mass manufacturing techniques. Policy related to PV in the longer term must address subsequent generations of PV technology, such as those based purely on organic materials. In a recent study, Nemet and Baker [107] combined an expert elicitation and a bottom-up manufacturing cost model to compare the effects of R&D and demand subsidies. They modeled the effects of these policy instruments on the future costs of a low-carbon energy technology that is not currently commercially available, namely, organic PV. That study found that production-related effects on technological advance – learning by doing and economies of scale – are not as critical to the long-term potential for cost reduction in organic PV as the investment in and success of R&D.

One example of a new technological generation is purely organic PV. It is particularly intriguing because of characteristics that distinguish it from the current generation of PV, which consists of cells made from crystallized silicon. Purely organic PV use a thin film of organic semiconductor material for photon conversion. Because they do not require a glass substrate, organic PV cells can be manufactured on highly flexible material, leaving open the possibility of a much wider range of applications. These manufacturing techniques are more amenable to automation and high throughput because they involve chemical rather than mechanical production processes. That they also require only a thin layer of light-absorbing PV material, rather than a crystal structure, means that the amount of input materials needed is very low. The combination of highly automated 'reel-to-reel' manufacturing processes and small materials consumption gives organic PV its most appealing distinguishing characteristics – the potential for very low manufacturing costs [108]. However, organic PV are not currently manufactured on a commercial scale. Moreover, the current models have very low efficiency, with the highest being around 5% in laboratory conditions [109]; this compares to about 15% efficiency for silicon-based solar cells. Finally, organic materials are susceptible to degradation in sunlight, leading to concerns about the lifetimes of these cells.

In this case of a new generation of technology like organic PV, policy can impact future cost in multiple ways. First, technology-push policies, such as direct government-sponsored R&D, can increase the likelihood of achieving technical breakthroughs. Nemet and Baker assume that government R&D has an impact on two technical characteristics of organic solar cells: (1) their electrical conversion efficiency and (2) their lifetime. Second, demand-pull policies, such as demand subsidies, increase demand for organic PV and thus create opportunities for cost reductions through economies of scale and learning by doing. That model focuses on these two avenues of technical change. Note, however, another potential impact: particularly at later stages of technology development, demand-pull policies may stimulate private sector R&D through the promise of a larger, less risky market.

1.05.5.1 An Approach to Modeling Nonincremental Technological Change

Nemet and Baker [106] developed the following methodology, taking the perspective that the combination of expert elicitation with a bottom-up manufacturing cost model provides a promising avenue for more robustly understanding future technology costs. Adoption subsidies are modeled as having an impact on cost by enabling economies of scale through increasing demand. R&D investment outcomes are modeled using the results of the expert elicitation. They use this schema to evaluate the uncertain impact of combinations of R&D investments and subsidies on the cost of electricity over time. The central question in that study was how R&D investment policies interact with demand subsidy policies to impact the cost of electricity from PV.

This model considers the effects of two demand-pull instruments: demand subsidies and carbon prices. The authors model subsidies as a decision variable and treat carbon prices as an exogenous sensitivity. (The reason for the focus on subsidies as the primary demand-pull decision variable in this model is that they can be designed to exclusively support organic PV, whereas carbon prices enhance demand for low-carbon technologies in general.) In order to assess the effectiveness with which technology policy can induce technical change in organic PV, they determined how the specific policies – investment in R&D and demand subsidies – affect technology improvements.

1.05.5.2 Results for Nonincremental Technological Change

They simulate efforts by the government to fund R&D and subsidize demand at three levels of policy intensity each, calculate the costs of PV electricity in 2040 and 2050 under the nine combinations of government technology programs (low R&D is $15 million yr^{-1} for 10 years, high R&D is $80 million yr^{-1} for 10 years; low subsidy is 20¢ kWh^{-1} for 5 years, high subsidy is 25¢ kWh^{-1} declining to 5¢ kWh^{-1} over 20 years). While both subsidies and successful R&D programs reduce costs, the effect of successful R&D on cost in 2050 is an order of magnitude larger than the effect of subsidies. Subsidies are relatively more effective in 2040 than in 2050, but the effect of successful R&D is still much larger, despite the fact that in their model only half of the benefits of R&D arrive by then. Even the highest subsidy levels do not achieve cost-effective organic PV without successful R&D. The cost of PV without successful R&D never falls below 16¢ kWh^{-1}, far from the target level of 4¢ kWh^{-1}. Note also the counterintuitive result that, under successful R&D programs, the high- and low-subsidy programs produce costs in 2050 that are slightly higher than without the subsidy program. This result occurs because the subsidy programs shift a substantial amount of PV production to earlier years; without subsidies, almost all of the demand for PV electricity in 2050 is met by production between 2040 and 2050. Consequently, without subsidies, the scale of manufacturing plants in 2050 reaches a larger, more efficient scale and the cost in 2050 is lower. The curves in **Figure 16** show the path of cost reductions over time and the relationships among the policy combinations. The three subsidy curves in **Figures 16(a)–16(c)** are much more similar to each other than the three R&D curves in **Figures 16(d)–16(f)**.

Interestingly, the relative effectiveness of successful R&D and subsidies does not change under varying assumptions about storage and carbon prices; under all four scenarios, R&D success has a greater effect on cost reductions than do subsidies in 2050. High carbon prices do enhance the relative impact of subsidies and free storage increases the relative impact of R&D success, but in both cases the effects are small. Furthermore, sensitivity analysis shows that the two main claims are robust to uncertainty in the data used to populate the model. First, the analysis supports the claim that the base case set of assumptions represents an upper bound

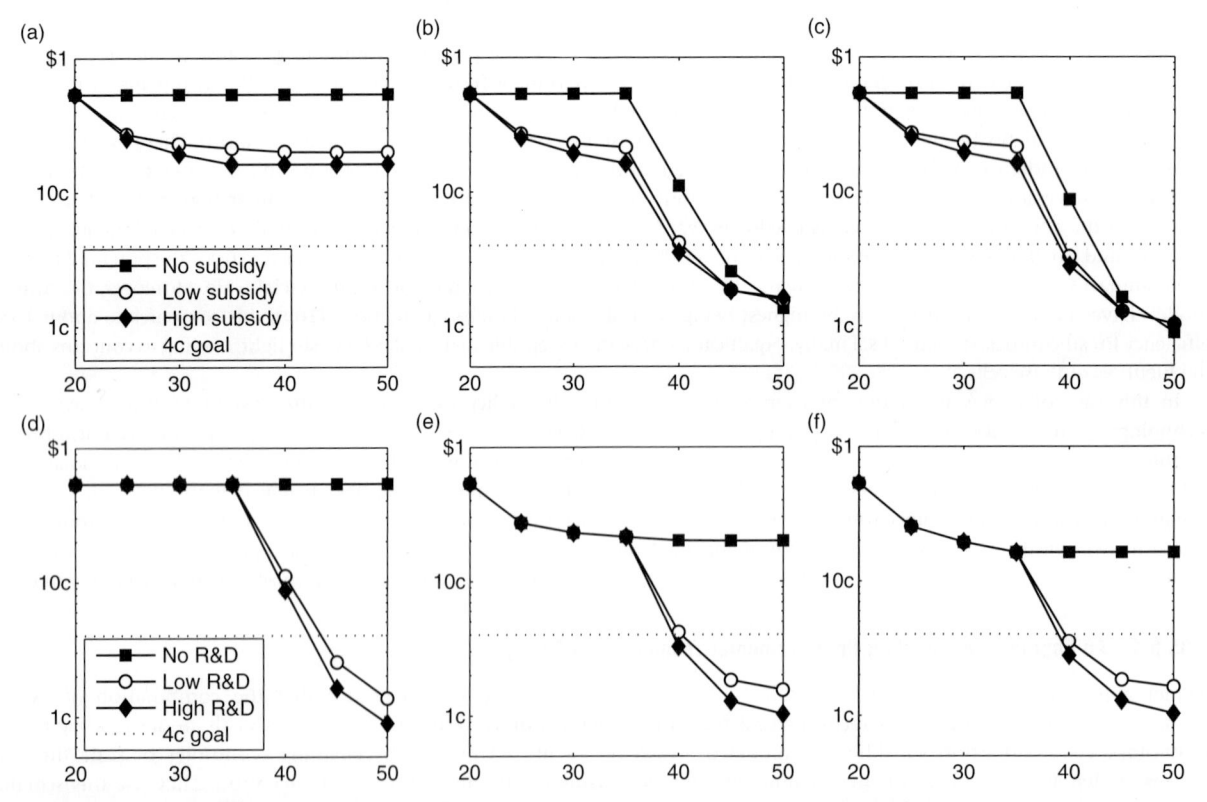

Figure 16 Impact of subsidies and R&D on cost per kWh of PV electricity: (a) no R&D; (b) low R&D; (c) high R&D; (d) no subsidy; (e) low subsidy; and (f) high subsidy. Low and high R&D cases are conditional on program goals for efficiency and lifetime being reached. Costs are on a log scale [106]. Reproduced from Nemet GF (2006) Beyond the learning curve: Factors influencing cost reductions in photovoltaics. *Energy Policy* 34(17): 3218–3232 [6].

on the effectiveness of a subsidy program. Second, all alternative scenarios support the finding that the cost-reducing effect of successful R&D is larger than the effects of subsidies.

Another result that is consistent across scenarios is that subsidizing a large demand for PV before the benefits of R&D arrive can be expensive. Under the base case assumptions, no carbon tax and no free storage, the net present social cost of subsidies is $5 billion for the low-subsidy program and $80 billion for the high-subsidy program. These values are in line with recent estimates of the cost of subsidizing the current generation of PV [110]. Note that they are considerably higher than the R&D amounts we have considered, which have a net present value of $0.1 billion and $0.7 billion. Also, the cost of each subsidy program increases as demand for solar electricity increases. For example, in the presence of a $1000 carbon tax, the cost of the low-subsidy program rises to $30 billion and that of the high-subsidy program rises to $3 trillion. Given the wide range of subsidy program costs, it may be useful in future work to use this model to optimize the timing and level of subsidies – especially given various assumptions about carbon prices and storage technology. The outcomes here are similar to those discussed above on sensitivity of learning curve predictions to expensive outlier cases.

Despite the possibility of expensive outcomes, a case can still be made for subsidies. A subsidy with no R&D is 'less risky', since it avoids the worst case of a very high electricity cost, and the expected cost is lower as well. This result implies that if (1) the goal were simply to achieve as low an electricity cost as possible and (2) the two programs had equal costs, the 'no R&D/high-subsidy program' would be strictly preferred by all risk averters. Note, however, that neither of these conditions necessarily holds. These results imply that the value of subsidies is that they provide a hedge against the possibility that breakthroughs in technical change fail to take place. In a choice under uncertainty framework, subsidies provide a benefit in reducing risk.

1.05.5.3 Summary of Nonincremental Modeling

The Nemet and Baker study found that (1) successful R&D enables PV to achieve a cost target of 4¢ kWh^{-1}, (2) the cost of PV does not reach the target when only subsidies – and not R&D – are implemented, and (3) production-related effects on technological advance – learning by doing and economies of scale – are not as critical to the long-term potential for cost reduction in organic PV as the investment in and success of R&D. Those results were insensitive to the intensity of either type of program, the level of a carbon price, the availability of storage technology, and uncertainty in the main parameters used in the model. The central policy implication of those results is that governments must find a way to engender this R&D, whether it is funded by the government itself or by the private sector in response to changing demand conditions. In fact, one might argue that the key question policy makers face, with regard to PV development, is how to encourage this R&D, rather than how to support economies of scale and learning by doing.

To be sure, that study found that a case could still be made for subsidies through analysis of risk. Because of the possibility of R&D failure, the benefits of subsidies stochastically dominate those of R&D. In the event of R&D failure, subsidies make the costs of PV much lower than they would otherwise be, albeit not at levels close to the target. The importance of subsidies as a hedge against inherently uncertain R&D programs depends on the value that society places on the availability of a low-carbon energy source that is moderately inexpensive – that is, unlikely to be competitive with all other technologies but perhaps inexpensive enough to be deployed at a large-enough scale to diversify energy supply.

Much work needs to be done to develop this and other methods for modeling discontinuous evolution of PV technology and the impacts on costs. Given the importance of historical nonincremental changes described in the previous section, as well as the possibility of even more significant changes in the future, the need for better models is great.

1.05.6 Future Progress and Development

The insights gained from assessing cost development in PV technology have some direct policy implications; they also clarify needs for modeling.

As a result of the assessment of the sources of historical cost reductions as well as modeling future costs, we now have several design criteria for public policies intended to reduce the costs of PV. We need an array of supporting policy instruments: for example, R&D, demand subsidies, and encouragement of intersectoral spillovers. Timing matters; making good decisions about when to switch from a focus on R&D to a more capital-intensive investment in wide-scale deployment is crucial. Multiyear demand subsidies are important because the benefits of demand subsidies come from expectations about markets in the long term. Intermittent demand supports may actually be worse than no support. R&D support also needs a long-term commitment; budgets or grants that span multiple years are important; supporting policies, such as Japan's Sunshine Program or US Project Independence, that demonstrated commitment by making this area of work a serious national priority were also successful. Niche markets have been crucial, especially when government support was lacking. The success of new technological generations may require renewed R&D support even while markets for the existing technology are expanding; new problems need to be worked and postdeployment experience needs to feed back into subsequent R&D decisions.

These insights imply a strong need for better tools with which to understand technological change in PV. Much is at stake, in terms of both the public's financial resources used to fund these programs and the environmental impacts these programs are designed to mediate. These decisions are too important – and mistakes too expensive – to rely on simple heuristics that mask large uncertainties and that are easily ignored. Promising developments exist. An important analytical improvement has certainly been the inclusion of explicit treatment of learning uncertainty in modeling [111–113]. Estimating technology costs through the summation of bottom-up characterization of technology dynamics in individual components provides an appealing alternative in that sources of uncertainty can be identified more precisely [114]. The combination of such bottom-up models with experience curves and expert opinion provides a method that is more robust to bias within any single method [83]. As discussed above, an alternative use of bottom-up methods is to integrate them with expert elicitation into a single model that represents both incremental and nonincremental technical change [107]. This integration will help account for the introduction of new technological generations, which seems especially likely in the case of PV. Improving the accuracy and precision of models such as these is an important research endeavor. Identifying the specific nonincremental changes that occurred, as described by Husman [115]., provides a methodology for connecting them to causes and impacts; this provides a potential means by which to supplement expert opinion on the effectiveness of future research investments. The policy implications described above reveal important decisions, such as timing and resource allocation between R&D and subsidies. Developments in modeling future costs have the potential to improve the efficiency and efficacy of these programs in fully realizing the very large potential societal benefits of widespread PV deployment.

References

[1] Nemet GF (2007) Policy and Innovation in Low-Carbon Energy Technologies. PhD Dissertation, University of California.
[2] FS (2009) *First Solar Passes $1 Per Watt Industry Milestone (25 Feb.)*. Tempe, AZ: First Solar.
[3] Schaeffer GJ, Seebregts AJ, Beurskens LWM, *et al.* (2004) Learning from the Sun. Analysis of the use of experience curves for energy policy purposes: The case of photovoltaic power. *Final Report of the PHOTEX Project*, Petten, The Netherlands. ECN Renewable Energy in the Built Environment.
[4] Wiser R, Barbose G, *et al.* (2009) *Tracking the Sun: The Installed Cost of Photovoltaics in the U.S. from 1998–2007*. Berkeley, CA: Lawrence Berkeley National Laboratory.
[5] GEA (2011) The energy technology innovation system. In: Nakicenovic N (ed.) *The Global Energy Assessment (GEA)*. Cambridge: Cambridge University Press.
[6] Nemet GF (2006) Beyond the learning curve: Factors influencing cost reductions in photovoltaics. *Energy Policy* 34(17): 3218–3232.
[7] Surek T (2003) Progress in U.S. photovoltaics: Looking back 30 years and looking ahead 20. In: *Proceedings of the 3rd World Conference on Photovoltaic Energy Conversion*, May 11–18, Osaka, Japan.
[8] Green MA (2005) Silicon photovoltaic modules: A brief history of the first 50 years. *Progress in Photovoltaics: Research and Applications* 13(5): 447–455.
[9] Taylor M, Nemet G, *et al.* (2007) *Government Actions and Innovation in Clean Energy Technologies: The Cases of Photovoltaic Cells, Solar Thermal Electric Power, and Solar Water Heating, CEC-500-2007-012*. Sacramento, CA: California Energy Commission.
[10] Moore RM (1982) Czochralski silicon solar cell modules: Present cost and future prospects. *Solar Cells* 5: 313–329.
[11] Shum KL and Watanabe C (2007) Photovoltaic deployment strategy in Japan and the USA – An institutional appraisal. *Energy Policy* 35(2): 1186–1195.
[12] Peevey MR and Malcolm K (2006) Interim Order Adopting Policies and Funding for the California Solar Initiative. California Public Utilities Commission, Rulemaking 04-03-017.
[13] Neuhoff K, Nemet G, *et al.* (2007) *The Role of the Supply Chain in Innovation: The Example of Photovoltaic Cells*. Cambridge: University of Cambridge – Electricity Policy Research Group.
[14] Jaeger-Waldau A (2004) *PV Status Report 2004: Research, Solar Cell Production and Market Implementation of Photovoltaics*. Ispra, Italy: European Commission, DG JRC, Institute for Environment and Sustainability, Renewable Energies Unit.
[15] Maycock PD (2005) PV technology, performance, cost 1995–2010. Williamsburg, VA: PV Energy Systems.
[16] Dutton JM and Thomas A (1984) Treating progress functions as a managerial opportunity. *Academy of Management Review* 9(2): 235–247.
[17] van Benthem A, Gillingham K, *et al.* (2008) Learning-by-doing and the optimal solar policy in California. *The Energy Journal* 29(3): 131.
[18] Shum KL and Watanabe C (2008) Toward a local learning (innovation) model of solar photovoltaic development. *Energy Policy* 36(2): 508–521.
[19] Menanteau P (2000) Learning from variety and competition between technological options for generating photovoltaic electricity. *Technological Forecasting and Social Change* 63(1): 63–80.
[20] Yu CF, van Sark WGJHM, *et al.* (2011) Unraveling the photovoltaic technology learning curve by incorporation of input price changes and scale effects. *Renewable and Sustainable Energy Reviews* 15: 324–337.
[21] Maycock PD and Stirewalt EN (1985) *A Guide to the Photovoltaic Revolution*. Emmaus, PA: Rodale Press.
[22] Wolf M (1974) Historic development of photovoltaic power generation. In Helmut R Loesch (ed.): *International Conference on Photovoltaic Power Generation.*, pp. 49–65. Hamburg, Germany: Deutsche Gesellschaft fuer Luft- und Raumfahrt.
[23] Roessner DJ (1982) Government–industry relationships in technology commercialization: The case of photovoltaics. *Solar Cells* 5(2): 101–134.
[24] Maycock PD (1984) U.S.–Japanese competition for the world photovoltaic market. In: Ebinger CK and Morse RA (eds.) *U.S.–Japanese Energy Relations: Cooperation and Competition*, pp. 207–217. London: Westview Press.
[25] Herfindahl OC (1950) *Concentration in the US Steel Industry*. New York: Columbia University.
[26] Hirschman AO (1945) *National Power and the Structure of Foreign Trade*. Berkeley; Los Angeles: University of California Press.
[27] Costello D and Rappaport P (1980) The technological and economic development of photovoltaics. *Annual Review of Energy* 5(1): 335–356.
[28] Nemet GF (2009) Interim monitoring of cost dynamics for publicly supported energy technologies. *Energy Policy* 37(3): 825–835.
[29] BCG (1972) *Perspectives on Experience*. Boston, MA: The Boston Consulting Group.
[30] Irwin DA and Klenow PJ (1994) Learning-by-doing spillovers in the semiconductor industry. *Journal of Political Economy* 102(6): 1200–1227.
[31] Watanabe C, Wakabayashi K, *et al.* (2000) Industrial dynamism and the creation of a "virtuous cycle" between R&D, market growth and price reduction – The case of photovoltaic power generation (PV) development in Japan. *Technovation* 20: 299–312.
[32] Laird FN (2001) *Solar Energy, Technology Policy, and Institutional Values*. New York: Cambridge University Press.
[33] van Sark W, Alsema E, *et al.* (2010) General aspects and caveats of experience curve analysis. In: Junginger M, van Sark W, and Faaij A (eds.) *Technological Learning in the Energy Sector: Lessons for Policy, Industry and Science*. Cheltenham, UK: Edward Elgar.
[34] Hoffmann W and Pellkofer T (in press, corrected proof) Thin films in photovoltaics: Technologies and perspectives. *Thin Solid Films*. http://dx.doi.org/10.1016/j.tsf.2011.04.146.
[35] Schumpeter JA (1947) *Capitalism, Socialism, and Democracy*. New York; London: Harper.
[36] Freeman C (1994) The economics of technical change. *Cambridge Journal of Economics* 18(5): 463–514.
[37] Mowery DC and Rosenberg N (1998) *Paths of Innovation: Technological Change in 20th-Century America*. Cambridge: Cambridge University Press.

[38] Rosenberg N (1994) *Exploring the Black Box: Technology, Economics, and History.* Cambridge: Cambridge University Press.
[39] Alchian A (1963) Reliability of progress curves in airframe production. *Econometrica* 31(4): 679–693.
[40] Rapping L (1965) Learning and World War II production functions. *The Review of Economic Statistics* 47(1): 81–86.
[41] Smith A (1776) Of the division of labor. In: *An Inquiry into the Nature and the Causes of the Wealth of Nations.* Chapter 1. London: Methuen and Co.
[42] Wright TP (1936) Factors affecting the costs of airplanes. *Journal of the Aeronautical Sciences* 3: 122–128.
[43] Arrow K (1962) The economic implications of learning by doing. *The Review of Economic Studies* 29(3): 155–173.
[44] Duke RD and Kammen DM (1999) The economics of energy market transformation initiatives. *The Energy Journal* 20(4): 15–64.
[45] van der Zwaan B and Rabl A (2003) Prospects for PV: A learning curve analysis. *Solar Energy* 74: 19–31.
[46] Azar C and Dowlatabadi H (1999) A review of technical change in assessment of climate policy. *Annual Review of Energy and the Environment* 24(1): 513–544.
[47] Grubler A, Nakicenovic N, et al. (1999) Dynamics of energy technologies and global change. *Energy Policy* 27: 247–280.
[48] Williams RH and Terzian G (1993) *A Benefit–Cost Analysis of Accelerated Development of Photovoltaic Technology.* Princeton, NJ: The Center for Energy and Environmental Studies, Princeton University.
[49] Wene C-O (2000) *Experience Curves for Technology Policy.* Paris: International Energy Agency.
[50] Neij L, Andersen PD, et al. (2003) The use of experience curves for assessing energy policy programs. In: *Proceedings of the EU/IEA Workshop on Experience Curves: A Tool for Energy Policy Analysis and Design*, 22–24 January. Paris, France.
[51] Edenhofer O, Lessmann K, et al. (2006) Induced technological change: Exploring its implications for the economics of atmospheric stabilization. Synthesis report from the Innovation Modeling Comparison Project. *Special Issue: Endogenous Technological Change and the Economics of Atmospheric Stabilisation. The Energy Journal* 27: 57–108.
[52] Grubb M, Koehler J, et al. (2002) Induced technical change in energy and environmental modeling: Analytic approaches and policy implications. *Annual Review of Energy and the Environment* 27: 271–308.
[53] Messner S (1997) Endogenized technological learning in an energy systems model. *Journal of Evolutionary Economics* 7(3): 291–313.
[54] Nordhaus WD (2002) Modeling induced innovation in climate change policy. In: Grubler A, Nakicenovic N, and Nordhaus WD (eds.) *Technological Change and the Environment*, pp. 182–209. Washington, DC: Resources for the Future; International Institute for Applied Systems Analysis.
[55] Freeman C and Louca F (2001) *As Time Goes By: From the Industrial Revolutions to the Information Revolution.* Oxford: Oxford University Press.
[56] Arthur WB (2006) Out-of-equilibrium economics and agent-based modeling. In: Judd K and Tesfatsion L (eds.) *Handbook of Computational Economics, Vol. 2: Agent-Based Computational Economics*, pp. 1551–1564. Elsevier; North-Holland: Amsterdam.
[57] Marx K (1867) Machinery and modern industry. In: *Capital.* Harmondsworth, Middlesex, UK.
[58] Junginger M, van Sark W, et al. (2010) *Technological Learning in the Energy Sector: Lessons for Policy, Industry and Science.* Cheltenham, UK: Edward Elgar.
[59] IPCC (2007) *Climate Change 2007: Mitigation. Contribution of Working Group III to the Fourth Assessment Report of the Intergovernmental Panel on Climate Change.* Cambridge; New York: Cambridge University Press.
[60] Stern N (2006) *Stern Review on the Economics of Climate Change.* Cambridge: Cambridge University Press.
[61] IEA (2008) Deployment and technology learning. In: *Energy Technology Perspectives.* Paris: International Energy Agency.
[62] Goldemberg J, Coelho ST, et al. (2004) How adequate policies can push renewables. *Energy Policy* 32(9): 1141–1146.
[63] CPUC (2009) California Solar Initiative Annual Program Assessment, California Public Utilities Commission (CPUC), June, 2009.
[64] CPUC (2003) Decision 03-06-071, Order Initiating Implementation of the Senate Bill 1078 Renewable Portfolio Standard Program. California Public Utilities Commission (CPUC).
[65] Sher B (2002) Senate Bill 1078: The Renewables Portfolio Standard of California – Chapter 516, Statutes of 2002, State of California.
[66] Yelle LE (1979) The learning curve: Historical review and comprehensive survey. *Decision Science* 10: 302–328.
[67] Wene CO (2007) Technology learning systems as non-trivial machines. *Kybernetes* 36(3–4): 348–363.
[68] McDonald A and Schrattenholzer L (2001) Learning rates for energy technologies. *Energy Policy* 29: 255–261.
[69] Argote L and Epple D (1990) Learning curves in manufacturing. *Science* 247(4945): 920–924.
[70] Romer PM (1990) Endogenous technological change. *The Journal of Political Economy* 98(5): S71–S102.
[71] Hall B and Mairesse J (2006) Empirical studies of innovation in the knowledge-driven economy. *Economics of Innovation and New Technology* 15: 289–299.
[72] Maycock PD (2002) *The World Photovoltaic Market.* Warrenton, VA: PV Energy Systems.
[73] Strategies Unlimited (2003) *Photovoltaic Five-Year Market Forecast, 2002–2007.* Mountain View, CA: Strategies Unlimited.
[74] Hall G and Howell S (1985) The experience curve from the economist's perspective. *Strategic Management Journal* 6(3): 197–212.
[75] Baloff N (1966) Learning curve – Some controversial issues. *Journal of Industrial Economics* 14(3): 275–282.
[76] Carlson JG (1973) Cubic learning curves: Precision tool for labor estimating. *Manufacturing Engineering and Management* 71(5): 22–25.
[77] Sheshinski E (1967) Tests of the learning by doing hypothesis. *Review of Economics and Statistics* 49(4): 568–578.
[78] Adler PS and Clark KB (1991) Behind the learning curve: A sketch of the learning process. *Management Science* 37(3): 267–281.
[79] Buonanno P, Carraro C, et al. (2003) Endogenous induced technical change and the costs of Kyoto. *Resource and Energy Economics* 25(1): 11–34.
[80] Miketa A and Schrattenholzer L (2004) Experiments with a methodology to model the role of R&D expenditures in energy technology learning processes: First results. *Energy Policy* 32: 1679–1692.
[81] Thompson P (2001) How much did the liberty shipbuilders learn? New evidence for an old case study. *Journal of Political Economy* 109(1): 103–137.
[82] Neij L and Astrand K (2006) Outcome indicators for the evaluation of energy policy instruments and technical change. *Energy Policy* 34(17): 2662–2676.
[83] Neij L (2008) Cost development of future technologies for power generation – A study based on experience curves and complementary bottom-up assessments. *Energy Policy* 36(6): 2200–2211.
[84] Rubin ES, Antes M, et al. (2005) *Estimating Future Trends in the Cost of CO_2 Capture Technologies.* Pittsburgh, PA: International Energy Agency Greenhouse Gas R&D Programme (IEAGHG).
[85] Koomey J and Hultman NE (2007) A reactor-level analysis of busbar costs for U.S. nuclear plants, 1970–2005. *Energy Policy* 35(11): 5630–5642.
[86] Borenstein S (2008) *The Market Value and Cost of Solar Photovoltaic Electricity Production.* Berkeley, CA: University of California Energy Institute's Center for the Study of Energy Markets.
[87] van Sark WGJHM (2008) Introducing errors in progress ratios determined from experience curves. *Technological Forecasting and Social Change* 75(3): 405–415.
[88] van Sark W, Alsema EA, et al. (2008) Accuracy of progress ratios determined from experience curves: The case of crystalline silicon photovoltaic module technology development. *Progress in Photovoltaics* 16(5): 441–453.
[89] SEIA (2004) *Our Solar Power Future: The Photovoltaics Industry Roadmap Through 2030 and Beyond.* Washington, DC: Solar Energy Industries Association.
[90] Gritsevskyi A and Nakicenovic N (2000) Modeling uncertainty of induced technological change. *Energy Policy* 28(13): 907–921.
[91] Baker E and Adu-Bonnah K (2008) Investment in risky R&D programs in the face of climate uncertainty. *Energy Economics* 30(2): 465–486.
[92] Schnapp R (2008) *Federal Financial Interventions and Subsidies in Energy Markets 2007.* Washington, DC: Energy Information Administration – Office of Coal, Nuclear, Electric and Alternate Fuels.
[93] Husmann D (2011) Identification of Breakthroughs in Photovoltaics. MS Thesis, University of Wisconsin.
[94] Garcia R and Calantone R (2002) A critical look at technological innovation typology and innovativeness terminology: A literature review. *Journal of Product Innovation Management* 19(2): 110–132.
[95] Saitoh T (2003) 30 Years of progress in crystalline silicon solar cells. In: *Proceedings of the 3rd World Conference on Photovoltaic Energy Conversion*, pp. A23–A28. Osaka, Japan, 18 May 2003.

[96] Podolny JM and Stuart TE (1995) A role-based ecology of technological change. *American Journal of Sociology* 100(5): 1224–1260.
[97] Perlin J (1999) *From Space to Earth: The Story of Solar Electricity*. Ann Arbor, MI: Aatec Publications.
[98] Bellis M (2009) History: Photovoltaics Timeline. *About.com* (accessed 10 February 2009).
[99] Goetzberger A, Hebling C, et al. (2003) Photovoltaic materials, history, status and outlook. *Materials Science and Engineering, R: Reports* 40(1): 1–46.
[100] Swanson RM (2006) A vision for crystalline silicon photovoltaics. *Progress in Photovoltaics* 14(5): 443–453.
[101] Dahlin KB and Behrens DM (2005) When is an invention really radical? Defining and measuring technological radicalness. *Research Policy* 34(5): 717–737.
[102] Hall BH and Ziedonis RH (2001) The patent paradox revisited: An empirical study of patenting in the US semiconductor industry, 1979–1995. *Rand Journal of Economics* 32(1): 101–128.
[103] von Wartburg I, Teichert T, et al. (2005) Inventive progress measured by multi-stage patent citation analysis. *Research Policy* 34(10): 1591–1607.
[104] Albert MB, Avery D, et al. (1991) Direct validation of citation counts as indicators of industrially important patents. *Research Policy* 20(3): 251–259.
[105] NREL (1991) *U.S. Photovoltaic Patents: 1988–1990*. Golden, CO: National Renewable Energy Laboratory.
[106] Nemet GF and Baker E (2009) Demand subsidies versus R&D: Comparing the uncertain impacts of policy on a pre-commercial low-carbon energy technology. *The Energy Journal* 30(4): 49–80.
[107] Berger A (2009) Personal communication.
[108] Brabec CJ (2004) Organic photovoltaics: Technology and market. *Solar Energy Materials and Solar Cells* 83(2–3): 273–292.
[109] Ginley D (2007) *National Solar Technology Roadmap: Organic PV in National Solar Technology Roadmap*. Golden, CO: National Renewable Energy Laboratory.
[110] IEA (2008) *Energy Technology Perspectives: Scenarios and Strategies to 2050*. Paris: International Energy Agency.
[111] Alberth S and Hope C (2007) Climate modelling with endogenous technical change: Stochastic learning and optimal greenhouse gas abatement in the PAGE2002 model. *Energy Policy* 35(3): 1795–1807.
[112] Rubin ES, Yeh S, et al. (2007) Use of experience curves to estimate the future cost of power plants with CO_2 capture. *International Journal of Greenhouse Gas Control* 1(2): 188–197.
[113] Uyterlinde MA, Junginger M, et al. (2007) Implications of technological learning on the prospects for renewable energy technologies in Europe. *Energy Policy* 35(8): 4072–4087.
[114] Keshner MS and Arya R (2004) *Study of the Potential Cost Reductions Resulting from Super-Large-Scale Manufacturing of PV Modules*. Golden, CO: National Renewable Energy Laboratory.
[115] Husmann D (2011) US Photovoltaic Breakthroughs from 1947 to 1993: their Identification, Origin and Commercialization. Masters thesis, University of Wisconsin-Madison.

1.06 Feed-In Tariffs and Other Support Mechanisms for Solar PV Promotion

D Jacobs, Freie Universität Berlin, Berlin, Germany
BK Sovacool, Vermont Law School, South Royalton, VT, USA

© 2012 Elsevier Ltd. All rights reserved.

1.06.1	**Introduction**	74
1.06.2	**Overview of Support Mechanisms for Renewable Electricity**	75
1.06.2.1	Quota-Based Support (TGC and RPS)	76
1.06.2.2	Tender Systems	77
1.06.2.3	Net Metering	77
1.06.2.4	Feed-In Tariffs	77
1.06.2.5	Tax and Investment Incentives	78
1.06.2.6	Assessment of Support Mechanisms (Effectiveness and Efficiency)	78
1.06.3	**Singapore**	79
1.06.3.1	Introduction	79
1.06.3.2	Existing Support Schemes	79
1.06.3.2.1	Solar capability scheme	80
1.06.3.2.2	Clean energy research and test-bedding program	81
1.06.3.2.3	Clean energy program office	81
1.06.3.2.4	Clean energy research program	81
1.06.3.2.5	Other efforts	81
1.06.3.3	Challenges and Prospects for the Future	82
1.06.4	**United States**	83
1.06.4.1	Introduction	83
1.06.4.2	Existing Support Schemes	84
1.06.4.2.1	Renewable portfolio standards	85
1.06.4.2.2	Net metering	86
1.06.4.2.3	Green power programs	86
1.06.4.2.4	Tax credits	87
1.06.4.2.5	Feed-in tariffs	88
1.06.4.3	Challenges and Prospects for the Future	89
1.06.5	**European Union (Germany and Spain)**	90
1.06.5.1	Introduction: Europe	90
1.06.5.2	Support Mechanisms	91
1.06.5.3	Germany	91
1.06.5.4	Spain	91
1.06.6	**Common Features of Best Practice Promotion Schemes**	93
1.06.6.1	Eligible Producers	94
1.06.6.2	Purchase Obligations	94
1.06.6.3	Tariff Calculation Methodology	94
1.06.6.4	Duration of Tariff Payment	97
1.06.6.5	Financing Mechanism	97
1.06.6.6	Progress Report	98
1.06.6.7	Tariff Differentiation According to Plant Size	98
1.06.6.8	Tariff Differentiation According to Plant Type (Location)	99
1.06.6.9	Tariff Degression	99
1.06.6.10	Inflation Indexation	101
1.06.6.11	Design Options for Better Market Integration	102
1.06.6.12	Challenges and Prospects for the Future	103
1.06.6.12.1	Managing volume success with price response	103
1.06.7	**Conclusion and Outlook**	103
1.06.7.1	Leveling the Playing Field	105
1.06.7.2	Investment Structure and Actor Groups on Future Electricity Markets	106
References		106

1.06.1 Introduction

This chapter explores support mechanisms for the promotion of solar photovoltaic (PV) electricity. Over the years, a range of support instruments have been applied in order to foster the deployment of solar PV installations around the world, including research and development (R&D) spending, investment and tax incentives, and market-based support instruments such as net metering and feed-in tariffs (FITs). In this chapter we will analyze existing support mechanisms in Singapore, the United States, Germany, and Spain.

The promotion of solar PV started to be of large interest for policymakers in the 1970s. After the oil crises of the 1970s, the quest for alternative energy sources became a major goal for energy policy strategies worldwide. However, the market for solar PV has really started to expand only in the past 10–15 years. While the global cumulative PV capacity was less than 1 GW in 1998, 10 years later it had already reached almost 15 GW (see **Figure 1**), about 23 GW in 2009, and more than 35 GW in 2010 [1]. This development is largely due to innovative support schemes that will be discussed in this chapter.

One record year is following another. In 2008, the newly installed capacity reached 5.5 GWp, and solar PV produced about 15 TWh of electricity. In 2009, about 7.2 GW new capacity was added. According to the European Photovoltaic Industry Association (EPIA), the global solar PV market could reach almost 30 GW annually by 2014 if appropriate policy frameworks are established in key markets [2].

Despite the fact that solar PV only supplies less than 1% of total electricity demand, the worldwide installed capacity of solar PV has experienced impressive growth rates over the last decade. Although the capacity increased by an average of 24% in the years 1998–2003, this figure jumped to 39% in the following 5 years (2003–08). Between 1999 and 2008, the installed capacity has increased by more than 10-fold [3] (see **Figure 2**).

There is a clear correlation between increasing markets and decreasing module prices. According to one recent assessment, a doubling of the cumulative installed PV capacity has led to price reduction for modules of 22% (see **Figure 3**). Based on these observations, further significant price reductions can be expected in the future [4].

Similarly, worldwide R&D spending has increased from about US $250 million in 2000 to US $500 million in 2007. At the same time, the generation costs for solar PV have decreased by more than 50% [5]. Based on these figures, the International Energy Agency (IEA) projected generation cost for solar PV until 2050 [6]. Accordingly, at good locations the costs for electricity from solar PV might be as low as 12 US¢ $(kWh)^{-1}$ in 2020, 7 US¢ $(kWh)^{-1}$ in 2030, and 4.5 US¢ $(kWh)^{-1}$ in 2050. Besides the cost reduction through mass markets, technological learning also took place regarding the average cell efficiency. In the case of crystalline cells, the average efficiency increased from 14.5% in 2004 to 16.5% in 2008. These efficiency gains will most likely continue in the future.

Notwithstanding the impressive development of the global PV market, world market growth in the last decade was substantially driven by a limited number of countries, namely Germany, Spain, and (to a certain extent) Japan. When looking at the regional distribution of the global PV market in 2009, the dominant role of Europe with respect to the rest of the world becomes apparent [5]. Of all newly installed capacity, about 70% was located in Europe, with Germany accounting for 54% of that world market.

The lesson appears to be that global market development depends crucially on the policy framework conditions within countries. Germany, Spain, and Japan make up about ¾ of the total installed capacity worldwide. Whereas Germany and Spain primarily relied on FITs for the promotion of solar power, Japan for the most part relied on investment subsidies and net metering mechanisms.

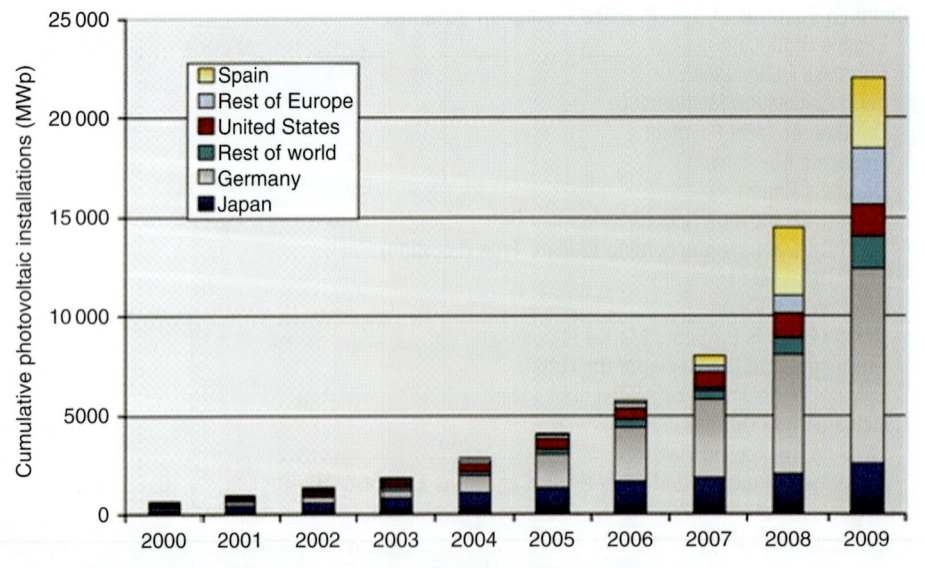

Figure 1 Accumulated, worldwide installed solar capacity per region (2000–09). Source: JRC (2010) PV status report 2010. Ispra, Italy: Joint Research Centre, Institute for Energy, European Commission [1].

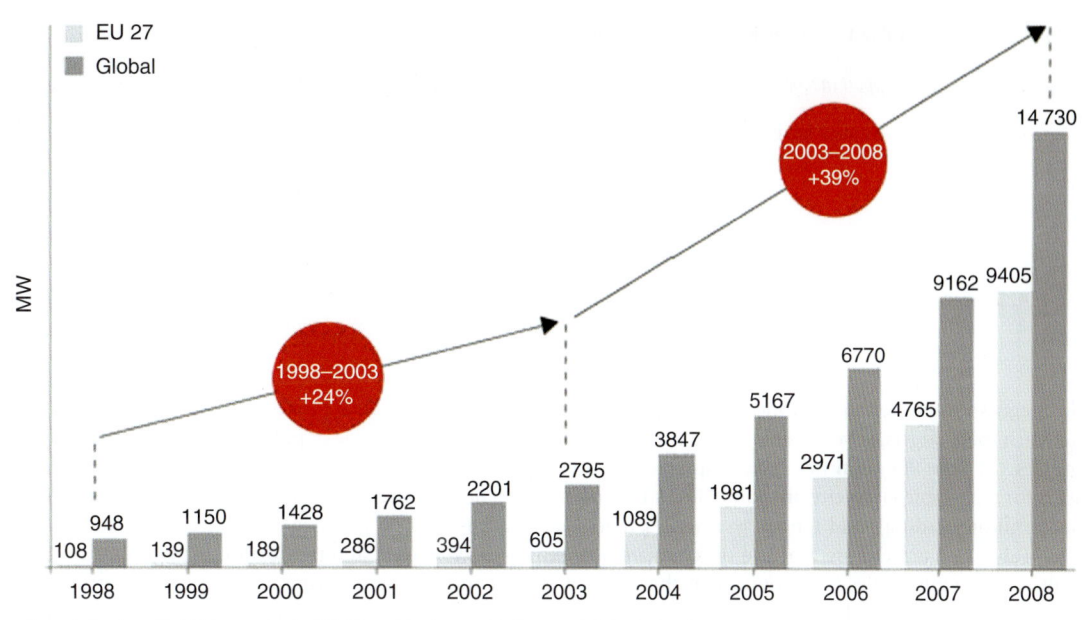

Figure 2 Cumulative installed PV capacity in EU-27 and in the world. Source: EPIA (2009) Set for 2020 – Solar photovoltaic electricity: A mainstream power source in Europe by 2020, executive summary [3].

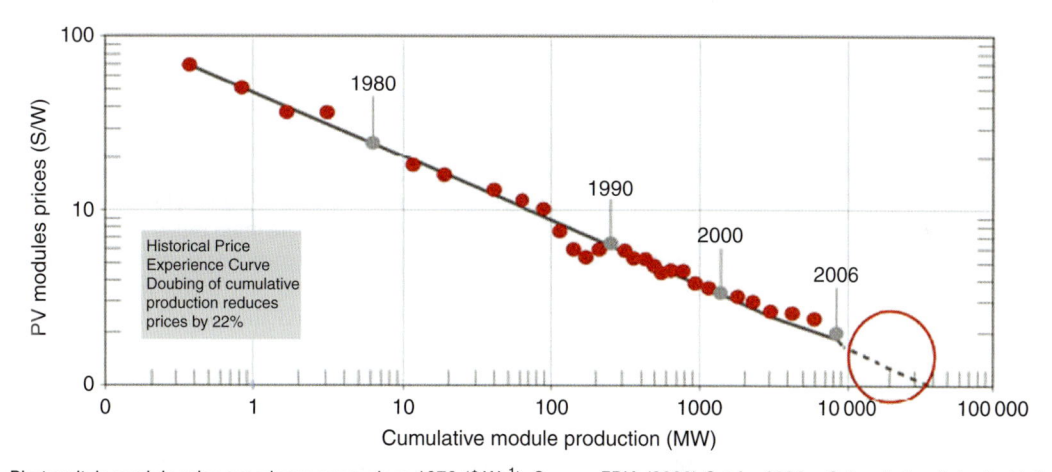

Figure 3 Photovoltaic module price experience curve since 1976 ($ W^{-1}). Source: EPIA (2009) Set for 2020 – Solar photovoltaic electricity: A mainstream power source in Europe by 2020, executive summary [3].

In this chapter, we elaborate on the reasons for success in promoting solar PV deployment. We focus on FITs with a special eye on design in Germany and Spain as these countries have been most successful in bringing about new PV capacity and because they have frequently been identified as international best practice. However, we do not exclusively focus on FITs. As will be shown, also Germany and Spain used other support mechanisms at an early stage of market development. Similarly to Germany in the 1980s, Singapore is (still) primarily focusing on R&D and investment subsidies. In the United States, a sort of evolutionary process of support instruments occurred, including R&D spending and tax credit schemes up to net metering and, most recently, FITs. In Singapore, a similar progression occurred from R&D spending to investment subsidies. However, before going into the more detailed case studies, we will give a more general overview about support instruments for renewable electricity in the following section.

1.06.2 Overview of Support Mechanisms for Renewable Electricity

The promotion of renewable energy sources has become a priority for scores of governments around the world. (This section draws largely on a policy paper which David Jacobs has prepared for an OSCE (Organization for Security and Co-operation in Europe) seminar paper (Baku, Azerbaijan).) As of 2010, more than 80 countries worldwide have adopted targets for the development of

Table 1 Overview of support mechanisms from renewable electricity

Support mechanisms	Price-based support	Quantity-based support
Investment focused	Research and development Investment subsidies Tax incentives Soft loans	Tender mechanism
Generation focused	FITs Net metering	Tender mechanism Quota obligations (TGC/RPS)

RPS, renewable portfolio standard; TGC, tradable green certificate scheme.

renewable energy sources. Medium or long-term targets are an advantage as they increase investment security for power producers. In order to reach these targets, governments around the world have adopted a wide range of policies for the promotion of renewable energy sources. At least 85 countries have implemented specific policies for renewables. The most frequently used support mechanisms for renewable electricity are public R&D, tax and investment incentives, FITs, net metering, quota-based mechanisms (based on certificate trading), and tender systems [7]. These mechanisms can be grouped into price-based and quantity-based support (see **Table 1**). Furthermore, one can differentiate between capacity-focused and production-focused incentives [8].

In recent years, many studies have found that the actual design of support mechanisms is more important for effective and efficient support than the mere choice of support schemes. Therefore, it is essential to take international best practice into account when designing a national support instrument. Well-designed support mechanisms guaranteeing a maximum of investment security can reduce costs for renewable energies by 10–30% [6]. If the investor is able to foresee the income revenue of a project, financial institutions will provide capital at lower cost, thus lowering the costs for renewable electricity.

1.06.2.1 Quota-Based Support (TGC and RPS)

Under quota-based mechanisms, the legislator obliges a certain market actor (consumers, producers, or suppliers) to provide a certain share of electricity from renewable energy sources. The choice of the obliged party (consumer, producer, or supplier) usually depends on the national market design. The obliged party can either produce electricity itself or buy it from other green electricity producers. In order to increase the flexibility of the system, in many countries the obliged party is also allowed to reach the share by trading certificates, which serve as proof for compliance [9]. Therefore, these mechanisms are often called tradable green certificate (TGC) schemes. In the United States and other parts of the world, they are often called renewable portfolio standards (RPSs), as supply companies are obliged to provide a certain share of the electricity portfolio from renewable energy sources. RPS mechanisms sometimes operate without certificate trading. They can also be combined with tender mechanisms or FITs.

In the case of certificate trading, renewable electricity producers have two income sources. First, they sell their electricity at the spot market for electricity at the given market price. Second, they can sell their certificates at the national green certificate market. In theory, the certificate sales shall compensate for 'greenness' of the electricity, that is, the positive attribute of renewable electricity compared with conventionally produced 'gray electricity'. The obliged party can either obtain certificates by producing renewable electricity itself or by buying them on the certificate market. The certificates allow the obliged party to prove that they have 'produced' a certain share of their electricity from renewable energy sources. If they cannot prove this, that is, they do not have a sufficient number of certificates, they have to pay a penalty.

In theory, quota-based mechanisms have the advantage of being cost-efficient as they focus on the least cost technologies and spur competition between green power producers. Producers will install only the cheapest renewable energy technologies as this support mechanism does not take the differences in generation costs for different renewable energy technologies into account. Theoretically, quota obligations are also thought to be most appropriate to reach a certain target, without overfulfilling or undergoing it. Besides, certificate trading gives the obliged party flexibility of how to reach particular policy goals, requirements, and targets. The can produce 'green' electricity themselves, buy certificates on the certificate market, and freely decide upon which technology to chose for meeting those targets. Unlike tax exemptions, publicly financed R&D, and other support mechanisms, quota-based mechanisms cost the legislator no money as the additional costs are passed on to the final consumer.

However, in practice, quota-based mechanisms face some disadvantages. In the case of certificate trading, they convey a high risk for renewable electricity producers as both revenue sources – the electricity spot price and the certificate price – are volatile. Due to fluctuations of the electricity price and the certificate price, long-term rates of return are difficult to predict, thus making the financing of renewable energy projects more expansive. In practice, the increased investors risk can offset the theoretical benefits from competition between renewable electricity producers. In the United Kingdom, not even one-third of all projects has actually been installed, see Reference 10. As quota-based mechanisms are generally technology neutral, they only support the least costly renewable energy sources. Therefore, less mature technologies, such as solar power, geothermal, and certain types of biomass, are not being developed. Nontechnology-specific certificate trading creates large excess profits for producers of relatively mature technologies, thus making the support of renewable electricity unnecessarily expensive [11]. By focusing on the least cost technologies and not promoting other, less mature technologies, technological learning is *de facto* penalized. Moreover, empiric findings suggest that European TGC schemes favor large players and especially incumbent industries. Therefore, small-scale, independent power producers have difficulties entering the market. Finally, renewable electricity producers will always try not to achieve the targets fixed by the quota obligation as this would mean that the certificate price will drop to zero. Therefore, quota-based mechanisms can even limit the expansion of renewable energy sources.

1.06.2.2 Tender Systems

Tender or bidding systems are quantity-based support instruments where the legislator issues a call for tender, that is, an auctioning mechanism, for a certain renewable energy project of a specific size. The financial support can be based either on the total investment cost or on the power generation cost per electricity unit. Instead of offering up-front support (investment cost), tender mechanisms are usually based on the power generation costs per unit of electricity, that is, bidders provide renewable electricity at a predefined price per kilowatt-hour over a certain number of years. The bidder with the lowest necessary financial support wins the tender and has the exclusive right to profit from the support granted.

In theory, tender schemes have a number of advantages. First and foremost, they are cost-effective, as the tender process initiates competition between producers. As the bidder with the lowest bid wins the contract for power generation, the total additional cost for the society can, in theory, be limited. Besides, the government has direct control over the amount of renewable electricity that is produced under the support mechanism.

However, in practice tender schemes have revealed considerable problems. The major disadvantage of tender schemes is their limited effectiveness in empirical practice. Due to competitive bidding process, projects are often not actually built as competitors issue bids which are too low for actually running power plants profitably. Therefore, these projects are frequently abandoned by developers. Besides, tender mechanisms have been criticized for not promoting local renewable energy development as all necessary equipments are imported from other countries. Moreover, tenders have created stop-and-go development cycles in the renewable energy industry as legislators have called for tenders irregularly.

1.06.2.3 Net Metering

Net metering is a concept mostly applied for the promotion of decentralized solar electricity. Theoretically, also other technologies can be eligible under net metering mechanisms. Generally speaking, independent power producers have the right to get connected to the grid, and the local utility or grid operator is obliged to purchase all excess electricity. The name of the support instrument refers to the meter measuring the electricity consumption. In the case of most net metering schemes, the meter starts turning 'backward' once excess electricity is fed into the grid. If the consumer has produced more electricity than consumed, the local utility or grid operator has to pay for the net production at the end of each month or year. The 'remuneration' for the excess electricity varies from one net metering program to the other. In some cases, excess electricity is paid according to the retail electricity price; in other cases, the wholesale electricity price is the benchmark. Further variations are possible.

Historically, consumers who intended to produce renewable electricity at home and sell the excess power to the grid had to use separate meters. This 'double metering' led to unfair conditions for consumers as utilities only wanted to pay very small rates for the electricity fed into the grid. With net metering, ostensibly the consumer at least gets the retail electricity price (as the meter simply turns backward).

Theoretically, net metering has a number of advantages. Solar PV is usually produced at daytime when electricity demand is highest in many countries. Therefore, consumers can provide valuable electricity during peak demand periods. If net metering is coupled with time of use electricity rates for final consumer (i.e., higher electricity tariffs during high demand periods), these mechanisms can generate considerable incomes for consumers.

However, in most cases, these incomes are not high enough in order to finance the solar modules. Therefore, using renewable electricity locally and not feeding it into the grid is inherently promoted by this support mechanism. Besides, net metering frequently focuses on small-scale solar PV systems, as only excess electricity is being accepted. Therefore, large-scale renewable energy plants – which are necessary for transforming the global energy system – are not being supported. In contrast to other price-based support mechanisms, namely FITs, investment security is still rather low as the profitability of a plant largely depends on the long-term development of electricity prices for final consumers.

1.06.2.4 Feed-In Tariffs

FITs set a fixed price for the purchase of one unit renewable electricity. This rate reflects the actual power generation cost of each renewable energy technology (plus a reasonable rate of return). Tariffs are usually guaranteed for a long period of time (e.g., 15–20 years). FITs normally require grid operators to purchase all renewable electricity, independent of total electricity demand. They are generally financed via a small top-up on the electricity price for final consumers, that is, additional costs are distributed between all rate payers via national burden-sharing mechanisms. When designing FITs, legislators are looking for a balance between investment security for producers and reduced costs for the final consumer.

The success of FITs largely depends on the high degree of investment security. Investors' risks (volume and price risk) can be significantly reduced by providing fixed tariff payment over a long period of time. Besides, renewable electricity producers are generally not subject to balancing risk (providing prenegotiated amounts of electricity at a given moment in time), as FITs include a purchasing obligation. The biggest advantage of FITs over other support mechanisms is the technology-specific approach. By being able to promote all renewable energy technologies according to their stage of technological development, the policymaker also has the chance to promote technologies which are still rather costly but have a large mid- or long-term potential (e.g., solar PV). Besides, mature technologies such as wind energy can be promoted in a cost-efficient manner.

Nonetheless, even FITs have some disadvantages. Especially in countries with liberalized energy markets, FITs have sometimes been criticized for not conforming to the principle of competition as the idea of 'fixing' tariffs is associated with state-dominated, monopolistic energy markets. Fixing tariffs has also been criticized for hindering technological learning. However, tariff degression and frequent assessments of tariff levels can help to address this problem. Besides, a purchase obligation, that is, the purchase of all renewable electricity independent of electricity demand patterns, can lead to network balancing problems and increased grid operation costs. Moreover, it might be difficult to predict the number of market players and consequently renewable electricity projects which are attracted by a certain tariff level. Therefore, emerging economies and developing countries have often chosen to operate with capacity caps.

1.06.2.5 Tax and Investment Incentives

Investment incentives, that is, capital grants, tax incentives, tax credits, and soft loans, were the major support mechanisms for renewable energies in the 1980s and at the start of the 1990s [12]. They were mostly used for the realization of demonstration projects. The above-mentioned support schemes, especially FITs, quota-based mechanisms, and tender schemes, are generally supplemented by additional tax and investment incentives at an early stage of market development. Investment incentives are normally capacity-based incentives and investment focused, that is, the state grants a certain financial incentive based on the size, that is, the installed capacity, of the power plant.

Capital grants are often given in the form of contributions to the total investment costs. Producers of renewable electricity are often exempted from certain taxes. This can be carbon taxes in the case of industrialized countries or taxes for imports of renewable energy equipment in developing countries. Tax exemptions are normally justified by the unfair competition with conventional energy sources due to the lack of internalizing the negative external costs. Many countries also operate with accelerated depreciation for renewable energy projects. This allows people investing in renewable energy projects to earlier profit from tax benefits [13]. In the United States, tax credit mechanisms have been used frequently to promote renewable energy sources. They can be separated into investment tax credits (ITCs) and production tax credits (PTCs). As implied by the name, ITCs guarantee favorable tax treatment to actors deciding to invest into renewable energy projects by providing a partial tax write-off. When buying renewable energy equipment, investors can receive a 5–50% tax credit [14].

Capital grants and tax incentives have the advantage of enabling clear and predictable investment incentives to renewable energy investors. They can be applied to one specific or a whole range of technologies. In contrast to governmental R&D funding, private actors are usually targeted by those mechanisms. As mentioned above, tax and investment incentives have proven to be a successful supplementary and/or complementary instrument for renewable energy deployment. Similar to all the above-mentioned support schemes, they socialize the costs from renewable electricity promotion by distributing them amongst all tax payers.

However, these support mechanisms also have certain drawbacks. Most obviously, investment incentives are (naturally) geared toward spurring investment in a technology only, and they do not offer any incentive to improve the long-term operating performance of renewable energy power plants. This has sometimes led to a situation where investors have profited from governmental grants but never operated renewable energy power plants properly. Such a situation occurred with wind energy in India, where the legislator now decided to move away from investment-based support toward production-based support instruments. Tax incentives such as accelerated depreciation and tax credit schemes also tend to favor large-scale power plants (due to economies of scale) and wealthy people as one needs to have sufficient income to use tax credits effectively. Therefore, they implicitly exclude individuals and small businesses from participating in the renewable energy market.

1.06.2.6 Assessment of Support Mechanisms (Effectiveness and Efficiency)

Support mechanisms for electricity from renewable energy sources have been frequently analyzed. From economic theory, price- and quantity-based mechanisms are ought to have the same impact. Both approaches create an artificial market in order to stimulate renewable electricity deployment. In the case of price-based support, the legislator fixes the 'price' and the market decides about the 'quantity' of renewable energy projects. In the case of quantity-based support, the legislator fixes the amount of renewable electricity that shall be produced and the market decides about the price [15]. However, in reality some support instruments have proven to be more successful than others.

Most recently, the European Commission and the IEA have evaluated the above-mentioned support instruments for green electricity. Their evaluations have found that the success of support mechanisms can be best measured by effectiveness and efficiency. Effectiveness refers to the ability of a support mechanism to deliver an increase of the share of renewable electricity, while efficiency is related to cost-efficiency, that is, a comparison of the total amount of support received and the generation cost. In the following section, the most prominent renewable electricity support mechanisms will be compared, namely quota-based mechanisms, tender schemes, net metering, and FITs. (Investment and tax incentives are not being considered as they are generally applied as additional support mechanisms and their success significantly depends on the specific design in each country.)

By now, technology-specific support mechanisms, namely FITs, have proven to be most effective. This is especially true in the case of wind energy, biogas, and solar PV. In the case of biomass, some quota-based mechanisms have also been able to bring about renewable electricity deployment, due to the fact that these mechanisms generally promote the least costly technologies, for example, landfill gas plants. The European Commission also stresses that production-based support is far more important for the development of renewable energy projects than investment-based support. This confirms that tax and investment incentives should be used as supplementary support instruments but not as the major policy for support.

The superiority of FITs is clearly related to the high degree of investment security, by guaranteeing fixed tariff payment over a long period of time. In the case of quota-based mechanisms, insecurity about the future rates of return slowed down investment, while tender-based mechanisms suffered from the fact that many projects had been abandoned because of low bids.

A similar picture emerges when comparing the efficiency of support mechanisms. Generally speaking, FIT countries made better use of the money dedicated to renewable electricity support. The higher degree of efficiency of FITs is also due to the high degree of investment security. By guaranteeing tariff for a long period of time, project developers have fewer difficulties financing the renewable energy projects, and financing conditions are generally better than with other support instruments. In the case of quota-based support instruments, capital is generally more expansive as banks normally take a risk premium for the uncertain development of the certificate price and the electricity price.

Furthermore, the higher degree of efficiency of FITs is also related to technology-specific support. As shown above, well-designed FITs calculate the tariff payment based on the generation costs for each technology, normally assuming an internal rate of return between 5% and 9%. By doing this, windfall profits can be avoided. In contrast, technology-neutral quota-based mechanisms grant the same support to all technologies. Therefore, cost-efficient technologies can normally count on very high internal rates of return while less mature technologies will not be developed at all.

With an eye for which mechanisms have proven most successful on the ground, as well as an appreciation that mechanisms are seldom implemented in isolation and instead policymakers often rely on a bundle of support schemes at once, the next section explores four case studies. It explores what the governments of Singapore, the United States, and Germany and Spain (in the European Union) have each done to promote solar PV.

1.06.3 Singapore

1.06.3.1 Introduction

Singapore, with better solar radiation than Germany, had installed only a few kilowatts of solar PV capacity by 2005 but has since shown a remarkable speed of policy and technology development. In 2004 the country had only 'token' efforts to attract manufacturing and R&D, but since then has signaled a strategic intent to invest in renewable energy generally and solar PV as a 'core' sector [16]. In the past few years, the country has seen a new Solar Energy Research Institute of Singapore (SERIS) launched, manufacturing and research companies established, a $350 million fund for clean energy created, and a variety of test-bed projects along with a solar capability scheme (SCS) to fund private sector projects. As **Figure 4** shows, installed solar PV capacity has increased more than 100-fold from 18 kWp in 2000 to 2000 kWp in 2009.

1.06.3.2 Existing Support Schemes

Singapore has a number of factors that make it well suited for solar PV and especially building integrated solar PV. Singapore's annual global solar radiation is 50% larger than Germany's and the provision of solar energy there is even, whereas other countries suffer from seasonal changes in output, and its high diffuse ratio in Singapore means vertical surfaces receive high solar radiation independent of their orientation. Amorphous silicon performs well under Singapore's tropical hot and humid conditions. Second, the ways that buildings are designed and constructed hold advantages for PV integration. Building orientation is often designed with respect to the sun in Singapore, meaning that subexposed facades have fewer windows to prevent solar heat from entering the interior and plentiful unused surfaces, especially roofs, available for installation. Moreover, Housing Development Board buildings are mostly prefabricated, meaning installations can be the same size and efficiently applied in large numbers. Third, PV systems can offer a variety of important ancillary services, including the shading of facades and rainwater collecting devices such as butterfly roofs, adding value to buildings [17].

Despite these potential benefits, up until 2004 the largest impediment to solar PV systems in Singapore was cost. With few government incentives, a homeowner investing in a solar panel had to wait about 50 years to make their money back (unlike 3–10 years in places such as Japan and Germany) [18]. A similar study also concluded that given current economics and rate structures, power generation solar PV is costlier than fossil fuels in Singapore because many of its positive attributes, such as improved reliability or security, were not valued [19]. The government has long adhered to an approach to energy and electricity regulation that avoided promoting any single source of electricity. Singapore's electricity market framework has attempted to ensure a 'level playing field' for all types of generation technology and fuel mixes. Central to this strategy is ensuring that the wholesale and retail electricity markets are competitive, and that the markets harness competition to drive down costs through improvements in innovation and efficiency. Both the electricity and natural gas markets are liberalized, an

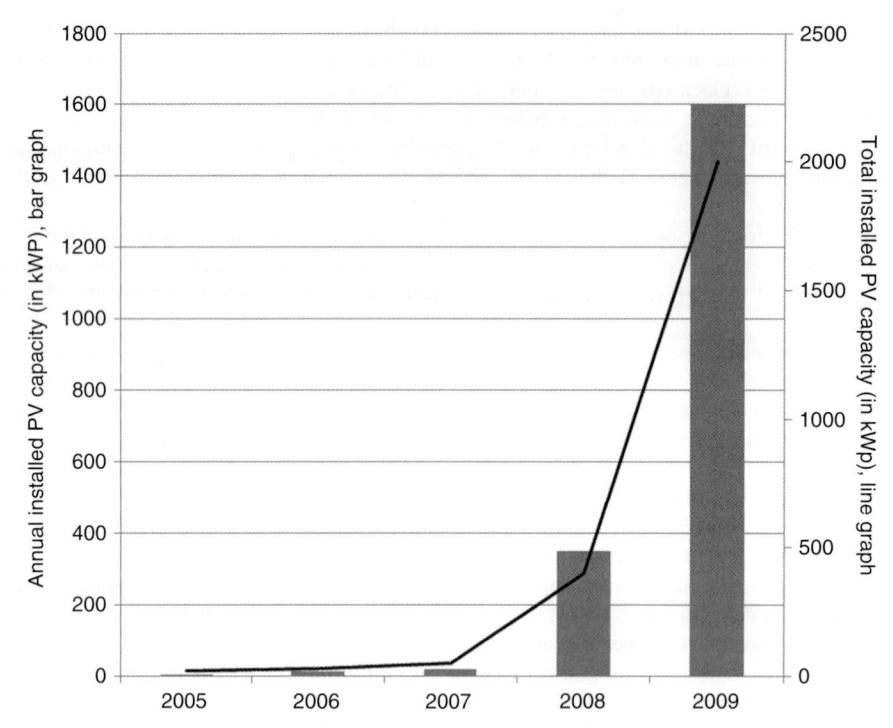

Figure 4 Annual and total installed PV capacity in Singapore, 2005–09. Source: Sovacool BK.

environment spurred by several important acts of legislation (including the Energy Market Authority of Singapore Act, the Gas Act, and the Electricity Act).

The 2001 Energy Market Authority of Singapore Act formally established (perhaps unsurprisingly) the Energy Market Authority (EMA), a statutory board in charge of regulating the electricity and gas markets in Singapore and promoting competition in these markets. Singapore's big three power companies – PowerSeraya, Senoko Power, and Tuas Power – were also all divested to the Singapore government's investment arm Temasek Holdings [18]. The EMA aims to protect the interests of consumers with regard to prices, reliability, and quality of electricity supply and services and performs the functions of economic and technical regulator. The EMA also promotes economic efficiency in the electricity industry and oversees a regulatory framework for the electricity industry that promotes competition and fair and efficient market conduct. The 2001 Gas Act extended EMA oversight to cover the shipping, retailing, management, and operation of natural gas and liquefied natural gas facilities. The 2001 Electricity Act, the most sweeping of the three, restructured the retail market for electricity, began the process of privatizing government-owned electric power plants, and encouraged private investment in the electricity sector.

Informally, while Singaporean regulators have added a host of voluntary agreements, two are the most notable: The Singapore Green Plan 2012 and the National Climate Change Strategy. The Singapore Green Plan 2012 focuses on promoting cleaner power plants, refineries, and vehicles as a way to improve ambient air quality. It sets voluntary standards to reduce energy consumption, states the government's preference for cleaner forms of electricity supply, and publicizes the importance of recycling and maintaining air pollution levels within 'good' ranges at least 85% of the year. The government has also formulated a progressive National Climate Change Strategy noting the importance of a variety of different mechanisms, ranging from energy audits and appliance standards to managing traffic congestion and improving the fuel economy of vehicles, to cut energy use and greenhouse gas emissions [20].

In terms of explicit support for solar PV, the SCS and Clean Energy Research and Test-bedding (CERT) program have been the most direct and influential followed by the creation of a clean energy research program and a clean energy program office (CEPO), along with a host of peripheral policies and programs.

1.06.3.2.1 Solar capability scheme

The SCS is a $20 million fund for nongovernment projects that provides a grant worth 30–40% of the capital cost for solar PV systems meeting formal criteria. It is capped at $1 million per project and requires that the building must achieve at least a Green Mark Gold certification by the Building Construction Authority, who recently introduced a Green Mark Scheme for landed properties. A minimum size of 10 kWp is required, putting it out of reach of most homeowners wanting to dabble in small-scale systems, but it has attracted many developers for commercial, industrial, and large-scale residential projects such as condominiums. **Table 2** presents a list of solar projects funded by SCS to date [21].

Table 2 Solar projects funded by the SCS, 2008–09

Name	Building type	System size (kilowatt-peak)
Applied materials manufacturing facility	Industrial	366
CDL Tampines Grande	Commercial	107
Lend Lease Retail 313@Somerset	Commercial	76
Lonza Biologics manufacturing facility	Industrial	181
Robert Bosch Southeast Asia HQ Building	Commercial	88

1.06.3.2.2 Clean energy research and test-bedding program

The CERT allocates $17 million to test-bed and integrate clean technologies making Singapore a 'field laboratory'. It was launched in August 2007 and primarily supports projects involving buildings and facilities of government agencies. It has so far funded a sizeable number of solar projects over the course of 2007–09, as described in **Table 3**. As of December 2009, the scheme has been fully apportioned.

1.06.3.2.3 Clean energy program office

Regulators established the CEPO as Singapore's key interagency working group responsible for planning and executing Singapore's strategy to become a clean energy hub. It was created in April 2007 to coordinate various research and test-bedding programs, including those of the National Research Foundation and Research, which identified clean energy as a key growth area for Singapore and announced a target of generating $1.7 billion of added value and 7000 jobs by 2015.

1.06.3.2.4 Clean energy research program

The clean energy research program has budgeted $170 million to accelerate R&D efforts to support the expansion of a clean energy industry in Singapore. It is a competitive funding initiative aimed at supporting 'upstream' and 'downstream' research efforts through demonstration projects. Most research projects to date have included a focus on solar energy, and $25 million has so far been awarded to research teams exploring thin-film PV and high-efficiency concentrator cells.

1.06.3.2.5 Other efforts

Indirect support for solar PV comes from a variety of areas, including BCA's Green Mark Award, which awards up to 20 bonus points for new commercial buildings that include solar PV. The EMA's Market Development Fund (MDF) also allocates $5 million to facilitate test-bedding of clean energy systems including solar PV, with support given for 5 years per project. The EMA and Building Construction Authority have also featured a series of PV system handbooks aimed at informing installers and homeowners about solar energy (see **Figure 5**).

Desiring to further support research on solar PV, the government launched the SERIS and hired Prof. Joachim Luther, former director of the Fraunhofer Institute for Solar Energy Systems in Germany, to lead it. SERIS will conduct industry-focused and application-oriented research on solar energy, aiming to become a 'world class' institute by working at the nexus of science and industry.

There is some evidence that these efforts are beginning to pay dividends. In January 2008, Oerlikon, the Swiss-based supplier of thin-film manufacturing equipment, chose to locate its Asian manufacturing hub in Singapore, and Norway's Renewable Energy Corporation (REC) has committed to establishing the largest solar manufacturing complex in the world there. The first phase of the REC facility involves $3 billion in investment and 1300 employees, and it will be producing silicon wafers, solar cells, and solar

Table 3 Solar projects funded by CERT

Name	System size (kilowatt-peak)
BCA Zero Energy Building	190
HDB Sembawang and Serangoon North	146
NParks Gardens by the Bay	TBC
PUB Marina Barrage	70
Singapore Polytechnic	47
Changi Airport Budget Terminal	250
Khoo Teck Puat Hospital	150
Ngee Ann Polytechnic	14
NEA Meteorological Services Building	25

TBC, to be confirmed.

Figure 5 Various Singapore handbooks for solar PV systems.

modules in early 2010. Once it is fully scaled up, REC intends to manufacture 1.5 GW of solar products in Singapore each year for global markets. The managing director of the Economic Development Board is hoping that the REC project will be "a queen bee to attract a hive of solar activities to Singapore" [22].

1.06.3.3 Challenges and Prospects for the Future

One challenge to solar PV penetration in Singapore is that the government is somewhat committed to fossil fuels. Singapore consumed 763 000 barrels of oil per day in 2005 but hosted crude refining capacity of 1.3 million barrels per day, making it one of the biggest refiners of oil in the world. In addition to three large refineries (ExxonMobil's Jurong/Pulau Ayer Chawan facility, Royal Dutch Shell's Pulau Bukom complex, and Singapore Petroleum Company's Pulau Merlimau refinery), Singapore also stores 112.4 billion barrels of oil and hosts the regional headquarters for many large oil companies. This has precipitated a general agreement amongst policymakers that oil and gas are intertwined with Singapore's future. When asked why Singapore has not decided to push more heavily for solar energy in 2008, one official working for the energy division of the Ministry of Trade and Industry explained that

> the core reason is economics. Gas-fuelled power generation is more competitive than oil-fired power generation (the primary source of electricity in Singapore before we started to switch to gas). Large scale renewable energy is not available to Singapore. Solar power is viable, but there are cost and technological issues, besides the issue of scale too. Coal power is cost competitive, but the environmental concerns need to be addressed. Therefore, we firmly believe fossil fuels will continue to be the best options for Singapore

(Research Interview at the Energy Division of the Ministry of Trade and Industry, 10 June 2008).

A secondary challenge concerns existing excess electricity capacity. Singapore only uses about 5200 MW worth of power plants to generate most of its power but has more than 10 200 MW installed. (Put another way, roughly 57% of capacity does not operate continually.) Because current installed electricity capacity in Singapore far exceeds existing peak demand, less incentive exists to push solar PV and other alternatives. Part of this is connected to the Asian financial crisis of 1997. Before the crisis, power plant operators, government planner, and nearly everyone else expected the Singaporean economy to grow much more rapidly than it did (along with almost every other Southeast Asian economy). Thus, developers committed to building a large amount of electricity capacity that was completed but has not yet been needed. If all existing power plants are taken into account, and assuming that electricity demand grows at a rate of 5% yr^{-1}, Singapore will not need to build any new capacity until about 2018. Given that a power plant that is already built is usually cheaper than one you have to build, such a large amount of excess capacity serves as a disincentive toward investing in more electricity supply, including solar PV and BIPV.

Third, the Singaporean government is generally wary of subsidies and support schemes. As one energy consultant working in Singapore explained, "there is a general belief in this country that decisions about energy should be left to the market, and that the market knows best" (Research interview with Andrew Symon, Asia Director for Menas Associates, 11 October 2008). As one executive of a solar company puts it (anonymous source)

> Many senior Singaporean policymakers recognize the potential of clean energy technology, and realize that PV is the best one applicable for Singapore. They understand that it needs some incentives to get going, because it is not yet ready to compete against established fossil-fuel based power generation. They suspect that feed in tariffs are the most efficient way of administering support because they replicate post-grid-parity market conditions and minimize government interference in the procedure. But they are not yet convinced enough of the short, medium and long-term economic value for Singapore to make a strong case for feed-in tariffs and the like. More conservative officials cannot let go of 1980s ideology that relies on pure market forces. They are prepared to be 'technology blind' and remove almost all administrative barriers to connecting solar PV units to the grid. But they refuse on principle to contemplate subsidizing it in any way, because that would violate their golden principle of not distorting the market. Never mind that the 'distortion' would be too small to measure, or could even bring net benefits to Singaporean customers and businesses.

The government is also hesitant to raise electricity prices through an FIT or other types of support schemes, since electricity rate increases are seen to hurt low-income families the hardest and to potentially jeopardize political relationships with Singaporean middle-class voters [23].

Overall, then, the future of solar PV in Singapore is uncertain. They have done an exceptional job attracting investments in solar PV manufacturing and in growing the local PV market from a few kWp in 2005 to 2000 kWp in 2009. Yet the government still lacks any type of sustained target for solar PV or renewable energy and has no FIT. The key challenge seems to be how to deploy more PV in Singapore and create incentives for residential and commercial users without raising electricity prices or creating subsidies. In the absence of any such support, it will remain unlikely that solar PV can compete commercially with conventionally generated electricity and unlikely to be widely embraced.

1.06.4 United States

1.06.4.1 Introduction

The market for solar photovoltaics in the United States is somewhat mixed. The US market is the fourth largest in the world, and the US Department of Energy (DOE) estimates that 65–75% of US water heating and about half of residential space heating needs could be met with solar-based energy [24, 46]. The DOE also estimates that solar PV erected on just 7% of the country's available roofs, parking lots, highway walls, and buildings (without substantially altering appearances or requiring currently unused land) could supply every kWh of the nation's current electricity requirements [26]. However, most PV capacity in the country is not integrated into buildings or configured for homes, but owned and operated by utilities and power providers in large and centralized installations, and more than 75% of US market for solar PV is in one state, California [27]. Although **Figure 6** shows that

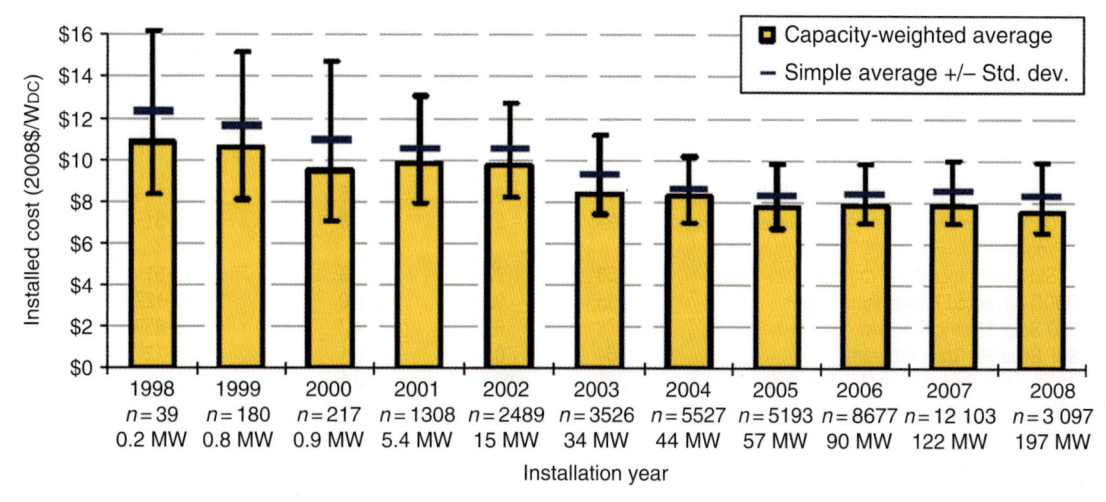

Figure 6 Installed solar PV costs in the United States, 1998–2008. Wiser R, Peterman GBC, and Darghouth N (2009) Tracking the Sun II: The installed cost of solar photovoltaics in the United States from 1998 to 2008. LBNL–2674E, February. Berkeley, CA: Lawrence Berkeley National Laboratory [28].

installation costs for solar PV systems in the United States have declined over time [28], the country has a total capacity of grid-connected solar of 478 MW, more than 100 times less than Germany [29].

1.06.4.2 Existing Support Schemes

Fixed-price incentives for solar energy have been around since the 1970s, although these early programs do not closely resemble modern FITs. The two most commonly mentioned historical policies are the Public Utility Regulatory Policies Act (PURPA) of 1978 and standard offer contracts in California.

As a consequence of the oil crises of the 1970s, PURPA was one of five statutes that were included in President Jimmy Carter's National Energy Plan as an attempt to reduce US dependence on foreign oil and vulnerability to supply interruptions and to develop renewable and alternative sources of energy. (For excellent summaries of PURPA, see References 30–32.) After the passage of PURPA, electricity suppliers were no longer able to hold a monopoly over power generation. PURPA enabled new actors, such as small power producers or 'qualifying facilities', to generate electricity on their own and forced the incumbent utilities to purchase this power at a reasonable fixed rate based on the 'avoided costs' to the utility. PURPA was a breakthrough in the sense that it opened the door to nonutility producers of power, although it did not catalyze widespread use of renewables because the 'avoided costs' were still too low, often ranging from a mere 2–5 ¢ kWh^{-1}. Despite its limitations, PURPA was perhaps the first major piece of legislation to offer a fixed payment to small-scale renewable power producers, and from 1980 to 1992 (before the next major legislative act relating to electricity was passed), about 40 000 MW of nonutility generating capacity was added to the country's grid [33]. The state of California, for example, implemented PURPA through standard offer contracts that saw the addition of 1200 MW of wind capacity between 1984 and 1994 [34].

Other states and utilities throughout the country have since experimented with 'performance-based incentive payments' to promote renewable electricity. Among the truly massive number of programs, the most significant ones are presented in **Table 4**; the programs were responsible for installing more than 52 000 systems constituting 566.3 MWp of capacity from 1998 to 2008. As just a few examples, Minnesota passed its 'Community-Based Energy Development Proposal' in 2005 to allow utilities to give wind projects within the state 5.5 ¢ kWh^{-1}, and the state of Washington signed a solar PV program into law that pays as much as

Table 4 Summary of state-level PV incentives in the United States [35]

State	PV incentive program	No. of systems	Total MWp	% of Total MWp (%)	Size range (kWp)	Year range
AZ	APS Solar & Renewables Incentive Program	912	6.2	1.1	0.4–255	2002–08
	SRP EarthWise Solar Energy Program	346	1.7	0.3	0.7–36	2005–08
CA	Anaheim Solar Advantage Program	69	0.3	0.1	1.4–18	2001–08
	CEC Emerging Renewables Program	27 947	146.4	25.9	0.1–670	1998–2008
	CEC New Home Solar Partnership	539	1.6	0.3	1.3–92	2007–08
	CPUC California Solar Initiative	11 533	146.7	25.9	1.2–1308	2007–08
	CPUC Self-Generation Incentive Program	796	144.9	25.6	33–1239	2002–08
	LADWP Solar Incentive Program	1 463	17.6	3.1	0.6–1200	1999–2008
	Lompoc PV Rebate Program	5	0.02	0.0	3.0–5.3	2008–08
	SMUD Residential Retrofit and Commercial PV Programs	170	1.0	0.2	1.3–97	2005–08
CO	Governor's Energy Office Solar Rebate Program	16	0.1	0.0	2.0–5.4	2008–08
CT	CCEF Onsite Renewable DG Program	66	5.6	1.0	1.6–480	2003–08
	CCEF Solar PV Program	557	3.1	0.5	0.8–17	2005–08
MA	MRET Commonwealth Solar Program	1 091	8.1	1.4	0.2–460	2002–08
MD	MEA Solar Energy Grant Program	230	0.8	0.1	0.5–45	2005–08
MN	MSEO Solar Electric Rebate Program	145	0.5	0.1	0.5–40	2002–08
NJ	NJCEP Customer Onsite Renewable Energy Program	3 167	54.2	9.6	0.8–702	2003–08
	NJCEP Solar Renewable Energy Credit Program	58	8.4	1.5	1.0–1588	2007–08
NV	NPC/SPPC RenewableGenerations Rebate Program	393	2.0	0.3	0.5–31	2004–08
NY	NYSERDA PV Incentive Program	1 158	7.2	1.3	0.7–51	2003–08
OH	ODOD Advanced Energy Fund Grants	35	0.3	0.0	1.0–122	2005–08
OR	ETO Solar Electric Program	878	6.6	1.2	0.8–859	2003–08
PA	SDF Solar PV Grant Program	164	0.7	0.1	1.2–12	2002–08
VT	RERC Small Scale Renewable Energy Incentive Program	225	0.8	0.1	0.6–38	2004–08
WA	Klickitat PUD Solar PV Rebate Program	5	0.01	0.0	0.3–3.0	2008–08
	Port Angeles Solar Energy System Rebate	2	0.004	0.0	1.4–2.7	2007–08
WI	Focus on Energy – Renewable Energy Cash-Back Rewards	386	1.7	0.3	0.2–38	2002–08
Total		52 356	566.3	100	0.1–1588	1998–2008

54 ¢ kWh^{-1} to produce solar electricity. California piloted a modest PV tariff in 2005 of 50 ¢ kWh^{-1} (funded out of their systems benefits charge), and Wisconsin, Vermont, and the Tennessee Valley Authority at the utility scale offer various types of fixed tariffs as part of their green power programs at the utility scale [36–41].

These state programs, however, do not have the key components that other successful FIT schemes do. Many are not based on the costs of solar energy generation and do not offer rates high enough to make investments in solar energy profitable. Most set caps on project size or cost. The majority do not differentiate tariffs by size of the project or type of technology. They are usually voluntary and do not guarantee access to the grid. And, crucially, they do not spread costs of the tariff amongst all customers, instead spreading it only amongst those willing to pay a premium. The Minnesota tariff for wind energy, for example, was initially limited to 100 MW, capped project size at 2 MW, did not have components guaranteeing interconnection and priority grid access, and did not mandate that utilities have to offer it.

The most significant mechanisms for driving renewables in the United States in recent years have included three state mechanisms, one federal mechanism, and one emerging tool: solar energy/portfolio standards, net metering, and green power programs at the state or interstate level; tax credits at the national level. A fifth mechanism, FITs, is just beginning to emerge at the local and state level.

1.06.4.2.1 Renewable portfolio standards

RPSs, sometimes called 'solar energy standards' or 'sustainable energy portfolio standards', are mandates for utilities to source a specific amount of their electricity sales (or generating capacity) from renewable sources (see References 42–44).

Efforts to mandate targets for renewable electricity generation at the federal level have been unsuccessful to date (as of printing). But, as noted above, more than half of US states have enacted RPS laws. Iowa was the first US state to pass such a policy in 1985, when legislation was enacted to

> encourage the development of alternate energy production facilities and small hydro facilities in order to conserve our finite and expensive energy resources and to provide for their most cost effective use [45].

The law mandated that utilities enter into power purchase agreements with solar energy producers and set the upper limit on aggregate purchases of solar energy at 105 MW. As of March 2009, 30 states and the District of Columbia had adopted some form of renewable electricity mandate or goal (**Table 5**).

Table 5 States with RPS, 2009

State	Amount	Year	Organization administering RPS
Arizona	15%	2025	Arizona Corporation Commission
California	20%	2010	California Energy Commission
Colorado	20%	2020	Colorado Public Utilities Commission
Connecticut	23%	2020	Department of Public Utility Control
District of Columbia	11%	2022	DC Public Service Commission
Delaware	20%	2019	Delaware Energy Office
Hawaii	20%	2020	Hawaii Strategic Industries Division
Iowa	105 MW		Iowa Utilities Board
Illinois	25%	2025	Illinois Department of Commerce
Massachusetts	4%	2009	Massachusetts Division of Energy Resources
Maryland	9.5%	2022	Maryland Public Service Commission
Maine	10%	2017	Maine Public Utilities Commission
Minnesota	25%	2025	Minnesota Department of Commerce
Missouri	11%	2020	Missouri Public Service Commission
Montana	15%	2015	Montana Public Service Commission
New Hampshire	16%	2025	New Hampshire Office of Energy and Planning
New Jersey	22.5%	2021	New Jersey Board of Public Utilities
New Mexico	20%	2020	New Mexico Public Regulation Commission
Nevada	20%	2015	Public Utilities Commission of Nevada
New York	24%	2013	New York Public Service Commission
North Carolina	12.5%	2021	North Carolina Utilities Commission
Ohio	12.5%	2025	Public Utility Commission of Ohio
Oregon	25%	2025	Oregon Energy Office
Pennsylvania	18%	2020	Pennsylvania Public Utility Commission
Rhode Island	15%	2020	Rhode Island Public Utilities Commission
Texas	5880 MW	2015	Public Utility Commission of Texas
Utah	20%	2025	Utah Department of Environmental Quality
Vermont	10%	2013	Vermont Department of Public Service
Virginia	12%	2022	Virginia Department of Mines, Minerals, and Energy
Washington	15%	2020	Washington Secretary of State
Wisconsin	10%	2015	Public Service Commission of Wisconsin

Early RPS mandates were intended to promote the development of solar energy technologies and diversify the fuels that America relies on for generating its electricity. As with other solar energy support mechanisms, policymakers meant for these regulations to correct three major failures of the existing market for electricity fuels: (1) electricity prices do not reflect the social costs of generating power; (2) energy subsidies have created an unfair market advantage for conventional fuels and technologies; and (3) solar energy is a 'common good' and thus is subject to a 'free rider' problem, enabling society at large to benefit from the investments of individuals without paying for them.

RPS policies provide electric utilities with choices similar to the way emissions control strategies implemented in the 1970s and 1980s worked to reduce lead pollution from refineries and chlorofluorocarbons from aerosols and in the 1990s lowered nitrogen oxide and sulfur dioxide emissions. Cap-and-trade policies set an upper limit for emissions for a given time period and emission limits declined over time. Polluters could either reduce their own pollution or buy certificates that represented emissions reductions beyond mandated targets. In a similar way, an RPS allows generators to generate their own solar energy, purchase solar energy from others, or buy credits. It therefore blends the benefits of a 'command and control' regulatory paradigm with a 'free' market approach to environmental protection.

While RPS mandates have done much to stimulate a market for renewable resources and spur additional research, they are not without problems. Impacts have varied from state to state depending on policy design and implementation, including what share of the market is affected and the existence or level of penalties for noncompliance. In addition, uncertainty about the bidding process and the future value of solar energy credits can increase risk for investors. RPS systems are best suited for large centralized plants, and they tend to promote the cheapest, most mature technologies (which is why some states have recently adopted solar 'carve-outs', see, e.g., [46]).

1.06.4.2.2 Net metering

Net metering enables owners of grid-connected renewable electricity systems to be credited for the electricity that they provide to the grid – in effect, to spin their meters in reverse. As of March 2009, net metering was available in 44 states plus Washington, DC (Note that four of these states have net metering programs that are offered voluntarily by one or more electric utilities.) [47]. Most states limit the aggregate capacity to a small percentage of a utilities' peak load. Also, in most states, producers are credited only up to the amount of electricity that they consume; any excess beyond the level of consumption goes to the utility. However, net metering has played a significant role in encouraging investment in distributed solar energy systems. Under two of the most successful net metering regimes, customers in California and New Jersey had installed more than 20 000 and 3000 distributed solar systems, respectively, by early 2008. Net metering has been described as "providing the most significant boost of any policy tool at any level of government...to decentralize and 'green' American energy sources" [48]. By compensating customers for reducing demand and sharing excess electricity, net metering programs are powerful, market-based incentives that states have utilized to promote solar energy.

One recent evaluation of state net metering programs found that the most successful programs did not set limits on maximum system capacity or restrictions on eligible renewable resources. These programs required that all utilities participate and included all classes of customers. They went hand-in-hand with interconnection standards and had little to no application fees, special charges, or tariffs [49]. As expected, since not all net metering programs meet these requirements, their effectiveness varies from state to state.

In addition, most metering programs only allow a 'credit' equivalent to the price of conventional electricity, therefore failing to reflect the full environmental benefits of solar energy. While net metering does tend to stimulate deployment of distributed solar energy systems at the residential and commercial scale, it does virtually nothing to promote large solar energy power plants. In no country has net metering managed to bring about a substantial shift in overall capacity to renewable resources. The explanation may be that the investment security for solar energy producers is relatively low compared with the fixed rates offered by FITs. We do not recommend linking the remuneration of solar energy projects to electricity prices because these prices will fluctuate. Net metering does not reduce or eliminate this form of uncertainty and volatility.

1.06.4.2.3 Green power programs

As of September 2008, more than 850 utilities in 40 states offered some type of green power program. While the numbers vary based on who does the counting, about 850 000 residential and commercial customers participated in these green power programs and purchased 18 TWh of electricity in 2007. Top municipal buyers of 'green power' included the city of San Diego, Austin Independent School District, and buying groups in Montgomery County, Maryland, New York State, and East Bay Municipal Utility District in California. Top commercial purchasers were the US Air Force followed by a list that includes Whole Foods Market, Johnson & Johnson, Starbucks, HSBC North America, University of Pennsylvania, and the World Bank Group.

Green power programs have two primary strengths. First, they have the advantage of allowing customers in places that do not have significant renewable resources to support the development of solar energy technologies elsewhere. Second, they do not impose the costs of solar energy on those that do not wish to pay for them.

These strengths, however, are offset by substantial weaknesses. First, green power marketing schemes provide no guarantee that additional solar energy capacity will be built. The most common experience with green power programs growing rapidly has been for program sponsors to cap or limit the program, not build more capacity. In 2005, for example, Xcel Energy and Oklahoma Gas & Electric quickly and fully subscribed their green power programs but then had to refuse to let additional customers participate.

Table 6 Number of utility green power participants for the 10 most successful programs, 2008

Rank	Utility	Program(s)	Participants
1	Xcel Energy	Windsource Solar Energy Trust	71 571
2	Portland General Electric	Clean Wind Green Source	69 258
3	PacifiCorp	Blue Sky Block Blue Sky Usage Blue Sky Habitat	67 252
4	Sacramento Municipal Utility District	Greenergy	45 992
5	PECO	PECO WIND	36 300
6	National Grid	GreenUp	23 668
7	Energy East (NYSEG/RGE)	Catch the Wind	22 210
8	Puget Sound Energy	Green Power Program	21 509
9	Los Angeles Department of Water & Power	Green Power for a Green LA	21 113
10	We Energies	Energy for Tomorrow	19 615

Similarly, Austin Energy was forced to implement a lottery when its GreenChoice product fell below standard electricity rates [50]. The lesson seems to be that green power program managers have little incentive to improve or expand their programs if they are already receiving a stable revenue stream from customers.

Second, green power programs rarely represent a significant fraction of energy use or electricity sales. For those programs run by electric utilities, participation rates rarely exceed 5%, and the most popular programs have never exceeded 20% [51]. Green power programs, in other words, are being used by a very small fraction of customers. In 2008, the top 10 largest green power programs, the ones with the highest participation rates, had only 398 488 customers enrolled (see **Table 6**). This number may sound impressive, but it represents less than half a percent of the nation's 120 million residential electricity customers. The problem here is that because green power programs are not mandatory, customers can opt for dirty and conventional electricity at cheaper rates and 'free ride' on the environmental benefits provided by those actually subscribing to the programs [52].

Third, green power programs, because they try to avoid charging consumers too much, tend to promote only the lowest cost renewable resources. Indeed, the programs in the United States have almost exclusively promoted large-scale wind farms, but not distributed solar panels, small-scale wind turbines, or other alternatives. In Europe, voluntary markets for green power have been primarily based on cheap hydroelectric power mostly produced and certified in Scandinavian countries and sold in central Europe.

Fourth, and ironic given the point above about keeping costs low, green power programs *do* tend to be more expensive than other policy mechanisms. This is because the programs need firms to certify credits, match buyers with sellers, track trades, and ensure no 'double counting' occurs (i.e., that the same credit is not used more than once). Some of these problems are discussed further below when talking about solar energy credits, but these extra transaction costs do add to the expense of green power programs. In 2009, for example, the average purchase price for wind electricity from a green power program in the United States was 9.1 ¢ kWh^{-1} [53] when the US DOE reports that the average cost of producing and transmitting that electricity was less than 7.0 ¢ kWh^{-1} [54]. This implies an extra cost of about 2 ¢ kWh^{-1} merely to manage the program.

Unfortunately, these extra costs mean green power programs are also the first to be cut during economic downturns. From 2007 to 2008, when the global economy was relatively healthy, local governments and municipalities increased their green power purchases by 200 GWh. From 2008 to 2009, in the midst of the global financial crisis, they increased their purchases by only 17 GWh. The City of Durango, Colorado, for example, used to buy electricity for all government buildings from green power programs, but the City Council canceled the program in 2009 to revert to electricity from coal plants to save money.

1.06.4.2.4 Tax credits

At the federal level, most support for solar energy has come in the form of investment and PTCs. ITCs provide a partial tax write-off to those who invest in a particular solar energy technology. PTCs, by contrast, provide the investor or owner of a qualifying property with an annual tax credit based on the amount of electricity generated by the facility during the course of a year. In the United States, this credit has been available to eligible wind, hydro power, landfill gas, municipal solid waste, and biomass facilities [35, 55].

The ITC currently covers up to 30% of the cost of a commercial solar or wind project and 10% of the cost of a geothermal project. It has tended to favor commercial installations. From the start of the credit until 31 December 2008, the ITC in the United States capped residential investments in solar energy at $2000 but had no upper limit for commercial installations, creating an asymmetry that heavily favored centralized and large-scale projects [56].

One drawback is that many homeowners and manufacturers lack sufficient income to use the ITC efficiently, since they must have all of the capital up-front for investment and can only claim the credit when filing for taxes [57]. Perhaps because of these reasons, ITCs have played a supplemental, but by no means primary or driving role in investment in solar PV [58].

In 2008, the PTC reduced the price of renewable electricity by about 2 ¢ kWh^{-1} (the initial credit was 1.5 ¢ kWh^{-1}, inflation adjusted) on a 20-year basis, in order to make investments in solar PV more attractive. To accomplish this incentive, however, the PTC also imposes a cost to US taxpayers in the form of displaced tax revenue. PTC disbursements amounted to about $4 million in 1995 but more than $210 million in 2004, and wind projects accounted for about 90% of all PTC-related tax credits [59]. A second shortcoming is that 90% of these expenditures were for one technology, wind, implying that the PTC does not promote diversification of the renewable resource base or investments in solar energy.

1.06.4.2.5 Feed-in tariffs

As of mid-2009, discussions for comprehensive FIT programs at the legislative or regulatory level were occurring in no less than 18 states (Figure 7): Arkansas, California, Florida, Hawaii, Illinois, Indiana, Iowa, Maine, Michigan, Minnesota, New Jersey, New Mexico, New York, Oregon, Rhode Island, Vermont, Virginia, and Washington.

The only formal FITs in the United States as of May 2009 were in Gainesville, Florida, and the state of Vermont. In Florida, the board of directors for the regional utility, the Gainesville City Commission, unanimously approved the creation of 'Solar Energy Purchase Agreements' in February 2009. The Gainesville FITs give eligible small solar projects (below 25 kW) 32 ¢ kWh^{-1} for the electricity they export to the grid and larger ground-mounted projects (greater than 25 kW) 26 ¢ kWh^{-1}, and they guarantee the rate for 20 years. Under the program, Gainesville regional utilities will purchase all of the electricity produced by these systems and then sell it back to residential and commercial customers for 12 ¢ kWh^{-1}. The tariff of 32 ¢ kWh^{-1} was designed to give investors in solar energy a 5% return on investment for larger projects. The difference in cost between the two tariffs will be paid for by all Gainesville utility customers, and it is expected that the extra costs will not exceed $4–5 per month (less than a large cup of Starbucks coffee; correspondence with Gainesville regional utilities official, 10 May 2009). The only caveat is that the Gainesville FIT does set a cap on total installations at 4 MW yr^{-1}, and even though the utility only serves 90 000 customers, the FIT has already been fully subscribed (Wilson Rickerson, correspondence with author, 22 May 2009) [60]. According to officials at Gainesville regional utilities, as of April 2009 the utility had received applications for more than 40 MW of solar PV capacity in their service area and have more or less booked projects through 2012 (Toby Courtre, correspondence with one of the authors, 24 May 2009).

Vermont became the first state to implement a full system of FITs in late May 2009, when they passed legislation (H. 446) altering the state's Sustainably Priced Energy Enterprise Development Program, or SPEED. The changes to SPEED provide FITs intended to cover generation costs plus a reasonable profit, with the costs of the program distributed by Vermont electricity ratepayers. The Vermont FITs provide long-term contracts for 20 years and provide a specific tariff for small-scale wind turbines less

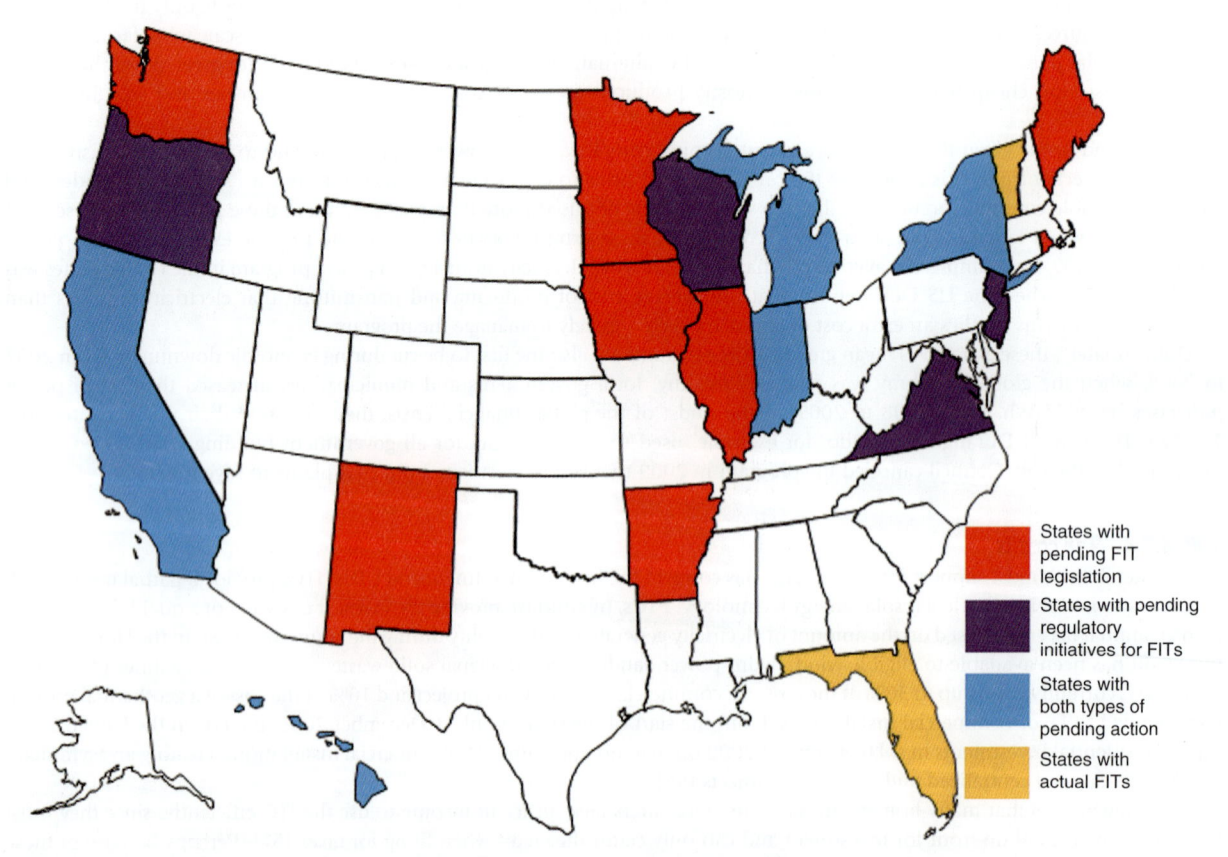

Figure 7 Locations in the United States with FIT legislation and/or regulatory initiatives (as of 2009).

Table 7 Vermont's recently enacted FITs

Program cap	50 MW
Project size cap	2.2 MW
Contract term	20 years
Rate of return	Profit set at same rate of return for Vermont electric utilities
Program evaluation	Every 2 years
Specific tariffs	
Wind energy < 15 kW	20 ¢ kWh^{-1}
Wind energy > 15 kW	14 ¢ kWh^{-1}
Landfill and biogas	12 ¢ kWh^{-1}
Solar	30 ¢ kWh^{-1}

than 15 kW (see **Table 7**). Tariffs are differentiated by technology and size, and the program will be reviewed periodically. The FIT legislation instructs the Vermont Public Service Board to review and reset the tariffs every 2 years to keep the program efficient. The executive director of Vermont, one of the groups that campaigned for the FITs, argued that "this law puts Vermont in a leadership role on solar energy policy and will help to bring vibrant growth and development to our local solar energy industry" [61].

State and city action has so far not been matched by serious commitment in the US Congress for an FIT at the federal level. In March 2008, representative Jay Inslee from Washington introduced a proposal for a national FIT under legislation named the 'Clean Energy Buy-Back Act', which was later renamed as the 'Solar energy Jobs & Security Act' (HR 6401) in June 2008. Inslee's proposal was backed by more than 70 solar energy companies and organizations, but never even passed committee in the US House of Representatives. Another federal bill was introduced in 2009 but would create tariffs *below* the avoided cost of generating electricity, hardly an FIT by our standards. Hopefully, as more cities and states enact their own FITs in the United States, that will start to change.

1.06.4.3 Challenges and Prospects for the Future

One challenge to investments in solar PV in the United States is the mismatch between government programs. For instance, federal research on solar energy systems has focused on centralized, large-scale, and utility-owned technologies whereas legislation has advanced decentralized, small-scale, and independently owned technologies. Legislations including the 1935 Public Utility Holding Company Act (PL 74-333), 1980 Wind Energy Systems Act (PL 96-345), 1984 Solar Energy Industry Development Act (PL 98-370), and provisions of the Energy Policy Act of 1992 (PL 102-486) were allowed to expire or never fully implemented. One study found that energy policy in the United States was the most inconsistent out of a sample of 17 countries [62].

Also, incentives for community ownership are largely absent in the United States. Large, investor-owned utilities and companies operate most of the country's renewable electricity capacity, and less than one-in-ten solar systems are used by ordinary people. Indeed, one recent study from the National Solar Energy Laboratory on the effectiveness of policy mechanisms for residential solar panels argued that policies have been completely ineffective at promoting small-scale, residential applications [63]. The United States also does not generally permit open market entry and access. Utilities and transmission operators have been able to oppose independent interconnection or access to the grid without extensive feasibility studies or exorbitant insurance rates.

As a broader financial constraint on the rapid uptake of solar PV in the United States, many homeowners simply do not have the resources to purchase their own solar panel. Connected to lack of capital is a concept known as the discount rate, or how consumers make investment decisions when they do have capital available. One study found a general aversion against solar PV systems in the housing market for precisely these reasons [64]. Such systems greatly add to the initial cost of purchasing a home. Moreover, when times are good and houses are selling well, builders and real estate agents view it as an indicator that alternative energy technologies are not needed to make sales. When times are bad, they place even more emphasis on minimizing costs and keeping house prices low. Homeowners also worry about project delays (and thus rising costs) associated with PV availability, installation scheduling, and utility interconnection. Builders believe that most homebuyers are not interested in PV, given its extra cost, and that many may even be opposed to it for concerns of aesthetics, maintenance, or reliability.

A recent 2008 study from the Harvard Business School is most telling here. After surveying hundreds of builders and contractors, given an extra $10 000 in construction budget to spend on discretionary items, more than 25% interviewed said they would do granite countertops while less than 15% said solar panels. The reasons had to do with the fact that granite countertops were perceived as less risky and more visible than solar panels [65]. The survey also found that consumers had unrealistic expectations about payback, many expecting a $4000 investment in solar PV to save more than 50% on monthly utility bills (when in reality it would tend to save 10–15%).

Political and regulatory obstacles play a role as well. One in-depth study of the 'red tape' involved in renewable energy projects found that systems installers frequently faced planners and building inspectors with little to no experience permitting solar PV systems [66]. The study noted that complex permitting requirements and lengthy review processes result in project delays and substantially add to the costs of projects. Multiple permitting standards across jurisdictions, such as competing or convoluted city, county, state, and national building codes, only add to the complexity. The study concluded that "these remaining bureaucratic hurdles stymie efforts by homeowners and business owners to install systems and hinder development of a national market for distributed renewable energy systems" [60].

1.06.5 European Union (Germany and Spain)

1.06.5.1 Introduction: Europe

Renewable energy promotion is at the core of EU energy policy in the twenty-first century. The European Union boasts the leading market for solar PV worldwide. There, legislation to increase the share of renewable energies was first implemented in the electricity sector. In 1996, the legislative process was initiated by the European Commission with the green paper on renewable energies [67] and the respective white paper a year later [68]. In the following years, a lengthy debate amongst the European institutions and the member states postponed the implementation of a European Directive several times. Finally, in 2001, the first Directive on the promotion of electricity produced from renewable energy sources (RES-e) was approved [69].

The Directive established indicative targets for all member states which amounts to the overall target of 21% of electricity consumption by 2010. Despite earlier efforts, no consensus was reached on mandatory targets, which would have required penalties in the case of noncompliance. This will be different under the new European Directive on renewable energies (2009/28/EC), which is setting the legislative framework for the years 2010–20. Besides the fact that in contrast to the Directive 2001/77/EC, now all sectors – electricity, heating/cooling, and transport – are included, the new Directive also includes mandatory national targets. Targets have proven to be important, as they signal long-term political commitment to investors. They indicate that support mechanisms will remain in place for a certain period of time and increase the likelihood of remuneration being sufficiently high.

Even though the Directive does not include specific targets for the electricity sector, member states will be obliged to issue so-called national action plans, including sector-specific targets and policy measures that will be taken to achieve the targets [70]. In line with the economic potential, the resource potential, and the already achieved potential, the European Commission has proposed and set targets for the EU member states (see **Table 8**).

Table 8 Share of energy from renewable sources in EU member states (2005 and 2020 targets)

	Share of energy from renewable sources in gross final consumption of energy, 2005 (S_{2005}) (%)	Target for share of energy from renewable sources in gross final consumption of energy, 2020 (S_{2020}) (%)
Belgium	2.2	13
Bulgaria	9.4	16
Czech Republic	6.1	13
Denmark	17.0	30
Germany	5.8	18
Estonia	18.0	25
Ireland	3.1	16
Greece	6.9	18
Spain	8.7	20
France	10.3	23
Italy	5.2	17
Cyprus	2.9	13
Latvia	32.6	40
Lithuania	15.0	23
Luxembourg	0.9	11
Hungary	4.3	13
Malta	0.0	10
The Netherlands	2.4	14
Austria	23.3	34
Poland	7.2	15
Portugal	20.5	31
Romania	17.8	24
Slovenia	16.0	25
Slovak Republic	6.7	14
Finland	28.5	38
Sweden	39.8	49
United Kingdom	1.3	15

Source: EU (2009) Directive 2009/28/EC of the European parliament and the council of 23 April 2009 on the promotion of the use of energy from renewable sources and amending and subsequently repealing Directives 2001/77/EC and 2003/30/EC. *Official Journal of the European Union* L 140/16 [70].

1.06.5.2 Support Mechanisms

Neither in the realms of the Directive 2001/77/EC nor during the negotiations of the current renewable energy framework Directive 2009/28/EC has consensus been reached on a harmonized European support scheme. According to the principle of subsidiarity, member states, therefore, have the right to implement the support mechanism of their choice.

In the European Union, essentially two support mechanisms have been applied to foster the electricity generation from renewable energy sources (RES-e): TGCs and FITs. The latter are currently established in 22 member states and are based on the payment of a (fixed) tariff in combination with a purchase obligation (price-based support mechanism). Only six member states make use of quota obligations. The FIT design in two especially successful countries will be discussed in the following section, the case studies Germany and Spain.

Even though the development of solar PV in Germany and Spain largely depended on the establishment and amendment of nationally implemented FITs in the 1990s and 2000s, market development was first stimulated by other support mechanisms. Similar to Singapore and the United States, European countries started promoting solar PV with R&D initiatives and investment subsidies. These were the primary support mechanisms for renewable electricity in the 1970s and 1980s. Especially in Germany, solar PV profited from extensive market development programs, including investment subsidies and state-drive soft-loan programs.

The German 1000 roof program for photovoltaics from 1989 granted investment aid of 60–70% of total costs. It was successful but did not lead to similar market development as in the case of wind energy because of the small market volume [72]. In January 1999, the new Red-Green coalition wanted to further enhance support for the PV market by setting up a 100 000 roof program. The new program was intended to breach the time gap between the finalized 1000 roof program and a new FIT law. The program intended to promote the installation of 100 000 photovoltaic plants with an average capacity of 3 kW. By those means, the installed capacity was to increase to 350 MWp by 2003 [73]. The program consisted of preferential financing conditions for private persons, self-employed people, and small and medium-sized companies. They were able to profit from a nominal interest rate of 1.9% p.a. over 10 years. The maximum amount of credit was limited at €6.500 kW^{-1} [74].

Only in 2003, additional support mechanisms in terms of investment subsidies and soft loans faded out. At the same time, the FIT level was increased significantly so that all costs could be covered by tariff payment alone. However, in the 1990s more and more European countries moved toward FITs for promotion of renewable electricity – nowadays the major success factors for the leading role of European countries in solar PV promotion. As FITs have proven to be the most successful support instrument, in the following section we are going to explore general design features of successful FIT legislation, including specific examples from Germany and Spain. (Further design options, which have not been implemented in Spain or Germany, will not be discussed in this chapter. For a more detailed description of all FIT design options, including design options for developing countries and emerging economies, see Reference 14.)

1.06.5.3 Germany

Germany was one of the first countries to set up an FIT scheme (only Portugal started at an earlier stage in 1988, see Reference 75) and can therefore be considered a forerunner with respect to innovative renewable energy policy [76]. The country started its support of electricity from renewable energy sources at the start of the 1990s. The Feed-in law (Stromeinspeisegesetz) established the major characteristics of a German FIT policy: a fixed tariff payment and a purchase obligation on the grid operator. Thereafter, the policy tool was amended several times. The FIT scheme was substantially changed in 2000 by passing the Renewable Energy Source Act (Erneuerbare-Energien-Gesetz). Subsequently, the support mechanism was amended periodically, every 4 years, in 2004 and 2008. The next amendment is expected to enter into force in January 2012.

Nowadays, Germany is the largest market for solar PV in terms of totally installed capacity. In 2008, the total installed capacity increased by 1.9 GW to about 5.3 GW. In 2009, about 3.8 GW was added and in 2010 about 7.4 GW. As of January 2011, the total installed PV capacity in Germany was about 17 GW – more than half of the worldwide installed capacity (see **Figure 8**; data based on BMU [77]; BSW [78]; Fulton *et al.* [79]).

Besides a robust support mechanism, the German market also relies on good financing opportunities and low interest loans provided by the state bank KfW, good availability of skilled PV companies, and a high degree of awareness of solar PV technologies [80].

1.06.5.4 Spain

The first major impulse for the development of electricity generation from renewable energy sources in Spain derived from Law 82/1980 on Energy Conservation [81]. The intention for promoting renewable energy sources at that time was clearly to diversify the energy portfolio and to reduce energy import dependency. At that time, environmental issues did not yet influence the political agenda in the energy sector [82].

The RD 2366/1994 on electricity produced by hydro sources, cogeneration, and RES [83] established basic contractual relations between the RES-e producer and the distribution companies. The 1994 legislation can be considered being the first feed-in style support mechanism in Spain. For the first time, fixed tariffs were set depending on technology and plant size. The technology differentiation, however, was relatively modest. The RD 2366/1994 established one overall tariff for almost all renewable energy technologies and a slightly lower tariff for biomass and municipal solid waste. The tariff payment was related to the average

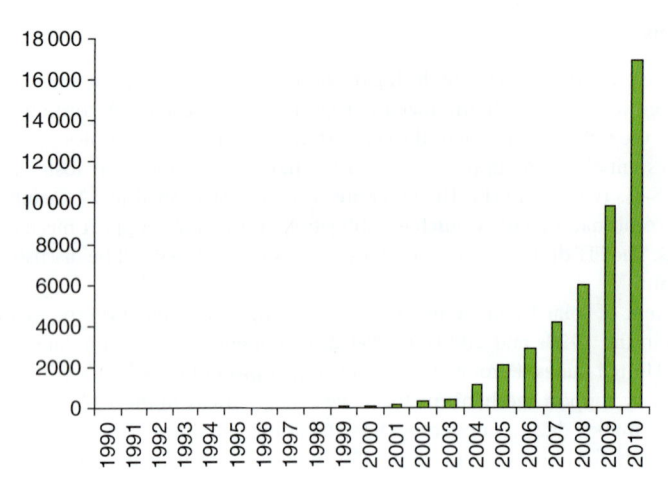

Figure 8 Installed solar photovoltaic capacity (MW) in Germany (1990–2010).

electricity price, which was established via a national decree on an annual basis. The RD 2818/1998 [84] can be seen as the turning point in the Spanish RES-e policy, since for the first time all RES-e regulations were gathered in a single piece of legislation, including fixed or premium tariffs for different technologies. (The Spanish FIT scheme only grants tariff payment for installations with a maximum capacity of 50 MW. This limitation is historically grounded. In the past, it was believed that renewable energy could only cover a small share of the electricity mix and that, by definition, renewable energy power plants had to be small-scale and decentralized installations. The recent experience in many countries, however, contradicts these assumptions. Even though the decentralized application is still one of the major advantages of renewable energies, the development in wind energy shows that wind farms with several hundred megawatts of installed capacity are feasible and economically viable. Large-scale plants are also expected for other technologies, such as PV, solar thermal, geothermal, and biomass)

A major revision of the Spanish FIT scheme took place in 2007. The RD 661/2007 was implemented after a lengthy debate between various Spanish actors, including the Ministry, the renewable energy associations, and the National Energy Council CNE. As a consequence, the decree entered into force almost 1 year later than expected [85]. The changes in the year 2007 have become necessary because of the rapidly increasing share of renewable power. However, the growth of the renewable energy sector as a whole was driven by very few technologies, mostly wind power. Other technologies, including biomass, biogas, and solar thermal power, were still far from reaching the 2010 targets as set out in the Spanish renewable energy plan. Therefore, tariff for these technologies needed to be increased.

In 2007, the target for solar PV set out in the National Renewable Energy Plan was reached. In September 2007, the MITYC issued a resolution which prolonged the payment period of the tariff for 1 year [86] – as it was foreseen by the RD 661/2007. At the same time, the Ministry of Industry started to work on transitional decree for the years 2008–10. Therefore, a new Royal Decree for solar PV was issued in 2008. The new Royal Decree RD 1578/2008 attempted to slow down market expansion [87]. Within the previous decree, the targets as set out in the Renewable Energy Plan PER have been exceeded by far. Under the new Royal Decree, tariffs for PV were reduced by 20–30%.

In Spain, the market development is traditionally limited by short- and mid-term caps, for example, targets determined by the National Plans for Renewables (PER). The Royal Decree for solar PV 1578/2008 has, for instance, limited newly installed capacity to 500 MW annually, whereas 233 MW is reserved for free-standing PV systems. This annual cap is increased by 10% every year. Even though Spain has a long tradition in regulating the newly installed capacity of renewable energy sources – the first national plan for the development of renewable energy sources was issued in the 1990s – the Spanish renewable energy industry wanted to avoid the cap by implementing flexible degression (see below). However, the tariff level, which in the case of some solar PV applications offered internal rates of return far above the envisaged 7%, forced the legislator to take drastic measures to control the costs by implementing a capacity cap (The Spanish Minister of Industry, Sebastián, stated that in 2008 alone, PV would cost Spanish taxpayers €800 million. In 2009, the figure could rise to more than €1.3 billion, see Reference 88.). It has been estimated that profits in Spain were about 50% higher than in Germany. Therefore, some observers have argued that the Spanish renewable energy industry itself was partly responsible for the implementation of a cap by calling for the highest possible tariffs in the first place [71].

Further changes were implemented in 2010 and came into effect in early 2011. Due to considerable cost reduction of solar PV systems and modules, the legislator further reduced the tariff payment via RD 1565/2010. The tariff for small-scale, roof-mounted systems was reduced by 5% and the tariff for larger-scale, roof-mounted systems by 25%. The remuneration for free-standing solar PV systems was reduced by 45%. Besides, the legislator tried to further avoid windfall profits by limiting the number of operating hours a PV producer is remunerated for. In very sunny areas, for instance, the maximum number of reference operating hours per year has been fixed at 1232 equivalent hours per year. If a solar PV system in this area should produce more electricity, the exceeding part will no longer be remunerated according to the FIT but instead according to the wholesale market price.

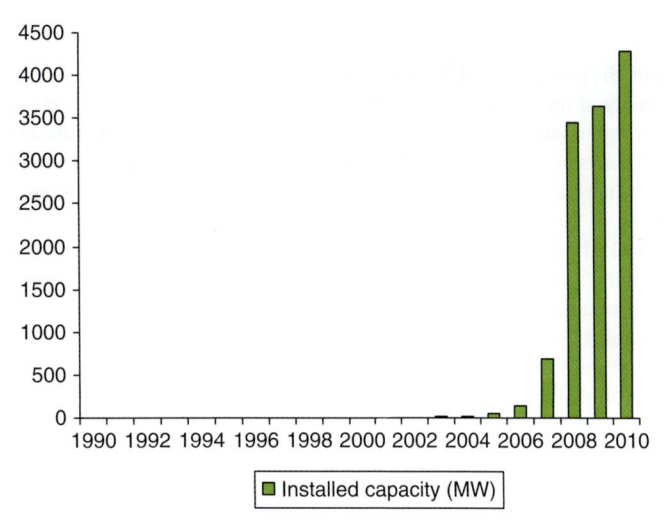

Figure 9 Installed solar PV capacity in Spain (1990–2010).

Still, at the end of 2008, the Spanish market was the second biggest worldwide. This was almost exclusively due to enormous market growth rates in the years 2007 and 2008. In 2008 alone, the installed capacity increased by more than 2.5 GW, reaching 3342 MW by the end of 2008 (see **Figure 9**, data based on CNE 2011 (CNE publishes all data from the so-called special regime on a monthly basis, see Reference 89)).

The extraordinary market growth in 2007 and especially 2008 was not only due to the high level of remuneration but also due to market distortions caused by the capacity limit as set out by the National Renewable Energy Plan. (The Spanish experience with very high growth rates of PV is also a showcase of 'negative' learning amongst European member states. A report of the French parliament stated that the objective of the French support scheme should be to control the growth of the PV sector and avoid 'anarchic growth' as it was experienced in Spain in 2007 and 2008, see Reference 90.) There was literally a race in the construction of PV plants in order to still be eligible under the significantly higher remuneration of RD 661/2007. An equity research institute estimated that the Spanish FIT scheme is almost "twice the value of funds received under the German solar subsidy program" [91]. After the capacity cap was reinforced in 2008, the market collapsed in 2009. Only 188 MW capacity was newly installed. In 2010, the Spanish market grew by 661 MW.

1.06.6 Common Features of Best Practice Promotion Schemes

This part of the chapter identifies 11 common elements of best practice FIT promotion schemes. It draws largely from examples from Germany and Spain, since these countries were amongst the first European countries to implement an FIT scheme. Following Portugal in 1988, Germany implemented FIT legislation in 1990 and Spain followed 4 years later. Both countries are still operating with this type of support instrument today and are therefore the two countries worldwide with the longest experience. (Other countries that have implemented FITs before, like Portugal and Denmark, have also experienced with other support instruments over the years.) Over the years – Germany is now working with an FIT mechanism for two decades – the complexity of the system has increased significantly. In Germany, for instance, the number of chapters of the FIT legislation increased from 5 chapters in 1990 to 13 chapters in 2000, 21 chapters in 2004, and even 66 chapters in 2009.

As both countries are leading in the promotion of renewable energy technologies and their support framework has frequently been identified as international best practice (For an analysis of FIT design options, please refer to Reference 92.) [14, 92–94, 96, 97], in the following the detailed design of the FIT in Germany and Spain will be analyzed. (The analysis of FIT design options in Germany and Spain is largely based on the PhD project of David Jacobs, which is sponsored by the German Federal Environmental Foundation (DBU) and will be published by Ashgate in 2012.)

When designing FITs, the idea is to provide a balance between investment security for producers, on the one hand, and the elimination of windfall profits (in order to reduce the additional costs for the final consumer), on the other hand. We isolate 11 separate factors common to successful FITs, supported by examples mostly from Germany and Spain. In order to increase investment security, the legislator has to (1) clearly define eligible producers, (2) establish a purchase obligation, (3) set up a clear and transparent tariff calculation methodology, and (4) guarantee tariff payment for a long period of time (duration of tariff payment). Additionally, (5) a robust financing mechanism needs to be established and (6) the success of the national FIT evaluated periodically (progress report). In order to decrease the costs for the final consumer, (7) policymakers can differentiate tariff payment according to the technology or (8) the size of power plants and the type of installations. Furthermore, (9) tariffs are generally reduced automatically on an annual basis (tariff degression) but (10) at the same time adjusted to inflation. More recently, (11) legislators have established a number of design options for market integration. All these design options are presented in this section.

1.06.6.1 Eligible Producers

At the start of each legal document, the policymaker defines which technologies will be eligible under the FIT mechanism. This decision generally depends on the availability of resources in a given country. To this respect, legislators often start with establishing national solar maps. Not all FIT schemes promote solar PV. Some developing countries have chosen to focus on the least costly renewable energy technologies. Kenya, for instance, has established an FIT scheme for small hydro, biomass, and wind energy in 2008 [98].

In most cases, including Germany and Spain, FIT schemes support a large basket of renewable energy technologies. As technology-specific support is one of the major advantages of FITs over other support mechanisms – e.g., quota-based support mechanisms such as RPS and TGC schemes – this generally also includes less mature and more expansive technologies, such as geothermal, tidal power, and solar PV. As an FIT mechanism can be considered a tool for technology development and cost reduction, the promotion of less mature technologies today enables us to use them in a cost-effective manner tomorrow. By supporting both fluctuating technologies, for example, wind energy and solar, and technologies that are more firm, for example, biomass, solar thermal, geothermal, and hydroelectric, the legislator can pave the pathway toward an energy system fully based on renewable energy sources [99]. Technology-specific support is necessary because of the large differences in generation costs amongst renewable energy technologies.

However, some countries or regions have chosen to promote exclusively solar PV with the FIT scheme. This is the case in jurisdictions where other support mechanisms are in place for the promotion of other technologies. In Italy, for instance, renewable energy technologies are promoted via a quota-based mechanism. As solar PV is more expensive than most other renewable energy technologies, they cannot be supported with a technology-neutral support instrument. Therefore, the Italian legislator has established an FIT exclusively for solar PV electricity producer. An FIT scheme for only one technology such as PV, however, includes certain risks which are most of all related to public acceptance. As the electricity costs for PV are significantly higher than that of conventional energy sources and other renewable energy technologies and the amount of electricity produced is comparatively small, the additional costs as distributed by financing mechanisms might seem rather high to the final consumer. In contrast, if a large portfolio of technologies is eligible under the FIT legislation, the average cost for one unit of renewable electricity is rather low. To a certain extent, more mature technologies such as wind power will help less mature technologies such as PV to be developed. In this way, public acceptance can be strengthened.

1.06.6.2 Purchase Obligations

Besides fixed tariff payment over a long period of time, the purchase obligation is one of the most important 'ingredients' for all FITs as it assures investment security. It obliges the nearest grid operator to purchase and distribute all electricity that is produced by renewable energy sources, independent of power demand. This means that, for instance, in times of low demand, the grid operator will reduce the amount of 'gray' electricity while all 'green' electricity is incorporated into the electricity mix. The purchase obligation is especially important for more variable renewable energy technologies, such as wind and solar PV, as the producer cannot control when the electricity will be generated. In contrast, gas- and coal-fired and nuclear-based power plants can increase and reduce output, along with hydroelectric dams, biomass facilities, and geothermal power stations.

The purchase obligation protects renewable electricity producers in monopolistic or oligopolistic markets where the grid operator might also dispatch power generation capacity. When it comes to electricity dispatch, when decisions are made concerning which power generation sources are used to meet electricity demand, such grid operators might be biased and dispatch power from power plants other than their own first. Therefore, the German legal text (Section 8, paragraph 1 of EEG 2009) states that the "grid system operators shall immediately and as a priority purchase, transmit and distribute the entire available quantity of electricity from renewable energy sources …" [100].

In Spain, the purchase obligation only applies for renewable energy producers who have chosen to be remunerated under the fixed tariff payment option. In the case of a premium FIT, for example, selling electricity on the spot market and receiving a reduced FIT payment on top of it (see further below), the renewable electricity producers are subject to the same conditions as any other electricity producer. In other words, the selection of power plants for meeting the hourly electricity demand depends on the short-term generation costs (the merit order). As solar power does not require any sort of fuel except sunlight (which is for free), the short-term generation costs are close to zero so that these technologies will always be accepted first in the merit order. Only if there is a risk of grid instabilities, these renewable energy sources might not be taken into consideration by the system operator.

1.06.6.3 Tariff Calculation Methodology

The tariff calculation methodology is one of the most crucial aspects when designing an FIT scheme. The methodology indirectly determines the level of remuneration for each technology. A tariff that is too low will not spur any investment in the field of renewable energies while a tariff that is too high might cause unnecessary profits and higher costs for the final consumer. In Germany and Spain, the methodology changed significantly over the period from 1990 to today.

In the 1990s, both Germany and Spain used a tariff calculation methodology which was based on the avoided costs for conventional power generation. Therefore, less mature technologies such as solar PV could not profit from the national FIT scheme in the same way as other technologies. Besides, in both countries the tariff level was determined as a percentage of the price of conventionally produced electricity.

In December 1990, German legislators passed an act on feeding renewable energy into the grid, in its *Stromeinspeisungsgesetz* (StrEG) [101]. According to this new law, beginning 1 January 1991, utilities in Germany were required by law to purchase electricity from nonutility generators of renewable energy at a fixed percentage of the retail electricity price. The percentage ranged from 65% to 90% depending on the technology type and the project size.

Similarly, the early Spanish FIT scheme of 1994 and the previous regulation for hydro power generation [102] based tariff calculation on the avoided cost for conventional power generation. The RD 2366/1994 even explicitly states that the tariffs for power feed into the grid should "take the avoided costs of the electricity sector into account, based on the concept of power generation, transport and distribution" [103]. Spain's Law of the Electricity Sector in 1997 [104] established prices for RES-e that ranged between 80% and 90% of the average retail price. Exceptions, that is, higher tariffs, were only possible for solar PV plants.

In the following years, both Germany and Spain (as well as most other countries which have been successful in promoting renewable electricity) have switched toward a tariff calculation methodology based on the generation costs of each technology. These FIT schemes offer a tariff payment based on the generation costs plus a small premium and thus offered sufficient returns on investment. In order to describe this methodology, different names have been used in Germany and Spain. While the German support scheme is based on the notion of 'cost-covering remuneration', the Spanish support mechanism speaks of a 'reasonable rate of return'. Despite the variety in names and notions, in all cases the legislator sets the tariff level in order to allow for a certain internal rate of return, usually between 5% and 10% return on investment per year.

This 'generation cost' tariff calculation methodology generally takes a number of common cost factors into account. This includes investment costs for each plant (including material and capital costs), grid-related and administrative costs (including grid connection cost, costs for the licensing procedure, etc.), operation and maintenance costs, fuel costs (in the case of biomass and biogas), and decommissioning costs (where applicable). Based on these cost factors, the policymaker can then calculate the nominal electricity production costs for each technology. Knowing the average operating hours of a standard plant and the duration of tariff payment, the legislator can fix the nominal remuneration level. For the estimate of the average generation costs, regulators can use standard investment calculation methods (such as the annuity method). The Spanish legislator even obliges renewable electricity producers to disclose all costs related to electricity generation in order to have optimal information when setting the tariff.

In Germany, this method of 'cost-covering remuneration' was first implemented on the local level in the case of solar PV in 1993. The cities of Freising, Hammelburg, and Aachen established an FIT scheme for solar PV, which allowed for full cost recovery. In the coming years, these early local FIT schemes became the role model for many other communities and later regions. In 1999, the Red-Green coalition decided to implement this scheme at the national level and apply the approach of cost-covering remuneration to all renewable energy technologies [105]. In 2000, the level of FITs was already exclusively based on the cost-covering remuneration approach (kostendeckendeVergütung) in order to guarantee sufficient returns on investment.

In 2000, a transparent, national tariff calculation methodology was developed. This methodology is used by the German Ministry for the Environment (BMU) for the initial tariff proposal in the framework of the so-called progress report. This report is issued every 4 years and serves as the base for the periodical revision of the FIT scheme. It has to be noted, however, that the initial tariff proposal of the BMU is sometimes changed during the consecutive political decision-making process. In contrast to many other countries, the German FIT scheme has the legal rank of a law – in contrast to Royal Decrees or Ministerial Orders. Therefore, the initial proposal of the Ministry has to pass the government and the parliament and might therefore be subject to modifications.

For the setting of the tariff, both the Ministry for the Economy and the Ministry for the Environment commission studies that are conducted by various independent research institutes. In addition, wide-ranging surveys on costs are conducted amongst producers of renewable electricity. The results are cross-checked with published cost data and empirical values from project partners of the ministries. In this way, the Ministry evaluates the average generation cost of plants. To finally determine the tariff level, several basic data and parameters are compiled. Generally, tariff payment is guaranteed for 20 years. For the tariff calculation of solar PV, the interest rate for capital is set at a nominal basic value of 5–8%. The expected annual inflation is 2%. The costs for specialized personnel and the expected annual operating hours are also taken into consideration. The detailed assumptions and data are summarized in **Table 9** (BMU [106]).

The German Ministry of the Environment applies this 'annuity method' to calculate the electricity generation costs for all renewable energy technologies except wind energy. This method of dynamic investment calculation allows for translating one-off payments and periodic payments of varying amount into constant, annual payments. All costs for renewable electricity generation are calculated on a real basis, adjusting them to inflation based on a specific reference year.

Besides the above-mentioned parameters, further input variables have to be taken into account for the specific cost calculation. This includes output data of average plants which are currently in operation, the purchasing costs for fuel in the case of biomass and biogas, investment cost (machinery, construction, grid connection, etc.), and operation costs (see **Figure 10**). Because of the unique regulatory environment in Germany, special investment cost subsidies from financial institutions are not included in the calculation, and the German FITs are based on pretax calculations.

Even though the electricity law of 1997 can be interpreted as a first step from the 'avoided cost' approach toward the 'generation cost' approach in Spain, the shift toward a tariff calculation approach based on the generation cost of each technology was triggered by the National Energy Commission CNE. In 2003, the CNE tabled a proposal for an objective methodology for tariff calculation which was sent to the Ministry of the Economy [107]. The methodology was applied for the first time for the FIT scheme of 2004 [108]. The tariff calculation methodology of the CNE was clearly based on a generation cost approach. For each technology, the generation costs consisted of three components (A + B + C). In the case of the premium FIT option, the generation cost minus the expected market price determines the premium tariff level.

Table 9 Summary of basic data and parameters used for profitability calculation

	Hydropower	Biomass	Landfill, sewage, and mine gas	Geothermal	Wind	Photovoltaics
Imputed period under review	30 a/15 a	20 a	Basic case: 20 a (6 a variant for landfill gas)	20 a	Basic case: 20 a (variant 16 a)	20 a
Nominal composite interest rate	Small plants 7%/a Large-scale plants 8%/a	8%/a	8%/a	8%/a	Variation within sector 5–8%/a
Inflation rate	2%/a					
Remuneration for heat (for CHP; ex-plant)	Basic case: € 25/MWh (Variation within sector € 10–40/MWh)					
Specialist personnel costs	€ 50 T per person-year					
Equivalent operating hours at full capacity of electricity-led plants	Dependent on degree of utilization	7700 h/a	Landfill gas 7000 h/a, sewage/mine gas 7700 h/a	7700 h/a	Dependent on conditions at location	
Equivalent operating hours at full capacity of heat-led plants	–	Dependent on model case	–	–	–	–

Source: BMU (2008) Depiction of the methodological approaches to calculate the costs of electricity generation used in the scientific background reports serving as the basis for the renewable energy source act (EEG) progress report 2007, extract from renewable energy source act (EEG), progress report 2007, Chapter 15.1 [106].

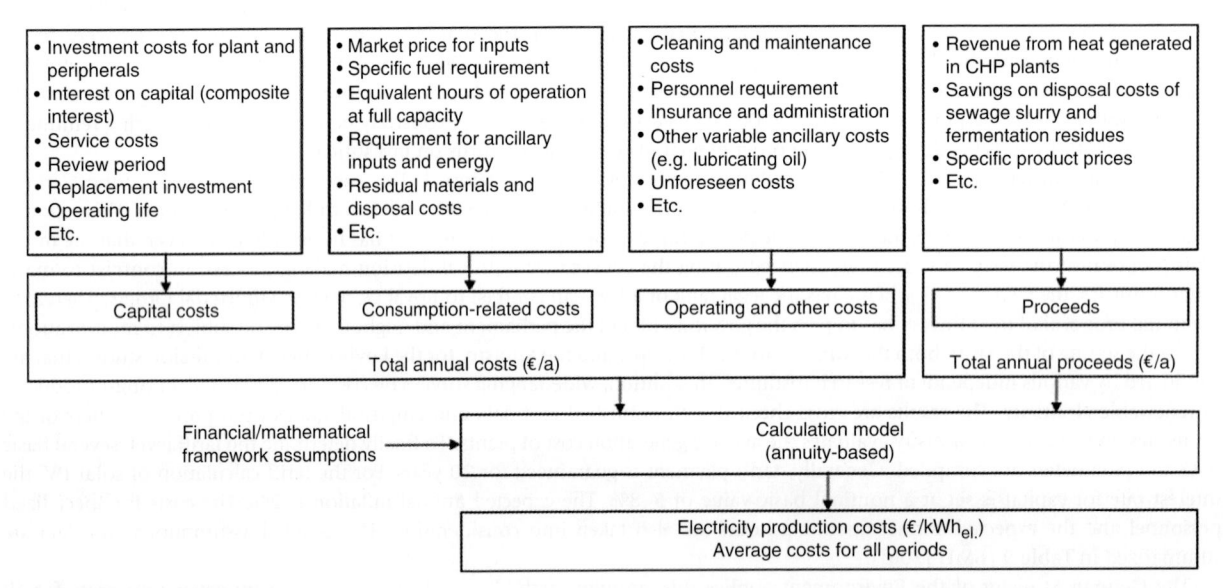

Figure 10 German methodology and input variables for calculating electricity production costs. Source: BMU (2008) Depiction of the methodological approaches to calculate the costs of electricity generation used in the scientific background reports serving as the basis for the renewable energy source act (EEG) progress report 2007, extract from renewable energy source act (EEG), progress report 2007, Chapter 15.1 [106].

Component A shall guarantee reasonable profitability for renewable energy projects, taking the generation costs and specific requirement of each technology into account. The income for power producers shall provide an internal rate of return of free cash flow after tax similar to a regulated financial activity. On average, the Spanish FIT levels are based on an internal rate of return of 7%. In the case of the Premium FIT option, the profitability varies between 5% and 9%, depending on the market price (Tembleque L (2008) personal communication, interview with Luis Jesús Sánchez de Tembleque, CNE, 13 February 2008, Madrid.)

The calculation model takes into account the operation hours per year, the performance of reference plants, the economic lifetime of projects and amortization period for investments, the investment costs, the tax burdens and benefits, the income from regional support programs, and the operation and maintenance costs (fuels, O&M costs, costs for insurance, rentals for land use, etc.). Component B assesses the additional energetic and environmental benefits of each reference plant. This additional component can increase the internal rate of return (IRR) of renewable energy projects. In order to determine the additional benefits, the national, technology-specific midterm objectives are compared with the actual growth rates of each technology. If the comparison shows that the target will be reached or even overfulfilled, no additional payment is granted based on component B. If one technology is underdeveloped and the technology-specific midterm targets will not be reached, then component B would consist of an additional payment which is to increase the IRR by X, a certain number of percentage points. In how far this applies to setting FITs can be observed within the Royal Decree 661/2007. When it became apparent that some technologies – including biomass, biogas, and concentrated solar power (CSP) – were still far from reaching the 2010 target, their tariffs were increased to a point that an average profitability margin of 8% was guaranteed (compared with 7% for all other technologies) [109].

Finally, component C is to measure the impact of the different technologies on the technical management of the electricity grid. Component C only includes those aspects which are not explicitly remunerated by additional tariff payments. This includes the capacity to participate in the national electricity market and the forecast of electricity generation. It only applies to power producers who opt to sell their electricity under the premium FIT (see below). In 2004, component C was taken into account by offering an additional incentive for participation in the power market (10% of the average electricity price) [110].

1.06.6.4 Duration of Tariff Payment

Fixing the payment duration is equally important for a good FIT mechanism. The duration of the tariff payment is closely related to the level of tariff payment. If a legislator desires a rather short period of guaranteed tariff payment, the tariff level has to be higher in order to assure the amortization of costs. If tariff payment is granted for a longer period, the level of remuneration can be reduced. FIT mechanisms around the world usually guarantee tariff payment for a period of 10–25 years, while a period of 15–20 years is the most common and successful approach. A payment of 20 years equals the average lifetime of many renewable energy plants. Longer remuneration periods are normally avoided because otherwise technological innovation might be hampered. Once tariff payment ends, the producer will have a stronger incentive to reinvest in new and more efficient technologies instead of running the old plant in order to keep receiving tariff payment.

In Germany and Spain, in the 1990s, tariff payment was only guaranteed for a short period of time of 1 year. Even though power purchase agreements were sometimes longer (in Spain generally 5 years), tariffs were subject to annual changes. This made financing of renewable electricity plants difficult. At this time, the remuneration for renewable electricity producers was linked to the retail electricity price. In Germany, retail electricity prices started to fall in the first years after the liberalization of energy markets and thus did the remuneration for renewable power producers [111]. Therefore, the 2000 amendment for the first time guaranteed fixed prices over a period of 20 years for all technologies except hydro power. In Spain, a long payment duration of at least 20 years was guaranteed from 2007 onward.

1.06.6.5 Financing Mechanism

The costs of generating electricity from renewable energy sources are still higher than in the case of conventionally produced electricity. Therefore, countries operating under FIT mechanisms have developed different financing mechanisms in order to cover the additional costs. In almost all countries, the additional costs are distributed equally amongst all electricity consumers. This financial burden-sharing mechanism permits the support of large shares of renewable electricity with only a marginal increase of the final consumer's electricity bill.

In this case, the national government only acts as a regulator of private actors in the electricity market by determining tariff payment and establishing the purchase obligation. However, no government financing is included under these conditions. In order to pass the price from the producer of renewable electricity to the final consumer, the costs, that is, the aggregated tariff payments, must be passed along the electricity supply chain. This is how it is done in Germany.

First, the producer of renewable electricity receives the tariff payment from his or her local grid operator. By legal obligation through the FIT scheme, this grid operator is obliged to pay, connect, and transmit the produced electricity. Normally, renewable electricity producers get connected to the next distribution system operator (DSO). In some cases, however, a producer of a large plant might also decide to connect directly to higher voltage lines, through the transmission system operator (TSO). Afterward, the costs and the accounting data are passed to the next highest level in the electricity system until the national TSO aggregates all costs and divides it by the total amount of renewable electricity produced. The costs are then equally distributed amongst all national supply companies in relation to the total amount of electricity provided to the final consumer (see **Figure 11**, from Jacobs and Kiene [112]). This way, all final consumers pay the same for the total amount of renewable electricity produced in a given territory.

In Spain, financing of the FIT mechanisms is also largely through a small increase of the electricity price of the final consumers. However, as the Spanish electricity market is not fully liberalized, electricity prices for certain consumer groups are still regulated by governmental authorities. Therefore, costs related to electricity generation, transportation, and distribution and other costs related to the electricity system are not fully passed on to the final consumers. The resulting 'gap' between the actual costs of the national electricity system and the income through selling the power leads to a national deficit, which has to be covered by the state budget. According to estimates of the Spanish Energy Council CNE, the electric deficit has accumulated to more than €15 billion between 2000 and 2008 [113]. This is one of the reasons why the Spanish government decided to keep the cap for solar PV as the national electricity deficit was to be reduced.

In 2009, a securitization fund was established (*Fondo de Titulización del Déficit del Sistema Eléctrico*). This fund is intended to enable power companies to recuperate the money they cannot charge to final consumers – the so-called tariff deficit. The money for the fund will be raised via the costs of the Spanish electricity system that eventually have to be paid by the final electricity consumer. For

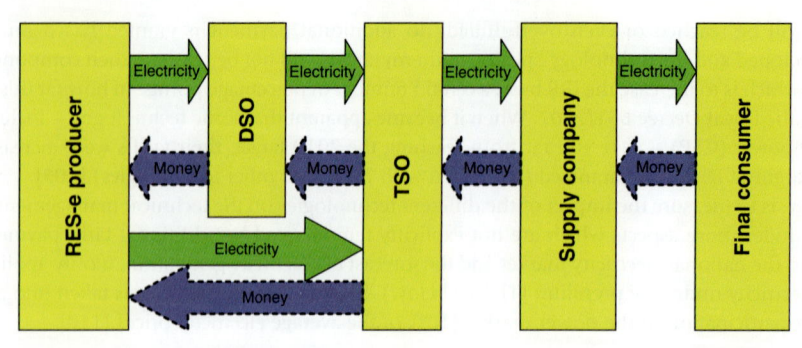

Figure 11 Flow of financing and electricity under the German FIT scheme. Reproduced with permission from Jacobs D and Kiene A (2009) Renewable energy toolkit – Promotion strategies in Africa. *World Future Council*, May 2009 [112].

2009–12, the electricity system deficit was expected to increase further as retail electricity prices are still regulated. However, the Royal Decree 6/2009 had already established annual upper limits for the new deficit. From 2013, electricity prices will have to reflect power generation costs and will no longer be regulated. Refinancing the existing tariff deficit has to be finalized by 2028. In other words, refinancing today's electricity deficit will result in higher future prices for the final consumer, when retail electricity prices will no longer be regulated. It should be noted, however, that the FIT mechanism in Spain is not financed via the general national budget [114].

An increase in the electricity price, even though it is minor, can have severe negative effects on some consumer groups. This might be especially the case for energy-intensive industries, where sometimes up to 80% of total production costs are energy related. Since these companies are often subject to international competition, exemptions from the general financing scheme have been incorporated in Germany. It has to be noted that environmental NGOs have often criticized this exemption as it reduces the necessity for the electricity-intensive industry to lower consumption. Besides, these consumer groups are often able to profit from preferential electricity tariffs anyway.

From 2004, German companies with a total electricity consumption of more than 100 GWh and total electricity costs exceeding 20% of the gross added value were partly exempt from renewable electricity support under the FIT. The increase of the electricity price due to the FIT payment was limited to 0.05 €cent kWh^{-1}. In the first years, only 40 companies profited from this exemption. In 2006, the criteria were loosened (10 GWh consumption and 15% of the gross added value), and almost 400 companies were exempt. Due to the exemption of these industries, the additional cost for all other electricity consumers increased by 17% in 2007 [115]. After the 2009 amendment, producers who wanted to become eligible for the financing exemption had in addition to prove and certify that energy-saving and energy efficiency measures had been adopted.

1.06.6.6 Progress Report

A periodic evaluation of the state and progress of FIT programs is crucial for long-term success. The Spanish and German FIT schemes, for instance, are modified every 4 years. This periodic revision guarantees stability for the producers, who know that the legislation will not be changed in the meantime, but it also gives politicians room for modifications.

Besides, Germany is evaluating the success of the national support scheme within periodically published progress reports. Reporting and evaluation are usually the task of the responsible ministry. They will ensure that the law is functioning well, and if necessary, how it could be improved or amended. In Germany, for instance, progress reports provide the scientific grounds for periodic amendments of the national FIT schemes. The Spanish and German FITs are modified every 4 years. This periodic revision guarantees stability for the producers, who know that the legislation will not be changed in the meantime, but it also gives politicians room for modifications.

Progress reports typically include an analysis of the growth rates and the average generation costs of all eligible technologies. They identify the economic, social, and environmental costs and benefits of renewable energy support (especially an estimate of greenhouse gas reductions). They review the additional costs for the final consumer. And they calculate the ecological effects of renewable energy plants, positive and negative, on nature and landscape.

1.06.6.7 Tariff Differentiation According to Plant Size

Besides technology-specific support, FIT schemes in Germany and Spain also differentiate the tariff payment according to the size of power plants. The underlying idea is that larger plants are generally less expensive due to economies of scale. Therefore, the FIT legislation sets specific tariffs for a particular technology in relation to plant size. The easiest way is to establish different groups according to the installed capacity. In Germany, tariff differentiation for solar PV installation depends on the following plant size groups:

0 kW < 0 kW < Tariff/Price ≤ 30 kW
30 kW < Tariff/Price ≤ 100 kW
100 kW < Tariff/Price ≤ 1000 kW
1000 kW and above

The choice for the range of each group does not necessarily have to be random. Many technologies offer standard products of a certain size range. In the case of PV, for instance, a typical rooftop installation for private households has a capacity of 3–30 kW. Larger-scale rooftop installations for industrial buildings or farms usually have an installed capacity of up to 100 kW. Therefore, an analysis of standard products of a certain technology in a given region or country will help to set plant size-specific tariffs. In order to avoid potential disruptive effects through size categories, the legislator also has the option to develop a formula which relates the plant size to the tariff payment. In Spain, the new Royal Decree for PV of 2007 also implemented size-specific tariffs. For roof-mounted PV systems, different tariffs are paid for installation of small 20 kW and larger 20 kW capacities. Besides, free-standing PV systems receive a flat-rate tariff.

1.06.6.8 Tariff Differentiation According to Plant Type (Location)

FITs can also be differentiated according to the location of the installed PV module. Generally speaking, there are three types of tariffs for solar PV depending on the location of the module. Free-standing PV systems are located on the ground, modules can be screwed on top of buildings (roof mounted), or they can be architecturally integrated (building integrated). Some countries focus on building integrated PV (BIPV) modules as they wish to minimize the visual impact. (With 25 €cent kWh^{-1} extra for building integrated solar PV modules, France has set up one of the most attractive markets for this segment in Europe. Clearly, the choice of promoting BIPV system was based on the intention to minimize the visual impact of solar PV modules in the most popular tourist destination worldwide.) The precise definition of the location of modules varies from country to country.

In Germany and Spain, higher tariffs are paid for roof-mounted PV systems. Until 2009, Germany even had an additional tariff payment of 5 €cent kWh^{-1} for BIPV modules. In Germany, there have also been discussions on granting a bonus tariff payment for thin-film PV modules, as they were considered to be an innovation in contrast to standard modules. Finally, however, the legislator decided to be technology neutral within this one technology area in order to avoid market interventions at an early stage of technological development. This avoided 'picking a winner' and directing technological development in a certain direction without sufficient information about the future potential of each of these technological options.

1.06.6.9 Tariff Degression

Germany was the first country to implement tariff degression. Tariff degression means that tariffs are reduced automatically on an annual basis. It was meant to both anticipate technological learning and provide an incentive for the industry to further improve renewable energy technologies. The cost reduction potential of renewable energy technologies is based on economies of scale and technological innovation. In the last decade, the generation costs for wind and solar power, for instance, dropped by over 60%.

This reduction, however, only affects new installation. In other words, once a power plant is installed, the tariff payment remains constant over a long period of time despite tariff degression. If the legislator decides to amend the FIT legislation periodically, for example, every 4 years, tariff degression allows for automatic reduction of the remuneration rate in the meantime without the negative effects of a lengthy political decision-making process. For instance, in 2009, a solar PV plant in a given country might be granted a tariff of 30 €cent kWh^{-1} for the following 20 years. Assuming an annual degression rate of 10%, the tariff payment for installations connected in 2010 will only be 27 €cent kWh^{-1}. Therefore, tariff degression also stimulated investors to speed up the planning process: the sooner you get connected to the grid, the higher will be the tariff payment for the power plant.

In line with the remaining learning potential of each technology, a low or a high degression rate is fixed by the legislator. Relatively mature technologies, such as wind energy, have either a very low degression rate or no degression rate. In Germany, for instance, the tariff is automatically reduced by 1% every year. Technologies whose generation costs are still declining rapidly will need to have a higher degression rate. The degression rate in Germany for solar PV can be up to 10% yr^{-1}. In **Table 10** you can find the full list of German degression rates for the different technologies as of 2009 (from Mendonca *et al.* [14]).

Table 10 Tariff degression rates under the German FIT scheme as of 2009

Renewable energy technology	Annual degression rate (%)
Hydro power (more than 5 MW)	1
Landfill gas	1.5
Sewage treatment gas	1.5
Mine gas	1.5
Biomass	1
Geothermal	1
Wind power offshore	5 (from 2015 onwards)
Wind power onshore	1
Solar PV	8–10

From Mendonca M, Jacobs D, and Sovacool B (2009) *Powering the Green Economy – The Feed-In Tariff Handbook*. London, UK: Earthscan [14].

In 2008, both Germany and Spain had implemented a design option into their respective FIT schemes, which links the degression rate to the market growth of a given technology. (This section is largely partly based on Reference 116.) In both cases, the new regulation only effected solar PV, a technology with a large potential for future cost reduction.

As described above, the cost reduction potential of a certain technology is partly due to economies of scale. If the installed capacity in a given country increased significantly, one can expect production costs to decrease simultaneously. Besides, the installed capacity and deployment rate for a given technology are a good indicator of whether the tariff level is too high or too low. In the case of unnecessarily high tariffs, producers will have a strong incentive to invest, and national objectives might even be exceeded. Thanks to the flexible degression, tariffs will be lowered automatically. In the case of low tariffs, the newly installed capacity will decline or come to a complete standstill. The implementation of the flexible degression feature will automatically lower the annual degression rate and spur investments again.

In Germany, the maximum deviation from the standard degression rate is only ±1%. The legislator fixed a predefined pathway of market growth until 2011, expecting the installed capacity to reach 1500 MW in 2009, 1070 MW in 2010 and 1900 MW in 2011. Depending on the actual installed capacity in those years, the degression rate can either be reduced or increased, as shown in **Table 11**.

The concept of flexible degression was further elaborated with the amendment of 2010. Under the new regulation, the government targets an annually installed capacity of 3.5 GW. If the market overshoots this target, the tariff will be lower by one additional percentage point for each GW. In other words, up to an installed capacity of 4.5 GW, the degression rate will increase by 1% point, up to 5.5 GW the degression rate will increase by 2% points, and so on. In 2011, the maximum additional degression due to market growth is limited to 4%. In 2012, the maximum degression rate will be 24% (see **Table 12** [99]).

Similarly, the Spanish legislator operates with a predefined pathway of market growth. However, the Spanish mechanism is even more complicated as the degression adjustment occurs every 4 months and not just once a year.

Initially, the Spanish PV association ASIF had proposed a mechanism linking the degression rate directly to the market growth, as it shows clearly how the degression rate could be linked to market growth [117]. The ASIF proposal envisaged a standard degression rate of 5% in the case of a 20% market growth. The deviations from this standard degression are shown in **Table 13**.

The ASIF proposal had two primary objectives. First, the extreme market growth of the years 2007 and 2008 had to be stopped in order to allow for a sustainable market development. Second, the PV industry wanted to avoid a total capacity cap, as it was proposed by the Spanish Industry Ministry MITYC. Unfortunately, the second objective could not be achieved.

Table 11 Flexible degression under the German FIT scheme according to the 2009 amendment

Additional capacity in 2009	Deviation from standard degression rate
Less than 1000 MW	Minus 1%
Between 1000 and 1500 MW	No deviation
More than 1500 MW	Plus 1%
Additional capacity in 2010	Deviation from standard degression rate
Less than 1100 MW	Minus 1%
Between 1100 and 1700 MW	No deviation
More than 1700 MW	Plus 1%
Additional capacity in 2011	Deviation from standard degression rate
Less than 1200 MW	Minus 1%
Between 1200 and 1900 MW	No deviation
More than 1900 MW	Plus 1%

Source: Jacobs D and Pfeiffer C (2009) Combining tariff payment and market growth. *PV Magazine*, pp. 220–224. May 2009 [116].

Table 12 Flexible degression under the German FIT scheme according to the 2010 amendment [90]

Scenario (GW)	MW to be installed in 2011 (projected)	Total (%)
Base case	3500	9
+1	4500	12
+2	5500	15
+3	6500	18
+4	7500	21
>+4	>7500	24

Table 13 Flexible tariff degression as proposed by the industry association ASIF (Spain)

Market growth (%)	Degression rate (%)
≤ 5	2
10	3
15	4
20	5
25	6
30	7
35	9
≥ 45	10

Source: Jacobs D and Pfeiffer C (2009) Combining tariff payment and market growth. *PV Magazine*, pp. 220–224. May 2009 [116].

In contrast to the ASIF proposal which was based on market growth, the degression rate for PV in Spain is linked to the installed capacity. To make this work, the legislator established a preallocation register for projects that were to become eligible for tariff payment. The major difference to the German legislation is that the implementation of flexible degression is combined with a capacity cap.

The new legislation, Royal Decree 1578/2008, establishes trimestrial capacity limits for the different types of PV systems, that is, small-scale rooftop installations (≤ 20 kW), large-scale rooftop installations (≥ 20 kW), and free-standing PV systems. For the year 2009, the tariff payment was limited to an overall capacity of 400 MW. More precisely, two-thirds (267 MW) is allocated to rooftop installations (of which 10% is reserved for small-scale installations) and the remaining 133 MW to dedicated free-standing PV systems. The producers who will sign up first in the registry will be granted tariff payment (first come, first served).

Tariff degression takes place if the installed capacity in the previous trimester exceeds 75% of the target. In this case, the tariff is reduced according to a given formula. Applying the formula, the total achievement of the target in one trimester would lead to a maximum tariff degression of 2.6% every 4 months. Tariffs might also increase according to the same formula. This happens if on two consecutive trimesters, not even 50% of the target is achieved.

Adjustments were announced for the first time in February 2009. Mostly due to administrative problems, the applications in the first quarter of 2009 did not reach 75% of the reserved capacity for rooftop installations. Therefore, the tariffs remained at 34 ¢ kWh^{-1} (small scale) and 32 ¢ kWh^{-1} (large scale) for the second quarter of 2009. However, tariffs were reduced for free-standing PV installations from 32 to 30.72 ¢ kWh^{-1} as more than 75% of the allocated capacity was reached. Further tariff reduction for free-standing PV systems took place in the following rounds. In mid-2010, the tariffs had already fallen to 32.19 €cent kWh^{-1} for small-scale roof-mounted systems, 28.68 €cent kWh^{-1} for larger-scale roof-mounted systems, and only 25.86 €cent kWh^{-1} for free-standing systems [118].

Flexible tariff degression can help to control market growth in rapidly expanding markets and thus limit the extra costs for final consumers. Ideally, this design option allows for a market development along a predefined growth path. In this case, an overall capacity cap in order to control costs would be needless. At the same time, drastic cuts in tariff payment could be avoided.

In both Germany and Spain, the primary proposal was significantly changed during the political decision-making process. Those modifications were implemented rather hastily. Therefore, the concept of flexible degression still needs to be improved during the coming amendments of national FIT schemes. In Germany, the variation in degression should be increased to several percentage points, as a variation of only 1% can have limited effect on market growth. In Spain, the capacity cap should be removed, since a well-designed 'flexible degression' scheme can help to control market growth and thus the additional system costs.

1.06.6.10 Inflation Indexation

The general lifetime of renewable energy power plants is in the range of 20–30 years (except hydro power), although efficiencies may dip in later years. Under good FIT schemes, the time for full cost recovery and paying all debts usually takes 15–20 years. As indicated above, tariff payment is generally guaranteed for 15–25 years.

As a matter of fact, such long-term investment projects are very sensitive to inflation effects. Therefore, it might be necessary to adjust tariff payment to annual inflation. This is especially important for countries with a high annual inflation rate, as after several years the 'real' remuneration rate will be significantly lower than the nominal rate as fixed by the FIT scheme. Inflation indexation generally affects both old and new installations.

In Spain, the legislator has decided to only partly adjust tariffs to inflation. Until December 2012, the tariffs are adjusted annually to the inflation index minus 25%. From 2013 onward, the tariffs will be adjusted to the national inflation index minus 50%. This leads to minor tariff degression for existing plants.

Germany is not explicitly adjusting tariffs to the annual inflation. However, when studying the German tariff calculation methodology in detail, it becomes clear that the inflation is implicitly taken into account. The relevant document indicates that an average inflation of 2% is factored in when calculating FITs in Germany (see above). Regarding the fact the inflation rate in Germany has been in this range and stable over decades, this is a feasible alternative to indexing tariffs explicitly. In most other countries, forecasting the inflation rate for the coming 15–20 years is, however, difficult.

1.06.6.11 Design Options for Better Market Integration

For better integration of renewable electricity into the conventional energy market, Germany and Spain have implemented a number of FIT design options. The most prominent design option is certainly the premium FIT. Premium FITs have first been implemented in Spain in 1998. The premium, or 'market-dependent' [119], tariff was also implemented by Denmark, Slovenia, the Czech Republic, Italy, Estonia, Argentina, and the Netherlands. Finland also plans to implement this remuneration option and Germany is still discussing it.

Under a Premium FIT, the remuneration for a green electricity producer consists of two elements: the general, hourly market price of electricity on the conventional power markets and a reduced tariff payment, which has to be sufficiently high to allow for reasonable profitability of renewable energy projects. This combination of two remuneration components makes it harder for the legislator to fix the FIT for each technology as market prices are fluctuating. The development of the market price has to be anticipated in order to avoid windfall profits (in the case of high market prices) and guarantee sufficient returns of investment (in the case of low market prices).

The Spanish legislator found that anticipating market prices is extremely difficult. Therefore, in 2007, the Spanish premium FIT scheme was complemented by a 'cap' and a 'floor'. The cap impedes the combined remuneration to exceed a certain limit in the case of high market prices while the floor prevents the remuneration falling below a minimum threshold in the case of low market prices. For onshore wind power, for instance, the premium was fixed at 2.9 €cent kWh^{-1}. The combined tariff payment (market price plus premium tariff) cannot exceed 8.5 €cent kWh^{-1} and cannot fall under 7.1 €cent kWh^{-1}. In 2010, the lower limit was fixed at 2.01 €cent kWh^{-1} and the upper limit at 9.17 €cent kWh^{-1} (RD 1614/2010).

Due to the fact that one part of the remuneration – the market price – is volatile, the investment security for the renewable electricity producer is lower than in the case of the normal fixed tariff option. This risk factor makes renewable energy projects slightly more expensive, as banks normally demand higher interest rates to compensate for such insecurity. Therefore, when calculating the tariffs, the expected return on investment has to be slightly higher under the Premium FIT option. To give you an example, the Spanish legislator calculated the tariffs based on 7% returns on investment under the fixed tariff option and 5–9% under the Premium FIT option.

For the moment, solar PV is still exempt from participating under the Spanish premium FIT option. This is mostly due to the (currently) relatively small share of solar PV in the total electricity portfolio (and thus the limited need to integrate solar PV into the gray electricity market) and the relatively large cost difference between one unit of electricity from solar PV and the Spanish spot market price (Samaniego MJ (2008) personal communication, interview with Mª José Samaniego Guerra, MITYC, 27 February 2008, Madrid).

In Spain and most other countries, premium FITs are implemented as an alternative option to the fixed tariff payment (and not a substitute for it). Without the alternative of a fixed tariff option, many potential renewable electricity producers might be excluded from the support scheme, especially private persons and small and medium companies. As a matter of fact, a private person with a small PV system on the roof will not be willing to engage in selling electricity on the spot market with all transaction costs that would be included. The same might be the case for community wind farms. On the contrary, large players and especially utilities are already experienced when it comes to selling electricity on the market. They will certainly opt for this remuneration option, especially when the expected rate of return is slightly higher.

The combination of two remuneration options forces the policymaker to decide on to what extent producers will be allowed to switch between both options. In Spain, producers have the chance to switch between both remuneration options on an annual basis. In Germany, a monthly change has been envisaged by the legislator. The policymaker should be careful when deciding upon these changes, as too short periods might incentivize 'cherry-picking'. In times with high market prices, producers will opt for the Premium FIT while in times of low market prices everyone changes back to the fixed tariff option.

Germany is also discussing the implementation of a premium FIT. However, the implementation of a premium FIT is opposed by certain actors in the German renewable energy business, including all renewable energy industry associations. The opponents fear a competitive advantage of large-scale utilities, which are engaged both in the power generation business and in grid operation. However, effective ownership unbundling (the strict separation of power producers and grid operators) is one of the essential prerequisites for establishing a premium FIT. Only this way fair grid access for renewable energy producers can be guaranteed. This is necessary as under the premium FIT green power producers can no longer rely on a purchase obligation (see above). Therefore, it is important that the grid system operator is not biased when dispatching power units.

Alternatively to the premium FIT, Germany discussed a different approach for better integrating renewable electricity into the conventional market: a special tariff payment for combining various renewable energy technologies. As the share of renewable electricity increases, it will become more and more important to improve the 'quality' of the green electricity, that is, the ability for renewable supply to match demand. In order to guarantee steady and demand-oriented electricity supply in the future, it will be necessary to combine different renewable energy technologies, for example, wind energy and biogas. Therefore, FITs can offer additional financial incentives to foster this combination of technologies. Accordingly, the German renewable energy association (BEE) proposed the so-called 4000 full load hours approach or integration bonus.

On average, wind power plants in Germany operate for 2000 full load hours annually. Through the combination with other technologies, such as biomass, hydro power, or other storage technologies, the total amount of full load can be doubled and, more importantly, electricity output can be planned. According to the calculations of the BEE, an additional tariff of 2 €cent kWh^{-1} could cover the related costs.

1.06.6.12 Challenges and Prospects for the Future

In the previous sections, best practice examples from Germany and Spain were elaborated. Despite the impressive record of renewable energy promotion in these countries, not all European countries are as successful in supporting renewable electricity. However, over the last couple of years, a process of mutual learning took place amongst European legislators. As all countries of the European Union are now confronted with binding targets for renewable energy sources by 2020, national legislators will have an even stronger incentive to look into best practice policies from other European countries such as Spain and Germany.

The experience from some countries with FITs shows that, even though they have good economic and grid access conditions, generation capacity for renewable electricity does not increase significantly. Despite having the best designed FIT scheme, the reasons for mediocre performance can include administrative barriers such as long lead times for project approval and a high number of involved authorities (see References 120, 121). Besides, European Commission recommends implementing quicker permitting procedures for small-scale projects because they differ fundamentally from large-scale coal-fired power plants [122]. It makes little sense to force both types of projects to go through the same permitting process. The most nefarious administrative barriers appear related to lead times, coordination, and spatial planning.

However, in the European Union, the major noneconomic barrier is long lead times. In the EU, lead times for small-scale hydro power development vary from 12 months (Austria) up to 12 years (Portugal and Spain). In France, wind power developers sometimes have to wait for 4–5 years to move from a project outline to electricity production. The same is the case for offshore wind power projects in Ireland. Policymakers can reduce this barrier by establishing a time limit on the entire permitting process, including all necessary documents from all organizations that are involved. National and local entities will be forced to deal with project permissions in time, and organizations opposed to renewable energies will lose 'teeth' when it comes to noneconomic barriers. Setting deadlines for the decisions of each authority will help, as long as authorities can keep to them. Especially on a local level, administrative bodies often lack experience in dealing with industrial-size projects. Complexity can be further reduced by clarifying the responsibilities of each authority. Most successful are those countries that authorize one single administrative body (a one-stop-shop organization) to deal with all subordinated authorities at different political levels. This approach was proposed by the European Commission in the framework of the New Directive for Renewable Energies.

With respect to the promotion of solar PV in Germany, in Spain one of the major challenges will be to control the costs for the final consumer. Germany is (still) the only market worldwide where the expansion of the solar PV market is not limited by some sort of capacity cap. However, the market growth in Germany in 2008, 2009, and 2010 has exceeded the envisaged scenario of the responsible ministry, thus putting pressure on national legislators to take action. As shown above, one design option to adjust tariff payment automatically to market growth is flexible degression. Contrary to other countries with capacity caps, Germany is trying to manage volume success with price responses.

1.06.6.12.1 Managing volume success with price response
In the future, Spain and Germany will also be confronted with more competition with other markets in the world. Especially the United States, Japan, South Korea, and other European countries will have a larger share in the worldwide installed capacity. On the one hand, this development might lead to a more evenly distributed world market and might therefore lead to a more sustained development. On the other hand, the creation of national markets in other countries with better sunshine conditions might encourage manufacturers to move their production capacity to other parts of the world than Germany.

1.06.7 Conclusion and Outlook

In the previous section we have analyzed the support instrument for solar PV in Singapore, the United States, Germany, and Spain. We have shown that R&D spending might create a market for several demonstration projects (see Section 1.06.3). However, in order to attract private financial resources, additional tax and investment incentives are necessary to create (at least) a niche market for solar PV (see Section 1.06.4). To create large-scale gigawatt markets the only proven support mechanism by now is FITs (see Section 1.06.5). This correlation between market size and the choice of support instruments is shown in **Figure 12**.

But what will follow FITs? Grid parity – the moment when solar PV generation costs equal the price of electricity for final consumers – is expected to further boost global market development. At this point, theoretically it will be more attractive to receive electricity from the solar PV module on my house than to purchase it from the local electricity supplier. Some commentators even go as far as saying that support for solar PV will no longer be necessary once grid parity will be achieved. This, however, would only be true if there are no equipment costs for a solar PV system. As this is not the case, solar PV generation costs will have to become so

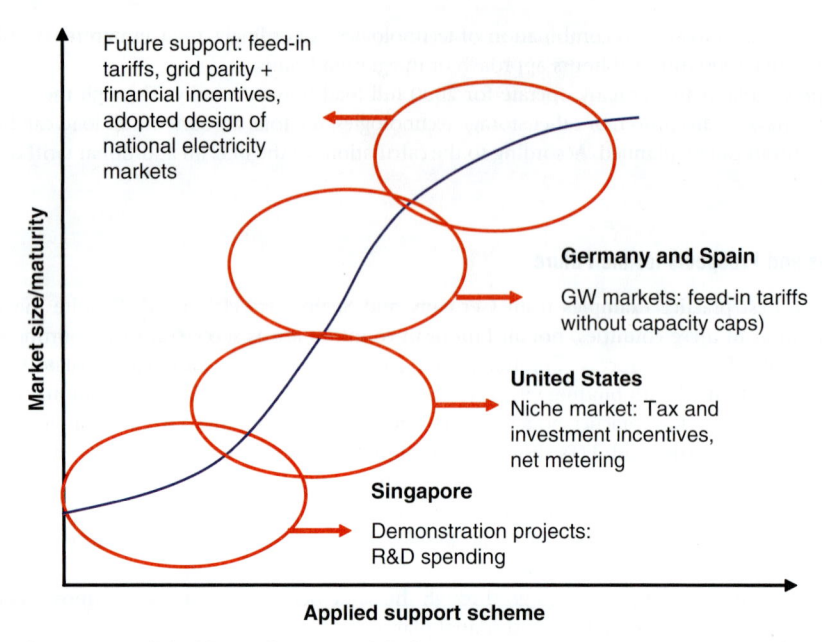

Figure 12 Market size in Singapore, the United States, Germany, and Spain in relation to applied support mechanism. Source: Own elaboration.

cost-effective that the difference between generation costs per unit and the retail electricity price also allows for purchasing the PV module in the first place. Additionally, battery systems for direct consumption might also have to be financed via the difference between power generation costs and retail electricity prices.

Besides, buyers of solar PV systems are expecting a certain internal rate of return. However, without the constant cash flow, which is guaranteed under FITs, these calculations will be far more complicated, since volatile income and cost components have to be calculated over the whole lifetime of the PV plant. Therefore, even in the case of solar PV generation costs below the electricity retail costs, electricity consumers might not opt for purchasing a PV system. A similar problem already occurs in the case of many energy efficiency measures. Even though it would make economic sense to tap certain energy efficiency potentials, investments are not being made. Therefore, additional financial incentives will still be necessary – even after grid parity is reached. Grid parity depends on two factors, the solar radiation intensity in a given country and the retail price for electricity. Thus, grid parity will be reached at different moments in time in different countries. Some countries and regions, including Italy, Hawaii, California, Spain, and Germany, will already reach it in the coming years.

The German legislator tried to anticipate 'grid parity' by offering an alternative remuneration option for autoconsumption, that is, solar electricity that is produced and consumed at the same location without feeding it into the grid. With this option, the legislator tried to give an additional incentive for decentralized electricity production/consumption. All producers of solar PV up to an installed capacity of 30 kW have the possibility to autoconsume the generated electricity and receive a reduced FIT. This possibility for autoconsumption of renewable electricity was first implemented in 2009 (§ 33, Section 2). Either the operator of the installation or a third party has to consume the power in the immediate vicinity of the plant. Instead of receiving 43.01 €cent kWh^{-1}, the tariff is reduced to 25.01 €cent kWh^{-1}. As the producer of PV electricity is obliged to pay sales taxes under the German law, this option becomes interesting for the owners of private PV installations when the gross electricity price for final consumers reaches 21.42 ¢ kWh^{-1}. This sales option for green electricity will become increasingly interesting in the coming years, as power prices are expected to increase and the tariff degression does not apply for the autoconsumption tariff. Thus, the difference with the standard FIT will decrease. In 2010, a final electricity price of 19.71 €cent kWh^{-1} will already guarantee higher profitability under this sales option [123].

This sales option was modified in 2010. It is now limited to installation with a total capacity of no more than 500 kW. (Interestingly, the Spanish legislator had implemented a very similar definition of direct consumers in 1998. The FIT legislation of the same year defined direct consumers as persons who primarily produced electricity for their own use and whose installations were no larger than 25 kW. However, this definition of direct consumers applied not to solar photovoltaic installations but to small-scale cogeneration units.) As before, the new legislation offers power producers that directly consume their electricity an average additional remuneration of 3.6 €cent kWh^{-1}. This incentive is paid in the event that direct consumption is below 30% of the total power consumption of a given consumer. Once direct consumption exceeds this 30% threshold, the additional tariff payment will rise to 8 €cent kWh^{-1} [124].

However, 'grid parity' is primarily a solution for small-scale generation units in the proximity of the final consumer (as grid-related costs can be avoided). For large-scale, free-standing PV systems, where renewable electricity is fed into the grid just as any other source of electricity, the long-term objective must be to reach 'production parity', that is, generation costs in the range of conventionally produced electricity.

While policymakers are still debating best practice of support mechanisms for renewable electricity, the real challenge is already appearing at the horizon: How do we need to design electricity markets in order to give renewable energy technologies the framework conditions they need for large-scale development? Changing the functioning and design of the electricity market as a whole will be necessary for several reasons. First, we need to establish a level-playing field. Second, an increasing share of renewable electricity generation capacity will decrease the price for electricity at the spot market and thus lower the income for renewable electricity producers (the merit-order effect). Third, the investment structure of renewable energy projects is fundamentally different from fossil fuel-based generation capacity, and the electricity market will no longer be dominated by large utilities but will consist of a more heterogeneous group of actors (utilities, small and medium sized companies, and private persons).

1.06.7.1 Leveling the Playing Field

Most energy markets in the world are distorted and therefore we need to level the playing field between renewable energy producers and conventional energy producers. The major sources of distortion are subsidies for conventional energy sources (fossil fuels and nuclear power) and the lack of internalizing the negative external costs of conventional energy generation technologies. Besides, electricity market rules do not reflect the needs of renewable electricity producer.

In the 2008 World Energy Outlook, the IEA confirmed that subsidies to the consumption of fossil fuels still exist in many non-OECD countries. In 2007, the accumulated energy subsidies of 20 non-OECD countries (accounting for more than 80% of total non-OECD energy demand) amounted to approximately $310 billion [125]. In these countries, the full cost is often not passed on to the final consumer, thus reducing the responsiveness of consumption to price increases. As a result, energy efficiency measures and alternative, renewable energy sources have difficulties to enter the market. Even though the reduction of energy subsidies is often politically challenging, it can help to set free budgetary resources in order to tackle certain social problems more directly [126].

Second, the use of fossil fuels and nuclear power often has an environmental impact, which covers costs for the society as a whole in terms of human health, climate change, and other serious damages. Not internalizing these external costs of fossil fuels means that the true costs of electricity generation are not reflected in electricity prices.

Third, the rules of today's electricity markets are tailored like a well-fitting tuxedo to the needs of conventional power generators. Some minor modifications have already been made in progressive countries, for instance, related to the cost-sharing methodology for grid connection. The so-called deep connection charging approach, which leaves the producer of renewable electricity with all costs, both for grid connection and for grid reinforcement, has been replace by the shallow connection charging approach in many European countries. Historically, the deep connection approach was employed for large-scale conventional power plants. In light of the high investment costs for these power plants, the additional expenditures for grid connection under the deep approach were negligible. This is different for renewable energy projects, which tend to have much lower overall costs per project than mammoth nuclear and coal-fired units. Furthermore, the deep approach provides an incentive to produce electricity in areas with a well-developed electricity grid. This makes sense in the case of coal- or gas-fired power plants but not in the case of renewable energy projects. Wind power plants, for instance, should be built in the windiest locations and not just in regions with available grid capacity. Under the shallow connection charging approach, the renewable energy producer only has to pay for the new electricity line to the next grid connection point, while the grid operator has to cover all costs for potential reinforcement of existing grid infrastructure. The costs covered by the grid operator will be passed on to the final consumer in terms of system charges. Under this approach, the renewable electricity producer will choose the location for the power plant depending on the resource availability (e.g., wind speed) and not infrastructure availability. Recently, a super shallow connection charging approach was implemented in some European countries to promote the deployment of offshore wind power plants, particularly in Denmark and Germany. Connection lines from offshore wind fields to the nearest onshore connection point are rather expensive because of the long distances involved. To free the offshore wind power developers from this financial burden, legislators decided that even the costs for the new connection line from the offshore wind park to the next onshore connection point have to be paid by the grid operator.

Moreover, Spain has established new gate closures for renewable electricity producers wanting to sell their power on the national spot market. For fluctuating technologies, such as wind power and solar PV, a high number of intraday gates are crucial in order to make short-term adjustment with respect to the amount of electricity that can be delivered to the system [127]. The Spanish regulation even allows wind power producers to make hourly adjustments to the power production forecasts.

However, further measures need to be taken in the future. As described above, 'grid parity' and 'generation parity' will be reached eventually, depending on the costs for conventional power generation and the solar resource conditions in a given country. Therefore, the future necessity for support for solar PV will largely depend on how these two factors vary from country to country. Consequently, time-of-use electricity retail prices could make investment into solar PV more attractive. This is already the case in California, where the electricity price for final consumers ranges from 10 US¢ kWh^{-1} in off-peak periods in winter time to 50 US¢ kWh^{-1} for peak periods in summer time (see **Figure 13**).

In many countries, solar generation matches medium or even peak electricity demand periods. Therefore, in liberalized electricity markets, the timely 'value' of solar PV electricity might be higher than a mere comparison of costs of conventional power generation and solar PV electricity production suggests [106].

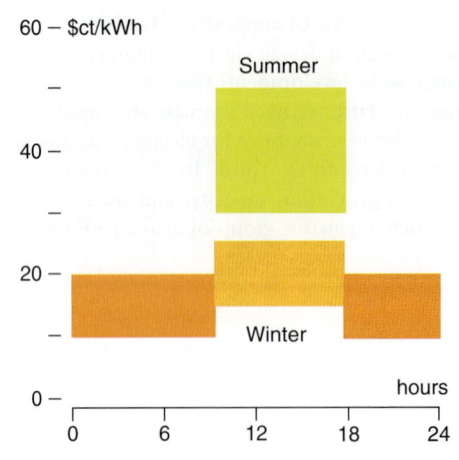

Figure 13 Range of household electricity price in California. Source: EPIA (2009) *2013 – Global Market Outlook for Photovoltaics until 2013*. Brussels, Belgium: European Photovoltaic Industry Association [80].

1.06.7.2 Investment Structure and Actor Groups on Future Electricity Markets

Renewable energy projects are defined by large-scale initial investment and relatively low costs for operation and maintenance forever after. Therefore, this different investment structure needs to be taken into account. For gas or coal-fired power plants, most financial resources are needed for the fuel provision over the lifetime of a power plant. However, in the case of wind power plants and other renewable energy technologies, almost all financial resources are needed at the start of the project in order to purchase the equipment. Due to this high, initial capital cost, long-term security and predictable returns on investment are essential for renewable electricity producers. Support mechanisms as described below often manage to create such conditions by significantly reducing investment risks. In other words, predictability of income is more important for renewable energy projects than excessive rates of return. This has to be taken into consideration when designing future power markets. Whether kilowatt-hour markets will be able to play this role remains to be seen.

After all, the actors engaged in the power production business will change. While nowadays, electricity markets are dominated by large-scale utilities, the decentralized nature of renewable energy projects will also attract 'smaller' actors. However, private actors and small and medium-sized companies are much more risk averse when it comes to the financing of renewable energy projects than large utilities. For those actors, risk minimization is certainly more important than high profits. Therefore, the choice of renewable energy support instruments and finally the market design as a whole will determine which actors will become involved in the power generation business. Support mechanisms such as FITs are generally conceived as being 'democratic' in nature, that is, allowing a heterogeneous group of actors to participate in the market. If future electricity will be designed in an equally democratic manner, the long-term outlook for solar PV is bright indeed.

References

[1] JRC (2010) PV status report 2010. Ispra, Italy: Joint Research Centre, Institute for Energy, European Commission.
[2] EPIA (2010) 2014 – Global market outlook for photovoltaics until 2014. Brussels, Belgium: European Photovoltaic Industry Association.
[3] EPIA (2009) Set for 2020 – Solar photovoltaic electricity: A mainstream power source in Europe by 2020, executive summary. Brussels: EPIA.
[4] Yu CF, van Sark WGJHM, and Alsema EA (2011) How to incorporate input price changes and scale effects into the learning curve? A photovoltaics case study. *Renewable and Sustainable Energy Reviews* 15: 324–337.
[5] IEA (2009) IEA photovoltaic roadmap. Review Draft.
[6] de Jager D and Rathmann M (2008) Policy instrument design to reduce financing costs in renewable energy technology projects. *IEA Implementing Agreement on Renewable Energy Technology Deployment (RETD)*, October 2008. Paris: International Energy Agency.
[7] REN21 (2010) Renewables 2010, global status report. Paris, France: REN21.
[8] IEA (2008) Deploying renewables: Principles for effective policies. Paris, France: International Energy Agency.
[9] EU Commission (2008) The support of electricity from renewable energy sources, commission staff working document, accompanying document to the proposal for directive of the European parliament and of the council on the promotion of the use energy from renewable sources. SEC(2008) 57, 23 January 2008. Brussels, Belgium: European Commission.
[10] Butler L and Neuhoff K (2008) Comparison of feed-in tariff, quota and auction mechanisms to support wind power development. *Energy Policy* 33: 1854–1867.
[11] Jacobsson S, Bergek A, Finon D, et al. (2009) EU renewable energy support policy: Faith or facts? *Energy Policy* 37: 2143–2146.
[12] Resch G, Lopez-Polo M-A, Auer H, and Haas R (2005): Electricity from renewable energy sources in EU15 countries – A review of promotion strategies. March 2005. Vienna: Energy Economics Group.
[13] Beck F and Martinot E (2004) Renewable energy policies and barriers. *Encyclopedia of Energy* 5: 365–383.
[14] Mendonca M, Jacobs D, and Sovacool B (2009) *Powering the Green Economy – The Feed-In Tariff Handbook*. London, UK: Earthscan.
[15] Hvelplund F (2005) Renewable energy: Political prices or political quantities. In: Lauber V (ed.) *Switching to Renewable Power. A Framework for the 21st Century*, pp. 228–245. London, UK: Earthscan.

[16] Inglin C (2008) Is Singapore Ready for Renewable Energy? *Presented at Lee Kuan Yew School of Public Policy*, Singapore, 16 July 2008. Singapore: National University of Singapore.
[17] Wittkopf S, Wong NH, and Hess W (2004) *Potential of Building Integrated Photovoltaics in Existing Urban High-Rise Housing in Singapore*. Singapore: Centre for Advanced Studies in Architecture, National University of Singapore.
[18] U.S. Energy Information Administration (2007) *Country Brief: Singapore*. Washington, DC: U.S. Department of Energy.
[19] Kannan R, Leong KC, Osman R, and Ho HK (2007) Life cycle energy, emissions and cost inventory of power generation technologies in Singapore. *Renewable and Sustainable Energy Reviews* 11: 702–715.
[20] Sovacool BK (2009) Cogeneration and trigeneration in the tropics: Singapore success. *Cogeneration and Onsite Power Production* 10(1): 29–35.
[21] Wong YS (2009) Development of renewable energy in Singapore. *ESI Bulletin* 2(2): 6–9.
[22] Economic Development Board (2007) World-scale integrated solar manufacturing complex marks watershed for clean energy industry. *EDB Press Release*. http://www.edb.gov.sg/content/edb/sg/en_uk/index/news/chapters/world-scale_integrated.print.html (accessed 1 December 2007).
[23] Toh M and Jamie Ee WW (2008) Power hikes: Low-income families to feel pinch most. *The Straits Times*, p. 8. 30 March 2008.
[24] Pratsch L (2004) Energy efficiency and solar energy, communication with Janet Sawin, Worldwatch Institute, 30 September 2004, U.S. Department of Energy.
[25] U.S. Department of Energy (2007) *Solar Energy Technologies Program: Applications*, p. 3. Washington, DC: DOE.
[26] Renewable Energy Policy Network for the 21st Century (REN21) (2009) Renewables global status report: 2009 update. Washington, DC: REN21.
[27] Wiser R, Peterman GBC, and Darghouth N (2009) Tracking the sun II: The installed cost of solar photovoltaics in the United States from 1998 to 2008. LBNL–2674E, February. Berkeley, CA: Lawrence Berkeley National Laboratory.
[29] Wiser R, Barbose G, and Peterman C (2009) Tracking the sun: The installed cost of solar photovoltaics in the United States from 1998 to 2007. LBNL–1516E, February. Berkeley, CA: Lawrence Berkeley National Laboratory.
[30] Joskow PJ (1979) Public utilities regulatory policy act of 1978: Electric utility rate reform. *Natural Resources Journal* 19: 787–810.
[31] Hirsh RF (1989) *Technology and Transformation in the American Electric Utility Industry*. Cambridge, UK: Cambridge University Press.
[32] Hirsh RF (1999) *Power Loss: The Origins of Deregulation and Restructuring in the American Electric Utility System*. Cambridge, MA: MIT Press.
[33] Edison Electric Institute (1996) *Statistical Yearbook of the Electric Utility Industry*. Washington, DC: EEI.
[34] Gipe P (1995) *Wind Energy Comes of Age*. New York: Wiley.
[35] Owens B (2004) Beyond the production tax credit (PTC): Solar energy support in the U.S. *ReFocus*, pp. 32–34. November/December, 2004.
[36] Gipe SP (2006) *Solar Energy Policy Mechanisms*. Tehachapi, CA: Wind Works Organization.
[37] Rickerson W and Grace RC (2007) *The Debate Over Fixed Price Incentives for Renewable Electricity in Europe and the United States: Fallout and Future Directions*. Washington, DC: Heinrich Boll Foundation.
[38] Grace R, Rickerson W, Porter K, et al. (2008) Exploring feed-in tariffs for California: Feed-in tariff design and implementation issues and options. CEC-300-2008-003–D, June 2008. Sacramento, CA: California Energy Commission and Kema Consulting.
[39] Cory K, Couture T, and Kreycik C (2009) Feed-in tariff policy: Design, implementation, and RPS policy interactions. NREL/TP-6A2–45549, March 2009. Golden, CO: National Solar Energy Laboratory.
[40] Grace R, Rickerson W, Corfee K et al. (2009) California feed-in tariff design and policy options. CEC-300-2008-009F, May 2009. Sacramento, CA: California Energy Commission.
[41] Couture T and Cory K (2009) State clean energy policy analysis: Solar energy feed-in tariffs. NREL/TP-6A2-45551, 12 February 2009. Golden, CO: National Renewable Energy Laboratory.
[42] Sovacool BK and Cooper C (2008) Congress got it wrong: The case for a national renewable portfolio standard (RPS) and implications for policy. *Environmental & Energy Law & Policy Journal* 3(1): 85–148.
[43] Sovacool BK (2008) A matter of stability and equity: The case for federal action on renewable portfolio standards in the U.S. *Energy & Environment* 19(2): 241–261.
[44] Sovacool BK and Cooper C (2007–2008) The hidden costs of state renewable portfolio standards (RPS). *Buffalo Environmental Law Journal* 15(1/2): 1–41.
[45] Moeller JW (2004) Of credits and quotas: Federal tax incentives for renewable resources, state renewable portfolio standards, and the evolution of proposals for a federal renewable portfolio standard. *Fordham Environmental Law Journal* 51: 91.
[46] Sawin JL (2004) National Policy Instruments: Policy lessons for the advancement and diffusion of solar energy technologies around the world. Thematic background paper #3. Presented at *International Conference for Renewable Energies*. Bonn, Germany, January.
[47] North Carolina State University (2007) *NC Solar Center Summary Maps*, Raleigh, North Carolina: NC State, accessed 10 October 2011 at http://www.dsireusa.org/library/includes/topic.cfm?TopicCategoryID=6&CurrentPageID=10&EE=0&RE=1.
[48] Network for New Energy Choices (2007) *Freeing the Grid 2007*. New York: Network for New Energy Choices.
[49] Haynes R (2007) Not your mother's net metering: Recent policy evolution in U.S. states. Presented at *Solar Power 2007 Conference*. Long Beach, CA, 25 September.
[50] Bird LA, Cory KS, and Swezey BG (2008) Solar energy price-stability benefits in utility green power programs. NREL/TP-670-43532, August 2008, p. 5. Golden, CO: National Solar Energy Laboratory.
[51] Bird LA, Cory KS, and Swezey BG (2008) Solar energy price-stability benefits in utility green power programs. NREL/TP-670-43532, August 2008, p. 1. Golden, CO: National Solar Energy Laboratory.
[52] Duke R, Williams R, and Payne A (2005) Accelerating residential PV expansion: Demand analysis for competitive electricity markets. *Energy Policy* 33: 1916.
[53] Gomez A (2009) Going green can eat a lot of green. *USA Today*, p. 3A. 5 May 2009.
[54] U.S. Department of Energy (2008) *Annual Report on U.S. Wind Power Installation, Cost, and Performance Trends: 2007*. Washington, DC: U.S. Department of Energy.
[55] Beck F and Martinot E (2004) Renewable energy policies and barriers. *Encyclopedia of Energy* 5: 365–383.
[56] National Renewable Energy Laboratory (2009) Solar leasing for residential photovoltaic systems. NREL/FS-6A2-43572, February 2009. Golden, CO: NREL.
[57] Bolinger M (2009) Financing non-residential photovoltaic projects: Options and implications. LBNL–1410E, January 2009. Berkeley, CA: Lawrence Berkeley National Laboratory.
[58] Lewis J and Wiser R (2005) Fostering a solar energy technology industry: An international comparison of wind industry policy support mechanisms. LBNL–59116, November 2005. Berkeley, CA: Lawrence Berkeley National Laboratory.
[59] Wiser R, Bolinger M, and Barbose G (2007) Using the federal production tax credit to build a durable market for wind power in the United States. *Electricity Journal* 20(9): 77–88.
[60] FITs in the U.S.A. *PV Magazine*, pp. 20–25. March 2009.
[61] Gipe P (2009) Vermont FITs become law: The mouse that roared. First North American jurisdiction with small wind tariff. *Renewable Energy World*, 28 May 2009.
[62] Haas R, Meyer NI, Held A, et al. (2008) Promoting electricity from solar energy sources – lessons learned from the EU, United States, and Japan. In: Sioshansi FP (ed.) *Competitive Electricity Markets: Design, Implementation and Performance*, pp. 91–140. Amsterdam, The Netherlands: Elsevier.
[63] Coughlin J and Cory K (2009) Solar photovoltaic financing: Residential sector deployment. NREL/TP-6A2–44853, March. Golden, CO: National Solar Energy Laboratory.
[64] Barbose G, Wiser R, and Bolinger M (2006) *Supporting Photovoltaics in Market-Rate Residential New Construction: A Summary of Programmatic Experience to Date and Lessons Learned*. Berkeley, CA: Lawrence Berkeley National Laboratory.
[65] Bulat O, Danford L, and Samarasinghe L (2008) *Project Sunshine: An Overview of the US Residential Solar Energy Market*. Cambridge, MA: Harvard Business School.
[66] Pitt D (2008) *Taking the Red Tape Out of Green Power*. New York: Network for New Energy Choices.

[67] EU Commission (1996) Energy for the future – Renewable sources of energy. Green paper for a community strategy and action plan. COM(97)599 final, 26 November 1997. Brussels, Belgium: European Commission.
[68] EU Commission (1997) Energy for the future – Renewable sources of energy. White paper for a community strategy and action plan. COM(97)599 final, 26 November 1997. Brussels, Belgium.
[69] EU (2001) Directive 2001/77/EC of the European Parliament and of the Council of 27 September 2001 on the promotion of electricity produced from renewable energy sources in the internal electricity market. *Official Journal of the European Communities* L 283/33.
[70] EU (2009) Directive 2009/28/EC of the European Parliament and the Council of 23 April 2009 on the promotion of the use of energy from renewable sources and amending and subsequently repealing Directives 2001/77/EC and 2003/30/EC. *Official Journal of the European Union* L 140/16.
[71] Photon International (2008) Adiós, España. *Photon Internacional*, p. 48. October 2008.
[72] Jacobsson S and Lauber V (2006) The politics and policy of energy system transformation – Explaining the diffusion of renewable energy technology. *Energy Policy* 34: 256–276.
[73] Bechberger M and Reiche D (2004) Renewable energy policy in Germany: Pioneering and exemplary regulation. *Energy for Sustainable Development* VIII(1): 47–57.
[74] Hirschl B, Hoffmann EZ, Hopper-Kilpper M, *et al.* (2002) Markt- und Kostenentwicklung erneuerbarer Energien, 2 Jahre EEG-Bilanz und Ausblick, Beiträge zur Umweltgestaltung A 151. Berlin, Germany: Erich Schmidt Verlag.
[75] Decreto-Lei n.º 189 de 27 de Maio 1988, D.R. n.º 123/88, Série I-A.
[76] Reiche D (2004) Rahmenbedingungen für erneuerbare Energien in Deutschland – Möglichkeiten und Grenzen einer Vorreiterpolitik, Frankfurt am Main.
[77] BMU (2010) *Entwicklung der erneuerbaren Energien in Deutschland im Jahr 2009*, Stand: 18. März 2010. Berlin, Germany: Federal Ministry for the Environment, Nature Conservation and Nuclear Safety.
[78] BSW (2010) Statistische Zahlen der deutschen Solarstrombranche (Photovoltaik), June 2010. Berlin, Germany: Bundesverband Solarwirtschaft.
[79] Fulton M, Mellquist N, Rickerson W, and Jacobs D (2011) *The German Feed-In Tariff for PV: Managing Volume Success with Price Response*. New York: DB Research.
[80] EPIA (2009) *2013 – Global Market Outlook for Photovoltaics until 2013*. Brussels, Belgium: European Photovoltaic Industry Association.
[81] BOE (1981) Ley 82/1980, de 30 de diciembre, sobre conservación de la Energía, BOE No. 23 of 27 January 1981, p. 1863. http://www.boe.es/boe/dias/1981/01/27/pdfs/A01863-01866.pdf (accessed 7 October 2011).
[82] del Río P (2008) Ten years of renewable electricity policy in Spain: An analysis of successive feed-in tariff reforms. *Energy Policy* 36: 2917–2929.
[83] BOE (1994) Real Decreto 2366/1994, de 9 de diciembre, sobre Produccion de energía eléctrica por instalaciones hidráulicas, de cogeneración y otras abastecidas por recursos o fuentes de energía renovables, Madrid, Spain, pp. 39595–39603. http://www.boe.es/boe/dias/1994/12/31/pdfs/A39595-39603.pdf (accessed 7 October 2011).
[84] BOE (1998) Real Decreto 2818/1998, de 23 de diciembre, sobre producción de energía eléctrica por instalaciones abastecidas por recursos o fuentes de energía renovables, residuos y cogeneración, BOE No. 313 of 30 December 1998, p. 44077. http://www.boe.es/boe/dias/1998/12/30/pdfs/A44077-44089.pdf (accessed 10 October 2011).
[85] Jacobs D (2008) Analyse des spanischen Fördermodells für erneuerbare Energien unter besonderer Berücksichtigung der Windenergie, Wissenschaft und Praxis, Studie im Auftrag des Bundesverbands WindEnergie e. V., August 2008, Berlin, Germany.
[86] BOE (2007) Resolución de 27 de septiembre de 2007, de la Secretaría General de Energía, por la que se establece el plazo de mantenimiento de la tarifa regulada para la tecnología fotovoltaica, en virtud de lo establecido en el artículo 22 del Real Decreto 661/2007, de 25 de mayo. Boletín Oficial del Estado No. 234 of 29 September 2007, p. 39745. http://www.cne.es/cne/doc/legislacion/Resol-Fotovoltaica-29-9-07.pdf (accessed 10 October 2011).
[87] IFIC (2009) *7th Workshop of the International Feed-In Cooperation, Conclusions*. Ljubljana, Slovenia, 28–29 May.
[88] Photon International (2008) Drying up. *Photon International*, p. 70. August 2008.
[89] CNE (2011) Información estadística sobre las ventas de energía del régimen especial, Dirección de Energía Eléctrica, February 2011. http://www.cne.es/ (accessed 7 October 2011).
[90] Assemblée Nationale (2009) Rapport d'information déposé en application de l'chapter 145 du règlement par la commission des affaires économiques, par M. Serge Poignant, député, Enregistré à la Présidence de l'Assemblée nationale le 16 juillet 2009. http://www.assemblee-nationale.fr/13/dossiers/engagement_environnement.asp (accessed 10 October 2011).
[91] Brothers L (2008) Spain solar subsidy analysis. *Equity Research*, 1 July 2008, New York.
[92] Klein A, Held A, Ragwitz M, *et al.* (2008) Evaluation of different FIT design options. Presented at *International Feed-In Cooperation*, April 22–24, 2008. Brussels: IFIC..
[93] Fell H-J (2009) FIT for renewable energies: An effective stimulus package without new public borrowing, March 2009.
[94] Roderick P, Jacobs D, Gleason J, and Bristow D (2007) Policy action on climate toolkit. wwww.onlinepact.org/ (accessed 23 May 2009).
[95] Mendonça M (2007) *FITs: Accelerating the Deployment of Renewable Energy*. London, UK: Earthscan.
[96] Grace R, Rickerson W, and Corfee K (2008) California FIT design and policy options. CEC-300-2008-009D. Sacramento, CA: California Energy Commission.
[97] Sösemann F (2007) *EEG – The Renewable Energy Sources Act: The Success Story of Sustainable Policies for Germany*. Berlin, Germany: Federal Ministry for the Environment, Nature Conservation and Nuclear Safety.
[98] Jacobs D and Kiene A (2009) Renewable energy policies for sustainable African development. *World Future Council*, April 2009.
[99] Mendonca M and Jacobs D (2009) Feed-in tariffs: The policy path to 100%. In: Droege P (ed.) *100 Per cent Renewable*. London, UK: Earthscan.
[100] BGB (2008) *Gesetz zur Neuregelung des Rechts der erneuerbaren Energien im Strombereich und zur Änderung damit zusammenhängender Vorschriften*, vom 25 Oktober 2008, Bundesgesetzblatt1 Nr 49, p. 2074.
[101] BGB (1990) Gesetz über die Einspeisung vom Strom aus erneuerbaren Energien in das öffentliche Netz (Stromeinspeisegesetz) vom 7. Dezember 1990, BGBl. I S.2633.
[102] BOE (1981) Real Decreto 1217/1981, de 10 de abril, para el fomento de la producción hidroeléctrica en pequeñas centrales, BOE No. 150 of 28 June 1981, p. 14435. http://www.boe.es/boe/dias/1981/06/24/pdfs/A14433-14433.pdf (accessed 7 October 2011).
[103] BOE (1994) Real Decreto 2366/1994, de 9 de diciembre, sobre Produccion de energía eléctrica por instalaciones hidráulicas, de cogeneración y otras abastecidas por recursos o fuentes de energía renovables, Madrid, Spain, pp. 39595–39603, Chapter 12.1.
[104] BOE (1997) Ley 54/1997, de 27 de noviembre, del sector eléctrico, BOE número 285, pp. 35097–35126.
[105] Fell H-J (2009) Feed-in tariffs for renewable energies: An effective stimulus package without new public borrowing. *Deutscher Bundestag*, March 2009.
[106] BMU (2008) Depiction of the methodological approaches to calculate the costs of electricity generation used in the scientific background reports serving as the basis for the Renewable Energy Source Act (EEG) Progress Report 2007. Berlin: Federal Environment Ministry of Germany.
[107] CNE (2004) Informe 4/2004 sobre la propuesta de Real Decreto por el que se establece la metodología para actualiziación y sistemantización del régimen jurídico y económico de la acticidad de producción de energía eléctrica en réginmen especial, 22 January 2004, Madrid, Spain.
[108] BOE (2004) Real Decreto 436/2004, de 12 de marzo, por el que se establece la metodología para la actualización y sistematización del régimen jurídico y económico de la actividad de producción de energía eléctrica en régimen especial, BOE No. 75, 27 March 2004, p. 13217.
[109] MITYC (2007) El Gobierno prima la rentabilidad y la estabilidad en el nuevo Real Decreto de energías renovables y cogeneración, Nota de prensa, 25 May 2007, Madrid, Spain.
[110] CNE (2007) Informe 3/2007 de la CNE relativo a la propuesta de Real Decreto por el que se regula la actividad de producción de energía eléctrica en el régimen especial y de determinadas instalaciones de tecnología asimilables del régimen ordinario, 14 February 2007, Madrid, Spain.
[111] Bechberger M (2000) Das Erneuerbare-Energien-Gesetz (EEG): Eine Analyse des Politikformulierungsprozesses. FFU-Report 00–06. Berlin: Environmental Policy Research Centre (FU Berlin).
[112] Jacobs D and Kiene A (2009) Renewable energy toolkit – Promotion strategies in Africa. *World Future Council*, May 2009.
[113] Calzada Álvarez G, Jara DM, Julián R, and García Bielsa J (2009) Study of the effects on employment of public aid to renewable energy sources, Universidad Rey Juan Carlos, March 2009.

[114] Jacobs D (2011) Renewable Energy Policy Convergence in the EU: The Evolution of Feed-In Tariffs in Germany, Spain and France. Dissertation, Environmental Policy Research Centre, Freie Universität Berlin.
[115] Wenzel B and Nitsch J (2008) *Ausbau erneuerbarer Energien im Strombereich, EEG-Vergütungen, Differenzkosten und –Umlagen sowie ausgewählte Nutzeneffekte bis 2030*, Teltow/Stuttgart, Dezember 2008.
[116] Jacobs D and Pfeiffer C (2009) Combining tariff payment and market growth. *PV Magazine*, pp. 220–224. May 2009.
[117] Asif (2008) *La Tarifa Fotovoltaica Flexible reduciría la retribución entre un 2 percent y un 10 percent cada año*, comunicado de prensa, Madrid, Spain, 13 de marzo de 2008.
[118] MITYC (2010) Industria incorpora 848 nuevas plantas fotovoltaicas al listado de instalaciones con derecho a retribución, press realease, press release, 20 July 2010. Madrid, Spain: Ministerio de Industria, Turismo y Comercio.
[119] Couture T (2009) An Analysis of FIT Policy Design Options for Renewable Energy Sources. Master's Thesis. University of Moncton.
[120] Coenraads R, Reece G, Voogt M, *et al.* (2008) Progress: Promotion and growth of renewable energy sources and systems. *Final Report*, TREN/D1/42-2005/S07.56988, 5 March 2008. Utrecht, The Netherlands: Ecofys.
[121] Ragwitz M, Held A, Resch G, *et al.* (2007) Assessment and optimisation of renewable energy support schemes in the European electricity market. *Final Report*, February 2007. Brussels: Intelligent Energy Europe.
[122] EU Commission (2005) The support of electricity from renewable energy sources. Communication from the commission. COM(2005) 627 Final, 7 December 2005. Brussels, Belgium: European Commission.
[123] Bröer G (2009) Klarheit beim PV-Eigenverbrauch, Solarthemen, No. 301, 9 April 2009, p. 1.
[124] BGBI (2010) *Erstes Gesetz zur Änderung des Erneuerbare-Energien-Gesetzes vom 11 August 2010*, Bundesgesetzblatt I, 17 August 2010, p. 1170.
[125] IEA (2008) *World Energy Outlook 2008*. Paris: International Energy Agency.
[126] IEA (2009) *World Energy Outlook 2009*. Paris: International Energy Agency.
[127] Morthorst PE, Wagemans S, Purchala K, *et al.* (2007) Detailed investigation of electricity market rules (D. 4.1.) – Cases of France, Germany, Netherlands, Spain and Denmark, TradeWind project. In: Morthorst PE (ed.) Risø National Laboratory, Technical University of Denmark, April 2007.
[128] Braun M, Saint-Drenan Y-M, Glotzbach T, *et al.* (2008) Value of PV energy in Germany – Benefit from the substitution of conventional power plants and local power generation. *23rd European Photovoltaic Solar Energy Conference*, Valencia, Spain, 1–5 September.

1.07 Finance Mechanisms and Incentives for Photovoltaic Technologies in Developing Countries

M Moner-Girona and S Szabo, Joint Research Centre, European Commission, Institute for Energy and Transport, Ispra, Italy
S Rolland, Alliance for Rural Electrification, Brussels, Belgium

© 2012 Elsevier Ltd. All rights reserved.

1.07.1	**Background: Photovoltaics, Rural Electrification, and Millennium Development Goals**	111
1.07.1.1	Development Assistance for Renewables in Developing Countries	113
1.07.1.2	Analytical Framework for Support Mechanism of PV in Rural Areas	114
1.07.2	**PV in Developing Countries: Current Situation**	114
1.07.2.1	Evolution of Grid-Connected/Off-Grid PV Systems	114
1.07.2.2	Evolution of Electrification Rates and Off-Grid PV Systems for Rural Areas	114
1.07.2.3	Energy Technology Options for Rural Areas	115
1.07.3	**Current Costs of PV in Developing Countries**	116
1.07.4	**Ownership, Organization, and Local Participation**	119
1.07.4.1	Community-Based Model	120
1.07.4.2	Private Ownership/Private Operator	120
1.07.4.3	Rural Energy Service Company Model	120
1.07.5	**Financing Channels for PV in Rural Renewable Energy**	120
1.07.5.1	Consumer Finance	121
1.07.5.1.1	Commercial banks and nonbank financing institutions	121
1.07.5.1.2	Microcredits	121
1.07.5.2	Market Development Finance	123
1.07.5.3	Public Sector Finance (Poverty Alleviation)	124
1.07.6	**PV Tariff Setting and Incentives for Rural Electrification**	124
1.07.6.1	Procedure for Annual Revision	125
1.07.7	**Finance Instruments to Promote PV Systems in Rural Areas in Developing Countries**	125
1.07.7.1	Capital Subsidies, Consumer Grants, and Guarantees	125
1.07.7.2	Renewable Energy Service Companies	126
1.07.7.3	Leasing or Hire Purchase Model	126
1.07.7.4	Renewable Portfolio Standards	127
1.07.7.5	Small Power Producer Regulation	127
1.07.7.6	Tender System	128
1.07.7.7	Fiscal Incentives: Reduction in VAT and Import Duty Reduction	128
1.07.7.8	Public Finance Pools	128
1.07.7.9	Bank Financing: Low Interest and Soft Loans	128
1.07.7.10	Carbon Financing	129
1.07.7.11	Transitions from Off-Grid to On-Grid Generation Systems	130
1.07.8	**Innovative Financing Mechanisms for Rural Renewable Energy**	130
1.07.8.1	Renewable Energy Premium Tariff	130
1.07.8.1.1	The RPT: Adapted FiT for mini-grids	131
1.07.8.1.2	RPT scheme under different regulatory and institutional frameworks	131
1.07.8.2	GET FiTs for Developing Countries	134
1.07.8.2.1	Alternatives for funding flows from GET FiT to projects	135
1.07.9	**Financial Risk Management**	135
1.07.9.1	Risk Characterization	136
1.07.9.1.1	Risk comparison of PV and other renewable technologies to fossil fuel-based technologies	136
1.07.9.1.2	Transforming risk dimensions into different return expectations	137
1.07.10	**Conclusions**	137
Acknowledgments		139
References		139

1.07.1 Background: Photovoltaics, Rural Electrification, and Millennium Development Goals

Lack of energy is among the key retarding forces preventing economic development and consequently slowing down poverty alleviation and growth of the rural sector. According to 2010 estimates, approximately 3 billion people worldwide rely on traditional biomass for cooking and heating, and about 1.4 billion have no access to electricity. Up to a billion more have access

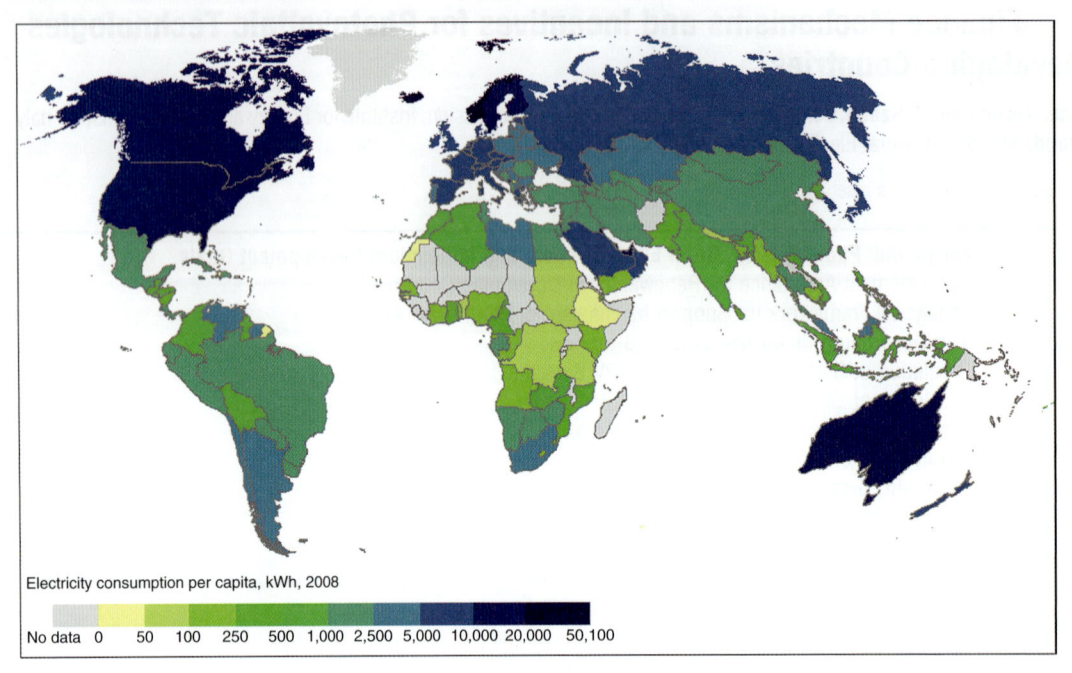

Figure 1 Electricity consumption per capita (kWh) in 2008. Source: Interpreted by K. Bodis (JRC–European Commission) with data compiled from the World Bank's Open Data.

only to unreliable electricity networks [1]. The electricity consumption per capita worldwide map (**Figure 1**) depicts the unbalanced figures: the need for the developed world to highly increase energy efficiency measures and adjust energy consumption patterns to decrease the impacts on climate change compared with the need for developing countries to increase access to modern energy to improve socioeconomic conditions of rural population.

According to the International Energy Agency (IEA) projections (the IEA projections are highly dependent on assumptions about incomes and electricity pricing) for the unelectrified population, the electrification rates and the number of unelectrified people will continue to diverge significantly among regions [2, 3]. Most of the people without access to electricity in 2030 will still be in sub-Saharan Africa (650 million) and South Asia (680 million), see **Figure 2**.

Current energy systems used in the developing world are inadequate to meet the needs of the world's poor and are jeopardizing the achievement of the Millennium Development Goals (MDGs) established by the United Nations for 2015 [4]. In recent years, many technological and financial innovations have been created to increase access to energy for the billions of people at the 'bottom of the pyramid'. Even with these advances, many remote communities face a present – and future – life without electricity [5]. Therefore, better-defined and more advanced sustainable energy models are needed to achieve the MDGs. On top of the optimized technological options depending on the local resources, financing schemes are essential to support the promotion of these sustainable initiatives in developing countries.

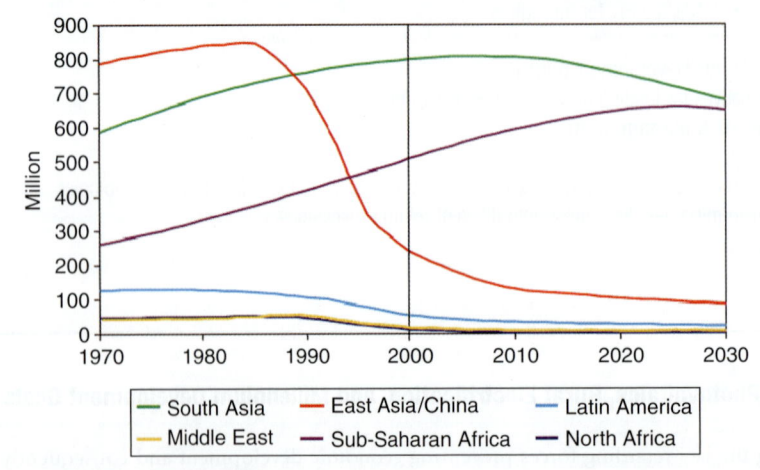

Figure 2 Number of people without electricity (1970–2030). Source: IEA analysis. Chapter 13: Energy and poverty. World Energy Outlook 2002, Organisation for Economic Co-operation and Development (OECD)/International Energy Agency (IEA), OECD/IEA Paris: 2002.

Remote communities turn to the nongovernmental organization (NGO) sector for electricity services because they are too far from the grid to hope for grid extension, unable to entice even social entrepreneurs because the community lacks a functioning economy, and located in a developing country without a central government able to fund remote electrification projects. In the case of these communities, financial mechanisms should be specifically tailored to overcome the barriers derived from the specific political and social conditions and to mitigate the effect of the relatively high initial investment needed using renewable or hybrid technologies [1].

1.07.1.1 Development Assistance for Renewables in Developing Countries

Development assistance for renewables in developing countries has multiplied more than twofold in 2009, exceeding $5 billion (compared with some $2 billion in 2008). The World Bank Group, including the International Finance Corporation (IFC) and the Multilateral Investment Guarantee Agency (MIGA), committed $1.38 billion to new renewables (solar, wind, geothermal, biomass, and hydro below 10 MW) and another $177 million for large hydropower. (These figures exclude Global Environment Facility (GEF) funds and carbon finance.) Germany's Kreditanstalt für Wiederaufbau (KfW) committed $381 million to new renewables and an additional $27 million to large hydropower. It also committed $1.1 billion at governmental level for renewable energy through its Special Facility for Renewable Energies and Energy Efficiency [6, 7].

Many other development assistance agencies committed large funds to renewables in 2009. The Inter-American Development Bank committed more than $1 billion in loans for renewable energy. The Asian Development Bank invested approximately $933 million in renewables, including $238 million in large hydropower. The Asian Development Bank also launched an Asian solar energy initiative (ASEI), which aims to generate some 3000 MW of solar power. The ASEI is identifying and developing large capacity solar projects and plans to provide $2.25 billion in finance, expecting to leverage an additional $6.75 billion in solar power investments over a period up to 2013–14. The other important institution is the GEF Trust Fund, which is a partnership of 10 entities (among them the United Nations Development Program (UNDP), the United Nations Environment Program (UNEP), World Bank, Food and Agriculture Organization (FAO), African Development Bank, and Asian Development Bank). The GEF funded 13 renewable energy projects with a total direct contribution of $51.2 million and with associated cofinance from other sources of $386.8 million. Agence Française de Développement (AFD) committed $293 million to renewable energy through direct financing and around $465 million through lines of credit to local banks. The Japan International Corporation Agency (JICA) provided $1.2 billion. The Netherlands Development Finance Company (NDFC) committed $370 million. Other official development assistance (ODA) figures from a variety of bilateral and multilateral development agencies suggest additional flows to renewables on the order of $100–200 million per year [6].

The European Union (EU) has also been, over the years, a significant supporter of renewables, in particular off-grid, in developing countries. The Energy Facility 1 and 2 launched, respectively, in 2005 and 2010 financed more than 150 projects with an outlay of more than €220 and €200 million, respectively, expecting to reach millions of people. Additionally, the EU has set up an investment fund, the Global Energy Efficiency and Renewable Energy Fund (GEEREF), planning to be as high as €250 million, which aims at participating in various regional funds specializing in renewable energy finance. The GEEREF includes the objective of energy access and has already contributed to the creation of five investment facilities throughout developing countries. The GEEREF is managed by the European Investment Bank (EIB). The EU, Germany, and Norway are GEEREF's founding investors. There is another relevant EU fund called the Global Climate Change Alliance (GCCA).

The following international funds are important drivers in energy-related investment in the developing world as they mobilize huge amounts of third-party investment in addition to their own contribution. The EU Energy Facilities mentioned above usually attract more than 25% third-party financing in addition to their contribution. The World Bank and the United Nations also manage similar funds to mobilize additional investment. The World Bank has the Climate Investments Fund (CIF) and the United Nations has the MDG Achievement Fund Environment and Climate Change Thematic Window; the United Nations Collaborative Program on Reducing Emissions from Deforestation and Forest Degradation in Developing Countries (UN-REDD), a collaboration between UNDP, UNEP, and FAO; and the United Nations Framework Convention on Climate Change (UNFCCC). Here the Kyoto Protocol Adaptation Fund must also be mentioned. These funds do not have a thematic focus on PV, but in the awarded projects of the EU Energy Facilities, the PV share is quite substantial.

There are also funds that are set up by national governments and have a significant portfolio for renewable energy investments. Sometimes they serve as the additional financing source for the above-mentioned international funds, sometimes they set up own priorities. These are the latest examples:

- International Climate Initiative, a German Fund. The International Climate Initiative (ICI) is an innovative, international mechanism for financing climate protection projects. It receives funding from the sale of tradable emission certificates. The overall objective of the fund is to provide financial support to international projects supporting climate change mitigation, adaptation, and biodiversity projects with climate relevance. Out of the €400 million, €120 million is dedicated for developing countries (half of it for sustainable energies).
- A UK-managed fund is the Environmental Transformation Fund International Window.
- A Japanese fund is the Hatoyama Initiative.

The fund called Fundo Amazonia managed by the Brazilian Development Bank must also be mentioned here.

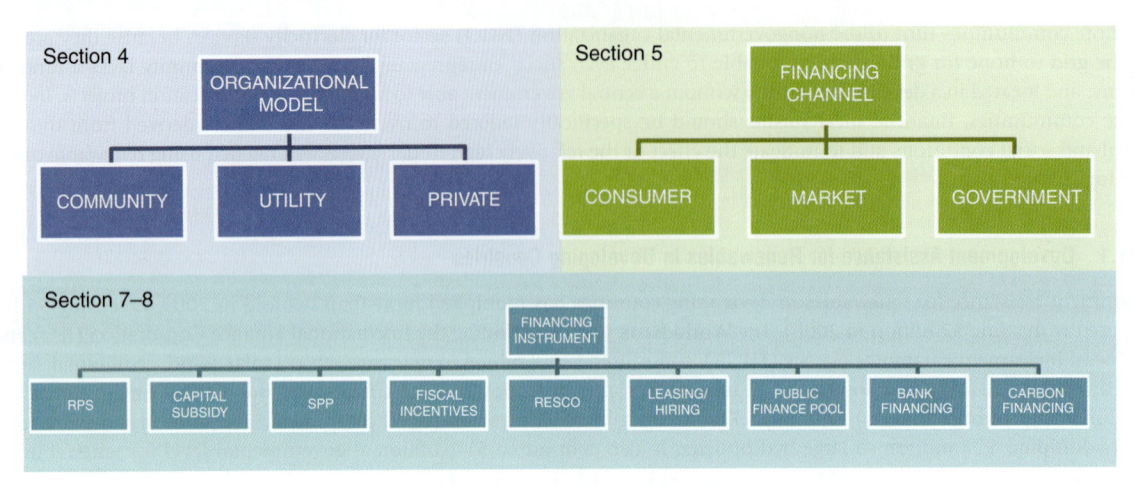

Figure 3 Analytical framework for financing PV in rural energy projects. Source: M Moner-Girona.

1.07.1.2 Analytical Framework for Support Mechanism of PV in Rural Areas

The wide range of existing support mechanisms for PV in rural areas can be analyzed from several perspectives depending on (1) how the community is organized, (2) to whom and from which institutes the financing is channeled, and (3) the specific instruments used for the financing (that will be the result of the combination of the options from the two first perspectives). **Figure 3** summarizes the analytical framework used in this chapter for analyzing the existing financing models that support PV in rural energy projects:

- Organizational *model*: defined as regulatory, legislative, and policy conditions (further described in Section 1.07.4);
- *Financing channel*: defined as the source of financing and how the financing is channeled (see Section 1.07.5);
- *Financing instrument*: defined as the specific delivering method of financing (see Sections 1.07.7 and 1.07.8).

Before discussing in detail the various instruments and models, we first provide a snapshot of the current market situation and cost trend of PV in the developing countries in the following two sections.

1.07.2 PV in Developing Countries: Current Situation

1.07.2.1 Evolution of Grid-Connected/Off-Grid PV Systems

In 2010, the worldwide PV market more than doubled; the volume of newly installed solar PV electricity systems varied between 17 and 19 GW, depending on the reporting consultancies [8]. Off-grid PV systems now constitute less than 5% of the total worldwide PV market. However, such applications still remain important in remote areas in developing countries that lack electricity infrastructure. In 2010, the off-grid PV capacity installed globally (including in both developed and developing countries) was between 400 and 800 MW. The new installed capacity is distributed approximately in 100–200 MW off-grid rural, 100–200 MW communication/signals, 100 MW off-grid commercial, and 100–200 MW consumer products. The main applications include very small scale systems (i.e., pico-PV programs) [9], water pumping units, communication units, solar home systems (SHSs), and PV integrated in mini-grids or hybrid systems.

Figure 4 presents the total capacity installed growth of off-grid PV (including off-grid PV in industrialized countries) from 1981 to 2010 compared with the PV grid-connected capacity. In the early years, the off-grid share was dominating the total PV market (>90%). However, the periods of strong growth have been driven by grid-connected applications. The share of off-grid PV in the total PV market began declining in 1996, from 90% to less than 5% in 2010 [8, 10].

1.07.2.2 Evolution of Electrification Rates and Off-Grid PV Systems for Rural Areas

In 2009, the number of people without access to electricity was 1.4 billion, 20% of the world's population [2, 3]. Some 85% of those people lived in rural areas (**Figure 5**). The number of rural households served by all forms of renewable energy is difficult to track, but may reach tens of millions. Regarding PV technology, an estimated 3 million households are electrified by small solar PV systems, with total cumulative off-grid PV capacity of 3.2 GW in 2009 [10].

The developing world offers a huge potential market for PV technologies and the PV price decrease can provide a more affordable electricity source for the people of this potential market. PV systems would provide reliable, clean, and environment-friendly energy and furthermore create direct and indirect employment via productive uses. Despite these appealing features, PV systems in rural areas of developing countries do not yet have broad market acceptance due to certain barriers [4]. In

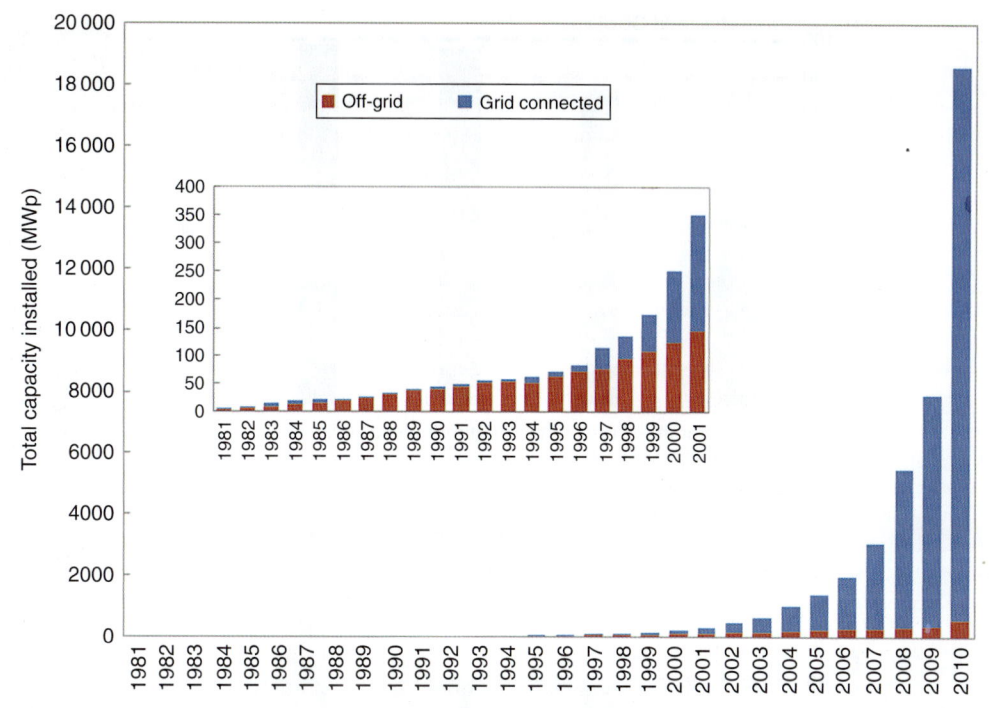

Figure 4 Off-grid/grid-connected yearly installed PV capacity growth. Source: Data compiled from Mints P (Navigant Consulting, May 2010); Reiche K, Grüner R, Attigah B, et al. GTZ. What difference can a pico-PV system make? May 2010 [10]; REN 21, Renewables Global Status Report 2010 [7]; and Jäger-Waldau A PV Status Report 2011. JRC-European Commission [9].

the near term, off-grid applications are the primary market for solar PV systems in developing countries – rural electrification programs are often integrated into either national infrastructure programs (including extension of the grid) or decentralized electrification of scattered population or isolated rural growth centers (by stand-alone systems or integrated into hybrid decentralized mini-grids). Eventually, where the grid infrastructure is maintained properly, the emergence of grid-connected PV systems is expected [4, 11].

In several developing countries, the PV installations are mainly off-grid systems; the figures are particularly high in Bangladesh (22 MWp), Indonesia (10 MWp), Kenya (7 MWp), Ethiopia (7 MWp), Nigeria (7 MWp), Sri Lanka (5 MWp), and Senegal (5 MWp). The coverage of population in these countries for the same capacity is higher, that is, 5 MWp SHSs with an average size of 50 Wp represent a solar power solution for 100 000 families [12]. In terms of SHSs, the most mature markets exist in India (450 000 SHSs), China (150 000 SHSs), Kenya (120 000 SHSs), Morocco (80 000 SHSs), Mexico (80 000 SHSs), and South Africa (50 000 SHSs). Kenya and China are by far the fastest growing markets, with annual growth rates of 10–20% in recent years. Many of these countries also manufacture components for SHSs, such as batteries, controllers, and lights [9].

1.07.2.3 Energy Technology Options for Rural Areas

The optimized energy option for unserved settlements depends not only on the distance to the existing grid but also on the load density and the natural resources available. Policy-makers and population in rural developing areas often hesitate to accept solar electric systems as a substitute for grid electricity because of the false perception of lower capacity service of solar electricity compared with electricity utility available in urban areas [10]. Paradoxically, the electricity grid infrastructure in many areas of the developing world suffers from frequent blackouts and requires significant upgrades [13], making the solar system option a much more reliable source of electricity for the unserved rural population.

The state of the network in most of the sub-Saharan African countries is very poor. The average lifetime of the transmission and distribution network is more than 36 years old [13]. **Figure 6(a)** gives the lifetime data for the transmission lines of the 27 countries where the average lifetime is older than 30 years. In two-thirds of these countries, the lifetime is more than 50 years. Maintaining a reliable service on this poor network is not feasible in many of these countries. Coupled with other factors (low payback ratios, inadequate regulation, different crisis situations), it can multiply the difficulties to manage the system. Moreover, most of the countries with old infrastructure occupy some of the first positions in the list of the longest blackout periods. **Figure 6(b)** gives the percentage of the year in which the service of electricity is down in the countries, where this proportion is higher than 5%. Besides the huge costs that occur due to the blackouts, this can undermine any potential extensions to new areas. Extending the grids to places further away from the power plants and connecting a smaller number of households with a low load factor may cost more than distributed renewable generation.

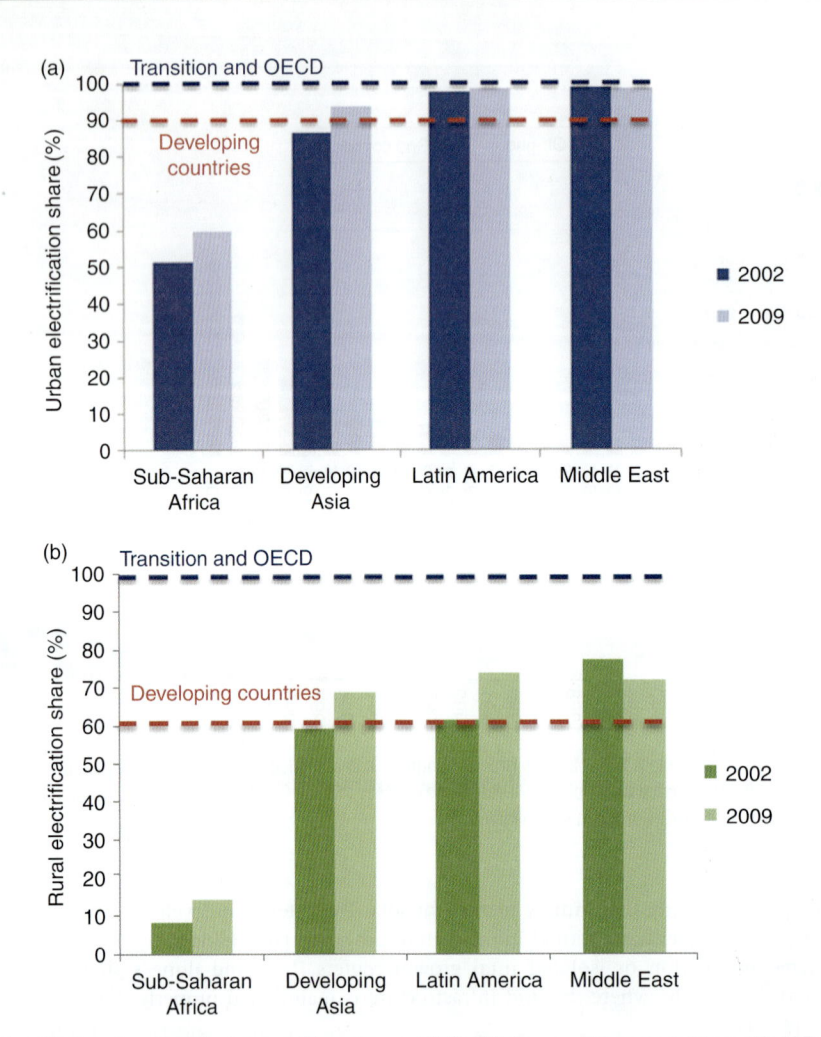

Figure 5 Evolution of electrification share for (a) urban and (b) rural areas (2002–09). Source: Data compiled from *World Energy Outlook 2010*. Paris: OECD/IEA [2] and *World Energy Outlook 2006*. Paris: OECD/IEA [3].

The grid extension is often more expensive in rural areas than in urban areas because of its lower load densities, low capacity utilization rates, high electricity line losses, and requirement for accompanying infrastructure development such as road building [13]. Stand-alone PV systems and decentralized hybrid systems are often the least expensive electrification options in sparsely populated areas with low electricity loads [6]. However, the high initial capital investment, the moderate operating and maintenance cost, and the lack of guarantee for the payments due to the specific socioeconomic conditions of the final consumers represent a bottleneck for their dissemination; adapted financial services to the potential rural users could help to address these barriers [14]. The success of a given mechanism depends on various factors ranging from selection of the right mechanism for the right location to the implementation strategy of the selected mechanism. However, financial schemes in rural areas of developing countries should be designed in such a way that they decrease financing risks and increase access to modern energy services to the poorest (see Sections 1.07.7 and 1.07.8).

1.07.3 Current Costs of PV in Developing Countries

In Africa, Asia, and Latin America, access to modern energy in isolated areas is driven partially by the use of pico-PV applications [9], PV for mini-grid, and off-grid systems, which in many instances are already at par with diesel genset prices [7, 15, 16]. Nevertheless, a recent study found that prices for solar PV modules and systems in Africa, Asia, and Latin America exceed those for grid-connected PV technology in Europe [7, 17].

Figure 7 depicts the evolution of PV module prices in Africa and Asia compared with world PV average price [12], that is, in Africa and Latin America, the PV price difference for small PV applications in low-income countries and the world price average can be more than 40%. In 2010, the PV price was as high as 4.52 US$ Wp^{-1} compared with the world average of 2.05 US$ Wp^{-1}.

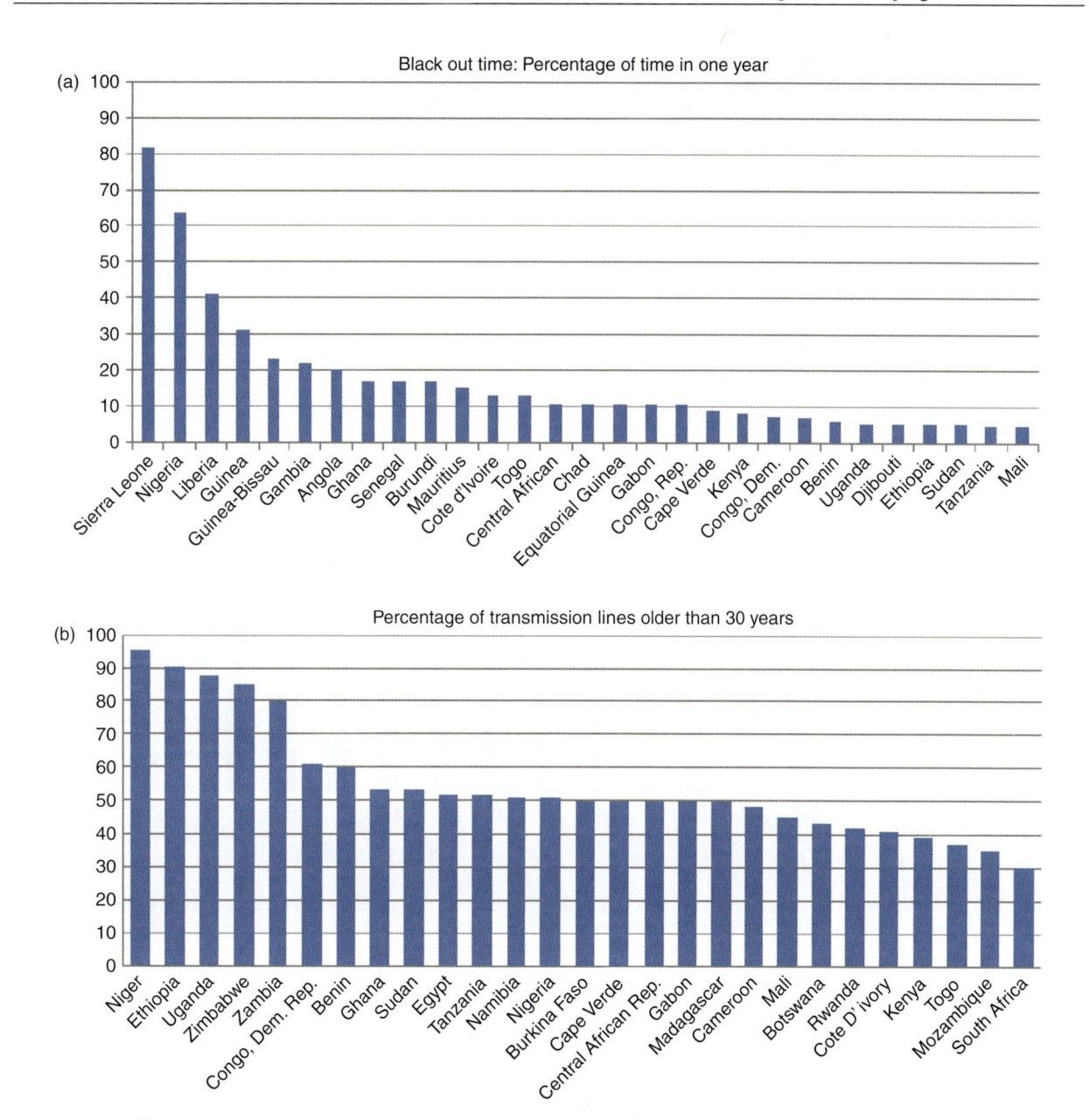

Figure 6 Reliability of African grid infrastructure: (a) percentage of transmission lines older than 30 years, (b) percentage of blackouts. Source: Data compiled from Foster V and Briceno-Garmendia C (eds.) Africa's Infrastructure: A Time for Transformation, Agence Française de Développement and the International Bank for Reconstruction and Development/The World Bank, Washington, USA, 2010 [13].

Moreover, PV system prices are higher in Africa than in other parts of the world (**Figure 7**). For example, a Ugandan may pay 2 times what an Asian customer pays for an equivalent PV system. High African prices are largely due to taxes and transaction costs in the process of delivering the system. One exception to this trend is the Kenyan solar market, where intense competition and import tariff reductions have played an important role in bringing prices down [18, 19], as exemplified in **Figure 8**, in which the SHS price is shown for various African countries.

Developing the supply markets is an important part of growing PV markets in developing countries. But perhaps more importantly, PV equipment is still beyond the reach of most rural Africans. Price decreases will be important for these markets to provide services to a larger portion of the population.

Table 1 compares the levelized cost of electricity (LCOE) generation (US$ kWh^{-1}) for various PV options. The LCOE allows for the quantification of the unitary cost of the electricity generated during the lifetime of the system; thus a direct comparison between the costs of different technologies becomes possible [21; ESMAP, 2007]. Typical energy costs are under best conditions, including system design, siting, and resource availability. Optimal conditions can yield lower costs, and less favorable conditions can yield substantially higher costs. PV electricity production depends primarily on the amount of solar radiation available. For

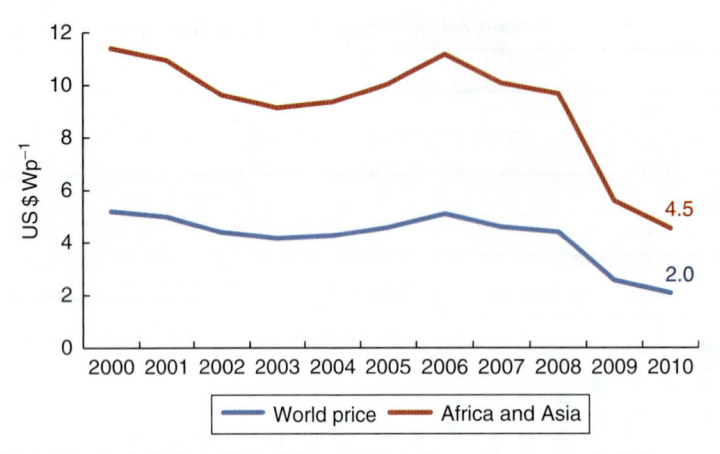

Figure 7 Comparison of the PV module price in US$ per Wp in Africa and Asia to the world average price [12].

Figure 8 SHS prices (US$ Wp^{-1}) in selected African countries [20]. Source: Nieuwenhout FDJ, van Dijk A, *et al.* (2001) Experience with solar home systems in developing countries: A review. *Progress in Photovoltaics: Research and Applications* 9: 455–474 [34] and Moner-Girona M, Ghanadan R, Jacobson A, and Kammen DM (2006) Decreasing PV costs in Africa: Opportunities for rural electrification using solar PV in Sub-Saharan Africa. *Refocus* 7(1) [20]. Note: Solar PV system cost includes solar panel, battery, four lights, charge controller, installation materials, and installation.

Table 1 Estimated PV costs (SHS, mini-grid, grid connected) under best conditions [7, 8]

	Size	LCOE (US$ kWh^{-1})	Social/economic impact
Grid connected	200 kW–100 MW	0.15–0.3 (end-users often subsidized)	Low to medium
Mini-grid	10–1000 kWp	0.25–1	High
SHS	20–100 W	0.4–0.6	High
Pico-PV lamps	1–10 W	0.10–0.60 (US$ klmh^{-1})	Very high

Source: REN 21, Renewables Global Status Report 2011 [8]; Intergovernmental Panel on Climate Change (IPCC) (2011) Summary for Policymakers, In: Edenhofer O, Pichs-Madruga R, Sokona Y, *et al.* (eds) *IPCC Special Report on Renewable Energy Sources and Climate Change Mitigation.* Cambridge, UK: Cambridge University Press; European Photovoltaic Industry Association (EPIA) (2011) *Global Market Outlook for Photovoltaics until 2015*; International Energy Agency, World Energy Outlook 2008, ISBN-13: 978-92-64-04560-6; Technical and Economic Assessment of Off-grid, Mini-grid, and Grid Electrification Technologies. Energy Sector Management Assistance Program (ESMAP). Technical Paper 121/07. December 2007. The International Bank for Reconstruction and Development/The World Bank, Washington, USA; Reiche K, Grüner R, Attigah B, *et al.* GTZ. What difference can a pico-PV system make? May 2010 [10].

grid-connected systems, the energy output can be approximated, being proportional to the total solar irradiation impinging on the PV modules. For off-grid systems, energy output fundamentally depends on the installed capacity size of the renewable energy (RE) resource conversion technology (i.e., PV, small hydro, and wind) [22]. Costs of off-grid hybrid power systems and mini-grids employing renewables depend strongly on system size, location, and associated items such as diesel backup and battery storage [7]. Pico-PV systems are small independent appliances providing light and/or additional small electrical services. They are powered by a solar panel and use a battery for electricity storage; their lighting service cost (initial investment divided by lighting output) ranges from 0.1 to 0.6 US$ klmh^{-1} [9].

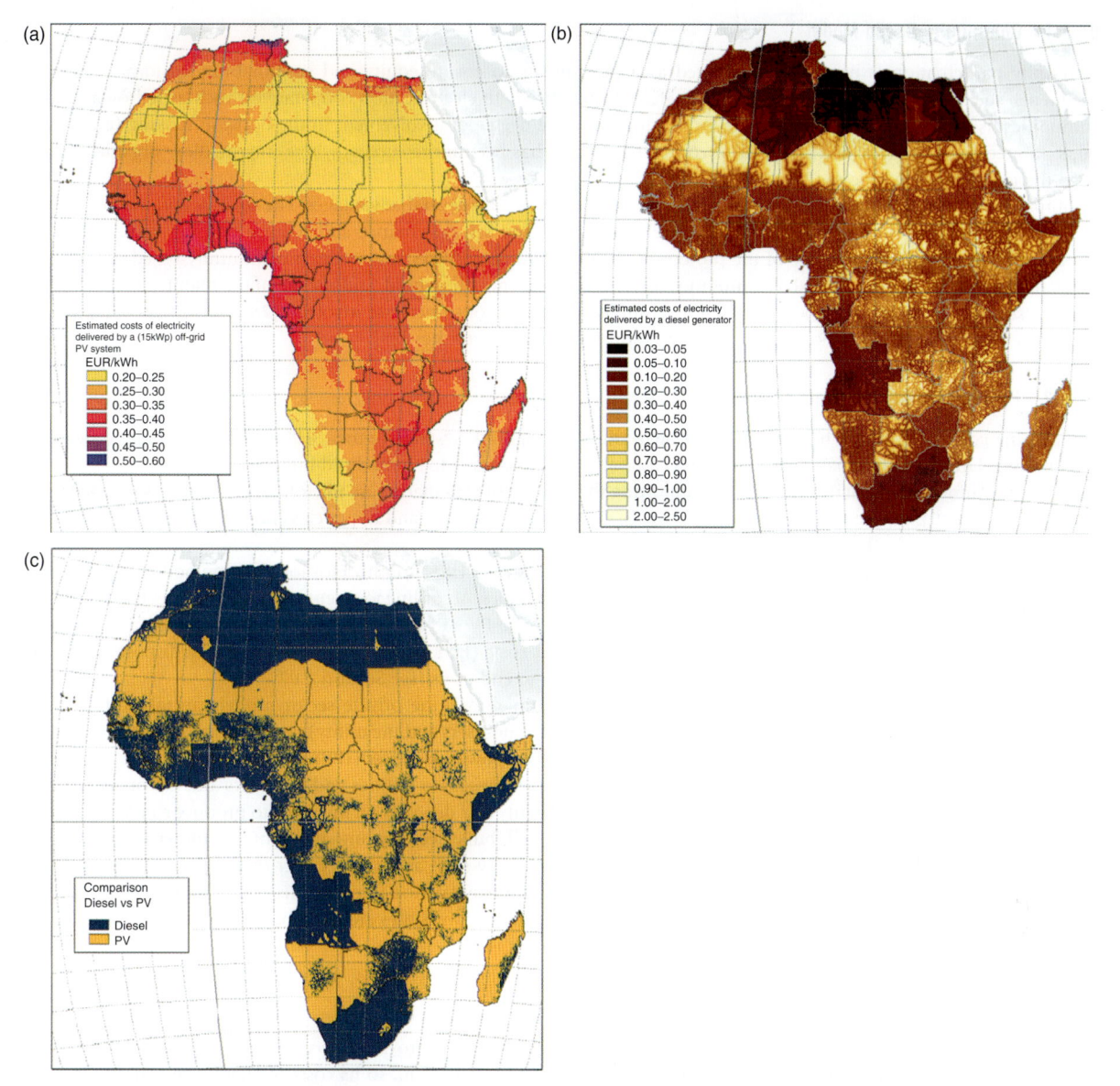

Figure 9 Estimated costs of electricity (€ kWh^{-1}) delivered by (a) off-grid PV system; (b) diesel generator; (c) off-grid options: economic comparison of diesel vs. PV. Source: Szabo S, Bodis K, Huld T, and Moner-Girona M (2011) Energy solutions in rural Africa: Mapping electrification costs of distributed solar and diesel generation versus grid extension. *Environmental Research Letters* 6: 9 [23]. Data based on PVGIS. http://re.jrc.ec.europa.eu/pvgis [24].

As a concrete example for PV off-grid electricity production cost, **Figure 9** compares the estimated costs of electricity for local mini-grid PV systems in Africa (15 kWp) ranging from 0.2 upto 0.55 € kWh^{-1} [23] with the costs of electricity delivered by a diesel generator (ranging from 0.03 to 2.5 € kWh^{-1}) using the diesel price for each country and taking into account the cost of diesel transportation. In most of the sub-Saharan countries, there are regions where from the two distributed generation technologies calculated, the PV offers a cheaper solution than the diesel gensets. The diesel option is dominantly cheaper only in countries where the diesel is heavily subsidized (Angola, Egypt, Lybia, Algeria, and Tunisia) and to a certain extent where these subsidies are lower but present (Nigeria and South African Republic). In the other sub-Saharan countries, PV is cheaper where the transport distance is high. As the road infrastructure density is far lower than in the rest of the world, PV would provide electricity competively to diesel genset in the majority of the rural parts of Africa (with the exception of the West African countries and South Africa).

1.07.4 Ownership, Organization, and Local Participation

The appropriate ownership and organizational model (**Figure 3**) for PV electrification varies according to the local socioeconomic conditions [25, 26] and the final energy services offered depending on power dimension and number of users, that is, multiuser PV systems, SHSs, and the pico-PV systems.

1.07.4.1 Community-Based Model

Community participation is now widely accepted as a prerequisite to ensure equity and sustainability of local infrastructure investments, such as rural electrification in remote areas. Experience with electrification cooperatives, such as self-organized solar communities, is variable and depends on the local culture and the degree of involvement in the decision making (e.g., women's groups, farmers' cooperatives, and chamber of commerce). There has been more success where intermediary organizations have helped the local planning process [27].

Compared with the alternatives, self-organized solar communities have several advantages. The owners and managers are also the consumers and therefore increase community self-sufficiency and self-governance and require training and operation and maintenance jobs during the lifetime of the project. Moreover, multiuser PV systems under a community-based model have in general an increased performance in the community, lower system cost per household, and a share of the maintenance costs among the final users. Nevertheless, the operation is more complex as several consumers are involved [28] and the potential for social conflict has to be addressed via sociological, technical, and economic approaches [29].

1.07.4.2 Private Ownership/Private Operator

In developing countries, private household-based ownership for small PV systems (either SHS or pico-PV) under a dealer sales model needs relatively high initial investment costs compared with the restricted household budgets.

The most common financial instruments for supporting the take-off of SHS market are microfinance or credit sales (see Sections 1.07.7.1 and 1.07.7.9). The end-users who own the SHSs are mainly the middle and upper class households because of relatively high initial system costs [19] (see Section 1.07.3).

Pico-PV systems offer lower cost energy access for lighting services (2–9 US$ month^{-1}) for low-income households in comparison to the actual monthly costs for lighting by kerosene lamps and candles. According to recent studies by the Deutsche Gesellschaft für Internationale Zusammenarbeit (GIZ) [9], the financing for the pico-PV end-users, particularly for consumers at the bottom of the income pyramid, to bridge the gap between one-time upfront costs (US$36–120) and their monthly disposable budget or lighting, can be supported through consumer credits from retailers to end-users (see Section 1.07.7.1).

In the case of multiuser PV systems (PV hybrid systems or mini-grids), the private sector model can take different forms according to the ownership of the system, the type of contracts (with end-users and the utility), and the type of subsidies [30]. One common case for a privately held PV facility is when an independent power producer (IPP) is involved. An IPP is an entity that without being a public utility owns facilities to generate electric power for sale to utilities and end-users and has no affiliation to a transmission or distribution company. The IPP is a privately held facility and depends on investors to produce electricity. When the ownership of the renewable energy facilities stays in the IPP, the IPP sells bulk electricity into the mini-grid under a long-term power purchase agreement (PPA). In this case, the agreement involves an entity such as a single buyer or the distribution company to purchase the power generated by the IPP under specified terms for a multiyear period (see Sections 1.07.7.5 and 1.07.8.1 for further details on the financial instruments). If a business plan is well structured, companies are also able to ensure long-term O&M and have the technical ability to address urgent problems and replacement issues.

1.07.4.3 Rural Energy Service Company Model

A rural energy service company (RESCO) is a quasi-governmental body that provides electricity to rural customers. Often the government gives subsidies to the RESCO to purchase PV systems and install them, so its costs of energy are typically lower than for an IPP. A RESCO is responsible to the public and has a board of elected commissioners; therefore, decisions are centralized. RESCO can, besides providing electricity, assist in developing a broad array of community services, such as water, waste, transportation, telecommunications, and other energy services. Because the ownership of the renewable energy facilities (either in the form of SHS, hybrid system, or mini-grid) stays in the RESCO, the company provides installation, operation, maintenance, repair, and additional services to end-users in return for monthly fees for connection and service. Due to their public or quasi-public position, RESCO also directly benefits from a privileged legal position and does have better access to financing mechanisms that it can sometimes apply itself (i.e., cross-subsidies) and can aggregate environmental benefits of individual systems (i.e., clean development mechanism (CDM)).

The utility-based model is an option that has been widely used around the world. According to the World Bank, utilities are the most common driver for rural electrification in developing countries [31]. In fee-for-service, ownership belongs to a RESCO. The customer pays a service fee for the use of the system – the electricity service. The monthly installment depends on the system size. Since the early 2000s, large concessions of SHSs through fee-for-service programs have taken place and helped to spread the use of SHSs (Morocco, South Africa, Zambia, Eritrea, Namibia, Senegal, Benin, Mauritania, Bangladesh, Argentina, Peru, Togo, and Cape Verde). While end-users may never own a system, they are able to receive guaranteed services from the company.

1.07.5 Financing Channels for PV in Rural Renewable Energy

The previous section described the possible types of ownership and organizational model for off-grid PV systems. The following sections describe the rural renewable energy finance channels [33] depending on which sector is being financed: consumer (Section 1.07.5.1), market sector (Section 1.07.5.2), and public sector (Section 1.07.5.3).

1.07.5.1 Consumer Finance

This section provides short definitions for various types of financing the consumers to purchase or rent the PV systems. When the financed sector is the final user, there are several financial instruments, which are described in more detail in Sections 1.07.7.1 and 1.07.7.9.

Almost all development stakeholders agree that the distribution of systems free of charge should be avoided. It is fundamental that customers contribute to be conscious of the value of the system. The high initial capital costs of PV systems, particularly if they come with an after-sales service, relative to household incomes, have resulted in the slow adoption of renewables in off-grid rural areas. As **Figure 10** shows, typical 50 Wp SHS prices are more than the average gross national income (GNI) per capita in most African countries, so only a very small part of the rural population has enough income to overcome such an investment in one stroke. This is why financial schemes have to be set up for local users (**Figure 10**).

Historically, the main problem for directly financing users has been the small projects size, their high geographical dispersion, and high risk depending on the political country situation, which has discouraged financial institutions from providing loans [9]. Providing loans to rural consumers is best handled by microfinance institutions and hire purchase organizations [33].

1.07.5.1.1 Commercial banks and nonbank financing institutions

Commercial banks and nonbank financing institutions providing loans can be a significant source of financing. But at the same time, it is necessary that the countries have a well-developed rural banking infrastructure with programs adapted to the needs of rural users and with links to the renewable energy sector. In most of the developing countries, traditional banking systems are still not active in financing rural renewable energy because of the high risk and low profit associated with these loans. Financial institutions are not always interested in giving or opening lines of credit for rural renewable energy [9].

1.07.5.1.2 Microcredits

The concept of microfinance or microcredit was proposed by Muhammad Yunus, the 2006 Nobel Peace Prize winner and the managing director of Grameen Bank. Microcredit gives loan to people without any guarantee. The loan is recovered from the borrowers in a number of regular installments. This financial system can reach a substantial population deprived of access to formal financial institutions. Apart from the economic perspective, its impact on empowering rural underprivileged women is quite significant [35].

Microfinance is a useful tool for financing users to purchase SHSs since it makes the markets less price sensitive and allows an emphasis on high-quality products that might be more expensive, but last longer. The link between quality and microfinance is crucial since reliability will be the most important condition to ensure that an end-user will be willing and able to pay for installments.

With microfinance, it is possible to lower the investment barrier and to reach middle and lower-income customers. In the case of Bangladesh, a down payment of 15% of the total price is required, as well as a monthly fee of US$11 for 3 years [29] (**Figure 11**).

Moreover, the savings (on kerosene, candles, etc.) resulting from the use of the SHS are generally what is going to be used to pay back the microloan. Hence, the design of the microfinance contract is often done according to the existing energy expenses in order to ensure that the users will be able to pay back the loan. The prices of SHS should also reflect those of the usual competitive technologies (e.g., diesel and candles). The customers can then fairly compare the prices and recognize that their money is better invested as a down payment for an SHS, particularly as the monthly fees are adapted to the regular energy expenditures [29].

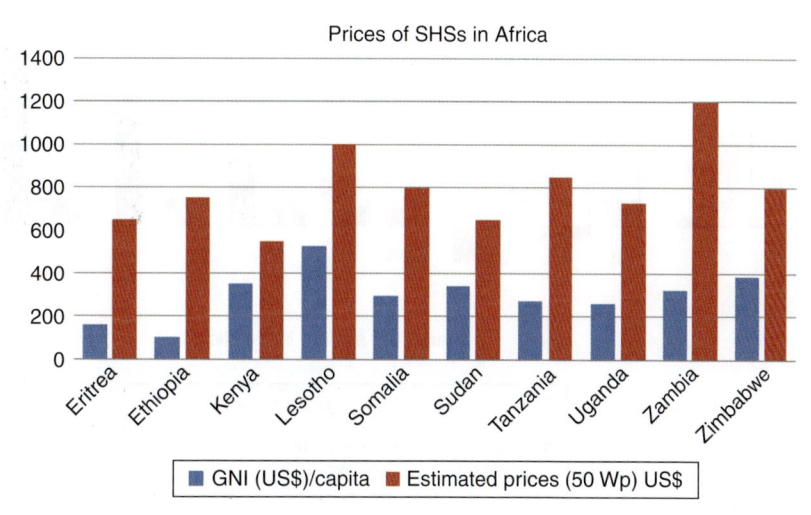

Figure 10 Comparison of SHS prices vs. GNI per each selected African country [20].

122 Economics and Environment

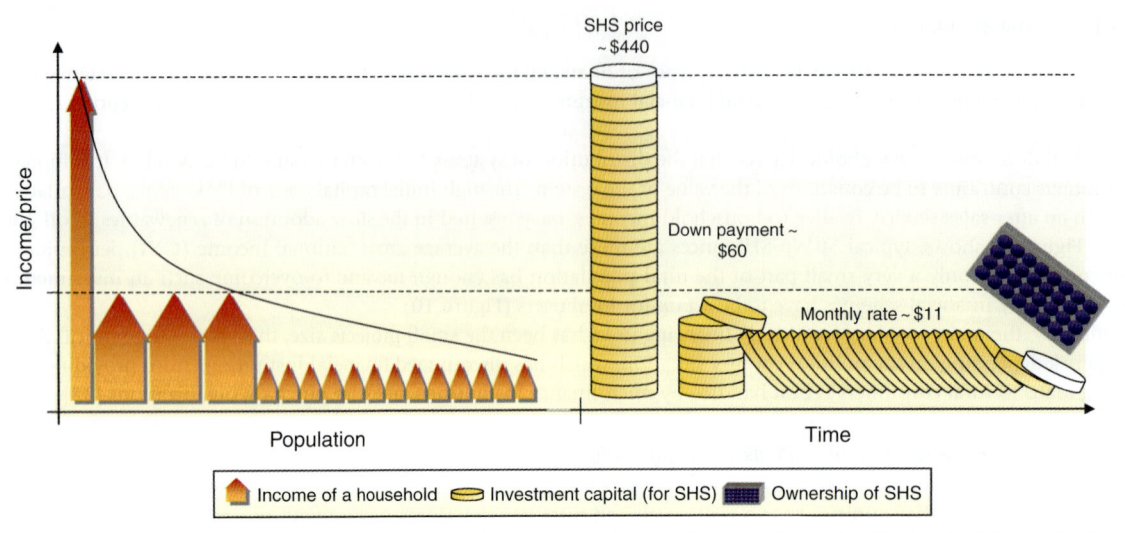

Figure 11 Overcoming the investment barrier for an SHS through microfinance. Source: Alliance for Rural Electrification (2009) Green light for renewable energy in developing countries [29].

Another important aspect for a well-designed SHS financing scheme is the adaptation to the depreciation and loss of value of the system over time, as is usual in leasing contracts. For the leasing company, the monthly payments have to reflect the system's resale value in case of payment failure. A well-tailored microfinance scheme is adapted on the one hand to the current expenses of the end-users and on the other hand to the loss of value of the system over time. For instance, in Bangladesh, where SHSs are standardized and where a large second-hand market exists, the 15% down payment reflects the costs of installation and deinstallation (in case of payment failure) and the loss of value of the system directly after installation (**Figure 12**).

Figure 13 shows the average expenses of Grameen Shakti [36] customers before and after they bought an SHS in comparison to battery and kerosene; after less than 5 years, the end-users start saving money.

Two different microfinance business models exist for energy services: the one-handed dealer credit model (Grameen Shakti/Bangladesh model) and the two-handed end-user credit model (SEEDS or Sri Lanka model).

1.07.5.1.2(i) One-hand business model

If there is no renewable energy product provider willing or able to develop its activities in a region, microfinance institutions (MFIs) can be trained by a renewable energy company or program to develop their own energy-funding departments or subsidiaries (also called the dealer credit model/Grameen Shakti/Bangladesh model). These will promote simple and standardized energy solutions and products together with their loans. MFIs can then replicate this model and their own energy department.

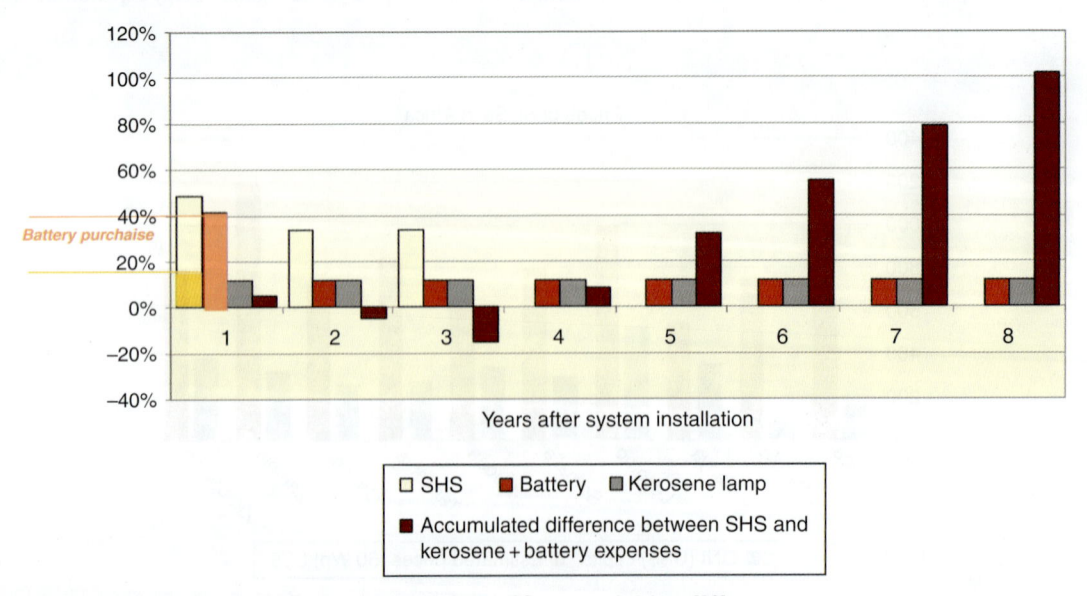

Figure 12 Comparison of costs. Source: Website of Grameen Shakti (GS), www.gshakti.org [36].

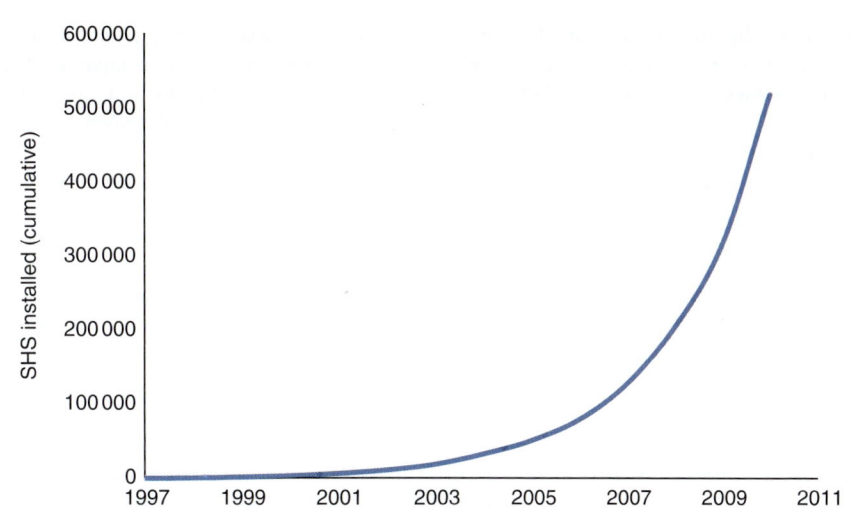

Figure 13 SHS installed in Bangladesh under the Grameen Shakti SHS program. Source: Compiled from data published in web site of Grameen Shakti (GS): http://www.gshakti.org/ [36].

The main challenge of the one-hand model is that the MFI must become part of the supply chain, develop stock logistics, and offer end-user training and maintenance services. Also, money collection in highly scattered and low populated rural areas might be a problem.

This model has been created by Grameen Shakti, a not-for-profit company, which is acting today as an energy system provider [36, 37]. It is a part of the Grameen Bank objective of alleviating poverty for the extreme poor through microcredit. Up to 2010, approximately 518 000 SHSs were installed under the Grameen Shakti SHS program. From **Figure 13**, it is evident that the Grameen Shakti SHS program is experiencing a rapid growth. The success of microfinance-based financial system has initiated a revolutionary movement in the energy sector of Bangladesh and beyond. The economic, social, and environmental impact of the SHS program has encouraged the Bangladesh government to adopt policies to promote the program to a wider and greater extent.

Following the success of Bangladesh, this model has been reproduced by energy companies that have been hiring microfinance specialists and have started offering end-user credits, such as Zara Solar in Tanzania or Solar Energy Uganda.

1.07.5.1.2(ii) Two-hand business model

This model is based on a long-term partnership between the MFIs and a committed rural energy service provider (also called the end-user credit model (SEEDS/Sri Lanka model)). In contrast to the one-hand business model, it is more suitable for diversification and customization of energy products. One provides the credit and the other the energy supply, knowledge, training, and maintenance.

This approach is more comfortable for MFIs, particularly in the starting phase as this type of structure, which requires only financial services from them, is closer to their core business. However, it is also usually more expensive because it involves two institutions and their respective infrastructures.

Furthermore, a strong partnership and a common vision shared by the energy provider and the MFI at the management and operational levels are crucial for ensuring the long-term success of the partnership. International experience shows that over time, MFIs tend to vertically integrate the energy business and to take over technical responsibilities, especially if the energy provider is not delivering proper services or product guarantees, which are crucial to loan repayment.

With both of the microfinance business models, the customers gain ownership over the system after the repayment period, but other approaches where the ownership stays with the provider are also widely developed.

Generally, the two-hand model is easier and cheaper to implement in its initial phase, but in the longer term, the double infrastructure of two companies can become costly. From this point of view, the fee-for-service and one-hand models are probably more viable approaches. Both these models generally need to involve companies with a technical know-how and experience or require training specialists; the one-hand model will always need capacity building, either on the microfinance side for technical companies or on the technical side for MFIs.

1.07.5.2 Market Development Finance

The United Nations Secretary General's advisory group on energy and climate change states that

> the private-sector participation in achieving the MDGs should be emphasized and encouraged. In the first instance, this will require the creation of long-term, predictable policy and regulatory frameworks to mobilize private capital. The creation of new and innovative investment mechanisms to enable accelerated technology deployment with active private-sector participation [1, 38]

One option is channeling the finance to the market development, where companies are financed to help them expand their import, distribution, retail, or other operations and to offer credit to downstream consumers or companies. A supply chain must be in place before financing of PV systems is considered [33]. To make rural electrification attractive and profitable to the private sector, a first solution is to design rural electrification projects around already existing business applications – or those close to existing, guaranteed off-takers that will make the projects attractive enough to private sector generation.

Central government might offer policies of opening electricity generation to private participation. To help the private sector, the market for PV should be created by considering a number of measures to raise awareness among investors, banking institutions, and potential consumers/off-takers on the viability of PV technologies [33]. Governments can also support the development of technical and business training in order to address the chain of supply and help the local companies to develop their activities.

The economic viability of large off-grid PV systems often depends on the presence of a productive activity or a local business (agriculture for instance). Many off-grid communities have activities that require energy or have a strong potential for initiating such activities, but are constrained by the lack of a stable and reasonably priced energy supply. Therefore, off-grid project designers should take advantage of opportunities that will significantly increase the prospects for long-term project sustainability through the direct generation of revenues [29].

A more global approach, but following the same logic, is to link a rural electrification project with a strong business development approach. This means that the project designers identify prior to the project implementation the likely local participants for a microbusiness and assist them in developing business activities. If this approach succeeds, it also dramatically increases the chances for the project to be sustainable over time. Collaboration prior to and during the project with local partners such as NGOs can be a good way to complement the outreach activities of the company [29].

1.07.5.3 Public Sector Finance (Poverty Alleviation)

Even with lower prices, well-established sales networks, and consumer financing, the poorer segments of the population will still not be able to afford PV. Questions then arise why donor funding is being used to help the upper quartile of the population to access PV systems and what is being done for low-income groups [33]. Where poverty alleviation is a primary objective, these questions must be asked. In such cases, public funding may be best used to increase access to electricity in an equitable way and use public funds for social buildings such as schools, hospitals, or power community with water supplies. Financing rural renewable energy is a part of financing rural electrification; it is an issue of improving social equity [38]. Public sector finance has been an important channel for financing rural renewable energy. Governments have a strong role to play in financing rural renewable energy by initiating national programs and providing financial incentives.

Major funding agencies have accepted PV power supplies and other renewable energy technologies as fully reliable for many social projects in developing countries. A number of additional agencies have also come into existence, combining an understanding of regional problem solving with novel new approaches to private and public funding [10]. International financing sources play a major role as incubator funds for the development of rural renewable energy. Many rural renewable energy projects worldwide have been financed by multilateral and bilateral organizations. The trend during the past decade has been to provide large amounts of funding to public financing institutions that are committed to support rural and renewable energy projects. They do not provide financing to households directly; rather, it is up to the private companies, concessionaires, NGOs, and microfinance groups to organize the demand for the energy service and to apply for project funding after developing a sound business plan to serve rural consumers [7]. This model has been successfully implemented in many countries, including Bangladesh, Mali, Senegal, and Sri Lanka. In practice, many of these funds specialize initially in a single technology, such as SHSs, but they are expanding increasingly to other renewable energy systems as well as to nonrenewable energy access [7].

1.07.6 PV Tariff Setting and Incentives for Rural Electrification

Tariff setting is a significant factor for the long-term sustainability of a PV project and strongly influences the project profitability. Therefore, tariff setting will be associated with the finance instrument (see Section 1.07.7) under which the PV program/projects are going to be developed. The kind of tariff can be flat tariff for individual systems or metering when connected to a collective central system.

The price structure for electricity generally consists of capital cost, generation and distribution cost, fuel cost (if applicable), annual operations, maintenance, management (both labor and materials), periodic equipment replacement, taxes and levies, profit for the operator, and return on equity for investors [29].

There is a balance to be struck such that the tariff setting reconciles sustainability of the project while meeting rural consumers' ability and willingness to pay (affordability) [40]. To achieve this balance, tariffs must be flexible and tailor-made taking into account the offer side (cost recovery for sustainability of business) and demand (tariff can be afforded by end-users) [41]. Tariffs should not be set at the level of the national utility on the grounds of being 'equitable'; neither should it be based on the consideration of the households' energy expenses (i.e., kerosene lamps and candles) before the project. The concept of affordability of course plays a crucial role but it can be balanced with subsidies and support schemes. In general, when setting a tariff for rural electrification projects, regardless of the scheme chosen, the tariff should at least cover the operating costs and replacements (e.g., batteries and inverters) to ensure the ongoing operation of a system throughout its lifetime. Two main types of tariffs are relevant [29]:

1. 'Breakeven tariffs' are designed to ensure that revenues cover operating, maintenance, and replacement costs. They are more easily affordable by most customers, especially if a subsidy is used in order to reduce the investment. In this case, the initial investment costs are entirely or greatly covered by other financial means (see Section 1.07.7).
2. 'Profitable' tariffs are designed to allow for sufficient return on investment to attract private sector investors. The private sector participation may result in higher tariffs or in higher incentives to keep tariffs affordable. The tariff is designed to cover the costs of all system components. The project implementation price includes the systems itself, the training, and the installation costs. If part of the investment cost is covered by the tariff, then the operator can expand to new customers. If the investment costs are not partially covered, and if the operators do not realize enough profit, then continuous public subsidies might be needed for expansion [41].

In the case of PV mini-grid systems, one can also follow a 'graded tariff regime' (low tariffs for the first kilowatt-hours and higher tariffs for heavier consumption), just as some grid systems do. This allows the tariffs to be set in better proportion to the customer's ability to pay and follows the assumption of a diminishing marginal utility of electricity. This also allows the setting up of different subsidy schemes better adapted to the consumption of the end-users.

1.07.6.1 Procedure for Annual Revision

Investors reduce their risk exposure by including provisions for regular changes in the tariff applied [41]. By doing so, they want to ensure that they maintain their original payback period and their liquidity even if the unforeseeable costs increase. The liquidity position can change due to many factors, among which the following are the most frequent:

- inflation rate and
- rate of exchange/US dollar (imported components)

In that respect, the advantage of the PV technology is that as the operational costs are quite minimal and as they rely on indigenous sources, most of these risks can be planned. In this respect, the fact that the capacity of payment of end-users or the income of inhabitants is not necessarily indexed to inflation should still be taken into account. So any procedure for revision has to take into account the local income generation properties.

Finally, tariff setting requires stakeholder participation as an iterative process; survey of income structures and percentage of inhabitants of an area that can be reached are key factors for optimizing tariff for various consumers and under different financial frameworks. The final output of the iterative process is critical for equity and sustainability [40, 41].

1.07.7 Finance Instruments to Promote PV Systems in Rural Areas in Developing Countries

Favorable regulatory, legislative, and policy conditions are critical for financing rural renewable energy [40]. These conditions strongly affect the possibilities and competitiveness of PV, sometimes in a way that economically viable rural renewable energy projects are financially not viable. Complementary to the tariff setting, and depending on the profit or nonprofit perspective, different combinations 'of support instruments' are needed to support poor rural areas in accessing modern energy services.

Possible instruments for finance and incentive mechanism to support the development of PV systems for rural renewable energy either as pico-PV, stand-alone, or hybrid systems with mini-grids are renewable portfolio standards (RPSs), seed capital (capital subsidies or grants), investment tax credits, sales tax or value-added tax (VAT) exemptions, green certificate trading, direct energy production payments or tax credits, net metering, direct public investment or bank financing (renewable energy finance initiatives), public competitive bidding, feed-in tariffs (FiTs) in the form of renewable premium tariff or under the Global Energy Transfer Feed-in Tariffs (GET FiTs), carbon financing, and long-term transitions from off-grid to on-grid generation systems.

1.07.7.1 Capital Subsidies, Consumer Grants, and Guarantees

This section gives an overview of the financial transfers of international donor organizations that play a mobilizing role in the international financing that was described in Section 1.07.5.3.

Grants do not require repayment: they are essentially 'gift' money with specific requirements or terms for use. Governmental and international organizations offer grants to promote environmental and development policies. Usually they include a statement of the work that will be performed using the money, including restrictions on how the money can be spent and the time frame during which it can be spent. Grants will often be directed toward the purchase of hardware and equipment required for the PV project and nowadays will usually include a training component. Grants often are given by private foundations; by international development organizations such as the World Bank, the GEF, bilateral funding organizations; or through national renewable energy funding divisions as well [43].

Currently, a seed capital payment by the government or utility covering a percentage of the capital cost of the PV system investment is the most common approach in the developing world. They are allied with a tariff scheme that covers the operational and maintenance costs. Some type of direct capital investment subsidy, grant, or rebate is offered in at least 45 countries and has been particularly instrumental in supporting solar PV markets [7].

Declining capital grants on a sliding scale over the life of the project are built into more recent projects to 'push' the market early on and then allow a transition to a fully commercial market. Some projects are offered fixed cash grants for each system installed once certification of the installation is available. For example, in the Chinese renewable energy development projects, a $100 cash grant is paid directly to the SHS dealer and in India the subsidies such as capital subsidy and interest subsidy are mainly provided by the Ministry of New and Renewable Energy Sources [38]. Another alternative is where state-owned electricity companies absorb the investment costs of the projects to provide a service and give access to the most remote regions; this is possible with cross-subsidies, and sometimes with the aid of municipalities or other organizations, actions are service oriented and nonprofit.

Guarantees are a contractual promise from a financing or well-capitalized organization to take responsibility for payment of a debt if the primarily liable organization fails to pay. Guarantees are offered by multilateral development banks (MDBs) and national development banks. For example, MIGA is organized by the World Bank to help investors and lenders to deal with political risks by insuring eligible projects against losses relating to currency transfer restrictions, breach of contract, expropriation, and war and civil disturbance, as these facilitate developing countries to attract and retain private investment [43, 44].

1.07.7.2 Renewable Energy Service Companies

The RESCO concept is most suitable for small-scale renewable energy systems like PV SHSs. Rather than selling SHSs to homeowners, RESCO sells the service that is produced by the SHS and in turn collects a monthly fee (see the fee-for-service model). RESCO can aggregate a large number of consumers into a single project rather than for each SHS. The consumer overcomes the high cost barrier by only having to make small monthly payments. Dozens of RESCOs have been set up to provide the services of sale and installation and maintenance of household solar PV systems in China and India and also in concession schemes throughout Africa and Latin America and solar water heating in India (**Figure 14**).

In this fee-for-service model, the operator provides the consumer with a certain amount of electricity according to the system capacity. The company, which retains ownership of the equipment, is responsible for maintenance and providing replacement parts over the life of the service contract. In exchange, the end-users pay a certain sum every month for the electricity service in cash or other methods (for instance, prepaid chip cards). The fee-for-service approach has the potential to provide high-quality systems to a broad range of rural households since companies providing fee-for-service can only be profitable if the systems they rent perform correctly. Moreover, the fee-for-service approach may be embedded in a stable regulatory framework increasing SHS penetration levels.

A successful model in Indonesia has been the credit sales model. In this model, the same company that provides loan and maintenance and that installs the system has a direct interest to keep them running in order to keep customers satisfied and get them to pay the credit.

1.07.7.3 Leasing or Hire Purchase Model

Leasing, or hire purchase, is a fee-for-service arrangement in which the leasing company (generally an intermediary company, cooperative, or NGO; not a dealer) buys stand-alone PV systems and installs them at customer sites (information from the World Bank's RE toolkit). The customer makes monthly payments, and the leasing company retains ownership of the systems until the customer has made all payments over the lease period, which is typically 5 years. Because the leasing periods are longer than most consumer finance terms, the monthly fees can be lower and the systems affordable to a larger segment of the rural population [46].

A leasing company investment has a longer return and a larger business risk than the consumer credit institutions. During the lease period, the leasing company makes monthly collections and provides maintenance service for the systems. Leasing companies often utilize seed money from government or donor grants to establish a revolving fund to buy an initial batch of systems. Experience with the leasing company approach has seen a few successes such as in China (Gansu Solar Electric Light Fund), Laos, and Dominican Republic (Enersol) (**Figures 15** and **16**) [46].

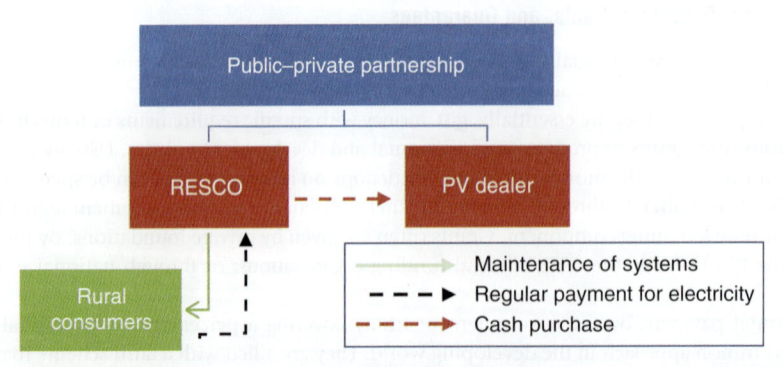

Figure 14 Framework for fee-for-service model. Source: Adapted from ISES. http://resum.ises.org/ and IEA PVPS Task 9 (2003) Summary of models for the implementation of photovoltaic solar home systems in developing countries. Report T9-02:2003 [45].

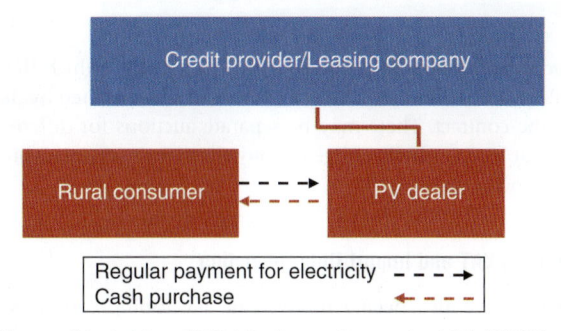

Figure 15 Lease/hire purchase model. Source: Adapted from ISES. http://resum.ises.org/ and IEA PVPS Task 9 (2003) Summary of models for the implementation of photovoltaic solar home systems in developing countries. Report T9-02:2003 [45].

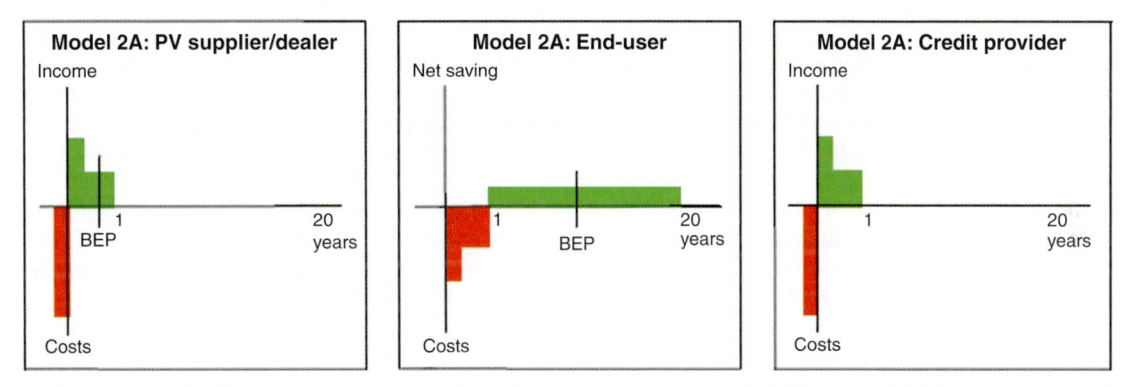

Figure 16 Cash flows for the PV dealer, end-user, and credit provider (dealer credit). Source: IEA PVPS Task 9 (2003) Summary of models for the implementation of photovoltaic solar home systems in developing countries. Report T9-02:2003 [45]. BEP, breakeven point.

The supplier and the user share the costs of the initial investment for 5 years. Usually the suppliers use some state support or evolving fund to secure the initial finance. The supplier does not share the risk with the end-user but retains the ownership until their costs are paid back, so in case of default it can take back the system. The end-users' advantage is that they can spread the payment for the system for longer periods (e.g., 5 years) and after that they take the ownership and the benefits from the system. This period gives enough time also to learn how to maintain and operate the system adequately.

1.07.7.4 Renewable Portfolio Standards

The RPSs also called renewable obligations or quota policies with green certificates aim to promote renewable energy generation by increasing the demand for renewable electricity. This is achieved by establishing the minimum percentage of generation of electricity or capacity installed to be provided by renewable energy [7]. Governments tend to use RPS for grid-connected systems, in accordance with the conditions of demand and generation, but it has not yet been adapted to reach renewable energy quota for off-grid systems. The RPS could choose the most appropriate type of renewable technology for off-grid areas (mostly based on mini-grids) and set country targets to be met.

1.07.7.5 Small Power Producer Regulation

The small power producer (SPP) regulations provide a supportive framework to facilitate standardized PPAs and grid-interconnection procedures for small distributed generation (typically renewable energy and cogeneration). SPP regulations typically cover generation under the 90 MW range (10 MW in some countries) and often are simple enough that much smaller generation (kW or hundreds of kW scale) can cost-effectively interconnect. While the main focus of SPP regulations is typically wholesale (to the utility), SPP regulations in some countries accommodate retail sales (direct sales to customers) and isolated mini-grid generation [31,48,49].

These policies aim to be administratively simple, assuming that developers' interest will increase (and regulation be more effective) with ease of contracting and administration of SPPs typically include a standardized PPA, technical and procedural guidelines for developers, standardized tariff calculations and methods, and rules for the regulator. In some countries, SPP arrangements have been put in place initially, providing renewable energy generators access to the grid for power export but paying tariffs equivalent to the utility's avoided costs. FiTs then build on the administrative and technical framework of SPP programs, providing higher, technology-specific tariffs [47–49].

1.07.7.6 Tender System

This system involves an auction process administered by the government, through which the entrepreneurs of renewable energy sources compete to win contracts (PPAs) or to receive a subsidy from a fund administered by the government. Those who make the most competitive offer are awarded the contract. There may be separate auctions for different types of technologies (known as technological bands), and energy companies are usually obliged to buy electricity at the price proposed by the winner of the contract (sometimes backed by a government fund).

1.07.7.7 Fiscal Incentives: Reduction in VAT and Import Duty Reduction

Investment and production tax credits have also been employed in developing countries. Reducing import duties can also have a dramatic influence on price and costs [31]. In fact, the relatively high cost of renewable technologies in Africa, for instance, can partly be attributed to high duties imposed on imported components, the high transaction costs in acquiring them, and the relatively low volume of purchases. Cases have been reported of solar PV systems being 3 times more expensive in Ghana than in Bangladesh and small hydro being twice as expensive in African countries as in Sri Lanka because of import duties [50].

This instrument can be applied in various ways to promote renewable energies: exemption of VAT or sales taxes on renewable energy technologies; reimbursement of taxes on green electricity; investment tax credits – allowing investments in renewable energy to be fully or partially deducted from tax obligations or income and direct energy production payments or tax credits – sometimes called 'premiums', provide the investor or owner of qualifying property with an annual tax credit based on the amount of electricity generated by that facility.

As a comparative example [38], in China, the imports of renewable energy technologies used to be exempt from payment of import duty; in India, this is the case for renewable energy technologies not produced in India. In China, the rate of VAT is 17%. VAT for biogas, wind power, and small hydro is only 3%, 8.5%, and 6%, respectively. VAT for power generation from municipal solid waste is 0%. In India, the VAT on renewable energy equipment is lower than the normal rate.

1.07.7.8 Public Finance Pools

Specific renewable financing support mechanisms established by the UNEP, the sustainable energy finance initiative [51], seek to provide financers with tools, support, and networks in order to promote sustainable energy investments in developing countries. The sustainable energy finance directory is a worldwide database of renewable energy lenders and investors.

These international sources of energy investments were discussed in Section 1.07.1.1. This database can be the very first step in harmonizing the existing sources and tools of energy investments in order to get to a scale that can help to change energy poverty in the rural part of developing countries, especially in rural Africa. The various schemes introduced before have accumulated already substantial experience in energy investment that could be utilized at a higher scale. If a pool of such initiatives would be set up, this could boost investment in rural electrification in an unprecedented way by reducing the risks associated with the single instruments (even the largest support facilities have nonpermanent features and can be stopped after a new phase). If part of the resources would be drawn together, its long-term credibility could offset the negative effects of the previous 'stop-and-go policies'. The initiative of the Deutsche Bank on the global energy transfer feed-in tariffs (GET FiTs) for developing countries [55] points to this direction as well.

1.07.7.9 Bank Financing: Low Interest and Soft Loans

Loans are a potential financing vehicle for rural electrification development projects because they continually replenish the development fund from which they are drawn (information taken from the World Bank's RE toolkit and the Renewable Energy and Energy Efficiency Partnership (REEEP)). The major sources of debt financing are international and national commercial banks, MDBs, the IFC, and debt/equity investment funds. International funds dedicated to development projects will often create loans with generous repayment terms, low interest rates, and flexible time frames. Such loans are called 'soft loans'. An additional consideration with loan funding is that foreign loans are subject to foreign currency oscillations [42].

Market-level interest rates are often prohibitive for high upfront cost projects such as renewable energy technologies, especially PV investment even if their lifetime costs could be competitive otherwise [21]. Why the cost of capital should be lowered for such specific technologies could be a valid argument. There are a lot of fundamental arguments that this could save societal costs. If an investment uses a local source for providing an energy service, this reduces geopolitical risks for the given country. The advantages connected with avoiding or mitigating climate change are also important arguments but not the only ones. Also the avoided external costs (such as medical expenses related to the use of fossil fuels, cost of accidents due to explosions, leakage from tanks, and transport needs) could justify the use of a long-term societal interest rate instead of market-based interests.

Another important feature of investment in public utilities is that while they provide the energy service to special consumers (students, patients), they teach them how to use these sustainable energy services, and this creates the long-term market for these services even in remote areas. Meeting the needs of disadvantaged population and creating a long-sustainable market is a social priority that needs to be addressed in the related policies.

Larger stand-alone PV systems, so-called solar residential systems (SRSs), usually provide electricity to large social infrastructures, that is, hospitals, schools, community and religious centers, and factories. Usually loans are quite limited for those community cooperatives that see the needs of prioritizing SRSs. Still there are options like opening lines of credit by development finance institutions, credit enhancements provided by the development finance institutions to soften the loans, or growth capital funds that are a mix of donor and commercial capital. Nonrecourse financing (i.e., a loan where the lending bank is only entitled to repayment from the profits of the project the loan is funding, not from other assets of the borrower) is usually not possible for SRS, SHS, or mini-grid PV projects, since it is generally not possible to sufficiently mitigate all risks attached with the project.

Other options are a standardized finance mechanism in the case of developing multiple projects and leveraging local financing, which seeks to stimulate local financing institutions to take a more participatory role in renewable energy projects [46].

1.07.7.10 Carbon Financing

The CDM under the Kyoto Protocol to the UNFCCC allows industrialized countries with a greenhouse gas (GHG) reduction commitment to invest in emission reducing projects in developing countries as an alternative to what is generally considered more costly emission reductions in their own countries [52]. These carbon finance mechanisms are project based, intending to provide financing for project activities that will cut off carbon emissions, in which renewable energy is an important component. Due to the abundance and prevalence of resources, solar energy is widely regarded as an ideal candidate for these mechanisms. However, the role of Kyoto Mechanisms to develop solar energy has remained relatively small as compared with other renewable energy projects, such as wind [53].

Approved CDM projects produce certified emission reductions (CERs), which can be traded with businesses, industries, or countries that do not meet their own CO_2 emission targets. Although CDM through the income of CERs is not likely to be a key investment driver, it is capable of acting as a catalyst in increasing return on investment, thus providing projects more credibility and facilitating the securing of funds from financial institutions [43]. The revenue from the sale of CERs is expected to help renewable energy projects compete with other generation technologies. However, it appears that the revenue from CERs has not provided sufficient financial advantages for PV technologies, which are relatively expensive and often installed in smaller system size configurations (**Figure 17**) [54].

PV projects can qualify as CDM where carbon emission reduction has a great potential; still systems are usually quite small. The CDM, which was regarded as a key instrument to promote GHG mitigation projects in developing countries, has not yet helped much in promoting solar power.

However, it is important to note that although there is a movement to include more PV within the CDM and the voluntary carbon markets, this technology and especially off-grid projects have been largely forgotten in the first periods of carbon finance especially in comparison with large wind or waste treatment projects. This is due not only to the small carbon savings that off-grid PV projects usually generate but also to the difficulties to understand the carbon finance procedures, the small amount of money that can be gained out of it, and the sectorial lack of organization (difficulties to identify and collaborate with overwhelmed national point of contacts, corruption, etc.). Therefore, there is a need to streamline CDM within country policies and financial instruments. One of the effective approaches to reduce the transaction cost of diffused, small-scale solar CDM projects is to bundle them into a single larger portfolio project. By bundling several small-scale CDM projects, transaction costs associated with the CDM

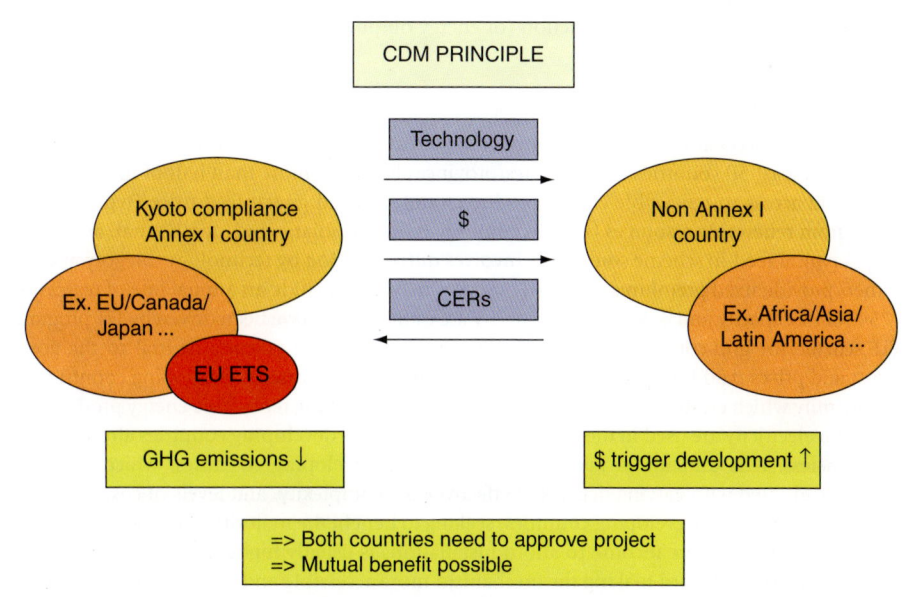

Figure 17 CDM principle. Source: Lemaire X and REEEP/SERN webinar (2009) Off grid regulation – How to provide cost-effective and sustainable rural energy services in remote areas of developing. www.leonardo-energy.org [41].

project cycle can be reduced. Different organizations can bundle applications, including private companies (e.g., energy service companies, ESCOs), financial institutions (e.g., the World Bank), government or NGOs [55]. As monitoring for off-grid projects (pico-PV, SHSs) is more difficult than grid-connected projects for which transaction costs are much higher [55], it would be necessary to provide further favorable conditions for the off-grid solar systems to reduce inhibitive transaction costs [53]. If procedures like projects have been created to offer an opportunity to smaller scale projects, carbon finance remains relatively unknown for local project promoters and should primarily be considered as an additional and complementary source of funding.

1.07.7.11 Transitions from Off-Grid to On-Grid Generation Systems

The map shown in **Figure 9(c)** points out how the subsidies channeled to fossil fuel use create barriers to many off-grid renewable and PV projects [48]. If the grid-connected electricity is subsidized, it could create a similar difficulty. When the end-user considers the off-grid PV option a low, subsidized electricity price in the national grid can prevent him from implementing the off-grid option. Even if the grid extension is not feasible due to the distance or other factors (low load density, network is already overloaded, etc.), the electricity price on the network serves as a reference for the new consumers.

Introducing changes in the tariff system that gives the proper price signals to the consumers on the real costs of producing, transporting, and distributing the electricity would be the first step in many developing countries to open the market for off-grid energy technologies.

Many developing countries have a range of service conditions, including an interconnected national grid, possible regional and/or mini-grids, off-grid stand-alone systems, and unconnected (i.e., unelectrified) households, and therefore a key issue is designing renewable policies that are adaptable to transitioning customers to connect services when those options become available (without penalizing them for exiting generation and services). For mini-grid customers, existing utility generators often do not recover the full operational cost through tariffs (as it is difficult to pass on the high costs of isolated diesel generation to consumers), and therefore these services can be a drain to utility finances. There is a strong incentive for generation of alternatives and policies like a renewable energy premium tariff (RPT), which can incentivize private renewable generators and reduce pressures on utility finances. SPPs also provide an important transitional policy when community-operated renewable systems become interconnected. For example, in Thailand, community mini-hydro systems have been able to sell power back to the utility when mini-hydro-based communities have become grid interconnected. A particularly promising aspect of SPPs is that they can function as regulatory and institutional starting points for future FiT/RPT programs. An SPP with tariffs based on utility-avoided cost can be a way of gaining experience (particularly for utilities that process applications and facilitate interconnection). An FiT can be later added once utility and regulatory capacity and procedures have been put in place and bottlenecks worked out. When Thailand's very small producer program (VSPP) (< 10 MW) added FiTs, a large number of PPAs (over 4000 MW) were signed between 2007 and 2010; however, it is not clear if all of these will be built [47]. This level of interest shows that well-designed pricing policies can support electrification and on-grid service transitions.

1.07.8 Innovative Financing Mechanisms for Rural Renewable Energy

The innovative financing mechanisms described in this section include the mechanisms that combine government and community financing with the concept of incentivizing the production (or energy output) of PV electricity.

1.07.8.1 Renewable Energy Premium Tariff

FiTs have been one of the most successful support mechanisms to increase the introduction of renewables and is rapidly spreading generation. By early 2010, at least 50 countries and 25 states/provinces had FiTs, more than half of these adopted only since 2005 [7]. The FiTs guarantee grid access to renewable energy producers and set fixed guaranteed price (typically 15–20 years) for the generation of electricity from renewable resources (most commonly biomass, solar, wind, geothermal, and small hydro), which is 'fed into' the grid [56]. A typical feed-in scheme sometimes involves differentiation by technology category and sometimes provides a fixed tariff while others provide fixed premiums added to market – may also include an annual rate of regression – or cost-related tariffs. Worldwide, 75% of PV capacity and 45% of wind capacity are estimated to have been driven by FiT programs as of 2008 [60]. Currently, in the FiT scheme for grid-connected systems, values are set by being revenue neutral to the government, with the difference between cost and prices paid implicitly by all utility consumers. In the case of developing countries, a key factor for the success of the FiT is to identify which entity should bear the cost of incentives for the renewable energy production. A wide variety of tariff modes of charging for electricity are used in the developing world, and 27 developing countries already use the grid-connected FiT scheme [58]. Nonetheless, it is difficult to justify higher tariffs in developing countries, which can impose a burden to consumers. FiTs have been adopted with varying degrees of effectiveness, complexity, and levels of cost/price in different contexts.

FiTs should be addressed carefully in developing countries, seeking to benefit the majority of the population. Conditions are very different than in developed nations, where income to afford installations is usually higher for a larger portion of the population. This has to be considered in working toward making the mechanism more accessible and not just benefit a small section of society. Besides, if FiT laws in developed economies have mainly followed an ethical/environmental purpose which has transformed into a flourishing economic success, this will not necessarily be the case in developing countries. However, some studies start suggesting that taking into account the excellent natural conditions of these regions, as well as the very high generation price of other technologies (especially in countries without gas/oil resources), grid-connected PV could very well be competitive nowadays or at least very soon even without subsidy and provide an immediate answer to the growing energy demand in these countries.

1.07.8.1.1 The RPT: Adapted FiT for mini-grids

For off-grid regions, the so-called RPT introduces a locally adapted variation of the FiT scheme to encourage the production of renewable electricity in isolated areas. Within the FiT model, payments are usually covered by distributing costs among all electricity end-users. The RPT can be a powerful mechanism for developing renewable energy in off-grid settings, as it ensures sustainability of systems by remunerating the cost of producing electricity, that is, delivery of the service rather than delivery of a project, for the project's lifetime (15 years). As the support is given for production of electricity and not for the initial capital investment, it incentivizes quality performance and ensures that the funds will be available to maintain its operation.

Because LCOE values for diesel generators throughout the developing world are estimated at 0.35–1.50 US$ kWh^{-1}, renewables can be highly cost-competitive compared with the high costs of running diesel mini-grid generators [57, 59, 60]. However, one of the key challenges in small-scale isolated systems in rural areas is that, load profiles tend to have high evening peaks and little or no consumption during the day or in the middle of the night. This has big implications for tariffs – since capital utilization is low if electricity is demanded only during a small portion of the day, tariffs have to be high to cover capital costs. The problem is compounded with renewable energy – because many renewable energy sources are intermittent and not dispatchable, yet electricity storage is expensive. A key factor for the success of the RPT support scheme is to define the financial flows involved to compensate the difference between electricity costs and prices paid and which entity should bear the cost of incentives for the renewable energy production [59]. Options include charging on-grid consumers a levy, subsidy through a local rural energy fund, or combination with international donors or mechanisms. It is therefore imperative to consider FiTs and RPT in the context of wider financial terms.

1.07.8.1.2 RPT scheme under different regulatory and institutional frameworks

The suitability of several RPT alternatives among different energy legal and institutional frameworks and different types of ownership is examined with the intention of facilitating decision-makers to exploit local renewable energy sources under the RPT scheme.

1.07.8.1.2(i) RPT scheme involving an IPP

In the case of involving an IPP, the local government provides to IPPs an RPT scheme including a renewable energy purchase agreement. The rural electrification agency, regulatory agency, or an equivalent governmental institution then offers the legal and regulatory RPT frameworks for IPPs to install solar, wind, biomass, small hydro power, and geothermal power generation technologies connected to a mini-grid (**Figure 18**). The tasks of the regulatory agency in a rural energy service concession include establishing the RPT premium tariff and guaranteeing the values for up to 20 years, supervising the power purchase and service agreements, and monitoring the energy concessions.

More than 25 developing countries have regulatory frameworks that allow IPPs to generate and sell power to utilities under PPAs [17]. In these countries, the adaptations of the purchase agreement to an RPT renewable energy purchase agreement can take place in a straightforward process. The factor to add on top for an RPT renewable energy purchase agreement is that the production of renewable electricity gets a supplementary value.

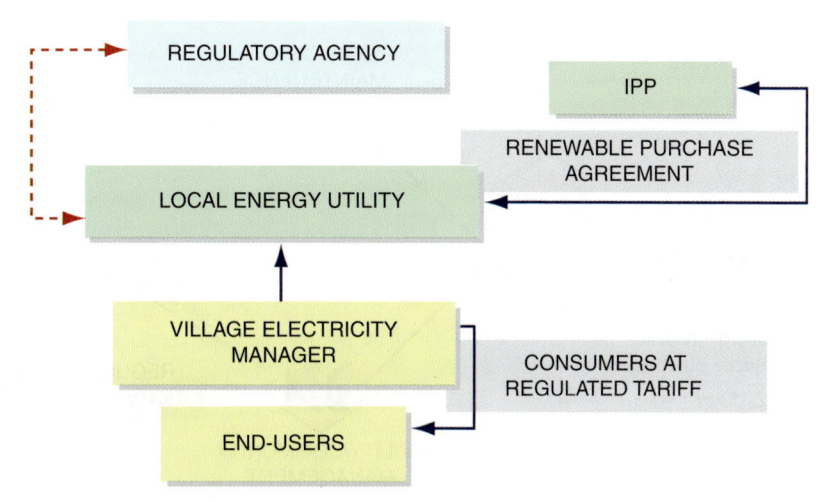

Figure 18 Independent power production regulatory framework under the RPT scheme for off-grid electrification support [59]. Note: red dashed arrows represent legal and regulatory framework and blue solid arrows represent the regulated purchase agreements.

1.07.8.1.2(ii) RPT scheme under an energy service concession

The affordability of electricity can be extended to a greater number of consumers when the ESCO offers electricity to a village-scale mini-grid under the RPT mechanism, rather than grid extensions. Under this legal arrangement, the government offers a concession in which the RESCO is competitively selected to provide off-grid electrification exclusively to designated rural areas with the obligation to serve all who request an electricity service and getting a premium for renewable electricity delivered. Under the RPT scheme, terms of the concession for the renewable energy provider may last up to 20 years (**Figure 19**).

The local energy development agency establishes the RPT premium tariff and guarantees the values for up to 20 years. The local electricity utility, or RESCO, deals with the electricity generation and distribution in the mini-grid. The RESCO retains the ownership of the mini-grid producing electricity by hybrid systems and is responsible for installing the electricity-measuring devices for controlling the amount of electricity generated by renewable energies (with a simple design with two-direction measurements, **Figure 20**).

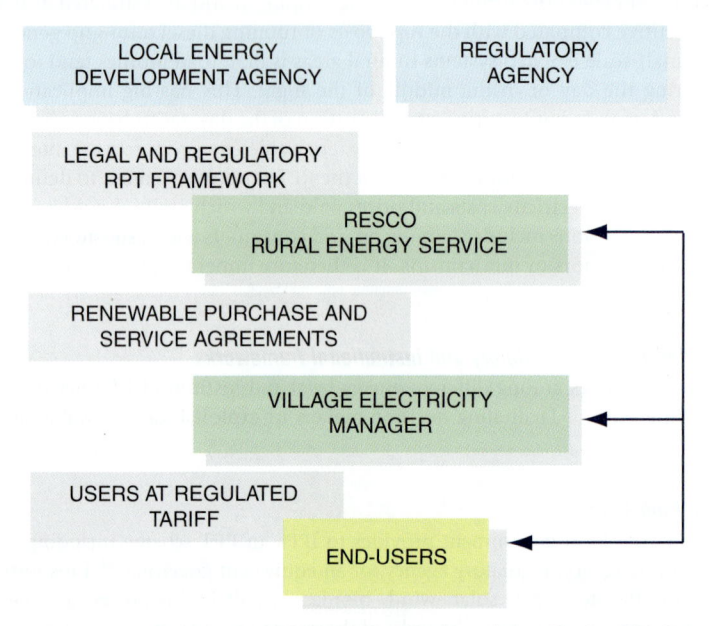

Figure 19 Framework for an energy service concession under RPT scheme for off-grid rural electrification [59]. Note: Arrows indicate regulated purchase agreements.

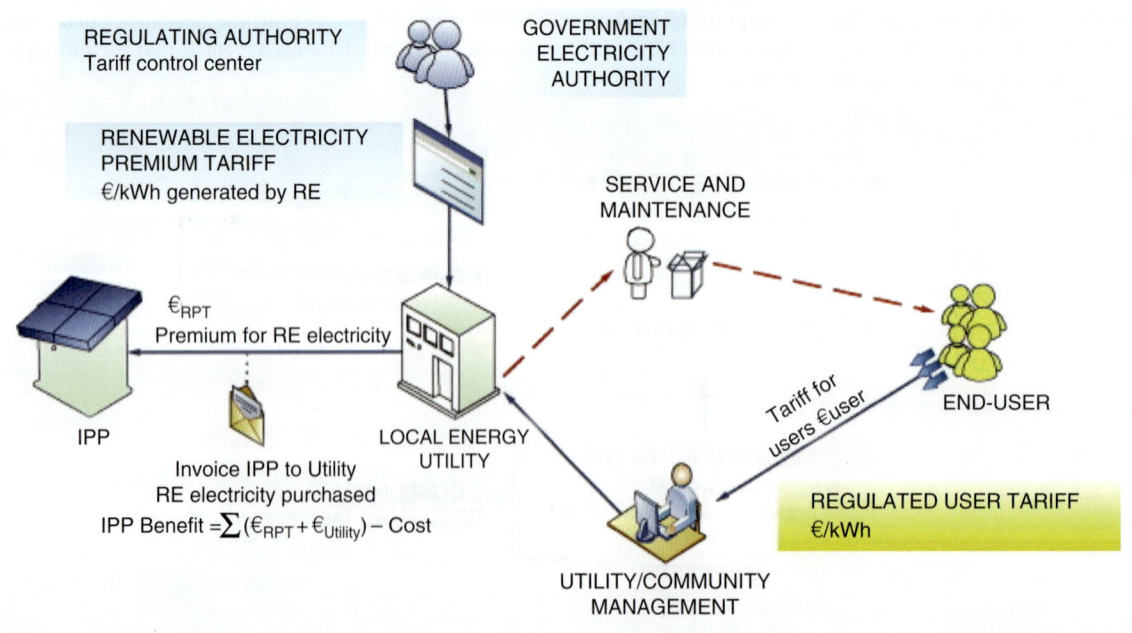

Figure 20 Energy service concessions under the RPT scheme for off-grid rural electrification promoting the use of renewable energy technologies [59]. Note: The blue arrows represent the money flows and the red slashed arrows the maintenance services.

Finance Mechanisms and Incentives for Photovoltaic Technologies in Developing Countries 133

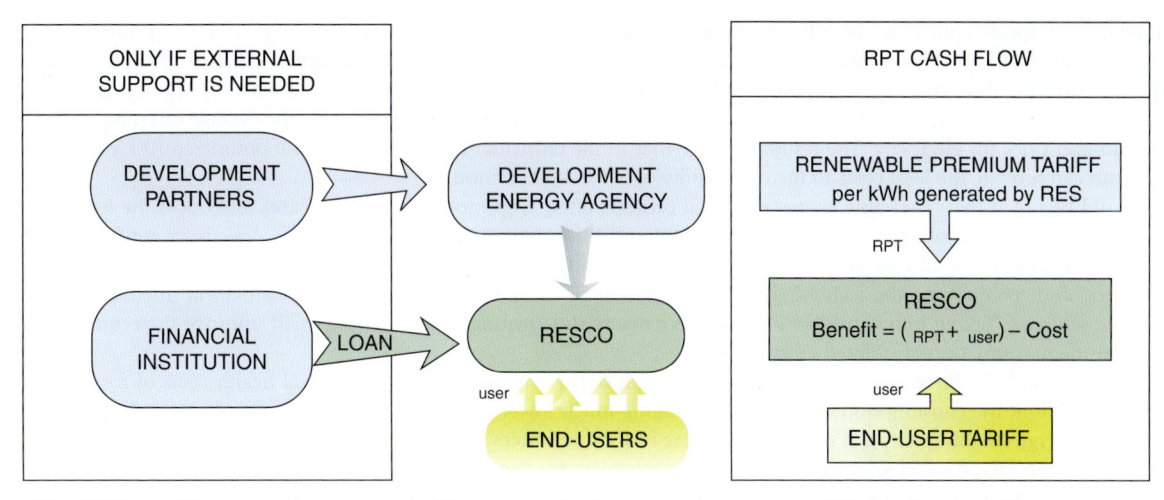

Figure 21 RPT financial flows for a village-scale mini-grid under a regulated energy service concession [59]. Note: The money flows are represented by the arrows.

In the situation where the local government cannot cover the premium value per kWh of renewable electricity delivered, funds can then be obtained from a multilateral donor (left reddish in the diagram). The development partners might enhance their support undertaking the necessary reforms for a coherent, transparent, and attractive investment framework (**Figure 21**).

Depending on the local political framework, additional financial instruments and incentives might be applied:

1. *Capital subsidies*: RESCO might receive yearly payments (decreasing annually) to cover a percentage of the capital cost.
2. *Production subsidies*: RESCO might receive overheads to cover a percentage of the capital cost depending on production generated.
3. Government-guaranteed loans: the government acts as an intermediary between the agency and the financial institutions as a guarantee of the loan.

At the same time, in the case of customers with their own generation, it would be helpful to introduce a net metering system in the mini-grid for a two-way flow of electricity between the electricity distribution mini-grid and customers with their own generation. The customer would only pay for the net electricity delivered from the utility (total consumption minus self-production) and then would get the RPT premium.

When performing indicative economic analysis to identify the range of the premium values that make the RPT scheme viable under a specific framework, the analysis determines the minimum renewable electricity premium value that makes the project financially viable (net present value (NPV) > 0) and the value of RPT to obtain a nonprofit outcome (NPV = 0) when using a 6% discount rate. The financial analysis under the RPT scheme with optimized values results in positive NPV and with internal rate of return (IRR) between 8% and 15%, which simply means a significant 8–15% return (see **Figure 22**). The minimum RPT value

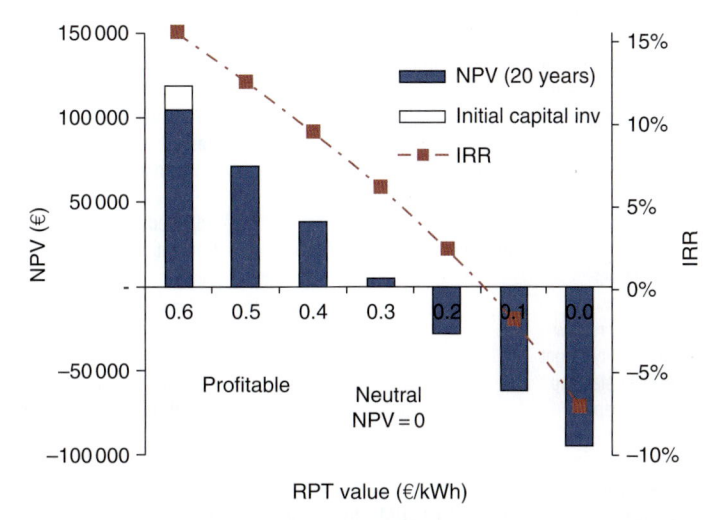

Figure 22 RPT analysis: NPV values (€) corresponding to each RPT value (€ kWh^{-1}) considered with their respective IRR (%) [59]. Note: The reddish shadow area represents the border for profitable and nonprofitable approach.

required for a nonprofit approach with NPV = 0 and interest rate of 6% is between 0.3 and 0.5 € kWh^{-1} and for a profit approach the RPT values range from 0.7 to 1.5 € kWh^{-1}. (When using a diesel-alone system and under the same electricity demand, the subsidies needed to cover the difference between end-user prices and real cost average from 0.7 to 0.3 € kWh^{-1}.) The results are used to compare the mini-grid with and without the RPT support mechanism in terms of total costs and the average incentive costs relative to the end-user price for electricity. The results indicate that in the particular case of applying the optimized RPT values, the RPT mechanism can provide the least costs to the community over a 20-year period.

It should be noted that renewable energy mini-grid projects often keep money in the local area and boost the local economy through the provision of jobs in the local area. The NPV and IRR calculations consider only the directly quantifiable costs and benefits; consequently, the calculations do not take into account indirect economic benefits such as the employment of local people in installing and maintaining the technologies. Consideration of these benefits may act to improve the financial viability of small-scale schemes. Taking into consideration the user's needs and creating productive uses will improve the economic, social, and environmental situation of isolated villages.

The RPT scheme will bring to isolated areas a way to reduce the environmental and external health costs of fossil-fuel-based electricity, will limit the consumption of fossil fuels bringing much lower operation and maintenance costs, and a higher energy security and energy flexibility through promoting the use of local resources.

To demonstrate that the RPT scheme is an effective mechanism for the introduction of renewable energy technologies in rural electrification programs, it is necessary to succeed with a few pilot cases under different operational frameworks.

1.07.8.2 GET FiTs for Developing Countries

In many developing countries, grants from external donors or government funds would be needed to pay for the marginal difference between the cost of renewable energy production and the price of electricity for users. (This section is based on the report of DB Climate Change Advisors [57].) As suggested by the DB Climate Change Advisors group [57], a possible way to cover the incremental necessary costs of the premium payment would be by a GET FiT [61]. The GET FiT program is a concept to specifically support both renewable energy scale-up and energy access in the developing world through the creation of new international public–private partnerships. GET FiT would efficiently combine a fund of public money directed for renewable energy incentives with risk mitigation strategies and coordinated technical assistance to address project development and financing barriers. This combined approach would catalyze the supply of, and the demand for, private sector financing of renewable energy projects in both middle- and low-income countries, while also ensuring maximum incentive capture of at least the cost to the funding partners [57]. Table 2 contains a summary of example design elements which could be adapted to the developing country context.

FiTs to date have targeted energy access in a limited range. For decentralized energy generation, especially mini-grids, in rural areas not included in current grid expansion plans, the design of the FiT mechanism should be adapted with the same principles of FiT design to create performance-based incentives and/or guarantees (see Section 1.07.8.1).

Table 2 Design elements to adapt FiT to developing countries' context (DB climate change advisors 2010 [57])

Fit design features	Key factors	Transparency, longevity, and certainty at the right price
Policy and economic framework	'Linkage' to mandates and targets	Yes
Core elements	Eligible technologies	All renewables eligible
	Specified tariff by technology	Yes
	Standard offer/guaranteed payment	Yes
	Interconnection	Yes
	Payment term	15–25 years 5–10 years
Supply and demand	Must take	Yes
	Who operates (most common)	Open to all
Fixed structure and adjustment		
How to set price	Fixed vs. variable price	Adjusted for inflation
	Generation cost vs. avoided cost	Generation
	IRR target	Yes
How to adjust price	Degression	Yes – ending at LCOE breakeven
	Periodic review	Yes
	Grid parity target	Yes
Caps	Project size cap	Depends on context
	Policy cap	Based on transmission constraints and/or ratepayer impact
Policy interactions	Eligible for other incentives	Yes – eligible to take choice
Streamlining	Transaction costs minimized	Yes
CDM linkage	Does the national FiT policy take CDM into account?	Yes

Source: Deutsche Bank Climate Change Advisors (2010) Global energy transfer feed-in tariffs for developing countries, April 2010 [57].

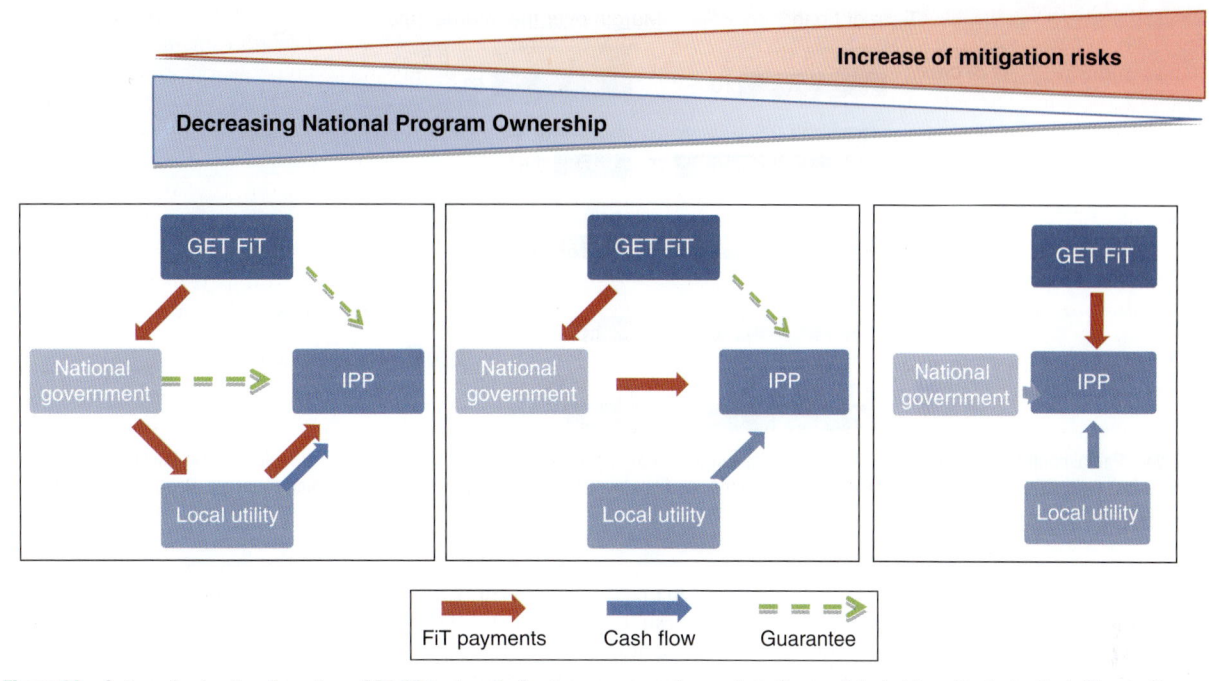

Figure 23 Options for funding flows from GET FiT to decentralized power generation project. Source: Adapted from Deutsche Bank Climate Change Advisors (2010) Global energy transfer feed-in tariffs for developing countries, April 2010 [57].

1.07.8.2.1 Alternatives for funding flows from GET FiT to projects

As seen in **Figure 23**, the GET FiT program would seek to maximize the involvement of national governments and utilities in the policy transactions. The flow of FiT payments to IPPs, however, can involve government and utilities to different degrees and there are potential trade-offs to consider (**Figure 23**).

While options directly involving the national institutions may introduce a longer term sustainable payment structure, these structures may introduce greater political risk and transaction costs, depending on the context. While options involving direct FiT payments to IPPs may be slightly better from a risk perspective from its financers as well as the risk perspective of GET FiT (e.g., reducing potential for corruption), it minimizes opportunities for national ownership and capacity building that are at the core of GET FiT.

This structure would help to mitigate revenue risk and could work in situations where the IPP serves the function of both generator and administrator of the mini-grid and in situations where the IPP provides power and technical services, but where the local community is responsible for aggregating and collecting electricity payments. The different options of how the financial flow would be distributed in the case of mini-grids are described in the case of the RPT scheme (see Section 1.07.8.1). The advantage of the GET FiT program is that the incentives provided would help mitigate off-take risk and make projects bankable because a substantial portion of revenue would come from the GET FiT program, channeled through the government or government agencies.

1.07.9 Financial Risk Management

Apart from the financing instruments, an array of technical and risk mitigation programs will need to be aggregated and coordinated as well. The financial mechanism should efficiently combine the renewable energy incentives with risk mitigation strategies and coordinated technical assistance to address project development and financing barriers. This combined approach would catalyze the supply of, and the demand for, private sector financing of renewable energy projects in both middle- and low-income countries [57].

Financial risks connected with the given countries can be a major barrier to PV development. Even the relatively small differences connected with the risk of different countries in Europe make a huge difference in PV deployment. A 2–4% additional country risk premium can prevent the PV market from growing rapidly.

The difference of the risk premium between the African and developed countries is so high that this creates a major barrier.

Hence, the donor country and international financial institution involvement is important from a risk mitigation point of view. This not only reduces the risk premium but also gives a good indication for the investors for the security of long-term revenues promised by the most advanced financial schemes presented above.

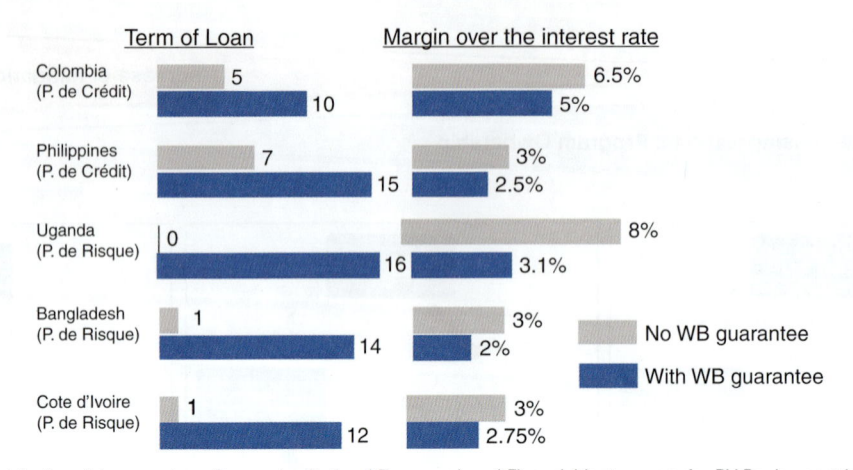

Figure 24 Partial contribution risk guarantees. Source: Institutional Framework and Financial Instruments for PV Deployment in Developing Countries, IEA PVPS Task 9 (2003) Summary of models for the implementation of photovoltaic solar home systems in developing countries. Report T9-02:2003 [45].

Without the above-mentioned properly designed risk management, "Investors are not interested in making investment due to high risks attached to projects and the returns on the investments will most probably be limited" (Financing Mechanisms and Public/Private Risk Sharing Instruments for Financing Small Scale Renewable Energy Equipment and Projects. UNDP, GEF 2007 [33]). On the other hand, proper risk management can create opportunity to achieve very favorable loan conditions that can boost investment (see **Figure 24**).

The development of partial risk guarantee and partial credit guarantee schemes is required to encourage private sector banks and investors to accept higher risk levels, longer term exposures, and lower interest rates. This type of partial risk guarantee can cover risk as refusal to accept an increase in tariffs as described in the escalation clause in the contract, public authority/regulator interference in a dispute settlement, impossibility of foreign exchange transfer through controls or nonavailability of foreign exchange.

1.07.9.1 Risk Characterization

Regulatory/policy risks and geopolitical risk dimensions give a comprehensive picture of how the investors perceive all the risk associated with the power investment options. These risk dimensions if not managed properly can pose an extra difficulty in the developing countries. The following two sections give an overview on how the investors convert their perceived risk associated with power technologies to return expectations. As was shown before, the higher the return expectation is in the energy technology market, the less favorable the conditions are for the high upfront technologies (like PV). Therefore, it is necessary to reduce these rates as much as possible. In order to achieve this, it is good to give a short analysis of the factors that have adverse effects on the return rates.

1.07.9.1.1 Risk comparison of PV and other renewable technologies to fossil fuel-based technologies

Investors' risk perceptions are affected by many factors that can have an influence on the returns of their investment. For analytical purposes, these risk effects are separated by dimensions that are independent from each other. **Tables 3** and **4** shows this conversion of the three risk levels (low, medium, and high) of the five independent risk types (technology risk, market risk, regulatory/policy risk, geopolitical risk, and stakeholder acceptance) for the selected power technologies. Besides the related renewable energy technologies, the risk levels associated with the conventional fossil/nuclear technologies are listed as a reference. To give a full spectrum, the biomass-based technologies are split into three technologies (bioenergy, first- and second-generation biofuels) distinctive from a risk point of view [21]; the solar-based technologies are differentiated as well to PV and concentrated solar technology. Specialist investors further subdivide the PV technology (crystalline, amorphous silicon, thin-film, concentrated PV, etc.); however, this chapter aims at the identification of the basic conditions and opportunities for the whole PV industry.

Without the systematic collection of state-of-the-art information on the performance and reliability of the various power technologies, most financial analysts would express reservations about the low-technology risk category for solar technologies. This negligence leads to the image of 'esoteric asset' type that is difficult to incorporate into the electricity portfolio. More than 84% of the modules have experienced less than 1% maximum power loss during 20 years outdoor measurements and only 3.5% experience more than 4% power loss [54]. These figures are well below the power failure and maintenance figures of the conventional technologies. Though these measurement results perhaps are well known among the industry experts, they are not known among the financial analysts who prepare the reports for the financial decision-makers. In fact, this misperception of the performances and risks associated with renewable energies is often shared at all levels in developing countries (from decision-maker to end-user levels) and contributes to their slow take-off in these regions.

Table 3 Risk levels and risk dimensions of different electricity technologies[21]

Risk type/technology	Technology risk	Market risk	Regulatory policy risk	Geopolitical risk	Stakeholder acceptance
PV	Low	Medium	Low	Low	High
Concentrated solar	Low/medium	Medium	Low	Low	Medium
Wind	Low	Medium	Low	Low	Medium
First-generation biofuel	Low-medium	High	High	Medium	High
Second-generation biofuel	High	Medium	Medium	Low	Low
Bioenergy	Low	Medium	Low	Low	High
Fossil/nuclear	Low/medium	Low	Medium	High	Medium/low

This is the most important message that can be concluded from the close analysis of the project appraisal and risk assessment method of the financial investors: there is a discrepancy between the industry and research experience and the perception of the financial analyst over the PV technology.

1.07.9.1.2 Transforming risk dimensions into different return expectations

After investors have evaluated the different risks associated with the different technologies, they assign one expected return value to the various technology-based projects with their given risk preferences (significance or weights of the presented risk dimensions). **Table 4** visualizes the process how investors convert their perceived risk levels to differentiate return expectations. The higher the risk they associate with the given type of technology, the investors adjust their expected minimum return rate requirement from the projects. This expected return can be decreased significantly if the financial institutions and investors would get complete information on technological performance for PV.

Due to its rapidly increasing deployment in the developing world, PV technology has gradually become a technology that can be characterized with relatively low risk, but the geopolitical regulatory/policy risks that are associated with the majority of the developing countries have to be also mitigated. The prevailing high discount rates can become the major barrier to the PV market in the developing countries. If the connected risks are managed properly, these additional return premiums can be diminished. The positive examples of this risk management in the form of risk guarantees can be seen in **Figure 24**. The expected returns can be reduced or even halved if a proper scheme is in place. The geopolitical and regulatory risks can be managed if international donor organizations would participate in the selected financial mechanisms in the different countries and would contribute to the credibility of these mechanisms.

1.07.10 Conclusions

Sustainable energy portfolios for off-grid areas in developing countries must be driven by goals of promoting long-term sustainability, improving basic energy services, fostering affordability and access, and improving reliability. All of these features are essential to effectively implementing PV support mechanisms in off-grid areas in the developing countries (including financing and pricing policies). In this sense, the existence of national targets is crucial for successful energy access programs.

Table 4 Conversion of risks to return expectations

Added return premium in %/risk class	PV (%)	Wind (%)	Bioenergy/first-generation biofuel (%)	Second-generation biofuel (%)	Fossil based (%)
The risk-free rate 3–5% for 10–20 year government bonds or the interest rate of a bank loan (see Section 1.07.5.1)	3	3	3	3	3
The equity risk premium related to the performance of similar listed asset classes (4% premium to compare with the typical return on equity of similar listed asset classes of 7–9%)	4–5	4–5	7–9	7–9	4–5
The shares cannot be sold as easily as liquid funds (illiquidity premium of about 3%)	3	3	3	3	3
The technology premium (unproven asset class) for new and unproven technologies	2–3 instead of 5–15	0	3	15	0
The regulatory risk premium reflecting the risks of the energy markets and renewable energy support schemes (−3% reduction for low risk to +3% extra for schemes with higher risk)	−3	−3	0	3	−3% to +3% (carbon prices)
Total	9–11	7–8	15	30	7–12

Source: S Szabo et al. [21].

The main factors relevant to long-term sustainability of effective support mechanisms are the participation of the national governments, the selection of the right mechanism for the specific location, considering the idiosyncrasies of the communities, the long-term financial guarantee, the orientation of the mechanism according to the demands of the beneficiaries, and the existence of stable regulatory frameworks.

This chapter has introduced an analytical framework for a number of financing, pricing, and policy support options to promote renewable energy for off-grid applications in developing countries. In particular, we analyzed PV technologies as a case study keeping in mind that the support mechanism should not be technologically driven prioritizing one clean energy technology over the others but taking into account the optimized technology option depending on the local resources and conditions. The chapter has described the potential of these policies to promote clean energy and energy service goals. Analyzing the pros and cons emphasizes that some of the mechanisms need adaptation/reforms in order to improve their effectiveness.

Two different ways of incentivizing energy access can be delimited according to target energy services and the objective of such schemes. The objective to electrify fundamental social infrastructure (schools, hospitals, social centers, etc.) on the one hand will have to follow a short-term highly supported policy, whereas the sustainable electrification of rural consumers (households and the private sector) will depend on long-term sustainable financing tools often relying on a private–public partnership approach.

Regarding social infrastructures, the objective is to provide a short-term scheme essentially based on capital subsidy along well-designed tariff setting (and a project approach). Certain support schemes should be used since some developing countries still lack public funds for covering these fundamental energy services. In the case of selecting the most effective support schemes for social infrastructures, the most relevant factor is to bring reliable energy services and building up added value for these services (students will rely later on the services learnt, e.g., computer use). Therefore, the short-term and secured incentive schemes should focus on this sector. Such a short-term support also contributes to building up the long-term market for the household segment.

In contrast, households and local business electrification should adopt a private–public partnership approach emphasizing the long-term sustainability of the projects/programs. The more market-oriented schemes could target long-term operation and performance of the systems (see **Table 5**) since highly subsidized rural energy projects without any cost recovery have not been sustainable for a long term. In the household and local business electrification projects, the pros of each suitable solution are summarized below.

The penetration of 'cash sale' small PV systems in developing countries has not yet reached its full potential, even if sales have been taking off in some countries, as, for example, in Kenya. Kenya has an active market for PV SHSs, with cumulative sales in excess of 100 000 units and sales of approximately 20 000 modules per year.

'Microcredit' and other types of small-scale consumer finance have played a key role in this development and definitely impose themselves as a useful tool to help end-users access energy services (as long as emphasis is placed on quality products). Of course, the fact that some countries already had an extensive microfinance network has strongly supported this scale-up.

The 'fee-for-service' approach has the potential to provide high-quality systems a broad range of rural households since the organizations providing fee-for-service can only be profitable if the systems they rent perform correctly. If the operator is financially solid (through profits and public support), this type of scheme is clearly a good solution to simultaneously address several key barriers to off-grid PV deployment (accessibility, affordability, poor O&M).

The 'CDM' and other carbon finance tools have not been very successful till now in promoting solar power in rural areas. There is a need to streamline CDM within country policies and financial instruments. One of the effective approaches to reduce the transaction cost of diffused, small-scale solar CDM projects is to bundle them into a single larger portfolio project. Currently, transaction costs for off-grid projects (pico-PV and SHSs) are much higher than grid-connected ones; therefore, favorable conditions for the off-grid solar systems are needed to reduce inhibitive transaction costs.

As is visible from **Figure 9**, the geographic distribution of the cost-competitive solutions is very mixed. And these include only a limited set of options. New technologies can be added to the portfolio that can further reduce the cost for many

Table 5 The strengths and weaknesses of the instruments

Instrument	Risk mitigation	Cost-competiveness	Long-term sustainability
Capital subsidies, consumer grants, and guarantees	+++	+++	−
Renewable ESCOs	+	+	++
Leasing and hire purchase model	+	+	+
RPSs	−	+	+
Microcredit	•	++	++
SPP regulation	+	−	−
Tender system	−	+	•
Fiscal incentives: reduction in VAT, import duty reduction	−	+	−
Public finance pools	+	+	•
Bank financing: low interest and soft loans	•	+	+
Carbon financing	+	+	+
GET FiTs	+++	+/++	+++
RPT	++	+/++	+++

Source: M Moner-Girona and S Szabo. The following symbols indicate that the instrument performs: +++, very strongly; ++, strongly; +, favorably; •, neutral; −, weakly.

locations. Finding these least cost-competitive solutions for the households cannot be planned by the governments; the local developers have to find them. The schemes can only give the proper incentives to these actors to act as quick as possible (like for mobile phones).

In the case of rural electrification projects using mini-grids, a new alternative, the 'GET FIT for developing countries', has the potential to deliver the target services in the most effective way and be adapted to each country depending on the fundamental design parameters. The use of this 'fund' would increase gradually and will have a strong long-term sustainability effect. The GET FiT concept could be flexibly adapted to specific national contexts and could be launched on a bilateral, regional, or global basis. There are two key factors for the success of the GET FiT. The first is the 'replicability' of the scheme in a large range of countries with different backgrounds, while the second is the credibility of the provided fund offering long-term guarantee for PV developers and financers in developing countries.

When it comes to choosing the most appropriate instrument for end-users, depending on the local conditions, we have considered three key factors (see **Table 5**): the degree of risk mitigation, the cost-competiveness, and the long-term sustainability of the energy project under the specific instrument.

While capital subsidies (including well-designed tariff schemes) remain the prevailing support mechanism for rural electrification, there is an evolution in the direction of subsidizing performance of the systems. These types of output-based aid subsidies are becoming more popular since they specifically target project sustainability.

If a performance subsidy can be applied to distributed systems in order to guarantee their long-term operation, a sustainable electrification policy should target a subsidy-free private sector-oriented approach. In order to overcome the barrier of investment, loans and other types of soft or normal financing tools should be made available, entrepreneurs should be trained properly on technology and business issues, and end-users should be involved (at least through a cost recovery tariff that should take into account an aspect of affordability). The fundamental logic behind this approach, targeting sustainable operation and profitability, with or without performance-linked support scheme (that should be phased out as soon as possible), is the only way to ensure the long-term full electrification.

Additional support can also involve technical assistance, site surveys, energy resource assessments (PVGIS [24], SWERA [16]), feasibility studies, market assessments, and capacity building provided to the investors or project developers during the project development phase (Alliance for Rural Electrification, ARE). On top of this, support schemes should be designed depending on the socioeconomic and cultural dimensions of the community in such a way that the level of organization already existing within the community/region is taken into account and, when appropriate, local/community ownership is encouraged. The participation of funds from the beneficiaries and the incorporation of the beneficiaries in the initial phases of the PV project organization would allow for the development of productive solutions with a higher potential to generate resources and to articulate sustainable proposals (ARE).

Acknowledgments

We would like to acknowledge the extensive work of the wider energy research community represented in this document; in particular ARE, Renewable Energy Policy Network for the 21st Century (REN 21), Grameen Shakti, International Solar Energy Society (ISES), Energy Sector Management Assistance Program (ESMAP) of the World Bank, UNDP, UNEP, United Nations-General's Advisory Group on Energy and Climate Change (UN-AGEC), GIZ, Energy for Sustainable Development (ESD), IEA, ENERGIA, Fundacion Bariloche, Climate Action, TERI (The Energy and Resources Institute, New Delhi), and DB Climate Change advisors.The authors would like to acknowledge Rebecca Ghanadan and Mauricio Solano-Peralta for their valuable contribution, comments, and suggestions.

References

[1] UN-AGECC (2010) *Energy for a Sustainable Future.* New York: United Nations Secretary. The Secretary-General's Advisory Group on Energy and Climate Change.
[2] World Energy Outlook (2010) Organisation for Economic Co-operation and Development (OECD)/International Energy Agency (IEA). Paris, France: OECD/IEA.
[3] World Energy Outlook (2006) Organisation for Economic Co-operation and Development (OECD)/International Energy Agency (IEA). Paris, France: OECD/IEA.
[4] Anisuzzaman M and Urmee TP (2006) Financing mechanisms of solar home systems for rural electrification in developing countries. In: *International Conference on Energy for Sustainable Development: Issues and Prospects for Asia.* Institute of Electrical and Electronic Engineers, Phuket, Thailand, March 2006.
[5] Chaurey A and Kandpal TC (2010) Assessment and evaluation of PV based decentralized rural electrification: An overview. *Renewable and Sustainable Energy Reviews* 14(8): 2266–2278.
[6] Pederson A (2010) Financing energy access on the edge of the world. *Colorado Journal of International Environmental Law* 21(2): 355–381.
[7] Renewable Energy Policy Network for the 21st Century, REN 21 (2011) Renewables 2011 Global Status Report. Paris, France: REN 21 Secretariat.
[8] Renewable Energy Policy Network for the 21st Century, REN 21 (2010) Renewables 2010 Global Status Report. Paris, France: REN 21 Secretariat.
[9] Jäger-Waldau A (2011) PV Status Report 2011, Office for Official Publications of the European Union, JRC- European Commission, EUR Report nr. JRC64900.
[10] Reiche K, Grüner R, Attigah B, *et al.* What difference can a PicoPV system make? Deutsche Gesellschaft für Technische Zusammenarbeit GmbH (GTZ), edn. *Eschborn*, May 2010.
[11] Mints P Off-grid solar: PV industry survivor. *Photovoltaics World*, May 2010.
[12] Werner C, Breyer CH, Gerlach A, and Adelmann P (2011) Global overview on cumulative installed photovolatic power. In: *2nd Symposium Small PV-Applications.* International Finance Corporation. Ulm, Germany, 6/7 June.

[13] Foster V and Briceño-Garmendia C (eds.) (2010) *Africa's Infrastructure: A Time for Transformation*. Washington, DC: Agence Française de Développement and the International Bank for Reconstruction and Development/The World Bank.
[14] Philips M and Browne B (2000) Accelerating PV markets in developing coutries. Washington, DC: Renewable Energy Policy Project (REPP) Center for Renewable Energy and Sustainable Technology (CREST), http://www.repp.org/repp/ (accessed November 2011).
[15] Schmidt F (2009) Off-grid PV back on the map with developing countries. *Renewable Energy Focus (Digital Edition)*, 9 June 2009.
[16] Solar and Wind Resource Assessment Programme. http://swera.unep.net/.
[17] Martinot E, Chaurey A, Lew D, et al. (2002) Renewable energy markets in developing countries. *Annual Review of Energy and the Environment* 27: 309–348.
[18] Acker DA and Kammen DM (1996) The quiet (energy) revolution: The diffusion of photovoltaic power systems in Kenya. *Energy Policy* 24: 81–111.
[19] Jacobson A (2007) Connective power: Solar electrification and social change in Kenya. *World Development* 35(1): 144–162.
[20] Moner-Girona M, Ghanadan R, Jacobson A, and Kammen DM (2006) Decreasing PV costs in Africa: Opportunities for rural electrification using solar PV in Sub-Saharan Africa. *Refocus* 7(1): 40–45.
[21] Szabo S, Jäger-Waldau A, and Szabo L (2010) Risk adjusted financial costs of photovoltaics. *Energy Policy* 38: 3807–3819.
[22] Huld T, Suri M, Dunlop E, et al. (2005) Integration of HelioClim-1 database into PVGIS to estimate solar electricity potential in Africa PVGIS. In: *Proceedings of the 20th European Photovoltaic Solar Energy Conference and Exhibition*. WIP Munich, Germany. Barcelona, Spain, June.
[23] Szabo S, Bodis K, Huld T, and Moner-Girona M (2011) Energy solutions in rural Africa: Mapping electrification costs of distributed solar and diesel generation versus grid extension. *Environmental Research Letters* 6: 9.
[24] Photovoltaic Geographical Information System (PVGIS)- European Commission, Joint Research Centre (2011) http://re.jrc.ec.europa.eu/pvgis (accessed November 2011).
[25] Terrado E, Cabraal A, and Mukherjee I (2008) Operational Guidance for World Bank Group Staff: Designing Sustainable Off-Grid Rural. Electrification Projects: Principles and Practices. Washington, DC: The World Bank, November 2008.
[26] Moner-Girona M (ed.) (2008) A New Scheme for the Promotion of Renewable Energies in Developing Countries. EU PV Technology Platform. WG4 European Commission, Joint Research Centre, Luxembourg: EUR23284 EN.
[27] Holland R, Lahim P, Sanchez T, and Wilkinson R (2000) Decentralized rural electrification: The critical success factors [experience of ITDG]. *World Renewable Energy Congress*. Brighton, UK, July 2000.
[28] Vallve X, Vosseler I, Cisneros EJ, et al. (2001) First experiences from the electrification of rural villages in Spain with multi-user solar hybrid grids. In: *Proceedings of the European Photovoltaic Solar Energy Conference*, 22–24 October 2001, WIP Munich, Germany.
[29] Alliance for Rural Electrification (2009) *Green Light for Renewable Energy in Developing Countries*. Brussels, Belgium: Alliance for Rural Electrification.
[30] Rolland S (2011) *Rural Electrification with Renewable Energy Technologies, Quality Standards and Business Models*. Brussels, Belgium: Alliance for Rural Electrification.
[31] Rolland S and Glania G (2011) *Hybrid Power Systems based on Renewable Energies: A Suitable and Cost-Competitive Solution for Rural Electrification*. Brussels, Belgium: Alliance for Rural Electrification and United States Agency for International Development (USAID).
[32] Reiche K, Tenenbaum B, and Torres de Mästle C (2006) Electrification and Regulation: Principles and a Model Law Paper, Paper No.18. Washington, DC: The International Bank for Reconstruction and Development/The World Bank.
[33] United Nations Environment Programme (UNEP) (2007) Financing Mechanisms and Public/Private Risk Sharing Instruments for Financing Small Scale Renewable Energy Equipment and Projects. Paris, France: United Nations Environment Programme (UNEP) and Global Environment Facility (GEF), September 2007.
[34] Nieuwenhout FDJ, van Dijk A, Lasschuit PE, et al. (2001) Experience with solar home systems in developing countries: A review. *Progress in Photovoltaics: Research and Applications* 9: 455–474.
[35] Khandker S (2009) Does micro-finance really benefit the poor? Evidence from Bangladesh. *Conference on Asia and Pacific Forum on Poverty: Reforming Policies and Institutions for Poverty Reduction*, 5–9 February 2009. Asian Development Bank, Manila, Philippines.
[36] Shakti G (2011) http://www.gshakti.org/ (accessed September 2011).
[37] Barua DC (2008) *Grameen Shakti: An Integrated and Sustainable Model for Bringing Light, Income, Health, and Affordable Climate Friendly Energy to the Rural People*. Dhaka, Bangladesh: Grameen Shakti.
[38] Barnes DF and Halpern J (2000) *Subsidies and Sustainable Rural Energy Services: Can We Create Incentives without Distorting Markets?* Washington, DC: World Bank.
[39] Liming H (2009) Financing rural renewable energy: A comparison between China and India. *Renewable and Sustainable Energy Reviews* 13: 1096–1103.
[40] Bess M (2006) Public private partnerships for access to community electricity. Tariff setting for rural electrification. *Mitigating Risk and Strengthening Capacity for Rural Investment in Africa (MIRREIA): Finance and Investment Workshop Proceedings*. Nairobi, Kenya, 18–19 July 2006.
[41] Lemaire X and REEEP/SERN webinar (2009) Off grid regulation – How to provide cost-effective and sustainable rural energy services in remote areas of developing. www.leonardo-energy.org (accessed October 2011).
[42] Martinot E and Reiche K (2000) Regulatory Approaches to Rural Electrification and Renewable Energy: Case Studies from Six Developing Countries. *World Bank Working Paper*, Washington, DC, June 2000.
[43] New J and Matteini M (eds.) Financing options for renewable energy and energy efficiency. Sustainable energy regulation and policymaking for Africa. United Nations Industrial Development Organization (UNIDO) and the Renewable Energy and Energy Efficiency Partnership (REEEP) training package. http://africa-toolkit.reeep.org/ (accessed November 2011).
[44] Multilateral Investment Guarantee Agency, MIGA (2011) www.miga.org (accessed November 2011).
[45] IEA PVPS Task 9 (2003) Summary of models for the implementation of photovoltaic solar home systems in developing countries. Report T9-02:2003. International Agency, Paris, France.
[46] World Bank (2008) REToolkit: A resource for renewable energy development. *World Bank*, June 30, Washington DC.
[47] Greacen C and Tenebaum B (2010) *On-Grid and Off-Grid Small Power Producers in Africa: Key Implementation Questions for Electricity Regulators*. Washington, DC: The World Bank, African Electrification Initiative (AEI).
[48] Ghanadan R (2010) Pricing Policies to Promote Renewable Energy and Energy Efficiency in Developing Countries. RE & EE Pricing Policy Memo prepared for World Bank.
[49] Ghanadan R and Eberhard A (2007) *Electricity Utility Management Contacts in Africa: Lessons and Experience from the TANESCO-NET Group Management Contract in Tanzania, 2002–2006*. Cape Town, South Africa: Management Program in Infrastructure Reform (MIR), Graduate School of Business, University of Cape Town.
[50] Karekezi S, Kithyyoma W, Oruta A, and Muzee K (2010) *Renewable Energies for Africa: Potential, Markets and Strategies*. Paris, France: REN 21.
[51] Makinson S (2005) *Public Finance Mechanisms to Catalyze Sustainable Energy Sector Growth*. Paris, France: UNEP, SEFI.
[52] United Nations Framework Convention on Climate Change (2011) *Benefits of the Clean Development Mechanism*. Bonn, Germany: United Nations Framework Convention on Climate Change, ISBN 92-9219-086-5.
[53] Byrne J, Kurdgelashvili L, Mathai MV, et al. (2010) World solar energy review: Technology, markets and policies center for energy and environmental policy and The World Bank.
[54] Federal Ministry for the Environment, Nature Conservation and Nuclear Safety (BMU) (2007) Renewable energy and the clean development mechanism. BMU Brochure. Bundesministeriums für Umwelt, Naturschutz and Reactorsicherheit (BMU), Berlin, Germany.
[55] Mariyappan J, Bhardwaj N, Coninck H, and Linden N (2007) A guide to bundling smallscale CDM projects. Report. Energy Research Center of the Netherlands (ECN). The Netherlands: Petten.
[56] Mendonca M (2007) *The Developing World, Feed-in Tariffs – Accelerating the Deployment of Renewable Energy*. London, UK: World Future Council, Earthscan.
[57] Fulton M (ed.) (2010) *Global Energy Transfer Feed-in Tariffs for Developing Countries*. Deutsche Bank Climate Change Advisors, New York, USA, April 2010.
[58] Bristow D (2007) The developing world. In: Mendonca M (ed.) *Feed-In Tariffs – Accelerating the Deployment of Renewable Energy*, pp. 76–86. London, UK: World Future Council, Earthscan.

[59] Moner-Girona M (2009) A new tailored scheme for the support of renewable energies in developing countries. *Energy Policy* 37(5): 2037–2041.
[60] Solano-Peralta M, Moner-Girona M, van Sark, W, and Vallve X (2009) Tropicalisation of feed-in tariffs: A custom-made support scheme for hybrid PV/diesel systems in isolated regions. *Renewable and Sustainable Energy Reviews* 13(9): 2279–2294.
[61] Rickerson W, Hanley C, Laurent C, and Greacen C Implementing a global fund for feed-in tariffs in developing countries: A case study of Tanzania. *World Renewable Energy Congress XI*. Abu Dhabi, UAE, September 2010.

1.08 Environmental Impacts of Photovoltaic Life Cycles

VM Fthenakis, Columbia University, New York, NY, USA; Brookhaven National Laboratory, Upton, NY, USA
HC Kim, Brookhaven National Laboratory, Upton, NY, USA

© 2012 Elsevier Ltd. All rights reserved.

1.08.1	Introduction	144
1.08.2	Background	144
1.08.3	Life Cycle of Photovoltaics	144
1.08.4	Life-Cycle Inventory	146
1.08.4.1	Modules	146
1.08.4.2	Balance of System	147
1.08.5	Energy Payback Times and Greenhouse Gas Emissions	147
1.08.5.1	Energy Payback Time	147
1.08.5.2	Greenhouse Gas Emissions	148
1.08.6	Criteria Pollutant and Heavy Metal Emissions	150
1.08.6.1	Criteria Pollutant Emissions	150
1.08.6.2	Heavy Metal Emissions	151
1.08.6.2.1	Direct emissions	151
1.08.6.2.2	Indirect emissions	151
1.08.7	Life-Cycle Risk Analysis	153
1.08.7.1	Risk Classification	153
1.08.7.2	Risks of Accidents in the Photovoltaic Life Cycle	153
1.08.7.3	Comparison with Other Energy Technologies	155
1.08.7.4	Limitation of the Study	157
1.08.8	Conclusion	157
Acknowledgment		158
References		158

Nomenclature

a-Si amorphous silicon
AC alternate current
BOS balance of system
c-Si crystalline silicon
CdS cadmium sulfide
CdTe cadmium telluride
CIGS copper indium gallium selenide
CIS copper indium diselenide
DC direct current
EPBT energy payback time
ESP electrostatic precipitator
FBR fluidized bed reactor
GaAs gallium arsenide
GHG greenhouse gas
GWP global warming potential
HCl hydrogen chloride
HF hydrogen fluoride
LCA life-cycle analysis (or assessment)
LCI life-cycle inventory
LPG liquefied petroleum gas
multi-Si multicrystalline silicon
mono-Si monocrystalline silicon
NAICS North American Industry Classification System
NG natural gas
NO_x nitrogen oxide
PM particulate matter
PR performance ratio
PSA probabilistic safety assessment
PSI Paul Scherrer Institute
PV photovoltaic
RMP risk management program
SiH_4 silane
$SiHCl_3$ trichlorosilane
SO_x sulfur oxide
TeO_2 tellurium dioxide
TPE thermoplastic elastomer
UCTE Union for the Co-ordination of Transmission of Electricity
VTD vapor transport deposition

1.08.1 Introduction

Currently, the main commercial photovoltaic (PV) materials are multicrystalline silicon (multi-Si), monocrystalline silicon (mono-Si), amorphous silicon (a-Si), and cadmium telluride (CdTe). A typical PV system consists of the PV module and the balance of system (BOS) structures for mounting the PV modules and power-conditioning equipment that converts the generated electricity to alternate current (AC) electricity of proper magnitude for usage in the power grid.

Life-cycle analysis (LCA) is a framework for considering the environmental inputs and outputs of a product or process from cradle to grave. It is employed to evaluate the environmental impacts of energy technologies, and the results are increasingly used in decisions about R&D funding and in formulating energy policies. In this chapter, we summarize the results of PV LCAs based on current data for two silicon and one thin-film technologies, emphasizing basic metrics including energy payback times (EPBTs), greenhouse gas (GHG) emissions, criteria pollutant emissions, toxic metal emissions, human injuries, and fatalities.

1.08.2 Background

Early life-cycle studies report a wide range of primary energy consumption for Si PV modules [1]. On the basis of normalized energy consumption per square meter, the researchers reported 2400–7600 MJ of primary energy consumption for multi-Si and 5300–16 500 MJ for mono-Si modules. Besides uncertainties in the data, these differences are due to different assumptions and allocation rules that each author adopted for modeling the purification and crystallization stages of silicon [1, 2]. Selecting only those process steps needed to produce solar-grade silicon, Alsema's [1] own estimates were 4200 and 5700 MJ m^{-2} for multi- and mono-Si modules, respectively. These values correspond to an EPBT of 2.5 and 3.1 years and life-cycle GHG emissions of 46 and 63 g CO$_2$-eq. kWh^{-1} for rooftop-mounted multi-Si PV with 13.2% efficiency and mono-Si with 14% efficiency, respectively, under Southern European (Mediterranean) conditions: insolation of 1700 kWh m^{-2} yr^{-1} and a performance ratio (PR; the ratio between the ideal and the actual electricity output) of 0.75. The BOS components, such as a mounting support, a frame, and electrical components, account for additional ~0.7 years of EPBT and ~15 g CO$_2$-eq. kWh^{-1} of GHG emissions.

Meijer et al. [3] more recently assessed a slightly higher energy expenditure of 4900 MJ m^{-2} to produce a multi-Si module. They assumed that the 270 µm thick PV cells with 14.5% cell efficiency were fabricated from electronic-grade high-purity silicon, which entails greater energy consumption. Their corresponding EPBT estimate for the module was 3.5 years excluding BOS components, that is, higher than Alsema's earlier determination of 2.5 years. The increase stems mainly from the low level of insolation in the Netherlands (1000 kWh m^{-2} yr^{-1}) compared with the average for Southern Europe (1700 kWh m^{-2} yr^{-1}), and, to a lesser degree, from the higher energy estimation for silicon [1, 3]. Jungbluth [4] reported the life-cycle metrics of various PV systems under environmental conditions in Switzerland in 2000. He considered the environmental impacts for 300 µm thick multi- and mono-Si PV modules with 13.2% and 14.8% conversion efficiency, respectively. Depending on which of the two materials he evaluated, and their applications (i.e., façade, slanted roof, and flat roof), he arrived at figures of 39–110 g CO$_2$-eq. kWh^{-1} of GHG emissions and 3–6 years of EPBT for the average insolation of 1100 kWh m^{-2} yr^{-1} in that country. He assumed that the source of silicon materials was 50% from off-grade silicon and 50% from electronic-grade silicon, which is distant from the composition of the current (2010s) PV supply [2, 4].

There are fewer life-cycle studies of thin-film PV technologies; evaluations of the life-cycle primary energy consumption of a-Si ranged between 710 and 1980 MJ m^{-2} [1]. The differences are largely attributed to the choice of substrate and encapsulation materials. The lowest estimate, made by Palz and Zibetta, considered a single glass structure, while the highest one by Hagedorn and Hellriegel was based on a double-glass configuration to protect the active layer [1, 5, 6]. For CdTe PV, Hynes et al. [7] based their energy analysis on two alternative technologies employed at that time. The first employed nonvacuum electrodeposition of a 1.5 µm absorber layer (CdTe), in conjunction with chemical-bath deposition of the 0.2 µm window layer (cadmium sulfide (CdS)); the second method deposited both these layers by thermal evaporation yielding an ~5 µm thick absorber layer and an ~1.7 µm thick window layer. Their primary energy estimate for the first technology was 993 MJ m^{-2} and that for the second was 1188 MJ m^{-2}. Kato et al.'s [8] energy estimates were pertinent to the scale of annual production; they suggested that energy consumption will decline as the scale of production rises; they cited values of 1523, 1234, and 992 MJ m^{-2} for frameless modules with annual capacities of 10, 30, and 100 MW$_p$ (peak power), respectively. However, these earlier estimates fall far short of describing present-day commercial-scale CdTe PV production, which, unlike previously, now encompasses many large-scale production plants.

1.08.3 Life Cycle of Photovoltaics

The life cycle of PVs starts from the extraction of materials from the ground (cradle) and ends in the disposal or recycling of the end-of-life products (grave). The main stages are (1) the production of raw materials, (2) their processing and purification, (3) the manufacture of modules and BOS components, (4) the installation and use of the systems, and (5) their decommissioning and disposal or recycling (**Figure 1**).

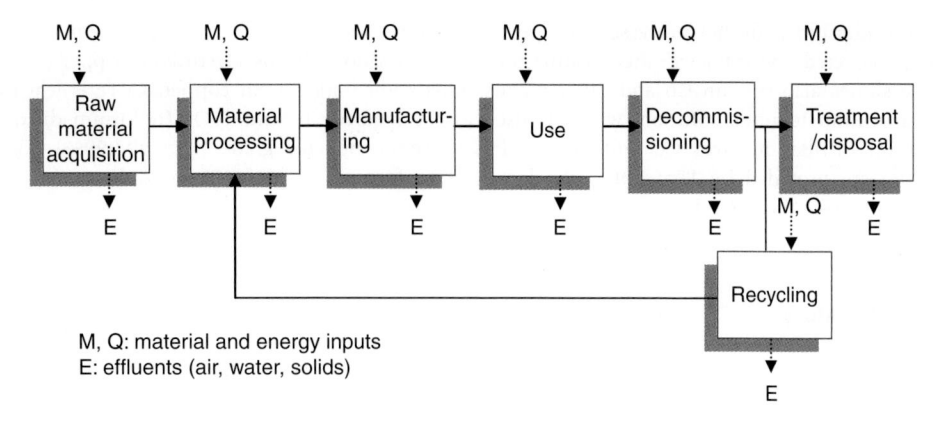

Figure 1 Flow of the life-cycle stages, energy, materials, and effluents for PV systems.

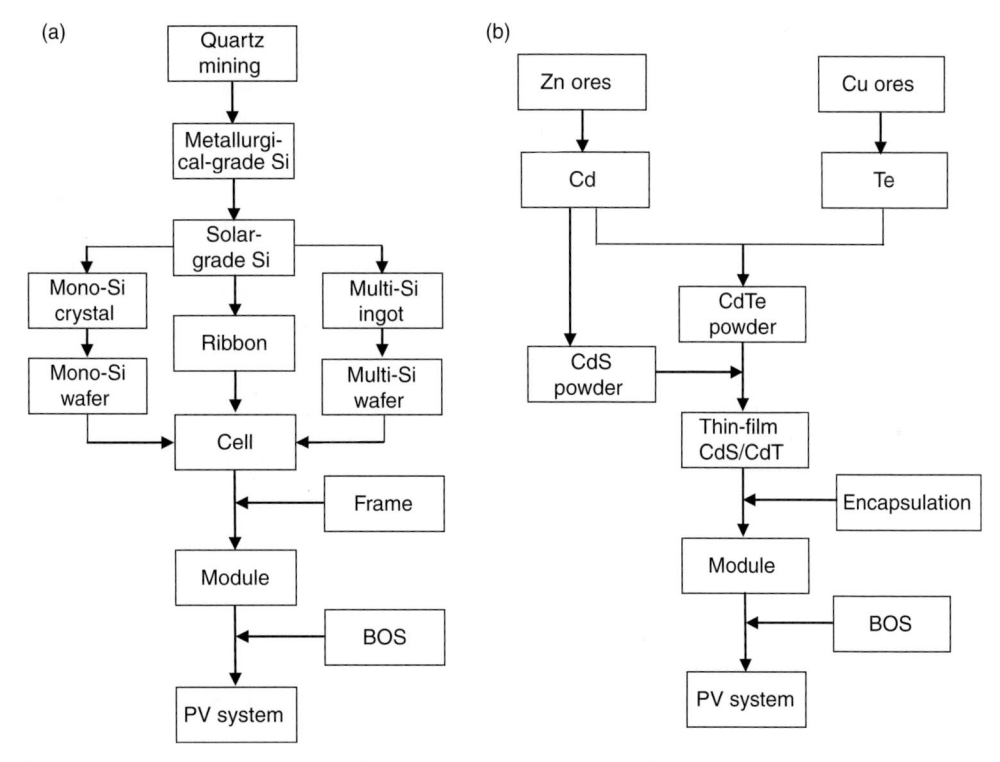

M, Q: material and energy inputs
E: effluents (air, water, solids)

Figure 2 Detailed flow diagram from raw material acquisition to the manufacturing stage of PVs [9]. (a) Silicon PVs and (b) CdTe PVs (frameless). BOS, balance of system; mono-Si, monocrystalline silicon; multi-Si, multicrystalline silicon.

Production starts with mining of the raw materials (i.e., quartz sand for silicon PV; Zn and Cu ores for CdTe PV), and continues with their processing and purification (**Figure 2**) [9]. The silica in the quartz sand is reduced in an arc furnace to metallurgical-grade silicon, which must be purified further into 'electronic-grade' or 'solar–grade' silicon, typically through a 'Siemens' process. Crystalline silicon (c-Si) modules typically are framed for additional strength and easy mounting. The recent LCAs of c-Si are based on life-cycle inventory (LCI) data provided, collectively, by 11 European and US PV companies participating in the European Commission's CrystalClear project. The data sets were published in separate papers by Alsema and de Wild-Scholten [2] and by Fthenakis and Alsema [10].

The LCIs of the minor metals used in thin-film PVs such as Cd, In, Mo, and Se are closely related to the production cycle of base metals (Zn, Cu). The allocations of emissions and energy use between the former (Cd, In, Mo, and Se) and the latter (Zn, Cu) during mining, smelting, and refining stages are described elsewhere [11]. Fthenakis [12] described the material flows of cadmium (Cd) and emissions from the entire life-cycle stages of CdTe PV. The life cycle starts with the production of Cd and Te, which are by-products, respectively, of smelting of Zn and Cu ores (**Figure 2**). Cadmium is obtained from the Zn waste streams, such as particulates collected in air pollution control equipment and slimes collected from Zn electrolyte purification stages. Cadmium is further processed and purified to meet the four or five 9s purity required for synthesizing CdTe. Tellurium is recovered and extracted after treating the slimes produced during electrolytic copper refining with dilute sulfuric acid; these slimes also contain Cu and other metals. After cementation with copper, CuTe is leached with caustic soda to produce a sodium telluride solution, which is used as the feed for Te and TeO_2 (tellurium dioxide). Additional leaching and vacuum distillation gives Cd and Te powders of semiconductor grade (i.e., 99.999%). The LCI data on thin-film CdTe PV were provided by First Solar, the largest manufacturer of CdTe PV modules, using vapor transport deposition (VTD) to deposit the CdTe layer.

1.08.4 Life-Cycle Inventory

Life-cycle assessments require data on material and energy use as well as emissions during the various stages of the life cycle of PVs. These data, called LCIs, are typically available from different databases for the modules and the BOS.

1.08.4.1 Modules

The material and energy inputs and outputs during the life cycles of Si PVs, namely, multi- and mono-Si, and also thin-film CdTe PV were investigated in detail based on actual measurements from PV production plants. Alsema and de Wild-Scholten recently updated the LCI for the technology for producing c-Si modules in Western Europe under the framework of the CrystalClear project, a large European integrated project focusing on c-Si technology, cofunded by the European Commission and the participating countries [2, 13]. Fthenakis and Kim [14] reported the LCI data for CdTe thin-film technology taken from the production data from First Solar's plant in Perrysburg, OH, USA. Table 1 presents the simplified LCIs for 2006, compiled from the data from 11 European and 2 US plants along with values in the literature [2, 14].

The typical thickness of multi- and mono-Si PVs is 200 and 180 μm, respectively; 60 individual cells of 243 cm^2 (156 mm × 156 mm) comprise a module of 1.6 m^2 for all Si PV types. The conversion efficiency of multi- and mono-Si modules is taken as 13.2%, and 14.0%, respectively. On the other hand, as of 2009, the frameless, double-glass, CdTe modules of 1.2 m × 0.6 m, manufactured by First Solar, are rated at 10.9% photon-to-electricity conversion efficiency with ~3 μm thick active layer.

The data for Si PVs extend from the production stage of solar-grade Si to the manufacturing stage of the module, while those for CdTe PV correspond to the deposition of the CdTe film and the manufacturing stage of the module. The metallurgical-grade silicon that is extracted from quartz is purified into solar-grade polysilicon by either a silane (SiH_4)- or a trichlorosilane ($SiHCl_3$)-based process. The energy requirement for this purification step is significant for c-Si PV modules, accounting for ~30% of the primary energy used for fabricating multi-Si modules [15]. Two technologies are currently employed for producing polysilicon from silicon gases: the Siemens reactor method and the fluidized bed reactor (FBR) method. In the former, which accounts for the majority (~90% in 2004) of solar-grade silicon production in the United States, silane or trichlorosilane gas is introduced into a thermal decomposition furnace (reactor) with high-temperature (~1100–1200 °C) polysilicon rods [16–18]. The silicon rods grow as silicon atoms in the gas deposit onto them, up to 150 mm in diameter and up to 150 cm in length [16]. The data on Si PVs in Table 1 are based on averages over standard and modified Siemens reactors. The former primarily produces the electronic-grade silicon with a purity of over nine 9s, while the latter produces the solar-grade silicon with a purity of six to eight 9s, consuming less energy than the former [19]. The scenario involving the scrap silicon from electronic-grade silicon production is not considered as the market share of this material accounts for only 5% in 2005 [20].

Table 1 Materials and energy inputs for PV systems to produce 1 m^2 of module including process loss, compiled in 2006 (excluding the frame for Si modules) [9]

Category	Inputs	Multi-Si	Mono-Si	CdTe
Components (kg)	Cell materials	1.6	1.5	0.065
	Glass	9.1	9.1	19.2
	Ethylene vinyl acetate	1.0	1.0	0.6
	Others	1.8	1.8	2.0
Consumables (kg)	Gases	2.2	7.8	0.001
	Liquid	6.8	6.6	0.67
	Others	4.3	4.3	0.4
Energy	Electricity (kWh)	248	282	59
	Oil (l)	0.05	0.05	0.05
	Natural gas (MJ)	308	361	–

1.08.4.2 Balance of System

Little attention has been paid to the LCA studies of the BOS, and so inventory data are scarce. Depending on the application, solar cells are either rooftop- or ground-mounted, both operating with a proper BOS. Silicon modules need an aluminum frame of 2.6 kg m^{-2} for structural robustness and easy installation, while a glass backing performs the same functions for the CdTe PV produced in the United States [2, 14]. For a rooftop PV application, the BOS typically includes inverters, mounting structures, cable, and connectors. Large-scale ground-mounted PV installations require additional equipment and facilities, such as grid connections, office facilities, and concrete.

A recent analysis of a 3.5 MW$_p$ mc-Si installation at the Springerville Generating Station in Arizona affords a detailed material and energy balance for a ground-mounted BOS (**Table 2**) [21]. For this study, Tucson Electric Power (TEP) prepared the BOS bill of material and energy consumption data for its mc-Si PV installations. The life expectancy of the PV metal support structures is assumed to be 60 years. Inverters and transformers are considered to last for 30 years, but parts must be replaced every 10 years, amounting to 10% of their total mass, according to well-established data from the power industry on transformers and electronic components. The inverters are utility-scale Xantrec PV-150 models with a wide-open frame, allowing failed parts to be easily replaced. The LCI includes the office facility's material and energy use for administrative, maintenance, and security staff, as well as the operation of maintenance vehicles. Aluminum frames are shown separately, since they are part of the module, not of the BOS inventory; there are both framed and frameless modules on the market.

De Wild-Scholten et al. [22] studied two classes of rooftop mounting systems based on an mc-Si PV system called SolarWorld SW220 with dimensions of 1001 mm × 1675 mm and 220 W$_p$: they are used for on-roof mounting where the system builds on existing roofing material and in-roof mounting where the modules replace the roof tiles. The latter case is credited in terms of energy and material use because roof tile materials then are not required. **Table 3** details the LCI of several rooftop mounting systems, cabling, and inverters. Two types (500 and 2500 W) of small inverters adequate for rooftop PV design were inventoried. A transformer is included as an electronic component for both models. The amount of control electronics will become less significant for inverters with higher capacity (>10 kW), resulting in less material use per PV capacity [22].

1.08.5 Energy Payback Times and Greenhouse Gas Emissions

The most frequently measured life-cycle metrics for the environmental analysis of PV systems are the EPBT and the GHG emissions.

1.08.5.1 Energy Payback Time

EPBT is defined as the period required for a renewable energy system to generate the same amount of energy (either primary or kWh equivalent) that was used to produce the system itself.

$$\text{EPBT} = \frac{E_{\text{mat}} + E_{\text{manuf}} + E_{\text{trans}} + E_{\text{inst}} + E_{\text{EOL}}}{E_{\text{agen}} - E_{\text{aoper}}}$$

where E_{mat} is the primary energy demand to produce materials that constitute PV system, E_{manuf} the primary energy demand to manufacture PV system, E_{trans} the primary energy demand to transport materials used during the life cycle, E_{inst} the primary energy

Table 2 Mass balance of major components for the 3.5 MW Tucson Electric Power Generating plant in Springerville, AZ, based on 30 years of operation [21]

	BOS	Mass (kg MW$_p^{-1}$)	Percentage of total
BOS	PV support structure	16 821	10.3
	Module interconnections	453	0.3
	Junction boxes	1 385	0.8
	Conduits and fittings	6 561	4.0
	Wire and grounding devices	5 648	3.4
	Inverters and transformers	28 320	17.3
	Grid connections	1 726	1.1
	Office facilities	20 697	12.6
	Concrete	76 417	46.6
	Miscellaneous	5 806	3.5
	Total	163 834	100.0
Frame[a]		18 141	

[a] Based on 12.2% rated efficiency for mc-Si module.
BOS, balance of system.

Table 3 Life-cycle inventory of balance of system [21,22]

(a) Mounting system (kg m^{-2})

	On-roof		In-roof	
	Phönix, TectoSun	Schletter Eco05+EcoG	Schletter, Plandach 5	Schweizer, Solrif
Low-alloy steel	0	0	0	0
Stainless steel	0.49	0.72	0.28	0.08
Aluminum	0.54	0.97	1.21	1.71
Concrete	0	0	0	0
Frame	3.04	0	0	0

(b) Cabling (g m^{-2})

	Helukabel, Solarflex 101, 4 mm^2, DC	Helukabel, NYM-J, 6 mm^2, AC
Copper	83.0	19.9
Thermoplastic elastomer (TPE)	64.0	0.0
PVC	0.0	16.9

(c) Inverters (g)

	Philips PSI 500 (500 W)	Mastervolt SunMaster 2500 (2500 W)
Steel	78	9800
Aluminum	682	1400
Copper	2	
Polycarbonate	68	
Acrylonitrile butadiene styrene (ABS)	148	
Other plastics	5.4	
Printed circuit board	100	1800[a]
Connector	50	
Transformers, wire-wound	310	5500
Coils	74	
Transistor diode	10	
Capacitor, film	72	
Capacitor, electrolytic	54	
Other electric components	20	

[a] Including electric components.
AC, alternate current; DC, direct current.

demand to install the system, E_{EOL} the primary energy demand for end-of-life management, E_{agen} the annual electricity generation in primary energy term, and E_{aoper} the annual energy demand for operation and maintenance in primary energy term.

Calculating the primary energy equivalent requires knowledge of the country-specific, energy conversion parameters for fuels and technologies used to generate energy and feedstock. The annual electricity generation (E_{agen}) is represented as primary energy based on the efficiency of electricity conversion at the demand side. The electricity is converted to the primary energy term by the average conversion efficiency of 0.29 for the United States and 0.31 for Western Europe [23, 24].

1.08.5.2 Greenhouse Gas Emissions

The GHG emissions during the life-cycle stages of a PV system are estimated as an equivalent of CO_2 using an integrated time horizon of 100 years; the major emissions included as GHG emissions are CO_2 (GWP = 1; GWP stands for global warming potential and is an indicator of the relative radiative effect of a substance compared to CO_2, integrated over a chosen time horizon), CH_4 (GWP = 25), N_2O (GWP = 298), and chlorofluorocarbons (GWP = 4750–14 400) [25]. Electricity and fuel use during the PV material and module production are the main sources of the GHG emissions for PV cycles. Upstream electricity generation methods also play an important role in determining the total GHG emissions. For instance, the GHG emission factor of the average US electricity grid is 40% higher than that of the average Western European (UCTE (Union for the Co-ordination of Transmission of Electricity)) grid although emission factors of fossil fuel combustion are similar, resulting in higher GHG estimates for the US-produced modules [23, 24].

With material inventory data from industry, Alsema and de Wild-Scholten [2] demonstrated that the life-cycle primary energy and GHG emission of complete rooftop Si PV systems are much lower than those reported in earlier studies. Primary energy consumption is 3700 and 4200 MJ m^{-2}, respectively, for multi- and mono-Si modules. Fthenakis and Alsema also report that the GHG emissions of multi- and mono-Si modules corresponding to 2004–05 production are within 37 and 45 g CO$_2$-eq. kWh^{-1}, with an EPBT of 2.2 and 2.7 years for a rooftop application under Southern European insolation of 1700 kWh m^{-2} yr^{-1} and a PR of 0.75 (**Figures 3** and **4**, respectively) [2, 10]. We note that in these estimates, the BOS for rooftop application accounts for 4.5–5 g CO$_2$-eq. kWh^{-1} of GHG emissions and 0.3 years of EPBT. De Wild-Scholten recently updated these estimates based on thinner modules and more efficient processes, reporting an EPBT of ~1.8 years and GHG emissions of ~30 g CO$_2$-eq. kWh^{-1} for both multi- and mono-Si PVs. Note that these figures include the effect of 'take back and recycling' of PV modules but do not take into account the frame that is typically required for structural integrity in single glass modules. After accommodating these factors, the GHG emissions correspond to 28 and 29 g CO$_2$-eq. kWh^{-1}, respectively, for multi- and mono-Si PVs, whereas the EPBT is ~1.7 years for both Si PV systems (**Figures 3** and **4**). These calculations were based on the electricity mixture for the current production of Si, within the context of the CrystalClear project.

For CdTe PV, we previously estimated the energy consumption as 1200 MJ m^{-2}, based on the actual production data of the year 2005 from the First Solar's 25 MW$_p$ plant in Ohio, USA, close to the early studies reviewed [7, 8]. The GHG emissions and EPBT of ground-mounted CdTe PV modules under the average US insolation condition, 1800 kWh m^{-2} yr^{-1}, were determined to be 24 g CO$_2$-eq. kWh^{-1} and 1.1 years, correspondingly. These estimates include 6 g CO$_2$-eq. kWh^{-1} of GHG and 0.3 years of EPBT contribution from the ground-mounted BOS [14]. On the other hand, Raugei *et al.* [26] estimated a lower primary energy

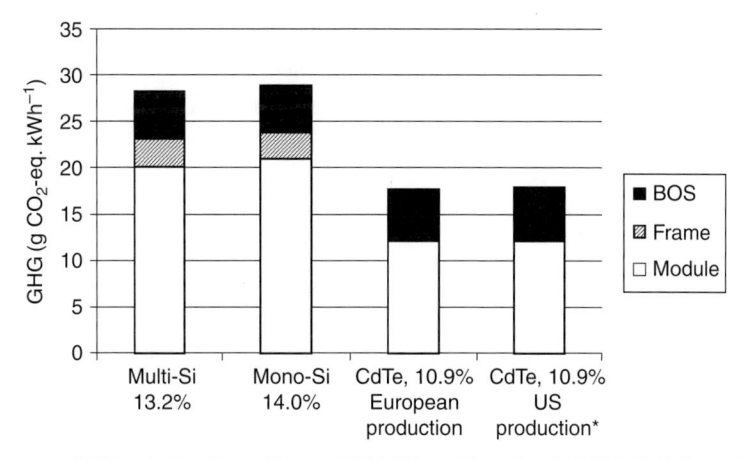

Figure 3 Life-cycle greenhouse gas (GHG) emissions from silicon and CdTe PV modules, wherein BOS is the balance of system, that is, the module supports, cabling, and power conditioning [2, 10, 13, 14, 26]. Unless otherwise noted, the estimates are based on rooftop-mounted installation, Southern European insolation of 1700 kWh m^{-2} yr^{-1}, a performance ratio of 0.75, and a lifetime of 30 years. *Based on ground-mounted installation, average US insolation of 1800 kWh m^{-2} yr^{-1}, and a performance ratio of 0.8. Mono-Si, monocrystalline silicon; multi-Si, multicrystalline silicon.

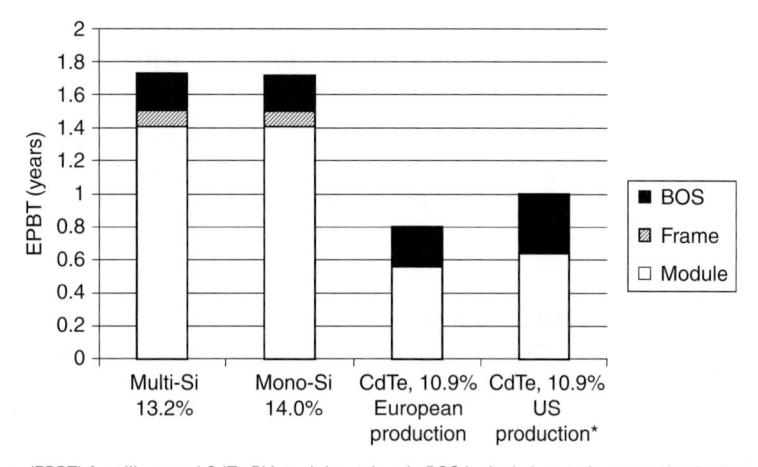

Figure 4 Energy payback time (EPBT) for silicon and CdTe PV modules, wherein BOS is the balance of system, that is, the module supports, cabling, and power conditioning [2, 10, 13, 14, 26, 27]. Unless otherwise noted, the estimates are based on rooftop-mounted installation, Southern European insolation of 1700 kWh m^{-2} yr^{-1}, a performance ratio of 0.75, and a lifetime of 30 years. *Based on ground-mounted installation, average US insolation of 1800 kWh m^{-2} yr^{-1}, and a performance ratio of 0.8. Mono-Si, monocrystalline silicon; multi-Si, multicrystalline silicon.

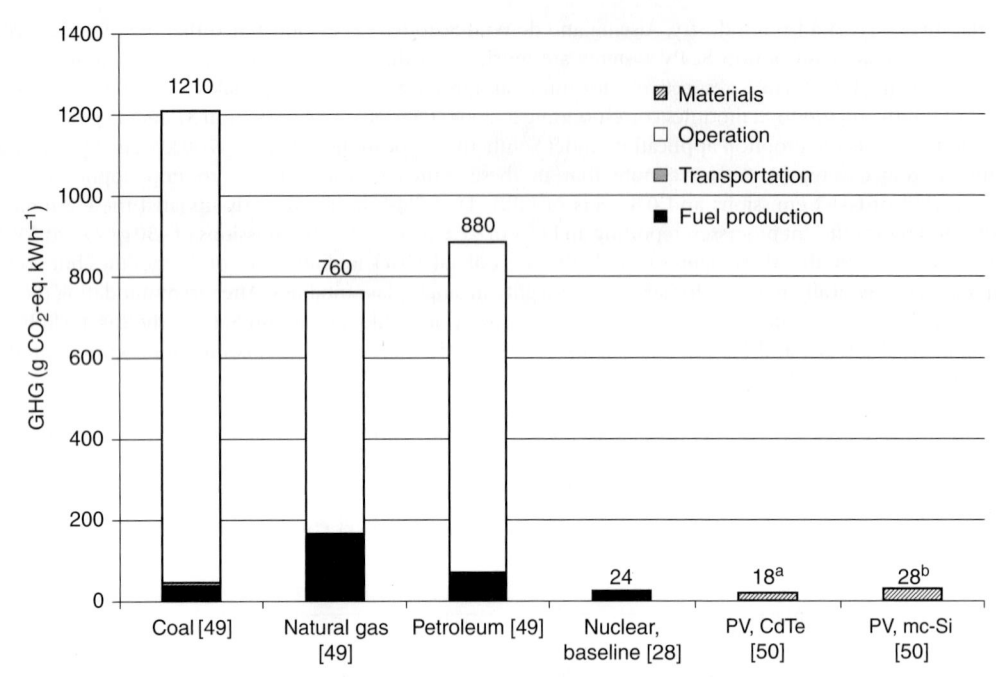

Figure 5 Comparison of emissions from PV with those from conventional power plants. [a]Based on the average US insolation of 1800 kWh m^{-2} yr^{-1} and a performance ratio of 0.8; [b]based on the Southern European insolation of 1700 kWh m^{-2} yr^{-1} and a performance ratio of 0.75. GHG, greenhouse gas; mc-Si, multicrystalline silicon.

consumption, ~1100 MJ m^{-2}, and thereby less GHG emissions and lower EPBT than ours, based on the data of the year 2002 from the Antec Solar's 10 MW$_p$ plant in Germany. However, the latter estimates are obsolete as their plant ceased producing CdTe PV.

With continued growth in efficiency and reduction of electricity use in the new production lines, Fthenakis et al. [50] updated CdTe PV's environmental indicators using new data from the plant in Perrysburg, OH, and two studies based on data from the plant in Frankfurt-Oder, Germany (**Figures 3** and **4**). The latest EPBT and GHG emissions based on the standard system boundary are 0.8 years and 18 g CO$_2$-eq. kWh^{-1} for CdTe PV for typical rooftop installation in Southern Europe, that is, with irradiation of 1700 kWh m^{-2} yr^{-1} and a PR of 0.75. Note that the US estimates of CdTe in **Figures 3** and **4** include R&D and administrative energy consumptions which are not included in other PV LCAs. These updated EPBT and GHG figures are 30–35% lower than the previous estimates by Fthenakis and Kim [14] and Fthenakis et al. [9].

We note that this picture is not a static one and expect that improvements in material and energy utilization and recycling will continue to improve the environmental profiles. A recent, major improvement is a recycling process for the sawing slurry, the cutting fluid that is used in the wafer cutting [27]. This recycling process recovers 80–90% of the silicon carbide and polyethylene glycol, which used to be wasted. On the other hand, any increases in the electrical conversion efficiencies of the modules will entail a proportional improvement of the EPBT. **Figure 5** compares these emissions with those of conventional fuel-burning power plants, revealing the considerable environmental advantage of PV technologies. The majority of GHG emissions are from the operation stage for the coal, natural gas, and oil fuel cycles, while the material and device production accounts for nearly all the emissions for the PV cycles. The GHG emissions from the nuclear fuel cycle are mainly related to the fuel production, that is, mining, milling, fabrication, conversion, and enrichment of uranium fuel. The details of the US nuclear fuel cycle are described elsewhere [28].

1.08.6 Criteria Pollutant and Heavy Metal Emissions

1.08.6.1 Criteria Pollutant Emissions

The emissions of criteria pollutants during the life cycle of a PV system are largely proportional to the amount of fossil fuel burned during its various phases, in particular, PV material processing and manufacturing; therefore, the emission profiles are close to those of the GHG emissions (**Figure 6**). Toxic gases and heavy metals can be emitted directly from material processing and PV manufacturing, and indirectly from generating the energy used at both stages. Accounting for each of them is necessary to create a complete picture of the environmental impact of a technology. An interesting example of accounting for the total emissions is that of cadmium flows in CdTe and other PV technologies, as discussed next.

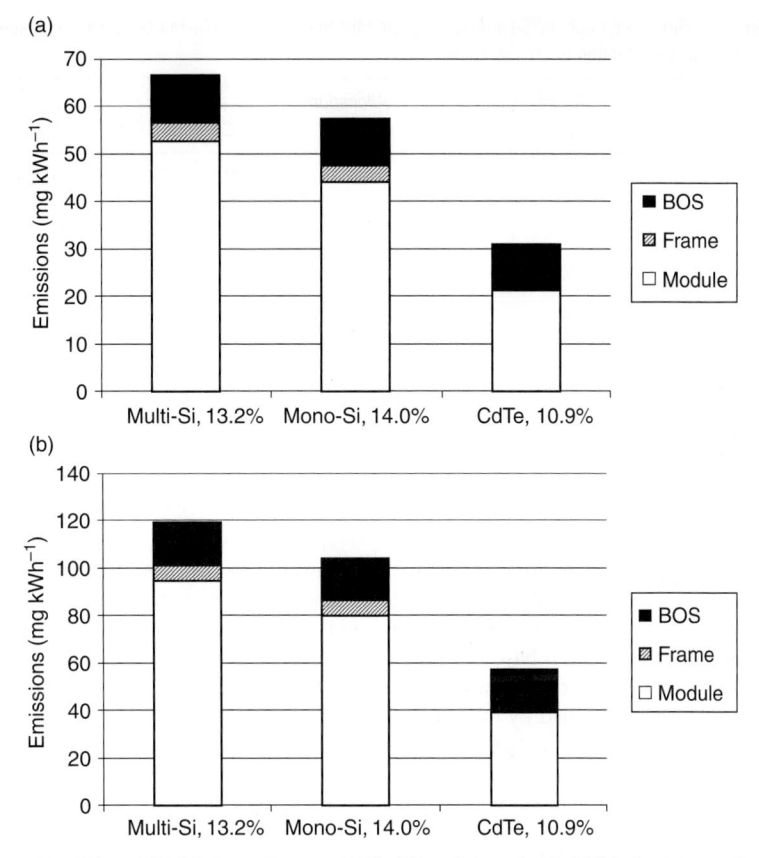

Figure 6 Life-cycle emissions of (a) NO_x and (b) SO_x from silicon and CdTe PV modules, wherein BOS is the balance of system (BOS), that is, module supports, cabling, and power conditioning. The estimates are based on rooftop-mounted installation, Southern European insolation of 1700 kWh m^{-2} yr^{-1}, a performance ratio of 0.75, and a lifetime of 30 years. It is assumed that the electricity supply for all the PV system is from the UCTE grid. Mono-Si, monocrystalline silicon; multi-Si, multicrystalline silicon.

1.08.6.2 Heavy Metal Emissions

1.08.6.2.1 Direct emissions

Cadmium is a by-product of zinc and lead, and is collected from emissions and waste streams during the production of these major metals. The largest fraction of cadmium, with ~99.5% purity, is in the form of a sponge from the electrolytic recovery of zinc. This sponge is transferred to a cadmium recovery facility and is further processed through oxidation and leaching to generate a new electrolytic solution. After selectively precipitating the major impurities, cadmium of 99.99% purity is recovered by electrowinning. It is further purified by vacuum distillation to the five 9s purity required for CdTe PV manufacturing. The emissions during each of these steps are detailed elsewhere [12]. They total up to 0.02 g GWh^{-1} of PV-produced energy under Southern European condition (Table 4). On the other hand, cadmium emissions during the life span of a finished CdTe module are negligible; the only conceivable pathway of release is if a fire broke out. Experiments at Brookhaven National Laboratory that simulated real fire conditions revealed that CdTe is effectively contained within the glass-to-glass encapsulation during the fire, and only minute amounts (0.4–0.6%) of Cd are released. The dissolution of Cd into the molten glass was confirmed by high-energy synchrotron X-ray microscopy [29].

1.08.6.2.2 Indirect emissions

The indirect emissions here are those emissions associated with the production of energy used in mining and industrial processes in the PV life cycle. Reporting indirect emissions separately from direct ones not only improves transparency in analyses but also allows calculating emissions for a certain mix of energy options as demonstrated in a recent study by Reich *et al.* [30]. Coal- and oil-fired power plants routinely generate Cd during their operation, as it is a trace element in both fuels. According to the data from US Electric Power Research Institute (EPRI), under the best/optimized operational and maintenance conditions, burning coal for electricity releases into the air between 2 and 7 g Cd GWh^{-1} [31]. In addition, 140 g Cd GWh^{-1} inevitably collects as fine dust in boilers, baghouses, and electrostatic precipitators (ESPs). Furthermore, a typical US coal-powered plant emits per GWh about 1000 tonnes of CO_2, 8 tonnes of SO_2, 3 tonnes of NO_x (nitrogen oxide), and 0.4 tonnes of particulates. The emissions of Cd from heavy oil-burning power plants are 12–14 times higher than those from coal plants, even though heavy oil contains much less Cd than coal (~0.1 ppm),

Table 4 Direct, atmospheric Cd emissions during the life cycle of the CdTe PV module (allocation of emissions to coproduction of Zn, Cd, Ge, and In)

	Air emissions (g Cd tonne^{-1} Cd[a])	Allocation (%)	Air emissions (g Cd tonne^{-1} Cd[a])	mg Cd GWh^{-1} [b]
Mining of Zn ores	2.7	0.58	0.016	0.02
Zn smelting/refining	40	0.58	0.23	0.3
Cd purification	6	100	6	9.1
CdTe production	6	100	6	9.1
PV manufacturing	3	100	3	4.5
Operation	0.3	100	0.3	0.3
Disposal/recycling	0	100	0	0
Total			15.55	23.3

[a] Tonne of Cd produced.
[b] Energy produced assuming average Southern European insolation (i.e., 1700 kWh m^{-2} yr^{-1}), 9% electrical conversion efficiency, and a 30-year life for the modules.

because these plants do not have particulate control equipment. Cadmium emissions are also associated with the life cycle of natural gas and nuclear fuel because of the energy used in the processing and material production of the associated fuel [23].

We accounted for Cd emissions in generating the electricity used in producing a CdTe PV system [32]. The assessment of electricity demand for PV modules and BOS was based on the LCI of each module and the electricity input data for producing BOS materials. Then, Cd emissions from the electricity demand for each module were assigned, assuming that the life-cycle electricity for the silicon and CdTe PV modules was supplied by the UCTE (European) grid. The indirect Cd emissions from electricity usage during the life cycle of CdTe PV modules (i.e., 0.2 g GWh^{-1}) are an order of magnitude greater than the direct ones (routine and accidental) (i.e., 0.016 g GWh^{-1}).

The complete life-cycle atmospheric Cd emissions, estimated by adding those from the electricity and fuel demand associated with manufacturing and material production for various PV modules and BOS, are compared with the emissions from other electricity-generating technologies (**Figure 7**) [9]. Undoubtedly, displacing the others with Cd PV markedly lowers the amount of Cd released into the air. Thus, every GWh of electricity generated by CdTe PV modules can prevent around 4 g of Cd air emissions if they are used instead of, or as a supplement to, the UCTE electricity grid. Also, the direct emissions of Cd during the life cycle of CdTe PV are 10 times lower than the indirect ones due to electricity and fuel use in the same life cycle, and about 30 times less than those indirect emissions from crystalline PVs [9]. Furthermore, we examined the indirect heavy metal emissions in the life cycle of the three silicon technologies discussed earlier, finding that, among PV technologies, CdTe PV with the lowest EPBT has the lowest heavy metal emissions (**Figure 8**) [9].

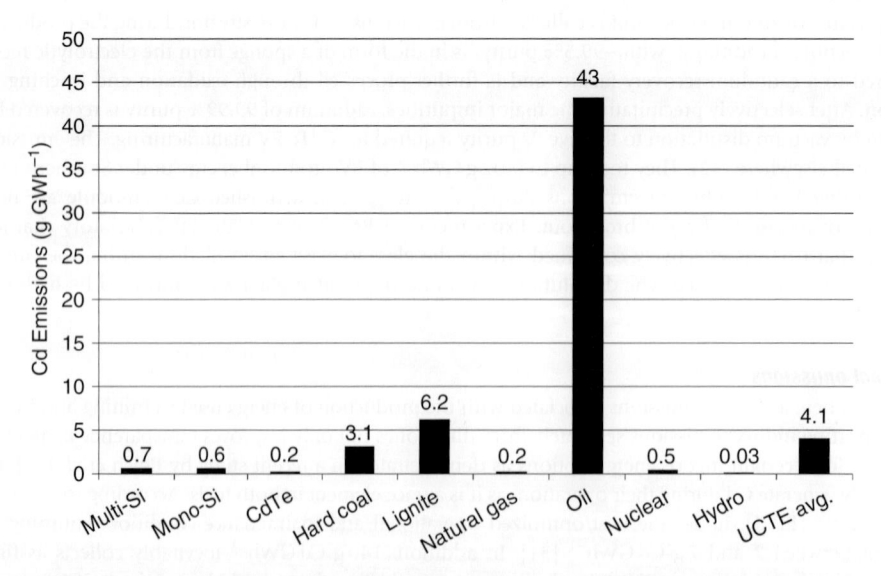

Figure 7 Life-cycle atmospheric Cd emissions for PV systems from electricity and fuel consumption, normalized for a Southern Europe average insolation of 1700 kWh m^{-2} yr^{-1}, a performance ratio of 0.8, and a lifetime of 30 years. A ground-mounted balance of system is assumed for all PV systems [9]. Mono-Si, monocrystalline silicon; multi-Si, multicrystalline silicon.

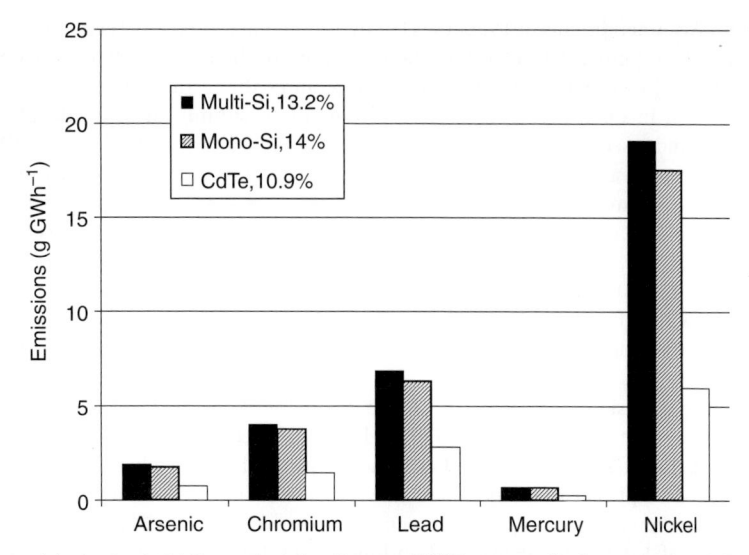

Figure 8 Emissions of heavy metals due to electricity use, based on European UTCE averages (Ecoinvent database). Emissions are normalized for Southern European average insolation of 1700 kWh m^{-2} yr^{-1}, a performance ratio of 0.8, and a lifetime of 30 years. Each PV system is assumed to include a ground-mounted balance of system as described by Mason et al. [21]. Mono-Si, monocrystalline silicon; multi-Si, multicrystalline silicon.

1.08.7 Life-Cycle Risk Analysis

1.08.7.1 Risk Classification

Perhaps the greatest potential risks of the PV fuel cycle are linked with chemical usage during material production and module processing [33, 34]. Although rare, accidents like leakage, explosion, and fire of toxic and flammable substances are the major concerns to be addressed to ensure public acceptance of PV technology. But little is known about their frequency and scale in terms of human fatalities, injuries, and economic losses during the PV fuel cycle. In its burgeoning stage, the PV industry has not experienced major accidents of the same scale as other energy sectors. Furthermore, the stages of the PV fuel cycle are closely connected to the semiconductor processes characterizing PV risks, that is, equitably allocating risks to the PV and semiconductor industries poses many difficulties.

The risks associated with energy technologies can be classified into four types based on their scale, frequency, and the severity of harmful events [35].

1. Risk during normal operation – risks the consequences of which are typically accepted, for example, GHG emissions, toxic chemical emissions, routine radioactive emissions, chemical/radioactive waste, and resource (fuel, water) depletion.
2. Risk of routine accidents – risk of accidents with high frequency and low consequences, for example, small-scale leakage of chemicals, small-scale explosion/fires, transportation accidents, and small-scale radioactivity release.
3. Risk of severe accidents – risk of accidents with low frequency and high consequences, for example, core meltdown, collapse of dam, and large-scale fire/explosion.
4. Difficult-to-evaluate risks – subject to, and sometimes reinforced by, perception. These include terrorist attacks on reactor/used fuel storage, geopolitical instability, military conflicts, energy security/national independence, and nuclear proliferation.

The first type of risk is characterized as routine under normal conditions as opposed to accidents, and its impact is usually limited by safety measures often established by regulation. This type of risk is usually determined by analytical tools, such as LCA and impact pathway analysis. The second and third types cover anomalous events or accidents. The general public is more concerned about the third type of risk, low-probability catastrophic events, than the second type, high-probability less severe accidents. The fourth type of risk is often associated with the public's perception, and the probability and consequences are difficult to evaluate [36].

1.08.7.2 Risks of Accidents in the Photovoltaic Life Cycle

The greatest potential risks of the PV life cycle involve the toxic and flammable chemicals used for producing PV materials and for manufacturing modules [34]. Fthenakis and Kim undertook a life-cycle risk analysis based on accident records from a national database, the risk management plan (RMP). The study focused on the stages of handling and using the chemicals while making solar cell materials and the modules [35]. The risks of potential accidents during installation, operation, and disposing/recycling of PV modules may be negligible, as then chemical usages are little or unnecessary.

According to the Clean Air Act Amendments of 1990, the US Environmental Protection Agency (EPA) is to publish regulations and guidance for facilities that use extremely hazardous substances to prevent chemical accidents. The US EPA developed the RMP rule to implement section 112 (r) of the amendments. This rule requires the facilities that produce, use, or handle toxic or flammable chemicals of concern in quantities over specific thresholds to submit an RMP. Regulated substances and their threshold quantities are listed under section 112 (r) of the Clean Air Act in 40 CFR Part 68. The RMP should include a 5-year accident history detailing the cause of accidents and the damages to the employees, environment, and local public. Other RMP components include a hazard assessment for the most likely and the worst-case accident scenarios, a prevention program covering safety precautions and maintenance, monitoring, and employee training measures, and an emergency response program that describes emergency health care, employee training measures, and procedures for informing the public and response agencies [37]. In 1999, around 15 000 relevant facilities in the United States first submitted their accident records during the previous 5-year period, along with other documents. The current (2005) updated RMPs mostly cover accidents that occurred since mid-1999 for 17 000 country-wide facilities. The program must be resubmitted every 5 years and revised whenever there is a significant change in usage.

Fthenakis *et al.* [35] estimated the risks of the chemicals used in the PV life cycle, that is, accidents, fatalities, and injuries during the production, storage, and delivery of the flammable and toxic chemicals listed in 40 CFR Part 68, based on the current and past histories in the RMPs reported. **Table 5** shows the number of accidents/death/injuries between 1994 and 2004 for substances involved in PV material and module production. Since there are very few data on the production/consumption of trichlorosilane (SiHCl$_3$), estimates are given based on polysilicon production and capacity data. About 2.5 kg of polysilicon is needed to produce a multi-Si module of 6 × 10 cells of 156 mm × 156 mm and an input of 11.3 kg of trichlorosilane is required to generate 1 kg of polysilicon [2, 19]. No accidents were reported in the RMP database for phosphine and diborane in these years.

We note that the number of occurrences shown in **Table 5** represents the total for all the US facilities that produce, process, handle, and store these chemicals in quantities over their specified thresholds. These statistics may include data irrelevant to the PV industry. For example, the majority (61%) of accidents/death/injuries attributed to hydrogen fluoride (HF) occurred in petroleum refineries (NAICS 32411 (North American Industry Classification System)), although refinery use accounts for only 6% of the US consumption [38]. The petrochemical industry uses 100% HF under high pressure in large, multicomponent units (e.g., alkylation units with many pipes, fittings, valves, compressors, and pumps) from where two-phase releases may occur, whereas the PV industry uses only aqueous solutions of HF (typically 49 wt.%) in etching baths. Moreover, the usage of HF and hydrogen chloride (HCl) in the US PV industry accounts for less than 0.1% of the total in the United States. Therefore, we excluded HF use in the petroleum industries and the corresponding accidents from our analysis of risks in the PV fuel cycle.

Table 5 Incident records and estimated production for substances used in PV operation and regulated under the RMP rule

Substance	Source	Total average (1994–2000) US production (1000 tonnes yr^{-1})	Incidents	Injuries	Deaths
Toxic					
Arsine (AsH$_3$)	GaAs chemical vapor deposition (CVD)	23	2	1	0
Boron trichloride (BCl$_3$)	p-type dopant for epitaxial silicon	NA	0	0	0
Boron trifluoride (BF$_3$)	p-type dopant for epitaxial silicon	NA	1	1	0
Diborane (B$_2$H$_6$)	a-Si dopant	~50	0	0	0
Hydrochloric acid (HCl)	Cleaning agent for c-Si	3500	28	12	1
Hydrogen fluoride (HF)	Etchant for c-Si	190	165 (57)[a]	209 (70)[a]	1
Hydrogen selenide (H$_2$Se)	CIGS selenization	N/A	4	17	0
Hydrogen sulfide (H$_2$S)	CIS sputtering	>110	40	47	1
Phosphine (PH$_3$)	a-Si dopant	N/A	0	0	0
Flammable					
Dichlorosilane (SiH$_2$Cl$_2$)	a-Si and c-Si deposition	N/A	2	0	0
Hydrogen (H$_2$)	a-Si deposition/GaAs	18 000 m^3	57	65	4
Silane (SiH$_4$)	a-Si deposition	8	5	2	0
Trichlorosilane (SiHCl$_3$)	Precursor of c-Si	110	14	14	2

[a] Number excludes incidents in petroleum refineries (NAICS 32411).

a-Si, amorphous silicon; c-Si, crystalline silicon; CIGS, copper indium gallium selenide; CIS, copper indium diselenide; RMP, risk management program.

Reproduced from Williams E (2000) *Global Production Chains and Sustainability: The Case of High-Purity Silicon and Its Applications in IT and Renewable Energy*. Tokyo, Japan: Institute of Advanced Studies, The United Nations University [19]; EPA (1992) *Hydrogen Fluoride Study. Report to Congress*. Washington, DC: Office of Solid Waste and Emergency Response, US Environmental Protection Agency [38]; Census of Bureau (2002) *Current Industrial Reports –? Inorganic Chemicals* (MQ325A) [39]; Board on Environmental Studies and Toxicology (BEST) (2003) *Acute Exposure Guideline Levels for Selected Airborne Chemicals*, vol. 3. The National Academic Press [40]; U.S. Geological Survey (2003) *Mineral Commodity Summary: Arsenic* [41]; Agency for Toxic Substances and Disease Registry (2004) *Toxicological Profile for Hydrogen Sulfide* [42]; Pichel JW and Yang M (2006) *2005 Solar Year-End Review & 2006 Solar Industry Forecast*. Piper Jaffray & Co [43].

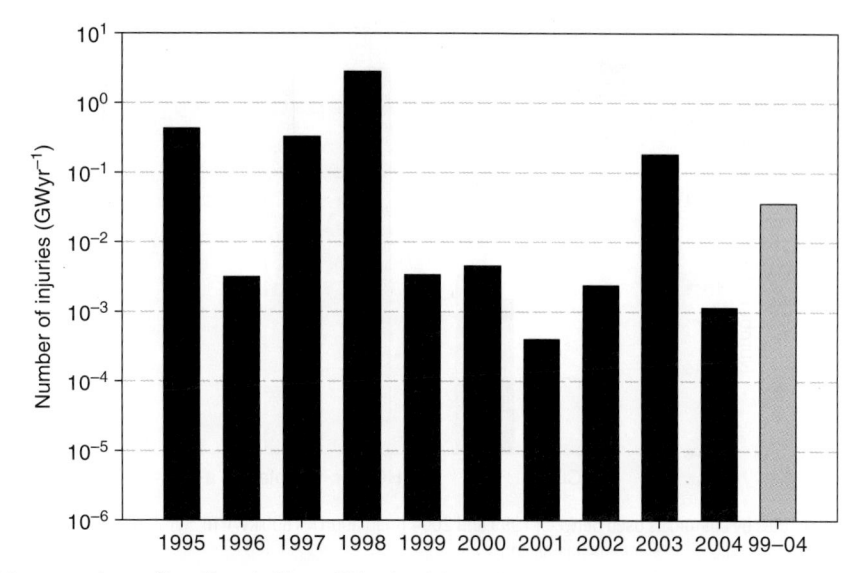

Figure 9 Estimated injury rates of crystalline silicon (c-Si) per GWyr electricity produced in the United States based on the year of accidents for HF, HCl, and SiHCl$_3$ (insolation = 1800 kWh m^{-2} yr^{-1}, performance ratio = 0.8).

To normalize the rate of accident/death/injuries, the figures are divided by the amount produced for those chemicals in the United States. The risks of each substance used in a 25 MW$_p$ yr^{-1} scale PV industry are determined based on the amount of materials in **Table 2**. Then, the number of accidents/death/injuries per GWyr of electricity generated is determined as a risk indicator of chemical accidents in the PV fuel cycle based on the average US insolation of 1800 kWh m^{-2} yr^{-1} and a PR of 0.8 (i.e., 20% system loss).

Figure 9 depicts the rates of accidents/death/injuries for c-Si per GWyr electricity produced based on the average US insolation, 1800 kWh m^{-2} yr^{-1}. The last column with the most recent incident data (i.e., data submitted from 1999 onward) may better represent the current evolution of the fast-growing PV industry. In general, for most chemicals, the numbers of accidents reported for the second cycle of the RMP (second half of 1999–2004) are lower than those reported in the first cycle (1994 to the first half of 1999). Specifically, only one accident involving silane was reported during the second cycle of the RMP, whereas four accidents occurred during the first. Likewise, the number of accidents during the second RMP cycle involving trichlorosilane fell from 13 to 1 between 1994–99 and 1999–2004. This across-the-board reduction of incidents likely represents improved safety in the whole US PV industry. For c-Si PV modules, SiHCl$_3$, the feedstock of polysilicon, presents greater risks than other chemicals (**Figure 10**). On the other hand, limited statistics suggest that silane poses the greatest risk in a-Si module manufacturing. The fatalities in **Figure 10** are related to HF. However, this risk is not based on the real events in PV facilities but is a virtual risk, derived from accident rates in other industries and the amount consumed in the PV industry. The real risk of HF in the PV industry, however, is likely to be lower than this current estimate due to the different characteristics of processes across industry sectors.

1.08.7.3 Comparison with Other Energy Technologies

Figure 11 compares fatality and injury rates across conventional electricity technologies and PV technologies. The figures for the conventional fuel cycles were extracted from the compilation of severe accident records of the GaBE project by the Paul Scherrer Institute (PSI), Energy-Related Severe Accident Database (ENSAD), from 1969 to 2000 [44]. Although such a direct comparison may not be entirely appropriate, the data imply that the expected risks in the PV fuel cycle are lower than the risks in other technologies, as we explain below. Thus, there are several caveats in directly comparing our estimate of PV risks and the risks estimated by the PSI's investigators. First, Hirschberg et al.'s assessments are based on severe accidents only, and small-scale accidents are ignored [44]; the former are defined as events with at least 5 fatalities, 10 injuries, $5 million of property damage, or 200 evacuees. On the other hand, only 20 out of the 318 incidents (**Table 5**) can be classified as severe accidents under the same definition. Therefore, the PSI's values for risk of conventional energy technologies may be underestimates. Also, we expect the safety records of the evolving PV industry to improve with time, whereas those for the mature conventional energy technologies are less likely to change. The risk estimate for the nuclear cycle in **Figure 11** relies on the probabilistic safety assessment (PSA) tool for the OECD countries rather than historical evidence due to insufficient experience related to the nuclear accidents. We note that the figures should be updated with the recent nuclear accident in Fukushima, Japan. Although PSA is a logical approach to identify plausible accidents, their rates, and consequences, it is not proven to provide absolute risk estimates due to its limitations associated with data uncertainty; for example, risks of unexpected events or those triggered by human errors are impossible to fully account for as evidenced in the recent nuclear

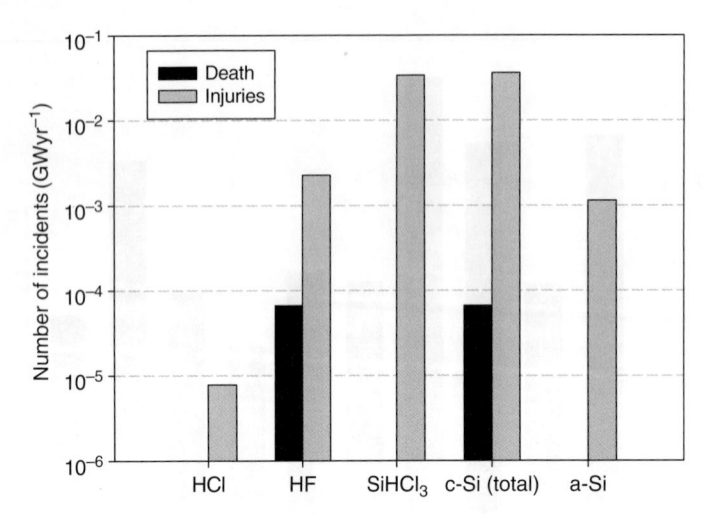

Figure 10 Estimated incident rates by chemicals used between 1999 and 2004 (insolation = 1800 kWh m^{-2} yr^{-1}, performance ratio = 0.8). The rate of a-Si covers 1997–2004. a-Si, amorphous silicon; c-Si, crystalline silicon.

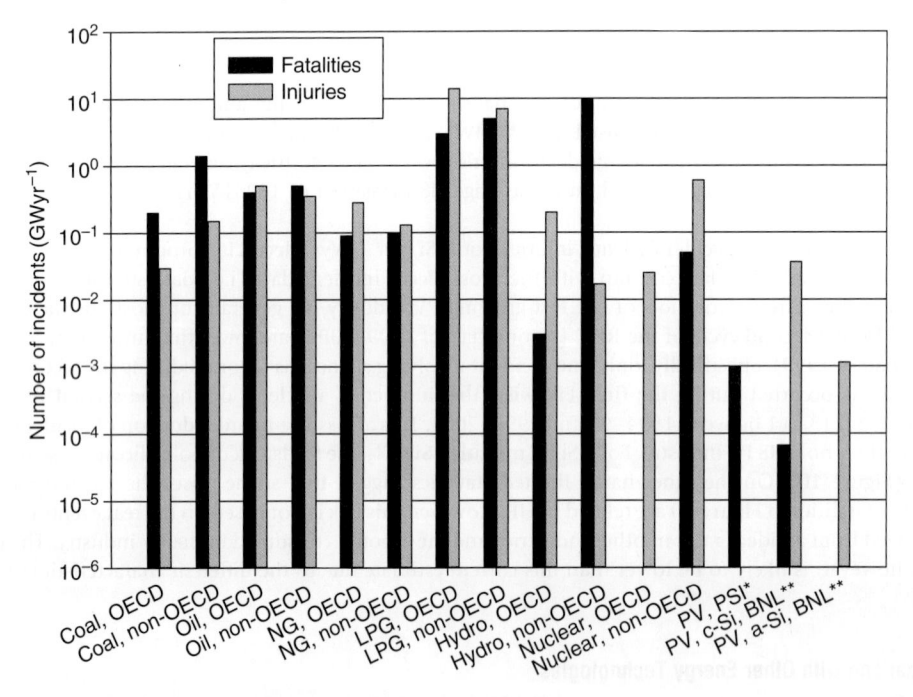

Figure 11 Comparison of fatality and injury rates across electricity generation technologies. The average US insolation of 1800 kWh m^{-2} yr^{-1} and a performance ratio of 0.8 were assumed. The incident rates for coal, oil, natural gas (NG), liquefied petroleum gas (LPG), hydro, nuclear, and PV technologies given by Paul Scherrer Institute (PSI) are from Hirschberg S, et al. (2004) *Sustainability of Electricity Supply Technologies under German Conditions: A Comparative Evaluation.* Switzerland: Paul Scherrer Institute [44]. *Module type is not specified and injuries are not estimated; **estimates of Brookhaven National Laboratory (BNL) based on US data [35]. a-Si, amorphous silicon; c-Si, crystalline silicon.

disaster in Japan [45, 46]. For a similar reason, the PSI's estimate for the PV cycle relied on data of the chemical industries handling similar substances used in the PV cycle (B. Peter, personal communication, 2006).

We also examined the maximum consequences of each energy technology. People are rarely neutral about risk; decision makers, risk analysts, and the public are more interested in unforeseen catastrophes, such as bridges falling, dams bursting, earthquakes and tsunami's occurring, and nuclear reactors exploding, than in adverse but routine events, such as transportation accidents. Comparing low-probability/high-damage risks with high-probability/low-damage events within one expected value frame often distorts the relative importance of consequences across technology options. Therefore, describing the maximum consequence potential makes sense [36]. **Figure 12** shows the maximum fatalities: figures for the fossil fuel and nuclear cycles are from a database

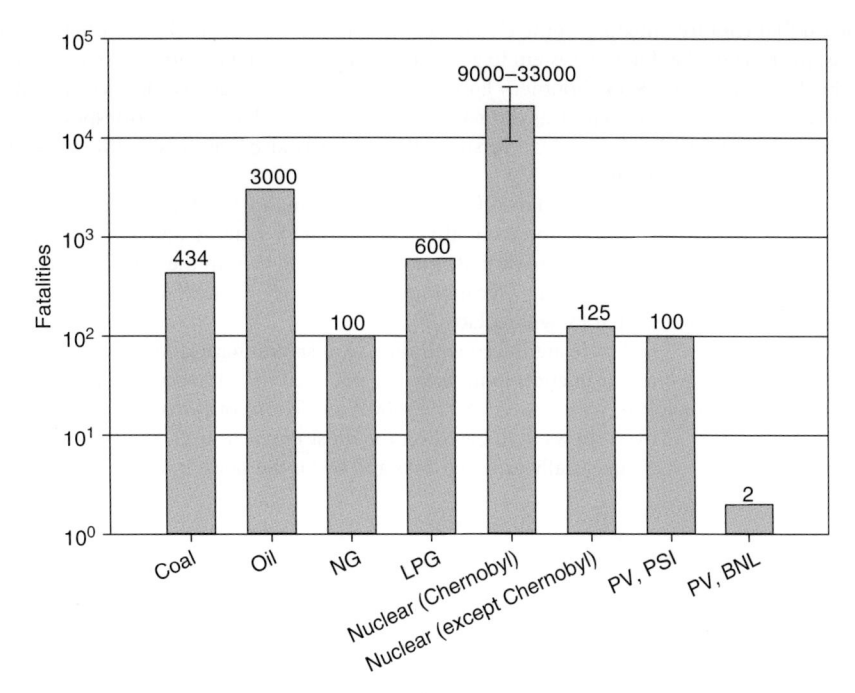

Figure 12 Maximum fatalities from accidents across energy sectors. The number for Chernobyl includes latent fatalities. The incident rates for coal, oil, natural gas (NG), liquefied petroleum gas (LPG), hydro, nuclear, and PV technologies given by Paul Scherrer Institute (PSI) are from Hirschberg S, Spikerman G, and Dones R (1998) *Severe Accidents in the Energy Sector*, 1st edn. Switzerland: Paul Scherrer Institute [33]. BNL, Brookhaven National Laboratory.

[33] and for PV from literature [35, 44]. From a scale of consequence perspective, PV technology is remarkably safer than other technologies. We anticipate that the maximum consequence will remain at the same level shown in **Figure 12** unless there is a significant change in PV production technologies.

The nature of risks varies with different energy technologies. The PSI analysis focuses on fuel mining, fuel conversion, power plant operation, and transportation of fuels. On the other hand, fuel-related or power plant-related risks are nonexistent in the PV fuel cycle. Instead, our analysis of PV risks focuses on accidents associated with feedstock materials as well as process consumables, that is, upstream risks, which the PSI analysis does not include.

1.08.7.4 Limitation of the Study

As discussed, the hazards of trichlorosilane when making modules of c-Si and that of silane for a-Si modules have dominated concerns over other chemicals due to the large amount required and their flammability. Their limited number of incident records in the RMP database prevents accurate measurement of the safety of the PV industry. Since death records are very rare for these chemicals, the risk of fatalities is highly sensitive to a single incident. On the other hand, injury rates are relatively stable against the incremental number of injuries. This illustrates that the scale of the PV industry in terms of capacity and employees is still small so that such analyses are inadequate to directly compare with other technologies. PV technology is still in the early stage of commercial application, and, with time, risk management programs complied through experience eventually should stabilize the number of abnormal incidents. Other technologies, such as nuclear power, experienced a similar period during the early years of commercialization [33].

Although PV technology is at an early stage compared with other energy systems, it is rapidly growing within the context of EU policy to increase the contribution of renewable energies to the total EU energy mix [47, 48]. Accordingly, there are strong efforts to boost the PV sector, and therefore, it should be treated more and more as an energy sector, avoiding comparisons with the chemical or semiconductor industry. Our analysis of risk in the PV life cycle is at a level lower than many other technologies. Given this situation, the PV industry should help by sharing information on risk, which, at the same time, could surely give PV more credibility and transparency.

1.08.8 Conclusion

This review offers a snapshot of the rapidly evolving life-cycle performances of PV technologies and underlines the importance of timely updating and reporting the changes. During the life cycle of PV, emissions to the environment mainly occur from using fossil fuel-based energy in generating the materials for solar cells, modules, and systems. These emissions differ in different countries, depending on that country's mixture in the electricity grid and the varying methods of material/fuel processing. The lower the EPBT, that is, the time it takes for a PV system to generate energy equal to the amount used in its production, the lower these emissions will be. Under average US and Southern Europe conditions (e.g., 1700 kWh m^{-2} yr^{-1}) with rooftop application, the EPBT of multi-Si, mono-Si, and CdTe systems was estimated to be 1.7, 1.7, and 0.8 years, correspondingly. The EPBT of CdTe PV is the lowest in the group, although electrical conversion efficiency was also the lowest; this was due to the low energy requirement in manufacturing CdTe PV modules.

The indirect emissions of Cd due to energy used in the life of CdTe PV systems are much greater than the direct emissions. CdTe PV systems require less energy input in their production than other commercial PV systems, and this translates into lower emissions of heavy metals (including Cd) as well as SO_2, NO_x, particulate matter (PM), and CO_2 in the CdTe cycle than in other commercial PV technologies. However, regardless of the particular technology, these emissions are extremely small in comparison to the emissions from the fossil fuel-based plants that PV will replace.

The greatest potential risks of the PV fuel cycle are linked with the use of several hazardous substances, although in quantities much smaller than in the process industries. In an effort to measure the potential risks associated with PV fuel cycle in comparison with other electricity generation technologies, we used the US EPA's RMP accident records that cover the entire major US chemical storage and processing facilities. Our analysis shows that, based on the most recent records, the PV fuel cycle is much safer than conventional sources of energy in terms of statistically expected risks and by far the safest in terms of maximum consequence.

Acknowledgement

The authors gratefully acknowledge support from the US DOE Office of Energy Efficiency and Renewable Energy, under contract DE-AC02-76CH000016, to Brookhaven National Laboratory.

References

[1] Alsema EA (2000) Energy pay-back time and CO_2 emissions of PV systems. *Progress in Photovoltaics: Research and Applications* 8: 17–25.
[2] Alsema E and de Wild-Scholten M (2005) Environmental impact of crystalline silicon photovoltaic module production. In: *Material Research Society Fall Meeting, Symposium G: Life Cycle Analysis Tools for "Green" Materials and Process Selection*, pp. 73–82. Boston, MA.
[3] Meijer A, Huigbregts MAJ, Schermer JJ, and Reijnders L (2003) Life-cycle assessment of photovoltaic modules: Comparison of mc-Si, InGaP and InGaP/mc-si solar modules. *Progress in Photovoltaics: Research and Applications* 11(4): 275–287.
[4] Jungbluth N (2005) Life cycle assessment of crystalline photovoltaics in the Swiss ecoinvent database. *Progress in Photovoltaics: Research and Applications* 13(8): 429–446.
[5] Hagedorn G and Hellriegel E (1992) *Umwelrelevante masseneinträge bei der herstellung verschiedener solarzellentypen – endbericht – teil I: konventionelle verfahren*. München, Germany: Forschungstelle für Energiewirtschaft.
[6] Palz W and Zibetta H (1991) Energy pay-back time of photovoltaic modules. *International Journal of Solar Energy* 10: 211–216.
[7] Hynes KM, Baumann AE, and Hill R (1994) An assessment of the environmental impacts of thin film cadmium telluride modules based on life cycle analysis. In: *IEEE 1st World Conference on Photovoltaic Conversion (WCPEC)*, pp. 958–961. Hawaii.
[8] Kato K, Hibino T, Komoto K, et al. (2001) A life-cycle analysis on thin-film CdS/CdTe PV modules. *Solar Energy Materials & Solar Cells* 67: 279–287.
[9] Fthenakis VM, Kim HC, and Alsema E (2008) Emissions from photovoltaic life cycles. *Environmental Science & Technology* 42: 2168–2174.
[10] Fthenakis V and Alsema E (2006) Photovoltaics energy payback times, greenhouse gas emissions and external costs: 2004–early 2005 status. *Progress in Photovoltaics: Research and Applications* 14: 275–280.
[11] Fthenakis V, Wang W, and Kim HC (2009) Life cycle inventory analysis of the production of metals used in photovoltaics. *Renewable and Sustainable Energy Reviews* 13: 493–517.
[12] Fthenakis VM (2004) Life cycle impact analysis of cadmium in CdTe PV production. *Renewable and Sustainable Energy Reviews* 8(4): 303–334.
[13] de Wild-Scholten M and Alsema E (2005) Environmental life cycle inventory of crystalline silicon photovoltaic module production. In: *Material Research Society Fall Meeting, Symposium G: Life Cycle Analysis Tools for "Green" Materials and Process Selection*, pp. 59–72. Boston, MA.
[14] Fthenakis VM and Kim HC (2006) Energy use and greenhouse gas emissions in the life cycle of CdTe photovoltaics. In: *Material Research Society Fall Meeting, Symposium G: Life Cycle Analysis Tools for "Green" Materials and Process Selection*, pp. 83–88. Boston, MA.
[15] Alsema EA and de Wild-Scholten MJ (2007) Reduction of the environmental impacts in crystalline silicon module manufacturing. In: *22nd European Photovoltaic Solar Energy Conference*, pp. 829–836. Milano, Italy.
[16] Aulich HA and Schulze F-W (2002) Crystalline silicon feedstock for solar cells. *Progress in Photovoltaics: Research and Applications* 10: 141–147.
[17] Woditsch P and Koch W (2002) Solar grade silicon feedstock supply for PV industry. *Solar Energy Materials & Solar Cells* 72: 11–26.
[18] Maycock PD (2005) National survey report of PV power applications in the United States 2004. *International Energy Agency*.
[19] Williams E (2000) *Global Production Chains and Sustainability: The Case of High-Purity Silicon and Its Applications in IT and Renewable Energy*. Tokyo, Japan: Institute of Advanced Studies, The United Nations University.
[20] Rogol M (2005) Silicon and the solar sector: Mapping a new world. In: *Presentation at the 2nd Solar Silicon Conference*. Munich, Germany, 11 April.
[21] Mason JE, Fthenakis VM, Hansen T, and Kim HC (2006) Energy payback and life-cycle CO_2 emissions of the BOS in an optimized 3.5 MW PV installation. *Progress in Photovoltaics: Research and Applications* 14: 179–190.
[22] de Wild-Scholten MJ, Alsema EA, ter Horst EW, et al. (2006) A cost and environmental impact comparison of grid-connected rooftop and ground-based PV systems. In: *21st European Photovoltaic Solar Energy Conference*, pp. 3167–3173. Dresden, Germany.
[23] Dones R, Bauer C, Bolliger R, et al. (2003) Sachbilanzen von Energiesystemen. Final report ecoinvent 2000, vol. 6. Swiss Centre for LCI, PSL, Dubendorf, CH.
[24] Franklin Associates (1998) *USA LCI Database Documentation*. Prairie Village, KS: Franklin Associates.
[25] Forster P, Ramaswamy V, Artaxo P, et al. (2007) Changes in atmospheric constituents and in radiative forcing. In: *Climate Change 2007: The Physical Science Basis. Contributions of Working Group I to the Fourth Annual Assessment Report of the Intergovernmental Panel on Climate Change*. Cambridge UK and New York: Cambridge University Press.
[26] Raugei M, Bargigli S, and Ulgiati S (2007) Life cycle assessment and energy pay-back time of advanced photovoltaic modules. CdTe and CIS compared to poly-Si. *Energy* 32: 1310–1318.

[27] Alsema EA, de Wild-Scholten MJ, and Fthenakis VM (2006) Environmental impacts of PV electricity generation – A critical comparison of energy supply options. In: *21st European Photovoltaic Solar Energy Conference*, pp. 3201–3207. Dresden, Germany.
[28] Fthenakis VM and Kim HC (2007) Greenhouse-gas emissions from solar electric- and nuclear power: A life-cycle study. *Energy Policy* 35: 2549–2557.
[29] Fthenakis VM, Fuhrmann M, Heiser J, *et al.* (2005) Emissions and encapsulation of cadmium in CdTe PV modules during fires. *Progress in Photovoltaics: Research and Applications* 13: 713–723.
[30] Reich NH, Alsema EA, van Sark WGJHM, *et al.* (2011) Greenhouse gas emissions associated with photovoltaic electricity from crystalline silicon modules under various energy supply options. *Progress in Photovoltaics: Research and Applications* 19: 603–613.
[31] Electric Power Research Institute (EPRI) (2002) PISCES data base for US power plants and US coal.
[32] Fthenakis VM and Kim HC (2007) CdTe photovoltaics: Life cycle environmental profile and comparisons. *Thin Solid Films* 515: 5961–5963.
[33] Hirschberg S, Spikerman G, and Dones R (1998) *Severe Accidents in the Energy Sector*, 1st edn. Switzerland: Paul Scherrer Institute.
[34] Fthenakis V (2003) Overview of potential hazards. In: Markvart T and Gastaner L (eds.) *Practical Handbook of Photovoltaics: Fundamentals and Applications*, pp. 857–868. Kidlington, UK: Elsevier.
[35] Fthenakis VM, Kim HC, Colli A, and Kirchsteiger C (2006) Evaluation of risks in the life cycle of photovoltaics in a comparative context. In: *21st European Photovoltaic Solar Energy Conference*, pp. 3194–3201. Dresden, Germany.
[36] Haimes YY (1998) *Risk Modeling, Assessment, and Management*. Hoboken, NJ: John Wiley & Sons.
[37] Environmental Protection Agency Risk Management Plan (RMP) Rule. http://www.epa.gov/osweroe1/content/rmp/ (accessed September 2011).
[38] EPA (1992) *Hydrogen Fluoride Study. Report to Congress*. Washington, DC: Office of Solid Waste and Emergency Response, US Environmental Protection Agency.
[39] Census of Bureau (2002) *Current Industrial Reports – Inorganic Chemicals* (MQ325A).
[40] Board on Environmental Studies and Toxicology (BEST) (2003) *Acute Exposure Guideline Levels for Selected Ariborne Chemicals*, vol. 3. Washington, DC: The National Academic Press.
[41] U.S. Geological Survey (2003) *Mineral Commodity Summary: Arsenic*.
[42] Agency for Toxic Substances and Disease Registry (2004) *Toxicological Profile for Hydrogen Sulfide*. http://www.atsdr.cdc.gov/.
[43] Pichel JW and Yang M (2006) *2005 Solar Year-End Review & 2006 Solar Industry Forecast*. Minneapolis, MN: Piper Jaffray & Co.
[44] Hirschberg S, Dones R, Heck T, *et al.* (2004) *Sustainability of Electricity Supply Technologies under German Conditions: A Comparative Evaluation*. Switzerland: Paul Scherrer Institute.
[45] Linnerooth-Bayer J and Wahlström B (1991) Applications of probabilistic risk assessments: The selection of appropriate tools. *Risk Analysis* 11(2): 239–248.
[46] Nuclear Energy Agency (1992) Probabilistic safety assessment: An analytical tool for assessing nuclear safety. In: *NEA Issue Brief: An Analysis of Principal Nuclear Issues*, No. 8, January 1992.
[47] Directive 2001/77/EC of the European Parliament and of the Council (2001) *Promotion of Electricity Produced from Renewable Energy Sources in the Internal Electricity Market*, 27 September.
[48] European Commission (1997) *Communication from the commission "Energy for the Future: Renewable Sources of Energy"*, White Paper for a Community Strategy and Action Plan.
[49] Kim S and Dale BE (2005) Life cycle inventory information of the United States Electricity System. *International Journal of Life Cycle Assessment* 10: 294–304.
[50] Fthenakis V, Kim HC, Held M, *et al.* (2009) Update of PV energy payback times and life-cycle greenhouse gas emissions. In: *24th European Photovoltaic Solar Energy Conference*, pp. 4412–4416. Hamburg, Germany.

1.09 Overview of the Global PV Industry

A Jäger-Waldau, Institution for Energy Transport, Ispra, Italy

© 2012 Elsevier Ltd. All rights reserved.

1.09.1	**Introduction**	162
1.09.2	**Development of the Photovoltaic Industry**	164
1.09.3	**The Photovoltaic Industry in 2010**	167
1.09.3.1	Technology Mix	168
1.09.3.2	Solar Cell Production Companies	169
1.09.3.2.1	Suntech Power Co. Ltd. (PRC)	169
1.09.3.2.2	First Solar LLC (USA)	169
1.09.3.2.3	JA Solar Holding Co. Ltd. (PRC)	170
1.09.3.2.4	Yingli Green Energy Holding Company Ltd. (PRC)	170
1.09.3.2.5	Trina Solar Ltd. (PRC)	170
1.09.3.2.6	Motech Solar (Taiwan)	170
1.09.3.2.7	Q-Cells AG (Germany)	170
1.09.3.2.8	Sharp Corporation (Japan)	170
1.09.3.2.9	Gintech Energy Corporation (Taiwan)	171
1.09.3.2.10	Neo Solar Power Corporation (Taiwan)	171
1.09.3.2.11	Canadian Solar Inc. (PRC)	171
1.09.3.2.12	Renewable Energy Corporation AS (Norway)	171
1.09.3.2.13	Solar World AG (Germany)	171
1.09.3.2.14	SunPower Corporation (USA)	171
1.09.3.2.15	Kyocera Corporation (Japan)	171
1.09.3.2.16	SANYO Electric Company (Japan)	172
1.09.3.2.17	E-Ton Solar Tech Co. Ltd. (Taiwan)	172
1.09.3.2.18	Sun Earth Solar Power Co. Ltd. (PRC)	172
1.09.3.2.19	Hanwha SolarOne (PRC)	172
1.09.3.2.20	Bosch Solar (Germany)	172
1.09.3.3	Polysilicon Supply	173
1.09.3.3.1	Silicon production processes	173
1.09.3.4	Polysilicon Manufacturers	173
1.09.3.4.1	Hemlock Semiconductor Corporation (USA)	174
1.09.3.4.2	Wacker Polysilicon (Germany)	174
1.09.3.4.3	OCI Company (South Korea)	174
1.09.3.4.4	GCL-Poly Energy Holdings Limited (PRC)	174
1.09.3.4.5	MEMC Electronic Materials Inc. (USA)	174
1.09.3.4.6	Renewable Energy Corporation AS (Norway)	174
1.09.3.4.7	LDK Solar Co. Ltd. (PRC)	174
1.09.3.4.8	Tokuyama Corporation (Japan)	175
1.09.3.4.9	Elkem AS (Norway)	175
1.09.3.4.10	Mitsubishi Materials Corporation (Japan)	175
1.09.4	**Outlook**	175
References		177

Glossary

EC Framework Programme This is the main instrument of the European Union for funding research.

Feed-in tariff A feed-in tariff is a policy mechanism that obliges regional or national electric grid utilities to buy renewable electricity (electricity generated from renewable sources, such as solar power, wind power, wave and tidal power, biomass, hydropower, and geothermal power) from all eligible participants at a fixed price over a fixed period of time.

Photovoltaics (PV) PV is a method of generating electrical power by converting solar radiation into direct current electricity using semiconductors that exhibit the photovoltaic effect. The energy conversion devices are called solar cells.

Photovoltaic capacity The capacity of photovoltaic systems is given in Wp (watt peak). This characterizes the maximum DC (direct current) output of a solar module under standard test conditions, that is, at a solar radiation of $1000\,\text{W}\,\text{m}^{-2}$ and at a temperature of 25 °C.

> **Photovoltaic electricity generation** The actual electricity generation potential of a photovoltaic electricity system depends on the solar radiation and the system performance, which depends on the balance of system component losses. For a solar radiation between 600 and 2200 kWh m^{-2} yr^{-1}, an average PV system can produce between 450 and 1650 kWh of AC electricity.
>
> **Photovoltaic (PV) energy system** A PV system is composed of three subsystems:
>
> - On the power generation side, a subsystem of PV devices (cells, modules, arrays) converts sunlight to direct current (DC) electricity.
> - On the power-use side, the subsystem consists mainly of the load, which is the application of the PV electricity.
> - Between these two, we need a third subsystem that enables the PV-generated electricity to be properly applied to the load. This third subsystem is often called the 'balance of system' or BOS.
>
> **Photovoltaic module and photovoltaic system** A number of solar cells form a solar 'module' or 'panel', which can then be combined to solar systems, ranging from a few watts of electricity output to multi-megawatt power stations.
>
> **Polysilicon or polycrystalline silicon** A material consisting of small silicon crystals.
>
> **Solar cell production capacities**
>
> - In the case of wafer silicon-based solar cells, only the cells.
> - In the case of thin films, the complete integrated module.
> - Only those companies that actually produce the active circuit (solar cell) are counted.
> - Companies that purchase these circuits and make cells are not counted.

1.09.1 Introduction

Since more than 10 years, photovoltaics (PV) is one of the fastest growing industries with growth rates well beyond 40% per annum. This growth is driven not only by the progress in materials and processing technology, but also by market introduction programs in many countries around the world and the increased volatility and mounting fossil energy prices. Despite the negative impacts of the economic crisis in 2009, PV is still growing at an extraordinary pace.

Production data for the global cell production in 2010 vary between 18 and 27 GW. The significant uncertainty in the data for 2010 is due to the very competitive market environment, as well as the fact that some companies report shipment figures, whereas others report sales or production figures. In addition, the difficult economic conditions and increased competition led to a decreased willingness to report confidential company data. The previous tight silicon supply situation reversed due to massive production expansions as well as the economic situation. This led to a price decrease from the 2008 peak of around 500 \$ kg^{-1} to about 50–55 \$ kg^{-1} at the end of 2009 with a slight upward tendency throughout 2010 and early 2011.

Our own data, collected from various companies and colleagues, were compared to various data sources and thus led to an estimate of 21.5 GW (**Figure 1**), representing again a production growth of about 80% compared to 2009 [1–3].

Since 2000, total PV production increased almost by 2 orders of magnitude, with annual growth rates between 40% and 80%. The most rapid growth in annual production over the last 5 years could be observed in China and Taiwan, which together now account for more than 50% of worldwide production.

The market has changed from a supply- to a demand-driven market and the resulting overcapacity for solar modules has resulted in a dramatic price reduction of more than 50% over the last 3 years. Especially for companies in their start-up and expansion phase with limited financial resources, the oversupply situation anticipated for at least the next few years in conjunction with the continuous pressure on average selling prices (ASPs) is of growing concern. The recent financial crisis added pressure as it resulted in higher government bond yields and ASPs have to decline even faster than previously expected to allow for higher project internal rate of returns (IRRs).

In 2008, new investments in solar power surpassed those in bioenergy and were second only to wind with US\$ 33.5 billion (€25.8 billion (exchange rate: €1 = US\$1.30)) or 21.6% of new capital [4]. Business analysts are confident that despite the current turmoil the industry fundamentals as a whole remain strong and that the overall PV sector will continue to experience a significant long-term growth. Following the stock market decline, as a result of the financial turmoil, the PPVX (photon pholtovoltaic stock index) declined from its high at over 6500 points at the beginning of 2008 to 2095 points at the end of 2008. (The PPVX is a noncommercial financial index published by the solar magazine *Photon* and ÖKO-INVEST. The index started on 1 August 2001 with 1000 points and 11 companies and is calculated weekly using the Euro as reference currency. Only companies that made more than 50% of their sales in the previous year with PV products or services are included.) At the beginning of April 2011, the index stood at 2571 points and the market capitalization of the 30-PPVX companies (please note that the composition of the index changes as new companies are added and others have to leave the index) was €43.5 billion.

Market predictions for the 2011 PV market vary between 17.3 GW by the Navigant Consulting conservative scenario [5], 19.6 GW by Macquarie [6], and 22 GW by iSuppli [7] with a consensus value in the 18–19 GW range. Massive capacity increases are under way or announced and if all of them are realized, the worldwide production capacity for solar cells would exceed 50 GW at the end of 2011. This indicates that even with the optimistic market growth expectations, the planned capacity increases are way above the market

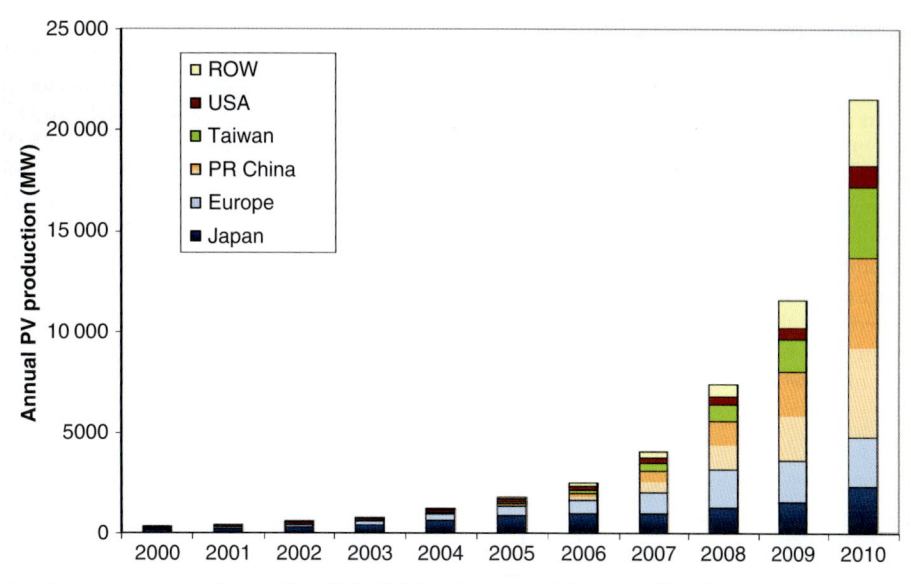

Figure 1 World PV cell/module production from 2000 to 2010. ROW, rest of world. Data source: Mints P *Manufacturer Shipments, Capacity and Competitive Analysis 2009/2010*. Palo Alto, CA: Navigant Consulting Photovoltaic Service Program [1]; Mints P (March 2010) *The PV Industry's Black Swan*. Photovoltaics World [2]; *PV News* (May 2010) Published by The Prometheus Institute, ISSN 0739-4829 [3]; our own analysis.

growth. The consequence would be the continuation of the low utilization rates and therefore a continued price pressure in an oversupplied market. Such a development will accelerate the consolidation of the PV industry and spur more mergers and acquisitions.

The current solar cell technologies are well established and provide a reliable product, with sufficient efficiency and guaranteed energy output for at least 25 years of lifetime. This reliability, the increasing potential of electricity interruption from grid overloads, as well as the rise of electricity prices from conventional energy sources add to the attractiveness of PV systems.

About 80% of the current production uses wafer-based crystalline silicon (c-Si) technology. A major advantage of this technology is that complete production lines can be bought, installed, and be up and producing within a relatively short time frame. This predictable production start-up scenario constitutes a low-risk placement with calculable returns on investments. However, the temporary shortage in silicon feedstock and the market entry of companies offering turnkey production lines for thin-film solar cells led to a massive expansion of investments in thin-film capacities between 2005 and 2009. More than 200 companies are involved in the thin-film solar cell production process ranging from R&D activities to major manufacturing plants.

Projected silicon production capacities available for solar in 2012 vary from 140 000 metric tons from established polysilicon producers, up to 185 000 metric tons, including the new producers [8], and 250 000 metric tons [9]. The possible solar cell production will in addition depend on the material use per Wp (watt peak). Material consumption could decrease from the current 8 to 7 g Wp^{-1} or even 6 g Wp^{-1}, but this might not be achieved by all manufacturers.

Similar to other technology areas, new products will enter the market, enabling further cost reduction. Concentrating photovoltaics (CPV) is an emerging market. There are two main tracks – either high concentration >300 suns (HCPV) or low to medium concentration with a concentration factor of 2 to ~300. In order to maximize the benefits of CPV, the technology requires high direct normal irradiation (DNI) and these areas have a limited geographical range – the 'Sun Belt' of the Earth. The market share of CPV is still small, but an increasing number of companies are focusing on CPV. In 2008, about 10 MW of CPV was produced, and market estimates for 2010 are in the 10–20 MW range and for 2011 about 50–100 MW is expected. In addition, dye-cells are getting ready to enter the market as well. The growth of these technologies is accelerated by the positive development of the PV market as a whole.

It can be concluded that in order to maintain the extremely high growth rate of the PV industry, different pathways have to be pursued at the same time:

- continuation to expand solar-grade silicon production capacities in line with solar cell manufacturing capacities;
- accelerated reduction of material consumption per silicon solar cell and Wp, for example, higher efficiencies, thinner wafers, and less wafering losses;
- accelerated ramp-up of thin-film solar cell manufacturing; and
- accelerated CPV introduction into the market, as well as capacity growth rates above the normal trend.

Further PV system cost reductions will depend not only on the technology improvements and scale-up benefits in solar cell and module production, but also on the ability to decrease the system component costs, as well as the whole installation, projecting, operation, permitting, and financing costs.

1.09.2 Development of the Photovoltaic Industry

With the oil crisis of the 1970s, many countries in the world started solar energy research and development (R&D) programs, but it took another 20 years until the first market implementation programs for grid-connected solar PV electricity generation systems started in the early 1990s and began to prepare the basis for the development of a PV industry.

Between 1982 and 1990, the annual shipments increased from roughly 8 to 48 MW per year. In the early 1980s, the PV market had been strongly dominated by the large-scale segment where the influence of the USA Carissa plains plant (1983–85) is obvious. Since then, the main driver for the production expansion was the increasing use of PV electricity for communication purposes, leisure activities (camping, boats), solar home systems, and water pumping. **Figure 2** gives a breakdown of the different applications in which PV systems were used during the period from 1990 to 1994 [10]. At that time, about 90% of PV applications worldwide were not grid connected with a somewhat higher share of 22% of grid-connected systems in Europe due to the German 1000 PV-roof program.

The development of the world PV cell production between 1988 and 1994 is shown in **Figure 3**.

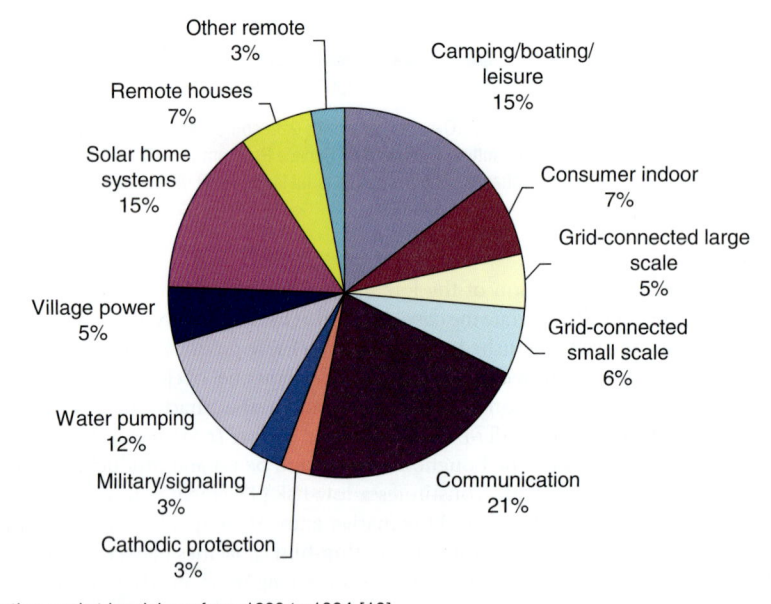

Figure 2 World PV application market breakdown from 1990 to 1994 [10].

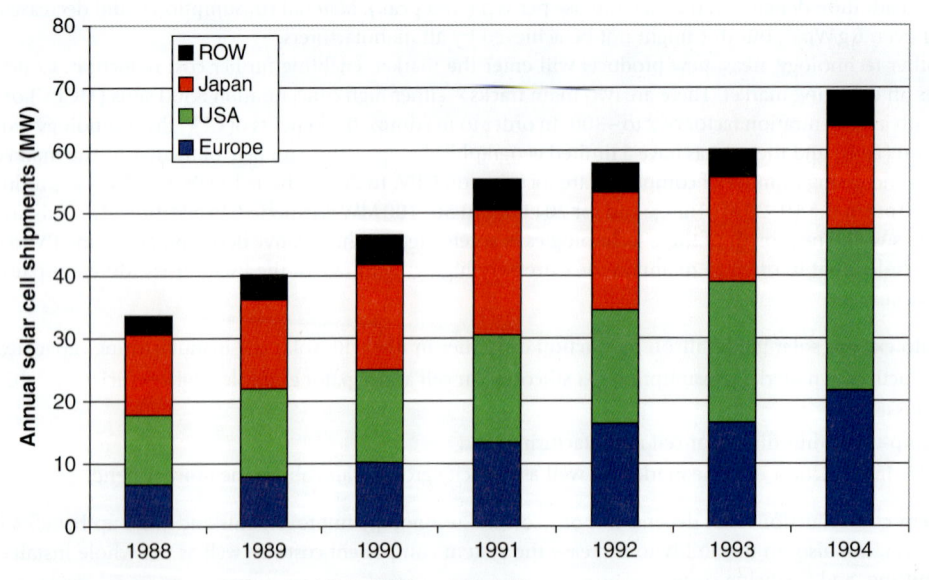

Figure 3 World solar cell production from 1988 to 1994 [11]. ROW, rest of world.

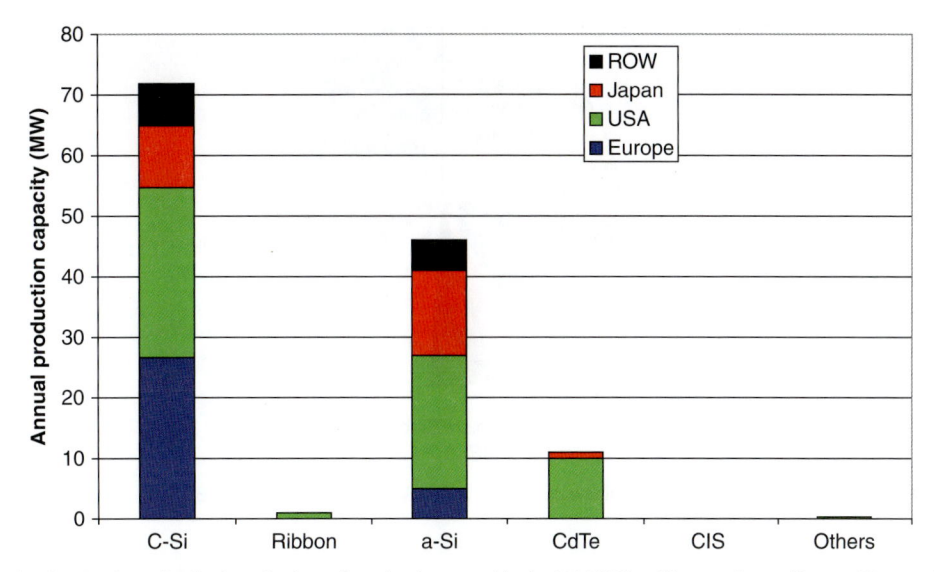

Figure 4 Regional and technology distribution of solar cell production capacities in 1994 [10]. a-Si, amorphous silicon; c-Si, crystalline silicon; ROW, rest of world.

In 1994, about 80 companies with a total production capacity of 130 MW existed worldwide and their activities ranged from research to production of solar cells. About half of them were actually manufacturing. Another 29 companies were involved in module production only. Out of the solar cell companies, 41 companies used c-Si, 2 ribbon silicon, 19 amorphous silicon (a-Si), 3 CdTe, 5 CIS (copper indium diselenide), and 10 companies worked on other concepts like III–V concentrator cells or spherical cells. The breakdown of the production capacities for the different technologies is shown in **Figure 4**.

The largest annual manufacturing capacity of a single company at that time was about 10 MW for single c-Si solar cells and 5 MW for a-Si. Most companies had an annual capacity of 1–3 MW. The annual production capacities and their utilization rates for 1992 and 1994 are shown in **Figure 5**.

The first large-scale program to introduce decentralized grid-connected PV systems started in September 1990 in Germany with the so-called 1000 PV-roof program. The aim of the program, which was initiated by the German ministry for Science and Technique, was to evaluate the current status of the technology and to determine the future research and development needs for small-scale grid-connected PV systems. Under the 1000 PV-roof program, applicants received 50% funding of investment costs from the federal government plus 20% from the Land government. Eventually, 2250 PV-roof systems with about 5 MW were installed between 1991 and 1995 [13]. However, with the end of the program, a number of solar cell manufacturers and a lot of smaller companies, especially installers, had financial problems, which were only partly compensated by some smaller local support programs.

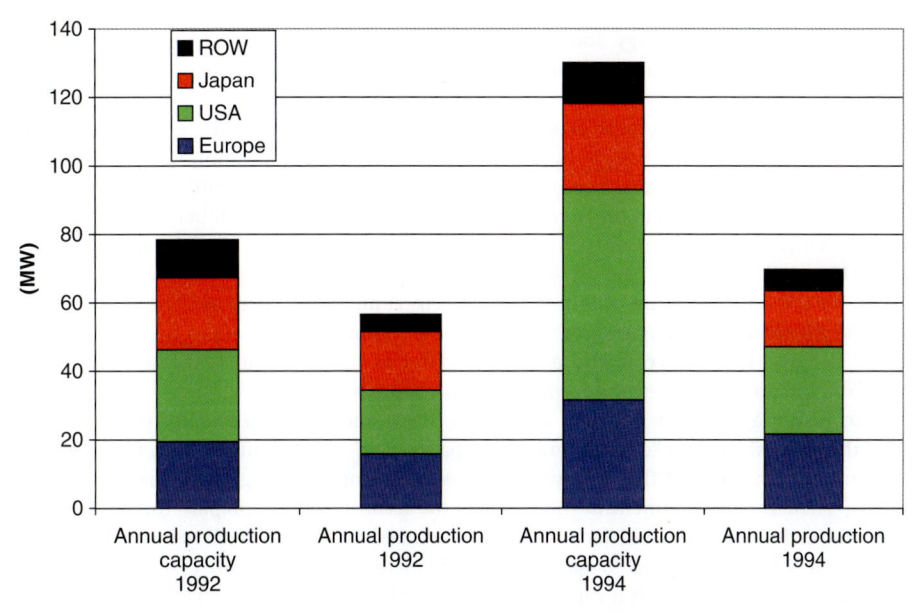

Figure 5 Geographical distribution of production and capacity in 1992 and 1994 [10, 12]. ROW, rest of world.

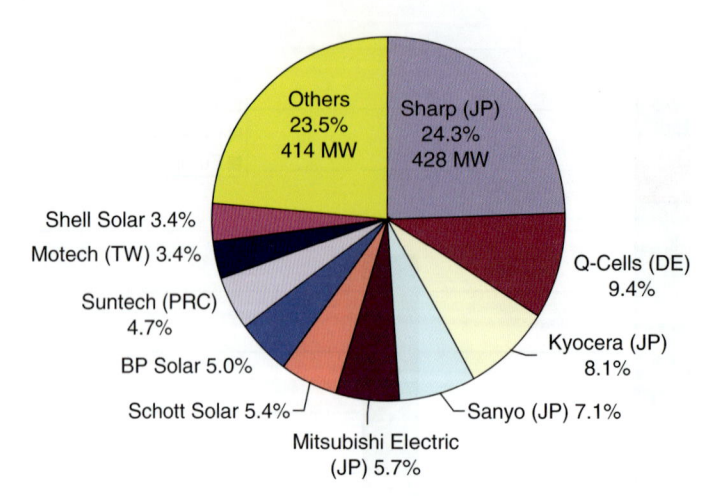

Figure 6 Top 10 photovoltaic companies in 2005 (total shipments in 2005: 1759 MW) [16]. Please note that BP Solar, Schott Solar, and Shell Solar have cell production capacities in more than one country.

In 1994, the first long-term PV implementation program, which led to a rapid increase in solar cell production capacities, was started in Japan. The first program to stimulate the implementation of PV in Japan was called 'Monitoring Programme for Residential PV Systems' and it lasted from 1994 to 1996 and was managed by the New Energy Foundation (NEF). Within this program, 50% of the installation costs were subsidized. The follow-up was the 'Programme for the Development of the Infrastructure for the Introduction of Residential PV Systems', which started in March 1997 and continued until October 2005. During this period, the average price for 1 kWp in the residential sector fell from 2 million ¥ kWp^{-1} in 1994 to 670 000 ¥ kWp^{-1} in 2004. These programs were not only expanding the Japanese PV market to a total cumulative installed capacity of 1420 MW at the end of FY 2005, but were also fostering the development of the Japanese PV industry [14, 15]. From 1994 to 2005, the production capacity of the Japanese PV industry increased from 25.2 to 1264 MW or about 50-fold. Actual production during this time span increased from 16.5 MW in 1994 to 819 MW in 2005 of which 528 MW or 65% was exported [15].

Between 1994 and 2005, the Japanese solar cell manufacturing industry grew much faster than the industry in other world regions and reached almost a 50% market share in 2005 (**Figure 6**).

The biggest boost for the development of the PV industry was the introduction of the German Renewable Energy Sources Act or Erneuer-Energien-Gesetz (EEG) in 2000 [17]. For the first time, this Act guaranteed a cost-covering feed-in tariff for 20 years of initially 50 €ct kWh^{-1} for PV-generated electricity. The setup of the scheme was to decrease this guaranteed feed-in tariff every year by 5% for new PV systems in order to put pressure on the reduction of the price for PV systems. In addition, the Kreditanstalt für Wiederaufbau (KfW), a public bank, gave loans with reduced interest rates to buyers of PV systems under the so-called 100 000-roof program. With these mechanisms a market for PV systems and consequently the basis for the accelerated buildup of the PV industry was created.

From the beginning, the Renewable Energy Sources Act foresaw a regular revision of the feed-in tariffs to react on price developments every 4 years. The first revision in 2004 accelerated the growth of the German market, which overtook the until then dominating Japanese market [18].

The structure of the PV industry changed quite drastically between the early 1990s and 2005. A significant number of the 80 companies that existed in 1994 were either bought by other companies or seized operation. The first company that exceeded a production capacity of 100 MW was Sharp (Japan) at the end of FY 2002 and it kept the position as No. 1 manufacturing company until 2008 when Q-Cells (Germany) moved to the front rank. Since the late 1990s, the number of new companies entering the PV manufacturing business started to increase, mainly in Germany, China, and Taiwan. This development can also be seen in the increase of shipments (**Figure 7**).

Between 1994 and 2004, the market share of thin-film solar cells continuously decreased from 30% to less than 10%. This development was due to the technology progress in the different c-Si technologies as well as the rapid expansion of production capacities where production lines for silicon could be faster realized due to the availability of the necessary equipment and ramped up than those in thin-film technologies, where the equipment was custom made.

The temporary silicon shortage, which stared to emerge in 2003, and the market entry of companies offering turnkey production lines for thin-film solar cells led to a massive expansion of investments in thin-film capacities. It opened the window of opportunities for a number of thin-film technologies and companies to get into the market. The most prominent example is First Solar (USA). The development to industrialize the technology and prepare for production started almost 25 years ago at First Solar's predecessor Solar cell Inc., which was founded back in 1986. When in 1999 First Solar was formed out of Solar Cell Inc., the company started to develop the production line, and full commercial operation of its initial manufacturing line started in late 2004 with a capacity of 25 MW. Since then on, the manufacturing capacity has grown to more than 1.2 GW in 2009.

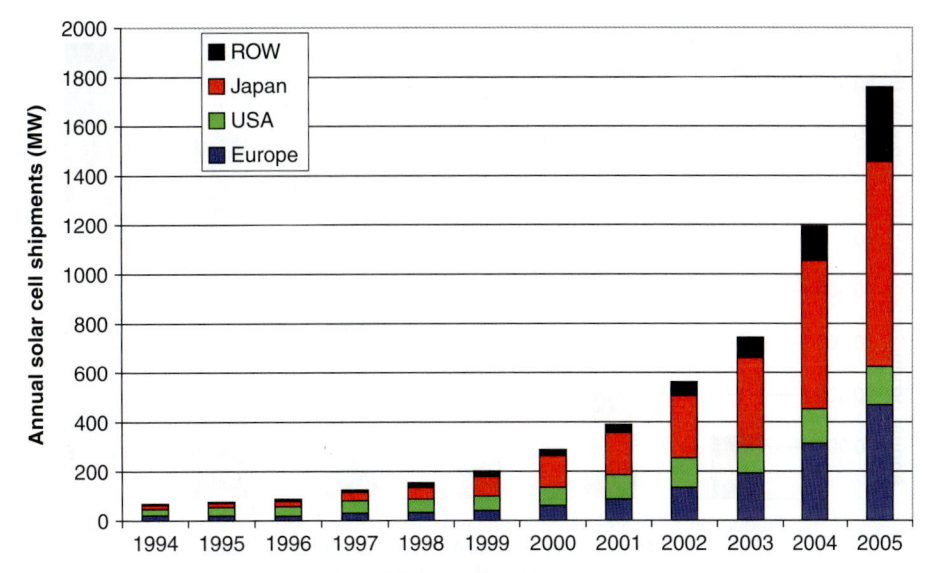

Figure 7 World solar cell production from 1994 to 2005 [11]. ROW, rest of world.

In the early 2000s, the buildup of solar cell manufacturing capacities in China and Taiwan started to gain pace and, in 2004, the Taiwanese company Motech Solar made it to the top-10 list, followed by Suntech from China in 2005. Since then, the growth of the PV industry in China and Taiwan outperformed that in the rest of the world.

PV industry activities in India existed since the 1980s, but it took almost 30 years until the Indian Government in 2009 recognized it as a promising industry with the launch of the Indian National Solar Mission in January 2010.

1.09.3 The Photovoltaic Industry in 2010

In 2010, the PV world market grew in terms of production by ~80% to 21–22 GW. The market for installed systems doubled again and the current estimates are between 16 and 18 GW, as reported by various consultancies. One could guess that this represents mostly the grid-connected PV market. To what extent the off-grid and consumer product markets are included is unclear. The difference of roughly 3–6 GW has therefore to be explained as a combination of unaccounted off-grid installations (~1–200 MW off-grid rural, ~1–200 MW communication/signals, ~100 MW off-grid commercial), consumer products (~1–200 MW), and cells/modules in stock.

In addition, the fact that some companies report shipment figures, whereas others report production figures, adds to the uncertainty. The difficult economic conditions added to the decreased willingness to report confidential company data. Nevertheless, the figures show a significant growth of the production, as well as a trend toward a silicon oversupply situation, for the next 2–3 years.

The announced production capacities – based on a survey of more than 300 companies worldwide – increased despite difficult economic conditions. Although a significant number of players announced a scale-back or cancellation of their expansion plans for the time being, the number of new entrants into the field, notably large semiconductor or energy-related companies, overcompensated this. At least on paper the expected production capacities are increasing. Only published announcements of the respective companies or their representatives and no third source info were used. The cutoff date of the used info was March 2011.

Therefore, the capacity figures just give a trend, but do not represent final numbers. It is worthwhile to mention that despite the fact that a significant number of players have announced a slowdown of their expansion, or cancelled their expansion plans for the time being, the number of new entrants into the field, notably large semiconductor or energy-related companies, is overcompensating this and, at least on paper, is increasing the expected production capacities.

It is important to note that production capacities are often announced taking into account different operation models such as number of shifts and operating hours per year. In addition, the announcements of the increase in production capacity do not always specify when the capacity will be fully ramped up and operational. This method has of course the setback (1) that not all companies announce their capacity increases in advance and (2) that in times of financial tightening, the announcements of the scale-back of expansion plans are often delayed in order not to upset financial markets. In addition, the assessment of all the capacity increases is further complicated by the fact that announcements of the increase in production capacity often lack the information about completion date. Therefore, the capacity figures just give a trend, but do not represent final numbers.

If all these ambitious plans can be realized by 2015, China will have about 38.4% of the worldwide production capacity of 88 GW, followed by Taiwan (18.0%), Europe (11.4%), and Japan (9.3%) (**Figure 8**).

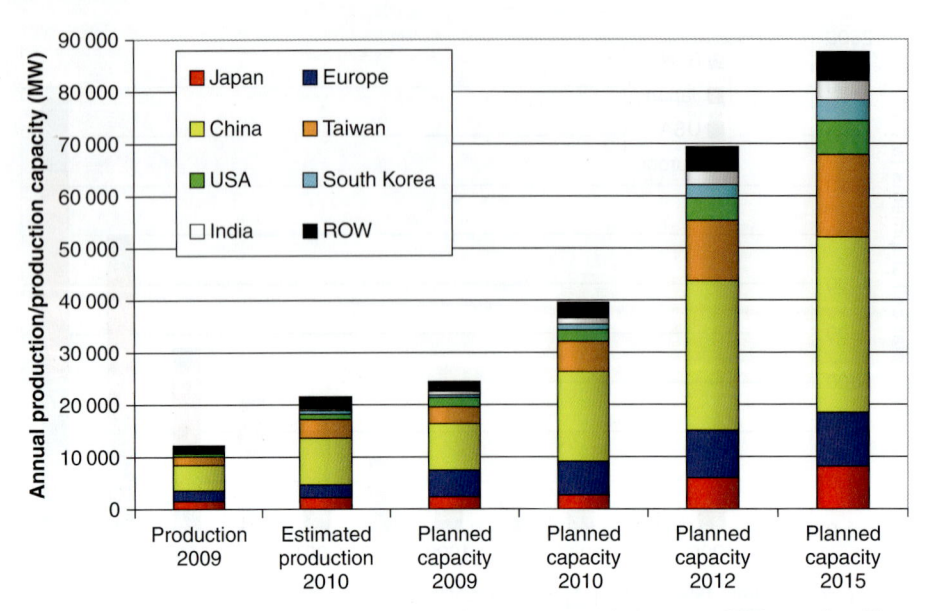

Figure 8 Worldwide PV production in 2009 and 2010 with future planned production capacity increases. ROW, rest of world.

All these ambitious plans to increase production capacities at such a rapid pace depend on the expectations that markets will grow accordingly. This, however, is the biggest uncertainty as the market estimates for 2010 vary between 9 and 24 GW with a consensus value in the 13 GW range. In addition, most markets are still dependent on public support in the form of feed-in tariffs, investment subsidies, or tax breaks.

Already now, electricity production from PV solar systems has shown that it can be cheaper than peak prices in the electricity exchange. In the first quarter of 2011, the German average price index for rooftop systems up to 100 kWp was given with €2546 kWp^{-1} without tax [19]. With such investment costs, the electricity generation costs are already at the level of residential electricity prices in some countries, depending on the actual electricity price and the local solar radiation level. But only if markets and competition will continue to grow, prices of the PV systems will continue to decrease and make electricity from PV systems for consumers even cheaper than from conventional sources. In order to achieve the price reductions and reach grid parity for electricity generated from PV systems, public support, especially on regulatory measures, will be necessary for the next decade.

1.09.3.1 Technology Mix

Wafer-based silicon solar cells are still the main technology and had around 80% market shares in 2010. Polycrystalline solar cells still dominate the market (45–50%), even if the market share has slightly decreased since the beginning of the decade. Commercial module efficiencies are within a wide range between 12% and 20%, with monocrystalline modules between 14% and 20% and polycrystalline modules between 12% and 17%. The massive manufacturing capacity increases for both technologies are followed by the necessary capacity expansions for polysilicon raw material.

In 2005, production of thin-film solar modules reached for the first time more than 100 MW per annum. Since then, the compound annual growth rate (CAGR) of thin-film solar module production is even beyond that of the overall industry, increasing the market share of thin-film products from 6% in 2005 to 10% in 2007 and 16–20% in 2010.

More than 200 companies are involved in thin-film solar cell activities, ranging from basic R&D activities to major manufacturing activities, and over 150 of them have announced the start or increase of production. The first 100 MW thin-film factories became operational in 2007. If all expansion plans are realized in time, thin-film production capacity could be around 22 GW, or 32% of the total 69.4 GW, in 2012 and about 30 GW, or 34%, in 2015 of a total of 87.6 GW (**Figure 9**). The first thin-film factories with GW production capacity are already under construction for various thin-film technologies.

One should bear in mind that only one-fourth of the over 150 companies with announced production plans have already produced thin-film modules on a commercial scale in 2009.

More than 100 companies are silicon based and use either a-Si or an amorphous/microcrystalline silicon structure. Thirty companies announced using Cu(In,Ga)(Se,S)$_2$ as absorber material for their thin-film solar modules, whereas nine companies use CdTe and eight companies go for dye and other materials.

CPV is an emerging technology which is growing at a very high pace, although from a low starting point. About 50 companies are active in the field of CPV development and almost 60% of them were founded in the last 5 years. Over half of the companies are located either in the United States of America (primarily in California) and in Europe (primarily in Spain).

Within CPV, there is a differentiation according to the concentration factors (high concentration >300 suns (HCPV), medium concentration $5 < x < 300$ suns (MCPV), low concentration <5 suns (LCPV)) and whether the system uses a dish (dish CPV) or lenses

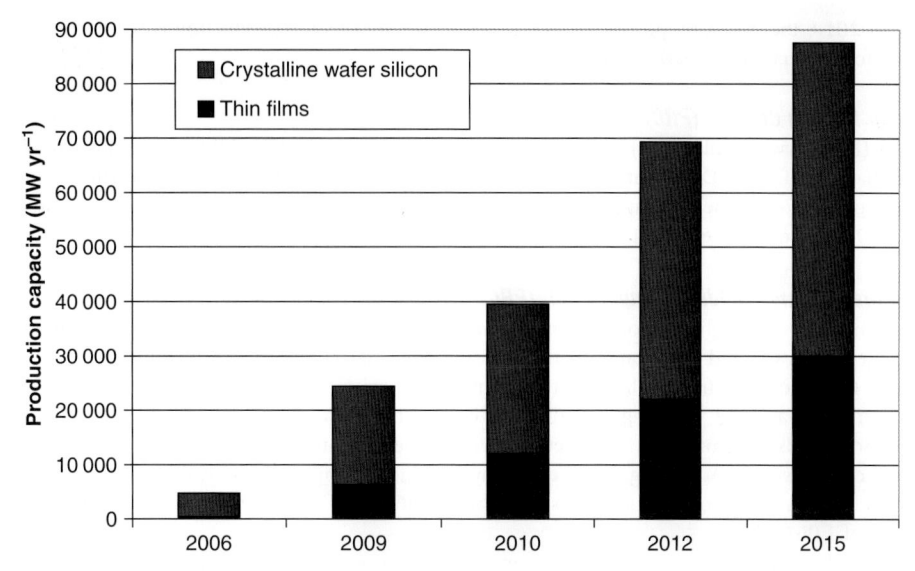

Figure 9 Annual PV production capacities of thin-film and crystalline silicon-based solar modules.

(lens CPV). The main parts of a CPV system are the cells, the optical elements, and the tracking devices. The recent growth in CPV is based on significant improvements in all of these areas, as well as the system integration. However, it should be pointed out that CPV is just at the beginning of an industry learning curve with a considerable potential for technical and cost improvements. The most challenging task is to become cost competitive with other PV technologies quickly enough in order to use the window of opportunities for growth.

With market estimates for 2010 in the 10–20 MW range, the market share of CPV is still small, but already for 2011 about 50–100 MW is expected and there is a wide consensus among consultancies and market analysts that CPV will reach a GW market size by 2015.

The existing PV technology mix is a solid foundation for future growth of the sector as a whole. No single technology can satisfy all the different consumer needs, ranging from mobile and consumer applications with the need for a few watts to multi-MW utility-scale power plants. The variety of technologies is an insurance against a roadblock for the implementation of solar PV electricity if material limitations or technical obstacles restrict the further growth or development of a single technology pathway.

1.09.3.2 Solar Cell Production Companies

Worldwide more than 300 companies produce solar cells. The following sections give a short description of the 20 largest companies, in terms of expected production capacity in 2010. (Solar cell production capacities mean the following: in the case of wafer silicon-based solar cells, only the cells; in the case of thin films, the complete integrated module; only those companies that actually produce the active circuit (solar cell) are counted; companies that purchase these circuits and make cells are not counted.) More information about additional solar cell companies and details can be found in various market studies and in the country chapters of the annual JRC PV Status Report [20]. The capacity, production, or shipment data are from the annual reports or financial statements of the respective companies or the cited references.

1.09.3.2.1 Suntech Power Co. Ltd. (PRC)

Suntech Power Co. Ltd. (http://www.suntech-power.com) is located in Wuxi. It was founded in January 2001 by Dr. Zhengrong Shi and went public in December 2005. Suntech specializes in the design, development, manufacturing, and sale of PV cells, modules, and systems. For 2010, Suntech reported shipments of 1.57 GW and held first place in the top-10 list. The takeover of the Japanese PV module manufacturer MSK was completed in June 2008. The company has a commitment to become the 'lowest cost per watt' provider of PV solutions to customers worldwide. The annual production capacity of Suntech Power was increased to 1 GW by the end of 2008 and the company plans to expand its capacity to 2.4 GW in 2011.

1.09.3.2.2 First Solar LLC (USA)

First Solar LLC (http://www.firstsolar.com) is one of the companies worldwide to produce CdTe thin-film modules. First Solar has developed a solar module product platform that is manufactured using a unique and proprietary vapor transport deposition (VTD) process. The VTD process optimizes the cost and production throughput of thin-film PV modules. The process deposits semiconductor material, while the glass remains in motion, completing deposition of stable, nonsoluble compound semiconductor materials.

The company has currently manufacturing plants in Perrysburg (USA), Frankfurt/Oder (Germany), and Kulim (Malaysia), which will have a combined capacity of 2.25 GW at the end of 2011. Further expansions are announced in France, the United States, and

Vietnam for 2012. In 2010, the company produced 1.4 GW and currently sets the production cost benchmark with 0.75 $ Wp^{-1} (0.58 € Wp^{-1}) in the fourth quarter of 2010.

1.09.3.2.3 JA Solar Holding Co. Ltd. (PRC)

JingAo Solar Co. Ltd. (http://www.jasolar.com) was established in May 2005 by the Hebei Jinglong Industry and Commerce Group Co. Ltd., the Australia Solar Energy Development Pty. Ltd., and Australia PV Science and Engineering Company. Commercial operation started in April 2006 and the company went public on 7 February 2007. The company reported a production capacity of 1.9 GW at the end of 2010 and shipments of 1.4 GW in 2010.

1.09.3.2.4 Yingli Green Energy Holding Company Ltd. (PRC)

Yingli Green Energy (http://www.yinglisolar.com/) went public on 8 June 2007. The main operating subsidiary, Baoding Tianwei Yingli New Energy Resources Co. Ltd., is located in the Baoding National High-New Tech Industrial Development Zone. The company deals with the whole set from solar wafers, cell manufacturing, and module production. On 29 April 2006, the groundbreaking ceremony was held for Yingli's 3rd-phase enlargement project, which aimed for production capacities of 500 MW for wafers, solar cells, and modules at the end of 2008. The investment included a PV system research center and a professional training center as well. According to the company, production capacity was 1.4 GW at the end of 2010. In 2011, a further expansion to 1.7 GW is under construction and should be operational in the first half of the year. The financial statement for 2010 gave shipments of 1.06 GW.

In January 2010, the Ministry of Science and Technology of China approved the application to establish a national-level key laboratory in the field of PV technology development, the State Key Laboratory of PV Technology at Yingli Green Energy's manufacturing base in Baoding.

1.09.3.2.5 Trina Solar Ltd. (PRC)

Trina Solar (http://www.trinasolar.com/) was founded in 1997 and went public in December 2006. The company has integrated product lines, from ingots to wafers and modules. In December 2005, a 30 MW monocrystalline silicon wafer product line went into operation. According to the company, the production capacity was 1.2 GW for cells and modules at the end of 2010. For 2011, an increase of the production capacities for ingot and wafers to 1.2 GW as well as for cells and modules to 1.9 GW is foreseen. For 2010, the company reported shipments of 1.06 GW.

In January 2010, the company announced that it was selected by the Chinese Ministry of Science and Technology to establish a state key laboratory to develop PV technologies within the Changzhou Trina PV Industrial Park. The laboratory is established as a national platform for driving PV technologies in China. Its mandate includes research into PV-related materials, cell and module technologies, and system-level performance. It will also serve as a platform to bring together technical capabilities from the company's strategic partners, including customers and key PV component suppliers, as well as universities and research institutions.

1.09.3.2.6 Motech Solar (Taiwan)

Motech Solar (http://www.motech.com.tw) is a wholly owned subsidiary of Motech Industries Inc., located in the Tainan Science Industrial Park. The company started its mass production of polycrystalline solar cells at the end of 2000 with an annual production capacity of 3.5 MW. The production increased from 3.5 MW in 2001 to 850 MW in 2010 with a production capacity of 1.15 GW. In August 2007, Motech Solar's Research and Development Department was upgraded to Research and Development Centre (R&D Centre), with the aim not only to improve the present production processes for wafer and cell production, but also to develop next-generation solar cell technologies.

At the end of 2009, the company announced that it acquired the module manufacturing facilities of GE in Delaware, USA.

1.09.3.2.7 Q-Cells AG (Germany)

Q-Cells SE (http://www.qcells.de) was founded at the end of 1999 and is based in Thalheim, Sachsen-Anhalt, Germany. Solar cell production started in mid-2001 with a 12 MWp production line. For 2010, the company reported a total production of 1014 MW solar cells including 75 MW of copper indium gallium diselenide (CIGS) thin-film modules. The production capacity at the end of 2010 was 1.1 GW c-Si (500 MW in Germany, 600 MW in Malaysia) and 135 MW CIGS thin films (Solibro, Germany).

1.09.3.2.8 Sharp Corporation (Japan)

Sharp (http://www.sharp-world.com) started to develop solar cells in 1959 and commercial production got under way in 1963. Since its products were mounted on 'Ume', Japan's first commercial-use artificial satellite, in 1974, Sharp has been the only Japanese maker to produce silicon solar cells for use in space. Another milestone was achieved in 1980, with the release of electronic calculators equipped with single-crystal solar cells. Sharp aims to become a 'zero global warming impact company by 2010' as the world's top manufacturer of solar cells.

In 2010, Sharp had a production capacity of 1070 MWp yr^{-1} and estimated sales of 1.3 GW [21]. Sharp has two solar cell factories at the Katsuragi, Nara Prefecture (550 MW c-Si and 160 MW a-Si triple-junction thin-film solar cell) and Osaka (200 MW c-Si and 160 MW a-Si triple-junction thin-film solar cell), five module factories, and the Toyama factory to recycle and produce silicon. Three of the module factories are outside Japan, one in Memphis, TN, USA, with 70 MW capacity, one in Wrexham, UK, with 500 MW capacity, and one in Nakornpathom, Thailand. In November 2008, the company announced to establish a joint venture with the Italian Enel SpA to build and operate a number of PV power plants with a total capacity of 189 MW by the end of 2012. In July 2010, the companies established the 3Sun S.r.l. joint venture in Catania, Italy, to set up a manufacturing plant with an initial capacity of 160 MW in 2011, which could later be expanded to 480 MW.

1.09.3.2.9 Gintech Energy Corporation (Taiwan)
Gintech (http://www.gintech.com.tw/) was established in August 2005 and went public in December 2006. Production at Factory Site A, Hsinchu Science Park, began in 2007 with an initial production capacity of 260 MW and has increased to 930 MW at the end of 2010. The company plans to expand capacity to 2.2 GW by 2013. In 2010, the company had a production of 827 MW [22].

1.09.3.2.10 Neo Solar Power Corporation (Taiwan)
Neo Solar Power (http://www.neosolarpower.com/) was founded in 2005 by PowerChip Semiconductor, Taiwan's largest dynamic random access memory (DRAM) company, and went public in October 2007. The company manufactures mono- and multi-crystalline silicon solar cells and offers SUPERCELL multicrystalline solar cell brand with 16.8% efficiency. Production capacity of silicon solar cells at the end of 2010 was 820 MW and an expansion to over 1.3 GW is foreseen for 2011. The company reported shipments of 500 MW in 2010.

1.09.3.2.11 Canadian Solar Inc. (PRC)
Canadian Solar Inc. (CSI; http://www.canadiansolar.com/) was founded in Canada in 2001 and was listed on NASDAQ in November 2006. CSI has established six wholly owned manufacturing subsidiaries in China, manufacturing ingot/wafer, solar cells, and solar modules. According to the company, it achieved 120–150 MW of ingot and wafer capacity in 2008 and plans to increase it to 400 MW in the first half of 2011. Solar cell capacity was 800 MW in November 2010 and the expansion to 1.3 GW should be operational in the first half of 2011. The module capacity was 1 GW in April 2010 and an expansion to 2 GW is under way. For 2010, the company reported module shipments of 803 MW with an internal cell production of 522 MW [22].

1.09.3.2.12 Renewable Energy Corporation AS (Norway)
Renewable Energy Corporation's (REC; http://www.recgroup.com/) vision is to become the most cost-efficient solar energy company in the world, with a presence throughout the whole value chain. REC is presently pursuing an aggressive strategy to this end. Through its various group companies, REC is already involved in all major aspects of the PV value chain. The company located in Høvik, Norway, has five business activities ranging from silicon feedstock to solar system installations.

REC ScanCell is located in Narvik, producing solar cells. From the start-up in 2003, the factory has been continuously expanding. In 2010, production of solar cells was 452 MW with a capacity at year end of 180 MWp in Norway and 550 MW in Singapore.

1.09.3.2.13 Solar World AG (Germany)
Since its founding in 1998, Solar World (http://www.solarworld.de/) has changed from a solar system and components dealer to a company covering the whole PV value chain from wafer production to system installations. The company now has manufacturing operations for silicon wafers, cells, and modules in Freiburg, Germany, and Hillsboro, OR, USA. Additional solar module production facilities exist in Camarillo, CA, USA, and since 2008 with a joint venture between SolarWorld and SolarPark Engineering Co. Ltd. in Jeonju, South Korea.

For 2010, solar cell production capacities in Germany were reported at 275 MW and at 500 MW in the United States. Total cell production in 2010 was 460 MW with 200 MW coming from Germany and 260 MW from the United States [22].

In 2003, the Solar World Group was the first company worldwide to implement silicon solar cell recycling. The Solar World subsidiary, Deutsche Solar AG, commissioned a pilot plant for the reprocessing of crystalline cells and modules.

1.09.3.2.14 SunPower Corporation (USA)
SunPower (http://us.sunpowercorp.com/) was founded in 1988 by Richard Swanson and Robert Lorenzini to commercialize proprietary high-efficiency silicon solar cell technology. The company went public in November 2005. SunPower designs and manufactures high-performance silicon solar cells, based on an interdigitated rear-contact design for commercial use. The initial products, introduced in 1992, were high-concentration solar cells with an efficiency of 26%. SunPower also manufactures a 22% efficient solar cell called Pegasus that is designed for nonconcentrating applications.

SunPower conducts its main R&D activity in Sunnyvale, California, and has its cell manufacturing plants (Fab. No. 1 & 2) outside of Manila in the Philippines. Fab. No. 3, a joint venture with AU Optronics Corporation (AUO), with a planned capacity of 1.4 GW by 2014 is currently under construction and ramp-up in Malaysia. Production in 2010 was reported at 584 MW.

1.09.3.2.15 Kyocera Corporation (Japan)
In 1975, Kyocera (http://global.kyocera.com/prdct/solar/) began with research on solar cells. The Shiga Yokkaichi Factory was established in 1980 and R&D and manufacturing of solar cells and products started with mass production of multicrystalline silicon solar cells in 1982. In 1993, Kyocera started as the first Japanese company to sell home PV generation systems.

Besides the solar cell manufacturing plants in Japan, Kyocera has module manufacturing plants in China (joint venture with the Tianjin Yiqing Group (10% share) in Tianjin since 2003), Tijuana, Mexico (since 2004), Kadan, Czech Republic (since 2005), and San Diego, USA (since 2010).

In 2010, Kyocera's solar cell production was estimated with 400 MW [21] and is also marketing systems that both generate electricity through solar cells and exploit heat from the sun for other purposes, such as heating water. The Sakura factory, Chiba Prefecture, is involved in everything from R&D and system planning to construction and servicing and the Shiga factory, Shiga Prefecture, is active in R&D, as well as the manufacturing of solar cells, modules, equipment parts, and devices, which exploit heat. Like solar companies, Kyocera is planning to increase its current capacity of 600 MW to 1 GW by 2012.

1.09.3.2.16 SANYO Electric Company (Japan)

Sanyo (http://sanyo.com/solar/) commenced R&D for a-Si solar cells in 1975. The year 1980 marked the beginning of SANYO's a-Si solar cell mass production for consumer applications. Ten years later, in 1990, research on the HIT (heterojunction with intrinsic thin layer) structure was started. In 1992, Dr. Kuwano (former president of SANYO) installed the first residential PV system at his private home. a-Si modules for power use became available from SANYO in 1993 and in 1997 the mass production of HIT solar cells started. In 2010, SANYO produced 400 MW solar cells [21]. The company is planning to increase its production capacity of 570 MW (565 MW HIT cells and 5 MW a-Si) to 1.5 GW by 2015.

At the end of 2002, SANYO announced the start of module production outside Japan. The company now has an HIT PV module production at SANYO Energy S.A. de C.V. Monterrey, Mexico and it joined Sharp and Kyocera to set up module manufacturing plants in Europe. In 2005, it opened its module manufacturing plant in Dorog, Hungary.

SANYO has set a world record for the efficiency of the HIT solar cell with 23% under laboratory conditions [23]. The HIT structure offers the possibility to produce double-sided solar cells, which offer the advantage of collecting scattered light on the rear side of the solar cell and can therefore increase the performance by up to 30% compared to one-sided HIT modules in the case of vertical installation.

1.09.3.2.17 E-Ton Solar Tech Co. Ltd. (Taiwan)

E-Ton Solar Tech (http://www.e-tonsolar.com) was founded in 2001 by the E-Ton Group, a multinational conglomerate dedicated to producing sustainable technology and energy solutions and was listed on the Taiwan OTC stock exchange in 2006.

At the end of 2010, the production capacity was 560 MW per annum and a capacity increase to 820 MW is foreseen for 2011. Shipments of solar cells were reported at 350 MW for 2010.

1.09.3.2.18 Sun Earth Solar Power Co. Ltd. (PRC)

Sun Earth Solar Power Co. Ltd. was established in 2010 (http://www.nbsolar.com/). Before, the company was known as Ningbo Solar or Sun-Earth and had been part of China's PuTian Group since 2003. The company has four main facilities for silicon production, ingot manufacturing, system integration, and solar system production. According to company information, Ningbo has imported solar cell and module producing and assembling lines from America and Japan.

In 2007, the company relocated to the Ningbo high-tech zone, with its global headquarters. There, the company produces solar silicon, ingots, wafers, solar cells, and solar modules. The second phase of cell and module production capacity expansion to 350 MW was completed in 2009. Further expansion to 800 MW is planned in 2011 and to 1 GW in 2012. For 2010, shipments of 450 MW were estimated [22].

1.09.3.2.19 Hanwha SolarOne (PRC)

Hanwha SolarOne (http://www.hanwha-solarone.com) was established in 2004 as Solarfun by the electricity meter manufacturer Linyang Electronics, the largest Chinese manufacturer of electric power meters. The company is a vertically integrated manufacturer of silicon ingots, wafers, PV cells, and modules. The first production line was completed at the end of 2004 and commercial production started in November 2005. The company went public in December 2006 and in September 2010, South Korea-based Hanwha Chemical invested in Solarfun Power Holdings Co., Ltd., purchasing 49.99% of its shares. As a result, the company changed its name to Hanwha SolarOne in December 2010. For 2011, the company has plans to increase cell capacity from 550 to 820 MW, wire saw capacity from 400 to 572 MW, and ingot capacity from 360 to 510 MW. Solar cell production was about 500 MW in 2010 [22].

1.09.3.2.20 Bosch Solar (Germany)

The Bosch Group, a leading global supplier of technology and services in the areas of automotive and industrial technology, consumer goods, and building technology, took over the 1997-founded ErSol Solar Energy AG Erfurt in 2008 and renamed it Bosch Solar (http://www.bosch-solarenergy.de/). Bosch Solar manufactures and distributes PV crystalline and thin-film silicon products. In 2010, the company had a production of 385 MW and a production capacity of 500 MW [22]. Further expansion to 700 MW is planned for 2011.

Bosch Solar holds a 35% interest in the joint venture company Shanghai Electric Solar Energy AG Co. Ltd., Shanghai, People's Republic of China (SESE Co. Ltd.), which was established in 2005 and has been producing solar modules since 2006. In 2009, Bosch Solar also acquired 68.7% of the German module manufacturer Aleo Solar AG and took over the majority of the German CIS company Johanna Solar GmbH.

1.09.3.3 Polysilicon Supply

The rapid growth of the PV industry since 2000 led to the situation where, between 2004 and early 2008, the demand for polysilicon outstripped the supply from the semiconductor industry. Prices for purified silicon started to rise sharply in 2007 and in 2008 prices for polysilicon peaked around 500 $ kg^{-1} and consequently resulted in higher prices for PV modules. This extreme price hike triggered a massive capacity expansion, not only of established companies, but many new entrants as well. In 2009, more than 90% of total polysilicon for the semiconductor and PV industry was supplied by seven companies: Hemlock, Wacker Chemie, REC, Tokuyama, MEMC, Mitsubishi, and Sumitomo. However, it is estimated that now about 70 producers are present in the market.

The massive production expansions, as well as the difficult economic situation, led to a price decrease throughout 2009 reaching about 50–55 $ kg^{-1} at the end of 2009 with a slight upward tendency throughout 2010 and early 2011.

For 2009, about 88 000 metric tons of solar-grade silicon production was reported, sufficient for around 11 GW under the assumption of an average materials need of 8 g Wp^{-1} [24]. China produced about 18 000 metric tons, or 20%, fulfilling about half of the domestic demand [25]. According to the Chinese Ministry of Industry and Information Technology, about 44 000 metric tons of polysilicon production capacity was reached with a further 68 000 metric tons capacity under construction in 2009.

Projected silicon production capacities available for solar in 2012 vary from 140 000 metric tons from established polysilicon producers up to 185 000 metric tons including the new producers [8] and 250 000 metric tons [9]. The possible solar cell production will in addition depend on the material use per Wp. Material consumption could decrease from the current 8 to 7 g Wp^{-1}, or even 6 g Wp^{-1}, but this might not be achieved by all manufacturers.

1.09.3.3.1 Silicon production processes

The high growth rates of the PV industry and the market dynamics forced the high-purity silicon companies to explore process improvements, mainly for two chemical vapor deposition (CVD) approaches – an established production approach known as the Siemens process and a manufacturing scheme based on fluidized bed (FB) reactors. Improved versions of these two types of processes will very probably be the workhorses of the polysilicon production industry for the near future.

1.09.3.3.1(i) Siemens process

In the late 1950s, the Siemens reactor was developed and has been the dominant production route since. About 80% of total polysilicon manufactured worldwide was made with a Siemens-type process in 2009. The Siemens process involves deposition of silicon from a mixture of purified silane or trichlorosilane (TCS) gas with an excess of hydrogen onto high-purity polysilicon filaments. The silicon growth then occurs inside an insulated reaction chamber or 'bell jar', which contains the gases. The filaments are assembled as electric circuits in series and are heated to the vapor deposition temperature by an external direct current. The silicon filaments are heated to very high temperatures of 1100–1175 °C at which TCS with the help of the hydrogen decomposes to elemental silicon and deposits as a thin-layer film onto the filaments. Hydrogen chloride (HCl) is formed as a by-product.

The most critical process parameter is temperature control. The temperature of the gas and filaments must be high enough for the silicon from the gas to deposit onto the solid surface of the filament, but well below the melting point of 1414 °C, so that the filaments do not start to melt. Second, the deposition rate must be well controlled and not too fast because otherwise the silicon will not deposit in a uniform, polycrystalline manner, making the material unsuitable for semiconductor and solar applications.

1.09.3.3.1(ii) Fluidized bed process

A number of companies develop polysilicon production processes based on FB reactors. The motivation to use the FB approach is the potentially lower energy consumption and a continuous production, compared to the Siemens batch process. In this process, tetrahydrosilane or TCS and hydrogen gases are continuously introduced onto the bottom of the FB reactor at moderately elevated temperatures and pressures. At a continuous rate high-purity silicon seeds are inserted from the top and are suspended by the upward flow of gases. At the operating temperatures of 750 °C, the silane gas is reduced to elemental silicon and deposits on the surface of the silicon seeds. The growing seed crystals fall to the bottom of the reactor where they are continuously removed.

MEMC Electronic Materials Inc., a silicon wafer manufacturer, has been producing granular silicon from silane feedstock using a FB approach for over a decade. Several new facilities will also feature variations of the FB. Several major players in the polysilicon industry, including Wacker Chemie and Hemlock, are developing FB processes, while at the same time continuing to produce silicon using the Siemens process as well.

Upgraded metallurgical-grade (UMG) silicon was seen as one option to produce cheaper solar-grade silicon with 5- or 6-nines purity, but the support for this technology is waning in an environment where higher purity methods are cost-competitive. A number of companies delayed or suspended their UMG silicon operations as a result of low prices and lack of demand for UMG material for solar cells.

1.09.3.4 Polysilicon Manufacturers

Worldwide more than 100 companies produce or start up polysilicon production. The following sections give a short description of the 10 largest companies in terms of expected production capacity in 2010. More information about additional polysilicon companies and details can be found in various market studies and the country chapters of the Annual PV Status Report [20].

1.09.3.4.1 Hemlock Semiconductor Corporation (USA)

Hemlock Semiconductor Corporation (http://www.hscpoly.com) is based in Hemlock, Michigan. The corporation is a joint venture of Dow Corning Corporation (63.25%) and two Japanese firms, Shin-Etsu Handotai Company, Ltd. (24.5%) and Mitsubishi Materials Corporation (12.25%). The company is the leading provider of polycrystalline silicon and other silicon-based products used in the semiconductor and solar industry.

In 2007, the company had an annual production capacity of 10 000 tons of polycrystalline silicon and production at the expanded Hemlock site (19 000 tons) started in June 2008. A further expansion at the Hemlock site, as well as a new factory in Clarksville, Tennessee, was started in 2008 and total production capacity was 36 000 tons in 2010. In 2009, 19 000 tons of production was reported [26].

1.09.3.4.2 Wacker Polysilicon (Germany)

Wacker Polysilicon AG (http://www.wacker.com) is one of the world's leading manufacturers of hyperpure polysilicon for the semiconductor and PV industry, chlorosilanes, and fumed silica. In 2010, Wacker increased its capacity to ~32 000 tons and produced 30 500 tons of polysilicon. The next 10 000 tons expansion stage became operational in April 2010 and another 10 000 tons expansion is under construction in Nünchritz (Saxony), Germany, which is scheduled to start up in 2011. Early 2010, the company received tax credits from the US Recovery Fund for their planned polysilicon plant in Tennessee, which is scheduled to start operation in 2013. For 2014, the company aims at a combined production capacity of 67 000 tons.

1.09.3.4.3 OCI Company (South Korea)

OCI Company Ltd. (formerly DC Chemical) (http://www.oci.co.kr/) is a global chemical company with a product portfolio spanning the fields of inorganic chemicals, petro and coal chemicals, fine chemicals, and renewable energy materials. In 2006, the company started its polysilicon business and successfully completed its 6500 metric ton P1 plant in December 2007. The 10 500 metric ton P2 expansion was completed in July 2009 and P3 expansion with another 10 000 metric tons went into trial production in December 2010. The expansion of P3 together with a new factory P4 with 20 000 tons capacity should bring the total capacity to 62 000 tons by 2013. For 2009, a silicon production of 6500 tons was reported [26].

1.09.3.4.4 GCL-Poly Energy Holdings Limited (PRC)

GCL-Poly (http://www.gcl-poly.com.hk) was founded in March 2006 and started the construction of its Xuzhou polysilicon plant (Jiangsu Zhongneng Polysilicon Technology Development Co. Ltd.) in July 2006. Phase I has a designated annual production capacity of 1500 tons and the first shipments were made in October 2007. Full capacity was reached in March 2008. Phase II, with an additional 1500 tons, started commercial operation in July 2008 and reached full capacity by the end of 2008. Construction for Phase III with 15 000 tons was started in December 2007 and commercial production started 1 year later in December 2008. Full capacity of all three plants, with a total capacity of 18 000 tons, was reached at the end of 2009. At the beginning of 2011, the company reported that it had a production capacity of 21 000 tons at the end of 2010 and announced its plans to increase this capacity up to 65 000 tons by 2012. For 2010, the company reported a production of 17 850 metric tons of polysilicon.

In August 2008, a joint venture Taixing Zhongneng (Far East) Silicon Co. Ltd. started pilot production of TCS. Phase I will be 20 000 tons to be expanded to 60 000 tons in the future.

1.09.3.4.5 MEMC Electronic Materials Inc. (USA)

MEMC Electronic Materials Inc. (http://www.memc.com/) has its headquarters in St. Peters, Missouri. It started operations in 1959 and the company's products are semiconductor-grade wafers, granular polysilicon, ultra-high-purity silane, TCS, silicon tetraflouride (SiF_4), and sodium aluminum tetraflouride (SAF). MEMC's production capacity in 2008 was increased to 8000 tons and the company planned to increase capacity further to 15 000 tons in 2010. In February 2011, the company entered into an agreement with Samsung Fine Chemicals to establish a 50/50 joint venture which will build and operate a new facility in Ulsan, South Korea, by 2013. For 2009, 10 000 tons of production was reported [26].

1.09.3.4.6 Renewable Energy Corporation AS (Norway)

Renewable Energy Corporation AS (http://www.recgroup.com/) took over Komatsu's US subsidiary Advanced Silicon Materials LLC ('ASiMI') in 2005, and announced the formation of its silicon division business area 'REC Silicon Division', comprising the operations of REC Advanced Silicon Materials LLC (ASiMI) and REC Solar Grade Silicon LLC (SGS). The company expanded the Moses Plant by adding 10 500 tons of new capacity. Plant III (6500 tons) was ramped up in 2009 and plant IV (4000 tons) was ramped up in the first half of 2010, bringing total capacity to about 17 500 tons. According to the company, about 13 600 tons was produced in 2010 and the production outlook for 2011 is 17 000 tons.

1.09.3.4.7 LDK Solar Co. Ltd. (PRC)

LDK (http://www.ldksolar.com/) was set up by the Liouxin Group, a company that manufactures personal protective equipment, power tools, and elevators. With the formation of LDK Solar, the company is diversifying into solar energy products. LDK Solar went public in May 2007. In 2008, the company announced that it completed the construction and commenced polysilicon production in its 1000 metric tons polysilicon plant. At the end of 2010, the company claimed a production capacity of 12 000 metric tons with plans to more than double this capacity to 25 000 tons in 2011. For 2010, a production of 5000 tons was reported.

1.09.3.4.8 Tokuyama Corporation (Japan)

Tokuyama (http://www.tokuyama.co.jp/) is a chemical company involved in the manufacturing of solar-grade silicon, the base material for solar cells. According to the company, Tokuyama had an annual production capacity of 5200 tons in 2008 and has expanded this to 8200 tons in 2009. Early 2011, the groundbreaking of a factory in Malaysia, which should become operational in 2013 with 6200 tons capacity, was announced.

A verification plant for the vapor-to-liquid deposition process (VLD method) of polycrystalline silicon for solar cells has been completed in December 2005. According to the company, steady progress has been made with the verification tests of this process, which allows a more effective manufacturing of polycrystalline silicon for solar cells. For 2009, silicon production of 8200 tons was reported [26].

Tokuyama has decided to form a joint venture with Mitsui Chemicals, a leading supplier of silane gas. The reason for this is the increased demand for silane gas due to the rapid expansion of amorphous/microcrystalline thin-film solar cell manufacturing capacities.

1.09.3.4.9 Elkem AS (Norway)

Elkem (http://www.elkem.com) is a subsidiary of Orkla ASA, and one of Norway's largest industrial companies and the world's largest producer of silicon metal. In January 2011, Orkla ASA has signed a binding agreement with China National Bluestar (Group) Co., Ltd. (Bluestar) for the purchase and sale of Elkem. Elkem Solar developed a metallurgical process to produce silicon metal for the solar cell industry. Elkem is industrializing its proprietary solar-grade silicon production line at Fiskaa in Kristiansand, Norway. According to the company, the first plant at Fiskaa has a capacity of 6000 tons of solar-grade silicon and was opened in 2009 with ramp-up in 2010. According to company data, about 2000 tons was produced in 2010.

1.09.3.4.10 Mitsubishi Materials Corporation (Japan)

Mitsubishi Materials (http://www.mmc.co.jp) was created through the merger Mitsubishi Metal and Mitsubishi Mining & Cement in 1990. Polysilicon production is one of the activities in their Electronic Materials & Components business unit. The company has two production sites for polysilicon, one in Japan and one in the United States (Mitsubishi Polycrystalline Silicon America Corporation), and is a shareholder (12.25%) in Hemlock Semiconductor Corporation. With the expansion of the polysilicon plant at Yokkachi, Mie, Japan, by 1000 tons in 2010, total production capacity increased to 4300 tons.

1.09.4 Outlook

New investment in clean energy technologies, companies, and projects increased in 2010 by 30% compared to 2099 and reached $243 billion (€187 billion) [27]. China held the largest share of investments with 22.4%, followed by Germany with 17% and the United States with 14% [28]. The total 2010 worldwide investment in solar energy reached $79 billion (€61 billion) and was second only to wind with $95 billion (€73 billion).

The PV industry has changed dramatically over the last few years. China has become the major manufacturing place followed by Taiwan, Germany, and Japan. Among the 15 biggest PV manufacturers in 2010, only three had production facilities in Europe, namely First Solar (the United States, Germany, and Malaysia), Q-Cells (Germany and Malaysia), and Solarworld (Germany and USA).

The implementation of the 100 000-roof program in Germany in 1990 and the Japanese long-term strategy set in 1994, with a 2010 horizon, was the start of an extraordinary PV market growth. Before the start of the Japanese market implementation program in 1997, annual growth rates of the PV markets were in the range of 10%, mainly driven by communication, industrial, and stand-alone systems. Since 1990, PV production has increased almost 500-fold from 46 MW to about 21.5 GW in 2010. This corresponds to a CAGR of 36% over the last 20 years. Statistically documented cumulative installations worldwide accounted for 38 GW in 2010. The interesting fact is, however, that cumulative production amounts to 53 GW over the same time period. Even if we do not account for the roughly 5 GW difference between the reported production and installations in 2010, there is a considerable 10 GW capacity of solar modules that is statistically not accounted for. Parts of it might be in consumer applications, which do not contribute significantly to power generation, but the overwhelming part is probably used in stand-alone applications for communication purposes, cathodic protection, water pumping, street, traffic, and garden lights, and so on.

The temporary shortage in silicon feedstock, triggered by the high growth rates of the PV industry over the last years, resulted in the market entrance of new companies and technologies. New production plants for polysilicon, advanced silicon wafer production technologies, and thin-film solar modules and technologies, like concentrator concepts, were introduced into the market much faster than expected a few years ago.

Even with the current economic difficulties, the increasing number of market implementation programs worldwide, as well as the overall rising energy prices, the need to re-evaluate the validity of a nuclear option after the tragic events in Fukujima, Japan, in March 2011, and the pressure to stabilize the climate, will continue to keep the demand for solar systems high. In the long term, growth rates for PV will continue to be high, even if the economic frame conditions vary and can lead to a short-term slowdown. This view is shared by an increasing number of financial institutions, which are turning toward renewables as a sustainable and secure long-term investment. Increasing demand for energy is pushing the prices for fossil energy resources higher and higher. Already in 2007, a number of analysts predicted that oil prices could well hit 100 $ bbl^{-1} by the end of 2007 or early 2008 [29]. After the spike of oil prices in July 2008, with close to 150 $ bbl^{-1}, prices have decreased due to the worldwide financial crisis and hit a low around 37 $ bbl^{-1} in December 2008. However, the oil price has rebounded and fluctuates in the 70–90 $ bbl^{-1} range since August 2009. It is obvious that the fundamental trend of increasing demand for oil will drive the oil price higher again. Already in March 2009, the IEA Executive Director Nobuo Tanaka warned in an interview that the next oil crisis with oil prices at around 200 $ bbl^{-1} due to a supply crunch could be as close as 2013 because of lack of investments in new oil production.

Over the last 20 years, numerous studies about the potential growth of the PV industry and the implementation of PV electricity generation systems were produced. In 1996, the Directorate General for Energy of the European Commission published a study 'Photovoltaics in 2010' [10]. The medium scenario of this study was used to formulate the White Paper target of 1997 to have a cumulative installed capacity of 3 GW in the European Union by 2010 [30]. The most aggressive scenario in this report predicted a cumulative installed PV capacity of 27.3 GW worldwide and 8.7 GW in the European Union for 2010. This scenario was called 'Extreme scenario' and it was assumed that in order to realize it a number of breakthroughs in technology and costs as well as continuous market stimulation and elimination of market barriers would be required. The reality check reveals that even the most aggressive scenario is lower than what we expect from the current developments. A cumulative installed capacity of about 38 GW worldwide and 28 GW in Europe was estimated as cumulative installations of PV systems at the end of 2010.

According to investment analysts and industry prognoses, solar energy will continue to grow at high rates in the coming years. The different photovoltaic industry associations, as well as Greenpeace, the European Renewable Energy Council (EREC), and the International Energy Agency, have developed new scenarios for the future growth of PV. **Table 1** shows the different scenarios of the Greenpeace/EREC study, as well as the different 2008 IEA Energy Technology Perspectives scenarios.

These projections show that there are huge opportunities for the PV industry in the future if the right policy measures are taken, but we have to bear in mind that such a development will not happen by itself. It will require the constant effort and support of all stakeholders to implement the envisaged change to a sustainable energy supply with PV delivering a major part. The main barriers to such developments are perception, regulatory frameworks, and the limitations of the existing electricity transmission and distribution structures.

The abovementioned scenarios will only be possible if new solar cell and module design concepts can be realized, as with current technology the demand for materials like silver would exceed the available resources within the next 30 years. Research to avoid such kind of problems is under way and it can be expected that such bottlenecks will be avoided.

The PV industry is developing into a fully fledged mass-producing industry. This development is connected to an increasing industry consolidation, which presents a risk and an opportunity at the same time. If the new large solar cell companies use their cost advantages to offer lower priced products, customers will buy more solar systems and it is expected that the PV market will show an accelerated growth rate. However, this development will influence the competitiveness of small and medium companies as well. To survive the price pressure of the very competitive market situation, and to compensate the advantage of the big companies made possible by economies of scale that come with large production volumes, they have to specialize in niche markets with high value added in their products. The other possibility is to offer technologically more advanced and cheaper solar cell concepts.

Despite the fact that Europe – especially Germany – is still the biggest world market, the European manufacturers are losing market shares in production. This is mainly due to the rapidly growing PV manufacturers from China and Taiwan and the new market entrants from companies located in India, Malaysia, Philippines, Singapore, South Korea, UAE, and so on. Should the current trend in the field of worldwide production capacity increase continue, the European share will further decrease, even with a

Table 1 Evolution of the cumulative solar electrical capacity scenarios until 2050 [31–33]

	2010 (GW)	2020 (GW)	2030 (GW)	2050 (GW)
Greenpeace[a] (reference scenario)	14	80	184	420
Greenpeace[a] ([r]evolution scenario)	18	335	1036	2968
Greenpeace[a] (advanced scenario)	21	439	1330	4318
IEA reference scenario	10	30	<60	Noncompetitive
IEA ACT map	22	80	130	600
IEA blue map	27	130	230	1150
IEA PV technology roadmap	27	210	870	3155

[a] 2010 values are extrapolated as only 2007 and 2015 values are given.

continuation of the growth rates of the last years. At the moment, it is hard to predict how the market entrance of the new players all over the world will influence future developments of the markets.

A lot of the future market developments, as well as production increases, will depend on the realization of the currently announced worldwide PV programs and production capacity increases. During 2009 and 2010, the announcements from new companies that wanted to start a PV production, as well as from established companies to increase their production capacities, continued to increase the expected overall production capacity. If all these plans are realized, thin-film production companies will increase their total production capacities even faster than the silicon wafer-based companies and increase their market share from the 2007 market share of 10% to about 30% in 2015. However, the number of thin-film expansion projects that are caught between the fact that margins are falling, due to decreasing module prices, and the need to raise additional capital to expand production in order to lower costs is increasing.

Already for a few years, we have now observed a continuous rise of oil and energy prices, which highlights the vulnerability of our current dependence on fossil energy sources, and increases the burden developing countries are facing in their struggle for future development. On the other hand, we see a continuous decrease in production costs for renewable energy technologies as a result of steep learning curves. Due to the fact that external energy costs, subsidies in conventional energies, and price volatility risks are generally not taken into consideration, renewable energies and PV are still perceived as being more expensive in the market than conventional energy sources. Nevertheless, electricity production from PV solar systems has already proved now that it can be cheaper than peak prices in the electricity exchange in a wide range of countries and if the new European Photovoltaic Industry Association (EPIA) and Solar Energy Industries Association (SEIA) visions can be realized, electricity generation cost with PV systems will have reached grid parity in most of Europe and the United States by 2020. In addition, renewable energies are, contrary to conventional energy sources, the only ones to offer a reduction of prices rather than an increase in the future.

References

[1] Mints P (2010) *Manufacturer Shipments, Capacity and Competitive Analysis 2009/2010.* Palo Alto, CA: Navigant Consulting Photovoltaic Service Program.
[2] Mints P (March 2010) *The PV Industry's Black Swan.* Photovoltaics World. Peterborough, NH, USA.
[3] *PV News* (May 2010) Published by The Prometheus Institute and Greentech Media, Boston, MA, USA. ISSN 0739-4829.
[4] UNEP and New Energy Finance (2009) *Global Trends in Sustainable Energy Investment 2009.* France: UNEP and New Energy Finance, ISBN 978-92-807-3038.
[5] Mints P (12 January 2011) *Global PV Demand 2011 and Beyond.* Webinar, Vote Solar.
[6] Mercom (2011) *Market Intelligence Report*, 4 April.
[7] iSuppli (2011) *PV Perspectives*, February.
[8] Homan G (2009) Presentation at Intersolar. Intersolar 2009, San Francisco, CA, USA.
[9] Bernreuther J and Haugwitz F (2010) The Who's Who of Silicon Production. *Bernreuter Research Photovoltaic Special Reports.* Germany: Bernreuter.
[10] European Commission, Directorate-General for Energy (1996) *Photovoltaics in 2010.* Office for Official Publications of the European Communities, ISBN 92-827-5347-6.
[11] Maycock PD (2003) *PV News*, ISSN 0739-4829. Casnova, VA.
[12] Maycock PD (1993) *Photovoltaic Technology, Performance, Cost and Market Forecast 1990–2010.* Casnova, VA: Photovoltaic Energy Systems Inc.
[13] Staiss F (ed.) (2000) *Jahrbuch Erneuerbare Energien 2000.* Radebeul: Bieberstein.
[14] Ikki O, Ohigashi T, Kaizuka I, and Matsukawa H (2005) Current status and future prospects of PV development in Japan: Beyond 1 GW of PV installed capacity. *Proceedings of the 20th European Photovoltaic Solar Energy Conference and Exhibition.* Barcelona, June 2005.
[15] Japan Photovoltaic Energy Association, Press Release, April 2006.
[16] Maycock PD (2006) *PV News*, ISSN 0739-4829. Casnova, VA.
[17] Gesetz über den Vorrang Erneuerbaren Energien (Erneuerbare-Energien-Gesetz – EEG), Bundesgestzblatt Jahrgang (2000) Teil I, Nr. 13, p. 305 (29.03.2000).
[18] Gesetz zur Neuregelung des Rechts der Erneuerbaren Energien im Strombereich (Erneuerbare-Energien-Gesetz – EEG), Bundesgestzblatt Jahrgang (2004) Teil I, Nr. 40, p. 1918 (31.07.2004).
[19] Bundesverband Solarwirtschaft, Preisindex Photovoltaik. http://www.solarwirtschaft.de/preisindex.
[20] Jäger-Waldau A (2011) Annual PV Status Report. http://re.jrc.ec.europa.eu/refsys/. Office for Official Publications of the European Union, Luxembourg, ISBN 978-92-79-20171-4.
[21] Osamu IKKI (March 2011) *PV Activities in Japan* 17(3).
[22] Photon International (March 2011).
[23] Taguchi M, Tsunomura Y, Inoue H, et al. (2009) High-efficiency HIT solar cell on thin (<100 μm) silicon wafer. In: *Proceedings of the 24th European Photovoltaic Solar Energy Conference*, p. 1690. Hamburg.
[24] Displaybank Briefing (28 January 2010). In 2010 130,000 tons of Global Solar Grade-Silicon Production Expected – Continuation of Over-Supply.
[25] Baoshan Li (2010) Research on the progress of silicon materials in China. *Presentation at the 6th China SoG Silicon and PV Conference.* 16–18 March 2010, Shanghai, PRC.
[26] Osamu IKKI (June 2010) *PV Activities in Japan* 16(6).
[27] World Economic Forum (2011) *Green Investment 2011.* http://www3.weforum.org/docs/WEF_IV_GreenInvesting_Report_2011.pdf.
[28] The PEW Charitable Trust (2011) *Who's Winning the Clean Energy Race? G-20 Investment Powering Forward.*
[29] International Herald Tribune 24 July 2007. http://www.iht.com/articles/2007/07/24/bloomberg/bxoil.php.
[30] Energy for the Future: Renewable Sources of Energy, White Paper for a Community Strategy and Action Plan, COM (1997)599 final (26 July 1997).
[31] Greenpeace International European Renewable Energy Council (EREC) (2010) *Energy [R]evolution*, June 2010.
[32] International Energy Agency (2008) *Energy Technology Perspectives – Scenarios & Strategies to 2050.* France: International Energy Agency, ISBN 9789264041424.
[33] International Energy Agency (2010) *PV Technology Roadmap.* France: International Energy Agency.

1.10 Vision for Photovoltaics in the Future

E Despotou, Formerly of the European Photovoltaic Industry Association, Brussels, Belgium

© 2012 Elsevier Ltd.

1.10.1	**Photovoltaics Today**	180
1.10.1.1	Markets	180
1.10.1.2	Technologies	181
1.10.1.3	Competitiveness	181
1.10.1.3.1	PV module prices	181
1.10.1.3.2	PV system prices	181
1.10.1.4	Electricity Prices	181
1.10.1.5	Policy Support	182
1.10.2	**Future Market Development**	183
1.10.2.1	PV as a Mainstream Power Source in Europe by 2020 and Beyond	183
1.10.2.2	US and Canadian Markets Slowly Taking Off	184
1.10.2.3	Japan Has a Moderately Ambitious PV Target for 2020	184
1.10.2.4	The Rise of Sunbelt Countries	184
1.10.2.5	Global PV Installed Capacity Could Reach More Than 4500 GW by 2050	185
1.10.3	**The EPIA Vision for 2050**	186
1.10.3.1	Introduction	186
1.10.3.2	A Dynamic Vision on PV Competitiveness and Grid Development	187
1.10.3.3	Necessary Steps to Unlocking PV Potential	187
1.10.3.3.1	Ensuring the gradual competitiveness of PV	187
1.10.3.3.2	Ensuring necessary infrastructure adaptations	188
1.10.3.3.3	Ensuring evolution of grid management practices and innovative market design	188
1.10.3.4	Policy Recommendations for a Bright 2050 Future	188
1.10.4	**Future Changes in Electricity Systems**	189
1.10.4.1	Managing Variability	189
1.10.4.2	From Centralized to Decentralized Energy Generation	189
1.10.4.3	Peak Load Shaving	190
1.10.4.4	Super Smart Grid	190
1.10.4.5	Decentralized Storage	191
1.10.4.6	DSM	191
1.10.5	**Future Market Segmentation**	191
1.10.6	**Future Share of On-Grid/Off-Grid Applications**	192
1.10.6.1	Extending the National Grid	192
1.10.6.2	Providing Off-Grid Solutions	192
1.10.6.3	Coupling Mini-Grids with Hybrid Power	192
1.10.7	**Future Technological Trends**	192
1.10.7.1	The Evolution of PV Module and System Prices	193
1.10.7.2	Cost of Electricity Generation	195
1.10.8	**Recommendations**	196
1.10.8.1	Policy Recommendations	196
1.10.8.1.1	Develop a long-term vision with precise milestones	196
1.10.8.1.2	Set up a supportive regulatory framework	196
1.10.8.1.3	Send the right signals to consumers	196
1.10.8.2	Investments in Technology and in PV Projects	196
1.10.8.2.1	The importance of a sustained PV cost reduction	196
1.10.8.2.2	Delivering research results in line with focus areas already identified	196
1.10.8.2.3	Financing necessary R&D investments	197
1.10.8.2.4	Encourage investments in Sunbelt countries	197
1.10.8.3	Grid Infrastructures Adaptations	197
1.10.8.3.1	Making necessary changes in the power distribution system	197
1.10.8.3.2	Adapting the transmission system	197
1.10.8.3.3	Financing infrastructure needs	197
1.10.9	**Conclusion**	197
References		198

1.10.1 Photovoltaics Today

1.10.1.1 Markets

Solar photovoltaic (PV) electricity is on the road to becoming a mainstream energy technology and is currently the fastest-growing renewable energy source in Europe, with a rise in installed capacity of almost 13 000 MW over the past year (see **Figure 1**), which is the second largest capacity increase in Europe just after gas. By the end of 2010, more than 28 GW were being installed. This corresponds to the electricity production of two coal-fired power plants or to the electricity consumption of 10 million households in Europe or half the current electricity demand in countries such as Greece.

Almost 40 GW were installed globally by the end of 2010 (see **Figure 2**), which corresponds to 50 TWh electricity generated. While these numbers are encouraging, solar PVs have the potential to achieve more. In fact, solar PV has a critical contribution to make to the three pillars of the European Union's (EU) energy policy: competitiveness, energy security, and sustainability.

In the future, should the right conditions be in place, solar PV could satisfy up to 12% of the EU's electricity needs. Achieving that desirable goal would cut down emission of 192 million tons of CO_2 per year, an important contribution to the EU's climate goals.

Ultimately, boosting the share of PVs in the electricity market will yield huge environmental, social, and economic benefits for Europe. However, to achieve a real paradigm, shift is needed. Policy-makers, regulators, and industry need to work together to drive PV mass penetration, fostering technological progress, and cost reductions as well as creating a predictable regulatory environment that attracts investments in the EU.

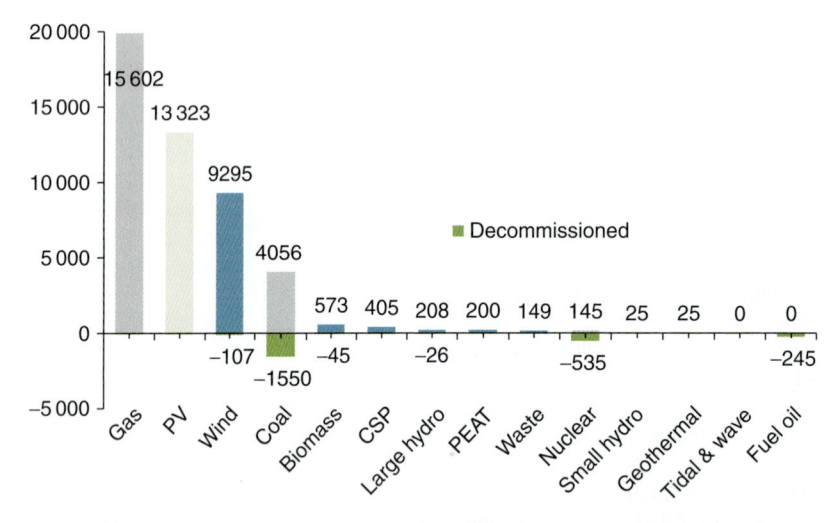

Figure 1 Power generation capacities added in 2010 at EU 27. Source: EPIA analysis [2].

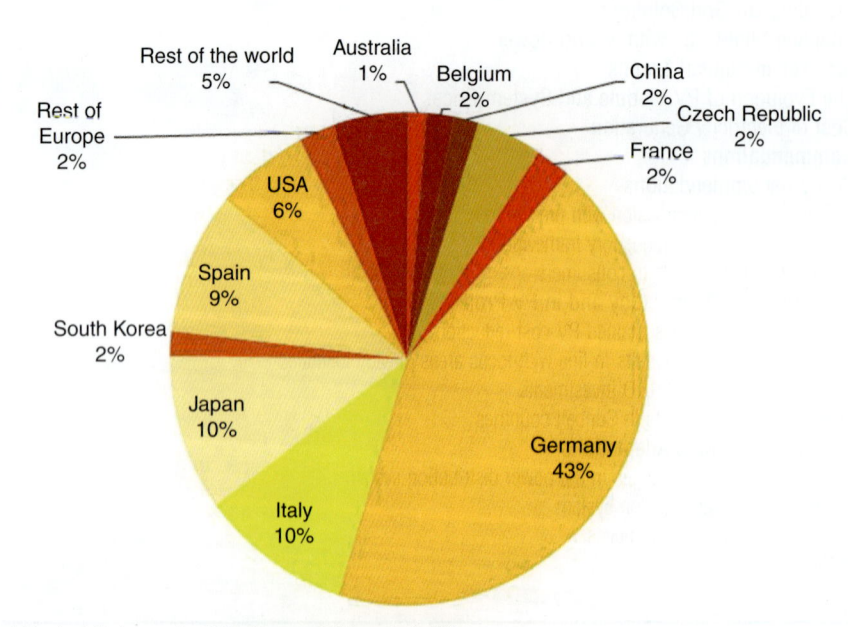

Figure 2 Global cumulative installed capacity 2010. Source: EPIA analysis [2].

With the Renewable Energy Sources Directive, 2009/28/EC [1], the EU has set the goal to reach 20% of EU energy demand satisfied by renewable energy sources by 2020. PV can play a major role in achieving this objective, provided the Member States realize the potential of the technology and set ambitious targets for its deployment.

PV technology is no longer just a gadget, or a device for powering space satellites, or useful only for small applications in remote areas. It is becoming a significant part of the energy mix. In Spain and Germany, the average annual contribution from PV to electricity generation is more than 2% of the total. However, with the right combination of regulatory framework, market conditions, and solar irradiation, PV can provide much more. For example, in the Spanish region of Extremadura, PVs made up 15% of the electricity mix of the yearly average of 2010 (with peaks up to 25% during summer). Thus, it has been proved that PV can compete with other generation sources.

Figure 2 demonstrates that Germany still represents the majority of the global market with 43% share. If we add up Italy and the rest of EU countries, Europe keeps by far the market leadership. Events such as the Fukushima disaster could potentially give an additional push to the PV market development for the years to come with a more important contribution.

1.10.1.2 Technologies

Crystalline silicon (c-Si) technologies have dominated the market for the last 30 years. Amorphous silicon (a-Si) technology has been the choice most widely used for consumer applications (e.g., calculators and solar watches) due to its low manufacturing cost, while c-Si technologies have been used mainly in both stand-alone and on-grid system applications.

In c-Si technologies, monocrystalline and multicrystalline are produced in equal proportion, but the trend is moving toward multicrystalline technology. Ribbon c-Si has a small market share that exists today less than 5%.

In the thin-film technologies, a-Si has lost some market share in the last decade, whereas other technologies such as CdTe have seen their market share to grow from 2% to 13% over the last 5 years [2].

Technologies such as concentrator PV, organics, and dye-sensitized solar cells are starting to enter the market and are expected to see an important growth in years to follow, with ~6% market share expected in 2020.

1.10.1.3 Competitiveness

PV competitiveness will be achieved before the end of this decade both from consumer and power-generator perspectives in most European countries. In addition, supported by smart, sustainable regulatory policies, PV will be an increasingly more desirable part of the energy equation and constitute a vital part of Europe's energy mix.

The competitiveness of PV electricity depends on the evolution of PV modules and system prices, as well as the cost of electricity generation. The following subsections explain the main drivers of the evolution of PV toward parity with conventional electricity producers and beyond.

1.10.1.3.1 PV module prices

Over the past 30 years, the PV industry has achieved significant and swift price reductions. The price of PV modules has been reduced by 22% for every doubling of the cumulative installed capacity (see **Figure 3**). The decrease in manufacturing costs and retail prices of PV modules and systems (including electronics and safety devices, cabling, mounting structures, and installation cost) has been possible thanks to the achieved economies of scale and acquired experience. Extensive innovation, research and development, and political support for market development have also been important drivers of cost reduction.

The 'module' price has fallen from about 75% of the total system price to between 50% and 60%, depending on the module efficiency, and is expected to further decrease down to 40% by the end of this decade.

1.10.1.3.2 PV system prices

The cost of solar PV is decreasing constantly across all segments: residential, commercial, and industrial installations as well as large ground-mounted power plants. In Europe, the price of PV systems has dropped 65% in the last decade.

The inverter, which represents ~15% of the total system price for a PV installation, has seen a decline in price similar to the one shown by PV modules.

Installation costs vary depending on the maturity of the market and type of application. For instance, with current technical improvements from new generation mounting structures, installations can be built faster and more efficiently.

1.10.1.4 Electricity Prices

Generating electricity from fossil and fissile fuels such as oil, gas, coal and uranium will become more expensive as supplies of these finite resources are exhausted. The growing economic and environmental costs of these energy sources will also add to cost increases. However, any quantification or potential indication on the electricity price increase at that time is considered as nonwise.

It should be pointed out that conventional electricity prices do not fully reflect actual production costs. Many governments still subsidize the coal industry and promote the use of locally produced coal by utilities through specific incentives. Given the strong backing of conventional energy sources over the past several decades, it should be entirely reasonable to view financial support

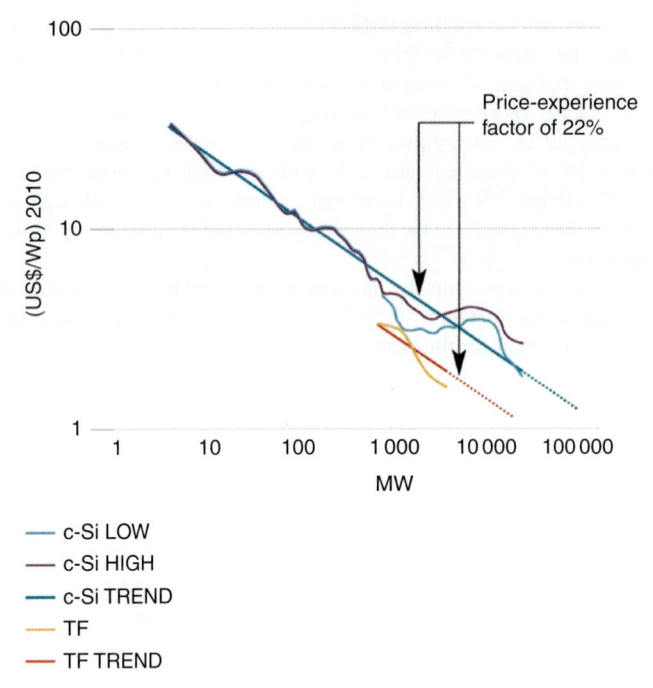

Figure 3 PV module price experience curve. Navigant consultant and EPIA internal analysis [3].

aimed at making renewable energy sources such as wind and solar fully competitive as appropriate, considering the strong backing of conventional sources over the past several decades.

Competitiveness of PV electricity (often referred to as 'grid parity') for consumers can be defined as the specific moment in a country when the savings in electricity cost and/or the revenues generated by the selling of electricity on the market are equal to or higher than the long-term cost of installing and financing a PV system.

Given the possible generation cost, "grid parity could be achieved progressively" across all market segments in Europe before the end of this decade. In most European countries, PV will be accessible to everyone at affordable prices in only a couple of years. The general rise in electricity prices as previously described, coupled with the reductions in the cost of generating PV electricity, is likely to abridge the time needed for PV to become competitive.

1.10.1.5 Policy Support

Over the years, the introduction of the feed-in tariff (FiT) support scheme has proven to be the most effective and efficient mechanism to kick off and help develop PV markets.

This is not just the view of the PV industry; it is also supported by key reports from the European Commission (industry surveys of 2005 and 2010) and The Stern Review on the Economics of Climate Change.

Globally, more than 40 countries have adopted such a mechanism; in Europe, Asia-Pacific, and North America, these countries have adjusted the system according to their regional- and national-specific needs.

FiT introduce the obligation by law for utilities to conclude purchase agreements for the solar electricity generated by PV systems. The cost of solar electricity purchased is passed on through the electricity bill and therefore does not negatively affect government finances. In markets where FiTs have been introduced as reliable and predictable market mechanisms, they have proven their ability to develop a sustainable PV industry that in return has progressively reduced costs and moved the sector toward grid parity. In order to be sustainable, it is critical that FiTs be guaranteed for a significant period of time (at least 20 years), without any possibility of retroactively reducing them.

FiT mechanisms remain a cornerstone for promoting the uptake of solar electricity in Europe.

To be successful, a support mechanism should be

- *temporary* – required only as a gap-filler until solar PV reaches full competitiveness;
- *paid by utilities, with costs passed on to all consumers* – thus protecting the tariff from frequently changing governmental budgets and limiting the increase in consumer cost;
- *used to drive costs down* – annual reductions in the tariffs (only for newly installed PV systems) keep pressure on the PV industry to cut costs each year;

- *used to encourage high-quality systems* – by rewarding people for generating solar electricity, not just for installing it, FiTs help owners keep output high over the entire lifetime of the system; and
- *structured to encourage easier financing* – by guaranteeing income over the lifetime of the system, a good tariff system encourages buyers to take out loans and simplifies loan structures for banks.

1.10.2 Future Market Development

1.10.2.1 PV as a Mainstream Power Source in Europe by 2020 and Beyond

Figure 4 provides a comparison of different industrial scenarios and targets; more specifically, the three scenarios from the 'SET For 2020' study (covering 4%, 6%, and 12%, respectively, of the electricity demand in 2020) as well as the two scenarios from the Global Market Outlook [4] providing a shorter-term perspective until 2015. The cumulative target of the National Renewable Energy Action Plans (NREAPs) is also shown. With only 84.38 GW in 2020 or 2.4% of the final gross electricity consumption, this target does not constitute a real lever for wide market deployment compared to the more ambitious PV industrial targets.

The Set For 2020 study [5] commissioned by the European Photovoltaic Industry Association (EPIA) and conducted by the strategic consultancy AT Kearney in 2008 highlights the potential for PV in Europe up to 2020. With the right regulatory frameworks in place, properly defined financial conditions and grid improvements including the introduction of smart grids, storage, and e-mobility, PV could reach up to 12% of the electricity demand in Europe by that time.

Even without substantial changes to the electricity distribution and transport system, scenarios in which PV provides 4% and 6% are possible. Achieving the 12% scenario will require addressing the capacity to distribute PV electricity across Europe, as well as the issue of storing part of the generated electricity (locally with decentralized storage solutions and more in large storage systems such as pumped hydro storage facilities) and of using more demand response from customers.

But even with those three scenarios – 4% (with 130 GW installed), 6% (195 GW), and 12% (390 GW) – the full potential is not reached. PV installations could rise even more in the decade following 2020, depending on the changes in the general electricity framework. The conditions for overtaking the 6% threshold of penetration will remain the same before and after 2020. Without any improvements in the current production, transportation, distribution, and consumption of electricity and in market design, the 6% mark will remain a maximum value.

However, this 6% mark may be overtaken if electricity systems evolve toward higher shares of renewable energy, adequate demand-side management (DSM), decentralized as well as large-scale storage, and smart inverters for PV systems that are able to provide services to the network (such as short-circuit current or reactive power production), and smart network management.

Once the adequate technical framework is in place, and with the right political decisions, PV can continue its growth of PV in the power generation mix. By 2050, the share of PV could reach between 19% [6] and 27.5% [7] in the EU. In most cases, 2050 targets

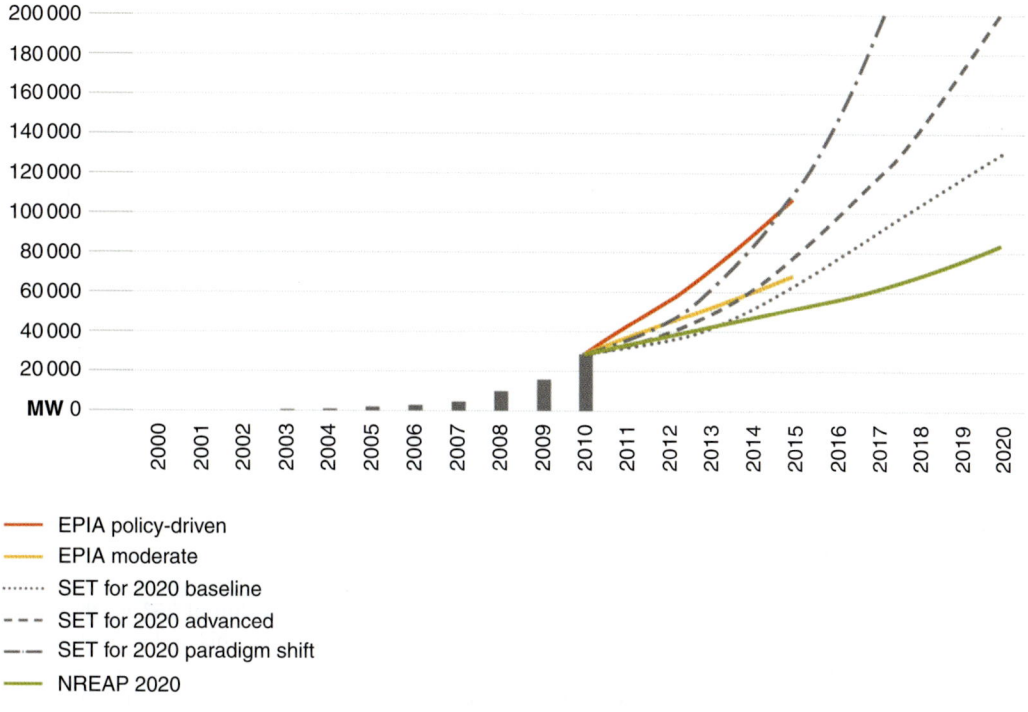

Figure 4 Market forecasts compared to 'SET For 2020' targets and NREAPs. Source: EPIA analysis [2].

take high shares of renewable energy sources in the power generation mix into account, ranging from 80% to 100%. The difference between these scenarios depends on technological choices, how the evolution of electricity networks will be shaped, and how the market segmentation of PV will evolve.

1.10.2.2 US and Canadian Markets Slowly Taking Off

US markets remain largely untapped considering the size of the country and its potential for PV. With its vast open spaces, high electricity demand, and strong correlation between demand peaks and PV production, everything is in place for rapid deployment.

Current PV capacity in the United States was higher than 2.5 GW at the end of 2010 – <10% of the installed capacity of the EU. Despite limited solar irradiation compared to the United States, Canada has continued the increasing PV uptake observed in 2009. An additional 105 MW capacity was connected to the grid in 2010. The province of Ontario is clearly driving the market due to a relatively generous FiT even though local content provisions have been introduced requiring developers to source at least 60% of their products and resources from Ontario-based goods and labor. Japan requested consultations with Canada through the World Trade Organisation (WTO) regarding Canada's measures relating to domestic content requirements in the FiT program. Industry associations vigorously oppose those provisions as they do not permit the establishment of a level playing field for global competition.

Around 200 MW are already foreseen for installation in 2011, all located in Ontario. EPIA considers that the Canadian market could reach up to 4.1 GW cumulative installed capacity by 2015 under a Policy-Driven scenario.

According to the EPIA scenarios, by 2020, the potential for PV in the United States and Canada could be between 77 and 144 GW. In the highest-case scenario, the United States and Canadian markets together would reach 14 GW of installed capacity per year.

By 2030, this could rise to between 285 and 460 GW and for 2050, the total installed capacity for PV in the United States and Canada could reach up to 980 GW.

1.10.2.3 Japan Has a Moderately Ambitious PV Target for 2020

Once the world PV leader, Japan has slid down in ranking due to its disruptive policy support. Before the dramatic events of March 2011, the Japan PV market was progressing, with "990 MW installed in 2010" and positive forecasts for the years to come. The 28 GW target defined for 2020 looked reasonable and achievable with a manageable increase in market volumes. Besides the residential systems that represented more than 95% of the market, ground-mounted installations were also expected to grow.

EPIA believes the lack of power generation following the destruction of many power plants will push forward PV development in the coming years. The rising electricity demand during the summer for air-conditioning could also favor PV as a preferred energy source in order to solve the current lack of power generation capacity in the short and medium terms.

Growth will certainly resume afterward, whatever the outcome of the current events, meaning that Japan will continue to be one of the leading PV countries worldwide.

The Japanese government, through the New Energy and Industrial Technology Development Organization (NEDO), has released its targets for 2020 (with a target upgraded from 14 to 28 GW) and 2030 (rising to 53 GW of PV installed capacity). A plan for 2050 is foreseen as well.

The electrical utilities plan to build 140 MW PV power plants in 30 locations across Japan by 2020. By 2010, they had already announced the construction of 30 plants for a total installed capacity of 100 MW. This shows that the final market share for utilities could be higher than foreseen. Japanese utilities will probably take a lion's share of large installations. Indeed, their experience in the electricity market makes them natural competitors with large project developers. This is less obvious for residential and commercial installations in the current context; however, it is highly conceivable to see utilities acting as intermediaries, for example, through virtual power plants to control the incoming millions of small rooftop installations.

1.10.2.4 The Rise of Sunbelt Countries

Outside the main existing markets, PV potential in the world is expected to grow rapidly in the coming decades, reaching between 17% and 21% of the world electricity demand according to the most favorable scenario in 2050 (**Figure 5**). The difference between both the scenarios will come from the possible gain in efficiency in energy consumption in the 40 coming years.

Worldwide, the PV penetration could reach 4670 GWp of cumulative installed capacity (4.67 TWp) by 2050 in the highest scenario (**Figure 6**). This represents a total electricity output of 6747 TWh yr^{-1}. This represents a reduction in CO_2 emissions of 4.05 billion tons by the year 2050, compared to the current power generation mix.

The term 'Sunbelt' refers to countries located in the sunniest latitudes, within the region of 35° north and south of the equator. While most are developing countries, lowering the price of PV will make this technology more and more competitive with conventional power generation sources. According to the development scenario, PV potential in Sunbelt countries could range from 60 to 250 GWp. Sunbelt countries would then represent 27–58% of the forecasted global PV installed capacity by 2030.

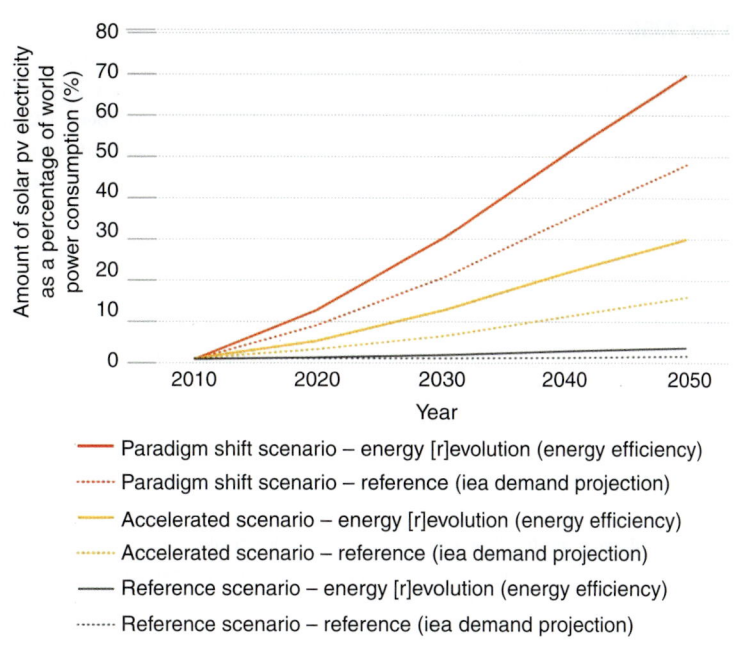

Figure 5 Amount of solar PV electricity as a percentage of world power consumption. Source: EPIA and Greenpeace (2011) *Solar Generation 6*. Brussels, Belgium: EPIA [8]. http://www.epia.org/index.php?eID=tx_nawsecuredl&u=0&file=fileadmin/EPIA_docs/documents/Solar_Generation_6__2011_Full_report_Final.pdf&t=1328180025&hash=76fb49badbaaffeaee2999bbff6bd977.

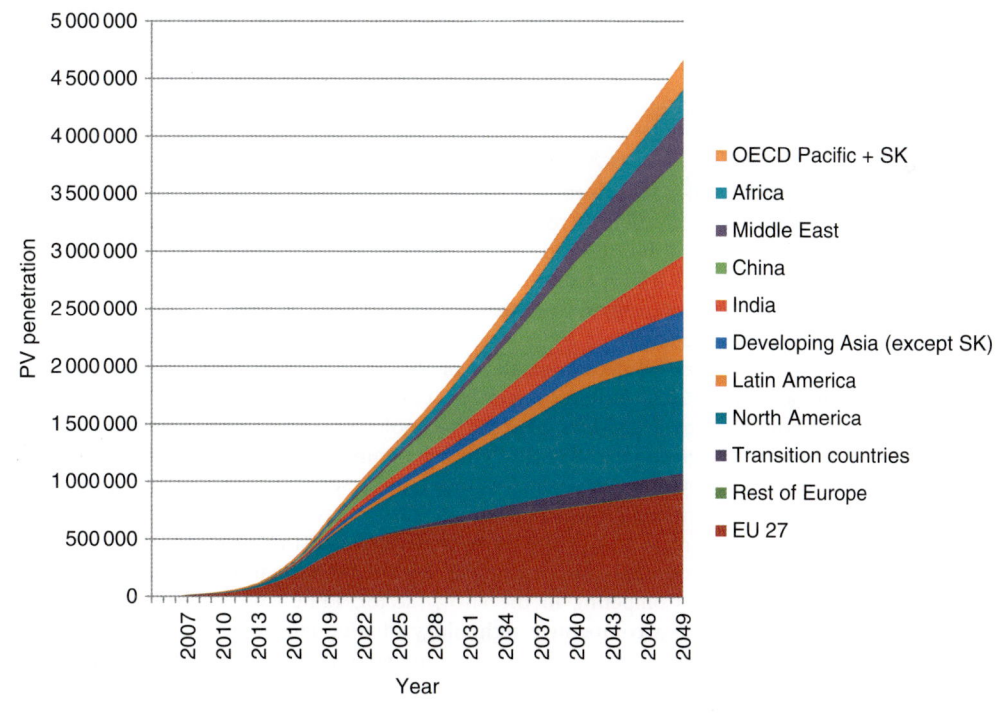

Figure 6 World PV penetration by region until 2050, it shows that by 2050, under a Paradigm Shift scenario over 4500 GW of PV installed worldwide is feasible. Source: EPIA and Greenpeace (2011) *Solar Generation 6*. Brussels, Belgium: EPIA [8].

1.10.2.5 Global PV Installed Capacity Could Reach More Than 4500 GW by 2050

According to EPIA statistics, global PV installed capacity reached almost 40 GW at the end of 2010. PV could in the near future compete with conventional energy sources as a mainstream energy source.

In 2010, PV had a record year, adding 13 GW installed capacity in the EU to reach almost 17 GW global annual installations.

The growth of PV is not constrained by raw material availability or by the industry's ability to handle growing demand. Even if temporary shortages occurred in years of heavy demand, the PV industry can cope with double-digit growth.

1.10.3 The EPIA Vision for 2050

Solar PV energy will, as part of a mix, participate in the "transition toward a 100% renewable European electricity sector by 2050."
In the upcoming debate on the Energy Roadmap 2050, it will be important to focus on some areas where further developments of EU energy policy may still be necessary in order to fully harvest the benefits of a massive deployment of PV in Europe:

- *Remove barriers on the road to PV competitiveness by 2020.* We need to ensure that gradual PV competitiveness will not be jeopardized by distorted market conditions. The clear prerequisites for the creation of a transparent electricity market are a full functioning of Emissions Trading System (ETS) system from 2013 onward and progressive phasing out of all conventional fuel subsidies (with a complete phase-out by 2020). In order to facilitate the upcoming debate on the future European energy mix, EPIA suggests that the European Commission present a comprehensive staff working document analyzing the instruments currently used to finance all sources of energy alongside the 2050 Energy Roadmap. This document should also serve to provide neutral and updated calculations on the costs of a range of energy technologies, based on transparent assumptions. Other important elements for accelerating PV competitiveness include systematic streamlining of national administrative and grid connection procedures and appropriate funding of the European Industrial Initiatives.
- *Adapt the grid infrastructure at all voltage levels to allow a well balanced mix of renewables, including massive PV integration and storage.* The regulatory framework needs to evolve considerably in order to better incentivize distribution system operators (DSOs) to invest in the intelligent upgrade of European distribution grids. Electricity storage infrastructures should also benefit from an appropriate regulatory framework. Regarding the transmission level, EPIA supports the current debate on actions to be taken (development of Electricity Highways) as needed for the projected mix of renewables.
- *Promote smart management of networks and innovative market design.* With the rise of decentralized production and decentralized storage, a paradigm shift in grid management will also be required. EPIA suggests that a task force gathering ENTSO-E, DSOs and renewable industry representatives should be created in order to exchange best practices on the integration of variable energy sources. Market rules will also have to evolve in order to integrate more flexible and distributed power production in an economically optimal way.

1.10.3.1 Introduction

The EU is at crossroads: in order to reach its 80–95% reduction of greenhouse gas emissions target by 2050, it will have to organize a complete shift in energy consumption and production. As recently pointed out by the European Commission (COM (2010) 677), one important evolution of this transition will be "the increase in electricity demand" driven by the multiplication of electric applications and technologies. EPIA believes that such a shift toward greater electricity consumption will only be sustainable if it relies entirely on decarbonized and indigenous energy sources that are accompanied by a very ambitious and sustained effort to fully tap into the remaining energy savings potential.

Meanwhile, in order to ensure a progressive decarbonization of the energy sector, EPIA believes that clear milestones should be set up, such as an "ambitious 2030 binding target for renewables." Such a shift in the energy system would reinforce Europe's competitive advantage as a provider of clean technologies, lower our dependency on third countries' supplies and support the creation of local green jobs. PV already offers significant benefits to the future renewable electricity market. As an indigenous energy source providing direct employment of over 300 000 people in Europe (Solar Generation 6, EPIA/Greenpeace, 2011), it represents enormous growth opportunities for many European companies in the international arena. Building on an impressive track record in terms of reducing its levelized cost of electricity (LCOE) (PV module prices decrease by 22% each time the cumulated installed capacity doubles. For more information on the huge potential for further PV generation cost decline, please see PV Competing in the energy sector, EPIA, 2011), PV, with a further 60% LCOE reduction expected until 2020, will become a competitive technology offering energy at low cost in the timeframe until 2050. PV's key assets include uncritical material availability, an existing voluntary take-back and recycling scheme (Via the PV Cycle Association: www.pvcycle.org), minimal impact on land use and seamless integration in populated areas. The technology also enjoys widespread popular support. According to a recent Eurobarometer survey (October 2010), 8 out of 10 European citizens consider that solar energy will have a positive effect on their life in the next 20 years, ranking it at the top of a long list of innovative technologies.

The recommendations presented here are based on a "dynamic vision of market and grid developments." They are not aimed at proving that the transition to a decarbonized energy system is economically and technically feasible, as this has already been done (See for instance Roadmap 2050: a practical guide to a prosperous, low-carbon Europe (Europe Climate Foundation - April 2010)); rather they concentrate on areas where further development of the EU energy policy may be necessary in order to fully harvest the benefits related to a massive deployment of PV. According to various studies, "this will correspond to between 19% and 27% of the electricity demand in Europe in 2050."

1.10.3.2 A Dynamic Vision on PV Competitiveness and Grid Development

While PV prices are dropping fast and will continue toward this path, this document aims to draw a realistic future of PV going mainstream in Europe by 2050. In this context, two parallel elements are shaping PV development:

- The "progress on the competitiveness of PV" (often partially described as 'grid parity')
- The "integration of large PV volumes in the electricity networks."

Taking these into account, PV deployment can be summarized in the following 'three main phases':

- Phase 1: The 'pre-grid parity era', when PV reduces cost but is not competitive yet, though its deployment does not require much infrastructure investment or coordination with other energy sources. This is the case in most European PV markets today.
- Phase 2: The 'transition to competitiveness' of electricity prices in the residential, commercial, and industrial segments and wholesale prices in the ground-mounted segment, along with high levels of PV penetration. This will require upgrading the grid infrastructure – first at the distribution level to cope with high level of decentralized power generation and then at the transmission level to ensure high reliability of the electricity network. In this phase, grid upgrades are not only driven by PV penetration but also stem from a combination of different evolutions (i.e., European market integration, enhanced security of supply, rollout of smart grids, electric vehicles development and increase of decentralized power generation sources). In certain cases, PV penetration levels could increase faster than the transformation of the network.
- Phase 3: 'Full PV competitiveness' in most European countries. In this 'paradigm shift era', further penetration of PV is highly interlinked with other energy sources and it is dependent on infrastructure development. Renewably generated electricity supports the shift toward progressive electrification of mobility.

1.10.3.3 Necessary Steps to Unlocking PV Potential

EPIA suggests concentrating on the following 'three objectives':

- ensuring that the gradual competitiveness of PV is achievable with the implementation of a transparent, level playing field;
- ensuring that the necessary infrastructure adaptations are undertaken on time in order to allow the optimal integration of PV and other sources of renewable power into the grid;
- ensuring that grid management practices are evolving according to the progressive integration of renewables.

1.10.3.3.1 Ensuring the gradual competitiveness of PV

Several studies (See notably: Solar Generation 6, EPIA/Greenpeace, 2011 and PV – Competing in the Energy Sector, EPIA, 2011) using LCOE calculations already show that PV competitiveness will be reached in most European markets by 2020. But achieving this will require "well-designed and predictable national support schemes." Apart from this, it will be necessary to regularly adjust the level of incentives over time in order to keep the return on PV investments within sustainable boundaries and to avoid speculative market overheat. Moreover – as the RES Directive stipulates – if desirable, two or more neighbor countries could align their support mechanisms and realize joint projects.

As PV reaches grid parity, a progressive shift from traditional support schemes such as FiTs to other models guaranteeing market access and predictable prices might be needed. As this development is gradual and dependent on local solar conditions and national characteristics, the transition will likely be driven by the individual Member States.

In the meantime, in order to reach competitiveness faster, it will be important to ensure a complete level playing field with other electricity generation technologies:

- The full "functioning of the ETS system should therefore be ensured from 2013 onward" in order to provide an efficient carbon price signal, which is an absolute prerequisite if a decarbonized energy system is to be achieved. The excess of allowances from Phase 2 of the ETS system already identified by the European Commission (COM(2010) 265 final) should therefore not keep the price of CO_2 certificates artificially low.
- "All inefficient fossil fuels subsidies should be phased out in the medium term," in line with the commitment taken by G-20 leaders in Pittsburgh in September 2009. A complete phase-out of subsidies for conventional fuels should be then achieved by 2020 at the latest. 'Transparency' on subsidies given to all low-carbon technologies should also be ensured.
- "Complex grid connection procedures and unjustified administrative barriers should be removed," taking the varying practices in the different Member States into account (The PV legal project already compares the impact of the legal-administrative barriers across 12 European countries. See the 1st PV Legal Status report, July 2010, www.pvlegal.eu). The PV Legal project should be used as a supporting tool to streamline those procedures.

Finally, sustained R&D efforts represent another key driver for a further decrease in the cost of PV systems. In order to speed up the achievement of Phase 2, the whole PV industry is fully committed to co-financing the priorities identified in the Solar European

Industrial Initiative (See the Press release presented on 1 June 2010: http://www.epia.org/fileadmin/EPIA_docs/public/100601_Solar_Europe_Industry_Initiative_-_Press_Release.pdf): in order to implement the initiative, EPIA suggests that its financing needs "are correctly reflected in the next multiannual financial framework, in which a shift toward a larger financing of clean energy technologies should be included."

1.10.3.3.2 Ensuring necessary infrastructure adaptations
Given the growing share of renewables in the electricity mix, "flexibility will be a key aspect of future power systems." For PV to contribute actively to grid management and network stability, this implies different prerequisites for 'infrastructure adaptations':

– During Phase 2, EPIA favors development of mobile (i.e., electric vehicles) and decentralized stationary storage as well as hydro capacities (large hydro for medium-term storage; pump hydro for short-term storage). Flexibility of the power generation mix (through an increased use of electricity from natural gas, for instance) and quick ramp rates for balancing power reserves will also be essential.
– During Phase 3, the high PV penetration rate will make power balancing necessary on a larger scale. This requires ensuring that existing infrastructures and market rules support the deployment of PV.

The recent EC Communication on energy infrastructure priorities for 2020 and beyond offers valuable input for ensuring consistency of infrastructure development with EU energy priorities. EPIA supports the Commission's call to establish Europe's leadership in 'electricity storage' at all voltage levels. The focus on roll-out of 'smart grids technologies' is also significant since DSM and on-site generation will play a key role in balancing Europe's electricity in the decades ahead.

Concerning the transmission infrastructure, EPIA supports the idea presented by the Commission to prepare a "modular development plan for 'Electricity Highways'." In particular, as pointed out by the Commission's Blueprint, interconnections in South-Western Europe would facilitate the transportation of PV electricity from the production to the consumption and storage centers. This applies not only to the interconnection between Spain and France, but also to PV electricity flows from north Africa to Europe. In addition, upgrades in countries that will be critical to south–north electricity flows (such as Italy or Spain) need to be strengthened. In this regard, implementation of the Desertec initiative and the Mediterranean Solar Plan could represent promising frameworks for importing PV-generated electricity.

The above-mentioned communication, however, neglects some necessary adaptations that will also have to be sorted out at the distribution level: "the biggest share of the investments needed in infrastructures will indeed have to be realized at the distribution level" (€400 billion). This is in line with International Energy Agency (IEA) calculations (World Energy Outlook 2010, table 7.2) according to which €489 billion will have to be invested in the distribution grid over the next 25 years in the EU. The strengthening of existing infrastructures will also constitute a challenge for the coming decades. Although those investments are not mainly driven by PV development, EPIA suggests that the EC, while taking due account of the responsibilities of each actor, proposes ways to better address these issues in the upcoming legislative and regulatory proposals. "Incentives to help DSOs making the necessary investments," in line with the upcoming findings of the task force on Smart Grids, 'will be crucial'.

1.10.3.3.3 Ensuring evolution of grid management practices and innovative market design
The rise of decentralized production together with decentralized storage will require a paradigm shift in grid management.

As the utility methods of electricity production, management, distribution and transportation change, the role of aggregators will rise, transforming the approach of utilities and grid operators in the electricity market with a major shift in added value generation process. A "closer cooperation between ENTSO-E, DSOs, and the renewable sector," notably in the context of the network codes development process, will most probably bring mutual benefits.

Higher PV penetration will also require "changes to market design and the optimization of renewable electricity deployment to the network." Given the decentralized character of PV power and the large number of small installations involved, "aggregation strategies through, for instance, virtual power plants" combining different renewable energy sources on a large scale, will also have to develop in order to facilitate market access for PV. Moreover, the current supply and demand concepts will probably need to be refined to take storage and DSM into consideration in a market dominated by RES electricity.

1.10.3.4 Policy Recommendations for a Bright 2050 Future
PV will contribute significantly to the shift toward a fully decarbonized European electricity sector by 2050. As a cost-competitive solution, its growing share in the energy mix will require adaptations to the grid infrastructure, both in physical and in managerial terms, as well as some evolutions in the market design.

In order to ensure this bright future, EPIA underlines the importance of the following policy recommendations:

– *Recommendation 1*. Full functioning of the ETS system from 2013 onward should be guaranteed. Excess allowances from Phase 2 of the ETS system should not keep the price of CO_2 certificates artificially too low.
– *Recommendation 2*. Progressive phasing-out of all fossil fuels subsidies via a thorough implementation of competition rules should be ensured in order to facilitate the creation of transparent electricity markets. No subsidy to conventional sources of energy should be granted after 2020.

- *Recommendation 3.* In order to facilitate the upcoming debate on the future energy mix, the European Commission should present a comprehensive staff working document analyzing the instruments currently used both at the national and at the European levels to finance different sources of energy alongside the 2050 Energy Roadmap. This document should also provide neutral and updated calculations on the costs of a range of energy technologies, based on transparent assumptions.
- *Recommendation 4.* The European Commission should ensure the full implementation of the Renewable Energy Directive, in particular the streamlining of national administrative procedures as described in its Article 13.
- *Recommendation 5.* The Technology Roadmaps of the European Industrial Initiatives should be given additional support. Sufficient public funding to balance out the private investments on R&D and innovation should be ensured in the next multiannual financial framework.
- *Recommendation 6.* The upcoming Energy Security and Infrastructure Instrument should not only focus on transmission grid needs but also address issues at all voltage levels.
- *Recommendation 7.* The regulatory framework should evolve in order to better incentivize DSOs to make the necessary investments in smart grids, reinforcement of the distribution grid and electricity storage infrastructures. Where necessary, public financial support should be able to step in.
- *Recommendation 8.* A task force comprising ENTSO-E, DSOs, and the renewable industry should be created in order to exchange best practices on the integration of variable energy sources into the electricity system.
- *Recommendation 9.* Market design should evolve to integrate more flexible and distributed power production in an economically optimal way.
- *Recommendation 10.* An ambitious 2030 binding target for renewables should be set.

1.10.4 Future Changes in Electricity Systems

In the first years of this decade, PV penetration will be ensured by a combination of adequate support measures and administration procedures. In many countries, a market instrument, such as the FiT, will be used.

In developed countries, other renewable energy sources will, along with PV, replace aging nuclear power plants and/or fossil fuels plants in the energy mix.

In developing countries, PV will not directly replace existing power plants but will initially complement them to cope with the growing electricity demand.

After this first phase, higher penetration will lead to adjustments to smooth out the impact on the network, including specific incentives to flatten the production curve from PV autoconsumption to favor consumption during production hours, and decentralized storage through low-cost fixed batteries. Moreover, as the penetration of electric vehicles increases, part of their storage capabilities will be used to smooth the curve.

From 2020, the growing penetration of PV will trigger a shift in our perception of electricity markets. Time and installed capacity will require the ability to import/export PV electricity, to introduce storage solutions and to adapt demand to production on a regular basis. This will progressively reshape the way grids are organized and managed to maintain reliability. Furthermore, the way decisions related to power generation investments will be considered, will also have to be strengthened, especially with regard to the planning of repowering.

Major issues will be solved progressively as described in the following subsections.

1.10.4.1 Managing Variability

Depending on solar irradiation, electricity production from PV is, by nature, variable. Hence, it is important to be able to predict the production and consumption of PV electricity on a daily basis in order to balance increases and decreases in power supply and demand. This way, network managers can ensure that the voltage and frequency of electricity remain between predefined boundaries.

The output from PV panels can be easily predicted when aggregated over a large area, allowing a network manager to easily plan the use of balancing power. As a result, variability, which can be significant in a limited area, is smoothed at regional level.

On a larger scale, the question of whether large amounts of PV electricity can be integrated into networks depends on the ability of the network manager to dispatch balancing power in due time. Recent studies confirm that the combination of different renewable energy sources on a large scale (such as across the EU) compensates the intermittencies from solar and wind to provide not only peak load generation but also medium and base loads (**Figure 7**). In addition to this, other conditions such as the ability to dispatch a part of the electricity consumption throughout the day (the so-called demand-side management) to better cope with electricity production, need to be fulfilled.

1.10.4.2 From Centralized to Decentralized Energy Generation

From the past totally centralized system, electricity is now moving to a largely decentralized generation system. In the case of wind turbines, small and medium biomass plants, and solar power plants, electricity can be produced anywhere in the network. This new way of conceiving network organization and management has led electricity grid operators (DSO – the operator of the low and medium voltage electricity grid; transport system operator (TSO) – the operator of the medium and high voltage electricity grid) to rethink the way to guarantee the quality of electricity delivery.

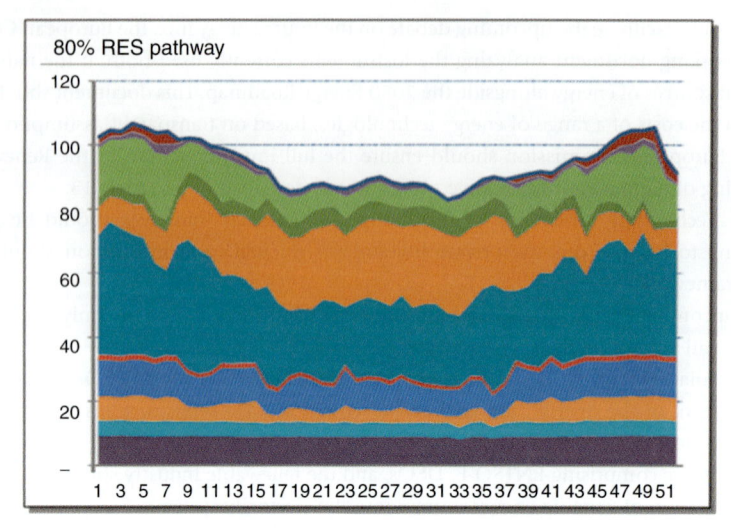

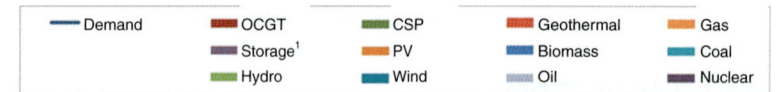

Figure 7 Energy balance in 2050, 20% demand response, TWh per week. European Climate Foundation (2010) *Roadmap 2050: A Practical Guide to a Prosperous, Low Carbon Europe.* Brussels, Belgium: ECF [6]. http://www.roadmap2050.eu/attachments/files/Volume1_fullreport_PressPack.pdf.

1.10.4.3 Peak Load Shaving

The electricity consumption curve during a day presents one peak at midday (in southern countries) and occasionally a second peak in the evening (mainly in northern countries). Naturally this depends on climate conditions but the trend is evident. In **Figure 8**, the effect of PV on the midday peak represents a real peak shaving, diminishing the power demand on the network. The use of daily storage allows a part of the electricity produced during the day to shave the evening peak as well.

1.10.4.4 Super Smart Grid

Variability of renewable sources can be smoothed over and balanced in large regions. This will require enhancing interconnections between countries and ensure a global management of the grid. It will also allow the mix of wind electricity from windy countries with solar electricity from sunny countries. **Figure 9** represents such a possibility, combining the European and Mediterranean countries capacities.

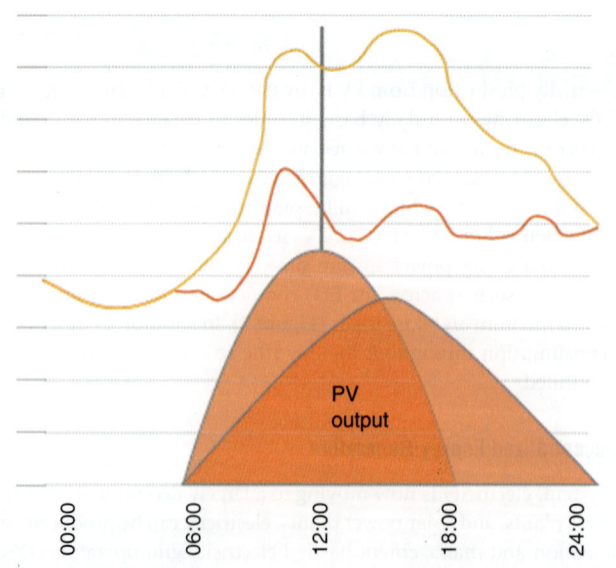

Figure 8 PV peak load shaving. Sources: IEA PVPS-Task 10 (2009) Overcoming PV grids issues in urban areas. http://iea-pvps-task10.org/IMG/pdf/rep10_06.pdf [9] and EPIA analysis [2].

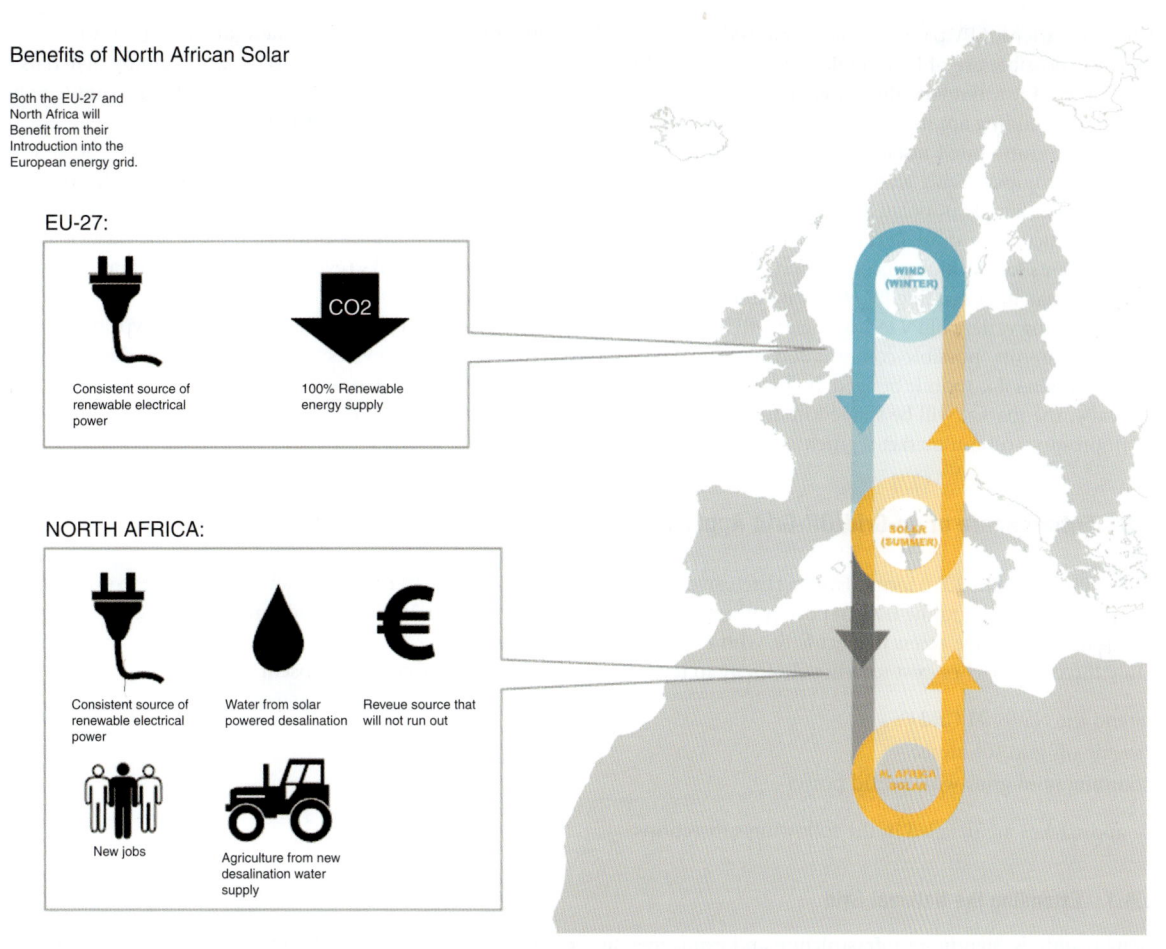

Figure 9 EU–North Africa solar electricity exchange. Source: European Climate Foundation (2010) *Roadmap 2050: A Practical Guide to a Prosperous, Low Carbon Europe*. Brussels, Belgium: ECF [6].

The smart grid concept refers to any improvement that could make the grid more resilient and more capable of coping with large shares of decentralized and/or intermittent energy sources. A better understanding of the supply and demand of electricity will be combined with the ability to intervene at the consumer level to better balance both supply and demand. EPIA supports the creation of a super smart grid to permit accommodation of all variable energy technologies.

1.10.4.5 Decentralized Storage

Decentralization of electricity production will subsequently require the decentralization of storage. Most of today's major storage systems are hydro pumped storage facilities, but future solutions could include small batteries or innovative concepts such as fly-wheels or hydrogen fuel-cells. The development of e-mobility will also be a factor, as the batteries from electric vehicles can be increasingly viewed as decentralized storage facilities. The concept behind this is known as V2G (vehicle-to-grid) and will require some intelligent charge and discharge management.

1.10.4.6 DSM

Load shaving is already used by electricity network managers to reduce the electricity demand of large electricity consumers. Instead of looking for new production capacities that are used only during peak periods, the DSM concept refers to the possibility of applying this load shaving to almost all electricity consumers. The functioning of many domestic electrical appliances may be delayed (from heat-pumps to washing machines, passing by the EVs recharge). This concept, hardly noticeable by final consumers, may be used to help balance out intermittent sources and obtain better use of energy when it is available.

1.10.5 Future Market Segmentation

It is difficult to predict PV market segmentation over the next 40 years. Current market segmentation depends on existing technologies, with PV panels that are well adapted to rooftops and large ground-mounted installations.

The wide variety of PV panels being introduced into the market in the coming years will allow new kinds of applications and will diversify the possible use of PV modules. First of all, building-integrated PV (BIPV) will be used to replace building materials – not just tiles or windows, but virtually any element of the building envelope. For aesthetic reasons, BIPV will probably complement and replace many building applied PV installations, especially in cities with strict architectural constraints.

Large ground-mounted installations will continue to exist, most likely in countries with vast empty spaces like deserts, where they do not compete with arable land or preserved areas. Their size will most probably vary from MW-scale to GW-scale applications. In densely populated areas, it is less conceivable to see ground-mounted installations taking large market shares.

The introduction of more flexible PV devices will allow for even more installation opportunities, including cars, creating new market segments for PV. More unconventional applications can be imagined with PV inks (even in spray), PV roads and much more, such as space satellites sending PV electricity to earth with microwave beams.

The increasing variety of PV technologies will lead to specific market segments, depending on the place (the type of irradiation), aesthetic constraints, possible combination with heating/cooling systems, storage devices, and of course the destination of PV support – whether it is mobile or fixed, on buildings, on cars, in deserts, or whether with or without moving parts to follow the Sun.

Basically, the market will be shaped in the coming decades largely by technological developments, as well as political choices that will promote certain market segments.

1.10.6 Future Share of On-Grid/Off-Grid Applications

While the PV market in 2010 focused almost exclusively on on-grid applications, part of the market will continue to exist for off-grid applications. According to the IEA's report on the world's access to energy [8], in 2008, ~1.5 billion people or 22% of the world's population did not have access to electricity, with 85% of them in rural areas.

Only three approaches exist to bring electricity to remote areas where grids are currently absent:

1. Extend the National Grid
2. Provide off-grid solutions
3. Coupling mini-grids with hybrid power

These approaches are detailed in the following subsections.

1.10.6.1 Extending the National Grid

In many countries, significant infrastructure and extrageneration costs preclude further development of the grid. In countries that need rural electrification, population growth is creating an increasing demand and a huge challenge for utilities.

According to the World Bank, grid extension prices vary from $6340 km^{-1} in a densely populated country such as Bangladesh to $19 070 km^{-1} in a country like Mali, making the option of extending the National Grid a difficult choice.

1.10.6.2 Providing Off-Grid Solutions

Off-grid power generation with renewable energy sources is becoming more competitive in remote communities and does not suffer from power loss due to long transmission lines. Energy Home Systems (EHS) are designed to power individual households and are competitive in developing countries and easy to maintain.

PV is probably the most suitable type of technology for home systems as shown by the hundreds of thousands of solar home systems deployed around the world. PV systems can cover the energy needs of single households, public buildings, and commercial units. In rural areas, they replace candles, kerosene, and biomass traditionally used for lighting, and they run other applications that are usually driven by dry-cell batteries or diesel generators.

1.10.6.3 Coupling Mini-Grids with Hybrid Power

The third approach combines the first two, providing local grids powered by more than one generation source (**Figure 10**). PV plays a significant role within this approach to rural electrification. 'Centralized' electricity generation at the local level can power both domestic appliances and local businesses using village-wide distribution networks. They can be driven by fossil fuel, renewable energy sources, or by a combination of the two. Backup systems (genset) or battery storage can complement the structure.

This solution offers many advantages; not only in terms of costs, but also with regard to the availability of energy in small communities. It improves the quality of electricity delivered as well as global system reliability. Finally, it can be connected to the National Grid once it is in place.

1.10.7 Future Technological Trends

Crystalline silicon technologies have dominated the market for the last 30 years, see data for 2000 and 2005 in **Figure 11**. EPIA expects that by 2020, a more balanced mix of existing technologies will be in place and new emerging technologies will be

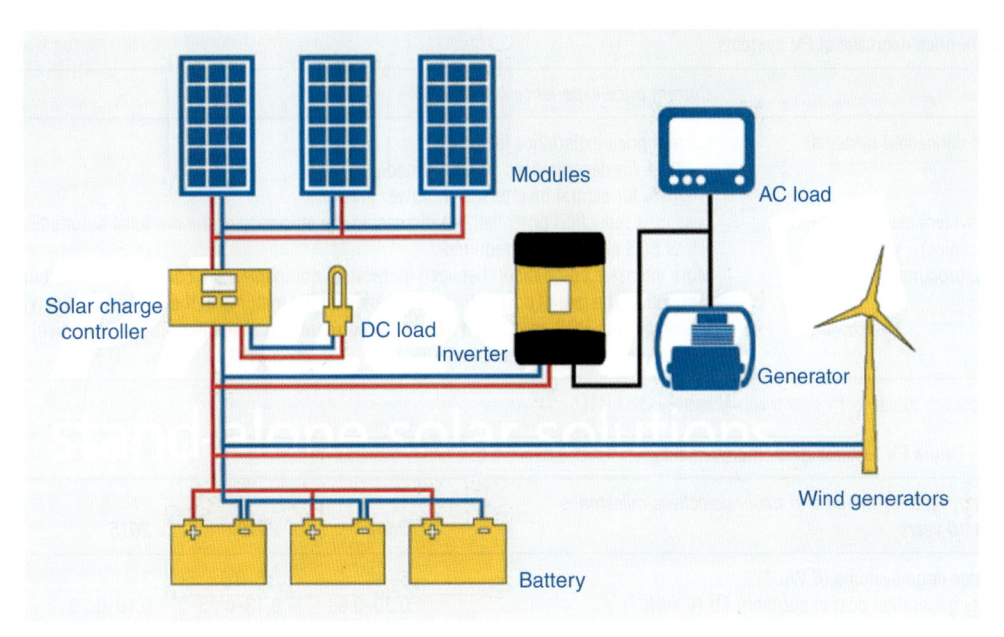

Figure 10 Mini-grid and hybrid system. Source: Phaesun GmbH, in EPIA and Greenpeace, p. 89.

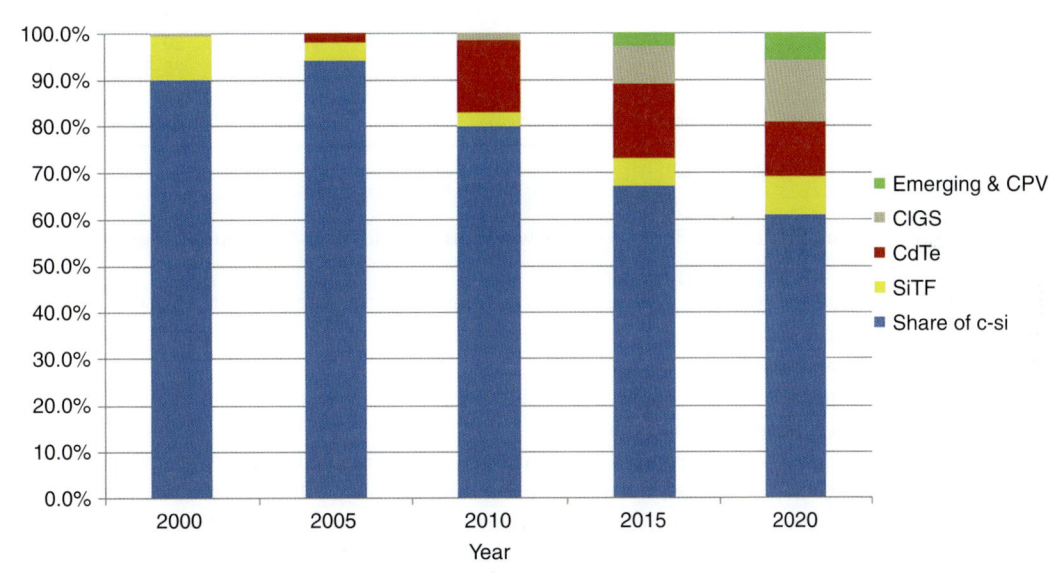

Figure 11 PV technologies market share. Source: Historical data (until 2009) based on Navigants Consultants, estimations based on EPIA analysis.

commercialized. Silicon wafer-based technologies will still account for about 61% of the market; the remainder will be shared by thin films (~33%) and CPV and emerging technologies (~6%).

1.10.7.1 The Evolution of PV Module and System Prices

PV system prices are currently (Summer 2011) between 2.2 and 4.8 and 6 € Wp^{-1} for BIPV. The difference depends on a number of factors, such as the size of the system, the type of application (ground-mounted, rooftop-applied, and building-integrated), the technology, and the country of installation. Decreases in PV system prices depend on installed PV capacity, as well as on scenarios outlined above. It is expected that by 2030, prices could be reduced to between 0.87 and 1.23 € Wp^{-1}.

The total price of a PV system depends on price evolution in the elements that make up a solar PV system, as well as the installation cost. **Table 1** lists the different elements in a PV system and their potential for further cost reductions.

Major factors that can lower the price of PV systems are

- Technological innovations (→ module cost)

   The solar industry is constantly innovating in order to improve PV module efficiency. Increased efficiency means that less material and energy are required to produce modules, and also that less area and less performing BOS elements

Table 1 Future price decrease of PV systems

PV modules	Current price-experience factor > 20%
Inverters (for grid-connected systems)	Current price-experience factor = – 20% for decentralized inverters/medium power – 10% for central inverters/high power inverters
Other balance of system elements (support structures and cables)	Less cost reduction potential, but increasing the efficiency of the modules automatically means that less BOS elements are required
EPC (engineering, procurement, and construction)	More intensive competition between installation companies will continue to contribute to shrinking margins. The rate of cost reduction depends on the maturity of the market and the type of application. Linkage with BOS cost: More sophisticated mounting structures (more expensive) can save installation time; for example, DOW's BIPV PV shingles [10]

Source: A strategic research agenda for PV solar energy technology, 2011 [11].

Table 2 Future PV technological improvements

PV technology state-of-the-art and major objectives/milestones for the next 10 years	2007	2010	2015	2020
Turn-key price large systems (€ Wp^{-1})	5	2.5–3.5	2	1.5
PV electricity generation cost in southern EU (€ kWh^{-1})	0.30–0.60	0.13–0.25	0.10–0.20	0.07–0.14
Typical PV module efficiency range (%)				
Crystalline silicon	13–18	15–20	16–21	18–23
Thin films	5–11	6–12	8–14	10–16
Concentrators	20	20–25	25–30	30–35
Inverter lifetime (years)	10	15	20	>25
Module lifetime (years)	20–25	20–25	25–30	35–40
Energy pay-back time (years)	2–3	1–2	1	0.5
Cost of PV + small-scale storage (€ kWh^{-1}) in southern EU (grid-connected)	–	0.35	0.22	<0.15

A strategic research agenda for PV solar energy technology, 2011 [11].

are required during installation. **Table 2** provides an overview of current efficiencies and expectations until the end of the decade.

The sector's primary goal is to reduce material use and energy requirements. Other areas make use of thinner and more efficient wafers and polysilicon substitutes (e.g., upgraded metallurgical silicon), and also increase the substrate areas and depositions speeds for thin film production.

- Production optimization (→ module cost) – Improving production processes and production efficiency can reduce wafer breakages, energy requirements, and production line downtime.
- Economies of scale (→ module cost) – As companies scale up production, they can benefit from the advantages of automation and larger line capacities. About a decade ago, cell and module production plants typically could produce just a few MW of solar modules. Today, market leaders have plants with over 1 GW capacity, which is a several hundredfold increase.
- Increasing the performance ratio of PV (→ system cost) – The quality of the PV system is reflected by its performance ratio. The higher the performance ratio, the lower the losses between the modules and the point at which the system feeds into the grid. Typically, current system performance ratios are between 80% and 85%. Monitoring systems can quickly detect faults and unexpected system behavior (e.g., due to unexpected shadows), and help maintain high performance ratios.
- Extension of PV system's lifetime (→ system cost) – Extending the system lifetime will increase the overall electrical output and improve the cost per generated kWh. Most module producers give module performance warranties for 25 years, which is now considered the minimum module lifetime. The component that has the most effect on product lifetime is the encapsulating material. There is currently intensive research in this field; however, the industry is cautious when using substitute materials because they need to be tested over the long term. Right now, modules are being produced with a lifetime of 30 years; the target is 40 years by the end of the decade (see **Table 2**). Likewise, the PV inverter industry is putting a lot of effort into increasing the lifetime of its products, which is expected to reach more than 25 years by the end of the decade (see **Table 2**).
- Development of standards and specifications – Developing standards and technical specifications will help to define a set of common goals for the PV industry. This will contribute to reducing costs in design, production and deployment. It will also foster fair and transparent competition since everyone will have to play by the same rules.
- The development of 'next generation' PVs – Efforts in the development of so-called emerging technologies, such as organic PVs, dye-sensitized solar cells, and advanced inorganic thin-film technologies are very promising. Completely new approaches, such as quantum technologies and technologies using nanostructures, are also possible. These innovative technologies can be produced at

very low costs. However, research is still needed in order to increase the stability of the new technologies over time and to increase the solar cell area. Some of these new products are already commercially available in specific consumer applications, and they are expected to enter the market at large within 5–10 years for emerging technologies and about 10–15 years for novel devices.

The industry targets for PV technology development in the period 2010–20 are summarized in **Table 2**. The table shows the expected technical developments as described within the Implementation Plan of the Solar Europe Industry Initiative, one of the initiatives within the framework of the European Commission's Strategic Energy Technology (SET) Plan [12].

1.10.7.2 Cost of Electricity Generation

The indicator used to compare PV electricity with other sources of energy is the cost per kWh generated. The LCOE is a measure used to compare different power plants using various kinds of energy. The LCOE takes into account all investment and operational costs, including fuels consumed.

With LCOE, we can compare, for instance, a PV installation with gas or nuclear power plants which have very different lifetimes and investment costs. The LCOE calculation for PV takes into consideration the location of its annual irradiation, which varies widely. For example,

Scandinavia: 700–800 kWh kWp^{-1}	Southern Europe: more than 1500 kWh kWp^{-1}
Middle East: 1800 kWh kWp^{-1}	Sub-Saharan Africa: up to 2100 kWh kWp^{-1}

Figure 12 shows current PV electricity generation costs for large ground-mounted systems based on these outputs, and a typical system performance ratio of 85%. The 2010 costs range from around 0.28 € kWh^{-1} in the north of Europe to 0.15 € kWh^{-1} in the south. The calculations are based on the average turn-key system price in Europe that is typically found in Germany.

These values will decrease significantly in the next decade. Expected generation costs in 2020 for large ground-mounted systems are in the range of 0.14–0.07 € kWh^{-1} in almost all of Europe. The potential is even larger in countries with higher solar irradiation, although the investment climate might be more uncertain for some of these countries.

It is expected that the current cost discrepancy between large-scale, ground-mounted systems and small-scale rooftop applications will decrease over time.

Moreover, a significant network of installation companies will be available in each geographical region to cover the demand for installations. In Germany (the most mature market), the discrepancy between the average selling price for a large-scale, ground-mounted system and a small-scale rooftop application is slightly more than 20%, whereas in France (a far less developed market), it is almost 45%.

As a consequence for all market segments, PV electricity generation cost has huge potential to decrease to levels that can easily compete with conventional power generation sources; this is not only for peak power, but also for medium and base power.

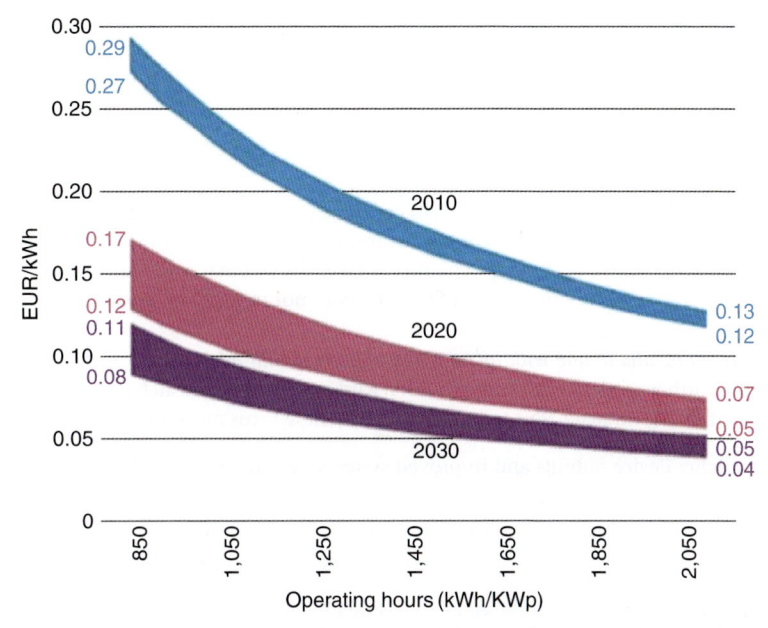

Figure 12 PV levelized cost of energy ranges. Source: EPIA and Greenpeace (2011) *Solar Generation 6*. Brussels, Belgium: EPIA [8].

1.10.8 Recommendations

1.10.8.1 Policy Recommendations

1.10.8.1.1 Develop a long-term vision with precise milestones

A long-term vision (2030–50) is essential to drive market and industry development. Quantitative targets – expressed, for instance, as a percentage of final consumption to be covered by energy from renewable sources – need to be set by decision-makers.

The EU has set mandatory national targets for the overall share of energy from renewable sources in gross final consumption of energy by 2020. In this context, the SET For 2020 study, developed by EPIA, shows that PV can become a mainstream electricity source, representing up to 12% of electricity demand in Europe by 2020. This is the vision developed under the 'Paradigm Shift Scenario', which requires a rapid and widespread adoption of power storage and smart grid technologies, optimized PV supply chains and improved operations and marketing strategies of the PV industry.

1.10.8.1.2 Set up a supportive regulatory framework

Sustainable support mechanisms should be put in place in order to ensure the market uptake of PV. The implementation of such schemes should consider the following suggestions:

- Draw a national roadmap to PV competitiveness, but also foresee support instruments afterward.
- Set transparent and simple permitting and connection procedures: simplicity attracts small-scale investors like the ones investing in private PV systems.
- Make procedures for PV system planning, constructing, and operating short and cheap: heavy bureaucracy discourages investments.
- Trigger growth of a mix of technologies and market segments by differentiating the level of support between different types of applications (notably, building integrated, adapted, and ground-mounted systems of residential, commercial, and industrial size).
- Allow for reasonable investment profitability: design and regularly adjust the support scheme at levels that trigger investment appetite but avoid speculations.
- Create a stable investment environment: announce adjustments to support schemes well in advance to allow investors to make their calculations. Avoid stop-and-go policies.

The establishment of supportive regulatory frameworks in Sunbelt countries should build upon a better understanding of PV characteristics and benefits. Significant awareness building and an information campaign will be very important in educating the public. Opinion leaders and decision-makers, and also development banks and other influencers, could play a major role in this respect.

Indeed in these countries, PV is still perceived as an expensive energy source mostly suitable for small- and medium-sized off-grid installations, despite its increasing competitiveness on a large scale. PV support would not necessarily imply large budgets or cost to the final consumer: simple bottleneck removal such as ensuring grid connections and net metering, as well as clear guidance by local and regional administrations for spatial planning and authorization procedures, could greatly help.

1.10.8.1.3 Send the right signals to consumers

Massive deployment of smart metering devices can turn household consumers into real actors of the electricity market, allowing them to make better use of decentralized production while helping them better control their consumption. Regarding energy sector regulation (at both national and European levels), time-of-use electricity billing, and net metering to facilitate the penetration of renewable energy sources, should therefore be promoted.

1.10.8.2 Investments in Technology and in PV Projects

1.10.8.2.1 The importance of a sustained PV cost reduction

PV companies must maintain their strong R&D commitment to continue the dynamic PV cost reduction momentum. A continuous cost reduction, together with the development and marketing of innovative PV applications to final consumers, will inspire trust among investors and policy-makers and will lead to rapid market uptake. The fact that competitiveness of PV investment versus grid purchase is being reached now in some southern regions of the EU, does not in itself, necessarily lead to market development.

1.10.8.2.2 Delivering research results in line with focus areas already identified

The PV R&D community must further accelerate its progress with regard to delivering research results in line with focus areas defined by the PV Technology Platform in the Strategic Research Agenda [11]. These focus areas are meant to

- enhance performance by higher device outputs and improved systems performance;
- improve manufacturability and reduce process costs;
- ensure sustainability aspects of technology through the entire lifecycle, from manufacturing to use and recycling; and
- address applicability by developing products and technologies to meet specific market needs.

PV industry companies and R&D institutes must collaborate to ensure the ready uptake of innovation in the end-product. They will have to fully lever research support granted by public authorities to this end.

1.10.8.2.3 Financing necessary R&D investments

Public and private funding must increase in order to support PV R&D efforts and large demonstration projects, with a focus on accelerated cost reduction. In Europe, for instance, the total public and private investment needed over the next 10 years in order to reach the Solar Europe Industry Initiative (SEII) objectives, is estimated at €9 billion.

The Seventh Framework Programme is the main instrument used by the European Commission to finance R&D projects. The subprogram, Cooperation, is devoted to supporting cooperation between universities, industry, research centers, and public authorities. Seven percent of the Cooperation budget, corresponding to €2.35 billion, is dedicated to energy issues, CO_2 capture, and storage included, over a period of 7 years. This budget is not high enough, especially when compared with 'Euratom', one of the European Commission's programs for nuclear energy, which accounts for €2.7 billion over a period of 5 years [13].

1.10.8.2.4 Encourage investments in Sunbelt countries

PV investments are still scarce in Sunbelt countries due to the limited PV know-how of financial players and to the early stage of policy support in these countries. To the extent that policy support becomes reliable, and word of the benefits of PV spreads, finance can be expected to follow. To accelerate this development, financial intermediaries need to play an active part in awareness building.

Transferring project finance experience from established PV markets and collaborating with industry and policy experts can turn banks into catalysts for PV deployment rather than constituting a bottleneck. For example, by understanding the functioning of mini-grids in rural communities, banks can also benefit from stimulating economic activity in areas and customer segments that were not the focus of their commercial activity.

1.10.8.3 Grid Infrastructures Adaptations

Climate change will not be addressed without a strong decarbonization of the energy system, which implies a larger share of renewable energy sources in the electricity mix.

The distribution and transport of electricity is currently relying on an aging network. In view of future massive penetration of renewables, it must be modernized and enhanced.

The cost of investments should be shared between consumers, grid operators, and public authorities.

1.10.8.3.1 Making necessary changes in the power distribution system

Grid operators must help decentralize infrastructure and become actively involved in implementing necessary smart grid technology such as improved measurement, communication, and control technologies (i.e., DSM). They also must help develop and install storage technologies to increase the absorption of distributed power in grids, while collaborating with the renewable energy sector to ensure that regulators reflect necessary investments in their distribution tariffs.

By seizing the opportunity offered by fast PV growth, DSOs will be able to quickly internalize related high-tech evolutions and create new sources of value for their customers and employees. This also applies to developing more harmonized interconnection standards for distributed energy resources.

In the future, electric vehicles will represent PV electricity storage facilities: policy-makers and standardization bodies will play a great role in their roll-out.

1.10.8.3.2 Adapting the transmission system

Deployment of renewable energies may also imply some adjustments or reinforcements of the transmission system (e.g., reinforced countries interconnections and a super grid in order to import solar production from the Mediterranean area to consumption centers in Europe), which can raise concerns of public acceptance. National governments, local authorities, and grids operators should cooperate in order to fully take into account this problem.

1.10.8.3.3 Financing infrastructure needs

These adaptations, at both distribution and transmission levels, as well as deployment of storage facilities and smart grids, will require huge investments. The role of the market (through well-defined tariffs) will be crucial here, but public support could also prove necessary for projects that do not directly bring commercial benefits but provide added value on a larger scale.

The sooner infrastructure adaptations are planned and developed, the lower the costs will be, and the quicker renewable electricity will gain a higher market share.

1.10.9 Conclusion

Solar PV technology is meant to be a mainstream technology and play an important role in the future energy mix, thus contributing to the decarbonization of the energy in Europe and globally. The technology made huge steps forward in the last 10 years mainly due to smart policy support, economies of scale, and technology developments. Competitiveness of solar PVs is expected to be reached before the end of the decade in all European markets and its market segments.

Considering the current market trend evolution, PV could reach 6% of the EU electricity demand by 2020. Cost has been decreased by 50% in the last 5 years and additional reduction is expecting in the following years. The PV industry is fully committed to further decrease the price should European governments make the right political choices. In order to be able to supply a substantial percentage of electricity into the electricity grid, grid integration of PV is an important issue and currently tackled by the industry. PV represents a solution as a contributor to security of supply. Considering the natural resource, the potential of deployment and the advance of the technology, PV is one of the world's most promising energy sources.

References

[1] Directive 2009/28/EC of The European Parliament and of the Council of 23 April 2009 on the promotion of the use of energy from renewable sources and amending and subsequently repealing Directives 2001/77/EC and 2003/30/EC.
[2] EPIA analysis.
[3] Navigant consultant and EPIA analysis.
[4] EPIA (2010) *2015: Global Market Outlook for Photovoltaics until 2015*. Brussels, Belgium: EPIA.
[5] Kearney AT and EPIA (2009) *SET for 2020 – Solar Photovoltaic Electricity: A Mainstream Power Source in Europe by 2020*. Brussels, Belgium: EPIA.
[6] European Climate Foundation (2010) *Roadmap 2050: A Practical Guide to a Prosperous, Low Carbon Europe*. Brussels, Belgium: ECF.
[7] European Renewable Energy Council (2010) *RE-Thinking 2050*. Brussels, Belgium: EREC.
[8] EPIA and Greenpeace (2011) *Solar Generation 6*. Brussels, Belgium: EPIA.
[9] IEA PVPS-Task 10 (2009) Overcoming PV grids issues in urban areas. http://iea-pvps-task10.org/IMG/pdf/rep10_06.pdf.
[10] For further reference, see for instance: http://building.dow.com/media/news/2010/20100119d.htm.
[11] Science, Technology and Applications group of the EU Photovoltaic Technology Platform (2011) *A Strategic Research Agenda for Photovoltaic Energy Technology*, 2nd edn. Luxembourg: Publications Office of the European Union.
[12] Commission of the European Communities (2007) *A European Strategic Energy Technology Plan (SET-PLAN) – Towards a Low Carbon Future*, COM(2007) 723. Brussels, Belgium: Commission of the European Communities.
[13] Breyer Ch, Birkner Ch, Kersten F, *et al*. (2010) Research and development investments in PV – A limiting factor for a fast PV diffusion? *25th EU PVSEC*, Valencia, Spain, 6–10 September.

1.11 Storage Options for Photovoltaics

VM Fthenakis, Columbia University, New York, NY, USA; Brookhaven National Laboratory, Upton, NY, USA
T Nikolakakis, Columbia University, New York, NY, USA

© 2012 Elsevier Ltd. All rights reserved.

1.11.1	Introduction	199
1.11.2	Grid Flexibility and Reliability	199
1.11.3	Energy Storage and Conventional Power Systems	200
1.11.4	Solar Electricity and Energy Storage	201
1.11.4.1	Impact on the Grid of Solar and Wind Electricity Penetration	201
1.11.4.2	Solar, Wind, and Energy Storage: Integration Applications	203
1.11.5	Energy Storage Technologies	204
1.11.6	Power Quality Storage Technologies	205
1.11.6.1	Superconducting Magnetic Energy Storage	205
1.11.6.2	Electric Double-Layer Capacitors	205
1.11.6.3	Flywheels	205
1.11.7	Bridging Power Storage Technologies: Batteries	206
1.11.7.1	Lead–Acid Batteries	206
1.11.7.2	Lithium-Ion Batteries	207
1.11.7.3	Flow Batteries	208
1.11.8	Energy Management Storage Technologies	208
1.11.8.1	Pumped Hydro Energy Storage	208
1.11.8.2	Compressed Air Energy Storage	210
1.11.9	Conclusions	211
References		211

1.11.1 Introduction

The intermittent generation of solar and wind power and the technical characteristics of conventional power systems pose limits to the amount of energy that can be utilized efficiently without energy storage. Storing energy is essential for two reasons: to increase the reliability and flexibility of current grids and to accommodate the projected high penetration of solar and wind energy in future grids.

This chapter describes the different beneficial services that energy storage affords in increasing the efficiency and the reliability of electricity grids, and gives an overview of current and emerging storage technologies.

1.11.2 Grid Flexibility and Reliability

A power system must reliably meet the demand at each moment. However, even though combustion releases chemical energy quickly, the speed at which this energy can be delivered to the costumer is constrained by the limited ability of the power plants' mechanical equipment to ramp power up and down. The flexibility of a power system, that is, its ability to vary its output to meet the demand, depends on the mix of its generators. The design of traditional electric power systems assures the maintenance of a dynamic balance between consumers' demand for electricity and the amount supplied by the generators. Meeting the demand requires keeping on constant standby a vast array of expensive equipment, including transformers, substations, and base load generators. Base load electricity is the minimum level of demand over a day, and it is generated by a number of units designed to run at nearly full capacity for 24 h a day (usually nuclear and coal power plants). Most of the time, base load generators operate via the simple or modified Rankine cycle [1], that is, a cycle that converts heat into work and their start and turn-off are very slow. The outputs of nuclear-power plants are inflexible and abrupt turn-offs can make them dangerous as demonstrated by the Fukushima, April 2011 events. The output of coal power plants can be varied, but the preference is to operate them at full capacity due to the low price of coal. The main constraint on the flexibleness of a grid power system primarily is due to the less flexible base load generators.

Cycling generators satisfy the additional cost needed to accommodate variations in the daily and seasonal demand. The higher the variation on demand, the costlier the operation of the system because this requires a larger number of peak generators to ensure high levels of reliability. Peak power plants are operated only for few hours a day (or only a few hours over the year); usually, they are natural gas turbines (GTs) and diesel generators. Because they operate through the thermodynamic Brayton cycle, they can be ramped up and down in a much more flexible way than steam turbine generators. The gap between peak and base load generation is filled by intermediate generators, mainly coal fired plants and GTs.

To maintain the reliability of the grid, an additional number of generators are operated at partial load, with their surplus megawatts available to ensure dependability under rapid changes on demand (frequency regulation), or an unplanned outage of a unit or a transmission line (contingency reserves). Frequency and contingency reserves are called spinning reserves; their existence both increases operational costs and lowers the overall power system's efficiency. Furthermore, a number of select units ensure the stability of the grid (its voltage, frequency, and reactive power). Detailed discussions on the dynamics of power systems are available elsewhere [2–4].

1.11.3 Energy Storage and Conventional Power Systems

The need to reduce the cost, and increase the reliability of power grids by introducing energy storage units was first recognized in the 1970s during the oil crisis triggered by the embargo on exports enacted by the Arab oil-producing nations. Concerns about security and oil supply led to the US Power Plant and Industrial Use Act that restricted the construction of new power plants using natural gas or oil as their primary fuels, and encouraged the use of pumped hydrotechnology; this resulted in 20 GW of pumped hydro power plants being deployed as a result. Subsequent efficiency improvements in GT technology along with a drop in the price of natural gas and in the costs of combined-cycle gas turbine (CCGT) and single-cycle GT engineering resulted in the Natural Gas Utilization Act of 1987 [5]. The latter repealed sections of the Power Plant and Industrial Use Act that restricted the usage of natural gas and oil, bringing both technologies back to the scene. GTs have become the dominant technology for load leveling since then, killing interest in, and the deployment of, storage technologies. However, there is renewed interest in them today mainly due to the deregulation of electricity markets, and the importance of storage when coupled with renewable sources of energy generation. Electricity markets have become more transparent, revealing the economic value of energy storage in assuring energy management and its ancillary services. Such services require a fast response and limited energy delivery, two characteristics that are well suited to energy storage technologies [4]. Some of the most important markets operated by Independent Service Organizations (ISOs) that support the participation of energy storage technologies are the following [6]:

1. Wholesale energy market: This encompasses the processes of day-ahead and real-time bidding. For example, around 95% of energy in New York is scheduled in the day-ahead market. Half of it is settled through bilateral contracts.
2. Ancillary services market: This ensures the reliability of the grid. Technologies offering frequency regulation and providing contingency reserves can participate in this market.
3. Installed capacity market (ICAM): This market ensures that there is sufficient capacity for generation to cover demand requirements. Energy storage systems that meet the ICAM criteria can participate simultaneously in the wholesale energy market.

The financial benefits of storage technologies are related to either revenues made when a technology is participating in one or more of the markets mentioned above or by avoiding costs that would have been incurred if no action was taken or if a conventional technology other than storage had been implemented instead. Energy storage technologies can offer more than one service at the same time and the total benefit is the aggregate revenue of each service. The most important services that can be provided by energy storage technologies are as follows [6]:

- Energy arbitrage: It participates in the energy market. It is the storing of cheap off-peak electricity and selling it as (more expensive) peak electricity. This requires having large capacities, high roundtrip efficiencies, and a large storage reservoir to be competitive economically; compressed air energy storage (CAES), and pumped hydro are appropriate for arbitrage.
- Load regulation: This entails responding to small rapid changes in demand. At any moment, supply may exceed demand or may be less than it. Regulation is used for dumping that difference; units operating online, spinning and only partly loaded, perform this function ready to increase or decrease power as needed. Storage technologies are well suited for frequency regulation because they have superior part-load efficiency and a very fast response. Frequency regulation is the most demanding of all storage applications as it requires very high reliability, a continuous change in output, and frequent cycling; flywheels, capacitors, and some battery types are most appropriate for frequency regulation. This function participates to the ancillary services market.
- Contingency reserves: This represents the reserve capacity for unpredicted outages of a generation unit, or a transmission line. There are three main types of reserves: (1) spinning reserve, (2) supplemental reserve, and (3) backup supply. The difference among them is in the order of action. Being loaded, spinning reserve is the first to take action first within 10 min of an outage; initially, unloaded and spinning supplemental reserve is what follows after all spinning reserve has been used. Backup supply is actually a backup for spinning and supplemental reserves. Storage devices should participate in the ancillary services market for this action.

Among arbitrage, reserves, and regulation, the latter garners the highest revenue per year. However, a storage technology can participate in more than one market. Modeling and cost analyses of storage options are needed to details possible revenues from combined uses. Other uses of electricity storage include:

- Load following: This is an ancillary service having the purpose of supplying flexible power that follows the demand up and down. The difference between load following and frequency control lies in the time scale. Regulation responds to rapid changes in demand (of about 1 min), and it constitutes the actual load minus the average of the 30 s moving average. Load following responds to changes more slowly (in about 5–30 min), and corresponds to the 30 min rolling average of demand. High-capacity energy storage devices are suitable for load following. Currently, a mix of conventional thermal power plants operated at partial load undertake load following. Under such conditions, efficiency is lower than it would have been if the plant were operated at full output, resulting in increased fuel consumption and emissions. In contrast, storage technologies are very suitable for load-following services because they can operate at partial load with little performance penalty.

- Capacity supply: Energy storage reservoirs might be used to defer or eliminate the need for utilities to buy additional peak capacity, mainly by replacing the numbers of simple cycle GTs required. The investor could rent generation capacity in the wholesale electricity marketplace. The size of the reservoir can be geared toward the characteristics of the market. Capacity supply also participates to the ICAM market.
- Transmission and distribution: As energy consumption and the demand grow with time, so does the annual peak demand, thereby stressing the transmission and distribution systems. Upgrading these systems is costly; storage can help defer or eliminate the need for such improvements. Energy storage enhances the capacity factor of base load generators, and reduces that of peak load generators by lowering the net load. Transmission lines are designed to meet peak demand conditions that occur only a few hours over the year. Placing energy storage reservoirs downstream of congested lines for this application could assure electricity during peak hours.
- There also are 'end-use' applications, like power quality equipment placed on load sites, and other such applications, like time-of-use shifting and backup supply. Detailed descriptions of such applications are given elsewhere [6, 7].

There is one further important usage of energy storage, viz., its coupling with renewable energy generation the implementation of which will realize enormous advantages which is the topic of the next section.

1.11.4 Solar Electricity and Energy Storage

1.11.4.1 Impact on the Grid of Solar and Wind Electricity Penetration

The intermittency of solar and wind energy poses limits to the grid's ability to absorb the electricity generated by such sources. Storage technologies can 'smoothen' this variability in solar and wind generation, or shift variable generation to times when the output is needed the most. Before looking at storage options, it is interesting to understand the interaction of the grid with wind and solar output.

A number of units operating at partial load account for the functions of load following, frequency regulation, and spinning reserves. Solar and wind penetration into a power system displaces generation from conventional units, and can be visualized as a reduction in the load (**Figure 1**). From a utility's perspective, the following are the main advantages of this penetration:

- Reduced need for overall system capacity. However, this primarily is true for solar electricity, rather than wind because usually solar output coincides better with the load (**Figure 1**). Usually, there is a 1 or 2 h lag between the peaks of solar generation, and

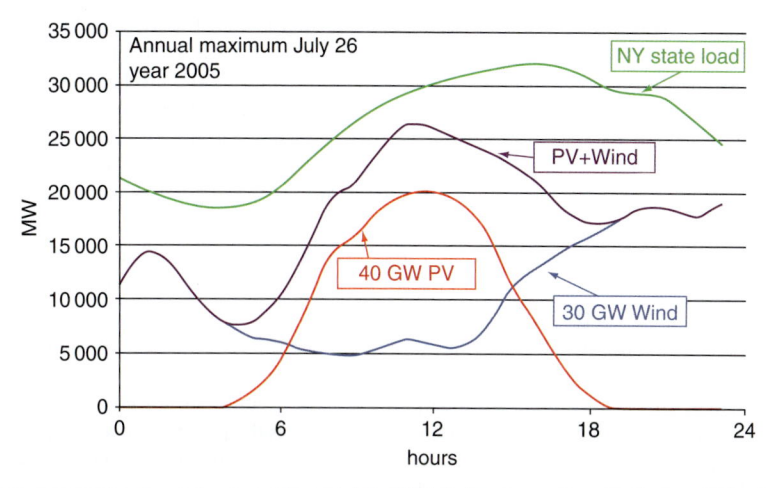

Figure 1 Simulations are based on real hourly wind, solar, and load data in NY State. The figure shows the load and PV and wind outputs for the 26 July 2005. This is the day where the highest load of the year appears. (Green) Actual hourly load in NY State. (Red) The hourly output of 40 GW PV tilted due south spread throughout the state. (Blue) The output from 30 GW wind turbines installed in areas with high wind resources within the NY State. (Purple) Combined solar and wind output. Source: Nikolakakis T and Fthenakis VM (in press) The optimum mix of electricity from wind and solar sources in conventional power systems: Evaluating the case for New York State. *Energy Policy*.

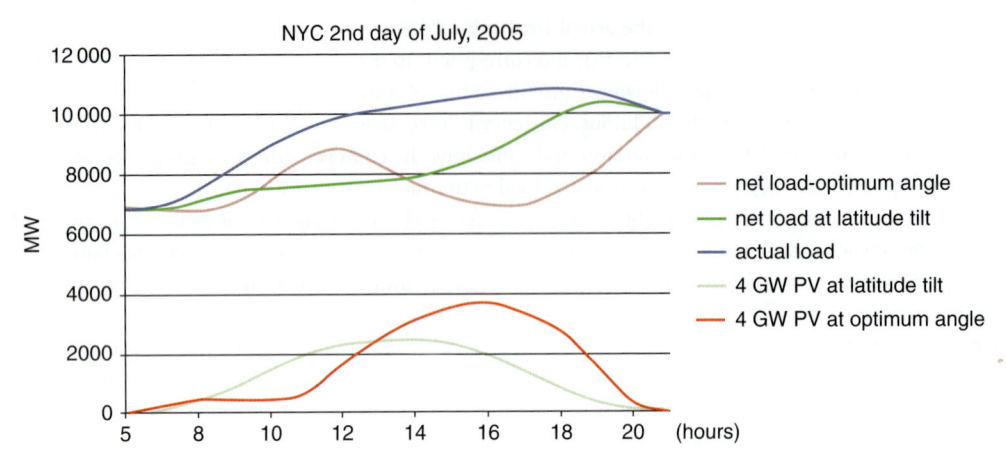

Figure 2 Reduction of the peak in the NY State control area after deploying 4 GW PV-generated power. PVs are placed in 11 different geographic regions throughout the state. Green: South facing panels at latitude tilt. (Red) Panels are tilted at 50° due south at an azimuth angle of 70° due west, viz., the optimum angle giving the maximum reduction on the peak during the summer months, May–September. Source: Nikolakakis T and Fthenakis VM (in press) The optimum mix of electricity from wind and solar sources in conventional power systems: Evaluating the case for New York State. *Energy Policy* [8].

load demand. One method to shift the solar peak to better match the summer afternoon load peak is to position the solar panels facing due west (**Figure 2**).
• Fuel economy.

Denholm *et al.* identified four main impacts of integrating a variable renewable energy supply into the grid [4]:

• Increased need for frequency regulation because of the variable availability of wind and solar power.
• Increase in the requirements for ramping rate of load-following units.
• Increase in overall ramp range (due to the difference between the daily minimum and maximum demand).

The total impact of such integration on the grid translates into additional costs to cover the greater amount of flexibility, ramping capability, and operating reserves needed in the system. Several studies on the variability in wind power show an impact on the order of $5 MWh^{-1}, adding 10% to the cost of this technology [4, 9, 10]. The costs of integrating solar energy drops dramatically when PVs are dispersed geographically over large regions; the costs can be as low as 7% of the cost incurred when the output is from one plant only [11, 12]. The penetration of renewable energy into an electricity grid depends on the mix of generators of the system; that is, the grid's flexibility, the solar and wind profiles of the region, as well as the amount of energy that is allowed to be curtailed. Each parameter is explained in detail beginning with the flexibility of the grid.

As described previously, there are two main types of generators: inflexible base load units, and the more flexible cycling units. The former units are designed to operate at full output using cheap fuel. In general, base load power constitutes around 35–40% of the annual peak capacity [3]. The penetration of wind and solar power cannot drive the net load below the limit imposed by the number and the type of base load generators, and the amount and type of reserves. This limit depends on the ability of conventional base load generators to reduce significantly their output, as well as on both economic and mechanical constraints. For example, coal plants can vary their output from full to half capacity, but experience shows that frequent cycling of the generators entails costly maintenance. The flexibility limit that separates the flexible capacity from the inflexible capacity and, hence, the flexibility of a system is defined as the percentage of the annual peak capacity that is flexible. There is no specific way to specify the exact flexibility limit of a power system. An approximation is based on the difference between the peak and the minimum load of the year. **Figure 3** depicts the hourly load of the New York State for 2 days when the peak and the minimum occurred. The NY peak of 34.2 GW occurs in summer; in 2005 it occurred on 26 July. The minimum load occurred in the spring was 12.2 GW; since there probably is additional cycling capacity to ensure reliability, along with the spinning reserves, the assumed inflexible capacity is around 10 GW. Thus, the flexibility limit was around 70% ((34.2−10)/34.2 MW).

High levels of wind and solar energy penetration may stress the system because of its flexibility limit; there will be hours throughout the year where the net load is brought below it. Then, the amount of energy below the flexibility limit cannot be absorbed and must be curtailed. This is a problem for incorporating wind technology since winds are stronger during the night when the load levels are low. The more flexible a power system is, the higher is the penetration achievable, and the less the restraint on renewable electricity (**Figure 4**). The amount of energy to be cutback can be determined with a cost analysis; often it makes economical sense to curtail small amounts of energy as a tradeoff in penetration.

The irregularity of renewable resources and the limit on the grid's flexibility both pose restrictions on the maximum penetration achievable in a system. Some interesting studies focused on the maximum renewable penetration (or amount of curtailed energy) that can be realized without storage. Denholm and Margolis [13] showed that the maximum annual energy penetration attainable from solar energy alone in the ERCOT system is around 10% if no energy is curtailed, while allowing 10% curtailment gives a 22%

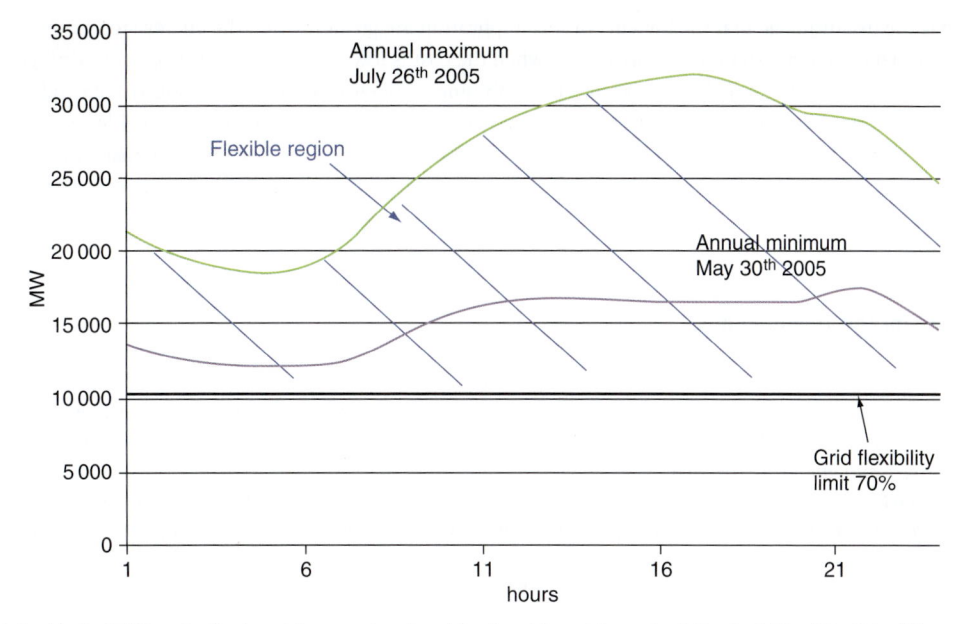

Figure 3 Hourly load in the NY State for the day of the annual peak and the day of the minimum load. The flexibility of the NY grid is approximately 70%. Source: Nikolakakis T and Fthenakis VM (in press) The optimum mix of electricity from wind- and solar-sources in conventional power systems: Evaluating the case for New York State. *Energy Policy*.

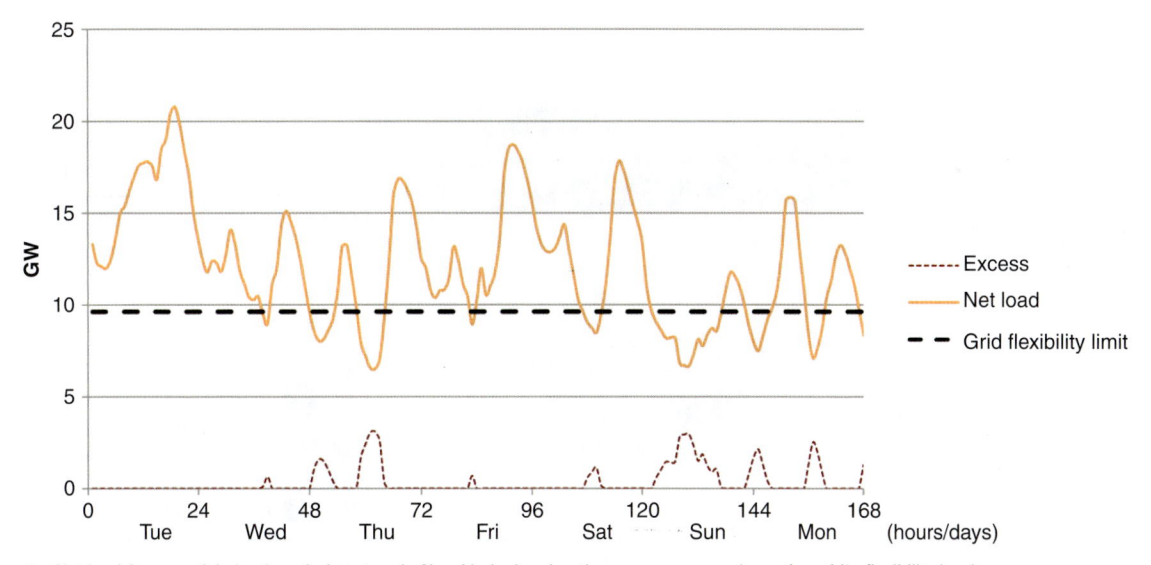

Figure 4 Net load for a modeled solar-wind system in New York showing the excess energy above the grid's flexibility level.

penetration (assuming 80% flexibility). Other studies focusing on the New York Independent System Operator (NYISO) yielded almost identical results, and additionally showed that wind energy alone achieves around a 6% higher penetration than solar energy, while the synergy of the two realizes a much higher value than either attains individually [8].

1.11.4.2 Solar, Wind, and Energy Storage: Integration Applications

Energy storage technologies can offer the two services discussed below that heighten the flexibility of the system and lower energy curtailment.

1. Renewable energy time-shift: This technology is almost the same as energy arbitrage. The difference is that instead of curtailing renewable energy, it is stored rather than used as off-peak base load. The source of this renewable source could be either wind or solar; however, because solar energy is produced at peak times, it is an unattractive option for this application. For example, low-value wind energy generated at night when the demand is low can be stored and sold later through the energy market.

However, it has the disadvantage that the benefits of this application are greatest when the energy storage operator can choose from all of the generators in a system, and store energy when the cost is lowest, instead of storing only wind-generated power.

2. Renewable energy capacity firming: This process refers to combining a storage technology with sources of wind or solar energy so that the output is somewhat-to-very constant. It offsets the need to purchase additional dispatchable capacity (for offsetting renewable generation ramping), relieves congestion and compensates for the need for having transmission and distribution equipment. A storage technology offering wind or solar capacity firming participates in the energy market. The storage used must be reliable because significant penalties accompany a nonconstant power output.

1.11.5 Energy Storage Technologies

Electric storage technologies are differentiated by various attributes, such as rated power and discharge time, as shown in **Figure 5**.

In general, there are three major categories of large-scale energy storage technologies: power quality, bridging power, and energy management [14, 15], as listed in **Table 1**. The main difference between them is the timescales over which they operate, and the extent to which power and energy are needed.

'Power quality' refers to the set of parameters that must be continuously satisfied for electrical systems to operate as expected. The storage technologies that are best suited for ensuring this continuity must provide a large power output on very short timescales, in about seconds. Since power delivery occurs in such a brief period, large storage capacities are not necessary. These technologies include superconducting magnetic energy storage (SMES), electric double-layer capacitors (EDLCs), flywheels, and batteries (**Figure 5**).

On the other hand, technologies that provide power over longer timescales for applications such as load leveling and peak shaving are used for 'energy management'. Whereas power quality applications deal with short-term and unpredictable fluctuations

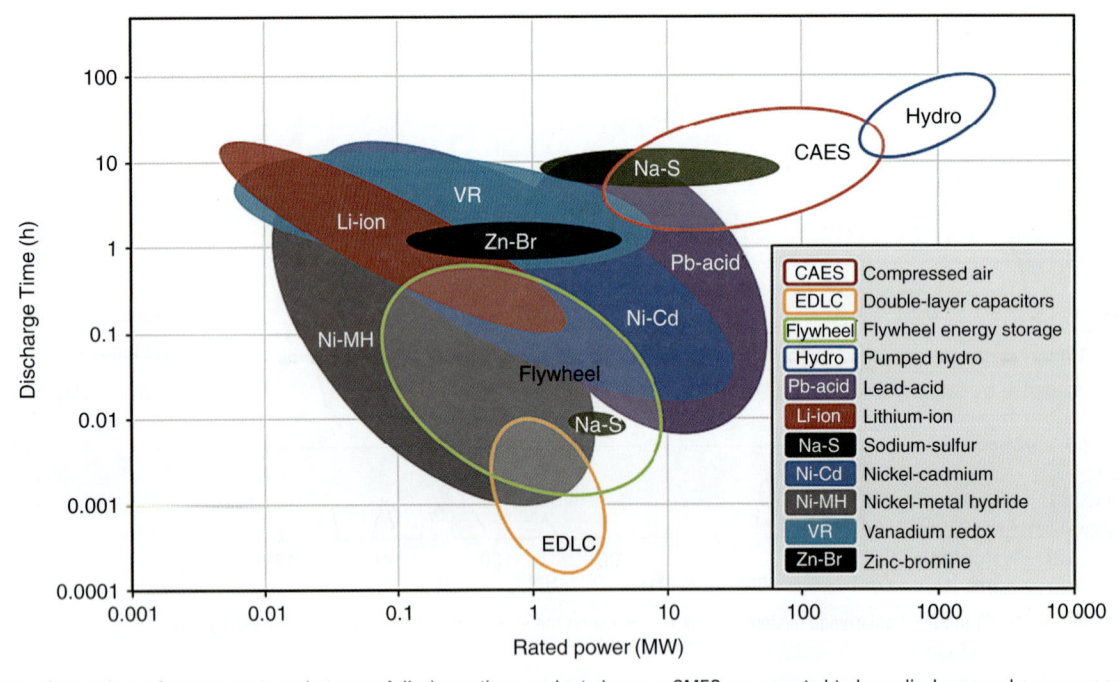

Figure 5 Comparison of storage systems in terms of discharge times and rated power; SMES are expected to have discharge and power properties comparable to EDLC. Source: Electricity Storage Association (2009) Technologies. http://www.electricitystorage.org/ESA/technologies/.

Table 1 Categories of electricity storage technologies

Categories	Applications	Operation timescale	Technologies
Power quality	Frequency regulation, voltage stability	Seconds to minutes	Flywheels, capacitors, superconducting magnetic storage, batteries
Bridging power	Contingency reserves, ramping	Minutes to ~1 h	High energy density batteries
Energy management	Load following, capacity, transmission and distribution deferral	Hours to days	CAES, pumped hydro, high energy batteries

in power output, energy management technologies address variability that largely is predicted by peak and off-peak demand. Emphasis is placed on storage capacity and less so on instantaneous power, and the timescales involved are much longer than those needed for power quality technologies. The upper region of **Figure** 5 provides a few examples of storage mechanisms used for energy management: pumped hydro, CAES, and flow batteries. Between these two boundaries lie storage technologies used for 'bridging power' to ensure continuity when switching from one source of energy to another.

In the following sections, we will describe what appear to be the most important candidates for energy storage applications.

1.11.6 Power Quality Storage Technologies

1.11.6.1 Superconducting Magnetic Energy Storage

Among the most efficient storage technologies are SMES systems. They store energy in the magnetic field created by passing direct current through a superconducting coil; because the coil is cooled below its superconducting critical temperature, the system experiences virtually no resistive loss. Four components comprise a typical SMES system: the superconducting coil magnet (SCM); the power conditioning system (PCS); the cryogenic system (CS); and the control unit (CU) [16].

The major disadvantage of SMES is the high cost of refrigeration and the material of the superconducting coil. Research is being made into high-temperature superconductor (HTSC) technology that does not require extremely low temperatures and utilizes liquid nitrogen rather than the costly liquid hydrogen required for a very low-temperature superconductor; nevertheless, the costs of HTSC material remain high. SMES systems with large capacities of 5–10 GWh involve large coils, several hundred meters in diameter, that must be kept underground [14], adding to the expense of the system.

However, these requirements result in very high round-trip efficiencies (e.g., ~95%). In addition, SMES systems can discharge almost all the energy stored in the system with a high power output in a very short time, making them ideal for power quality applications [14, 15].

SMES systems improve power quality and system stability in several ways [16]. Following an interruption, such as a downed power line or generator, an SMES unit can dampen low-frequency oscillations and mitigate voltage instability by providing both real and reactive power to the power system. On the demand side, an SMES can balance fluctuating loads by releasing or absorbing electricity according to demand. They also can be used as a backup power supply for critical loads that may be sensitive to disturbances in power quality; their fast response time allows them to inject power in less than one power cycle. SMES can provide a wide range of services like reactive power control, black start capability, transient voltage dip improvement, and frequency regulation. Micro-SMES have been used so far in industrial settings to control voltage sag problems. Large-scale applications (e.g., load following) are still in the experimental phase.

1.11.6.2 Electric Double-Layer Capacitors

EDLCs, also known as supercapacitors or ultracapacitors, offer another solution to ensure quality and short-term reliability in power systems. Like a conventional capacitor, electricity in an EDLC is stored in the electrical field between separated plates; the capacitance is a function of the plates' area, the distance between them, and the dielectric constant of the separating medium. However, whereas standard capacitors employ two plates of opposite charge separated by a dielectric, EDLCs consist of two porous electrodes immersed in an electrolyte solution, a structure giving a highly effective surface area and minimal distance between electrodes [17].

Compared to regular batteries, EDLCs have lower energy densities and higher power densities, making them suitable for power quality applications. For short-term, high-power applications, electricity discharge in an EDLC is not limited by the rates of chemical reaction rates as is the case with batteries [18]. In addition, EDLC–battery hybrids that incorporate the benefits of both technologies often are used for distributed energy storage.

This hybrid storage offers a dynamic solution to problems related to off-grid PV: the EDLC provides the power necessary for large fluctuations in power demand, while the battery remains the source of continuous electricity over long periods. In this arrangement, the battery's size is geared for a constant load rather than for peak current demand, which can be up to 10 times the normal operating current, and may only need to be satisfied for a few seconds at a time. Because the EDLC handles high currents, the battery does not experience deep discharges, and thus its life is extended [18].

Batteries in off-grid PV hybrid storage systems, when paired with EDLCs, experience less discharge depth, which translates to longer lifetimes and smaller batteries. In addition, the hybrid arrangement increases the reliability of the PV system on both large and small timescales. Increased power quality ensures that fluctuations in load demand will not adversely affect the stand-alone system, making off-grid PV systems a viable option where they might not be without energy storage technology.

1.11.6.3 Flywheels

Energy in a flywheel is stored in the form of rotating mechanical energy, in contrast with batteries and SMES where energy is stored in chemical and electrical form, respectively. Peak power for flywheels depends on the application, ranging anywhere from the kW scale (satellite, hybrid bus, utility power quality) to the MW scale (hybrid combat vehicle, train) and even into the GW scale (electromagnetic launcher) [19].

One major advantage of flywheels is long life, upwards of 20 years and independent of depth of discharge; that is, unlike electrochemical batteries, flywheels operate equally well whether discharges are few and deep or frequent and shallow. In addition, the flywheel's state of charge (SOC) can be directly determined from its rotational velocity, whereas battery SOC is more difficult to measure [20].

The most mature commercial application for flywheels is providing an uninterruptible power supply, taking advantage of the flywheel's high power density and fast recharge time [20]. Short bursts of power are administered when power line disturbances occur, 80% of which last for less than a second [21]. For some applications, a flywheel can coast for over an hour to zero charge. Field tests at the University of Texas at Austin showed that batteries on hybrid electric buses can be replaced by smaller, lighter, and longer lasting flywheels, with a mass of 60 kg, capacity of 7.2 MJ, peak power of 150 kW, and ability to accelerate a fully loaded bus to 100 km h^{-1} [19, 22].

Another developing application for flywheel energy storage is in isolated grids with renewable energy sources. High penetration of renewable and distributed energy sources in an isolated grid is limited by spinning reserve requirements, conventional generator minimum loading, conventional generator step load, system stability, and reactor power, and voltage control requirements. These limitations can be overcome with a flywheel energy storage system, as demonstrated in a wind/diesel/hydro power system on the island of Flores, Azores, where such a system is expected to increase wind energy penetration by 33% while decreasing diesel fuel usage by 150 000 l per year [23].

Another study examined a wind-diesel generator in an isolated grid where regular wind oscillations were compensated by a continuously operating diesel engine. The addition of a flywheel energy storage unit, designed to supply up to 1.8 min of rated power, provided enough active and reactive power to counteract the wind irregularities, allowing the diesel generator to be run less frequently and resulting in reduced fuel consumption [24, 25].

As a demonstration of the feasibility of building-integrated photovoltaics (BIPVs) in modern cities, a high-speed flywheel incorporated into a doubly salient permanent magnet (DSPM) was used to improve the performance of a BIPV system in Hong Kong. The original BIPV system was designed to supply a constant lighting load of 4 kW between 9 a.m. and 3 p.m.; however, additional energy was not stored. With the addition of the DSPM flywheel, this excess energy was stored and used to power the lights until 6 p.m. and beyond, lengthening the time period by over 70% [26].

The flywheel is an old storage technology being made through new improvements in materials, magnetic bearing control, and power electronics. Unable to ensure continuous supplies of energy, renewable sources such as wind and solar have long relied on lead–acid batteries for storage, but developing technology and decreasing costs are making flywheels an increasingly viable substitute to conventional batteries [19]. In addition to their technical advantages in some applications when compared to conventional batteries, flywheels also exhibit lower environmental impacts, particularly in the disposal stage [19, 26, 27]. As both penetration of renewable energy resources and the search for battery alternatives continue to grow, the next generation of flywheels may provide an increasing share of energy storage to utilities, isolated grids, and urban centers.

1.11.7 Bridging Power Storage Technologies: Batteries

1.11.7.1 Lead–Acid Batteries

The low cost and good availability of lead–acid batteries historically lead to their dominating PV electricity storage; this is the technology of choice for PV residential systems [28]. However, their short life cycle and issues of corrosivity/toxicity long have plagued their success [29]. With the growing adoption of PV, research is underway to improve lead–acid battery lifetime and their integration with PV systems.

Lead–acid batteries can be either flooded or sealed. Sealed batteries, also known as valve-regulated lead–acid (VRLA) batteries, do not require the regular addition of water as do flooded batteries. Low-maintenance design, high efficiency, and low cost make VRLA batteries the most common battery used in stand-alone PV systems [30].

There are two types of VRLA batteries: absorbed glass mat (AGM) and gelled electrolyte. The former store the electrolyte on a glass mat separator composed of woven glass fibers soaked in acid. The latter immobilize the electrolyte in a gel. Hybrid VRLA batteries encompass the power density of AGM design and the improved thermal properties of the gel design. Of all types of lead–acid batteries, the hybrid VRLA proved to be the technology best suited for PV stand-alone lighting systems [31].

PV panels are not ideal sources for charging lead–acid battery because they generate power intermittently. One proposed method to extend the lifetime of the VRLA batteries is combining them with supercapacitors into a hybrid storage system [17] utilizing the high power density, longer life cycle, and fast charge/discharge times of the supercapacitor to supply short bursts of power during times of peak demand and motor starting. The much more energy-dense VRLA battery supplies energy continuously over longer periods. Incorporating a supercapacitor allows the battery to be sized according to the demands of normal operating current rather than to that of peak current, while avoiding deep discharge, maintaining a high SOC, preventing sulfation and stratification, and extending the battery's life. Though supercapacitors are expensive, cost reduction through technology development and market growth may enable such supercapacitor–VRLA battery hybrids affordably to provide more reliable storage for PV systems.

1.11.7.2 Lithium-Ion Batteries

Among all battery technologies, lithium-ion (Li-ion) batteries have the largest potential for future development and implementation [32]. Both their energy density and power density are high compared to other battery technologies (**Figure 6**), making them ideal for portable applications.

Li-ion batteries have long lifetimes and low self-discharge rates. Electricity can be charged and discharged very quickly with high power output, with no memory effect [14]. Round-trip efficiency is 90% or higher. An Li-ion battery stores electricity when voltage is applied to it causing Li-ions to travel from the metal oxide cathode through the electrolyte separator to the graphitic-carbon anode. Electricity is discharged when the ions travel in the opposite direction. **Figure 7** depicts this mechanism.

The disadvantages of this technology include its high cost and sensitivity to extreme conditions. Despite the large power density of a Li-ion battery, like any battery it deteriorates when exposed to deep discharging and overcharging. In fact, much of the cost of Li-ion batteries lies in the overcharge protection units to prevent such events from occurring. High temperatures further decrease the battery's life.

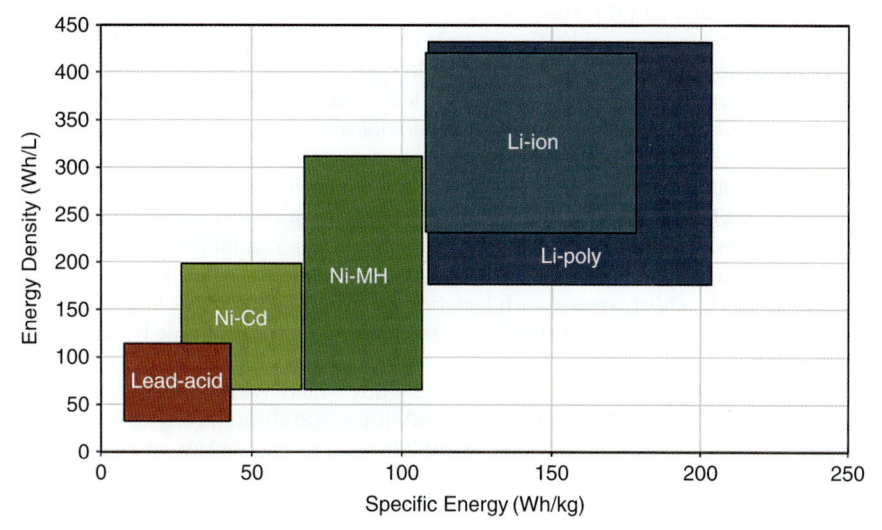

Figure 6 Battery types: energy density comparisons.

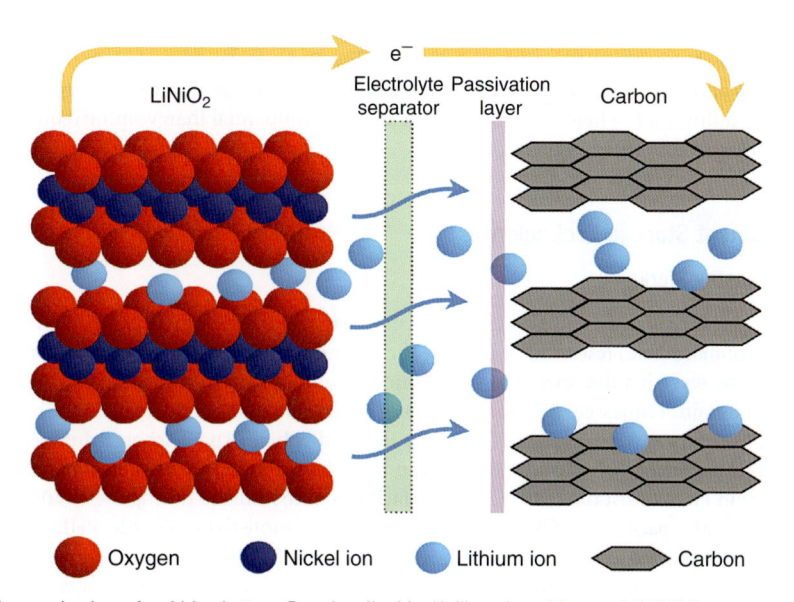

Figure 7 The basic working mechanism of an Li-ion battery. Based on Ibrahim H, Ilinca A, and Perron J (2008) Energy storage systems: Characteristics and comparisons. *Renewable and Sustainable Energy Reviews* 12: 1221–1250.

However, despite its drawbacks, Li-ion battery technology offers an interesting solution to grid-scale energy storage. Due to their high storage capacities, fast charging rates, and relatively small sizes, Li-ion batteries are popular for use in electric vehicles. If implemented on a large scale, fleets of plug-in electric vehicles can offer not only as cleaner modes of transportation but also distributed sources of stored energy for the grid [33, 34]. Large numbers of electric vehicles powered by Li-ion batteries would add flexibility and stability to the grid, and enable further penetration of renewable energy.

Another rechargeable Li-based technology with potential automotive applications is the lithium-ion polymer (Li-poly) battery that is based on the Li-ion battery, wherein the liquid electrolyte is replaced by a solid polymer electrolyte. The cost of Li-poly batteries currently is prohibitive, but their increased production may lower the cost in future. Hyundai announced plans to use Li-poly batteries in its HEVs [35], and an Audi A2 powered by Li-poly batteries recently set the record for distance travelled on a single battery charge [36].

1.11.7.3 Flow Batteries

In flow batteries, chemical energy is stored in an electrolyte containing dissolved species and converted to electricity when the electrolyte flows through electrochemical cells in a reactor. Unlike conventional batteries, the charged electrolyte can be stored in a separate tank and circulated when desired [37]. This configuration essentially decouples the power and energy aspects of the batteries and allows them to be sized independently: The power is determined by the size of the reactor, and the energy storage is limited only by the size of the external storage tank and volume of electrolyte. It also avoids the problem of self-discharge present in most battery technologies. However, flow batteries typically have lower energy densities than most portable batteries when the storage and reactor tanks are accounted for; it also requires using additional components, such as pumps and sensors [38].

There has been limited deployment of at least two types of flow batteries, vanadium redox, and zinc bromine; other types are under development, such as polysulfide bromide ones [39]. Because ruthenium exhibits fast kinetics and exhibits three redox states in solution, an all-ruthenium redox flow battery was deemed a promising design for future applications in solar energy storage [40]. Redox flow batteries consist of two half cells, each containing dissolved species in different oxidation states, separated by an ion-exchange membrane. For example, the two half cells in an iron–chromium redox battery involves the two reactions $Fe^{3+} + e = Fe^{2+}$ and $Cr^{2+} - e = Cr^{3+}$ [41]. Other types of such batteries include vanadium redox flow batteries, polysulfide bromide batteries, and uranium redox flow batteries [42]. Hybrid flow batteries, such as zinc bromine batteries, contain metallic species deposited in one of the half cells.

VRB Power (currently Prudent Energy) invented the vanadium redox battery energy storage system (VRB-ESS™) built on a 175 kW modular basis [43]. Large-scale installations include a 1 MWh per 500 kW storage system for the China Electric Power Research Institute (CEPRI) as part of a project that includes 78 MW of wind capacity, 640 kW of PV capacity, and 2.5 MW of total energy storage [44]. In addition, the company is building in California vanadium redox battery systems with SunPower's PV systems, in cooperation with Pacific Gas and Electric (PG&E), KEMA, and Sandia National Laboratories [45].

Flow batteries are being developed on the residential PV system scale. HomeFlow is a 30 kWh/10 kW zinc bromine flow battery intended for such usage. The product is being developed by Premium Power, which strives to become the 'Dell Computers of flow batteries' by bringing the technology directly to homes through modular design and inexpensive manufacturing [46]. Its product line also includes larger zinc bromine batteries with capacities/rated powers of 45 kWh/15 kW, 100 kWh/30 kW, and 2.8 MWh/500 kW that can be installed at the community level to curb peak power demand.

The key characteristic of flow batteries is their independent scalability: Reactors can be scaled up in response to increasing power demand, while storage tanks and electrolyte solution can be added for more energy storage capacity to accommodate additional renewable generators. At the utility scale, where capacity and cost are more influential than volume requirements, flow batteries are a promising technology for renewable energy systems.

1.11.8 Energy Management Storage Technologies

1.11.8.1 Pumped Hydro Energy Storage

Pumped hydro energy storage (PHES) is the most widely used energy storage technology in the United States. It utilizes elevation difference between natural (or manmade) reservoirs to increase the potential energy of water by pumping it into the higher reservoir and later produce electricity by reversing the operation of the pump running it as a turbine. The schematics of a pumped storage plant located at Raccoon Mountain, Tennessee, are shown in **Figure 8**. The water falls 990 feet from the high reservoir to run 4 units supplying 1.5 GW and supplying peak load electricity when the demand is high. The discharge duration is 22 h [47]. In general, PHES plants have a round-trip efficiency of around 75% and can have discharge capacities of more than 20 h.

Like the Raccoon Mountain Plant, most of the PHES storage facilities were initiated during the 1970s right after the big increase of oil prices reaching today a total capacity of 20 GW in the United States. For more than a decade, PHES was considered a cheap and viable alternative for peak power production. Even though the capital cost of PHES was always higher than conventional generation, the difference was small till late 1980s (capital cost of a 10 h PHES plant versus a CCGT generator was $110–$280 and $175–$275, respectively [3, 48]). However, PHES fuel variable costs have been much lower than the fuel cost of gas and oil generators since mid-1970s [4]. PHES, originally planned to compliment nuclear plants providing peak electricity, started being less competitive since the 1980s after (a) reductions in energy efficient CCGT technology capital cost, (b) reductions in the price of natural gas,

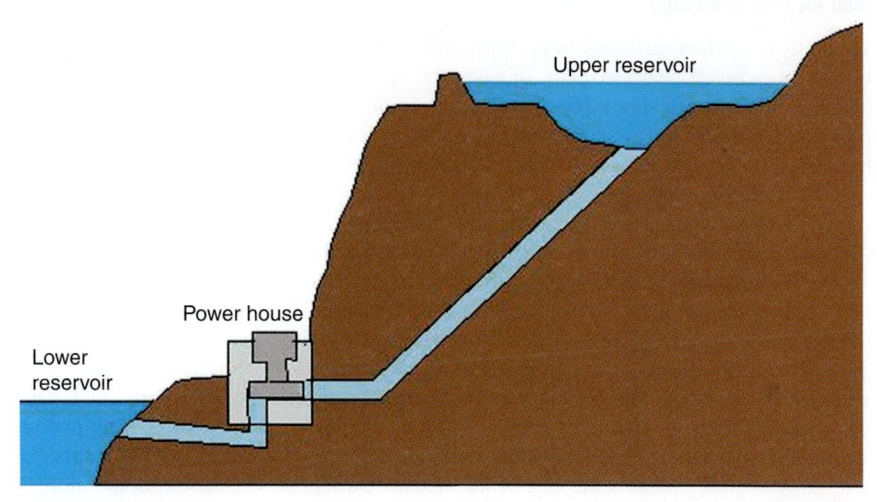

Figure 8 Conceptual schematic of a PHS plant.

(c) improvements in the efficiency of GT technology, and (d) nuclear power deployment becoming standstill. Moreover, at this moment the capital cost of PHES is almost twice that of CCGT (the overnight capital cost of CCGT in 2006 was around $800–$1100 [49] compared to the estimated cost of $2100 of a 10 h conventional PHES plant in 2009 [50]).

Even though expensive compared to CCGT for peak production, PHES is much cheaper on a kWh basis compared to most of energy storage technologies (see **Table 2**). Additional advantages include the following:

- High discharge time
- High power output for large-scale production (>100 MW)
- Proven technology

In the deregulated electric system of the United States, pumped hydro plants can make revenues by participating in the wholesale energy market, providing ancillary services or providing available capacity. More specifically, pumped hydro plants having high ramp rates and high power output qualify for load regulation, VAR support, black start up, ancillary capacity reserve, load following, energy arbitrage, transmission upgrade deferral, energy time shift, and renewables' capacity firming [6].

Table 2 Energy storage technology cost estimate by the Electric Power Research Institute, 2009

Storage type	$ kW^{-1}	$ kWh^{-1}	Hours	Total capital $ kwh^{-1}
Compressed air energy storage				
Large (100–300 MW underground storage)	590–730	1–2	10	600–750
Small (10–20 MW above ground storage)	700–800	200–250	3	1300–1500
Pumped hydro (conventional 1000 MW)	1300	80	10	2100
Battery (10 MW)				
Lead–acid, commercial	420–660	330–480	4	1740–2580
Sodium–sulfur (projected)	450–550	350–400	4	1850–2150
Flow battery (projected)	425–1300	280–450	4	1545–3100
Lithium-ion (small cell)	700–1250	450–650	4	2300–3650
Lithium-ion (large cell, projected)	350–500	400–600	4	1950–2900
Flywheel (10 MW)	3360–3920	1340–1570	0.25	3695–4313
Superconducting magnetic storage (commercial)	200–250	650 000–860 000	1 s	380–489
Supercapacitors (projected)	250–350	20 000–30 000	10 s	300–450

Source: Rastler D *Overview of Electric Energy Storage Options for the Electric Enterprise, EPRI.* http://www.greentechmedia.com/images/wysiwyg/News/EPRIEnergyStorageOverview%20DanRastler.pdf.
Notes: Total capital cost = $/kW + (number of hours × $ kWh^{-1}). All figures are rough order of magnitude estimates and are subject to changes as better information becomes available. Total capital costs include PCS and all equipment necessary to supply power to the grid. Not included are battery replacement costs, site permitting, interest during construction, and substation costs. These costs are for the hours shown ± 25%. Cost may vary depending on the price of commodity materials and location of project.

1.11.8.2 Compressed Air Energy Storage

CAES converts grid electricity to mechanical energy in the form of compressed air stored in underground (or surface) reservoirs. The source of input energy can be excess off-peak electricity, or renewable electricity coming from wind or solar farms. To convert stored energy back to electricity, the compressed air is released through a piping system into a turbine generator system after having been heated. When compression and expansion are rapid, the processes are near adiabatic; heat is generated during compression, and cooling occurs during expansion. The first is associated with large energy losses as compression to 70 atm can produce temperatures of about 1000 °C, so necessitating cooling.

For large CAES plants, a large storage volume is required and underground reservoirs are the most economically viable solution. Such reservoirs can be a salt formation, an aquifer, or depleted natural gas field. When the volume confining the air is constant, pressure fluctuates throughout the compression cycle. Constant pressure operation in hard rock mined caverns is achievable by using a head of water applied by an aboveground reservoir. For smaller CAES plants (e.g., <5 MW), air can be stored in above-ground metallic tanks or large onsite pipes, such as those designed for carrying natural gas under high pressure.

A typical CAES power plant comprises a compression and a generation train connected through a motor/generator device. During the compression mode, electricity runs dynamic compressors that compress air at pressures of 70 bars or more. Because of the high pressure ratio required, compression takes place in a series of stages separated by cooling periods. Cooling the air is necessary to reduce power consumption and meet the cavern's volume requirements. The higher the number of stages, the greater is the efficiency attained; however, this increases the cost of the system. During the expansion mode, motor operation stops and clutches engage the generator drive. Air is released to run the expanders after having first being heated in properly designed combustors. Heating the air assures high efficiency and avoids damaging of the turbomachinery due to low temperatures resulting from the rapid expansion of air and the Joule–Thompson effect. A recuperator sited after the exit from the expanders recovers some of the energy of the heated air before it is released to the atmosphere. Even though fuel is needed to run a CAES power plant, the input for a certain power capacity is around 65% less than the amount required to run a GT because around two-thirds of the energy produced by a GT is used to run its compressor. Thus, when the compressors are fed by renewable electricity, the emissions of a CAES power plant are 35% of those produced by a GT of the same capacity. **Figure 9** is a scheme of a typical CAES power plant.

Currently, two CAES power plants are operating. The world's first facility is the Huntorf CAES plant that has operated since 1978 in Bremen, Germany. It is a 290 MW facility, designed to provide black-start services to nuclear power plants located nearby, along with spinning reserves and VAR support as well as cheap off-peak electricity. It stores air up to 1000 psi (68 atm) in two depleted salt caverns located 2100 and 2600 feet under the ground; it offers up to 4 h of power generation. The second CAES plant is a 110 MW power plant operating in McIntosh, Alabama, since 1991 (**Figure 10**). It pressurizes air to 1100 psi (75 atm) and has electricity generation cycle of up to 26 h between full charges. The McIntosh plant also has a heat recuperator in the expansion train that reduces fuel consumption by 25% compared to the Huntorf plant that does not include recuperation [53].

Deregulation and the current structure of electricity markets now allow storage technologies to participate in the market and profit from their operation. As an example, the NYISO includes markets for installed capacity, energy, ancillary services, and transmission congestion contracts [54]. Several specific advantages of CAES power plants make them suitable for large-scale, diurnal, multiday and seasonal energy storage:

1. CAES and pumped hydro are the only storage technologies that offer the high capacities (>100 MW) for long periods.
2. CAES has an approximately flat heat rate at part-load conditions.
3. CAES has the lowest annual anticipated cost for an 8 h discharge system that includes the cost for O&M, electricity used during the charging cycle, fuel requirements (if nonadiabatic CAES systems are used), and capital carrying charges [39].

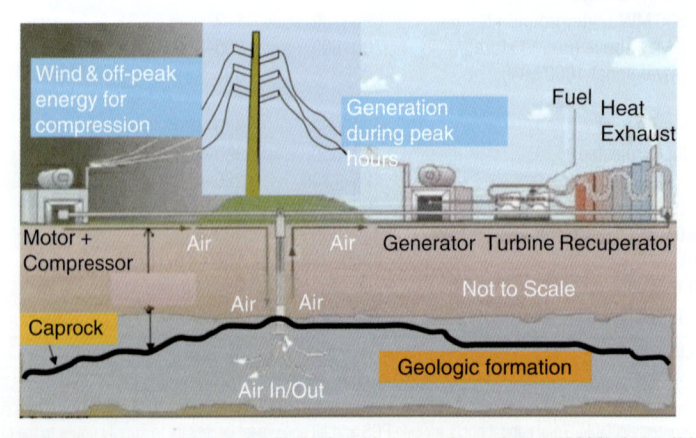

Figure 9 Schematics of a typical CAES power plant. Source: Sandia National Laboratories webpage (2008). https://share.sandia.gov/news/resources/releases/2008/images/compressor.gif [51].

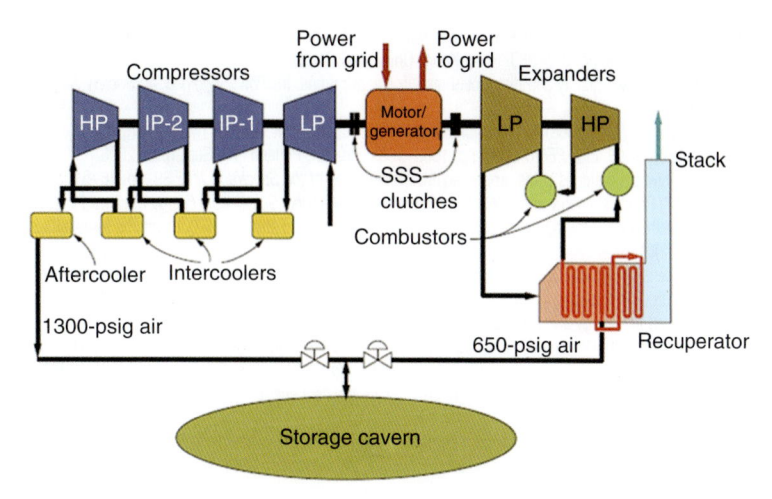

Figure 10 A schematic of the McIntosh, Alabama, CAES compression and expansion system. Source: Integrating Renewables, Technology Solutions, CAES. http://integrating-renewables.org/integrating-renewables-technology-solutions/ [52]. www.espcinc.com

4. CAES has the potential for the lowest levelized annual cost ($ kW-yr^{-1}) due to inexpensive storage (per hour of discharge capability) and greater operational efficiency than other systems, both of which translate into lower operational costs than batteries and other storage systems shown in **Figure 5**.

A CAES power plant can participate in the capacity market, provide load-following services and energy arbitrage, operate as an ancillary reserve, and offer VAR control or energy shift for renewable applications. More than one of these services are possible at the same time.

1.11.9 Conclusions

The increased role of renewable generation has prompted concerns about grid reliability and raised the question of how great the penetration of these resources can be before energy storage is needed. However, adding storage in the grid accomplishes more than just supporting renewable energy penetration. The current structure of conventional electricity grid systems is inefficient due to the technical limitations posed by base load and cycling thermal generators. Emerging storage technologies can participate in modern deregulated markets, and offer a wide number of services that will enhance the total efficiency and the economics of a power system.

References

[1] Sontag R, Borgnakke C, and Van Wylen G (2003) *Fundamentals of Thermodynamics*, 6th edn. Hoboken, NJ: John Wiley and Sons.
[2] Connors S, Martin K, Adams M, and Kern E (2004) Future electricity supplies: Redefining efficiency from a system's perspective. *MIT Engineering Systems Symposium*. http://esd.mit.edu/symposium/pdfs/papers/connors.pdf.
[3] Cordaro M (2008) Understanding base load power. In Conjunction with New York Affordable Reliable Electricity Alliance. http://www.area-alliance.org/documents/base%20load%20power.pdf.
[4] Denholm P, Ela E, Kirby B, and Milligan M (2010) The role of energy storage with renewable electricity. *Technical Report: NREL/TP-6A2-47187*.
[5] EIA (2009) Repeal of the Powerplant and Industrial Fuel Use Act (1987). http://www.eia.doe.gov/oil_gas/natural_gas/analysis_publications/ngmajorleg/repeal.html (accessed December).
[6] Rahul W and Apt J (2008) Market analysis of emerging electric energy storage systems. *Final Report to DOE, Report ID:DOE/NETL-2008/1330*.
[7] Eyer J and Corey G (2010) Energy storage for the electricity grid: Benefits and market potential assessment guide. *Sandia Report: SAND2010-0815*.
[8] Nikolakakis T and Fthenakis VM (2011) The optimum mix of electricity from wind- and solar-sources in conventional power systems: Evaluating the case for New York State. *Energy Policy* 39: 6972–6980.
[9] DeCesaro J, Porter K, and Milligan M (2009) Wind energy and power system operations: A review of wind integration studies to date. *The Electricity Journal* 22: 34–43.
[10] Parsons B, Milligan M, Smith JC, et al. (2006) Grid impacts of wind power variability: Recent assessments from a variety of utilities in the United States. *National Renewable Energy Laboratories, Conference Paper, ID: NREL/CP-500-39955*.
[11] Mills A and Wiser R (2010) Implications of wide-area geographic diversity for short-term variability of solar power. *LBNL-3884E*. Berkeley, CA: Ernest Orlando Lawrence Berkeley National Laboratory.
[12] Hurlbut JD (2009) Colorado's prospects for interstate commerce in renewable power. *Technical Report, ID: NREL/TP-6A2-47179*.
[13] Denholm P and Margolis PR (2007) Evaluating the limits of solar photovoltaics (PV) in traditional electric power systems. *Energy Policy* 35: 2852–2861.
[14] Ibrahim H, Ilinca A, and Perron J (2008) Energy storage systems: Characteristics and comparisons. *Renewable and Sustainable Energy Reviews* 12: 1221–1250.
[15] Electricity Storage Association (2009) Technologies. http://www.electricitystorage.org/ESA/technologies/.

[16] Sutanto D and Cheng KWE (2009) Superconducting magnetic energy storage systems for power system applications. In: *International Conference on Applied Superconductivity and Electromagnetic Devices, 2009. ASEMD 2009*, pp. 377–380. Hong Kong, China, 2-6 October 2005.
[17] Barker PP (2002) Ultracapacitors for use in power quality and distributed resource applications. In: *Power Engineering Society Summer Meeting, 2002 IEEE*, vol. 1, pp. 316–320. Chicago, IL, USA, 21-25 July 2002.
[18] Glavin ME, Chan PKW, Armstrong S, and Hurley WG (2008) A stand-alone photovoltaic supercapacitor battery hybrid energy storage system. In: *Proceedings of the 13th Power Electronics and Motion Control Conference, 2008. EPE-PEMC 2008*, pp. 1688–1695. Poznan, Polland, 1-3 September 2008.
[19] Hebner R, Beno J, and Walls A (2002) Flywheel batteries come around again. *Proceedings of the Spectrum, IEEE* 39, pp. 46–51. doi: 10.1109/6.993788.
[20] Bolund B, Bernhoff H, and Leijon M (2007) Flywheel energy and power storage systems. *Renewable Sustainable Energy Reviews* 11: 235–258. doi: 10.1016/j.rser.2005.01.004.
[21] Varatharajoo R and Fasoulas S (2001) Methodology for the development of combined energy and attitude control systems for satellites. *Aerospace Science and Technology* 6: 303–311. doi: 10.1016/S1270-9638(02)01157-4.
[22] Hayes RJ, Kajs JP, Thompson RC, and Beno JH (2000) Design and testing of a flywheel battery for a transit bus. *SAE Transactions* 108: 2199–2207.
[23] Hamsic N, Schmelter A, Mohd AI, et al. (2007) Increasing renewable energy penetration in isolated grids using a flywheel energy storage system. In *Proceedings of the 1st International Conference of Power Engineering, Energy and Electrical Drives 2007*, pp. 195–200. Setúbal, Portugal, 12–14 April.
[24] Iglesias IJ, García-Tabarés L, Agudo A, et al. (2000) Design and simulation of a stand-alone wind-diesel generator with a flywheel energy storage system to supply the required active and reactive power. In: *Proceedings of the 31st Annual Conference of Power Electronics Specialist Conference 2000*, pp. 1381–1386. Galway, Ireland, 18–23 June.
[25] Okou R, Sebitosi AB, Khan A, and Pillay P (2009) The potential impact of small-scale flywheel energy storage technology on Uganda's energy sector. *Journal of Energy in Southern Africa* 20: 14–19.
[26] Kan HP, Chau KT, and Cheng M (2001) Development of doubly salient permanent magnet motor flywheel energy storage for building integrated photovoltaic system. In: *Proceedings of the 16th Annual Conference of Applied Power Electronics Conference and Exposition 2001*, pp. 314–320. Anaheim, CA, USA, 4–8 March. doi: 10.1109/APEC.2001.911666.
[27] Hartikainen T, Mikkonen R, and Lehtonen J (2006) Environmental advantages of superconducting devices in distributed electricity generation. *Applied Energy* 84: 29–38.
[28] Rand DAJ, Moseley PT, Garche J, and Parker CD (eds.) (2004) *Valve-Regulated Lead-Acid Batteries*. Amsterdam: Elsevier.
[29] Koutroulis E and Kalaitzakis K (2004) Novel battery charging regulation system for photovoltaic applications. *IEE Proceedings – Electric Power Applications* 151: 191–197. doi: 10.1049/ip-epa:20040219.
[30] Schaber C, Mazza P, and Hammerschlag R (2004) Utility-scale storage of renewable energy. *Electricity Journal* 17: 21–29. doi: 10.1016/j.tej.2004.05.005.
[31] Hariprakash B, Martha SK, Ambalavanan S, et al. (2008) Comparative study of lead-acid batteries for photovoltaic stand-alone lighting systems. *Journal of Applied Electrochemistry* 38: 77–82.
[32] Divya KC and Vøstergaard J (2009) Battery energy storage technology for power systems: An overview. *Electric Power Systems Research* 79: 511–520.
[33] Tomic J and Kempton W (2007) Using fleets of electric-drive vehicles for grid support. *Journal of Power Sources* 168: 459–468.
[34] University of Delaware (2007) Car prototype generates electricity, and cash. *ScienceDaily*. 9 December.
[35] Lysaght M (2009) Hyundai To Unveil 2011 Sonata at Detroit Auto Show-Edmunds Inside Line.
[36] Nicola S (2010) German Electric Car Sets World Record – UPI.com.
[37] Ponce de León C, Frías-Ferrer A, González-García J, et al. (2006) Review: Redox flow cells for energy conversion. *Journal of Power Sources* 160: 716–732.
[38] Woodbank Communications (2011) Electropaedia: Flow batteries. http://www.mpoweruk.com/flow.htm (accessed 30 March).
[39] Denholm P, Ela E, Kirby B, and Milligan M (2010) *The Role of Energy Storage with Renewable Electricity Generation*. NREL/TP-6A2-47187. NREL: Golden, CO.
[40] Chakrabarti MH, Lindfield Roberts EP, Bae C, and Saleem M (2011) Ruthenium based redox flow battery for solar energy storage. *Energy Conversion and Management* 52: 2501–2508. doi: 10.1016/j.enconman.2011.01.012.
[41] Bartolozzi M (1989) Development of redox flow batteries: A historical bibliography. *Journal of Power Sources* 27: 219–234. doi: 10.1016/0378-7753(89)80037-0.
[42] Shiokawa Y, Yamana H, and Moriyama H (2000) An application of actinide elements for a redox flow battery. *Journal of Nuclear Science and Technology* 37: 253–256. doi: 10.3327/jnst.37.253.
[43] Prudent Energy Corporation (2009) Press Release: Prudent Energy announces its assets acquisition of VRB Power Systems Inc. http://www.pdenergy.com/press_012909_acquisition.html (accessed 30 March 2011).
[44] Prudent Energy Corporation (2011) Press Release: Prudent Energy announces installation of a MW class VRB™ Energy Storage System for CEPRI. http://www.pdenergy.com/press_030211_cepri.html (accessed 30 March 2011).
[45] Prudent Energy Corporation (2011) Press Release: Prudent Energy announces solar energy storage initiative with CPUC, SunPower, PG&E, Others in California. http://www.pdenergy.com/press_030911_california.html (accessed 30 March 2011).
[46] Kanellos M (2010) Flow batteries coming into homes? *Greentech Media, Inc.*, 11 November. http://www.greentechmedia.com/articles/read/flow-batteries-coming-into-homes/ (accessed 30 March 2011).
[47] Tennessee Valley Authority website. http://www.tva.gov/sites/raccoonmt.htm.
[48] EPRI (1976) Assessment of energy storage systems suitable for use by electric utilities. *EPRI-EM-264*, July.
[49] NREL (2010) Energy Technology Cost and Performance Data. http://www.nrel.gov/analysis/costs.html.
[50] Rastler D (2009) *Overview of Electric Energy Storage Options for the Electric Enterprise', EPRI*. http://www.greentechmedia.com/images/wysiwyg/News/EPRIEnergyStorageOverview%20DanRastler.pdf.
[51] Sandia National Laboratories webpage (2008) https://share.sandia.gov/news/resources/releases/2008/images/compressor.gif.
[52] Integrating Renewables, Technology Solutions, CAES. http://integrating-renewables.org/integrating-renewables-technology-solutions.
[53] EPRI-DOE (2003) *Handbook of Energy Storage for Transmission and Distribution Applications*.
[54] Gregory P (2009) Compressed air energy storage engineering and economic study. *Report 10-9, NYSERDA*.

1.12 Solar Radiation Resource Assessment for Renewable Energy Conversion

DR Myers, National Renewable Energy Laboratory, USA

© 2012 Elsevier Ltd. All rights reserved.

1.12.1	**Introduction**	214
1.12.1.1	The Sun as Star	214
1.12.1.2	The Earth and the Sun	215
1.12.2	**Fundamentals of Solar Radiation**	215
1.12.2.1	Solar Geometry	215
1.12.2.2	The Atmospheric Filter	216
1.12.2.3	Spectral Considerations	216
1.12.3	**Fuel for Solar Energy Collectors**	217
1.12.3.1	Photovoltaic and Solar Thermal Flat Panels	218
1.12.3.2	Solar Thermal Systems	219
1.12.3.3	Sustainable Applications	219
1.12.4	**Measuring Solar Radiation**	219
1.12.4.1	Solar Radiometers and Detectors	219
1.12.4.2	Radiometer Calibration	221
1.12.4.3	World Radiometric Reference: the Calibration Reference	221
1.12.4.4	Traceability	222
1.12.4.5	Pyrheliometer Calibrations	223
1.12.4.6	Pyranometer Calibrations	223
1.12.4.7	Radiometric Uncertainty and Performance	224
1.12.5	**Modeling Solar Radiation**	225
1.12.5.1	Physics-Based Models	225
1.12.5.2	Empirical Models	225
1.12.5.3	Satellite-Based Models	225
1.12.5.4	Geographical Information System Models	226
1.12.6	**Converting Solar Radiation Data to Application-Specific Data**	226
1.12.6.1	Estimating Hemispherical Radiation on a Tilt	226
1.12.6.2	Estimating Direct Beam (DNI) from Global Horizontal Radiation	226
1.12.6.3	Estimating Diffuse Hemispherical Radiation from Global or DNI	227
1.12.7	**Measured and Model Data Set Properties**	227
1.12.7.1	Period of Record	227
1.12.7.2	Temporal Resolution	228
1.12.7.3	Spatial Coverage	228
1.12.7.4	Modeled Data Sets	228
1.12.8	**Model Estimate Uncertainties**	229
1.12.9	**Developing Solar Radiation Resource Databases**	229
1.12.9.1	Developing the NSRDB	229
1.12.9.2	Sources of Solar Radiation and Meteorological Data	230
1.12.9.2.1	Data acquisition	230
1.12.9.2.2	Meteorological data – TD-3280	230
1.12.9.2.3	Precipitable water	230
1.12.9.2.4	Snow depth – TD-3210	230
1.12.9.2.5	Ozone	230
1.12.9.2.6	Filling gaps in the data record	230
1.12.9.2.7	Deriving precipitable water data	230
1.12.9.2.8	Deriving broadband aerosol optical depth	231
1.12.9.2.9	Modeling cloud transmittance, scattering, and statistical effects	231
1.12.9.2.10	Output products and data quality checks	231
1.12.9.2.11	Updating the database	232
1.12.10	**Applications: Calculating Solar Radiation for Flat-Plate and Concentrating Collectors**	232
1.12.11	**Future Directions**	234

References	236
Further Reading	237
Relevant Websites	237

Glossary

Aerosol optical depth (AOD) Dimensionless parameter quantifying the extinction of solar radiation by scattering particulates and absorption between the point of observation and the top of the atmosphere.

Air mass (AM) The path length from an observer's location to the top of the atmosphere, which passes through the center of the sun, relative to the zenith (perpendicular to the local horizontal = air mass 1).

Albedo (r) For the ground. The ratio of the magnitude of reflected radiation to incident radiation. The bulk reflectivity of the ground.

Broadband radiation Photons in a wide electromagnetic spectral wavelength range, typically several hundred nanometers (nm) wide.

Circumsolar radiation (CSR) The solar aureole, sky radiation surrounding the solar disk which is scattered out of the direct normal irradiance.

Diffuse hemispherical radiation (F) Photons scattered in the atmosphere, excluding those from the solar disk, arriving on a horizontal surface originating from the 2π steradian hemisphere of the sky dome.

Direct beam irradiance (B) See Glossary term 'Direct normal irradiance'.

Direct normal irradiance (DNI) Nearly parallel rays of photons arriving on a surface perpendicular to the line from the observer to the center of the solar disk originating from within the 0.5° solid angle centered on the solar disk, plus additional sky radiation within 2.5° to 3° of the center of the solar disk.

Electron volt (eV) Measure of photon energy, dependent on wavelength of the light.

Extinction Loss of amplitude or attenuation in a signal propagating through an absorbing or scattering medium.

Extraterrestrial solar radiation (ETR) Direct normal radiation at the top of the Earth's atmosphere.

Global hemispherical radiation (G) The combination of photons from the sky dome and solar disk (diffuse hemispherical and projection of the direct normal radiation) received on a horizontal surface.

Incidence angle (i) The angle between the center of the solar disk and the foot of the normal (perpendicular) of a receiving surface.

Pyranometer A radiometer with a 2π steradian (hemispherical) field of view used to measure global hemispherical or diffuse hemispherical radiation.

Pyrheliometer A radiometer with a restricted field of view (typically 5°–6°) used to measure direct normal radiation.

Responsivity (R_s) The ratio of the output signal of a radiometer to the optical power intercepted by the sensor.

Solar radiation Electromagnetic emissions from the sun between 250 and 2500 nm.

Zenith angle (Z) The angle between the local vertical and the center of the solar disk; complement of the solar elevation angle (angle from the center of the solar disk to the horizon).

1.12.1 Introduction

With the present recognition that fossil fuels are not sustainable and that their use damages the planetary environment, alternative, noncarbon emitting sources of energy such as solar energy are recognized as a path to a clean and sustainable energy sources. It has long been recognized that the sun is the ultimate source of all of our energy sources, whether for fuel for the economy or food as fuel for our bodies. This chapter addresses the measurement and modeling of solar energy as fuel for solar energy conversion systems. In this sense, the sun provides unlimited 'reserves', relatively easy to access and harvest, for a truly sustainable energy supply. Despite the intermittent and relatively low energy density of sunlight, information on the quantity and quality of terrestrial solar radiation can be used to optimize solar conversion systems. Developing innovative designs for capturing and converting solar radiation is only one-half of the equation. Identifying, locating, and prospecting for the appropriate quantity and quality of solar resources to fuel these systems is critical to designers, investors, financiers, and owner/operators. This chapter addresses the fundamental elements and state of the art for measuring, modeling, and evaluating solar radiation resources and applications to system design.

1.12.1.1 The Sun as Star

Modern classification of stars is similar to the classification of species in the plant, animal, and insect kingdoms. The astrophysical classification scheme is used to express the approximate age, size, and luminosity, or energy content, of stars. Presently, the classification consists of single letter designations OBAFGKMN. The letters represent, in order, young, hot, energetic stars to old, cool, low energy stars. Subclassification numbers and small letter designations are used for subdividing the stellar classes according to sometimes esoteric features of the stellar spectra. Our sun is a typical 'average' star classified by astronomers as a 'G2-V dwarf', in the middle of its evolutionary lifetime of about 20×10^9 years. The sun emits 2.009×10^7 watts per square meter per steradian (W m^{-2}-sr^{-1}) from its surface, and 2.845×10^{26} W in all directions. The Earth resides in an elliptical orbit about the sun with an eccentricity of 0.0167 (1.4710×10^6 km at perihelion, 1.5210×10^6 km at aphelion). At the mean Earth–sun distance, the sun subtends a solid angle of 9.24 mrad, or 0.529°. Thus, the sun is not truly a point source, and the rays from the sun are not truly parallel, but diverge into a cone with a nominal half angle of 0.529°. Many scientists have investigated the energy output of the sun, sometimes referred to as the 'solar constant', or the magnitude of the energy reaching the top of the Earth's atmosphere, referred to here as 'extraterrestrial radiation', or ETR. Since the late 1970s, measurements from earth orbit by orbiting 'total solar irradiance' sensors have attempted to measure 'solar constant' at the Earth. Despite the identification of the 'sunspot' cycle of approximately 11 years, and rather small (less than one-fifth of 1%) variation in solar emission as a result of sunspots, there is a widely accepted definition of the solar constant, at 1 astronomical unit or 1.495979×10^9 km, as $1366.1\,\mathrm{Wm^{-2}} \pm 7.0\,\mathrm{Wm^{-2}}$.

1.12.1.2 The Earth and the Sun

As mentioned above, the Earth's orbit about the sun is elliptical. Treating the sun as a point source, the variation in the Earth–sun distance produces a '1 over R-square' variation in the ETR defined above. This $1/R^2$ effect increases the ETR above the mean value by 3% at perihelion (December) and decreases the ETR by 3% at aphelion (July). This effect must be taken into account when modeling, or mathematically computing, solar radiation resources throughout the year. The 23° tilt of the Earth's rotation axis with respect to the plane of the Earth orbit about the sun results in variations in the solar path through the daytime sky dome throughout the year (as well as the procession of the seasons).

1.12.2 Fundamentals of Solar Radiation

The Earth intercepts the ETR within a very slender cone, or beam, of photons, called the direct normal irradiance (DNI), or direct beam radiation, since it is typically measured on a surface perpendicular to the quasi-collimated 'beam' of photons within the cone. The flux density of this beam at the top of the atmosphere (at the average Earth–sun distance) is the ETR, or solar constant defined above. The atmosphere acts as an absorbing and scattering medium through which the beam propagates to the ground. Photons are scattered (their directed of propagation is changed) or absorbed by molecules and particles in the atmosphere. Photons that are not absorbed contribute to uncollimated diffuse irradiance of the sky dome. The changing constituents of the atmosphere (clouds, water vapor, aerosols, smoke, pollutants, etc.) change the optical properties of the atmosphere. This in turn affects the distribution of power as a function of the wavelength (or energy) of the photons moving through the atmosphere. The combination of direct normal and diffuse sky radiation constitutes the total solar radiation impinging on surface. The geometrical relationship between the surface or plane of interest, the sky dome and ground, and the direction of the direct beam from the solar disk determine the relative contribution of each component to the total solar radiation available to a surface. The optical properties of the surfaces or system elements also affect the amount of solar energy that can be converted to useful energy. Each of these elementary contributions to the modification of solar energy available to solar conversion systems are discussed below.

1.12.2.1 Solar Geometry

Solar radiation flux on a horizontal surface is referred to as total hemispherical solar radiation; sometimes 'global horizontal' radiation, G. This hemispherical radiation is comprised of a combination of the nearly collimated direct beam radiation (B) from the solar disk and some portion of the diffuse sky radiation (F). Solar flux on an arbitrarily tilted surface is referred to as total hemispherical radiation on a tilted surface, generally shortened to 'global tilt' radiation (GT). For tilted surfaces, contributions from the sky radiation are reduced because of the 'unseen' part of the sky radiation. Ground-reflected radiation (R) may contribute to the global tilt radiation, and its magnitude depends on the optical properties (albedo) of the ground in the field of view. In all cases, the contribution of the direct beam to the radiation on the surface depends upon the incidence angle (i), the angle between the normal to the surface, and the projection of the direct beam radiation on the surface. This component is computed as the direct beam magnitude multiplied by the cosine of the incidence angle i. For a horizontal surface, the incidence angle for the beam is the zenith angle, Z, defined as the angle between the center of the solar disk and the normal to the surface, which points to the zenith. **Figure 1** illustrates the terms utilized in solar geometry calculations.

For incidence angle i, direct beam magnitude B, diffuse sky radiation value F, and possibly ground-reflected radiation R, the total hemispherical radiation on a surface is

$$G = B\cos(i) + F + R$$

From **Figure 1**, note that as the solar elevation angle (e) increases, or the zenith angle decreases, the effective path length (through a plane atmosphere) decreases. The reference altitude for the path length calculation is sea level. Geometrically, the path length is a function of the reciprocal of the sine of the incidence angle $\sin(i)$, or cosine of the zenith angle $\cos(Z)$. The common term for this path length in the solar energy community is the air mass, (AM), and AM = $1/\sin(e) = 1/\cos(Z)$. Thus, a solar elevation of 30° (Z = 60°) results in AM = 2.0, and AM = 1.0 means the elevation angle is 90°, the zenith angle is 0°, and the sun is directly overhead.

Note this definition is appropriate for a plane atmosphere only. The curvature of the Earth's atmosphere and refraction, or bending of the beam radiation due to optical properties of the atmosphere, cause deviations from this 'geometrical' AM and the 'absolute AM', represented by an integration over the (curved) path through the atmosphere, accounting for the decrease in atmospheric pressure with height above the ground. For solar Z less than about 70° (elevations above 20°), the geometrical

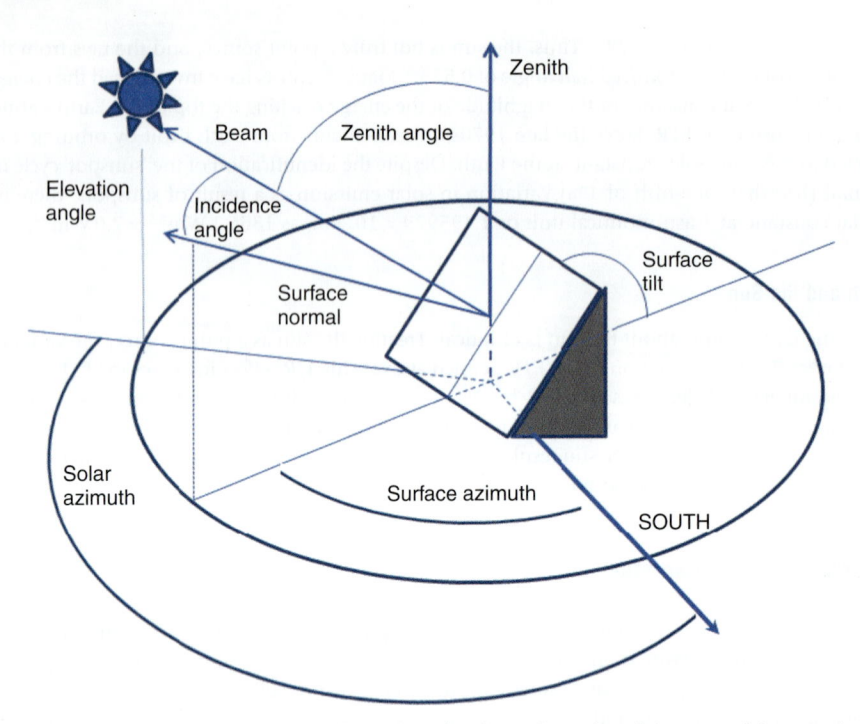

Figure 1 Example of solar geometry terms for a general case. For horizontal surfaces, the surface tilt is zero, and the normal points to the zenith, the 'surface azimuth' is undefined, and the incidence angle is equal to the zenith angle, Z, (complement of the solar elevation angle). Thus, the total hemispherical radiation becomes $G = B \cos(Z) + F$.

approximation is very good, as the atmosphere approximates a flat plate, due to the large curvature of the Earth. For solar Z greater than 70° (elevations < 20°), corrections are often applied to account for the effects of refraction, which always increase the AM. Lastly, absolute AM is a function of elevation, since the density of the atmosphere decreases with altitude.

1.12.2.2 The Atmospheric Filter

The Earth's atmosphere acts as a continuous variable filter, changing the relative magnitudes of the direct beam and diffuse sky radiation (and thus the total global radiation), as well as modifying the spectral distribution, or amplitude as a function of wavelength of the light, for each of these components. The changes induced on the ETR beam and resulting global total and diffuse sky radiation are functions of many factors, including the solar geometry (AM) and constituents of the atmosphere.

1.12.2.3 Spectral Considerations

Figure 2 is a graph of the extraterrestrial spectral distribution of sunlight at the top of the atmosphere, and typical direct beam, diffuse sky, and total hemispherical spectral distributions for a specific set of atmospheric conditions and single given air mass = 1.5.

The ETR spectrum in **Figure 2** can be approximated by a smooth blackbody radiation curve for a body at a temperature of about 5400 K. However, the sun is not truly a blackbody radiator. The ETR curve contains various absorption features ('valleys' in the curve), especially apparent below 500 nm. These result from various elements and conditions such as gradients in temperature and density in the solar atmosphere. These features were first identified and associated with the physics of the solar atmosphere by Fraunhofer, and are named in his honor. Most are apparent in the wavelengths below 500 nm. For longer wavelengths, the ETR curve is relatively smooth.

Conversely, the terrestrial beam and total hemispherical curves show absorption features that depend on the path length between the top of the atmosphere and the observation site. Basic atmospheric gases such as oxygen and nitrogen, and mainly water vapor, ozone, and pollutants have their own absorption features. Gas molecules in the atmosphere that are approximately the same size as the wavelength of light within the spectrum are more efficient at scattering radiation out of the beam. This is Rayleigh scattering, after Lord Rayleigh, who first investigated this phenomenon. Lastly, suspended particulates of varying sizes and optical properties scatter some wavelengths better than others. These particulates are usually lumped together as 'aerosols'. The Swedish scientist Kurt Ångstrom related the extinction due to aerosols to two parameters, α (related to the size of the aerosols) and β (related to the optical properties of the aerosols). Once the effects of Rayleigh scattering, atmospheric gas absorption, and water vapor absorption are accounted for, the formula for the relationship of collected incident radiation I to incident radiation I_o is

$$I = I_0 \exp(-tm) \quad \text{where } t = \beta \lambda^{\alpha}.$$

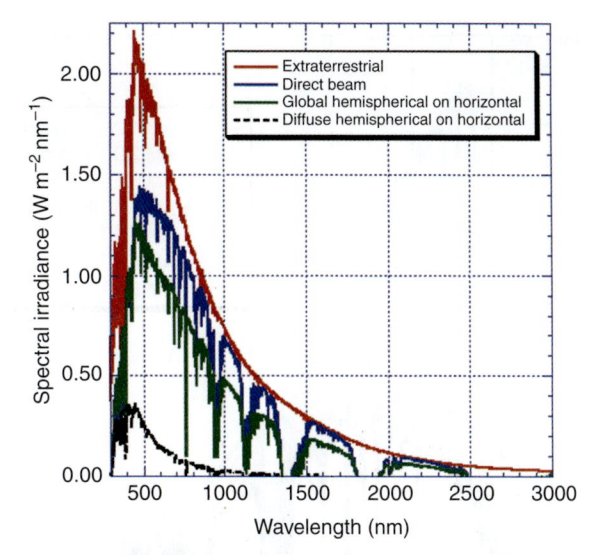

Figure 2 Extraterrestrial and clear-sky AM 1.5 terrestrial component spectral distributions under certain atmospheric conditions. Top to bottom, the curves are: extraterrestrial, direct normal beam, total hemispherical on a horizontal surface, diffuse sky radiation on a horizontal surface.

where t is often referred to as 'turbidity', m = air mass AM, and λ is wavelength. The more correct term for t is aerosol optical depth. The phrase optical depth refers to the attenuation of radiation passing through a plane parallel medium.

A typical range for α is 0.5–2.5, with an average for natural atmospheres of around 1.3 ± 0.5. Larger values of α, when the t value for longer wavelengths is much smaller than the t value for the shorter wavelengths, imply a relatively high ratio of small particles to large ($r > 0.5\,\mu m$) particles. As t for a longer wavelength approaches the t for a shorter wavelength, larger particles dominate the distribution and α becomes smaller. It is not physically reasonable for the t value of longer wavelengths to equal or exceed the t value of shorter wavelengths.

For both broadband and spectral solar radiation, if one considers the transmittance, T_x, or ratio of collected to incoming ETR irradiance, for each atmospheric constituent 'x' described above, such as

Rayleigh scattering transmittance: T_r
Mixed gas transmittance: T_g
Water vapor transmittance: T_w
Ozone transmittance: T_o
Aerosol scattering transmittance: T_a

each of which is dependent on the AM and concentration, or amount of the constituents present.

Then an expression for the dependence of clear-sky direct beam terrestrial solar radiation on these parameters can be written as the product of transmittances and the direct beam ETR, (I_o):

$$I = I_o T_r T_g T_w T_o T_a$$

For broadband estimates, each of the transmittance parameters can be considered as a 'bulk' transmittance integrated over all wavelengths. For spectral estimates, each parameter becomes a function of wavelength.

Besides clouds, discussed below, the single largest impact on the amplitude of both broadband and spectral irradiance is the air mass, or path length through the atmosphere. **Figure 3** shows the impact of increasing air mass on direct beam irradiance. **Figure 3** illustrates how the air mass affects the spectral distribution of direct beam and global hemispherical solar radiation. Both figures are for a fixed set of atmospheric conditions/constituents and clear skies.

For cloudy or partly cloudy skies, the situation becomes more complex. Absolute or relative 'effective' cloud 'transmittance' is difficult to parameterize. Various types of clouds have different optical properties ('cloud optical depth', similar to aerosol optical depth). The spatial distribution (in three dimensions) of clouds with respect to the position of the sun, mixture of cloud types present, and varying physical structure of clouds present formidable barriers to precise calculation of the impact of clouds on the transfer of solar radiation through the atmosphere. That topic is discussed in more detail below in the section on Modeling Solar Radiation.

1.12.3 Fuel for Solar Energy Collectors

Estimating or quantifying the available fuel for solar conversion systems is the aim of solar resource assessment. The 'quantity' or magnitude of the resource is often of first concern. The 'quality' of the resource is represented by inherent properties of the radiation, such as the spectral distribution, relative contribution of direct beam, diffuse, and total hemispherical components, duration, and

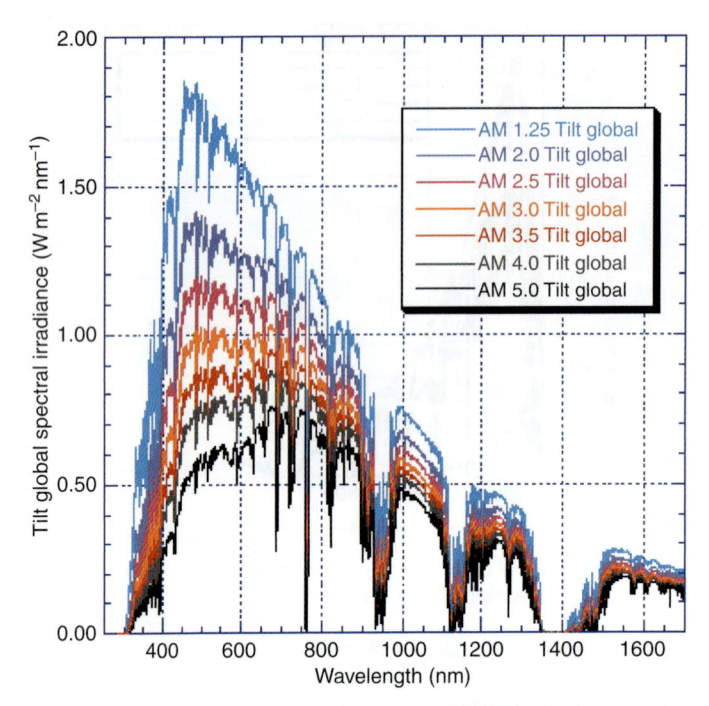

Figure 3 Air mass (AM)-dependent shift in global spectral irradiance distributions on a 37° tilted surface for specific atmospheric conditions. Curves are labeled in top to bottom order.

temporal and spatial variability. The relative importance of each of these aspects of solar radiation resources depends on the technology of the conversions systems in question. A few examples of the most common applications for solar radiation resource assessment are discussed next.

1.12.3.1 Photovoltaic and Solar Thermal Flat Panels

Photovoltaic technologies utilize various semiconductor materials that release electrons from their constituent atomic structure that become available for conduction, or for the production of electric current. The electrons are kicked out of there orbital bands by absorbing photons of above a suitable threshold energy. The 'suitable energy' of course depends on the materials used.

Most photovoltaic panels deployed today are made of crystalline silicon. If a silicon atom absorbs a photon of wavelength shorter than about 1100 nm, or a photon with energy of at least 1.1 eV, an electron may be released into the conduction band of the material. Less expensive cells, such as 'thin film' amorphous (i.e., noncrystalline) silicon, or more easily produced 'multicrystalline' silicon response differently. Cadmium telluride (CdTe), copper indium gallium selenide (CuInGaSe$_2$, or CIGS), and gallium arsenide (GaAs) cells use photons from different spectral bands into conduction electrons. Some materials can be stacked to produce 'multijunction' cells. Each layer absorbs and converts a specific part of the spectrum, thus using more of the solar spectrum. Figure 4 plots the spectral response functions for several materials systems.

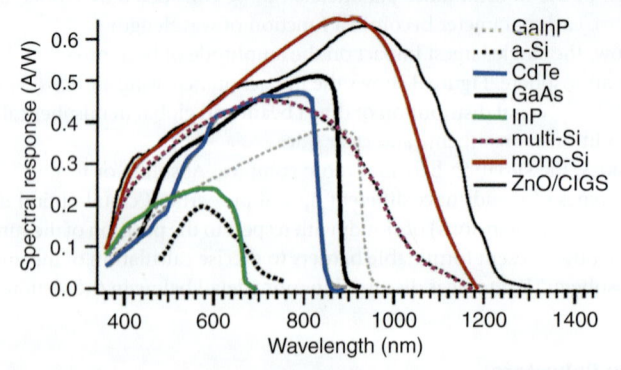

Figure 4 PV material system spectral responses. GaInP = gallium indium phosphide; a-Si = amorphous silicon thin film; CdTe = cadmium telluride; GaAs = gallium arsenide; InP = indium phosphide; multi-Si = multicrystalline silicon; mono-Si = monocrystalline silicon; ZnO/CIGS = zinc oxide-coated copper indium gallium diselenide film. Source: Field H (1997) Solar cell spectral response measurement errors related to spectral band width and chopped light waveform. *26th IEEE Photovoltaic Specialists Conference, Anaheim, California, NREL/CP-530-22969, 29 September–3 October 1997*. Golden CO: National Renewable Energy Laboratory [1].

The challenge for photovoltaic conversion systems is to find a combination of material conversion efficiency manufacturing processes and deployment applications for optimum economic and or energy impact. The spectral quality of the sunlight available becomes important for photovoltaic systems, in that it is the integral of the product of the spectral response of the materials and the available spectral distribution that determines the total number of electrons that become available for conduction. Energy outside the spectral response of the materials is absorbed to produce heat, or if the material is thin enough, and the wavelength long enough, passes through the material to be absorbed by the substrate holding the material.

1.12.3.2 Solar Thermal Systems

Solar thermal collectors use the concept of 'selective absorber' materials to absorb as much of the solar spectrum as possible. These are essentially black absorbers that convert the photon energy to heat. The heat then is used in thermal applications to produce hot water or steam, sometimes at high pressure and temperatures. Flat plate absorbers are commonly used to produce domestic hot water. By using parabolic reflectors, either as long troughs with absorbers running through the focal axis of the trough or dishes with absorbers at the focus of the parabola, the flux density of the solar radiation (energy per unit area) can be increased several orders of magnitude (powers of 10). Similarly, Fresnel lenses or other focusing optical systems can also be used to concentrate solar radiation. For thermal systems, part of the overall efficiency of the systems is the optical efficiency of the reflectors and absorbers. Heat transfer and energy transport through the system contribute to the overall system efficiency. It is critical to note that concentrating collectors can only utilize the direct beam irradiance. These are the only photons that are redirected to the absorbers by the reflecting or lens components. Diffuse sky and ground-reflected radiation propagate in random directions, and cannot be focused. Thus, the relative contribution of direct beam to the total available solar radiation resource becomes important for concentrating systems.

1.12.3.3 Sustainable Applications

Solar radiation resources are important for other sustainable energy applications, such as daylighting, solar desalinization, and detoxification of contaminated water, 'passive solar' construction (which manages the heat loads for buildings based on architecture and materials). For building applications it is usually necessary to have solar radiation information in combination with weather or climate data. The solar radiation in combination with the exposure, materials, and orientation of buildings, and the parameters defining the comfort of the occupants, generates the heating and cooling loads that must be met.

For daylighting applications, the substitution of natural sunlight for artificial lighting, the relevant solar geometry for a location, in combination with the relative contributions of sky and direct beam radiation, and spectral transmittance of window materials become important. The human eye has a limited spectral response (the photopic response) between 380 and 800 nm, peaking at 550 nm, which also has to be considered. The 'luminous efficacy' of a source, such as the sun or a lamp, is the ratio of the integration of the eye response multiplied by the spectral distribution of the source divided by the integrated source spectral distribution over the eye response region. The variation of the spectral distribution of daylight is dependent on location and atmospheric conditions, and can impact the quality of available illumination for lighting applications.

Water quality and availability can be improved through the use of solar energy to evaporate sea water, leaving behind salt, and then recondensing the water vapor. Water contaminated with toxic compounds can be purified by using titanium dioxide (TiO_2) as a catalyst in combination with the ultraviolet part of the solar spectrum (or an artificial source) to remove the contaminants. For these applications, the relative availability and amplitude of broadband and ultraviolet spectral components of solar radiation are important.

The following sections discuss the measurement, modeling, and organization of solar radiation to meet the needs of these sustainable technologies.

1.12.4 Measuring Solar Radiation

1.12.4.1 Solar Radiometers and Detectors

Radiometers for measuring total hemispherical or diffuse hemispherical radiation are called pyranometers. Two types of sensors, thermal sensors using thermopiles or other thermoelectric generating sensors, such as resistance thermometers, or solid-state sensors using photovoltaic devices, typically silicon photodiodes, are most often used.

Thermal sensors are in thermal contact with a black absorbing surface that heats up proportionally to the incident radiation. A thermopile sensor generates voltages when junctions of dissimilar metals such as copper and constantan are heated. A second set of reference junctions are held at a reference temperature. The voltage generated by the thermopile is proportional to the temperature difference of the heated and reference junctions. Thermal devices respond over the entire solar spectral range of wavelengths, though they may be protected by windows or domes with broad spectral transmittance range from 285 to 2500 nm. When calibrated with respect to a reference radiometer with no window, a small missing part of the spectrum beyond 2500 nm in the test unit is accounted for.

Silicon detectors generate a photocurrent proportional to the solar incident radiation. The photocurrent can be passed through stable 'dropping' resistors to generate a voltage. These radiometers have the same limited spectral response range as crystalline silicon photovoltaic cells, from 300 to 1100 nm. The energy within this range represents only about 75% of that in the total solar spectrum. The solar terrestrial solar spectrum beyond 1000 nm is susceptible to considerable variation due to water vapor absorption. The silicon detectors do not respond to these variations. This leads to additional uncertainty in the measurement of total solar radiation above that for thermal radiometers. **Figure 5** shows the relative spectral response windows for a thermal detector under a quartz dome and a silicon photodiode detector under an acrylic diffuser. **Figure 6** shows typical examples of radiometers used to measure hemispherical radiation.

A pyrheliometer is used to measure the direct beam or direct normal irradiance (DNI). These instruments are designed with sensors at the bottom of view limiting tubes with field of view limiting apertures. These apertures are designed to provide acceptance angles of 5–5.7°. This permits some limited error in pointing or tracking of the 0.5° diameter of the solar disk, which should be centered in the field of view. These designs were defined before the availability of highly accurate computer-controlled solar tracking equipment, so $\pm 2°$ tolerance for tracking were needed. The geometry of the tube designs are defined by the World Meterorological Organization (WMO) Committee on Instrumentation, Measurements, and Observations (CIMO) Guide No. 8, published by the WMO. This reference has an excellent chapter, number 8, on the measurement of solar radiation. That chapter also includes a classification scheme and specifications for solar radiometer quality.

Within the 5–5.7° total field of view, the area of scattered radiation near the solar disk, the solar aureole or circumsolar radiation is within the field seen by the pyrheliometer. This sometimes raises questions as to the impact of comparing DNI measurements from pyrheliometers with different fields of view. However, the decline in radiance or brightness of sky within the solar aureole is very steep, falling by a factor of 1000 over a very short angular distance from the solar disk limb. The small amplitude of the aureole, in combination with the additional 0.35° increment on the outer edge of the field of view of a 5.7° field results in the additional radiation below the noise level of the detectors involved.

Diffuse hemispherical radiation, F, is measured using pyranometers behind shading devices that block at least the same 5 or 5.7° field of view, centered on the sun, that the pyrheliometer uses. This conserves the component summation relation $G = B \cos(Z) + F$ for measured data, as the missing part of F is included in B. Shade devices that produce the most accurate diffuse measurements are opaque disks or balls mounted on solar trackers that follow the sun and shade the pyranometer through the day. An older alternative is band, oriented to obscure the entire path of the sun through the day. This approach shades part of the diffuse sky where

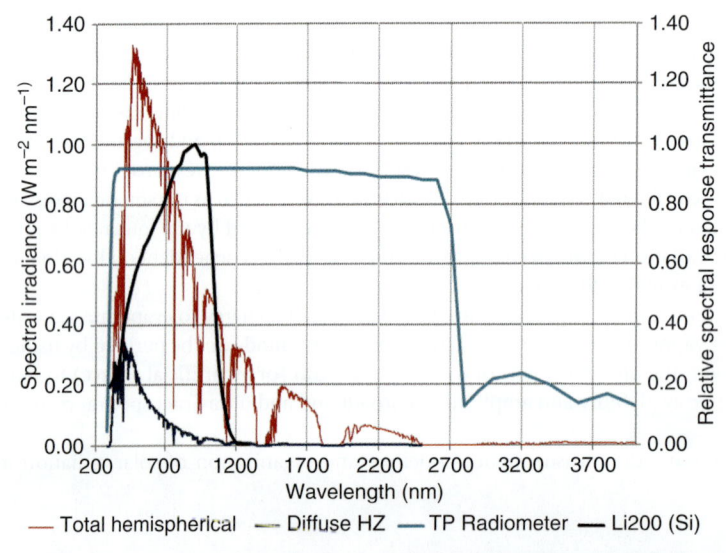

Figure 5 Total hemispherical and diffuse spectral solar radiation distributions with spectral response regions for thermal detector (TP) under quartz window (with large flat region), and silicon photodiode (curve cutoff at 1100 nm).

Figure 6 Examples of silicon detector (left) and thermopile detector pyranometers (right) for measuring total hemispherical solar radiation on a horizontal.

Total (global) G, Direct beam, B, Diffuse sky (scattered), F
$G = B \cos(i) + F$ i = incidence angle

Pyranometer

Pyrheliometer

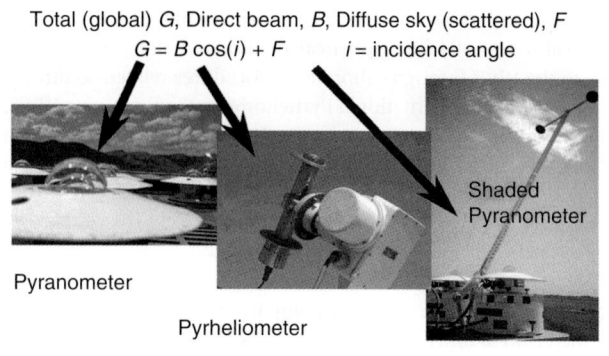

Shaded Pyranometer

Figure 7 Typical solar radiation sensors for the three solar components.

the solar disk is not located. Many algorithms for correcting for this source of error, which varies according to cloud cover and seasons have been published, but most are no more accurate than about ± 25% of the diffuse magnitude. **Figure 7** shows examples of typical instrumentation for measuring solar radiation components.

1.12.4.2 Radiometer Calibration

In 1970, Kendall [2] and later Willson [3] at the Jet Propulsion Laboratory developed electrical compensation radiometers utilizing conical blackened silver cavities with thermojunctions attached that could be calibrated using electrical heating in place of heating from solar radiation. These and instruments of similar design by Crommelynck [4], Brusa and Frohlich [5], and Hickey [6] became the standard for the current World Radiometric Reference (WRR) now in use [7, 8]. **Figure 8** is a photograph of the instruments that constitute the World Standard Group, or WSG, which are used to define the present scale for solar radiation measurements. These standard pyrheliometers are the foundation of the radiation scale and calibration of field pyrheliometers and pyranometers as described in more detail below.

1.12.4.3 World Radiometric Reference: the Calibration Reference

The International System or SI unit of solar irradiance is the WRR established and maintained by the WMO at the Physical Meteorological Observatory, Davos, Switzerland, World Radiation Center (PMOD/WRC). WRR was introduced in 1977 in order to ensure homogeneity of solar radiation measurements. WRR is determined from the weighted mean of the measurements of a group of six absolute cavity radiometers, which were fully characterized for electrical performance and physical attributes (such as limiting aperture area). It has an estimated accuracy of 0.3%. The WRR is realized by a group of absolute cavity pyrheliometers designated the World Standard Group (WSG). There have been laboratory comparisons between a WMO/WRC cavity radiometer and a cryogenic absolute cavity radiometer, the SI standard for realizing the radiometric scale for laboratory measurements. The comparisons showed that the WRR radiometer reproduced the SI laboratory irradiance scale to within 0.05% [9–11].

Figure 8 Photo of the Working Standard Group (WSG) of the WRR at PMOD/WRC.

Note that the WRR reference is with respect to direct beam radiation only. There are presently no internationally accepted reference instruments or radiation scales for total hemispherical or diffuse hemispherical radiation. The result is that all such measurements must be traced back to the WRR through calibration procedures related to direct beam measurements.

Every 5 years, since 1970, WMO sponsors the International Pyrheliometer Comparisons (IPC). The WMO representatives of any country bring their reference solar radiometers to Davos to compare them with the WSG and derive a WRR correction factor. As of this writing, the latest IPC was IPC XI, conducted in 2010. The test radiometers are compared with the WSG using a rigorous data collection and processing protocol [12].

1.12.4.4 Traceability

Traceability of measurements requires an unbroken chain of comparisons with defined uncertainties to stated references. The traceability of the WSG cavity radiometers to SI units is with respect to electrical (volt, ohm, and ampere) and physical-dimensional (length, area) standards maintained by national standardizing laboratories. Detailed characterization of the aperture area, absorption of the cavity, and electrical components of the measurement system substantiates the 'absolute' nature of the WSG measurements. WMO representatives and reference pyrheliometer manufacturers of any country are invited to bring reference pyrheliometers to IPCs to compare them with the WSG and derive a WRR correction factor. **Figure 9** shows the traceability path for

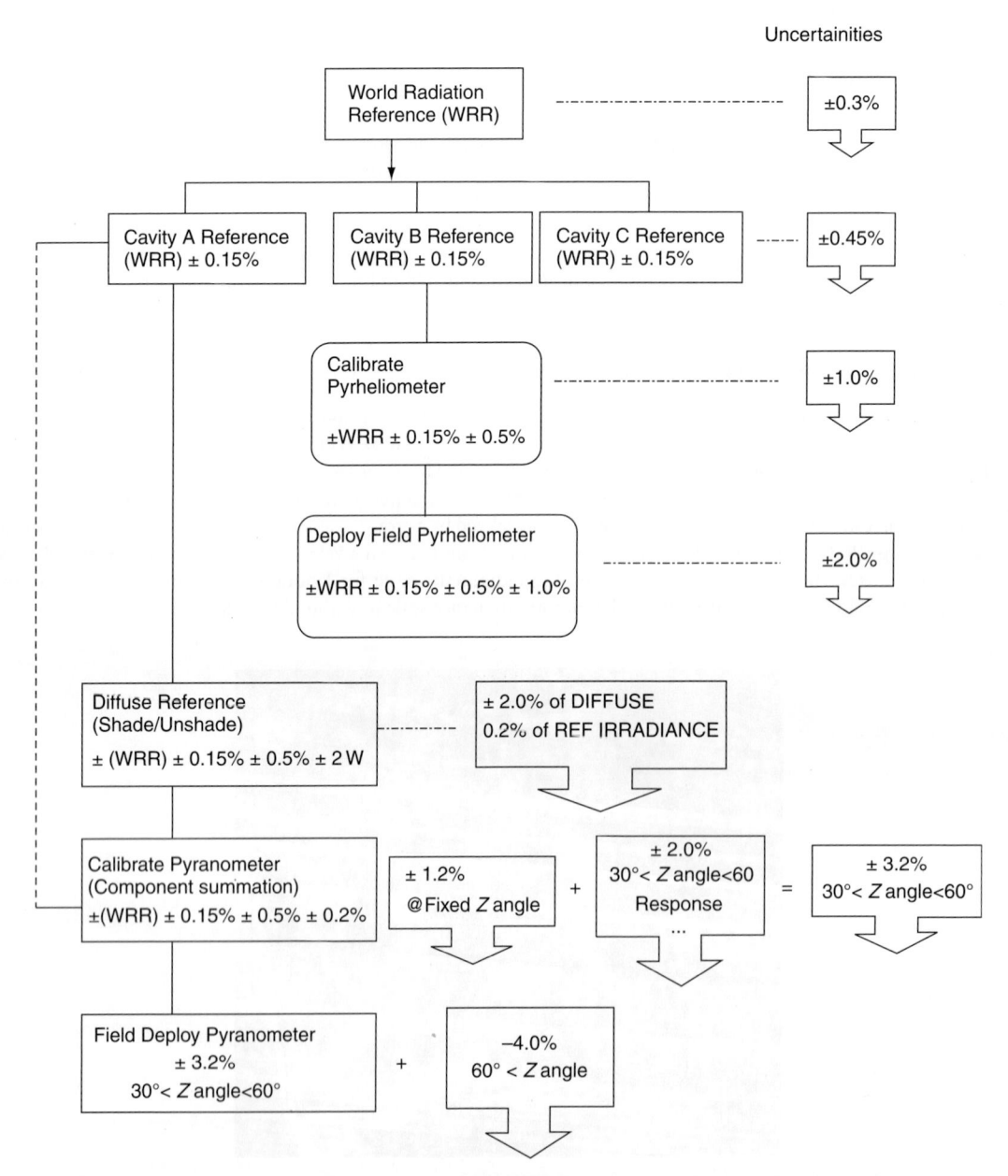

Figure 9 Traceability diagram of the transfer of WRR scale and propagation of uncertainty from reference to field radiometers.

working field radiometers to WRR through the WSG. Increasing uncertainty at each level for field radiometer calibrations including transfer process and test radiometer stability is indicated.

1.12.4.5 Pyrheliometer Calibrations

Pyrheliometer responsivities (R_s, or output signal per stimulus unit) are derived by direct comparisons with reference cavity pyrheliometers traceable to WRR. The approach is much like the transfer of WRR between cavity radiometers. The ratio of test pyrheliometer signals to the reference irradiance from the reference cavity pyrheliometer is computed over the course of a clear day or several clear days. **Figure 10** shows typical data for such a 'Broadband Outdoor Radiometer Calibration' (BORCAL) at the National Renewable Energy Laboratory. Example calibration reports are available online at http://www.nrel.gov/aim/borcal.html. National and international standards documents describe the procedures for calibration of field pyrheliometers from primary (absolute cavity) pyrheliometers and reference pyrheliometers [13–15].

The shape of the response function seen in **Figure 10** is of concern, as the distribution of the responsivities is not random but biased differently in the morning and afternoon. The cause for this bias is a current topic of research. Possible explanations are the different fields of view of the reference (5°) and test (5.7°) pyrheliometers, environmental influences (ambient temperature, wind speed, and direction), and test instrument design (thermal gradients between detector and reference thermocouples).

1.12.4.6 Pyranometer Calibrations

Pyranometer responsivities may be derived using two techniques. The first is a 'shade/unshade' technique [13]. Responsivity for a pyranometer, R_s, is derived in a shade/unshade calibration using the formula

$$R_s = \frac{(U-S)}{[B\cos(Z)]}$$

where U and S are the unshaded and shaded output voltages from the sensor, Z is the zenith angle, and B is DNI measured by a reference pyrheliometer. Procedures for this calibration are described in the American Society for Testing and Materials Standard G167 and international standard ISO 9060 [13, 15].

Shade/unshade calibrations are subject to several sources of uncertainty. The pyranometer under test has several time constants, caused by differing heating and cooling rates of the domes and detectors as the shade is imposed and removed. For the shaded pyranometer, sky radiation, particularly the infrared (IR) radiation temperature, remains relatively constant, while the detector cools down significantly. Therefore, the net IR exchange between the instrument and the sky is different in the shade and unshade condition [16, 17]. This produces thermal offsets in the detector. Variations in the direct beam radiation over the shade and unshade periods (at the beginning and end of the shade period) can lead to errors. A modified shade/unshade pyranometer calibration that determines an average responsivity at 45° zenith angle for three instrument azimuths averages out azimuth response variations [18].

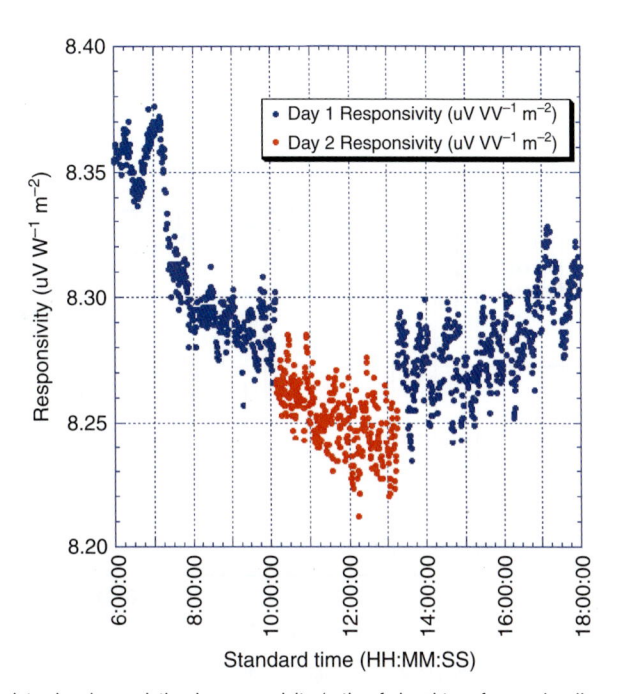

Figure 10 Pyrheliometer calibration data showing variation in responsivity (ratio of signal to reference irradiance) over 2 days.

For a 'component summation' calibration of a pyranometer, the reference global irradiance (G_r) is derived from an absolute cavity radiometer beam measurement (B) and shaded pyranometer (diffuse) measurement (F) using $G_r = B \cos(Z) + F$. The ratio of the test pyranometer signal to the reference global irradiance is the responsivity, or calibration value, for the pyranometer.

This technique requires a shade/unshade calibrated pyranometer to measure the 'reference diffuse' irradiance, F, during the calibration. The instantaneous voltage signals of the test radiometers are divided by the reference global irradiance G_r to generate instantaneous responsivities typically in units of microvolts per watt per square meter ($\mu V W m^{-2}$). **Figure 11** shows a typical plot of responsivity versus zenith angle throughout a day.

As with the pyrheliometer example discussed above, the response of the pyranometer is not constant with respect to the solar incidence angle. Every individual pyranometer will have a distinct, unique, individual 'signature', even for a given model designation. Similar signatures are obtained from pyranometers calibrated if the shade/unshade techniques are used over a large range of zenith angles. Selection criteria for a reported responsivity (or calibration factor, C_f, equal to $1/R_s$), and range of R_s (or C_f) must be described to adequately characterize the uncertainty in solar radiation measured with the pyranometer.

1.12.4.7 Radiometric Uncertainty and Performance

Using the shade/unshade technique the direct beam irradiance can be measured with an absolute cavity pyrheliometer to about 0.4%. The clear-sky diffuse irradiance can be measured with an uncertainty of $\pm(3\%$ of reading $+ 1.0 W m^{-2})$. Under clear-sky calibration conditions, the diffuse irradiance is on the order of 10–15% of the total global hemispherical irradiance. This means that the contribution of uncertainties in the diffuse to the total global reference irradiance is rather small, about 0.3%, comparable to the uncertainty in the direct beam irradiance measured with an absolute cavity radiometer of 0.4%. Thus, the very lowest uncertainty in a reference irradiance or total global hemispheric irradiance in general is about 0.7%.

In combination with the precision and accuracy of a (very good) data logger system, of about 0.1%, the uncertainty in the determination of each individual R_s computation is about 0.5–0.7%. This represents about 1 standard deviation, or 1-sigma 'standard uncertainty'. In accordance with the processes of uncertainty analysis spelled out in the International Bureau of Weights and Measures (French acronym BIPM) Guide to the Uncertainty in Measurements (GUM) [19] an expanded uncertainty is obtained by multiplying this standard uncertainty by a coverage factor k, resulting in an expanded uncertainty with a specified confidence interval. A confidence interval of 95%, assuming a normal or Gaussian distribution of errors sources, requires a $k = 2$. Thus, the expanded uncertainty about each individual R_s data point is about 1.8%.

This 1.8% is the smallest uncertainty that can be expected of a pyranometer under conditions identical to the calibration conditions, including the infrared thermal offset (generated by infrared exchange between the cold sky and warm radiometer), at a specific zenith angle. It is possible to estimate the thermal offset during calibration, using long-wave radiometers (Pyrgeometers, with their own inherent uncertainties) and compensate for this effect during the calibration. Responsivity at a given zenith angle at the time of measurement, $R_s(Z)$, can be obtained from a fit to the response curve from calibration data versus zenith angle.

To simplify data collection and logging, an average responsivity is used to compute the calibration factor to convert sensor signal to engineering units. Since the average zenith angle for an isotropic, homogeneous, uniform irradiance distribution in the sky dome is 45°, this is usually the preferred Z for reporting $R_s(Z)$. If used, there will be a regular pattern of systematic errors introduced into the pyranometer measurements, especially of clear-sky data, from morning to afternoon and winter to summer. These errors result from the deviation of the true instrument responsivity signature from the $Z = 45°$ $R_s(Z)$ as a function of Z, and can exceed 5% for $Z > 60°$, and grow beyond 10% for $Z > 70°$ [20]. Compensation for these errors can occur by averaging data over a day. Morning and

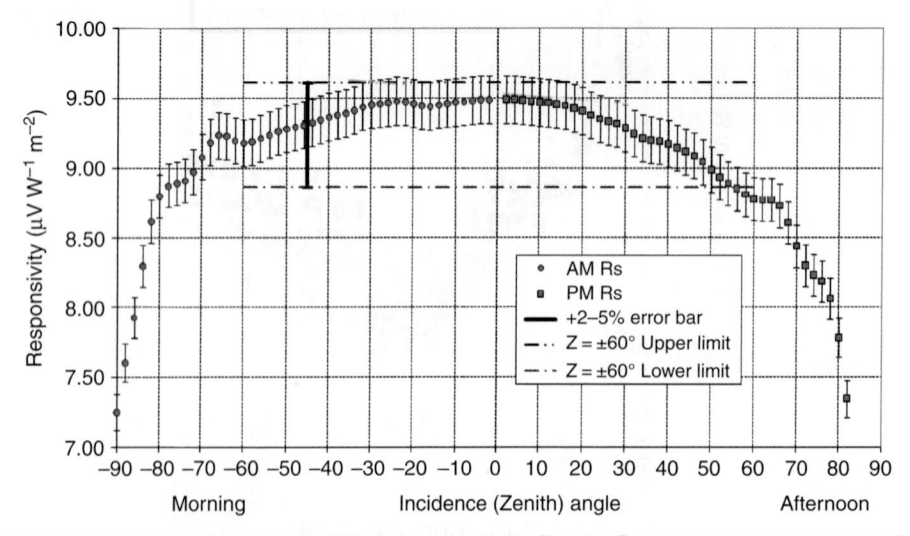

Figure 11 Typical pyranometer response as function of zenith angle throughout a day. Negative Z angles correspond to morning. 1.8% error bar on each R_s, and limits of +2% and 5% bound data between $30° < Z < 60°$.

afternoon errors of overestimation (in the example of **Figure 11**) tend to cancel midday underestimation errors. For solar resource assessment purposes, relatively small contributions to the daily total of (clear-sky) solar resources come from the early morning and late afternoon ($Z < 60°$) part of the day.

For conversion system performance, acceptance testing, or rating, the story is a little different. Minute-by-minute system efficiency and performance data is a direct function of the available energy. For these tests, it is best to measure the solar resource as accurately as possible, for example, by applying the $R_s(Z)$ or responsivity as a function of zenith angle throughout the test period.

1.12.5 Modeling Solar Radiation

Different solar energy conversion systems configurations depend on different solar radiation components or combinations of components (hemispherical, direct, or diffuse). Concentrating systems rely on the availability of direct beam radiation. Low-concentration systems may be able to utilize some diffuse sky radiation through light trapping techniques. Fixed or variable tilt flat-plate collectors utilize all radiation components, possibly including ground-reflected radiation from behind the panels in the case of bifacial modules. Buildings and daylighting applications require solar components contributing to heat loads or available for skylight and window configurations.

Long-term measured solar radiation data sets are rare, have variable periods of record (with usually many data gaps), and vary in their ease of access. Measurement networks or stations providing high-accuracy, 'up-to-the-minute' measured data are typically oriented toward scientific research and are very sparse. Given the variety of solar radiation applications, and the small number of available measurements, solar radiation models are necessary to provide suitable information for solar energy conversion systems.

1.12.5.1 Physics-Based Models

Physics-based models use the principles of physics, radiative transfer, and the properties of the atmosphere. They can be complex, and usually require esoteric, rarely found input parameters. Examples are cloud droplet radii, aerosol size distributions, single scattering albedo, cloud layer heights, cloud types, and so on. Simple transmission and scattering functions for the atmosphere can be derived or parameterized from the complex functions in the most complicated physical models. These models generate clear-sky direct beam radiation and use correlations or special algorithms to generate the total hemispherical and or diffuse sky radiation. Examples include the popular Bird and Hulstrom [21, 22] clear-sky models and the REST2 model of Gueymard [23]. Survey articles covering such models have been published by several researchers in the journal literature [24, 25].

1.12.5.2 Empirical Models

Empirical or parametric models use correlations developed between input independent variables and solar radiation data as the dependent or output result. Linear or multilinear regression analyses relate the solar radiation output to functions of the independent variables. Independent variables often used are sunshine hours, temperature, cloud cover, and so on. An example is the so-called Ångstrom relation [26, 27] between daily total solar irradiance, G, and sunshine hours, H:

$$G = G_o(a + b(H/H_o))$$

where G_o is the ETR on a horizontal surface (ETR $\cos(Z)$), H is the number of hours of sunshine duration (defined by WMO as direct beam irradiance above $120\,\text{W m}^{-2}$), and H_o is the total maximum hours of sunshine possible for the day. G_o and H_o are computed from basic formulas [28].

Since temperature can be correlated with the solar radiation and relative humidity with temperature and dew point caution is needed here, as the independent variables are often cross-correlated. This multicollinearity inflates correlation coefficients [29]. Unstable model coefficients, that is, coefficients that change dramatically with differences in the input variable data sets, can result [29]. For example, in models 18 and 19 of [28], coefficients a, b, and c in a parabolic equation differ by 34, 25, and 97%. For two models based on identical cubic equation formulations in [28], namely models 20 and 21, the square term coefficients are different by 2218%. These models are often site-dependent and not generally applicable worldwide, unless the development and (independent, different) validation data sets are very comprehensive.

1.12.5.3 Satellite-Based Models

Brightness (radiance) data from geosynchronous weather satellite images can be transformed into solar radiation fluxes at the surface. This is the basis of satellite-based models. Combinations of physical and empirical correlations of solar radiation with variables such as surface albedo, cloud cover, and relations between radiation components are then used to produce radiation total hemispherical, diffuse sky on a horizontal surface, and direct beam radiation components [30–32]. Individual gridded or matrix layers of information are constructed from pixel brightness. Then ancillary information, usually from some other database such as aerosol climatology, snow cover, water vapor, ground albedo, and so on, are gridded or interpolated to match the desired grid size, and are combined to produce surface flux estimates.

1.12.5.4 Geographical Information System Models

Geographical Information Systems (GIS) represent a combination of the station and satellite-based approaches to modeling solar radiation. This approach is particularly powerful if complex terrain (say for distributed solar systems in mountains) is involved. GIS tools for importing digital terrain data, interpolating between station data, and overlaying gridded satellite data are quite powerful. Algorithms exist for computing the solar clear-sky total hemispheric irradiance that modify the irradiance with weather data and produce gridded map products (and the underlying data). Under the United Nations Solar and Wind Energy Program (UNEP), GIS toolkits have been developed allowing one to evaluate solar (and other renewable resources) potential for various countries. The toolkits permit the overlaying of land use, transmission line, road, railway, river, and political layers of information with the solar radiation information (typically 10 or 40 km spatial resolution) grids. Examples can be found on the National Renewable Energy Laboratory website at http://www.nrel.gov/international/geospatial_toolkits.html.

1.12.6 Converting Solar Radiation Data to Application-Specific Data

Typically, because it is the cheapest and most simple solar radiation measurement, the only available measured or modeled solar radiation data are global horizontal total hemispherical radiation. Conversion models are then used to derive estimates of the appropriate quantities, such as radiation on a tilted surface. The solar radiation scientific research community, peer-reviewed publications, and published reports are presently relied upon to evaluate, validate, and assess the quality of these conversion algorithms. The primary objective of many of the models is to compute total (global) hemispherical irradiance, sometimes decomposed into the direct normal irradiance and the sky diffuse irradiance. Examples include the METSTAT model of Maxwell [33] and other models based on meteorological inputs [34]. The next step is to estimate the solar resources available on various solar energy collector configurations. Algorithms are used to convert either available measured or modeled data (e.g., total hemispherical on a horizontal surface) to the radiation incident on some other configuration, a tilted plane, tracking focusing collector, window area, tilted roof, or building facade.

1.12.6.1 Estimating Hemispherical Radiation on a Tilt

Tilted surfaces may be fixed or variable in tilt angle. Examples include south-facing surfaces tilted at the latitude of a location and vertical surfaces facing various azimuth directions, or surfaces that track the sun or change their tilt from vertical east at sunrise, to horizontal at noon, to vertical west at sunset. The radiation on these surfaces is a combination of the direct beam (if the surface is hit by the beam radiation), a portion of the sky radiation from that portion of the sky seen by the surface, and ground-reflected radiation within the field of view of the surface.

Similar to horizontal surfaces, the incidence angle, θ, of the direct beam with respect to the normal perpendicular to the surface will determine the contribution of the direct beam component on a tilted surface, or plane of array, POA, B_t. B_t is just DNI $\times \cos(\theta)$. The contributions of the portions of the sky and ground-reflected radiation hitting the POA are much more variable and difficult to describe without direct measurement of the total hemispherical radiation in the POA. If the total hemispherical radiation on the POA, H_s, can be measured, and the direct beam, B, can be measured independently, the total diffuse radiation on a tilted surface, F_s, can be computed using the relation $F_s = H_s - B_t = H_s - B \times \cos(\theta)$.

Note that the total diffuse on a tilted surface, F_s, is the sum of the sky radiation, S_s, and ground-reflected radiation G_s, or $F_s = S_s + G_s$. It is a difficult measurement problem to separate the incident beam radiation, sky, and ground-reflected radiation from the total hemispherical radiation on a POA. Models have been developed to accomplish this, depending on the optical properties of the ground in the field of view of the tilted surface.

Many models have been derived for computing hemispherical radiation on a tilt from global horizontal hemispherical radiation. The most accurate models use at least two measured components to compute the irradiance on the tilted surface; however, a few (less accurate) models estimate the irradiance on a tilted surface from a single parameter, usually global horizontal irradiance. Validation of the modeled data against experimentally measured data has shown that these models possess systematic bias errors of 2–5% and random errors of 5–10% with respect to the validation data sets. One of the most popular and accurate of the former is the Perez Anisotropic Model for Diffuse on a tilted surface [35]. This model is embedded in many flat-plate photovoltaic performance models. The Perez model was developed using hourly average data and thermopile radiometer data. The Perez model has systematic and random errors on the lower end of the range of errors mentioned above. Applicability of the Perez model, or any of the transposition models, to higher time-resolution (e.g., sub-hourly) periods or data derived from nonthermopile radiometers is also an open research question.

1.12.6.2 Estimating Direct Beam (DNI) from Global Horizontal Radiation

A few models estimate direct beam from global horizontal radiation. The Maxwell DISC (Direct Solar Insolation Code) [36] and the Perez variation on this approach, DIRINT [37], are the most popular. The model is based on empirical relations between clearness indices: K_t, the ratio of ground global hemispherical radiation to ETR on a horizontal surface, ETR $\cos(Z)$, and K_n, the ratio of ground-measured direct beam to ETR direct beam. The model was derived using hourly average data and thermopile radiometer data. Applicability to higher time-resolution data and nonthermopile radiometers, which do not sense the entire solar spectrum, is an open research question. Basic systematic error in the DISC model is around $\pm 50\,\mathrm{W\,m^{-2}}$, with random errors on the order of $\pm 150\,\mathrm{W\,m^{-2}}$ in hourly data. The model was developed and validated using mid-latitude data in the United States, so it may not have included a wide enough range of solar elevation angles to be appropriate for worldwide application, but the model has been checked for northern European sites as well as US sites with results similar to those quoted above.

1.12.6.3 Estimating Diffuse Hemispherical Radiation from Global or DNI

Diffuse sky radiation is often a relatively small part (<30%) of the total hemispherical radiation under clear and partly cloudy conditions. Global hemispherical and diffuse sky radiation should be identical for dense overcast conditions. Estimates of the diffuse may be needed in conjunction with global hemispherical data to estimate direct beam (as in the Maxwell DISC model discussed above). Diffuse sky radiation is also useful for daylighting applications. Many models based on empirical correlations between global hemispherical and diffuse sky radiation data have been developed, the most famous of which is due to Liu and Jordan [38], for estimating monthly average hourly diffuse horizontal radiation. Many other examples are to be found in the literature [39–41], generally use correlations of K_t and K_d [(diffuse sky radiation)/ETR $\times \cos(Z)$]. These models have large ($\pm 30\%$) scatter about regression formulas of K_d versus K_t.

1.12.7 Measured and Model Data Set Properties

Applying solar and meteorological data from different sources requires attention to the following key considerations:

Period of record. Solar resource data vary from year to year, seasonally, monthly, weekly, daily, and on timescales down to a few seconds. For this reason, climate normals are based on 30 years of meteorological data, and updated every 10 years. A popular approach is to produce a Typical Meteorological Year (TMY) data set from a statistical analysis of multiyear data, preferably the same 30-year period corresponding to climate normals, to derive a single year of data representative of a longer-term record [42, 43].

Temporal resolution. Solar resource data can range from annually averaged daily-integrated power (kWh day^{-1}) typically used for mapping resource distributions to 1 s samples of irradiance (W m^{-2}) for operational time-series analyses. As mentioned above, hourly averages, and monthly average daily total integrated data are popular. Daily total radiation values in either megajoules or kilowatt-hours are sometimes used in system simulation programs.

Spatial coverage. The area represented by the data can range from a single station, a sample geographic region, or to a global perspective.

Spatial resolution. Ground-based measurements are site-specific. Current satellite-remote sensing estimates can be representative of 10 km × 10 km or less or larger areas, such as 1° by 1° latitude–longitude grids.

Data elements and sources of the data. The usefulness of solar resource data may depend on the available data elements (especially DNI) and whether the data were measured, modeled, or produced in combination.

Data quality control and quality assessments. A description of the measurement operations, model validation methods, and data adjustments or corrections to indicate data quality.

Estimated uncertainties. Stated uncertainties should include a description of the methodology used to provide this information.

Availability. Are data distributed in the public domain, for purchase, or license?

Updates. The need to include the most recent data and other revisions require database updates.

Some detailed discussion on these topics follows.

1.12.7.1 Period of Record

Few sets of measured data for long periods of record (i.e., more than a few years) are available to the public. Examples are:

University of Oregon Solar monitoring network (since 1975 at some sites in northwest US): http://solardat.uoregon.edu

National Renewable Energy Laboratory Solar Radiation Research Laboratory (since 1981): http://www.nrel.gov/solar_radiation/data.html

US Department of Energy (DOE) Atmospheric Radiation Measurement sites (since 1997): http://www.arm.gov/measurements

BSRN (since approximately the mid-1990s but varies by station): http://www.bsrn.awi.de/en/home

World Meteorological Organization World Radiation Data Center (WMO/WRDC): (mostly daily total radiation values) http://wrdc.mgo.rssi.ru

Some modeled data sets, such as

US National Solar Radiation Data Base (NSRDB) [44–46]: http://rredc.nrel.gov/solar/old_data/nsrdb/
National Aeronautics and Space Administration Surface Solar Energy (NASA SSE) data set [47]: http://eosweb.larc.nasa.gov/sse/
European Solar Radiation Atlas (ESRA) [48–50]: http://www.helioclim.net/esra/index.html

contain modeled data over extended periods of time (20–30 years). The preferred period for TMY data sets is the 30-year climate normal period, as it has been shown that shorter periods represent less faithfully the average conditions for the longer period [51].

1.12.7.2 Temporal Resolution

Hourly average solar radiation data have been the most prevalent time resolution for solar radiation data (measured or modeled) to date. Measured data have usually been averaged over an hour, based on measurements at higher-resolution (e.g., 1, 5, or 10 min) intervals. The underlying higher time-resolution data are usually not available.

The WMO World Radiation Data Center (WRC) in St. Petersburg, Russia, is the designated WMO archive for daily solar radiation data in the form of daily total radiation, typically global hemispherical radiation, summed over daylight hours. Monthly averages (e.g., monthly average daily total of hourly data) are popular to evaluate the suitability of a proposed solar energy conversion system. Because of the impact of transient effects of clouds on the transient response of large photovoltaic systems and the stability of the electric grid, efforts are being initiated to produce higher time-resolution measured and modeled data down to 1 min, or even 1 s intervals.

The NSRDB for the United States hosts hourly data. The highest time-resolution NASA SSE data are daily totals. Stations in the WMO/WRC data archive report daily totals (usually of percent sunshine and/or global horizontal daily totals), and the period of record for individual stations varies widely from a few months to years.

1.12.7.3 Spatial Coverage

Solar radiation measurements at a single station represent point measurements. Networks of stations separated by microscale (less than a kilometer), mesoscale (up to 40 km), and larger (1° of latitude by 1° of longitude, about 250 km square) can provide data for specific regions. However, microclimates induced by coastlines, mountains, mountain to piedmont transitions, desert regions with dry lakebeds, and so on, are very difficult to characterize even with relatively dense measurement networks. Analysis of measured and modeled data correlations with distances between stations show that correlations fall off with both increasing station spacing, and with higher time-resolution (e.g., 15 min vs. hourly) data integration periods. One study of 17 sites in Wisconsin [52] showed that correlations for hourly data fall from 0.995 to 0.97 as spacing increases from 5 to 60 km. For 15 min data, the correlations fall from 0.98 to less than 0.75 at more than 100 km spacing.

Prevailing winds and cloud motion patterns can also affect both spatial and temporal variability over distances from a few kilometers to hundreds of kilometers. A study of a dense solar measurement network in Oklahoma [57] showed correlation between stations degrade from 95% or better for nearby stations to less than 45% for stations >300 km away, depending on the geographical relationship (east, west, northwest, etc.) between the stations. Attempts to interpolate 'between stations' to estimate solar resources should be used with caution.

Spatial coverage by geosynchronous satellites appears to be highly advantageous, but even at 37 000 km altitude, even high-resolution sensors are affected by curvature of the Earth, resulting in the projection effects with respect to higher latitudes. Acquiring the appropriate ancillary data for the state of the atmosphere at the same spatial resolution as the satellite images (often better than 1 km) is problematical as well. Satellites are not perfectly stable in their orbits, and navigational corrections are constantly needed to negate drift in the apparent locations within the images.

GIS-based estimates face many of the same problems as the satellite models, especially regarding ancillary atmospheric parameter data, and not only the spatial but also temporal or timing increment basis of the information. While powerful, the accuracy and usefulness of data interpolated to high spatial resolution requires careful analysis.

1.12.7.4 Modeled Data Sets

The so-called 'Typical Meteorological Year' (TMY) data sets mentioned above are important site-specific data sets representing the so-called normal conditions. TMY data sets were originally designed for building heating and cooling load calculations. Data for a given TMY month are near (but not equal to) the weighted mean of meteorological parameters (e.g., temperature, wind speed, etc.) and solar radiation for all months in the period of record (generally, 30 years is preferred) that the TMY represents. The TMY consists of 8760 hourly data points for a single, synthetic year. The representative months may come from different years but are joined together to give a continuous yearly time-series. These data sets are used mainly to evaluate relative performance of different conversion system designs with respect to a 'standard' data set and may not be appropriate for optimizing performance. The DOE EnergyPlus data sets [36] contain TMY-derived and TMY-like data sets for many world cities, as well as access to some real-time measurement data.

Examples of modeled data sets with hourly time resolution that are available to the public, either free online or for purchase, are the above-mentioned US NSRDB, the Swiss Meteotest METEONORM software (worldwide coverage), the European Solar Radiation Atlas (European coverage), the NASA SSE data set, and the DOE EnergyPlus weather data sets, similar to TMY years (worldwide coverage).

1.12.8 Model Estimate Uncertainties

Empirical models derived from correlations of measured data with independent parameters inherently carry measurement uncertainty embedded in model. Models based on 2, 5, or 10% accurate data can be no more accurate than the data used to generate the model. Typically, scatter about model regression lines increases the random component of uncertainty further. Models based on first principles of physics and radiation transfer cannot be validated or verified to accuracy any greater than that of the measurements. The uncertainties, including validation data uncertainties, accumulate in a fashion similar to the calibration transfer uncertainty increments shown in **Figure 9**.

Final uncertainties accounts for accuracy of measurement instrumentation, accounting for environmental influences, above and beyond calibration uncertainty. Station meteorological and Satellite data systematic (bias) and random values are typical values derived from mean bias differences and root mean square published in available satellite model validation studies. These must be combined with the measurement and environmental sources of uncertainty. Total expanded or final uncertainties are root sum square combinations of the bias (Type B uncertainties in the BIPM GUM) and (2 standard deviation) random components (Type A in the GUM) of uncertainty along with the measurement component, which cannot be eliminated. The latter, measurement component, is itself treated as random to account for the wide variety of conditions in which the limits of uncertainty can be achieved. For satellite data, additional sources of uncertainty – such as poor spatial resolution at high latitudes imaged at low incidence angles and coarse (typically 15–30 min) time resolution of images – can come into play. Table 1 shows a list of uncertainty sources for each solar component, and the total expanded uncertainty presently observed with respect to ground-based validation measurements.

Sample benchmarking of satellite-based data by the European Management and Exploitation of Solar Resource (MESOR) group has arrived at similar uncertainties for daily average estimates for total hemispherical radiation of about 9% and 20% for direct beam radiation. Model versus measurement validation of many of the empirical and station-based models can be found in several recent books, and often appear in the journal literature [37–39].

1.12.9 Developing Solar Radiation Resource Databases

Developing a solar radiation resource database is not easy. This section describes the development of the US 1961–90 National Solar Radiation Data Base (NSRDB) mentioned several times above. The NSRDB was developed at the US NREL, in conjunction with the National Oceanic and Atmospheric Administration (NOAA) National Climatic Data Center (NCDC), to meet the needs of the solar energy system designers for projects in the United States in the late twentieth century. Early in the twenty-first century, updates to the database to cover the period 1991–2005 were accomplished, using new and modified model approaches, including satellite-derived solar fluxes. These modifications will be briefly summarized.

1.12.9.1 Developing the NSRDB

The NSRDB, Version 1.1, was completed in March 1994 by NREL and was published by NOAA/NCDC. A complete detailed description of the NSRDB and how it was produced is presented in its *User's Manual NSRDB-Vol. 1*, and a Final Technical Report, published in 1992 [44, 45]. The NSRDB contains hourly values of measured or modeled solar radiation and meteorological data for 239 stations for the 30-year period from 1961 to 1990. WMO protocols call for the use of a 30-year period of record to establish normals, means, and extremes of meteorological variables. Because updates for normals, means, and extremes for the United States each decade, the period from January 1961 through December 1990, were used for the NSRDB. The foundation for the NSRDB is the (limited) hourly measured solar radiation data collected by the US National Weather Service (NWS) over several decades [46]. Although measured solar radiation data constitute less than 7% of the NSRDB up until 1991, and less than 0.5% of the 1991 to 2005 update to the NSRDB, they provided the benchmark for model estimates of solar radiation.

Table 1 List of uncertainty sources and total uncertainty

Uncertainty source	Total hemispherical (%)	Direct normal (%)	Diffuse (%)
Measurement (site/model development/validation)	6	5	6
Station meteorological data bias	2	4	2
Station meteorological data random (2 s)	8	15	8
Total expanded uncertainty: meteorological model	10	16	10
Satellite data bias	0	4	1
Satellite data random	5	14	5
Total expanded uncertainty: satellite model	8	15	8

The meteorological/statistical model (METSTAT) [33], developed at NREL, produced approximately 93% of the solar radiation data in the NSRDB. The model was developed using relatively good quality solar radiation data collected by the NWS from 1977 through 1980, for about 25 stations. These measured and modeled solar radiation data were combined with meteorological data (used by the solar energy industry to evaluate the performance of its systems) to form the NSRDB.

Besides solar radiation and meteorological elements, the database includes temperature, wind speed, precipitation, snow cover, aerosol optical depths (or turbidity), total precipitable water vapor, and codes for typical weather conditions (fog, haze, hail, rain, etc.). All data are referenced to local standard time. The solar radiation elements are the radiant energy integrated over the hour preceding the designated time. Meteorological elements are the values observed at the designated time. When a station contains only modeled solar radiation data, it is referred to as a Secondary station. Primary stations contain some measured solar radiation data for at least a portion of the 30-year record. The NSRDB contains a total of 56 Primary and 183 Secondary stations distributed rather uniformly over the United States.

1.12.9.2 Sources of Solar Radiation and Meteorological Data

The sources of solar radiation and meteorological data and the methods used to derive model estimates of solar radiation data in the NSRDB. This section also gives a flavor for the detailed work needed to produce such a solar resource data set.

1.12.9.2.1 Data acquisition
NCDC provided all of the meteorological data for the entire period of record. NCDC also provided solar radiation data that had been collected by NWS. Solar radiation data were also acquired from WEST Associates (a consortium of Southwest utilities), the University of Oregon, three DOE SEMRTS (Solar Energy & Meteorological Research & Training Sites), and the NREL Historically Black College and University (HBCU) network in the Southeast. Periodically, solar radiation data from other sources may be acquired and added to the database, creating updated versions.

1.12.9.2.2 Meteorological data – TD-3280
Most of the meteorological data (cloud cover observations, temperatures, relative humidity, wind speed and direction, etc.) required for the database were available from NCDC-archived TD-3280 tape deck files at NCDC with data from surface airways hourly observations.

1.12.9.2.3 Precipitable water
NCDC provided precipitable water within 5 atmospheric pressure levels from 1013 to 300 mB from radiosonde data. The values in the five layers were summed to obtain total precipitable water from the surface to 300 mB. The data indicate that no more than 1 mm of precipitable water is likely to exist above the 300 mB level. Linear interpolation between soundings was used to obtain hourly values of precipitable water. Hourly values were input to the model used to estimate solar radiation.

1.12.9.2.4 Snow depth – TD-3210
Snow depth data were used for estimating ground albedo. High-surface albedos produced by snow cover increases diffuse radiation from the clouds and atmosphere. Snow depth data were extracted by NREL from copies of TD-3210 archive tapes supplied by NCDC.

1.12.9.2.5 Ozone
Ozone data are not generally available for most locations for the entire period from 1961 to 1990. However, ozone has a relatively small effect on the transmittance of solar radiation between 0.3 and 3.0 μm. Thus, monthly mean values of ozone for geographic regions were obtained from surface and satellite data. These values were assumed to be the same for each year, and were incorporated into the model as a look-up table.

1.12.9.2.6 Filling gaps in the data record
Missing meteorological data had to be derived or created to produce serially complete model input data sets. Data were missing for periods ranging from an hour to a year. Short gaps in the data record were filled by linear interpolation between data points. For gaps of 48 h to 1 year, data from other years for the same time periods were selected to fill the gap. The selection was based on finding a year for which the data before and after the period of the gap had the best match with data before and after the actual gap.

1.12.9.2.7 Deriving precipitable water data
It is known that long-term monthly means of surface vapor pressure are well correlated with monthly means of total precipitable water. Correlations between hourly surface vapor pressure measurements and precipitable water were calculated from individual radiosonde soundings. Thus, surface temperature, relative humidity, and pressure data were used to derive hourly values of precipitable water for times and locations for which radiosonde data were not available.

1.12.9.2.8 Deriving broadband aerosol optical depth

Broadband aerosol optical depth data were linked to the METSTAT model used to estimate solar radiation. Algorithms were used to calculate direct normal transmittances for ozone absorption (T_o), Rayleigh scattering (T_r), absorption by uniformly mixed gases (T_g), and water vapor absorption (T_w) described in the section on Spectral Considerations. These were combined to obtain a value for molecular transmittance, T_m:

$$T_m = T_o T_r T_g T_w$$

Aerosol transmittance T_a was then calculated as $T_a = B/I_o T_m$ using B = the measured direct normal radiation and I_o = the extraterrestrial direct normal radiation to estimate transmission of aerosols only, T_a, as a function of optical depth t and path length (air mass) m from Beer's law, $T_a = e^{-tm}$. Thus, the broadband aerosol optical depth, t, is computed from $t = -\ln(T_a)/m$. This method produced broadband aerosol optical depths when measured direct normal data were already available.

Calculated aerosol optical depths were then used to derive seasonal functions for estimating aerosol optical depths for any day of the year. A sine function, $t = A \sin[(360/365)d - \phi]$, where d is the day of the year, A is a scaling coefficient, and ϕ is a phase shift angle to account for seasonal shifts in peak aerosols, produced the best fit to the data. Coefficients for the sine functions were then mapped to establish climatic/geographic relationships.

Laser-induced atmospheric reflection (LIDAR) measurements of the effects of volcanic eruptions, such as El Chichon, were used to determine the effects of other volcanic eruptions from 1961 through 1990. The effects of volcanic eruptions were used to form a look-up table of daily optical depth increases.

Interest in aerosol optical properties and the impact of aerosols has increased in the twenty-first century, so more measurement campaigns and data sets are becoming available. An example is the NASA AERONET network of sunphotometer data. This data set provides daily, monthly, annual, and climatological values of aerosol and precipitable water estimates for a large worldwide measurement network.

1.12.9.2.9 Modeling cloud transmittance, scattering, and statistical effects

The single largest modifier of solar radiation is clouds. The NSRDB data sources included opaque and translucent cloud cover estimates in tenths of sky cover. Empirical correlations were used to determine transmittance factors T_{opq} and T_{trn} for these respective parameters. These factors, as functions of cloud cover, are used to compute the direct normal transmittance, T_n, of the beam radiation:

$$T_n = T_o T_r T_g T_w T_a T_{opq} T_{trn}$$

More empirical algorithms were developed to account for scattering of radiation into the diffuse sky component by opaque and translucent clouds, K_{sopq} and K_{strn}, and angular and spatial diffusion of sky radiation by the Rayleigh and aerosol scattering centers, K_{sr}, K_{sa}. Some solar radiation is scattered from the ground back toward the atmosphere. Some backscattered radiation is in turn scattered back to the surface by the atmosphere and/or clouds, and the process repeats itself. This increases the total diffuse radiation incident upon the surface. The increase is a function of the albedo (solar spectrum reflectance) of the surface and the atmosphere and clouds, so algorithms for multiple ground/sky/cloud/ground reflections were developed.

The random effects of cloud position, type, and size dominate the random variation of the direct normal component of solar radiation. Cumulative frequency distributions (CFDs) of direct normal radiation were used to derive the CFDs representing the random effect of opaque cloud position. A random number generator with a uniform distribution from 0 to 1 was used with tables of the CFDs to obtain values of effective opaque cloud cover. These values were then used to calculate statistically representative cloud transmittances.

More recently, Internet availability of cloud cover estimates and properties of clouds are available through programs such as the International Satellite Cloud Climatology Program (ISCCP). Data sets such as these may be useful for future database development projects.

1.12.9.2.10 Output products and data quality checks

After the collection, organization, and filling of appropriate input meteorological (and when available, measured solar data sets), two paths of output product were available. Measured solar radiation data were evaluated for quality by comparison with physically realistic limits, comparison with clear-sky envelopes, or specially developed solar radiation data quality evaluation algorithms.

Where and when solar data were missing, the model algorithms were applied to the meteorological input data. The process included (1) deterministic (clear-sky) algorithms based on the transmission and scattering algorithms, (2) statistical algorithms to produce monthly statistics (means and standard deviations) then mimic as accurately as possible the monthly statistics of measured data, (3) quality assessment of the modeled data, using the component summation equation and comparison with measured data when available, and (4) assignment of source (measured, modeled) and uncertainty (estimated from combinations of model systematic and random errors, and measurement errors).

Each hourly data record for the period of record was then exported to a structured text file with data elements and associated source and uncertainty flags. From these hourly data records, product such as statistical summaries (month by month and averages and standard deviations for each year, and for the entire 30-year period of record) was produced. Finally, the entire detailed hourly data set and statistical summaries were published in CD-ROM format, and made available over the Internet through NREL and NCDC websites. Two volumes of documentation, a User's manual and a detailed technical report all totaling over 500 printed pages, were published [44, 45].

1.12.9.2.11 Updating the database

Once the 1961–90 NSRDB was completed and published in 1992, it became out of date with respect to more recent data. An update to provide data representative of more recent times was initiated in 2000 to provide a 1991–2000 update, eventually completed as a 1991–2005 update [53–55]. This update still included measured solar data when available. However, measured data were even rarer, devoted mainly to scientific research, and not resource assessment goals. The meteorological station-based approach, using basically the same METSTAT model, was used. Modifications to the model were required because cloud observations were now automated, and human-observed opaque and translucent coverage was lacking. This required changing the cloud cover transmittance algorithms in the METSTAT model. However, there were many more automated stations, over 1400, compared to the original 239 stations in the earlier NSRDB.

Second, satellite-based estimates of solar fluxes began to be developed in the late 1990s. These models permitted estimation of solar data over the entire nation at relatively high spatial resolution (10 km). In addition, the estimates are based on an actual measurement of photons (reflected irradiance from the Earth and atmosphere). For consistency, the METSTAT approach was applied to the larger station set (including overlap with the original 239 stations) [56]. The satellite models were used to produce 10 m gridded data sets for the United States, on an hourly basis, from 1998 to 2005. The resulting 1991–2005 NSRDB update includes 1400 station sites with METSTAT estimates for each hour of the 15-year period, and the hourly satellite-based estimate for each hour in the 1998–2005. This permits research into the relative differences between the two approaches for each hour. The 1995–2000 5-hourly data sets are available as station-specific or grid cell-specific downloads over the Internet directly from the NCDC, NREL, or through Internet tools such as the NREL Solar Power Prospector, (http://maps.nrel.gov/node/10) or NREL In My Backyard (http://www.nrel.gov/eis/imby) internet applications.

1.12.10 Applications: Calculating Solar Radiation for Flat-Plate and Concentrating Collectors

The primary application of solar radiation resource data is to produce estimates of the performance of solar energy conversion systems. These systems depend on the magnitude and quality (relative contribution of the various components) available to the particular configuration under study. A user may require hourly TMY data to run through a solar system performance calculator. He or she may want to run many years of data through a simulator to estimate interannual system performance and financial and economic variability.

Alternatively, a simple summary of monthly mean solar resources can be sufficient to establish the resources available to various system configurations over the long term. The 1961–90 NSRDB data set was used to generate a data manual product summarizing the monthly and annual resources available to popular solar collector configurations. This US Data Manual for Flat-Plate and Concentrating Solar Collectors summarizes monthly and yearly average solar radiation values for various flat-plate and concentrating collectors to enable quick estimates of the incident solar energy for common collectors. The approach used in producing these summaries is quite similar to the approach used in most hour-by-hour solar conversion system simulation programs, so is outlined here.

Statistical summaries of solar radiation values were computed from the hourly values using a diffuse irradiance on tilted surfaces conversion model and NSRDB values of direct beam and diffuse horizontal solar radiation. The total solar radiation received by a flat-plate collector (G_p) is a combination of direct beam radiation (B), diffuse sky radiation (F_s), and radiation reflected from the surface in front of the collector (R_g):

$$G_p = B\cos(\theta) + F_s + R_g$$

where θ is the incident angle of the sun's rays to the collector. For tracking collectors, these algorithms also were used to compute collector tilt angles from the horizontal. Direct beam solar radiation hourly values from the NSRDB were used to determine the direct beam contribution ($B\cos(\theta)$) for each hour. Except for the first and last daylight hour, incident angles were calculated at the midpoint of the hour. For the first and last daylight hours, incident angles were calculated at the midpoint of the period during the hour when the sun was above the horizon.

The diffuse (sky) radiation, F_s, received by the collector was calculated by an anisotropic diffuse radiation model developed by R. Perez of the State University of New York at Albany. The model is an improved and refined version of their original model that was recommended by the International Energy Agency for calculating diffuse radiation for tilted surfaces. This model is often embedded in solar energy system simulation software. The Perez model equation for diffuse sky radiation for a tilted surface is

$$F_p = F[0.5(1-F_1)(1+\cos(\beta)) + F_1(a/b) + F_2\sin(\beta)]$$

where F = diffuse solar horizontal radiation, F_1 = circumsolar anisotropy coefficient, function of sky condition, F_2 = horizon/zenith anisotropy coefficient, function of sky condition, β = tilt of the collector from the horizontal, $a = 0$ or the cosine of the incident angle, whichever is greater, and $b = 0.087$ or the cosine of the solar zenith angle, whichever is greater.

The model coefficients F_1 and F_2 are organized as an array of values that are selected for use depending on the solar zenith angle, the sky's clearness, and the sky's brightness.

Ground-reflected radiation received by a collector is a function of the global horizontal radiation (G), the tilt of the collector from the horizontal (β), and the surface reflectivity or albedo (ρ):

$$R_g = 0.5\rho G[1-\cos(\beta)]$$

Surface albedo was adjusted depending on the presence of snow cover, as indicated by the snow depth data in the NSRDB.

The concentrating collectors portrayed in the manual have small fields-of-view and do not receive diffuse (sky) radiation or ground-reflected radiation. Consequently, solar radiation for these concentrating collectors is solely a function of the direct beam radiation and the sun's incident angle to the collector. Solar radiation received by the concentrating collectors, B_c, simplifies to

$$B_c = B\cos(\theta)$$

Example summary tables from the data manual for a single 1961–90 NSRDB station, Sacramento, California, are shown in **Table 2** for several popular collector system configurations.

Table 2 Representative solar collector configuration solar resources for Sacramento, California

	Value	Jan	Feb	Mar	Apr	May	Jun	Jul	Aug	Sep	Oct	Nov	Dec	Year
(a) Solar radiation for flat-plate collectors facing south at a fixed tilt (kWh m^{-2} day)														
Tilt														
0	Average	1.9	3.0	4.3	5.9	7.2	7.9	7.9	7.0	5.7	4.0	2.4	1.7	4.9
	Minimum	1.6	2.3	3.4	4.6	6.2	7.0	7.4	6.3	5.1	3.5	1.9	1.4	4.6
	Maximum	2.4	3.8	5.4	6.6	7.8	8.4	8.2	7.4	6.1	4.3	3.0	2.3	5.1
Latitude – 15	Average	2.6	3.9	5.2	6.5	7.3	7.6	7.8	7.5	6.7	5.3	3.3	2.4	5.5
	Minimum	1.9	2.8	3.9	4.9	6.2	6.8	7.3	6.7	5.9	4.4	2.3	1.7	5.1
	Maximum	3.6	5.3	6.6	7.2	7.9	8.1	8.1	7.9	7.2	5.8	4.5	3.7	5.8
Latitude	Average	2.9	4.2	5.4	6.3	6.8	7.0	7.2	7.2	6.9	5.7	3.7	2.7	5.5
	Minimum	2.0	2.9	3.9	4.7	5.9	6.2	6.7	6.4	5.9	4.8	2.5	1.8	5.0
	Maximum	4.1	5.9	6.9	7.1	7.4	7.4	7.5	7.6	7.3	6.3	5.1	4.4	5.9
Latitude + 15	Average	3.1	4.3	5.2	5.9	6.0	6.0	6.3	6.5	6.6	5.8	3.9	2.9	5.2
	Minimum	2.0	2.9	3.8	4.4	5.2	5.4	5.8	5.8	5.7	4.8	2.5	1.8	4.7
	Maximum	4.3	6.2	6.8	6.6	6.5	6.3	6.4	6.9	7.1	6.4	5.4	4.7	5.6
90	Average	2.7	3.6	3.8	3.6	3.0	2.7	2.9	3.6	4.5	4.6	3.4	2.6	3.4
	Minimum	1.6	2.3	2.8	2.7	2.7	2.5	2.8	3.3	3.9	3.8	2.1	1.5	3.0
	Maximum	3.9	5.2	5.0	4.0	3.2	2.8	2.9	3.7	4.8	5.2	4.9	4.4	3.8
(b) Solar radiation for 2-axis tracking flat-plate collectors (kWh m^{-2} day)														
Tracker														
2-Axis	Average	3.4	5.0	6.7	8.6	10.2	11.0	11.4	10.4	9.2	7.2	4.5	3.2	7.6
	Minimum	2.1	3.2	4.6	6.0	8.4	9.4	10.4	9.1	7.6	5.8	2.8	1.9	6.7
	Maximum	5.0	7.4	9.1	9.9	11.4	12.2	12.0	11.3	10.0	8.1	6.4	5.5	8.1
(c) Solar radiation for 1-axis tracking flat-plate collectors with a north-south axis (kWh m^{-2} day)														
Axis tilt														
0	Average	2.5	4.0	5.9	8.1	9.9	10.8	11.1	10.0	8.3	5.8	3.3	2.2	6.8
	Minimum	1.7	2.7	4.1	5.7	8.2	9.2	10.1	8.8	6.8	4.8	2.2	1.5	6.2
	Maximum	3.4	5.7	7.9	9.3	11.1	11.9	11.7	10.8	9.0	6.5	4.5	3.5	7.2
Latitude – 15	Average	3.0	4.7	6.6	8.6	10.1	10.8	11.2	10.4	9.1	6.8	4.0	2.8	7.3
	Minimum	2.0	3.0	4.5	5.9	8.3	9.2	10.2	9.1	7.5	5.6	2.6	1.8	6.5
	Maximum	4.3	6.8	8.9	9.8	11.3	11.9	11.8	11.2	9.9	7.6	5.6	4.6	7.8
Latitude	Average	3.3	4.9	6.7	8.5	9.8	10.3	10.8	10.2	9.2	7.1	4.3	3.0	7.4
	Minimum	2.0	3.2	4.6	5.9	8.0	8.8	9.8	8.9	7.5	5.8	2.7	1.9	6.5
	Maximum	4.7	7.3	9.1	9.8	10.9	11.4	11.3	11.1	10.0	7.9	6.1	5.1	7.9
Latitude + 15	Average	3.4	5.0	6.6	8.2	9.2	9.7	10.1	9.8	9.0	7.2	4.5	3.2	7.2
	Minimum	2.1	3.2	4.5	5.6	7.6	8.2	9.2	8.5	7.4	5.8	2.7	1.9	6.3
	Maximum	4.9	7.4	9.0	9.4	10.3	10.6	10.6	10.6	9.8	8.0	6.4	5.4	7.7

(Continued)

Table 2 (Continued)

	Value	Jan	Feb	Mar	Apr	May	Jun	Jul	Aug	Sep	Oct	Nov	Dec	Year
(d) Direct beam solar radiation for concentrating collectors (kWh m^{-2} day)														
Tracker														
1-X, E-W HZ Axis	Average	1.8	2.6	3.4	4.3	5.5	6.2	6.6	5.8	5.2	4.1	2.5	1.7	4.1
	Minimum	0.7	1.2	1.8	2.1	4.0	4.9	5.6	4.7	3.8	3.2	1.1	0.6	3.4
	Maximum	3.0	4.6	5.3	5.4	6.5	7.3	7.1	6.6	5.8	4.8	4.1	3.6	4.6
1-X, N-S HZ Axis	Average	1.3	2.4	3.8	5.6	7.3	8.3	8.8	7.7	6.3	4.1	2.0	1.2	4.9
	Minimum	0.5	1.0	2.0	2.8	5.3	6.4	7.4	6.3	4.4	3.1	0.9	0.4	4.1
	Maximum	2.2	4.2	6.1	7.0	8.7	9.8	9.6	8.8	7.2	4.9	3.2	2.5	5.3
1-X, N-S Tilt=Lat	Average	1.9	3.1	4.4	5.9	7.1	7.8	8.4	7.9	7.1	5.2	2.8	1.8	5.3
	Minimum	0.8	1.4	2.3	2.9	5.2	6.0	7.1	6.4	5.0	3.9	1.3	0.7	4.4
	Maximum	3.2	5.5	7.1	7.4	8.5	9.2	9.1	8.9	8.0	6.1	4.6	3.8	5.8
2-X	Average	2.1	3.2	4.4	6.0	7.5	8.4	9.0	8.1	7.1	5.3	2.9	1.9	5.5
	Minimum	0.8	1.4	2.3	3.0	5.5	6.5	7.6	6.6	5.0	4.0	1.3	0.7	4.5
	Maximum	3.5	5.7	7.1	7.5	9.0	10.0	9.8	9.2	8.0	6.2	4.8	4.1	6.1
(e) Average climatic conditions														
Element														
Temperature (°C)		7.3	10.4	12.0	14.6	18.5	22.0	24.3	23.9	21.9	17.9	11.8	7.4	16.0
Daily minimum (°C)		3.2	5.2	6.2	7.5	10.2	12.9	14.5	14.4	13.2	10.2	6.3	3.2	8.9
Daily maximum (°C)		11.5	15.6	17.8	21.7	26.8	31.0	34.0	33.4	30.7	25.5	17.3	11.5	23.1
Record low (°C)		−5.0	−5.0	−3.3	0.0	2.2	5.0	8.9	9.4	6.1	2.2	−3.3	−7.8	−7.8
Record high (°C)		21.1	24.4	31.1	33.9	40.6	46.1	45.6	42.8	42.2	38.3	30.6	22.2	46.1
HDD, base = 18.3 C		341.0	222.0	198.0	128.0	44.0	7.0	0.0	0.0	9.0	43.0	195.0	339.0	1527.0
CDD, base = 18.3 C		0.0	0.0	0.0	16.0	49.0	117.0	184.0	174.0	117.0	29.0	0.0	0.0	687.0
Relative humidity percent		83.0	77.0	72.0	64.0	59.0	55.0	53.0	56.0	57.0	63.0	76.0	83.0	66.0
Wind speed (m s^{-1})		2.5	3.1	3.5	3.6	3.9	4.0	3.8	3.6	3.1	2.5	2.5	2.5	3.2

Station No. 23232, Latitude (N): 38.52, Longitude (W): 121.50, Elevation (m): 8, Station Pressure (mB): 1015, Station Type: Secondary. (a) Flat-plate collectors facing south at a fixed-tilt; (b) 2-axis tracking flat-plate collectors; (c) 1-axis tracking flat-plate collectors with a north–south axis; (d) direct beam solar radiation for concentrating collectors; (e) average climatic conditions. HDD are equivalent heating degree days, the sum of the product of the number of hours where the temperature was lower than the base level, and the difference between the base and ambient temperature, converted to days. CDD are equivalent cooling degree days, the sum of the product of the number of hours where the temperature was higher than the base level and the difference between the temperature and the base level, converted to days. Source: NREL Data Manual for Flat-Plate and Concentrating Solar Collectors.

Table 2 includes maximum and minimum values for monthly solar radiation resources. The user is able to see the range of variability encountered over the 30-year period of record. For example, the tables show that a concentrating system has the highest available annual average solar resource of 7.6 kWh m^{-2} day. The resource can vary up to ±0.85 kWh m^{-2} day or about ±11% over 30 years. Thus, there can be up to a 22% difference from one year to the next.

Flat-plate fixed tilt at latitude collectors average 5.5 kWh m^{-2} day of available resource. That resource can vary about ±0.5 kWh m^{-2} day, or also ±10%, with a difference of 20% from year to year possible. The designer must factor in infrastructure costs, load requirements (which may be a function of the climatic conditions), financial restrictions, and so on, to determine which system design meets the client's needs.

As of 2010, there are a number of Internet tools that permit the hour by hour and monthly summarized simulation of photovoltaic and hybrid renewable energy conversion systems. Despite their sophistication, those tools all rely on the sort of solar radiation resource data described here to produce output results. The quality of the output from those tools is directly proportional to the quality of the input data, which is why solar radiation resource data are a focus of continued research and development.

1.12.11 Future Directions

Because of the important role of solar radiation resource input data and system simulation output, the International Energy Agency (IEA) has in the past conducted research on radiometer performance, calibration and correction techniques, solar radiation modeling, and model validation. With the explosion in satellite and computer technology and Internet connectivity, an IEA task on Solar Resource Knowledge Management (IEA Task 36) was established. This activity is an international undertaking to provide the solar energy industry, the electricity sector, governments, and renewable energy organizations and institutions with the most suitable and accurate information of the solar radiation resources at the Earth's surface in easily accessible formats and understandable quality metrics.

The main objectives of this task are

- The standardization and benchmarking of international solar resource data sets
- To provide improved data reliability, availability, and accessibility
- To develop methods that improve the quality and the spatial and temporal coverage.

Subtask activities to meet this objective are

- Select and qualify ground data: survey and document of existing data sources, and the production and reporting of validation data
- Define measures of model quality for product validation: and model intercomparison procedures
- Develop methods for establishing coherent benchmarking of products
- Apply benchmarking procedures to include characterization of model performance as a function of input data sets.

Newer approaches to evaluating model performance and quality of satellite data estimates versus ground validation data have been developed. The main new tool now being used to evaluate model quality is not just systematic or random error, but comparisons of cumulative frequency or probability distributions of the data using the Kolmogorov–Smirnov statistic. This statistic measures the difference the distributions of modeled and measured or other comparable data sets to give a quantitative value for the data or model quality. Approaches to providing a centralized data portal on the Internet for accessing high-quality and properly distributed resource data sets are being developed.

Forecasting of solar radiation resources is of importance to large, utility scale multisquare kilometer systems and mesoscale distributed energy systems with respect to the stability of the utility grid. Techniques for using numerical weather forecasting models in conjunction with solar radiation estimates from satellites are under development. Operation tools for these applications are needed before large-scale penetration of solar renewable energy systems into the electricity infrastructure can be fully accepted.

In the past, a map of annual average solar radiation for a specific conversion system, such as **Figure 12**, showing direct normal annual average resources for a concentrator system, might help a designer start down the road of evaluating the potential of site. In the future, a 15 min, hourly, or 6 hourly forecasts, on a continuing real time basis, for solar radiation resource availability, such as shown in **Figure 13**, will be required. Getting to that point with sufficient accuracy and reliability relies on expertise and innovation as the future of solar radiation resource assessment.

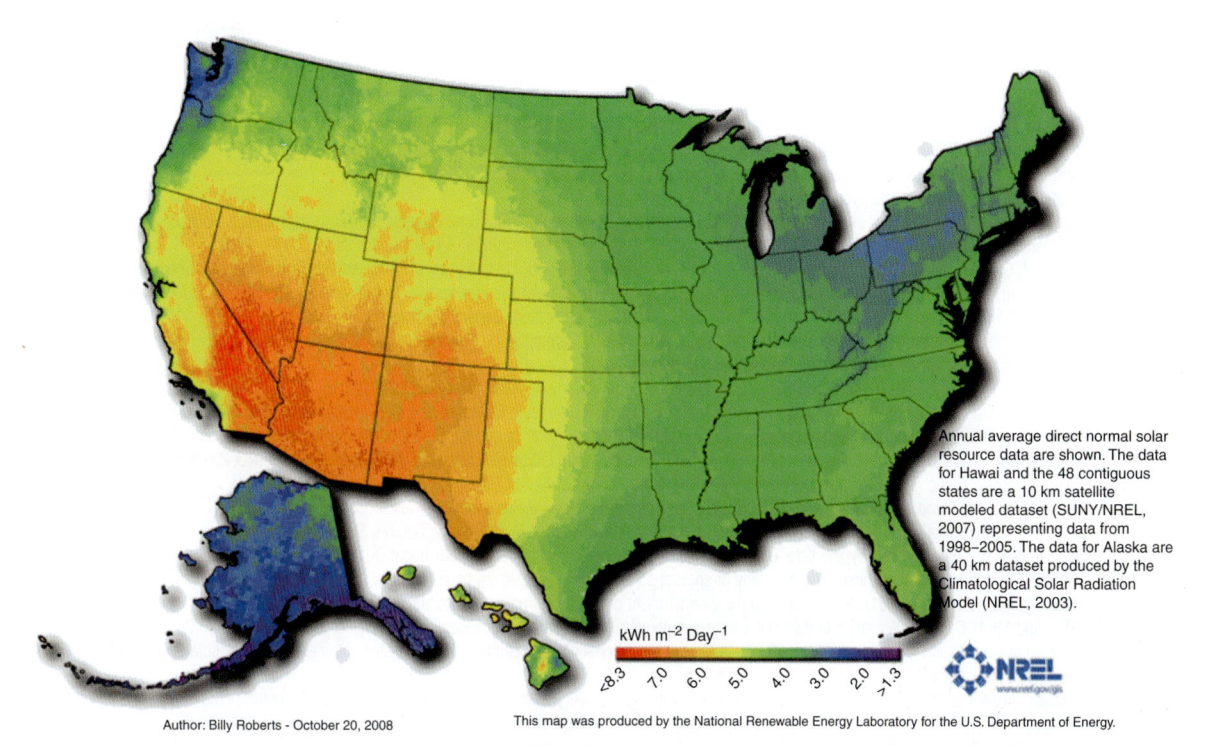

Figure 12 Annual average direct beam irradiance resource for concentrating solar power systems for the United States. A high resolution (10 km) grid GIS product presently available for evaluating potential solar system sites.

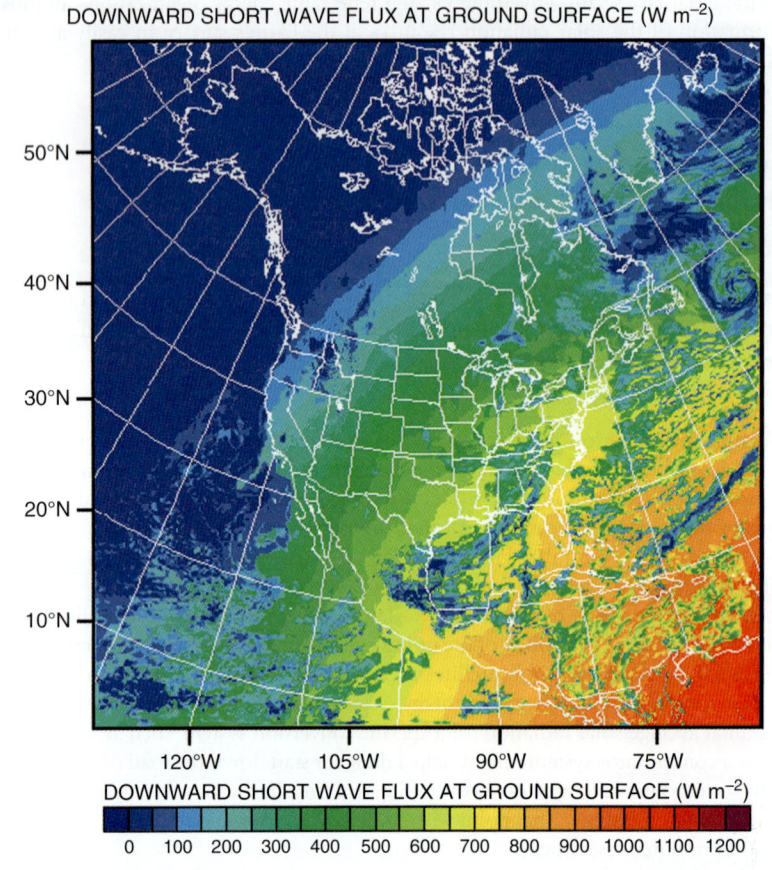

Figure 13 Simulated 6 h forecast of global horizontal solar radiation resource derived from high time and space resolution satellite data and numerical weather prediction models for the North and Middle Americas. In the future, updates on periods of as little as 15 min may be needed by utility scale entities.

References

[1] Field H (1997) Solar cell spectral response measurement errors related to spectral band width and chopped light waveform. In: *26th IEEE Photovoltaic Specialists Conference*, pp. 471–474, NREL/CP-530-22969, Anaheim, CA, 29 September–3 October. Golden, CO: National Renewable Energy Laboratory.
[2] Kendall JM and Berdahl CM (1970) Two blackbody radiometers of high accuracy. *Applied Optics* 9(5), 1082–1091.
[3] Willson RC (1980) Active cavity radiometer type V. *Applied Optics* 19(19), 3256–3257.
[4] Mekaoui Si, Dewitte S, Crommelynck D, et al. (2004) Absolute accuracy and repeatability of the RMIB radiometers for TSI measurements. *Solar Physics* 224, 237–246.
[5] Brusa RW and Frohlich C (1986) Absolute radiometers (PMO6) and their experimental characterization. *Applied Optics* 25(22), 4173–4180.
[6] Hickey JR, Alton BM, Griffin FJ, et al. (1982) Extraterrestrial solar irradiance variability two and one-half years of measurements from Nimbus 7. *Solar Energy* 29(2), 125–127.
[7] Rüedi I, Fröhlich C, and Schmutz W, Wehrli Ch (2000) Report on the International Pyrheliometer Comparisons – The Maintenance and Dissemination of the World Radiometric Reference. IOM Report No. 74 (WMO/TD-No. 1028), 64–67. World Meteorological Organization, Geneva, Switzerland.
[8] WMO (2008) Measurement of radiation, in World Meteorological Organization (WMO) Committee on Instrumentation, Measurements, and Observations (CIMO) Guide No. 8. *Guide to Meteorological Instruments and Methods of Observation.* Switzerland: WMO.
[9] Romero J, Fox NP, and Fröhlich C (1991) First comparison of the solar and an SI radiometric scale. *Metrologia* 28, 125.
[10] Romero J, Fox NP, and Fröhlich C (1995/1996) Improved comparison of the World Radiometric Reference and the SI radiometric scale. *Metrologia* 32(6), 523–524.
[11] Romero J, Fox NP, and Fröhlich C (2008) Third comparison of the World Radiometric Reference and the SI radiometric scale. *Metrologia* 45, 377–381.
[12] Reda I (1996) Calibration of a solar absolute cavity radiometer with traceability to the world radiometric reference. *NREL Report No. TP-463-20619*, p. 79, Golden, CO: National Renewable Energy Laboratory. http://www.nrel.gov/docs/legosti/fy96/20619.pdf.
[13] ASTM Standard G167 (2010) *Standard Test Method for Calibration of a Pyranometer Using a Pyrheliometer.* West Conshohocken, PA: ASTM International. wwww.astm.org.
[14] ISO Standard 9059 (1990) *Calibration of Field Pyrheliometers by Comparison to a Reference Pyrheliometer.* Geneva, Switzerland: International Organization for Standards.
[15] ISO Standard 9846 (1993) *Calibration of a Pyranometer Using a Pyrheliometer.* Geneva, Switzerland: International Organization for Standards.
[16] Gulbrandsen A (1978) On the use of pyranometers in the study of spectral solar radiation and atmospheric aerosols. *Journal of Applied Meteorology* 17, 899–904.
[17] Haefflin M, Kato S, Smith AM, et al. (2001) Determination of the thermal offset of the Eppley precision spectral pyranometer. *Applied Optics* 40(4), 472–484.
[18] Reda I, Stoffel T, and Myers D (2003) A method to calibrate a solar pyranometer for measuring reference diffuse irradiance. *Solar Energy* 74, 103–112.
[19] International Bureau of Weights and Measures (BIPM) (2008) Evaluation of measurement data – Guide to the expression of uncertainty in measurement JCGM 100. http://www.bipm.org/utils/common/documents/jcgm/JCGM_100_2008_E.pdf
[20] Reda I, Myers D, and Stoffel T (2008) Uncertainty estimate for the outdoor calibration of solar pyranometers: A metrologist perspective. *Journal of Measurement Science* 3(4), 58–66.
[21] Bird RE and Hulstrom RL (1981) Review, evaluation, and improvement of direct irradiance models. *Journal of Solar Energy Engineering* 103, 182–1992.
[22] Bird RE and Hulstrom RL (1981) A simplified clear sky model for direct and diffuse insolation on horizontal surfaces. *SERI/TR-642-751.* Golden, CO: Solar Energy Research Institute, 46 p. http://www.nrel.gov/docs/legosti/old/761.pdf
[23] Gueymard C (2008) REST2: High-performance solar radiation model for cloudless-sky irradiance, illuminance, and photosynthetically active radiation – Validation with a benchmark data set. *Solar Energy* 82, 272–285.

[24] Ineichen P (2006) Comparison of eight clear sky broadband models against 16 independent data banks. *Solar Energy* 80, 468–478.
[25] Perez R and Stewart R (1986) Solar irradiance conversion models. *Solar Cells* 18, 213–222.
[26] Prescott JA (1940) Evaporation from water surface in relation to solar radiation. *Transactions Royal Society of Australia* 46, 114–118.
[27] Gueymard C and Estrada-Cajigal V (1995) A critical look at recent interpretations of the Angstrom approach and its future in global solar radiation prediction. *Solar Energy* 54(5), 357–363.
[28] Menges HO, Ertekin C, and Sonmete MH (2006) Evaluation of global solar radiation models for Konya, Turkey. *Energy Conversion and Management* 47, 3149–3173.
[29] Myers R (2006) *Classical and Modern Regression with Applications*, 2nd edn. Pacific Grove, CA: Duxbury Press.
[30] Perez R, Ineichen P, Moore K, et al. (2002) A new operational model for satellite-derived irradiances: description and validation. *Solar Energy* 73(5), 307–317.
[31] Rigollier C, Lefèvre M, and Wald L (2004) The method Heliosat-2 for deriving shortwave solar radiation data from satellite images. *Solar Energy* 77(2), 159–169.
[32] Pinker RT, Frouin R, and Li Z (1995) A review of satellite methods to derive surface shortwave irradiance. *Remote Sensing of Environment* 51(1), 108–124.
[33] Maxwell EL (1998) METSTAT: The solar radiation model used in the production of the National Solar Radiation Data Base (NSRDB). *Solar Energy* 62(4), 263–279.
[34] Muneer T, Gul MS, and Kubie J (2000) Models for estimating radiation and illuminance from meteorological parameters. *Journal of Solar Energy Engineering* 122, 146–153.
[35] Perez R, Seals R, Ineichen P, et al. (1987) A new simplified version of the Perez diffuse irradiance model for tilted surfaces. *Solar Energy* 39(3), 221–231.
[36] Maxwell EL (1987) A quasi-physical model for converting hourly global to direct normal insolation, *SERI/TR-215-3087*. Golden, CO: Solar Energy Research Institute and *Proceedings Annual Meeting American Solar Energy Society*, pp. 35–46. Portland, OR, 12–16 July. http://rredc.nrel.gov/solar/pubs/PDFs/TR-215-3087.pdf
[37] Perez RR, Ineichen P, Maxwell EL, Seals RD, and Zalenka A (1992) Dynamic global-to-direct irradiance conversion models. *ASHRAE Transactions: Research Series 3578* Vol 98 Pt.1, RP-644.
[38] Liu BYH and Jordan RC (1960) The interrelationship and characteristic distribution of direct, diffuse, and total solar radiation. *Solar Energy* 4, 1–19.
[39] Erbs DG, Klein SA, and Duffie JA (1982) Estimation of the diffuse radiation fraction for hourly, daily and monthly average global radiation. *Solar Energy* 28, 293–302.
[40] Ilyas SZ, Nasir ShM, and Kakac S (2007) Estimation and comparison of diffuse solar radiation over Pakistan. *International Scientific Journal for Alternative Energy and Ecology* 3 (47), 109–111.
[41] Coppolino S (1990) A new model for estimating diffuse solar radiation in Italy from clearness index and minimum air mass. *Solar and Wind Technology* 7(5), 549–553.
[42] Wilcox S and Marion W (2008) *User's Manual for TMY3 Data Sets, NREL/TP-581-43156*. Golden, CO: National Renewable Energy Laboratory.
[43] Wilcox S and Marion W (2008) Development of an updated typical meteorological year data set for the United States. In: Campbell-Howe R (ed.) *Proceedings of the 2008 American Solar Energy Society Annual Conference*, San Diego, CA, 3–8 May. Boulder, CO: American Solar Energy Society.
[44] NREL (1992) *NSRDB Vol. 1 User's Manual National Solar Radiation Data Base (1961-1990) Version 1.0*. Golden, CO: National Renewable Energy Laboratory (http://rredc.nrel.gov/solar/pubs/NSRDB/cover.html).
[45] Maxwell EL, Marion W, Myers D, et al. (1995) *National Solar Radiation Data Base, Vol. 2 – Final Technical Report (1961–1990). NREL Report No. TP-463-5784*. 318 p. Golden, CO: National Renewable Energy Laboratory.
[46] Maxwell EL, Myers DR, Rymes MD, et al. (1991) Producing a national solar radiation data base. In: Denver C, Arden ME, Burley SMA, Coleman M (eds.), *Solar World Congress: Proceedings of the Biennial Congress of the International Solar Energy Society*. pp. 1007–1012, Part II, Vol. 1, 19–23 August. New York: Pergamon Press.
[47] Chandler WS, Hoell JM, Westberg D, et al. (2010) Near real-time global radiation and meteorology web services available from NASA. In: Campbell-Howe R (ed.) *Proceedings of the ASES National Solar Conference*, Phoenix, AZ, 17–22 May. Boulder CO: American Solar Energy Society.
[48] Scharmer K (1994) Towards a new atlas of solar radiation in Europe. *International Journal of Solar Energy* 15, 81–87.
[49] Sharmer K and Greif J (2000) *The European Solar Radiation Atlas, Vol. 1: Fundamentals and Maps*. Paris: Les Presses de l'Ecole des Mines. http://catalog.ensmp.fr/Files/ESRA11res.pdf
[50] Sharmer K and Grief J (2000) *The European Solar Radiation Atlas, Vol. 2: Database and Exploitation Software*. Paris: Les Presses de l'Ecole des Mines.
[51] Vignola FE and McDaniels DK (1993) Value of long-term solar radiation data. In: Campbell-Howe R (ed.) *Proceedings of the American Section of the International Solar Energy Society*, pp. 468–473. Washington, DC, April 1993. Boulder, CO: American Solar Energy Society.
[52] Long CK and Ackerman TP (1995) Surface measurements of solar irradiance: A study of the spatial correlation between simultaneous measurements at separated sites. *Journal of Applied Meteorology* 34, 1039–1046.
[53] Wilcox S, Anderberg M, Beckman W, et al. (2006) Towards production of an updated national solar radiation database. In: Campbell-Howe R (ed.) *Proceedings of the Solar 2006 Conference*, Denver, CO, 9–13 July. Boulder, CO: American Solar Energy Society.
[54] Wilcox S, Anderberg M, George R, et al. (2007) Completing production of the updated national solar radiation database for the United States. In: Campbell-Howe R (ed.) *Proceedings of the Solar 2007 Conference*, Cleveland, OH, 8–12 July. Boulder, CO: American Solar Energy Society.
[55] George R, Wilcox S, Anderberg M, and Perez R (2007) National Solar Radiation Database (NSRDB): 10 km gridded hourly solar database. In: Campbell-Howe R (ed.) *Proceedings of the Solar 2007 Conference*, Cleveland, OH, 8–12 July. Boulder, CO: American Solar Energy Society.
[56] Wilcox S (2007) National Solar Radiation Database 1991–2005 Update: User's Manual. *NREL Report No. TP-581-41364*. 472 p. http://www.nrel.gov/docs/fy07osti/41364.pdf.
[57] Barnett TP, Ritchie J, Foat J, and Stokes G (1998) On the space–time scales of the surface solar radiation field. *Journal of Climate* 11, 88–96.

Further Reading

Badescu V (ed.) (2008) *Modeling Solar Radiation at the Earth Surface*. Berlin: Springer.
Duffie JA and Beckman WA (2006) *Solar Engineering of Thermal Processes*, 3rd edn. Hoboken, NJ: John Wiley and Sons.
Dubayah R and Rich PM (1996) GIS-based solar radiation modeling. In Goodchild M, Parks, BO, Steyaert, LT (eds.) *GIS and Environmental Modeling: Progress and Research Issues*, pp. 129–134. New York: John Wiley and Sons.
Gray RO and Corbally CJ (2009) *Stellar Spectral Classification*. Princeton, NJ: Princeton University Press.
Hulstrom R (ed.) (1989) *Solar Resources*. Cambridge, MA: Massachusetts Institute of Technology.
Iqbal M (1983) *An Introduction to Solar Radiation*. Toronto, ON: Academic Press.
Jashek C and Jashek K (1987) *The Classification of Stars*. Cambridge, UK: Cambridge University Press.
Kreider J, Kreith JA, and Goswami D (2000) *Principles of Solar Engineering*, 2nd edn., Philadelphia: Taylor and Francis.
McCluny R (1994) *Introduction to Radiometry and Photometry*. Boston: Artech House.
Muneer, T (ed.) (2004) *Solar Radiation and Daylight Models*. Burlington, MA: Elsevier Butterworth-Heinemann.
World Meteorological Organization (WMO) (2008) Committee on Instrumentation, Measurements, and Observations (CIMO) Guide No. 8 Guide to Meteorological Instruments and Methods of Observation. Geneva, Switzerland.

Relevant Websites

http://www.asrc.cestm.albany.edu/perez/directory/ResourceAssessment.html – Consists publications of great interest to the solar radiation resource and modeling community
http://www.wmo.int/pages/index_en.html – World Meteorological Organization

1.13 Prediction of Solar Irradiance and Photovoltaic Power

E Lorenz and **D Heinemann,** University of Oldenburg, Oldenburg, Germany

© 2012 Elsevier Ltd. All rights reserved.

1.13.1	**Introduction**	240
1.13.2	**Applications of Irradiance and PV Power Forecasts**	241
1.13.2.1	Grid Integration of PV Power	241
1.13.2.2	Stand-Alone Systems and Small Networks	243
1.13.2.3	Other Applications	243
1.13.3	**Models for the Prediction of Solar Irradiance and PV Power**	243
1.13.3.1	Basic Steps in a Power Prediction System	244
1.13.3.2	Irradiance Forecasting	246
1.13.3.2.1	Basic characteristics of solar irradiance	246
1.13.3.2.2	Time series models	248
1.13.3.2.3	Cloud motion vectors from satellite images	249
1.13.3.2.4	Cloud motion vectors from ground-based sky imagers	251
1.13.3.2.5	NWP model irradiance forecasts	252
1.13.3.2.6	Postprocessing of NWP model output	257
1.13.3.3	PV Power Forecasting	260
1.13.3.3.1	Irradiance on the module plane	260
1.13.3.3.2	PV simulation	262
1.13.3.3.3	Upscaling to regional power prediction	264
1.13.3.3.4	Statistical methods	265
1.13.4	**Concepts for Evaluation of Irradiance and Power Forecasts**	265
1.13.4.1	Specification of Test Case	265
1.13.4.2	Graphical Analysis	265
1.13.4.3	Statistical Error Measures	266
1.13.4.4	Selection of Data for Evaluation and Normalization	267
1.13.4.5	Reference Forecasts	268
1.13.4.6	Skill Scores and Improvement Scores	269
1.13.4.7	Evaluation of Forecast Accuracy in Dependence on Meteorological and Climatological Conditions	269
1.13.4.8	Uncertainty Information	270
1.13.5	**Evaluation and Comparison of Different Approaches for Irradiance Forecasting**	271
1.13.5.1	Measurement Data	271
1.13.5.2	NWP-Based Forecasts	271
1.13.5.3	Results for NWP-Based Forecasting Approaches	273
1.13.5.3.1	Detailed results for Germany	273
1.13.5.3.2	Comparison of forecast accuracies for the different regions	273
1.13.5.4	Comparison of Satellite-Based Irradiance Forecasts with NWP-Based Forecasts	275
1.13.5.5	Summary and Outlook	277
1.13.6	**Example of a Regional PV Power Prediction System**	277
1.13.6.1	Measurement Data	279
1.13.6.1.1	Irradiance measurements	279
1.13.6.1.2	PV power measurements	279
1.13.6.1.3	Quality control of measured PV power	279
1.13.6.2	Overview of the Power Prediction Scheme	280
1.13.6.3	Irradiance Forecasts	280
1.13.6.3.1	Refinement of ECMWF irradiance forecasts	280
1.13.6.3.2	Accuracy of different approaches for site-specific and regional forecasts	281
1.13.6.4	Power Forecasts	281
1.13.6.4.1	Tilted irradiance and PV simulation model	281
1.13.6.4.2	Postprocessing: Empirical approach to predict snow cover on PV modules	283
1.13.6.4.3	Regional upscaling	284
1.13.6.4.4	Evaluation of local and regional power forecasts	285
1.13.7	**Summary and Outlook**	288
References		289

Glossary

Cloud motion vector The speed and direction determined from tracking clouds in satellite imagery. If the clouds tracked are neither growing nor decaying, then the vector approximates the wind vector.

Direct-normal irradiance ($I_{beam,n}$) The amount of solar radiation from the direction of the sun (synonym for 'beam radiation').

Diffuse horizontal irradiance (I_{diff}) The radiation component that strikes a point from the sky, excluding circumsolar radiation. High values are produced by a turbid atmosphere or reflections from clouds.

Global horizontal irradiance (I) Total solar radiation; the sum of direct and diffuse horizontal radiation. For nonhorizontal surfaces, usually the ground-reflected radiation component has to be added as well.

Irradiance (or radiant flux density) The rate at which radiant energy in a radiation field is transferred across a unit area of a surface in a hemisphere of directions. In general, irradiance depends on the orientation of the surface. The radiant energy may be confined to a narrow range of frequencies (spectral irradiance) or integrated over a broad range of wavelengths. Its unit is $W\,m^{-2}$.

Mean bias error (MBE) Metric to compare forecasts to actual data. MBE can be negative (forecast is too small, on average) and positive (forecast is too large, on average). The MBE gives the average amount of over- or underestimation in the forecasted variable.

Model output statistics (MOS) Statistical method of postprocessing the numerical weather prediction (NWP) output to correct systematic deviations due to either model errors or local influences not considered by the NWP model.

Numerical forecasting (or numerical weather prediction, NWP) Weather forecasting using computer models for the integration of the governing hydrodynamic equations by numerical methods subject to given initial conditions.

Radiance The rate at which radiant energy from a unit solid angle around a particular direction is transferred across a unit area of a surface projected onto this direction. Unlike irradiance, radiance is a property solely of a radiation field, not of the orientation of the surface. The unit of radiance is $W\,m^{-2}\,sr^{-1}$.

Root mean square error (RMSE) Metric to compare forecasts to actual data. The RMSE value is the positive square root of the mean-square error. It is equal to the standard error only when the mean error is zero.

Zenith angle The angle between the direction of interest (e.g., of the sun) and the zenith (directly overhead).

1.13.1 Introduction

Renewable energies will contribute a major share of the future global energy supply. In particular, the contribution of photovoltaic (PV) power production to the electricity supply is also constantly increasing. This transition to a sustainable energy supply not only implies the introduction of the renewable energy technologies but will also have important consequences for the organization, structure, and management of all levels of electricity supply systems. Power generated from solar and wind energy systems shows fundamentally different generation characteristics than that from conventional energy sources (e.g., fossil fuels). While power production from conventional sources can easily be matched to the given electricity demand, the availability of solar and wind energy is largely determined by the prevailing weather conditions and is therefore highly variable.

These different characteristics pose a major challenge for the integration of renewable energies into the energy supply system and make new methods of balancing supply and demand necessary. Today, this task is mainly addressed by adapting the schedule of conventional, flexible power plants in order to compensate fluctuations in renewable power production. Shifting loads to periods where enough and cheap energy is available is another concept that may be applied to better match demand and renewable power supply, currently investigated in the context of demand-side management. In the longer term, storage technologies are also expected to play an important role in reducing the mismatch between electricity demand and renewable power production.

All these concepts require detailed information on the expected power production as an essential input for management and operation strategies. Hence, reliable forecasts of solar and wind power are important for an efficient integration of large shares of solar and wind power into the electricity supply system. Today, wind power prediction systems are already an essential part of the grid and system control in countries with a substantial wind power generation. Accordingly, the prediction of solar yields is becoming more and more important, especially for countries where legislation encourages the deployment of solar power plants (e.g., Germany and Spain). The first PV power prediction systems became operational recently [1–4], and contribute to an increase in the value of the PV energy produced in the market. In addition to the direct economic benefit, reliable PV power forecasts will also increase the general acceptance of PV as a major power source, and hence will support the change to a sustainable energy system.

The benefit of PV power forecasts for grid integration is directly connected with their accuracy. Consequently, increasing effort is currently spent on research to improve irradiance forecasts as a basis for corresponding PV power forecasts. The need for detailed and precise forecast data for the energy sector will be a key motivation for further research activities in this field. Hence, apart from its relevance for improving the cost efficiency of renewable energies, research on solar irradiance forecasting in the context of energy meteorology also addresses new scientific questions and is expected to contribute to basic research with respect to cloud and radiation modeling.

Depending on the application and its corresponding timescale, different forecasting approaches are appropriate. Time series models with on-site measured irradiance data as input are adequate for the very short term timescale ranging from minutes up to few hours. Intrahour forecasts of clouds and irradiance with a high spatial and temporal resolution may be obtained from ground-based sky imagers. Forecasts based on cloud motion vectors from satellite images show a good performance for a temporal range of 30 min to 6 h. Grid integration of PV power mainly requires forecasts up to 2 days ahead or even beyond. These forecasts are based on numerical weather prediction (NWP) models.

This chapter gives an overview of the applications and models for irradiance and power prediction, and presents results for selected prediction systems.

First, the benefits of PV power forecasting for various applications are presented. The next section starts with a description of the basic elements in a PV power prediction system, followed by an overview of state-of-the-art approaches for solar irradiance forecasting for different timescales. The section is completed by an introduction to the modeling of PV power when the forecasted irradiance is given. In Section 1.13.4, the basic concepts for evaluation of irradiance and power prediction are presented. The following sections provide evaluation results of irradiance and power predictions: Section 1.13.5 addresses the intercomparison of different approaches for irradiance forecasting and Section 1.13.6 focuses on a detailed evaluation of different aspects in regional PV power prediction. Finally, a summary and a brief outlook on future research are given.

1.13.2 Applications of Irradiance and PV Power Forecasts

An efficient use of the fluctuating energy output of PV systems requires reliable forecast information for management and operation strategies. This forecast is necessary for the grid integration of PV systems as well as for small networks and stand-alone systems.

1.13.2.1 Grid Integration of PV Power

The most important application of PV power forecasts is to support a cost-effective integration of large amounts of solar power into the electricity supply system. The contribution of renewable power production – particularly PV systems, solar thermal power plants, and wind energy converters – to the electric power supply is constantly increasing. Utility companies and transmission system operators have to cope with the fluctuating input from these different renewable energy sources. This is a new challenge compared with power production from conventional power plants that can be adjusted to the expected load profiles (**Figure 1**). Predicted load patterns for the next 2 days provide the basis for scheduling of power plants and planning transactions in the electricity market in order to balance the supply and demand of energy and to assure reliable grid operation.

Electricity demand can be predicted with high accuracy. When fluctuating renewable energies are integrated into the grid, the load profiles are modified (**Figure 1**), given that all power is directly integrated into the grid as is the case, for example, in Germany. Forecasts of solar and wind power input to the grid are necessary to adjust the respective load forecasts. These forecasts are used by utility companies, transmission system operators, energy service providers, energy traders, and independent power producers.

The required forecast horizon is partly defined by technical constraints, for example, the mix of power plants in energy systems with their specific start-up times. Even more important is its dependence on the organizational framework of the energy market. A major fraction of electric power transactions is realized on the so-called day-ahead market. Power purchase and sale bids for the next day have to be placed at a certain time, usually around noon, announcing the supply of or the request for electric power in dependence on the daytime. Therefore, power forecasts with a forecast horizon up to 2 days ahead are of particular relevance for grid integration purposes.

Additionally, energy markets offer the possibility of intraday trading. This allows for an adaptation of the day-ahead schedule to updates of the forecast for the respective day, which are expected to be more accurate than day-ahead forecasts. The corresponding time horizon of the forecast is in the range of some hours. The remaining deviations between scheduled and needed power may be adjusted by using balancing energy and reserve power on the very short term timescale. However, this is costly and reduces the value of the produced energy.

Summarizing these considerations, a major objective of PV power prediction is to increase the value of the produced energy in the market. From the technical point of view, this is achieved by reducing the need for balancing energy and reserve power.

The need for forecast information on the expected solar and wind power production is increasing with the amount of installed power. Today, wind power prediction systems are widely used operationally and have shown their strong economic impact and benefit for the integration of wind energy into the electricity grid [5–8]. Accordingly, the prediction of solar yields is becoming more and more important for utilities that have to integrate increasing amounts of solar power, especially for countries where legislation encourages the deployment of solar power plants. For example, in Germany, about 17.3 GW of PV power was installed at the end of 2010 [9], and a share of 2% of the total electricity supply was covered by PV power production. On sunny summer days, solar energy can contribute more than 25% of the overall electricity demand at noon, as illustrated in the lower right graph in **Figure 1**. This graph also shows a good correlation of load and PV power on sunny days. PV power especially contributes for hours with high demand and correspondingly high values of energy. This peak shaving capability is even more pronounced in hot and sunny regions, where a considerable amount of electricity is used for cooling (e.g., see Reference 10).

As a consequence of this new and rapidly evolving situation on the energy market, various operational PV power prediction systems have been introduced recently [1–4], and respective services are requested, for example, by grid operators. The use of these forecasts and the corresponding spatial and temporal scales depend on the regulatory framework of the respective countries and the structure of the energy system. In the following, we will give some examples.

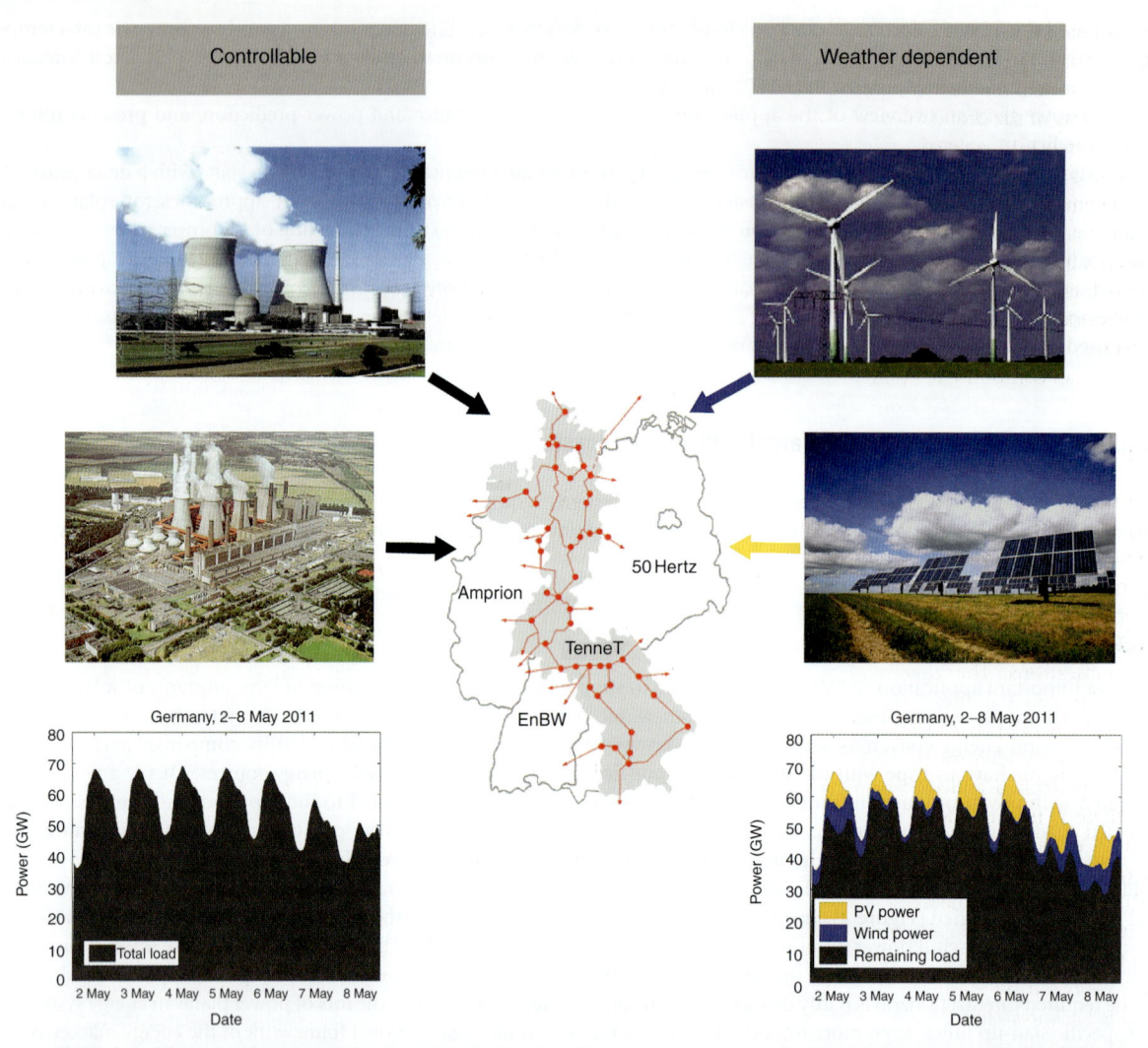

Figure 1 Illustration of the current structure of the electricity supply system. The bottom graphs show load (left) and load in combination with feed-in of wind and PV power (right) for 1 week in May 2011 for the control area of the German transmission system operator TenneT. Data published according to EEG transparency guidelines.

In Germany, according to the current feed-in law, PV system operators may feed in their complete electricity production with priority to conventional electricity for a fixed price. Hence, grid operators are in charge of balancing the fluctuating input for the corresponding control areas, and regional forecasts are required.

A comprehensive description of the situation of the Spanish energy market with respect to the feed-in of solar power is given in Reference 11. Two possibilities are offered to solar plant operators. The fixed tariff model is similar to the German feed-in tariff model. With this model, solar system operators have a guaranteed right to feed in all produced power and are paid a fixed price, independent of the market price of energy. In addition, operators of plants with an installed power of more than 1 MW are allowed to directly participate in the electricity market, placing bids on the day-ahead and intraday market. By choosing this model, solar plant operators are obliged to deliver power according to the schedule specified in the contract. If they fail, they are charged a penalty, depending on the deviation between scheduled and delivered power. Due to the weather dependence of solar and wind power, this is a clear disadvantage for owners of renewable power plants. In order to balance this disadvantage and to encourage the operators of renewable power plants to participate in the market, an additional premium per kilowatt-hour is paid by the Spanish National Energy Commission (premium tariff model). Especially in combination with a storage system, the premium tariff may be advantageous compared with the fixed tariff. When participating in the premium tariff model, plant operators will need site-specific forecasts of the produced power for the current and next day. The use of irradiance forecasts for optimized operation strategies of solar thermal power plants with thermal storages was investigated in a recent case study [11].

A study on the scheduling of PV power station output based on solar radiation forecasts specific to the situation of the Japanese energy market is presented in Reference 12. In Japan, the input of PV power to the grid has to be delivered according to a day-ahead schedule, and schedule violations are associated with an additional fine. In order to achieve improved controllability and adjustability of PV power, the investigated large-scale PV system is combined with a battery storage system. The authors propose and compare different methods for determining an optimal operating schedule for the PV power station with the storage system using day-ahead and current-day forecasts of the solar radiation. The described optimization strategies are based on a cost function, implying generation cost savings in dependence on the daytime and additional costs associated with schedule violation. The effectiveness of the proposed procedures was shown on the basis of simulations and measured data of power output.

In Reference 10, an evaluation of the end-use accuracy of power forecasts for grid integration is presented for two case studies in the United States. The authors emphasize the ability of PV power to contribute at critical load demand times, especially when the load demand is driven by air-conditioning. During peak load times, the grid is stressed and energy values and penalties for schedule violations are high. Hence, forecasts of the peak load reduction by PV power are of high importance for utility companies, which have to adjust the predicted load demand for conventional generation. The authors analyze the predicted and actual utility peak load reduction capability of PV power input for different scenarios of grid penetration of PV, ranging from 2% to 20%. Capacity credit values are used as measures to evaluate predicted in comparison to simulated PV power output in combination with measured load data. A good agreement between predicted and simulated capacity credit values is found, suggesting that solar forecasts can contribute to effective management of solar resources on the power grid.

1.13.2.2 Stand-Alone Systems and Small Networks

Also, the performance of small networks including PV and stand-alone PV systems can be improved using solar radiation and power forecasts. Several studies have recently reported different applications of forecasting in this domain.

A power forecasting system designed to optimize the scheduling of a small energy network including PV power is described in Reference 13. Due to environmental concerns, there is growing interest in energy networks with local power generation integrating PV systems, other low-emission generators, fuel cells, and batteries. Electric power and heat in these networks may be controlled with advanced communication networks taking advantage of new developments in the field of communications. The effectiveness of these networks may be increased by optimizing the schedule for the distributed generators and batteries, with the aim of, for example, minimizing energy cost and CO_2 emissions. The authors express the need for predictions of generated power for a forecast horizon up to 24 h as a basic input for corresponding operation strategies. They identify several problems that may occur when forecast accuracy is low and considerable deviations between actually generated and predicted power are found, for example, waste of heat if the backup power is provided by fuel cells and there is no heat demand at that time.

Also, the authors of Reference 14 highlight the importance of decentralized and autonomous generation networks, so-called microgrids, for a future sustainable energy system. As an example, they investigate the stability of the Kythnos island power system with special focus on the influence of weather disturbances. Several case studies have been performed varying the share of PV power from about 9% to 60% and using different sources of irradiance data as a basis for corresponding simulations. The authors show that the system operates close to the stability boundary for high penetration of PV. They state that the stability and effectiveness of the system can be improved if information on cloud cover approaching the island is available 15 min in advance. This allows starting backup systems, for example, a diesel generator, in time, and noncritical loads may be disconnected. As a consequence, less reserve power is required during periods of sunshine with high PV power production. The authors recommend satellite-based nowcasting and short-term forecasting to obtain the required information on cloud motion.

An example of the use of irradiance forecasts for a stand-alone PV system is presented in Reference 15. The authors investigate a forecast-based control method for a PV–diesel hybrid generation system on a ship. The proposed operation strategy aims at keeping the diesel engine at the most efficient operating point as well as keeping charge power into the battery as small as possible. This allows for an improved overall system design by minimizing the capacity of the batteries. Irradiance forecasts for the current day with hourly resolution are the basic input for the control algorithm. The applicability of the method is demonstrated on the basis of numerical simulations.

1.13.2.3 Other Applications

Finally, it shall be mentioned that – of course – there is also a variety of applications of irradiance forecasts not related to PV. The use of direct irradiance forecasts to optimize operation strategies for solar thermal power plants has already been mentioned [11]. In addition, on the very short term timescale of few minutes, forecasts of direct irradiance could be useful for the control of receivers in solar thermal power plants. Further examples include the use of weather and solar energy forecasts for the control of heating, ventilating, and cooling of buildings [16]; the use of irradiance forecasts to improve the management of district heating grids that integrate solar thermal water heating; load forecasting [16]; and the use of forecasts in agriculture, for example, for crop harvesting.

1.13.3 Models for the Prediction of Solar Irradiance and PV Power

In this section, we give an overview of solar irradiance and PV power prediction models and introduce the basic principles of the different approaches.

1.13.3.1 Basic Steps in a Power Prediction System

Power prediction of PV systems usually involves several modeling steps in order to obtain the required forecast information from different kinds of input data.

A typical model chain of a PV power forecasting system, as illustrated in **Figure 2**, comprises the following basic steps:

- Forecast of site-specific global horizontal irradiance
- Forecast of irradiance on the module plane
- Forecast of PV power.

For regional forecasts, an additional step has to be applied:

- Upscaling to regional power production.

All these steps may involve physical or statistical models or a combination of both. Not all approaches for PV power prediction necessarily include all modeling steps explicitly. Several steps may be combined by the use of statistical models, for example, relating power output directly to input variables like measured power of previous time steps or forecast variables of NWP systems.

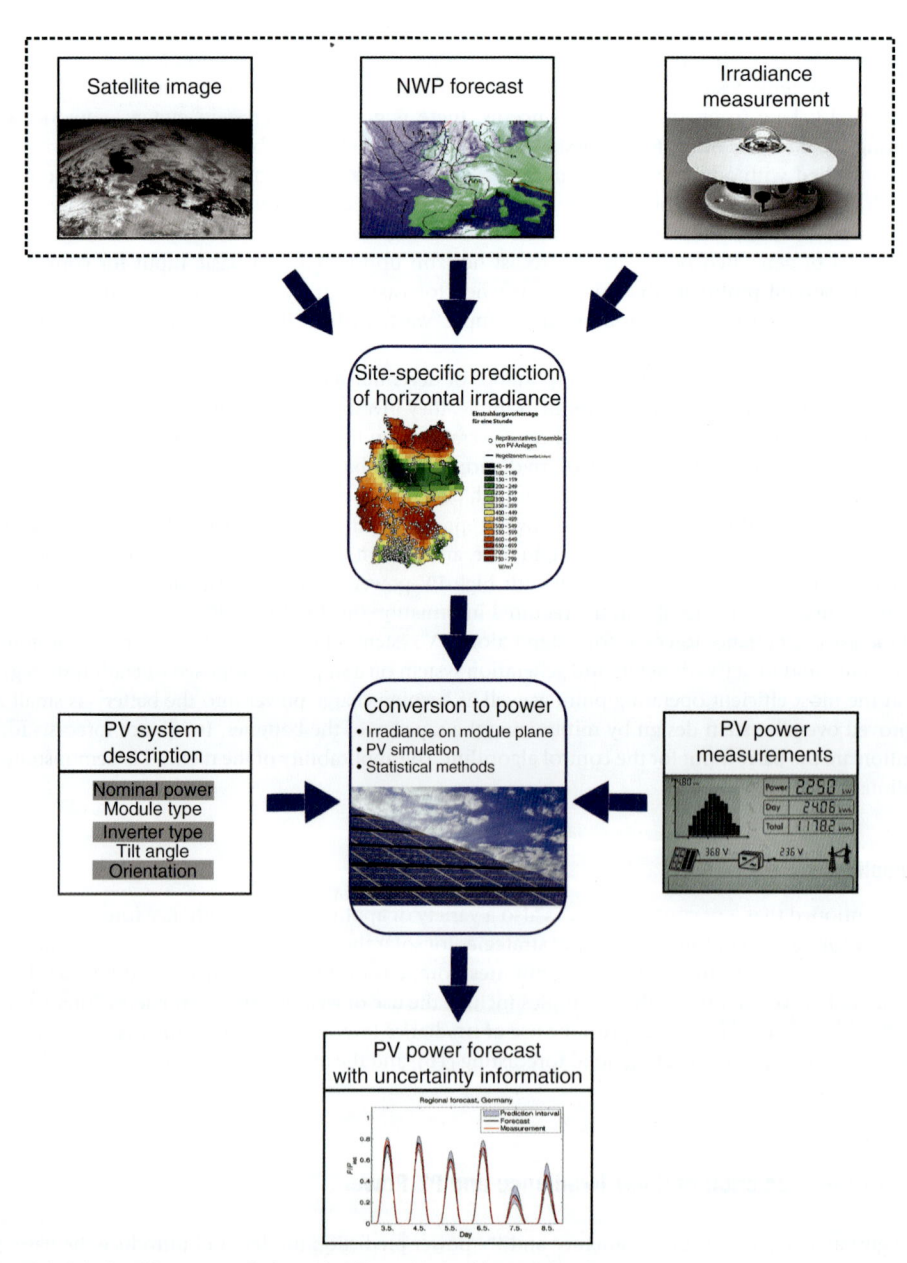

Figure 2 Typical model chain for PV power prediction with different kinds of input data sets.

In the following, we briefly describe the different steps and necessary input data. A more detailed description is provided in the subsequent sections.

Forecasting of global horizontal irradiance is the first and most essential step in most PV power prediction systems. Depending on the forecast horizon, different kinds of input data and models are used.

- For the very short term timescale ranging from minutes to few hours, on-site measured irradiance data in combination with time series models are appropriate. Examples of direct time series models are Kalman filtering, autoregressive (AR), and autoregressive moving average (ARMA) models. Furthermore, artificial neural networks (ANNs) may be applied to derive irradiance forecasts using only measurements.
- Information on the temporal development of clouds, which largely determine surface solar irradiance, may be used as a basis for short-term irradiance forecasting.
  - Forecasts based on satellite images show a good performance for up to 6 h ahead. Subsequent images deliver information on cloud motion which can be extrapolated to the next few hours.
  - For the subhour range, cloud information from ground-based sky imagers may be used to derive irradiance forecasts with much higher spatial and temporal resolution compared with the satellite-based forecasts. Forecast horizons here are limited by the spatial extension of the monitored cloud scenes and corresponding cloud velocities.
- From about 4–6 h onward, forecasts based on NWP models typically outperform the satellite-based forecasts (see also Section 1.13.6.4). Hence, power prediction systems in the context of PV grid integration are based on this approach. The weather service's global NWP models describe the complete Earth with a comparatively coarse spatial and temporal resolution. They are initialized on the basis of meteorological observations. Mesoscale models allow for calculations on a finer grid covering selected regions. Boundary and initial conditions are then taken from a global model. However, recent improvements in the resolution of the global models more and more make this difference less critical. Some weather services, for example, the European Centre for Medium-Range Weather Forecasts (ECMWF), directly provide surface solar irradiance as forecast model output. This allows for site-specific irradiance forecasts with the required temporal resolution produced by downscaling and interpolation techniques. However, surface solar irradiance is still not a standard prediction variable of all weather services. Statistical models may be applied to derive surface solar irradiance from available NWP output variables and to adjust irradiance forecasts to ground-measured or satellite-derived irradiance data.

In the second step, the irradiance on the plane of the PV modules has to be calculated. Different possible installation types have to be considered:

- For systems with a fixed orientation, the forecast values of global horizontal irradiance have to be converted according to the specific orientation of the modules. Various models are available for this task. They require information on the tilt angle and orientation of the PV system as input.
- For one- and two-axis tracking systems, these models have to be combined with respective information on the tracking algorithm.
- Concentrating PV systems require forecast information on direct normal irradiance. These forecasts may be derived from global horizontal irradiance forecast by applying a direct/diffuse fraction model or by directly using forecasted cloud and atmospheric parameters as input to radiative transfer calculations.

The forecast of the PV power output is finally obtained by applying a PV simulation model to the forecasted irradiance on the module plane.

In general, PV simulation involves a model to calculate the direct current (DC) power output in the first step and an inverter model in the second step. The dependence of PV system power output on the incoming irradiance has been extensively investigated and a number of models are available, ranging from very simple to sophisticated models. For power prediction systems, the use of more simple models is adequate, because the uncertainty in power prediction is largely determined by the uncertainty of the irradiance forecast.

To consider the influence of temperature on the power output of a PV system, forecasted temperature data are beneficial input to PV system models as well. Temperature forecasts are a standard product of all weather services and therefore can easily be integrated into prediction systems. For very short term predictions up to some hours, on-site temperature measurements may be integrated using standard time series modeling. In case of missing temperature predictions, the expected ambient temperature can be estimated combining irradiance forecasts with climatological temperature information.

In addition to the meteorological input data, the characteristics of the PV systems have to be specified. This implies information on the nominal power in the first place. Depending on the complexity of the simulation model, information, for example, on the part-load behavior and temperature coefficients of the module type used and on the inverter characteristics is required.

As a last step to derive optimized power forecasts for a single PV system, the forecasted power output may be adapted to measured power data by statistical postprocessing. Self-calibrating recursive models are most beneficial if measured data are available online. Off-line data can also be used effectively for model calibration.

PV power prediction for utility applications usually requires forecasts of the cumulative PV power generation for a specified area rather than for a single site. Upscaling to the regional PV power production from a representative set of single PV systems is the final step for this type of application. A simple summation of the power output of thousands of systems installed in a given area would be hardly feasible due to excess computational and data handling efforts. Furthermore, detailed system information necessary for simulation is generally not available for all PV systems. Especially, small PV systems which largely contribute to the overall power production often lack this information. A proper upscaling approach leads to almost no loss in accuracy, given that the representative set correctly represents the regional distribution of installed power and installation type of the systems.

In addition to the power prediction, a specification of the expected uncertainty of the predicted value is important for an optimized application. This uncertainty information provides the basis, for example, to assess the risk associated with decisions based on the forecasts or to estimate the necessary reserve power determined by the largest forecast errors [17]. In Reference 12, it is shown that the performance of a forecast-based operating schedule for a PV power station with storage can be optimized if additional information on forecast uncertainty is integrated. Information on the expected uncertainty may be provided in the form of confidence or prediction intervals (**Figure 2**) which indicate the range in which the actual value is expected to appear with a quantified probability of typically 90%. A more specific description of the forecast uncertainty is given using the probability distribution function of forecast errors. In general, the uncertainty associated with regional power prediction is much smaller than that for single PV systems, because the correlation of forecast errors rapidly decreases with the increase in the distance between the systems.

In this section, we have given an overview of different approaches for PV power prediction. According to the importance of power forecasts for grid integration of large shares of PV power with the corresponding time constant of 1 day ahead, most PV power prediction systems will be based on NWP models. In principle, two different approaches may be distinguished to derive PV power forecasts from NWP output parameters. Using the physical approach, site-specific irradiance forecasts are derived in a first step, followed by a conversion to irradiance on the module plane and PV simulation with physical models. The statistical approach in a pure form establishes relations between measured power data from the past and NWP variables. In practice, most approaches for power prediction will combine elements from both concepts in order to achieve optimized forecasts.

1.13.3.2 Irradiance Forecasting

PV system output is essentially determined by the incoming solar irradiance. Therefore, irradiance forecasting is the most important step for most PV power prediction approaches.

As we have outlined in the previous section, irradiance forecasting approaches may be categorized according to the input data used which also determine the forecast horizon. Time series models based on online irradiance measurements are applied for the very short term timescale. For the subhour range also, cloud information derived from ground-based sky imagers may be used to calculate forecasts with a very high temporal and spatial resolution. Satellite data are useful to derive irradiance forecasts up to 6 h ahead. For longer forecast horizons, NWP-based forecasts are the most suitable choice. Of course, there are also combined approaches that integrate different kinds of input data to derive an optimized forecast in dependence on the forecast horizon.

In the following, we briefly describe the different approaches for irradiance forecasting. Emphasis will be on approaches based on NWP models, reflecting their importance for grid integration of PV power. Prior to this, the basic characteristics of solar radiation are summarized and common quantities used in irradiance modeling are introduced.

1.13.3.2.1 Basic characteristics of solar irradiance

The amount of solar irradiance arriving at the Earth's surface is influenced by several factors. The normal extraterrestrial solar radiant flux is determined by the radiative properties of the Sun and the actual distance between the Sun and the Earth. The extraterrestrial irradiance received by a plane with a given orientation can be calculated knowing the position of the Sun with respect to the receiving surface. Finally, as solar radiation passes through the Earth's atmosphere, it is partly absorbed and scattered by air molecules, water vapor, aerosols, and clouds. These extinction processes reduce the extraterrestrial radiation and thereby the amount of energy available at surface level. For a detailed description and basic understanding of radiative processes in the atmosphere processes, we refer to References 18 and 19.

The value of the solar radiant flux passing through a surface of a unit area perpendicular to the Sun's direction at the average Sun–Earth distance outside the Earth's atmosphere (i.e., the solar constant I_{SC} or total solar irradiance (TSI)) has been determined to be $1366 \pm 4\,W\,m^{-2}$. This value varies by 3% due to the varying distance between the Sun and the Earth. This variation can be expressed by using the eccentricity correction factor ε_0, and the extraterrestrial radiation at normal incidence is then given as $I_0 = \varepsilon_0 I_{SC}$.

To determine the amount of extraterrestrial solar irradiance I_{ext} received by a horizontal plane, the angular displacement of the Sun's position from normal incidence has to be considered, and I_{ext} is calculated as

$$I_{ext} = I_0 \cos \theta_Z \qquad [1]$$

where θ_Z is the solar zenith angle describing the position of the Sun in the sky. The diurnal pattern of irradiance depends on trigonometric relationships describing the influence of the Earth's rotation around its own axis and the Earth's revolution around the Sun. The seasonal variation of the irradiance is mainly caused by the varying position of the polar axis with respect to the Sun. This strong deterministic pattern is a special feature of solar irradiance compared with other meteorological parameters, which influences irradiance models in many aspects, as will be discussed later.

To finally determine the solar irradiance at ground level, atmospheric extinction processes have to be considered. On the way through the Earth's atmosphere, radiation can be absorbed or scattered by air molecules, water vapor, aerosols, and clouds. The solar radiation that passes through directly to the Earth's surface is called direct or beam solar irradiance I_{beam}. The part of the radiation that has been scattered is called diffuse solar radiation I_{diff}. The beam and the diffuse component sum up to global solar irradiance I.

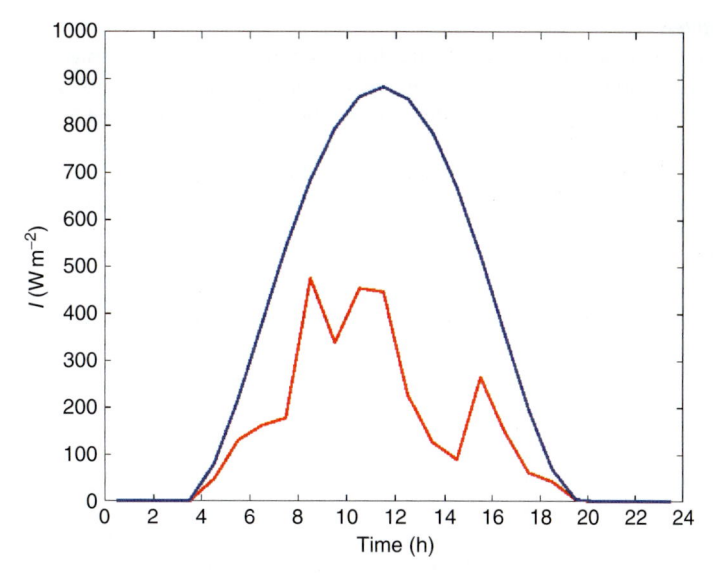

Figure 3 Typical daily pattern of solar irradiance for a clear-sky day (blue) and a cloudy day (red).

A variety of models exists to calculate the irradiance for cloudless skies, usually referred to as clear-sky irradiance I_{clear}, with reasonable accuracy. A typical clear-sky day is illustrated in **Figure 3**. An overview of different models is presented by Ineichen [20]. Clear-sky models range from empirical models [21] to radiative transfer-based calculations [22]. All these models need information on the state of the atmosphere as input. Some of the models are based on turbidity measures, integrating the influence of all atmospheric parameters, while other models require detailed input parameters describing the optical properties of aerosols, water vapor, and other gases separately. Up to now, mostly climatological values of the atmospheric parameters have been used to model clear-sky irradiances. Recently, the use of aerosol information with high temporal resolution derived from NWP and chemical transport models has also been investigated [23, 24].

Besides the deterministic daily and annual patterns of irradiance, clouds have the strongest influence on solar irradiance at surface level. For an optically thick cloud cover, the global irradiance may be reduced to 5–10% of clear-sky irradiance with a direct component I_{beam} reduced to 0. Clouds show a strong variability in time and space, as illustrated in **Figure 3**. Hence, determination of clouds at a designated time is an essential task in irradiance forecasting and modeling. Irradiance for all sky conditions including cloudy skies may be derived using radiation transfer models (e.g., see Reference 25) requiring input on the vertical structure of cloud physical parameters, for example, cloud and ice water content or droplet radius. Also, NWP models imply parameterizations of radiative transfer calculations.

In practice, many irradiance models also involve an empirical or statistical component. For statistical models, it may be favorable to treat the influences of the deterministic solar geometry and the nondeterministic atmospheric extinction separately. for this purpose, two transmissivity measures have been introduced: clearness index (k) and clear-sky index (k^*).

The clearness index k is defined as the ratio of irradiance at ground level to extraterrestrial irradiance on the horizontal plane:

$$k = \frac{I}{I_{ext}} \qquad [2]$$

It describes the overall extinction by clouds and atmospheric constituents in relation to the extraterrestrial irradiance. This approach strongly reduces seasonal and daily patterns by considering the influence of the zenith angle Θ_Z, which is modeled by I_{ext}. The clearness index is widely applied to reduce the deterministic trend in irradiance time series.

However, the clearness index accounts for only the trends caused by geometric effects on solar position. As atmospheric extinction depends on the length of radiation's path through the atmosphere, it is also governed by solar geometry. The clear-sky index therefore decreases with increasing zenith angle. To account for this influence as well, the clear-sky index k^* is introduced. It relates the surface solar irradiance to a defined clear-sky irradiance instead of the extraterrestrial irradiance:

$$k^* = \frac{I}{I_{clear}} \qquad [3]$$

For the calculation of the clear-sky index, a clear-sky model and information on atmospheric input parameters are required.

The quantities introduced in this section are frequently used in solar modeling and forecasting. For example, some time series models explicitly require input parameters free of trend; hence, clearness or clear-sky index is an adequate choice. Also, satellite-based forecasts of irradiance are based on the concept of separately describing the influence of clouds and other atmospheric components by using the clear-sky index and a clear-sky model. Furthermore, most empirical models to derive the diffuse fraction of irradiance, necessary to calculate the irradiance on a tilted plane, are generally based on the clearness or clear-sky index.

1.13.3.2.2 Time series models

The basic idea of using time series models to forecast solar irradiance is to utilize only on-site measured values of solar irradiance as a basis for the predictions. In addition, further measurement values related to solar irradiance, for example, cloud cover, may be included. Time series models may also be applied directly to derive PV power forecasts, using measured power as input.

Time series models make use of the high autocorrelation for short time lags in time series of solar irradiance and cloud cover. Dynamic phenomena like motion and formation or dissolution of clouds may not be accounted for. Considering these effects makes the use of physical modeling necessary, for example, numerical models or models to describe cloud movement and to derive irradiance from satellite images. However, these models show an inherent uncertainty by modeling of surface solar irradiance, caused, for example, by limits in spatial and temporal resolution, uncertainty in input parameters, and simplifying assumptions within the models. As a consequence, although transient clouds may not be predicted well, for the very short term timescales, typically up to 1 or 2 h ahead, forecasts based on accurate on-site measurements will be advantageous.

Two principal time series approaches may be distinguished:

- the statistical or direct time series approach
- the learning or artificial intelligence (AI) approach.

Using the statistical approach, relations between predictors, variables used as an input to the statistical model, and predictand, the variable to be predicted, are derived from statistical analysis. An early approach in direct time series irradiance forecasting based on autoregressive integrated moving average (ARIMA) models has been proposed in Reference 26. Since then, several studies with respect to direct time series modeling have been performed. In Reference 27, different time series models are compared, and in Reference 28, the authors investigate the use of a simpler AR model to directly predict PV power in comparison with other models.

In the AR model – the simplest of the time series models – the value to be predicted y_t is expressed as a linear combination of previous values $y_{t-i\Delta t}$ and the stochastic residual ε_t:

$$y_t = a_0 + \sum_{i=1}^{n} a_i y_{t-i\Delta t} + \varepsilon_t \qquad [4]$$

where a_i denotes the model parameters that have to be identified and Δt the temporal resolution of the irradiance data.

For about one decade, there has been great interest in research on AI techniques, not only for forecasting but also for a broad range of applications, including control, data compression, optimization, pattern recognition, and classification. An overview of the application of AI techniques in the field of solar radiation modeling and forecasting is given in Reference 29, with special focus on ANNs which are being widely used.

ANNs offer the possibility of overcoming the limitations of conventional linear approaches and solving complex and nonlinear problems that are difficult to model analytically. The relation between the desired output and input data is learned using data of a so-called training set. In the case of solar irradiance forecasting, the output of the ANN is the predictand I_t and the inputs are irradiance values or related meteorological parameters at previous time steps. Irradiance forecasting approaches based on ANN and other AI techniques have been proposed by several research groups [30–35]. A short description of the basic principles and an overview of different types of ANNs are given in Reference 31.

Most of the proposed forecasting algorithms based on on-site measured data aim at forecast horizons of one or several hours ahead, which extended to some hours as given in References 27 and 28. Forecasts in the subhour range were also investigated [26, 27, 33]. In addition, ANNs are used to predict the solar radiation sum for the next day [30, 32, 33]. However, as discussed earlier, day-ahead forecasts strongly benefit from using NWP predictions. In Reference 36, the authors update their approach presented in Reference 32, using also NWP output variables as an additional input to ANNs. In Reference 28, the results of a pure AR model are compared with those of an AR model with exogenous input from NWP models, which allows for a direct comparison of the importance of different kinds of input parameters for different forecasting lead times. This analysis revealed that up to 2 h ahead measured data are the most important input to the model, while for next day horizons the use of NWP forecast parameters is adequate.

For both statistical and AI techniques, the choice of suitable input data is of critical importance. For direct time series modeling in particular, the time lags, which have the strongest impact on the predictand, have to be identified. Statistical analysis of the autocorrelation or partial autocorrelation for different time lags can support this choice and may be complemented by sensitivity analysis in a second step. For 1 h-ahead forecasts, the authors agree that the most important input to the model is the latest available measured value y_{t-1h}, corresponding to a time lag of 1 h, and the hourly value y_{t-24h} of the preceding day at the same time as the value to be predicted. Some authors also include the value with a time lag of 2 h y_{t-2h}.

In the next step, additional data sets may be identified, again using correlation and sensitivity analysis as a basis. Additional parameters that are found to be useful include humidity, cloud cover [27], atmospheric pressure [30], temperature [30, 31], wind direction, and time [31].

Preprocessing of the input data can considerably contribute to improving the accuracy of forecasts, and different approaches are proposed. As mentioned earlier, stationary, trend-free time series are required for classical time series approaches, and might be beneficial also for ANNs. Hence, the use of the clear-sky or clearness index instead of irradiance data seems suitable. This approach is followed, for example, in References 26, 28, and 30. The latter work uses power values normalized to power at clear-sky conditions, which is an equivalent approach. On the other hand, the authors of References 31 and 34 argue that time series of the clearness or clear-sky index are mostly random, and hence do not provide a good basis for any learning algorithm. They recommend using irradiance values as input. Other examples of preprocessing of input data are the use of wavelets [32] and the use of the logarithm of irradiance values [27].

A comparison of ANNs and classical time series models has been carried out in References 27 and 31. Both studies find that the error of a simple regression model can be reduced considerably by a factor in the range of 0.6–0.8 when using advanced models. In Reference 27, best results are achieved with an advanced ARIMA model that outperforms also the investigated ANN, while in Reference 31, a feed-forward ANN is identified as most appropriate. The analysis in Reference 27 for several stations with different climatic conditions also shows that there is a strong influence of the climatic conditions on both forecast accuracy and potential for improvement by the use of advanced models.

The statistical and AI models described offer the possibility of including not only on-site measured data but also input from NWP models instead or in addition, which allows for an extension of the forecast horizon from some hours to some days. This topic will be addressed in more detail in Section 1.13.3.2.4(i).

1.13.3.2.3 Cloud motion vectors from satellite images

With increasing forecast horizon, the description of the development of clouds is becoming increasingly important. For forecast horizons up to some hours, the temporal change of cloud structures is strongly influenced by cloud motion as a result of horizontal advection. Geostationary satellites with their high temporal and spatial resolution offer the potential to derive the required information on cloud motion.

An early approach to forecast solar irradiance based on Meteosat satellite images as a basis for PV power forecast was proposed in Reference 37. Subsequently, we investigated and compared various methods to derive motion vector fields from Meteosat data [38, 39], and applied them to forecast solar irradiance up to some hours ahead. In Reference 40, the results of irradiance forecasts based on the images of the Geostationary Operational Environmental Satellite (GOES) with a similar approach patterned after Reference 39 are shown. The first steps to set up a similar approach for the Geosynchronous Meteorological Satellite (GMS) are reported in Reference 41.

Cloud motion vectors from satellite images may not only be used to predict irradiance but also play an important role in meteorology and weather forecasting in general. Hence, corresponding methods have been investigated intensively by many research groups and different approaches have been proposed. An overview of methods for cloud tracking with satellite imagery is given in Reference 42, covering the development from pioneering work to the present state of the art.

To demonstrate the basic principles of irradiance forecasting based on motion vector fields from satellite images, we briefly describe our approach presented in Reference 39.

The algorithm consists of the following steps, as illustrated in **Figure 4**:

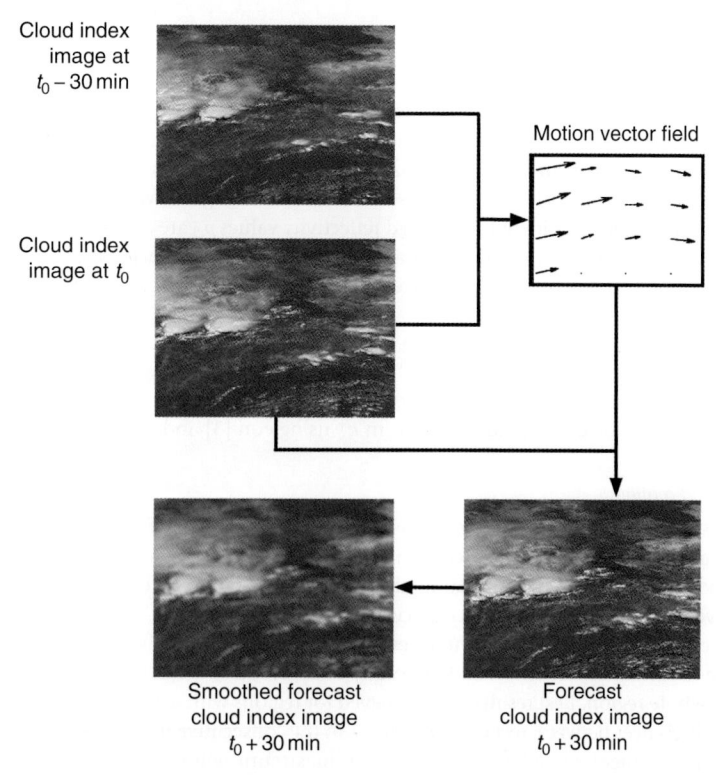

Figure 4 Short-term forecasting scheme using cloud index images.

- As a measure of cloudiness, cloud index images according to the Heliosat method [43], a semiempirical method to derive solar irradiance from satellite data, are calculated from the satellite data.
- Motion vector fields are calculated from consecutive cloud index images.
- The future cloud situation is estimated by the extrapolation of motion, that is, by applying the calculated vector field to the current image.
- A smoothing filter is applied to the predicted cloud index image in order to eliminate randomly varying small-scale structures that are not predictable. Filtering this 'noise' considerably improves the forecast accuracy in terms of root mean square error (RMSE) as defined in eqn [19] (see Section 1.13.4.3).
- Solar surface irradiance is derived from the smoothed forecast cloud index images using the Heliosat method.

A brief description of the algorithms used to derive irradiance predictions from satellite images is given in the following sections: first, the frequently used Heliosat method to derive irradiance from satellite data is introduced, and then, the algorithm for detecting cloud motion in satellite images is presented.

1.13.3.2.3(i) Irradiance from satellite data

The main application of satellite-derived irradiance data is to provide long-term mean values for solar resource assessment. With respect to forecasting, in addition to the motion vector approach shown here, satellite-derived irradiance values may also be used as reference values for training in a statistical forecasting system if ground measurement data are not available.

Images in the visible range of the geostationary Meteosat satellites are used as input data for the forecast. The Meteosat satellites at prime meridian position (0° N/0° E) basically view Europe, Africa, and the eastern part of Brazil. The satellites of the new Meteosat Second Generation (MSG) provide images of the full Earth disk every 15 min with a spatial resolution of approximately 1 km × 1 km at subsatellite point. The resolution of GMS satellites positioned at 0° N/140° E is in the same range, and the resolution of the satellite model applied to the US satellite GOES in Reference 40 is 0.1° × 0.1°.

Surface irradiance and cloud information are derived from the satellite measurements using an enhanced version of the Heliosat method [43]. In the visible range, the satellite measures radiation reflected by the Earth's atmosphere and surface and clouds. For cloud detection, the differences in the reflectivity of the Earth's surface and clouds are used. The Earth's surface – except when covered with snow – appears dark in the satellite images, while clouds show a much higher reflectivity and appear bright (see also satellite image in **Figure 2**).

In a first step, the original satellite radiometer count c is reduced by an offset c_0 to account for the sensor offset and a relative reflectivity value ρ is calculated from this corrected signal by applying a normalization with respect to the solar zenith angle. In a second step, the cloud index n is derived from the relative reflectivity ρ for each pixel as a dimensionless measure of cloudiness. The definition of the cloud index n is based on the concept that the reflectivity values are composed as a mixed signal emanating from clouds ρ_{cl} and a signal emanating from the ground ρ_{gr}, including the relative reflectivity of the clear-sky atmosphere. The share of the signal emanating from clouds defines the cloud index n:

$$\rho = n\rho_{cl} + (1-n)\rho_{gr} \qquad [5]$$

Using this relation, the cloud index may be directly inferred from the reflectivity values if the ground and cloud reflectivity values ρ_{gr} and ρ_{cl} are known. Ground reflectivity values ρ_{gr} are determined by applying an iterative procedure to select cloud-free pixels with minimum reflectivity for each satellite pixel and time slot separately on a monthly basis. In this way, spatial and temporal changes on the ground albedo – for example, due to different types of soil or seasonal changes of vegetation – as well as the anisotropy of the reflection by ground and atmosphere are considered. The cloud reflectivity values ρ_{cl} are derived from histograms of satellite images in dependence on the Sun–satellite geometry to account for anisotropic reflection characteristics.

A linear relationship is assumed to describe the influence of the cloud index n on cloud transmissivity, characterized by the clear-sky index k^*:

$$k^* = 1 - n \qquad [6]$$

For overcast situations ($n > 0.8$), this relation is modified according to Reference 44.

Finally, the global irradiance I can be directly calculated from k^* using eqn [3] and a clear-sky model to determine I_{clear}.

1.13.3.2.3(ii) Detection of cloud motion

The forecast algorithm operates on cloud index images and is therefore independent of the diurnal pattern of solar irradiance. As stated earlier, a number of algorithms exist to detect cloud motion. In Reference 39, we use a comparatively simple procedure, resulting in the same accuracy as the advanced statistical method we investigated in Reference 38.

To derive cloud motion vectors, cloud structures in consecutive images are identified, assuming that cloud structures of a certain spatial scale are stable for the considered short-term timescales. As a first step in this analysis, rectangular regions are defined which should be both large enough to contain information on temporally stable cloud structures and small enough so that the same vector describes the motion for the whole region. Best results were achieved for regions with a minimum size of 90 km × 90 km. In the next step, the mean square pixel differences between rectangular regions in the consecutive images are calculated for displacements in all directions. The maximum displacement considered is defined by maximum wind speeds at typical cloud heights. Finally, the motion vectors are determined by the displacements that yield the minimum mean square pixel differences.

The future cloud index images are calculated by applying the derived motion vectors to the latest available image. Here, the additional assumption that cloud motion stays constant for the considered timescale up to some hours ahead is used.

An evaluation of the satellite-based irradiance forecasts in dependence on the forecast horizon in comparison with other forecasting approaches is given in Section 1.13.6.4.

1.13.3.2.4 Cloud motion vectors from ground-based sky imagers

Information on cloud motion as a basis for short-term forecasting may also be derived from ground-based sky imagers as proposed in a recent study [45]. Compared with satellite data, ground-based sky imagers offer a much higher spatial and temporal resolution, including the possibility of capturing sudden changes in the irradiance – often referred to as ramps – on a temporal scale of less than 1 min. The maximum possible forecast horizon strongly depends on the cloud condition and is limited by the time until the monitored cloud scene has passed the location or area of interest. This time is determined by the spatial extension of the monitored cloud scenes in combination with cloud velocities. In Reference 45, forecasts up to 5 min ahead were evaluated for 4 partly cloudy days. An estimation of a maximum possible extension of the forecast horizon in dependence on the cloud scene resulted in values ranging from 5 to 25 min.

The forecasting procedure involves similar steps as described for satellite-based forecasts in the previous section, including a method to derive cloud and irradiance information from raw data, a method to detect cloud motion, and the extrapolation of cloud motion.

1.13.3.2.4(i) Clouds and irradiance from sky imagers

In Reference 45, binary cloud decision maps are derived from the original images (**Figure 5**) as a basis for forecasting. For time series with very high spatial and temporal resolution as considered here, binary information on the presence of clouds between the Sun and ground location in combination with a clear-sky model and a suitable representation of cloudy skies provides a good basis for estimating the solar surface irradiance (**Figure 6**). As described earlier, this is different for satellite-derived irradiances, where varying cloud positions are integrated to spatial and temporal averages and the continuous variable n is also used for a quantitative description of partly cloudy conditions.

The cloud decision algorithm is based on an evaluation of the ratio of red light to blue light (red–blue ratio, **Figure 5(b)**), which is measured using different spectral channels of the total sky imager. Different spectral scattering properties of clouds and clear sky result in different red–blue ratios. Clouds with rather uniform scattering properties in the visible range of the spectrum show a red–blue ratio close to 1. In contrast, due to the strong wavelength dependence of scattering by molecules and atmospheric particles, clear parts of the sky appear blue and correspondingly show a low red–blue ratio. These differences in the red–blue ratio of clouds and clear sky are used for detection of clouds.

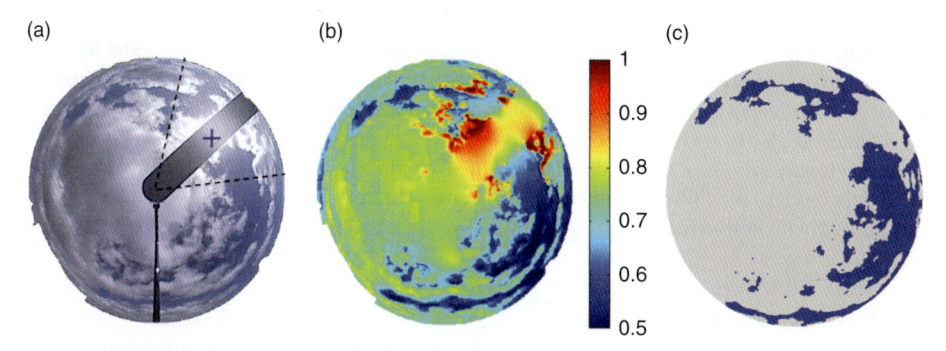

Figure 5 Processing chain of a total sky image taken on 4 October 2009 at 15:45:30 at the UC San Diego solar energy testbed (32.9° N, 117.2° W): (a) raw image; (b) red–blue ratio; and (c) cloud decision image. Source: University of San Diego.

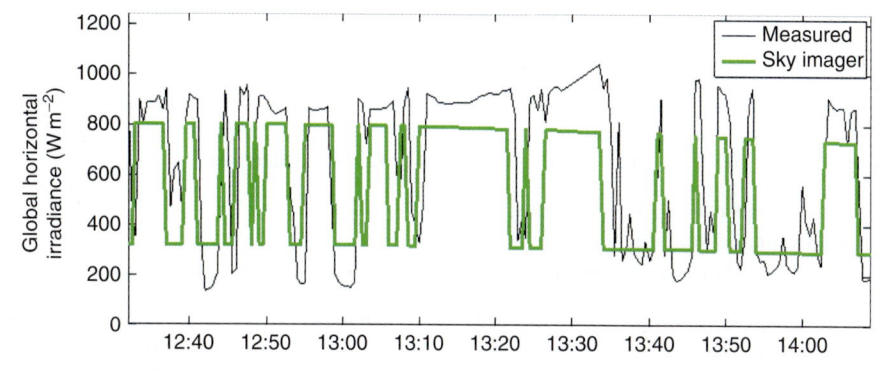

Figure 6 Nowcast from total sky imager in comparison with measured irradiance, 4 October 2009, 15:45:30, at the UC San Diego solar energy testbed (32.9° N, 117.2° W). Source: University of San Diego.

Using a threshold procedure, the measured red–blue ratio is compared with the signal expected for clear-sky conditions for each pixel of the image. A pixel is decided to be cloudy, if the red–blue ratio is larger than the corresponding clear-sky value. As the clear-sky signal is not uniform over the whole sky hemisphere (**Figure 13**), which is caused by atmospheric scattering properties, a clear-sky library in dependence on the solar zenith angle and the Sun-pixel-angle is calculated as a reference, based on the images of a cloud-free day. Besides this basic threshold procedure, an additional sunshine parameter is evaluated to better account for the circumsolar region. **Figure 6** illustrates that clouds and sudden changes in the irradiance conditions are generally detected well with the proposed approach.

1.13.3.2.4(ii) Forecasting cloud motion

The method to determine cloud motion applied in Reference 45 is based on the identification of matching cloud structures in consecutive sky images, similar to the approach described in Section 1.13.3.2.3(ii). Here, cross-correlation coefficients (see also eqn [23]) instead of mean square pixel differences are used to quantify the match between image segments. An average cloud motion vector for the complete scene is obtained after applying a quality control, including an evaluation of the calculated cross-correlation coefficients. Forecast images are derived by shifting the cloud decision images along the corresponding motion vector.

The proposed method was evaluated for forecast horizons up to 5 min ahead for 4 partly cloudy days on the basis of cloud decision images. Forecast accuracy was characterized by the number of falsely classified pixels in the forecast images and in addition related to the corresponding persistence error, that is, applying the simple assumption that the cloud situation persists without advection (see also Section 1.13.4.5). A considerable reduction of forecast errors in comparison with persistence was found, indicating the potential of the method to predict short-scale variations of solar irradiance.

1.13.3.2.5 NWP model irradiance forecasts

NWP models are operationally used to forecast the state of the atmosphere up to 15 days ahead. The temporal development of the state of the atmosphere is modeled by numerically solving the basic differential equations that describe the physical laws governing the weather.

Starting from initial conditions that are derived from worldwide observations, in a first step, the future state of the atmosphere is calculated with a global NWP model. Global NWP models are currently in operation at about 15 weather services. Examples are the Global Forecast System (GFS) run by the US National Oceanic and Atmospheric Administration (NOAA) and the Integrated Forecast System (IFS) operated at the ECMWF. Global models usually have a coarse resolution and do not allow for a detailed mapping of small-scale features, although resolution has increased rapidly during the last years and nowadays – depending on the model – is in the range of 16–50 km.

In the next step, different concepts may be applied to account for local effects and to derive improved site-specific forecasts. One possibility is the downscaling by mesoscale models, which are also referred to as local area or regional models. Mesoscale models cover only a part of the Earth but can be operated with a higher spatial resolution. They are routinely run by national weather services and private weather companies.

Also, postprocessing methods, for example, model output statistics (MOS), may be applied to model local effects. In addition, they allow for the correction of systematic deviations in dependence on different meteorological parameters and for modeling of the irradiance if irradiance is not provided as output parameter of an NWP model. Postprocessing may be applied directly to the output of a global model and likewise also to regional model output.

In this section, we first briefly introduce the general features of NWP models. Next, we exemplarily describe the ECMWF global model and two mesoscale models, the fifth-generation mesoscale model MM5 developed by the Pennsylvania State University – National Center for Atmospheric Research (PSU-NCAR) and the weather research and forecasting (WRF) mesoscale model, with respect to irradiance forecasting.

1.13.3.2.5(i) Numerical weather prediction

NWP models are based on prognostic equations describing the physical processes in the atmosphere. These equations are numerically solved on a grid, involving parameterizations to describe processes that are not explicitly resolved by the model. To initialize the forecasts, data assimilation tools are applied to make efficient use of available observations. A detailed description of the basic features briefly introduced here is given in Reference 46.

1.13.3.2.5(i)(a) Physical processes and prognostic equations The basis for any NWP model is given by the physical laws governing the processes in the atmosphere. An illustration of different atmospheric processes relevant for weather prediction is given in **Figure 7**.

In an NWP model, the state of the atmosphere is described by a basic set of variables, the prognostic variables, including the three-dimensional field of wind speed, temperature, humidity, and pressure. The temporal development of these variables is determined by the conservation equations that form the basic set of prognostic equations:

- Conservation of momentum (Navier–Stokes equations)
- Mass conservation for dry air and humidity
- Energy conservation (first law of thermodynamics).

This set of equations to be solved is completed by the equation of state (perfect gas law) relating the variables pressure and temperature to the density of air. Transport equations for other physical or chemical parameters (e.g., ozone, water, or ice content) may be added, extending the set of prognostic variables. Further parameters, the diagnostic variables, are inferred from the predicted fields without modeling their temporal development explicitly.

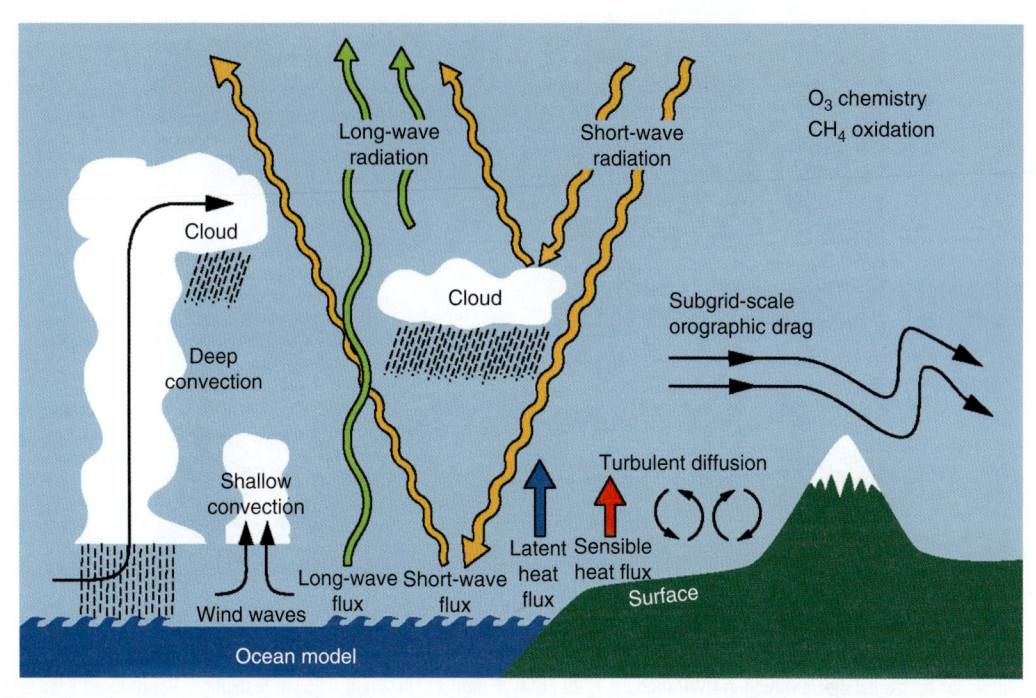

Figure 7 Illustration of processes in the atmosphere. Reproduced from Hagedorn R http://www.ecmwf.int/newsevents/training/meteorological_presentations/pdf/DA/ECMWF.pdf [47].

In hydrostatic models, hydrostatic equilibrium is assumed, where gravity and buoyant force are in balance, and vertical momentum becomes a diagnostic variable. This is a reasonable assumption for macroscale systems, but is not valid for some mesoscale phenomena, for example, convective storms. The typical spatial scale where nonhydrostatic processes become relevant is about 10 km horizontal resolution. With a hydrostatic model, mesocale phenomena may not be calculated directly and must be approximated. Global NWP models with comparatively coarse horizontal resolution are generally hydrostatic models, while mesoscale models with the aim to resolve processes with higher resolution often include nonhydrostatic processes.

The conservation properties defined in the prognostic equations essentially depend on boundary conditions. This requires the modeling of sinks and sources in the atmosphere and exchange with the Earth's surface. In particular, boundary conditions for energy conservation are determined by the incoming radiation at the top of the atmosphere and interactions between radiation and atmospheric components in the atmosphere. The corresponding absorption and scattering processes are modeled using radiation transfer equations.

1.13.3.2.5(i)(b) Solving equations on a grid The prognostic equations describing the temporal development of the prognostic variables are solved on a grid with appropriate numerical methods, involving temporal and spatial discretization. In general, with increasing resolution, a more realistic description of physical processes and a better forecast accuracy are expected. However, the resolution of an NWP model is limited by the numerical effort that is necessary to do calculations for a large number of grid points.

The temporal resolution of internal calculations in NWP models usually is considerably higher than that of the output variables. Output variables are delivered with a resolution of typically 1 h for local area models and 3–6 h for global models. The internal time step gives the period over which the change of the atmospheric variables is described by the dynamic equations. This internal time step may be down to 30 s for highly resolved calculations with mesoscale models and is about 10 min for global NWP models.

The horizontal resolution (**Figure 8**) determines the spatial extent of weather phenomena that can be directly simulated. Grid points are usually distributed equally in the horizontal range. The resolution of global NWP models nowadays is in the range of 16–50 km. In mesoscale models, the horizontal resolution may be down to 1 km; weather services typically operate mesoscale models with a spatial resolution in the range of 5–20 km. The resolution of vertical levels is generally adapted to the occurrence of physical processes that take place in certain regions of the atmosphere.

1.13.3.2.5(i)(c) Parameterizations The need for parameterizations is a direct consequence of solving the basic differential equations on a grid with finite resolution, rather than on the continuum. The finite-difference equations represent the evolution of a space–time average of the true solution and can only describe phenomena on spatial scales that are larger than twice the grid size. However, the full spectrum of atmospheric processes as described by the original fundamental equations ranges from micro- to macroscale processes and a lot of physical processes occur on spatial scales that are much smaller than the scale explicitly resolved by the grid. Although these subgrid processes are not directly included in the model, their statistical effect on their mean flow can be taken into account. The effect of the unresolved scales on the average flow expressed in terms of the large-scale parameters is mathematically modeled by using parameterizations.

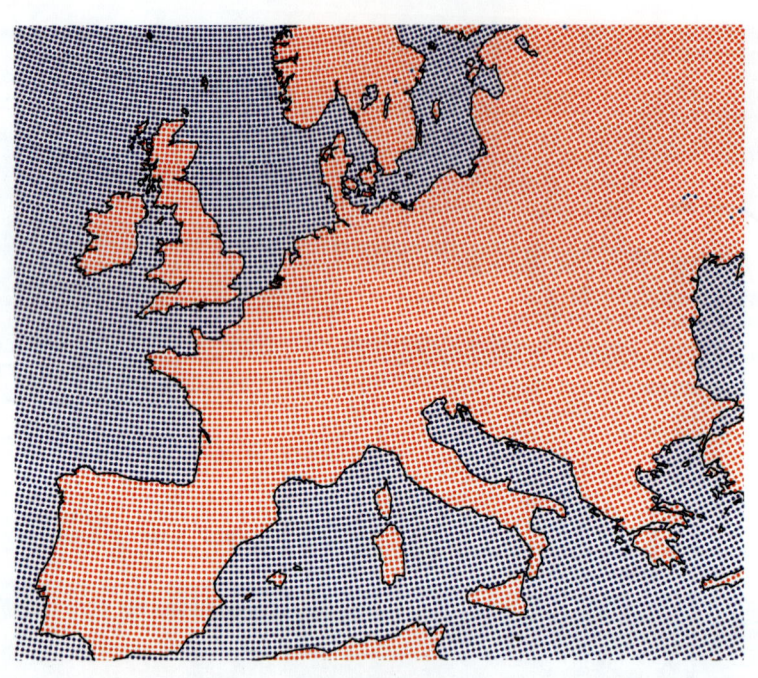

Figure 8 Example for horizontal discretization in NWP models: T799 ECMWF model with 25 km × 25 km resolution. Reproduced from Untch A http://www.ecmwf.int/newsevents/training/meteorological_presentations/pdf/NM/Adiabatic.pdf [48].

Parameterizations are applied to represent different physical processes, including condensation, convection, turbulence, and land surface processes. For irradiance forecasting, the parameterization of radiation transfer and clouds is of special interest.

1.13.3.2.5(i)(d) Starting a forecast – The initial conditions To start a forecast, information on the current state of the atmosphere is necessary. For global NWP models, this information is obtained from a worldwide network of meteorological observations and measurements. The key variables needed are the three-dimensional fields of wind, temperature, and humidity and the two-dimensional field of surface pressure. Boundary variables like snow cover or sea surface temperature are also of high importance. Depending on the forecast system, further observations may be integrated, for example, those on precipitation and clouds. Different kinds of complementary platforms utilized for the observations are shown in **Figure 9**.

To make the most efficient use of the available measurements, modern data assimilation systems use the forecast model to process the observations and to produce a more complete picture of the state of the atmosphere. The data assimilation process starts with the previous analysis. In the second step, a short-term forecast is made for the current analysis time. Finally, this forecasted state is corrected using the new observations. In this way, not only are data gaps in time and space filled, but also indirect satellite measurements are integrated in a consistent way into the forecasting model.

Regional models use initial conditions as well as lateral boundary conditions from global NWP model output, and also offer the possibility of integrating local measurements.

1.13.3.2.5(ii) Irradiance forecasts of the ECWMF global model

The ECMWF provides weather forecasts up to 15 days ahead, including solar surface irradiance and different cloud parameters as model output. ECMWF forecasts have shown their high quality as a basis for both wind and solar power forecasts. These forecasts are described here as an example of global NWP model forecasts.

From the time ECMWF started operation in August 1979, there has been development in many aspects and model performance has been constantly increasing. Here, we focus on the aspect of increasing grid resolution and the improvements with respect to radiation and cloud schemes.

Due to the rapid development in computer performance, horizontal as well as vertical resolution has increased at a faster rate. In 1985, the model T106 became operational with a horizontal resolution of approximately 200 km × 200 km and 16 vertical levels, followed by the model T213 in 1991 with a horizontal resolution of 90 km × 90 km and 31 vertical levels. Since then, several upgrades of the resolution have been performed. The evaluations of ECMWF-based irradiance and PV power predictions [4, 49, 50] presented below are based on the T799 model with a spatial resolution of 25 km × 25 km. The current model T1279 was implemented in January 2010 and shows a horizontal resolution of 16 km × 16 km, which is getting close to typical operational resolutions of regional models. Ninety-one hybrid vertical levels resolve the atmosphere up to 0.01 hPa corresponding to approximately 80 km. The temporal resolution of the forecasts is 3 h for the first 3 forecast days that are most relevant for PV power prediction.

Prediction of Solar Irradiance and Photovoltaic Power

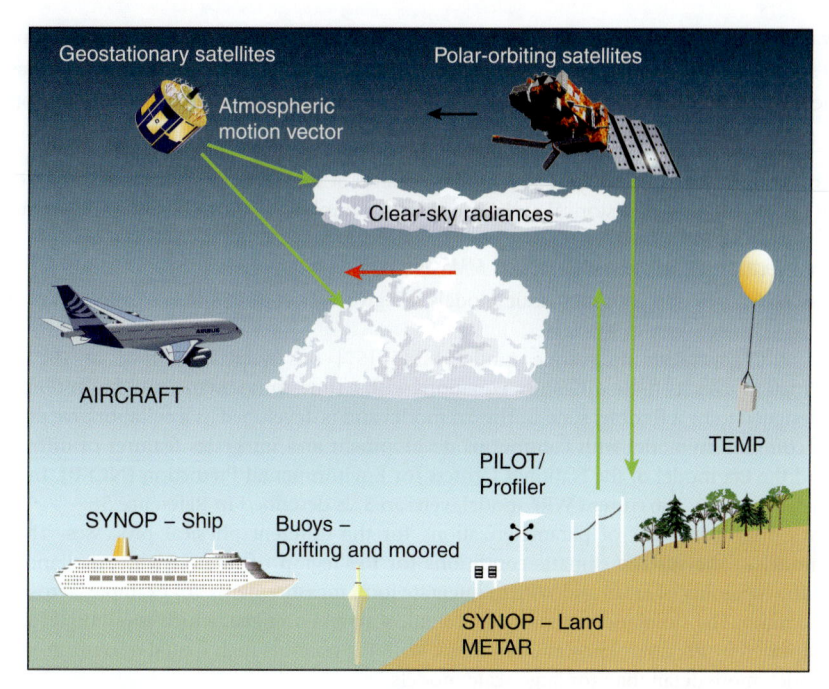

Figure 9 Overview of observation platforms. Reproduced from Taniguchi H, Otani K, and Kurokawa K (2001) Hourly forecast of global irradiation using GMS satellite images. *Solar Energy Materials & Solar Cells* 67(1–4): 551–557. doi:10.1016/S0927-0248(00)00327-5 [41].

The modeling of radiation transfer in NWP models requires parameterization of scattering and absorption processes in the atmosphere. As a first approximation, the short- and long-wave spectral ranges, corresponding to radiation emitted by the Sun and the Earth, respectively, are modeled with different schemes, solving the radiation transfer equations on spectral bands. For clear-sky situations, state-of-the-art parameterized radiative transfer schemes show good accuracy in comparison with detailed line-by-line radiation models. But the situation is much more complex for cloudy skies. Clouds are extremely variable in space and their representation in global models with coarse resolution is one of the major challenges in the parameterization of physical processes. The parameterization of geometric effects of clouds requires specification of the fraction of cloud cover in a grid box, the subgrid variability of cloud variables, and overlap assumptions for clouds in the vertical columns. Other important factors are the representation of the cloud optical properties (optical thickness, single scattering albedo, and asymmetry factor) and parameterizations of cloud microphysical processes.

A description of the first implementation of radiation and cloud properties in the ECMWF model is given in Reference 50. In the first version, a two-stream formulation of the radiative transfer equations was employed together with a photon path distribution method to model transmission through the layers of the atmosphere. The transmission functions were evaluated for two spectral intervals in the short wave. Aerosols were considered as one background type. Cloud cover was basically diagnosed as a function of relative humidity, and the cloud optical parameters were derived from the cloud liquid water path using an empirical relation. To assess the quality of the radiation schemes, radiative fluxes and the vertical profile of heating rates are evaluated in comparison with detailed radiation models with spectrally highly resolved line-by-line calculations as a reference. It was shown that the latest version of the radiation scheme including major changes in radiation parameterizations, in aerosol description, and in the assignment of cloud optical properties showed better agreement with the detailed models than the prior ones.

Since then, model development with respect to cloud and radiation schemes has been an ongoing process [51–54]. This process integrates scientific progress and information on model deficiencies. Information on model deficiencies is obtained by comparing the modeled and predicted variables with observations or simulations with detailed models. Evaluations in this context are not restricted to analysis of radiative fluxes, energy budgets, and cloud parameters. Also, the influence of cloud and radiation schemes on the performance of the complete system is investigated, by, for example, analyzing temperature and wind fields, and the anomaly correlation of geopotential as an objective score of forecast skill. An evaluation with focus on surface radiation fields and cloudiness is given in Reference 55.

Here, two of the major revisions are highlighted.

- In 1995, the diagnostic cloud scheme was replaced by a prognostic cloud scheme, as proposed in Reference 52. The temporal development of clouds is described by large-scale budget equations for cloud water content and cloud cover, resulting in a strong coupling of cloudiness to the physical processes. In particular, the formation, maintenance, and dissipation of clouds are directly related to the physical processes of convection, large-scale condensation, vertical diffusion, and radiation. A comparison of observed values of cloud cover and cloud water content demonstrated the improved performance using the new scheme.
- A new approach to represent subgrid cloud structures was introduced with the new radiation package McRad [54], which was implemented in July 2007. The most important feature of this new scheme is a Monte Carlo independent column approximation for radiation transfer that ensures an unbiased description of radiation fields in comparison with more detailed radiation models.

In addition, the new radiation package includes a short-wave radiation scheme with 14 spectral intervals and revised cloud optical properties. The new scheme is evaluated against observations and the previous operational model for seasonal simulations and 10-day forecasts. The positive impact of the new scheme on different forecast parameters, in particular tropical temperatures and winds, is shown.

Detailed information on continuous development and model updates at the ECMWF is available in Reference 56, where a full scientific and technical documentation of historical and current model implementations of the IFS is provided.

1.13.3.2.5(iii) Irradiance forecast with the mesoscale models MM5 and WRF

As examples of the irradiance prediction with mesoscale models, we give a short description of MM5 and WRF with respect to this purpose.

The nonhydrostatic, fifth-generation mesoscale model MM5 [57] has been developed at the PSU-NCAR. It uses a terrain-following coordinate, solves its finite-difference equations with a time-split scheme, and has multiple nesting capabilities.

The WRF model is designed to be a flexible, state-of-the-art model and is developed as a collaborative effort of several institutes. WRF is supported as a community model with continuous development and integrates features of different mesoscale models, including also MM5 and the Eta model of the National Centers for Environmental Prediction (NCEP). In this sense, WRF can be seen as a follow-up model to MM5. The current WRF model, version 3, is described in Reference 58.

Both WRF and MM5 offer a number of parameterizations for the different physical processes. This allows adapting the configuration of the model to the specific climatic conditions for the region of interest with irradiance as designated output parameter. In addition, the capability of MM5 and WRF to integrate local measurements, for example, aerosols, may also contribute to improving forecast accuracy. The simulation of meso- and small-scale phenomena, which is essential for calculations with high spatial resolution, is supported by the nonhydrostatic dynamics. With the possibly high spatial resolution, the effects of topography may be considered in much more detail than for large-scale models.

Mesoscale models require input from global NWP models for initialization and boundary conditions. Frequently, GFS data of NOAA are used to initialize MM5 or WRF for operational applications, because – in contrast to ECMWF data – they are available for free. The input data used have a significant influence on the results, especially for cloudy conditions. This has been demonstrated in a case study reported in Reference 59, where different NWP models – ECMWF and the global and local models of the German Weather Service DWD – were compared for initialization.

To achieve the intended high spatial resolution in a mesoscale model with reasonable computing time, the resolution of the driving global model is increased stepwise with internal nesting. For example, in the study reported in Reference 59, the outer domain of MM5 covering large parts of Europe has a resolution of 27 km × 27 km, the next domain has a resolution of 9 km × 9 km, and the final resolution of the innermost domain is 3 km × 3 km. The nested domains used in this study are shown in **Figure 10**.

MM5 and WRF offer different long- and short-wave transfore schemes (e.g., see Dudhia 60) that describe the interaction of radiation with the atmosphere including cloud and precipitation fields as well as with the surface. Several parameterizations are also available for cloud physical processes, for example, cumulus parameterizations and moisture schemes. A basic difference of MM5 and WRF in comparison with global NWP models concerning the cloud scheme is the specification of grid boxes as either cloudy or clear sky, assuming a horizontally homogeneous structure of clouds in a grid box. In contrast, in global NWP models, the subgrid variability of cloud structures is described by several parameters including the cloud cover that can take continuous values between 0 and 1, as described above. This different treatment of clouds is motivated by the assumption that with the high spatial resolutions of MM5 and WRF cloud structures can be explicitly resolved, while for large-scale models unresolved cloud structures have to be parameterized.

First studies on the performance of MM5 with respect to solar irradiance forecasting in the context of model development are reported in References 61–63. The investigations in References 61 and 62 focus on the evaluation of clear-sky situations and the influence of the aerosol optical depth (AOD) not only on irradiance but also on other parameters. The authors show that MM5 can model clear-sky irradiances with good accuracy for low aerosol load, but that considerable overestimation of the irradiances is found for AOD larger than 0.1. This overestimation also affects the surface energy balance, resulting in errors in the estimation of surface heat fluxes, surface temperature, and depth of the mixing layer. The authors emphasize the importance of a detailed representation of aerosols in the model to avoid systematic errors and recommend that future research should address the assimilation of measurements of AOD into the model.

In Reference 63, a detailed analysis of cloud and radiation fields predicted with MM5 is given in comparison with data collected by the Atmospheric Radiation Measurement (ARM) Climate Research Facility at Southern Great Plains. This unique data set includes radiative flux measurements as well as radar and lidar measurements providing vertical profiles of cloud parameters, and offers an excellent basis for evaluation and improvement of cloud and radiation schemes in atmospheric models. MM5 simulations are performed with initial and lateral boundary conditions from the Eta model and assimilating available local measurements. Although the representation of low clouds, cirrus clouds, and – again – aerosols is identified as a weak point of the model, it is shown that overall a reasonable agreement between predicted and measured cloud and radiation fields is achieved using MM5.

Recently, several research groups have investigated the potential of MM5 and WRF irradiance forecasts for solar energy applications. In a first step, an appropriate setup of MM5 or WRF has to be determined. In Reference 59, we have addressed this task by comparing different configurations of the cumulus, moisture, and planetary boundary layer parameterizations with respect to irradiance calculations in a case study. To limit the computational effort when rerunning simulations for several configurations, a set of 6 test days is defined covering different cloud conditions: clear sky, broken clouds, and overcast. The comparison revealed

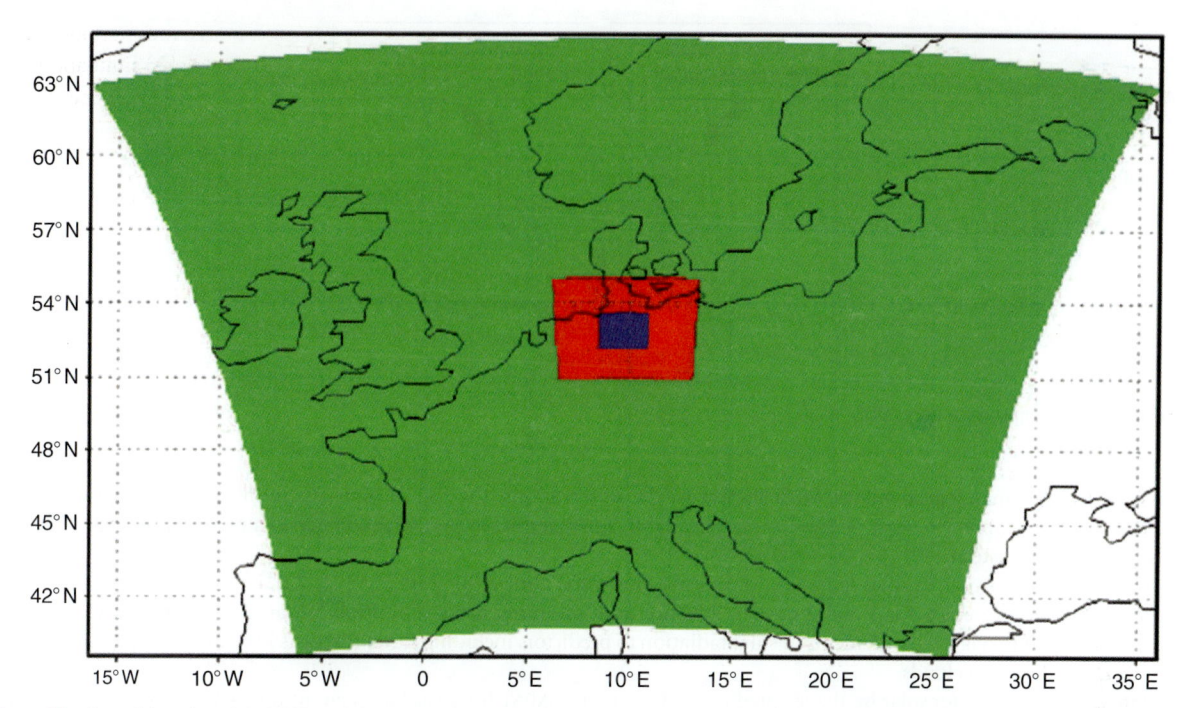

Figure 10 Nested domains of the WRF model as used in Reference 59. Green, outermost domain with a spatial resolution of 27 km × 27 km; red, middle domain with a spatial resolution of 9 km × 9 km; blue, study area with a spatial resolution of 3 km × 3 km.

significant differences in the error of the irradiance prediction depending on the combination of parameterizations and also on the cloud conditions. Corresponding investigations in Reference 64 focus on the evaluation of different schemes of the planetary boundary parameterization due to its strong impact on radiation and heat fluxes near the surface. The prediction of irradiance in complex topographic terrain is the focus of another case study [65]. The influence of the topographic parameterization of MM5 describing the effects of slope and aspect on the surface irradiance is investigated for a set of clear-sky days.

Once the operational setup of MM5 or WRF is defined, simulations for longer periods may be run and evaluated. In Reference 59, we show an evaluation of MM5 forecasts for a 40-day period in summer 2003 in Southern Germany in comparison with other forecasting approaches. Two studies comparing different methods to predict solar irradiance including WRF forecasts for different locations in the United States are reported in References 66 and 67. In Reference 68, a detailed evaluation study of WRF irradiance forecasts in Andalusia (Southern Spain) is given with calculations of 1 month for each of the seasons. The results of WRF irradiance forecasts in comparison with other approaches for different European countries [69] are presented in Section 1.13.5.3.

1.13.3.2.6 Postprocessing of NWP model output

Postprocessing methods are frequently applied to refine the output of NWP models. Especially, detailed local weather features are generally not resolved by NWP predictions although spatial resolution has increased rapidly during the last years. In addition, systematic deviations for certain weather situations may be assigned to both global and mesoscale model predictions. Hence, there is potential for improvement by statistical or other postprocessing methods, and many irradiance forecasting approaches imply a statistical component.

In particular, postprocessing methods may be utilized to

- reduce systematic forecast errors (correction of systematic deviations);
- account for local effects (e.g., topography);
- account for the influence of selected variables in more detail (e.g., aerosols);
- derive parameters that are not directly provided by the NWP models (e.g., solar surface irradiance is still not a standard output parameter);
- optimize the scaling of the amplitude of the forecasts; and
- combine the output of different models in an optimum way.

Various – mostly statistical – approaches have been proposed to address these issues, some of which are presented in the following sections.

1.13.3.2.6(i) Model output statistics

MOS [70] is an established and widely used technique to refine the output of NWP models, often with focus on adjustment to local conditions. Observations of the designated forecast variable – the predictand – are related to model forecast variables – the predictors – with a statistical approach (**Figure 11**). The set of predictors may be extended by including, for example, prior

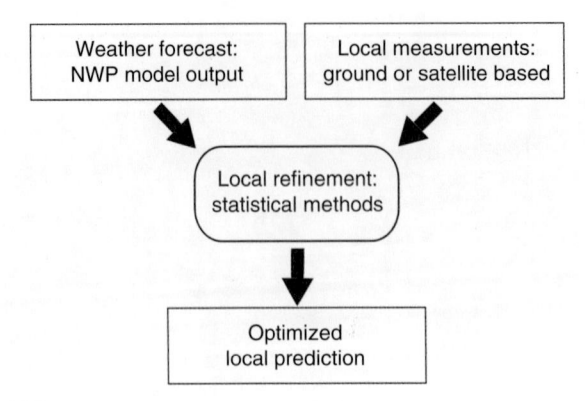

Figure 11 Forecasting scheme using MOS.

observations and climatological values. With respect to the observations, the use of high-quality measurements from ground stations is most favorable. However, if these are not available, for example, in case of irradiance as a predictand, satellite-derived values may be used instead.

One of the first attempts in solar radiation forecasting, presented almost 30 years ago [71, 72], is based on MOS techniques. Daily solar radiation forecasts for 1 and 2 days in advance were produced using a multiple linear regression scheme. Statistical regression was used to relate measurements of solar radiation to predictors including cloud forecasts in terms of probability for clear sky, overcast, and broken clouds.

A state-of-the-art MOS for solar irradiance predictions based on ECMWF forecasts has been introduced in Reference 1. Multiple regression is applied to modify long-term monthly mean values of the predictand. Direct model output of ECMWF and statistically derived predictors are used. The MOS is operated on the basis of ground-measured irradiance values when available. For locations without irradiance measurements, irradiance derived from Meteosat data with the Heliosat method (see also Section 1.13.3.2.3(i)) is used instead. A comparison of irradiance forecasts using this MOS scheme with WRF forecasts and other approaches is given in References 59 and 69.

Although traditionally MOS schemes are mostly based on linear regression, any statistical approach relating observed variables to NWP output fits to the concept of MOS. In particular, ANNs have also been used to improve NWP output with respect to irradiance prediction [36, 73, 74]. In Reference 73, an ANN is applied to irradiance forecasts of the NCEP Eta model run operationally at the Brazilian Center for Weather Forecasts and Climate Studies (CPTEC/INPE). An evaluation with measurements for two stations in the south of Brazil reveals a strong overestimation of the irradiance by the original forecasts, and a considerable improvement is achieved by the application of an ANN using different atmospheric forecast parameters of the Eta model as input. In Reference 74, the authors present a novel high-performance approach combining discrete wavelet transformation with ANNs. This postprocessing approach is applied to forecast errors of the nonhydrostatic Advanced Regional Prediction System (ARPS) for a location in the south of Brazil, resulting in a significant reduction of the forecast errors for daily radiation prediction.

An empirical approach for solar radiation forecasting based on sky cover forecasts of the US National Digital Forecast Database (NDFD) is presented in Reference 75. NDFD forecasts with a grid resolution of $0.05° \times 0.05°$ are generated as a combination of US national model output, mesoscale model runs, and human input. Solar irradiance is not provided as an NDFD forecast parameter. Hence, the main aim of the postprocessing here is to infer a parameter that otherwise would not be available. The proposed approach relates sky cover forecasts to clear-sky index values, derived from measured irradiance values according to eqn [3], with an exponential fit function. A preliminary evaluation of one site in the United States shows a good correlation between forecasted and measured irradiances.

Systematic deviations of NWP output variables often depend on the meteorological situation. In Reference 49, a bias correction in dependence on the predicted cloud situation for the application to ECMWF irradiance forecasts is introduced. The original forecasts show a considerable overestimation of irradiance for intermediate cloud cover, as shown in more detail in Section 1.13.4.7. To avoid this systematic deviations, in a first step, the bias (see eqn [20], Section 1.13.4.3) is modeled as a polynomial function of the predicted clear-sky index k^* and the solar zenith angle θ_Z. The corrected forecast is then obtained by subtracting the modeled Bias(k^*, θ_Z) from the original predicted values. Training of the fit function is performed with a sliding window technique using measurements of the previous 30 days of weather stations in the region of interest. The number of training data pairs is a critical issue and we found that using a network of stations for training is favorable compared with training using data of individual stations only. The results of this approach applied to ECMWF irradiance forecasts for measurement stations in Germany are presented in detail in Section 1.13.7.2.2. The proposed approach for bias correction has been adapted and evaluated also for other NWP models and different climates in two recent studies [76]. Reference 77 provides an analysis of irradiance forecasts of three different NWP models (GFS, North American Model (NAM), and ECMWF) for stations in the continental United States. For all the three models, forecast accuracy could be improved by applying the weather-dependent bias correction.

An evaluation of the Canadian Global Environmental Multiscale (GEM) model for stations in Canada and the United States is given in Reference 76. A method for bias removal of irradiance forecasts using Kalman filtering is introduced and compared with the bias correction according to Reference 49. Kalman filters are designed to efficiently extract a signal from noisy data and are therefore expected to show a more robust performance if only limited training data are available, which is the case if the training is performed on the basis of individual stations. Pelland et al. [76] found that the most suitable realization of their approach was a set of Kalman filter equations established separately for each forecast horizon and modeling the bias in dependence on the forecasted irradiances. The accuracy assessment was performed for single stations and for regional average values. At the level of individual stations, the bias removal based on Kalman filtering outperforms the other approach. However, the improvement compared with the original forecasts is small for single stations, while for regional averages both bias removal approaches significantly reduced the RMSE, which is in agreement with the evaluations shown in Section 1.13.7.2.2.

1.13.3.2.6(ii) Temporal interpolation

Global model forecasts are provided with a temporal resolution of 3–6 h. The management of electricity grids, however, needs forecasts of the expected solar power input at least on an hourly basis. Different interpolation techniques may be applied in order to derive hourly forecasts from global NWP output.

In Reference 49, we propose an approach combining the forecast data with a clear-sky model to account for the typical diurnal course of irradiance. This approach is applied to 3-hourly ECMWF irradiance forecasts and compared with a simple linear interpolation of irradiance values. Linear interpolation is performed for the clear-sky index k^*, which is almost independent of the deterministic course of irradiance, as described in Section 1.13.3.2.1. Hence, it provides a more suitable basis for linear interpolation than irradiance, which clearly shows nonlinear time dependence for the investigated temporal resolution of 3 h, particularly during morning and evening hours as well as around noon. In a first step, 3-hourly mean values of $k^*_{3h} = I_{pred,3h}/I_{clear,3h}$ are calculated from the forecasted values $I_{pred,3h}$. In a second step, hourly values of k^* are derived by linear interpolation, and finally, the hourly resolved irradiance values are obtained as $I_{pred} = k^* I_{clear}$. Particularly for clear-sky situations, linear interpolation of k^* performs significantly better than linear interpolation of the irradiance.

1.13.3.2.6(iii) Spatial averaging

As already mentioned in Section 1.13.3.2.3, forecast accuracy in terms of RMSE can be improved by applying a smoothing filter or spatial averaging. For ECMWF forecasts with an original spatial resolution of 25 km × 25 km and temporal resolution of 3 h, best results are achieved for average values of 4 × 4 grid points corresponding to a region of 100 km × 100 km [49]. However, the improvement compared with forecasts that evaluate only the next grid point is small due to the already coarse spatial and temporal resolution of the original forecasts.

Spatial averaging has a much stronger impact for mesoscale or multiscale model output with hourly values and a finer grid resolution. An analysis of the high-resolution WRF forecasts presented in Reference 59 showed that averaging irradiance predictions over an area of 180 km × 180 km reduces the RMSE to approximately 85% of the RMSE when evaluating the nearest grid point only. Similar improvements are achieved for WRF forecasts provided by Meteotest that are delivered as average values of 10 × 10 model pixels, corresponding to an area of 50 km × 50 km [69], and also for irradiance forecasts with the Canadian GEM model, where averaging areas in the range of 300 km × 300 km to 600 km × 600 km gave best results [76].

Mathiesen and Kleissl [77] report 100 km × 100 km as a suitable averaging area for irradiance forecasts of the GFS model and the NAM model, which is also WRF based.

The benefits of spatial averaging can be explained as follows:

- For a low correlation between forecast and measurement, it is favorable to reduce variations of the forecasts around their mean values. In the extreme case of 0 correlation, a minimum RMSE is obtained if the forecasts are replaced by their mean value. In this way, the magnitude of forecast errors is limited to maximum possible deviation from the mean value, while otherwise forecast errors might get as large as the difference between maximum and minimum possible values. A quantitative description and formal derivation of the relation between RMSE, correlation, and further statistical quantities is given, for example, in Reference 78.
- For variable cloud situations, it is hardly possible to predict the exact position of a cloud for a certain hour 1 day or even more in advance. The correlation of predicted and measured cloud cover is low and large forecast errors may occur, as quantitatively shown in Section 1.13.4.7.
- Spatial averaging reduces the amplitude of the forecasts for situations with variable cloud cover, which is beneficial because of the low correlation for these situations.
- For stable, homogeneous clear-sky or overcast situations, the averaging procedure introduces only minor changes to the forecast values. This is desirable, because these situations usually show good forecast accuracy, as shown in Section 1.13.4.7.

Summarizing, the spatial averaging procedure reduces fluctuations of forecast values in variable cloud situations where this is favorable, but preserves the good quality of the original forecasts in homogeneous clear-sky and overcast situations.

Finally, it must be emphasized here that the spatial averaging is considered in the context of postprocessing of NWP output only. Of course, an increasing resolution of the NWP model allowing for a better representation of physical processes may be beneficial for forecast accuracy.

1.13.3.2.6(iv) Physical postprocessing approaches

Few studies also investigate physical postprocessing procedures involving radiation transfer calculations. This allows for integrating additional parameters that are generally not modeled in detail with NWP models, for example, aerosols. Additionally, radiation transfer calculations directly provide information on both global and direct normal irradiance, which is relevant for concentrating PV or solar thermal power plants.

In Reference 23, a forecasting system for global and direct irradiance including aerosol forecasts derived with a chemical transport model is proposed and evaluated. The irradiance calculations are performed with the libRadtran software package for radiative transfer [25]. Input parameters are the aerosol forecasts, cloud cover and water vapor forecasts with MM5, and satellite-derived ground albedo and ozone values. Special focus of the study is on the evaluation of clear-sky situations, which are mainly determined by aerosols.

In Reference 68, the authors analyze the reliability of 3-day-ahead hourly forecasts global and direct normal irradiance forecast in Andalusia (Southern Spain) based on the WRF mesoscale atmospheric model. The direct normal irradiance forecasts are calculated on the basis of WRF model output and satellite retrievals with a physical postprocessing procedure based on radiation transfer calculations.

A partly physical postprocessing procedure for topographic downscaling of solar irradiance forecasts in mountainous regions is proposed in Reference 79. The disaggregation is carried out by accommodating the initial WRF irradiance estimates to the elevation of a target digital elevation model with a spatial resolution of 90 m × 90 m. The proposed method accounts for shading, sky-view reduction, reflected irradiance, and scaling to the inclined terrain surface.

1.13.3.2.6(v) Human interpretation of NWP output

Finally, a traditional method to obtain improved local forecasts from NWP model output is the participation of a human forecaster [16]. Meteorologists at weather services routinely analyze and compare the output of different global and local NWP models and meteorological measurements. In particular, they also use their expert knowledge to decide on the final forecast values, for example, of cloud cover. Solar irradiance forecasts may be derived by combining the cloud cover forecasts of meteorologists with a clear-sky model. An advantage of this approach is that forecasts may be adjusted for local events or weather situations difficult to forecast with NWP models or statistical methods, like, fog. An evaluation of solar irradiance forecasts involving human interpretation (HI) of numerical weather forecasts is given later, as part of the benchmarking study presented in Section 1.13.5.

1.13.3.3 PV Power Forecasting

Forecasts of global irradiance as described in the previous section provide the basis for most PV power prediction schemes. In recent years, different approaches to infer aggregated electric power output from irradiance forecasts have been proposed. These approaches may be grouped into the following categories, already introduced above:

- Physical approaches explicitly model the different processes determining the conversion of solar irradiance to electricity. This includes conversion of horizontal irradiance to the array plane in a first step and PV simulation in a second step (**Figure 2**). Temperature forecasts are useful as additional forecast parameter influencing PV power generation.
- Statistical or learning algorithms do not model the physical processes directly but try to establish the relation between power output and irradiance forecasts on the basis of historical data sets. Input data to statistical approaches are not limited to irradiance forecasts. As alternative or complementary input, different NWP output variables and prior observations, particularly of PV power output, may also be used.
- Combined or hybrid approaches apply physical models in a first step and correct the obtained results with a statistical model.

Explicit PV power prediction approaches are presented, for example, in References 1, 4, 35, and 50. Examples of the use of purely statistical methods are given in Reference 80, where PV power forecasts are derived from prior observations of PV power, different irradiance components, and temperature, and in Reference 28, where PV power is derived from prior observations and NWP forecast variables using AR models with exogenous input. A direct comparison of an explicit and a statistical model based on NWP input is shown in Reference 13, with better results for the statistical approach. In Reference 50, a hybrid method is proposed, involving statistical adjustments at different stages of the modeling chain.

Power prediction for utility applications usually requires upscaling to regional power as an additional step. Only few studies have addressed this topic so far. A preparatory study is presented in Reference 1 and further work is described in Reference 4.

The basic features of the modeling steps of an explicit physical PV power forecasting approach are introduced in the next sections. After that, we address upscaling to regional power prediction, and some aspects of statistical postprocessing specific to PV power prediction are discussed.

1.13.3.3.1 Irradiance on the module plane

To calculate the irradiance on the module plane actually utilized by the PV system, systems with fixed tilt angles, tracked systems, and concentrating PV systems have to be distinguished.

The majority of PV systems receive the incoming irradiance on a tilted plane, and the forecasted global horizontal irradiance has to be converted according to the orientation and declination of the modules. Irradiance conversion for tilted planes is also necessary

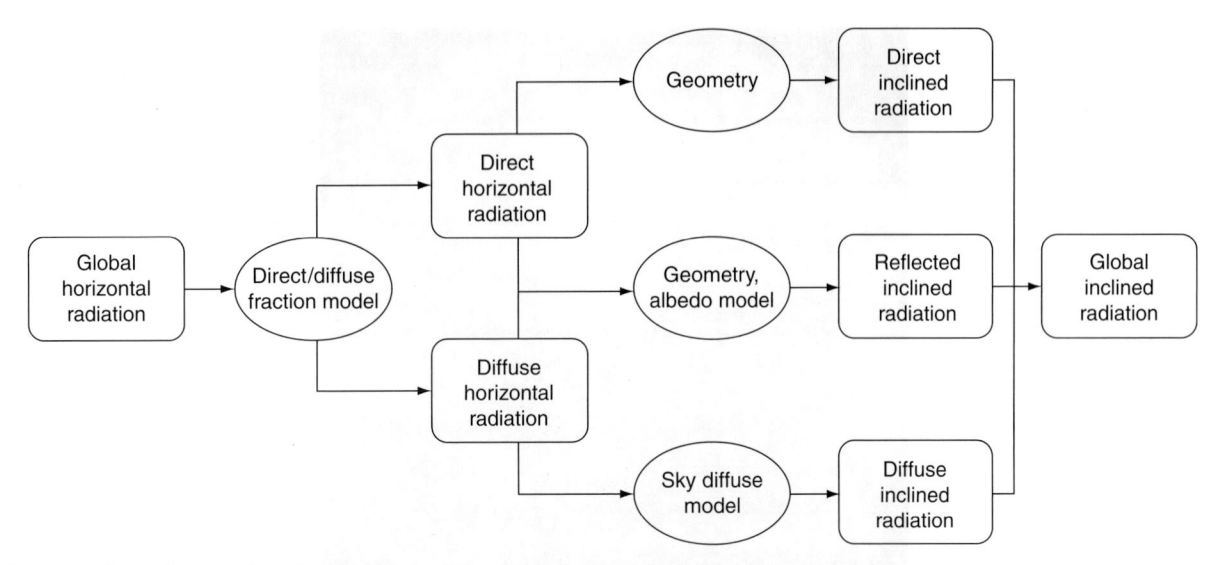

Figure 12 Conversion steps for estimating global radiation on tilted surfaces from global horizontal radiation.

for PV system yield estimation and for planning and sizing of PV systems. In this context, a large number of empirical tilted irradiance models have been developed that may be directly used for PV power prediction as well.

It is current practice to decompose the solar radiation on a tilted plane into the components direct beam, sky diffuse, and ground-reflected radiation:

$$I_t = I_{beam,t} + I_{diff,t} + I_{r,t} \quad [7]$$

where the indices denote radiation on the tilted plane (t) and reflected radiation (r), respectively.

The different steps to derive these components are illustrated in **Figure 12**. In a first step, information on the diffuse and direct components of the horizontal irradiance has to be derived. These components may be inferred from global horizontal irradiance values with empirical direct/diffuse fraction models. They all use the strong dependency of the diffuse fraction on atmospheric conditions (e.g., clouds, aerosols, and water vapor) as well as on solar geometry and surface parameters. In References 80 and 81, for the first time, the diffuse fraction was related to the clearness index, using a statistical method to determine the functional relationship $I_{diff}/I = f(k)$. Since then, many variations of this basic approach have been presented. For example, in Reference 82, solar elevation and a cloud variability parameter are considered in addition to the clearness index. Recently, models that treat the influence of clouds and clear-sky atmospheric components separately have also been proposed. In Reference 83, the direct fraction is modeled as an empirical function depending on the clear-sky index and a clear-sky model for direct and global irradiance:

$$\frac{I_{beam}}{I} = \frac{f(k^*)I_{beam,clear}}{I_{clear}} \quad [8]$$

The parametric function $f(k^*)$ has been derived by fitting to measured beam fraction values.

Some forecasting systems also directly provide the direct and diffuse irradiance components derived with radiative transfer calculations, as described in Section 1.13.3.2.5(iv).

Consecutively, separate models for the three components of the tilted irradiance are applied.

The modeling of the direct component of the tilted irradiance is straightforward by applying a geometric conversion factor (to the horizontal beam component):

$$I_{beam,t} = \frac{\cos\Theta}{\cos\Theta_Z} I_{beam} \quad [9]$$

where Θ_Z denotes the solar zenith angle and Θ the angle of incidence. The angle of incidence Θ is geometrically determined by the direction toward the Sun (latitude, declination, hour angle) and the orientation (tilt, azimuth) of the given PV plane.

Modeling of the diffuse irradiance on a tilted plane component is more complex, because the directional distribution of radiance over the sky strongly depends on the atmospheric situation. For overcast situations, the assumption of an isotropic (i.e., uniform) radiance distribution over the sky is usually a good approximation. Clear skies, on the other hand, show a significant anisotropic distribution of sky radiance. Due to atmospheric scattering processes, the sky horizon and the circumsolar region of the sky show enhanced amounts of radiance compared with the overall sky (**Figure 13**). Most difficult to model are broken cloud situations with large and spatially inhomogeneous deviations from a uniform distribution.

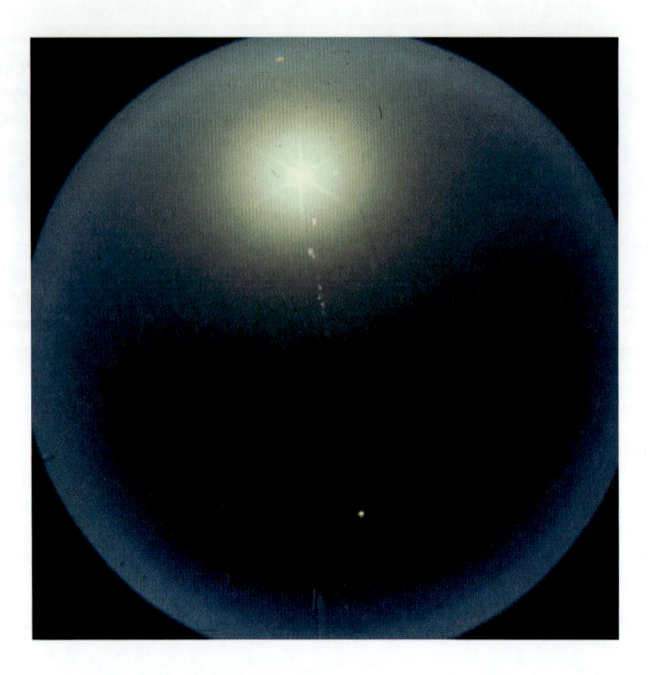

Figure 13 Image of a clear sky.

Existing tilted irradiance models use different assumptions on the radiance distribution depending on the cloud situation. The simple model in Reference 81 assumes a uniform distribution of radiance and accounts for only the geometric view factor describing the part of the sky seen from the module plane, which is determined by the module's tilt angle β:

$$I_{\text{diff},t} = \frac{I_{\text{diff}}(1 + \cos \beta)}{2} \quad [10]$$

Advanced models also consider anisotropic effects in dependence on the cloud situations, for example, the anisotropic-all-sky models formulated by Perez [84] and Klucher [85]. The latter is also used for the PV power prediction system presented in Section 1.13.6.

The ground-reflected irradiance component depends on the module slope β and ground reflectivity ρ. Again, assumptions of the distribution of radiances have to be made. Assuming isotropic reflection, we obtain

$$I_{r,t} = \frac{I\rho(1 - \cos \beta)}{2} \quad [11]$$

In comparison with the other components, ground-reflected irradiance is generally of minor importance. Typical reflectivity values are in the range of 0.1–0.3. An exception is snow cover with reflectivities close to 1, leading to a considerably enhanced contribution by snow reflection.

Finally, the three components direct, diffuse, and ground-reflected irradiance are combined to give the irradiance on a tilted plane.

To calculate the irradiance on the module plane for tracking systems, tilted irradiance models have to be combined with the corresponding information on the tracking algorithm.

Power prediction for concentrating PV systems requires forecasts of the direct normal irradiance $I_{\text{beam},n}$. These forecasts may be derived from global horizontal irradiance forecast by applying a direct/diffuse fraction model and converting the horizontal beam component according to the position of the Sun:

$$I_{\text{beam},n} = \frac{I_{\text{beam}}}{\cos \Theta_Z} \quad [12]$$

As presented in Section 1.13.3.2.5(iv), radiation transfer calculations may also be used to forecast direct normal irradiance based on NWP model output and other parameters.

1.13.3.3.2 PV simulation

Methods for PV simulation have been investigated extensively (e.g., see References 86–90) and are mainly used in the context of planning and sizing of PV systems and for yield estimation. As a result, a large number of PV simulation software tools are available. Often, these tools also include routines for irradiance conversion.

As an example, a PV simulation model for DC reported in Reference 86 is briefly described. A basic advantage of this model is the applicability to both classic crystalline silicon (c-Si) and thin-film technologies, which is demonstrated exemplarily for modules of c-Si, amorphous silicon (a-Si), and copper indium diselenide (CIS). This meets the requirements for PV power forecasting, in particular also for regional forecasts, where generally various different module types have to be considered. The power prediction scheme presented and evaluated in Section 1.13.6 and the approach described in Reference 1 are based on this model.

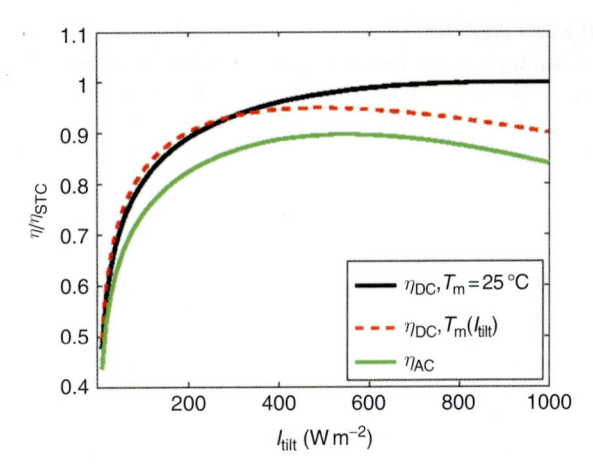

Figure 14 Example of normalized MPP efficiency as a function of irradiance on the module plane. Black, η_{MPP} at $T_m = 25$ °C; red, η_{MPP} for an ambient temperature of $T_a = 15$ °C; green, η_{AC} for an ambient temperature of $T_a = 15$ °C.

The proposed model estimates the efficiency η_{MPP} of PV generators operated at maximum power point (MPP) conditions in dependence on irradiance I_t and module temperature T_m. In a first step, the basic influence of the irradiance for $T_m = 25$ °C is described with a parametric model, based on the analysis of the characteristics of different module types and suggestions in Reference 87:

$$\eta_{MPP}(I_t, 25 \text{ °C}) = a_1 + a_2 I_t + a_3 \ln I_t \qquad [13]$$

where a_1, a_2, and a_3 are device-specific parameters. A typical efficiency curve for $T_m = 25$ °C in dependence on the incoming irradiance is given by the red curve in **Figure 14**. The curve is normalized to the efficiency at standard test conditions (STCs) η_{STC}. STCs are defined by $T_m = 25$ °C, $I = 1000$ W m^{-2}, and the standard spectrum of air mass AM1.5. Most modules show a decreasing performance for low irradiance values, as shown in Reference 88.

The performance at module operating temperatures T_m differing from 25 °C is modeled by the standard approach using a single temperature coefficient α:

$$\eta_{MPP}(I_t, T_m) = \eta_{MPP}(I_t, 25 \text{ °C})(1 + \alpha(T_m - 25 \text{ °C})) \qquad [14]$$

The four model parameters may be determined from the manufacturer's data sheet information or from the measured data.

Necessary information on the module temperature may be estimated from the ambient temperature and an additional term describing the heating of the module in dependence on the irradiance received by the module:

$$T_m = T_a + \gamma I_t \qquad [15]$$

The parameter γ is given by the mounting type of the system. A roof- or facade-integrated system generally heats up faster than a free-standing installation. The blue curve in **Figure 14** illustrates the part-load behavior of a typical module for an ambient temperature of 15 °C. Heating of the module at high solar irradiance leads to reduced efficiency in comparison with STCs.

The DC power output of a PV generator with module area A and nominal power P_{nom} can be predicted by inserting eqns [13]–[15] in the equation

$$P_{DC} = \eta_{MPP}(I_t, T_m) \times I_t \times A = \frac{\eta_{MPP}(I_t, T_m)}{\eta_{STC}} \times \frac{I_t}{1000 \text{ W m}^{-2}} \times P_{nom} \qquad [16]$$

with forecasted irradiances and temperatures as input. The model requires specification of the model parameters, the installation type, and the nominal power.

For grid-connected PV systems, also the efficiency of the inverter has to be considered in addition to the DC performance. The model presented in Section 1.13.6 uses a standard approach for modeling the conversion from DC to alternating current (AC) as given in Reference 90. The parametric model describes the efficiency as a function of DC power input, using given efficiencies at three points of the curve as a basis. **Figure 14** also shows an exemplary curve for overall conversion efficiency η_{AC} from irradiance to AC. Other miscellaneous losses further reducing the system performance may be taken into account by an additional factor.

The approach for PV simulation shown here is applicable for c-Si and various thin-film technologies as stated above. Concentrating PV systems equipped with triple-junction cells require different modeling techniques. In particular, they show a strong dependency on the spectral distribution of the irradiance. The development of suitable models is a new research topic and is addressed in Reference 91.

Summarizing, available PV simulation models and models for irradiance conversion to the module plane meet the requirements for PV power prediction for most conventional PV technologies. To apply these models, the specification of module and inverter characteristics, as well as the description of the orientation and tilt angle of the modules, is necessary. Although these parameters are usually at hand for forecasts for specific systems, it is not straightforward for regional power forecasts, because detailed system information is generally not available for all PV systems, especially for small PV systems.

1.13.3.3.3 Upscaling to regional power prediction

Renewable power prediction for utility applications usually requires forecasts of the cumulative power generation for the corresponding control areas. For wind power forecasts, this is routinely done by upscaling from a representative set of single wind farms (e.g., see Reference 17). Also for PV power prediction, first operational systems rely on this approach (**Figure 15**) [4].

There are several reasons why upscaling is performed rather than simulation and summation of the larger number of systems in a region, as briefly discussed above:

- Computational and data handling efforts are reduced to a practicable amount.
- There is almost no loss in accuracy by the upscaling approach, given that the representative set approximates the basic properties of the total data set with good accuracy. Due to spatial averaging effects, small-scale variability plays a minor role for regional forecasts and does not have to be modeled in detail. Variations on larger scales with impact on the regional prediction, for example, by approaching cloud fronts, can be modeled using representative systems, because the energy output of nearby systems is similar for spatially homogeneous cloud fields or clear sky.
- Detailed system information necessary for simulation is generally not available for all PV systems contributing to regional power production. Small PV systems largely contribute to the overall power production and the required details are not accessible for many of these systems.

The quality of the upscaling procedure depends on the appropriate definition of a representative data set. Once defined, the estimation of the regional power output $P_{pred,all}$ by upscaling of the predicted power for the representative systems $P_{pred,rep}$ is straightforward:

$$P_{pred,all} = P_{pred,rep} \frac{P_{nom,all}}{P_{nom,rep}} \qquad [17]$$

where $P_{nom,all}$ denotes the overall nominal power of all systems in the area and $P_{nom,rep}$ the nominal power of the representative systems.

The representative subset should show a similar response to the irradiance conditions as the full ensemble. A correct representation of the spatial distribution of the nominal power is most important in this respect. In addition, the distribution of system orientations has an influence on the ensemble power production and the subset should reflect the original orientations. Finally, the mix of module types has to be considered, because different module types show different part-load behavior; for example, thin-film technologies generally show a better efficiency for low irradiance values. An incorrect representation of module types in the subset can therefore lead to systematic deviations.

In order to determine a suitable set of representative systems, in a first step the basic characteristics of the complete set of systems in an area have to be described. Available information here depends on the regulatory framework in a country. For example, in Germany, according to the Renewable Energy Sources Act (here denoted as EEG), all PV systems receiving feed-in tariff have to be registered with address and nominal power. Thus, most essential information on the spatial distribution of the nominal power of PV systems is available (**Figure 15(b)**). However, more detailed information on module type, tilt, tracking, and so on, is not recorded. The distribution of these parameters has to be estimated from existing databases.

In Section 1.13.6.4.4, we show an evaluation of the accuracy of an upscaling approach based on measured data of approximately 500 PV systems.

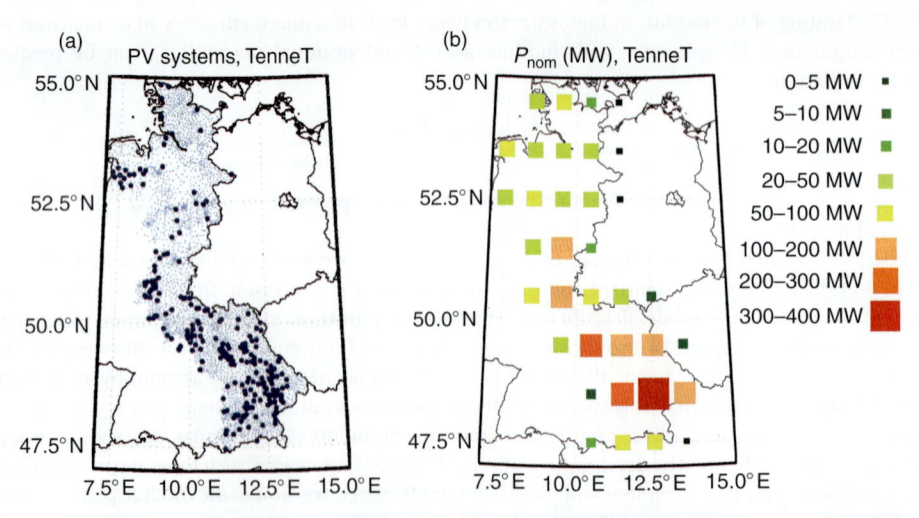

Figure 15 (a) Example of a representative set of PV systems (large dark blue dots) as a basis for upscaling to the power production of all systems (small light blue dots) in the area of the German transmission system TenneT. The position of the systems in the overall data set is determined by the postal codes, which leads to a limited spatial resolution. (b) Distribution of nominal power in the control area of TenneT with a spatial resolution of 1°, based on EEG data from December 2008.

1.13.3.3.4 Statistical methods

Statistical methods may be applied to directly forecast PV power on the basis of NWP output or previous measurements or to improve local or regional PV power forecasts derived with explicit physical modeling. The applicable methods are largely the same as for irradiance forecasts ranging from simple regression techniques to more advanced AI techniques, as described in Sections 1.13.3.2.2 and 1.13.3.2.6(i).

An example of a purely statistical algorithm is the method proposed in Bacher *et al.* [28]. An AR model with exogenous input is used to predict PV power on the basis of measured power data and NWP global irradiance predictions. The optimum weight for the two different kinds of input data sources is adjusted in dependence on the forecast horizons, ranging from 1 h ahead up to 2 days ahead. The model coefficients are obtained by recursive least-squares fitting with forgetting using online measured data. In this way, the model may be adjusted to temporal changes that affect PV power output, for example, reduced performance due to snow cover on the modules during winter or shading of the modules, which depend on the position of the Sun with its seasonal variations. Furthermore, the influence of systematic deviations of the NWP parameters may be reduced.

An approach combining forecasts of different NWP models with a statistical method to derive optimized PV power predictions is presented in Reference 92. Measured PV power and measured and predicted meteorological parameters of various NWP models are integrated with a combination procedure based on the classification of different weather situations. A considerable improvement compared with forecasts based on a single NWP model is shown.

An example of a PV power prediction method combining physical and statistical methods is given in Section 1.13.6.4. Adaptive statistical corrections are applied at different stages of the explicit modeling chain. First, an adaptive bias correction using values of the previous 30 days is applied to NWP-forecasted irradiances that mainly aims at the correction of weather-dependent deviations. In a second step, during winter, the forecasted power output is adjusted with an empirical approach that aims at improving PV power predictions for snow-covered PV modules, where the original forecasts usually show a strong overestimation of the power production.

1.13.4 Concepts for Evaluation of Irradiance and Power Forecasts

In this section, we present and discuss different aspects of evaluation of irradiance and PV power forecasts. The specification of the forecast accuracy is important for different purposes. Users benefit from knowing the accuracy of the forecasts when using them as a basis for decisions. Furthermore, accuracy information assists them to choose between different forecasting products. In research, evaluations are an indispensable basis for model testing and further model development.

To assess the accuracy of the predictions, they are compared with the corresponding measured irradiance or PV power values. A lot of different aspects can contribute to forecast evaluation. An extensive overview of forecast verification methods is given in Jolliffe and Stephenson [78]. Depending on the target group and on the aim of the accuracy assessment, different methods to assess prediction quality may be selected. For users of the forecast, the verification scheme should be kept as simple as possible and must comprise only a minimum set of accuracy measures. From the scientific point of view, a detailed analysis of different aspects of forecast accuracy is necessary as a basis for improving the forecasting system.

Here, we give an overview of evaluation methods commonly applied in the field of energy meteorology. Exploratory methods, as well as a basic set of statistical error measures, are presented. Another useful quality check in short-term forecast evaluation is the comparison with trivial reference models. In Section 1.13.4.5, we introduce reference prediction models for irradiance and power forecasts, followed by a short introduction to the concept of skill scores. As an example of a detailed accuracy assessment, we investigate the influence of weather conditions on forecast accuracy in Section 1.13.4.7. Finally, we describe concepts to provide uncertainty information in the form of confidence intervals or the probability distribution function of forecast errors. The different procedures for uncertainty assessment are illustrated by application to a test case.

1.13.4.1 Specification of Test Case

The different measures of forecast quality given below are illustrated using an example data set. This data set includes measurement data as well as a corresponding set of forecast data.

Measured data are hourly global irradiance values from a meteorological station of the German Weather Service (DWD) in Mannheim, Germany (49.2° N, 9.56° E; station height: 96 m). The evaluations are done for the period from 1 January 2007 to 31 October 2007. Forecast data are based on the 0:00 UTC model run of the ECMWF deterministic global model with a spatial resolution of 25 km × 25 km and a temporal resolution of 3 h in combination with the postprocessing procedure as described in Reference 49.

1.13.4.2 Graphical Analysis

Graphical analysis of forecasted values in comparison with measured values gives a first and intuitive impression of forecast accuracy. Furthermore, it provides a deep insight into the performance of the methods. This is especially important for understanding the reasons for forecast errors and improving the forecast. Several examples of graphical analysis are shown in the following.

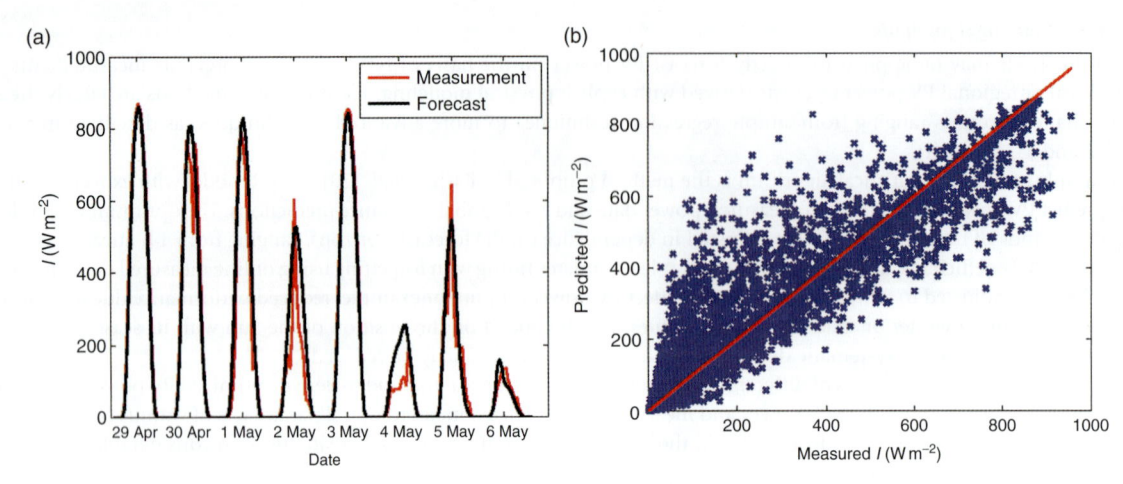

Figure 16 (a) Time series of predicted and measured global irradiance for the period from 29 April 2007 to 6 May 2007. (b) Scatter plot of predicted vs. measured global irradiance.

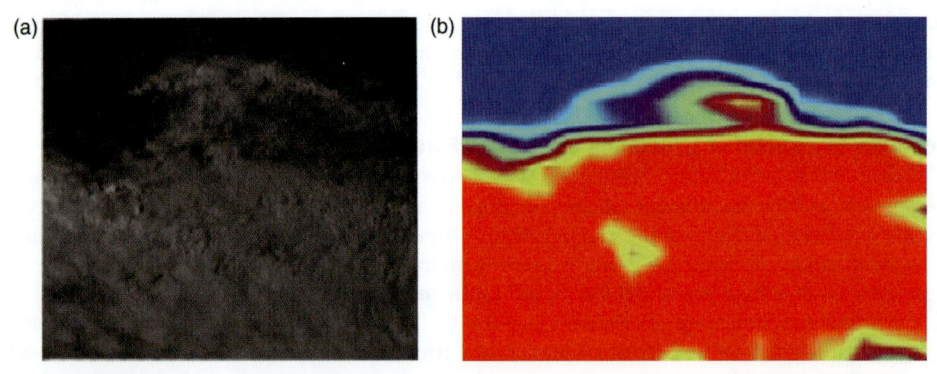

Figure 17 Cloud scenes for the area 47–55° N, 5–16° E, 25 April 2005, 15:00 UTC. (a) Meteosat 8 (high-resolution visible channel). (b) ECMWF forecast parameter total cloud cover; color scale: blue (0) to light red (1).

Time series of predicted irradiance in comparison with measured irradiance visualize forecast quality in a comprehensive way (**Figure 16(a)**). The example time series illustrates the high forecast accuracy in clear-sky situations and also illustrates that larger errors may occur in broken cloud situations. In particular, the strong variation in irradiance for days with variable clouds is not correctly reproduced by the forecast.

Scatter plots showing the predicted irradiance over measured irradiance are another way to graphically examine the relation between forecasts and observations (**Figure 16(b)**). These plots can reveal systematic deviations in dependence on the irradiance conditions and show the range of deviations that are related to the forecasts.

The analysis of spatial fields can give further insight into the performance of forecasting algorithms, as well for single scenes as for average fields. **Figure 17** shows a satellite-derived cloud field in comparison with a NWP forecast field of total cloud cover. The figure illustrates similar positions of predicted and satellite-measured cloud fronts for the given example. The investigation of average spatial fields is frequently applied in the context of NWP model evaluation (e.g., see Reference 54).

1.13.4.3 Statistical Error Measures

A quantitative description of forecast accuracy can be obtained using statistical error measures. For the evaluation of wind and solar power forecasts, it is common practice to use the RMSE as a main score [4, 93, 94]. Also, several additional error measures will be introduced.

The error of a single measurement is given as

$$\varepsilon_i = x_{\text{pred},i} - x_{\text{meas},i} \qquad [18]$$

where $x_{\text{pred},i}$ denotes a predicted irradiance or power value and $x_{\text{meas},i}$ the corresponding measured value. For positive errors ε_i, the calculated value exceeds the measured value.

One of the most common measures to assess the forecast accuracy is the RMSE:

$$\text{RMSE} = \frac{1}{\sqrt{N}} \sqrt{\sum_{i=1}^{N} \varepsilon_i^2} \qquad [19]$$

where N denotes the number of data pairs evalutated. The RMSE can be split into different parts, related to systematic and statistical components of forecast errors.

The Bias is defined as

$$\text{Bias} = \bar{\varepsilon} = \frac{1}{N}\sum_{i=1}^{N}\varepsilon_i \qquad [20]$$

and describes the difference between the mean values of predicted and measured values and corresponds to the systematic part of the error.

The standard deviation of the error (STDERR) is defined as

$$\text{STDERR} = \sigma(\varepsilon) = \frac{1}{\sqrt{N}}\sqrt{\sum_{i=1}^{N}(\varepsilon_i - \bar{\varepsilon})^2} \qquad [21]$$

and gives information on the fluctuation of the errors around their mean value.

In combination with a model for the distribution of forecast errors, STDERR may be used as a basis for calculating confidence intervals (see also Section 1.13.4.8).

These error measures are related to each other by

$$\text{RMSE}^2 = \text{Bias}^2 + \text{STDERR}^2 \qquad [22]$$

The STDERR may be further decomposed into one part related to the amplitude error ($\sigma(x_{\text{pred}}) - \sigma(x_{\text{meas}})$) and another part related to the cross-correlation of the time series.

The cross-correlation is defined as

$$\text{CC} = \frac{\sum_{i=1}^{N}(x_{\text{pred},i} - \bar{x}_{\text{pred}})(x_{\text{meas},i} - \bar{x}_{\text{meas}})}{\sqrt{\sum_{i=1}^{N}(x_{\text{pred},i} - \bar{x}_{\text{pred}})^2 \sum_{i=1}^{N}(x_{\text{meas},i} - \bar{x}_{\text{meas}})^2}} \qquad [23]$$

The complete decomposition of the RMSE is then given by

$$\text{RMSE}^2 = \text{Bias}^2 + \text{STDERR}^2 + (\sigma(x_{\text{pred}}) - \sigma(x_{\text{meas}}))^2 + 2\sigma(x_{\text{meas}})\sigma(x_{\text{pred}})(1 - \text{CC}) \qquad [24]$$

Another common measure to assess forecast accuracy is the mean absolute error (MAE):

$$\text{MAE} = \frac{1}{N}\sum_{i=1}^{N}|\varepsilon_i| \qquad [25]$$

The MAE is appropriate for applications with linear cost functions, that is, where the costs that are caused by a wrong forecast are proportional to the forecast error. The RMSE is more sensitive to large forecast errors, and hence is suitable for applications where small errors are more tolerable and larger errors cause disproportionately high costs, as is, for example, the case for utility applications.

For applications where decisions are related to threshold values, the additional investigation of the distribution of the predictions is of special importance. The agreements of the distribution function of measured and predicted time series can be evaluated, for example, using the Kolmogorov–Smirnov test integral (KSI) described in Reference 95.

1.13.4.4 Selection of Data for Evaluation and Normalization

For consistent validation procedures, it has to be defined which data pairs should be included in the evaluation. A characteristic feature of solar irradiance data is the strong deterministic component caused by the daily variation of the Sun and – most importantly – the period with 0 irradiance during nighttime. Different concepts have been introduced to deal with these night values in solar irradiance evaluations. Within the solar resource assessment community, usually only daytime values, that is, with nonzero solar irradiance, are considered for accuracy assessment. The trivial case of deriving perfect forecasts of $I_{\text{glob}} = 0$ at night is neglected. The electric utility sector, however, is used to evaluate energy production forecasts including all hours of the day. Obviously, the choice of including night values or not has a significant impact on the values of statistical error measures, and has to be clearly indicated when providing quantitative evaluation results. The evaluations in the remainder of this chapter use daylight hours as a basis, unless noted otherwise.

Evaluation results are usually grouped according to forecast days. For a model run at 0:00 UTC, the results for the first forecast day (intraday) integrate forecast horizons up to 24 h, the second forecast day (day-ahead) integrates forecast horizons from 25 to 48 h, and the third day includes forecast horizons from 49 to 72 h. The reason for grouping results according to forecast days rather than forecast hours is the strong dependency of forecast accuracy on the daytime caused by the daily course of irradiance.

Often, relative error measures are given in addition to absolute errors. Knowledge of the absolute uncertainty of the forecast is necessary for most applications. However, if these absolute uncertainty values are set in relation to a reference value, it is easier to judge the quality of a forecast. Relative values, obtained by normalization to a reference value, give a comprehensive impression of the forecast quality. Again, different concepts for the choice of reference values are applied by different communities.

In the context of solar resource assessment, normalization is generally done with respect to mean measured irradiance for the considered period:

$$\text{RMSE}_{rel} = \frac{\text{RMSE}}{\bar{x}^{\text{meas}}} \quad [26]$$

This definition is used for the evaluations presented below, unless indicated otherwise.

For wind and PV power predictions in utility applications, it is common practice to normalize forecast errors to the installed power [4, 93, 94], which is independent of the climatic conditions and known *a priori*. This leads to much smaller relative error values than normalization with respect to mean values.

1.13.4.5 Reference Forecasts

In addition to the accuracy information in terms of statistical error measures, it should be checked whether the forecast model provides better results than any trivial reference model. It is worthwhile to implement and run a complex forecasting tool only if it is able to clearly outperform trivial models.

Probably, the most common reference model or baseline for short-term forecasts is persistence. We investigate different concepts of persistence and compare them with the use of climatological values as reference forecasts. For both, we have to consider the deterministic daily irradiance pattern as an additional constraint.

As a baseline for intraday forecasts of irradiance and PV power, a very simple and commonly applied approach of persistence x_{per} is to consider the measured value of the previous day at the same time as a forecast value:

$$x_{\text{per},24h}(t) = x_{\text{meas}}(t - 24\,\text{h}) \quad [27]$$

where t denotes the time of the forecasted value. In this way, the daily course of irradiance and power production is modeled and no additional clear-sky model is necessary. Of course, this approach may also be extended to longer forecast horizons.

However, if this direct persistence approach is applied to forecast horizons of some hours, the daily variation of solar irradiance will considerably increase persistence errors. A better option for irradiance here is to combine persistence of the clear-sky index with a clear-sky model in order to account for the deterministic daily course of irradiance and to define $I_{\text{per},k^*,\Delta t}$ for the forecast horizon Δt as

$$I_{\text{per},k,\Delta t}(t) = k^*_{\text{meas}}(t - \Delta t) I_{\text{clear}}(t) \quad [28]$$

This approach is applicable straightforward for irradiance forecasts, and is applied in the evaluations shown below. Using a PV simulation model, it may also be transferred to power forecasts, given that measured irradiance values are available as a basis to calculate k^*.

Also for forecast horizons of some days ahead, an improved persistence model can be derived with this concept. The time lags considered for persistence without introducing additional errors due to the daily course of irradiance are no longer limited to multiples of 24 h. This allows considering average values of the clear-sky index:

$$I_{\text{per},\bar{k}\cdot\Delta t}(t) = 1/m \sum_{i=-m}^{0} k^*_{\text{meas}}(t - \Delta t + i) I_{\text{clear}}(t) \quad [29]$$

which can reduce the persistence error considerably. The parameter m specifies the range of values used for averaging. The mean value of k^* of all daylight hours of the previous days is a suitable and simple choice to obtain improved persistence forecasts. For example, for the test case described in Section 1.13.4.1, the error of day-ahead persistence with this approach is reduced to 58% in comparison with 68% using the approach defined in eqn [27]. For forecast horizons of more than 1 day, further improvements could be achieved by using average values of k^* of several days. However, as persistence is meant as a trivial reference model, not too much effort should be spent on optimization, and we recommend using the simple approach with k^* values of only the latest day. This concept of persistence is also used in the remainder of this chapter.

If long-term time series of measured irradiance values I_{meas} are available, these can be used as a basis for reference forecasts as well:

$$I_{\text{ref,mean}}(t) = \bar{k}^*_{\text{meas}} I_{\text{clear}}(t) \quad [30]$$

The use of an average value $\bar{k}^*_{\text{meas}}$, determined on the basis of the available long-term irradiance measurements, instead of directly using the mean irradiance value allows for modeling the daily course of the irradiance. Obviously, this model, referred to as climatological mean, is independent of the forecast horizon.

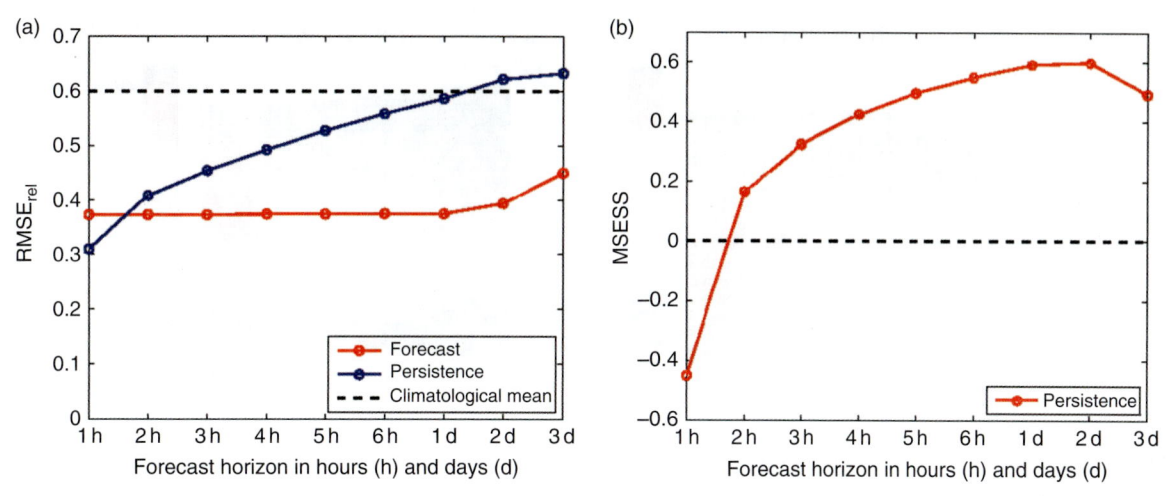

Figure 18 (a) RMSE$_{rel}$ of the ECWMF-based forecasts and of the reference models over forecast horizon. (b) MSESS$_{per}$ over the forecast horizon.

A comparison of the ECMWF-based forecast with the two reference models for the test case defined earlier is given in **Figure 18(a)**. Persistence up to few hours ahead is compared with the intraday ECMWF-based forecast, because ECMWF forecasts are not available for these very short-term timescales. After 2 h, the ECWMF-based forecast performs significantly better than persistence. For the prediction of hourly irradiance values, for example, 3 h ahead, it is therefore preferable to use the NWP-based intraday irradiance forecast than extrapolate measured irradiance values using eqn [28]. For forecasts for the next hour, it is favorable to use persistence instead of the available intraday NWP forecasts. The comparison of the two reference models illustrates that from the second forecast day onward, long-term mean values of k^* show lower errors and should be used as the most suitable reference model for the given test case.

1.13.4.6 Skill Scores and Improvement Scores

The use of Skill scores is a common concept in meteorology to evaluate the performance of forecast models by comparison with trivial reference models. The gain of forecast quality when using the forecast model compared with the reference model is set in relation to the difference between the scores of a perfect forecast and the reference forecast:

$$\text{Skill score} = \frac{\text{Score}_{forecast} - \text{Score}_{reference\_forecast}}{\text{Score}_{perfect\_forecast} - \text{Score}_{reference\_forecast}} \quad [31]$$

The Skill score takes the value '1' for a perfect forecast and the value '0' for the reference forecast. If a forecast model performs worse than the reference model, the Skill score is negative.

To judge the skill in terms of the RMSE score, in Reference 78 the mean square error Skill score (MSESS) is proposed, defined as

$$\text{MSESS} = \frac{1 - \text{MSE}_{forec}}{\text{MSE}_{ref}} \quad [32]$$

where MSE$_{forec}$ is the mean square error for the evaluated forecast model and MSE$_{ref}$ the mean square error for the reference model. The MSESS$_{per}$ in comparison with persistence is displayed in **Figure 18(b)** for the test case.

Evidently, eqns [31] and [32] may be applied not only for comparison with a trivial reference model but also for intercomparison of different forecasting approaches. Improvement scores are obtained by replacing the score for the trivial reference forecast with the corresponding score for the forecast algorithm, which is used as a base-line in the evaluation.

1.13.4.7 Evaluation of Forecast Accuracy in Dependence on Meteorological and Climatological Conditions

The results of forecast evaluation will depend not only on the forecast model but also on the climatic conditions at the selected site and the period for evaluation. An analysis of the forecast quality in dependence on the actual weather situation and for different regions and seasons can give valuable additional information. Examples of seasonal and regional performance assessments are given in Section 1.13.5.3. Here, we show an approach to quantify the influence of weather conditions on forecast accuracy [49]. Measurement and forecast data used for the evaluation are described in Section 1.13.6.1.1 and Section 1.13.6.3.2, respectively.

Forecast accuracy strongly depends on the cloud situation. Variable cloud situations are generally more difficult to forecast and show a lower accuracy than forecasts for clear skies. Additionally, again, the daily course of irradiance should be considered. The cosine of the solar zenith angle ($\cos\theta_z$) determines the limit of maximum possible irradiances, and hence also influences the magnitude of forecast errors. Therefore, a detailed error assessment in dependence on the two factors is performed. As a main parameter to characterize the cloud situation, we use the clear-sky index k^*.

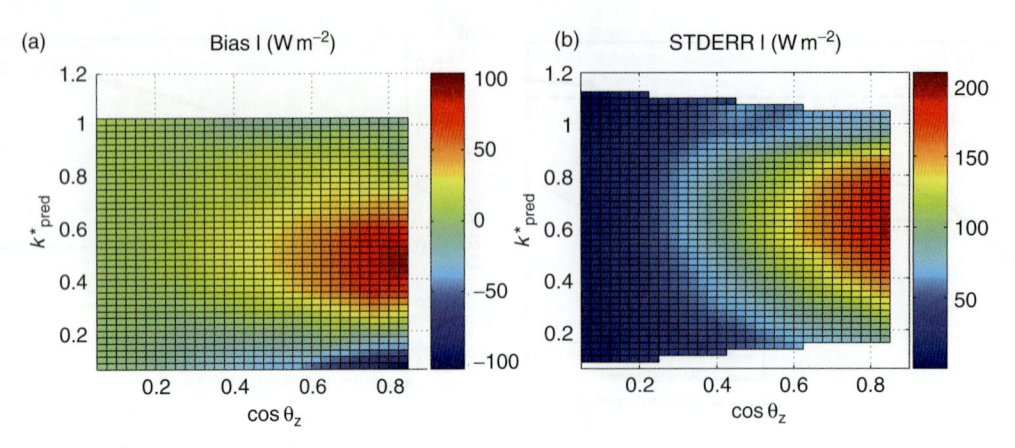

Figure 19 (a) Bias and (b) STDERR of the forecast as a function of $\cos\theta_z$ and k^*.

The Bias of the forecast in dependence on the predicted clear-sky index (k^*_{pred}) and the cosine of the solar zenith angle ($\cos\theta_z$) is displayed in **Figure 19(a)**. A considerable overestimation of the irradiance occurs for intermediate cloud situations ($0.3 < k^*_{pred} < 0.8$), which in its magnitude also depends on the solar zenith angle. For situations predicted as overcast ($k^*_{pred} < 0.2$) the actual measured irradiance is underestimated, and for clear-sky situations no systematic deviations are found. This analysis has been used as a basis for the weather-dependent Bias correction introduced in Section 1.13.3.2.6(i).

Figure 19(b) shows the STDERR of the forecast in dependence on the two parameters k^*_{pred} and $\cos\theta_z$. Forecast errors are comparatively small for situations predicted as clear sky ($k^*_{pred} \approx 1$) and for overcast situations with low irradiance ($k^*_{pred} < 0.2$). The largest deviations between measurement and forecast are found for situations with variable cloud cover, characterized by intermediate values of the clear-sky index. Again, the strong influence of the solar elevation is also obvious. The knowledge of the situation-specific STDERR can provide a basis for the calculation of weather-specific uncertainty information, as outlined in the following.

1.13.4.8 Uncertainty Information

In addition to the forecast information itself, the specification of the expected uncertainty of irradiance or power predictions is beneficial for the application of the forecasts, as briefly described in Section 1.13.3.1.

As a basis for quantifying the expected uncertainty of a forecast, the probability distribution functions of forecast errors or – equivalently – irradiance or power predictions have to be known. Using this information, confidence or prediction intervals can be derived that indicate the range in which the actual value is expected to appear with a quantified probability. Confidence intervals are often given for uncertainty levels of 90% or 95%, as illustrated in **Figure 20** for site-specific and regional forecasts. This uncertainty information may be further refined by providing confidence intervals for different uncertainty levels.

In principle, two essentially different approaches may be applied to derive uncertainty information:

- use of the output of ensemble prediction systems
- analysis of historical time series of forecasts in comparison with measurements.

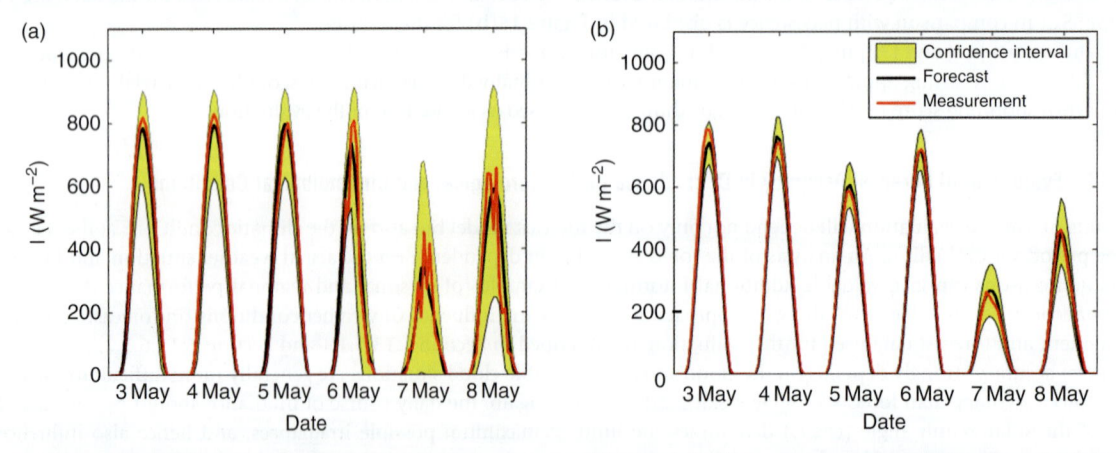

Figure 20 Forecast of global irradiance I with confidence intervals of an uncertainty level of 95% compared with measured irradiance for 6 days in May 2007 (a) for a single site and (b) for the mean value of the measurement stations in Germany displayed in **Figure 26**.

In ensemble prediction systems, not only one but several forecast runs are computed at the same time starting from slightly different initial conditions (e.g., see Reference 96). Each of these forecast runs will result in a different forecast. Due to the high complexity and nonlinearity of atmospheric processes, even small changes to the initial conditions can change the results significantly. The result of an ensemble forecast can be described as probability density function; that is, uncertainty information is a direct result of ensemble predictions. This approach – although already used in the wind power sector – has not been applied so far for solar irradiance or power predictions, but shows a high potential for future applications.

Existing methods to derive uncertainty information [28, 49] rely on the analysis of historical time series of forecasted and measured values. Different techniques may be applied to obtain the required information on the distribution of forecast errors.

In Reference 49, we determine weather-specific prediction intervals on the basis of a detailed error analysis. As a first approach, we assume a normal distribution of forecast errors for different cloud and solar elevation situations. The distribution function of errors is then completely described by the STDERR of the forecasts, given that the Bias is negligible. Although this assumption would not be appropriate for the entire data set, it leads to reasonable results by application to defined classes of clear-sky index (k^*) and cosine of the solar zenith angle ($\cos\theta_z$). Accordingly, specific values of the STDERR are determined in dependence on the two parameters as shown in **Figure 19(b)**. The dependence of the STDERR on the two parameters can be modeled with a polynomial function of fourth order f_STDERR($\cos\theta_z, k^*$) with good accuracy. Confidence intervals with an uncertainty level of 95% are then given by

$$\left[I_{\text{pred}} - 2\text{f\_STDERR}(\cos\Theta_Z, k^*), I_{\text{pred}} + 2\text{f\_STDERR}(\cos\theta_z, k^*) \right] \quad [33]$$

A quantitative evaluation of the proposed method on a test data set has demonstrated the reliability of the described method. As an example, **Figure 20(a)** shows forecasted irradiance values with 95% confidence intervals in comparison with measured irradiance for 6 days in May 2007 for a single site. The figure illustrates that the changes of forecast quality with the meteorological situation are well modeled by the proposed approach. For clear-sky situations, the prediction intervals are narrow and the forecast is very reliable. On days with variable clouds, large deviations are to be expected for forecasts with hourly resolution for single stations. For regional forecasts, a much better agreement between forecast and measurements is achieved (see also Section 1.13.6.3.2), resulting in narrow confidence intervals for different weather situations (**Figure 20(b)**).

Another approach to determine the probability distribution of forecast values is presented in Reference 28. The authors propose the use of quantile regression to determine the probability distribution of normalized power values in dependence on predicted normalized power. The advantage of this method is that no assumption on distribution functions is necessary. However, more computational effort is involved because different uncertainty levels have to be calculated separately.

1.13.5 Evaluation and Comparison of Different Approaches for Irradiance Forecasting

In this section, different approaches for irradiance forecasting are evaluated and compared. First, the basic information and main results of a comparison of NWP-based forecasting approaches for different European countries are summarized [69]. Then, one of the NWP-based approaches is compared with a satellite-based irradiance forecasting scheme.

As shown in Sections 1.13.3.2.5 and 1.13.3.2.6, a considerable number of different NWP-based methods are available to derive irradiance forecasts for some days ahead that may be directly applied also for PV power forecasting. For the users of these forecasts, it is important that standardized methodology be used when presenting results on the accuracy of prediction models in order to get a clear idea of the advantages of a specific approach.

A common benchmarking procedure has been set up in the framework of IEA SHC Task 36 "Solar Resource Knowledge Management" [97]. The proposed procedure for benchmarking is applied to compare irradiance forecasting procedures of seven participants of IEA SHC Task 36. The different methods include the use of mesoscale NWP models, the application of statistical postprocessing tools to forecasts of NWP models, and also one approach involving the meteorologist's expert knowledge to interpret and combine forecast data of different sources.

1.13.5.1 Measurement Data

As a basis for the benchmarking, we have defined a common measurement data set. Due to the weather dependence of forecast accuracy, the evaluation site and period may significantly influence the performance of a given forecasting system. Therefore, it is important to use the same measurement data for evaluation when comparing different prediction methods. The selected data set with hourly measured irradiance values covers four regions in Europe with different climatic conditions, as illustrated in **Figure 21**: Southern Germany, Switzerland including mountain stations, Austria, and Southern Spain. German, Swiss, and Spanish measurement data were provided by the national weather services DWD, MeteoSwiss, and AEMet, respectively. Austrian measurement data were supplied by the private company Blue Sky. The period of evaluation is July 2007 until June 2008.

1.13.5.2 NWP-Based Forecasts

Hourly irradiance forecasts up to 3 days ahead provided by seven participants of IEA SHC Task 36 are included in the benchmarking. The different forecasting approaches are all based on global NWP model predictions, either ECMWF global model forecast data or GFS data. For the local refinement of these coarse resolution forecasts, different methods are proposed within IEA SHC Task 36.

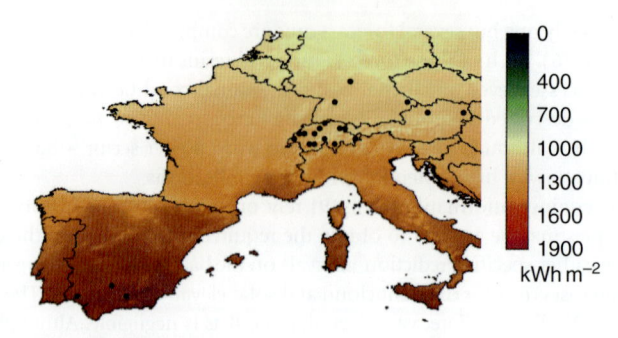

Figure 21 Map of mean yearly irradiation sums (1995–2004) with locations of measurement stations.

Table 1 Overview of forecasting approaches used for benchmarking within IEA SHC Task 36

Team and abbreviation	Approach	NWP model with spatial and temporal resolution
University of Oldenburg, Germany, ECMWF-OL	Statistical postprocessing in combination with a clear-sky model [49]	ECMWF 0.25° × 0.25° 3 h
Blue Sky, Austria (a) BLUESKY-HI (b) BLUE	(a) HI of cloud cover forecast (b) BLUE FORECAST: statistical forecast tool	For (b) GFS 1° × 1° and 0.5° × 0.5° 3 and 6 h
Meteomedia GmbH, Switzerland, MM-MOS	MOS	ECMWF 0.25° × 0.25° 3 h
Ciemat, Spain, HIRLAM-CI	Bias correction	AEMet-HIRLAM 0.2° × 0.2° 1 h
CENER, Spain, CENER	Postprocessing based on learning machine models	Skiron [98]/GFS 0.1° × 0.1° 1 h
Meteotest, Switzerland, WRF-MT	Direct model output of global irradiance, averaging of 10 × 10 pixels	WRF [58]/GFS 5 km × 5 km 1 h
University of Jaén, Spain, WRF-UJAEN	Direct model output of global irradiance [68]	WRF [58]/GFS 3 km × 3 km 1 h

Table 1 gives an overview of the forecasting approaches with the used NWP models. A short introduction to the main features of each approach and further references are given in Reference 69. Summarizing, the algorithms can be grouped into four categories:

- The approaches ECMWF-OL, BLUE, and MM-MOS combine a global NWP model with a postprocessing method involving historical ground measurement data or satellite-derived irradiance data.
- The models proposed by CENER and Ciemat apply a postprocessing procedure based on historical ground measurement data to predictions of a mesoscale NWP model.
- Meteotest and the University of Jaén provide forecasts of the mesoscale model WRF without any integration of measured values.
- The BLUESKY-HI approach involves human interpretation (HI) of numerical weather forecasts.

1.13.5.3 Results for NWP-Based Forecasting Approaches

First, we provide the results of the benchmarking of different forecast algorithms for Germany, using RMSE, MAE, and Bias as a basic set of accuracy measures. Following this, a comparison of the performance of the forecast algorithms for the different regions is given.

1.13.5.3.1 Detailed results for Germany

For Germany, irradiance forecasts of the University of Oldenburg, Meteotest, CENER, Blue Sky, and Meteomedia GmbH were available for the evaluation.

To illustrate the performance of the different forecasting methods, predicted irradiances are compared with measured irradiances for an example time series in **Figure 22**. All forecasting algorithms show a good agreement between forecasts and measurements for clear-sky days. For days with variable clouds, significant deviations between the different forecasts and also in comparison with the measurements occur.

An overview of the statistical error measures for the complete German data set consisting of three stations is given in **Table 2** for the first, second, and third forecast day, respectively. The relative RMSE in dependence on the forecast horizon is also visualized in **Figure 25(a)**. With respect to RMSE and MAE, the forecasting approaches combining a global model with postprocessing (ECMWF-OL, BLUE, MM-MOS) show better results than mesoscale models. Comparing the approaches based on a global model, best accuracy is found for the ECMWF forecasts combined with the postprocessing proposed by the University of Oldenburg, closely followed by the statistical forecasts by Blue Sky and the MM-MOS. The two mesoscale models show a similar performance, with slightly lower RMSE values for the CENER approach. Here, it has to be considered that the WRF-MT forecasts are direct model output of global irradiance and only an averaging procedure is applied, while the postprocessing proposed by CENER involves measured data. The Bias is small for the evaluated forecasting approaches, except for the approach of CENER with systematic overestimation of the irradiance of more than 5% for the first forecast day. All approaches show a significant improvement in comparison with persistence for all forecast horizons. For persistence, a comparatively strong decrease of forecast accuracy occurs from intraday (day 1) to day-ahead (day 2) forecasts, while the NWP-based approaches show only a small increase of forecast errors.

Figure 23 shows the relative RMSE for the first forecast day for the three measurement stations separately. The RMSE of the global model-based forecasts is very similar for the three stations. For the mesoscale model forecasts, the RMSE values vary from 47% for Fürstenzell to 55% for Würzburg.

In order to evaluate the seasonal dependence of forecast errors, the absolute RMSE and Bias in dependence on the month are given in **Figure 24**. During winter months with low solar elevations and low clear-sky irradiances, absolute errors (**Figure 24(a)**) are small and relative errors (**Figure 24(b)**) are large. The improvement in comparison with persistence is low during December. For all other months, the NWP-based forecasts perform significantly better than persistence. With respect to the intercomparison of the five NWP-based approaches, a strong dependence on the month is observed. For July and August 2007, the forecasting approaches perform quite similarly. For October 2007 and for April and May 2008, the RMSE of the mesoscale model forecasts is considerably larger than for the global model-based approaches.

Summarizing the evaluation of the German stations, the global model-based forecasts show higher accuracy than the forecasts based on a mesoscale model. A detailed analysis shows that the difference between mesoscale models and global models with postprocessing strongly depends on the month of evaluation. Furthermore, the accuracy of the mesoscale model forecasts shows a stronger dependence on the location of evaluation. All five NWP-based approaches perform significantly better than persistence.

1.13.5.3.2 Comparison of forecast accuracies for the different regions

Detailed forecast evaluations for Austria, Switzerland, and Spain are given in Reference 69; here, we briefly summarize the main results and focus on the differences in forecast accuracy due to differences in the climatic conditions.

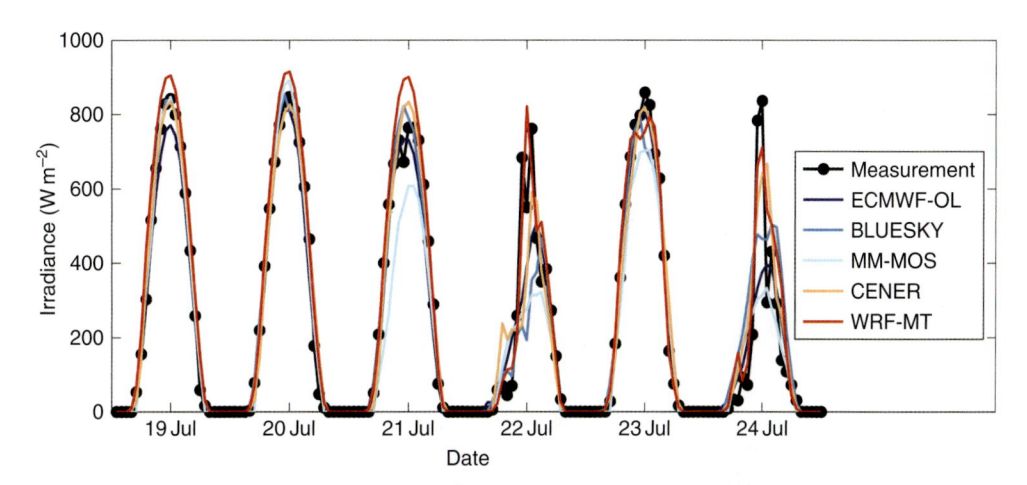

Figure 22 Measured irradiance in comparison with predicted irradiances for 6 days in July 2007 for the station Fürstenzell, Germany.

Table 2   RMSE, MAE, and Bias for the five forecasting approaches and persistence for the complete German data set

Error measure	RMSE ($W\,m^{-2}$) ($RMSE_{rel}$ (%))			MAE ($W\,m^{-2}$) (MAE_{rel} (%))			Bias ($W\,m^{-2}$) ($Bias_{rel}$ (%))		
Forecast horizon	Day 1	Day 2	Day 3	Day 1	Day 2	Day 3	Day 1	Day 2	Day 3
ECWMF-OL	92 (40.3)	95 (41.6)	102 (44.9)	59 (26.2)	63 (27.5)	67 (29.5)	−7 (−2.9)	−7 (−3.1)	−8 (3.3)
BLUE	94 (41.5)	100 (43.9)	104 (45.6)	62 (27.2)	66 (29.0)	69 (30.4)	−3 (−1.4)	−3 (−0.9)	−2 (−0.8)
MM-MOS	99 (43.5)	103 (45.1)	107 (46.8)	67 (29.6)	70 (30.5)	73 (32.0)	−2 (−1.0)	−2 (−1.4)	−2 (−1.1)
CENER	113 (49.9)	121 (52.9)	–	72 (31.5)	77 (33.6)	–	13 (5.9)	9 (3.7)	–
WRF-MT	118 (51.8)	125 (54.9)	138 (60.6)	74 (32.6)	79 (34.5)	86 (37.7)	−1 (−0.3)	−10 (−4.5)	−13 (−5.7)
Persistence	144 (63.5)	161 (70.2)	167 (73.3)	92 (40.5)	104 (45.6)	109 (47.9)	−4 (−1.8)	−6 (−2.7)	−7 (−2.9)

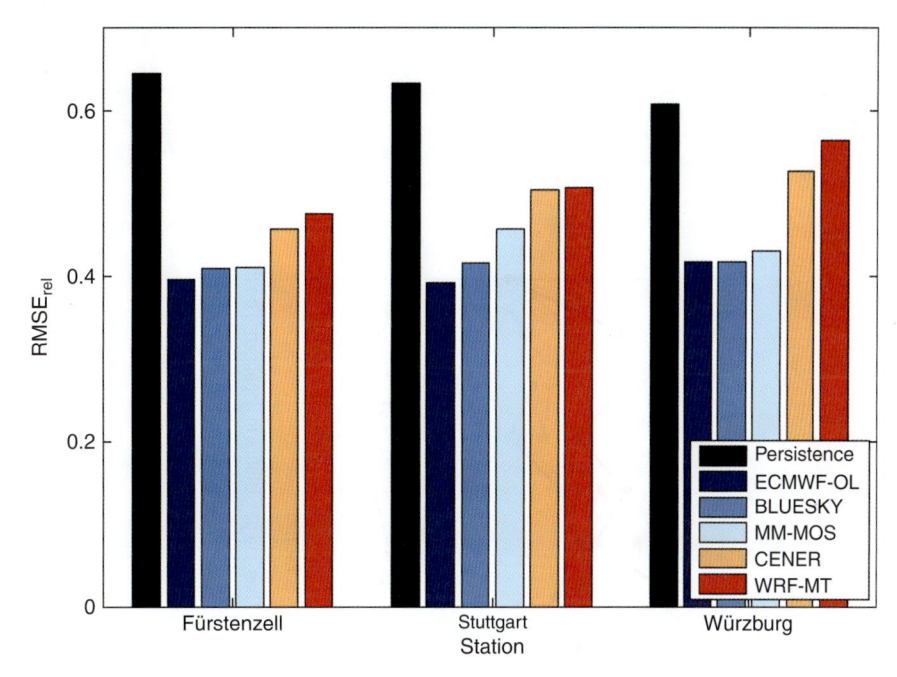

Figure 23 RMSE of the five forecasting approaches and persistence per station for the first forecast day.

In **Figure 25**, the overall RMSE as a main score for irradiance forecast evaluation is given in dependence on the forecast day for the four countries for the approaches available in each case. With respect to intercomparison of the models, the general trend is similar for all countries: the approaches using a global model in combination with postprocessing perform clearly better than the different mesoscale models. The two available mesoscale approaches for Central Europe show similar performance. In Spain (**Figure 25(d)**), WRF forecasts processed at the University of Jaén, Spain, even without postprocessing using historical measurement data, perform better than the other mesoscale models. For Austria (**Figure 25(c)**), an approach based on HI of forecasts was also available. These forecasts also outperform the mesoscale model forecasts, but show slightly higher RMSE values than the two approaches involving statistical postprocessing of global model output.

Looking at the differences between the countries, we observe that forecast errors in Spain are considerably smaller than in Central Europe. For intraday forecasts, the relative RMSE values in Spain range from $80\,\text{W}\,\text{m}^{-2}$ (20%) for the best forecasts to $125\,\text{W}\,\text{m}^{-2}$ (35%) for persistence, in comparison with about $100\,\text{W}\,\text{m}^{-2}$ (40%) for the best forecasts and $150\,\text{W}\,\text{m}^{-2}$ (60%) for persistence in Central Europe.

As shown earlier, forecast accuracy strongly depends on the meteorological situation, and sunny days generally show smaller forecast errors than cloudy ones. In the sunny climate of Southern Spain, this leads to smaller absolute errors than in Central Europe, despite the contrary effect of the influence of the cosine of the solar zenith angle (**Figure 19(b)**), which is higher in Southern Spain than in Central Europe. Concerning relative error values, there is an additional effect by normalization to the higher average irradiance in Spain.

1.13.5.4 Comparison of Satellite-Based Irradiance Forecasts with NWP-Based Forecasts

In this section, we give a short evaluation of a satellite-based irradiance forecasting scheme in comparison with the ECMWF-OL forecasts and persistence in dependence on the forecast horizon.

Short-term forecasts up to 6 h ahead are derived with the algorithm proposed in Reference 39 and briefly presented in Section 1.13.3.2.3 based on Meteosat-8 data. Persistence is calculated from ground-measured irradiance data using eqn [28]. The validation is performed for irradiance measurement stations in Germany (**Figure 26**) for the period from 1 July 2011 to 30 September 2011. Only hours where the satellite-based forecasts are available for all forecast horizons up to 5 h ahead are included in the evaluation. This basically restricts the evaluation to afternoon hours. Cloud information derived with the described version of the Heliostat method [43] is based on the visible channel of Meteosat 8 and is available only during daytime. Therefore, satellite-based forecast may be calculated only after sunrise, and a reliable performance is achieved for solar elevations above 10°.

Figure 27, where the RMSE_{rel} of the different approaches is displayed for single sites and regional average values, illustrates the benefits of each data source and forecasting approach for the various forecast lead times. The main characteristics are as follows:

- For forecast horizons between 1 h and several hours, the approach based on satellite data is superior to the other methods. Compared with NWP-based methods, the improvement is larger for regional averages than for single sites.
- For forecast horizons of about 6 h onwards, NWP-based forecasts are the best choice.

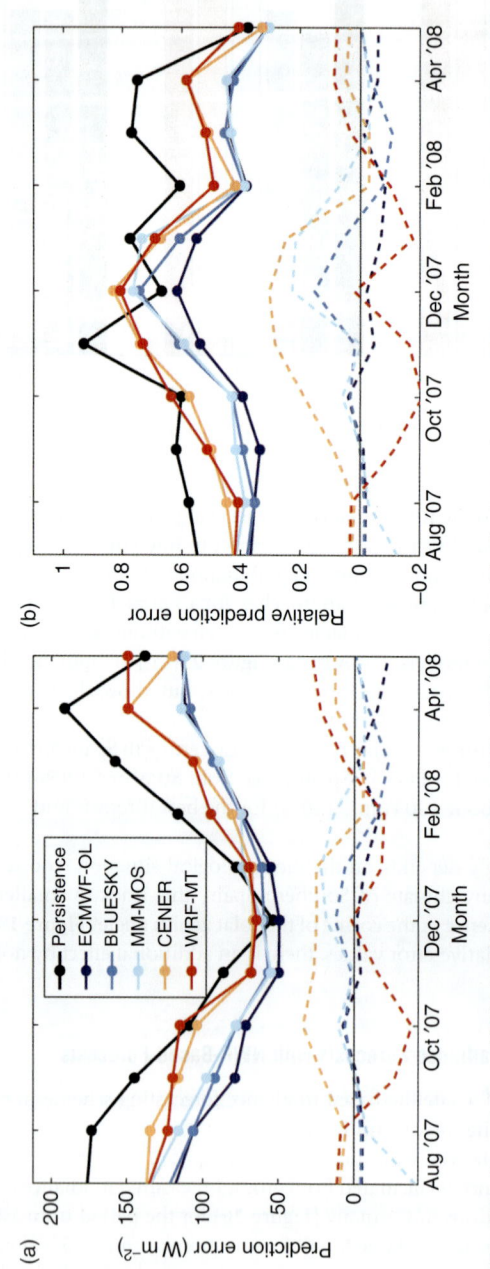

Figure 24 (a) Absolute and (b) relative forecast errors: RMSE (solid lines with circles) and Bias (dashed lines) of the five forecasting approaches and persistence in dependence on the month for the first forecast day using the complete German data set.

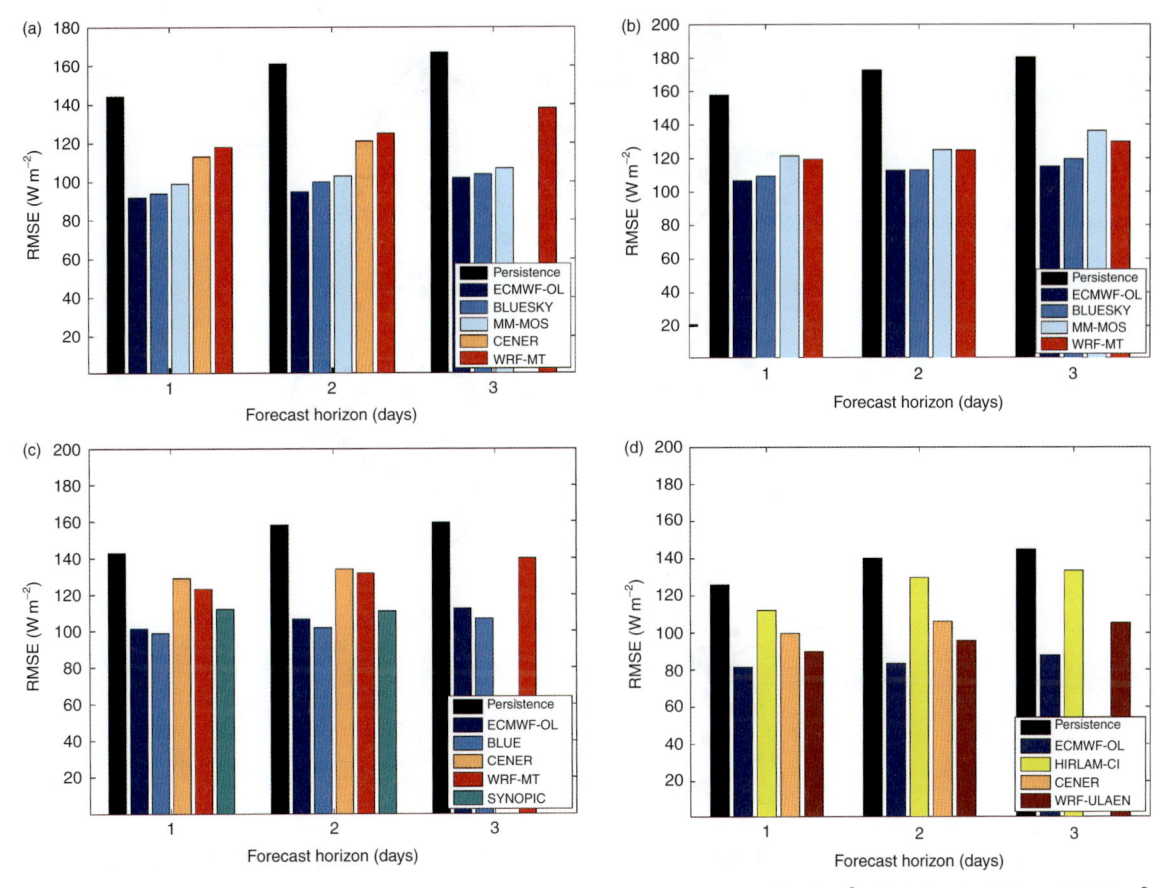

Figure 25 RMSE for the first, second, and third forecast day for stations in (a) Germany (I_{mean} = 227 W m^{-2}), (b) Switzerland (I_{mean} = 267 W m^{-2}), (c) Austria (I_{mean} = 222 W m^{-2}), and (d) Spain (I_{mean} = 391 W m^{-2}). I_{mean} denotes the average of hourly measured irradiances including only daylight hours.

- Persistence of ground-measured clear-sky index values shows a better performance than the NWP-based forecasts up to 2 h ahead for single sites and up to 3 h for regional averages for the given database and algorithms. For this very short term timescale, further optimization can be expected by the use of an advanced time series modeling approach instead of persistence.

For forecasts in the subhour range not shown here, the use of persistence, time series models, or information from ground-based sky imagers is favorable compared with the satellite-based method. A lower limit for the forecast accuracy achievable by the satellite-based method is given by the inherent uncertainty of the irradiance retrieval from satellite data.

The results and conclusions presented here are in agreement with a similar comparison for the United States [40].

1.13.5.5 Summary and Outlook

The basic results of the application of a benchmarking procedure developed in the framework of IEA SHC Task 36 to eight different NWP-based forecasting algorithms and one approach based on motion vectors from satellite images have been presented.

A strong dependence of the forecast accuracy on the climatic conditions is found. For the Central European stations, the relative RMSE of the NWP-based methods for intraday and day-ahead forecast horizons ranges from 40% to 60%, and for the Spanish stations with more of clear-sky days, the relative RMSE values are in the range of 20–35%. Irradiance forecasts based on global NWP models in combination with postprocessing show better results than the investigated mesoscale NWP models. All proposed methods perform significantly better than persistence. For short-term horizons up to about 6 h, the satellite-based approach leads to best results.

As there is ongoing development of the methods to predict irradiance not only by the IEA SHC Task 36 members, improved forecast accuracies are expected and evaluation and comparison of different forecast algorithms will be continued.

1.13.6 Example of a Regional PV Power Prediction System

Several PV power prediction services are now available on the market, e.g., References [1–4, 92]. As an example, here we present and evaluate the operational PV power prediction system of the University of Oldenburg and Meteocontrol GmbH [4, 50], which was one of the first PV power prediction services operationally employed by transmission system operators in Germany. The PV power

278 Resource and Potential

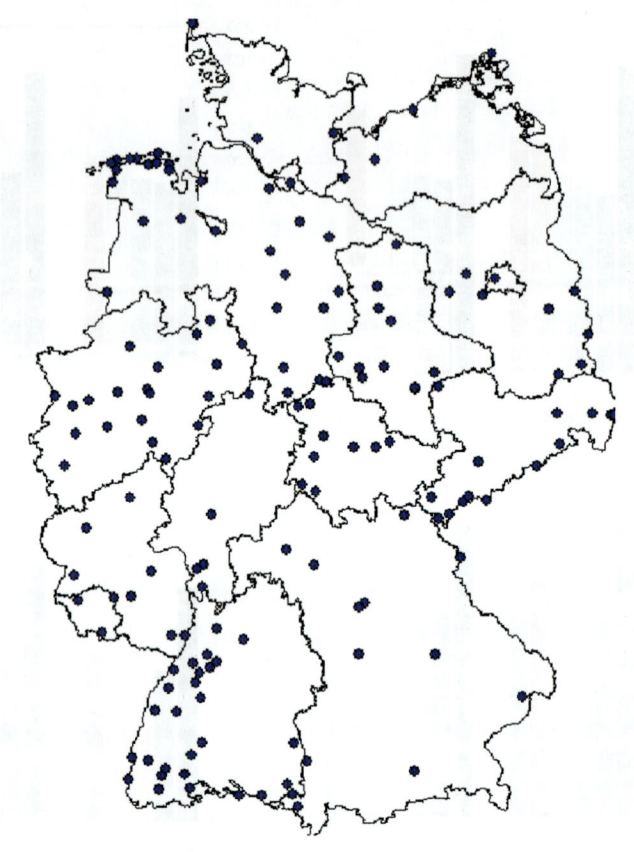

Figure 26 Distribution of irradiance measurement stations in Germany used for the evaluations in Sections 1.13.4.8, 1.13.5.4 and 1.13.6.3.

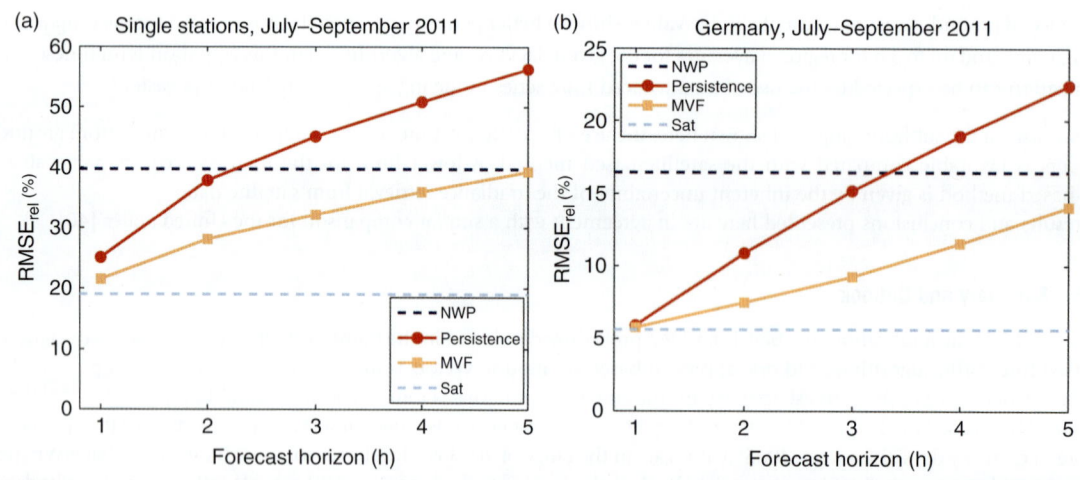

Figure 27 RMSE$_{rel}$ of global irradiance forecast for single sites (a) and regional average values (b) based on motion vectors from satellite images (orange) depending on the forecast horizon in comparison with the RMSE$_{rel}$ of forecasts ECMWF-OL (dark blue), satellite-based irradiance values (light blue), and persistence (red).

prediction scheme for hourly forecasts up to 3 days ahead combines explicit physical modeling with statistical tools at different stages of the modeling chain. Measured data of thousands of PV systems monitored by Meteocontrol GmbH in Germany are available as a basis for statistical postprocessing, continuous evaluation, and further development of the PV power prediction system.

The performance of the predictions is analyzed for the underlying irradiance forecasts as well as for the power forecasts. The evaluation of irradiance forecasts [49] focuses on the accuracy of regional forecasts in dependence on the region size and on the impact of different postprocessing procedures. The accuracy assessment of the PV power forecasts is performed for control areas of two German transmission system operators. Special focus is on the investigation of a proper upscaling [4] and the assessment of an empirical postprocessing to improve the forecasts during periods of snow cover [50].

1.13.6.1 Measurement Data

1.13.6.1.1 Irradiance measurements

For the evaluation and postprocessing of irradiance forecasts, hourly measured irradiance data of more than 200 meteorological stations in Germany are available, partly operated by the German Weather Service DWD and partly by Meteomedia GmbH. The distribution of these stations in Germany is shown in **Figure 26**. The evaluation period is January–October 2007.

1.13.6.1.2 PV power measurements

PV power forecasts are evaluated in comparison with hourly power output data of the monitoring database of Meteocontrol GmbH for a 1-year period from October 2009 to September 2010. The considered PV sites are located in the control areas of the German transmission system operators 50Hertz (**Figure 28**) and TenneT (**Figure 15**(a)).

With respect to the evaluation of regional forecasts, the problem that PV power output is not recorded for the majority of PV systems has to be dealt with. Therefore, the actual regional power production has to be estimated from available measurements by upscaling as done also for the predictions (see also Section 1.13.3.3.3). A correct representation of the overall ensembles – in particular with respect to the spatial distribution of the installed power – is very important to obtain reliable reference values for forecast evaluation, which are essential to obtain reliable estimates of forecast accuracy.

In order to assess the effect of upscaling from a representative data set to a larger data set, the regional power forecasts for the control area of 50Hertz based on 77 representative PV systems are evaluated against measurements of all systems monitored by Meteocontrol GmbH in this area during the evaluation period (**Figure 28**). This data set comprising more than 500 PV systems covered about 20% of the overall installed power in the control area of 50 Hertz during the period of evaluation. For the control area of TenneT, the actual power production is estimated using the same representative systems as for the forecasts.

For the evaluation all regional power values are normalized to the time dependent overall installed power $P_{nom}(t)$, in order to obtain a better comparability between different data sets and to account for changes in the installed power during the period of evaluation.

1.13.6.1.3 Quality control of measured PV power

A good quality of measurement data is essential for evaluations as well as for any postprocessing approach using these data as an input. A basically automatic quality control [4] was applied to the measured power data. As a first step, this implies a unification of the time system, because different PV systems may deliver measured data in different time systems, for example, following daylight saving time or not. In a second step, clearly too high values are filtered out. Finally, we have to deal with the problem that outages of the measurement system are not always clearly indicated, but often measured values of 0 are provided in this case. Without further information it is difficult to decide whether 0 power values during day time are caused by an outage of the measurement system and

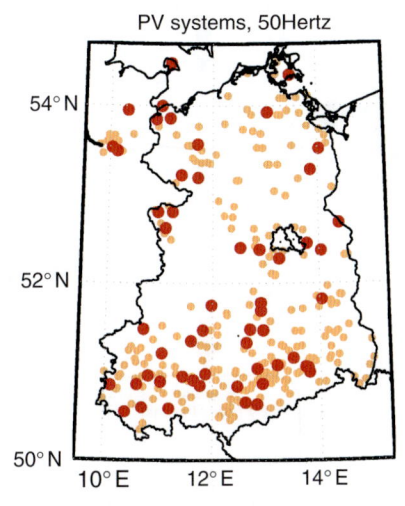

Figure 28 Locations of PV systems used for the evaluation. Large red dots, representative PV systems; small orange dots, all PV systems monitored by Meteocontrol GmbH in the control area in 2010.

hence should be filtered out, or if the PV system actually does not deliver power, for example, due to snow cover or due to technical reasons, and should remain in the evaluation data set. We excluded values of 0 during daytime only for the months when no snow cover is to be expected.

1.13.6.2 Overview of the Power Prediction Scheme

The prediction of the PV power production is based on irradiance and temperature forecasts of the ECMWF global model up to 3 days ahead. **Figure 29** illustrates the different steps to derive forecasts of PV power production from ECMWF irradiance forecasts. As a first step, site-specific hourly forecasts are derived from the low-resolution ECWMF forecasts for the representative system sites, involving a postprocessing procedure using measured irradiance data. As a second step, the forecasts of the global horizontal irradiance are converted to the module plane with a tilted irradiance model. The power forecasts are derived by applying a PV simulation model to the forecasted tilted irradiances and further improved by application of a second statistical postprocessing including also additional meteorological parameters. Finally, the regional forecasts are obtained by upscaling the power production from the representative set of PV systems.

1.13.6.3 Irradiance Forecasts

1.13.6.3.1 Refinement of ECMWF irradiance forecasts

The ECMWF global model irradiance forecasts had a temporal resolution of 3 h and a spatial resolution of 25 km × 25 km during the period of evaluation; the radiative transfer scheme is described in Morcrette et al. [54].

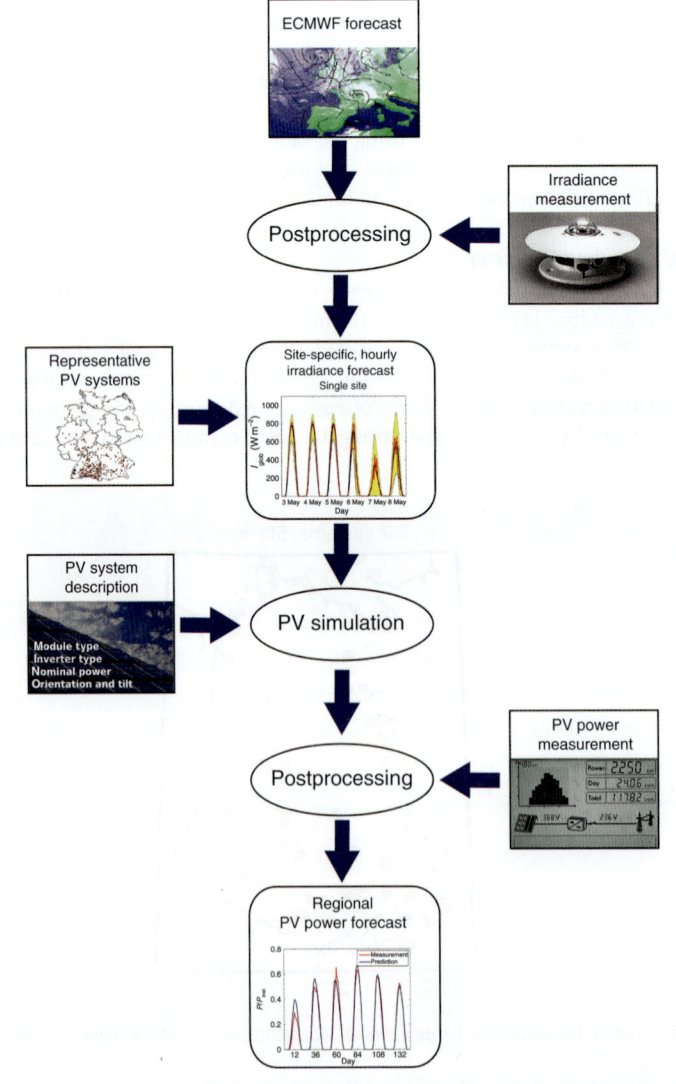

Figure 29 Overview of the regional power prediction system of the University of Oldenburg and Meteocontrol GmbH.

We have investigated different approaches to derive optimized hourly and site-specific irradiance forecasts and these are briefly described in the following. A more detailed description is given in Reference 49. As a first step, a spatial averaging procedure is applied. An analysis of the forecast accuracy in dependence on the area of averaging revealed that best results are achieved with a region of approximately 100 km × 100 km (see also Section 1.13.3.2.6(iii)).

For the temporal interpolation, two different approaches are considered:

- Linear interpolation of the 3-hourly mean values that are provided by the ECMWF (version V1)
- Combination of the forecast data with a clear-sky model to better account for the diurnal course of the irradiance. The temporal interpolation is performed for the clear-sky index k^*, as explained in Section 1.13.3.2.6(ii) (version V2).

As a third approach (version V3), we have applied the weather-specific bias correction, described in Sections 1.13.3.2.6(i) and 1.13.4.7, to the forecasts derived with version V2. In the current version of our forecasting system, this bias correction function is continuously updated using measured irradiance values of the last 30 days of the stations given in **Figure 26**. In the evaluations shown here, the correction function was fitted on a training data set and evaluated on a test set.

1.13.6.3.2 Accuracy of different approaches for site-specific and regional forecasts

An overall evaluation of the forecast accuracy of the different approaches using the test data set in dependence on the forecast horizon is given in **Figure 30**. **Figure 30(a)** shows the results for single stations; in **Figure 30(b)**, the mean irradiance of all stations was evaluated.

For single sites with the best approach V3, the $RMSE_{rel}$ amounts to 36.9% for the first forecast day, and increases to 46.3% for the third forecast day. Due to spatial averaging effects, the forecast accuracy for the average irradiance of an ensemble of distributed stations is much higher than for a single system. The $RMSE_{rel}$ for the ensemble of all stations with V3 amounts to 13.4% for the first forecast day. For the third forecast day, the $RMSE_{rel}$ increases to 22.5%. An illustration of the different forecast accuracies for single sites and regional forecasts is given in **Figure 20**, displaying time series of measured and forecasted irradiances with confidence intervals.

With respect to the intercomparison of the different approaches, **Figure 30** shows that best results are achieved with approach V3 for single sites and regional forecasts. However, for site-specific forecasts, the improvement using k^* interpolation and applying the bias correction is only small, because forecast errors are mainly determined by the scattering of errors around the mean value – that is, whether the occurrence of clouds is predicted correctly for this particular location for the respective hours – rather than by systematic deviations. For regional forecasts, where small-scale fluctuations are strongly reduced by averaging effects, a significant improvement is achieved by the correction of systematic deviations using V3. All the following results for irradiance and PV power predictions are derived using approach V3.

A more detailed description of the accuracy of regional forecasts for arbitrary ensembles of stations in dependence on the size of the region is given in the following. The reduction of errors when considering an ensemble of stations instead of a single station is determined by the cross-correlation of forecast errors of the systems that are part of the ensemble.

The correlation coefficient is defined in eqn [23]. To obtain the cross-correlation of the forecast errors of two stations, x_{pred} and x_{meas} have to be replaced by forecast errors of these stations.

The correlation coefficient of the forecast errors ε_i and ε_j of two stations i and j, respectively, depends on the distance between the stations, as illustrated in **Figure 31(a)**. This dependence may be modeled with an exponential function [49]:

$$CC_{i,j}(d_{i,j}) = e^{(a_1 d_{i,j})^{a_2}} \qquad [34]$$

where $d_{i,j}$ denotes the distance between the two stations and a_1 and a_2 are the fit parameters. The red dots in **Figure 31(a)** show the model curve.

This model combined with a statistical approach to derive the expected errors of mean values allows for the estimation of forecast errors $RMSE_{ensemble}$ for arbitrary scenarios of ensembles of stations.

Figure 31(b) shows the error reduction factor $f = RMSE_{ensemble}/RMSE_{single}$ calculated with this model for different ensembles of stations over the size of the region where the stations are distributed. For comparison, the error reduction factor determined directly from the data is given. A good agreement between measured and modeled error reduction factors is achieved. The figure shows that for ensembles of stations equally distributed over a region of a size of 3° × 3° the RMSE of the forecast is about half the RMSE of a single site. The RMSE is reduced to one-third of the site-specific RMSE for regions of a size of about 8° × 8°.

1.13.6.4 Power Forecasts

1.13.6.4.1 Tilted irradiance and PV simulation model

Conversion of the predicted global irradiance to the PV module plane and PV simulation are the next steps in the PV power prediction modeling chain, as shown in **Figure 29**. Here, we use the tilted irradiance model formulated by Klucher [85], including anisotropic effects like horizon brightening and circumsolar irradiance for tilted irradiance conversion. In the current version of the forecasting scheme, the representative set of PV systems consists of converters with a fixed tilt angle. In order to derive PV power forecasts, the robust simulation model for MPP performance [86] described in Section 1.13.3.3.2 is applied to the forecasted

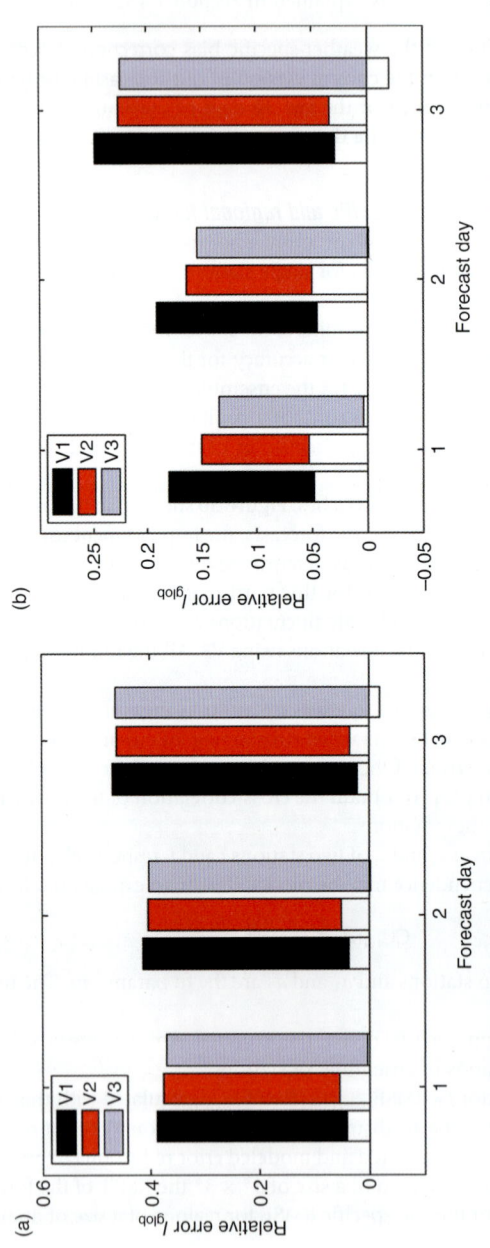

Figure 30 Relative forecast errors for hourly global irradiance I_{glob} in dependence on the forecast horizon for the different forecasting approaches. *V1*, linear interpolation of I_{glob}; *V2*, linear interpolation of k^*; *V3*, linear interpolation of k^* and bias correction. Colored bars represent RMSE$_{rel}$ and the respective white bars show Bias$_{rel}$. (a) Site-specific forecasts and (b) ensemble of all stations in Germany.

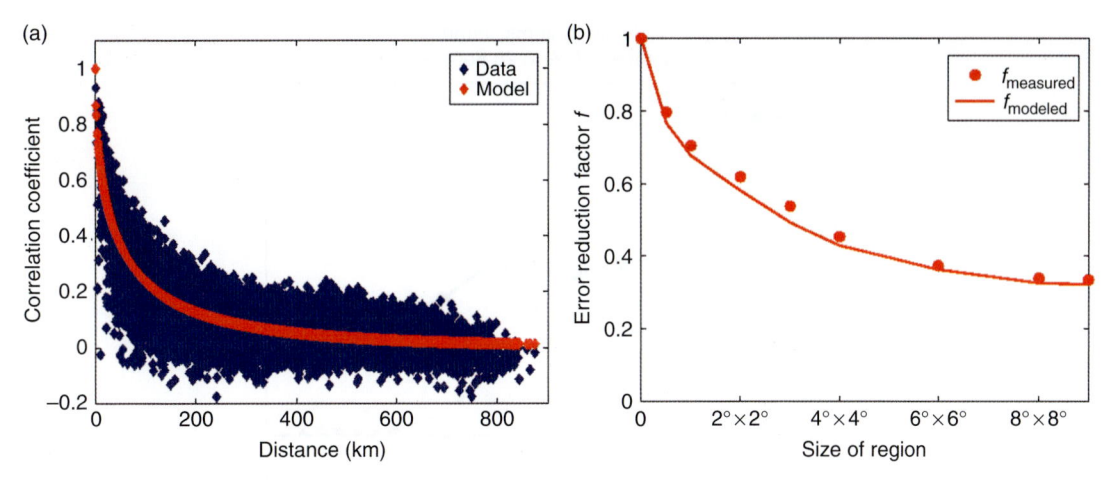

Figure 31 (a) Correlation coefficient of forecast errors of two stations over the distance between the stations. The blue dots represent measured values and the red dots the model curve. (b) Error reduction factor RMSE$_{ensemble}$/RMSE$_{single}$ for regions with increasing size.

irradiances on the tilted plane and corresponding temperature forecasts. Finally, models of the efficiency characteristics of the inverter and the different system losses are applied [4].

1.13.6.4.2 Postprocessing: Empirical approach to predict snow cover on PV modules

PV modules may be covered by snow during winter in Germany, which can almost completely suppress power production. This is not considered in the PV power prediction approach based on irradiance forecasting and PV simulation described so far. A typical example of forecast performance during winter is shown in **Figure 32**(a), where PV power predictions and measurements are displayed for several days in December 2009 together with the ECMWF forecast parameters temperature T_{pred} and snow depth SD_{pred}. In addition, irradiance measurements and predictions for the same days are given in **Figure 32**(b). Although a good agreement between irradiance predictions and measurements is found, strong deviations occur between measured and predicted PV power: while the actual PV power production is reduced to almost 0 for the period 18–20 December 2009, which is caused by snow cover on the PV modules, the PV power forecast reflects the irradiance forecasts and therefore shows a strong overestimation. This period is related to both predicted snow cover and frost in this region, confirming that the overestimation is caused by snow cover on the PV modules.

We have proposed an empirical approach to improve PV power predictions during periods of snow cover, integrating measured PV power production data and additional meteorological parameters, which is described in detail in Reference 50. To detect situations with snow-covered PV modules, we investigated the forecast parameters T_{pred} and SD_{pred} and the temporal development

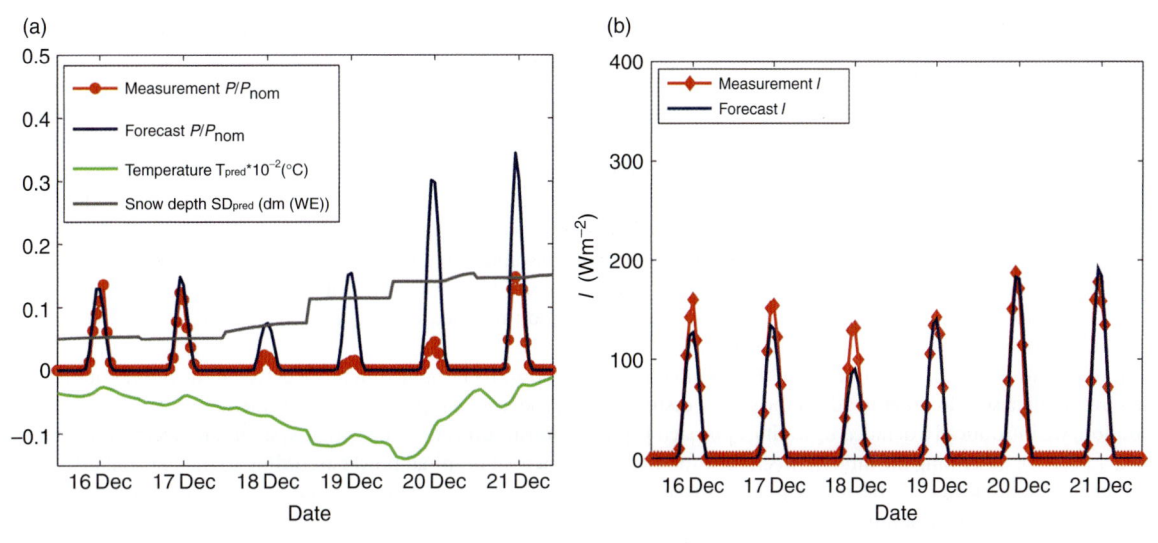

Figure 32 Time series of (a) normalized PV power intraday forecasts and measurements with additional information on predicted snow cover (predicted snow depth SD_{pred} in dm of water equivalent (WE)) and temperature T_{pred} and (b) irradiance intraday forecasts and measurements for average values of the region of 2° × 2° indicated in **Figure 28**.

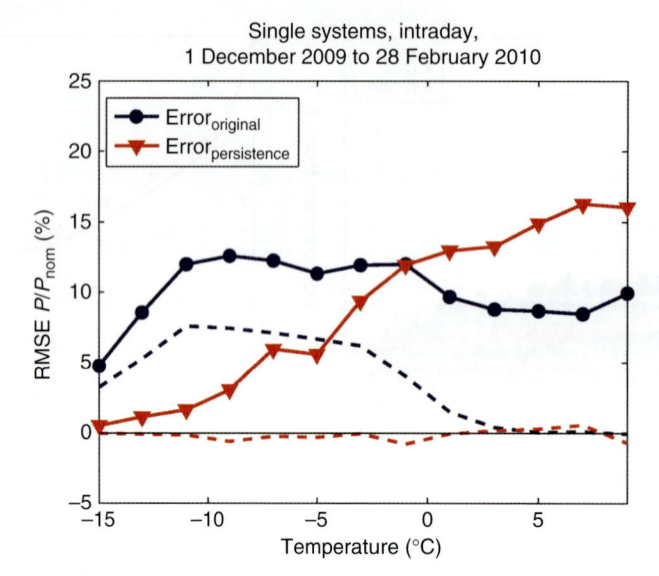

Figure 33 RMSE and bias of the original forecasts and persistence in dependence on the predicted temperature T_{pred}.

of the latter, indicating snowfall. Furthermore, we evaluated if the PV module was likely to be covered with snow on the previous day, which is estimated on the basis of measured power output and irradiance conditions. For an appropriate representation of PV power from snow-covered modules, we found persistence (eqn [27]) to be a suitable choice. **Figure 33** shows the RMSE and Bias of the original PV power forecasts and persistence in dependence on T_{pred}. The figure illustrates the advantage of persistence in comparison with the original forecasts for $T_{\text{pred}} < 0\ °C$. In particular, the large Bias of the original forecasts may also be adjusted.

The adapted power output during winter time is predicted for each PV system as

$$P_{\text{pred, snow}}(t) = (1-a)P_{\text{pred, orig}}(t) + aP_{\text{per}}(t) \qquad [35]$$

where the parameter a denotes the probability of snow cover on the module, characterized by one or more of the criteria briefly described above and determined by training with measured data. When evaluating the different criteria to detect snow cover, we found information on the predicted temperature or 'snow cover on the previous day' to be robust criteria, while information on the predicted SD_{pred} alone was not sufficient. With a combination of different criteria, a small additional improvement could be achieved. However, the investigated simple training approach was found to be very sensitive to detailed configurations of the training procedure.

Finally, it shall be mentioned that statistical postprocessing,of course, may also be beneficial for situations not related to snow cover, but is not evaluated here.

1.13.6.4.3 Regional upscaling

Upscaling from the representative data set is the last step in the processing chain to derive regional PV power predictions. As described earlier, a correct reproduction of the actual overall data set by the representative subsets is essential for a proper upscaling.

The quality of the representative subsets for the two control areas used during the first year of operation was investigated by analyzing the basic properties of these subsets in comparison with the corresponding properties of the overall data sets [4]. Information on the spatial distribution of the overall installed power was based on the data published by the transmission system operators according to the transparency guidelines of the German Renewable Energy Sources Act EEG. As a reference for information on the module type and orientations, we use the monitoring database of Meteocontrol GmbH.

With respect to system orientations and mix of modules, the study revealed a reasonable agreement between representative subsets and the overall data set.

With respect to the spatial distribution of the installed power, we found a notable difference between the representative subsets and the overall data sets. In order to adjust the spatial distribution of the installed power of the representative data sets to the actual distribution, we introduced a detailed upscaling approach [4]. The contributions from the single systems are weighted with a scaling factor $f_{\text{scale}}(\Phi, \lambda, t)$, describing the ratio between the time-dependent overall nominal power according to the EEG data $P_{\text{nom,all}}(\Phi, \lambda, t)$ and the nominal power of the representative subset $P_{\text{nom,rep}}(\Phi, \lambda)$ in dependence on the geographic location (latitude Φ, longitude λ) with a spatial resolution of $1° \times 1°$:

$$f_{\text{scale}}(\Phi, \lambda, t) = \frac{P_{\text{nom,all}}(\Phi, \lambda, t)}{P_{\text{nom,rep}}(\Phi, \lambda)} \qquad [36]$$

The regional power sums $P_{\text{scale}}(t)$ are then calculated as

$$P_{\text{scale}}(t) = \sum_{i=1}^{N} f_{\text{scale}}(\Phi_i, \lambda_i, t) P_i(t) \qquad [37]$$

where $P_i(t)$ and $P_{\text{scale}}(t)$ can be predicted or measured values.

1.13.6.4.4 Evaluation of local and regional power forecasts

The evaluation of the power forecasts starts with an overview of the results for different versions of the power prediction scheme. This is followed by a more detailed analysis with respect to the performance of the forecasts for different weather situations and seasons. Three versions of the power prediction scheme are included in the evaluation, to assess the impact of different modifications:

- Forecasts with simple upscaling according to eqn [17], and without snow detection. These forecasts were delivered operationally during the first year of operation, corresponding to the period of evaluation from October 2009 to September 2010.
- Forecasts with detailed upscaling, but without snow detection.
- Forecasts with detailed upscaling and snow detection based on temperature forecasts, corresponding to the operational version during winter 2010/2011.

1.13.6.4.4(i) Overall evaluation

The basic accuracy measures for the different forecast versions and persistence are summarized in **Tables 3** and **4** for intraday and day-ahead forecast horizons for the two control areas. For better comparison, the RMSE values as main scores of forecast evaluation are additionally visualized in **Figure 34**. All regional power values are normalized to the time dependent overall installed power $P_{\text{nom}}(t)$, in order to obtain a better comparability between different data sets and to account for changes in the installed power during the period of evaluation. This is common practice for utility companies and transmission system operators, who are the main users of regional PV power predictions. The evaluation includes all 24 h of the day.

With RMSE values in the range of 4.3–4.8% for intraday and 4.6–5.3% for day-ahead forecast horizons already during the first year of operation, a reasonable accuracy far better than persistence was achieved. This could be further improved by the proposed modifications. With the new approach integrating detailed upscaling and snow detection, intraday RMSE values could be reduced below 4% and day-ahead RMSE values to 4.1–4.6%. These RMSE values are in the same range as for current operational wind power prediction systems (e.g., see Reference 17) that have already demonstrated their value and importance for the grid integration of large shares of wind power.

Table 3 Bias and RMSE of P/P_{nom} for different forecasting approaches for the control area of 50Hertz (all 24 h of the day included)

	Bias		RMSE	
	Intraday (%)	Day-ahead (%)	Intraday (%)	Day-ahead (%)
Original	0.7	0.6	4.8	5.3
Detailed upscaling	0.2	0.2	4.3	4.8
Detailed upscaling and snow detection	0.0	0.0	3.9	4.6
Persistence	0.01	0.02	8.2	10.2

Mean $P_{\text{meas}}/P_{\text{nom}}$ amounts to 10.4%.

Table 4 Bias and RMSE of P/P_{nom} for different forecasting approaches for the control area of TenneT (all 24 h of the day included)

	Bias		RMSE	
	Intraday (%)	Day-ahead (%)	Intraday (%)	Day-ahead (%)
Original	0.6	0.6	4.3	4.6
Detailed upscaling	0.4	0.4	4.1	4.4
Detailed upscaling and snow detection	0.1	0.1	3.6	4.1
Persistence	−0.04	−0.04	6.8	8.8

Mean $P_{\text{meas}}/P_{\text{nom}}$ amounts to 10.8%.

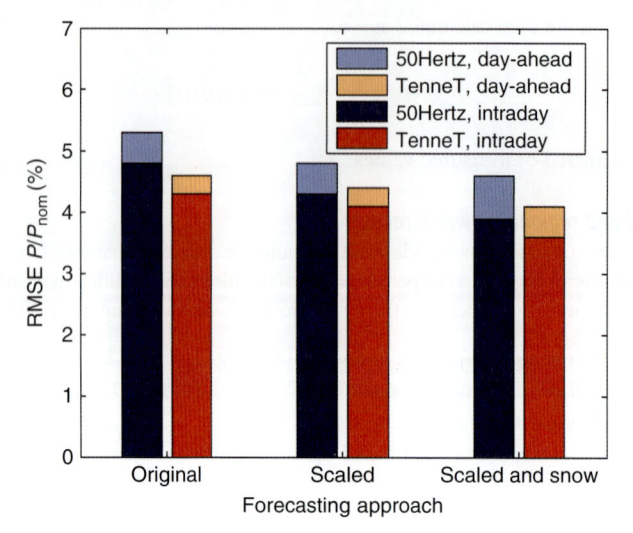

Figure 34 RMSE of different forecasting approaches in dependence on forecast horizon in days for the control areas of 50Hertz and TenneT.

1.13.6.4.4(i)(a) Evaluation of upscaling The comparison of the first operational version with the modified upscaling approach shows a considerable improvement by the new approach with respect to both RMSE and Bias. The improvement is more pronounced for the control area of 50Hertz due to larger deviations between the spatial distribution of the representative subset and the actual installed power for this control area. These results emphasize the importance of a correct modeling of the spatial distribution of the installed power for upscaling approaches.

The evaluations for 50Hertz also include upscaling from the representative data set to all systems monitored by Meteocontrol GmbH in the control area (**Figure 28**). In order to assess the effect of upscaling, we additionally evaluated the forecasts against regional power values derived from measurements of the same representative subset as used for the forecasts with the detailed upscaling approach. RMSE values based on the two different data sets to estimate the actual regional power agreed within ±0.1% of the nominal power. This indicates that – given a correct representation of the overall data set – using the same representative data sets as a basis for upscaling for regional predictions and measurements can provide a reasonable estimate of forecast accuracy. The additional error introduced by upscaling to a larger database is small.

1.13.6.4.4(i)(b) Evaluation of snow detection The algorithm for snow detection has an impact only during winter. Still the improvement is also notable for the complete year with reduced RMSE values and a bias of almost 0. The improvement is larger for intraday than for day-ahead forecasts. A more detailed evaluation of the algorithm for snow detection is given in the next section.

1.13.6.4.4(i)(c) Evaluations for different control areas and site-specific forecasts Forecast errors are smaller for the control area of TenneT (**Figure 15**), extended from the south of Germany (47° N) to the north of Germany (55° N), than for the control area of 50Hertz (**Figure 28**), covering the smaller area 50.5–54.5° N and 10–15° E. With increasing size of the region, forecast errors are decreasing due to spatial averaging effects, as described quantitatively in the detailed study of irradiance forecasts, presented in Section 1.13.6.3.2.

Forecast errors for single PV systems are summarized in **Table 5**. The RMSE values are in the range of 8.1% for intraday and 8.6% for day-ahead forecast horizons, which is about double the RMSE of the control areas.

Table 5 Bias and RMSE of P/P_{nom} for different forecasting approaches for single PV systems, located in the control area of 50Hertz (all 24 h of the day included)

	Bias		RMSE	
	Intraday (%)	Day-ahead (%)	Intraday (%)	Day-ahead (%)
Original	0.5	0.4	8.1	8.6
Snow detection	0.2	0.1	8.0	8.5
Persistence	0.0	0.0	12.4	14.0

Mean P_{meas}/P_{nom} amounts to 10.8%.

1.13.6.4.4(ii) Detailed analysis

A detailed view on forecast accuracies is obtained by visual inspection of predicted and measured values in comparison. In particular, we investigate and discuss the influence of different weather conditions and solar elevation on power production and forecast accuracy. These factors lead to a typical seasonal dependence of power production and forecast accuracy. The analysis in this section is exemplarily performed on the basis of the intraday forecasts for the control area of 50Hertz. The performance of the original forecasts is compared with that of the new forecast including detailed upscaling and snow detection.

Measured and predicted PV power production is compared in **Figure 35** for two selected periods covering different weather situations in December 2009 and June 2010. A scatter plot (**Figure 36**) of forecasted over measured power values gives a complementary picture of the performance of the forecasts during the complete evaluation period.

Apart from the deterministic course of irradiance, cloud cover is the main factor influencing power production. As for the example given in **Figure 35**(a), changes in weather conditions are mostly predicted well and cloudy days (e.g., 1 and 2 June 2010) are clearly distinguished from clear-sky days (e.g., 4 and 5 June 2010). Consequently, most data points are relatively close to identity in **Figure 36**. With the detailed upscaling, a slight overestimation of the power production occurring for the complete range of power values is adjusted.

During winter, snow cover on PV modules is an additional factor that has to be considered, as described in Section 1.13.6.4.2. With the original forecasting algorithm, a strong overestimation of the actual power production is found for snow-covered PV modules from 19 to 21 December 2009 as illustrated in **Figures 32**(a) and **35**(b). Also, in the scatter plot (**Figure 36**), an accumulation of data points with a considerable overestimation due to snow-covered PV modules is noticeable for low power

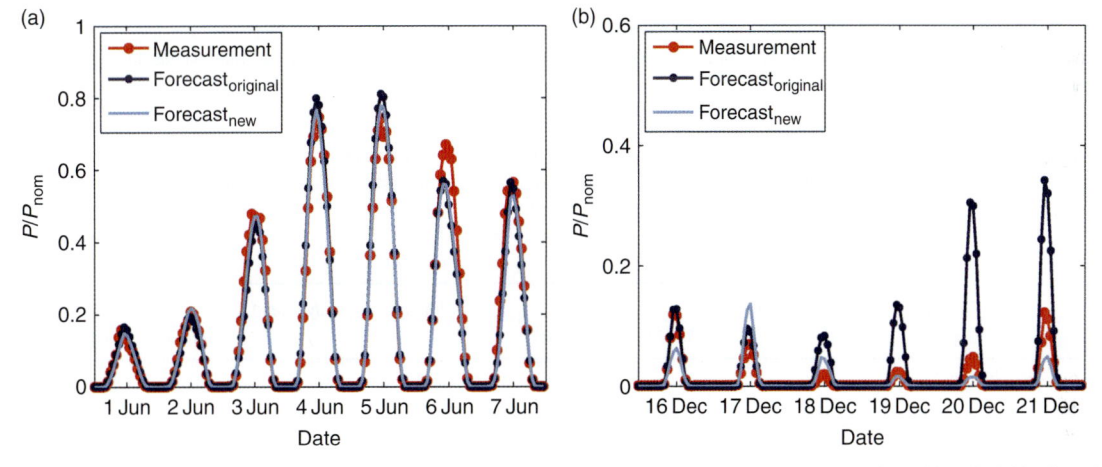

Figure 35 Comparison of time series of measured (red line with circles) and predicted power output with the original algorithm (dark blue line with small circles) and the new version (light blue line). Intraday forecasts for the control area of 50Hertz: (a) 1–7 June 2010 and (b) 16–21 December 2009.

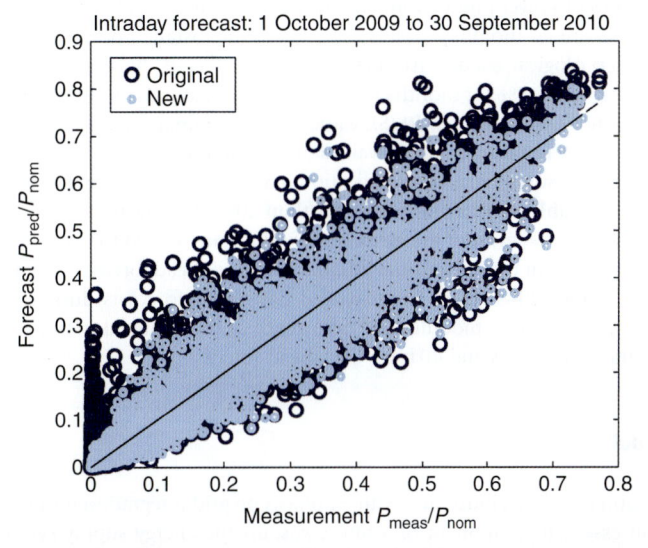

Figure 36 Scatter plot of predicted over measured PV power with the original (dark blue) and the new approach (light blue).

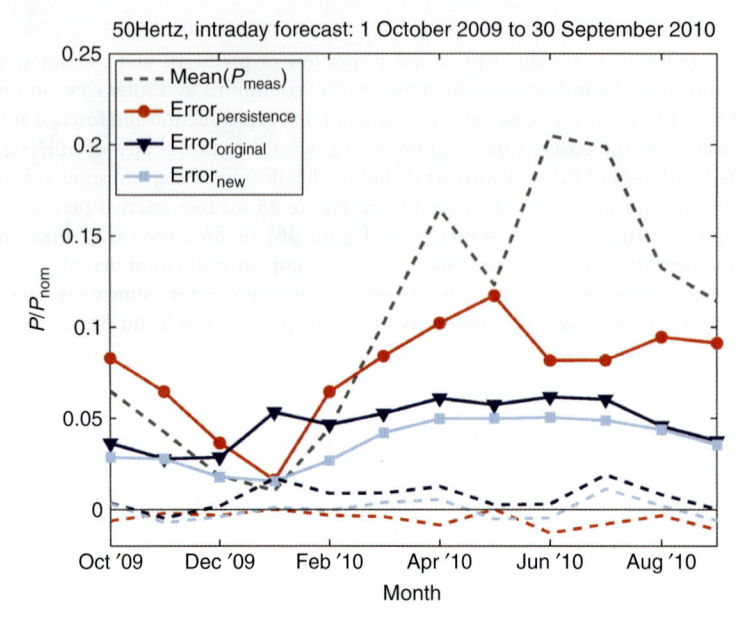

Figure 37 Monthly mean values (dashed gray line) and error measures for persistence (red line), the original PV power forecasts (dark blue line), and the new PV power forecasts (light blue line) for the control area of 50Hertz. Solid lines with markers correspond to RMSE values and dashed colored lines represent the Bias.

Table 6 Maximum over- and underestimation by the forecasts and number of hours with deviations of more than 20% of the nominal power for the two forecasting approaches and intraday and day-ahead forecasts for the control area of 50Hertz

	Maximum		Hours ($P_{pred}-P_{meas}$) > -20% P_{nom}		Maximum		Hours ($P_{pred}-P_{meas}$) < -20% P_{nom}	
	Intraday (%)	Day-ahead (%)	Intraday	Day-ahead	Intraday (%)	Day-ahead (%)	Intraday	Day-ahead
Operational	35.7	40.9	78	90	−26.8	−32.9	21	35
New	33.1	34.9	20	40	−27.6	−31.4	20	27

values ($P_{meas}/P_{nom} < 0.2$). With the proposed approach for snow detection, this overestimation is corrected and a good agreement between forecast and measurements is also achieved for snow situations.

Figure 37 shows the seasonal dependence of forecast errors (RMSE and Bias) for the original and new forecasts and persistence in relation to the monthly mean values of power production. The strong seasonal dependence of the power production approaching 20% of the installed power in the summer months and less than 2% of the installed power in January 2010 is a consequence of changing solar elevation and meteorological conditions, including snow-covered PV modules during winter. The RMSE of both forecasting approaches is in the range of 3–5% for months without snow-covered PV modules, and a clearly better performance in comparison with persistence is found. During winter, RMSE values of the original forecasts can be reduced significantly with the proposed algorithm for snow detection, resulting in RMSE values of less than 3%.

In addition to the statistical error measures that give an indication of the average performance forecasts, extreme deviations of the forecasts have also been investigated (**Table 6**). Deviations of more than 20% of the nominal power are considered as critical by the utility companies. For the original forecasts, most of the extreme deviations are related to overestimation. The maximum observed overestimation is between 35% and 40% for the operational intraday and day-ahead forecasts. An overestimation of more than 20% of the nominal power occurs for about 80–90 h for intraday and day-ahead forecasts during the complete year. As this overestimation is often related to snow cover on PV modules, the occurrence of these large deviations may be reduced drastically with the new approach to 20 h for intraday forecasts and 40 h for day-ahead forecasts.

1.13.7 Summary and Outlook

The benefits of PV power prediction have been illustrated with emphasis on grid integration purposes and increasing cost efficiency. PV power forecasting will be an essential component of a future sustainable energy supply system integrating large amounts of fluctuating renewable power.

Research on solar irradiance forecasting has started more than 30 years ago. Currently, increasing effort is spent on forecasting of solar irradiance and solar electricity generation as a consequence of the need for precise and detailed forecast data in the energy sector. We have presented a state-of-the-art review and basic features of solar irradiance and power prediction approaches, including time series models based on on-site measured data, models based on the detection of cloud motion in satellite images or ground-based sky images, and NWP-based models. This overview has been complemented by an introduction to PV simulation models.

The introduction of different concepts for evaluation has been a special focus of this chapter, reflecting its importance for various purposes. Detailed evaluations are an indispensable basis for model testing and further model development. Furthermore, proper accuracy assessment provides valuable information for users that rely on the forecasts as a basis for decision making. In particular, the specification of the expected uncertainty of forecast values in the form of confidence intervals or probability density functions is beneficial for an effective application of forecasts. We have proposed a first approach to derive weather-specific confidence intervals and outlined further options like the use of ensemble prediction systems.

The presented accuracy measures have been applied for the evaluation and comparison of various irradiance prediction algorithms. It has been shown that in the temporal range of 1–6 h forecasts based on cloud motion vectors from satellite images are superior to both time series models and NWP-based forecasts. Time series models outperform NWP-based forecasts for forecast horizons up to 1 or 2 h. From more than 6 h onward, the use of NWP-based forecasts is the best choice. With respect to the intercomparison of different NWP-based models, we have shown that at the current state of the scientific knowledge, forecasts based on global NWP models in combination with postprocessing perform superior to the investigated mesoscale approaches.

In a detailed evaluation of an operational PV power prediction system, we have quantified the effect of spatial averaging on the accuracy of regional forecasts. With RMSE values in the range of 4–5% with respect to the nominal power, these regional power forecasts can at the current state of the art contribute to improved grid integration of PV power. Still, as the benefit of the forecasts is directly related to their accuracy, there is a strong need for further research and development.

Evidently, progress in NWP-based irradiance forecasting will be strongly linked to general development and improvement of NWP models including several aspects like enhancement with respect to resolution, parameterizations, input data, and data assimilation systems. Nevertheless, modeling and parameterizations of clouds and radiation in both global and mesoscale NWP models are of particular importance for irradiance forecasting. In addition, integration of enhanced aerosol information is of special relevance for direct irradiance forecasting, which is necessary for concentrating PV as well as for solar thermal power plants.

Another promising approach toward improved solar irradiance forecasts is the use of ensemble prediction systems. Apart from the inherent uncertainty information, ensemble prediction systems perform superior to deterministic models for forecast horizons longer than typically 1 or 2 days ahead.

Still, whatever model is used for forecasting, partly stochastic and partly systematic errors will remain after all modeling efforts. Statistical postprocessing techniques, applicable to all classes of numerical models, can eliminate systematic errors mainly introduced by a model bias or by the influence of local effects not covered by the model, as also demonstrated in the presented evaluations. Hence, statistical methods will significantly contribute to future enhancement of irradiance and power predictions. Apart from model development, here the availability of high-quality and up-to-date measurement data of both irradiance and PV power will be of critical importance. Statistical models may also be applied to combine input of different data sources, including on-site measured data, satellite-based forecasts, and output of one or various NWP models, in order to derive optimized forecasts for horizons ranging from a few minutes up to several days ahead.

With respect to regional PV power prediction, an additional task will be the proper characterization of the large ensembles of PV systems contributing to the overall power production in an area.

Finally, in order to make an efficient use of the available forecasts with corresponding uncertainty information, the development of optimized management and operation strategies in close cooperation with different users is required.

References

[1] Bofinger S and Heilscher G (2006) Solar electricity forecast: Approaches and first results. In: *Proceedings of the 21st European Photovoltaic Solar Energy Conference and Exhibition*, pp. 2641–2645. Dresden, Germany, 4–8 September. München, Germany: WIP Renewable energies.

[2] Remund J, Schilter C, Dierer S, *et al.* (2008) Operational forecast of PV production. In: *Proceedings of the 23rd European Photovoltaic Solar Energy Conference and Exhibition*, pp. 3138–3140. Valencia, Spain, 1–5 September. München, Germany: WIP Renewable energies. doi: 10.4229/23rdEUPVSEC2008-4BV.1.44.

[3] Le Pivert X, Sicot L, and Merten J (2009) A tool for the 24 hours forecast of photovoltaic production. In: *Proceedings of the 24th European Photovoltaic Solar Energy Conference and Exhibition*, pp. 4076–4079. Hamburg, Germany, 21–25 September. München, Germany: WIP Renewable energies. doi: 10.4229/24thEUPVSEC2009-5BV.2.14.

[4] Lorenz E, Scheidsteger T, Hurka J, *et al.* (2010) Regional PV power prediction for improved grid integration. *Progress in Photovoltaics: Research and Applications* 19: 757–771. doi: 10.1002/pip.1033.

[5] Lange M (2006) A mature market? The history of short-term prediction services. *POW'WOW Best-Practices Workshop*. Delft, The Netherlands. http://powwow.risoe.dk/publ/ems-research_to_business_powwow_Delft_2006.pdf (accessed 18 January 2011).

[6] Landberg L, Giebel G, Nielsen HA, *et al.* (2006) Short-term prediction – An overview. *Wind Energy* 6(3): 273–280. doi: 10.1002/we.96.

[7] Costa A, Crespo A, Navarro J, *et al.* (2008) A review on the young history of the wind power short-term prediction. *Renewable & Sustainable Energy Reviews* 12(6): 1725–1744. doi: 10.1016/j.rser.2007.01.015.

[8] Giebel G (2011) The state-of-the-art in short-term prediction of wind power. *Anemos Report*. http://www.prediktor.dk/publ/GGiebelEtAl-StateOfTheArtInShortTermPrediction_ANEMOSplus_2011.pdf (accessed 18 January 2011).

[9] Böhme D, Dürrschmidt W, and Van Mark M (2011) *Renewable Energy Sources in Figures: National and International Development*, p. 7. Berlin, Germany: Federal Ministry for the Environment, Nature Conservation and Nuclear Safety (BMU) – Public Relations Division.

[10] Perez R, Kmiecik M, Schlemmer J, *et al.* (2007) Evaluation of PV generation capacity credit forecast on day-ahead utility markets. In: Campbell-Howe R (ed.), *Proceedings of the ASES Annual Conference*, pp. 945 Cleveland, OH, USA, 8–12 July. Curran Associates, Inc.

[11] Wittmann M, Breitkreuz H, Schroedter-Homscheidt M, and Eck M (2008) Case studies on the use of solar irradiance forecast for optimized operation strategies of solar thermal power plants. *IEEE Journal of Selected Topics in Applied Earth Observations and Remote Sensing* 1(1): 18–27. doi: 10.1109/JSTARS.2008.2001152.

[12] Takayama S, Iwasaka Y, Hara R, *et al.* (2009) Study on scheduling of PV power station output based on the solar radiation forecast. In: *Proceedings of the 24th European Photovoltaic Solar Energy Conference and Exhibition*, pp. 4127–4131. Hamburg, Germany, 21–25 September. München, Germany: WIP renewable energies. doi: 10.4229/24thEUPVSEC2009-5BV.2.31.

[13] Kudo M, Takeuchi A, Nozaki Y, *et al.* (2009) Forecasting electric power generation in a photovoltaic power system for an energy network. *Electrical Engineering in Japan* 167(4): 16–23. doi:0.1002/eej.20755.

[14] Rikos E, Tselepis S, Hoyer-Klick C, and Schroedter-Homscheidt M (2008) Stability and power quality issues in microgrids under weather disturbances. *IEEE Journal of Selected Topics in Applied Earth Observations and Remote Sensing* 1(3): 170–179. doi: 10.1109/JSTARS.2008.2010557.

[15] Yamamoto S, Park JS, Takata M, *et al.* (2003) Basic study on the prediction of solar irradiation and its application to photovoltaic–diesel hybrid generation system. *Solar Energy Materials & Solar Cells* 75(3–4): 577–584. doi: 10.1016/S0927-0248(02)00160-5.

[16] Traunmüller W and Steinmaurer G (2010) Solar irradiance forecasting, benchmarking of different techniques and applications to energy meteorology. In: *Proceedings of EuroSun 2010*. Graz, Austria, 28 September-1 October. International Solar Energy Society. ISBN:3-901425-13-6, 978-3-901425-13-4.

[17] Ernst B, Oakleaf B, Ahlstrom ML, *et al.* (2007) Predicting the wind. *IEEE Power & Energy Magazine* 5(6): 78–89. doi: 10.1109/MPE.2007.906306.

[18] Liou KN (1980) *An Introduction to Atmospheric Radiation.* Orlando, FL: Academic Press.

[19] Iqbal M (1983) *An Introduction to Solar Radiation.* Toronto, ON: Academic Press.

[20] Ineichen P (2006) Comparison of eight clear sky broadband models against 16 independent data banks. *Solar Energy* 80(4): 468–478. doi: 10.1016/j.solener.2005.04.018.

[21] Rigollier C, Bauer O, and Wald L (2000) On the clear sky model of the ESRA – European Solar Radiation Atlas – with respect to the Heliosat method. *Solar Energy* 68(1): 33–48. doi: 10.1016/S0038-092X(99)00055-9.

[22] Müller RW, Dagestad KF, Ineichen P, *et al.* (2004) Rethinking satellite based solar irradiance modelling: The SOLIS clear-sky module. *Remote Sensing of Environment* 91(2): 160–174. doi: 10.1016/j.rse.2004.02.009.

[23] Breitkreuz H, Schroedter-Homscheidt M, Holzer-Popp T, and Dech S (2009) Short range direct and diffuse irradiance forecasts for solar energy applications based on aerosol chemical transport and numerical weather modeling. *Journal of Applied Meteorology and Climatology* 48(9): 1766–1779. doi: 10.1175/2009JAMC2090.1.

[24] Cebecauer T, Perez R, and Suri M (2011) Comparing performance of SolarGIS and SUNY satellite models using monthly and daily aerosol data. In: *Proceedings of the ISES Solar World Congress 2011*, pp. 30–138. Kassel, Germany, 28 August–2 September. Freiburg, Germany: International Solar Energy Society.

[25] Mayer B and Kylling A (2005) Technical note: The libRadtran software package for radiative transfer calculations – Description and examples of use. *Atmospheric Chemistry and Physics* 5: 1855–1877. doi: 10.5194/acp-5-1855-2005.

[26] Chowdhury BH (1990) Short-term prediction of solar irradiance using time-series analysis. *Energy Sources* 12(2): 199–219. doi: 10.1080/00908319008960199.

[27] Reikard G (2009) Predicting solar radiation at high resolutions: A comparison of time series forecasts. *Solar Energy* 83(3): 342–349. doi: 10.1016/j.solener.2008.08.007.

[28] Bacher P, Madsen H, and Nielsen HA (2009) Online short-term solar power forecasting. *Solar Energy* 83(10): 1772–1783. doi: 10.1016/j.solener.2009.05.016.

[29] Mellit A (2008) Artificial intelligence technique for modelling and forecasting of solar radiation data: A review. *International Journal of Artificial Intelligence and Soft Computing* 1(1): 52–76. doi: 10.1504/IJAISC.2008.021264.

[30] Kemmoku Y, Orita S, Nakagawa S, and Sakakibara T (1999) Daily insolation forecasting using a multi-stage neural network. *Solar Energy* 66(3): 193–199. doi: 10.1016/S0038-092X(99)00017-1.

[31] Sfetsos A and Coonick AH (2000) Univariate and multivariate forecasting of hourly solar radiation with artificial intelligence techniques. *Solar Energy* 68(2): 169–178. doi: 10.1016/S0038-092X(99)00064-X.

[32] Cao JC and Cao SH (2006) Study of forecasting solar irradiance using neural networks with preprocessing sample data by wavelet analysis. *Energy* 31(15): 3435–3445. doi: 10.1016/j.energy.2006.04.001.

[33] Chaabene M and Ben Ammar MN (2008) Euro-fuzzy dynamic model with Kalman filter to forecast irradiance and temperature for solar energy systems. *Renewable Energy* 33(7): 1435–1443.

[34] Hocaoglu FO, Gerek ON, and Kurban M (2008) Hourly solar radiation forecasting using optimal coefficient 2-D linear filters and feed-forward neural networks. *Solar Energy* 82(8): 714–726. doi: 10.1016/j.solener.2008.02.003.

[35] Voyant C, Muselli M, Paoli C, *et al.* (2009) Predictability of PV power grid performance on insular sites without weather stations: Use of artificial neural networks. In: *Proceedings of the 24th European Photovoltaic Solar Energy Conference and Exhibition*, pp. 4141–4144. Hamburg, Germany 21–25 September. München, Germany: WIP renewable energies. doi: 10.4229/24thEUPVSEC2009-5BV.2.35.

[36] Cao JC and Lin XC (2008) Study of hourly and daily solar irradiation forecast using diagonal recurrent wavelet neural networks. *Energy and Conversion Management* 49(6): 1396–1406. doi: 10.1016/j.enconman.2007.12.030.

[37] Beyer HG, Costanzo C, Heinemann D, and Reise C (1994) Short range forecast of PV energy production using satellite image analysis. In: *Proceedings of the 12th European Photovoltaic Solar Energy Conference and Exhibition*, pp. 1718–1721. Amsterdam, The Netherlands, April 11 – 15. Begford, United Kingdom: H.S. Stephens & Associates.

[38] Hammer A, Heinemann D, Lorenz E, and Lückehe B (1999) Short-term forecasting of solar radiation: A statistical approach using satellite data. *Solar Energy* 67: 139–150. doi: 10.1016/S0038-092X(00)00038-4.

[39] Lorenz E, Heinemann D, and Hammer A (2004) Short-term forecasting of solar radiation based on satellite data. In: *Proceedings of EuroSun 2004*, pp. 841–848. Freiburg, Germany 20–24 June. Freiburg, Germany: PSE GmbH. ISBN 3-9809656-0-0.

[40] Perez R, Kivalov S, Schlemmer J, *et al.* (2009) Validation of short and medium term operational solar radiation forecasts in the US. In: *Proceedings of the ASES Annual Conference*. Buffalo, NY, USA, 11–16 May. Curran Associates, Inc.

[41] Taniguchi H, Otani K, and Kurokawa K (2001) Hourly forecast of global irradiation using GMS satellite images. *Solar Energy Materials & Solar Cells* 67(1–4): 551–557. doi: 10.1016/S0927-0248(00)00327-5.

[42] Menzel WP (2001) Cloud tracking with satellite imagery: From the pioneering work of Ted Fujita to the present. *Bulletin of the American Meteorological Society* 82(1): 33–47. doi: 10.1175/1520-0477(2001)0822.3.CO;2.

[43] Hammer A, Heinemann D, Hoyer C, *et al.* (2003) Solar energy assessment using remote sensing technologies. *Remote Sensing of Environment* 86(3): 423–432. doi: 10.1016/S0034-4257(03)00083-X.

[44] Fontoynont M, Dumortier D, Heinemann D, *et al.* (1998) Satellight: A WWW server which provides high quality daylight and solar radiation data for Western and Central Europe. In: *9th Conference on Satellite Meteorology and Oceanography*, pp. 434–437. Paris, France. Boston, MA: American Meteorological Society.

[45] Chow CW, Urquhart B, Lave M, *et al.* (2011) Intra-hour forecasting with a total sky imager at the UC3 San Diego solar energy testbed. *Solar Energy* 85(11): 2881–2893. doi: 10.1016/j.solener.2011.08.025.

[46] Kalnay E (2002) *Atmospheric Modeling, Data Assimilation and Predictability.* Cambridge, UK: Cambridge University Press.

[47] Hagedorn R http://www.ecmwf.int/newsevents/training/meteorological_presentations/pdf/DA/ECMWF.pdf (accessed 18 January 2011).

[48] Untch A http://www.ecmwf.int/newsevents/training/meteorological_presentations/pdf/NM/Adiabatic.pdf (accessed 18 January 2011).

[49] Lorenz E, Hurka J, Heinemann D, and Beyer HG (2009) Irradiance forecasting for the power prediction of grid-connected photovoltaic systems. *IEEE Journal of Special Topics in Earth Observations and Remote Sensing* 2(1): 2–10. doi: 10.1109/JSTARS.2009.2020300.

[50] Lorenz E, Heinemann D, and Kurz C (2011) Local and regional photovoltaic power prediction for large scale grid integration: Assessment of a new algorithm for snow detection. *Progress in Photovoltaics: Research and Applications.* doi: 10.1002/pip.1224.

[51] Morcrette JJ (1991) Radiation and cloud radiative properties in the European Center for Medium Range Weather Forecasts forecasting system. *Journal of Geophysical Research* 96(D5): 9121–9132. doi: 10.1029/89JD01597.

[52] Tiedtke M (1993) Presentation of clouds in large-scale models. *Monthly Weather Review* 121(11): 3040–3061. doi: 10.1175/1520-0493(1993)1212.0.CO;2.

[53] Gregory D, Morcrette JJ, Jakob C, *et al.* (2000) Revision of convection, radiation and cloud schemes in the ECMWF integrated forecasting system. *Quarterly Journal of the Royal Meteorological Society* 126(566): 1685–1710. doi: 10.1002/qj.49712656607.

[54] Morcrette JJ, Barker HW, Cole JNS, *et al.* (2008) Impact of a new radiation package, McRad, in the ECMWF integrated forecasting system. *Monthly Weather Review* 136(12): 4773–4798. doi: 10.1175/2008MWR2363.1.

[55] Morcrette JJ (2002) Assessment of the ECMWF model cloudiness and surface radiation fields at the ARM SGP site. *Monthly Weather Review* 130(2): 257–277. doi: 10.1175/1520-0493(2002)1302.0.CO;2.

[56] ECMWF http://www.ecmwf.int/research/ (accessed 18 January 2011).

[57] Grell GA, Dudhia J, and Stauffer DR (1995) A description of the fifth-generation Penn State/NCAR mesoscale model (MM5). Technical Note NCAR/TN-398+STR, 121pp. Boulder, CO: National Center for Atmospheric Research.

[58] Skamarock WC, Klemp JB, Dudhia J, *et al.* (2008) A description of the advanced research WRF version 3. Technical Note NCAR/TN-475+STR. Boulder, CO: Mesoscale and Microscale Meteorology Division, National Center for Atmospheric Research.

[59] Heinemann D, Lorenz E, and Girodo M (2006) Forecasting of solar radiation. In: Dunlop ED, Wald L, and Suri M (eds.) *Solar Resource Management for Electricity Generation from Local Level to Global Scale*, pp. 83–94. New York: Nova Science Publishers.

[60] Dudhia J (1989) Numerical study of convection observed during the winter monsoon experiment using a mesoscale two-dimensional model. *Journal of the Atmospheric Sciences* 46: 3077–3107. doi: 10.1175/1520-0469(1989)0462.0.CO;2.

[61] Zamora RJ, Solomon S, Dutton EG, *et al.* (2003) Comparing MM5 radiative fluxes with observations gathered during the 1995 and 1999 Nashville southern oxidants studies. *Journal of Geophysical Research* 108(D2): 4050. doi: 10.1029/2002JD002122.

[62] Zamora RJ, Dutton EG, Trainer M, *et al.* (2005) The accuracy of solar irradiance calculations used in mesoscale numerical weather prediction. *Monthly Weather Review* 133(4): 783–792. doi: 10.1175/MWR2886.1.

[63] Guichard F, Parsons DB, Dudhia J, and Bresch J (2003) Evaluating mesoscale model predictions of clouds and radiation with SGP ARM data over a seasonal timescale. *Monthly Weather Review* 131(5): 926–944. doi: 10.1175/1520-0493(2003)1312.0.CO;2.

[64] Ruiz-Arias JA, Pozo-Vázquez D, Sánchez-Sánchez N, *et al.* (2009) Evaluation of two MM5-PBL parameterizations for solar radiation and temperature estimation in the south-eastern area of the Iberian Peninsula. *Il Nuovo Cimento* 31: 5–6. doi: 10.1393/ncc/i2009-10343-6.

[65] Pozo-Vázquez AD, Lara-Fanego V, and Al-Samamra H (2008) Using NWP models for solar radiation estimates in a complex-topography area in Southeastern Spain In: *Proceedings of EuroSun 2008.* 7–10 October. Lisbon, Portugal: International Solar Energy Society (ISES).

[66] Remund J, Perez R, and Lorenz E (2008) Comparison of solar radiation forecasts for the USA. In: *Proceedings of the 23rd European Photovoltaic and Solar Energy Conference and Exhibition*, pp. 3141–3143. Valencia, Spain 1–5 September. München, Germany: WIP renewable energies. doi: 10.4229/23rdEUPVSEC2008-4BV.1.45.

[67] Perez R, Beauharnois M, Hemker K, *et al.* (2011) Evaluation of numerical weather prediction solar irradiance forecasts in the US. In: *Proceedings of the ASES Annual Conference.* Raleigh, NC, USA, 17–21 May.

[68] Lara-Fanego V, Ruiz-Arias JA, Pozo-Vázquez D, *et al.* (2011) Evaluation of the WRF model solar irradiance forecasts in Andalusia (southern Spain). *Solar Energy.* doi: 10.1016/j.solener.2011.02.014.

[69] Lorenz E, Remund J, Müller SC, *et al.* (2009) Benchmarking of different approaches to forecast solar irradiance. In: *Proceedings of the 24th European Photovoltaic and Solar Energy Conference and Exhibition*, pp. 4199–4208. Hamburg, Germany, 21–25 September. München, Germany: WIP renewable energies. doi: 10.4229/24thEUPVSEC2009-5BV.2.50.

[70] Glahn HR and Lowry DA (1972) The use of model output statistics (MOS) in objective weather forecasting. *Journal of Applied Meteorology* 11: 1203–1211. doi: 10.1175/1520-0450(1972)0112.0.CO;2.

[71] Jensenius JS and Cotton GF (1981) The development and testing of automated solar energy forecasts based on the model output statistics (MOS) technique. In: *Proceedings of the 1st Workshop on Terrestrial Solar Resource Forecasting and on the Use of Satellites for Terrestrial Solar Resource Assessment.* Newark, NJ: American Solar Energy Society.

[72] Jensenius JS (1989) Insolation forecasting. In: Hulstrom RL (ed.) *Solar Resources*, pp. 335–349. Cambridge, UK: MIT Press.

[73] Guarnieri RA, Pereira EB, and Chou SC (2006) Solar radiation forecast using artificial neural networks in South Brazil. In: *Proceedings of the 8th International Conference on Southern Hemisphere Meteorology and Oceanography (ICSHMO)*, pp. 1777–1785. Foz do Iguaçu, Brazil, 24–28 April.

[74] Kratzenberg MG, Colle S, and Beyer HG (2008) Solar radiation prediction based on the combination of a numerical weather prediction model and a time series prediction model. In: *Proceedings of EuroSun 2008.* 7–10 October 2008. Lisbon, Portugal: International Solar Energy Society.

[75] Perez R, Moore K, Wilcox S, *et al.* (2007) Forecasting solar radiation: Preliminary evaluation of an approach based upon the national forecast database. *Solar Energy* 81(6): 809–812. doi: 10.1016/j.solener.2006.09.009.

[76] Pelland S, Gallanis G, and Kallos G (in press) Solar and photovoltaic forecasting through post-processing of the global environmental multiscale numerical weather prediction model. *Progress in Photovoltaics: Research and Applications.* doi:10.1002/pip.1180.

[77] Mathiesen P and Kleissl J (2011) Evaluation of numerical weather prediction for intra-day solar forecasting in the continental United States. *Solar Energy* 85(5): 967–977. doi: 10.1016/j.solener.2011.02.013.

[78] Jolliffe IT and Stephenson DB (2003) *Forecast Verification: A Practitioner's Guide in Atmospheric Science.* Chichester, UK: John Wiley & Sons Ltd.

[79] Ruiz-Arias JA, Pozo-Vázquez D, Lara-Fanego V, *et al.* (2011) A high-resolution topographic correction method for clear-sky solar irradiance derived with a numerical weather prediction model. *Journal of Applied Meteorology and Climatology* 50(12): 2460–2472. doi:10.1175/2011JAMC2571.1.

[80] Suzuki H, Watanabe Y, and Wakao S (2008) Short-term PV output forecast using just-in-time modeling. In: *Proceedings of the 23rd European Photovoltaic Solar Energy Conference and Exhibition*, pp. 3406–3408. Valencia, Spain, 1–5 September. München, Germany: WIP renewable energies. doi: 10.4229/23rdEUPVSEC2008-5BV.2.13.

[81] Liu BYH and Jordan RC (1963) The long-term average performance of flat-plate solar energy collectors. *Solar Energy* 7: 53–74.

[82] Skartveit A, Olseth JA, and Tuft ME (1998) An hourly diffuse fraction model with correction for variability and surface albedo. *Solar Energy* 63: 173–183. doi: 10.1016/S0038-092X(98)00067-X.

[83] Kemper A, Lorenz E, Hammer A, and Heinemann D (2008) Evaluation of a new model to calculate direct normal irradiance based on satellite images of Meteosat second generation. In: *Proceedings of EuroSun 2008 – 1st International Conference on Solar Heating, Cooling and Buildings.* Lisbon, Portugal, 7–10 October. International Solar Energy Society.

[84] Perez R, Seals R, Ineichen P, *et al.* (1987) A new simplified version of the Perez diffuse irradiance model for tilted surfaces. *Solar Energy* 39(3): 221–231.

[85] Klucher TM (1979) Evaluation of models to predict insolation on tilted surfaces. *Solar Energy* 23: 111–114. doi: 10.1016/S0038-092X(87)80031-2.

[86] Beyer HG, Betcke J, Drews A, *et al.* (2004) Identification of a general model for the MPP performance of PV modules for the application in a procedure for the performance check of grid connected systems. In: *Proceedings of the 19th European Photovoltaic Solar Energy Conference and Exhibition*, pp. 3073–3076. Paris, France, 7–11 June. International Solar Energy Society.

[87] Randall JF and Jacot J (2003) Is AM1.5 applicable in practice? Modelling eight photovoltaic materials with respect to light intensity and two spectra. *Renewable Energy* 28: 1851–1864. doi: 10.1016/S0960-1481(03)00068-5.

[88] Reich NH, van Sark WGJHM, Alsema EA, *et al.* (2009) Crystalline silicon cell performance at low light intensities. *Solar Energy Materials & Solar Cells* 93: 1471–1481. doi: 10.1016/j.solmat.2009.03.018.
[89] Skoplaki E and Palyvos JA (2009) On the temperature dependence of photovoltaic module electrical performance: A review of efficiency/power correlations. *Solar Energy* 83(5): 614–624. doi: 10.1016/j.solener.2008.10.008.
[90] Reich NH, van Sark WGJHM, and Turkenburg WC (2011) Charge yield potential of indoor-operated solar cells incorporated into product integrated photovoltaic (PIPV). *Renewable Energy* 36: 642–647. doi: 10.1016/j.renene.2010.07.018.
[91] Schmidt H and Sauer DU (1996) Wechselrichter-Wirkungsgrade. *Sonnenenergie* 4: 43–47.
[92] Peharz G, Siefer G, Araki K, and Bett AW (2008) Spectrometric outdoor characterization of CPV modules using isotype monitor cells. In: *33rd IEEE Photovoltaic Specialists Conference*, pp. 1–5. San Diego, CA, USA. Institute of Electrical and Electronics Engineers (IEEE) and Electron Devices Society (EDS). doi: 10.1109/PVSC.2008.4922735.
[93] Schmelter J and Focken U (2011) Operationelle Erfahrungen mit kombinierten Solarleistungsvorhersagen für deutsche ÜNBs und VNBs. In: *Proceedings of the 26th Symposium on Photovoltaische Solarenergie*, pp. 376–381. Bad Staffelstein, Germany, 2-4 March. Regensburg, Germany: Ostbayrisches Technologie_transfer-Institut e.V. (OTTI).
[94] Lange M and Focken U (2005) *Physical Approach to Short-Term Wind Power Prediction*. Berlin, Heidelberg, New York: Springer.
[95] Nielsen TS, Madsen H, Nielsen HA, *et al.* (2006) Advanced statistical modelling and uncertainty assessment for wind power forecasting. In: *Proceedings of the European Wind Energy Conference*. Athens, Greece, 27 February - 2 March.
[96] Espinar B, Ramírez L, Drews A, *et al.* (2009) Analysis of different error parameters applied to solar radiation data from satellite and German radiometric stations. *Solar Energy* 83(1). doi: 10.1016/j.solener.2008.07.009.
[97] Molteni F, Buizza R, Palmer TN, and Petroliagis T (1996) The ECMWF ensemble prediction system: Methodology and validation. *Quarterly Journal of the Royal Meteorological Society* 122: 73–119. doi: 10.1002/qj.49712252905.
[98] http://www.iea-shc.org/task36 (accessed 18 January 2011).
[99] Kallos G (1997) The regional weather forecasting system SKIRON. In: *Proceedings of the Symposium on Regional Weather Prediction on Parallel Computer Environments*. University of Athens, Athens, Greece, 15–17 October.

1.14 Principles of Solar Energy Conversion

LC Hirst, Imperial College London, London, UK

© 2012 Elsevier Ltd. All rights reserved.

1.14.1	Introduction	294
1.14.2	The PV Effect	294
1.14.3	Solar Cells in Circuits	294
1.14.4	Solar Resource	295
1.14.4.1	Blackbody Radiation	295
1.14.5	Absorption Profile of a Solar Cell	296
1.14.6	Semiconductors	297
1.14.6.1	Energy Band Structure	297
1.14.6.2	Carrier Populations in Semiconductor Materials	298
1.14.6.2.1	Density of electron states	298
1.14.6.2.2	Occupation of electron states	299
1.14.6.2.3	Carrier density	299
1.14.6.3	Doping	300
1.14.6.4	Pn Junction	301
1.14.7	Generation and Recombination	301
1.14.7.1	Thermal Generation and Recombination	302
1.14.7.2	Radiative Generation and Recombination	302
1.14.7.3	Carrier–Carrier Generation and Recombination	303
1.14.7.4	Impurity and Surface Generation and Recombination	303
1.14.8	Thermal Energy into Chemical Energy	304
1.14.8.1	Current Extraction	305
1.14.9	Generalized Planck	305
1.14.9.1	Density of Photon States	306
1.14.9.2	Geometrical Factor	306
1.14.9.3	Occupation of Photon States	307
1.14.10	Detailed Balance	308
1.14.10.1	Shockley–Queisser Limiting Efficiency	308
1.14.10.1.1	Shockley–Queisser assumptions	308
1.14.10.1.2	Photon recycling	308
1.14.10.2	Real-World Devices	309
1.14.11	Intrinsic Loss Mechanisms in Solar Cells	309
1.14.11.1	Below E_g Loss	310
1.14.11.2	Emission Loss	311
1.14.11.3	Thermalization	311
1.14.11.4	Carnot Loss	311
1.14.11.5	Boltzmann Loss	311
1.14.12	Exceeding the Shockley–Queisser Limiting Efficiency	312
1.14.13	Summary	312
References		313

Glossary

Acceptor An impurity atom with fewer valence electrons than necessary to bond with the host semiconductor.

Bandgap The forbidden energy gap between valence and conduction bands which creates the step-like absorption profile of a semiconductor.

Blackbody A body which absorbs all wavelengths of light and emits light according to Planck's Law of radiation.

Donor An impurity atom with more valence electrons than necessary to bond with the host semiconductor.

Doping The process of replacing atoms in a semiconductor lattice with impurity atoms with a different number of valence electrons.

Fermi-level The energy at which half of all states are occupied.

Generation When an electron and a hole pair are formed in a semiconductor.

n-Type semiconductor A semiconductor doped with acceptor atoms.

Open circuit voltage (V_{oc}) The voltage across a solar cell when no current flows.

> **pn Junction** A diode formed of layers of oppositely doped semiconductor material.
> **p-Type semiconductor** A semiconductor doped with donor atoms.
> **Recombination** The process of an electron and hole pair annihilating.
> **Shockley–Queisser limit** The fundamental limit for solar energy conversion in a single junction device under one Sun illumination (31%)
>
> **Short circuit current (J_{sc})** The current passing through a solar cell when the voltage across the solar cell is zero.
> **Thermalization** The process by which excited electrons lose energy as heat to the surrounding atomic lattice.
> **Valence band** The highest band of electronic energy levels that is filled at absolute zero.

1.14.1 Introduction

Sunlight can be directly converted into electricity in solar cells via the photovoltaic (PV) effect. This chapter examines the fundamental mechanisms behind this energy conversion process. PV conversion will only occur in a device exhibiting two necessary behaviors. First, a solar cell must absorb solar radiation, converting the Sun's heat energy into chemical energy in the device. When light is absorbed, electrons are excited into higher energy levels, temporarily storing chemical energy. Excited electrons behave as charge carriers (current) in an electrical potential. Second, a solar cell must exhibit asymmetric electrical resistance. Under solar illumination, this generates an electrical potential (voltage) across a device, which is defined by the chemical energy stored in the electron population. In this way, a solar cell can supply useful electrical work to a load resistance.

All semiconductor materials exhibit the first necessary behavior. They make efficient solar absorbers because they have a continuum of electronic energy levels as well as a forbidden energy gap. This absorption profile allows much of the solar spectrum to be absorbed while preventing excited electrons rapidly returning to their original ground state via thermal transitions. Semiconductors can also be structured in such a way that they exhibit the second necessary behavior. A pn junction is a semiconductor device that behaves as a diode, defining the direction of current flow and allowing a voltage to be generated. The way in which semiconductors interact with light is considered in this chapter along with the behavior of electrons in these materials.

The conversion of solar radiation into useful electrical work can never be 100% efficient. This chapter derives and explains intrinsic loss mechanisms occurring in solar cells and shows how these lead to a fundamental limit in conversion efficiency.

1.14.2 The PV Effect

PV devices convert light directly into useful electrical work. This conversion relies on the PV effect [1], which causes a voltage to develop across a material with asymmetric electrical resistance, under illumination. When light is incident on matter, it can provide sufficient energy to excite atomic electrons into higher energy states. In the case of semiconductor materials, such as silicon or germanium, this energy allows electrons to escape from their bound state and become free charge carriers, moving along a path of least resistance. Asymmetry in the material allows negatively charged free electrons to move to one side of the material, leaving the opposite side positively charged. As electrons accumulate at one terminal, a potential that opposes the motion of the charge carriers is generated. This potential defines the voltage across the device. When the terminals of a solar cell are short-circuited, no charge will accumulate at the terminals as electrons will flow uninhibited across the short circuit to the opposite terminal. In this instance, the maximum current will flow but no voltage will be generated. When a large load resistance is placed across the terminals, a large electron population will collect at the terminals, generating a large voltage across the device but restricting current flow.

1.14.3 Solar Cells in Circuits

The PV effect requires both photocurrent generation and asymmetric electrical resistance, and as such, a solar cell is electrically equivalent to a photosensitive current source connected in parallel to a diode (**Figure 1**) [2]. The short-circuit photocurrent (J_{sc}) is proportional to the intensity of the incident illumination. This photo-generated current is divided between a load resistance and a diode. The current flowing through the diode ($J_D(V)$) is a function of voltage across the device and flows in the direction opposite to J_{sc}. A rectifying diode has a nonlinear resistance, which produces an asymmetric current–voltage characteristic [3, 4]. Equation [1] is the ideal diode equation: J_0 is a constant, e is the electron charge, V is the voltage across the device, k is Boltzmann's constant (1.38×10^{-23} J K^{-1}), and T is the device temperature.

$$J_D(V) = J_0 \left[\exp\left(\frac{eV}{kT}\right) - 1 \right] \quad [1]$$

Current flowing through the diode generates a voltage, enabling charge separation. Without the asymmetry of the diode, no voltage would be developed across the device. Sign convention defines J_{sc} as the positive direction of current flow. The net flow of current ($J(V)$) is the product of photo and diode currents, eqn [2].

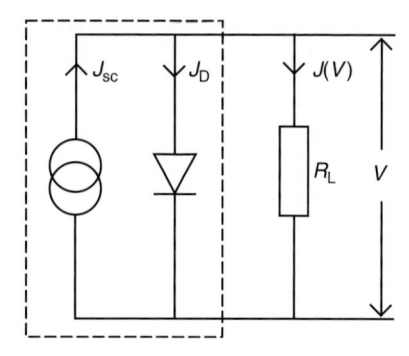

Figure 1 A solar cell is electrically equivalent to a current source and a diode connected in parallel.

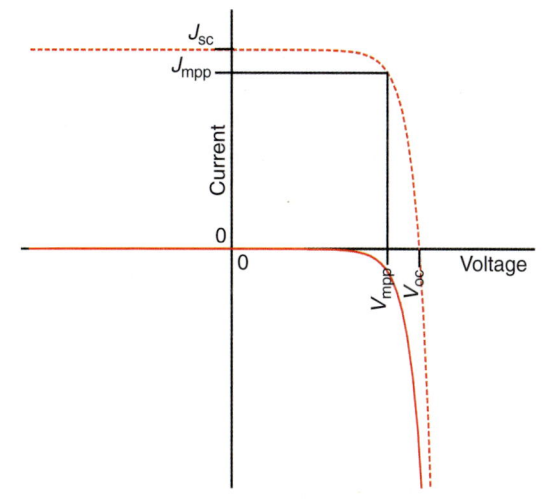

Figure 2 The Shockley ideal diode equation describes the current–voltage characteristics of a pn junction. Behavior in the dark (solid line) and under illumination (dashed line) are shown.

$$J(V) = J_{sc} - J_D(V) \quad [2]$$

The current–voltage (J–V) characteristic of a solar cell is therefore defined by both the incident intensity of light and the diode characteristics (**Figure 2**). A device operates at a set position along its J–V characteristic determined by the load resistance (R_L) between the two terminals of the solar cell. When $R_L = 0$, all the generated photocurrent passes through the load and the device is effectively short-circuited ($J(V) = J_{sc}$). No current passes through the diode and therefore no voltage is developed across the solar cell. As R_L increases, current will start to flow through the diode reducing the current passing through the load and resulting in a voltage developing across the solar cell. In the case of $R_L = \infty$, no current will flow through the load and the open circuit voltage V_{oc} will be generated by the diode.

Output electrical power (P_{out}) is the product of $J(V)$ and V. The optimal operating current (J_{mpp}) and voltage (V_{mpp}) is defined by the maximum power point of the current–voltage characteristic. A solar cell requires the photosensitive current source to generate current and the diode to generate voltage. Both elements are therefore required to extract electrical power from a device. A pn junction is a semiconductor device that exhibits both necessary behaviors and is therefore the foundation of most real-world PV devices.

1.14.4 Solar Resource

The primary application of PV devices is the conversion of solar energy into electricity. The parameters of the solar resource define the requirements of a solar energy conversion system. Light is quantized into energy packets, or particles, called photons. The human eye detects photon energy as color and is sensitive in the energy range 1.5 (red light) to 3 eV (blue light). White light consists of a spectrum of different energy photons over the visible range. The Sun emits light over a broad range of energies including ultraviolet, visible, and infrared light. This radiation can be approximated as the emission from a blackbody of temperature 6000 K.

1.14.4.1 Blackbody Radiation

A blackbody is a body that absorbs all wavelengths of light. No light is reflected and therefore, at low temperature, it appears black. Emission from a blackbody is temperature dependent and at high temperature, a blackbody will emit a spectrum of photon energies

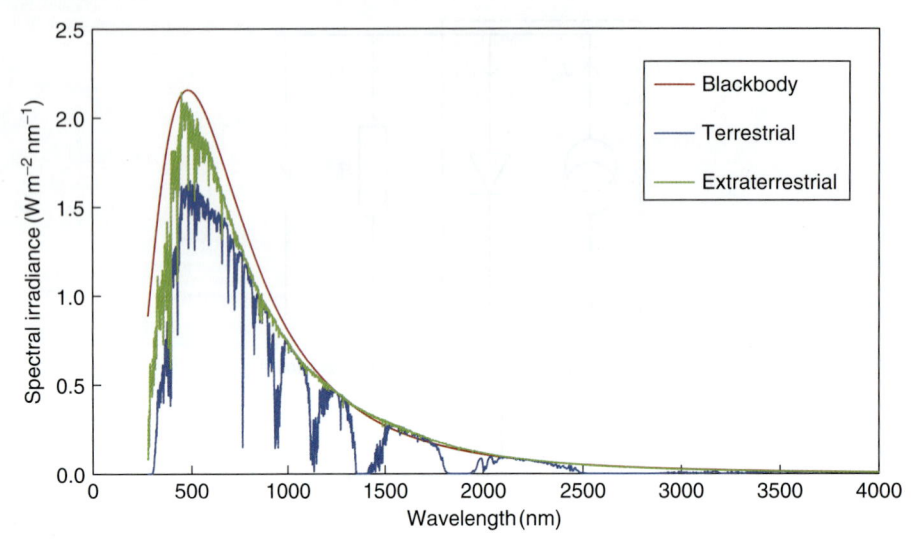

Figure 3 Terrestrial, extraterrestrial, and 6000 K blackbody spectra are compared. The terrestrial spectrum shown is ASTM G173-03 global tilt reference spectra, which is used to characterize and compare real-world solar cells [5].

that span the visible range, and therefore it will appear white. The Sun is an example of a high-temperature blackbody. Planck's law of radiation, eqn [3], quantifies photon flux, emitted through the surface of a blackbody into a defined solid angle, per unit area, per unit energy interval.

$$n_{\text{ph}}(E, T, \Omega) = \frac{2\Omega}{c^2 h^3} \frac{E^2}{\exp[E/kT] - 1} \quad [3]$$

E is the photon energy, T is the temperature of the emitting body, Ω is the solid angle of emission, c is the speed of light, h is Planck's constant, and k is Boltzmann's constant. Planck's law of radiation provides a good approximation of the incident solar radiation; however, many other factors such as daily and annual cycles and atmospheric absorption and scattering will have a significant effect on real-world device performance. Many of these factors are highly site specific and will be very important in evaluating the suitability of certain device designs and the operating capacity of a solar power station. Terrestrial and extraterrestrial spectra used to characterize real-world solar cells are shown in **Figure 3** alongside a 6000 K blackbody spectrum.

1.14.5 Absorption Profile of a Solar Cell

A solar cell must have an absorption profile that complements the broad solar spectrum. The monochromatic absorption of a single atomic transition is a poor match for the Sun's spectrum. A material exhibiting a broad continuum of electron energy levels is required to access a large portion of the available irradiance. Metals with rough surfaces behave like blackbodies. They have a broad continuum of electronic energy levels and hence are able to absorb most of the solar spectrum. Despite being good absorbers, metals do not make efficient PV materials because of a process called thermalization, in which excited electrons lose energy to the surrounding atomic lattice.

Above absolute zero, atoms in a solid vibrate. These vibrations can be quantized into energy packets called phonons. Phonons and electrons in a solid interact, exchanging energy and momentum and allowing photo-excited electrons to return to their original ground state via the continuum of electronic levels. These interactions occur on an extremely rapid timescale ($>10^{-12}$ s), preventing the electron populations forming an excited steady state from which useful energy can be extracted. A gap in available electron states is required to halt phonon emission and prevent excited electrons cascading through energy levels back to their original state. This can be achieved in a gray body with a threshold absorption profile (**Figure 4**).

A gray body, like a blackbody, has an emission profile defined by the temperature of the emitting body; however, in a gray body, this profile also contains an energy-dependent emissivity term, $\varepsilon(E)$. Such a material will emit light according to eqn [4], which is the product of the blackbody emission spectrum and $\varepsilon(E)$.

$$n_{\text{ph}}(E, T, \Omega) = \varepsilon(E) \frac{2\Omega}{c^2 h^3} \frac{E^2}{\exp[E/kT_S] - 1} \quad [4]$$

A gray body will also have an energy-dependent absorption profile, $a(E)$. According to Kirchhoff's law of thermal radiation, $\varepsilon(E) = a(E)$. A gray body with a threshold absorption profile will only absorb and emit photons with energy above the threshold. This limits the amount of solar radiation that can be absorbed; however, without the threshold, excited electrons instantaneously return to their original states and no useful electrical work can be extracted from the device.

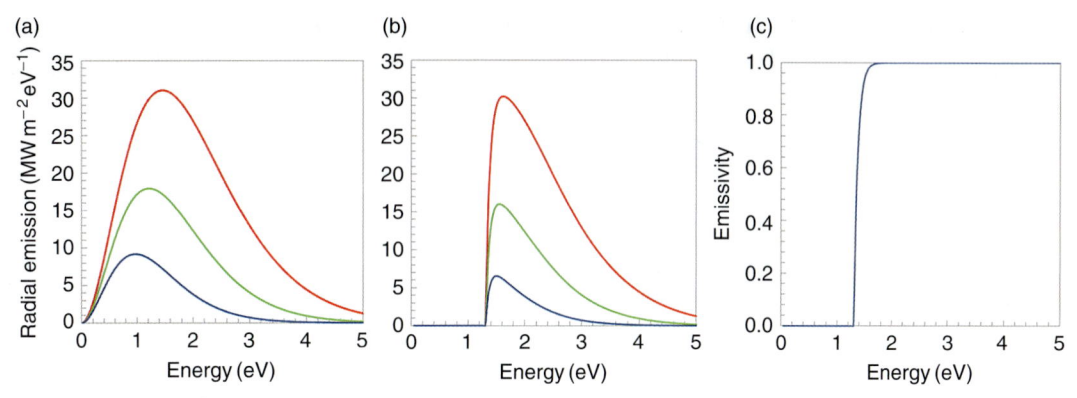

Figure 4 (a) Emission from a blackbody with $a(E) = \varepsilon(E) = 1$ and $T = 1000$ K (blue), $T = 3000$ K (green), and $T = 6000$ K (red). (b) Emission from a gray body with step-like absorption and emission profile shown in (c).

1.14.6 Semiconductors

Semiconductors are gray bodies. They have a continuum of electronic energy levels that are interrupted by a forbidden region, called the energy bandgap (E_g). As isolated atoms come together in a solid, their discrete atomic energy levels split into degenerate bands of allowed electron states (**Figure 5**) [6]. The valence band describes the highest filled band of electron states at absolute zero. The energy band directly above is called the conduction band.

Partial occupation of the conduction band is required for a material to behave as an electrical conductor. When all valence band states are fully occupied with electrons, no current can flow. This is because there are no vacant states for the electrons to move into. When an electron is promoted into the conduction band, it leaves behind a positively charged vacancy. It is convenient to consider this vacancy as a particle called a hole. The conduction band is no longer empty and the valence band is no longer full, and hence a current will flow under an applied field.

The separation between conduction and valence bands defines E_g and the absorption and emission threshold of the material. Photons with energy greater than E_g can be absorbed by the material. In the case of metals, conduction and valence bands overlap, making them good electrical conductors and giving them an uninterrupted continuum of electronic energy states. An insulator has a large energy bandgap (>3 eV), and therefore, practically no electrons occupy the conduction band at room temperature. The large forbidden energy region also prevents the absorption of most of the solar spectrum because most incident photons will not have sufficient energy to excite an electron into the conduction band. Semiconductor materials have an energy bandgap in the region 0.5–3 eV. This absorption threshold balances the requirements of broad spectral absorption and energy discontinuity, to make efficient solar converters. At room temperature in the dark, most semiconductors are highly electrically resistive. Under illumination, however, electrons are promoted to the conduction band, allowing the material to behave as a conductor. This is known as photoconductivity.

1.14.6.1 Energy Band Structure

The minimum energy state in the conduction band occurs at the conduction band edge (E_c). Electrons in this energy state have zero kinetic energy. Electrons with kinetic energy occupy higher energy levels in the conduction band. The reverse is true for holes in valence band states.

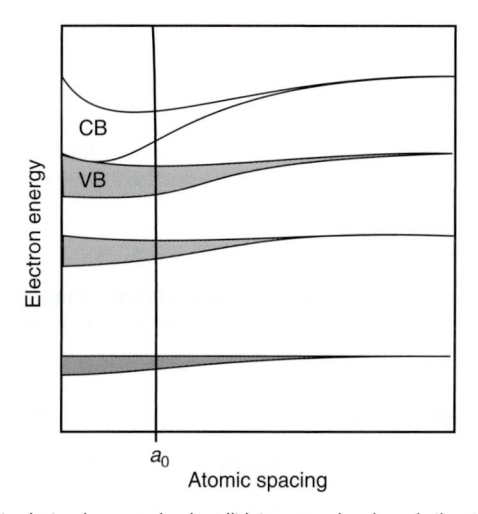

Figure 5 As atoms come together their discrete electronic energy levels split into energy bands. a_0 is the atomic spacing in a semiconductor crystal lattice.

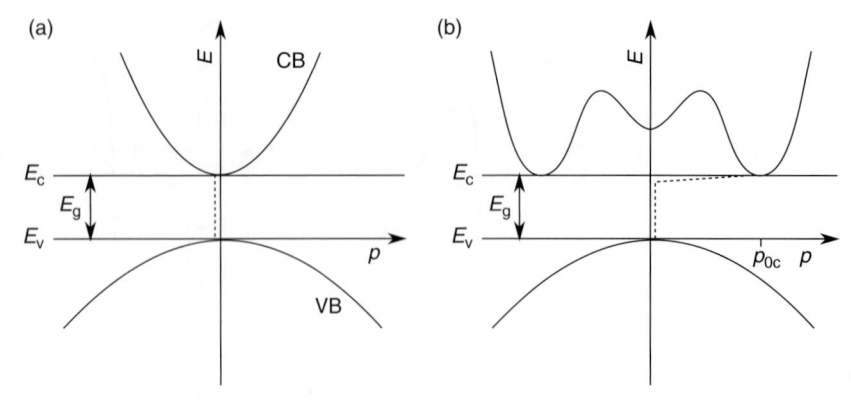

Figure 6 (a) Electronic band structure for a direct bandgap semiconductor. E_c and E_v both occur at crystal momentum $p = 0$. Photons with energy E_g can promote electrons into the conduction band without a change in momentum (dashed line). (b) Electronic band structure for an indirect bandgap semiconductor. E_c does not occur at the same crystal momentum as E_v. A change in momentum is required for a photon of energy E_g to promote an electron into the conduction band (dashed line). This extra momentum can come from a lattice phonon.

The energy (E) and momentum (p) of free electrons are described by the parabolic relationship shown in eqn [5], where m is the mass of the particle.

$$E = \frac{p^2}{2m} \quad [5]$$

In a crystalline structure, the motion of electrons and holes is affected by the periodic potentials around the atoms. An expression analogous to eqn [5] can be applied to carriers in a solid, accounting for the crystalline structure with an effective mass term [6]. This approximation is only valid close to the band edges. Equation [6] describes the energy of conduction band electrons with effective mass m_e^*. Equation [7] describes the energy of valence band holes with effective mass m_h^*.

$$E = E_c + \frac{p^2}{2m_e^*} \quad [6]$$

$$E = E_v - \frac{p^2}{2m_h^*} \quad [7]$$

Momentum is defined along the crystal axis of the structure and therefore it is possible for the kinetic energy minima, E_c and E_v, to occur at a nonzero momentum value relative to this axis. It is also possible for E_c and E_v to occur at different momenta relative to each other. Equations [6] and [7] describe electrons and holes in direct bandgap semiconductors, where E_c and E_v occur at the same value of momentum (**Figure 6(a)**). GaAs is an example of a direct bandgap material.

Indirect bandgap semiconductors have E_c and E_v at different momentum values (**Figure 6(b)**). The energy–momentum relations for electrons and holes in indirect materials are given by eqns [8] and [9], respectively. The momentum shift between the band edges and zero crystal momentum is given by p_{0c} and p_{0v}. Silicon and germanium are examples of indirect bandgap materials.

$$E = E_c + \frac{(p - p_{0c})^2}{2m_e^*} \quad [8]$$

$$E = E_v - \frac{(p - p_{0v})^2}{2m_h^*} \quad [9]$$

When a photon is absorbed in a semiconductor, promoting an electron from the conduction band into the valence band, momentum and energy must be conserved. Photons have effectively zero momentum with respect to electrons and therefore indirect transitions require momentum from another source. A lattice phonon can provide sufficient momentum to enable the transitions; however, the requirement of an additional particle reduces the likelihood of the interaction occurring. Photon absorption and emission from indirect transitions are suppressed relative to direct transitions.

1.14.6.2 Carrier Populations in Semiconductor Materials

The population of carriers in a semiconductor is described by a density of states function, which defines the electron states in the material system, and a distribution function, which determines the occupation of those states according to Fermi–Dirac statistics.

1.14.6.2.1 Density of electron states

The density of electron states $D_e(E)$ can be derived from the uncertainty principle, eqn [10], where h is Planck's constant.

$$\Delta p \Delta x = h \quad [10]$$

For two electron states to be distinct, they must differ in momentum and space by Δp and Δx, respectively; hence, the volume in momentum space (Δp^3) occupied by each state can be described as shown in eqn [11], where $V = \Delta x^3$.

$$\Delta p^3 = \frac{h^3}{\Delta x^3} = \frac{h^3}{V} \quad [11]$$

The number of electron states ($N_e(p)$) with momentum less than $|p|$ is given by dividing the volume of a sphere in phase space of radius $|p|$ by the volume occupied by each state, as shown in eqn [12]. An additional factor of 2 is included because two electrons of opposite spin can occupy each state.

$$N_e(p) = 2\frac{\left(\frac{4}{3}\pi|p|^3\right)}{h^3/V} \quad [12]$$

The parabolic energy–momentum relationship, eqn [6], is then substituted to give the number of electron states with energy less than E, eqn [13].

$$N_e(E) = 2\frac{\frac{4}{3}\pi(2m_e^*(E-E_c))^{3/2}}{h^3/V} = \frac{8\pi(2m_e^*)^{3/2}V}{3h^3}(E-E_c)^{3/2} \quad [13]$$

The density of electron states per unit energy interval in unit volume ($V = 1$) is determined by taking the derivative of $N_e(E)$ with respect to energy, eqn [14].

$$D_e(E) = 4\pi\left(\frac{2m_e^*}{h^2}\right)^{3/2}(E-E_c)^{1/2} \quad [14]$$

A similar equation can be derived for the density of hole states, eqn [15] [7].

$$D_h(E) = 4\pi\left(\frac{2m_h^*}{h^2}\right)^{3/2}(E_v-E)^{1/2} \quad [15]$$

1.14.6.2.2 Occupation of electron states

At absolute zero, electrons populate the lowest available energy levels, according to Pauli exclusion principle, with each state supporting two electrons of opposite spin. As the temperature increases, electrons acquire kinetic energy and are able to occupy higher energy levels. Electrons are fermions and as such the probability of an electron state being occupied is described by the Fermi–Dirac distribution, eqn [16]. Fermi level (E_f) is the energy at which half of all the states are occupied.

$$f_e(E, T, E_f) = \frac{1}{\exp[(E-E_f)/kT]+1} \quad [16]$$

A hole describes the absence of an electron and hence the distribution function of holes is given by eqn [17].

$$f_h(E, T, E_f) = 1 - f_e(E, T, E_f)$$
$$= \frac{1}{\exp[(E_f-E)/kT]+1} \quad [17]$$

1.14.6.2.3 Carrier density

Multiplying the Fermi–Dirac distribution by the density of electron states gives an expression for the density of electrons ($n_e(E, T, E_f)$) in the conduction band, eqn [18]. The density of holes in the valence band ($n_h(E, T, E_f)$) is similarly derived, eqn [19].

$$n_e(E, T, E_f) = D_e(E)f_e(E, T, E_f)$$
$$= 4\pi\left(\frac{2m_e^*}{h^2}\right)^{3/2}\frac{(E-E_c)^{1/2}}{\exp[(E-E_f)/kT]+1} \quad [18]$$

$$n_h(E, T, E_f) = D_h(E)f_h(E, T, E_f)$$
$$= 4\pi\left(\frac{2m_h^*}{h^2}\right)^{3/2}\frac{(E_v-E)^{1/2}}{\exp[(E_f-E)/kT]+1} \quad [19]$$

Figure 7 shows the density of states, the Fermi–Dirac distribution, and the density of carriers.

The total number of conduction band electrons is calculated by integrating ($n_e(E, T, E_f)$) with respect to energy over the energy range $E_c \to \infty$, eqn [20] [8]. To allow an analytical solution to this integration, the '+1' in the denominator of the Fermi function must be ignored. This is a valid approximation for nondegenerate semiconductors, for which $E_f < E_c - 3kT$ and carriers form an ideal gas. This approximation is valid for semiconductors at 300 K under 1 sun illumination. The approximation breaks down for devices under high concentration (>100 suns). The total number of holes in the conduction band is given by eqn [20].

$$n_e(T, E_f) = \int_{E_c}^{\infty} n_e(E, T, E_f) dE$$
$$= N_c \exp\left(-\frac{E_c-E_f}{kT}\right) \quad [20]$$

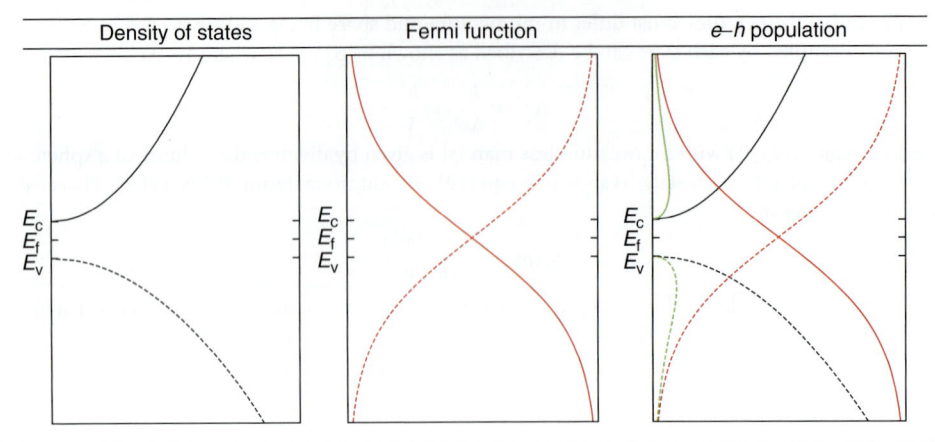

Figure 7 The electron population in the conduction band ($n_e(E, T, E_f)$) (green lines) is the product of density of electron states ($D_e(E)$) (black lines) and the Fermi–Dirac distribution ($f_e(E, T, E_f)$) (red lines). The hole population in the valence band is similarly defined. Solid lines refer to electrons and dotted lines refer to holes.

where

$$N_c = 2\left(\frac{2\pi m_e^* kT}{h^2}\right)^{3/2} \quad [21]$$

The total number of holes in the conduction band is given by eqn [22].

$$n_h(T, E_f) = \int_{E_v}^{\infty} n_h(E, T, E_f) dE$$
$$= N_v \exp\left(-\frac{E_f - E_v}{kT}\right) \quad [22]$$

where

$$N_v = 2\left(\frac{2\pi m_h^* kT}{h^2}\right)^{3/2} \quad [23]$$

The number of conduction band electrons and valence band holes is a function of temperature and Fermi level. Varying the temperature changes the shape of the Fermi distribution. Changing the Fermi level shifts the Fermi distribution in energy, without affecting the shape of the function. The Fermi distribution will be shifted in a semiconductor under illumination and also with the addition of impurity atoms to the semiconductor lattice.

1.14.6.3 Doping

Doping is the process of replacing atoms in a semiconductor lattice with impurity atoms with a different number of valence electrons (**Figure 8**). Donor impurity atoms have more valence electrons than necessary to bond with the host semiconductor. The impurity atom is bound to the lattice with strong covalent bonds fixing the position of the atom. Additional electrons are not required for bonding and therefore only experience a weak Coulomb attraction to the donor atom. This is easily overcome thermally

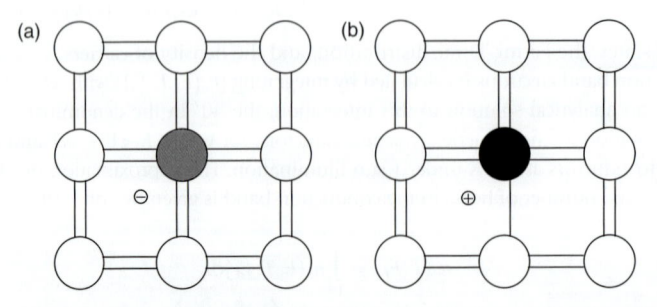

Figure 8 (a) A donor atom (gray) in a semiconductor lattice. The additional electron makes the material n-type. (b) An acceptor atom (black) in a semiconductor lattice. The electron vacancy makes the material p-type.

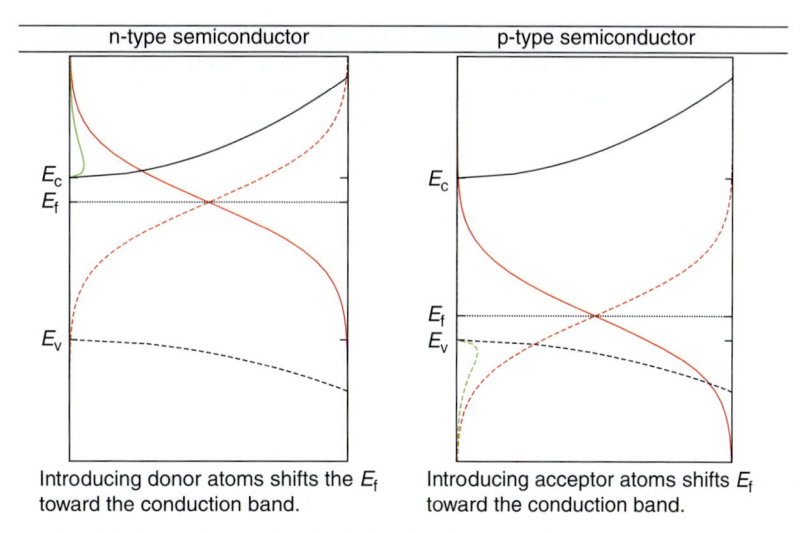

Figure 9 Density of states functions (black lines), Fermi–Dirac distributions (red lines), and the density of carriers (green lines) are shown for n-type and p-type doped semiconductors. Solid lines refer to electrons and dotted lines refer to holes.

and at 300 K, almost all donor atoms are positively ionized. A semiconductor doped in this way is called n-type as negative electrons are the principal charge carriers in this material. The increase in conduction band electron population is characterized by a shift in E_f toward the conduction band edge (**Figure 9**). Acceptor atoms have too few electrons to bond with the host semiconductor lattice. The impurity bond is completed by removing a valence electron from the surrounding structure, populating the valence band with additional holes. This is known as a p-type semiconductor as positively charged holes are the principal charge carriers. This increase in valence band hole population can be described by a shift in E_f toward the valence band edge (**Figure 9**).

1.14.6.4 Pn Junction

In order for a semiconductor to start behaving like a solar cell, the device requires some built-in resistive asymmetry to draw excited carriers into an electrical circuit. A pn junction is a diode formed from layers of oppositely doped semiconductor material that forces excited carriers to flow in one direction. When n-type and p-type semiconductor materials are brought together in a pn junction, the random thermal motion of the carriers allows them to diffuse across the junction along concentration gradients. This is a result of the greater electron population in the n-type semiconductor and the greater hole population in the p-type semiconductor. The impurity ions are fixed in the semiconductor lattice and so get left behind, creating an electric field across the junction. This field opposes the motion of the carriers, causing carriers to drift back across the junction. Equilibrium is achieved when diffusion and drift mechanisms balance, establishing an area of transition across the junction called the depletion region. E_f is constant across the junction under equilibrium conditions creating a potential step in conduction and valence band edges, referred to as built-in voltage. Over the depletion region, the gradient of carriers forms a smooth energy profile across the junction (**Figure 10**).

1.14.7 Generation and Recombination

Generation is the process of promoting an electron from the valence band into the conduction band, generating a hole in the valence band. The reverse process, in which a conduction band electron relaxes into the valence band, is called recombination.

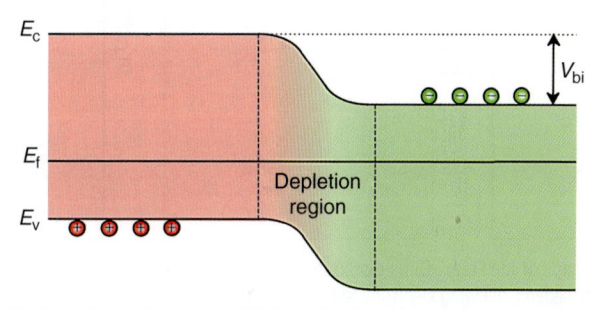

Figure 10 A pn junction in the dark is in thermal and chemical equilibrium. The Fermi levels of the p-type and n-type materials align, leaving a built-in voltage (V_{bi}) across the junction.

In a semiconductor, the energy required to excite an electron into the conduction band primarily can be derived from three main sources: phonons, carriers, and photons. During recombination, energy can be emitted via the same three interaction pathways. Phonon and carrier interactions are called nonradiative processes, whereas photon interactions are called radiative processes. Additional electronic states created by impurities and crystal defects can also act as generation and recombination centers.

1.14.7.1 Thermal Generation and Recombination

Thermal generation is the process of electron promotion via phonon interaction. Thermal energy in the lattice can be transferred to a valence band electron, exciting it into the conduction band, in a process called thermal generation. The reverse mechanism, in which electrons relax into lower energy states, returning energy to the lattice, is called thermal recombination. Fermi–Dirac statistics (eqn [16]) describe the occupation of electronic energy levels as a function of temperature (**Figure 11**). At absolute zero, $f_e(E, T, E_f)$ is a step function with no conduction band levels occupied. In this case, the semiconductor will behave as a perfect insulator as it has no charge carriers. At room temperature, the Fermi–Dirac distribution will only permit a small free carrier population and as such most intrinsic semiconductors will be highly electrically resistive. An increase in free carrier population created by an increase in temperature will allow the material to behave like a conductor. Increasing temperature increases the rate of thermal generation of electrons. The rate of thermal recombination also increases, maintaining thermal and electrochemical equilibrium between the carrier population and the lattice.

The intrinsic carrier density (n_i) gives the density of thermally promoted electrons in the conduction band of a nondoped semiconductor, eqn [24]. This must equal the number of thermally generated valence band holes.

$$n_i^2 = n_e(T, E_f) n_h(T, E_f)$$
$$= N_c N_v \exp\left(\frac{-E_g}{kT}\right) \quad [24]$$

1.14.7.2 Radiative Generation and Recombination

A photon incident on a semiconductor with energy greater than E_g can promote an electron into the conduction band, generating a hole in the valence band. This process is called radiative generation. Conduction band electrons can release energy as a photon and return to the valence band, radiatively recombining with holes. Three radiative generation and recombination mechanisms must be considered in a semiconductor: stimulated absorption, stimulated emission, and spontaneous emission. A two-level model is used to illustrate these mechanisms in **Figure 12**.

Both stimulated processes rely on incident photons and so the rate with which these occur is dependent on the incident spectrum. Stimulated absorption will occur relatively frequently under normal solar cell operating conditions because it can result from any photon with $E > E_g$ and hence can be induced by a large component of the solar spectrum. The thermalization of excited carriers means that emission processes are approximately monochromatic and therefore stimulated emission can only be achieved with an incident photon of energy $\sim E_g$, which accounts for a very small component of the solar spectrum. Spontaneous emission is therefore the dominant radiative recombination mechanism.

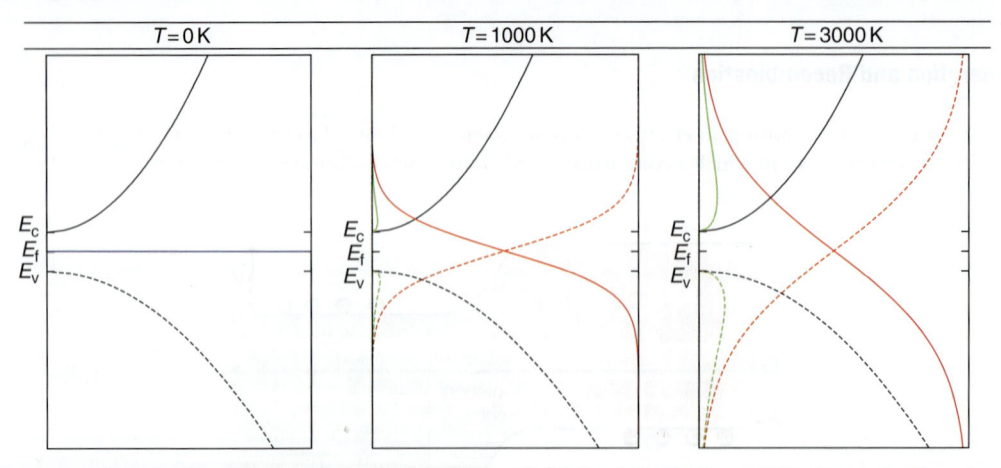

Figure 11 Temperature describes the shape of the Fermi–Dirac distribution. At 0 K, the electron–hole population is described by a step function. With increasing temperature, the distribution broadens, allowing electrons to populate the conduction band and holes to population the valence band. E_f is not temperature dependent. Black lines show density of states functions, red lines show Fermi–Dirac distributions, and green lines show the density of carriers. Solid lines refer to electrons and dotted lines refer to holes.

Stimulated absorption	Stimulated emission	Spontaneous emission
A photon with energy $E2-E1$ is absorbed, promoting an electron from state 1 to state 2.	A photon with energy $E2-E1$ stimulates an electron to relax from state 2 into state 1, releasing its energy as a photon of the same energy.	An electron spontaneously relaxes from state 2 to state 1, releasing its energy as a photon of energy $E2-E1$.
$f_{ph}f_1(1-f_2)$	$f_{ph}f_2(1-f_1)$	$f_2(1-f_1)$

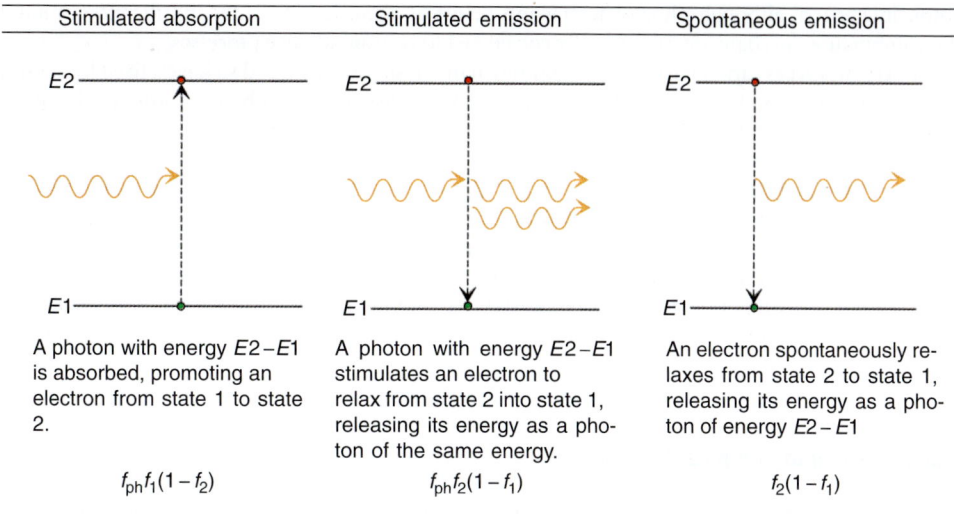

Figure 12 Mechanisms for radiative generation and recombination of electron–hole pairs with corresponding probabilities. f_{ph} is the probability of a photon existing. f_1 is the probability that level 1 is occupied by an electron. f_2 is the probability that level 2 is occupied by an electron.

1.14.7.3 Carrier–Carrier Generation and Recombination

Impact ionization is a carrier–carrier scattering process that promotes an electron into the conduction band (**Figure 13(a)**). In this process, a high-energy conduction band electron exchanges energy and momentum with a low-energy valence band electron, producing two low-energy conduction band electrons. The electron population does not acquire any additional energy despite an extra electron being promoted into the conduction band. This process occurs with a very low probability because it requires a high-energy conduction band electron, which is unlikely to exist as a result of thermal generation. The reverse process is called Auger recombination (**Figure 13(b)**), where two low-energy conduction band electrons interact. One electron recombines with a valence band hole, transferring energy and momentum to the other electron, exciting it high into the conduction band. Following Auger recombination, the remaining high-energy conduction band electron will experience rapid thermalization, returning it to the conduction band edge, and as such, energy is lost from the carrier population as heat. The probability with which carrier–carrier interaction mechanisms occur is dependent on the carrier density. Auger processes can become a significant source of loss in highly doped materials or at high temperature. Carrier–carrier processes have a greater effect in indirect bandgap semiconductors, such as silicon, where radiative mechanisms are suppressed.

1.14.7.4 Impurity and Surface Generation and Recombination

In real-world solar cells, the semiconductor lattice cannot be produced perfectly uniformly without defects. Impurities are unavoidably introduced into the structure during crystal growth. The crystal lattice of a real-world device will not be infinite in extent, and additional impurities and broken bonds are concentrated at surfaces and material interfaces. These impurities and defects can create additional electronic states in the forbidden energy region of the semiconductor. Carriers can access these states via

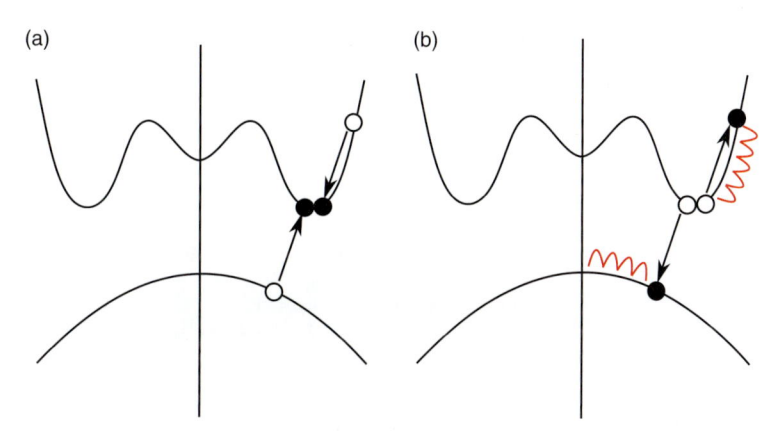

Figure 13 (a) Impact ionization and (b) Auger recombination are carrier–carrier generation and recombination mechanisms, respectively. Electrons before interaction (white dots) and electrons after interaction (black dots) are shown along with thermalization steps (red lines).

phonon or photon interaction, although phonon interaction occurs at a much faster rate, and therefore impurity and surface generation and recombination mechanisms are generally considered to be nonradiative processes.

Impurity and defect states act as carrier traps. They are bound in the crystal structure and so have a fixed location. Any free carrier caught in this state is then also fixed in location until either it can be released thermally or a carrier of the opposite polarity is captured into the same state, forcing recombination. Trap states reduce device efficiency in two ways: acting as recombination centers and impeding carrier transport.

In the absence of any radiative generation, trap state generation and recombination are equal. The rate at which electrons are captured in impurity states is dependent on the density of electrons in the conduction band and the density of holes in the impurity states. The rate of generation, however, only depends on the density of electrons in the impurity states. Under illumination, the electron density of the conduction band increases and trap state recombination mechanisms occur at a faster rate than the competing generation processes. Recombination occurring via impurity states is often referred to as Shockley–Read–Hall [9] recombination, and in many real-world devices, this is the dominant recombination mechanism.

1.14.8 Thermal Energy into Chemical Energy

Instantaneously after stimulated absorption occurs, carriers have an energy distribution that is described by that of the incident spectrum. Excited carriers rapidly interact with lattice phonons and the carrier populations cool to the band edges, as they form distributions with the minimum free energy. For most realistic PV operating conditions, thermalization occurs at a much faster rate than any band-to-band transition; hence, under constant illumination, the excited carriers form steady-state populations in thermal equilibrium with the lattice. The shape of the Fermi–Dirac distribution is determined by the temperature of the carrier population. The value of the Fermi level is described by the steady-state carrier density. In a solar cell under constant illumination, electron and hole populations are described by a Fermi–Dirac distribution at room temperature, although the two distributions have separate Fermi levels [10].

The density of the electron and hole populations is determined by the relative rates of the generation and recombination processes. Under solar illumination, the rate of generation exceeds that of recombination and net generation occurs. This results in an increase in electron density in the conduction band, which causes the Fermi level describing the electron population (E_{fc}) to shift toward the conduction band edge. A corresponding increase in the hole density in the valence band causes the Fermi level describing the hole population (E_{fv}) to shift toward the valence band edge. The separation between E_{fc} and E_{fv} is the chemical potential (μ) generated in the device per electron–hole pair, eqn [25].

$$\mu = E_{fc} - E_{fv} = eV \qquad [25]$$

The chemical potential describes the entropy free energy that can be extracted as useful electrical work and that an electron–hole pair can deliver to a load [11] (**Figure 14**). The chemical potential is given by the product of electron charge (e) and the voltage (V) across the device. Illuminating a semiconductor is often referred to as optical biasing.

The increase in carrier density that derives from net generation in a device will also result in an increase in spontaneous emission and trap state recombination as the density of the excited state carrier population increases. When no current is extracted (open circuit) and the rate of stimulated absorption is equal to the sum of spontaneous emission and trap state recombination, a steady-state carrier population will be established under constant illumination.

An expression for device open circuit voltage, as a function of absorbed photons ($n_{ph}(E > E_g)$), can be derived from the carrier population densities. The total number of conduction band electrons and valence band holes in a device under illumination is given by eqns [26] and [27]. The expressions are analogous to eqns [20] and [22] but allow electron and hole Fermi levels to take separate values.

$$n_e(T, E_{fc}) = N_c \exp\left(-\frac{E_c - E_{fc}}{kT}\right) \qquad [26]$$

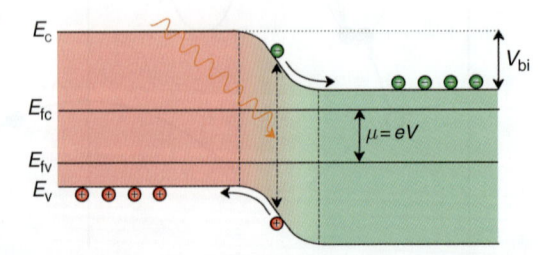

Figure 14 A pn junction under illumination is no longer in chemical equilibrium. V_{bi} draws photo-excited carriers to their respective terminals causing a splitting of electron and hole quasi-Fermi levels. Chemical potential, proportional to incident photon flux, develops across the device.

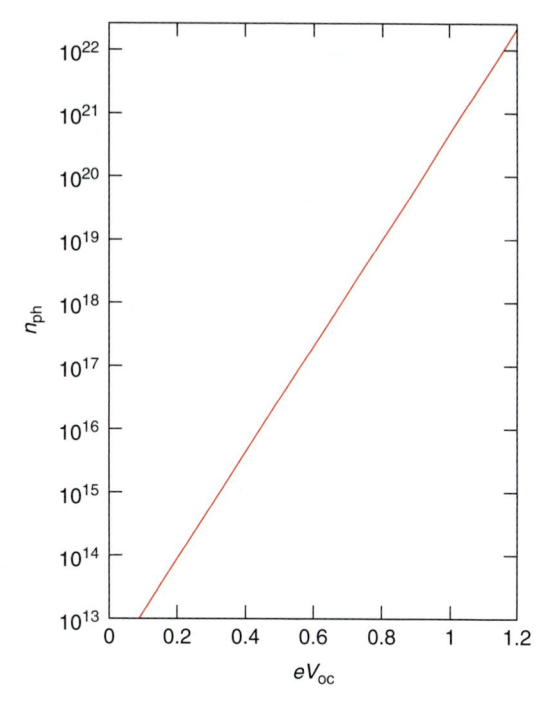

Figure 15 The open circuit voltage of an idealized device is logarithmically dependent on the incident photon flux.

$$n_h(T, E_{fv}) = N_v \exp\left(-\frac{E_{fv} - E_v}{kT}\right) \qquad [27]$$

The product of $n_e(T, E_{fc})$ and $n_h(T, E_{fv})$ is a function of μ, eqn [28].

$$n_e(T, E_{fc})n_h(T, E_{fv}) = N_c N_v \exp\left(-\frac{E_g}{kT_c}\right)\exp\left(\frac{E_{fc} - E_{fv}}{kT}\right)$$
$$= n_i^2 \exp\left(\frac{\mu}{kT}\right) \qquad [28]$$

The sum of absorbed photons ($n_{ph}(E > E_g)$) and thermally generated pairs (n_i), all squared, is given by the product of electron number and hole number, eqn [29].

$$(n_{ph}(E > E_g) + n_i)^2 = n_e(T, E_{fc})n_h(T, E_{fv}) \qquad [29]$$

Substituting this expression into eqn [28] provides eqn [30]. This relationship is illustrated in **Figure 15**.

$$eV_{oc} = 2kT \ln\left(\frac{n_{ph}(E > E_g) + n_i}{n_i}\right) \qquad [30]$$

1.14.8.1 Current Extraction

When a finite load resistance is placed across the terminals of an illuminated solar cell, some current will flow. As carriers are extracted, the density of the steady-state carrier populations is reduced and hence the associated chemical potential is also reduced. For zero load resistance, the device is operating at short circuit and all photo-generated carriers are extracted. Under this condition, the steady-state carrier density is the same as for a device in the dark and hence the chemical potential of the electron and hole populations is zero. **Figure 16** shows the effect of current extraction on the electron and hole populations and quasi-Fermi-level splitting.

1.14.9 Generalized Planck

The generalized Planck equation is an adaptation of Planck's law of radiation, which can be used to describe photon emission from a carrier population with chemical potential. The emitted photon population is in thermal and chemical equilibrium with the steady-state electron and hole populations and therefore also has a chemical potential associated with it. The generalized Planck equation is derived by considering the density of photon states in the body $dN_{ph}(E)/dE$ and the probability that those states are occupied ($f_{ph}(E, T)$). A geometrical factor is also required to describe the angular emission out of the surface of the body [12].

$R_L = 0$	$0 < R_L < \infty$	$R_L = \infty$
All photo-generated carriers pass through the load and only the intrinsic thermal population remains.	Not all carriers pass through the load; hence, there is a splitting of quasi-Fermi levels.	No carriers can pass through the load; hence, the splitting of quasi-Fermi levels is maximized.

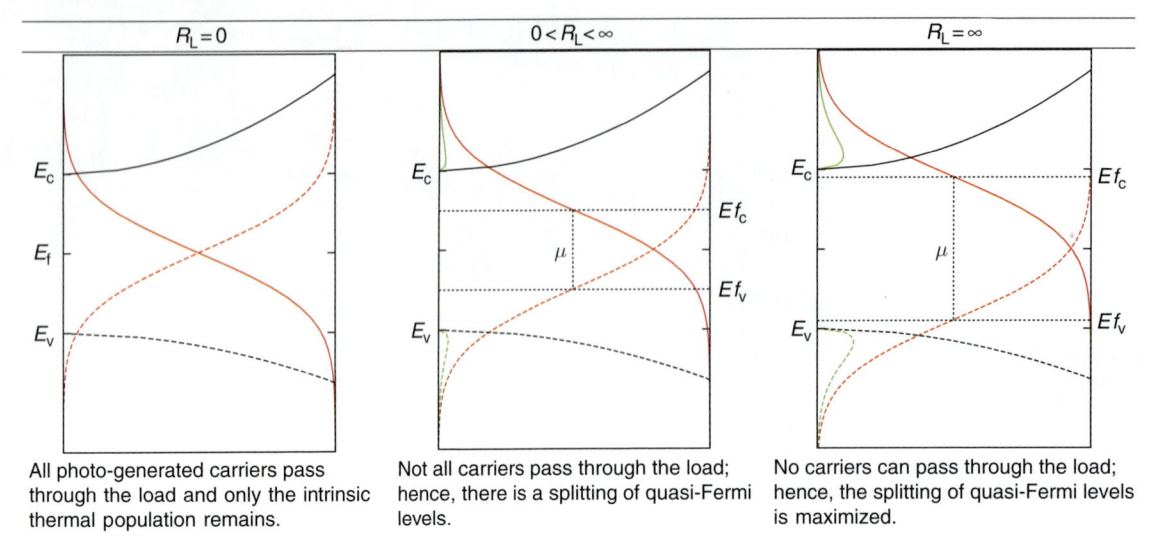

Figure 16 The load resistance connecting the two terminals of a solar cell determines the position along the current–voltage characteristic at which a device operates. This figure shows density of states functions (black lines), Fermi–Dirac distributions (red lines), and the steady-state carrier populations (green lines) for $R_L = 0$ (short-circuit), $0 < R_L < \infty$ (power-producing), and $R_L = \infty$ (open circuit) operating conditions. Solid lines refer to electrons and dotted lines refer to holes.

1.14.9.1 Density of Photon States

The density of photon states $D_{ph}(E)$ can be derived from the uncertainty principle, analogous to $D_e(E)$. The number of electron states $N_{ph}(p)$ in a unit sphere in phase space is the same as for electron states, eqn [31].

$$N_{ph}(p) = N_e(p) \quad [31]$$

Photon energy and momentum are related by the expression shown in eqn [32], allowing conversion between momentum and energy space.

$$E = pc \quad [32]$$

Equation [32] is substituted into eqn [12] to give the number of photon states with energy less than E in volume V, eqn [33].

$$N_{ph}(E) = 2 \frac{\left(\frac{4}{3}\pi \frac{E^3}{c^3}\right)}{h^3/V} = \frac{8\pi E^3 V}{3c^3 h^3} \quad [33]$$

The density of photon states per unit energy interval is found by taking the derivative of $N_{ph}(E)$, with respect to energy, eqn [34].

$$\frac{dN_{ph}(E)}{dE} = \frac{8\pi E^2 V}{c^3 h^3} \quad [34]$$

1.14.9.2 Geometrical Factor

Black and gray bodies are radial emitters; however, often only a limited range of emission angles will be relevant to the calculation. In the case of solar radiation, only light emitted out of the surface of the Sun into a small cone subtended by the solar disk will reach a solar cell on the surface of the Earth. A further geometrical factor is required to calculate the photon flux escaping the surface of the body into the relevant angular range.

The solid angle of a sphere in steradians (sr) is 4π and therefore the fraction of total radiation emitted from a body into solid angle $d\omega$ is given by $d\omega/4\pi$. Photons will travel a distance $c\,dt$ in a time interval dt, where c is the speed of light in vacuum. Photons emitted at angle θ from the normal, out of surface element dS, will be generated in volume $V = c\,dt\cos\theta\,dS$ of the body (**Figure 17**).

Substituting this value of V into eqn [34] and multiplying by $d\omega/4\pi$ will give an expression for the density of photon states per unit energy interval, emitted through surface element dS into solid angle $d\omega$ in time interval dt (eqn [35]).

$$\frac{dN_{ph}(E,\omega)}{dE} = \frac{8\pi E^2}{c^3 h^3} c\,dt\,\cos\theta\,dS\,\frac{d\omega}{4\pi}$$

$$= \frac{2E^2}{c^2 h^3}\cos\theta\,d\omega\,dS\,dt \quad [35]$$

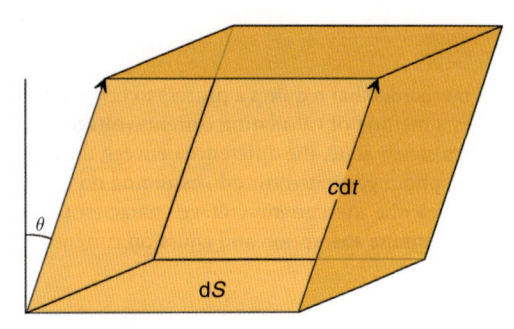

Figure 17 Photons emitted through a surface dS, in time dt, at angle θ to the normal of the surface, originating from a blackbody volume $V = c\,\mathrm{d}t\cos\theta\,\mathrm{d}S$.

Integrating over the relevant solid angle and taking dt = dS = 1 gives an expression for the flux of photon states emitted from a body per unit surface area per unit energy interval, eqn [36].

$$D_{\mathrm{ph}}(E,\Omega) = \frac{2\Omega}{c^2 h^3} E^2 \qquad [36]$$

Emission into a hemisphere is described by $\Omega_{\mathrm{hemi}} = \pi$. This can be used to describe emission from a solar cell. The solid angle subtended by the Sun is given by $\Omega_S = 6.8 \times 10^{-5}$.

1.14.9.3 Occupation of Photon States

Photons are bosons and therefore their distribution is described with Bose–Einstein statistics. The Bose–Einstein distribution, eqn [37], gives the probability of a photon state being occupied. T is the temperature of the emitting body and k is Boltzmann's constant.

$$f_{\mathrm{ph}}(E,T) = \frac{1}{\exp[E/kT] - 1} \qquad [37]$$

The occupation of photon states in a population with nonzero chemical potential ($f_{\mathrm{ph}}(E, T, \mu)$) is calculated by considering generation and recombination mechanisms occurring in the emitting body [13]. Equation [38] shows the probability (R) with which any radiative process occurs. This is the sum of the probabilities of each individual radiative process, shown in **Figure 12**.

$$R = f_{\mathrm{ph}} f_1 (1-f_2) + f_{\mathrm{ph}} f_2 (1-f_1) + f_2(1-f_1) \qquad [38]$$

The rate of change to $f_{\mathrm{ph}}(E, T, \mu)$ resulting from radiative generation and recombination mechanisms is given by eqn [39], where C is a constant scaling factor. When temperature and chemical potential are constant, the photon population forms a steady state and hence this rate of change is zero.

$$\frac{\mathrm{d}f_{\mathrm{ph}}(E,T,\mu)}{\mathrm{d}t} = CR = 0 \qquad [39]$$

An expression for photon occupation probability in a body with nonzero chemical potential follows, eqn [40].

$$f_{\mathrm{ph}}(E,T,\mu) = \frac{1}{\frac{f_1(1-f_2)}{f_2(1-f_1)} - 1}$$

$$= \frac{1}{\exp\left(\frac{E-\mu}{kT}\right) - 1} \qquad [40]$$

Electron and hole occupation probabilities, f_2 and f_1, are described by eqns [16] and [17], respectively. The photon flux ($n_{\mathrm{ph}}(E, T, \mu, \Omega)$) emitted from a black or gray body per unit energy interval is the product of available photon states, eqn [36], the probability of their occupation, eqn [40], and the emissivity of the material, $\varepsilon(E)$. This expression is called the generalized Planck, eqn [41].

$$n_{\mathrm{ph}}(E,T,\mu,\Omega) = \varepsilon(E)\frac{2\Omega}{c^2 h^3} \frac{E^2}{\exp[(E-\mu)/kT] - 1} \qquad [41]$$

The generalized Planck can be used to describe the Sun's emission using $\varepsilon(E) = 1$, $\mu = 0$, and $\Omega = 6.8 \times 10^{-5}$, corresponding to eqn [3]. In the case of emission from a solar cell, $\varepsilon(E)$ can be approximately described by a step function with the emission threshold at E_g, $\mu = eV$, and emission is over a hemisphere giving $\Omega = \pi$.

1.14.10 Detailed Balance

Detailed balance is a principle of statistical mechanics that requires a process to occur at the same rate as the reverse process when a system is in equilibrium. This basis provides a method of calculating current–voltage characteristics for a device by balancing the relative rates of absorption and emission. In a steady state, the difference between the number of photons absorbed by the device and the number of photons emitted gives the photo-generated current, assuming no trap state recombination occurs. The method can be evaluated with real spectral data to describe the current–voltage characteristic of a real-world device. Alternatively, the generalized Planck equation can be used to determine absorption and emission currents, allowing ultimate solar conversion limits of idealized devices to be calculated.

1.14.10.1 Shockley–Queisser Limiting Efficiency

The Shockley–Queisser limiting efficiency is derived using a detailed balance, generalized Planck formalism, and is the ultimate conversion efficiency achievable in a single-junction device, under 1 sun illumination [14]. The difference between the number of photons absorbed by the device, $n_{ph}(E, T_S, \mu = 0, \Omega_S)$, and the number of photons emitted, $n_{ph}(E, T_C, \mu, \Omega_C)$, integrated over all photon energies, gives the number of carriers contributing to the photo-generated current, eqn [42]. Multiplying by the electron charge converts carrier number into current.

$$J = e\int_0^\infty [n_{ph}(E, T_S, \mu = 0, \Omega_S) - n_{ph}(E, T_C, \mu, \Omega_C)]dE$$
$$= e\int_0^\infty \left[a(E)\left(\frac{2\Omega_S}{c^2 h^3}\right) \frac{E^2}{\exp[E/kT_S] - 1} - \varepsilon(E)\left(\frac{2\Omega_C}{c^2 h^3}\right) \frac{E^2}{\exp[(E-\mu)/kT_C] - 1} \right] dE \quad [42]$$

$a(E)$ and $\varepsilon(E)$ can be approximated as a step function, eqn [43]. This is incorporated into eqn [42] by changing the lower limit of integration to E_g, as shown in eqn [44].

$$a(E) = \varepsilon(E) = \begin{cases} 0 & E < E_g \\ 1 & E \geq E_g \end{cases} \quad [43]$$

$$J = e\int_{E_g}^\infty \left[\left(\frac{2\Omega_S}{c^2 h^3}\right) \frac{E^2}{\exp[E/kT_S] - 1} - \left(\frac{2\Omega_C}{c^2 h^3}\right) \frac{E^2}{\exp[(E-\mu)/kT_C] - 1} \right] dE \quad [44]$$

Electrical power that can be extracted from the device is the product of current and voltage; the efficiency of the device is determined by dividing output power by the total power in the incident solar spectrum (P_{in}), eqn [45].

$$\eta = \frac{JV}{P_{in}} \quad [45]$$

Figure 18 shows current–voltage characteristics for idealized devices with a range of E_g. The power efficiency of each device is also shown; $E_g = 1.31$ eV provides the maximum device efficiency of 31%, at the optimal operating voltage. Devices with a lower E_g absorb more of the solar spectrum and hence have a larger J_{sc}; however, more energy is dissipated in the lattice as heat giving lower V_{oc}. Devices with a higher E_g have a lower J_{sc} as more of the solar spectrum is transmitted; however, it will have a higher V_{oc} because excited carriers retain more of their energy.

1.14.10.1.1 Shockley–Queisser assumptions
Several assumptions have been made in deriving the Shockley–Queisser limit:

1. The solar cell has a step-like absorption and emission profile and 100% of incident photons with energy above E_g are absorbed. This would only occur in an infinitely thick device because light incident on an absorber is attenuated exponentially with penetration depth.
2. Each incident photon produces a single electron–hole pair. No impact ionization or Auger recombination occurs in the device. This is a reasonable assumption for many real-world devices. However, Auger recombination can be a significant loss mechanism in indirect bandgap materials such as silicon.
3. The crystal is perfect and infinite, with no trap states and therefore no impurity of surface recombination.

1.14.10.1.2 Photon recycling
In a solar cell photon emission necessarily occurs, according to the generalized Planck equation. Some of the emitted photons will escape through the surface of the device and therefore cannot contribute to the extracted current. However, some of the emitted phonons will be reabsorbed in the device, generating another electron–hole pair. This reabsorption process is known as photon recycling and can provide a significant efficiency enhancement in a real-world device.

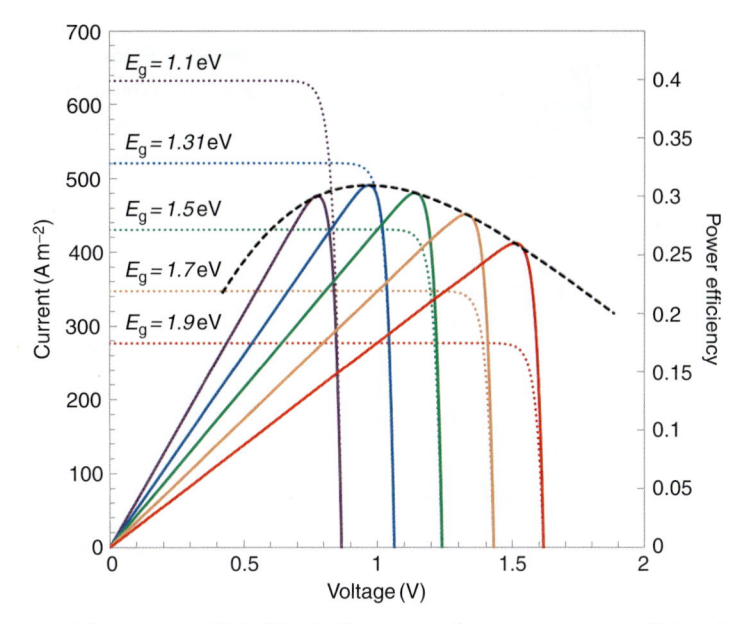

Figure 18 Current–voltage characteristics are shown (dotted lines) with corresponding power conversion efficiency (solid lines) for devices with E_g = 1.1, 1.31, 1.5, 1.7, and 1.9 eV. The dashed line indicates maximum power conversion efficiency and shows that E_g = 1.31 eV is optimal for the given conditions. Solar and cell temperatures are taken to be 6000 and 300 K, respectively.

The Shockley–Queisser limiting efficiency model includes the effects of photon recycling [15]. The geometric factor used in deriving the generalized Planck only includes photons exiting the surface of the body. All photon recycling occurring below the surface of the cell is therefore taken into account in this model.

1.14.10.2 Real-World Devices

A detailed balance approach can be used to model device current–voltage characteristics more realistically, where the Shockley–Queisser approximations are not made. The path of incident photons can be calculated and the probability of each interaction process considered. Device thickness, absorption and emission coefficients, refractive indices, parasitic resistances, and the rates of nonradiative processes are all key variables in such a model. Photon recycling must also be taken into account separately. This additional complexity allows a model to describe solar cell behavior more realistically but it will never result in efficiency exceeding the Shockley–Queisser limit.

1.14.11 Intrinsic Loss Mechanisms in Solar Cells

The Shockley–Queisser efficiency limit of 31% is the ultimate theoretical limit for PV conversion in a single-junction device under 1 sun illumination. The Shockley–Queisser model describes solar conversion in a perfect physical system in which all avoidable losses are eliminated. Loss mechanisms ignored in this model are here referred to as extrinsic losses.

Auger recombination is unavoidable in certain material systems; however, it is not included in the detailed balance model and it is considered to be an extrinsic loss mechanism because the rate at which Auger recombination occurs varies with different material systems and operating conditions. Auger recombination is a significant loss mechanism in some materials under certain operating conditions; however, materials with a large direct bandgap under 1 sun illumination will be dominated by other recombination mechanisms, and in the ultimate limit, this carrier–carrier process will occur at a negligibly slow rate. When considering the ultimate limit for PV conversion in a single-junction device under 1 sun illumination, it is therefore inappropriate to consider Auger effects.

The loss mechanisms leading to the Shockley–Queisser limiting efficiency are called intrinsic losses. These losses are fundamentally unavoidable in single-junction devices under 1 sun illumination. There are five intrinsic loss processes. Both below E_g loss and emission loss result in a reduction in current, whereas thermalization loss, Carnot loss, and Boltzmann loss limit device voltage. **Figure 19** illustrates the effect of each loss mechanism on the optimal operating current and voltage, dictating the maximum power output of the device. **Figure 20** shows the maximum power output and intrinsic loss mechanisms accounting for all incident radiation [16].

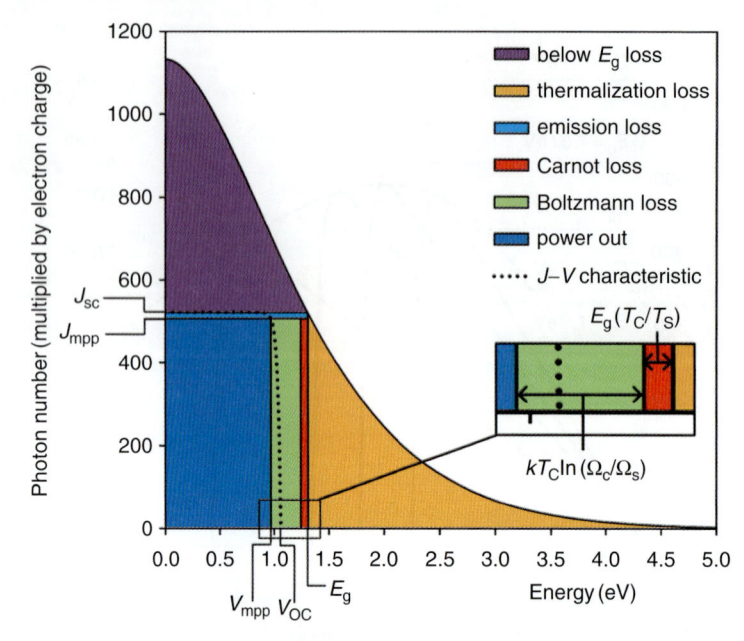

Figure 19 Intrinsic loss mechanisms are shown for a Shockley–Queisser solar cell with $E_g = 1.31$ eV, under 1 sun illumination. The outer curve is given by the number of incident solar photons with energy more than or equal to the x-axis value; hence, the total area of the shaded region describes the power of the incident solar spectrum. The power sacrificed to different intrinsic loss mechanisms is given by the areas of the different shaded regions. Photon number (y-axis) is multiplied by electron charge and energy (x-axis) is expressed in units of eV to allow a current–voltage curve for this idealized device to be superimposed on the plot. Intrinsic loss mechanisms can then be defined as either current limiting or voltage limiting. This plot shows that both emission loss and below E_g loss reduce J_{mpp}, whereas Carnot loss, Boltzmann loss, and thermalization loss all reduce V_{mpp}. Changing E_g moves the J_{sc}–V_{oc} point along the outer curve, changing the relative significance of the different intrinsic loss mechanisms [16].

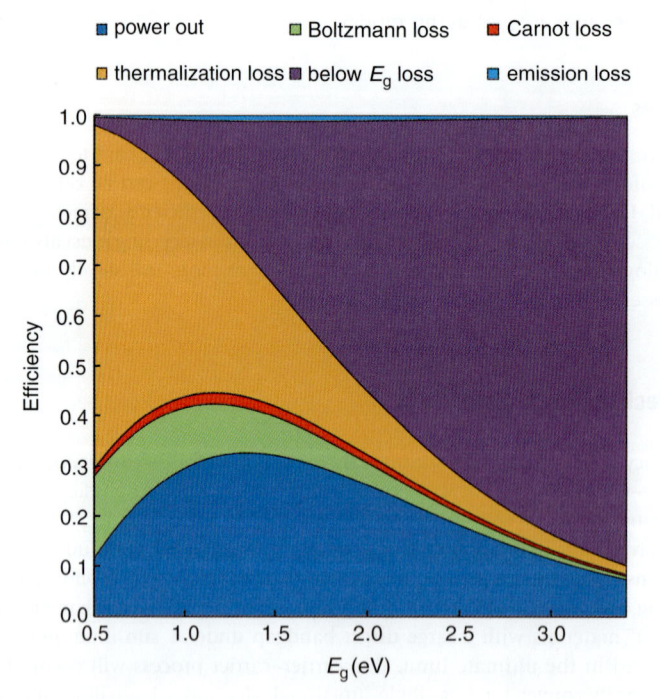

Figure 20 Intrinsic loss mechanisms and extracted electrical work cumulatively account for all incident solar radiation, demonstrating that intrinsic loss mechanisms lead to fundamental limiting efficiency [16].

1.14.11.1 Below E_g Loss

Only photons with energy above the bandgap of the semiconductor will have sufficient energy to excite an electron from the valence band into the conduction band. In this idealized model, all photons with sufficient energy will be absorbed, and other photons are transmitted and will not contribute to the useful power output. Below E_g loss derives from the spectral mismatch between the broad solar spectrum and the single threshold absorption of a semiconductor device. This loss mechanism reduces the number of incident photons able to induce stimulated absorption. The first term in eqn [44] describes stimulated absorption in the device. In a higher bandgap material, the range of integration will be reduced as will be the available current.

1.14.11.2 Emission Loss

Spontaneous emission in a solar cell is described by the second term in eqn [44]. This emission is described by the device temperature and the voltage across the device. The radiative recombination of carriers competes with stimulated absorption and therefore reduces the available current. In a device under 1 sun illumination, at room temperature, emission loss is approximately zero in a device under short-circuit conditions. As load resistance increases and the device moves toward optimal operating voltage, emission loss increases.

1.14.11.3 Thermalization

Similarly to below E_g loss, thermalization loss derives from the spectral mismatch between the solar spectrum and the semiconductor absorption profile. Following photo-generation, excited carriers rapidly interact with lattice phonons, losing energy as heat to the surroundings. Thermalization occurs at a much faster rate than any radiative process in the solar cell and therefore, under constant illumination, steady-state electron and hole populations are in thermal equilibrium with the lattice. Effectively all photon energy above the bandgap of the material is lost as heat. Thermalization loss reduces the free energy available per carrier and therefore is a voltage loss mechanism. It is the dominant loss mechanism in many real-world devices. Without thermalization, carriers would remain hot and the device would behave much like a solar thermal heat engine, with heat energy rather than chemical energy driving a load.

1.14.11.4 Carnot Loss

As thermalization takes place, the electron and hole populations acquire chemical energy. The shape of the cooled carrier distribution is described by the lattice temperature, but the number of carriers in that distribution is much higher because of photo-generation, leading to quasi-Fermi-level splitting. The efficiency with which thermal energy is transferred into chemical energy can be derived from eqn [45].

The maximum efficiency of a solar cell is described by two independent variables: the bandgap of the device and the voltage at which the device is operated. Therefore, the Shockley–Queisser efficiency limit can be derived by evaluating two partial differential equations (eqns [46] and [47]).

$$\left(\frac{\partial \eta}{\partial E_g}\right)_V = 0 \qquad [46]$$

$$\left(\frac{\partial \eta}{\partial V}\right)_{E_g} = 0 \qquad [47]$$

Equation [46] can be solved analytically by neglecting the '−1' in the denominator of eqn [44]. This approximation is valid for realistic bandgaps ($E_g > 0.5$).

$$eV_{mpp} = E_g\left(1 - \frac{T_C}{T_S}\right) - T_C k \ln\left(\frac{\Omega_C}{\Omega_S}\right) \qquad [48]$$

Once carriers are fully thermalized with the lattice, they have energy equal to the bandgap of the semiconductor; however, the free energy per carrier that can be extracted as useful work is lower. The free energy is described by the chemical potential of the carrier populations, eqn [48].

Equation [48] shows that the optimal operating voltage is described by two entropic terms. The first term of eqn [48] is referred to as Carnot factor [17] because it takes the form of Carnot's equation, which describes the work that can be extracted when energy is transferred from a hot source to a cold sink. As the carrier population cools, thermal energy is transferred into entropy free chemical energy, which can be extracted as useful electrical work. In a lattice at 0 K, all thermal energy will be transferred in this way; however, real-world cells will have some finite temperature and therefore not all thermal energy can be converted. The reduction in free energy available per carrier as a result of incomplete thermalization is described by the Carnot factor. In a colder lattice, more thermal energy is transferred into chemical energy, making colder devices fundamentally more efficient solar converters.

1.14.11.5 Boltzmann Loss

The second term in eqn [48] is referred to as the Boltzmann factor because it takes the form of Boltzmann's equation describing entropy generation with the increased occupancy of available states. Boltzmann loss derives from the mismatch between the solid angle of absorption (Ω_S) and the solid angle of emission (Ω_C). Photons are absorbed through the solid angle subtended by the solar disk, $\Omega_S = 6.8 \times 10^{-5}$. By contrast, emission from the cell is over a hemisphere, $\Omega_C = \pi$ (**Figure 21**). This irreversible expansion of photon modes generates entropy, further reducing the free energy available per carrier.

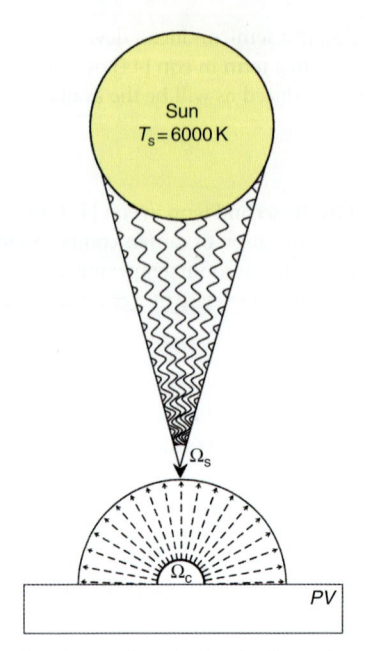

Figure 21 Solar radiation described by $T_S = 6000$ K and $\mu = 0$ (wavy lines) is absorbed in a solar cell through solid angle $\Omega_S = 6.8 \times 10^{-5}$. Emission from the cell is over a hemisphere ($\Omega_C = \pi$) and is characterized by $T_C = 300$ K and $\mu = eV_{mpp}$ (dashed lines).

This mismatch means that there are more photon states allowing spontaneous emission than those allowing stimulated absorption. Under constant illumination, carriers will form a steady-state population in thermal equilibrium with the lattice. The number of carriers in this population is determined by the relative rates of photo-generation, current extraction, and photo-recombination. The solid angle mismatch favors recombination, reducing the carrier population and therefore reducing the quasi-Fermi-level splitting and the resulting carrier chemical potential.

Lenses and mirrors can be used to focus the light onto the solar cell, expanding the solid angle of absorption. This increases the number of photon states available for stimulated absorption. Equally, novel cell structuring or sophisticated cell coatings can be used to restrict the angle of emission, reducing the recombination rate. Both methods have the effect of enabling a larger steady-state carrier population, increasing the free energy available per carrier.

1.14.12 Exceeding the Shockley–Queisser Limiting Efficiency

While the Shockley–Queisser limiting efficiency is the fundamental limit for solar conversion in a single-junction device under 1 sun illumination, it is far from the ultimate limit for any method of solar conversion. Devices can be designed to exceed the Shockley–Queisser limit by accessing the five intrinsic loss mechanisms. Solar cells exceeding this limit are often referred to as third-generation devices [18]. These devices are designed to access the dominant intrinsic loss mechanisms that lead to Shockley–Queisser limiting efficiency. Thermalization loss, below E_g loss, and Boltzmann loss account for 30%, 25%, and 10% of the incident solar spectrum, respectively. Substantial efficiency benefits can only come from targeting these loss mechanisms.

The use of multiple pn junctions made from materials with different bandgaps is a common approach for reducing below E_g and thermalization losses. This device is known as a multijunction device. An idealized three-junction solar cell, under 1 sun illumination, has limiting efficiency of 49.3% [19]. Boltzmann loss can be accessed by concentrating light onto a solar cell using lenses and mirrors to increase the angle of absorption (Ω_S). In the limit $\Omega_S = \Omega_C$, Boltzmann loss is eliminated and the limiting efficiency of a single-junction device is given by 40.8% [14]. Often a multijunction device will be implemented in a concentrator system, and it will benefit from a reduction in Boltzmann loss as well as a reduction in below E_g and thermalization losses. This leads to a limiting efficiency of 68.3% in a three-junction device under maximum concentration [19]. Other cell designs including hot carrier [20] and intermediate band devices [21] in theory offer substantial efficiency advantages and are an interesting prospect for future development.

1.14.13 Summary

Solar energy can be directly converted into useful electrical work in a PV device. Such a conversion will only occur in a device exhibiting two necessary behaviors: photosensitive current generation and asymmetric electrical resistance.

The Sun behaves as a blackbody, emitting photons over a broad spectrum of energies. An efficient solar cell should be well matched to the solar spectrum and so must be able to absorb a broad range of energies. This requires a material with a continuum of electronic energy transitions. A continuum of electronic energy transitions can also act as a staircase where excited electrons will rapidly descend, in search of thermal equilibrium. The thermalization of excited carriers can be interrupted by a break in the available electronic transitions. A semiconductor has a continuum of electronic energy levels broken up by a forbidden energy region called a bandgap (E_g). This acts to interrupt thermalization; however, it also limits the range of photon energies that will be absorbed. Only photons with energies greater than E_g will be absorbed in the device.

In a semiconductor, the band of energy levels below E_g is called the valence band and the band of energies above E_g is called the conduction band. Electrons excited into the conduction band are free to move in the semiconductor and act as current carriers. A pn junction is a semiconductor device made from two layers of oppositely doped material. This device has a built-in voltage across it, which draws charge carriers to their respective terminals. A pn junction provides resistive asymmetry, which is necessary to deliver carriers to an electrical circuit.

Generation in a solar cell is the process of electron promotion from the valence band into the conduction, leaving a positively charged electron vacancy (a hole) in the valence band. Recombination describes an electron returning to the valence band and occupying a vacancy. These processes require the conservation of energy and momentum. Interaction particles, which supply or dissipate energy and momentum, are required for generation or recombination to occur. Photons, thermal lattice vibrations (phonons), and other carriers can all act as interaction particles. The absorption of a photon is a generation process in which a photon supplies the necessary energy to promote an electron into the conduction band.

Under illumination, the carrier density in a solar cell increases. Thermalization occurs at a much faster rate than band-to-band processes and therefore, under constant illumination, the steady-state carrier population is in thermal equilibrium with the surrounding lattice. After thermalization, electron and hole populations cease to be in chemical equilibrium, and the two populations are separated by a chemical potential. This chemical potential describes the free electrical work each electron–hole pair can perform on a load and is the product of electron charge and voltage. When the two terminals of a solar cell are connected by a finite load, some current will flow. This reduces the density of the carrier population, which in turn reduces the chemical potential across the device. Current and voltage in a solar cell, therefore, have an inverse relationship.

The maximum solar conversion efficiency achievable in a single-junction device under 1 sun illumination is 31% and is called the Shockley–Queisser limiting efficiency. Five intrinsic loss mechanisms lead to this fundamental limit: below E_g loss, emission loss, thermalization loss, Boltzmann loss, and Carnot loss. Both below E_g loss and thermalization loss derive from the mismatch between the broad solar spectrum and the single threshold absorption of a semiconductor. Emission loss occurs because of radiative recombination in the device. Boltzmann and Carnot losses are both entropic terms that describe the difference between the energy of the carriers and the free energy available to be extracted as useful electrical work. Solar energy converters can be made to exceed the Shockley–Queisser limit and substantial efficiency advantages can be achieved by targeting the dominant intrinsic loss mechanisms.

References

[1] Becquerel AE (1839) Mémoire sur les effects électriques produits sous l'influence des rayons solaires. *Comptes Rendus des Séances Hebdomadaires* 9: 561–567.
[2] Nelson J (2003) *The Physics of Solar Cells*. London: Imperial College Press.
[3] Shockley W (1949) The theory of p-n junctions in semiconductors and p-n junction transistors. *Bell System Technical Journal* 28: 435.
[4] Sze S and Ng KK (2006) *Physics of Semiconductor Devices*. New York/Chichester: Wiley.
[5] National Renewable Energy Laboratory. Reference Solar Spectral Irradiance. http://rredc.nrel.gov/solar/spectra/am1.5.
[6] Yu PY and Cardona M (2005) *Fundamentals of Semiconductors: Physics and Materials Properties*, 3rd edn. Berlin/London: Springer.
[7] Sze SM (2002) *Semiconductor Devices: Physics and Technology*. New York/Chichester: Wiley.
[8] Würfel P (2009) *Physics of Solar Cells: From Basic Principles to Advanced Concepts*, 2nd edn. Weinheim/Chichester: Wiley-VCH.
[9] Shockley W and Read WT (1952) Statistics of the recombinations of holes and electrons. *Physical Review* 87(5): 835–842.
[10] Würfel P (1995) Is an illuminated semiconductor far from thermodynamic equilibrium? *Solar Energy Materials and Solar Cells* 38(1–4): 23–28.
[11] Würfel P (1982) The chemical-potential of radiation. *Journal of Physics C – Solid State Physics* 15(18): 3967–3985.
[12] De Vos A (2008) *Thermodynamics of Solar Energy Conversion*. Weinheim/Chichester: Wiley-VCH.
[13] Fox M (2001) *Optical Properties of Solids*. Oxford: Oxford University Press.
[14] Shockley W and Queisser HJ (1961) Detailed balance limit of efficiency of p-n junction solar cells. *Journal of Applied Physics* 32(3): 510–519.
[15] Martí A, Balenzategui JL, and Reyna RF (1997) Photon recycling and Shockley's diode equation. *Journal of Applied Physics* 82(8): 4067–4075.
[16] Hirst LC and Ekins-Daukes NJ (2011) Fundamental losses in solar cells. *Progress in Photovoltaics* 19: 286–293.
[17] Landsberg PT and Markvart T (1998) The Carnot factor in solar-cell theory. *Solid-State Electronics* 42(4): 657–659.
[18] Green MA (2006) *Third Generation Photovoltaics: Advanced Solar Energy Conversion*. Berlin: Springer.
[19] Martí A and Araújo GL (1996) Limiting efficiencies for photovoltaic energy conversion in multigap systems. *Solar Energy Materials and Solar Cells* 43(2): 203–222.
[20] Würfel P (1997) Solar energy conversion with hot electrons from impact ionisation. *Solar Energy Materials and Solar Cells* 46(1): 43–52.
[21] Luque A and Martí A (1997) Increasing the efficiency of ideal solar cells by photon induced transitions at intermediate levels. *Physical Review Letters* 78(26): 5014–5017.

1.15 Thermodynamics of Photovoltaics

V Badescu, Polytechnic University of Bucharest, Bucharest, Romania

© 2012 Elsevier Ltd. All rights reserved.

1.15.1	Introduction	316
1.15.2	Thermodynamics of Thermal Radiation	316
1.15.2.1	Photon Gas	316
1.15.2.2	The Continuous Spectrum Approximation	317
1.15.2.3	Fluxes of Photon Properties	318
1.15.2.4	Spectral Property Radiances for Blackbodies and Bandgap Materials	318
1.15.2.5	Geometrical Factor of Radiation Sources	319
1.15.2.5.1	Isotropic radiation sources	319
1.15.2.5.2	Geometric factor of nonisotropic blackbody radiation sources	321
1.15.2.6	Diluted Thermal Radiation	322
1.15.3	Concentration of Solar Radiation	325
1.15.3.1	The *Étendue* of Beam Radiation	325
1.15.3.2	Upper Bounds on Beam Solar Radiation Concentration	326
1.15.3.3	Upper Bounds on Scattered Solar Radiation Concentration	327
1.15.4	Upper Bounds for Thermal Radiation Energy Conversion	328
1.15.4.1	Available Work of Enclosed Thermal Radiation	328
1.15.4.2	Available Work of Free Thermal Radiation	330
1.15.4.3	Available Work of Blackbody Radiation as a Particular Case	332
1.15.4.3.1	Upper bound for PT conversion efficiency	332
1.15.4.3.2	Upper bound for PV conversion efficiency	332
1.15.4.4	Discussion	333
1.15.5	Models of Monogap Solar PV Converters	334
1.15.5.1	Modeling Absorption and Recombination Processes	334
1.15.5.1.1	The solar cell equation	337
1.15.5.1.2	The Shockley–Queisser model	338
1.15.5.2	Modeling Multiple Impact Ionization	339
1.15.5.2.1	Solar cell efficiencies	339
1.15.5.2.2	Optimum voltage across solar cells	342
1.15.5.2.3	Discussion	345
1.15.6	Models of Omnicolor Solar Converters	345
1.15.6.1	Omnicolor PT Converters	345
1.15.6.2	Omnicolor PV Converters	347
1.15.6.3	Unified Model of Omnicolor Converters	349
1.15.6.4	Discussion	349
1.15.7	Conclusions	350
References		350
Further Reading		351

Glossary

Auger recombination Recombination of an electron and a hole in which no electromagnetic radiation is emitted, and the excess energy and momentum of the recombining electron and hole are transferred to another electron or hole.

Circulator A waveguide component having a number of terminals is so arranged that energy entering one terminal is transmitted to the next adjacent terminal in a particular direction.

Diffuse solar radiation Downward scattered and reflected solar radiation, coming from the whole hemisphere with the exception of the solid angle of the sun's disc.

Direct (beam) solar radiation The component of solar radiation received by the earth's surface only from the direction of the sun's disk (i.e., it has not been reflected, refracted, or scattered).

Fermi level (energy) The Fermi level (energy) of a system of noninteracting fermions is the smallest possible increase in the ground-state energy when exactly one particle is added to the system. It is equivalent to the chemical potential of the system in the ground state at zero thermodynamic temperature.

Gibbs free energy The thermodynamic potential for a system whose independent variables are the thermodynamic temperature, pressure, mass variables,

and other independent, extensive variables. The change in Gibbs free energy, as a system passes reversibly from one state to another at constant temperature and pressure, is a measure of the work available in that change of state.
Impact ionization Ionization produced by the impact of a high-energy charge carrier on an atom of semiconductor material; the effect is an increase in the number of charge carriers.

Lambertian surface A surface that emits or reflects radiation isotropically, according to Lambert's law.
Quantum efficiency Ratio between the number of electric carriers (or photons) generated by an elementary absorption process and the number of absorbed photons.
Selective absorber Absorber whose optical properties depend on wavelength or on radiation's incidence angle.

1.15.1 Introduction

The spectrum of extraterrestrial solar radiation resembles the spectrum of a blackbody of temperature 5760 K. At Earth's surface, the short-wavelength solar radiation consists of direct and diffuse radiation. The spectrum of the direct component is characterized by many dips, due to absorption by water vapor, oxygen, and other gases in the atmosphere. The spectrum of the diffuse radiation contains less energy and has a narrower spread of wavelengths than that of the direct component. Many calculations involving direct solar radiation can be made by using the blackbody spectra approximation rather than the correct solar spectrum. Also, diffuse solar radiation is sometimes treated as diluted blackbody radiation.

Solar energy transformation into other forms of energy involves interaction between the solar photons and the particles constituting the conversion devices. The energy levels of these particles (e.g., electrons, holes, excitons, and phonons) are quantified and transition of particles to higher energy levels is allowed just for particular values of the energy of the incoming photons. The photons having the appropriate energy are interacting with the conversion device's particles (i.e., they are absorbed) and the device is practically transparent for the other incoming photons. Also, transition of particles is allowed to lower quantified energy levels and the emitted photons have, accordingly, quantified energies, corresponding to the differences between the energy levels in the conversion device.

Solar energy converters may be scholastically grouped into two categories: devices based on thermal processes and devices based on nonthermal processes. Usually, the processes in the latter category of converters are called quantum processes, but this is rather inappropriate because both categories in fact involve quantum particles. In the first category, most part of the solar energy is transformed into internal energy of the body receiving radiation. This way of dealing with solar energy is called photothermal (PT) conversion. Very often, the body receiving radiation is a metal or an alloy. The internal energy may be subsequently used directly (as in case of a device providing heat to an end user) may be stored or may be transformed into mechanical, electrical, or chemical work. Converters based on quantum processes transform part of the energy of solar radiation directly into electrical energy (as happens in a photovoltaic cell) or store that energy in the form of chemical energy (as it happens in case of water photodissociation into oxygen and hydrogen). The first process is called photovoltaic (PV) conversion, while the second one is called photochemical (PC) conversion. Most PV devices are built with energy bandgap materials like semiconductors. Photosensible substances are used within PC conversion devices. In this chapter, we consider mainly the thermodynamics of PV solar energy conversion.

The chapter is structured as follows. Section 1.15.2 treats the thermodynamics of enclosed and free thermal radiation. Basic quantities such as the continuous photon spectrum and photon fluxes are defined. Also, the geometrical factors are introduced for both isotropic and nonisotropic radiation sources. Solar radiation is sometimes concentrated before reaching the converter. The Lagrange invariant (the *étendue*) of concentrated radiation is defined and discussed in Section 1.15.3. Also, the maximum concentration ratio for both direct and diffuse solar radiation is treated there. Upper bounds for the conversion efficiency of thermal radiation are derived in Section 1.15.4. A general theory of the exergy of enclosed and free thermal radiation is developed. This theory is subsequently applied to bandgap materials used in PV applications. Section 1.15.5 presents a thermodynamic model for PV conversion. The solar cell equation is derived from photon number fluxes arguments. Models for omnicolor converters are presented in Section 1.15.6. The approach allows a unique description of both PV and PT converters. Finally, Section 1.15.7 presents the conclusions.

1.15.2 Thermodynamics of Thermal Radiation

1.15.2.1 Photon Gas

Radiation emitted by hot bodies, such as the Sun, is called thermal radiation. Thermal radiation is a particular type of electromagnetic radiation. From a thermodynamic point of view, thermal radiation is often modeled by using the photon gas approximation. The next derivation does not involve the assumption of thermodynamic equilibrium.

A cavity of volume V containing a mixture of photons of various wavelengths is considered. One denotes by $P(N_1,N_2,\ldots)$ the probability to find N_1 photons in quantum state 1, N_2 photons in quantum state 2, and so on. Also, one denotes by $p(N_j)$ the probability to find N_j photons in quantum state j. The following two assumptions denoted 1 and 2 are adopted [1]:

1. The single quantum state probabilities $p(N_1), p(N_2), \ldots$, are independent, that is,

$$P(N_1, N_2, \ldots) = p(N_1) \times p(N_2) \ldots \qquad [1]$$

2. When a new photon is added to the system, the probability that this particle is in quantum state j is independent of the number of particles already existing in that state. This means $p_j(N_j) = q_j^{N_j}$, where q_j is a positive (but otherwise undetermined) number. Through the normalization condition, one finds:

$$p_j(N_j) = (1-q_j)q_j^{N_j} \qquad (0 \leq q_j \leq 1) \qquad [2]$$

One denotes by n_j the mean occupation number of the state j. Then,

$$n_j = \sum_{N_j=0}^{\infty} N_j p_j(N_j) = \sum_{N_j=0}^{\infty} N_j q_j^{N_j}(1-q_j) = \frac{q_j}{1-q_j} \qquad [3]$$

Equation [3] allows correlating q_j to n_j.

The entropy S of the photon gas is obtained from the Shannon formula [1]:

$$\begin{aligned}
S &= k \sum_{N_1=0}^{\infty} \ldots \sum_{N_j=0}^{\infty} \ldots P(N_1, N_2, \ldots) \ln P(N_1, N_2, \ldots) \\
&= -k \sum_j \sum_{N_j=0}^{\infty} \left\{ (1-q_j)q_j^{N_j} \ln \left[(1-q_j)q_j^{N_j} \right] \right\} \\
&= -k \sum_j \left[(1+n_j) \ln (1+n_j) - n_j \ln n_j \right]
\end{aligned} \qquad [4]$$

Here, k is Boltzmann's constant.

1.15.2.2 The Continuous Spectrum Approximation

The distance between the photon energy levels decreases by increasing the volume V containing radiation. The model of a continuous spectrum is often used when that distance is very small. Integration replaces in this case the summation over quantum states. This requires an expression for the number of photon quantum states in the frequency range $(v, v + dv)$.

A surface element is considered, which may be part of the surface of the volume V or may be placed inside that volume. A flux of radiation is incident on that surface element in the solid angle $d\Omega$ from a direction, making the angle θ with the normal at the surface. When the surface element is part of volume's surface, the normal is oriented toward outside the volume. For convenience, the refractive index of the medium inside the volume equals unity. Then, the number of photon quantum states in the frequency range $(v, v + dv)$ is given by [2]

$$dN_v = \frac{d\Omega V l v^2}{c^3} dv \qquad [5]$$

where c is the speed of light while $l = 1$ and $l = 2$ stand for polarized and unpolarized radiation, respectively. The number of photons in the frequency interval $(v, v + dv)$ is obtained from the density of quantum states dN_v times the mean occupation number n_v of the quantum state of frequency v. The total number N of photons in the volume V is obtained through integration over all frequencies and the total solid angle [2]:

$$N = V \iint \tilde{n}_v \, dv d\Omega \qquad [6]$$

$$\tilde{n}_v \equiv \frac{l v^2}{c^3} n_v \qquad [7]$$

The internal energy of the radiation is given by

$$U = V \iint \tilde{u}_v \, dv d\Omega \qquad [8]$$

$$\tilde{u}_v \equiv \frac{l v^2 h v}{c^3} n_v \qquad [9]$$

Using eqn [4], one obtains the entropy of the radiation confined to the volume V:

$$S = V \iint \tilde{s}_v \, dv d\Omega \qquad [10]$$

$$\tilde{s}_v \equiv \frac{l k v^2}{c^3} \left[(1+n_v) \ln (1+n_v) - n_v \ln n_v \right] \qquad [11]$$

The quantities $\tilde{n}_v$, $\tilde{u}_v$, and $\tilde{s}_v$ are photon number, internal energy, and entropy densities, respectively. Their units are number of photons, energy unit, or entropy unit, respectively, per unit volume, unit frequency, and unit solid angle.

Conversion between the frequency v and the energy e per photon may be easily obtained from $e = hv$, where h is Planck's constant. This allows changing the frequency range $(v, v + dv)$ into the energy range $(e, e + de)$. The quantities defined by eqns [6], [8], and [10] can be obtained by integration over photon energies. In this case, the number of photon quantum states in the energy range is given by

$$dN_e = \frac{d\Omega V e^2}{h^3 c^3} de \qquad [12]$$

Sometimes, $\omega \equiv 2\pi v$ is used as a frequency and the Planck relation becomes $e = \hbar\omega$ with $\hbar \equiv h/(2\pi)$.

1.15.2.3 Fluxes of Photon Properties

Photons traveling in free space are carrying properties, such as the number of particles, energy, and entropy. The thermodynamics of free thermal radiation is shortly presented here under the assumption of the continuous approximation.

One denotes by $K_{N,v}$ the photon number spectral radiance given by

$$K_{N,v} = c\tilde{n}_v = \frac{lv^2}{c^2} n_v \qquad [13]$$

The factor c (the light speed) takes into account that the number of photons in the frequency range Δv incident from the solid angle $d\Omega$ perpendicularly on the surface area ΔA during the time interval Δt is given by $K_{N,v} dv d\Omega \Delta A \Delta t = \tilde{n}_v dv d\Omega \Delta A (c\Delta t)$, where the radiation is contained by a cylinder whose axis length is $c\Delta t$ [2]. Then, the photon number flux density γ received by a Lambertian plane surface is given by [3]

$$\gamma = \iint K_{N,v} \cos\theta \, dv \, d\Omega \qquad [14]$$

The factor $\cos\theta$ projects the plane surface area in such a way to be perpendicular on the propagation direction of the radiation.

Similar arguments apply for the energy and entropy spectral radiances, denoted $K_{E,v}$ and $K_{S,v}$, respectively, which are given by [3]

$$K_{E,v} = c\tilde{u}_v = \frac{lhv^3}{c^2} n_v \qquad [15]$$

$$K_{S,v} = c\tilde{s}_v = \frac{lkv^2}{c^2}[(1 + n_v)\ln(1 + n_v) - n_v \ln n_v] \qquad [16]$$

The energy and entropy fluxes, φ and ψ, respectively, are given by

$$\phi = \iint K_{E,v} \cos\theta \, dv \, d\Omega \qquad [17]$$

$$\psi = \iint K_{S,v} \cos\theta \, dv \, d\Omega \qquad [18]$$

For isotropic radiation, the radiances $K_{N,v}$, $K_{E,v}$, and $K_{S,v}$ do not depend on direction and the photon number, energy, and entropy fluxes come to the simplest form:

$$\gamma = B \int K_{N,v} \, dv \qquad [19]$$

$$\phi = B \int K_{E,v} \, dv \qquad [20]$$

$$\psi = B \int K_{S,v} \, dv \qquad [21]$$

where

$$B \equiv \int \cos\theta \, d\Omega \qquad [22]$$

which is the so-called geometric (or view) factor that captures the geometrical relation between the source and the receiver of radiation. More details on the geometric factor of radiation sources are shown in Section 1.15.2.5.

1.15.2.4 Spectral Property Radiances for Blackbodies and Bandgap Materials

In the case of a blackbody or a bandgap material, the mean occupation number n_v of the quantum state of energy hv is given by the following Shockley–Roosbroeck-like relationship [4]:

$$n_v = \frac{1}{\exp\left(\dfrac{h\nu - \mu}{kT}\right) - 1} \qquad [23]$$

where T is the temperature of the body and μ is the chemical potential of the emitted radiation. In case of blackbody radiation, $\mu = 0$ and eqn [23] reduces to the usual Planck expression. In case of a bandgap material (for instance, a semiconductor), $\mu = q(E_{Fe} - E_{Fh})$, where E_{Fe} and E_{Fh} are the quasi-Fermi levels for electrons and holes, respectively, and q is electron electric charge [5, 6]. For a semiconductor solar cell, the usual approximation is $E_{Fe} - E_{Fh} = V$, where V is the voltage across the cell [7]. Then, eqn [23] for $\mu = qV$ becomes

$$n_v = \frac{1}{\exp\left(\dfrac{h\nu - qV}{kT}\right) - 1} \qquad [24]$$

Equations [23] and [24] may be used in eqns [13], [15], and [16] to compute the photon number, energy, and entropy spectral radiances, respectively, for blackbodies or bandgap materials.

1.15.2.5 Geometrical Factor of Radiation Sources

PV converters may receive radiation from various sources. A common case corresponds to a spherical source of radiation (e.g., the Sun). Generally, the incident radiation is nonisotropic, but the isotropic approximation is very often used as far as solar direct radiation is concerned.

1.15.2.5.1 *Isotropic radiation sources*

We shall consider now isotropic radiation that is not necessarily blackbody. The position of a typical luminous element of the sphere at A will be specified by the zenith angle θ and the azimuthal angle λ (**Figure 1**). One denotes by δ the half-angle of the cone

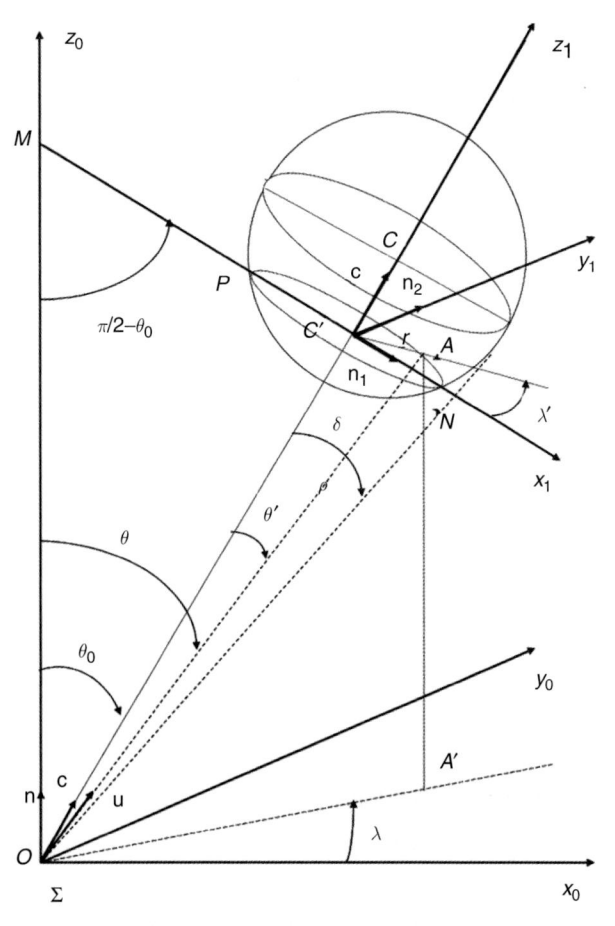

Figure 1 Notation used and arrangement of the source (center C) and the receiver Σ. The points C and C' are in the plane (x_0, z_0). The line OA' is the intersection of the plane (OC, OA) with the plane (x_0, y_0).

subtending the sphere when viewed from the observer. A common case corresponds to a spherical source of radiation (e.g., the Sun) whose center C is on the zenith line ($\theta_0 = 0$) and for which $0 \leq \lambda \leq 2\pi$ and $0 \leq \theta \leq \delta$. This case corresponds to the largest direct solar energy flux. The geometrical factor (eqn [22]) is in this case:

$$B(\theta_0 = 0) = \int_0^{2\pi} d\lambda \int_0^{\delta} \cos\theta \sin\theta \, d\theta = \pi \sin^2\delta \quad [25]$$

In terms of the solid angle Ω subtended by the spherical radiation source, the same geometric factor B is given by [8–10]

$$B(\Omega) = \Omega\left(1 - \frac{\Omega}{4\pi}\right) \quad [26]$$

Sometimes, the source of radiation is a hemispherical dome ($\delta = \pi/2$ and $\Omega = 2\pi$). This happens, for example, in case of diffuse solar radiation received by a horizontal surface. Then, from eqns [25] and [26], one finds $B = \pi$.

Generally, the spherical source of radiation is not vertically above the receiving surface, but at a zenith angle θ_0 (see **Figure 1**). In that case, eqn [22] gives rise to the following generalization of eqn [25] [11]:

$$B(\theta_0) = \pi \sin^2\delta \cos\theta_0 \quad [27]$$

A variant of eqn [27] is

$$B(\Omega, \theta_0) = \Omega\left(1 - \frac{\Omega}{4\pi}\right)\cos\theta_0 \quad [28]$$

in terms of the solid angle Ω subtended by the source at the receiver.

Derivation of eqn [27] is shown next [12]. Let a spherical source of radiation subtend a solid angle Ω at a flat receiver Σ (**Figure 1**). Let **n** be a unit vector on the axis z_0 normal to Σ at a point O, and let **c** be the unit vector in the direction of the center C of the source, θ_0 being the angle between **n** and **c**. Let A be an arbitrary point on the sphere. One constructs a plane through A and perpendicular to OC. Its intersection with the sphere determines a circle of center C'. At the point C', one can set up a Cartesian coordinate system (x_1, y_1, z_1), with the z_1-axis a continuation of OC. The other axes in **Figure 1** are determined as follows: **n** and z_1 determine a plane that cuts the circle of center C' in N and P, and the plane Σ in Ox_0. The axis y_0 is perpendicular to x_0 and z_0. The axis x_1 is specified by unit vector $\mathbf{n}_1$ on C'N. The axis y_1 of unit vector $\mathbf{n}_2$ is chosen perpendicular to the plane ($\mathbf{n}_1$, **c**). One can see that y_1 is parallel to y_0 as they both are perpendicular on the plane (x_0, z_0). Then, the vector **u** can be expressed as

$$\mathbf{u} = \mathbf{c}\cos\theta' + \mathbf{n}_1 \sin\theta' \cos\lambda' + \mathbf{n}_2 \sin\theta' \sin\lambda' \quad [29]$$

where θ' and λ' are shown in **Figure 1**. Also

$$\mathbf{n} \cdot \mathbf{u} = \mathbf{n} \cdot \mathbf{c}\cos\theta' + \mathbf{n} \cdot \mathbf{n}_1 \sin\theta' \cos\lambda' + \mathbf{n} \cdot \mathbf{n}_2 \sin\theta' \sin\lambda' \quad [30]$$

Next, note that

$$\mathbf{n} \cdot \mathbf{c} = \cos\theta_0, \quad \mathbf{n} \cdot \mathbf{n}_1 = \cos(\pi/2 + \theta_0) = -\sin\theta_0, \quad \mathbf{n} \cdot \mathbf{n}_2 = 0 \quad [31]$$

Thus

$$\mathbf{n} \cdot \mathbf{u} = \cos\theta_0 \cos\theta' - \sin\theta_0 \sin\theta' \cos\lambda' \quad [32]$$

An expression for the geometrical factor

$$B = \int \mathbf{n} \cdot \mathbf{u} \, d\Omega \quad [33]$$

is readily obtained from eqns [32] and [22]. We have from eqns [32] and [33]

$$B(\theta_0) = \int_0^{2\pi} d\lambda' \int_0^{\delta} \sin\theta' d\theta' [\cos\theta_0 \cos\theta' - \sin\theta_0 \sin\theta' \cos\lambda'] = \pi \sin^2\delta \cos\theta_0 \quad [34]$$

since the λ'-integration extends from 0 to 2π, while the θ'-integration extends from 0 to δ. The second term in eqn [34] does not contribute since it involves $\int_0^{2\pi} \cos\lambda' d\lambda'$. Hence, eqn [34] leads to eqn [27].

The solid angle subtended by the spherical radiating source at Σ is, in analogy with eqn [34],

$$\Omega = \int_0^{2\pi} d\lambda' \int_0^{\delta} \sin\theta' d\theta' = 2\pi(1 - \cos\delta) \quad [35]$$

It is therefore independent of the angle θ_0, as expected. However, in order that the whole radiator is visible from Σ, we require

$$\Omega + 2\pi \sin \theta_0 \leq 2\pi \qquad [36]$$

Otherwise, part of the emitting disc is cut off by the horizon.

Eliminating δ from eqns [27] and [35] yields

$$B(\theta_0) = \pi(1 - \cos \delta)(1 + \cos \delta)\cos \theta_0 = \pi \left(\frac{\Omega}{\pi}\right)\left(1 - \frac{\Omega}{4\pi}\right)\cos \theta_0 \qquad [37]$$

If Σ is part of a unifacial solar cell that sits under a hemispherical radiating dome, then $\delta = \pi/2$ and we can chose $\theta_0 = 0$, so that

$$B(\theta_0 = 0) = \pi, \quad \Omega = 2\pi \qquad [38]$$

The geometrical factor, normalized to a hemisphere, is then

$$\Gamma \equiv B(\theta_0 = 0)/\pi \qquad [39]$$

If there are several distinct sources, each with its own value of B and Ω, then all the Γ's involved must add up to unity [13]. For a bifacial cell, they should add up to 2.

1.15.2.5.2 Geometric factor of nonisotropic blackbody radiation sources

When nonisotropic sources of radiation are considered, strictly, a geometrical factor does not exist. However, an average geometric factor can still be used, as shown below for the case of the Sun.

In the case of a spherical source of isotropic blackbody radiation (chemical potential $\mu = 0$) at temperature T, one obtains the energy flux from eqns [15], [20], and [23]:

$$\phi(\theta_0) = \frac{B(\theta_0)}{\pi}\sigma T^4 = \frac{\Omega}{\pi}\left(1 - \frac{\Omega}{4\pi}\right)\sigma T^4 \cos \theta_0 \qquad [40]$$

where the geometrical factor $B(\theta_0)$ is given by eqn [28].

It is known that the solar brightness falls considerably with the distance from the center of the disc. This effect, which is referred to as limb darkening, is a consequence of the fact that the Sun is not an isotropic source of radiation. Several empirical correlations have been proposed to describe the limb darkening effect [14, 15]. The nonisotropic luminance of the Sun can be described by the simple widely used relationship [16]:

$$L(\varepsilon) = L_0 \left(\frac{2 + 3\cos \varepsilon}{5}\right) \qquad [41]$$

where L_0 is a measurable constant, namely the solar luminance normal to the Sun's (pseudo)surface, and ε is the zenith angle measured also from the normal to the solar surface (**Figure 2**). Equation [41] predicts the observed values within 5% [15]. We shall use here the popular equation [41] as an example even if better approximations can be inferred from the experimentally observed darkening data. The luminance of an isotropic source of radiation is obtained by replacing $\cos\varepsilon$ with 1 in eqn [41].

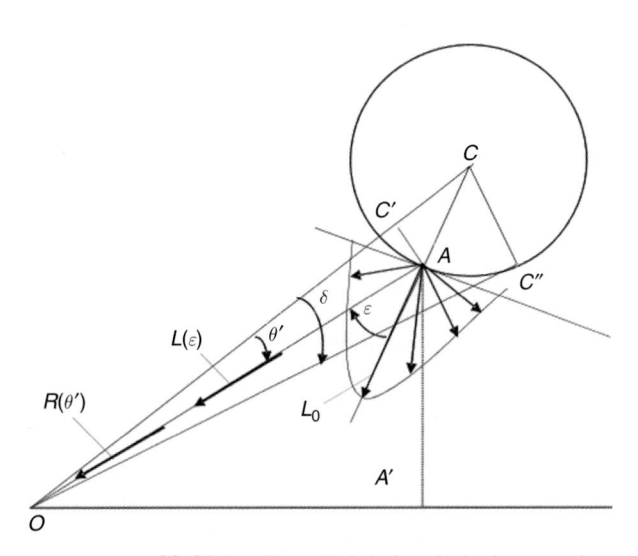

Figure 2 The source (center C) crossed by the plane (OC, OA) (see **Figure 1**). L_0 is the solar luminance on the normal at the Sun's surface. A plot of the luminance $L(\varepsilon)$ at zenith angle ε is included in the diagram. $R(\theta')$ is the radiance of the radiation incident under the angle θ' on the receiver Σ.

Consequently, by using eqn [40] and taking into account that the Sun emits the energy flux $\int L_0 \cos\theta d\Omega = \sigma T^4$ in all directions ($\Omega = 2\pi$) one obtains

$$L_0 = \frac{\sigma T^4}{\int \cos\theta d\Omega} = \frac{\sigma T^4}{B(\theta_0 = 0)} = \frac{\sigma T^4}{\pi} \qquad [42]$$

The solar energy flux incident on a Lambertian surface is given by eqn [15], that is,

$$\phi = \int_\Omega R(\theta)\cos\theta d\Omega \qquad [43]$$

where $R(\theta) = \int K_{E,\nu} d\nu$ is the spectrally integrated solar energy radiance. The energy radiance $R(\theta)$ could also be noted $R(\theta')$ as the radiation direction (unit vector **u** in **Figure 1**) is characterized by any of the angles θ or θ'. **Figure 2** shows a cross section passing through OC and A in **Figure 1**. One neglects all loss processes associated with light travel from the Sun to the Earth. Consequently, the energy radiance $R(\theta')$ of the radiation incident on the receiver equals the solar luminance $L(\varepsilon)$. By using eqns [40]–[43] and **Figure 2**, one obtains after some algebra

$$L(\varepsilon)(=R(\theta) = R(\theta')) = \frac{\sigma T^4}{\pi}\left[\frac{2\sin\delta + 3(\sin^2\delta - \sin^2\theta')^{1/2}}{5\sin\delta}\right] \qquad [44]$$

By replacing eqns [44] and [41] in eqn [43], one obtains through a change of coordinates $(\rho,\theta,\lambda) \rightarrow (\rho,\theta',\lambda')$ [12]:

$$\phi(\theta_0) = \frac{\sigma T^4}{\pi}\frac{4}{5}\Omega\left(1 - \frac{\Omega}{4\pi}\right)\cos\theta_0 \qquad [45]$$

This energy flux can be put into the form similar to that of the isotropic blackbody radiation flux (eqn [40]):

$$\phi(\theta_0) = \frac{B_{\text{non-is}}(\theta_0)}{\pi}\sigma T^4 \qquad [46]$$

where

$$B_{\text{non-is}}(\theta_0) \equiv \frac{4}{5}B(\theta_0) = \frac{4}{5}\Omega\left(1 - \frac{\Omega}{4\pi}\right)\cos\theta_0 \qquad [47]$$

is an equivalent, or average, geometrical factor of the Sun, regarded as a nonisotropic source of radiation. From eqn [47], one sees that the nonisotropically emitting Sun is equivalent to a star of about 80% smaller size, emitting isotropically.

Equation [46] is valid at any distance from the Sun. At the mean Sun–Earth distance, the observed values are [17]

$$\Omega_{\text{obs}}(\cong B_{\text{obs}}) = 6.835 \times 10^{-5} \qquad [48a]$$

$$\phi_{\text{obs}}(\theta_0 = 0) = 1366.1 \text{ W m}^{-2} \qquad [48b]$$

Using eqns [48] in eqns [40], [46], and [47] leads to two different values of the Sun's temperature. If the limb darkening effect is neglected, the Sun temperature is $T = 5769.8$ K. When this effect is included by using eqn [41], a higher temperature is obtained: $T_{\text{non-is}} = 6100.8$ K. In this case, the equivalent geometric factor of the nonisotropic source falls below that of an isotropic source subtending the same solid angle. In order that the energy flux received from both sources be equal, the temperature of the nonisotropic has therefore to exceed that of the isotropic source. Finally, one should mention that a more accurate description of the limb darkening effect (e.g., by using $L(\varepsilon) = L_0(11 + 9\cos\varepsilon)/20$ instead of eqn [41]) yields a Sun temperature of about 6000 K, which is often used in PV efficiency calculations.

1.15.2.6 Diluted Thermal Radiation

Diffuse solar radiation may be treated as diluted blackbody radiation [3, 8, 18]. A full account on this subject may be found in the work of Landsberg and Tonge [19]. The most significant results are reviewed in Reference 8.

Entropy and energy fluxes of diluted radiation may be written as

$$\phi = A(\Omega)\varepsilon\sigma T_R^4 \qquad [49]$$

$$\psi = \frac{4}{3}A(\Omega)\sigma\varepsilon\chi(\varepsilon)T_R^3 \qquad [50]$$

where $\varepsilon \leq 1$ is the so-called dilution factor, T_R refers to the undiluted blackbody radiation ($\varepsilon = 1$), and $\chi(\varepsilon)$ is a function exactly calculated in Reference 19, which can be approximated for small ε (i.e., less than 0.1) by

$$\chi(\varepsilon) \cong 0.9652 - 0.2777 \ln\varepsilon + 0.0511\varepsilon \qquad [51]$$

and such that $\chi(1) = 1$. Another useful approximation is $\chi(\varepsilon) \cong 1 - 45/(4\pi^4) \times (2.336 - 0.260\varepsilon) \times \ln\varepsilon$, which can be used for $0.005 < \varepsilon < 1$ [20]. The function $A(\Omega)$ from eqns [49] and [50] refers to a geometrical factor that depends on the solid angle Ω subtended by the source of radiation by

$$A(\Omega) \equiv \frac{B(\Omega)}{\pi} = \frac{\Omega}{\pi}\left(1 - \frac{\Omega}{4\pi}\right) \qquad [52]$$

By using eqns [49] and [50], the effective temperature T_e of the diluted radiation can be derived from the usual definition:

$$T_e \equiv \left(\frac{\partial \phi}{\partial \psi}\right)_{\varepsilon\Omega} = \frac{4}{3}\frac{\phi}{\psi} = \frac{T_R}{\chi(\varepsilon)} \qquad [53]$$

Although T_e is not an equilibrium temperature, with its help the thermodynamics of diluted radiation is formally coincident with the thermodynamics of blackbody radiation. Indeed, by using eqns [49] and [53], we derive another form of the energy flux of diluted radiation [19]:

$$\phi = \beta T_e^4 \qquad [54]$$

with

$$\beta \equiv A(\Omega)\varepsilon\sigma\chi^4(\varepsilon) \qquad [55]$$

After dilution, the thermal radiation may be considered as undiluted with respect to the blackbody radiation of temperature T_e.

Two papers approached the theoretical maximum efficiency of diffuse solar radiation [8, 21]. Very different results were reported. In Reference 8, one proved that the maximum efficiency is 0.573. A significantly smaller value (i.e., 0.096) was obtained in Reference 21. In Reference 18, we showed that both results are consistent if the more general model presented next is used.

Now, one assumes the Sun at zenith. Also, one assumes that the Earth's atmosphere does not absorb solar radiation and radiation scattering is forward (in other words, there is no backscattered radiation). Then, we define a perfectly forward diffuser, that is, a finite thin body situated between the Sun and the observer whose surface elastically scatters into a 2π solid angle any narrow pencil of radiation incident on it. We assume this diffuser as subtending a solid angle Ω_1 when viewed from the Earth. Consider first the direct sunlight (dilution factor ε_0) incident on a point M placed on the diffuser surface. Then, $\varepsilon_0 = 1$ and

$$A(\Omega_0) = \frac{\Omega_0}{\pi}\left(1 - \frac{\Omega_0}{4\pi}\right) \approx \frac{\Omega_0}{\pi} \qquad [56]$$

where $\Omega_0 = 6.835 \times 10^{-5}$ sr is the solid angle subtended by the Sun (see eqn [48b]). Consequently, the flux of beam radiation is given by eqn [4]

$$\phi_0 = \frac{\Omega_0}{\pi}\varepsilon\sigma T_s^4 \qquad [57]$$

where T_s is Sun temperature (5760 K).

The flux φ_0 is scattered over a $\Omega_1 = 2\pi$ solid angle around the point M. After scattering, solar radiation has a dilution factor $\varepsilon_1 < 1$ and the effective temperature $T_{e,1}$. For an observer situated at the point M, the scattered radiation has a geometrical factor $A(\Omega_1) = 1$. The flux φ_1 of dilute radiation is equal to the incoming flux φ_0. By using eqns [49] and [57], we obtain

$$\phi_1 = A(\Omega_1)\varepsilon_1\sigma T_s^4 = \frac{\Omega_0}{\pi}\sigma T_s^4 = \phi_0 \qquad [58]$$

Consequently, the dilution factor is

$$\varepsilon_1 = \frac{\Omega_0}{\pi} \qquad [59]$$

and the effective temperature of the scattered radiation can be derived by using eqn [53]:

$$T_{e,1} = T_s/\chi(\varepsilon_1) = 1459.5 \text{ K} \qquad [60]$$

This result was first reported in Reference 8.

Until now, we have analyzed the scattered radiation from the point of view of an observer situated on the surface of the diffuser. For an observer placed on the Earth's surface, the source of singly scattered radiation may be formally described as a blackbody of temperature $T_{e,1}$ (dilution factor $\varepsilon_1' = 1$), which subtends the solid angle Ω_1. To determine Ω_1, we use eqn [49] and the assumption that on the Earth's surface the flux φ_1 of scattered radiation equates the flux φ_0

$$\phi_1 = A(\Omega_1)\varepsilon_{e,1}\sigma T_{e,1}^4 = \frac{\Omega_0}{\pi}\sigma T_s^4 = \phi_0 \qquad [61]$$

By using eqn [52], we obtain

$$\Omega_1 = 2\pi \left[1 - \left(1 - \frac{\Omega_0}{\pi}\chi^4(\varepsilon_1)\right)^{1/2}\right] = 0.01665 \text{ sr} \quad [62]$$

The solid angle Ω_1 is enveloped by a cone symmetrically disposed around the nadir–zenith direction and whose half-angle δ_1 can be derived from the relation:

$$\Omega_1 = 2\pi(1 - \cos\delta_0) \quad [63]$$

We obtain

$$\delta_1 = 2.083° \quad [64]$$

We conclude that after a single scattering solar radiation is still strongly anisotropic (compare δ_1 with the half-angle $\delta_0 = 0.265°$ of the cone subtended by the Sun).

The second scattering is described next. This case implies the existence of a second perfectly forward diffuser. The incoming radiation consists in the flux φ_1 of singly scattered solar radiation (dilution factor $\varepsilon_1 = \Omega_0/\pi$) or, which is equivalent, blackbody radiation of temperature $T_{e,1}$ (dilution factor $\varepsilon'_1 = 1$). The flux φ_1 is again dispersed over a solid angle $\Omega_2 = 2\pi$, the scattered radiation having a geometrical factor $A(\Omega_2) = 1$ and a dilution factor $\varepsilon_2 < 1$.

The flux φ_2 of doubly scattered radiation equates to the incoming flux φ_1. By using eqn [58], we obtain

$$\phi_2 = A(\Omega_2)\varepsilon_2 \sigma T_{e,1}^4 = \phi_1 = \phi_0 = \frac{\Omega_0}{\pi}\sigma T_s^4 \quad [65]$$

From eqn [65], we find

$$\varepsilon_2 = \frac{\Omega_0}{\pi}\chi^4(\varepsilon_1) = 5.281 \times 10^{-3} \quad [66]$$

and the effective temperature of the doubly scattered radiation is given by eqn [53]:

$$T_{e,2} = \frac{T_{e,1}}{\chi(\varepsilon_2)} = \frac{T_s}{\chi(\varepsilon_1)\chi(\varepsilon_2)} \quad [67]$$

For an observer placed on the Earth's surface, the source of thermal radiation is a blackbody of temperature $T_{e,2}$ (dilution factor $\varepsilon'_2 = 1$) which subtends a solid angle Ω_2. To determine Ω_2, we use eqn [49] and the assumption that the energy flux φ_2 incident on the Earth's surface equates to the flux φ_0:

$$\varphi_2 = A(\Omega_2)\varepsilon'_2 \sigma T_{e,2}^4 = \varphi_0 = \frac{\Omega_0}{\pi}\sigma T_s^4 \quad [68]$$

By using eqn [52], we obtain

$$\Omega_2 = 2\pi\left[1 - \left(1 - \frac{\Omega_0}{\pi}\chi^4(\varepsilon_1)\chi^4(\varepsilon_2)\right)^{1/2}\right] = 0.599 \text{ sr} \quad [69]$$

The half-angle δ_2 of the cone that envelops the solid angle Ω_2 can be determined by a relation similar to eqn [63] and is

$$\delta_2 = 12.609° \quad [70]$$

As we see, the doubly scattered solar radiation is still anisotropic.

The above procedure can be repeated for three and four scatterings with the following results:

$$\varepsilon_i = \frac{\Omega_0}{\pi}\prod_{j=1}^{i-1}\chi^4(\varepsilon_j) \quad [71]$$

$$T_{e,i} = \frac{T_s}{\prod_{j=1}^{i}\chi(\varepsilon_j)} \quad [72]$$

$$\Omega_i = 2\pi\left[1 - \left(1 - \frac{\Omega_0}{\pi}\prod_{j=1}^{i}\chi^4(\varepsilon_j)\right)^{1/2}\right] \quad (i = 3, 4) \quad [73]$$

where we noted $T_{e,0} \equiv T_s$. **Table 1** shows the results. After four scatterings, solar radiation is completely isotropic and an observer at the ground would see a uniformly brilliant sky. This case was first analyzed in Reference 21. There are some indications that for a clear sky most of the diffuse solar radiation is received within a cone of half-angle $\delta_{real} = 20 - 30°$ [22, 23]. This implies a mean number of three scatterings.

Table 1 Maximum efficiency of singly or multiply scattered solar radiation

Number of scatterings, i	$T_{e,i}$ (K)	δ_i (deg)	C_{max}
0	5760	0.265	45963
1	1459.5	2.083	189.5
2	602.8	12.609	5.5
3	418.9	30.961	1.3
4	393.4 (389.9)[a]	90	1

[a] Value computed from eqn [51] which is a good approximation only for small values of the dilution factor ε.

T_e, the effective temperature of scattered radiation; δ, the half-angle of the cone that subtends a blackbody at temperature T_e; C_{max}, the maximum concentration ratio.

1.15.3 Concentration of Solar Radiation

A solution to increase the useful energy flux provided by the solar energy conversion system is to concentrate the incoming solar radiation. Another solution is to increase the surface area of the absorber. The former solution has the advantage that it yields an increase of the conversion efficiency and that the cost per unit surface area of the concentrating device is smaller than that of the absorber. Also, radiation concentration allows obtaining a higher absorber temperature.

Two types of solar concentrators are often used in practice: three-dimensional (3D) and two-dimensional (2D) concentrators. In a 3D concentrator, the transversal surface area of the incident beam is diminished on two perpendicular directions. The beam radiation is concentrated into a spot, which ideally reduces to a point. In a 2D concentrator, the transversal surface area is diminished on a single direction. The beam radiation is concentrated into a strip, which ideally reduces to a line.

There is an upper limit for solar radiation concentration. In this section, we show how this limit may be theoretically derived for both 3D and 2D concentrators.

1.15.3.1 The *Étendue* of Beam Radiation

Figure 3 shows an optical system consisting of two homogeneous media [24]. A light incident ray passing through the point P_1 (medium 1) enters medium 2 and arrives in the point P_2 as an emerging ray. The points P_1 and P_2 may be thought as emitting and receiving rays, respectively. We shall examine the influence that small displacements of point P_1 and small changes in emitted ray direction exhibit on the emerging ray. These small displacements and direction changes make the beam of emerging rays to have a certain transversal surface area and angular extent. The refractive index of the two media is denoted n_1 and n_2, respectively.

Coordinates systems are defined in both media. The incident ray is defined by the coordinates (x_1, y_1, z_1) of P_1 and the unit vectors (u_1, v_1, w_1) of its direction. The small displacements of P_1 are described by the variations dx_1 and dy_1 of x_1 and y_1, respectively, while the small changes in the direction of the incident ray are described by the variations du_1 and dv_1 of u_1 and v_1, respectively. Thus, a ray beam of surface area $dx_1 dy_1$ and angular extent $du_1 dv_1$ is defined. Similarly, the emerging ray is defined by the coordinates (x_2, y_2, z_2) of P_2 and the unit vectors (u_2, v_2, w_2) of its direction. Small variations may be defined in case of the emerging ray and they are denoted $dx_2 dy_2$ and $du_2 dv_2$, respectively.

The small variations introduced above allow to define the infinitesimal variation of the Lagrangean U for a bundle of rays in a medium of refractive index n:

$$dU = n^2 dx dy du dv \quad [74]$$

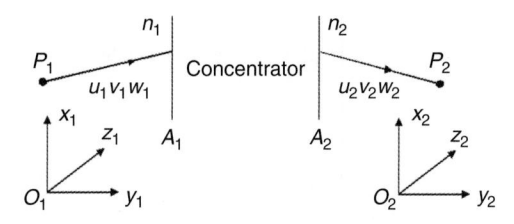

Figure 3 The Lagrangean of a radiation beam.

Sometimes, in practice a different expression of dU is used, as shown next. The distance between P_1 with P_2 is denoted r. Then

$$du = \frac{dx}{r} \qquad [75]$$

$$dv = \frac{dy}{r} \qquad [76]$$

An average of the bundle of rays is defined, which connects the center of the emitting element P_1 with the center of the receiving element P_2. One denotes by i the angle between the normal at the surface determined by dx_1 and dy_1 and this average direction. Also, one denotes by dA the area of the emitting surface. Then, the following relation applies

$$dxdy = dA\cos i \qquad [77]$$

where d$A\cos i$ is the emitting area projected on the average direction of the incident rays. Also, one denotes by A' the surface area of the receiving surface element, while i' is the angle between the emerging ray and the surface of area A'. Taking account of eqns [75] and [76], one may write

$$dudv = \frac{dxdy}{r^2} = dA'\frac{\cos i'}{r^2} \qquad [78]$$

Using eqns [74], [77], and [78] yields

$$dU = n^2 dA dA' \frac{\cos i \cos i'}{r^2} \qquad [79]$$

A classical result of geometrical optics states that the Lagrangean U is conserved for those ray beams free from energy losses. Therefore, U is referred to as the Lagrange invariant or *l'étendue*.

1.15.3.2 Upper Bounds on Beam Solar Radiation Concentration

Two parameters are commonly used to characterize the concentrator performance: the geometric concentration ratio C_g and the energetic concentration ratio C_e. The geometric concentration ratio C_g is defined by

$$C_g \equiv \frac{A_1}{A_2} \qquad [80]$$

where A_1 is the inlet surface area and A_2 is the outlet surface area (**Figure 3**). The energetic concentration ratio C_e is given by

$$C_e \equiv \frac{\phi_2}{\phi_1} \qquad [81]$$

where ϕ_2 and ϕ_1 are the energy radiation flux densities at concentrator exit and inlet, respectively. For a given concentrator, C_g and C_e have generally different values. When radiation passes through interfaces separating two optical media with different refractive index, energy losses occur, mainly due to reflection. This makes the energetic concentration ratio C_e to be in general smaller than the geometric concentration ratio C_g.

The principle of a 2D concentrator is shown in **Figure 4**. The incident and emerging ray beams subtend cones of angles $2\theta_1$ and $2\theta_2$, respectively, while the inlet and outlet surface areas are denoted $2a_1$ and $2a_2$, respectively. The Lagrangean U_1 of the incident radiation beam is given by

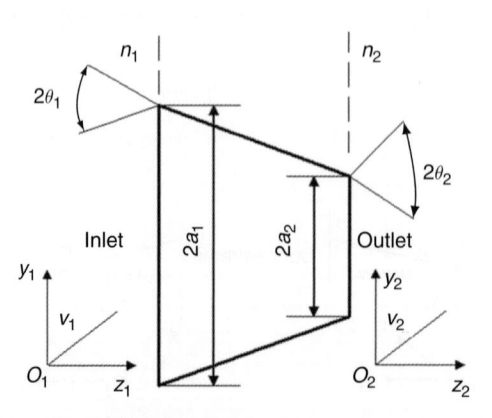

Figure 4 The maximum concentration ratio for a 2D concentrator.

$$U_1 = \int_{\text{inlet}} n_1 \mathrm{d}y_1 \mathrm{d}v_1 = n_1 \int_0^{2a_1} \mathrm{d}y \int_{-\theta_1}^{\theta_1} \mathrm{d}(\cos\theta) = 4a_1 n_1 \sin\theta_1 \qquad [82]$$

A similar expression holds for the Lagrangean U_2 at the level of the exit surface. The Langrangean is conserved in case no energy loss occurs between the inlet and exit surfaces. This means $U_1 = U_2$, that is,

$$4a_1 n_1 \sin\theta_1 = 4a_2 n_2 \sin\theta_2 \qquad [83]$$

The geometric concentration ratio of the 2D concentrator is given by

$$C_g^{2D} = \frac{a_1}{a_2} = \frac{n_2 \sin\theta_2}{n_1 \sin\theta_1} \qquad [84]$$

Among the four parameters entering eqn [84], only n_2 and θ_2 may be changed according to the designer's will. To obtain the maximum concentration ratio ($C_{g,\max}^{2D}$, say), one looks for the maximum value of θ_2 (i.e., $\theta_{2,\max} = \pi/2$). Then

$$C_{g,\max}^{2D} = \frac{n_2}{n_1 \sin\theta_1} \qquad [85]$$

Similar arguments show that the maximum concentration ratio of 3D concentrators with axially symmetric geometry, $C_{g,\max}^{3D}$ is given by

$$C_{g,\max}^{3D} = \left(\frac{n_2}{n_1 \sin\theta_1}\right)^2 \qquad [86]$$

We now apply the above results for concentrators placed on the Earth's surface. When seen from the Earth, the Sun subtends a cone of half-angle $\theta_1 \approx 16'$. The same value of the refractive index may be assumed at both concentrator inlet and exit ($n_2 = n_1$). Then, eqns [85] and [86] yield

$$C_{g,\max}^{2D} \approx 215 \qquad [87]$$

$$C_{g,\max}^{3D} \approx 46\,200 \qquad [88]$$

Slightly different values may be found in literature, due to (slightly) different values adopted for the half-angle θ_1. **Table 1** shows, for example, the maximum concentration ratio for a 3D concentrator in case a more accurate value is adopted for the half-angle of the cone subtended by the Sun (i.e., $\theta_1 = 0.265°$).

At the Earth's surface, the medium at concentrator inlet is air ($n_1 = 1$). Note that C_g increases in proportion to the square of n_2 (see eqns [85] and [86]). Then, a significant increase of the concentration ratio may be obtained in case the medium at concentrator exit is optically denser than the air ($n_2 > 1$). For example, when oil is used ($n_2 \approx 1.5$), the maximum concentration ratio of a 3D concentrator may exceed 1 00 000. This yields at concentrator exit an energy flux density higher than on the surface of the Sun, which is about 63 MW m^{-2}. Note that this is not a violation of the second law of thermodynamics, because the temperature of the bundle of concentrated radiation does not exceed the temperature of the radiation source (the Sun) [25].

1.15.3.3 Upper Bounds on Scattered Solar Radiation Concentration

Regardless of the number i of scatterings, the flux ϕ_{in} of scattered solar radiation incident on a horizontal surface is given by (see Section 1.15.2.6)

$$\phi_{\text{in}} = A(\Omega_i)\varepsilon_i \sigma T_{e,i}^4 = \phi_0 = \frac{\Omega_0}{\pi}\sigma T_s^4 \qquad [89]$$

However, scattered solar radiation is generally anisotropic (see **Table 1**). Consequently, it can be concentrated. The flux ϕ_p incoming on the receiver of a concentrator is

$$\phi_p = C\phi_{\text{in}} \qquad [90]$$

where C is the concentration ratio.

To determine the maximum concentration ratio of a i times scattered diffuse radiation, we must observe that fully concentrated scattered radiation implies that the receiver sees over the hemispherical solid angle 2π a blackbody at temperature $T_{e,i}$. Consequently, the maximal value of ϕ_p is

$$\phi_{p,\max} = \sigma T_{e,i}^4 \qquad [91]$$

Now, we can determine the maximum concentration ratio from eqns [89], [90], and [91]:

$$C_{\max,i} = \left[\frac{\Omega_i}{\pi}\left(1 - \frac{\Omega_i}{4\pi}\right)\right]^{-1} \qquad [92]$$

Results are shown in **Table 1** [18]. The maximum concentration ratio decreases by increasing the number of scatterings, as expected. Of course, fully isotropic diffuse radiation cannot be concentrated.

1.15.4 Upper Bounds for Thermal Radiation Energy Conversion

The maximum conversion efficiency of thermal radiation energy into work has been often derived from available work (exergy) considerations. The vast majority of authors considered the case of blackbody radiation (i.e., thermal radiation with zero chemical potential). The diversity of results generated a long-term debate in literature. Three efficiency-like factors affecting the radiation energy were proposed and defended in this context [26–30]. Among these, there is the Jeter (Carnot-like) factor and the Petela–Landsberg–Press (PLP) factor. The old problem is reiterated from time to time with different arguments pro or against one or another factor (for early and recent reviews, see References 31–34).

In this section, a more general theory of radiation energy conversion into work is developed by using a simple statistical thermodynamics approach [35]. This allows covering the particular case of dead-state radiation of nonzero chemical potential.

1.15.4.1 Available Work of Enclosed Thermal Radiation

A (fixed) volume V containing thermal radiation is considered and the continuum spectrum hypothesis is adopted. The energy representation is used here instead of the frequency representation used in most part of Section 1.15.2. As described in Section 1.15.2.2, dN_e denotes the number of photons in V with energy between e and $e + de$. Equation [12] shows that dN_e is given by the product between the number of energy states dg_e and the state occupation number n_e:

$$dN_e \equiv n_e dg_e \qquad [93]$$

The number of energy states of enclosed thermal radiation equals the number of vibration modes in volume V and is given in Reference 2 (see also Section 1.15.2.2):

$$dg_e \equiv \frac{64\pi^4}{c^3 h^3} V e^2 de \equiv A V e^2 de \qquad [94]$$

Here the extensivity assumption was adopted, which means interactions are weak. In some cases, not all the energy states are occupied by photons and here the following expression in generalization of eqn [23] is adopted for the mean occupation number of the state:

$$n_e \equiv \begin{cases} \dfrac{1}{\exp\left(\dfrac{e-\mu}{kT}\right)-1} & \text{for } e_g \leq e \leq e_m \\ 0 & \text{otherwise} \end{cases} \qquad [95]$$

In eqn [95], T is the temperature of the body emitting thermal radiation while e_g and e_m are some minimum and maximum allowed energy levels, respectively. For instance, e_g and μ in eqn [95] may be the bandgap energy and the radiation quasi-chemical potential appearing in the Shockley–Roosbroeck relationship, in case the radiation is in interaction with two electronic populations in a bandgap material [4]. For usual equilibrium, blackbody radiation $e_g = 0$, $e_m \to \infty$, and $\mu = 0$.

The number of particles N in volume V and their (internal) energy U is obtained after integration over all energy levels. Results are shown in rows 1 and 2 of **Table 2**. There, the following notation has been used:

$$x \equiv \frac{e}{kT} \qquad [96a]$$

$$x_\mu \equiv \frac{\mu}{kT} \qquad [96b]$$

$$x_g \equiv \frac{e_g}{kT} \qquad [96c]$$

$$x_m \equiv \frac{e_m}{kT} \qquad [96d]$$

and

$$i_s(x_\mu, x_g, x_m) \equiv \int_{x_g}^{x_m} \frac{x^s dx}{\exp(x - x_\mu) - 1} \qquad [97]$$

The entropy S of the particles inside volume V is defined in the equation in row 3 of column 2 of **Table 2**. For Bose statistics, the following function $s(n_e)$ applies (see eqns [10] and [11] in the frequency representation):

$$s(n_e) = -k[n_e \ln n_e - (1 + n_e) \ln (1 + n_e)] \qquad [98]$$

Table 2 Extensive thermodynamic properties of thermal radiation derived from microscopic quantities in energy representation

Quantity	Symbol and definition	Relationship
Number of particles	$N = \int_{e_g}^{e_m} n_e \, de_e$	$AVi_2(x_\mu, x_g, x_m)(kT)^3$
Internal energy	$U = \int_{e_g}^{e_m} e n_e \, de_e$	$AVi_3(x_\mu, x_g, x_m)(kT)^4$
Entropy	$S = \int_{e_g}^{e_m} s(n_e) \, de_e$	$-kAVj_2(x_\mu, x_g, x_m)(kT)^3$
Helmholtz free energy	$F \equiv U - TS$	$AV[i_3(x_\mu, x_g, x_m) + j_2(x_\mu, x_g, x_m)](kT)^4$
Pressure	$p = \dfrac{\mu N + TS - U}{V}$	$-A[i_3(x_\mu, x_g, x_m) + j_2(x_\mu, x_g, x_m) - i_2(x_\mu, x_g, x_m)x_\mu](kT)^4$
Enthalpy	$H \equiv U + pV$	$-AV[j_2(x_\mu, x_g, x_m) - i_2(x_\mu, x_g, x_m)x_\mu](kT)^4$

Equation [98] covers both equilibrium and nonequilibrium states. Relationships to compute other thermodynamic quantities are shown in rows 4–6 of **Table 2**. There, the following notation has been used:

$$j_s(x_\mu, x_g, x_m) \equiv \int_{x_g}^{x_m} \{\tilde{n}(x) \ln [\tilde{n}(x)] - [1 + \tilde{n}(x)] \ln [1 + \tilde{n}(x)]\} x^s dx \qquad [99]$$

Where

$$\tilde{n}(x) \equiv [\exp(x - x_\mu) - 1]^{-1} \qquad [100]$$

A few comments about the results of **Table 2** follow. For a given spectrum, the extensive thermodynamic functions N, U, and S depend on one extensive variable (V) and two intensive variables (T and μ). For given V, T, and μ, the same thermodynamic functions depend on the spectrum, which put its signature on the values i_2, i_3, and j_2 entering the expressions in column 3 of **Table 2**. In the particular case of a blackbody radiation spectrum ($e_g = 0$, $\mu = 0$, and $e_m \to \infty$), the extensive thermodynamic functions depend just on V and T.

The pressure definition $p \equiv -(\partial F/\partial V)_{T,N}$ has not been used in **Table 2**, because the number N of particles is not conserved. Instead, we have used the thermodynamics relationship $U - TS + pV = \mu N$, and this finally yields the result in the equation in row 5 of column 2 of **Table 2**. Use of the equations in column 3 of the first three rows in **Table 2** yields the state equation for the thermal radiation:

$$pV = -\frac{i_3(x_\mu, x_g, x_m) + j_2(x_\mu, x_g, x_m) - i_2(x_\mu, x_g, x_m)x_\mu}{i_3(x_\mu, x_g, x_m)} NkT \qquad [101]$$

Equation [101] is similar to the state equations of other simple Bose systems whose potential energy is neglected.

The mean energy $\bar{e}$ per particle inside the volume V is obtained from equations in row 1 of column 3 and row 2 of column 3 in **Table 2**, that is, $\bar{e} = U/N = [i_3(x_\mu, x_g, x_m)/i_2(x_\mu, x_g, x_m)](kT)$. In the particular case of blackbody radiation ($e_g = 0$, $\mu = 0$, and $e_m \to \infty$), $i_2(0,0,\infty) = 2\zeta(3) \cong 2.404$ and $i_3(0,0,\infty) = \pi^4/15 \cong 6.494$. Consequently, $\bar{e} \cong 2.701(kT)$.

The available work is generally defined as the maximum work extractable from a system by bringing it to mechanical, thermal, and chemical equilibrium with the environment. The environment (subscrip. 0) is defined as consisting of m given constituents of chemical potentials μ_0, i ($i = 1, m$) in equilibrium at pressure p_0 and temperature T_0. The list of the environment constituents and their composition is adopted by convention, sometimes in relation with the average Earth's crust composition. In practice, most available work calculations are based on the reference environment published in Reference 36, but several other reference environments are also used.

The chemical equilibrium condition is not trivial in the present case. To avoid this obstacle, we neglect most systems constituting the environment, which is simply reduced to the thermal radiation it contains. The same way of defining the environment has been always used when the available work of blackbody radiation was evaluated [32].

However, in most cases, the equilibrium radiation in real-world environments is different from blackbody radiation. Indeed, the equilibrium radiation frequency distribution depends strongly on the nature of the other components of the environment, with which radiation interacts. A simple example is the equilibrium radiation of an environment consisting of a gray body inside an enclosure with perfectly reflecting walls. The radiation with spectra described by Shockley–Roosbroeck relationship is another simple example. Also, common experience shows that the environment bodies emitting radiation are usually not covering the whole hemisphere. This makes the environment radiation to be nonisotropic in general. The academic equilibrium radiation is a particular case of the equilibrium thermal radiation in a real-world environment (i.e., it is associated with equilibrium radiation emitted by a single hemispherical blackbody).

The radiation in volume V reaches a dead state when equilibrated with the environment. The chemical potential and temperature of dead-state radiation are denoted μ_0 and T_0, respectively (its pressure p_0 is a unique function of T_0 and μ_0, see equation in row 5 of column 3 in **Table 2**). For generality, here one assumes the state occupation number (say $n_{0,e}$) associated with the dead-state radiation is characterized by specific quantities e_{g0} and e_{m0} in eqn. [95].

The system's available work X is the maximum theoretical amount of work that can be produced as the system reaches the dead state [37]:

$$X \equiv \Delta(U - T_0 S + p_0 V) = (U - U_0) - T_0(S - S_0) + P_0(V - V_0) \qquad [102]$$

where U_0, S_0, and V_0 are the dead-state extensive properties of the system. Use of the equations in column 3 of rows 2, 3, and 5 in **Table 2** for $T = T_0$, $\mu = \mu_0$, $e_g = e_{g0}$, and $e_m = e_{m0}$ shows that the dead-state Gibbs free energy $G_0 \equiv U_0 - T_0 S_0 + p_0 V_0 = \mu_0 N_0$, as expected. Then, use of eqn [102] and the equations in column 3 of rows 2, 3, and 5 in **Table 2** yields

$$X = \eta_X U \qquad [103]$$

where

$$\eta_X \equiv 1 + \frac{j_2(x_\mu, x_g, x_m)}{i_3(x_\mu, x_g, x_m)}\left(\frac{T_0}{T}\right) - \left[\frac{i_3(x_{\mu 0}, x_{g0}, x_{m0}) + j_2(x_{\mu 0}, x_{g0}, x_{m0})}{i_3(x_\mu, x_g, x_m)} + \left(\frac{V_0}{V} - 1\right)\frac{i_2(x_{\mu 0}, x_{g0}, x_{m0})}{i_3(x_\mu, x_g, x_m)}x_{\mu 0}\right]\left(\frac{T_0}{T}\right)^4 \qquad [104]$$

The efficiency-like available work factor η_X affecting the internal energy in eqn [103] contains the dead-state and radiation temperatures and the initial and dead-state volumes. This factor is different from the usual Carnot factor appearing in the available work carried by heat.

Two cases, denoted 1 and 2 in the following, may be of interest:

1. In the first case, the dead-state volume V_0 equals the initial volume V. Then, from eqn [104], one derives

$$\eta'_X \equiv 1 + \frac{j_2(x_\mu, x_g, x_m)}{i_3(x_\mu, x_g, x_m)}\left(\frac{T_0}{T}\right) - \left[\frac{i_3(x_{\mu 0}, x_{g0}, x_{m0}) + j_2(x_{\mu 0}, x_{g0}, x_{m0})}{i_3(x_\mu, x_g, x_m)}\right]\left(\frac{T_0}{T}\right)^4 \qquad [105]$$

Equation [105] shows that $\eta'_X(T_0 = 0) = 1$. Two assumptions are very often (implicitly) adopted. First, both the radiation and the environment radiation have the same chemical potential (a zero chemical potential is usually considered). Second, the same spectrum dependence on temperature and chemical potential applies to both the radiation and the environment radiation. The two assumptions yield $\eta'_X(T = T_0) = 0$. This result does not hold when one of the above assumptions is relaxed.

2. In the second case, the dead-state volume vanishes, that is, $V_0 = 0$. Consequently, η_X given by eqn [104] is a maximum:

$$\eta''_X \equiv 1 + \frac{j_2(x_\mu, x_g, x_m)}{i_3(x_\mu, x_g, x_m)}\left(\frac{T_0}{T}\right)$$
$$- \left[\frac{i_3(x_{\mu 0}, x_{g0}, x_{m0}) + j_2(x_{\mu 0}, x_{g0}, x_{m0}) - i_2(x_{\mu 0}, x_{g0}, x_{m0})x_{\mu 0}}{i_3(x_\mu, x_g, x_m)}\right]\left(\frac{T_0}{T}\right)^4 \qquad [106]$$

This rather unusual case of a vanishing dead state may be assimilated to radiation absorption. In general, η'_X obeys $\eta''_X(T_0 = 0) = 1$ and $\eta''_X(T = T_0) = [i_2(x_{\mu_0}, x_{g0}.x_{m0})/i_3(x_{\mu_0}, x_{g0}.x_{m0})]x_{\mu_0}$. This is reasonable, because a particle system at dead-state temperature may still provide (mechanical, electrical, or chemical) work. A well-known example is absorption of radiation in a bandgap material followed by electric carrier separation in the valence and conduction bands, which is associated with storage of Gibbs free energy.

1.15.4.2 Available Work of Free Thermal Radiation

A simple statistical model follows. It is inspired by the usual nonequilibrium thermodynamics treatment of free non-interacting particles where intensive parameters such as (effective) temperature, pressure, and chemical potential are still in use (see Section 1.15.2.4). Definitions for the most important flux quantities are shown in **Table 3** in the energy representation. There, θ and λ are incidence and azimuth angles, respectively, while Ω is the solid angle covered by all directions of photons of energy e with velocity $c(\theta, \lambda)$ (see Section 13.9 in Reference 22 and Chapter 4 in Reference 38). The following expression is adopted for the speed $c(\theta, \lambda)$ of a photon:

$$c(\theta, \lambda) \equiv c f_e(\theta, \lambda) \qquad [107]$$

Table 3 Quantities related to the flux of property Ξ

Quantity	Symbol and definition	Units
Spectral property radiance	$K_{\Xi,e}(\theta,\lambda) \equiv \frac{c(\theta,\lambda)}{4\pi V}\frac{d_e \Xi}{de}$	$\frac{\text{Property units}}{\text{m}^2 \text{ J sr}}$
Property flux density for solid angle $d\Omega$ and energy interval de	$d^2_{e,\Omega}J_{\Xi,e} \equiv K_{\Xi,e}(\theta,\lambda)\cos\theta\, de\, d\Omega$	$\frac{\text{Property units}}{\text{m}^2}$
Property spectral flux density	$d_e J_{\Xi,e} \equiv \int_\Omega d^2_{e,\Omega} J_{\Xi,e} = \int_\Omega K_{\Xi,e}(\theta,\lambda)\cos\theta\, d\Omega$	$\frac{\text{Property units}}{\text{m}^2 \text{ J}}$
Property flux density	$J_\Xi \equiv \int_e d_e J_{\Xi,e} = \int_{\Omega,e} K_{\Xi,e}(\theta,\lambda)\cos\theta\, de\, d\Omega$	$\frac{\text{Property units}}{\text{m}^2}$

Ξ may be the number of particles N, the energy U, and the entropy S.

where the function $f_e(\theta,\lambda)$ gives the photon direction. The following geometric factor $\bar{f}_e$ is defined as

$$\bar{f}_e \equiv \int_\Omega f_e(\theta,\lambda)\cos\theta\, d\Omega \qquad [108]$$

For example, in case the speed directions are isotropically distributed over the whole hemisphere, $\Omega = 2\pi$ and $f_e(\theta,\lambda) = 1$. Taking account that $d\Omega = \sin\theta\, d\theta\, d\lambda$, $\theta \in [0,\pi/2]$ and $\lambda \in [0,2\pi]$ one easily finds from eqn [108] that $\bar{f}_e = \pi$.

Use of equations in **Table 3** allows writing the flux density J_Ξ of a certain property Ξ as follows:

$$J_\Xi = D\Xi \qquad [109]$$

where the coefficient D is defined by

$$D \equiv \frac{c\bar{f}_e A}{4\pi} \qquad [110]$$

Here, A is a shortcut notation defined by eqn [94].

Some flux properties of thermal radiation are given in column 3 of **Table 4**. Equations in column 3 of rows 1 and 2 in **Table 4** show that the particle number flux and the energy of thermal radiation, respectively, are proportional to the third and fourth power of the effective temperature T, respectively, as known from the case of blackbody radiation. Use of the equations in column 3 of rows 2 and 3 in **Table 4** allows to writing $J_S = [-j_2(x_\mu, x_g, x_m)/i_3(x_\mu, x_g, x_m)]J_U/T$. This gives $J_S = (4/3)(J_U/T)$ in case of blackbody radiation ($e_g = 0$, $\mu = 0$, and $e_m \to \infty$), as expected.

A simple model is developed here to evaluate the available work of free thermal radiation. It is formally similar to the model of the available work of incoherent electromagnetic radiation [39]. In case of free radiation, the solid angles Ω and Ω_0 subtended by the radiation source and the dead-state radiation are generally different from each other. The spectral available work radiance d^2K_X is given by

$$d^2 K_X = [K_U - K_{U_0} - T_0(K_S - K_{S_0})]de\, d\Omega \qquad [111]$$

Finally, integration over the solid angle Ω subtended by the radiation source and over all energy levels yields the available work flux density:

$$J_X \equiv \iint d^2 K_X = J_U - J_{U_0} - T_0(J_S - J_{S_0}) \qquad [112]$$

Using eqn [112] and the equations in column 3 of rows 2 and 3 in **Table 4**, one finds the available work flux density, which is given by

$$J_X = \eta'_{J_X} J_U \qquad [113]$$

Table 4 Flux properties of thermal radiation

Quantity	Symbol and definition	Relationship
Particle number flux density	J_N	$Di_2(x_\mu, x_g, x_m)(kT)^3$
Energy flux density	J_U	$Di_3(x_\mu, x_g, x_m)(kT)^4$
Entropy flux density	J_S	$-kDj_2(x_\mu, x_g, x_m)(kT)^3$
Helmholtz free energy flux density	$J_F \equiv J_U - TJ_S$	$D[i_3(x_\mu, x_g, x_m) + j_2(x_\mu, x_g, x_m)](kT)^4$

where

$$\eta'_{J_X} \equiv 1 + \frac{j_2(x_\mu, x_g, x_m)}{i_3(x_\mu, x_g, x_m)} \left(\frac{T_0}{T}\right) - \left(\frac{D_0}{D}\right) \left[\frac{i_3(x_{\mu 0}, x_{g0}, x_{m0}) + j_2(x_{\mu 0}, x_{g0}, x_{m0})}{i_3(x_\mu, x_g, x_m)}\right] \left(\frac{T_0}{T}\right)^4 \quad [114]$$

Here, the dead-state constant D_0 generally differs from D because the geometric factors $\bar{f}_{0,e}$ and $\bar{f}_e$ are generally different from each other. Equation [114] is useful in the rather uncommon case when $\Omega_0 < \Omega$. However, in most cases, $\Omega_0 \geq \Omega$ and the integration over the solid angle Ω in eqn [112] yields $D_0 = D$. In this case

$$\eta'_{J_X} = \eta'_X \quad [115]$$

where η'_X is given by eqn [105]. In the case $\Omega_0 \geq \Omega$, eqn [21] with $\eta'_{J_X} = \eta'_X$ may be derived directly by using eqn [109] twice, for $\Xi \equiv U$ and $\Xi \equiv X$. Of the two cases considered in Section 1.15.4.1, only the available work factor given by eqn [105] (which corresponds to $V_0 = V$) is compatible with eqn [112] (which requires of course a finite volume dead state).

1.15.4.3 Available Work of Blackbody Radiation as a Particular Case

The particular case of free blackbody radiation ($e_g = 0$, $\mu = 0$, and $e_m \to \infty$) is considered next. This case is important, mainly because solar radiation is often modeled as blackbody radiation.

Two different particular subcases will be treated. Each case is characterized by its own (unique) dead state. In the first subcase, the dead state consists of radiation of zero chemical potential. In the second subcase, the dead state corresponds to luminescence radiation (nonzero chemical potential). Both cases may be used to describe, more or less accurately, situations existing in natural world. In the more limited world of man-made devices, the dead state of the first subcase is similar to the radiation emitted by a thermal converter, while the dead state of the second subcase may be assimilated to the radiation emitted by a common single gap solar cell. Therefore, the two available work factors derived below represent upper bounds for the efficiency for PT and PV conversion of radiation energy into mechanical and electrical work, respectively.

1.15.4.3.1 Upper bound for PT conversion efficiency

First, the case when the dead state consists of radiation emitted by a blackbody is considered ($e_{g0} = 0$, $\mu_0 = 0$, and $e_{m0} \to \infty$). This means that the incident blackbody radiation is finally degraded to radiation emitted by a blackbody receiver and the available work derived below corresponds to the maximum work extractable from solar radiation by using a PT (nonselective) blackbody converter. From eqns [115] and [105], one finds

$$\eta'_{J_X} \equiv \eta'_X = 1 - \frac{4}{3}\frac{T_0}{T} + \frac{1}{3}\left(\frac{T_0}{T}\right)^4 \quad [116]$$

This is precisely the PLP efficiency-like factor previously derived when the available work of isotropic blackbody radiation has been studied [26, 28, 29].

In case the dead state is associated with radiation emitted by a selective blackbody converter ($e_{g0} \neq 0$, $\mu_0 = 0$, and $e_{m0} \to \infty$), the available work factor is given by

$$\eta'_{J_X} \equiv \eta'_X = 1 - \frac{4}{3}\frac{T_0}{T} - \left[\frac{i_3(0, x_{g0}, \infty) + j_2(0, x_{g0}, \infty)}{6.4939}\right] \left(\frac{T_0}{T}\right)^4 \quad [117]$$

Figure 5 shows that the available work factor η'_{J_X} predicted by eqn [117] is strongly dependent on the ratio T_0 / T, as expected. The quantity x_{g0} (defined by eqn [96c], with $e_g \equiv e_{g0}$ and $T \equiv T_0$) is related to the properties of the selective converter, which does not emit photons with energy lower than e_{g0}. In case $x_{g0} = 0$ (i.e., when the dead state consists of blackbody radiation), the available work factor (eqn [117]) reduces to the PLP factor, which is always positive, whenever T is higher or lower than T_0, and is zero only for $T = T_0$. This last result is a consequence of the fact that both the radiation and the environment radiation have the same (null) chemical potential and a similar (blackbody-type) spectrum. Note that the PLP factor may exceed unity in case $T < T_0/1.587$, and this restricts somewhat its usage for $T < T_0$. These features are in agreement with previous knowledge [26].

For $x_{g0} >$, the spectrum of the radiation and the environment radiation is different from each other and the available work factor does not fulfill $\eta'_X(T = T_0) = 0$ (**Figure 6(a)**). Negative η'_X values mean that transforming blackbody radiation into nonblackbody radiation requires receiving external work. The influence of x_{g0} on the available work factor is rather weak and decreases when $T \to \infty$.

Equation [117] is a more accurate upper bound for the conversion efficiency than the PLP factor. However, the PLP factor may be used as a very good approximation at small values of the ratio T_0 / T. This happens, for example, in case of the PT conversion of solar energy where $T_0/T \cong 300/6000 = 0.05$.

1.15.4.3.2 Upper bound for PV conversion efficiency

Second, the case when the dead state consists of radiation with $e_{g0} \neq 0$, $\mu_0 \neq 0$, and $e_{m0} \to \infty$ is considered. It corresponds to an environment filled with radiation emitted by a bandgap material, for example. Thus, the available work factor derived below corresponds to the maximum work extractable from blackbody radiation by using a monogap PV cell. Then, $x_{g0} = e_g/(kT_0)$ and

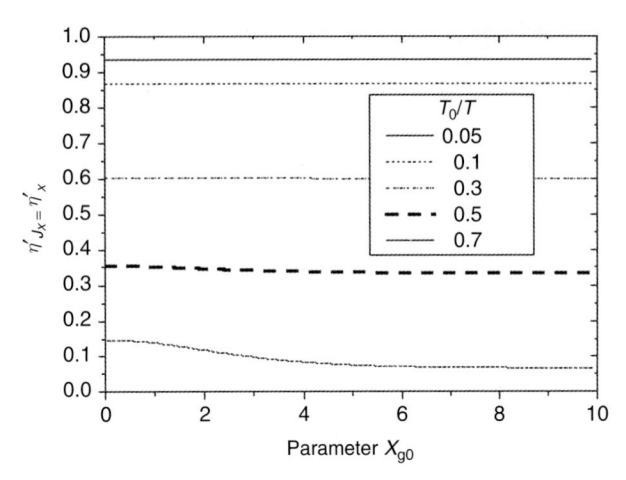

Figure 5 Dependence of the available work factor $\eta'_{J_X} = \eta'_X$ given by eqn [117] on the parameter x_{g0}, for several values of the ratio T_0/T.

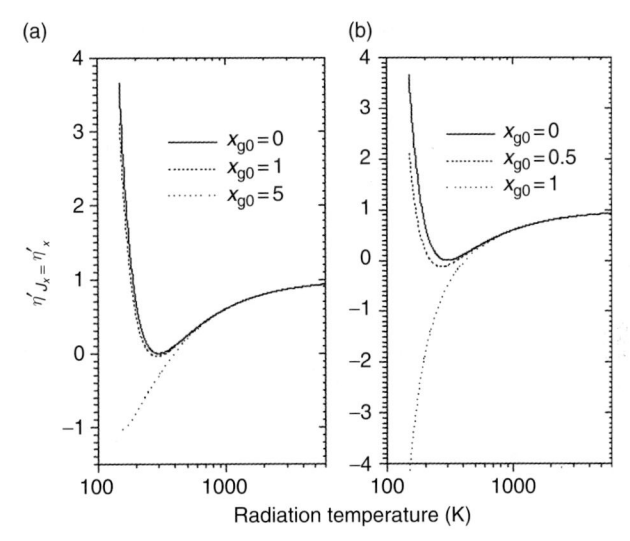

Figure 6 Dependence of the available work factor $\eta'_{J_X} = \eta'_X$ on the radiation temperature T, for several values of x_{g0}. The environment temperature is $T_0 = 300$ K. (a) Case of PT conversion: η'_{J_X} is given by eqn [117]; (b) case of PV conversion: η'_{J_X} is given by eqn [118] (computations performed for $x_{\mu 0} = 0.9 x_{g0}$).

$x_{\mu 0} = (qV^0)/(kT_0)$ where e_g, V_0, and T_0 are the bandgap energy, the voltage across the cell, and the cell temperature, respectively. From eqn [115], one finds

$$\eta'_{J_X} \equiv \eta_X = 1 - \frac{4}{3}\frac{T_0}{T} - \left[\frac{i_3(x_{\mu 0}, x_{g0}, \infty) + j_2(x_{\mu 0}, x_{g0}, \infty)}{6.4939}\right]\left(\frac{T_0}{T}\right)^4 \qquad [118]$$

Figure 6(b) shows the dependence of η'_{J_X} on the radiation temperature T, for a particular value of the environment temperature T_0. Again, negative η'_X values mean that transforming blackbody radiation into nonblackbody radiation requires receiving external work. **Figure 7** shows that the available work factor η'_{J_X} is significantly dependent on $x_{\mu 0}$ (i.e., on the voltage across the cell) at high values of the ratio T_0/T, as expected. This makes the formula (eqn [118]) of practical interest in case of thermophotovoltaic conversion. For small values of T_0/T, the influence of both x_{g0} (which is proportional to the cell bandgap) and $x_{\mu 0}$ on η'_{J_X} decreases and PLP factor is a very good approximation for the more exact eqn [118] (compare **Figures 6(a)** and **6(b)**).

1.15.4.4 Discussion

Equations [103] and [113] are important findings of this section. They show that the available work (or the available work flux density) of thermal radiation is given by the internal energy (or the energy flux density) times an available work factor η_X (or η'_{J_X}) containing the dead-state temperature and the radiation temperature, among other factors.

In most usual cases, eqn [105] provides a general upper bound for the efficiency of thermal radiation conversion into work. Efficiency-like relationships for less usual cases are also given (see eqn [106] for a dead state of vanishing volume and eqn [114] for dead-state radiation subtending a solid angle narrower than that of the radiation source).

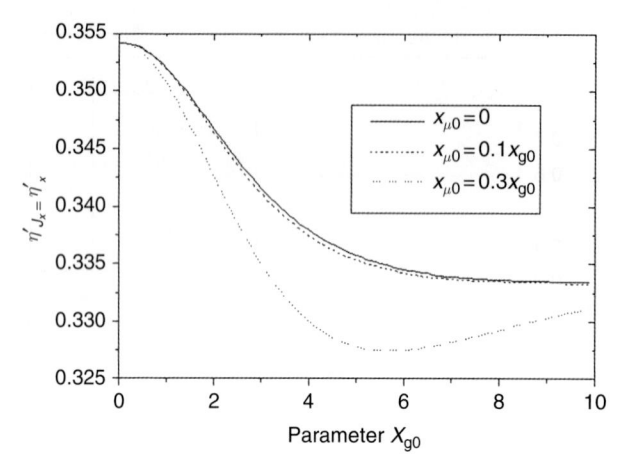

Figure 7 Upper bound for PV conversion efficiency of blackbody radiation energy into electrical work. Dependence of available work factor $\eta'_{J_x} = \eta'_x$ given by eqn [118] on x_{g0}, for several values of $x_{\mu 0}$ in case of $T_0 / T = 0.5$.

The theory is used to predict the best (ideal) performance of various conversion devices such as blackbody and selective thermal converters and monogap PV cells. If accurate results are needed, eqns [117] and [118] should be used as upper bounds for the efficiency of PT and PV conversion, respectively. However, the PLP factor and even the Carnot factor may be used as rough first approximations whatever the type of conversion is.

It is known that the optimum voltage across the solar cell, which maximizes the conversion efficiency, is given by References 40 and 41 (see also Section 1.15.5.2.2):

$$qV^{0,\text{opt}} = qe_{g0}\left(1 - \frac{T_0}{T_c}\right) \quad [119]$$

where T_c is the temperature of the cell. In the model studied here, the cell operates at dead-state temperature (i.e., $T_c = T_0$) and the optimum voltage $V^{0,\text{opt}}$ vanishes (as well as $x_{\mu 0}$). Thus, the available work factor predicted by eqn [118] is associated with $x_{\mu 0} = 0$ (**Figure 7**) and reduces to the case of the selective thermal converter (i.e., eqn [117]). In nonoptimal cases ($V^0 \neq V^{0,\text{opt}}$), the upper bound for the PV efficiency eqn [118] is lower than the upper bound of the PT efficiency (eqn [117]), for similar e_{g0} values.

1.15.5 Models of Monogap Solar PV Converters

The converter considered here consists of a photon absorber and a work extractor. The general case covering both PV and PT conversion can be found in References 42 and 43. Here we refer only to PV conversion. In this case, the (electrical) work extractor produces electrical energy.

The converter is intended to operate continuously; the electrical work extractor ensures that equilibrium does not establish itself. The absorber is normally a solid body consisting of

1. the nuclei of the lattice and their core electrons (subscript l);
2. the electrons of highest energy band (the conduction band) (subscript e);
3. the electrons or holes of the valence band (the band below the conduction band) (subscript h); and
4. the traps in the forbidden gap between the conduction band and the valence band (subscript t). Their concentration is assumed low so that impurity band effects and hopping can be neglected.

The electrical work extractor is a *p-n* or metal–semiconductor junction, together possibly with an external battery.

As a result of the incident external radiation, the characteristics of the subsystems l, e, h, and t in a volume element of the absorber are a function of position. The interaction between these subsystems consists of collisions within a volume element and influences due to neighboring volume elements. The latter are in part due to particle fluxes. The components of the converter can be subject to external field of forces such as mechanical stress and gradients of electrostatic potential or temperature. The general statistical approach has been described by using Boltzmann transport equations [42]. Local continuity equations were obtained by using the usual Chapman–Enskog procedure. The theory developed in the quoted paper has been applied to PV conversion [43]. Results from both papers are presented in this section.

1.15.5.1 Modeling Absorption and Recombination Processes

We consider the case of a converter (c) receiving radiation from a source of radiation (s) (e.g., the Sun) and a sink (a) (e.g., the ambient) and emitting radiation. The radiation emitted or received by the converter, pump, or sink may be partially polarized.

The balance of exergy per unit time in the two electronic bands (i.e., the valence and the conduction band) is given by eqn [3.1] in Reference 43:

$$P + \dot{E}^{elast} = \dot{G} + \dot{G}_t - T_c\dot{\Sigma}_G \qquad [120]$$

where P is the net electric power; $\dot{G}$ and $\dot{G}_t$ are the rate of change of Gibbs free energy due to electronic interband transitions and transitions involving traps, respectively; $\dot{E}^{elast}$ is the net elastic phonon energy leaving absorber per unit time, T_c is converter temperature, and $\dot{\Sigma}_G$ is the entropy generation rate in the two electronic bands. Basically, there is a single irreversibility taken explicitly into account, namely the dissipation accompanying the flow of charge.

One denotes by γ_{sc}, γ_{ac} the photon number flux received by the converter from the radiation source and ambient, respectively. Also, γ_{ct} denotes the photon number flux emitted by the absorber in all directions. Moreover, A_{cs} and A_{ca} are the areas where the fluxes γ_{sc} and γ_{ac} are received and A_{ct} is the emitting area of the converter. For simplicity we assume

$$A_{cp} = A_{cs} = A_{ct} = A \qquad [121]$$

One denotes by qV the chemical potential of the radiation emitted by the absorber. The assumption of small gradients of qV is adopted here.

The rate of change of Gibbs free energy due to electronic interband transitions, $\dot{G}$, can be expressed in terms of the photon number fluxes γ_i (i = sc, ac, cT) (see eqn [A15] in Reference 43). Use of eqn [3.1] and the expression of $\dot{G}$ yields eqn [3.2] in Reference 43:

$$P = qVA[f_{abs}(\gamma_{sc} + \gamma_{ac}) - f_{rec}\gamma_{ct}] + \dot{G} - \dot{E}^{elast} - T_c\dot{\Sigma}_G \qquad [122]$$

where the absorption and recombination factors, f_{abs} and f_{rec}, respectively, are given by

$$f_{abs} \equiv \left\langle \frac{\eta_{abs}}{1 - T^{t \leftrightarrow e}} \right\rangle \qquad [123a]$$

$$f_{rec} \equiv \left\langle \frac{1 - r\eta_{abs}\eta_{rec}}{\eta_{rec}(1-r)(1 - T^{t \leftrightarrow e})} \right\rangle \qquad [123b]$$

Here the brackets < > denote an average value over the converter volume, while the terms they contain are efficiency – like factors defined in **Table 5** by using symbols defined in **Table 6**.

The maximum efficiency η_{max} of converting the energy of the pump radiation into electrical work will be estimated by using the so-called endoreversibility hypothesis, which assumes that all the processes occurring in a given system are reversible. The main feature of an endoreversible PV converter is that any photon absorbed or emitted has no thermal effect and, consequently, should affect only the Gibbs free energy of the converter. As a result, each photon collision should be associated with precisely one electronic jump between the two bands. So, $(\dot{N}_{total,abs} - \dot{n}^{h \to e})_{rev} = 0$ and $(\dot{N}_{c,em} - \dot{n}^{e \to h})_{rev} = 0$. In this case, from **Table 5** we learn that $\eta_{abs,rev} = 1 > \eta_{abs}$ and $\eta_{abs,rev} = 1 > \eta_{rec}$. Consequently, by using eqns [131], we derive $f_{abs,rev} = 1 > f_{abs}$ and $f_{rec,rev} = 1 < f_{rec}$.

In all real cases, neither η_{rec} could vanish nor could $T^{t \leftrightarrow e}$ equal unity. There is, however, a possibility for the photon recycling efficiency to equal unity in some regions of the converter volume. The contribution of those regions to the volume average in eqn [123b] is zero [43]. By using **Table 5**, we see that normally η_{abs} and η_{rec} are less than unity because some of the photons absorbed thermalize and some of the carrier recombinations are nonradiative.

The following assumptions are adopted now:

1. The converter is transparent for the radiation of frequency $v < v_0 = E_g/h$, where E_g is the energy gap.

Table 5 Efficiency-like expressions (functions of space and time)

Definition	Meaning
$T^{t \leftrightarrow e} \equiv \dfrac{\dot{n}^{t \to e} - \dot{n}^{e \to t}}{\dot{n}^{coll}}$	Net ionization rate as a fraction of the total rate of change $\dot{n}^{coll}$
$r \equiv \dfrac{\dot{N}_{c,abs}}{\dot{N}_{c,em}}$	Efficiency of photon recycling in the converter
$\eta_{abs} \equiv \dfrac{\dot{n}^{h \to e}}{\dot{N}_{total,abs}}$	Efficiency of interband carrier generation of photon absorption
$\eta_{rec} \equiv \dfrac{\dot{N}_{c,em}}{\dot{n}^{e \to h}}$	Efficiency of photon emission by interband carrier recombination

The converter consists of electrons in the conduction band e and traps t, holes in the valence band h, and the lattice l. The photons are from the radiation source s and ambient a, or emitted by the converter c. Symbols are defined in Table 6.

Table 6 Symbols and meaning for rate of change of electron and photon number densities due to collisions (function of space and time) entering **Table 5**.

Symbol	Meaning
$\dot{n}^{coll}$	Rate of increase of electron number density in the conduction band, due to collisions with particles from all the subsystems j of the converter (j = e, t, h, l)
$\dot{n}^{e \rightarrow h}$	Rate of interband carrier recombination
$\dot{n}^{h \rightarrow v}$	Rate of interband carrier generation
$\dot{n}^{t \rightarrow e}$	Rate of carrier generation due to traps
$\dot{n}^{e \rightarrow t}$	Rate of carrier recombination due to traps
$\dot{N}_{total, abs}$	Absorption rate of all types i of photons (i = s, a, c) by all the subsystems j of the converter (j = e, t, h, l)
$\dot{N}_{c, em}$	Rate of photon emission by all the subsystems j of the converter (j = s, t, h, l)

The converter consists of electrons in the conduction band e and traps t, holes in the valence band h, and the lattice l. The photons are from the radiation source s and ambient a or emitted by the converter c.

Table 7 Temperatures and chemical potential for photon emitted by various sources i (i = s, a, c)

	Chemical potential μ_i	Temperature T_i
Radiation source (s)	0	T_s
Ambient (a)	0	T_a
Converter (c)	qV	T_c

2. Each source of radiation is characterized by a different photon distribution function. Under the steady-state assumption, the following distributions apply:

$$f_{Ni} = \frac{l_i(v)}{2} \left[\exp\left(\frac{hv - \mu_i}{kT_i} \right) - 1 \right]^{-1} \quad (i = s, a, c) \quad [124]$$

where the chemical potentials μ_i and the temperatures T_i (i = s, a, c) are shown in **Table 7**. Also, $l_i(v) = 1$ or 2 are polarization factors for polarized or unpolarized radiation, respectively.

3. The radiation entering or leaving the converter is characterized by reflectance ρ_{Ni} (i = s, a, c). Here, ρ_{Ns} and ρ_{Na} refer to the reflectance for the radiation source and ambient to enter into the converter, while ρ_{Nc} refers to the reflectance for the converter radiation to leave the converter.

4. The solid angles subtended by the pump and sink, when viewed from the converter, are Ω_{sc} and Ω_{ac}, respectively. Each point of the converter emits radiation in the solid angle $\Omega_t = 2\pi$.

5. When the radiation is partially polarized, the photon number flux can be expressed as a function of the flux of unpolarized (up) radiation, which corresponds to $l_i(v) = 2$ in eqn [124] of the same temperature:

$$\gamma_i = \frac{2 - P_i}{2} \gamma^{up} \quad (i = sc, ac, ct) \quad [125]$$

where P_i is the degree of polarization ($0 \leq P_i \leq 1$), which is assumed to be independent of frequency.

6. The following notation is adopted:

$$a \equiv \frac{T_a}{T_s} \quad [126a]$$

$$b \equiv \frac{T_c}{T_s} \quad [126b]$$

$$x_s \equiv \frac{E_g}{kT_s} \quad [126c]$$

$$v_s \equiv \frac{qV}{kT_s} \quad [126d]$$

7. The following functions are defined:

$$F_j(u, v) \equiv \int_u^\infty \frac{x^j dx}{e^{x-v} - 1} \quad [127]$$

Table 8 Different photon number fluxes

Flux	Meaning
$\gamma_{sc} = \frac{15\sigma}{\pi^5 k}(1-\rho_{Ns})\frac{2-P_s}{2}B_{sc}T_s^3 F_2(x_s, 0)$	Flux from radiation source to converter
$\gamma_{ac} = \frac{15\sigma}{\pi^5 k}(1-\rho_{Na})\frac{2-P_a}{2}B_{ac}T_a^3 F_2\left(\frac{x_s}{a}, 0\right)$	Flux from ambient to converter
$\gamma_{ct} = \frac{15\sigma}{\pi^5 k}(1-\rho_{Nc})\frac{2-P_c}{2}B_{ct}T_c^3 F_2\left(\frac{x_s}{b}, \frac{v_s}{b}\right)$	Flux emitted by converter in all directions

σ and k are the Stefan–Boltzmann and Boltzmann constants, respectively.

By taking into account the assumptions 1–7, we obtain the net photon number fluxes of **Table 8**.

An upper bound (P_{max}) for the useful power delivered by the converter can be derived by considering the flow of charge in the two electronic bands as a reversible process (i.e., $\dot{\Sigma}_G = 0$) and, in addition, $\dot{E}^{elast} = \dot{G}_t = 0$. Consequently, from eqn [122], one obtains

$$P_{max} = qVA[f_{abs}(\gamma_{sc} + \gamma_{ac}) - f_{rec}\gamma_{ct}] \qquad [128]$$

Note that $\dot{G}_t = 0$ implies $T^{t \leftrightarrow e} = 0$. As a result, the absorption and recombination factors (eqns [123]) become

$$f_{abs} \equiv \langle \eta_{abs} \rangle \qquad [129a]$$

$$f_{rec} \equiv \left\langle \frac{1 - r\eta_{abs}\eta_{rec}}{\eta_{rec}(1-r)} \right\rangle \qquad [129b]$$

Define the upper bound, η_{max}, of the maximum PV conversion efficiency as

$$\eta_{max} = \frac{P_{max}}{A\phi_{sc,inc}} = \frac{P_{max}}{A\frac{\sigma}{\pi}\frac{2-P_s}{2}B_{sc}T_s^4} \qquad [130]$$

where $\phi_{sc,inc}$ is the energy flux falling on the converter from the radiation source. By using eqns [128] and [130] and **Table 8**, one obtains

$$\eta_{max} = \frac{15 v_s}{\pi^4}\left[(1-\rho_{Ns})F_2(x_s, 0) + (1-\rho_{Na})\frac{2-P_a}{2-P_s}\frac{B_{sc}}{B_{sc}}a^3 F_2\left(\frac{x_s}{a}, 0\right) - (1-\rho_{Nc})\frac{2-P_c}{2-P_s}\frac{B_t}{B_{sc}}b^3 F_2\left(\frac{x_s}{b}, \frac{v_s}{b}\right)\right] \qquad [131]$$

Note that η_{max}, even if defined in energy terms (see eqn [130]), is a function of the photon number fluxes (i.e., of the function F_2).

A few results reported in Reference 43 are listed now. The highest conversion efficiency is obtained when the PV converter is kept at the lowest possible temperature, that is, at the ambient temperature ($T_c = T_a$). By increasing the ambient temperature T_a, the efficiency decreases, as expected. The efficiency has a shallow maximum as a function of the voltage V. In all cases, the efficiency decreases to zero as a threshold voltage (say V_{oc}) is reached. The efficiency increases slightly and the V_{oc} considerably by increasing the geometric factor of the pump (in other words, by increasing the radiation concentration ratio C). The dependence of the efficiency on the degree of polarization P_s is negligible. The power density P is greatest in the limit of unpolarized radiation ($P_s = 0$).

When the endoreversible converter is considered, the maximum efficiency is as high as 0.408 for fully concentrated radiation. It occurs for $x_s/b \approx 2.14$. This corresponds to a bandgap energy $E_g \approx 1.06$ eV, which is slightly smaller than the bandgap of silicon (1.12 eV). In case of nonconcentrated solar radiation, the efficiency decreases to 0.305. It occurs for $x_s/b \approx 2.54$ (i.e., $E_g \approx 1.26$ eV). This is lower than the bandgap of InP (1.29 eV). The optimum voltage ranges between 1.01 and 0.92 V for concentration ratio C decreasing from about 46 200 to 1. For a more realistic PV converter, the efficiency decreases from 0.318 to 0.233 for the full range of C considered here. The optimum values of x_s / b increase, but the optimum values of v_s / b decrease, as compared to the reversible PV converter.

1.15.5.1.1 The solar cell equation

The model will be used to derive the so-called solar cell equation, which is a widely used relation between the electric current density I leaving the solar cell and the voltage V across the converter. For this purpose, one uses equation $P = I \cdot V$ and eqn [130] and one obtains

$$I = \eta_{max}\frac{A\phi_{s,inc}}{V} \qquad [132]$$

By using eqns [131] and [132], we derive

$$I = qA\frac{15}{\pi^5}\frac{\sigma}{k}T_s^3 \left\{ \begin{array}{l} f_{abs}\left[(1-\rho_{Ns})\frac{2-P_s}{2}B_{sc}F_2(x_s, 0) + (1-\rho_{Na})\frac{2-P_a}{2}B_{ac}a^3 F_2\left(\frac{x_s}{a}, 0\right)\right] \\ -f_{rec}(1-\rho_{Nc})\frac{2-P_c}{2}B_t b^3 F_2\left(\frac{x_s}{b}, \frac{v_s}{b}\right) \end{array} \right\} \qquad [133]$$

The following relationship exists:

$$B_{ac} = B_t - B_{sc} \quad [134]$$

The equilibrium state (eq) is obtained in the dark (when $B_{sc} = 0$ and $B_{ac} = B_t$ as a result of eqn [134] with $V = 0$ (i.e., $v_s = 0$). Then, $I = 0$ so that eqn [133] becomes

$$f_{abs,eq}(1-\rho_{Na})\frac{2-P_a}{2}a^3 F_2\left(\frac{x_s}{a},0\right) = f_{rec,eq}(1-\rho_{Nc})\frac{2-P_c}{2}b^3 F_2\left(\frac{x_s}{b},\frac{v_s}{b}\right) \quad [135]$$

By using eqns [133]–[135], we obtain a useful relation between I and V:

$$I = qA\frac{15}{\pi^5}\frac{\sigma}{k}T_s^3 \left\{ \begin{array}{l} f_{abs}B_{sc}\left[(1-\rho_{Ns})\frac{2-P_s}{2}F_2(x_s,0) - (1-\rho_{Na})\frac{2-P_a}{2}a^3 F_2\left(\frac{x_s}{a},0\right)\right] \\ -f_{rec}B_t(1-\rho_{Nc})\frac{2-P_c}{2}b^3\left[F_2\left(\frac{x_s}{b},\frac{v_s}{b}\right) - c_f F_2\left(\frac{x_s}{b},0\right)\right] \end{array} \right\} \quad [136]$$

where:

$$c_f \equiv \frac{f_{abs}}{f_{abs,eq}}\frac{f_{rec,eq}}{f_{rec}} \quad [137]$$

The usual solar cell equation is a particular case of the more general result (eqn [136]). To see this, suppose that $qV \ll E_g$ (i.e., $v_s \ll x_s$). Then,

$$F_2\left(\frac{x_s}{b},\frac{v_s}{b}\right) \cong F_2\left(\frac{x_s}{b},0\right)\exp\left(-\frac{v_s}{b}\right) \quad [138]$$

By introducing eqn [138] in eqn [136], one obtains

$$I = I_L - I_0\left[\exp\left(\frac{qV}{kT_c}\right) - c_f\right] \quad [139]$$

where:

$$I_L \equiv qA\frac{15}{\pi^5}\frac{\sigma}{k}T_s^3 f_{abs} B_{sc}\left[(1-\rho_{Ns})\frac{2-P_s}{2}F_2(x_s,0) - (1-\rho_{Na})\frac{2-P_a}{2}a^3 F_2\left(\frac{x_s}{a},0\right)\right] \quad [140]$$

$$I_0 \equiv qA\frac{15}{\pi^5}\frac{\sigma}{k}T_s^3 f_{rec} B_t(1-\rho_{Nc})\frac{2-P_c}{2}b^3 F_2\left(\frac{x_s}{b},0\right) \quad [141]$$

If $c_f = 1$, eqn [139] is precisely the usual solar cell equation. In this case, I_L and I_0 can be identified with the illumination current density and the dark saturation current density, respectively. Note that $c_f = 1$ if photon absorption and emission are considered reversible processes ($f_i = f_{i,eq} = f_{i,rev} = 1$ ($i = $ abs, rec)).

The approximation (eqn [138]) breaks down at higher solar radiation concentration when the open-circuit voltage V_{oc} obtained by putting $I = 0$ in eqn [133] is close to the value E_g/q.

1.15.5.1.2 The Shockley–Queisser model

One of the first detailed balance model of PV conversion was proposed by Shockley and Queisser [44]. It continues to be very attractive because of its simplicity. Compared with the more accurate model described above, we note that it neglects

1. the loss of energy due to radiation from the converter;
2. incident radiation from the ambient;
3. the effect of the front face reflection of radiation; and
4. the irreversibilities associated with the absorption of radiation.

With these assumptions, our eqn [131] yields the Shockley–Queisser efficiency η_{SQ}:

$$\eta_{SQ} = \frac{15 v_s}{\pi^4} F_2(x_s, 0) \quad [142]$$

The maximum efficiency predicted by the Shockley–Queisser model is 0.439 and $x_{s,opt} \approx 2.17$. This corresponds to an optimum bandgap energy $E_{g,opt}$ of about 1.08 eV.

From eqns [122], [128], and [130], one can deduce two efficiency relations. First,

$$\frac{P}{A\phi_{sc,inc}} = \frac{P_{max}}{A\phi_{sc,inc}} + \frac{\dot{G}_t - \dot{E}^{elast} - T_c\dot{\Sigma}_G}{A\phi_{sc,inc}} \quad [143]$$

The last term is the one neglected in eqns [128] and [130]. Second,

$$\frac{P}{A\phi_{sc,inc}} = \frac{qVA[f_{abs}(\gamma_{sc}+\gamma_{ac})-f_{rec}\gamma_{ct}]}{A\phi_{sc,inc}} + \frac{\dot{G}_t - \dot{E}^{elast} - T_c\dot{\Sigma}_G}{A\phi_{sc,inc}} \qquad [144]$$

The Shockley–Queisser result (eqn [142]) is part of the term γ_{pC} shown in **Table 8**. It is obtained by choosing unpolarized pump radiation and no reflection of photons from the pump: $P_s = 0$; $\rho_{Ns} = 0$. Equating eqns [143] and [144], one finds

$$\eta_{max} = f_{abs}\frac{2-P_s}{2}(1-\rho_{Ns})\eta_{SQ} - \frac{qV}{\phi_{sc,inc}}(f_{rec}\gamma_{ct} - f_{abs}\gamma_{ac}) \qquad [145]$$

which is the desired relation between the efficiency η_{max} and the Shockley–Queisser efficiency η_{SQ}. The coefficient of η_{SQ} is less than unity. Also, the photon number flux emitted by the converter normally exceeds that received from the ambient ($\gamma_{ct} > \gamma_{ac}$) while $f_{rec} > f_{abs}$, whence η_{max} is less than η_{SQ}, as expected. However, one sees from eqn [145] that η_{SQ} need not be a good upper efficiency limit, namely, if $\gamma_{ct} < \gamma_{ac}$, which could arise for a hot ambient and a well-cooled converter.

1.15.5.2 Modeling Multiple Impact Ionization

The influence of impact ionization on solar cell performance has been studied by many authors [45–52]. For example, the probability that a charge carrier will, when it has adequate energy, actually impact ionize was estimated [53]. This, together with Auger recombination, reduces the beneficial effects of impact ionization [54]. In one case (Si–Ge), the experimentally observed effect of impact ionization on the measured efficiency was actually quite small [55]. Increasing radiation concentration proved to be beneficial.

In this section, the combined effects of both impact ionization and radiation concentration on solar cell performance will be described by using thermodynamic models. Four different ways are used to derive expressions for the solar cell efficiency. They allow for both solar and ambient inputs, as well as for the occurrence of separate cell and ambient temperatures. A Carnot-type upper bound is found for the reduced driving force in PVs that exhibit impact ionization.

1.15.5.2.1 Solar cell efficiencies

Direct solar radiation can be concentrated. The following notation will be used:

$$s \equiv \frac{B_s}{\pi} \qquad [146]$$

where B_s is the geometrical factor of the Sun when viewed from the Earth. Equation [90] allows to write the energy flux of concentrated radiation, ϕ_{conc}:

$$\phi_{conc} = C\frac{B_s}{\pi}\sigma T_s^4 = Cs\sigma T_s^4 \qquad [147]$$

where C is the energetic concentration ratio. Note that $Cs = 1$ in eqn [147] corresponds to maximum solar concentration assuming a loss-free optical system that collects all incident solar radiation at the top of the atmosphere. Use of the assumption (eqns [48a] and [146]) allows to find $s \approx 2.176 \times 10^{-5}$. Then, the maximum value of the concentration ratio at the level of the Earth level is about $C_{max} = 1/s \approx 45\,963$.

On the Earth's surface, the product Cs may be smaller than 2.176×10^{-5}. For example, extraterrestrial solar radiation for $C = 1$ at the orbit of the Earth is about $1367\,\mathrm{Wm}^{-2}$, while global solar irradiance at the Earth's surface in sunny days decreases to about $1000\,\mathrm{Wm}^{-2}$. Equation [147] yields $Cs = 0.731 \times 10^{-5}$ for this last case and $\ln(Cs) = -11.82$.

The output power of a solar cell is considered in the usual way, as resulting from three contributions:

1. Power from the main source of radiation, the Sun, which is treated as a blackbody at temperature T_s. The term (1) related to the main source of radiation is affected by the factor Cs ($0 \le Cs \le 1$) which allows for different values of the solar concentration ratio C ($0 \le C \le 45\,963$).
2. Power from the surroundings that cover the remaining solid angle of the solar cell. This is taken to act as an effective blackbody at temperature T_a. Note that T_a is a few centigrade degrees lower than the ambient temperature. However, usually the ambient temperature is adopted as an approximation value for T_a. The term (2) related to the ambient radiation has the matching factor $1-Cs$.
3. Power reduction due to carrier recombination. This term has also a Bose denominator of the form $\exp[(e-Q(e)qV)/kT_c]-1$. It appears in an integral over the photon energy e. Here, T_c is cell temperature, qV is the driving force in the solar cell, and $Q(e)$ is a quantum efficiency representing the number of electron–hole pairs generated by a photon of energy e. Here, $Q(e)$ is a staircase function of e (i.e., it equals zero for $0 < e < E_g$ and equals M for $ME_g < e < (M+1)E_g$). The probability of impact ionization was taken to be unity, but in fact it is lower [53].

The quantum efficiency also appears as a multiplier of each of the three terms. Other multipliers inside the integral (over the photon energies from $e = 0$ to $e = \infty$) are

(a) $(2\pi/h^3c^2)e^2\,de \equiv ge^2\,de$, which converts the three terms (1)–(3) to photon number fluxes (note that this relationship defines the factor g); and

(b) the photovoltage V produced across the cell, which converts each integral to a power density.

We now have the output power density of the cell for the given illumination. Dividing by the input power density due to the Sun, this procedure yields an expression for the efficiency, η, of the solar cell. The relevant equations are displayed on page 419 of Reference 49, where $qVQ(e)$ has been interpreted as the chemical potential, $\mu(e)$, of the photons of energy e and the solar cell was kept at the ambient temperature (i.e., $T_c = T_a$). The resulting equation is

$$\eta = \frac{15}{\pi^4 Csk^4T_s^4} \int_0^\infty \left[\frac{Cs}{\exp\left(\frac{e}{kT_s}\right)-1} + \frac{1-Cs}{\exp\left(\frac{e}{kT_a}\right)-1} - \frac{1}{\exp\left(\frac{e-\mu(e)}{kT_a}\right)-1} \right] \mu(e)e^2\,de \quad [148]$$

For a maximum efficiency, one needs to derive a supplementary equation, denoted by below eqn [152], obtained from the condition:

$$\partial\eta/\partial\mu(e) = 0 \quad [149]$$

Four common ways will be presented now to deal with the problem of deriving maximum efficiencies under different conditions from eqn [148].

1.15.5.2.1(i) Approximation for narrow band semiconductors

In the first method, one takes into consideration that impact ionization is particularly important for narrow bandgap semiconductors. Thus, let $E_g \to 0$ and $M \to \infty$ but make ME_g of the order 20 (i.e., large). Then, e/E_g approximates $Q(e)$ because the staircase function tends toward a straight line in this limit. The following notation will be used:

$$t \equiv \frac{T_a}{T_s} \quad [150a]$$

$$v \equiv \frac{qV}{E_g} \quad [150b]$$

This yields the efficiency:

$$\eta = (1-t^4)v + \frac{t^4v}{Cs}\left[1 - \frac{1}{(1-v)^4}\right] \quad [151]$$

The use of eqn [149] applied to eqn [151] yields the following result:

$$[Cs(1-t^4) + t^4](1-v)^5 = t^4 + 3vt^4 \quad [152]$$

1.15.5.2.1(ii) Maximum efficiency for maximum concentration

By considering a special case treated in Reference 49, we now proceed on the assumption of maximum solar concentration, $Cs = 1$, to find, for this case, the following relations:

$$\eta = \left[1 - \left(\frac{t}{1-v}\right)^4\right]v \quad [153]$$

$$(1-v)^5 = (1+3v)t^4 \quad [154]$$

They are given here without use of the variable $x \equiv t/(1-v)$ used in eqns [6] and [7] of Reference 49. The maximum efficiency for this case is

$$\eta = 0.854, \quad [155]$$

as explained in the quoted paper.

1.15.5.2.1(iii) Open-circuit voltage for narrow band semiconductors

Returning to the case of narrow semiconductors and keeping the product Cs general, one finds the following generalization of eqn [153]:

$$\eta = \frac{4v^2t^4}{Cs(1-v)^5} \quad [156]$$

which must be equivalent to eqn [151]. In order to test this, equate eqns [151] and [156]. The condition for equality is just eqn [152], thus proving the validity of eqn [156]. If we rewrite eqn [152] in the form

$$Cs = \left[\frac{1+3v}{(1-v)^5} - 1\right]\frac{t^4}{1-t^4} \quad [157]$$

we see that Cs increases with v if t is given. Greater values of the product Cs lead to a larger voltage. **Figure 8** gives this curve for $t = 0.05$, corresponding to $T_a/T_s \sim 300/6000$, that is, the solar case. The limiting value $Cs = 1$ occurs for the reduced driving force $v = 0.882$ [40]. Under normal conditions, this represents an upper limit for qV/E_g.

Next we consider how the open-circuit voltage $V_{oc}(v_{oc} \equiv qV_{oc}/E_g)$ depends on the product Cs. This can be discussed by putting $\eta = 0$ in eqn [151], since η vanishes when the current density vanishes. Some simple manipulation then yields

$$v_{oc} = 1 - \frac{t}{[Cs + (1-Cs)t^4]^{1/4}} \quad [158]$$

V_{oc} shows the expected increase for given t as the incident radiation energy is increased (**Figure 9**). But it drops for given insolation as the radiation source temperature T_s is decreased (T_a being kept fixed). This applies in case of diffuse radiation, for example (see Section 1.15.2.6).

A short explanation follows. There are two ways of changing incident radiation: change its blackbody temperature (i.e., T_s) or change its composition, which would mean concentrating or diluting it while still keeping it blackbody radiation. The increase of

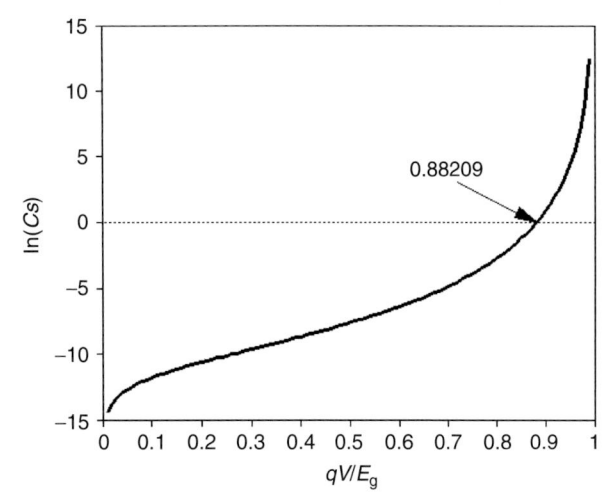

Figure 8 Concentration factor Cs as a function of the reduced driving force qV/E_g as predicted by eqn [157] for $t = T_a/T_s = 0.05$. E_g, energy bandgap; T_a, ambient temperature; T_s, radiation source temperature (e.g., the Sun).

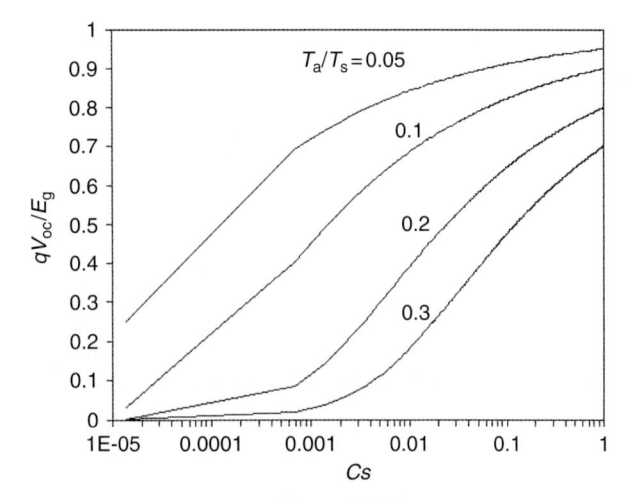

Figure 9 Reduced open circuit driving force qV_{oc}/E_g as a function of the concentration factor Cs and T_a/T_s as predicted by eqn [158]. For notation, see **Figure 8**.

insolation by concentrating the radiation would be expected to increase the V_{oc}. If T_s drops but keeps the total insolation, the frequency distribution of the blackbody radiation is changed and the consequence is that the incident radiation has now a lower maximum and V_{oc} may be expected to drop as well.

1.15.5.2.1(iv) General approach

Perhaps the most general procedure is to apply eqn [149] to eqn [148] and to avoid the limiting procedure of Section 1.15.5.2.1(i) and also to omit the assumption $Cs = 1$ of Section 1.15.5.2.1(ii) (as was already done in Section 1.15.5.2.1(iii)). This yields a supplementary condition that is different from eqn [152], namely eqn [163] below. First, use the notation

$$u \equiv \frac{e}{kT_a} \qquad [159a]$$

$$ut \equiv \frac{e}{kT_s} \qquad [159b]$$

$$x \equiv \frac{\mu}{kT_a} \qquad [159c]$$

$$A \equiv \frac{15}{\pi^4 k^4 Cs T_s^4} \qquad [159d]$$

One can identify u as the new variable, with the efficiency η now a functional depending on the function $x(u)$. The aim is to find that function $x_{opt}(u)$ that maximizes η given by eqn [149] and written as

$$\eta = A \int_0^\infty F[x(u), u] du \qquad [160]$$

where

$$F[x(u), u] \equiv \left[\frac{Cs}{\exp(ut) - 1} + \frac{1 - Cs}{\exp(u) - 1} - \frac{1}{\exp[u - x(u)] - 1} \right] x(u) u^2 \qquad [161]$$

This is a classical variational calculus problem where $F[x(u), u]$ is the argument function, which does not depend on the derivatives of $x(u)$. Consequently, the attached Euler–Lagrange equation is

$$\frac{\partial F[x(u), u]}{\partial x} = 0 \qquad [162]$$

By using eqns [161] and [162], one finds the equation for $x_{opt}(u)$:

$$\frac{Cs}{\exp(ut) - 1} + \frac{1 - Cs}{\exp(u) - 1} - \frac{[1 + x_{opt}(u)] \exp[u - x_{opt}(u)] - 1}{\{\exp[u - x(u)] - 1\}^2} = 0 \qquad [163]$$

The optimum chemical potential of photons as a function of photon energy is obtained by solving eqn [163] for $x_{opt}(u)$. Here $x_{opt}(u)$ and the associated maximum efficiency are both found to increase with illumination, that is, with Cs (**Figures 10** and **11**). Indeed, the incident flux on the cell consists of photons rich in energy from the Sun (first term in eqn [161], geometric factor Cs) and less energetic photons from the ambient (second term in eqn [161], geometric factor $1 - Cs$). Increasing Cs increases the contribution of solar photons; hence, the increase in solar cell efficiency, as eqns [160] and [161] show.

1.15.5.2.2 Optimum voltage across solar cells

1.15.5.2.2(i) Impact ionization neglected

Returning to the case $M = 1$ (i.e., no impact ionization), the electrical current density I is given by

$$\frac{I}{q} = A \left[Cs \int_{E_g}^\infty \frac{e^2 de}{\exp\left(\frac{e}{kT_s}\right) - 1} + (1 - Cs) \int_{E_g}^\infty \frac{e^2 de}{\exp\left(\frac{e}{kT_a}\right) - 1} - \int_{E_g}^\infty \frac{e^2 de}{\exp\left(\frac{e - qV}{kT_c}\right) - 1} \right] \qquad [164]$$

The first term in the square brackets is the contribution of the solar energy flux, the second term is the gain from the ambient, while the last term is the loss due to carrier recombination. Here, the general case of a cell at temperature $T_c \neq T_a$ is considered. To find the voltage V that gives the maximum of I with respect to the bandgap E_g, compute the derivative:

$$\left[\frac{\partial (I/q)}{\partial E_g} \right]_V = 0 \qquad [165]$$

One finds the following equation to be fulfilled by the optimum voltage V:

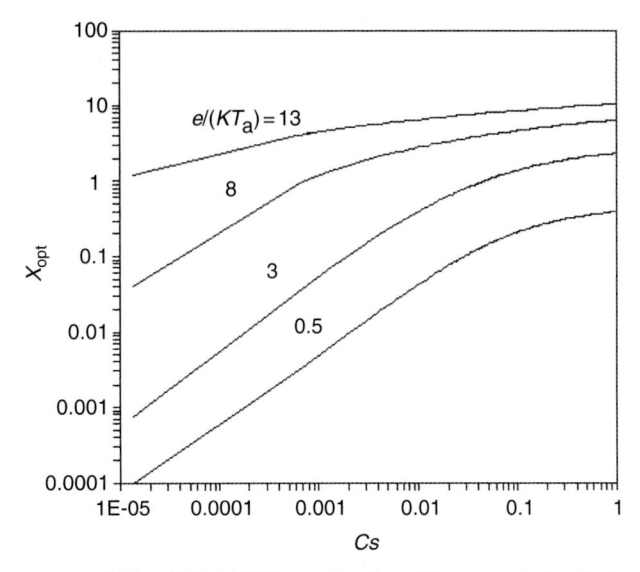

Figure 10 Dimensionless parameter $x_{opt} \equiv \mu/(kT_a) \equiv qVQ(e)/(kT_a)$ as a function of the concentration factor Cs and $u \equiv e/(kT_a)$. Equation [163] has been used. $Q(e)$, quantum efficiency for photons of energy e; V, voltage across the cell; $T_s (= 300\,K)$, ambient temperature.

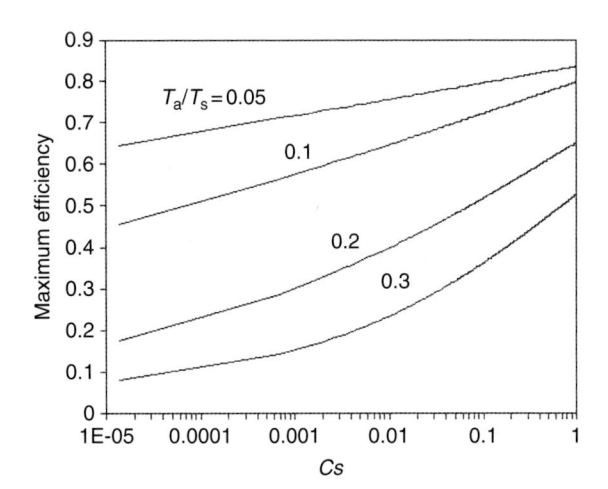

Figure 11 Maximum PV conversion efficiency defined by eqn [160] as a function of the concentration factor Cs and T_a/T_s. For notation, see **Figure 8**.

$$\frac{Cs}{\exp\left(\frac{E_g}{kT_s}\right)-1} + \frac{1-Cs}{\exp\left(\frac{E_g}{kT_a}\right)-1} - \frac{1}{\exp\left(\frac{E_g-qV}{kT_c}\right)-1} = 0 \qquad [166]$$

One can associate a V with each Cs. Three special cases denoted (1)–(3) are detailed now:

1. Operation at maximum radiation concentration. Maximum radiation concentration means $Cs = 1$. By using eqn [166], one finds for the reduced optimum driving force:

$$\frac{qV}{E_g} = 1 - \frac{T_c}{T_s} \qquad [167]$$

One can see the occurrence of the Carnot factor $(1 - T_c/T_s)$. Equation [167] is a generalization of the result first obtained in Reference 40 where the solar cell temperature T_c was assumed to be equal to the ambient temperature T_a and the Carnot factor was found to be $1 - T_a/T_s$. Generally, the two temperatures are different (with $T_c > T_a$) and eqn [167] gives a more accurate upper bound for the cell voltage [41].

2. Operation in darkness. The case when the cell operates in darkness (i.e., $Cs = 0$) is also of interest. From eqn [166], one finds [56]

$$-\frac{qV}{E_g} = \frac{1}{\frac{T_a}{T_c - T_a}} \qquad [168]$$

Let us suppose that $T_c > T_a$. One sees in the denominator of the positive right-hand side of eqn [168] the coefficient of performance of a Carnot refrigeration engine operating between the temperatures T_a and T_c. The voltage V is negative. This means that the cell has to receive energy from outside in order to keep its temperature T_c higher than the ambient temperature T_a.

3. Operation at null voltage. The solar cell voltage vanishes (i.e., $V = 0$) in case of the following value of the product between the concentration ratio and the reduced geometrical factor of the Sun:

$$(Cs)_0 = \frac{\left(\dfrac{1}{\exp\left(\dfrac{E_g}{kT_c}\right) - 1}\right) - \left(\dfrac{1}{\exp\left(\dfrac{E_g}{kT_a}\right) - 1}\right)}{\left(\dfrac{1}{\exp\left(\dfrac{E_g}{kT_s}\right) - 1}\right) - \left(\dfrac{1}{\exp\left(\dfrac{E_g}{kT_a}\right) - 1}\right)} \qquad [169]$$

Using eqns [169] and [166], one can easily check this result.

The cases (1)–(3), above, apply for particular cases of the concentration factor Cs and for arbitrary temperatures $T_a < T_c < T_s$. Figure 12 shows the dependence of the reduced driving force qV/E_g for some intermediate values of Cs. For convenience, the following values were considered: $T_s = 6000\,K$ and $T_a = 300\,K$ and the cell temperature is $T_c = 350\,K$. The voltage V is negative for Cs less than $(Cs)_0$ given by eqn [169].

1.15.5.2.2(ii) Impact ionization included

The case with impact ionization included is analyzed under the assumptions of Section 1.15.5.2.1(i) (i.e., $E_g \to 0$; $M \to \infty$, and ME_g = finite). Then, the current density is given by

$$\frac{I}{q} = A' \left[Cs \int_{E_g}^{\infty} \frac{\left(\dfrac{e}{E_g}\right) e^2 \, de}{\exp\left(\dfrac{e}{kT_s}\right) - 1} + (1 - Cs) \int_{E_g}^{\infty} \frac{\left(\dfrac{e}{E_g}\right) e^2 \, de}{\exp\left(\dfrac{e}{kT_a}\right) - 1} - \int_{E_g}^{\infty} \frac{\left(\dfrac{e}{E_g}\right) e^2 \, de}{\exp\left(\dfrac{e - qV(e/E_g)}{kT_c}\right) - 1} \right] \qquad [170]$$

where A' is a constant.

To find the voltage V that gives the maximum of I with respect to the bandgap E_g, one computes the derivative (eqn [165]). After some algebra, one obtains eqn [166] again. It is interesting to remind ourselves that eqn [166] was previously derived under the assumption of no impact ionization ($M = 1$) and arbitrary E_g.

All exponential functions in eqn [166] include the factor E_g. Also, $qV < E_g$. Keeping the assumptions of Section 1.15.5.2.1(i), one can see that these functions can be approximated by $\exp(z) \approx 1 + (z)$. Thus, eqn [166] yields

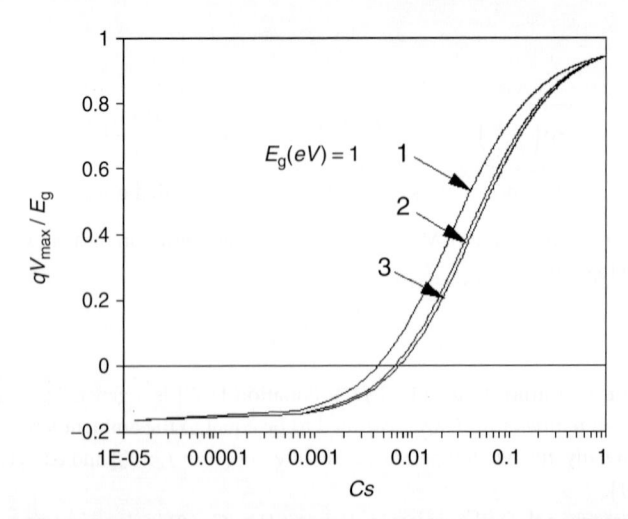

Figure 12 Dependence of the reduced driving force qV/E_g on the concentration factor Cs and energy bandgap E_g. Equation [166] has been used. T_a (=300 K), ambient temperature; T_s(=6000 K), radiation source temperature (the Sun); T_c(=350 K), cell temperature.

$$\frac{qV}{E_g} = 1 - \frac{T_c}{T_s}\left[\frac{1}{Cs + (1-Cs)\frac{T_a}{T_s}}\right] \leq 1 - \frac{T_c}{T_s} \qquad [171]$$

The last inequality in eqn [171] is due to the square bracket being bigger than unity. The Carnot factor occurs again (this time for arbitrary concentration) as an upper bound of the optimum reduced driving force qV/E_g, when the number of impact ionization is unlimited.

The three particular cases of eqn [166] can be reiterated in case of eqn [171].

1. For maximum concentration ($Cs = 1$), eqn [171] yields eqn [167] again.
2. In case of a cell operation in darkness ($Cs = 0$), eqn [171] yields again eqn [168].
3. The voltage vanishes ($V = 0$) in case of the following concentration factor:

$$(Cs)_0 = \frac{T_c - T_a}{T_s - T_a} \qquad [172]$$

Equation [172] can also be obtained from eqn [169] under the hypothesis $E_g \to 0$.

1.15.5.2.3 Discussion

Multiple impact ionization increases, of course, solar cell efficiency. Its counterpart is the Auger recombination process, which has also been discussed in this section, eqn [148], using appropriate multiples of the normal photon chemical potential. Since these two rates are equal in equilibrium, they are both liable to be important also out of equilibrium.

Impact ionization and Auger recombination are particularly important for narrow bandgap semiconductors. For maximum solar concentration and an infinite number of impact ionizations, one obtains the maximum efficiency of 0.845 [46, 48, 49]. In the solar case (i.e., $t \equiv T_a/T_s \approx 300/6000$), that maximum efficiency is associated with an optimum driving force $qV/E_g = 0.882$ [40]. The open-circuit voltage increases for given t as the insolation is increased and drops for given insolation as t is decreased.

The optimum reduced driving force qV/E_g for PV cells with single impact ionization is obtained by solving eqn [166]. With full concentration, the optimum reduced driving force is proportional to the Carnot factor as shown by eqn [167]. In the absence of illumination, the reduced driving force is negative and the efficiency is related to the coefficient of performance of a Carnot refrigerating engine (see eqn [168]). For arbitrary concentration, the Carnot factor is an upper bound of the reduced driving force qV/E_g (eqn [171]).

The averaged probability that a charge carrier will (when it has the correct energy) actually impact ionize was estimated theoretically. This together with consideration of Auger recombination reduces the expected beneficial effects of impact ionization.

1.15.6 Models of Omnicolor Solar Converters

Various ways of converting solar radiation into electrical energy were conceived, most of them based on single gap systems. It has been soon realized that the use of a system involving more than one energy gap should enable higher efficiency to be obtained. It is believed that the highest efficiency can be realized by an infinite stack of p–n junctions with smoothly varying bandgaps from infinity to zero, such that there is a single junction adapted to each frequency in the solar spectrum. In the system proposed in Reference 57, all individual cells are selective blackbodies such that the photons of frequency v of the solar spectrum are completely absorbed by the cell with bandgap $E_g = hv$. Such a system is denoted as a fully selective or omnicolor PV converter. Useful approximations for their mathematical treatment were proposed subsequently [58]. A small error in the model was corrected and a simple relation between the Carnot efficiency of thermodynamic engines and PV energy conversion was outlined [59, 60]. A new improvement of the model was performed [61]. The influence of radiation concentration on the efficiency of omnicolor converters was studied [62]. Note that the geometric factors affecting the ambient radiation incident on the collector have to be corrected in that paper. However, this error has little influence on the results. Some of the above papers were reviewed [63, 64].

This section provides an introduction to the thermodynamics of PT and PV omnicolor converters [65]. An unifying approach is also presented.

1.15.6.1 Omnicolor PT Converters

The maximum conversion efficiency with a thermal system is obtained, in the limit, with an infinite collector array, as shown in **Figure 13**. Each radiation splitter selects from the (concentrated) radiation spectrum the photons from a narrow band of width dv around a given frequency v used to heat a collector that absorbs and emits around that frequency. This collector has a temperature $T_c(v)$ and its absorptance $a(v)$ is supposed to be given by

$$a(v) = \begin{cases} 1 & \text{for } v \in [v - dv/2, v + dv/2] \\ 0 & \text{for all other frequencies} \end{cases} \qquad [173]$$

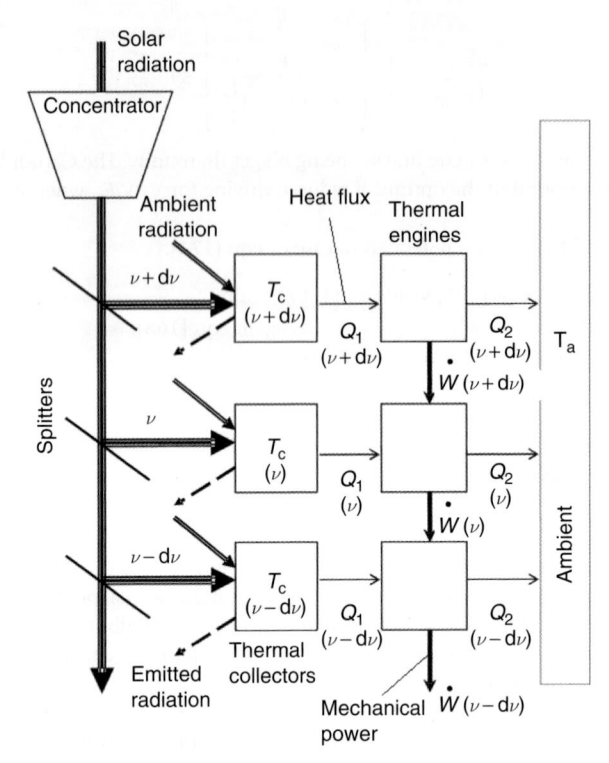

Figure 13 Omnicolor PT converter. For details, see the body of the text.

The spectral irradiance φ from a source of blackbody radiation at temperature T may be written in the form:

$$\phi(v, T) = \frac{B}{\pi} I_P(v, T) hv \qquad [174]$$

where B is the geometric factor and

$$I_P(v, T) = \frac{2v^2}{c^2} \left[\exp\left(\frac{hv}{kT}\right) - 1 \right]^{-1} \qquad [175]$$

is Planck's distribution.

The net thermal flux $\dot{Q}_1(v)$ supplied by the collector of surface area A at temperature $T_c(v)$ toward its accompanying heat engine is supposed to be given by

$$\dot{Q}_1(v)/A = \phi_s(v, T_s) + \phi_a(v, T_a) - \phi_c[v, T_c(v)] \qquad [176]$$

where the indices s, a, and c refer to the Sun, ambient, and collector, respectively. The first two terms from the right-hand side of eqn [176] represent the incident solar and ambient radiation, respectively, while the last term is the flux of radiation emitted by the collector.

In a first approximation, the Sun can be considered as a source of isotropic radiation. In this case, $T \approx 5760$ K and the following equation (derived from eqn [27]) applies for the geometric factor of the Sun:

$$B_s(\Omega_s, \Theta) = \pi u^2(\Omega_s) \cos \Theta \qquad [177]$$

where, from eqns [25] and [26], one sees that

$$u(\Omega_s) = \left[\frac{\Omega_s}{\pi} \left(1 - \frac{\Omega_s}{\pi} \right) \right]^{1/2} = \sin \delta \qquad [178]$$

Here, Ω_s is the solid angle subtended by the Sun when viewed from the receiving surface, while θ_0 is the angle between the normal of the receiving surface and the direction to the center of the solar disc (i.e., the Sun's zenith angle – see **Figure 1**). Also, δ is the half-angle of the cone subtended by the Sun. Equation [177] can be used only when the following condition (eqn [36]) is fulfilled, that is, when the sun is completely visible.

In case of concentrated radiation, one notes that in the presence of the concentrator, the Sun is viewed from the collector surface under an enlarged angle (say Ω_c). The concentration ratio C is naturally defined as [66]

$$C = \frac{B_s(\Omega_c, \Theta=0)}{B_s(\Omega_s, \Theta=0)} \qquad [179]$$

that is, the ratio between the geometric factors of the concentrated and the nonconcentrated radiation, respectively, both evaluated at normal incidence ($\theta_0 = 0$). By using eqns [179], [177], and [178], one obtains

$$C = \frac{\Omega_c(4\pi - \Omega_c)}{\Omega_s(4\pi - \Omega_s)} \qquad [180]$$

Consequently, for a given distance to the sun and concentration ratio C, eqn [180] can be used to compute the enlarged solid angle Ω_c. Then, the energy flux density $\varphi_s(\nu, T_s)$ can be evaluated by means of eqn [174].

The geometric factor B_a of the ambient radiation flux is given by [66]

$$B_a = \pi - B_s \qquad [181]$$

Note that eqn [181] is rigorous in the case of concentrated solar radiation, when the concentrator's mirror covers part of the celestial vault [67]. However, this equation is a very good approximation in the case of unconcentrated radiation too, because of the negligible value which B has in this case (at the mean Earth–Sun distance $B_s \approx 6.83 \times 10^{-5}$ – see eqn [48a]). Equation [181] was accepted by several authors [61, 62]. In Reference 62, the following assumption has been adopted: $B_a = \pi$. We proved that each of the two hypotheses is valid under special circumstances [67]. Throughout this section, we accept eqn [181] because Haught's assumption [62] $B_a = \pi$ could lead to significant error for large values of C.

The collector is supposed to emit radiation toward the whole hemisphere ($\Omega = 2\pi$); consequently, its geometric factor is B_c ($\Omega = 2\pi, \theta_0 = 0) = \pi$, as eqn [177] shows.

By using eqns [174], [175], and [181], we obtain the net thermal flux $\dot{Q}_1(\nu)$ entering the thermal engine working at frequency ν:

$$\frac{\dot{Q}_1(\nu)}{A} = \frac{2\pi h \nu^3}{c^2} \alpha(\nu) \left\{ \frac{B_s}{\pi}\left[\exp\left(\frac{h\nu}{kT_s}\right)-1\right]^{-1} + \left(1 - \frac{B_s}{\pi}\right)\left[\exp\left(\frac{h\nu}{kT_a}\right)-1\right]^{-1} - \left[\exp\left(\frac{h\nu}{kT_c}\right)-1\right]^{-1} \right\} \qquad [182]$$

If we take into account eqn [173], we see that this engine uses the energy of solar radiation in a narrow range around frequency ν only. Of course, the neighboring engines use the radiation from other infinitesimal frequency intervals. As usual, the thermal engines are supposed to be of Carnot type. The power provided by the engine working at frequency ν is given by $\dot{W}d\nu = \dot{Q}_1(\nu)\eta_{Carnot}d\nu$, where η_{Carnot} is Carnot efficiency. Consequently, the mechanical power $\dot{W}_{tot}$ supplied by the array of monochromatic converters (i.e., by the whole omnicolor converter) can be obtained by summing up the contributions of all thermal engines:

$$\dot{W}_{tot} = \int_0^\infty \dot{W}(\nu)d\nu = \int_0^\infty \dot{Q}_1(\nu)\left[1 - \frac{T_a}{T_c(\nu)}\right]d\nu \qquad [183]$$

Remember that $\dot{Q}_1(\nu)$ is a function of $T_c(\nu)$. The maximum power supply $\dot{W}_{tot,max}$ can be obtained by optimizing the collector temperature $T_c(\nu)$ for conversion of the radiation of frequency ν. Consequently, we have to solve the equation

$$\frac{\partial \dot{W}_{tot}}{\partial T_c(\nu)} = 0 \qquad [184]$$

and then replace its root (say $T_{c,opt}(\nu)$) in eqn [182]. The maximum efficiency of the omnicolor PT is simply given by

$$\eta_{PT,max} \equiv \frac{\dot{W}_{tot,max}}{\int_0^\infty \varphi_s(\nu)d\nu} = \frac{\dot{W}_{tot,max}}{\frac{B_s}{\pi}\sigma T_s^4} \qquad [185]$$

An omnicolor PT converter yields $\eta_w = 0.868$ for terrestrial applications, and even higher efficiencies in case of some space applications (due to the lower environmental temperature).

1.15.6.2 Omnicolor PV Converters

The maximum conversion efficiency with a PV system is obtained, in the limit, with an infinite stack of cells, as shown in **Figure 14**. Note that this set of galvanically separated cells provides higher performance than the case of current-coupled tandem cells [11].

The following usual idealizations are made in order to avoid trivial loss processes [60]:

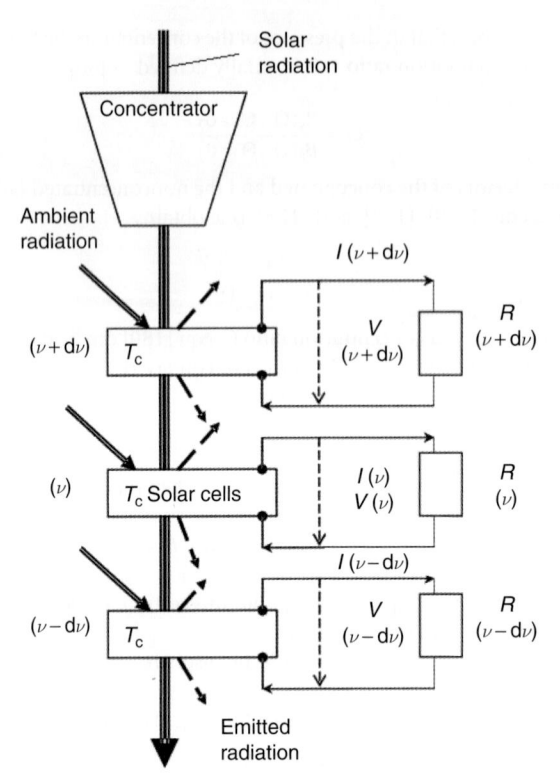

Figure 14 Omnicolor PV converter. *R*, electrical resistance; *I*, electric current; *V*, voltage. For other details, see the body of the text.

1. Light can only be absorbed by creating an electron–hole pair (i.e., light cannot be absorbed by exciting an electron from one level to another level in the same energy band).
2. An electron–hole pair can only recombine by emission of a photon (radiative recombination).
3. The difference in quasi-Fermi levels at the place of creation of electrons and holes equals the difference at the place of extraction of this carrier (the contacts), that is, it equals the elementary electric charge q times the basic voltage $V(v)$.

The spectral number flux density of photons from a source of blackbody radiation of temperature T is given by

$$\psi(v,T) = \frac{B}{\pi} I_P(v,T) \qquad [186]$$

Equation [186] can be used in the case of photons incident on the infinite stack of cells from the Sun and the ambient. When the number flux of photons emitted by a semiconductor is considered, a different equation has to be used. So, for any cell from the stack, the photon number flux density emitted is

$$\psi_c[v, V(v), T_c] = \frac{B_c}{\pi} I_{SR}[v, V(v), T_c] \qquad [187]$$

where

$$I_{SR}[v, V(v), T_c] \equiv \frac{2v^2}{c^2} \left[\exp\left(\frac{hv - qV(v)}{kT_c}\right) - 1 \right]^{-1} \qquad [188]$$

is the Shockley–Roosbroeck relationship that was first reported in the theory of photoluminescence [60]. Note that in eqn [188] all the cells were considered to be at the same temperature T_c. According to the above hypothesis (a), the net number flux density of photons ψ absorbed by the cell working at frequency v equals the number of electron–hole pairs generated.

By using eqns [175] and [186]–[188], and taking into account that $B_c = \pi$, we obtain the net number flux density of photons:

$$\psi(v) = \frac{2v^2}{c^2} \left\{ \frac{B_s}{\pi} \left[\exp\left(\frac{hv}{kT_s}\right) - 1 \right]^{-1} + \left(1 - \frac{B_s}{\pi}\right) \left[\exp\left(\frac{hv}{kT_a}\right) - 1 \right]^{-1} - \left[\exp\left(\frac{hv - qV(v)}{kT_c}\right) - 1 \right]^{-1} \right\} \qquad [189]$$

Consequently, the electric current is

$$I(v) = qA\Psi(v) \qquad [190]$$

where again A is the collection surface area.

Now, we neglect the loss of power in the external resistance $R(v)$. Each cell provides an electrical power $W(v) = I(v)V(v)$ and the total electrical power $\dot{W}_{tot}$, supplied by the whole stack is

$$\dot{W}_{tot} = \int_0^\infty \dot{W}(v)dv = \int_0^\infty I(v)V(v)dv \qquad [191]$$

The maximum electrical power $\dot{W}_{tot,max}$ is provided when each cell is working at its optimum voltage $V_{opt}(v)$ satisfying

$$\frac{\partial \dot{W}_{tot}}{\partial V(v)} = 0 \qquad [192]$$

$\dot{W}_{tot,max}$ is obtained by replacing in eqn [191] the optimum voltage we derived by solving eqn [192]. Of course, the maximum efficiency of the omnicolor PV converter $\eta_{PV,max}$ can be computed again by using eqn [185].

1.15.6.3 Unified Model of Omnicolor Converters

De Vos and Vyncke [61] observed that η_{PV} and η_{PT} can be put in a unique form if the following notation is used:

1. In the case of the PT omnicolor converter:

$$x(v) = 1 - \frac{T_a}{T_c(v)} \qquad [193]$$

2. In the case of the PV omnicolor converter:

$$x(v) = \frac{qV(v)}{hv} \qquad [194]$$

First we have to replace eqns [193] and [194] in eqns [183] and [191], respectively, in order to obtain the mechanical and electrical power as a function of the new variable $x(v)$. Then the derivatives in eqns [184] and [192] have to be evaluated to determine the optimum value $x_{opt}(v)$ for which the maximum power $\dot{W}_{tot,max}$ is obtained. Finally, the maximum efficiency $\eta_{max}(\equiv \eta_{PT,max}; \eta_{PV,max})$ is computed by using eqns [183] and [193] (or eqns [191] and [194]) and eqn [185]. The following notation and change of variable, respectively, will be used:

$$\tau_a \equiv \frac{T_a}{T_s} \qquad [195a]$$

$$u \equiv \frac{hv}{kT_a} \qquad [195b]$$

Then the efficiency is given by [61]

$$\eta_{max}(\equiv \eta_{PT,max}; \eta_{PV,max}) = \frac{15\tau_a^4}{\frac{B_s}{\pi}\pi^4} \int_0^\infty x_{opt}(u) \left\{ \frac{B_s/\pi}{\exp(\tau_a u)-1} + \frac{1-B_s/\pi}{\exp(u)-1} - \frac{1}{\exp[u-ux_{opt}]-1} \right\} u^3 du \qquad [196]$$

Here the optimum value $x_{opt}(u)$ is obtained by solving the equation:

$$\frac{(1+ux_{opt})\exp(u-ux_{opt})-1}{[\exp(u-ux_{opt})-1]^2} = \frac{B_s/\pi}{\exp(\tau_a u)-1} + \frac{1-B_s/\pi}{\exp(u)-1} \qquad [197]$$

If we take into account eqns [193–195], we see that once $x_{opt}(u)$ is known, the optimum dependence of $T_{c,opt}(u)$ and $V_{opt}(v)$ can be computed with

$$T_{c,opt}(u) = \frac{T_s}{1-x_{opt}(u)} \qquad [198a]$$

$$V_{opt}(v) = \frac{ux_{opt}(u)kT_s}{q} \qquad [198b]$$

1.15.6.4 Discussion

The limiting value for the efficiency η_{PV} of a standard single gap PV cell under fully concentrated sunlight is about 0.408 [68]. For a two-cell stack, the maximum efficiency increases to 0.557 while when advanced techniques such as up-converters and down-converters are used the efficiency becomes 0.638 [69]. A further increase is obtained in case of omnicolor PV converters (this time under one-sun illumination) with a maximum efficiency of 0.687 [61]. The omnicolor PV converters under fully concentrated radiation yields $\eta_{PV} = 0.868$ for terrestrial applications and even higher efficiencies in the case of some space applications [65, 70]. This is the highest solar energy conversion efficiency possible in a solar energy conversion system with reciprocity between light absorption and emission [69].

Nonreciprocal converters based on circulators yield the PLP efficiency that is about 0.93 in case of terrestrial applications. An ideal solar cell combined with an ideal monochromatic light filter acts as an ideal Carnot converter of heat emitted by a blackbody (conversion efficiency about 0.95 for the Earth-based applications) [69].

All these theoretical results are far beyond experimental results. The best laboratory result is $\eta_{PV} = 0.415$ (for a three-cell tandem under concentration). First-generation silicon solar modules have efficiencies in the range 10–15% and second-generation thin-film cells have even lower values of 4–9% [69, 71].

1.15.7 Conclusions

Thermodynamic modeling of solar energy conversion system operation means a description of the various processes taking place inside in terms of intensive physical quantities (such as temperature, pressure, and chemical potential) and property fluxes (such as the energy and entropy fluxes).

The energy conversion system consists of one or more devices and these devices are described by various design and operation parameters. The essential part of any solar energy conversion system is the radiation absorber. A radiation concentrator is sometimes part of the systems. The other devices, if any, are just assisting in operation of these two main components. This chapter presented simple, idealized models for concentrator and absorber operation. Only the essential parameters and processes were included in the models.

The performance of the device is quantified by performance indicators. In case of PV converters, the most important performance indicator is the radiation energy conversion efficiency. The main objective of any (solar) energy conversion theory is to estimate accurately the effective performance of the conversion system. Two steps are necessary in practice to increase the accuracy of simple thermodynamic models. First, additional relevant processes should be included in the models. The second step consists of taking account of the imperfections and irreversibilities associated with these additional processes. Here we showed the procedures in case of the recombination and impact ionization processes. [65, 66, 67, 68, 69, 70, 71]

References

[1] Landsberg PT (1961) *Thermodynamics with Quantum Statistical Illustrations.* New York: Wiley.
[2] Landsberg PT (1990) *Thermodynamics and Statistical Mechanics.* New York: Dover.
[3] Landsberg PT and Tonge G (1980) Thermodynamic energy conversion efficiencies. *Journal of Applied Physics* 51: R1–R20.
[4] Landsberg PT (1991) *Recombination in Semiconductors.* Cambridge, UK: Cambridge University Press.
[5] Landsberg PT (1981) Photons at non-zero chemical potential. *The Journal of Physics C* 14: L1025–L1027.
[6] Würfel P (1982) The chemical potential of radiation. *The Journal of Physics C* 15: 3967–3985.
[7] De Vos A (2000) Thermodynamics of photovoltaics. In: Sieniutycz, S and De Vos, A (eds.) *Thermodynamics of Energy Conversion and Transport*, pp. 50–71. New York: Springer.
[8] Castans M, Soler A, and Soriano F (1987) Theoretical maximal efficiency of diffuse radiation. *Solar Energy* 38: 267–270.
[9] Kabelac S (1991) A new look at the maximum conversion efficiency of black-body radiation. *Solar Energy* 46: 231–236.
[10] Bell LN and Gudkov ND (1993) *Thermodynamics of Light Energy Conversion.* The Hague, the Netherlands: SPB Publishing.
[11] Dinu C and Badescu V (1998) Optimisation of four-colour photothermal converters used for power generation on interplanetary stations. *International Journal of Energy Research* 22: 857–866.
[12] Landsberg PT and Badescu V (2000) The geometrical factor of spherical radiation sources. *Europhysics Letters* 50: 816–822.
[13] Landsberg PT, De Vos A, Baruch P, and Parrott JE (1996) Multiple source photovoltaics. In: Shiner JS (ed.) *Entropy and Entropy Generation*, p. 192. Dordrecht, the Netherlands: Kluwer Academic Publishers.
[14] Kamada O (1965) Theoretical concentration and attainable temperature in solar furnaces. *Solar Energy* 9: 39–47.
[15] Negi BS, Bhowmik NC, Mathur SS, and Kandpal TC (1986) Ray trace evaluation of solar concentrators including limb darkening effects. *Solar Energy* 36: 293–296.
[16] Giovanelli RG (1975) The nature of solar energy. In: Messel H and Butler ST (eds.) *Solar Energy.* London: Pergamon.
[17] Gueymard CA and Myers DR (2008) Solar radiation measurement: Progress in Radiometry for improved modeling. In: Badescu V (ed.) *Modeling Solar Radiation at Earth Surface*, pp. 1–27. Heidelberg, Germany: Springer.
[18] Badescu V (1991) Maximum conversion efficiency for the utilization of multiply scattered solar radiation. Journal of Physics D 24: 1882–1885.
[19] Landsberg PT and Tonge G (1979) Thermodynamics of the conversion of diluted radiation. *Journal of Physics* A 12: 551–561.
[20] Wright SE (2007) Comparative analysis of the entropy of radiative heat transfer and heat conduction. *International Journal of Thermodynamics* 10: 27–35.
[21] Badescu V (1988) L'exergie de la radiation solaire directe et diffuse sur la surface de la Terre. *Entropie* 145: 41–45.
[22] Perez R, Seals R, Ineichen P, *et al.* (1987) A new simplified version of the Perez diffuse irradiance model for tilted surfaces. *Solar Energy* 39: 221–231.
[23] Harrison AW and Coombes CA (1988) Angular distribution of clear sky short wavelength radiance. *Solar Energy* 40: 57–63.
[24] Bernard R, Menguy G, and Schwartz M (1980) *Le Rayonnement Solaire. Conversion Thermique et Applications.* Paris, France: Technique et Documentation.
[25] Winston R, Minano JC, and Benitez P (2005) *Nonimaging Optics.* London: Elsevier Academic Press.
[26] Petela R (1964) Exergy of heat radiation. *Journal of Heat Transfer* 86: 187–192.
[27] Spanner DC (1964) *Introduction to Thermodynamics*, p. 218. London: Academic Press.
[28] Landsberg PT and Mallinson JR (1976) Thermodynamic constraints, effective temperatures and solar cells In: Coll. Int. sur l'Electricite Solaire, pp. 27–35. Toulouse: CNES.
[29] Press WH (1976) Theoretical maximum for energy from direct and diffuse sunlight. *Nature* 264: 734–735.

[30] Jetter SJ (1981) Maximum conversion efficiency for the utilization of direct solar radiation. *Solar Energy* 26: 231–236.
[31] Bejan A (1987) Unification of three different theories concerning the ideal conversion of enclosed radiation. *Journal of Solar Energy Engineering* 109: 46–51.
[32] Bejan A (1988) *Advanced Engineering Thermodynamics*. New York: Wiley.
[33] Petela R (2003) Exergy of undiluted thermal radiation. *Solar Energy* 74: 469–488.
[34] Sieniutycz S and Kuran P (2006) Modeling thermal behavior and work flux in finite-rate systems with radiation. *International Journal of Heat and Mass Transfer* 49: 3264–3283.
[35] Badescu V (2008) Unified upper bound for photothermal and photovoltaic conversion efficiency. *Journal of Applied Physics*. 103: 054903.
[36] Szargut J, Morris DR, and Steward FR (1988) *Exergy Analysis of Thermal, Chemical, and Metallurgical Processes*, Hemisphere. Berlin, Germany: New York; Springer-Verlag.
[37] Landau L and Lifchitz E (1967) *Physique Statistique*. Moscow: Mir.
[38] Landsberg PT and Badescu V (2000) Some methods of analysing solar cell efficiencies. In: Sieniutycz S and De Vos A (eds.) *Thermodynamics of Energy Conversion and Transport*, pp. 46–48. New York: Springer.
[39] Karlsson S (1982) Exergy of incoherent electromagnetic radiation. *Physics Scripta* 26: 329–332.
[40] Landsberg PT and Markvart T (1998) The Carnot factor in solar-cell theory. *Solid-State Electron* 42: 657–659.
[41] Landsberg PT and Badescu V (2000) Carnot factor in solar cell efficiencies. *Journal of Physics* D 33: 3004.
[42] Badescu V and Landsberg PT (1995) Statistical thermodynamics foundation for photovoltaic and photothermal conversion II. Application to photovoltaic conversion. *Journal of Applied Physics* 78: 2793–2802.
[43] Badescu V and Landsberg PT (1995) Statistical thermodynamics foundation for photovoltaic and photothermal conversion. I. Theory. *Journal of Applied Physics* 78: 2782–2792.
[44] Shockley W and Queisser H (1961) Detailed balance limit of efficiency of p-n junction solar cells. *Journal of Applied Physics* 32: 510.
[45] Landsberg PT, Nussbaumer H, and Willeke G (1993) Band-band impact ionisation and solar cell efficiency. *Journal of Applied Physics* 74: 1451–1452.
[46] Werner J, Kolodinski S, and Queisser H (1994) Novel optimization principles and efficiency limits for semiconductor solar cells. *Physical Review Letters* 72: 3851–3854.
[47] Brendel R, Werner J, and Queisser H (1996) Thermodynamic efficiency limits for semiconductor solar cells with carrier multiplication. *Solar Energy Materials and Solar Cells* 41/42: 419–425.
[48] Wurfel P (1997) Solar energy conversion with hot electrons from impact ionisation. *Solar Energy Materials and Solar Cells* 46: 43.
[49] De Vos A and Desoete B (1998) On the ideal performance of solar cells with larger-than-unity quantum efficiency. *Solar Energy Materials and Solar Cells* 51: 413.
[50] Andreev VM (1999) Heterostructure solar cells. *Semiconductors* 33: 942–945.
[51] Badescu V, Landsberg PT, De Vos A, and Desoete B (2001) Statistical thermodynamic foundation for photovoltaic and photothermal conversion. IV. Solar cells with larger-than-unity quantum efficiency revisited. *Journal of Applied Physics* 89: 2482–2490.
[52] Metzger WK (2001) Auger recombination in low-band-gap n-type InGaAs. *Applied Physics Letters* 79: 3272.
[53] Liakos JK and Landsberg PT (1995) A simple model calculation of impact ionisation probability and its consequences for photovoltaic cell efficiencies. In: *13th European Photovoltaic Solar Energy Conference*, p. 1235. Nice, France.
[54] Liakos JK and Landsberg PT (1996) Auger recombination and impact ionization in heterojunction photovoltaic cells. *Semiconductor Science and Technology* 11: 1895–1900.
[55] Wolf M, Brendel R, Werner JH, and Queisser HJ (1998) Solar cell efficiency and carrier multiplication in $Si_{1-x}Ge_x$ alloys. *Journal of Applied Physics* 83: 4213.
[56] Landsberg PT and Badescu V (2002) Solar cell thermodynamics including multiple impact ionization and concentration of radiation. *Journal of Physics* D35: 1236–1240.
[57] De Vos A (1980) Detailed balance limit of the efficiency of tandem solar cells. *Journal of Physics* D13: 839–846.
[58] Grosjean CC and De Vos A (1981) On the upper limit of the efficiency of conversion in tandem solar cells. *Journal of Physics* D 14: 883–894.
[59] De Vos A and Pauwels H (1981) On the thermodynamic limit of photovoltaic energy conversion. *Journal of Applied Physics* 25: 119–125.
[60] Pauwels H and De Vos A (1981) Determination and thermodynamics of the maximum efficiency photovoltaic device. In: *Proceedings of the 11th IEEE Photovoltaic Specialists Conference*, pp. 377–338. Orlando, FL, USA.
[61] De Vos A and Vyncke D (1983) Solar energy conversion: Photovoltaic versus photothermal conversion. In: *Proceedings of the 5th E. C. Photovoltaic Solar Energy Conference*, pp. 186–190. Athens, Greece.
[62] Haught AF (1984) Physics considerations of solar energy conversion. *Journal of Solar Energy Engineering* 106: 3–15.
[63] Sizmann JR (1990) Solar radiation conversion. In: Winter Cl, Sizmann R, and Vant-Hull L (eds.) *Solar Power Plants*, pp. 17–93. Berlin, Germany: Springer.
[64] De Vos A (1992) *Endoreversible Thermodynamics of Solar Energy Conversion*. Oxford, UK: Oxford University Press.
[65] Badescu V and Dinu C (1995) Maximum performance of omnicolor photothermal and photovoltaic converters in our planetary system. *Renewable Energy* 6: 765–777.
[66] Landsberg PT and Baruch P (1989) The thermodynamics of the conversion of radiation energy for photovoltaics. *Journal of Physics* A 22: 1911–1926.
[67] Badescu V (1992) Thermodynamics of the conversion of partially polarized black-body radiation. *Journal of Physics III France* 2: 1925–1941.
[68] Badescu V (2005) Spectrally and angularly selective photothermal and photovoltaic converters under one-sun illumination. *Journal of Physics* D 38: 2166–2172.
[69] Green MA (2003) *Third Generation Photovoltaics: Advanced Solar Energy Conversion*. New York: Springer.
[70] Badescu V and Dinu C (1996) Optimization of multicolor photothermal power plants in the solar system: a finite-time thermodynamic approach. *Journal of Physics III France* 6: 143–163.
[71] Landsberg PT and Badescu V (1998) Solar energy conversion: list of efficiencies and some theoretical considerations. Part II – Results. *Progress in Quantum Electronics* 22: 231–255.

Further Reading

1. Green MA (1982) *Solar Cells: Operating Principles, Technology and System Applications*. New Jersey: Prentice-Hall. [Authoritative book in the field of photovoltaic conversion.]
2. Fahrenbruch AL and Bube RH (1983) *Fundamentals of Solar Cells – Photovoltaic Solar Energy Conversion*. New York: Academic Press. [Authoritative book in the field of photovoltaic conversion.]
3. Hough TP (ed.) (2006) *Solar Energy: New Research*. New York: Nova Science Publishers. [A compendium of technical articles on most types of solar energy conversion systems written by authoritative authors.]
4. Badescu V and Paulescu M (eds.) (2010) *The Physics of Nanostructured Solar Cells*. New York: Nova Science Publishers. [A compendium of technical articles on third-generation photovoltaics written by authoritative authors.]
5. Badescu V and Landsberg PT (1993) Theory of some effects of photon recycling in semiconductors. *Semiconductor Science and Technology* 8: 1267–1276. [This paper is recommended for those readers interested to see how realistic models of photovoltaic cell operation may be developed.]
6. Badescu V (1998) Accurate upper bounds for the conversion efficiency of black-body radiation energy into work. *Physics Letters* A244: 31–34. [This paper shows the basic procedure to improve the accuracy of models treating solar energy conversion into mechanical work.]
7. Badescu V (2005) Spectrally and angularly selective photothermal and photovoltaic converters under one-sun illumination. *Journal of Physics* D38: 2166–2172. [This paper uses thermodynamic methods in analyzing the performance of advanced photothermal and photovoltaic devices.]
8. Markvart T and Landsberg PT (2002) Thermodynamics and reciprocity of solar energy conversion. *Physica E* 14: 71–77. [This paper proposes a treatment based on irreversible thermodynamics for photochemical conversion.]

9. Badescu V and De Vos A (2007) Influence of some design parameters on the efficiency of solar cells with down-conversion and down shifting of high-energy photons. *Journal of Applied Physics* 102: 073102. [This paper proposes detailed balance thermodynamic models for solar cells assisted by down-converters.]
10. Badescu V and Badescu AM (2009) Improved model for solar cells with up-conversion of low-energy photons. *Renewable Energy* 34: 1538–1544. [This paper proposes detailed balance thermodynamic models for solar cells assisted by up-converters.]
11. De Vos A, Szymanska A, and Badescu V (2009) Modelling of solar cells with down-conversion of high energy photons, anti-reflection coatings and light trapping. *Energy Conversion and Management* 50: 328–336. [This paper proposes a thermodynamic model for solar cells assisted by up-converters and light-trapping devices.]

1.16 Crystalline Silicon Solar Cells: State-of-the-Art and Future Developments

SW Glunz, R Preu, and D Biro, Fraunhofer Institute for Solar Energy Systems, Freiburg, Germany

© 2012 Elsevier Ltd. All rights reserved.

1.16.1	**General Introduction**	353
1.16.1.1	Photovoltaic Market	353
1.16.1.2	Historical Development of Cell Efficiency	354
1.16.1.3	Maximum Achievable Efficiency	354
1.16.2	**Current Status of Silicon Solar Cell Technology**	355
1.16.2.1	Basic Structure of a Silicon Solar Cell	355
1.16.2.2	Physical Structure of an Industrial Silicon Solar Cell	355
1.16.2.3	Process Sequence	358
1.16.3	**Influence of Basic Parameters**	363
1.16.4	**Strategies for Improvement**	364
1.16.4.1	Dielectric Surface Passivation	364
1.16.4.1.1	Influence of surface passivation	364
1.16.4.1.2	Passivation mechanisms of dielectric layers	365
1.16.4.1.3	Layers and processes for surface passivation	365
1.16.4.2	Metallization	366
1.16.4.2.1	Front contacts	366
1.16.4.2.2	Back contacts	368
1.16.4.3	Bulk Properties	368
1.16.5	**High-Efficiency Cell Structures on p-type Silicon**	371
1.16.5.1	Main Approaches for High Efficiencies in p-type Devices	371
1.16.5.2	Passivated Emitter and Rear Cell	371
1.16.5.3	Metal Wrap-Through Solar Cells	372
1.16.5.4	MWT-PERC	373
1.16.5.5	Emitter Wrap-Through Solar Cells	374
1.16.6	**High-Efficiency Structures on n-type Silicon**	375
1.16.6.1	Aluminum-Alloyed Back Junction	375
1.16.6.2	n-Type Cells with Boron-Diffused Front Emitter	376
1.16.6.3	Back-Contact Solar Cells with Boron-Diffused Back Junction	377
1.16.6.4	Heterojunction Solar Cells	379
1.16.6.5	Alternative Emitters	380
1.16.6.5.1	Polysilicon emitters	380
1.16.6.5.2	Implanted emitters	381
1.16.7	**Conclusion**	381
References		381

1.16.1 General Introduction

1.16.1.1 Photovoltaic Market

Crystalline silicon photovoltaic (PV) is the working horse of the PV energy market from its invention in the 1950s up to today. In the last decade, the market share of crystalline silicon PV has always been in the range between 80% and 90% (see blue sections in **Figure 1**).

Crystalline silicon PV can be subdivided into cells made of multicrystalline, monocrystalline, and ribbon silicon, with multicrystalline silicon (mc-Si) playing the most important role closely followed by monocrystalline silicon (mono-Si). The dominance of crystalline silicon PV has historical reasons: the early invention of this solar cell type and the parallel development of the microelectronic industry; in addition, the superior properties of silicon and silicon solar cells have also contributed to the dominance of crystalline silicon PV:

- Silicon is an *abundant* material (about 25% of the earth's crust is comprised of silicon).
- Silicon is *nontoxic*. This is especially important for a green technology.
- PV modules with crystalline silicon solar cells are *long-term stable* outdoors (>20 years). This is decisive for the cost competitiveness of PV because currently investment starts to pay back around the 10th year after the initial installation of the PV system.
- *High energy conversion efficiency*. A high efficiency reduces system costs and enables installation of high-power systems at sites with limited available space like rooftops. The best commercial silicon solar cells available today exceed 20% efficiency [1].

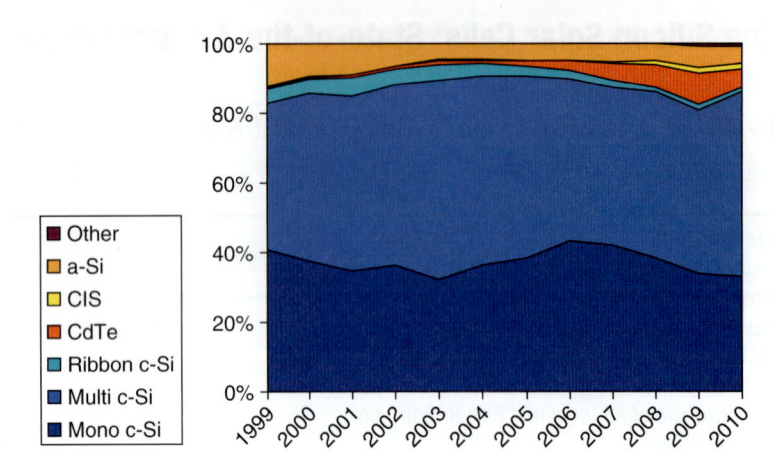

Figure 1 Market shares of different photovoltaic technologies. Data based on the yearly market surveys published in *Photon International*. Aachen, Germany: Photon Europe.

- *Considerable potential for further cost reductions.* Although there have been returning predictions that silicon PV has reached its cost minimum, the costs went down following a learning curve with a learning rate of 20% [2] (20% cost reduction for doubling the cumulated installed power) which will quite probably be extended in the future.

1.16.1.2 Historical Development of Cell Efficiency

In 1941, the first silicon solar cell was reported by Ohl [3]. It featured a melt-grown pn-junction and an energy conversion efficiency of less than 1%. A great progress was made in the early 1950s when Pearson, Fuller, and Chapin at the Bell Laboratories prepared silicon solar cells with a diffused pn-junction. The first cells were fabricated on p-type silicon and reached an efficiency of up to around 4.5% [4]. Then they switched to arsenic-doped n-type silicon with a boron-doped emitter [5]. This increased efficiency to a value of more than 6%. The first application of these 'solar batteries' was as power source for satellites. They won the competition against other power supplies such as chemical batteries [6]. The space race was of national interest for Americans and Soviets during the cold war and solar cells played an important technical role. In fact, today, PV panels are still the dominant power source for satellites and other space applications. Up to the end of the 1950s, the cells were mainly fabricated on n-type silicon, leading to superior efficiencies of up to around 14%. However, it was found that space radiation hardness was less detrimental for cells with a p-type base [7]. This became more clear when a high-atmosphere nuclear bomb was ignited by the Americans, leading to failure of the solar panels of satellites [8]. Thus, in the early 1960s, there was a switch to cells on p-type silicon with a phosphorus-doped emitter [9]. These cells had a higher radiation hardness but started with a lower efficiency. It took up to 1973 to achieve higher efficiencies with cells on p-type silicon than those reached in the early 1960s with cells on n-type base.

A second strong phase of cell development started in the 1980s with the passivated emitter solar cell (PESC) clearing the important 20% hurdle in 1985 [10]. The PESC and also its successors the passivated emitter and rear cell (PERC) [11] and the passivated emitter, rear locally diffused cell (PERL) [12] have a very important feature in common: surface passivation in order to reduce recombination of charge carriers at the surfaces. Indeed this is a crucial prerequisite for all high-efficiency silicon solar cells particularly for interdigitated back-contact cells [13, 14] where the collecting junction is at the rear side and most carriers have to diffuse a long way. Back-contact cells have always played an important role in the race for record efficiencies and are the base structure for today's best commercial solar cells with efficiencies greater than 22%. The best efficiency for a mono-Si solar cell is 25% [4, 15] getting quite close to the 'practical' limit of around 26% [16].

Although cell efficiencies on mono-Si are significantly higher, it is very important to keep an eye on cells on mc-Si since 5 out of 10 solar cells today are made of this material type. Mc-Si is cheaper than mono-Si but unfortunately also has a lower material quality due to a higher amount of crystal defects and metal impurities. Since this difference in material quality is especially relevant for record solar cells where hyper-pure floating-zone (FZ) silicon is used for monocrystalline cells, it is fair to report record efficiencies for multicrystalline cells separately. The major interest in mc-Si started in the mid-1970s with record efficiencies of around 15%. In this case, the historical increase in efficiency was mainly influenced by the improvement in material quality either during the crystallization process or during the cell process utilizing gettering and internal hydrogen passivation of crystal defects (see Section 1.16.4.3). An effective way to reduce the influence of material quality is the reduction of cell thickness and usage of effective surface passivation. This path led to today's record solar cell on mc-Si with an efficiency of 20.4% and a thickness of only 99 μm [17, 18].

1.16.1.3 Maximum Achievable Efficiency

A major question related to efficiencies of solar cells is of course how far one can get. The answer to this question was given in a very elegant way by Shockley and Queisser in the 1960s [19]. Based on a detailed balance calculation for the ideal case that the only

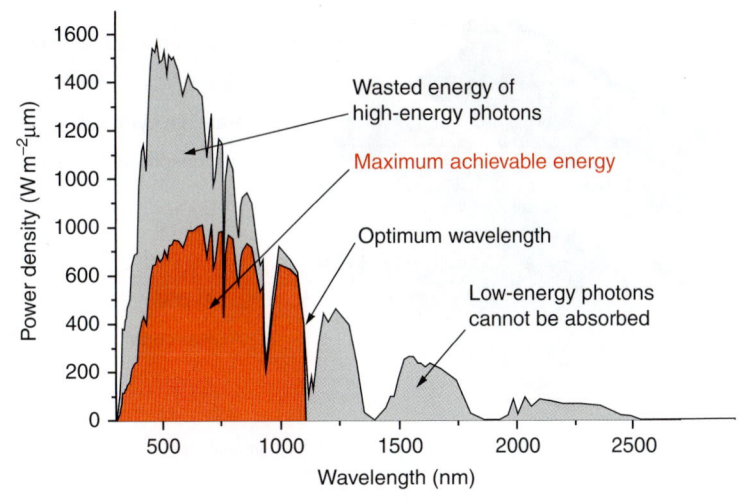

Figure 2 Spectral losses in a solar cell. The figure shows the maximum achievable energy of a silicon solar cell in relation to the sun spectrum (AM1.5).

recombination channel is radiative recombination, they calculated the maximum achievable efficiency, which is around 30% for a band gap of 1.1 eV (sic!).

Figure 2 visualizes the main loss mechanism in a silicon solar cell: spectral losses. It shows the maximum achievable energy of a silicon solar cell in relation to the sun spectrum. Photons carrying a specific energy can generate only one electron–hole pair even if their energy is higher. The energy greater than the band-gap energy is lost in thermalization of the hot carriers, that is, as heat (see the upper gray part in **Figure 2**). Photons with energies lower than the band-gap energy cannot generate an electron–hole pair (nonabsorption; see the right gray part in **Figure 2**). These two losses account for about 50% of the power carried in the sun spectrum.

In contrast to the calculation of Shockley and Queisser, in a realistic crystalline silicon solar cell radiative recombination does not play a dominant role due to the indirect band structure of silicon. Instead of this, Auger recombination plays a dominant role. Recent accurate determination of the Auger coefficients in silicon has led to the calculation of the maximum achievable efficiency of a silicon solar cell as being 29% [20]. However, such an idealized device without contacts is only of theoretical interest and cannot be realized. For a realistic but optimized silicon solar cell, an efficiency limit of 26% was predicted [16].

1.16.2 Current Status of Silicon Solar Cell Technology

1.16.2.1 Basic Structure of a Silicon Solar Cell

This section will give an overview of the technology currently used in industry to produce a silicon solar cell. A solar cell technology is defined by two features:

- the physical structure of the solar cell, which consists of a geometrical order of structure elements, and
- the production technology, that is, equipment, materials, and processes applied to realize such a product.

For a working solar cell, at least three structure elements are needed:

- An absorber that absorbs incoming photons and translates their energy to an excited state of a charge carrier. Typically, a semiconductor like silicon is used as the absorber and the absorption process generates an electron in the conduction band, that is, an electron from the valence band is transferred to the conduction band leaving behind a 'hole' in the valence band.
- A membrane that prevents the reverse process in which the excited carrier recombines with its ground state. Such a recombination may transfer the excitation energy of the electron into the excitation of a photon, transfer the energy of the electron to another already excited electron, or lead to lattice vibration. In the current technology, a junction formed by adjacent areas of p- and n-conducting semiconductor layers called the pn-junction is used.
- Contacts that allow for collection of carriers and interconnection with other solar cells or an outer load.

In principle, these elements would be sufficient, but an industrial solar cell is more complex as described in the following section.

1.16.2.2 Physical Structure of an Industrial Silicon Solar Cell

The currently dominating physical structure of mono-Si and mc-Si solar cells is mostly denoted as a co-fired screen-printed aluminum back surface field (Al-BSF) cell.

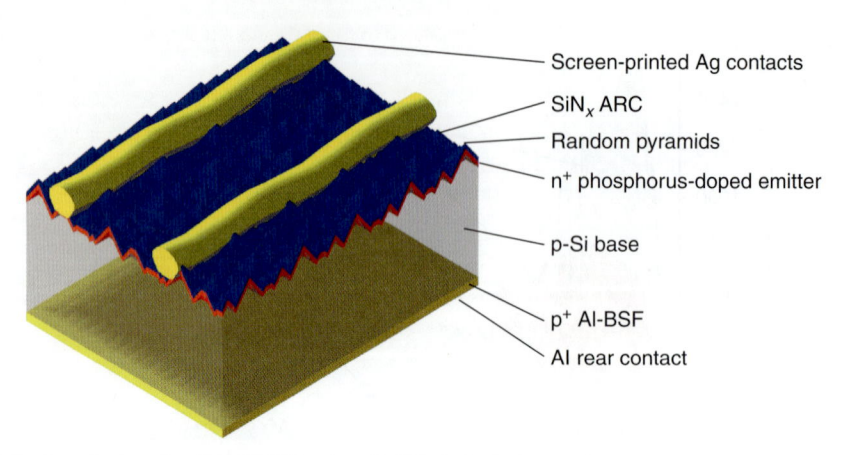

Figure 3 Structure of aluminum back surface field (Al-BSF) solar cell. ARC, Antireflection coating.

Although there are a number of variations within the family of Al-BSF cells, all have several distinct structure elements in common, making up around 80% of the world market share. In the following, these common characteristics are described (compare **Figure 3**):

1. The cell is most probably made from a $156 \times 156 \times 0.2$ mm^3 sized boron-doped crystalline silicon wafer with an acceptor density N_A of around 10^{16} cm^{-3}, which corresponds to a base resistivity of around $1 \, \Omega$ cm (p-type substrate). The wafers are from either mono-Si or mc-Si. Mono-Si is typically grown and cut with the (100) plain parallel to the large surface of the wafer. Furthermore, these wafers are typically not full-square, but rather pseudo-square, that is, the diagonal measures about 5–20 mm shorter than a matching full-square and are with radial geometry at the corners. Mc-Si wafers are full-square with only slightly beveled corners. Multicrystalline means that the crystal area size is typically in the range of mm^2 to cm^2; thus, the number of crystals per wafer is in the range of several 10^3. The wafers are typically extremely pure, with metallic impurity levels below 1 ppm. In mono-Si wafers, oxygen is the dominant impurity with concentrations typically in the range of several 10^{17} cm^{-3}. Mc-Si wafers show comparatively higher concentrations of metals and carbon, which accumulate in the grain boundaries. The oxygen concentration is rather in the range of 10^{17} cm^{-3} or below [21]. The main functions of a p-type substrate are to efficiently absorb incoming photons on a large surface, to enable diffusion of minority carriers (electrons), and to behave as a good conductor to enable efficient transport of majority carriers (holes) to the contacts.
2. The front side (within this text, front side refers to the side of a solar cell that faces the sun) of the solar cell is textured with a texture depth of typically a few micrometers. While mono-Si features upstanding randomly distributed pyramids, the surface of mc-Si solar cells mostly features a randomly distributed order of round-shaped valleys (compare **Figure 4**). The main functions of the texture are to increase the transmission of incoming photons into the silicon absorber and to increase the path length of the photons inside the absorber (oblique direction of the photon propagation relative to the surface and high internal reflection at the surfaces).
3. The top layer at the front side of the cell is doped with phosphorus. The donor concentration N_D falls steeply from more than 10^{20} cm^{-3} at the silicon surface to values below N_A in a depth of less than 1 µm forming a net n-type layer with a sheet resistivity of around $75 \, \Omega$ sq^{-1} and a pn-junction of several hundreds of nanometers. The main functions are to allow the formation of this pn-junction with reasonable thickness to separate charge carriers, to enable a sufficient diffusion length of minority carriers

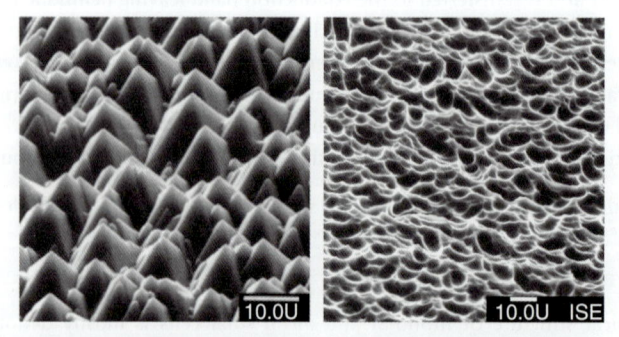

Figure 4 Texture on the front side of monocrystalline (left) and multicrystalline (right) silicon solar cells.

(holes) within the layer, and to allow for effective conduction to enable efficient transport of majority carriers (electrons) to the contacts.
4. The front side is further coated with an approximately 75 nm thin layer of amorphous hydrogenated silicon nitride. The layer is slightly silicon-rich leading to a refractive index of approximately 2.1 [22] for an effective reduction of front reflection. The amorphous structure allows for the incorporation of hydrogen concentration of typically more than 10 at.%. The main functions are to provide antireflection coating based on refractive index matching and quarter-wavelength thickness and passivation (the term passivation is used in order to indicate reduction of carrier recombination rates, typically by technical means; passivation can take place at the surface or within the volume and is denoted accordingly) of the n-type surface as well as the volume based on the incorporated hydrogen [23, 24].
5. At the front surface an H-like pattern of sintered silver paste is formed [25], which punches through the silicon nitride layer [26, 27]. The H-like pattern is continuous and makes up approximately 8% of the front surface. Below the sintered paste, pure silver crystallites are penetrating through the silicon nitride into the silicon along the (111) planes with a depth of up to around 100 nm and a surface area fraction of typically around 10–30%. The bulk of the sintered silver paste is densely formed from round- and flake-shaped silver particles, which are interconnected to each other by sinter necks (compare **Figure 5**). The volume in between the silver particles is filled with glass frit. The main function of the H-like pattern is efficient carrier transport and transparency for the incoming light, that is, low shading. It can be subdivided into two device elements, which are denoted contact busbars and contact fingers, which fulfill specific functions:
   - Mostly three busbars are used, which are approximately 1.5 mm wide and 20 µm high, equally spaced in parallel to the wafers edge. Their main functions are collection of current from the contact fingers and allow for a soldering interconnection to a coated copper ribbon with good electrical and mechanical contact (minimum adhesion force 1 N).
   - Contact fingers are approximately 100 µm wide and 20 µm high and are situated perpendicular to the busbars with a pitch of typically 2 mm. At the outer edges of the wafer which are parallel to the busbars, the fingers are frequently interconnected to each other. At all edges there is a range of typically 1.5 mm which is not covered by contacts at all. The main functions of the contact fingers are to provide low contact resistance to the underlying n-type silicon surface and an excellent lateral conductivity for efficient carrier transport. The interconnection of fingers at the edge enables good carrier collection from the edge of the solar cell and tolerance to individual finger interruptions at the outer side of the cells. Analysis of the microstructure of the contact area between screen-printed finger and silicon has revealed that the silver bulk is typically separated by a thin glass from the silicon surface. Different current transport paths have been discussed and found including grown-in silver crystals in close contact with the silver bulk as well as enhanced carrier transport due to metallic particles in the glass layer allowing for multistep tunneling (compare **Figure 5**) [28, 30–32].
6. The rear side is fully metallized. The main function is efficient carrier transport. Again the rear side metallization can be subdivided into two areas.
   - Around 5% of the rear side area is used as contact pads, which are situated on the opposite side of the front busbar. They form either a continuous or an interrupted line. These contact pads are typically 4 mm wide and consist of approximately 20 µm thick silver paste. Frequently, a low fraction of aluminum is also incorporated. The vertical structure at the rear silver contact pads is similar to the one at the front contacts. The aluminum allows for a slight doping underneath the silver contact pads [33]. The main functions of these contact pads are to collect the current from the metallized area and to enable a high-conducting electrode for later soldering to the interconnector ribbon with good mechanical contact (minimum adhesion force 1 N).
   - The remaining area of the rear side consists of a multilayer area which is surrounded by a nonmetallized 1.5 mm wide area all around the wafer edge. The silicon surface at the metallized rear area is doped with aluminum of approximately 5 µm deep to a

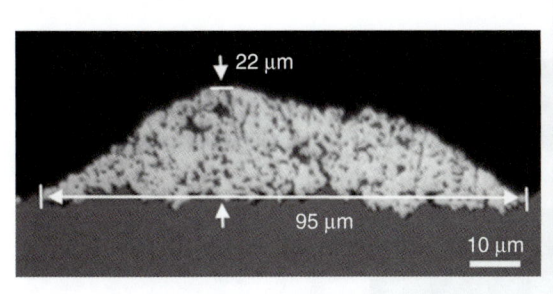

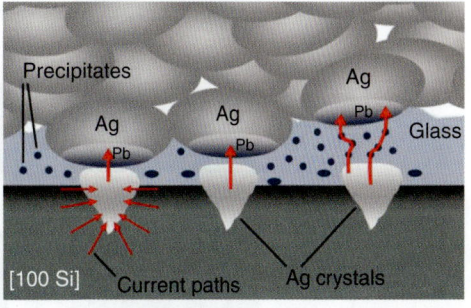

Figure 5 (Left) Picture of a current screen-printed contact. (Right) Model for the current transport at the screen-printed silver contact. Three different current transport routes between silver crystals and silver bulk are proposed: direct contact, tunneling through the glass, and multitunneling via metal precipitates in the glass. Reproduced with permission from Kontermann S, Hörteis M, Kasemann M, et al. (2009) Physical understanding of the behavior of silver thick-film contacts on n-type silicon under annealing conditions. *Solar Energy Materials and Solar Cells* 2009(93): 1630–1635 [28] (copyright 2009 Elsevier) after Schubert G (2006) Thick Film Metallisation of Crystalline Silicon Solar Cells. Dissertation, Universität Konstanz [29].

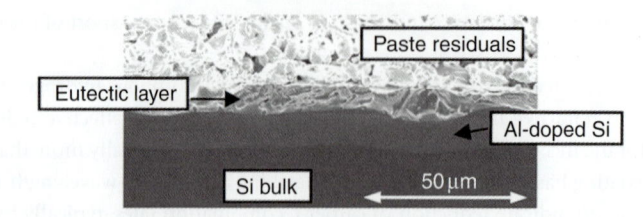

Figure 6 Scanning electron microscopy (SEM) image of the cross section of the rear Al contact and the underlying doped area (aluminum back surface field (Al-BSF)). Reproduced with permission from Krause J, Woehl R, and Biro D (2010) Analysis of local Al-p$^+$-layers for solar cells processed by small screen-printed structures. In: *Proceedings of the 25th European Photovoltaic Solar Energy Conference and Exhibition*, pp. 1899–1904. Valencia, Spain [36]. Copyright 2010, WIP, Munich.

maximum concentration of around $3-4 \times 10^{18}$ cm^{-3}, which slowly decreases toward the surface [34, 35]. On top of the doped silicon surface, there is a eutectic layer, also approximately 10 µm (see **Figure 6**). On top of the eutectic layer, there is a layer of sintered aluminum paste with substantial in-diffusion of silicon [36]. The main functions of these areas are to provide a low contact and lateral resistance as well as a passivation of the rear side by implementing a high–low junction or back surface field (BSF).

7. The edge of the solar cell consists of an interruption of the highly n-doped layer on the front and the p-doped layer on the rear side of the solar cell. This interruption is at least a few micrometers wide. The main function of this area is to interrupt an unwanted carrier transport from the n-type emitter at the front to the rear p-layer in order to prevent parasitic shunting.

Typical efficiencies for this cell structure in current production lines are 17.5–18.0% for mono-Si and 16.5–17.0% for mc-Si. The main drivers for the enormous success of this cell structure are as follows:

- The simplicity of the production technologies related to realize the structure in comparison to the efficiency which can be obtained.
- The tolerance of structure and process against variations of wafer quality, that is, variations in the concentration of base material doping, metallic and other impurities as well as grain boundaries.
- One of the most important points for the success of this cell structure is the availability of the associated production technology. None of the vital structure elements or process sequences is severely protected by patents or other legal issues. This allowed many equipment and material manufacturers to join the competition for best and lowest cost products.

Due to the enormous demand for production technology on the market, these drivers were keys to a very rapid increase in production capacity.

1.16.2.3 Process Sequence

In the following, the individual process steps are discussed in detail. The corresponding process flow is shown in **Figure 7**.

1. Incoming inspection and sorting into carriers

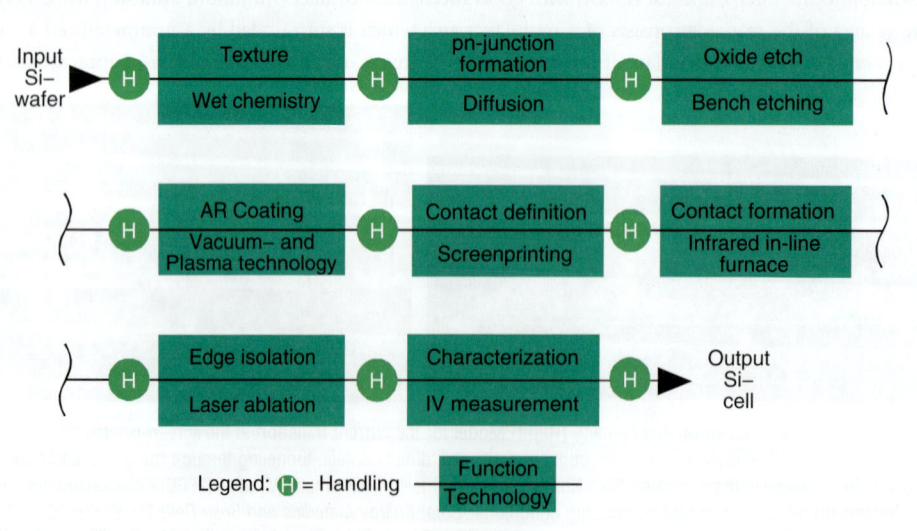

Figure 7 Schematic process flow for an industrial crystalline silicon solar cell line.

The entrance interface is the wafer in a stack. As a first step the wafers are typically inspected for microcracks using infrared transmission. Then they are either sorted into wet chemical carriers or directly put onto a belt for further processing depending on whether further processing is batch or in-line processing, respectively.

2. Saw damage removal, texturing, and cleaning

Differences in the texturing process used depend mostly on the crystallinity of the wafer. Mono-Si wafers are etched in 70–80 °C hot aqueous sodium hydroxide with organic additives (typically isopropanol) for approximately 20–30 min to attain the random pyramidal structure. The main reaction can be summarized as

$$2KOH + Si + H_2O \rightarrow K_2SiO_3 + 2H_2 \uparrow \qquad [1]$$

Care has to be taken with the released molecular hydrogen and eventually evaporated organic additives. Due to the long etching time and high temperature, batch-type wet benches are the standard for this process in order to achieve high capacity and throughput. The etching is typically stopped using a short dip in an acidic solution. Specific cleaning is partially applied at this point to remove metal ions and other impurities from the surface. Then rinsing is performed and the wafers are dried.

Mc-Si is textured by treating with acidic agents that are simultaneously oxidizing and oxide etching like mixtures of deionized water, HNO_3, and HF for approximately 1–2 min. The process temperature is typically reduced to values of 10–15 °C for better control and reduced etching since the process is strongly exothermic. The main reaction that takes place is

$$3Si + 4HNO_3 + 12HF \rightarrow 3SiF_4 + 4NO + 8H_2O \qquad [2]$$

Care has to be taken with the nitrous oxide released during the process. After the texturing, a thin porous surface layer (stain), which remains after the etching process, is removed in aqueous potassium hydroxide. The low temperature and short process times enable the use of in-line wet bench systems, which offer improved material flow compared to the carrier-based wet bench processing. The wafers are rinsed in cascade benches and dried.

3. Phosphorus diffusion

The textured and cleaned wafers are then transferred into quartz carriers for phosphorus diffusion. Narrow wafer distance in the carrier and back-to-back processing allow for up to 500 wafers being processed simultaneously in one tube. The quartz carrier is then transferred into a hot tube and the furnace is closed. For phosphorus diffusion, pure nitrogen is used as a carrier gas, which is guided through a container of liquid phosphorus oxychloride ($POCl_3$) and released to the chamber together with oxygen to perform the following reaction on the wafer surface:

$$4POCl_3 + 3O_2 \rightarrow 2P_2O_5 + 6Cl_2 \qquad [3]$$

The production of chlorine is beneficial in terms of the removal of metallic impurities like sodium. This part of the process is typically denoted predeposition. A second reaction takes place from the phosphorus oxide, which can be described as

$$2\,P_2O_5 + 5\,Si \rightarrow 5\,SiO_2 + 4\,P \qquad [4]$$

This phosphorus silicate glass (PSG) is grown to a thickness of a few tens of nanometers and then the flow of $POCl_3$ is turned off to keep the phosphorus content at a finite level. This allows a deeper diffusion for a given surface concentration during the subsequent drive-in. The temperature is typically increased for this part of the process to plateau temperatures in the range of 820–850 °C. At the end of the process, the furnace is purged and the carrier is taken out of the furnace. A typical cycle time is around 1 h [37].

In-line diffusion has been used for many years instead of tube furnace diffusion. Here the phosphorus dopant is applied outside the furnace, for example, by ultrasonic spraying. In-line diffusion has clearly lost market share due to several reasons even though low contamination furnaces based on ceramic rolls or strings have proven to enable clean processing [38].

4. Phosphorus glass removal

The PSG is removed in a further wet chemical etching processing. Hydrofluoric acid is used due to its excellent etch selectivity with the ratio of etching rate of phosphorus glass to silicon around 400:1 for standard processing conditions. Nevertheless, since the phosphorus surface concentration is very high after the diffusion, a controlled etch back of a few nanometers of the highly doped surface area is desirable and is used in many production lines. Again rinsing and drying is applied after processing. The full process cycle takes just a few minutes and can be applied in either batch- or in-line-type wet benches.

5. Deposition of antireflection coating

As a next step, the hydrogenated amorphous silicon nitride layer is deposited. The dominating technology is plasma-enhanced chemical vapor deposition (PECVD) based on silane and ammonia. There are a number of different PECVD approaches in the field, two most important being a low-frequency direct plasma or a microwave plasma based on linear antennas for in-line processing (compare **Figure 8**). The plasma partially dissociates the silane and ammonia and the deposition takes place via different mechanisms [40].

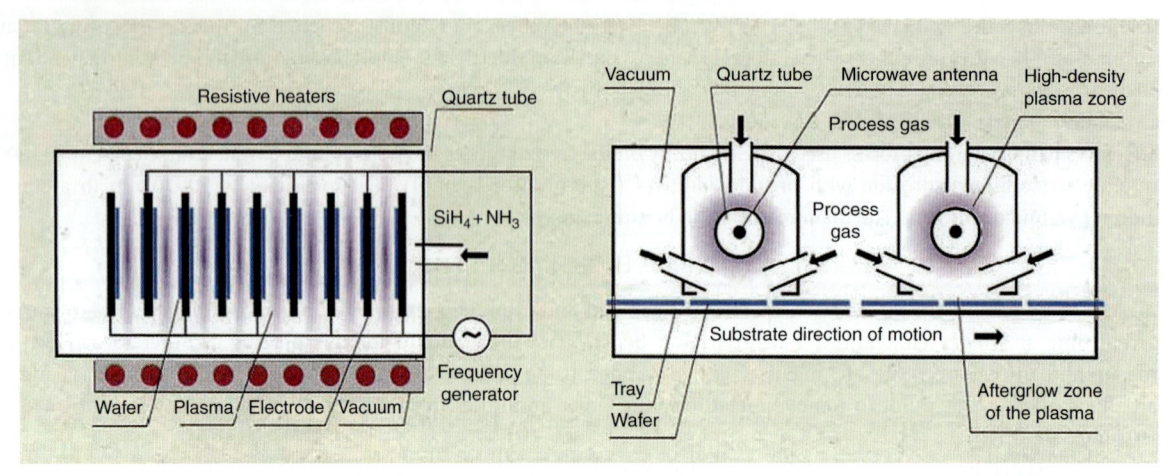

Figure 8 Schematic drawing of the two dominating plasma-enhanced chemical vapor deposition (PECVD) techniques. (Left) Direct low-frequency plasma and (right) microwave antenna. Reprinted with permission from Photon International, March 2003 [39]. Copyright 2003 Photon Holding GmbH.

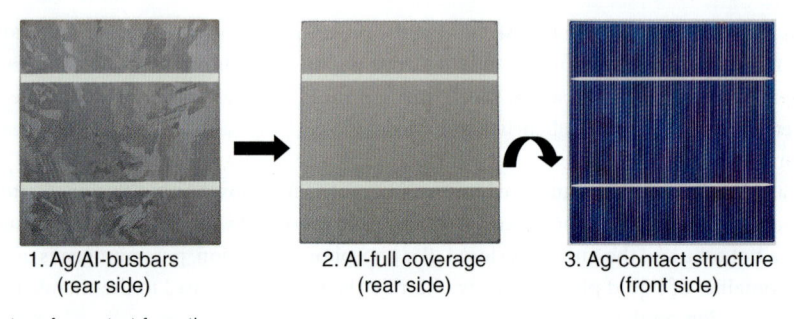

Figure 9 The three print steps for contact formation.

Reactive sputtering based on silicon-containing targets and nitrogen and ammonia as reactive gases was introduced as an alternative with excellent lateral homogeneity and optical performance, but has not succeeded in substituting the dominating PECVD approach [41].

6. Screen printing of contacts

The contact definition is performed via subsequent printing of three different pastes – rear Ag, rear Al, and front Ag paste – and subsequent drying. During the printing process, the paste is distributed by the fast moving squeegee. The paste makes contact with the wafer substrate through the openings of the screen. A typical procedure is shown in **Figure 9**, but the printing can also be applied in a different order, for example, printing the front H-like pattern first. The pastes typically contain particles of metal and glass frits with maximum size in the range of 10 μm to prevent clogging of the screen and efficient formation of sinter necks in the following high-temperature steps. Further constituents are solvents and other organic compounds that are added in order to improve the printability and give the pastes their thixotropic behavior, that is, reduced viscosity under the application of shear stress during printing. Substantial developments have taken place in the formulation of the pastes, which enabled a large part of the efficiency development within the last 10 years. Consequently, the emitter sheet resistance could be increased from 40 to nearly 80 $\Omega\,\text{sq}^{-1}$. Also the formulation of the rear paste has been improved substantially, which allows the formation of a more homogeneous and highly doped BSF and reduced mechanical stress which appears due to the quite different expansion coefficients of silicon and aluminum. Drying at 200 °C is important to remove the solvents from the paste to prevent spreading. The last drying step can be included in the final firing step.

7. Contact firing

After the last printing step, the wafers undergo a further thermal treatment in a conveyor belt furnace. During temperature ramp-up, the organic compounds with low boiling temperature that have been added by the last printing step are removed. In the second phase, the remaining organic compounds are burned in an oxygen-containing atmosphere at around 400 °C. Then the wafers are heated to temperatures around 800 °C within a few seconds and cooled directly thereafter. The front and rear contact formation takes place during this part of the process. The most widely used models for the contact formation are shown in schematic graphs in **Figures 10** and **11**.

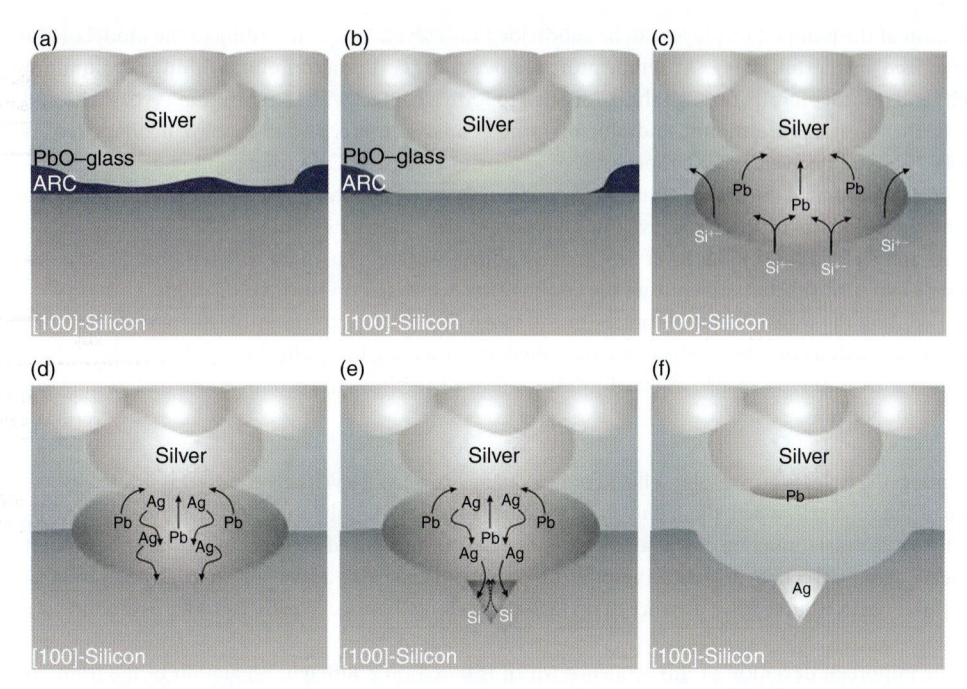

Figure 10 Simplified model of contact formation. (a) Schematic cross section of Ag thick film paste on <100> Si after combustion of organics. (b) Glass etches through SiNx layer. (c) Redox reaction between Si and glass. Pb is formed. (d) Liquid Pb starts to melt Ag. (e) Ag–Pb melt reacts with Si. Inverted pyramids are formed. (f) On cooling down, Ag recrystallizes on (111)-Si planes. Reproduced with permission from Schubert G (2006) Thick Film Metallisation of Crystalline Silicon Solar Cells. Dissertation, Universität Konstanz [29].

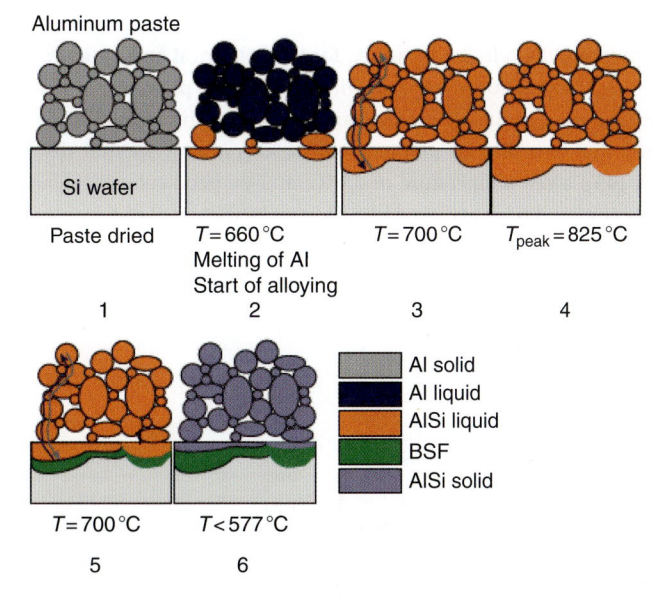

Figure 11 Formation of the aluminum back surface field and rear contact from a screen-printed aluminum paste: (1) paste after drying; (2) at 660 °C, melting of aluminum occurs and silicon dissolves in a mixed phase; (3) around 700 °C, all the aluminum is completely molten and substantial incorporation of silicon occurs; (4) at the peak temperature, the liquid phase has its maximum thickness; (5) during cooling down, the silicon recrystallizes with incorporation of aluminum, while the silicon content in the mixed liquid phase reduces, (6) at the eutectic temperature, the mixed phase of aluminum and silicon solidifies. Reproduced with permission from Huster F (2005) Investigation of the alloying process of screen printed aluminium pastes for the BSF formation on silicon solar cells. In: *Proceedings of the 20th European Photovoltaic Solar Energy Conference*, pp. 1466–1469. Barcelona, Spain [42]. Copyright 2005 WIP, Munich.

The front contact formation process is described in the model of Schubert [29]. Within the firing process, the glass contained in the paste etches the dielectric layer and gets into direct contact with the underlying silicon. Then, the liquid glass promotes dissolution of silver from the silver particles and silicon into this liquid phase as well as of the metallic glass particles into the silver particles. The dissolution of the silicon appears preferentially along the strongly bound (111) planes within the silicon forming the special shape of the crystallites [28].

The formation of the p-doped rear layer can be subdivided into several steps according to the model of Huster [42], and is briefly summarized in the following. At temperatures above 660 °C, the aluminum within the aluminum oxide-coated particles melts and punches locally through the oxide shell to form a contact with the surrounding particles and the underlying silicon. On further heating, aluminum and silicon form a mixed liquid phase at the silicon surface, with a ratio of approximately 70/30 at the peak wafer temperature of approximately 825 °C. During cooling down, the process is reversed, but aluminum is incorporated during the epitaxial regrowth of the silicon at the surface. The concentration of the aluminum is determined by the solubility at the respective temperature. At the eutectic temperature ($T = 577$ °C), the remaining mixed phase solidifies and yields a continuous layer on top of the silicon surface. Due to the different thermal expansion coefficients, the wafer is typically bent substantially during the cooling process. Based on his investigations, Huster [43] proposed stress relief cooling: cooling the wafers to temperatures in the range of −40 °C accelerates plastic reformation of the rear contact layer, which can be used to completely eliminate the otherwise occurring bow. This has partly been used in the industry, but adapted formulations of the paste also allowed minimization of the bow to current values of 1–2 mm for standard wafer thicknesses of 180–200 μm.

8. Edge isolation

After contact firing, the wafer is now a solar cell and power can be extracted. Nevertheless, power is limited by a severe shunt path over the edge of the solar cell, where the highly doped emitter meets the highly doped Al-BSF and yields high–high junctions, which allow for substantial tunneling or worse. The process that was introduced 10 years ago is the removal of the n-conducting layer in the near-edge areas by laser ablation. Typically, the area is ablated using a UV solid-state laser featuring nanosecond pulse duration. The laser beam is guided in a distance of up to 200 μm along the edge to form a groove of around 10 μm in depth and 30 μm in width.

There is one important deviation of this sequence which is based on a different separation of the front and rear junction. Recently, the separation using single-sided wet chemical etch back of the rear phosphorus-doped layer has become a favorable technology for junction isolation. It is performed in combination with the PSG glass removal, which keeps equipment and consumable costs low. Compared to laser edge isolation from the front side, it saves a small amount of active cell area and typically delivers a slight efficiency gain.

9. I–V measurement and sorting

After processing of the cell is finished, the cells are measured for their electrical and optical characteristics. The current–voltage characteristic is determined using illumination via a flash with an intensity plateau of a few tens of milliseconds. The whole measurement from $V = 0$ to $V = V_{oc}$ takes about 20 ms (compare **Figure 12**). The measurement is performed as close to standard testing conditions as possible, that is, using an irradiance of 1000 W m^{-2}, a spectral distribution in accordance with the normalized AM1.5g spectrum [45], a cell temperature of 25 °C, and perpendicular incidence of the light. The deviations of the irradiance from standard testing conditions are taken into account by the signal of a monitor cell placed adjacent to the tested cell. Furthermore, the cell is tested under a reduced light level and in the dark in order to extract further information on the electrical performance of the cell. Further visual measurements are performed, especially to control the visual appearance of the cell. Finally, the cells are sorted into performance bins.

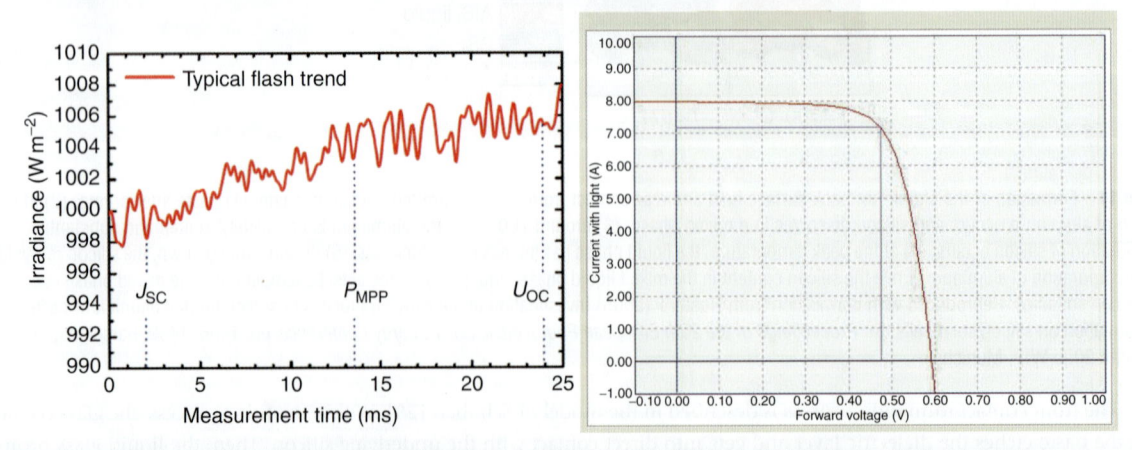

Figure 12 (Left) Typical irradiance within the plateau of a flash tester. The dotted lines indicate typical incidence with the electrical measurement of short-circuit current density (J_{sc}), maximum power point (P_{MPP}), and open-circuit voltage (V_{oc}). (Right) I–V curve taken by a flash tester. Reproduced from Krieg A (2007) Inbetriebnahme und Weiterentwicklung eines automatisierten IV-Kennlinienmessplatzes und Entwicklung eines Verfahrens zur Materialverfolgung in der Solarzellenproduktion. Masterarbeit, Fachhochschule für Technik und Wirtschaft Berlin [44].

1.16.3 Influence of Basic Parameters

To optimize the efficiency, that is, to reduce the power losses of silicon solar cells, it is important to understand the influence of different cell and material parameters such as bulk lifetime and cell thickness. In general, the influence of basic parameters can be classified based on the associated loss mechanisms:

1. The ratio of electrons that are not excited to the conduction band per incoming photon, often referred to as optical losses. Here further differentiation can be applied based on whether
   - the loss occurs since the photon does not enter the solar cell. This might be due to reflection from the metallized areas of the active surface of the cell.
   - the photon enters the cell but leaves it again without absorption within the cell. This is mainly controlled by the internal reflectance at front and rear and takes place for near-band-gap photons.
   - the photon is absorbed in the cell but no excitation of an electron from the valence to the conduction band occurs, which mainly takes place by free carrier absorption of infrared radiation in heavily doped regions.
2. Electrons that are excited but not delivered to an outer circuit, often referred to as electrical losses. The electrical losses can be subdivided into
   - Losses due to recombination of electrons with holes. The recombination takes place in every structure element of the wafer (excluding deposited layers and contacts).
   - Losses due to scattering of the (majority) charge carriers, which leads to ohmic heat. This takes place in all structure elements of the solar cells.

The physics of the solar cell can be described well by a number of basic equations, partially being of differential type in time and space. Thus, exact calculations of the performance of a solar cell can be obtained by only one- to three-dimensional numerical simulators. Since sound multidimensional calculations are time consuming in both the description of the problem and the computer-based numerical calculation, a one-dimensional approach using the program PC1D is probably the most widely used approach to simulate solar cells [46]. A number of lumped parameters are used due to the one-dimensional characteristic of the simulator. Table 1 gives an overview of a standard set of parameters that can be used to describe and simulate a screen-printed mono-Si solar cell yielding an efficiency of 18.0%.

It is of specific interest to assess the impact of the variation of relevant parameters on solar cell's efficiency. Three parameters are most relevant to determine recombination in the base of the solar cell: the thickness of the solar cell, the bulk carrier lifetime, and the rear surface recombination velocity. Changing the thickness and the bulk carrier lifetime of the solar cell can only be achieved by changing the wafers used for processing, which is of specific importance since the wafer covers a substantial cost share of the whole solar cell (60–70%). We have performed PC1D simulations to visualize the effect of variation of these parameters for a standard industrial cell based on the parameter set shown in Table 1 applying a variation of the rear surface recombination velocity in the range of $S_{\text{rear}} = 1250\,\text{cm s}^{-1}$ (bad Al-BSF), $500\,\text{cm s}^{-1}$ (standard Al-BSF), and $200\,\text{cm s}^{-1}$ (excellent Al-BSF). A value as low as $80\,\text{cm s}^{-1}$ has so far been demonstrated only for dielectric passivation with localized Al-BSFs, which also changes the internal reflectivity at the rear side to values of up to 95% [50, 51].

Table 1 Cell and material parameters used for model calculation of a equation monocrystalline silicon solar cell yielding an efficiency of 18.0% ($V_{\text{oc}} = 620\,\text{mV}$, $J_{\text{sc}} = 36.5\,\text{mA cm}^{-2}$, FF = 79.5%)

Parameter	Value
Base resistivity, ρ_{base}	$\rho_{\text{base}} = 2\,\Omega\,\text{cm}$, typical value of industrial monocrystalline silicon solar cells
Oxygen concentration, $[O_i]$	$6 \times 10^{17}\,\text{cm}^{-3}$
Bulk recombination due to boron–oxygen complex, τ_{CZ}	Fundamental limit given by Bothe et al. [48] with a factor of 2 due to improvements by high-temperature steps [48, 49] Using $\rho_{\text{base}} = 2\,\Omega\,\text{cm}$, which corresponds to $N_{A,\text{base}} = 7.2\,\text{cm}^{-3}$, $[O_i] = 7 \times 10^{17}\,\text{cm}^{-3}$, and yields $\tau_{\text{CZ}} = 84\,\mu\text{s}$
Shaded area fraction due to front metallization, f_{shaded}	7%
Reflection on active cell area	Measured data with $R_{\text{weighted}} = 3\%$
Emitter doping and passivation	$R_{\text{sheet}} = 75\,\Omega\,\text{sq}^{-1}$, error function profile, $S_{\text{front}} = 4 \times 10^4\,\text{cm s}^{-1}$
Rear recombination and internal reflectance (due to the difficulties in describing an aluminum BSF properly in PC1D)	$S_{\text{rear}} = 500\,\text{cm s}^{-1}$ [50] $R_{\text{int}} = 65\%$ [50, 51]
Lumped series resistance	$R_s = 0.6\,\Omega\,\text{cm}^2$
Lumped parallel resistance	$R_p = 10\,\text{k}\Omega\,\text{cm}^2$

The used internal reflectance and surface recombination velocity data are based on accurate internal quantum efficiency analysis of current solar cells [47].

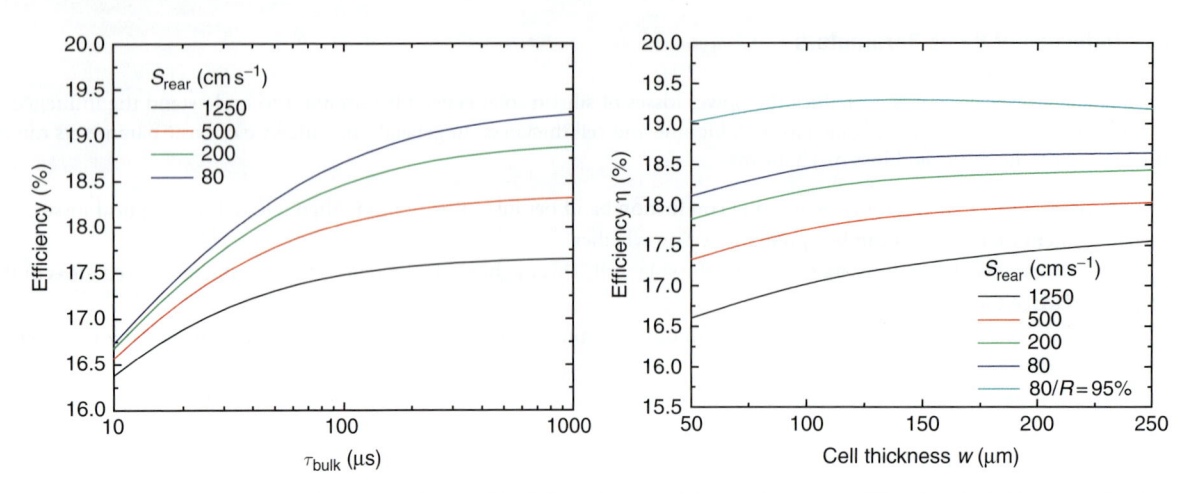

Figure 13 PC1D simulation of cell efficiency for variations of the bulk lifetime τ_{bulk} (left, cell thickness $w = 200\,\mu m$) and cell thickness w (right, $\tau_{bulk} = 84\,\mu s$) for different rear surface recombination velocity S_{rear}. The figure on the right also includes the result for an increased internal rear reflectance (95%). $S_{rear} = 500\,cm\,s^{-1}$ can be taken as state-of-the-art.

In **Figure 13**, the result of PC1D simulations for variations of bulk lifetime and cell thickness is shown for different rear recombination velocities. The high impact of the bulk lifetime on the efficiency in the range from 10 to 1000 µm is clearly visible. A reduced rear recombination velocity substantially increases the sensitivity due to the more dominant bulk recombination.

The impact of the cell thickness on the efficiency is clearly dependent on the rear recombination velocity. For high S_{rear} of $1250\,cm\,s^{-1}$, a reduction of the thickness will greatly reduce the efficiency of the solar cell. This reduction is only small but still apparent, if S_{rear} is reduced to $80\,cm\,s^{-1}$. But if we further turn on the increased internal reflectivity of a dielectrically passivated rear, then the efficiency actually increases to a thickness of around 100 µm and is just reduced after this.

1.16.4 Strategies for Improvement

1.16.4.1 Dielectric Surface Passivation

1.16.4.1.1 Influence of surface passivation

All cell structures that have shown efficiencies greater than 20% feature an efficient surface passivation with dielectric layers. Especially the rear side is of great importance as shown before. To achieve surface passivation in a cell structure, nearly the full rear surface (around 99%) is covered with a dielectric layer like SiO_2, SiN_x, or Al_2O_3 to greatly reduce the rear surface recombination velocity S_{rear}. Only small point-like or line metal structures on the rear form the base contact (see **Figure 14**).

However, the present state-of-the-art rear surface structure of industrial silicon solar cells is a screen-printed and thermally fired Al-BSF (see Section 1.16.2), which has two major restrictions: (1) the wafer bow due to the firing process and (2) the lower electrical

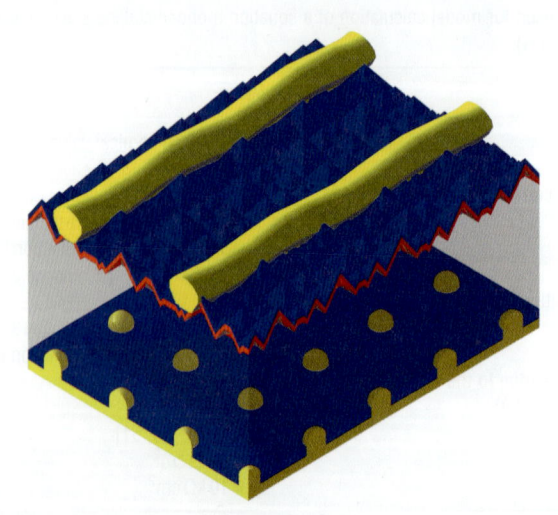

Figure 14 Silicon solar cell with surface passivation (blue) at front and rear surface. Only small point-like metal points (yellow) form the base contact.

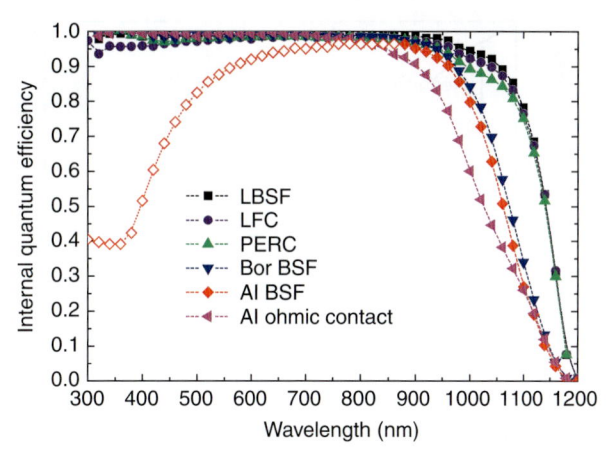

Figure 15 Internal quantum efficiency (IQE) of different rear surface structures on 1 Ω cm 250 μm thick floating-zone (FZ)-Si with a high-efficiency front structure. Note: The low IQE for short wavelengths of the Al-BSF cell (open diamonds) is due to a degradation of front surface passivation during firing. Nevertheless, the IQE starting at 900 nm is identical to the performance of industrial cells. For abbreviations, see **Table 2**.

Table 2 Internal reflectance (R_{int}) and rear surface recombination velocity (S_{rear}) as extracted from the data in **Figure 15**

Structure	R_{int} (%)[a]	S_{rear} (cm s^{-1})
LBSF (local boron back surface field) [55]	94.5	60
LFC (laser-fired contacts) [56]	95.5	110
PERC (random pyramids, passivated emitter and rear cell) [11]	95.0	200
Bor-BSF (boron-diffused back surface field)	71	430
Al-BSF (screen-printed alloyed Al back surface field)	65	750
Ohmic Al contact (evaporated)	83	10^7

[a]Note that for a proper description, it is necessary to introduce a Phong-like characteristic.
The dielectric passivation layer for the LBSF, LFC, and PERC structure was a thermally grown 105 nm thick oxide.

and optical quality. In particular, the rear surface recombination velocity S_{rear} is a crucial parameter, but exhibits a great range of values found in literature. This makes it difficult to evaluate the potential of Al-BSFs versus dielectric passivation.

Thus, an experimental study of different rear surface structures combined with a high-efficiency front structure which does not limit the cell performance was performed [52]. This makes it possible to determine the surface recombination velocity S_{rear} and the internal reflectance R_{int} quite accurately [53].

Figure 15 shows the measured internal quantum efficiencies (IQEs) of different rear structures starting from a low-quality ohmic Al contact up to a PERL [54]/local back surface field (LBSF) [55] rear surface. The effective S_{rear} and R_{int} have been extracted by fitting a simulation model to the IQE and reflection measurement (see **Table 2**). It should be noted that the quality of the Al-BSF formation has been improved since this investigation. Therefore, in the simulation in Section 1.16.3, S_{rear} values of 500 cm s^{-1} have been used.

1.16.4.1.2 Passivation mechanisms of dielectric layers

There are two different mechanisms leading to good surface passivation (for a comprehensive overview about this topic, see Reference 57): (1) the reduction of interface states D_{it} and (2) field effect passivation, that is, the strong reduction of one carrier type by incorporation of fixed charges Q_f in the passivation layer. Although these mechanisms or the combination of both leads to low surface recombination velocities for different excess carrier densities Δn, the resulting $S(\Delta n)$ curve shows different characteristics (see **Figure 16**). The reduction of interface states is more effectively reached for thermally grown SiO$_2$ layers, while the field effect passivation together with a moderate reduction of D_{it} is more typical for PECVD-deposited layers like SiN$_x$. Typical values for SiO$_2$ are $D_{it} = 10^{10}$ cm^{-2} eV^{-1} and $Q_f = 10^{10}$ cm^{-2}, while values for SiN$_x$ are $D_{it} = 10^{11}$ cm^{-2} eV^{-1} and $Q_f = 10^{11}$ cm^{-2}.

1.16.4.1.3 Layers and processes for surface passivation

Due to the successful implementation of passivation layers for high-efficiency devices in the 1980s, the respective processing technologies have been a field of intense research and development in the past decade. According to their main passivation mechanisms, we can subdivide these layers into four groups:

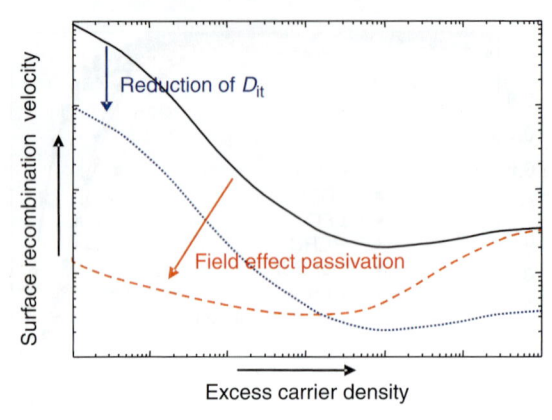

Figure 16 Sketch of the impact of the two passivation schemes, reduction of interface state density D_{it} (dotted) and field effect passivation (dashed).

1. Thermally grown SiO$_2$ was the passivation layer utilized for the first solar cells with efficiencies greater than 20%. Thermally (800–1000 °C) grown SiO$_2$ yields excellent passivation on p- and n-type surfaces. The oxidation process is unique as it is not a mere deposition process as all the other layers described in the following, but it actually consumes silicon of a defined thickness of approximately 45% of the total layer thickness during processing [58]. This leads to the fact that the rate of layer formation is linear only for a thickness in the range of a few nanometers and it is limited by diffusion of the reaction species through the already existing oxide layer. The growth rate is thus described by a linear-parabolic model [59, 60]. Under standard conditions, the oxidation takes place at both sides simultaneously. It can be used as a rather thin layer of around 10 nm or rather in the range of 100 nm. The latter thickness is usually used if the layer is meant to also show optical functionality to serve as an antireflection layer on the front or a reflection layer on the rear side. Silicon oxide is not temperature stable when it is covered by aluminum and exposed to temperatures above 500 °C. A capping layer of silicon nitride can be an appropriate choice in such cases. Oxidation was considered to be too expensive, but higher capacity of tube furnaces and in-line oxidation allow for lower cost [61].
2. Excellent passivation on p-type surfaces has been demonstrated with amorphous hydrogenated silicon nitride (a-SiN$_x$:H) [62], silicon oxide (a-SiO$_x$:H) [63], and silicon carbide (a-SiC$_x$:H) [64] layers. These layers have in common that they can provide high densities of positive fixed charges in the range of 10^{12} cm^{-2}, especially for silicon nitride. Deposition of these layers is typically performed using PECVD. Also sputtering has been successfully applied for surface passivation purposes [65]. A substantial practical problem of a-SiN$_x$:H passivation layers with their high built-in positive charge is that they yield inversion layers for lowly doped p-type silicon, which can lead to shunting of nonoptimum junctions [66]. In principle, they are better suited for n-type silicon passivation where they lead to the accumulation of majority carriers at the surface. In general, the same large variety of plasma excitation systems as for antireflection layers can be used to deposit these layers.
3. Aluminum oxide has been demonstrated with excellent passivation and high negative charge density after thermal treatment based on single-wafer atomic layer deposition (ALD) [67]. Several attempts have been undertaken to convert the ALD approach into an industrially feasible system. Nevertheless, excellent passivation results have also been shown for layers deposited by in-line PECVD or sputtering [68]. For industrial p-type Si passivation, this seems to be an alternative high-quality, low-cost option. Silicon nitride capping layers have proven to improve the thermal stability of aluminum oxide also appropriate for contact firing [69].
4. Intrinsic amorphous silicon (i a-Si) is a semiconductor and yields outstanding passivation [70], but it is thermally unstable at $T > 450$ °C [71]; thus a full low-temperature process is preferably applied like the heterojunction with intrinsic thin-layer (HIT) approach of Sanyo (see Section 1.16.6.4).

1.16.4.2 Metallization

1.16.4.2.1 Front contacts

As the front contacts are facing the sun they have to fulfill various requirements at the same time:

- Low shading losses due to the coverage of the active cell area by metal.
- Low metal/silicon contact resistivity.
- High conductivity in order to allow efficient current transport to collecting structures (e.g., busbars or via holes).
- Solderability and mechanical strength against pull-off forces in the module.

This resulted in screen-printed contacts made of a silver paste that has to be fired after the printing process. Screen printing is a very reliable process and allows for rather small structures especially if they are aligned in parallel such as the front contact fingers of the standard solar cell. Even though very fine lines can be printed at lab scale (~60 μm), currently most production lines fabricate wider fingers to allow for robust production. Very remarkable progress has taken place on the printing equipment side as well as on the materials side where paste vendors are developing paste that is capable of contacting lowly doped high-performance emitters maintaining all the abovementioned requirements at very high yield. In addition to screen printing, stencil printing [72] is also used at lab scale, but it has not found its way into production so far. A special challenge to transfer this well-known technology from printed circuit board (PCB) industry to PV is the shape of the contact grid of the solar cells. The parallel fingers cut through the screens, considerably reducing their stability. Small bridge-like structures increase this stability, but this adds cost to the screens and threatens to interrupt the contacts at these places. Another printing technology to form front contacts is based on extrusion. In this process, the paste is forced through a small orifice and a very high aspect ratio contact line can be deposited on the wafer surface by the relative movement of orifice and wafer. Clogging has to be avoided in this technology and a set of parallel operating orifices should be used to allow high throughput. Recently, very promising results for this noncontact technology have been demonstrated by various authors [73–75].

A very powerful approach to improve the front contact is based on a two-step process [76]. In this process, a seed layer is deposited in a first step. This seed layer is optimized for low contact resistivity and mechanical adhesion to the wafer. Further, it can be deposited in very fine structures as it does not have to feature high aspect ratios. On these fine structures, a second metal is deposited which has electrical contact with the seed. This second layer will carry the current and therefore must have a corresponding cross-sectional area.

There are various options to achieve this structure. Double printing of different pastes is most related to the standard fabrication process. Promising results are already shown by various workers and even production data are already available that show advantages compared to the standard single print [77, 78].

Aerosol printing [79, 80] or inkjet printing [81] of the seed layer allows for very fine structures of the seed layer, and using a plating step this seed layer can be enforced by plating of metal on it. Using a light-induced plating process [82–84] (**Figure 17**), this process can be carried out in a very efficient manner using in-line plating systems. Excellent results have been achieved by this type of contact formation, and various materials and production tools are already tested and used in industrial lines and R&D environments.

Interestingly, this type of plating also allows for plating of copper. Copper could become very important in order to reduce the material cost of the solar cell and to avoid a silver resource issue [85]. Currently, very promising results are achieved by various groups [86–89]; especially the investigation of the impact of copper metallization on solar cell performance is an important subject, as effective copper barriers would allow the use of this cost-effective material [86, 90].

The abovementioned seed layers have in common that they are fired through the antireflection coating. If by a prior process the antireflection coating is already opened (e.g., by laser ablation or local etching), other seed layers can be used [91, 92]. In the early high-efficiency research, metal stack layers have been applied (e.g., Ti/Pd/Ag). The company BP Solar has used plated nickel contacts exploiting the fact that the Ni will deposit on exposed silicon [93]. These Ni layers can be annealed to form nickel silicides, which allow for good mechanical properties. On these seed layers, silver or other metals can be plated (**Figure 18**). Nickel together with copper could become a very cost-effective combination which can also be integrated in high-efficiency concepts [94].

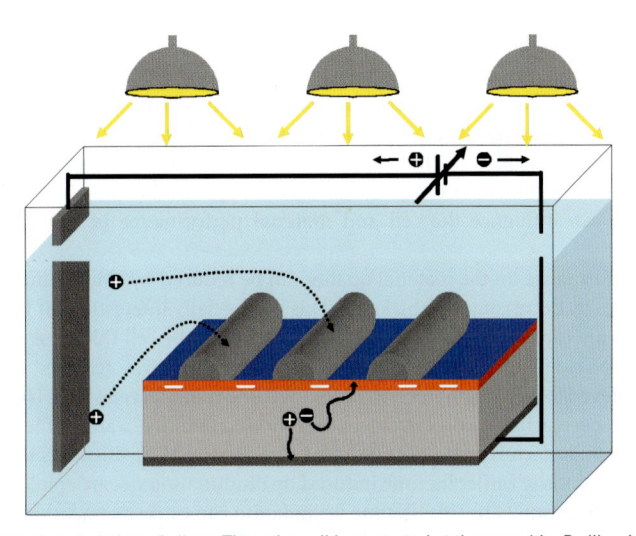

Figure 17 Working principle of light-induced plating of silver. The solar cell is contacted at the rear side. By illuminating the cell, a negative potential at the front contacts is created which attracts the positive silver ions.

Figure 18 Plated front contact finger consisting of a thin Ni seed layer (see front part) and a thick Ag conductive layer.

1.16.4.2.2 Back contacts

The back contacts of the current solar cells are described in Sections 1.16.2.2 and 1.16.2.3. The applied metal pastes have been optimized in the past in order to allow the usage of thin wafers without too much wafer bow. Furthermore, the surface recombination velocities of the contacts formed have been reduced over the years by various methods. Huster and Schubert [35] describe the effect of added boron to increase the doping level of the back surface field. However, only very limited literature is available that focuses on improving the optical properties of the aluminum contacts [95]. During the transition to a locally contacted rear surface of the solar cell, the role of the aluminum paste changes. It will be in contact with only a small fraction of silicon, whereas the largest share of the aluminum will be placed on a passivating dielectric layer, which also results in high internal reflectance. Therefore, the optimization of pastes for this purpose is still ongoing, but various workers have already reported excellent efficiencies on PERC solar cells with modified conventional aluminum pastes.

A further approach to form the back contact is the usage of physical vapor deposition methods [96, 97]. Here, sputtering or either thermal or e-gun-based evaporation is used. As the formed layers achieve very high conductivities, these methods allow realization of the same performance with considerably lower metal sheet thicknesses.

1.16.4.3 Bulk Properties

Certainly, even the best cell structure will not result in high efficiencies if the material quality is too low. Therefore, the investigation of electrically active defects is of great importance for PV material. Especially for mc-Si with its high amount of metal contaminations [98, 99] and crystal defects, it is very important to understand thermal treatments, gettering [100–102], and hydrogen passivation [103] in order to increase the carrier diffusion length. These measures were extremely important to obtain the record efficiencies on small (20.4% on 1 cm^2) [17] and large area (19.5% on 243 cm^2) [104] multicrystalline substrates.

In a standard cell process, gettering is mainly accomplished by the phosphorus diffusion process. Metal impurities can be removed quite effectively by this step [100]. However, if the main lifetime-limiting effects are crystal defects, it is crucial to apply hydrogen passivation [103] to increase carrier lifetime.

Additional effects caused by defects in mc-Si are shunts and junction breakdowns [105, 106]. This is especially important for the application of these cells in a module where solar cells that are shaded can be driven in reverse by the other illuminated cells.

In order to reduce the material costs, a number of attempts have been made to use other procedures such as the classical Siemens process to clean the metallurgical silicon. The resulting material is called solar-grade or upgraded metallurgical silicon (umg-Si). It seems that the common characteristic of this material type is the unavoidable compensation of boron and phosphorus doping atoms. This can influence the cell and material performance in different ways and is currently under investigation [107–112].

The dependence of the cell performance on the material quality can be reduced by using thinner wafers. Thus, the decisive ratio diffusion length/thickness increases by decreasing the thickness. This is especially interesting for high-efficiency cell structures since the high-quality surface structures are capable of retaining cell performance as the cell thickness decreases. For example, the world record efficiency of 20.4% on mc-Si using a fully surface-passivated cell structure was achieved on 99 µm thick material while an efficiency of 'only' 19.9% was achieved for a 218 µm thick wafer of the same material type [17]. Using high-efficiency cell structures, efficiencies greater than 20% have been achieved on extremely thin monocrystalline wafers of less than 50 µm [113].

Most of the mono-Si solar cell manufacturers use boron-doped Czochralski (Cz) silicon as the starting material. This material type shows a severe degradation of minority carrier lifetime induced by illumination or carrier injection [114, 115] reaching a stable final value after a rather short time of about 24 h. This lifetime degradation can cause degradation of cell efficiency of several tenths to more than 1%$_{absolute}$ depending on the quality of the cell structure. The responsible metastable defect is related clearly to the existence of boron and oxygen [116, 117].

Table 3 Cell and material parameters used for model calculation

Parameter	Value
Shadow loss due to front metallization	5%
Recombination in emitter, J_{oe}	100 fA cm^{-2} (–>$V_{oc,max}$ ~ 685 mV)
Maximum achievable FF due to J_{02} and R_p, PFF	~82.5%
Bulk recombination due to boron–oxygen complex, τ_{CZ}	Fundamental limit given by Bothe *et al.* [48] with a factor of 2 due to improvements by high-temperature steps [48, 49]
Residual SRH (Shockley–Read–Hall) bulk recombination due to metal contamination, τ_{metal}	1000 µs
Intrinsic bulk recombination (Auger and direct), τ_{intr}	Doping-dependent parameterization [118]
Base resistivity, ρ_{base}	Variation between 0.1 and 10 Ω cm
Oxygen concentration, $[O_i]$	0 and 6–9 × 10^{17} cm^{-3}
Surface recombination velocity at the rear dielectric layer, S_{pass}	Doping-dependent parameterization for annealed thermally grown oxide [119]
Surface recombination velocity at laser-fired metal contact points, S_{met}	Doping-dependent parameterization for laser-fired contacts [120]
Effective surface recombination velocity at the rear surface, S_{rear}	Calculation using S_{met} and S_{pass} with Fischer equation [121]
Effective base resistance, R_{base}	Spreading resistance calculation using Cox and Strack's equation [122]
Distance of rear point contacts	Optimum distance calculated for each base doping using PitchMaster software
Additional series resistance due to metallization and emitter, $R_{s,residual}$	0.3 Ω cm^2

In order to calculate a realistic potential for solar cells from boron-doped Cz silicon, an industrial high-efficiency cell structure featuring fine-line metallization, shallow and well-passivated emitter, and a rear surface structure with dielectric passivation and local laser-fired point contacts was taken into account (see **Table 3**).

Bothe *et al.* [48] have given a fundamental limit of the lifetime in the degraded state as a function of oxygen and boron concentration. It is important to note that this lifetime is valid for an unprocessed wafer. In several publications [48, 49], it was reported that the concentration of the metastable defect is reduced by a factor of 2–3 by high-temperature steps above 700 °C. Since this is the case for our cell process (emitter diffusion, …), we have assumed the fundamental lifetime limit of Bothe *et al.* multiplied by a factor of 2:

$$\tau_{C_z} = 2 \times 7.675 \times 10^{45} [B_s]^{-0.824} [O_i]^{-1.748} \quad [5]$$

For the calculations presented here, typical oxygen concentrations between 6 and 9 × 10^{17} and 0 cm^{-3} as a reference were chosen. This results in bulk diffusion lengths are shown in **Figure 19**. The quite dramatic difference between the material with no oxygen content and the ones with realistic concentrations is obvious. At low base resistivities, intrinsic recombination channels such as Auger recombination play a dominant role especially for the ideal material. It has to be kept in mind that we have chosen a very high residual lifetime of 1000 µs. This is not always easy to achieve under realistic conditions since the lifetime in p-type silicon is reduced even by low impurity concentrations due to the asymmetric capture cross sections of most metal impurities [123]. However, it is a valuable case study to evaluate the potential of our cell structure under ideal conditions.

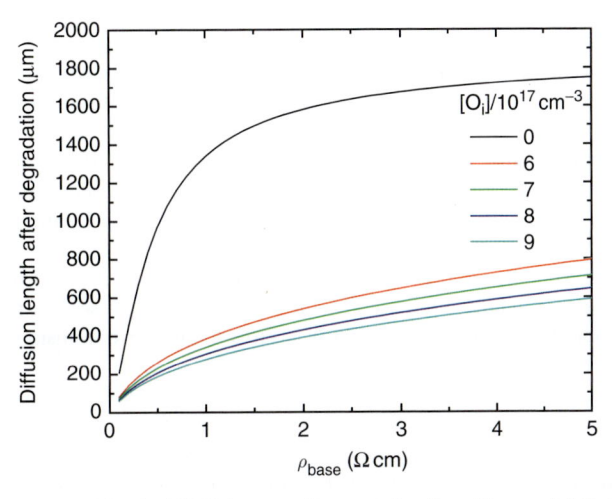

Figure 19 Bulk diffusion length in boron-doped Czochralski (Cz)-grown silicon as a function of base resistivity for different oxygen concentrations.

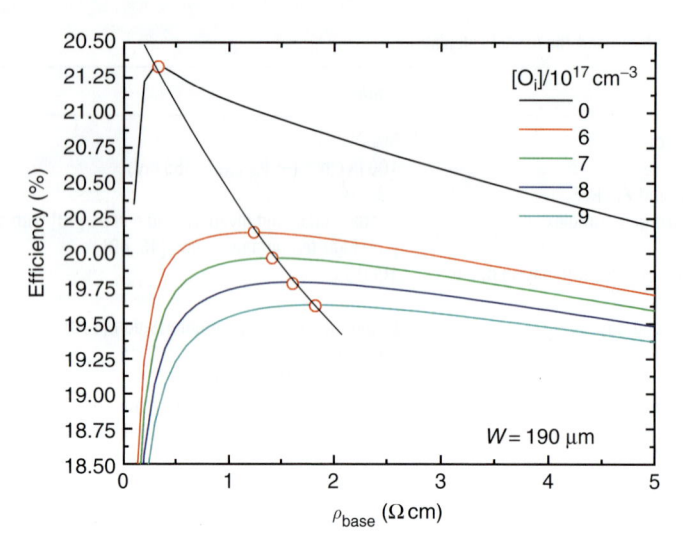

Figure 20 Efficiency as a function of base resistivity for different oxygen concentrations. The maximum efficiencies for each oxygen concentration are denoted by a circle. The pitch of the rear contacts was optimized for each base resistivity. The dots indicate the point of highest efficiency for each individual curve.

For the rear surface structure, we have selected a combination of laser-fired contacts (LFCs) and annealed thermally grown oxide since this results in very high efficiencies and a doping-dependent parameterization of the surface recombination velocity is known [119, 120]. For technical reasons, that is, low deposition temperature, it might be preferable to choose Al_2O_3 as a rear surface passivation layer. However, it will not change the result of our calculation significantly since from a recent publication [124] it is known that using Al_2O_3 nearly identical cell parameters can be achieved as with thermally grown oxide. The pitch of the point contacts is optimized by the spreadsheet-based software PitchMaster [125] as a compromise of recombination losses and base spreading resistance. PitchMaster calculates the cell parameters for the optimum point contact pitch for each individual base doping concentration. The results as a function of base resistivity for a cell thickness W of 190 μm are given in **Figure 20**.

While the cell structure offers an efficiency potential of more than 21%, the best values for oxygen-contaminated materials are in the range between 19.6% and 20.1% for low and high oxygen concentration, respectively. This shows clearly the reduced potential for cells on today's boron-doped Cz-grown silicon and increases the urge for alternatives.

Three options are promising for a reduction of this degradation: (1) the use of thinner wafers to improve the ratio diffusion length/cell thickness [126]; (2) decreasing the boron or oxygen concentration to reduce the light-induced degradation [49, 127]; or (3) the application of the regeneration process as recently demonstrated by Herguth et al. [128].

In addition, alternative material types are also of interest. In fact, cells from gallium-doped Cz-silicon show no degradation [129]. The only issue occurring with this material might be the large variation of doping concentration over the ingot due to the low segregation coefficient of gallium. Nevertheless, adapted cell structures show excellent results over a wide doping range [130].

A strong reduction of the oxygen concentration to values below 1 ppma also results in a perfect suppression of light-induced degradation. Magnetic Czochralski silicon (MCz) has shown a very high efficiency potential [129, 131]. Another material, PV-FZ™ [132], with a negligible oxygen concentration was reported to be introduced into the large-scale PV production a few years ago. This material type has shown very high and stable carrier lifetimes for p- and n-doping, but unfortunately the availability of this material type is still not clear at the moment.

Another material type of interest is certainly n-type silicon. n-type Cz-grown material shows no carrier-induced degradation even in the presence of a significant oxygen concentration [116, 133]. Also for mc-Si, excellent minority carrier lifetimes have been measured [134]. This superior material quality is mainly due to the fact that for most relevant defects the ratio of electron to hole capture cross sections is much greater than unity [123] (**Figure 21**).

Therefore, compared to p-type silicon, the minority carrier lifetime for the same defect concentration is much greater in the case of n-type silicon since this parameter is mainly influenced by the hole capture cross section (σ_p). Thus, although the diffusion constant for minority carriers is about a factor of 2.5–3, which reduces the effective diffusion length, this effect is by far overcompensated by the higher lifetime in realistic material.

These superior recombination characteristics also apply for surfaces. The capture cross sections for the silicon interface of common dielectric passivation layers such as SiO_2 or SiN_x are also highly asymmetric, that is, $\sigma_n \gg \sigma_p$ [135–137]. In practice, this means that the n-type surfaces are easier to passivate. In contrast to these physical advantages, a technological drawback is the fact that the classical cell process as described in Section 1.16.2 is not directly compatible with n-type silicon.

In the following two sections, cell structures for p- and n-type silicon, respectively, will be discussed in more detail.

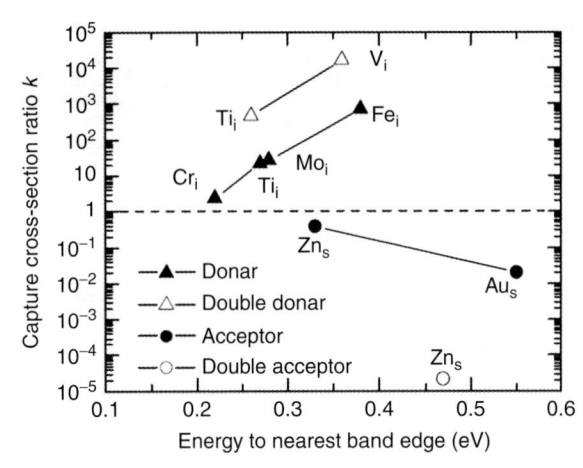

Figure 21 Capture cross sections as a function of energy level for different impurities in crystalline silicon. Reproduced with permission from Macdonald D and Geerligs LJ (2004) *Applied Physics Letters* 85(18): 4061–4063 [123]. Copyright 2004, American Institute of Physics.

1.16.5 High-Efficiency Cell Structures on p-type Silicon

1.16.5.1 Main Approaches for High Efficiencies in p-type Devices

Fortunately, various options exist that allow to surpass the currently industrially achieved solar cell efficiencies. A part of these options can be incorporated into the current solar cell production process without the need to significantly alter the module fabrication, as the concept of having contacts on both sides of the cells will be untouched. The other set of options relate to structural changes of the solar cell. Hereby the first target is the reduction of shading losses by forming back-contacted solar cells. However, up to now, these concepts have not been implemented without a change in the module fabrication process, which is a hurdle for market entry. As this second set of changes also aim at an improved performance of the entire solar cell module, finally an individual gain will be expected at both the cell level and the module level, which should make the development of a suitable module technology very attractive on the midterm.

1.16.5.2 Passivated Emitter and Rear Cell

While solar cell mainstream fabrication was focusing on the Al-BSF solar cell (as described in Section 1.16.2), various research groups fabricated very highly efficient solar cells with contacts on both sides. But a technological gap between the requirements for mass production and the need for clean room environments, photolithography processes, and special cleaning sequences to fabricate the high-efficiency cells did not allow a direct transfer of the developed concepts right away in order to improve and alter the Al-BSF cells. Currently, various technologies have come into the reach of the PV industry, allowing transfer of those concepts that were developed in the early days of PV research and which rose to an extraordinarily high level of performance already at that time.

In 1989, Blakers *et al.* presented the PERC (see **Figure 22**) solar cell reaching solar cell efficiencies of 22.8% [11] and even exceeding 23% in a later work [138]. This concept is based on fundamental device structure improvements by introducing a dielectrically passivated rear surface with local point contacts. Due to reduced surface recombination velocity and improved optical performance, cell parameters were improved compared to cells that do not feature dielectrically passivated surfaces. To further

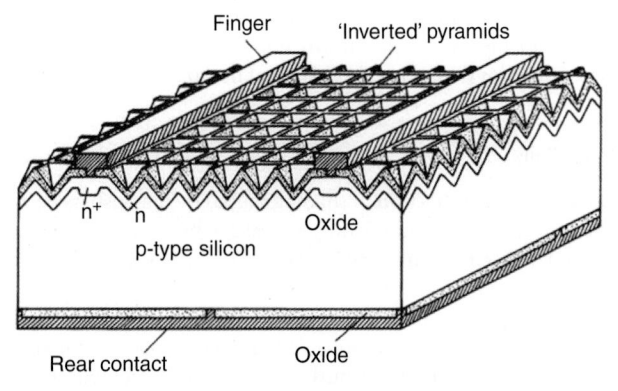

Figure 22 Structure of the PERC (passivated emitter and rear cell) solar cell as proposed in Reference 11. Reprinted with permission from Blakers AW *et al.* (1989) *Applied Physics Letters* 55(13): 1363. Copyright 1989, American Institute of Physics.

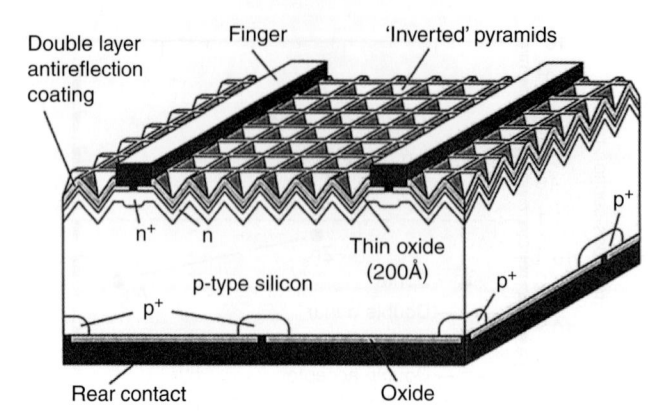

Figure 23 Structure of the PERL (passivated emitter, rear locally diffused cell) solar cell. Reprinted with permission from Zhao *et al.* (1990) *Solar Energy Materials and Solar Cells* 41–42: 87–89. [139]. Copyright 1990 Elsevier.

reduce the recombination of the point contacts and to allow for the use of high-resistivity material, the PERL (see **Figure 23**) solar cell structure was introduced by Zhao *et al.* [140] in 1990. With this concept, cell efficiencies of up to 25% have been achieved [4].

These concepts relate to the passivation and contacting concept used for point contacted back-contact solar cells introduced by Sinton and co-workers [141, 142].

Although these results for PERC and PERL were all achieved on high-quality FZ silicon wafers, excellent results have been achieved on mc-Si substrates [101, 143] and on Cz silicon [144, 145] using such structures. A very substantial reduction of the process complexity was achieved by the so-called RP-PERC (random pyramids, passivated emitter and rear cell) approach, in which amongst other things the inverted pyramid process for front texturing has been replaced by a random pyramid texture (see also Section 1.16.2) saving up to four photolithography steps and achieving excellent efficiencies of up to 21.6% on small-area FZ devices [144]. Further work concentrated on simplification of the formation of the local rear contacts by opening the dielectric passivation using laser ablation processes [146].

Remarkable reduction in the complexity and cost of the process is achieved using the LFC approach in which the point contacts are punched through the passivation layer using a laser while the aluminum layer is already present [147]. Alternatively, the so-called industrial Passivated Emitter and Rear Cell (i-PERC) process [148], in which the dielectric layer is opened before screen-printed aluminum deposition with subsequent firing, can be applied. The i-PERC process was successfully applied by various groups [50, 149]. Detailed analysis of the complex local alloying process was carried out by various researchers [150–152]. It has been reported that during the alloying process considerable amounts of silicon originating from the volume below the local contact are distributed within the aluminum layer which contains liquid phases allowing for fast transport of the silicon in the melt [150]. This silicon depletion can lead to voids depending on the process conditions and contact size and is subject to ongoing investigations [152, 153].

Nekarda *et al.* [154] demonstrated that also the LFC approach is compatible with a screen-printed aluminum layer, which allowed integration of LFC into the already widespread screen-printed aluminum back-contact process which is also compatible with screen-printed front contacts. Recent progress achieved with this type of cells is reported in the literature [96, 104, 155–158] demonstrating efficiencies exceeding 19%. Remarkably high values even on mc-Si substrates have been achieved using LFC technology, leading to large-area multicrystalline solar cells with a maximum efficiency of 19.5% [104]. In this paper also modules have been fabricated from such cells leading to a 17.8% efficient multicrystalline Si-based module, which represents a further world record.

Using high-volume systems the aluminum layers can also be deposited by physical vapor deposition (PVD) mass fabrication [97], and remarkable progress has been reported on using LFC in combination with PVD layers [159].

As these improvements are also accompanied and supported by improved understanding of the underlying physics, the reader is encouraged to look into related publications for deeper understanding of the corresponding structures [53, 120, 121, 125, 160–163].

1.16.5.3 Metal Wrap-Through Solar Cells

Looking at the standard Al-BSF solar cell, the large fraction of shading caused by the busbars becomes immediately apparent. In the current modules, up to three busbars (of approx. 1.5 mm width) are used, which adds up to a total shading loss of approximately 3% of the incoming light (based on a $156 \times 156 \, mm^2$ sized solar cell). Further, the interconnection ribbons cannot be made arbitrarily thick, but the mechanical impact on the cells has to be considered, which leads to the use of rather thin ribbons that cause series resistance losses in the module. Based on this challenge, the metal wrap-through (MWT) concept was introduced by Kerschaver *et al.* [164]. In this concept, the busbars of the solar cell are placed on the rear surface. A set of small metallized via holes, which can be drilled by laser processing, connect this busbar through the wafer with the front contact grid (see **Figure 24**).

The size and number of via holes depend strongly on the overall cell design but can be varied with a large degree of freedom. If the current of a large part of the solar cell is supposed to be transported through the hole, then the diameter is usually larger in order

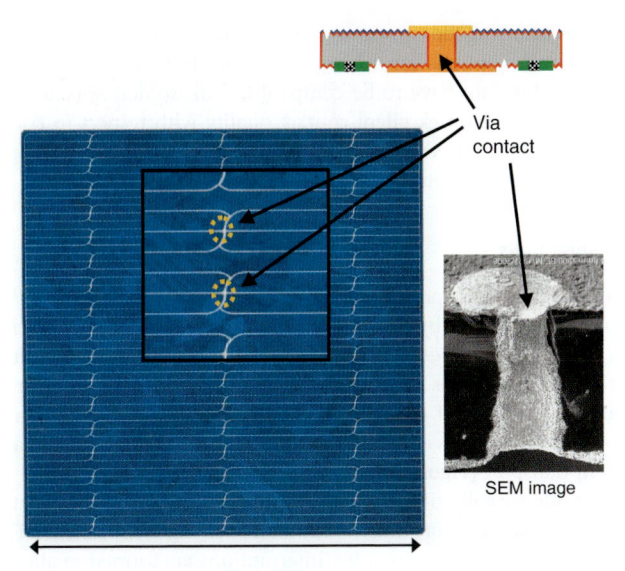

Figure 24 Picture and structure of an MWT (metal wrap-through) solar cell.

to allow a low series resistance contribution of the hole. This has led to the idea of the so-called PUM (pin-up module) [165, 166], which is strongly related to a concept introduced already in 1975 by Hughes Aircraft Company [167, 168].

In concepts similar to Kerschaver's original design suggestions [164], more and smaller holes are applied, which is compatible with the standard front grid in which the fingers are parallel. In both cases, the solar cell features a current collecting grid on the front side, but the interconnection terminals are located on the back surface, which allows new module concepts to be applied. This way the series interconnection can be done by connecting the solar cells to a structured and conducting substrate [169]. It has been demonstrated that this type of interconnection can be carried out by very efficient pick and place automation, leading to very high throughput and very low breakage rates [170, 171]. The fact that no interconnection ribbons are used in this technology allows minimization of the resistive loss that occurs in the standard module fabrication process. Furthermore, the use of conductive adhesives becomes possible, which allows reduction of the mechanical stress within the modules considerably. In total, it has been demonstrated by various workers that the MWT technology allows an efficiency gain of 0.4–0.6% absolute at cell level and an additional gain of 0.3–0.4% at module level, leading to a total gain of approximately 1% absolute for MWT-based modules [172–174]. This has led to excellent module efficiency of up to 16.4% on mc-Si, which represented a world record module at that time [174]. The corresponding proposed MWT solar cell fabrication processes are remarkably close to the standard process mostly used for the fabrication of Al-BSF solar cells. The only amendments to the standard cell process are hole drilling and rear contact isolation, which is applied to ensure a separation of the back minus busbar from the aluminum plus pole. Optionally, a third process is added if the rear minus busbar (which is simultaneously metallizing the vias) is printed with a paste that is different from the paste used for the solder pads of the plus polarity. Choosing different pastes can lead to a slight efficiency advantage, which can overcompensate the cost for the additional process. Various companies and institutes have demonstrated that the fabrication of this cell seems to be feasible [175–178]. Currently, the module production technology and the cost of the related materials seem to be the limiting factors for the introduction of the MWT solar cell, even though very promising technologies are currently evolving such that a near-term large-volume fabrication of MWT modules seems to be possible.

1.16.5.4 MWT-PERC

By combining the advantages of the PERC cells described in Section 1.16.5.2 with the advantages of MWT solar cells described in the previous section, a very attractive concept of an MWT solar cell with passivated surfaces, the so-called MWT-PERC, is obtained. This cell has been demonstrated by various groups [179–181] and it has been shown that the concept – as it is still very close to the standard fabrication process – benefits from most developments that are initially meant to support the standard cell such that the MWT-PERC cell is capable of taking advantage of improvements of the standard process while allowing for significantly higher efficiencies [182]. Most interestingly, a structural advantage of the MWT-PERC solar cell can be worked out by placing the rear minus busbar on top of the rear passivation layer. This way a synergetic effect is achieved as the busbar is not only moved to the back surface but is also eliminated in terms of recombination as it is placed on a passivating layer. Further simplification of the MWT-PERC cells is achieved by the high-performance MWT (HIP-MWT) approach in which the rear minus busbar is not only placed on top of the rear passivation layer, but is also located on top of a p-type doped area while the rear surface emitter is omitted. This approach allows fabrication of HIP-MWT-PERC solar cells by applying simple single-side etching processes, which leads to a remarkably simple process sequence allowing for excellent efficiencies exceeding 20.2% on 125 × 125 mm^2 FZ substrates as recently presented by Thaidigsmann et al. [183]. This value represents the highest efficiency achieved with screen-printed contacts and diffused junctions on p-type substrates, showing the enormous power of the MWT-PERC approach which has only recently entered the R&D centers around the world. Further options for the improvement of MWT solar cells can be found when looking at the metallization of the front surface as it does not have to be compatible with soldering technologies and no busbar needs to be formed. Therefore, it can solely be optimized for excellent contact quality with respect to contact resistance, that is, minimum shading at high aspect ratios. Simplified approaches for seed and plate technology as well as dispensing technology can be applied and further combined with selective emitter concepts.

1.16.5.5 Emitter Wrap-Through Solar Cells

Compared to the MWT solar cells described in the previous sections, the emitter wrap-through (EWT) solar cell concept includes a total ban of the front metallization (first proposed by Gee *et al.* [184]). This is realized by replacing the front contact structure by a set of densely placed vias (approx. one via per mm^2 of cell area) of small diameter (approx. 50 µm). The rear surface of the wafer and the vias feature a further emitter structure which is connected through the vias with the front surface emitter. Only the emitter located on the rear surface is metallized in the EWT concept. The rear emitter is interrupted in a regular and rather dense (pitch is approx. 2 mm) pattern in order to expose the basis of the cell for contact formation. This way an interdigitated metal grid can be formed allowing for efficient current transport (**Figure 25**).

The emitters on the front and rear side are collecting carriers, which makes the EWT cell very attractive for low-lifetime materials. Early EWT solar cells showed rather limited fill factors due to two main challenges with the EWT solar cells. The first challenge was the long exposed pn-junction which was formed as the emitter interruptions are formed to allow the exposure of the basis. As the pitch of this structure is roughly 2 mm, the total length of this type of open pn-junction is about 20 m for a 156×156 mm^2 cell. This issue was overcome by introducing passivation layers and suitable technologies to expose the basis without forming a highly recombinative open pn-junction. The second major challenge is the series resistance of the EWT solar cells. First, the current transport through the vias results in additional loss and more severely interdigitated contact grid pattern on the rear surface leads to very long finger structures which essentially extend to the total length of the used wafers. Various groups have addressed these challenges with different technological approaches [185–189]. Using high-performance clean room technologies, it was possible to demonstrate that EWT solar cells are in principle capable of yielding very high efficiencies. Kray *et al.* [190] have achieved remarkably high efficiencies of 22% on very thin substrates using photolithography processes. Mingirulli *et al.* [191] demonstrated 18.8% efficient EWT solar cells with screen-printed fingers (cell size approx. 40×40 mm^2) allowing to reach an acceptable series resistance. To reduce the series resistance of the EWT solar cells, Eikelboom *et al.* [192] suggested a busbarless EWT solar cell and a corresponding interconnection method based on conductive adhesives. In a later work, again cell/module concepts have been proposed by Gee and Hacke targeting at reducing the series resistance by distributed terminals [193–195], but during the financial meltdown in 2009 Advent Solar did not get a chance to bring these ideas to market and was finally taken over by the company Applied Materials, at which Gee was able to continue some of the EWT work showing excellent results, with EWT cells of 19% efficiency on large-area Cz substrates featuring distributed screen-printed contact terminals [196]. In parallel to the development of the EWT with screen-printed contacts, Engelhart *et al.* [197] worked on a solar cell that was featuring evaporated contacts which have been structured without photolithography using a PVD metallization process together with very unique contact separation process called RISE (rear interdigitated single evaporation). Furthermore, they have optimized the emitter of the solar cell by exploiting the fact that the front side emitter does not need to be contacted; it thus may have a rather low surface concentration, which allowed together with a very efficient passivation to achieve low sheet resistance emitters (about 40–50 Ω sq^{-1}) which still feature very low saturation current densities of about 100 fA cm^{-2}, which was very important for achieving high open-circuit voltages. This structure allowed to achieve very high conductivities and has led to excellent efficiencies of 21.4% on 91.9 cm^2 Cz substrates [198]. Ulzhöfer *et al.* [199, 200] have continued the work on this cell structure, which has considerably increased the understanding of the limiting

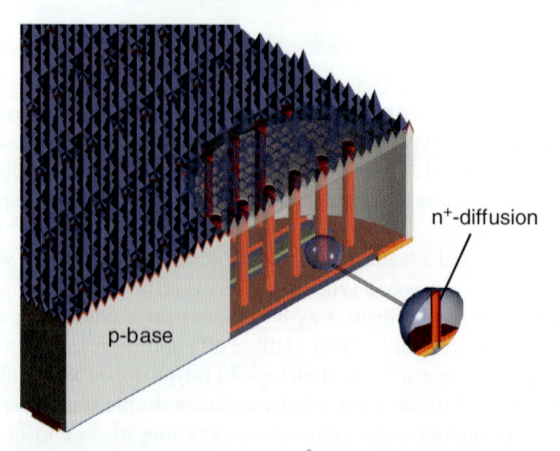

Figure 25 Structure of an EWT (emitter wrap-through) cell.

factors of EWT solar cells. The perspective of EWT solar cells is currently unclear given the fact that only few publications appear per year on this topic; currently, it does not seem to be in the main focus of R&D. Nevertheless, the advantages of the cell concept remain preserved and the concept could be reconsidered if the technological basis for fabrication of such a cell has become more advanced.

1.16.6 High-Efficiency Structures on n-type Silicon

In the previous section, it was shown that improved cell structures with good surface passivation have the potential to reach very high efficiencies. But as was shown in Section 1.16.4.3, the cell performance is also limited by the bulk properties. Therefore, it might be useful to use n-type Cz silicon with its superior physical properties (see Section 1.16.4.3). However, it is not possible to use the well-known and reliable phosphorus diffusion for the emitter formation and alternatives have to be found.

1.16.6.1 Aluminum-Alloyed Back Junction

The easiest way to realize a solar cell on n-type silicon is to utilize the full-area screen-printed Al-alloyed BSF of standard industrial p-type cell structures as the p$^+$-back junction of n-type cells. As effective passivation of the front surface is an important prerequisite for a high efficiency of back-junction cells, a special metallic ink for aerosol printing of the grid has been developed which also allows weakly doped surfaces to be contacted (**Figure 26**). Even without an additional passivation layer on the rear side, high efficiencies of 19.3% on large cells [201, 202] and 19.8% on small cells [203] were achieved (see **Table 4**).

By the addition of a passivation layer on the rear emitter surface, the emitter dark saturation current (J_{oe}) can be reduced [204] and the internal optical reflectivity increased. In this way, efficiencies exceeding 20% have been demonstrated [203].

By using a structured aluminum-doped emitter on the back surface, it is possible to move the front contacts to the rear surface of the solar cell by forming an interdigitated structure in which plus and minus terminals alternate in a dense pattern. The cell formed this way is a back-contacted back-junction solar cell. Gong et al. [205] have presented such a solar cell in which they used screen-printed aluminum paste that was alloyed in a fast firing furnace to form the emitter. In this initial work, the aluminum was printed on a photolithographically structured mask in order to allow the formation of the structured aluminum emitter. After forming the alloy, the aluminum paste residuals as well as the diffusion barrier were etched away. This way in the subsequent process the aluminum emitter could be passivated allowing for low emitter recombination. This process has led to remarkable 19.1% (aperture area 2 × 2 cm) efficient solar cells fabricated on n-type Cz substrates. Bock et al. [206] have applied printed aluminum pastes on unmasked wafers. After firing the paste and etching away the paste residuals and parts of the eutectic layer, the rear surface was structured and a phosphorus diffusion was carried out in order to form an n^{++} region in designated regions of the cell. The cell was passivated on both sides and contacted with a PVD process followed by a contact separation step which allowed to form the interdigitated grid [206]. Within this approach, 19.0% (aperture area 3.97 cm^2) efficient solar cells have been achieved on n-type Cz substrates. Using screen-printed contacts it would be very cost effective if the printed aluminum paste which forms the emitter could also be used as conductor. Furthermore, the minus polarity contact could be formed within the same firing step by a

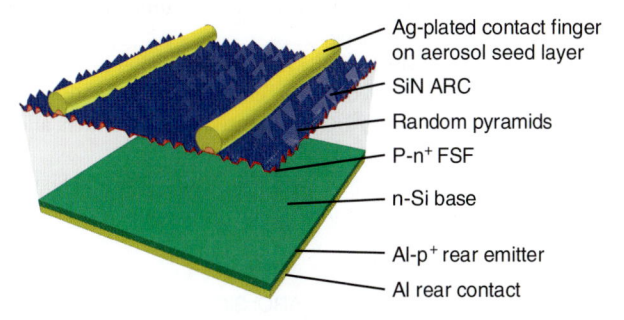

Figure 26 Cell structure with Al-alloyed rear emitter. ARC, antireflection coating; FSF, front surface field.

Table 4 Results of cells with Al-alloyed back junction and no additional rear passivation layer

Process type	A (cm^2)	V_{oc} (mV)	J_{sc} (mA cm^{-2})	FF (%)	η (%)
Industrial	12.5 × 12.5	640	37.7	80	19.3[a]
Laboratory	4.0	642	38.7	79.6	19.8[a]

[a] Measurements confirmed by Fraunhofer ISE Callab.

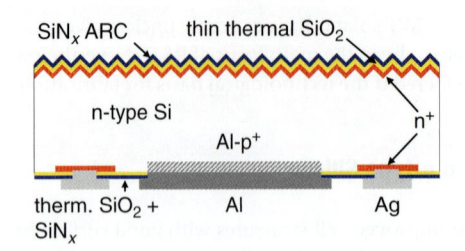

Figure 27 Structure of a back-contacted back-junction solar cell using screen-printed pastes for forming both an aluminum-alloyed emitter and the contact grid [208].

silver-containing paste. This approach is demonstrated by Woehl *et al.* [207]. The corresponding solar cell is shown in **Figure 27**. This approach has resulted in solar cells with an efficiency of 20.0% (aperture area 16.65 cm^2) on n-type FZ silicon substrates [208].

As the various approaches summarized in this section are still in the very early stage of development, there is a lot of potential to increase the achieved efficiency.

1.16.6.2 n-Type Cells with Boron-Diffused Front Emitter

To create a solar cell on n-type silicon and thus utilize the superior characteristics of this material, one can just convert the structure of a standard solar cell resulting in a p$^+$nn$^+$ structure (**Figure 28**). The p$^+$-emitter is created by a boron diffusion, while the n$^+$-BSF is generated by a phosphorus diffusion. In an industrial process, both profiles are fabricated in a co-diffusion process. Such structures are currently transferred to industry [209, 210]. Significantly higher efficiencies of more than 19% have been reached in lab and pilot line production [211, 212].

The phosphorus BSF is well understood and can be passivated and contacted like the standard emitter of a p-type cell. The contacting, and especially the passivation, of the front boron emitter is more demanding. The standard passivation layer SiN$_x$ [213–215] and the thermally grown SiO$_2$ layers [213, 216–218] have shown a poor performance. Thus, new layers had to be developed. In most cases, the front surface layer of such cells consists of a thin layer passivating the boron-doped emitter plus a thick layer of PECVD-SiN$_x$ serving as the antireflection coating and hydrogen reservoir. A layer that is easy to realize is created by a wet chemical passivation in a solution of nitric acid [219]. This increases significantly the blue response compared to cells with a pure PECVD-SiN$_x$ layer. To achieve even better surface passivation, it is worth having a closer look at the passivation system. Therefore, lifetime samples with symmetrical boron- and phosphorus-doped emitters were passivated with thermally grown SiO$_2$. Subsequently, the oxide layers were charged with a corona setup and the carrier lifetime was measured. The measured lifetime can be easily converted to an implied voltage, which indicates the potential of the emitter including passivation (see **Figure 29**).

When no charges are applied, the implied voltage for an oxide-passivated emitter is much better than for the boron-doped emitters. The phosphorus-doped emitter can be improved by adding positive charges resulting in an accumulation of majority carriers. The same field effect passivation can be achieved by adding negative charges on the SiO$_2$-passivated boron-doped emitter. In fact, the quality of both emitters is identical for a charge resulting in strong accumulation. Therefore, the ideal surface passivation for boron-doped emitters should have a strong negative charge.

A dielectric layer that fulfills this requirement and which can be deposited at rather low temperatures is Al$_2$O$_3$. Hoex *et al.* [221] have shown that an Al$_2$O$_3$ layer deposited by ALD can reduce the emitter dark saturation current J_{oe} very effectively. Emitter saturation currents down to 10 fA cm^{-2} were measured on Al$_2$O$_3$-passivated boron emitters allowing for open-circuit voltages far above 700 mV and perfect blue response.

In order to evaluate the potential of such emitters at cell level, the cell structure shown in **Figure 30** was fabricated by Benick *et al.* [220]. The rear side of the cell shown is passivated with a thermally grown oxide and locally diffused phosphorus BSFs.

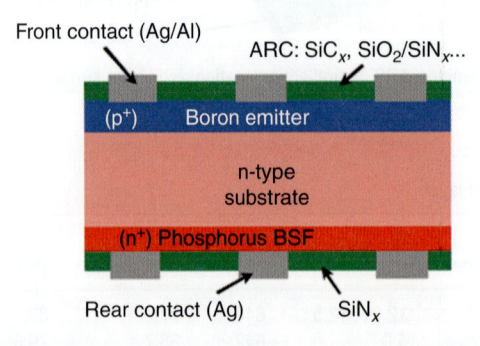

Figure 28 Structure of p$^+$nn$^+$ solar cell. BSF, back surface field. Reproduced with permission from Weeber A, Naber R, Guillevin N, *et al.* (2009) Status of n-type solar cells for low-cost industrial production. In: *Proceedings of the 24th Photovoltaic Solar Energy Conference*, pp. 891–895. Hamburg, Germany [209]. Copyright 2009, WIP, Munich.

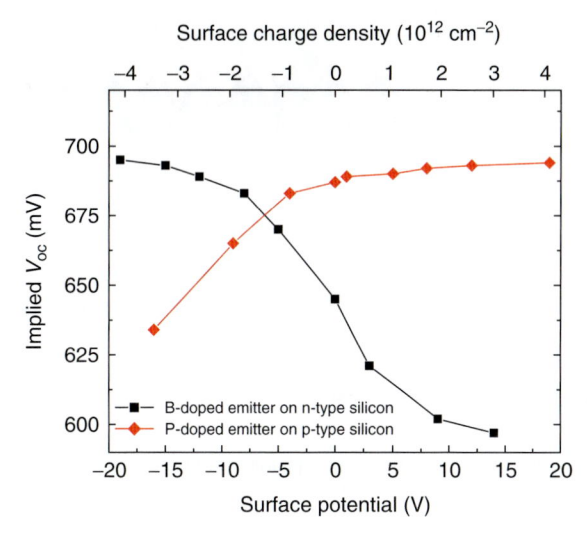

Figure 29 Implied voltages measured on lifetime samples with boron- and phosphorus-doped emitter passivated by a SiO$_2$ layer as a function of corona charge density. Reproduced from Benick J, Hoex B, van de Sanden MCM, *et al.* (2008) High efficiency n-type Si solar cells on Al$_2$O$_3$-passivated boron emitters. *Applied Physics Letters* 92(253504): 253504/253501–253503 [220].

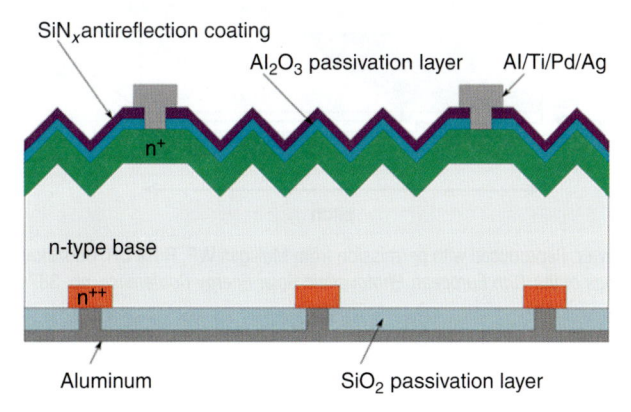

Figure 30 Cell structure with boron-diffused front emitter.

Although this cell still has no selective emitter, which gives room for further improvement, recently an efficiency of 23.9% [222] for a calibrated aperture area (illuminated area includes busbar) measurement has been achieved (see **Table 5**).

In order to transfer this technology from the laboratory to an industrial environment, several processes have to be simplified. The locally diffused P-BSFs of the lab process using masking oxides and photolithography are too complex for industrial application. Therefore, a new process consisting of two steps was developed: (1) PECVD deposition of phosphorus-containing passivation layer system called *PassDop* and (2) simultaneous opening of the layer with a laser and generation of local P-BSFs (see **Figure 31**). Using this new and easy-to-fabricate rear surface process [223], it was possible to achieve a maximum efficiency of 22.4% (see **Table 5**).

1.16.6.3 Back-Contact Solar Cells with Boron-Diffused Back Junction

The A-300 of SunPower [224] (compare **Figure 32**) is a strongly simplified version of the point-contact cell originally developed for concentrator applications at Stanford University [13].

Table 5 Results of cells with boron-diffused front junction ($A = 4$ cm^2)

Rear structure	V_{oc} (mV)	J_{sc} (mA cm^{-2})	FF (%)	η (%)
Thermal oxide + locally diffused P-BSF	705	41.1	82.5	23.9[a]
New PassDop layer + laser-fired P-BSF	701	39.8	80.1	22.4[a]
Full-area P-BSF + printed front contacts	654	38.7	80.8	20.5

[a] Measurements confirmed by Fraunhofer ISE Callab.
P-SF, phosphorus back surface field.

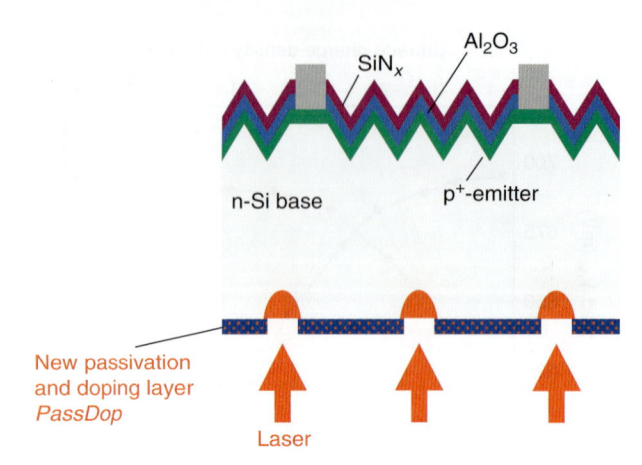

Figure 31 Laser process to create contact openings and local P-BSF (phosphorus back surface field) using the *PassDop* layer. After this process step, an Al layer is evaporated on the rear surface [201].

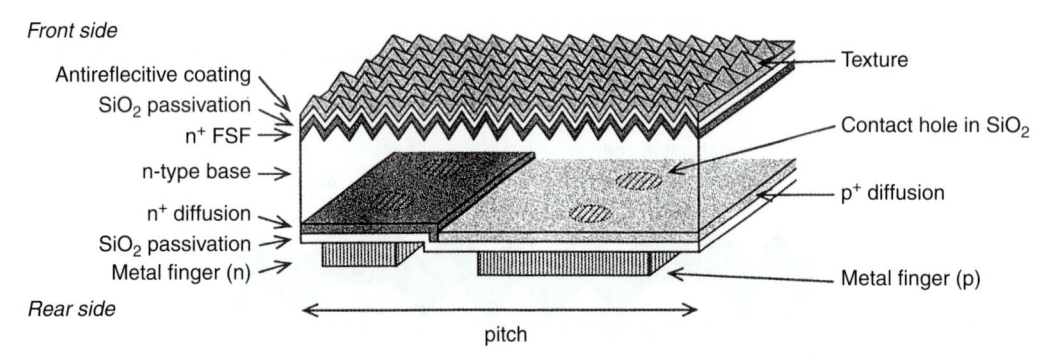

Figure 32 Point-contact cell of SunPower. Reproduced with permission from Mulligan WP, Rose DH, Cudzinovic MJ, *et al.* (2004) Manufacture of solar cells with 21% efficiency. In: *Proceedings of the 19th European Photovoltaic Solar Energy Conference*, pp. 387–390. Paris, France [1]. Copyright 2004, WIP, Munich.

The main feature of this 22% efficient cell in mass production [225] is the absence of any metal contacts on the front side since both electrodes are placed on the rear surface as an interdigitated grid. Thus, nearly all carriers have to diffuse from the front surface where they are photogenerated to the collecting pn-junction at the rear surface. Therefore, the bulk diffusion length has to be high (see previous section) and especially the surface recombination velocity at the front has to be very low. This task is managed by an excellently passivating SiO_2 layer on a lowly doped n^+ front surface field. Although back-contact cells are obviously extremely attractive in terms of efficiency and aesthetics, they also pose very high demands on material quality and process technology. Especially the fabrication of the rear surface structure, that is, the separation of p- and n-diffused regions or p- and n-electrodes, is an issue. One interesting opportunity for this task is the use of laser technologies [226].

Another important design aspect of interdigitated rear contact solar cells is the so-called 'electrical shading' effect [225, 227–229]. Although rear contact solar cells have no metal contacts on the front side and thus optical shading is avoided, regions with lower collection efficiency can occur. Since the width of the BSF regions in industrial back-junction cells is in the region of several times the cell thickness, minority carriers that are generated in this region have to travel considerably longer than carriers that are generated directly above the collecting emitter (see **Figure 33**). Even in high-lifetime material, the collection efficiency for these carriers is reduced, leading to a lower short-circuit current as can be seen on the right side of **Figure 33**. Therefore, the BSF region should be reduced to a minimum. SunPower has successfully reduced or even eliminated the electrical shading and increased efficiency by more than 1% in production [225].

However, when reducing the BSF region, one has to consider that the metallization for the p-contact should have approximately the same width as the emitter contacts. Thus the n-contact will overlap the emitter region in the finished cell and measures have to be taken to avoid a shunt. This can be achieved by the so-called 'buried emitter' concept, where the emitter profile is overcompensated by BSF at the surface [230–233] leading to improved cell performance [234]. The other possibility is to cover the rear surface with a passivating and insulating layer which avoids shunts (see **Figure 34**) and allows for a decoupling of the emitter/BSF and grid geometry. Such layers are available and resulted in cells with excellent performance and without electrical shading [227].

The most recent generation of A300 cells have additionally used passivated contacts to reduce the impact of metal–semiconductor interface recombination. The record efficiency of these cells is 24.2% with a remarkable open-circuit voltage of 721 mV [235].

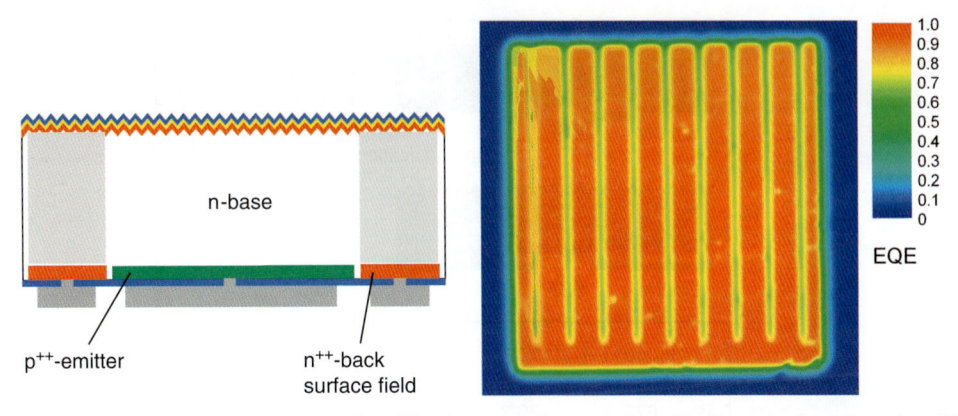

Figure 33 Back-junction solar cell and electrical shading effect. Minority carriers that are generated in the gray regions above the n-BSFs (back surface fields) have to travel laterally to the collecting p-emitter. Since the distances are much larger compared to the cell thickness, carrier collection in this region is strongly reduced (see light beam-induced current map on the right side) [229]. EQE, External quantum efficiency.

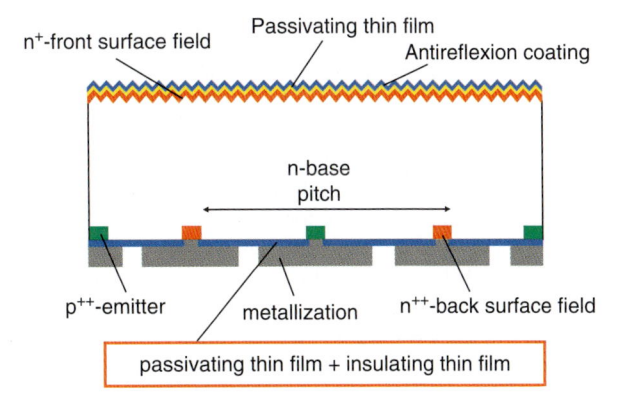

Figure 34 Interdigitated back-junction solar cell with decoupled emitter/BSF and grid geometry using a passivating and insulating film [227].

1.16.6.4 Heterojunction Solar Cells

The p^+-emitter on the n-substrate for the HIT cell of Sanyo [236, 237] is not based on boron diffusion but is formed by the deposition of a p-doped a-Si layer resulting in a heterojunction (see **Figure 35**). Also, the rear surface is passivated by an a-Si layer in order to obtain the full potential of the monocrystalline n-type silicon. The HIT cells by Sanyo prove the excellent surface passivation quality of solar cells with heterojunctions resulting in voltages of 743 mV on 98 μm thick n-type wafers [239]. Efficiencies well above 22% can be achieved using this cell structure.

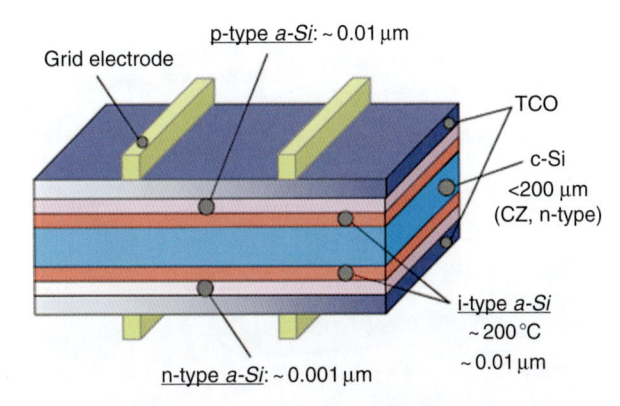

Figure 35 Front structure of the HIT (heterojunction with intrinsic thin-layer) cell. Reproduced from Taira S, Yoshimine Y, Baba T, *et al.* (2007) Our approaches for achieving hit solar cells with more than 23% efficiency. In: *Proceedings of the 22nd European Photovoltaic Solar Energy Conference*, pp. 932–935. Milan, Italy [238]. Copyright 2007, WIP, Munich. TCO, Transparent conducting oxide.

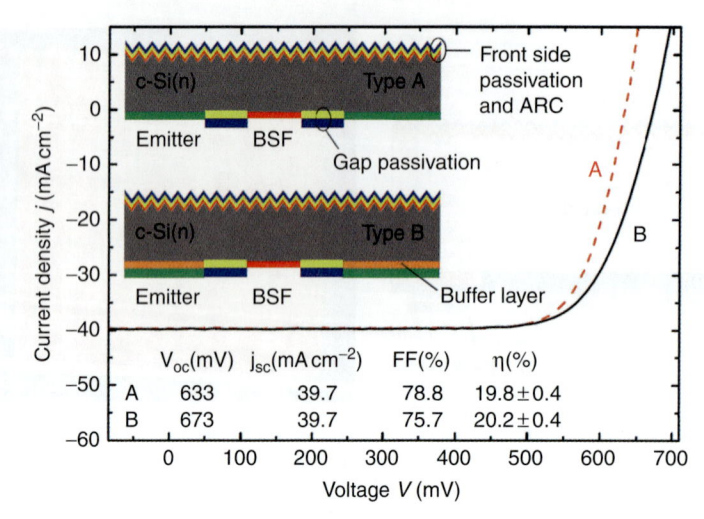

Figure 36 Results on interdigitated heterojunction back-contact cells. BSF, back surface field; ARC, antireflection coating. Reprinted with permission from Mingirulli N et al. (2011) *Physica Status Solidi RRL* 5(49): 159–161 [253]. Copyright 2011, Wiley VCH, Weinheim, Germany.

Up to now, the HIT cell has only been produced by Sanyo, but this situation will change since important patents are running out. Therefore, several institutes and also the equipment manufacturers have intensified their research activities to develop an HIT-like cell structure [240–248].

The major advantage of the HIT cell structure is its perfect surface passivation, which allows for very high open-circuit voltages. In contrast, the achieved currents are only moderate. This is due to the parasitic absorption of photons in the amorphous emitter on the front side. The diffusion length is quite small so that IQE for short-wavelength photons is relatively low. Therefore, a cell structure with front heteroemitter is always a compromise between high-voltage, good transport properties and blue response. A possibility to avoid this parasitic effect is to use heterojunctions in an interdigitated back-junction cell design. Several groups have been working in this field [249–252]. The best efficiency reported so far is 20.2% [253], but of course the potential of this structure is much higher since it combines in an ideal way the advantages of a back-contact solar cell (high current) with those of a standard heterojunction cell (high voltage) (**Figure 36**).

1.16.6.5 Alternative Emitters

1.16.6.5.1 *Polysilicon emitters*

Instead of using a-Si, one can also deposit doped polysilicon [254–256]. This has the advantage that the absorption in polysilicon is lower and the temperature stability is higher. To obtain best results, it is advantageous to use a thin intermediate dielectric layer to passivate the interface and to block diffusion out of the polysilicon emitter resulting in a very abrupt junction (**Figure 37**). This concept was revisited using modern microelectronic equipment and a thin rapid thermal oxide (RTO) as an interfacial layer [257]. Open-circuit voltages of up to 678 mV have been reached with this promising approach.

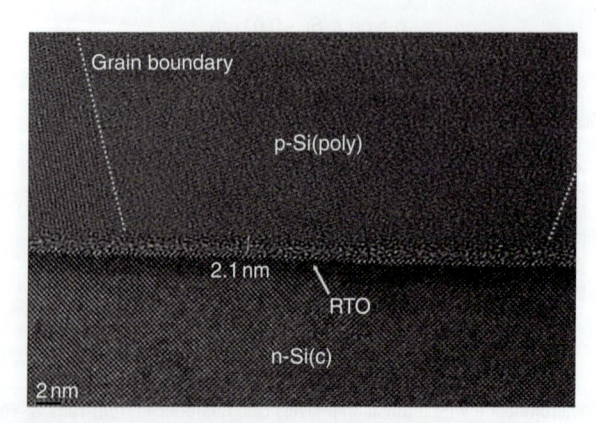

Figure 37 Cross section through a polysilicon emitter. RTO, rapid thermal oxide. Reprinted with permission from Borden P, et al. (2008) *Proceedings of the 23rd Photovoltaic Solar Energy Conference*, pp. 1152. [257]. Copyright 2008, WIP, Munich.

1.16.6.5.2 Implanted emitters

Another technology from microelectronic industry to generate doped layers is ion implantation. Ion implantation allows to generate exactly defined doping profiles and to achieve very uniform doping. After the ion implantation, the wafers have to be annealed to remove the damage introduced by the implantation process. This is extremely critical for solar cells in order to obtain low emitter saturation currents, J_{oe}. Recently, it was shown that with an appropriate high-temperature anneal process very low saturation currents of 20 and 24 fA cm^{-2} for boron and phosphorus emitters, respectively, can be achieved [222]. This would allow in both cases open-circuit voltages above 700 mV.

An interesting feature of ion implantation is the *in situ* masking of implantation allowing locally defined doping profiles. This feature was utilized to generate monocrystalline cells with ion-implanted selective emitters. Efficiencies of greater than 19% have been achieved [258]. Local doping is even more interesting for interdigitated back-junction solar cells with their complex doping pattern on the rear. Using this technique, efficiencies of up to 20% have been reported [259].

1.16.7 Conclusion

This chapter on the current status and new activities of crystalline silicon PV could only give a small insight into the enormous spectrum of research and technology activities in this field and is thus condemned to incompleteness. On the other hand, this is also a very good sign for the sustainability of crystalline silicon PV. The strong research activities show that crystalline silicon PV, which is often regarded as the 'old technology' of PV, is alive and kicking and will remain so in the coming decades. To ensure such a bright future, a strong cooperation between research and industry is crucial.

References

[1] Mulligan WP, Rose DH, Cudzinovic MJ, *et al.* (2004) Manufacture of solar cells with 21% efficiency. In: *Proceedings of the 19th European Photovoltaic Solar Energy Conference*, pp. 387–390. Paris, France. Munich, Germany: WIP Renewable Energies.
[2] van Sark WGJHM, Alsema EA, Junginger HM, *et al.* (2008) Accuracy of progress ratios determined from experience curves: The case of photovoltaic technology development. *Progress in Photovoltaics* 16: 441–453.
[3] Ohl RS (1941) Light Sensitive Electric Device. US Patent 240,252.
[4] Green MA (2009) The path to 25% silicon solar cell efficiency: History of silicon cell evolution. *Progress in Photovoltaics* 17(3): 183–189.
[5] Chapin DM, Fuller CS, and Pearson GL (1954) A new silicon p-n junction photocell for converting solar radiation into electrical power. *Journal of Applied Physics* 25: 676–677.
[6] Perlin J (1999) *From Space to Earth*. Ann Arbor, MI: Aatec Publications.
[7] Wolf M (1963) The effects of a drift field on solar cells. In: *Proceedings of the 3rd IEEE Photovoltaic Specialists Conference*, p. B12. Washington, DC, USA. Piscataway, NJ, USA: IEEE.
[8] Hess WN (1964) The effects of high altitude explosions. In: LeGalley D and Rosen A (eds.) *Space Physics*, pp. 573–610. New York: Wiley.
[9] Mandelkorn J, McAfee C, Kesperis J, *et al.* (1962) Fabrication and characteristics of phosphorous-diffused silicon solar cells. *Journal of the Electrochemical Society* 109(4): 313–318.
[10] Blakers AW and Green MA (1986) 20% efficiency silicon solar cells. *Applied Physics Letters* 48(3): 215–217.
[11] Blakers AW, Wang A, Milne AM, *et al.* (1989) 22.8% efficient silicon solar cell. *Applied Physics Letters* 55(13): 1363–1365.
[12] Zhao J, Wang A, Altermatt PP, *et al.* (1994) 24% efficient silicon solar cells. In: *Proceedings of the 1st World Conference on Photovoltaic Energy Conversion*, pp. 1477–1480. Waikoloa, HI, USA. Piscataway, NJ, USA: IEEE.
[13] Sinton RA, Kwark Y, Gan JY, and Swanson RM (1986) 27.5-percent silicon concentrator solar cells. *IEEE Electron Device Letters* 7(10): 567–569.
[14] Swanson RM (1986) Point-contact solar cells: Modeling and experiment. *Solar Cells* 17(1): 85–118.
[15] Zhao J, Wang A, and Green MA (1999) 24.5% efficiency silicon PERT cells on MCZ substrates and 24.7% efficiency PERL cells on FZ substrates. *Progress in Photovoltaics: Research and Applications* 7(6): 471–474.
[16] Swanson RM (2005) Approaching the 29% limit efficiency of silicon solar cells. In: *Proceedings of the 31st IEEE Photovoltaic Specialists Conference*, pp. 889–894. Orlando, FL, USA. Piscataway, NJ, USA: IEEE.
[17] Schultz O, Glunz SW, and Willeke G (2004) Multicrystalline silicon solar cells exceeding 20% efficiency. *Progress in Photovoltaics: Research and Applications* 12(7): 553–558.
[18] Green M, Emery K, Hishikawa Y, and Warta W (2010) Solar cell efficiency tables (version 35). *Progress in Photovoltaics: Research and Applications* 18: 144–150.
[19] Shockley W and Queisser HJ (1961) Detailed balance limit of efficiency of p-n junction solar cells. *Journal of Applied Physics* 32(3): 510–519.
[20] Kerr MJ, Cuevas A, and Campbell P (2003) Limiting efficiency of crystalline silicon solar cells due to Coulomb-enhanced Auger recombination. *Progress in Photovoltaics: Research and Applications* 11(2): 97–104.
[21] Tajima M, Ikebe M, Ohshita Y, and Ogura A (2010) Photoluminescence analysis of iron contamination effect in multicrystalline silicon wafers for solar cells. *Journal of Electronic Materials* 39(6): 747–750.
[22] Bustarret E, Bensouda M, Habrard MC, and Bruyere JC (1988) Configurational statistics in a-Si$_x$N$_y$H$_z$ alloys: A quantitative bonding analysis. *Physical Review B* 38(12): 8171.
[23] Hezel R and Jaeger K (1989) Low-temperature surface passivation of silicon for solar cells. *Journal of the Electrochemical Society* 136(2): 518–523.
[24] Szlufcik J, De Clercq K, De Schepper P, *et al.* (1994) Improvement in multicrystalline silicon solar cells after thermal treatment of PECVD silicon nitride Ar coating. In: *Proceedings of the 12th European Photovoltaic Solar Energy Conference*, pp. 1018–1021. Amsterdam, The Netherlands. Munich, Germany: WIP Renewable Energies.
[25] Ralph EL (1975) Recent advancements in low cost solar cell processing. In: *Proceedings of the 11th IEEE Photovoltaic Specialists Conference*, pp. 315–316. Scottsdale, AZ, USA. Piscataway, NJ, USA: IEEE.
[26] Frisson L, Honoré M, Mertens R, *et al.* (1980) Silicon solar cells with screen printed diffusion and metallization. In: *Proceedings of the 14th IEEE Photovoltaic Specialists Conference*, pp. 941–942. San Diego, CA, USA. Piscataway, NJ, USA: IEEE.
[27] Mardesich N, Pepe A, Bunyan S, *et al.* (1980) A low-cost photovoltaic cell process based on thick film techniques. In: *Proceedings of the 14th IEEE Photovoltaic Specialists Conference*, pp. 943–947. San Diego, CA, USA. Piscataway, NJ, USA: IEEE.
[28] Kontermann S, Hörteis M, Kasemann M, *et al.* (2009) Physical understanding of the behavior of silver thick-film contacts on n-type silicon under annealing conditions. *Solar Energy Materials and Solar Cells* 2009(93): 1630–1635.
[29] Schubert G (2006) Thick Film Metallisation of Crystalline Silicon Solar Cells. Dissertation, Universität Konstanz.

[30] Ballif C, Huljic DM, Willeke G, and Hessler-Wyser A (2003) Silver thick-film contacts on highly doped n-type silicon emitters: Structural and electronic properties of the interface. *Applied Physics Letters* 82(12): 1878–1880.

[31] Schubert G, Horzel J, Kopecek R, *et al.* (2005) Silver thick film contact formation on lowly doped phosphorous emitters. In: *Proceedings of the 20th European Photovoltaic Solar Energy Conference*, pp. 934–937. Barcelona, Spain. Munich, Germany: WIP Renewable Energies.

[32] Li ZGL and Cheng LK (2009) Electron microscopy study of front-side Ag contact in crystalline Si solar cells. *Journal of Applied Physics* 105(6): 066102.

[33] Rauer M, Woehl R, Rühle K, *et al.* (2011) Aluminum alloying in local contact areas on dielectrically passivated rear surfaces of silicon solar cells. *IEEE Electron Device Letters* 32(7): 916–918.

[34] Lölgen P, Leguijt C, Eikelboom JA, *et al.* (1993) Aluminium back-surface field doping profiles with surface recombination velocities below 200 cm/s. In: *Proceedings of the 23rd IEEE Photovoltaic Specialists Conference*, pp. 1490, 1236–1442. Louisville, KY, USA.

[35] Huster F and Schubert G (2005) ECV doping profile measurements of aluminium alloyed back surface fields. In: *Proceedings of the 20th European Photovoltaic Solar Energy Conference*, pp. 1462–1465. Barcelona, Spain. Munich, Germany: WIP Renewable Energies.

[36] Krause J, Woehl R, and Biro D (2010) Analysis of local Al-p$^+$-layers for solar cells processed by small screen-printed structures. In: *Proceedings of the 25th European Photovoltaic Solar Energy Conference and Exhibition*, pp. 1899–1904. Valencia, Spain. Munich, Germany: WIP Renewable Energies.

[37] Bentzen A (2006) Phosphorus Diffusion and Gettering in Silicon Solar Cells. Dissertation, University of Oslo.

[38] Voyer C, Biro D, Wagner K, *et al.* (2006) Fabrication of textured solar cells using sprayed phosphoric acid as the dopant source for the in-line emitter diffusion. In: *21st European Photovoltaic Solar Energy Conference*, pp. 1157–1160. Dresden, Germany. Munich, Germany: WIP Renewable Energies.

[39] Aichberger SV (2003) Deeper than blue: Market survey on deposition systems for silicon nitride. *PHOTON International* (March).

[40] Hofmann M (2008) Rear Surface Conditioning and Passivation for Locally Contacted Crystalline Silicon Solar Cells. Dissertation, Universität Konstanz.

[41] Wolke W, Jäckle A, Preu R, *et al.* (2004) SiN:H anti-reflection coatings for c-Si solar cells by large scale inline sputtering. In: *Proceedings of the 19th European Photovoltaic Solar Energy Conference*, pp. 419–422. Paris, France. Munich, Germany: WIP Renewable Energies.

[42] Huster F (2005) Investigation of the alloying process of screen printed aluminium pastes for the BSF formation on silicon solar cells. In: *Proceedings of the 20th European Photovoltaic Solar Energy Conference*, pp. 1466–1469. Barcelona, Spain. Munich, Germany: WIP Renewable Energies.

[43] Huster F (2005) Aluminium-back surface field: Bow investigation and elimination. In: *Proceedings of the 20th European Photovoltaic Solar Energy Conference*, pp. 635–638. Barcelona, Spain. Munich, Germany: WIP Renewable Energies.

[44] Krieg A (2007) Inbetriebnahme und Weiterentwicklung eines automatisierten IV-Kennlinienmessplatzes und Entwicklung eines Verfahrens zur Materialverfolgung in der Solarzellenproduktion. Masterarbeit, Fachhochschule für Technik und Wirtschaft Berlin.

[45] International Electrotechnical Commission (2008) International Standard, IEC 60904-3, Edition 2. Photovoltaic devices – Part 3: Measurement principles for terrestrial photovoltaic (PV) solar devices with reference spectral irradiance data. ISBN 2-8318-9705-X.

[46] Basore PA and Clugston DA (1996) PC1D version 4 for windows: From analysis to design. In: *Proceedings of the 25th IEEE Photovoltaic Specialists Conference*, pp. 377–381. Washington, DC, USA.

[47] Thaidigsmann B, Wolf A, and Biro D (2009) Accurate determination of the IQE of screen printed silicon solar cells by accounting for the finite reflectance of metal contacts. In: *Proceedings of the 24th European Photovoltaic Solar Energy Conference*, pp. 2056–2059. Hamburg, Germany.

[48] Bothe K, Sinton R, and Schmidt J (2005) Fundamental boron–oxygen-related carrier lifetime limit in mono- and multicrystalline silicon. *Progress in Photovoltaics: Research and Applications* 13: 287–296.

[49] Glunz SW, Rein S, Lee JY, and Warta W (2001) Minority carrier lifetime degradation in boron-doped Czochralski silicon. *Journal of Applied Physics* 90(5): 2397–2404.

[50] Gatz S, Hannebauer H, Hesse R, *et al.* (2011) 19.4%-efficient large-area fully screen-printed silicon solar cells. *Physica Status Solidi Rapid Research Letters* 5(4): 147–149.

[51] Hermle M (2008) Analyse Neuartiger Silizium- und III-V-Solarzellen Mittels Simulation und Experiment. Dissertation, Universität Konstanz.

[52] Hermle M, Schneiderlöchner E, Grupp G, and Glunz SW (2005) Comprehensive comparison of different rear side contacting methods for high-efficiency solar cells. In: *Proceedings of the 20th European Photovoltaic Solar Energy Conference*, pp. 810–813. Barcelona, Spain.

[53] Kray D, Hermle M, and Glunz SW (2008) Theory and experiment on the back side reflectance of silicon wafer solar cells. *Progress in Photovoltaics: Research and Applications* 16: 1–15.

[54] Zhao J, Wang A, Altermatt PP, *et al.* (1994) 24% efficient PERL silicon solar cell: Recent improvements in high efficiency silicon cell research. In: *Proceedings of the 1st World Conference on Photovoltaic Energy Conversion*, pp. 87–99. Waikoloa, HI, USA.

[55] Knobloch J, Aberle A, Warta W, and Voss B (1990) Starting points for raising the efficiency of practical silicon solar cells. In: *Proceedings of the 5th International Photovoltaic Science and Engineering Conference*. Kyoto, Japan. Tokyo, Japan: ICS.

[56] Schneiderlöchner E, Preu R, Lüdemann R, and Glunz SW (2002) Laser-fired rear contacts for crystalline silicon solar cells. *Progress in Photovoltaics: Research and Applications* 10: 29–34.

[57] Aberle AG (1999) *Crystalline Silicon Solar Cells: Advanced Surface Passivation and Analysis of Crystalline Silicon Solar Cells*. Sydney, NSW, Australia: Centre for Photovoltaic Engineering.

[58] Goetzberger A, Voß B, and Knobloch J (1997) *Sonnenenergie: Photovoltaik, Physik und Technologie der Solarzelle*. Stuttgart, Germany: Teubner.

[59] Deal BE and Grove AS (1965) General relationship for the thermal oxidation of silicon. *Journal of Applied Physics* 36(12): 3770–3778.

[60] Han C-J and Helms CR (1987) Parallel oxidation mechanism for Si oxidation in dry O_2. *Journal of the Electrochemical Society: Solid-State Science and Technology* 134(5): 1297–1302.

[61] Biro D, Mack S, Wolf A, *et al.* (2009) Thermal oxidation as a key technology for high efficiency screen printed industrial silicon solar cells. In: *Proceedings of the 34th IEEE Photovoltaic Specialists Conference*, pp. 1594–1599. Philadelphia, PA, USA. Piscataway, NJ, USA: IEEE.

[62] Schmidt J, Lauinger T, Aberle AG, and Hezel R (1996) Record low surface recombination velocities on low-resistivity silicon solar cell substrates. In: *Proceedings of the 25th IEEE Photovoltaic Specialists Conference*, pp. 413–416. Washington, DC, USA. Piscataway, NJ, USA: IEEE.

[63] Mueller T, Schwertheim S, Scherff M, and Fahrner WR (2008) High quality passivation for heterojunction solar cells by hydrogenated amorphous silicon suboxide films. *Applied Physics Letters* 92(033504): 033504/033501–033503.

[64] Vetter M, Martín I, Ferre R, *et al.* (2007) Crystalline silicon surface passivation by amorphous silicon carbide films. *Solar Energy Materials and Solar Cells* 91: 174–179.

[65] Wolke W, Catoir J, Emanuel G, *et al.* (2005) Surface passivation for solar cells by large scale inline sputtering of silicon nitride. In: *Proceedings of the 20th European Photovoltaic Solar Energy Conference*, pp. 733–736. Barcelona, Spain. Munich, Germany: WIP Renewable Energies.

[66] Dauwe S, Mittelstädt L, Metz A, and Hezel R (2002) Experimental evidence of parasitic shunting in silicon nitride rear surface passivated solar cells. *Progress in Photovoltaics: Research and Applications* 10(4): 271–278.

[67] Hoex B, Heil SBS, Langereis E, *et al.* (2006) Ultralow surface recombination of c-Si substrates passivated by plasma-assisted atomic layer deposited Al_2O_3. *Applied Physics Letters* 89(042112): 042112/042111–042113.

[68] Saint-Cast P, Kania D, Hofmann M, *et al.* (2009) Very low surface recombination velocity on p-type c-Si by high-rate plasma-deposited aluminum oxide. *Applied Physics Letters* 95: 151–502.

[69] Schmidt J, Veith B, and Brendel R (2009) Effective surface passivation of crystalline silicon using ultrathin Al_2O_3 films and Al_2O_3/SiN_x stacks. *Physica Status Solidi Rapid Research Letters* 3(9): 287–289.

[70] Dauwe S, Schmidt J, and Hezel R (2002) Very low surface recombination velocities on p- und n-type silicon wafers passivated with hydrogenated amorphous silicon films. In: *Proceedings of the 29th IEEE Photovoltaic Specialists Conference*, pp. 1246–1249. New Orleans, LA, USA. Piscataway, NJ, USA: IEEE.

[71] Hofmann M, Saint-Cast P, Bareis D, *et al.* (2009) Towards a-Si:H rear passivated industrial-type silicon solar cells. In: *Proceedings of the 24th European Photovoltaic Solar Energy Conference*, pp. 1539–1543. Hamburg, Germany. Munich, Germany: WIP Renewable Energies.

[72] Hoornstra J and Heurtault B (2009) Stencil print applications and progress for crystalline silicon solar cells. In: *Proceedings of the 24th European Photovoltaic Solar Energy Conference*, pp. 1–4. Hamburg, Germany. Munich, Germany: WIP Renewable Energies.

[73] Chen X, Church K, Yang H, *et al.* (2011) Improved front side metallization for silicon solar cells by direct printing. In: *IEEE Photovoltaic Specialists Conference*. Seattle, WA, USA. Piscataway, NJ, USA: IEEE.

[74] Pospischil M, Zengerle K, Specht J, *et al.* (2011) Investigations of thick-film-paste rheology for dispensing applications. In: *Proceedings of the 1st SiliconPV*. Freiburg, Germany. Freiburg, Germany: PSE.

[75] Specht J, Zengerle K, Pospischil M, *et al.* (2010) High aspect ratio front contacts by single step dispensing of metal pastes. In: *Proceedings of the 25th European Photovoltaic Solar Energy Conference and Exhibition*, pp. 1867–1870. Valencia, Spain. Munich, Germany: WIP Renewable Energies.

[76] Glunz SW, Aleman M, Bartsch J, *et al.* (2008) Progress in advanced metallization technology at Fraunhofer ISE. In: *Proceedings of the 33rd IEEE Photovoltaic Specialists Conference*, pp. 1–4. San Diego, CA, USA. Piscataway, NJ, USA: IEEE.

[77] Galiazzo M, Furin V, Tonini D, *et al.* (2010) Double printing of front contact Ag in c-Si solar cells. In: *25th European Photovoltaic Solar Energy Conference and Exhibition*, pp. 2338–2340. Valencia, Spain. Munich, Germany: WIP Renewable Energies.

[78] Raabe B, Huster F, McCann M, and Fath P (2005) High aspect ratio screen printed fingers. In: *20th European Photovoltaic Solar Energy Conference*, pp. 931–933. Barcelona, Spain. Munich, Germany: WIP Renewable Energies.

[79] Mette A, Richter PL, Hörteis M, and Glunz SW (2007) Metal aerosol jet printing for solar cell metallization. *Progress in Photovoltaics: Research and Applications* 115: 621–627.

[80] Hörteis M and Glunz SW (2008) Fine line printed silicon solar cells exceeding 20% efficiency. *Progress in Photovoltaics: Research and Applications* 16(7): 555–560.

[81] Ebong A, Rounsaville B, Cooper I, *et al.* (2010) High-efficiency silicon solar cells with ink jetted seed and plated grid on high sheet resistance emitter. In: *IEEE Photovoltaic Specialists Conference*, pp. 1364–1367. Honolulu, HI, USA.

[82] Durkee LF (1979) Method of Plating by Means of Light. US Patent 4,144,139, 13 March 1979.

[83] Grenon LA (1981) Electroplating Method. US Patent 4,251,327, 17 February 1981.

[84] Mette A, Schetter C, Wissen D, *et al.* (2006) Increasing the efficiency of screen-printed silicon solar cells by light-induced silver plating. In: *Proceedings of the 4th World Conference on Photovoltaic Energy Conversion*, pp. 1056–1059. Waikoloa, HI, USA. Piscataway, NJ, USA: IEEE.

[85] Green MA (2011) Ag requirements for silicon wafer-based solar cells. *Progress in Photovoltaics* 19(8): 911–916. doi: 10.1002/pip.1125.

[86] Bartsch JM, Mondon A, Schetter C, *et al.* (2010) Copper as conducting layer in advanced front side metallization processes for crystalline silicon solar cells, exceeding 20% efficiency on printed seed layers. In: *Proceedings of the 35th IEEE Photovoltaic Specialists Conference*. Honolulu, HI, USA. Piscataway, NJ, USA: IEEE.

[87] Braun S, Emre E, Raabe B, and Hahn G (2010) Electroless nickel and copper metallization: Contact formation on crystalline silicon and background plating behavior on PECVD SiN$_x$:H layers. In: *25th European Photovoltaic Solar Energy Conference and Exhibition*. Valencia, Spain. Munich, Germany: WIP Renewable Energies.

[88] Hernández JL, Tous L, Allebe C, *et al.* (2010) Application of CMOS metal barriers to copper plated silicon solar cells. In: *25th European Photovoltaic Solar Energy Conference and Exhibition*, pp. 1479–1483. Valencia, Spain. Munich, Germany: WIP Renewable Energies.

[89] Posthuma NE, Hernandez JL, Lazov V, *et al.* (2009) Investigation of copper plated contacts for silicon solar cells. In: *24th European Photovoltaic Solar Energy Conference*, pp. 997–1001. Hamburg, Germany, 21–25 September. Munich, Germany: WIP Renewable Energies.

[90] Bartsch J, Mondon A, Bayer K, *et al.* (2010) Quick determination of copper-metallization long-term impact on silicon solar cells. *Journal of the Electrochemical Society* 157(10): H942–H946.

[91] Aleman M, Bay N, Barucha D, *et al.* (2009) Advances in electroless nickel plating for the metallization of silicon solar cells using different structuring techniques for the arc. In: *Proceedings of the 24th European Photovoltaic Solar Energy Conference*, pp. 1414–1418. Hamburg, Germany. Munich, Germany: WIP Renewable Energies.

[92] Knorz A, Aleman M, Grohe A, *et al.* (2009) Laser ablation of antireflection coatings for plated contacts yielding solar cell efficiencies above 20%. In: *Proceedings of the 24th European Photovoltaic Solar Energy Conference*, pp. 1002–1005. Hamburg, Germany. Munich, Germany: WIP Renewable Energies.

[93] Bruton TM, Mason NB, Roberts S, *et al.* (2003) Towards 20% efficient silicon solar cells manufactured at 60 MWp per annum. In: *Proceedings of the 3rd World Conference on Photovoltaic Energy Conversion*, pp. 899–902. Osaka, Japan. Piscataway, NJ, USA: IEEE.

[94] Shi Z, Wenham S, and Ji J (2009) Mass production of the innovative PLUTO solar cell technology. In: *Proceedings of the 34th IEEE Photovoltaic Specialists Conference*, pp. 1922–1926. Philadelphia, PA, USA. Piscataway, NJ, USA: IEEE.

[95] Rohatgi A, Narasimha S, Ebong AU, and Doshi P (1999) Understanding and implementation of rapid thermal technologies for high-efficiency silicon solar cells. *IEEE Transactions on Electron Devices* 46(10): 1970–1977.

[96] Nekarda J-F, Hörteis M, Lottspeich F, *et al.* (2010) Comparison of the three different metallization concepts for LFC cells. In: *Proceedings of the 25th European Photovoltaic Solar Energy Conference and Exhibition*, pp. 2245–2249. Valencia, Spain.

[97] Nekarda J, Reinwand D, Grohe A, *et al.* (2009) Industrial PVD metallization for high efficiency crystalline silicon solar cells. In: *Proceedings of the 34th IEEE Photovoltaic Specialists Conference*, pp. 1–5. Philadelphia, PA, USA. Piscataway, NJ, USA: IEEE.

[98] Istratov AA, Buonassisi T, McDonald RJ, *et al.* (2003) Metal content of multicrystalline silicon for solar cells and its impact on minority carrier diffusion length. *Journal of Applied Physics* 94(10): 6552–6559.

[99] Buonassisi T, Istratov AA, Pickett MD, *et al.* (2006) Chemical natures and distributions of metal impurities in multicrystalline silicon materials. *Progress in Photovoltaics: Research and Applications* 14(6): 513–531.

[100] Bentzen A, Holt A, Kopecek R, *et al.* (2006) Gettering of transition metal impurities during phosphorus emitter diffusion in multicrystalline silicon solar cell processing. *Journal of Applied Physics* 99: 093509.

[101] Schultz O, Glunz SW, Riepe S, and Willeke GP (2006) High-efficiency solar cells on phosphorus gettered multicrystalline silicon substrates. *Progress in Photovoltaics: Research and Applications* 14: 711–719.

[102] Macdonald D and Cuevas A (2000) The trade-off between phosphorus gettering and thermal degradation in multicrystalline silicon. In: *Proceedings of the 16th European Photovoltaic Solar Energy Conference*, pp. 1707–1710. Glasgow, UK. Munich, Germany: WIP Renewable Energies.

[103] Hahn G, Käs M, and Herzog B (2010) Hydrogenation in crystalline silicon materials for photovoltaic application. *Solid State Phenomena* 156–158: 343–349.

[104] Engelhart P, Zimmermann G, Klenke C, *et al.* (2011) R&D pilot-line production of multi-crystalline Si solar cells with top efficiencies exceeding 19%. In: *IEEE Photovoltaic Specialists Conference*. Seattle, WA, USA. Piscataway, NJ, USA: IEEE.

[105] Breitenstein O, Bauer J, Wagner J-M, *et al.* (2009) Physical mechanisms of breakdown in multicrystalline silicon solar cells. In: *Proceedings of the 34th IEEE Photovoltaic Specialists Conference*. Philadelphia, PA, USA. Piscataway, NJ, USA: IEEE.

[106] Kwapil W, Kasemann M, Gundel P, *et al.* (2009) Diode breakdown related to recombination active defects in block-cast multicrystalline silicon solar cells. *Journal of Applied Physics* 106: 063530.

[107] Cuevas A (2008) The paradox of compensated silicon. In: *Conference on Optoelectronics and Microelectronic Materials and Devices*, pp. 238–241. Sydney, NSW, Australia. Piscataway, NJ, USA: IEEE.

[108] Macdonald D, Rougieux F, Cuevas A, *et al.* (2009) Light-induced boron–oxygen defect generation in compensated p-type Czochralski silicon. *Journal of Applied Physics* 105: 093704.

[109] Peter K, Kopecek R, Pernau T, *et al.* (2005) Analysis of multicrystalline solar cells from solar grade silicon feedstock. In: *Proceedings of the 31st IEEE Photovoltaic Specialists Conference*, pp. 927–930. Orlando, FL, USA. Piscataway, NJ, USA: IEEE.

[110] Petter K, Ludwig Y, Bakowskie R, *et al.* (2010) Latest results on production of solar cells from UMG-Si feedstock. In: *Silicon for the Chemical and Solar Industry X*. Ålesund – Geiranger, Norway. Trondheim, Norway: NTNU.

[111] Haunschild J, Glatthaar M, Riepe S, and Rein S (2010) Quality control using luminescence imaging in production of mc-solar cells from UMG feedstock. In: *Proceedings of the 35th IEEE Photovoltaic Specialists Conference*. Honolulu, HI, USA.

[112] Kwapil W, Wagner M, Schubert MC, and Warta W (2010) High net doping concentration responsible for critical diode breakdown behavior of upgraded metallurgical grade multicrystallilne silicon solar cells. *Journal of Applied Physics* 108: 023708.

[113] Kray D, Kampwerth H, Schneiderlöchner E, *et al.* (2004) Comprehensive experimental study on the performance of very thin laser-fired high-efficiency solar cells. In: *Proceedings of the 19th European Photovoltaic Solar Energy Conference*, pp. 608–611. Paris, France. Munich, Germany: WIP Renewable Energies.

[114] Fischer H and Pschunder W (1973) Investigation of photon and thermal induced changes in silicon solar cells. In: *Proceedings of the 10th IEEE Photovoltaic Specialists Conference*, pp. 404–411. Palo Alto, CA, USA. Piscataway, NJ, USA: IEEE.

[115] Knobloch J, Glunz SW, Henninger V, *et al.* (1995) 21% efficient solar cells processed from Czochralski grown silicon. In: *Proceedings of the 13th European Photovoltaic Solar Energy Conference*, pp. 9–12. Nice, France. Munich, Germany: WIP Renewable Energies.

[116] Schmidt J, Aberle AG, and Hezel R (1997) Investigation of carrier lifetime instabilities in Cz-grown silicon. In: *Proceedings of the 26th IEEE Photovoltaic Specialists Conference*, pp. 13–18. Anaheim, CA, USA.

[117] Glunz SW, Rein S, Warta W, *et al.* (1998) On the degradation of Cz-silicon solar cells. In: *Proceedings of the 2nd World Conference on Photovoltaic Energy Conversion*, pp. 1343–1346. Vienna, Austria. Piscataway, NJ, USA: IEEE.

[118] Kerr MJ and Cuevas A (2002) General parameterization of Auger recombination in crystalline silicon. *Journal of Applied Physics* 91(4): 2473–2480.

[119] Schultz O, Mette A, Hermle M, and Glunz SW (2008) Thermal oxidation for crystalline silicon solar cells exceeding 19% efficiency applying industrially feasible process technology. *Progress in Photovoltaics: Research and Applications* 16: 317–324.

[120] Kray D and Glunz SW (2006) Investigation of laser-fired rear-side recombination properties using an analytical model. *Progress in Photovoltaics: Research and Applications* 14: 195–201.

[121] Fischer B (2003) Loss Analysis of Crystalline Silicon Solar Cells Using Photoconductance and Quantum Efficiency Measurements. Dissertation, Universität Konstanz.

[122] Cox RH and Strack H (1967) Ohmic contacts for GaAs devices. *Solid State Electronics* 10: 1213–1218.

[123] Macdonald D and Geerligs LJ (2004) Recombination activity of interstitial iron and other transition metal point defects in p- and n-type crystalline silicon. *Applied Physics Letters* 85(18): 4061–4063.

[124] Saint-Cast P, Benick J, Kania D, *et al.* (2010) High-efficiency c-Si solar cells passivated with ALD and PECVD aluminum oxide. *IEEE Electron Device Letters* 31(7): 695–697.

[125] Wolf A, Biro D, Nekarda J-F, *et al.* (2010) Comprehensive analytical model for locally contacted rear surface passivated solar cells. *Journal of Applied Physics* 108(124510): 1–13.

[126] Münzer KA, Holdermann KT, Schlosser RE, and Sterk S (1998) Improvements and benefits of thin crystalline silicon solar cells. In: *Proceedings of the 2nd World Conference on Photovoltaic Energy Conversion*, pp. 1214–1219. Vienna, Austria.

[127] Rein S, Warta W, and Glunz SW (2000) Investigation of carrier lifetime in p-type Cz-silicon: Specific limitations and realistic prediction of cell performance. In: *Proceedings of the 28th IEEE Photovoltaic Specialists Conference*, pp. 57–60. Anchorage, AK, USA. Piscataway, NJ, USA: IEEE.

[128] Herguth A, Schubert G, Kaes M, and Hahn G (2006) A new approach to prevent the negative impact of the metastable defect in boron doped cz silicon solar cells. In: *Proceedings of the 4th World Conference on Photovoltaic Energy Conversion*, pp. 940–943. Waikoloa, HI, USA. Piscataway, NJ, USA: IEEE.

[129] Glunz SW, Rein S, Knobloch J, *et al.* (1999) Comparison of boron- and gallium-doped p-type Czochralski silicon for photovoltaic application. *Progress in Photovoltaics: Research and Applications* 7(6): 463–469.

[130] Glunz SW, Rein S, and Knobloch J (2000) Stable Czochralski silicon solar cells using gallium-doped base material. In: *Proceedings of the 16th European Photovoltaic Solar Energy Conference*, pp. 1070–1075. Glasgow, UK. Munich, Germany: WIP Renewable Energies.

[131] Zhao J, Wang A, and Green MA (2001) 24.5% efficiency PERT silicon solar cells on SEH MCZ substrates and cell performance on other SEH CZ and FZ substrates. *Solar Energy Materials and Solar Cells* 66: 27–36.

[132] Vedde J, Clausen T, and Jensen L (2003) Float-zone silicon for high volume production of solar cells. In: *Proceedings of the 3rd World Conference on Photovoltaic Energy Conversion*, pp. 943–946. Osaka, Japan.

[133] Yoshida T and Kitagawara Y (1996) Bulk lifetime decreasing phenomena induced by light-illumination in high-purity p-type CZ-Si crystals. In: *Proceedings of the 4th International Symposium on High Purity Silicon IV*, pp. 450–454. San Antonio, TX, USA. Pennington, NJ, USA: ECS.

[134] Cuevas A, Kerr MJ, Samundsett C, *et al.* (2002) Millisecond minority carrier lifetimes in n-type multicrystalline silicon. *Applied Physics Letters* 81(26): 4952–4954.

[135] Aberle AG, Glunz S, and Warta W (1992) Impact of illumination level and oxide parameters on Shockley–Read–Hall recombination at the Si–SiO$_2$ interface. *Journal of Applied Physics* 71(9): 4422–4431.

[136] Eades WD and Swanson RM (1984) Determination of the capture cross section and degeneracy factor of Si–SiO$_2$ interface states. *Applied Physics Letters* 44(10): 988–990.

[137] Schmidt J, Schuurmans FM, Sinke WC, *et al.* (1997) Observation of multiple defect states at silicon–silicon nitride interfaces fabricated by low-frequency plasma-enhanced chemical vapor deposition. *Applied Physics Letters* 71(2): 252–254.

[138] Green MA, Blakers AW, Zhao J, *et al.* (1990) Characterization of 23-percent efficient silicon solar cells. *IEEE Transactions on Electron Devices* 37(2): 331–336.

[139] Zhao J, Wang A, Altermatt PP, *et al.* (1996) 24% efficient PERL silicon solar cell: Recent improvements in high efficiency silicon cell research. *Solar Energy Materials and Solar Cells* 41/42: 87–99.

[140] Zhao J, Wang A, and Green MA (1990) 24% efficient PERL structure silicon solar cells. In: *Proceedings of the 21st IEEE Photovoltaic Specialists Conference*, pp. 333–335. Kissimmee, FL, USA.

[141] Sinton RA, Kwark Y, Gruenbaum P, and Swanson RM (1985) Silicon point contact concentrator solar cells. In: *Proceedings of the 18th IEEE Photovoltaic Specialists Conference*, pp. 61–65. Las Vegas, NV, USA. Piscataway, NJ, USA: IEEE.

[142] King RR, Sinton RA, and Swanson RM (1988) Front and back surface fields for point-contact solar cells. In: *Proceedings of the 20th IEEE Photovoltaic Specialists Conference*, pp. 538–544. Las Vegas, NV, USA. Piscataway, NJ, USA: IEEE.

[143] Zhao J, Wang A, and Green MA (1998) 19.8% efficient multicrystalline silicon solar cells with 'honeycomb' textured front surface. In: *Proceedings of the 2nd World Conference on Photovoltaic Energy Conversion*, pp. 1681–1684. Vienna, Austria. Piscataway, NJ, USA: IEEE.

[144] Glunz SW, Knobloch J, Biro D, and Wettling W (1997) Optimized high-efficiency silicon solar cells with J_{sc} = 42 mA/cm^2 and ⊠ = 23.3%. In: *Proceedings of the 14th European Photovoltaic Solar Energy Conference*, pp. 392–395. Barcelona, Spain. Munich, Germany: WIP Renewable Energies.

[145] Glunz SW, Köster B, Leimenstoll T, *et al.* (2000) 100 cm^2 solar cells on Czochralski silicon with an efficiency of 20.2%. *Progress in Photovoltaics: Research and Applications* 8(2): 237–240.

[146] Glunz SW, Preu R, Schaefer S, *et al.* (2000) New simplified methods for patterning the rear contact of RP-PERC high-efficiency solar cells. In: *Proceedings of the 28th IEEE Photovoltaic Specialists Conference*, pp. 168–171. Anchorage, AK, USA. Piscataway, NJ, USA: IEEE.

[147] Preu R, Schneiderlöchner E, Grohe A, *et al.* (2002) Laser-fired contacts – Transfer of a simple high efficiency process scheme to industrial production. In: *Proceedings of the 29th IEEE Photovoltaic Specialists Conference*, pp. 130–133. New Orleans, LA, USA.

[148] Agostinelli G, Choulat P, Dekkers HFW, *et al.* (2005) Advanced dry processes for crystalline silicon solar cells. In: *Proceedings of the 31st IEEE Photovoltaic Specialists Conference*, pp. 1149–1152. Orlando, FL, USA. Piscataway, NJ, USA: IEEE.

[149] Münzer KA, Schöne J, Teppe AMH, *et al.* (2011) Physical properties of industrial 19% rear side passivated Al-LBSFR- solar cells. In: *Proceedings of the 1st SiliconPV*, pp. 415–420. Freiburg, Germany: PSE.
[150] Uruena A, John J, Beaucarne G, *et al.* (2009) Local Al-alloyed contacts for next generation Si solar cells. In: *Proceedings of the 24th European Photovoltaic Solar Energy Conference*, pp. 1–4. Hamburg, Germany. Munich, Germany: WIP Renewable Energies.
[151] Urrejola E, Peter K, Glatz-Reichenbach J, *et al.* (2010) Influence of the Al–Si alloy formation in narrow dielectric barrier openings on the specific contact resistance. In: *Proceedings of the 25th European Photovoltaic Solar Energy Conference and Exhibition*, pp. 2176–2178. Valencia, Spain. Munich, Germany: WIP Renewable Energies.
[152] Urrejola E, Peter K, Plagwitz H, and Schubert C (2011) Silicon diffusion in aluminum for rear passivated solar cells. *Applied Physics Letters* 98(153508): 1–3.
[153] Urrejola E, Peter K, Plagwitz H, and Schubert G (2010) Al–Si alloy formation in narrow p-type Si contact areas for rear passivated solar cells. *Journal of Applied Physics* 107(124516): 1–5.
[154] Nekarda J, Stumpp S, Gautero L, *et al.* (2009) LFC on screen printed aluminium rear side metallization. In: *Proceedings of the 24th European Photovoltaic Solar Energy Conference*, pp. 1411–1415. Hamburg, Germany. Munich, Germany: WIP Renewable Energies.
[155] Böscke T, Hellriegel R, Wütherich T, *et al.* (2011) Fully screen-printed PERC cells with laser-fired-contacts – An industrial cell concept with 19.5% efficiency. In: *37th IEEE PVSC*. Seattle, WA, USA (in press). Piscataway, NJ, USA: IEEE.
[156] Hofmann M, Saint-Cast P, Suwito D, *et al.* (2009) Overview on crystalline silicon solar cells using PECVD rear passivation and laser-fired contacts. In: *Proceedings of the 24th European Photovoltaic Solar Energy Conference*, pp. 1517–1522. Hamburg, Germany. Munich, Germany: WIP Renewable Energies.
[157] Mack S, Jäger U, Kästner G, *et al.* (2010) Towards 19% efficient industrial PERC devices using simultaneous front emitter and rear surface passivation by thermal oxidation. In: *Proceedings of the 35th IEEE Photovoltaic Specialists Conference*, pp. 34–38. Honolulu, HI, USA. Piscataway, NJ, USA: IEEE.
[158] Mack S, Jäger U, Wolf A, *et al.* (2010) Simultaneous front emitter and rear surface passivation by thermal oxidation – An industrially feasible approach to a 19% efficient PERC device. In: *Proceedings of the 25th European Photovoltaic Solar Energy Conference and Exhibition*, pp. 2218–2222. Valencia, Spain. Munich, Germany: WIP Renewable Energies.
[159] Wolf A, Wotke EA, Mack S, *et al.* (2010) Pilot processing of 18.6% efficient rear surface passivated silicon solar cells with screen printed front contacts. In: *Proceedings of the 25th European Photovoltaic Solar Energy Conference and Exhibition*, pp. 1391–1395. Valencia, Spain. Munich, Germany: WIP Renewable Energies.
[160] Catchpole KR and Blakers AW (2000) Modelling of the PERC structure with stripe and dot back contacts. In: *Proceedings of the 16th European Photovoltaic Solar Energy Conference*, pp. 1719–1722. Glasgow, UK. Munich, Germany: WIP Renewable Energies.
[161] Catchpole KR and Blakers AW (2002) Modelling the PERC structure for industrial quality silicon. *Solar Energy Materials and Solar Cells* 73(2): 189–202.
[162] Schöfthaler M, Rau U, Füssel W, and Werner JH (1993) Optimization of the back contact geometry for high efficiency solar cells. In: *Proceedings of the 23rd IEEE Photovoltaic Specialists Conference*, pp. 315–320. Louisville, KY, USA. Piscataway, NJ, USA: IEEE.
[163] Plagwitz H and Brendel R (2006) Analytical model for the diode saturation current of point-contacted solar cells. *Progress in Photovoltaics: Research and Applications* 14: 1–12.
[164] van Kerschaver E, Einhaus R, Szlufcik J, *et al.* (1998) A novel silicon solar cell structure with both external polarity contacts on the back surface. In: *Proceedings of the 2nd World Conference on Photovoltaic Energy Conversion*, pp. 1479–1482. Vienna, Austria. Piscataway, NJ, USA: IEEE.
[165] Burgers AR, Bultman JH, Tip AC, and Sinke WC (2001) Metallisation patterns for interconnection through holes. *Solar Energy Materials and Solar Cells* 65(1–4): 347–353.
[166] Bultman JH, Weeber AW, Brieko MW, *et al.* (2000) Pin up module: A design for higher efficiency, easy module manufacturing and attractive appearance. In: *Proceedings of the 16th European Photovoltaic Solar Energy Conference*, p. 1210. Glasgow, UK. Munich, Germany: WIP Renewable Energies.
[167] DeJong PN (1975) Solar Cell Contact Design. US Patent 3,903,428, 2 September 1975.
[168] Pack GJ (1975) Solar Cell Connections. US Patent 3,903,427, 2 September 1975.
[169] Gee JM (1997) Simplified module assembly using back-contact crystalline-silicon solar cells. In: *Proceedings of the 26th IEEE Photovoltaic Specialists Conference*, pp. 1085–1088. Anaheim, CA, USA.
[170] Späth M, De Jong PC, Bennett IJ, *et al.* (2008) A novel module assembly line using back contact solar cells. In: *Proceedings of the 16th IEEE Photovoltaic Specialists Conference*, pp. 1–6. San Diego, CA, USA. Piscataway, NJ, USA: IEEE.
[171] Späth M, de Jong PC, Bennett IJ, *et al.* (2008) First experiments on module assembly line using back-contact solar cells. In: *Proceedings of the 23rd European Photovoltaic Solar Energy Conference*. pp. 2917–2921. Valencia, Spain. Munich, Germany: WIP Renewable Energies.
[172] van Kerschaver E, De Wolf S, Allebé C, and Szlufcik J (2001) High performance modules based on back contacted solar cells. In: *Proceedings of the 17th European Photovoltaic Solar Energy Conference*, pp. 417–420. Munich, Germany: WIP Renewable Energies.
[173] Clement F, Lutsch M, Kubera T, *et al.* (2007) Industrially feasible multi crystalline metal wrap through (MWT) silicon solar cells exceeding 16% efficiency. In: *Technical Digest of the 17th International Photovoltaic Solar Energy Conference*, pp. 406–407. Fukuoka, Japan.
[174] Bennett IJ, Tjengdrawira A, Mewe A, *et al.* (2009) World record module efficiency for large and thin mc-Si MWT cells. In: *Proceedings of the 24th European Photovoltaic Solar Energy Conference*, pp. 3258–3261. Hamburg, Germany.
[175] Dross F, Allebé C, Ma Y, *et al.* (2007) High-efficiency (average 16.0%) industrial-type rear-contacts multicrystalline silicon solar cells. In: *Technical Digest of the 17th International Photovoltaic Solar Energy Conference*, pp. 410–411. Fukuoka, Japan. Tokyo, Japan: ICS.
[176] Lahmer D, Lossen J, Meyer K, *et al.* (2009) Pilot-line processing of Cz-Si MWT solar cells with an efficiency gain of 0.3%. In: *Proceedings of the 24th European Photovoltaic Solar Energy Conference*, pp. 2168–2171. Hamburg, Germany. Munich, Germany: WIP Renewable Energies.
[177] Späth M, De Jong PC, Lust S, and Clasen H (2006) Solder version of 8 inch back-contacted solar cells. In: *Proceedings of the 15th International Photovoltaic Science & Engineering Conference*, pp. 1003–1004. Shanghai, China. Tokyo, Japan: ICS.
[178] van den Donker MN, Wijnen PAM, Krantz S, *et al.* (2008) The Starfire project: Towards in-line mass production of thin high efficiency backcontacted multicrystalline silicon solar cells. In: *Proceedings of the 23rd European Photovoltaic Solar Energy Conference*, pp. 1–3. Valencia, Spain. Munich, Germany: WIP Renewable Energies.
[179] Dross F, van Kerschaver E, Allebé C, *et al.* (2006) Impact of rear-surface passivation on MWT performances. In: *Proceedings of the 4th World Conference on Photovoltaic Energy Conversion*, pp. 1291–1294. Waikoloa, HI, USA. Piscataway, NJ, USA: IEEE.
[180] Romijn I, Lamers M, Stassen A, *et al.* (2007) Aspire: A new industrial MWT cell technology enabling high efficiencies on thin and large mc-Si wafers. In: *Proceedings of the 22nd European Photovoltaic Solar Energy Conference*, pp. 1043–1049. Milan, Italy. Munich, Germany: WIP Renewable Energies.
[181] Thaidigsmann B, Wolf A, Clement F, *et al.* (2010) Combining the advantages of wrap through metallization and rear surface passivation into industrial MWT-PERC devices. In: *Proceedings of the 25th European Photovoltaic Solar Energy Conference and Exhibition*, pp. 2227–2230. Valencia, Spain. Munich, Germany: WIP Renewable Energies.
[182] Biro D, Thaidigsmann B, Clement F, *et al.* (2011) MWT meets PERC: Towards 20% efficient industrial silicon solar cells. In: *IEEE Photovoltaic Specialists Conference*. Seattle, WA, USA. Piscataway, NJ, USA: IEEE.
[183] Thaidigsmann B, Lohmüller E, Jäger U, *et al.* (2011) Large-area p-type HIP-MWT silicon solar cells with screen printed contacts exceeding 20% efficiency. *Physica Status Solidi Rapid Research Letters* 5(8): 286–288.
[184] Gee JM, Schubert WK, and Basore PA (1993) Emitter wrap-through solar cell. In: *Proceedings of the 23rd IEEE Photovoltaic Specialists Conference*, pp. 265–270. Louisville, KY, USA.
[185] Kress A, Fath P, Willeke G, and Bucher E (1998) Low-cost back contact silicon solar cells applying the emitter-wrap-through (EWT) concept. In: *Proceedings of the 2nd World Conference on Photovoltaic Energy Conversion*, pp. 1547–1550. Vienna, Austria. Piscataway, NJ, USA: IEEE.
[186] Haverkamp H, Scholz S, and Hahn G (2008) Screen printed EWT cells: Limitations and alternative approaches to the manufacturing process. In: *Proceedings of the 23rd European Photovoltaic Solar Energy Conference*, pp. 1945–1948. Valencia, Spain. Munich, Germany: WIP Renewable Energies.
[187] Faika K, Wagner M, Fath P, and Bucher E (2000) Simplification of EWT (emitter wrap-through) solar cell fabrication using Al–P-codiffusion. In: *Proceedings of the 28th IEEE Photovoltaic Specialists Conference*, pp. 260–263. Anchorage, AK, USA. Piscataway, NJ, USA: IEEE.

[188] Schönecker A, de Moor HHC, Burgers AR, *et al.* (1997) An industrial multi-crystalline EWT solar cell with screen printed metallization. In: *Proceedings of the 14th European Photovoltaic Solar Energy Conference*, pp. 796–799. Barcelona, Spain. Munich, Germany: WIP Renewable Energies.

[189] Fallisch A, Stüwe D, Neubauer R, *et al.* (2010) Inkjet structured EWT silicon solar cells with evaporated aluminum metallization and laser-fired contacts. In: *Proceedings of the 35th IEEE Photovoltaic Specialists Conference*, pp. 3125–3130. Honolulu, HI, USA. Piscataway, NJ, USA: IEEE.

[190] Kray D, Dicker J, Osswald D, *et al.* (2003) Progress in high-efficiency emitter-wrap-through cells on medium quality substrates. In: *Proceedings of the 3rd World Conference on Photovoltaic Energy Conversion*, pp. 1340–1343. Osaka, Japan. Piscataway, NJ, USA: IEEE.

[191] Mingirulli N, Stüwe D, Specht J, *et al.* (2009) 18.8% EWT-cells with screen-printed metallization and single step side selective emitter formation. In: *Proceedings of the 24th European Photovoltaic Solar Energy Conference*, pp. 1979–1984. Hamburg, Germany. Munich, Germany: WIP Renewable Energies.

[192] Eikelboom DWK, Burgers AR, Goris MJAA, *et al.* (2001) Conductive adhesives for interconnection of busbarless emitter wrap-through solar cells on a structured metal foil. In: *Proceedings of the 17th European Photovoltaic Solar Energy Conference*, pp. 1547–1550. Munich, Germany: WIP Renewable Energies.

[193] Gee JM, Meakin D, Southimath S, *et al.* (2009) Development of commercial-scale photovoltaic modules using monolithic module assembly. In: *34th IEEE Photovoltaic Specialists Conference*, pp. 2133–2137. Philadelphia, PA, USA. Piscataway, NJ, USA: IEEE.

[194] Hacke P, Gee J, Kumar P, *et al.* (2009) Optimized emitter wrap-through cells for monolithic module assembly. In: *34th IEEE Photovoltaic Specialists Conference*. Philadelphia, PA. Piscataway, NJ, USA: IEEE.

[195] Haller I (1990) Ion–molecule reactions in the silane–ammonia system. *Journal of Physical Chemistry* 1990(94): 4135–4137.

[196] Gee JM, Kumar P, Howarth J, *et al.* (2010) Development of industrial high-efficiency back-contact Czochralski-silicon solar cells. In: *25th European Photovoltaic Solar Energy Conference and Exhibition*, pp. 1342–1345. Valencia, Spain. Munich, Germany: WIP Renewable Energies.

[197] Engelhart P, Teppe A, Merkle A, *et al.* (2005) The RISE-EWT (rear interdigitated single evaporation – emitter wrap through) solar cell – A new approach towards simple high efficiency silicon solar cells. In: *Laseranwendungen in der Photovoltaik*. Dieburg, Germany: Coherent Lambda Physik GmbH.

[198] Engelhart P (2007) Lasermaterialbearbeitung als Schlüsseltechnologie zum Herstellen rückseitenkontaktierter Siliciumsolarzellen. PhD Thesis, Universität Hannover.

[199] Ulzhöfer C, Hermann S, Harder N-P, *et al.* (2008) The origin of reduced fill factors of emitter-wrap-through-solar cells. *Physica Status Solidi Rapid Research Letters* 2(6): 251–253.

[200] Ulzhöfer C, Altermatt PP, Harder NP, and Brendel R (2010) Loss analysis of emitter-wrap-through silicon solar cells by means of experiment and three-dimensional device modeling. *Journal of Applied Physics* 107(10): 104–509.

[201] Glunz SW, Benick J, Biro D, *et al.* (2010) n-type silicon – Enabling efficiencies >20% in industrial production. In: *Proceedings of the 35th IEEE Photovoltaic Specialists Conference*, pp. 50–56. Honolulu, HI, USA.

[202] Schmiga C, Rauer M, Rüdiger M, *et al.* (2010) Aluminium-doped p$^+$ silicon for rear emitters and back surface fields: Results and potentials of industrial n- and p-type solar cells. In: *Proceedings of the 25th European Photovoltaic Solar Energy Conference and Exhibition*, pp. 1163–1168. Valencia, Spain. Munich, Germany: WIP Renewable Energies.

[203] Schmiga C, Hörteis M, Rauer M, *et al.* (2009) Large-area n-type silicon solar cells with printed contacts and aluminium-alloyed rear emitter. In: *Proceedings of the 24th European Photovoltaic Solar Energy Conference*, pp. 1167–1170. Hamburg, Germany. Munich, Germany: WIP Renewable Energies.

[204] Rauer M, Schmiga C, Hermle M, and Glunz SW (2009) Passivation of screen-printed aluminium-alloyed emitters for back junction n-type silicon solar cells. In: *Proceedings of the 24th European Photovoltaic Solar Energy Conference*, pp. 1059–1062. Hamburg, Germany.

[205] Gong C, Van Kerschaver E, Robbelein J, *et al.* (2010) Screen-printed aluminium-alloyed p$^+$ emitter on high-efficiency n-type interdigitated back-contact silicon solar cells. *IEEE Electron Device Letters* 31(6): 576–578.

[206] Bock R, Mau S, Schmidt J, and Brendel R (2010) Back-junction back-contact n-type silicon solar cells with screen-printed aluminium-alloyed emitter. *Applied Physics Letters* 96(263507): 1–3.

[207] Woehl R, Krause J, Granek F, and Biro D (2011) 19.7% efficient all-screen-printed back-contact back-junction silicon solar cell with aluminum-alloyed emitter. *IEEE Electron Device Letters* 32(3): 345–347.

[208] Woehl R, Keding R, Rüdiger M, *et al.* (2011) 20% efficient screen-printed and aluminium-alloyed back-contact back-junction cells and interconnection scheme of point-shaped metallized cells. In: *IEEE Photovoltaic Specialists Conference*. Seattle, WA, USA. Piscataway, NJ, USA: IEEE.

[209] Weeber A, Naber R, Guillevin N, *et al.* (2009) Status of n-type solar cells for low-cost industrial production. In: *Proceedings of the 24th Photovoltaic Solar Energy Conference*, pp. 891–895. Hamburg, Germany.

[210] Mihailetchi VD, Jourdan J, Edler A, *et al.* (2010) Screen-printed n-type silicon solar cells for industrial application. In: *Proceedings of the 25th European Photovoltaic Solar Energy Conference*, pp. 1446–1448. Valencia, Spain.

[211] Guillevin N, Heurtault BJB, Geerligs LJ, and Weeber AW (2011) Development towards 20% efficient Si MWT solar cells for low-cost industrial production. In: *Proceedings of the 1st SiliconPV*, pp. 9–16. Freiburg, Germany: PSE.

[212] Richter A, Henneck S, Benick J, *et al.* (2010) Firing stable Al$_2$O$_3$/SiN$_x$ layer stack passivation for the front side boron emitter of n-type silicon solar cells. In: *Proceedings of the 25th European Photovoltaic Solar Energy Conference and Exhibition*, pp. 1453–1459. Valencia, Spain. Munich, Germany: WIP Renewable Energies.

[213] Altermatt PP, Plagwitz H, Bock R, *et al.* (2006) The surface recombination velocity at boron-doped emitters: Comparison between various passivation techniques. In: *Proceedings of the 21st European Photovoltaic Solar Energy Conference*, pp. 647–650. Dresden, Germany. Munich, Germany: WIP Renewable Energies.

[214] Kerr MJ (2002) Surface, Emitter and Bulk Recombination in Silicon and Development of Silicon Nitride Passivated Solar Cells. Dissertation, Australian National University.

[215] Libal J, Petres R, Buck T, *et al.* (2005) N-type multicrystalline silicon solar cells: BBr$_3$-diffusion and passivation of P$^+$-diffused silicon surfaces. In: *Proceedings of the 20th European Photovoltaic Solar Energy Conference*, pp. 793–796. Barcelona, Spain.

[216] King RR and Swanson RM (1991) Studies of diffused boron emitters: Saturation current, bandgap narrowing, and surface recombination velocity. *IEEE Transactions on Electron Devices* 38(6): 1399–1409.

[217] Cuevas A, Stuckings M, Lau J, and Petravic M (1997) The recombination velocity of boron diffused silicon surfaces. In: *Proceedings of the 14th European Photovoltaic Solar Energy Conference*, pp. 2416–2419. Barcelona, Spain. Munich, Germany: WIP Renewable Energies.

[218] Zhao J, Schmidt J, Wang A, *et al.* (2003) Performance instability in n-type PERT silicon solar cells. In: *Proceedings of the 3rd World Conference on Photovoltaic Energy Conversion*, pp. 923–926. Osaka, Japan. Piscataway, NJ, USA: IEEE.

[219] Mihailetchi VD, Komatsu Y, and Geerligs LJ (2008) Nitric acid pretreatment for the passivation of boron emitters for n-type base silicon solar cells. *Applied Physics Letters* 92(063510): 1–3.

[220] Benick J, Hoex B, van de Sanden MCM, *et al.* (2008) High efficiency n-type Si solar cells on Al$_2$O$_3$-passivated boron emitters. *Applied Physics Letters* 92(253504): 253504/253501–253503.

[221] Hoex B, Schmidt J, Bock R, *et al.* (2007) Excellent passivation of highly doped p-type Si surfaces by the negative-charge-dielectric Al$_2$O$_3$. *Applied Physics Letters* 91(112107): 112107/112101–112103.

[222] Benick J, Richter A, Li T-A, *et al.* (2010) Effect of a post-deposition anneal on Al$_2$O$_3$/Si interface properties. In: *Proceedings of the 35th IEEE Photovoltaic Specialists Conference*, pp. 891–896. Honolulu, HI, USA. Piscataway, NJ, USA: IEEE.

[223] Suwito D, Jäger U, Benick J, *et al.* (2010) Industrially feasible rear passivation and contacting scheme for high-efficiency n-type solar cells yielding a V$_{oc}$ of 700 mV. *IEEE Transactions on Electron Devices* 57(8): 2032–2036.

[224] McIntosh KR, Cudzinovic MJ, Smith DD, *et al.* (2003) The choice of silicon wafer for the production of low-cost rear-contact solar cells. In: *Proceedings of the 3rd World Conference on Photovoltaic Energy Conversion*, pp. 971–974. Osaka, Japan.

[225] De Ceuster D, Cousins P, Rose D, *et al.* (2007) High volume production of >22% efficiency silicon solar cells. In: *Proceedings of the 22nd European Photovoltaic Solar Energy Conference*, pp. 816–819. Milan, Italy. Munich, Germany: WIP Renewable Energies.

[226] Huljic D, Zerres T, Mohr A, *et al.* (2006) Development of a 21% back-contact monocrystalline silicon solar cell for large-scale production. In: *21st European Photovoltaic Solar Energy Conference*, pp. 765–768. Dresden, Germany. Munich, Germany: WIP Renewable Energies.

[227] Reichel C, Reusch M, Granek F, *et al.* (2010) Decoupling charge carrier collection and metallization geometry of back-contacted back-junction silicon solar cells by using insulating thin films. In: *Proceedings of the 35th IEEE Photovoltaic Specialists Conference*, pp. 1034–1038. Honolulu, HI, USA. Piscataway, NJ, USA: IEEE.

[228] Hermle M, Granek F, Schultz-Wittmann O, and Glunz SW (2008) Shading effects in back-junction back-contacted silicon solar cells. In: *Proceedings of the 33rd IEEE Photovoltaic Specialists Conference*, pp. 1–4. San Diego, CA, USA. Piscataway, NJ, USA: IEEE.

[229] Reichel C, Granek F, Hermle M, and Glunz SW (2010) Enhanced current collection in backcontacted back-junction Si solar cells by overcompensating a boron emitter with a phosphorus base-type doping. *Physica Status Solidi A* 207(8): 1978–1981.

[230] Moehlecke A, Del Cañizo C, Zanesco I, and Luque A (1998) Floating junction passivation of p$^+$ emitters. In: *Proceedings of the 2nd World Conference and Exhibition on Photovoltaic Solar Energy Conversion*, pp. 1551–1554. Vienna, Austria.

[231] Harder N-P, Mertens V, and Brendel R (2008) Buried emitter solar cell structures: Decoupling of metallisation geometry and carrier collection geometry of back contacted solar cells. *Physica Status Solidi Rapid Research Letters* 2(4): 148–150.

[232] Benick J, Schultz-Wittmann O, Schön J, and Glunz SW (2008) Surface passivation schemes for high-efficiency n-type Si solar cells. *Physica Status Solidi Rapid Research Letters* 2(4): 145–147.

[233] Granek F, Hermle M, Reichel C, *et al.* (2008) High-efficiency back-contact back-junction silicon solar cell research at Fraunhofer ISE. In: *Proceedings of the 23rd European Photovoltaic Solar Energy Conference*, pp. 991–995. Valencia, Spain.

[234] Mertens V, Bordihn S, Larionova Y, *et al.* (2009) The buried emitter solar cell concept: Interdigitated back-junction structure with virtually 100% emitter coverage of the cell area. In: *Proceedings of the 24th European Photovoltaic Solar Energy Conference*, pp. 934–936. Hamburg, Germany.

[235] Cousins PJ, Smith DD, Luan H-C, *et al.* (2010) Generation 3: Improved performance at lower cost. In: *Proceedings of the 35th IEEE Photovoltaic Specialists Conference*, pp. 275–278. Honolulu, HI, USA. Piscataway, NJ, USA: IEEE.

[236] Kawamoto K, Nakai T, Baba T, *et al.* (2001) A high-efficiency HIT^{TM} solar cell (21.0% ~ 100 cm^2) with excellent interface properties. In: *Technical Digest of the International PVSEC-12*, pp. 289–290. Jeju, Korea. Tokya, Japan: ICS.

[237] Fujishima D, Inoue H, Tsunomura Y, *et al.* (2010) High-performance HIT solar cells for thinner silicon wafers. In: *Proceedings of the 35th IEEE Photovoltaic Specialists Conference*, pp. 3137–3140. Honolulu, HI, USA. Piscataway, NJ, USA: IEEE.

[238] Taira S, Yoshimine Y, Baba T, *et al.* (2007) Our approaches for achieving hit solar cells with more than 23% efficiency. In: *Proceedings of the 22nd European Photovoltaic Solar Energy Conference*, pp. 932–935. Milan, Italy. Munich, Germany: WIP Renewable Energies.

[239] Taguchi M, Tsunomura Y, Inoue H, *et al.* (2009) High-efficiency HIT solar cell on thin (< 100 μm) silicon wafer. In: *Proceedings of the 24th European Photovoltaic Solar Energy Conference*, pp. 1690–1693. Hamburg, Germany. Munich, Germany: WIP Renewable Energies.

[240] van Sark WGJHM, Korte L, and Roca F (2011) *Physics and Technology of Amorphous–Crystalline Heterostructure Silicon Solar Cells*. Heidelberg, Germany: Springer.

[241] Bätzner DL, Andrault Y, Andreetta L, *et al.* (2011) Properties of high efficiency silicon heterojunction cells. In: *Proceedings of the 1st SiliconPV*. Freiburg, Germany: PSE.

[242] Korte L, Conrad E, Angermann H, *et al.* (2009) Advances in a-Si:H/c-Si heterojunction solar cell fabrication and characterization. *Solar Energy Materials and Solar Cells* 93(6–7): 905–910.

[243] Schulze TF, Korte L, Conrad E, *et al.* (2010) Electrical transport mechanisms in a-Si:H/c-Si heterojunction solar cells. *Journal of Applied Physics* 107: 023711.

[244] Ballif C, Olibet S, De Wolf S, *et al.* (2009) High efficiency heterojunction solar cells: Fundamental and practical aspects. In: *Proceedings of the 18th International Photovoltaic Science and Engineering Conference*. Kolkata, India. Tokyo, Japan: ICS.

[245] Pysch D, Meinhardt C, Ritzau K.-U, *et al.* (2010) Comparison of intrinsic amorphous silicon buffer layers for silicon heterojunction. In: *Proceedings of the 35th IEEE Photovoltaic Specialists Conference*, pp. 3570–3576. Honolulu, HI, USA. Piscataway, NJ, USA: IEEE.

[246] Mueller T, Schwertheim S, Mueller N, *et al.* (2010) High efficiency silicon heterojunction solar cell using novel structure. In: *Proceedings of the 35th IEEE Photovoltaic Specialists Conference*, pp. 683–688. Honolulu, HI, USA. Piscataway, NJ, USA: IEEE.

[247] Rahmouni M, Datta A, Chatterjee P, *et al.* (2010) Carrier transport and sensitivity issues in heterojunction with intrinsic thin layer solar cells on N-type crystalline silicon: A computer simulation study. *Journal of Applied Physics* 107: 054521.

[248] Branz HM, Teplin CW, Young DL, *et al.* (2008) Recent advances in hot-wire CVD R&D at NREL: From 18% silicon heterojunction cells to silicon epitaxy at glass-compatible temperatures. *Thin Solid Films* 516(5): 743–746.

[249] Desrues T, De Vecchi S, Souche F, *et al.* (2011) Development of interdigitated back contact silicon heterojunction (IBC Si-HJ) solar cells. In: *Proceedings of the 1st SiliconPV*, pp. 294–300. Freiburg, Germany: PSE.

[250] Lu M, Bowden S, Das U, and Birkmire R (2007) Interdigitated back contact silicon heterojunction solar cell and the effect of front surface passivation. *Applied Physics Letters* 91(063507): 1–3.

[251] Tucci M, Serenelli L, Salza E, *et al.* (2007) Novel scheme of amorphous/crystalline silicon heterojunction solar cell. In: *Proceedings of the 22nd European Photovoltaic Solar Energy Conference*, pp. 1600–1603. Milan, Italy. Munich, Germany: WIP Renewable Energies.

[252] Stangl R, Bivour M, Conrad E, *et al.* (2007) Recash – A novel high efficiency buried grid rear contact amorphous/crystalline silicon heterojunction solar cell concept. In: *Proceedings of the 22nd European Photovoltaic Solar Energy Conference*, pp. 870–874. Milan, Italy. Munich, Germany: WIP Renewable Energies.

[253] Mingirulli N, Haschke J, Gogolin R, *et al.* (2011) Efficient interdigitated back-contacted silicon heterojunction solar cells. *Physica Status Solidi Rapid Research Letters* 5(4): 159–161.

[254] Yablonovitch E, Gmitter T, Swanson RM, and Kwark YH (1985) A 720 mV open circuit voltage SiO$_x$:c-Si:SiO$_x$ double heterostructure solar cell. *Applied Physics Letters* 47(11): 1211–1213.

[255] Tarr NG (1985) A polysilicon emitter solar cell. *IEEE Electron Device Letters* 6(12): 655–658.

[256] Green MA (1995) *Silicon Solar Cells: Advanced Principles and Practice*. Sydney, NSW, Australia: Centre for Photovoltaic Devices and Systems UNSW.

[257] Borden P, Xu L, McDougall B, *et al.* (2008) Polysilicon tunnel junctions as alternates to diffused junctions. In: *Proceedings of the 23rd European Photovoltaic Solar Energy Conference*, pp. 1149–1152. Valencia, Spain. Munich, Germany: WIP Renewable Energies.

[258] Rohatgi A and Meier D (2010) Developing novel low-cost, high-throughput processing techniques for 20%-efficient monocrystalline silicon solar cells. *Photovoltaics International* 10: 87–94.

[259] Bateman N, Sullivan P, Reichel C, *et al.* (2011) High quality ion implanted boron emitters in an interdigitated back contact solar cell with 20% efficiency. In: *Proceedings of the 1st SiliconPV*, pp. 509–514. Freiburg, Germany: PSE.

1.17 Thin-Film Silicon PV Technology

M Zeman, Delft University of Technology, Delft, The Netherlands
REI Schropp, Utrecht University, Utrecht, The Netherlands

© 2012 Elsevier Ltd. All rights reserved.

1.17.1	Introduction	389
1.17.2	Thin-Film Silicon Solar Cell Structures	389
1.17.2.1	Amorphous Silicon	389
1.17.2.2	Microcrystalline Silicon	391
1.17.2.3	Multijunction Solar Cell	392
1.17.2.4	Light Trapping	393
1.17.2.5	Heterojunction *a*-Si/*c*-Si Solar Cells	393
1.17.3	Challenges of Thin-Film Si PV Technology	394
1.17.4	Fabrication of Thin-Film Si Modules	395
1.17.5	Applications	396
1.17.6	Conclusions	397
References		397

Glossary

Photon management. The manipulation of incident light such that photons are absorbed in the active layer as efficiently as possible and not in the inactive layers.

Multijunction solar cell A stack of cells where the respective absorber layers in each component cell are tailored to absorb a specific part of the solar spectrum.

Plasmonics The coupling of light to an absorber material by the integration of metal nanostructures which scatter light over a range of angles into the absorber.

1.17.1 Introduction

The solar photovoltaic (PV) market generated $82 billion in global revenues in 2010, up 105% from $40 billion in 2009 [1], and its compound annual growth rate (CAGR) is on average at 25%, but lately at even >50%. This means that the solar module market is one of the fastest growing markets in the world (**Figure 1**). The total production of solar modules reached a record high of 18.2 GW in 2010 and was dominated by crystalline silicon (*c*-Si) solar cells, which accounted for 80–85% of the total production [2]. As the *c*-Si solar cells, which represent the first-generation solar cells for terrestrial applications, have matured, the cost of these solar cells has become dominated by material costs, namely, those of the silicon wafer, the glass cover plate, and the encapsulants.

One way to decrease the cost of solar electricity is to reduce the thickness of the semiconductor materials that form a solar cell. In comparison with bulk *c*-Si solar cells, in which the silicon wafer has a thickness of 200–300 µm, the total thickness of the semiconductor absorbers in thin-film solar cells is less than a few micrometers. There are several semiconductors that are excellent candidates for thin-film solar cells, such as silicon, copper indium gallium diselenide ($CuInGaSe_2$, CIGS), and cadmium telluride (CdTe). At present, about half of all accumulated thin-film modules is thin-film silicon technology [2]. In 2009, 14% of the thin-film PV (MW-dc) production was hydrogenated amorphous silicon (*a*-Si:H) based (i.e., 7% CIGS based and 79% CdTe based).

Most of the commercial thin-film silicon solar cells today are represented by *a*-Si:H-based solar cells [3]. A distinct feature of these solar cells is that silicon-based layers are deposited in a low-temperature regime, mainly by plasma-enhanced chemical vapor deposition (PECVD) techniques. For solar cells with a thin-film silicon absorber film of <2 µm, the deposition temperature (*T*) usually is <250 °C, while for polycrystalline thin-film silicon absorber films of <100 µm, the deposition temperature (*T*) usually is <600 °C. Since in silicon solar cell technology the term 'thin-film' usually covers a range of 0.1–100 µm thick layers, in this chapter thin-film silicon solar cells refer to the low-temperature silicon-based solar cells.

1.17.2 Thin-Film Silicon Solar Cell Structures

1.17.2.1 Amorphous Silicon

In 1965, Sterling and Swann [4] published work on glassy (i.e., amorphous) layers deposited in a radio-frequency discharge using silane. In 1968, Vepřek and Mareček [5] deposited microcrystalline silicon (*µc*-Si:H), by exposing *c*-Si to a hydrogen plasma. With the microscopy techniques in these days, they could not discern whether the structure was in fact nanocrystalline. Nowadays, the term

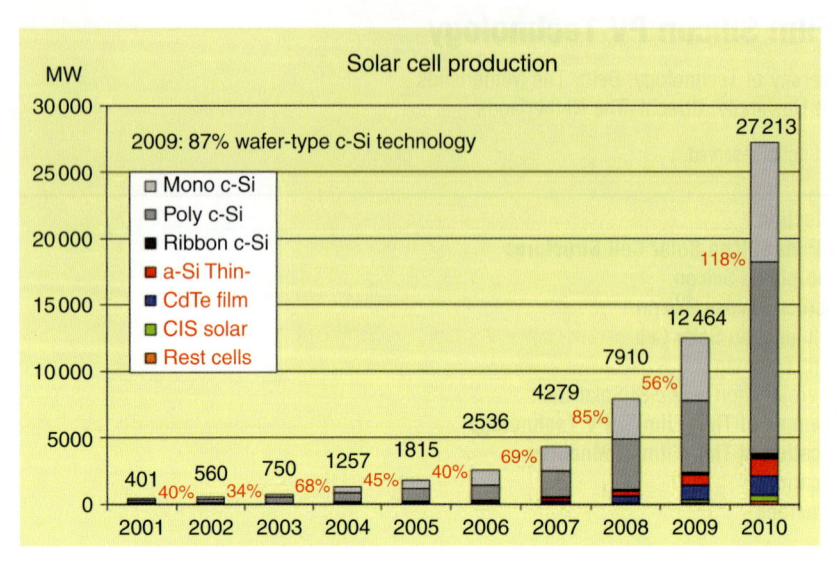

Figure 1 Global solar cell production between 2000 and 2010 [2].

hydrogenated microcrystalline silicon (μc-Si:H) is used irrespective of the actual size of the crystalline grains, which may consist of coherent regions from nanometer scale to micrometer scale [6].

In 1975, Walter Spear and Peter LeComber reported that amorphous silicon had semiconducting properties by demonstrating that the conductivity could be manipulated by several orders of magnitude by adding some phosphine or diborane gas to the gas mixture [7]. This was a far-reaching discovery since until that time it had been thought that amorphous silicon could not be made n-type or p-type by substitutional doping. Amorphous silicon suitable for electronic applications, where doping is required, is an alloy of silicon and hydrogen. Therefore, the electronic-grade amorphous silicon is called a-Si:H.

The successful doping of a-Si:H created tremendous interest in this material for two reasons. First, the material had several interesting properties that opened up many opportunities for semiconductor device applications, especially in optoelectronics and PVs. For example, due to the high absorption coefficient of a-Si:H in the visible range of the solar spectrum, a 1 μm-thick a-Si:H layer is sufficient to absorb 90% of the usable solar energy. Second, the glow discharge deposition technique, also referred to as PECVD, enabled production of a-Si:H films over a large area (>1 m^2) and at a low temperature (100–400 °C). The low processing temperature allows the use of a wide range of low-cost substrates such as a glass sheet and a metal or polymer foil. The a-Si:H can be simply doped and alloyed by adding appropriate gases to a silane source gas. These features made a-Si:H a promising candidate for low-cost thin-film solar cells.

At present, most thin-film Si solar cells are based on the single-junction structure. The solar cell structure is such that light enters the intrinsic a-Si:H layer that serves as the absorber layer through the p-type layer. This is in order to facilitate the collection of holes from the absorber layer, which have a lower mobility than electrons in a-Si:H. There are two basic configurations of thin-film Si solar cells, namely, a superstrate and substrate configuration, which depend on the sequence of the silicon layer deposition, p-i-n or n-i-p, respectively. In case of the superstrate configuration, the p-i-n deposition sequence requires a transparent substrate carrier. Usually, a glass plate coated with a transparent conductive oxide (TCO) layer with a rough surface is used as the carrier. **Figure 2** shows a typical superstrate single-junction a-Si:H solar cell. The back contact is a highly reflecting metal layer, usually deposited onto a TCO interlayer, which is used to improve the reflection from the back contact by matching the refractive indices between the n-type silicon and metal. An encapsulant and/or another glass plate usually form the backside of the superstrate cell.

In case of the substrate configuration, the substrate carrier forms the backside of the cell. This allows the use of opaque substrates, such as stainless steel. Also a polymer foil can be used as a substrate. Since the polymer need not be transparent, a temperature resistant type of polymer can be applied, such as polyimid. The foils can be thin enough to be flexible, which opens up a possibility to employ a roll-to-roll processing. A highly reflecting back contact with textured surface that consists of a metal layer of silver or aluminum and a TCO layer is deposited on the carrier. The surface texture is required in order to scatter the reflected light back to the cell at the angles that are large enough to facilitate total internal reflection. After depositing the sequence of the n-i-p a-Si:H-based layers, a TCO top layer with a metal grid is formed as the top contact. The front side of the substrate cell is finished by a transparent encapsulant layer with an additional glass plate. The use of conductive carriers such as stainless steel complicates the monolithic series interconnection of cells on the substrate.

Some important features of a-Si:H solar cells become apparent from **Figure 2**. The front contact layer is formed by the TCO. The top TCO film has to fulfill several stringent requirements, such as high optical transmission in the spectrum of interest, low sheet resistance, temperature durability, and good chemical stability and adhesion. In the superstrate configuration, the surface of the TCO layer has to be textured in order to enhance light absorption inside the solar cell due to the scattering at internal rough interfaces. The carriers generated in the p-type layer do not contribute to the photocurrent and it is thus desirable that the light

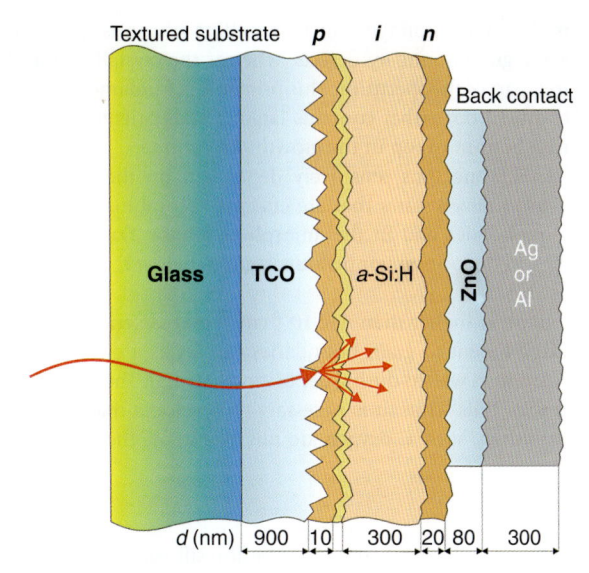

Figure 2 A schematic structure of a superstrate single-junction a-Si:H solar cell.

absorption in this layer is small. A smaller absorption is achieved by alloying the a-Si:H with carbon, which increases the optical band gap to about 2 eV. A sufficiently high electrical conductivity is required for both p- and n-type layers in order to form low-resistance contacts with the electrodes and a high built-in voltage across the p-i-n junction. The intrinsic layer with an optical band gap of about 1.75 eV serves as an absorber. The thickness of the intrinsic layer can vary between 100 and 300 nm, which depends whether it is incorporated in single or multijunction cells. Because the intrinsic layer is sandwiched between the doped layers, an internal electric field is present across the intrinsic layer. The internal electric field facilitates separation of electron–hole pairs that are generated in the intrinsic layer. The electric field strongly depends on the defect distribution inside the intrinsic layer and at the interfaces with the doped layers.

The first a-Si:H solar cell was made by Carlson and Wronski in 1976 and exhibited an energy conversion efficiency of 2.4% [8]. Inherent to a-Si:H is the creation of metastable defects when the material is exposed to light. This is a manifestation of what is called a Staebler–Wronski effect [9], which is clearly undesirable in solar cells. The extra created defects in the intrinsic layer act as recombination and trap centers for photogenerated charge carriers. As a result of the trapping, the space charge distribution in the layer changes and distorts the internal electric field. This leads to a lower drift and thus to a lower collection efficiency. The performance degradation of a-Si:H-based solar cells due to illumination can be partly avoided by using thinner intrinsic layers in which the internal electric field is higher and therefore less sensitive to any distortion. However, the employment of thinner absorber layers results in a lower absorption. The solution for having cells with better stability is the use of a stacked or multi-junction solar cell structure. The total thickness of the complete cell is the same as for a single-junction solar cell, but each component cell is thinner and therefore less sensitive to the light-induced defects. Another way to minimize the Staebler–Wronski effect is to develop an amorphous silicon material that is more stable against light exposure [10].

1.17.2.2 Microcrystalline Silicon

The first solar cell with a μc-Si:H i-layer was reported in 1994 by Meier *et al.* [11] at IMT Neuchâtel, Switzerland, with $\eta = 4.6\%$. In this mixed-phase material (μc-Si:H), the charge-carrier transport mechanism is not yet completely understood. Whether the electrical properties are determined by the amorphous or the crystalline fraction of the volume is dependent on the transport path. If the crystalline fraction is high enough, percolation takes place along interconnected paths through the crystallites. From geometrical considerations, the percolation threshold is 33%. In n-type and p-type microcrystalline silicon, percolation is observed at even lower crystalline volume fractions. Of these two doping types, n-type material seems to exhibit percolation at the lowest crystalline content, in experiments at Utrecht University at only 10%, much lower than theoretical predictions [12]. For intrinsic microcrystalline silicon, the threshold has been found at a crystalline content that is instead higher than predicted. For example, Kočka *et al.* [13] observe this threshold at 65%. Overall, it can be stated that the transport of charge carriers in μc-Si:H is influenced by (1) the crystalline fraction, (2) electronic barriers because of the difference in mobility gaps of crystalline grains and grain boundaries or amorphous tissues between grains, (3) doping due to impurities such as oxygen, and (4) grain boundary defects.

Obviously, grain boundary properties play an important role in carrier transport in μc-Si:H. Matsui *et al.* [14] studied electron and hole transport in separate devices and concluded that μc-Si:H becomes more n-type at higher crystalline fractions, leading to low activation energies for the dark conductivity. Elsewhere, it has been found that the grain boundary defect density increases with the crystalline fraction [15].

The performance of solar cells based on transition-type microcrystalline silicon is based on the principle that a considerable amorphous silicon content passivates the grain boundary defects, whereas the crystalline fraction is high enough to bring about sufficient absorption in the near-infrared part of the spectrum. This principle is fundamentally different from that in polycrystalline silicon [16, 17] which has no a-Si:H content but rather contains large crystals oriented in the [110] direction, with a low grain boundary defect density, extending from bottom to top in the growth direction.

The optoelectronic properties of μc-Si:H are thus sensitively dependent on the structure of the crystallites and the grain boundaries. Dangling bonds give rise to localized states that are effective recombination centers for charge carriers. Most of the defects are concentrated at the grain boundaries and in the amorphous phase. Dangling bond densities N_d can be as low as 10^{16} cm^{-3} for compact a-Si:H, but in the low deposition temperature regime (below T_s = 180 °C), N_d is usually reported to be higher [18, 19].

The presence of oxygen in concentrations higher than 1×10^{18} cm^{-3} may deteriorate the electronic properties of the layers considerably [20]. Interconnected voids adjacent to grain boundaries can act as a diffusion path for impurities, such as oxygen (acting as an n-type dopant), after deposition as well as during deposition [21–23]. The n-type doping effect leads to an unfavorable field distribution in p-i-n or n-i-p type solar cells. Thus, it is necessary to develop a material with high compactness, so that grain boundaries are fully passivated and impurities, such as oxygen, do not deteriorate the transport mechanism.

1.17.2.3 Multijunction Solar Cell

The concept of a multijunction solar cell is already widely used in thin-film silicon solar cell technology. In the multijunction solar cell structure, two [24] or more [25] solar cells are stacked on top of each other. The multijunction solar cell approach means that the absorber layer in each component cell can be tailored to a specific part of the solar spectrum. Top cells efficiently absorb the short-wavelength part of the spectrum (high-energy photons), whereas bottom cells absorb the remaining long-wavelength part of the spectrum (low-energy photons). In this way, the thermalization losses are minimized, which is reflected in higher open-circuit voltages of the devices. Absorber layers in multijunction thin-film silicon solar cells are based on a-Si:H, alloys of a-Si:H such as hydrogenated amorphous silicon germanium (a-SiGe:H), and μc-Si:H. For a tandem cell, the highest efficiency is predicted for a combination of absorber materials having band gaps of 1.7 and 1.1 eV for the top and bottom cell, respectively. With a band gap of 1.1 eV, μc-Si:H is the ideal material for a tandem cell with a-Si:H. The University of Neuchâtel introduced a micromorph tandem solar cell in 1994, which comprised an a-Si:H top cell and a μc-Si:H bottom cell [26]. An additional advantage is the stability of the component μc-Si:H solar cell against light exposure. The useful thickness of the μc-Si:H absorber is in the range of 1.0–3.0 μm. In order to obtain current matching, a relatively thick (> 300 nm) a-Si:H layer is required in the top cell, which therefore still suffers from light-induced degradation. It is expected that by implementing improved light-trapping techniques, especially for near-infrared light, the thickness of both absorber layers can be reduced. The best laboratory efficiency of a single-junction a-Si:H cell is 10.09% (stabilized) [27], that of a micromorph tandem a-Si:H/μc-Si:H cell is 14.1% (initial) [28], and 11.91% stable [29]. The best efficiency of a triple-junction a-Si:H/a-SiGe:H/μc-Si:H cell is 12.52% [30], that of a triple-junction a-Si:H/a-SiGe:H/a-SiGe:H cell is 10.4% [31], and 12.41% for an a-Si/μc-Si/μc-Si triple-junction cell [32]. The potential of practical triple-junction thin-film silicon solar cells is clear from the recent achievement of 16.3% initial efficiency at Unisolar [33]. In **Figures 3(a)** and **3(b)**, a typical double-junction silicon solar cell structure and a triple-junction solar cell structure are presented, respectively.

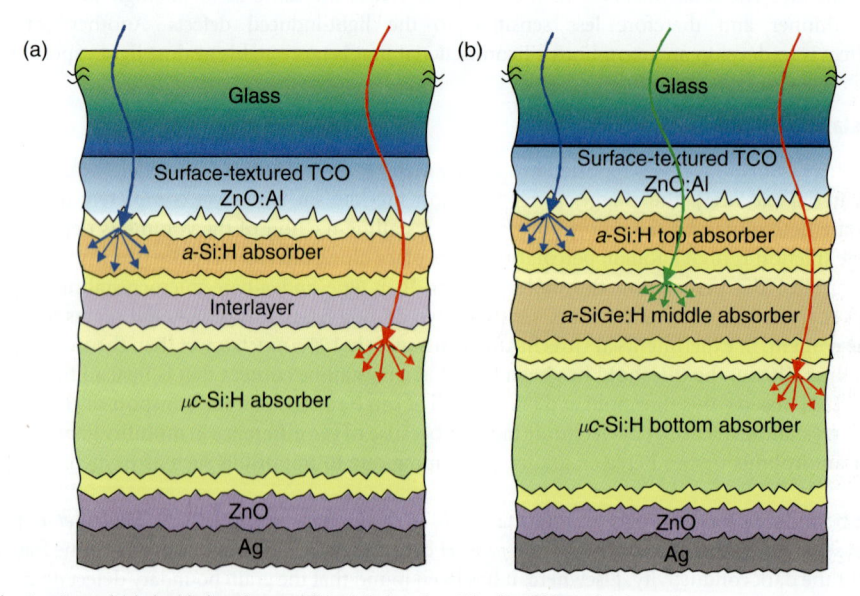

Figure 3 A schematic structure of (a) double-junction and (b) triple-junction thin-film Si-based solar cell.

A few of the highest values for stabilized total-area module efficiencies are presently 10.0% (Oerlikon, 1.4 m², tandem module 143 W), 10.0% (Sanyo, 1.54 m²), 9.5% (Sharp, 1.42 m²), 9.0% (Kaneka, 1.22 m²), 8.9% (Nexpower, 1.58 m²), and 8.4% on the largest area modules (Sunfilm, 5.72 m²) [34]. The latest recorded initial efficiency value on an intermediate-sized module is 12.0% (Unisolar, 400 cm²) [33]. Such modules stabilize at 11.2%, indicating the near-term potential of triple-junction large-area module technology.

1.17.2.4 Light Trapping

Light-trapping techniques help to capture light in the desired parts of a solar cell, which are the absorber layers, and prevent it from escaping. The most important role of light trapping is to keep the physical thickness of the absorber layer as thin as possible and to maximize its effective optical thickness. The following techniques are used to trap photons inside the absorber layer [35]:

- In-coupling of incident photons at the front side
- Reflection at the backside
- Intermediate reflectors in tandem solar cells
- Scattering at rough interfaces
- Scattering at metal nanoparticles (plasmonic effects).

Two research areas can be distinguished regarding the development of light-trapping techniques. The first area deals with the manipulation of photon propagation throughout a solar cell. The techniques are related to the development and implementation of 'optically active layers' such as antireflection coatings, single or stack of layers for index matching, and intermediate and back reflectors [31]. These layers take care that photons reach the absorber layer and undergo multiple passes inside the absorber.

The second area deals with the enhancement of an average photon path length inside the absorber layer. This is achieved by scattering of light at rough interfaces and/or metal nanoparticles. These techniques are related to the design and fabrication of a 'surface texture' on substrate carriers. The surface texture of a substrate introduces rough interfaces into the solar cell structure. Scattering at rough interfaces prolongs the effective path length of photons and partially leads to the total internal reflection between the back and front contacts, confining the light inside the absorber. Recently, layers of 'metal nanoparticles' and composite materials with embedded metal nanoparticles for efficient in-coupling and scattering of light into the absorber layer have attracted a lot of attention [36, 37].

In today's thin-film silicon solar cells, the standard trapping techniques are based on scattering of light at rough interfaces, the employment of high-reflective layers at the back contacts, and refractive-index matching layers. The rough interfaces are introduced into the solar cell by using substrate carriers that are coated with a randomly surface-textured TCO layer, such as fluorine-doped tin oxide (FTO) of Asahi U-type substrate with a pyramidal-like surface structure (**Figure 4(a)**) and sputtered aluminum-doped zinc oxide (AZO) that after etching in an HCl solution shows a crater-like surface texture (**Figure 4(b)**).

1.17.2.5 Heterojunction *a*-Si/*c*-Si Solar Cells

As described above, thin-film silicon solar cells based on *a*-Si:H and *μc*-Si:H are promising candidates for low-cost PV technology due to their low material consumption and low-temperature processing in comparison with wafer-based *c*-Si solar cells. However, a low module efficiency may be the principle limitation for this PV technology. A so-called heterojunction silicon solar cell approach benefits from combining both wafer-based *c*-Si and thin-film silicon solar cells. Heterojunction silicon solar cells can achieve high conversion efficiencies while using thin-film silicon processes to lower the cost in comparison with *c*-Si solar cells [38].

In **Figure 5**, a schematic structure of the heterojunction *a*-Si/*c*-Si solar cell is presented; it is denoted as the HIT (heterojunction with intrinsic thin-layer) solar cell [39]. The *n*-type *c*-Si wafer is randomly textured to provide effective light trapping. Intrinsic *a*-Si:H

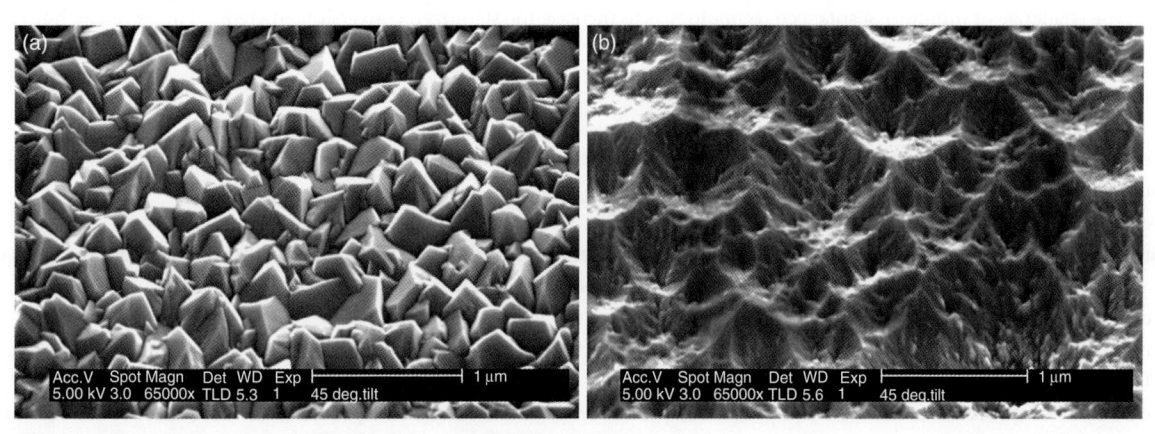

Figure 4 (a) Pyramidal-like and (b) crater-like surface morphology of TCO layers.

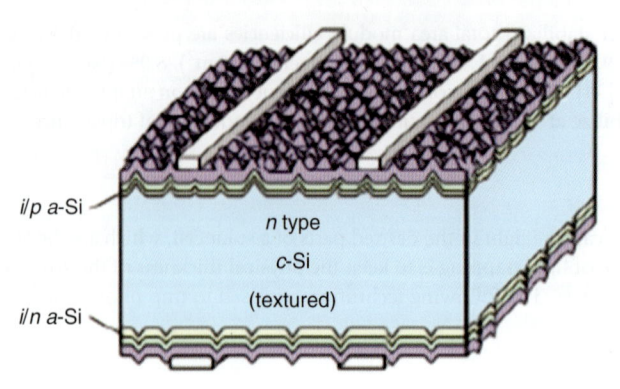

Figure 5 Solar cell structure of the HIT solar cell made by Sanyo [39].

is deposited on both sides of the wafer for passivation. The *p*-type *a*-Si:H is deposited on one side as an emitter, while an *n*-type *a*-Si:H is deposited on the other side to form the back-surface field (BSF). TCO layers are required to enhance carrier transport to the contacts because the *a*-Si:H layers are thin and highly resistive. Fabrication of HIT solar cells is relatively simple. The wafer surface is randomly textured, and the emitter and BSF are formed by depositing *a*-Si:H and/or *μc*-Si:H layers at temperatures below 250 °C in a PECVD process.

Although the heterojunction silicon solar cell comprises both *a*-Si:H and *c*-Si materials, it does not exhibit a strong performance degradation under light exposure, as is the case for thin-film *a*-Si:H solar cells, nor a strong temperature dependence of the performance, as is the case for wafer-based *c*-Si solar cells. This is because the *a*-Si:H layers in heterojunction silicon solar cells are very thin (i.e., only several nanometers) and therefore provide a negligible contribution to the overall power generation. The heterojunction silicon solar cell exhibits a smaller drop in performance with increasing temperature in comparison with conventional *c*-Si solar cells. It has been observed that a solar cell with improved surface passivation, and a correspondingly higher V_{oc}, exhibits an improved temperature dependence [40]. However, the reasons for this are not yet clear, and so further work is required to explain this phenomenon.

It took over 20 years for Sanyo to develop an HIT solar cell with 23.7% efficiency; recently, they reported on opportunities to reach impressive efficiencies over 23% based on the utilization of very thin wafers (<100 μm) [41]. Such improvements will mainly focus on the following: (1) the optical losses that limit the J_{sc}, (2) the recombination losses that mainly influence the V_{oc}, and (3) the resistance losses affecting the *FF*. Several solutions have been considered to reduce these losses. To reduce the optical losses, the following approaches have been made: surface-texturing of wafers to provide efficient light trapping, optimization of TCO and *a*-Si:H layers to reduce their absorption, and increasing the aspect ratio of the grid electrodes to reduce the shaded area. To reduce recombination losses, the cleaning of wafer surfaces prior to *a*-Si:H deposition is very important, as this removes recombination centers from the surface, such as metallic contamination and particles. The interface defect-state density can be reduced by saturating the dangling bonds on the wafer surface with hydrogen termination, and by using high-quality *a*-Si:H deposition. The resistance losses can be suppressed by decreasing the series resistance of the device. In this respect, highly conductive TCO and good ohmic contacts at the contact interfaces can contribute to the minimization of resistance.

1.17.3 Challenges of Thin-Film Si PV Technology

Today, the challenge of thin-film Si solar cell technology is to increase the stabilized conversion efficiency. Future research involves the following areas:

Improvement of the opto-electronic quality of *a*-Si:H, *a*-SiGe:H, and *μc*-Si:H absorbers

Full understanding of metastable changes in the properties of *a*-Si:H-based materials under light exposure

Optimization of the doped *p*- and *n*-type layers and the interfaces between the doped layers and intrinsic absorbers, the role of buffer, and profiled layers

Development of the TCO front material and optimization of the TCO/*p*-type layer interface

Photon management for effective use of the energy of the solar radiation and the maximization of absorption in desired parts of a solar cell that are called absorbers; novel concepts such as plasmonics, photonics, and nano-3D geometries

Increasing the deposition rate of absorber materials while maintaining their quality

Development of next generation devices (single and multijunction) for >15% stabilized large-area efficiency; predictive modeling rather than explanatory simulations

Development of advanced fabrication equipment for productivity enhancement and processes for cost-effective fabrication of thin-film silicon solar cells.

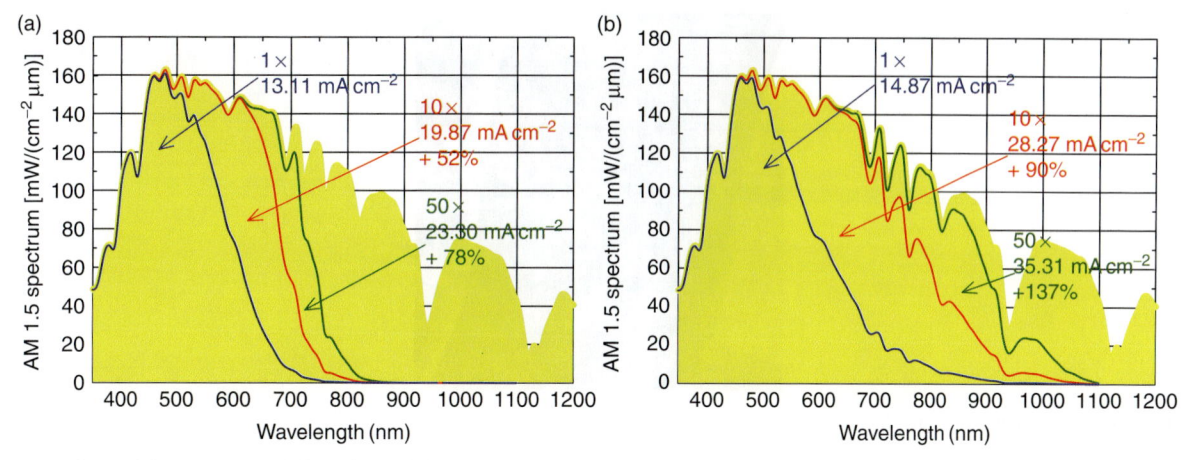

Figure 6 Spectral absorption in (a) 300 nm-thick *a*-Si:H layer and (b) 1 μm-thick μ*c*-Si:H layer matched to the AM1.5 spectrum, when the effective optical thickness of the layers is increased 10 and 50 times, respectively [42].

Photon management is one of the key issues for improving the performance of thin-film silicon solar cells and decreasing the production costs by shortening deposition times and using less material. The aim of the photon management is the effective use of the energy of the solar radiation and the maximization of absorption in desired parts of a solar cell that are called absorbers. Photon management in thin-film solar cells is accomplished by a number of techniques that are related to the following areas:

1. Effective use of the solar spectrum
2. Minimization of absorption outside the absorber layers
3. Trapping of photons inside the absorber layers (light-trapping techniques).

Computer simulations using advanced programs such as the ASA program from Delft University of Technology [42] and the Sunshine program from Ljubljana University [43] are a valuable tool to investigate the potential of photon management in thin-film silicon solar cells. **Figures 6(a)** and **6(b)** show calculated spectral absorption in a 300 nm-thick *a*-Si:H layer and 1 μm-thick μ*c*-Si:H layer, respectively, when the effective optical thickness of the layers is increased 10 and 50 times. When matching the absorption in the layers to the AM1.5 spectrum, one can calculate a potential photocurrent generated in the layers when used as absorbers in thin-film silicon solar cells. Increasing the optical thickness of the *a*-Si:H layer 10 and 50 times results in 52% and 78% potential enhancement of the photocurrent, respectively. The simulations demonstrate that in case of μ*c*-Si:H absorber, the light trapping plays an even more important role. Increasing the optical thickness of 1 μm-thick μ*c*-Si:H layer 10–50 times results in 90% and 138% enhancement of the photocurrent, delivering a potential photocurrent of 28 and 35 mA cm^{-2}, respectively.

1.17.4 Fabrication of Thin-Film Si Modules

Thin-film silicon solar cells have improved considerably, capable of achieving initial efficiencies exceeding 15% (tandem micromorph) [44, 45]. Based on the companies' announcements, the global production of all thin films is expected to reach well above 2 GWp yr^{-1} in 2012. The announced capacity for thin-film production is 20 GWp for 2015 [46]. It can be expected that in 2030, the PV market will be equally divided into three parts: 30% of the PV market is thin film, 30% *c*-Si, and 30% novel technologies. Of course, all segments will grow enormously. The thin-film silicon PV market is dominated by amorphous silicon-based modules; however, it is expected that the micromorph tandem modules will take over in the near future.

The electrical power delivered from a small-area solar cell is not enough for practical applications. Therefore, solar cells are connected in series or parallel to form a module that delivers a required power and voltage. A key step to practical industrial production of *a*-Si:H solar cells was the development of the monolithically integrated type of *a*-Si:H solar cell [47]. Monolithic series connection of cells to modules that can be easily implemented in the fabrication process is an attractive feature of thin-film Si solar cell technology.

The manufacturing for amorphous silicon solar cells is divided into two routes: (1) processing on glass plates and (2) processing on flexible substrates. Both manufacturing approaches include the following main steps:

Substrate conditioning
Large-area deposition of the contact layers, that is, the TCO as front electrode and the back reflector that is usually a double layer of metal and TCO
Large-area deposition of thin Si:H-based layers
Monolithic series connection of cells (at present applied only for manufacturing on glass) using laser scribing of contact and silicon layers

Figure 7 A flexible module from the Nuon Helianthos company [50].

Final module assembly including encapsulation, applying electrical connections, and framing.

A novel approach to fabricate a-Si:H modules has been developed in the Netherlands in the Helianthos project coordinated by the multinational corporation Akzo Nobel [48] and since 2006 by Nuon Helianthos company. The aim is to demonstrate that flexible thin-film silicon PV modules manufactured by means of automated roll-to-roll processes offer a versatile lightweight thin-film silicon PV product that will offer competitive kilowatt-hour costs in a wide range of applications [49]. The production technology is based on a temporary superstrate concept, which combines the advantages of both superstrate- and substrate-type a-Si:H solar cell technologies. The deposition of a high-quality top TCO layer using the atmospheric pressure chemical vapor deposition and monolithic series integration that offers the superstrate technology is combined with the roll-to-roll processing that is used in the substrate technology. An example of a flexible module from the Nuon Helianthos company is shown in **Figure 7** [50].

1.17.5 Applications

Due to the versatility of thin-film Si technology to produce rigid as well as flexible modules and the high energy yield, the application possibilities for thin-film Si-based modules are very broad. In addition, due to the fact that a-Si:H modules have a substantially lower conversion efficiency temperature coefficient than crystalline silicon modules [51], their yield (in kWh/kWp) is superior at higher operational temperatures. This feature favors the implementation of a-Si:H modules in high-temperature conditions.

The applications cover the following market areas:

Consumer products where small solar cells provide electricity for calculators and watches. Small modules with power ranging from 3 to 50 Wp are used as (portable) battery chargers, in car roofs, and a variety of other leisure products.

Residential and commercial grid-connected systems that are mainly designed for building-integrated photovoltaics (BIPVs). The modules usually have a 20-year power output warranty and can be structurally and aesthetically integrated as roofing or façade elements. Taking advantage of the laser techniques that are applied during manufacturing of a-Si:H modules, partly transparent modules can be fabricated. Offering both eco-friendly performance and a compelling design, these types of products open up new possibilities in BIPV applications.

Several large grid-connected systems have been realized with thin-film Si-based modules. An example is the amorphous silicon solar power plant (installed power of 1 MWp) that was completed in the beginning of 2005 in the German city of Buttenwiesen in the suburbs of Munich. The power plant comprises approximately 10 000 amorphous silicon single-junction superstrate-type modules. The plant is annually expected to deliver 1 million kWh. Another example is the larger 12 MW rooftop system of Unisolar modules at General Motors in Zaragoza, Spain [52] (**Figure 8**). This is at present perhaps the world's largest rooftop solar installation.

Off-grid and remote area applications include solar systems with a rated power of 30–50 Wp that are mainly designed for lighting in remote homes and construction sites without access to the power grid. Larger systems are designed to generate power for villages, remote homes, water pumping, telecommunications, traffic control signals, and so on.

Special applications. The lightweight, flexible features of thin-film silicon modules in connection with the inherent radiation hardness and superior high-temperature performance make the technology a candidate for space PV application.

Figure 8 Part of the 12 MW rooftop system of Unisolar modules at General Motors in Zaragoza, Spain [52].

1.17.6 Conclusions

The flexibility of thin-film silicon solar cell technology to deliver modules for a large variety of applications is its most important asset. The technology has a strong potential to produce modules with an attractive cost-to-performance ratio generating electricity with a price competitive to that of conventional electricity. The cost reduction of thin-film silicon modules will be determined by the scaling rate of the production capacity. At present, thin-film silicon solar cell technology has to concentrate on solving several issues that are discussed in Section 1.17.3, in order to become a fully mature technology.

Further development of thin-film silicon solar cell technology, in general, requires an increase in the performance of solar cells. One has to realize that two-thirds of the power generated by a promising micromorph tandem (a-Si:H/μc-Si:H) solar cell comes from the a-Si:H top cell. In the near future, attention will be paid to enhancing light trapping inside the cells, that is, improving the TCO material quality and optimizing the surface texture. At the same time, research will continue on a-Si:H-based materials, which has recently resulted in a completely new class of nanostructured silicon films.

References

[1] Marketbuzz (2011) *Annual PV Market Report 2011*. http://solarbuzz.com (accessed 15 March).
[2] Hering G (2011) *Year of the Tiger*. Photon International, March, pp. 186–218.
[3] Schropp REI and Zeman M (1998) *Amorphous and Microcrystalline Silicon Solar Cells: Modeling, Materials, and Device Technology*. Boston; Dordrecht; London: Springer.
[4] Sterling HF and Swann RGC (1965) Chemical vapour deposition promoted by rf discharge. *Solid-State Electronics* 8: 653.
[5] Vepček S and Mareček V (1968) The preparation of thin layers of Ge and Si by chemical hydrogen plasma transport. *Solid-State Electronics* 11: 683.
[6] Houben L, Luysberg M, Hapke P, *et al.* (1998) Structural properties of microcrystalline silicon in the transition from highly crystalline to amorphous growth. *Philosophical Magazine A* 77: 1447.
[7] Spear W and LeComber P (1975) Substitutional doping of amorphous silicon. *Solid State Communications* 17: 1193.
[8] Carlson DE and Wronski CR (1976) Amorphous silicon solar cell. *Applied Physics Letters* 28: 671.
[9] Staebler DL and Wronski CR (1977) Reversible conductivity changes in discharge-produced amorphous Si. *Applied Physics Letters* 31: 292.
[10] Zeman M, van Elzakker G, Tichelaar FD, and Sutta P (2009) Structural properties of amorphous silicon prepared from hydrogen-diluted silane. *Philosophical Magazine* 89: 2435.
[11] Meier J, Flückiger R, Keppner H, and Shah A (1994) Complete microcrystalline p-i-n solar cell: Crystalline or amorphous cell behavior? *Applied Physics Letters* 65(7): 860.
[12] Gordijn A, Rath JK, and Schropp REI (2003) High temperature n- and p-type doped microcrystalline silicon layers grown by VHF PECVD layer-by-layer deposition. *Materials Research Society Symposium Proceedings* 762: 637.
[13] Kočka J, Fejfar A, Stuchlíková H, *et al.* (2003) Basic features of transport in microcrystalline silicon. *Solar Energy Materials and Solar Cells* 78: 493.
[14] Matsui T, Muhida R, Kawamura T, *et al.* (2002) Microstructural dependence of electron and hole transport in low-temperature-grown polycrystalline-silicon thin-film solar cells. *Applied Physics Letters* 81: 4751.
[15] Baia-Neto AL, Lambertz A, Carius R, and Finger F (2002) Relationships between structure, spin density and electronic transport in 'solar-grade' microcrystalline silicon films. *Journal of Non-Crystalline Solids* 299–302: 274.
[16] Rath JK, Meiling H, and Schropp REI (1997) Purely intrinsic poly-silicon films for n-i-p solar cells. *Japanese Journal of Applied Physics* 36: 5436.
[17] van Veenendaal PATT, Savenije TJ, Rath JK, and Schropp REI (2002) Microwave mobility in profiled poly-Si thin films deposited on glass by hot-wire CVD. *Thin Solid Films* 403–404: 175.
[18] Kluth O, Rech B, Houben L, *et al.* (1999) Texture etched ZnO:Al coated glass substrates for silicon based thin film solar cells. *Thin Solid Films* 351: 247.
[19] Matsuda A (2004) Microcrystalline silicon: Growth and device application. *Journal of Non-Crystalline Solids* 338–340: 1.
[20] Kamei T and Wada T (2004) Oxygen impurity doping into ultrapure hydrogenated microcrystalline Si films. *Journal of Applied Physics* 96: 2087.
[21] Kondo M and Matsuda A (2002) An approach to device grade amorphous and microcrystalline silicon thin films fabricated at higher deposition rates. *Current Opinion in Solid State & Materials Science* 6: 445.
[22] Kočka J, Stuchlíková H, Stuchlík J, *et al.* (2002) Model of transport in microcrystalline silicon. *Journal of Non-Crystalline Solids* 299–302: 355–359.

[23] Konagai M, Tsushima T, Kim M-K, *et al.* (2001) High-rate deposition of silicon thin-film solar cells by the hot-wire cell method. *Thin Solid Films* 395: 152.
[24] Fischer D, Dubail S, Anna Selvan JA, *et al.* (1996) The micromorph solar cell: Extending a-Si:H technology towards thin film crystalline silicon. In: *Proceedings of 25th IEEE PVSC*, p. 1053. Washington, DC, USA.
[25] Guha S and Yang J (2005) Thin film silicon photovoltaic: From R&D to commercialization. In: Quinhao Y (ed.) *Technical Digest of the 15th International Photovoltaic Scientific Engineering Conference PVSEC-15*, p. 35. Shanghai: Shanghai Scientific & Technical.
[26] Meier J, Dubail S, Fluckiger R, *et al.* (1994) Intrinsic microcrystalline silicon (μc-Si:H): A promising new thin film solar cell material. In: *Proceedings of the 1st World Conference on Photovoltaic Energy Conversion, WPSEC-1*, p. 409. Hawaii, USA.
[27] Benagli S, Borrello D, Vallat-Sauvain E, *et al.* (2009) High-efficiency amorphous silicon devices on LPCVD-ZnO TCO prepared in industrial KAI TM-M R&D reactor. In: *Proceedings of the 24th European Photovoltaic Solar Energy Conference*, p. 2293. Hamburg, Germany.
[28] Yamamoto K, Yoshimi M, Tawada Y, *et al.* (2002) Large area thin film Si module. *Solar Energy Materials and Solar Cells* 74(1–4): 449–455.
[29] Bailat J, Fesquet L, Orhan J-B, *et al.* (2010) Recent developments of high-efficiency Micromorph® tandem solar cells in KAI-M PECVD reactors. In: *Proceedings of the 25th European Photovoltaic Solar Energy Conference*, p. 2720. Valencia, Spain.
[30] Guha S, Cohen D, Schiff E, *et al.* (2011) Industry–academy partnerships helps drive commercialization of new thin-film silicon technology. *Photovoltaics International* 13: 144.
[31] Dagamseh AMK, Vet B, Tichelaar FD, *et al.* (2008) ZnO:Al films prepared by rf magnetron sputtering applied as back reflectors in thin-film silicon solar cells. *Thin Solid Films* 516: 7844–7850.
[32] Banerjee A, Su T, Beglau D, *et al.* (2011) High efficiency, multi-junction nc-Si:H based solar cells at high deposition rate. In: *Proceedings of the 37th IEEE PVSC*. Seattle, June.
[33] United Solar Announces NREL Measurement of World Record 12% Efficient Thin-Film Silicon Cell. http://www.uni-solar.com (accessed 31 January 2011).
[34] Schropp REI (2012) Large area thin film silicon: Synergy between displays and solar cells. *Japanese Journal of Applied Physics* 51.
[35] Zeman M, Isabella O, Jaeger K, *et al.* (2010) Advanced light trapping in thin-film silicon solar cells. *Materials Research Society Symposium Proceedings* 1245: 1245-A03-03.
[36] Ferry VE, Verschuuren MA, Li HBT, *et al.* (2010) Light trapping in ultrathin plasmonic solar cells. *Optics Express* 18: A237.
[37] Ferry VE, Verschuuren MA, van Lare MC, *et al.* (2011) Optimized spatial correlations for broadband light trapping nanopatterns in high efficiency ultrathin film a-Si:H solar cells. *Nano Letters* 11: 4239.
[38] WGJHM van Sark, L Korte, F Roca (eds.) (2011) *Physics and Technology of Amorphous-Crystalline Heterostructure Silicon Solar Cells*, 580p. Heidelberg, Germany: Springer.
[39] Mishima T, Taguchi M, Sakata H, and Maruyama E (2011) Development status of high-efficiency HIT solar cells. *Solar Energy Materials and Solar Cells* 95: 18.
[40] Sawada T, Terada N, Tsuge S, *et al.* (1994) High-efficiency a-Si/c-Si heterojunction solar cell. In: *Proceedings of the 24th IEEE Photovoltaic Specialists Conference*, pp. 1219–1226.
[41] Kinoshita T, Fujishima D, Yano A, *et al.* (2011) The approaches for high efficiency HIT[TM] solar cell with very thin (<100 μm) silicon wafer over 23%. In: *Proceedings of the 26th European Photovoltaic Solar Energy Conference and Exhibition*, pp. 871–874.
[42] Zeman M, Willemen JA, Vosteen LLA, *et al.* (1997) Computer modelling of current matching in a-Si:H/a-Si:H tandem solar cells on textured TCO substrates. *Solar Energy Materials and Solar Cells* 46: 81.
[43] Krč J, Smole F, and Topič M (2003) Analysis of light scattering in amorphous Si:H solar cells by a one-dimensional semi-coherent optical model. *Progress in Photovoltaics: Research and Applications* 11: 15.
[44] Yang J, Banerjee A, Lord K, and Guha S (1998) Correlation of component cells with high efficiency amorphous silicon alloy triple-junction solar cells and modules. In: *Proceedings of the 2nd World Conference on Photovoltaic Energy Conversion, WPSEC-2*, p. 387. Vienna, Austria.
[45] Zeman M and Krč J (2008) Optical and electrical modeling of thin-film silicon solar cells. *Journal of Materials Research* 23: 889.
[46] Jäger-Waldau A (2010), *JRC Photovoltaic Status Report*. European Commission, Joint Research Center, Institute for Energy, Ispra, Italy.
[47] Kuwano Y, Imai T, Ohnishi M, and Nakano S (1980) A horizontal cascade type amorphous Si photovoltaic cell module. In: *Proceedings of the 14th IEEE Photovoltaic Specialist Conference*, p. 1408.
[48] Middelman E, van Andel E, Schropp REI, *et al.* (1998) New temporary superstrate process for roll-to-roll production of thin-film solar cells. In: *Proceedings of the 2nd World Conference and Exhibition on Photovoltaic Solar Energy Conversion, Vol. 1*, p. 816–819.
[49] Jongerden GJ (2003) Monolithically series integrated flexible PV modules manufactured on commodity polymer substrates. In: *Proceedings of the 3rd World Conference and Exhibition on Photovoltaic Solar Energy Conversion*, p. 6LN-C-05. Osaka, Japan.
[50] Nuon Helianthos. http://www.nuon.com/nl/het-bedrijf/innovatieve-projecten/helianthos/index.jsp (accessed 26 November 2011).
[51] Lechner P and Schade H (2002) Photovoltaic thin-film technology based on hydrogenated amorphous silicon. *Progress in Photovoltaics: Research and Applications* 10: 85.
[52] Uni-Solar GM plant source photograph. http://www.uni-solar.com/real stories/ (accessed 26 November 2011).

1.18 Chalcopyrite Thin-Film Materials and Solar Cells

T Unold and CA Kaufmann, Helmholtz Zentrum für Materialien und Energie GmbH, Berlin, Germany

© 2012 Elsevier Ltd.

1.18.1	Introduction	399
1.18.2	Material Properties	400
1.18.2.1	Structure	400
1.18.2.2	Optical Properties	401
1.18.2.3	Electrical Properties	403
1.18.2.3.1	Surfaces and grain boundaries	405
1.18.3	Deposition Methods	406
1.18.3.1	Single-Step Deposition	407
1.18.3.1.1	Single-stage process	407
1.18.3.1.2	Two-stage process	407
1.18.3.1.3	Three-stage or multistage process	407
1.18.3.2	Sequential Deposition	408
1.18.3.3	General Considerations	410
1.18.4	Device Structure	410
1.18.4.1	Substrate	410
1.18.4.1.1	Glass	410
1.18.4.1.2	Metal substrates	411
1.18.4.1.3	Polyimide substrates	412
1.18.4.2	Barrier Layers	412
1.18.4.3	Back Contact	412
1.18.4.4	Buffer Layer	412
1.18.4.5	Front Contact	414
1.18.5	Device Properties	414
1.18.6	Outlook	417
References		418

1.18.1 Introduction

Chalcopyrite-type materials are currently considered to be the most promising thin-film solar cell materials, because they exhibit direct band gaps well matched to the solar spectrum and because of their very favorable electronic properties that have recently led to solar cell efficiencies surpassing 20%. The chalcopyrite crystal structure family lends its name from the mineral $CuFeS_2$, which is one of the most important copper (Cu) ores. Chalcopyrite-type materials comprise the compounds formed either from group I, III, and VI (I-III-VI$_2$) or from group II, IV, and V (II-IV-V$_2$) elements of the periodic table [1].

Artificial chalcopyrite-type crystals were first synthesized and structurally characterized by Hahn *et al.* in the early 1950s [2]. The optical and electrical properties of chalcopyrite-type crystals were investigated by Shay and Wernick at Bell labs in the 1970s, originally for the application in optoelectronic devices [1]. First single-crystal homojunction devices based on $CuInSe_2$ were realized and electroluminescence was demonstrated also at Bell labs in 1974 by short anneals of n-type crystals in Se vapor [3]. The first single-crystal solar cell based on $CuInSe_2$ as an absorber material was demonstrated in the same year, using a $CuInSe_2$/CdS heterojunction device. This device, which contained a very thick, several micron n-type CdS as emitter window layer, showed a photoconversion efficiency of 5% [4]. Soon after photoconversion, efficiencies above 10% were obtained by further optimization of such device structures [5].

First real thin-film solar cells based on chalcopyrite-type absorbers were prepared by Kazmerski also using $CuInSe_2$/CdS heterojunctions [6]. These types of solar cells started to receive considerable attention when Mickelson *et al.* demonstrated solar cells based on polycrystalline $CuInSe_2$ absorber layers with an efficiency of 9.4% in 1981 by co-evaporation from elemental sources [7]. Already in 1982, an impressive thin-film solar cell efficiency of 14.6% was reported by the same group by optimizing the co-evaporation process [8]. Since then, a number of technological breakthroughs, such as the discovery of Na doping, alloying with Ga, and replacing the thick CdS window layer by a thin CdS buffer and thick conductive ZnO window layer, have led to a current record device efficiency of 20.3% for $Cu(In,Ga)Se_2$-based thin-film solar cells [9].

Over the last 30 years, chalcopyrite materials and solar cells have been investigated by many groups worldwide, and we will attempt to give an overview of the most salient findings and lessons learned with respect to these types of solar cells. Also industry has been involved in research and commercialization of chalcopyrite solar cells early on starting with Boeing and ARCO Solar in the 1980s. Since then, large-scale production facilities for chalcopyrite-based thin-film photovoltaic modules have been built and ramped up, with an estimated current capacity close to 1 GW year^{-1}. Although m^2-sized modules with record efficiencies of 17%

have been demonstrated recently [10], there is still a considerable gap between efficiencies achieved on small area devices in the laboratory and actual module efficiencies obtained in large-scale production. Here we will try to address the current state of knowledge and relevant challenges for commercialization with respect to chalcopyrite-type solar cells. We would like to mention that a number of excellent reviews on chalcopyrite-type materials and solar cells have been published previously, which may provide additional information that is not covered in this chapter [11–17].

1.18.2 Material Properties

1.18.2.1 Structure

The crystal structure of chalcopyrite-type semiconductors can be derived from the diamond lattice in accordance with the Grimm-Sommerfeld or 8-N rule [18]. This means that chalcopyrite semiconductors, just like group IV elements silicon or germanium, exhibit tetrahedral bonding, that is, every atom has four nearest neighbors. In this review, we will restrict ourselves to the Cu-chalcopyrite semiconductors formed from group I-III-VI elements. Starting from the sphalerite structure of ZnS (**Figure 1**), the chalcopyrite lattice is obtained by the ordered substitution of the group II element (Zn) by the group I (Cu) and group III (In or Ga) elements. This leads to a doubling of the unit cell in the c-direction, the so-called tetragonal crystal structure as shown in **Figure 1**. Because of the different bond strength and bond lengths of the group I–VI and III–V bonds, the lattice parameter c in general is not exactly $2a$, which is also called the tetragonal distortion of the unit cell [1].

Because chalcopyrite-type materials consist of at least three elements, a number of different phases are possible depending on the exact compositions and the growth conditions. In **Figure 2**, a ternary phase diagram with the corner points Cu, In, and Se is shown. Because chalcopyrites are usually synthesized at sufficient chalcogen excess (here Se) the composition of, in this example $CuInSe_2$, the thin-film materials prepared at varying Cu/(In + Ga) composition usually conform to the tie-line spanned by Cu_2Se and In_2Se_3. The desired chalcopyrite phase in this diagram is at the center of the tie-line. As will be discussed further below, many deposition techniques use this finding by moving from the In-rich to the Cu-rich side and back to an experimentally determined ideal composition at the end of the process. An equilibrium pseudobinary phase diagram composed of a mixture of In_2Se_3 and Cu_2Se, corresponding to the tie-line in **Figure 2** is shown in **Figure 3** [19]. Observed phases are indicated as a function of growth temperature: α denotes the chalcopyrite phase, β denotes ordered defect chalcopyrite phases, such as $CuIn_5Se_8$ or $CuIn_3Se_5$ and δ is the sphalerite phase occurring only at high temperatures. It can be seen that there is a small region between stoichiometry and the copper-poor side where single-phase chalcopyrite is obtained at 500 °C. This region narrows further for lower temperatures. On the Cu-rich side, Cu_xSe phases segregate and on the Cu-poor side a coexistence of chalcopyrite and defect chalcopyrite phases is expected. It is interesting to note that at low temperatures even for stoichiometric composition Cu_xSe phase segregation is expected, which has to be considered in the design of growth processes for these compounds. It has been found that the width of the chalcopyrite single-phase region is increased by alloying with gallium (Ga) and/or doping with Na [20].

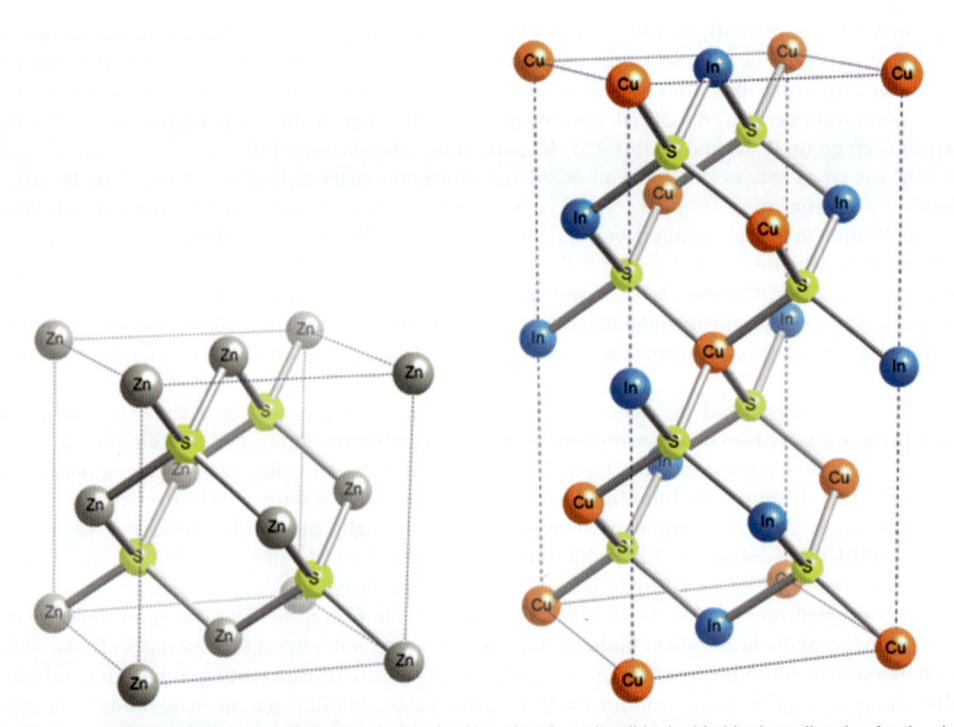

Figure 1 Crystal structure of (ZnS) sphalerite and ($CuInS_2$) chalcopyrite. Note that the unit cell is doubled in the c-direction for the chalcopyrite lattice.

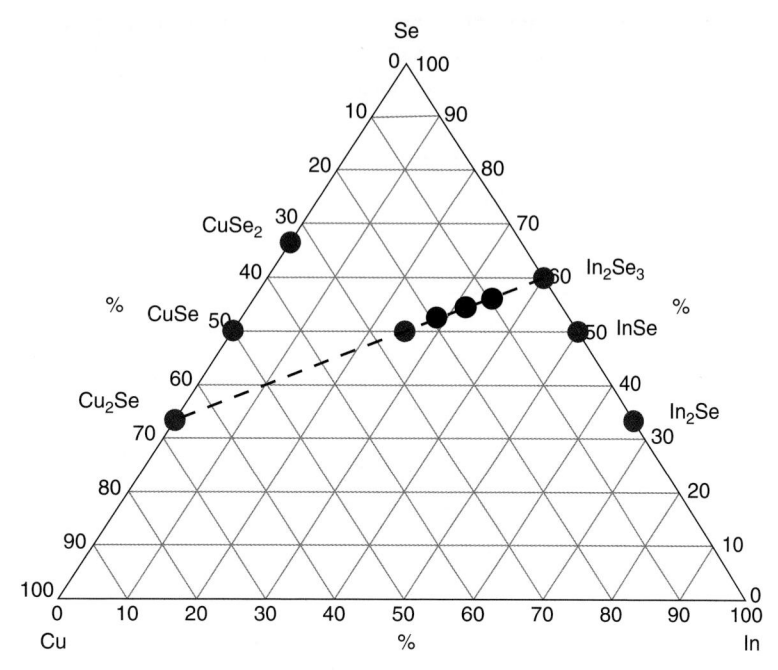

Figure 2 Ternary phase diagram for Cu–In–Se. The dashed line indicates the pseudobinary tie-line between Cu$_2$Se and In$_2$Se$_3$. Material phases occurring during different growth processes are indicated as black circles.

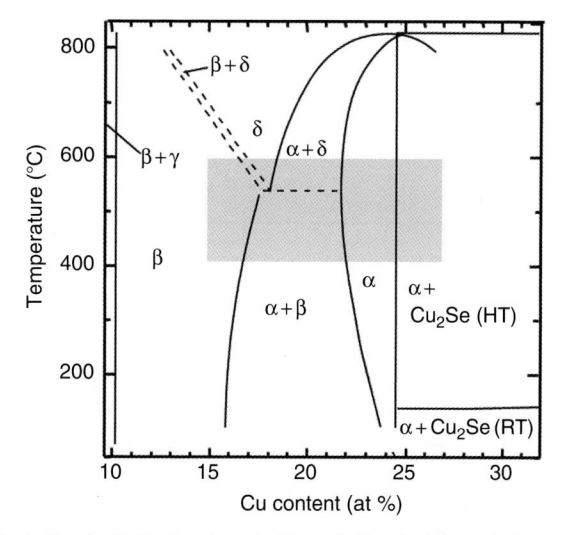

Figure 3 Pseudobinary phase diagram for In$_2$Se$_3$–Cu$_2$Se tie-line shown in **Figure 2**. The shaded area indicates the regions in the phase diagram relevant to multistage coevaporation of high-efficiency chalcopyrite solar cells.

CuInSe$_2$ can be readily alloyed with Ga and forms a solid solution CuIn$_{1-x}$Ga$_x$Se$_2$ over the whole composition range $0 < $ Ga/(In + Ga) $ < 1$. This means that lattice constants change continuously from the lattice constants for pure CuInSe$_2$ to those of pure CuGaSe$_2$, in accordance with Vegards law [21] as illustrated in **Figure 4**. Note also that the c/a ratio, that is the tetragonal distortion, changes with composition from a mismatch value of +1% on the CuInSe$_2$ to −3.5% for CuGaSe$_2$. For a Ga content of about $x = 0.23$, the tetragonal distortion vanishes and $c/a = 2.0$. Recently, it has been found that for exactly this composition ratio (or c/a ratio) the grain size is significantly enhanced in Cu(In,Ga)Se$_2$ thin films [23].

1.18.2.2 Optical Properties

Chalcopyrite semiconductors have direct band gaps leading to large absorption coefficients $\alpha > 10^4$ cm^{-1} above the band gap. This fact makes these materials very suitable as absorber materials in thin-film solar cells, as only thicknesses of about 1–2 μm are needed to absorb most of the above-band gap light from the solar spectrum, without the need for light trapping. Absorption coefficients of some Cu-chalcopyrite materials are shown in **Figure 5** [24]. The band gaps of Cu-chalcopyrite materials strongly depend on the specific composition and range from about 1 to 2.7 eV [1]. The most researched photovoltaic material CuIn$_{1-x}$Ga$_x$Se$_2$ exhibits band

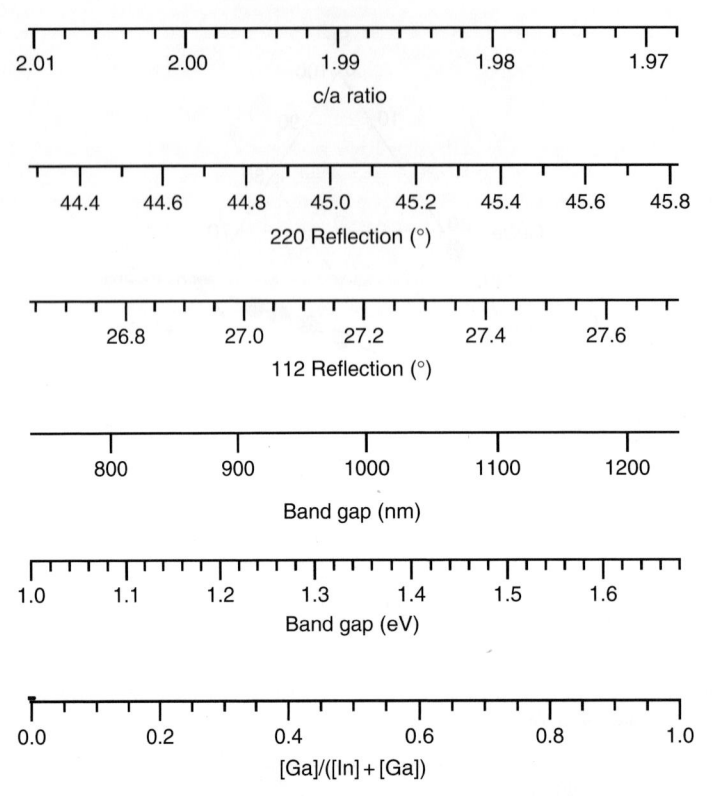

Figure 4 Structural and optical parameters of CuIn$_{1-x}$Ga$_x$Se$_2$ as a function of gallium content. Data from Suri DK, Nagpal KC, and Chadha GK (1989). *Journal of Applied Crystallography* 22: 578 [21] and Ishizuka S, Sakurai K, Yamada A, *et al.* (2005). *Japanese Journal of Applied Physics* 44: L679–682 [22].

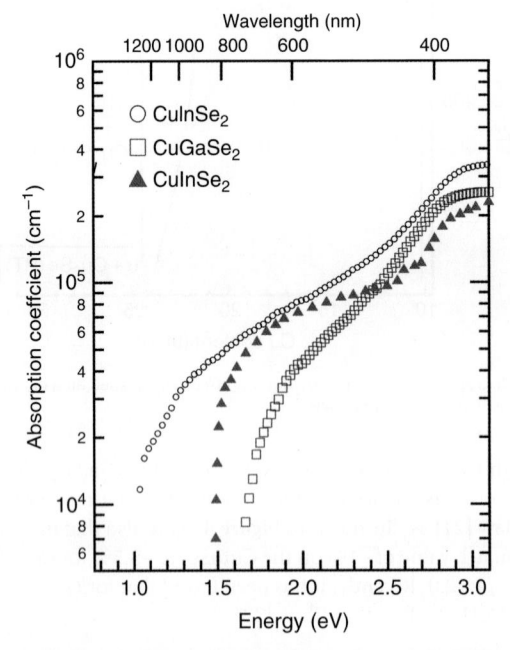

Figure 5 Absorption coefficients of CuInSe$_2$, CuGaSe$_2$, and CuInS$_2$. Data from Scheer R and Schock HW (2011) *Chalcogenide Photovoltaics: Physics, Technologies, and Thin Film Devices*. Weinheim, Germany: Wiley-VCH [16].

gaps between 1.04 and 1.68 eV [22, 24, 25]. The band gap of CuIn$_{1-x}$Ga$_x$Se2 increases monotonically with Ga content with a very small bowing between the end points. This functional dependence can be described by

$$E_g(x) = 1.0 + 0.564x + 0.116x^2 \qquad [1]$$

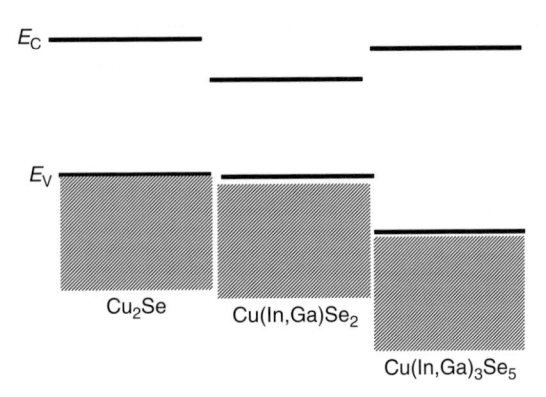

Figure 6 Band line-up for Cu(In,Ga)Se$_2$ and secondary phases for Cu(In,Ga)$_3$Se$_5$, Cu$_2$Se.

The highest efficiencies with chalcopyrite solar cells have been achieved with a Ga content between $0.2 < x < 0.35$ corresponding to a band gap between 1.15 and 1.25 eV. It has been found that alloying with Ga mainly reduces the electron affinity of CuIn$_{1-x}$Ga$_x$Se$_2$ leading to an upward shift of the conduction band whereas the valence band stays at the same energetic position [25–27]. This fact is important to consider when constructing band diagrams of CIGSe heterojunction devices. In state-of-the-art Cu(In,Ga)Se$_2$ devices grown by the three-stage co-evaporation method, a significant Ga gradient is found in the absorber layers. This means that the band gap, and in particular the conduction band minimum, varies accordingly throughout the device. In addition to or instead of Ga, sulfur can be added to CuInSe$_2$ to widen the band gap of CuIn$_{1-x}$Ga$_x$Se$_2$. However, in contrast to the effect of Ga, the addition of sulfur both lifts the conduction band and lowers the valence band [26]. For a number of industrially used deposition processes, sulfur is added to CuIn$_{1-x}$Ga$_x$Se$_2$ in order to widen the band gap close to the heterojunction [28].

Defect chalcopyrite phases are observed on the Cu-poor side of the phase diagram of CuIn$_{1-x}$Ga$_x$Se$_2$, whereas Cu$_x$Se secondary phases appear for Cu-rich growth conditions of CuIn$_{1-x}$Ga$_x$Se$_2$. This means that not only the structural and electronic properties of these phases may be relevant for the final device performance, but also their optical properties, in particular there band gap and band line-up with respect to the main chalcopyrite phase. The expected band line-up for CuIn$_{1-x}$Ga$_x$Se$_2$ is shown in **Figure 6** where it can be seen that for Ga contents of $x \approx 0.3$ a perfect line-up of Cu$_2$Se and mostly a lowered valence band maximum for the defect chalcopyrite compound is expected [29]. This may be one of the keys why CuIn$_{1-x}$Ga$_x$Se$_2$ exhibits maximum efficiencies within this Ga-composition ratio.

1.18.2.3 Electrical Properties

Cu-based chalcopyrite materials can be made p- or n-type depending on composition and growth conditions, solely due to the presence of intrinsic defects without the need for doping by external impurities. Cu(In,Ga)Se$_2$ grown Cu-rich and under chalcogen-excess is always found to be p-type [30]. N-type doping of CuInSe$_2$ can be obtained for low Cu/In ratios. Also, conversion of n-type CuInSe$_2$ into p-type CuInSe$_2$ by annealing in high Se pressure has been demonstrated [31]. Typical charge carrier densities of Cu-poor Cu(In,Ga)Se$_2$ used in solar cells grown on soda-lime glass are between 10^{15} cm^{-3} and 10^{17} cm^{-3}. Since the Cu/(In + Ga) ratio in these materials is usually between 0.8 and 0.9, large amounts of defects in the percent range must be present, despite the fact that the measured charge carrier densities are much lower. This can be explained by the fact that Cu-poor chalcopyrite compounds with large deviations from stoichiometry such that Cu/(In + Ga) < 1 are heavily compensated, with simultaneous formation of acceptors and donors, and a corresponding much lower net carrier density [32]. Also, the net doping density is found to strongly increase with the concentration of sodium incorporated in the films. This is shown in **Figure 7** where the charge carrier density is shown for Cu(In,Ga)Se$_2$ deposited on polymide foil with different NaF precursor layer thicknesses [33]. The effect of sodium on the net charge carrier density has been explained with a passivation of shallow donors such as In$_{Cu}$ antisites [34], or an increase in the acceptor density via Na$_{In}$ antisite defects [35]. Also a catalytic effect of Na on the passivation of V_{Se} vacancy donors by oxygen has been discussed [36]. There is also evidence that Na acts preferentially at grain boundaries (GBs) rather than in the bulk of the individual grains of the thin films [35, 37] and it has been found to significantly influence the diffusion of elements and morphology of the chalcopyrite-type thin films [38].

In principle, there are 12 intrinsic defects possible in a ternary chalcopyrite: three vacancies, three interstitials, and six antisite defects. Obviously, the quaternary Cu(In,Ga)Se$_2$ or pentenary Cu(In,Ga)(S,Se)$_2$ systems even provides for substantially more possible defects. The formation of defects in thermal equilibrium can be described by defect chemical models with the formation of the defects depending on the specific formation energies, the formation enthalpies, and the chemical potentials [39]. For charged defects, the formation enthalpy also directly depends on the position of the Fermi-level during defect formation. It has been found from density functional theory (DFT) calculations under most conditions the formation energy of the copper-vacancy in CuInSe$_2$ and CuGaSe$_2$ is very low and can be even negative, depending on the position of the Fermi level [40–42]. These calculations also show that the defect transition levels for CuInSe$_2$ can be rather shallow and that the formation of neutral defect pairs such as 2V$_{Cu}$-In$_{Cu}$ is very likely [40]. The DFT calculations predict that the ionization levels of these defect pairs are pushed out of the band gap, thus rendering them electronically inactive, in particular with respect to minority carrier recombination.

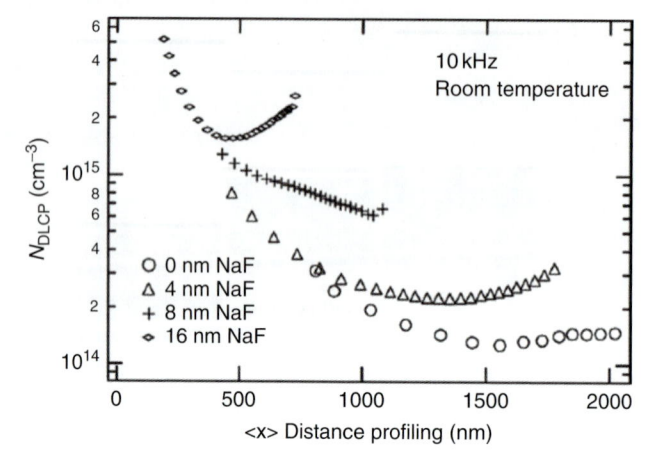

Figure 7 Charge carrier density for Cu(In,Ga)Se$_2$ solar cells obtained from drive-level capacitance profiling (DLCP) measurements at room temperature for different Na contents. Figure from Caballero R, Kaufmann CA, Eisenbarth T, et al. (2009) The effect of NaF precursors on low temperature growth of CIGS thin film solar cells on polyimide substrates. *Physica Status Solidi a – Applications and Materials Science* 206(5): 1049–1053 [33].

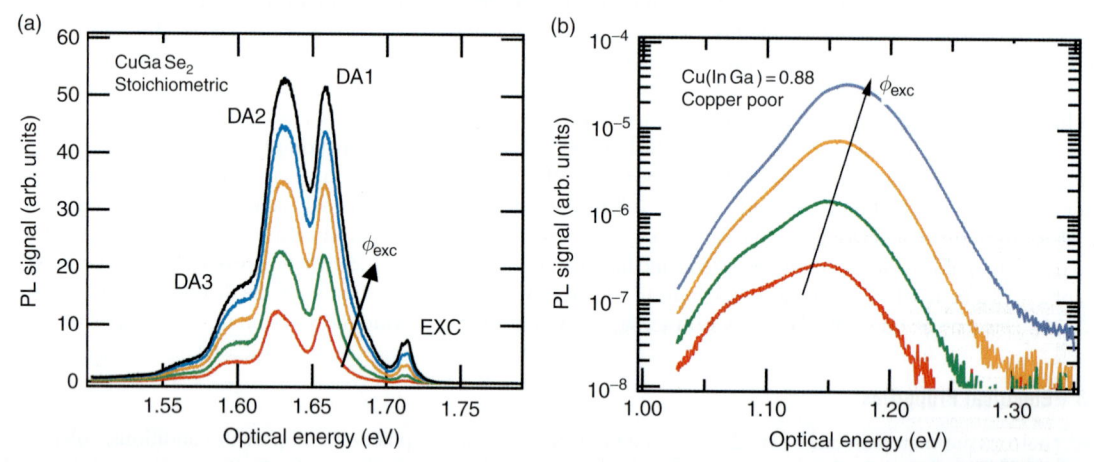

Figure 8 Low-temperature photoluminescence (T = 10 K) as a function of excitation intensity for (a) stoichiometric epitaxially grown CuGaSe$_2$ (data from Unold T and Gutay L (2011) Photoluminescence of thin film solar cells. In: Abou-Ras D, Kirchatz T, and Rau U (eds.) *Advanced Characterization of Thin Film Solar Cells*. Wiley [51]) and (b) Cu-poor Cu(In,Ga)Se$_2$.

Defects in chalcopyrite thin films have been investigated by admittance [43–46], Deep Level Transient Spectroscopy (DLTS) [47], and photoluminescence measurements [48–51]. However, the unambiguous assignment of ionization energies to different defects remains elusive, because of the large number of possibilities to assign a transition found with these measurements. Shallow defects can be best observed by photoluminescence measurements, whereas deep defects can be observed by admittance, DLCP, or DLTS measurements. As expected from the phase diagram shown in **Figure 3**, the defect physics is expected to differ significantly for the Cu-rich versus the Cu-poor composition range for chalcopyrite solar cells. Low-temperature photoluminescence measurements of stoichiometric CuGaSe$_2$ show excitonic transitions and shallow donor–acceptor pair transitions at low temperatures, as shown in **Figure 8(a)** for a an epitaxial thin film grown by metal-organic chemical vapor deposition (MOCVD) [51, 52]. Photoluminescence measurements on Cu-poor grown Cu(In,Ga)Se$_2$ films which lead to the highest conversion efficiencies in devices do not show distinct, narrow defect transitions either at low temperatures or at room temperature as shown in **Figure 8(b)**. As is typical for this material only one or two very broad defect transitions without excitonic signatures are observed, with very strong shifts of the peak energy with excitation intensity [32, 51, 53]. This has been interpreted as a signature of significant potential fluctuations present in these films because of the high degree of compensation as discussed above.

Photoconductivity, admittance, and capacitance voltage measurements have shown metastable effects, such as persistent conductivity after light soaking [54–56]. These metastabilities have been discussed in conjunction with metastabilities in the current-voltage characteristics, such as the increase in open-circuit voltage upon illumination with AM1.5 light, which has been observed for chalcopyrite solar cells and modules [57, 58]. The charge carrier density determined by capacitance profiling is found to increase after light soaking [59]. Also application of a reverse bias has been shown to lead to an increase in the charge carrier density and defect profile as measured by capacitance techniques [20]. There are a number of different models explaining these effects [56], among them a DX-center model [60], photodoping of CdS [61], the presence of a p$^+$-layer close to the heterointerface [62], and an amphoteric defect model [63].

Mobilities of charge carriers in chalcopyrite materials have been determined for single crystals and to a much lesser extent for polycrystalline thin films. The mobilities are found to differ strongly for the single-crystal and polycrystalline materials, as can be understood from the dominant role of GBs in the latter materials. As also found for other semiconductor materials, the mobilities generally depend strongly on the measurement temperature and material's composition. Hole mobilities for $CuInSe_2$ up to $60 cm^2 V^{-1} s^{-1}$ [48] at room temperature have been measured for single crystals, and much lower values around $1 cm^2 V^{-1} s^{-1}$ have been obtained for polycrystalline thin films [50, 64, 65]. These values have been inferred mostly from Hall measurements, which are difficult to interpret for polycrystalline and strongly compensated materials. Hole mobility values smaller than $1 cm^2 V^{-1} s^{-1}$ have been inferred from time-of-flight techniques [66], which has been explained by trapping in a large density of subgap states. Electron mobilities of up to $900 cm^2 V^{-1} s^{-1}$ have been reported for $CuInSe_2$ single crystals by Hall measurements [31]. The determination of electron mobilities in polycrystalline thin films, which are usually p-type remains elusive.

1.18.2.3.1 Surfaces and grain boundaries

GBs generally are expected to cause increased recombination of minority carriers because of the high density of broken or incorrect bonds occurring at such planes between two differently oriented crystals. In addition, potential barriers at GBs can significantly reduce the effective mobility of carriers and cause carrier depletion in the bulk of the grains. In contrast to other semiconductor materials such as silicon and GaAs, GBs in chalcopyrites seem to play a remarkably small role for recombination of minority carriers and therefore device performance [67]. Electron back scatter diffraction (EBSD) investigations on different chalcopyrite thin-film materials have shown that most of the GBs are highly symmetric twin boundaries, for which much lower defect densities are expected to be present when compared with randomly oriented GBs [68]. In fact, relatively little dependence of the device performance on the grain size has been found, as long as the grain size reaches a certain size of several hundred nanometers. In **Figure 9**(a), we show EBSD pattern quality maps of several $Cu(In,Ga)Se_2$ solar cells that have been deposited with different Ga content. It can be seen that the grain size varies significantly between $x = 0$ ($CuInSe_2$) and $x = 1$ ($CuGaSe_2$). As is shown in **Figure 9**(b), the efficiency of these devices increased for grain sizes of up to $0.6 \mu m$, but does not correlate with the grain sizes for larger grains [23].

Different models have been proposed to explain GB physics in chalcopyrites as summarized in **Figure 10**. Downward band bending at the GB (**Figure 10(a)**), as it is commonly assumed for silicon [69] or CdTe [70], has also been proposed for CIGSe [71].

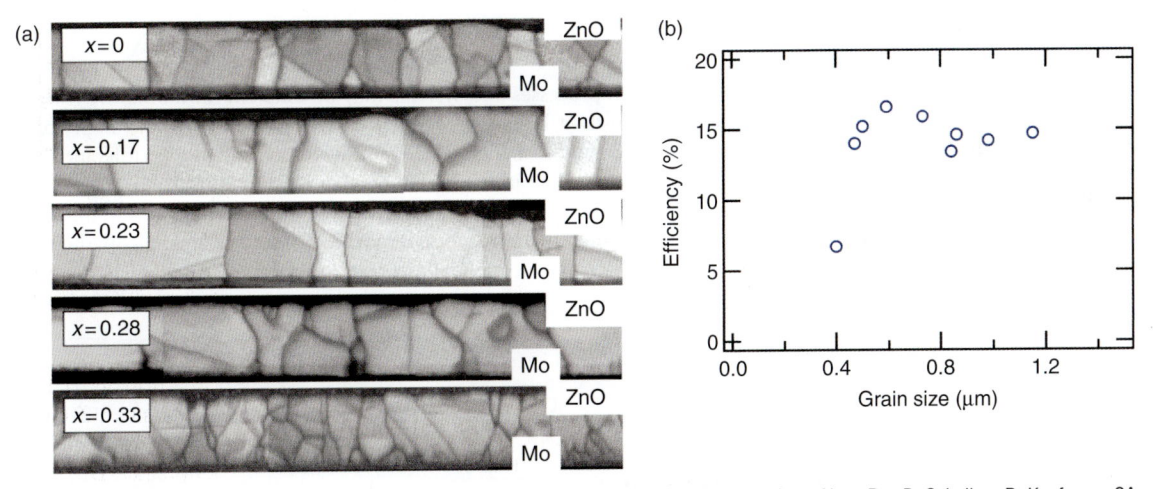

Figure 9 (a) EBSD pattern quality maps of CIGSe. (b) Dependence of efficiency on grain size. Data from Abou-Ras D, Caballero R, Kaufmann CA, et al. (2008) Impact of the Ga concentration on the microstructure of $CuIn_{1-x}Ga_xSe_2$. *Physica Status Solidi-Rapid Research Letters* 2(3): 135–137 [23].

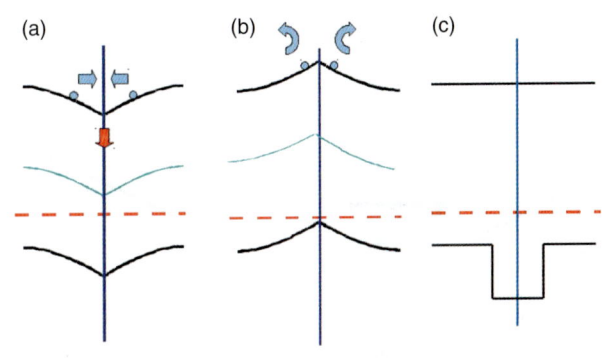

Figure 10 Band diagrams of different grain boundary models for polycrystalline thin films. (a) Inversion due to donors at grain boundary; (b) upward bending of grain boundary potential due to a high acceptor density at grain boundary; (c) neutral grain boundary with lowered valence band.

Such a band bending at GBs may aid in the current collection of polycrystalline chalcopyrite solar cells and reduce recombination, as the minority carriers are attracted and the majority carriers are repelled. However, numerical simulations have shown that, on the one hand, significant band bending is needed to effectively induce type inversion at the GB and that, on the other hand, such a configuration leads to significant open-circuit voltage losses in the devices [72, 73]. The same simulations predict some improvement in device efficiency for upward bending of the GBs (**Figure 10(b)**). A significant reduction in the GB recombination activity, however, is predicted by two-dimensional (2D) device simulation for the case of a valence band barrier (**Figure 10(c)**) at the GBs [72]. In this case, the minority carriers are unaffected while the holes are kept away from the zone of increased recombination at the GB. Such a valence band barrier can be caused by copper depletion because the states at the valence band maximum are due to antibonding states of Se-p and Cu-d hybrid orbitals [74]. Reduction of the copper content at the GB or also at the surface is thus expected to lower the energy of the valence band maximum. For an extended region of Cu depletion, an ordered defect compound may be formed (β phase), which also exhibits a lowered valence band maximum as discussed above. Copper depletion has been predicted for either the anion- or the cation-terminated polar surfaces of $CuInSe_2$, which may be stable because of the low formation energy of Cu-vacancies or In_{Cu} antisites [74]. Note that in order to reduce recombination in such a GB scenario the region of lowered valence band maximum (VBM) must be at least about 3 nm wide in order to prevent tunneling of holes into the recombination region [73].

Experimental evidence on the composition, electronic structure, and recombination activity of GBs in chalcopyrites is very diverse, and it has not been possible to confirm a single GB model [67, 75, 76]. This may be in part due to the fact that many of the experimental techniques are surface sensitive, and thus may be strongly influenced by surface, impurity, or oxidation effects [77]. Kelvin probe force microscopy (KPFM), scanning tunneling microscopy (STM), and Hall measurements all indicate a considerable large distribution of barrier heights at GB from 0 to 300 mV [67, 77]. It is important to note that upward bending and downward bending have been found for different grain boundaries on single samples. With respect to recombination, it has been shown by cathodoluminescence [78] and electron beam-induced current (EBIC) measurements [79] that high symmetry twin GBs show much reduced recombination activity. However, similarly as for the case of band bending detected by KPFM measurements, vastly differing behavior for different GBs on single samples has been found, which so far could not be correlated to specific structural models of GBs.

1.18.3 Deposition Methods

The main criteria for the choice between different deposition processes and systems may be different for laboratory research and industrial production and scale up. In the former case, mostly a high level of control over composition and high conversion efficiencies are aimed at. In the latter case, apart from efficiency, low cost, high yield, reproducibility, and process tolerance have also to be considered. Not every deposition technique that performs well in the laboratory can be scaled up to homogeneously and reproducible cover square meter substrates at low cost. In this section, we will give an overview of the most important fabrication routines and highlight advantages and disadvantages of the different approaches. Deposition processes for chalcopyrite thin films can be generally divided into two main categories: 'single-step' and 'sequential' deposition processes. A schematic for these two principal types of deposition methods is shown in **Figure 11**.

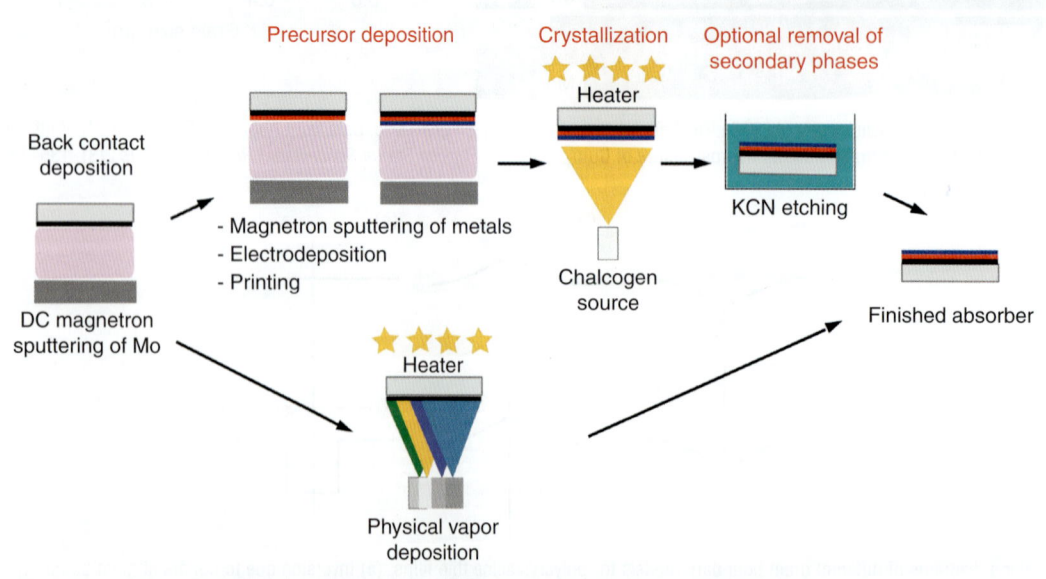

Figure 11 Single-step (bottom) and sequential (top) deposition methods for chalcopyrite-type thin-film solar cells.

1.18.3.1 Single-Step Deposition

In single-step deposition, the complete thin-film absorber is fabricated within one production step. Although it may be required to remove undesired by-product phases, or to treat the thin film in some way to improve its overall quality before proceeding with the solar cell manufacturing process, the synthesis of the chalcopyrite absorber in its proper crystallographic phase as such is complete.

Co-evaporation was among the first methods used for the fabrication of chalcopyrite-based CuInSe$_2$ thin-film solar cell devices [6]. In the last 30 years, many modifications of this process have been developed, which can be categorized by their number of stages in which elements are deposited at different rates. **Figure 12** displays the variations of the co-evaporation process as they are currently generally referred to (1) the single layer process, which consists of only one evaporation rate for each element and remains Cu-deficient throughout the whole process; (2) the bilayer process, which utilizes Cu-rich growth in the initial stage of the deposition process and ends up with an overall Cu-poor composition by reduction of Cu-supply in the last stage of the process; and (3) the three-stage approach.

1.18.3.1.1 Single-stage process

For this most simple growth recipe, either complete compounds [80] or single elements are evaporated either by evaporation boats or by Knudsen-type effusion cells in a high vacuum system. For low cost and increased control of composition at varying deposition conditions, single-element sources are preferable over compound source material. Best efficiencies for Cu(In,Ga)Se$_2$ have always been found for Cu-poor material with Cu/In + Ga < 0.9, that is, within the single-phase region expected from the thermodynamic equilibrium phase diagrams. Therefore, single-stage deposition requires precise control of the evaporation rates, which can be achieved by advanced evaporation source design or by means of optical process control such as atomic absorption spectroscopy (AAS) or electron impact emission spectroscopy (EIES) [81]. Relatively high device efficiencies of up to 16% have been obtained by this deposition method [82]. However, the average grain size for these films is rather small below 500 nm. It has been found that the grain size of chalcopyrite thin films depends not only on growth temperature and final composition, but also on whether the thin film has been Cu-rich at some point during the deposition process. On the other hand, as can also be seen from the equilibrium phase diagram, films grown in the Cu-rich regime contain significant amounts of Cu$_x$Se secondary phases that have been found to be detrimental to device performance. Therefore, the secondary phases either have to be etched by, for example, KCN or have to be converted into the chalcopyrite phase by use of several deposition stages with varying elemental ratios, as discussed in the following sections.

1.18.3.1.2 Two-stage process

These co-evaporation recipes include a Cu-rich and a Cu-poor step, with the aim to obtain large-grained, Cu-poor films after the deposition is completed. For example, a reactive 'two-stage' co-evaporation method using elemental Cu, In, and Se was developed in the early 1980s, to remove secondary Cu-Se phases within an initially Cu-rich grown thin film, by applying a second stage where only In, Ga, and Se are evaporated. This deposition recipe is also commonly referred to as the 'Boeing' process [83].

1.18.3.1.3 Three-stage or multistage process

The highest conversion efficiencies to date have been achieved using CIGSe thin-film absorber layers that were deposited using co-evaporation procedures based on the three-stage process [9, 84]. This process was originally implemented in the following way [85]. During the first stage, In, Ga, and Se are evaporated at a substrate temperature of about 330 °C, which leads to the formation of a very small grained (In,Ga)$_2$Se$_2$ compound layer. During the second stage, In and Ga evaporation rates are turned to zero and only Cu is evaporated together with Se, while at the same time the temperature is increased to the final deposition temperature between 500 and 600 °C. The Cu-Se evaporation continues until the composition of the compound becomes Cu-rich, that is Cu/(In + Ga) > 1, which leads to a rapid recrystallization of the compound and to the segregation of Cu$_x$Se phases. The Cu-Se

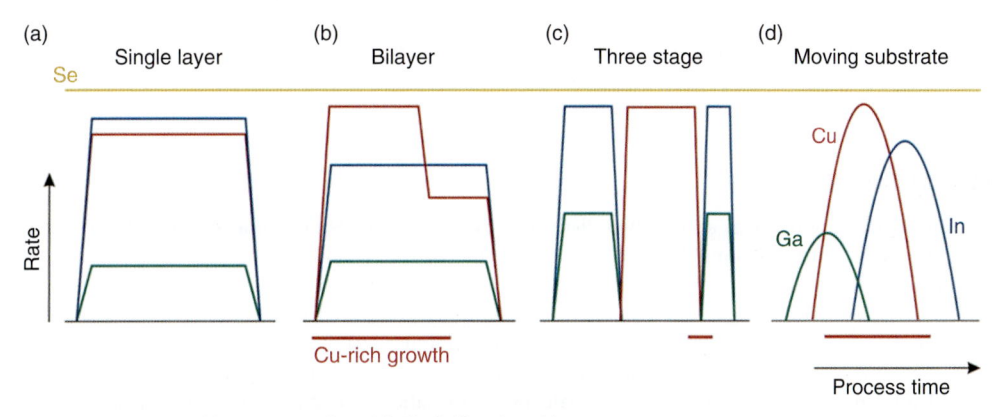

Figure 12 Different rate profiles used in co-evaporation of Cu(In,Ga)Se$_2$ deposition.

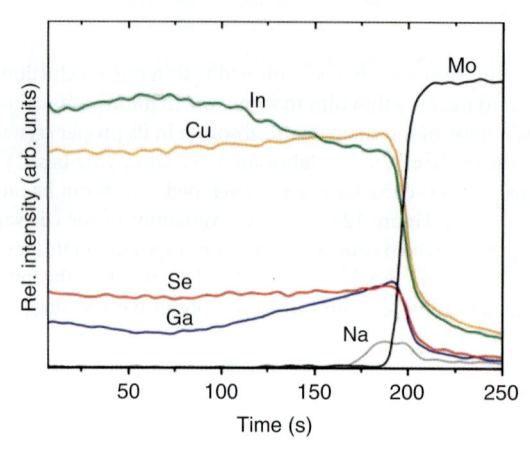

Figure 13 Typical depth-dependent compositional gradient in a multistage deposited Cu(In,Ga)Se$_2$ thin film, measured via glow discharge optical emission spectroscopy (see also Caballero R, Kauffmann CA, Efimova V, et al. [87]).

deposition is continued until the overall composition is about Cu/(In + Ga) ≈ 1.15, after which the Cu deposition is turned off, and a final stage consisting of the evaporation of In, Ga, and Se proceeds until the semiconducting layer has the desired final composition, typically Cu/(In + Ga) < 0.9. Devices grown with this three-stage process usually show a depth-dependent compositional grading with respect to the Ga content of the thin film, which is a natural consequence of the three-stage deposition sequence [86, 87]. A Ga gradient, as it is typical for such a device, is displayed in **Figure 13**. While the positive gradient toward the back interface of the device is a standard feature for the vast majority of processes, the slight increase toward the absorber surface and its effect on the later device performance is highly dependent on the individual process parameters.

Several growth models for this optimized process were published [85, 88–90]. They consider the diffusion of Cu or Cu-Se compounds into thin layers of In$_2$Se$_3$ or (In,Ga)$_2$Se$_3$ and can – in principle – be transferred to other fabrication methods. According to these growth models, a Cu-rich growth phase ensures the simultaneous presence of Cu-Se phases along with the chalcopyrite compound. This enhances the 'recrystallization' of the growing films. Although the precise details regarding recrystallization are still a matter of debate, the literature agrees on the fact that after recrystallization the electronic quality of a chalcopyrite thin-film absorber is much enhanced [87, 91–93]. Aspects such as grain size, crystal structure, and atomic defects are all under discussion to be affected.

The Cu-poor/Cu-rich transition of the growing thin film at the end of the second stage of the three-stage or multistage co-evaporation process can be easily monitored via pyrometry, laser light scattering (LLS) or by the heater's power input [94], because the material properties change drastically at the stoichiometry point. Most importantly, the segregation of Cu$_x$Se phases on the surfaces leads to a change in the surface morphology, which can be detected by LLS, and to a change in the emissivity, which can be detected by pyrometry or thermometry. In that sense, the important features and final composition of the films can be very precisely controlled by monitoring the stoichiometry point, which is to be followed by a relatively short third stage. While the application of LLS was originally developed using a He:Ne laser as a light source and the measurement of the diffusely scattered portion, a charge-coupled device (CCD) camera used as detector together with a white light source can provide spatially resolved information [95]. Further *in situ* methods are available and are applicable also to co-evaporation methods other than the three-stage process [96, 97].

The three-stage process has also been applied to sulfide compounds [98], but for these materials conversion efficiencies have not exceeded 12.6 % so far [99].

A possible implementation of the three-stage process in commercial inline systems is shown in **Figure 12(d)**. Here, the rates of the individual evaporation sources are fixed in time, and the time-dependence of the deposition rates used in static laboratory systems has to be translated into different locations of the sources within the inline system [100]. Note that in this case the use of line sources is beneficial in order to ensure homogenous evaporation of the typically 0.3–0.6 m wide substrates [101]. With a certified conversion efficiency of 19.3% the in-line adaptation of the three-stage co-evaporation process has proven the potential for its application in large-scale fabrication of high-efficiency thin-film modules [102].

1.18.3.2 Sequential Deposition

Sequential deposition generally involves at least two distinct steps: (1) the deposition of a precursor layer (usually metal) and (2) the crystallization step that transforms the precursor into a chalcopyrite absorber layer, usually performed by heating and chalcogenization [15]. As for the single-step deposited absorber thin films, further treatment before proceeding with the solar cell fabrication may be required. While single-step deposition is commonly performed in vacuum chambers, sequential deposition methods can be generally classified into vacuum and nonvacuum techniques [103].

Formation of chalcopyrite compounds by sequential processing has been studied using thermodynamic and reaction kinetic approaches, as well as by *in situ* observations during the chalcopyrite formation by energy-dispersive X-ray diffraction (EDXRD) and Raman techniques [104–106].

Precursor layers can be deposited by a wide variety of techniques, because low-temperature process can be used, they do not need to contain the chalcogens, and because the crystal quality does not need to be very good. Among the most used precursor fabrication techniques are magnetron sputtering [107], evaporation [108, 109], electrodeposition [110, 111], solution processing of nanoinks, or nanocrystals [112–114]. Magnetron sputtering offers the advantage that it can be very fast, is highly controllable, and profits from its application and experience in the architectural glass industry. Precursors can also be evaporated fast at room temperature. However, standard equipment for large area evaporation is not so readily available as for magnetron sputtering. Electrodeposition can in principle also produce uniform precursor layers over large areas and at high deposition speed [115, 116]. Finally, solution processing of nanoinks and nanocrystals, as, for example, doctor blading, spin coating, or printing has been used successfully to deposit precursor layers for chalcopyrite-type compounds [113, 114].

During the second step of these processing techniques, the chalcopyrite-type material is formed either by annealing, reactive annealing, rapid thermal processing (RTP) or by rapid thermal annealing in a reactive chalcogen atmosphere. If the precursor already contains the chalcogen, simple heating in an inert gas atmosphere could in principle be used to form the absorber layer. However, if the system is not sealed, chalcogen loss during this process is very likely leading to undesirable defects and defect phases in the absorber layer. Metallic precursors can be used to react at high temperatures (400–500 °C) in H_2S or H_2Se for the formation of $Cu(In,Ga)Se_2$ or $Cu(In,Ga)S_2$ [117, 118]. Alternatively, elemental selenium or sulfur can also be used. The annealing step in this process can last from tens of minutes to several hours. The advantage of this method is a high level of control over the reaction, whereas the disadvantage is that it is very slow and has to be compatible with temperatures the substrate withstands for extended periods of time.

Much faster reactions are obtained by RTP, again either without or in the presence of the Se or S [28, 119–121]. By this process, high-quality chalcopyrite absorbers can be obtained from metal layers within several minutes. The drawback of this method is that it is much harder to control as the reactions leading to precursor phases, secondary phases, and finally the desired chalcopyrite phase occur within a very short time span, which depends, for example, on temperature, temperature ramp, pressure and chalcogen pressure. Reactions occurring during the sulfurization step of $CuInS_2$ have been observed *in situ* by EDXRD [122–125] as shown in **Figure 14**. From such measurements, the reaction sequence

$$Cu, CuIn_2 \rightarrow Cu_{11}In_9 \rightarrow CuS, InS, CuInS_2 \rightarrow CuIn_5S_8, CuInS_2, Cu_{2x}S \rightarrow CuInS_2, Cu_{2x}S \quad [2]$$

has been determined for the reaction of Cu/In precursors with elemental sulfur in a rapid thermal anneal process [123]. The experiments were performed for sulfur partial pressures of 1 mbar and $1\,K\,s^{-1}$ heating ramps. Note that the presence of secondary phases and reaction paths strongly depend on these processing parameters as also has been found for the Cu-In-Ga-Se system [122].

For both the long-time thermal anneal and the rapid thermal anneal chalcogenization, the formation of $MoSe_x$ or MoS_x at the back contact, the formation of large voids close to the back contact, and adhesion of the absorber layer to the substrate in general pose major challenges. The formation of thin $MoSe_x$ or MoS_x at the back contact interface to the absorber is desirable as it improves the electrical performance; however, thick $MoSe_x$ or MoS_x layers lead to a very large series resistance that deteriorates device performance. Adhesion at the back contact has to be maximized by the proper choice of substrates and adjustment of the morphology and microstructure of the molybdenum back contact.

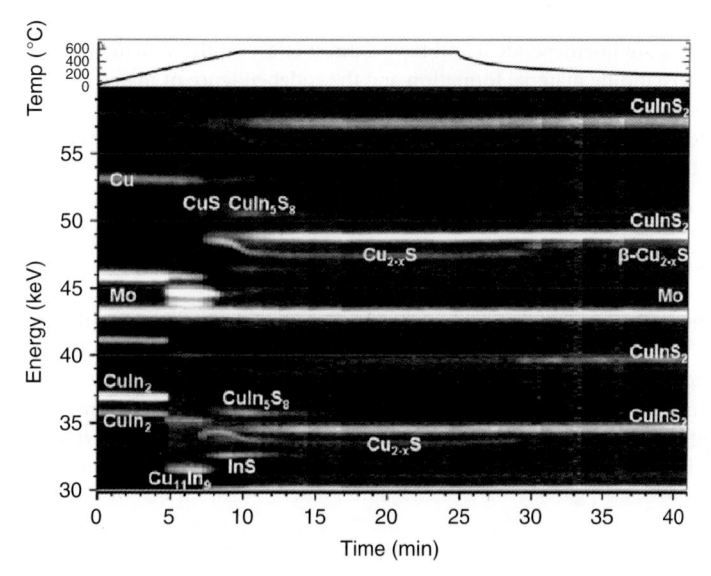

Figure 14 Energy dispersive X-ray diffraction (EDXRD) performed *in situ* during the RTP of $CuInS_2$. Figure from Rodriguez-Alvarez H, Mainz R, Marsen B, *et al.* (2010) Recrystallization of Cu-In-S thin films studied *in situ* by energy-dispersive X-ray diffraction. *Journal of Applied Crystallography* 43: 1053–1061 [93].

1.18.3.3 General Considerations

The following issues have to be considered in deposition of chalcogenides:

- Maximum process temperature T: Depending on the thermal stability of the kind of substrate in use (see also Section 1.18.4), different maximum substrate temperatures are used for the deposition process. Processes, which exert only little thermal stress on the substrate during thin-film deposition using maximum temperatures between 330 and 450 °C, have successfully been developed [82, 126] and it is has been shown that despite the diffusion limitation at low growth temperatures, multistep co-evaporation growth processes can produce absorbers of remarkably high electronic quality [127]. The use of high process temperatures, on the other hand, speeds up diffusion during film deposition and helps to decrease compositional inhomogeneity within the complete thin film [128, 129]. Pulsed laser-assisted co-evaporation has been evaluated to compensate for low process temperatures [130].
- Ga content GGI (=[Ga]/([Ga]+[In])): As described in Section 1.18.2, the Ga content of the material determines the band gap of the deposited material. The use of high deposition temperatures has proven beneficial when using high Ga contents [129]. Alternative routines to improve growth with high GGI, as, for example, ionization of Ga, have also been applied [131].
- Cu content CGI (=[Cu]/([Ga]+[In])) during and at the end of the deposition: The amount of Cu present during thin film preparation is important because recrystallization may be enhanced in the presence of secondary Cu-Se/S phases and also due to the fact that Cu-deficient phases may play a critical role in the energy band line up at the absorber surface, that is, at the absorber/buffer interface (see Section 1.18.2). Therefore, it is necessary to consider not only the final composition of the absorber thin film, but also the path in the phase diagram along which the synthesis of the thin film proceeds [87, 132].
- Chalcogen flux during layer deposition: The Se partial pressure in the deposition chamber must be high enough to impede the re-evaporation of Se and In_2Se from the surface of the growing thin film, in particular at high deposition temperatures [133]. Structural and optoelectronic characteristics of the deposited thin film are affected by the selenium/metal ratio of the deposition rates [134, 135]. Activation of evaporated Se species has been studied in terms of improved material yield and also to support Se integration in the absorber growth process when low process temperatures are used [136, 137].
- Amount of Na present and supply method: As mentioned in Section 1.18.2, the incorporation of Na in CIGSe has a beneficial impact on the final quality of the absorber layer, although no such effect has been found for Cu-rich deposited sulfide compounds. A variety of methods are used in order to supply Na. On standard float glass without a diffusion barrier coating Na will diffuse through the Mo back contact into the deposited thin-film material at the elevated process temperatures. If a barrier layer is applied or a Na-free substrate is used, Na needs to be supplied externally. This can be achieved by co-evaporation of NaF during the CIGSe deposition process [138], by a NaF posttreatment of the CIGSe thin film after deposition [139] or by use of a NaF precursor layer that is evaporated onto the Mo back contact (see Section 1.18.4) prior to CIGSe deposition [140], where it could have also a direct impact on the CIGSe/Mo interface conditioning [141]. Alternatively, on flexible substrates, Na has also successfully been supplied by a soda-lime glass layer that is located beneath the Mo back contact [142] or by adding Na to the back contact material [143]. The most successful method to date is the NaF posttreatment [127]. The presence of a certain element, such as Na, may have a catalytic effect on the formation of particular material phases. Thus, Na is, for example, assumed to promote the formation of oxides within CIGSe thin films [144].

Most of these process parameters are interdependent and have a direct effect on the structural and electronic characteristics of the growing CIGSe thin film. Understanding material formation and the codependence of material characteristics and resulting device properties are critical for achieving high conversion efficiencies and reproducibility. Since co-evaporation so far has produced the highest efficiency devices, offers reasonable process control, and gives access to a wide range of process parameters, it is the model system mostly used to study these topics.

1.18.4 Device Structure

Chalcopyrite solar cells are heterojunction devices consisting of a large number of layers with different functional properties. A schematic of a typical device is shown in **Figure 15**. Unlike amorphous or microcrystalline silicon devices, which are commonly fabricated in the superstrate configuration (sun light enters through the glass substrate), chalcopyrite solar cells are so far generally made in the substrate configuration (sunlight enters from the top). This is due to the fact that molybdenum has been found to be a very stable contact in this configuration and because the high temperatures used in the chalcopyrite absorber growth (>500 °C) lead to undesirable diffusion and intermixing if the window and buffer layers are deposited prior to the absorber.

1.18.4.1 Substrate

1.18.4.1.1 Glass

Currently, the most commonly used substrate in CIGSe thin-film solar cells and modules is conventional soda-lime glass. This is due to the fact that this glass is readily available through its use in the architectural industry, has favorable thermal expansion

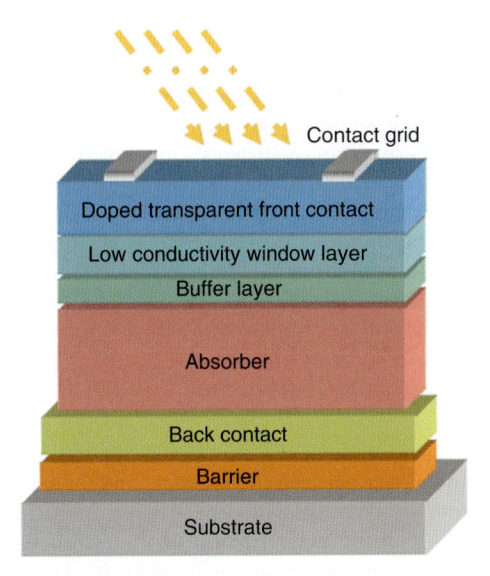

Figure 15 Schematic of a chalcopyrite-type thin-film heterojunction solar cell.

coefficients, and contains a large amount of sodium oxide on the order of 15–20% [145]: As mentioned above (Section 1.18.2), sodium has been found to significantly improve the solar cell efficiencies by increasing the effective carrier density [33, 146]. If appropriate deposition processes are used, the sodium diffuses through the back contact into the chalcopyrite absorber layer in adequate quantities to yield good electronic performance. Typically, glass thicknesses between 1 and 3 mm are used.

The drawback of soda-lime glass is that it contains various impurities across the periodic table and that it can only be heated up to about 550 °C, above which temperature it softens and begins to warp. Therefore, efforts were taken to develop high-temperature stable glass that can be heated to temperatures of above 600 °C and have a suitable thermal expansion coefficient. Indeed, first experiments with such high-temperature glass have shown promising results indicating improved devices efficiencies for Cu(In,Ga)Se$_2$ solar cells [128,129]. Selected properties for different substrate materials are summarized in **Table 1**.

1.18.4.1.2 Metal substrates

Flexible substrates have several advantages over rigid glass substrates, such as reduced weight, ease of storage in rolled-up form, new application areas, for example, in building-integrated PV, and maybe most importantly they allow for roll-to-roll processing [153]. A number of metal substrates have been used in the fabrication of CIGSe solar cells such as stainless steel [142, 154, 155], industrial steel [156], titanium foil [142, 157, 158], aluminum foil [159], and copper foil [160]. Major considerations for the selection of appropriate metal substrates are the thermal expansion coefficient, surface roughness, impurity content, and cost. Very high efficiencies close to 18% have been obtained on (expensive) titanium foil and on stainless steel [155, 157]. Reasonable efficiencies in the 13% range have also been obtained on industrial steel with appropriate barrier layers to prevent the diffusion of impurities, particularly the diffusion of Fe from the substrate [156].

Table 1 Selected properties of different substrate materials used for thin-film chalcopyrite-based solar cells

Material	Thickness	Thermal expansion ($\times 10^{-6}$ K^{-1})	Max temperature (°C)	Density (g cm^{-3})	Roughness (nm)
Moly	0.5–1 µm	4.8		10.3	
Soda lime	1–3 mm	10 [147]	<550	2.5	10–15 [148]
Borosilicate [151]		3.3	<800	2.2	
Quartz glass		<0.6 [150]	>1000	2.2	
Ti	25 µm	8.6 [148]	>600	4.5 [148]	1900 [148]
					75 [152]
steel	25 µm	>10	>600	>7.4	38–120 [152]
Polyimide [149]	25–50 µm	>20	<500	1.5	30–150
					3–16 [152]

Data from Hedstrom J, Ohlsen H, Bodegard M, et al. (1993) Zno/Cds/Cu(IN,GA)Se2 thin-film solar-cells with improved performance, pp. 364–371. *Conference Record of the Twenty Third IEEE Photovoltaic Specialists Conference*. May 1993 [147]; Herz K, Kessler F, Wächter R, et al. (2002) Dielectric barriers for flexible CIGS solar modules. *Thin Solid Films* 403–404: 384–389 [148]; Dupont [149]; Hereaus [150]; Duran [151]; Wuerz R, Eicke A, Kessler F, et al. (2011) Alternative sodium sources for Cu(In,Ga)Se2 thin-film solar cells on flexible substrates. *Thin Solid Films* 519(21): 7268–7271 [152].

1.18.4.1.3 Polyimide substrates

Polyimide foil is an electrically insulating material. Monolithic integration therefore becomes a viable option for on-substrate module interconnection without additional barrier layers, as they are required for conductive substrates. In comparison to metal foils, it offers a further weight advantage, smoother surfaces, and is the cheaper substrate. Disadvantages are the low tolerance to thermal stress and large thermal expansion coefficients. High-quality CIGSe thin films with efficiencies approaching 20% normally require temperatures of up to 600 °C during deposition. Currently, commercially available polyimide foils are only stable up to ~450 °C and can turn rather brittle once exposed to such temperatures. Na supply also becomes an important issue at these low deposition temperatures [33, 127, 139]. High thermal expansion of the substrate results in mechanical stress in the thin-film layer stack and poor adhesion. Despite the relatively low deposition temperatures, high-quality lab-sized CIGSe devices have been reported [140, 142, 161], with maximum efficiencies above 18% [162]. Industrial production of CIGSe on polyimide foil has surpassed the pilot stage with the first commercial modules soon to be available.

1.18.4.2 Barrier Layers

There are a number of reasons why a barrier layer between the substrate and the back contact may be appropriate. Since the supply of sodium to the absorber layer from the glass substrate depends on many factors, such as the actual sodium content of the glass, the morphology, density, oxygen content, and thickness of the (normally Mo) back contact layer, the substrate temperature during growth, and the duration of the deposition process, it may be advantageous to supply the sodium independently of the outdiffusion from the substrate [139]. In that case, however, if soda-lime glass is used as a substrate, a barrier layer has to be inserted to prevent additional out diffusion of sodium from the glass. Suitable barrier layers can be SiN_x or SiO_x layers [163]. The sodium can then be incorporated by use of a sodium-fluoride precursor layer deposited onto the back contact, by co-evaporation of sodium during the absorber deposition, or by incorporation of sodium after completion of the absorber deposition [139].

Barrier layers on the substrate may also be advisable on steel substrates in order to prevent or reduce the out diffusion of impurities, most prominently iron. It has been found that iron diffuses readily through the Mo back contact into the CIGS absorber layer at elevated temperatures above 400 °C [164], and that the detrimental defects are formed and the device efficiency is significantly reduced [154]. SiN_x, SiO_x, or also thin Cr layers have proved useful to prevent the diffusion of iron from steel substrates into CIGSe absorber layers [154, 156, 164].

Monolithic interconnection of solar cells on conducting substrates such as steel also requires the use of barrier layers, to prevent shunting from one solar cell to the other. This task requires a barrier layer with good electrical insulation. Although the use of such barrier layers has been mainly in research, most manufacturers using conducting substrates currently employ a single-type interconnection of single cells, similar to the module fabrication for crystalline silicon wafers.

1.18.4.3 Back Contact

The most commonly used material used as a back contact in chalcopyrite solar cells is molybdenum. This is due to its low resistivity and its stability at high temperatures during the absorber growth process. Molybdenum is usually deposited on the substrate material by magnetron sputtering or e-gun deposition. Since in many cases the sodium has to diffuse from the glass through the back contact into the absorber layer, the specific thickness [165], morphology, and state of tension of this back contact is very critical [166, 167]. In particular, the intrinsic stress of the molybdenum layer has to be minimized during the deposition process. Mo back contact layers usually show compressive stress. There have been conflicting reports about whether Mo forms an Ohmic contact with CiGSe [168, 169] or a Schottky-type contact [170, 171]. Recently, a back contact barrier on the order of 0.2 eV has been attributed to characteristic admittance signatures [46, 56]. The disagreement between different analyses on different devices may be due to an essential role of sodium during the contact and absorber formation [141]. Alternative back contacts have been investigated [172], but have not led to device efficiencies comparable to state-of-the-art CIGSe devices with Mo back contacts. Because Mo itself is a relatively poor reflector for long wavelength light and because Mo is a relatively rare metal, replacement of Mo by an alternative back contact would be highly desirable.

1.18.4.4 Buffer Layer

First chalcopyrite solar cells were made from $CuInSe_2$ single crystals with ~2 μm thick CdS emitter layer. Since the band gap of CdS is only about 2.4 eV and it cannot be doped very highly, it is not an optimal heteroemitter material. Therefore, CdS was later replaced by a ZnO emitter layer, but it was soon found that the inclusion of a thin, ~50 nm thick, CdS buffer layer, resulting in a CIGSe/CdS/ZnO structure, greatly improved the device performance. There are many possible reasons why this buffer layer may be beneficial for the heterojunction operation. Because it is not highly doped, it serves as an insulating layer to prevent shunting from pinholes or other local defects in the absorber layer. It may passivate macroscopic or microscopic defects on the chalcopyrite absorber surface. It may provide proper band alignment between absorber and window layer and it may cause type inversion at the heterointerface through surface donors at or close to the interface.

Over the years, many buffer layer materials and deposition techniques have been evaluated with varying results. Still to date, the best solar cells are obtained with buffer layers obtained from chemical bath deposition (CBD) of CdS. The reason for this is not clear since the CBD is a relatively 'dirty' process and the formed layers have low electronic quality and contain high amounts of hydrogen, nitrogen, and oxygen impurities.

CBD deposition of CdS for CIGSe solar cells generally uses an alkaline aqueous solution and three components: cadmium salt, complexing agent NH_3, sulfur precursor, for example, thiourea ($SC(NH_2)_2$). There are published recipes for CBD of CdS layers on CIGSe solar cells, but commonly every lab will perform some optimization of the process itself, which will also depend on the specifics of the absorber layer composition and deposition processes [173]. The chemical reaction can be described as follows [174]:

$$Cd^{2+} + NH_2 - CS - NH_2 + 2OH^- \rightarrow CdS + H_2CN_2 + 2H_2O\cdot \qquad [3]$$

The role of the NH_3 is to supply the ligand for the Cd and to control the hydrolysis of the thiourea. It also, to some extent, removes oxides from the surface of the CIGSe thin film just before CdS nucleates in the chemical bath during the deposition process [175]. This may be one possible reason why the CBD-deposited buffer has proven so advantageous in the fabrication of chalcopyrite-based solar cell devices. Depending on the process time, the CdS may grow in an ion-by-ion heterogeneous growth mode, which can switch into a homogeneous growth mode where the CdS particles nucleate in solution and precipitate at the surface of the film. Because CBD is a wet chemical process, it is not directly compatible with vacuum processing, and because Cd is toxic there has been substantial research into alternative buffer layers and alternative deposition techniques (**Table 2**) [190, 191, 192]. In addition, the 2.4 eV band gap of CdS leads to non-negligible absorption losses in the current response despite the fact that thicknesses below 60 nm are used for this layer [193].

So far ZnS-based alternative buffer layers have yielded the best device efficiencies (after CBD CdS) and are currently used in large-scale module production. Many alternative buffer layers have been found to be very prone to light-soaking metastability effects, that is, the electrical characteristics of the devices change – sometimes drastically – under illumination [194]. This may be due to differences in the structure of the heterojunction interface, band offsets, defect densities, and/or doping level. Some buffer

Table 2 Alternative buffer materials on CIGSe

Buffer material	Method	Absorber	Performance (η/η_{CdS})	Treatment	Comments	Lit
Without		CIGSe	0.80	Not specified		[Contreras]
Without		CIGSSe	0.99	Not specified	ILGAR ZnO	[Baer]
Zn(O,S)	CBD	CIGSe	0.84	After light soaking	ZnMgO/ZnO:Al	[Buffiere]
Zn(O,S)	CBD	CIGSe	1.00	After light soaking	ZnMgO/ZnO:Al	[Hariskos]
ZnS(O,OH)	CBD	CIGSe	(17.9%)	Not specified	no CdS Reference	[Yagioka]
ZnS(O,OH)	CBD	CIGSe	0.99	Not specified		[Contreras2]
Zn(S,O)	CBD	CIGSSe	(14.2%)	After light soaking	no CdS Reference	[Saez]
$ZnO_{1-x}S_x$	RF sputtering	CIGSe	0.90	Not specified		[Okamoto]
ZnSe	MOVPE	CIGSe	0.98	Not specified		[Engelhardt]
ZnSe	MOCVD	CIGSSe	0.97	Not specified		[Siebentritt]
$In_x(OH,S)_y$	CBD	CIGSe	0.74	After annealing		[Huang]
In_xS_y	Ultrasonic spray	CIGSe	0.70	After light soaking		[Ernits]
In_xS_y	Spray ILGAR	CIGSe	0.88	Not specified		[Allsop]
In_2S_3	Spray ILGAR	CIGSSe	0.99	No annealing		[Fischer]
In_xS_y	Evaporation	CIGSe	0.87	After annealing		[Pistor]
In_2S_3	Co-evaporation	CIGSe	0.65–0.92	Not specified	Ga/III dependent	[Couzinié]

Data from Allsop N, Kauffmann CA, Neisser A, *et al.* (2005) Presented at the *Materials Research Society. Symposium Proceeding*. San Francisco, CA, 2005 (unpublished [176] Buffière M, Harel S, Arzel L, *et al.* (2011) Fast chemical bath deposition of Zn(O,S) buffer layers for Cu(In,Ga)Se2 solar cells. *Thin Solid Films* 519 (21): 7575–7578) [177]; Contreras M, Egaas B, Ramanathan K, *et al.* (1999) Progress toward 20% efficiency in Cu(In,Ga)Se2 polycrystalline thin-film solar cells. *Progress in Photovoltaics* 7: 311–316) [155]; Contreras MA, Nakada T, Hongo M, *et al.* (2003) Presented at the 3rd WCPEC. Osaka, Japan, 2003 (unpublished); [178] Couzinié-Devy F, Barreau N, and Kessler J (2009) Influence of absorber copper concentration on the Cu(In,Ga)Se2/(PVD)In2S3 and Cu(In,Ga)Se2/(CBD)CdS based solar cells performance. *Thin Solid Films* 517(7): 2407–2410 [179]; Engelhardt F, Bornemann L, Kontges M, *et al.* (1999) Cu(In,Ga)Se-2 solar cells with a ZnSe buffer layer: Interface characterization by quantum efficiency measurements. *Progress in Photovoltaics* 7(6): 423–436 [180]; Ernits K, Brémaud D, Buecheler S, *et al.* (2007) Characterisation of ultrasonically sprayed InxSy buffer layers for Cu(In,Ga)Se2 solar cells. *Thin Solid Films* 515(15): 6051–6054 [181]; Fischer C-H, Allsop NA, Gledhill SE, *et al.* (2011) The spray-ILGAR® (ion layer gas reaction) method for the deposition of thin semiconductor layers: Process and applications for thin film solar cells. *Solar Energy Materials and Solar Cells* 95(6): 1518–1526 [182]; Huang CH, Li SS, Shafarman WN, *et al.* (2001) Study of Cd-free buffer layers using Inx (OH,S)y on CIGS solar cells. *Solar Energy Materials and Solar Cells* 69(2): 131–137 [183]; Hariskos D, Menner R, Jackson P, *et al.* (2011) Presented at the 26th EUPVSEC. Hamburg, Germany, 2011 (unpublished); [184] Okamoto A, Minemoto T, and Takakura H (2011) Application of sputtered ZnO1-xSx buffer layers for Cu(In, Ga)Se2 solar cells. *Japanese Journal of Applied Physics* 50: 04DP10 [185]; Pistor P, Caballero R, Hariskos D, *et al.* (2009) Quality and stability of compound indium sulphide as source material for buffer layers in Cu(In,Ga)Se solar cells. *Solar Energy Materials and Solar Cells* 93(1): 148–152 [186]; Sáez-Araoz R, Ennaoui A, Kropp T, *et al.* (2008) Use of different Zn precursors for the deposition of Zn(S,O) buffer layers by chemical bath for chalcopyrite based Cd-free thin-film solar cells. *Physica Status Solidi (a)* 205(10): 2330–2334 [187]; Siebentritt S, Walk P, Fiedeler U, *et al.* (2004) MOCVD as a dry deposition method of ZnSe buffers for Cu(In,Ga)(S,Se)2 solar cells. *Progress in Photovoltaics: Research and Applications* 12(5): 333–338 [188]; Yakioka T and Nakada T (2009) Cd-Free Flexible CI8(In, Ga)Se2 Thin Film solar Cells with ZnS(O,OH) Buffer Layers on Ti Foils. *Applied Physics Express* 2: 072201 [189].

layers have been combined directly with the high conductive window layer without a thin-resistive window layer. Obviously, the concept of 'buffer' and 'high resistive window' becomes blurry when large band gap materials such as ZnS, ZnMgO, or ZnO are employed as buffer layers. An overview on different alternative buffer layers is given in **Table 2**.

1.18.4.5 Front Contact

An n-type emitter layer is needed to form a heterojunction device. Since during the optimization of these devices, the n-type CdS layer has been thinned down to about 50 nm to become more of a buffer than a real emitter layer, a highly conducting n-type semiconductor layer with appropriate band gap and band edge line-up has to be deposited onto the absorber and buffer layer. This layer is also called window layer because it is desirable that it is transparent for the light to be absorbed in the absorber layer. It has to be highly doped to induce most of the band bending in the absorber layer and it has to be highly conductive in order to be able to carry the photocurrent laterally to the contacts without significant ohmic losses. Typically, a bilayer of ZnO is used in CIGSe devices, consisting of a thin intrinsic ZnO-layer and a thicker degenerately n-doped ZnO layer. The band gap of ZnO is 3.3 eV and the conduction band is reasonably aligned with the CIGSe absorber and the CdS buffer layer. ZnO can be readily deposited by radio frequency (RF) or direct current (DC) magnetron sputtering at temperatures below 200 °C. The purpose of the intrinsic window layer is to provide some shunt isolation (in addition to this function provided by the buffer layer), if local defects such as pin holes or rough spots in the substrate are present. Intrinsic ZnO layers of ~100 nm lead to sheet resistances on the order of 1 MΩsquare [195]. Also the intrinsic buffer layer seems to reduce the vulnerability to damp heat degradation of the solar cells and also helps to prevent the diffusion of dopants such as Al from the doped ZnO into the absorber layer [196].

An aluminum or Ga-doped ZnO layer is commonly used as the highly conductive window layer. The thickness and doping level of this ZnO layer have to be optimized to carry the current of the solar cell with minimized resistive losses and still maximum transmission in the spectral range of the absorber layer. Since high doping leads to increased free carrier absorption in the near-infrared region, a compromise between these two requirements has to be found. $Zn_{1-x}Mg_xO$ has been studied as a window layer material for CIGSe solar cells [197]. This material system allows for the tuning of the band gap and conduction band offset with the CIGSe absorber layers.

1.18.5 Device Properties

Current–Voltage (IV) analysis under standard conditions (AM1.5 illumination, $100\,\text{mW}\,\text{cm}^{-2}$, 25 °C) represents the most commonly applied device characterization. The IV curve can be described analytically or modeled numerically by 1D or more-dimensional device simulation. The IV curve under illumination can be approximated by

$$J(V) = J_0 \left[\exp\left(\frac{qV - R_s J(V)}{AkT} \right) - 1 \right] + \frac{qV - R_s J(V)}{R_p} - J_{ph}(V)$$

$$J_0 = J_{00} \exp\left(-\frac{E_a}{AkT} \right)$$

[4]

where $J_{ph}(V)$ is the photocurrent density, k the Boltzmann constant, T the temperature, A diode quality factor, R_s the series resistance, R_p the shunt resistance, J_{00} the dark current density prefactor, and E_a the barrier which limits recombination in the dark. If the photocurrent collection does not depend on the voltage across the device, the superposition principle can be applied and J_{ph} can be simply subtracted from the dark current. Unfortunately for chalcopyrite thin-film devices, this is very often not the case. The IV curve of a high-efficiency, 19.4%, solar cell is shown in **Figure 16** yielding a V_{oc} of 702 mV, $J_{sc} = 35.6\,\text{mA}\,\text{cm}^{-2}$, and fill factor (FF) = 77.5%. This solar cell was deposited using a multistage co-evaporation process at 600 °C substrate temperature [128]. The series resistance $R_s = 0.3\,\Omega$, shunt resistance $R_p = 5\,\text{k}\Omega$, and diode factor A = 1.4 were obtained from the dark IV curve. Very often a cross-over between the dark IV and illuminated IV is observed, indicating that superposition does not hold. The cross-over can be caused by internal barriers to photocollection that change under illumination and has been related to a barrier at the CdS/CIGSe interface or to a heavily doped p+-layer in the CIGSe absorber close to the heterointerface [198, 199].

External quantum efficiency curves for two $Cu(In,Ga)Se_2$ solar cells are displayed together with the AM1.5 and AM0 norm spectrum in **Figure 17**. The photocurrent obtained from an integration of the quantum efficiency multiplied by the AM1.5 spectrum gives a value of $36.2\,\text{mA}\,\text{cm}^{-2}$ for an effective band gap of 1.17 eV estimated from the steepest slope at long wavelengths. This is to be compared to a possible photocurrent of $43\,\text{mA}\,\text{cm}^{-2}$ that could be obtained if all photons incident on the solar cell could be collected under short-circuit condition. The losses occurring are (1) reflection losses, (2) loss due to absorption in the ZnO layer, (3) losses due to absorption in the CdS layer, and (4) losses due to recombination in the device. Reflection losses can be reduced by application of suitable antireflection coating designed to minimize reflection of the complete layer stack. Absorption losses in the ZnO layer can be reduced by optimization of the transmission of the ZnO layer, but here enough conductivity should be retained to ensure lateral current collection at the maximum power point to keep the FF high. Absorption losses in the CdS layer can be minimized by choice of a suitable buffer layer deposition and thickness and recombination losses can be reduced by minimizing the recombination in the volume and at the heterointerface.

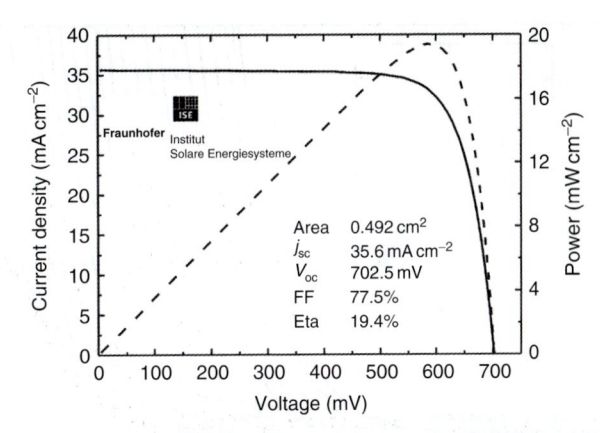

Figure 16 Current–voltage characteristic of 19.4% efficient glass/Mo/CuIn$_{1-x}$Ga$_x$Se$_2$/CdS/ZnO device. Figure from Haarstrich J, Metzner H, Oertel M, et al. (2011) Increased homogeneity and open-circuit voltage of Cu(In,Ga)Se(2) solar cells due to higher deposition temperature. *Solar Energy Materials and Solar Cells* 95(3): 1028–1030 [128].

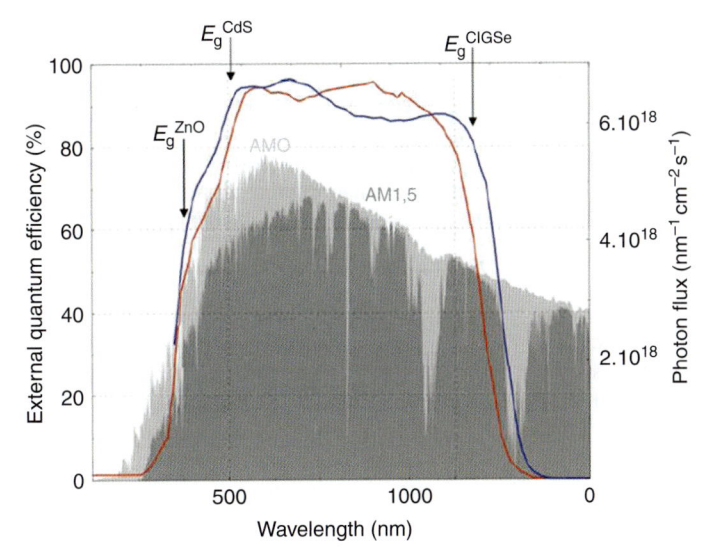

Figure 17 External quantum efficiency of two glass/Mo/CuIn$_{1-x}$Ga$_x$Se$_2$/CdS/ZnO devices, together with AM1.5 and AM0 norm spectrum.

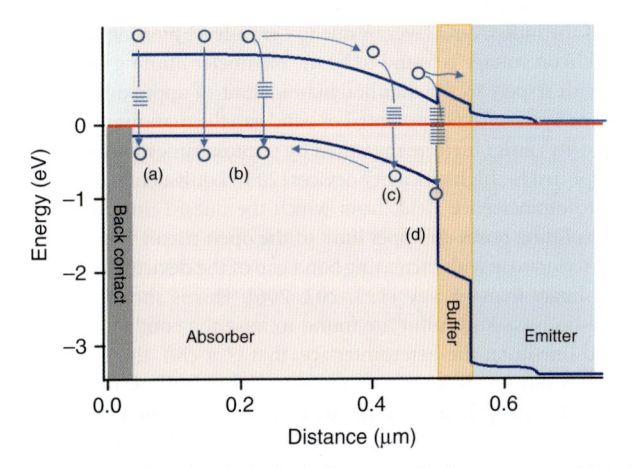

Figure 18 Band diagram for chalcopyrite-type heterojunction device indicating recombination processes: (a) back contact recombination; (b) bulk recombination; (c) space-charge region recombination; (d) interface recombination.

In **Figure 18**, a band diagram for a chalcopyrite thin-film solar cell is shown. The main recombination processes that can occur in such thin-film solar cells are recombination in the quasi-neutral region, recombination in the space-charge region, and recombination at the CdS/CIGSe heterointerface. In general, it is of interest whether bulk recombination or interface recombination limits

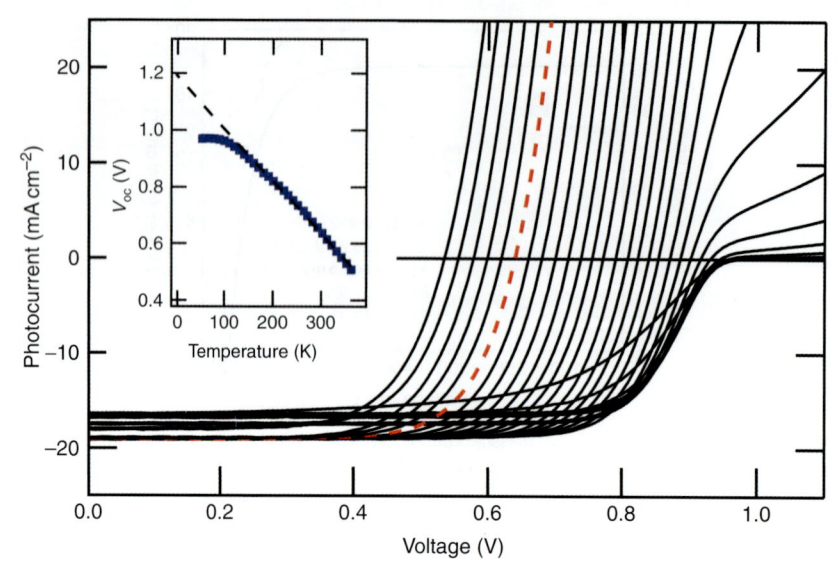

Figure 19 Current–voltage–temperature measurement for glass/Mo/CuIn$_{1-x}$Ga$_x$Se$_2$/CdS/ZnO device. Inset shows the open-circuit voltage vs. temperature.

device performance, and in particular the open-circuit voltage V_{oc}. The dominant recombination process limiting the device efficiency can be deduced from temperature-dependent IV measurements, since the temperature dependence of the dark saturation current and the diode-quality factor differ for different recombination processes [200]. The open circuit can be derived from the diode equation given above for the condition that the photocurrent equals the dark current

$$V_{oc} = \frac{kT}{q}\left(\frac{J_{ph}}{J_0}\right) = \frac{E_a}{q} - \frac{AkT}{q}\ln\left(\frac{J_{00}}{J_{ph}}\right) \quad [5]$$

Therefore, a plot of the V_{oc} versus temperature extracted temperature-dependent IV (IVT) measurements yields the activation energy of the dark current. IVT measurements are shown in **Figure 19**. It can be seen the open-circuit voltage increases with lower temperature and that at temperatures lower than 100 K a rollover occurs, which is due to photocurrent barriers. An extrapolation of the open-circuit voltage to 0 K yields a value of 1.1 V, which is very close to the band gap value for this device, indicating that bulk recombination is the limiting process for this device. If, in contrast, activation energy significantly smaller than the band gap value found, dominant recombination at the heterointerface is indicated. In the general case, the values of the diode factor and saturation current have to be carefully evaluated [201]. The fact that interface recombination does not seem to play a dominant role in optimized devices is somewhat surprising, since this heterointerface in CIGSe/CdS solar cells is not lattice matched and should therefore contain a large number of interface defects. The minor role of interface recombination may be explained by either a lowering of the VBM in the absorber layer close to the heterointerface due to copper depletion at this interface or, due to type inversion in the same absorber region, either due to heavy doping of the buffer/ZnO layer or due to Fermi-level pinning by shallow donors at the heterointerface.

In general, the value of the open-circuit voltage is found to be the parameter limiting high efficiencies in polycrystalline thin-film devices [202]. The missing voltage with respect to the thermodynamic limit of approximately $E_g - 0.3$ V, can be explained either by residual nonradiative recombination or by the effect of potential or band gap fluctuations in the material. A strong correlation between the open-circuit voltage and the minority carrier lifetime measured by photoluminescence decay has been observed [203, 204], with highest values of more than 250 ns reported for high-efficiency devices [205]. Equivalent information about the recombination activity can also be obtained from the photoluminescence yield, from which the quasi-Fermi level splitting in the absorber layer can be deduced [51]. The quasi-Fermi level splitting poses an upper limit to the open-circuit voltage attainable from PV devices.

The open-circuit voltage is found to increase with increasing band gap of the device up to a certain band gap value in chalcopyrite devices but saturates for band gaps larger than ~1.3 eV [129, 202, 206]. This is shown in **Figure 20** for a series of devices with different Ga and S/Se content. Since both Ga and sulfur are found to raise the conduction band minimum (CBM), this could be explained with an unfavorable band line-up at the heterointerface, that is, a cliff, thus preventing type inversion in the interface region. However, a number of studies did not identify interface but rather bulk recombination as the limiting recombination processes in wide band gap devices [12, 207]. It thus seems that for $x_{Ga} > 0.3$, the electronic quality of the absorber materials deteriorates significantly with increasing Ga content, and an optimum is reached at band gap values around 1.2 eV.

Module fabrication of chalcopyrite solar cells can be monolithic if insulating substrates are used or by series connection of individual cells. Both concepts are currently pursued by different thin-film companies. The monolithic interconnection works very similar to the interconnection scheme in amorphous silicon or CdTe photovoltaic modules and is shown schematically in **Figure 21**. The so-called P1 cut is scribed into the molybdenum after the back contact deposition. This can be easily performed by laser scribing using nanosecond pulsed laser systems. After the deposition of the chalcopyrite absorber and buffer layer, the so-called P2 cut is made, which is commonly scribed using a needle-based system, but can also now be performed by laser scribing either using picosecond or

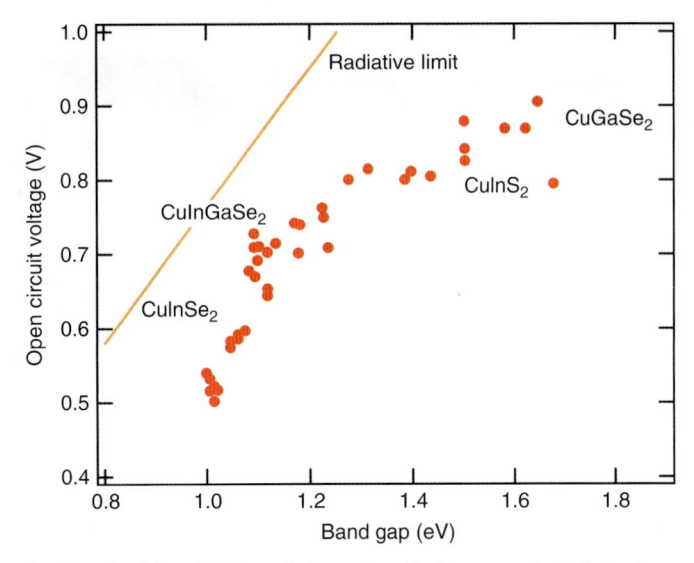

Figure 20 Open-circuit voltage vs. band gap for different chalcopyrite-type solar cells. The orange line indicates the open circuit voltage achievable only if radiative recombination occurs in the device. Data from Contreras M, Mansfield LM, Egaas B, et al. presented at the 37th IEEE PVSEC, Seattle, USA, 2011 (unpublished); Unold T and Schock HW (2011) Nonconventional (non-silicon-based) photovoltaic materials. In: Clarke DR and Fratzl P (eds.) *Annual Review of Materials Research*, vol. 41, pp. 297–321; and Schock HW, Rau U, Dullweber T, et al. presented at the EC PVSEC, Glasgow, Scottland, 2000 (unpublished).

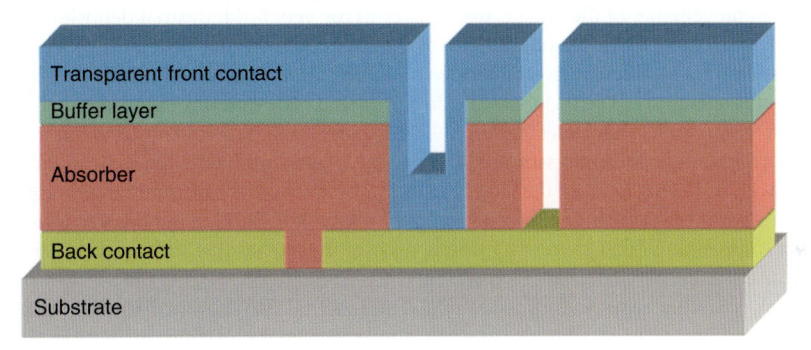

Figure 21 Monolithic interconnect scheme for chalcopyrite-type thin-film modules.

using nanosecond laser systems [208]. After the deposition of the ZnO front contact layer, the final P3 cut is made, again usually by needle scribing, but also possible using picosecond or nanosecond laser systems. The function of the P1 and P3 cuts is to isolate the neighboring cells from each other, whereas the P2 cut enables the series connection between the neighboring cells by allowing a contact between the doped ZnO of one cell with the Mo back contact of the neighboring cell. The interconnection geometry has to be optimized to minimize losses of (1) series resistance losses in ZnO related to the cell width, (2) distance between P1 and P2, and (3) distance between P2 and P3. After serial interconnection, the modules have to be protected against environmental influences, in particular oxygen and moisture. This can be achieved by using a top glass pane that is laminated onto the active device using a polymer such as EVA, as is used in crystalline silicon modules. Additional edge sealants may be required to keep moisture from entering the module. The modules have to be certified by elaborate test procedures according to the international IEC protocols, which include the so-called damp heat test (1000 h at 85 °C and 85% humidity) and additional electrical and mechanical stress and stability testing. Significant light-induced degradation, as generally observed for amorphous silicon, is not generally found for chalcopyrite technology but should be demonstrated for specific and in particular new device and module structures [15]. A possible implementation of an inline manufacturing of chalcopyrite-based thin-film solar cells is shown in **Figure 22**.

1.18.6 Outlook

The fact that chalcopyrite materials can be deposited successfully by such a large variety of different process technologies proves both an advantage and a disadvantage. The disadvantage is certainly that so far no critical mass of standardized deposition equipment has evolved such that the capex could be lowered substantially in the manufacturing, without the need for scale up to very large volumes. On the other hand, very simple low-cost techniques such as solution processing may generate a break-through during the coming years, which could allow such substantial lowering of cost with regard to standard crystalline silicon technology.

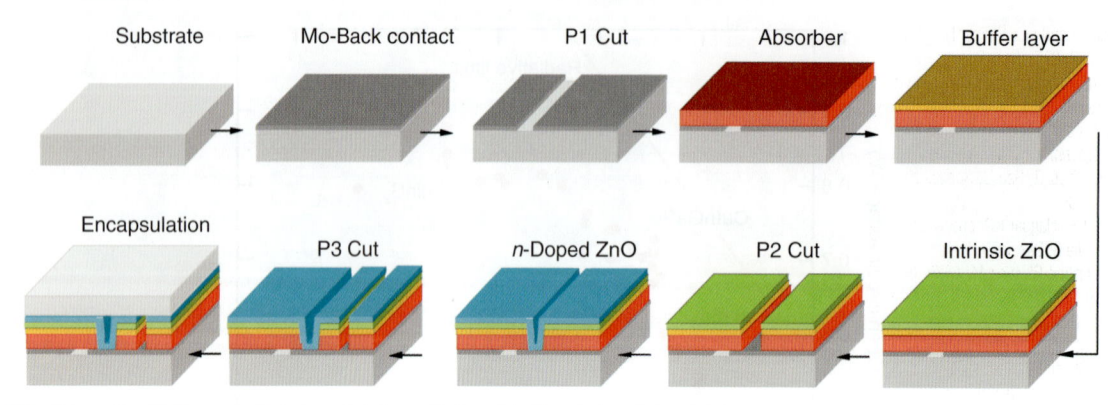

Figure 22 Schematic of inline manufacturing of chalcopyrite-type thin-film photovoltaic modules.

In this vein, the replacement of all vacuum equipment also for the back contact and front contact deposition could be an attractive long-term vision.

At present, the major challenges for chalcopyrite-type solar cells involve the bridging of the gap between three-stage-process-deposited high-efficiency devices (>20%) and the efficiencies obtained with industrial technologies on module size, which can be up to almost 18% for single sub-m^2 modules. Currently, commercially sold Cu(In,Ga)Se$_2$ modules are sold at total area efficiency of 12–13%. For a further increase, we believe that more processing and quality control has to be implemented, in particular to improve the large- and small-scale homogeneities of these large area devices in the very fast industrial deposition processes applied. At the same time, many questions with regard to the material science of the different functional layers, the processing of these layers, and in particular the interplay between these different layers are open and need to be understood more properly.

Considering the renewable energy needs on a global scale during the next 40 years, one can foresee contributions of photovoltaic electricity on the terawatt (TW) scale. This raises additional questions about the scarcity of elements used and the need for environmentally friendly compounds and processes [202]. Here, the biggest problems for chalcopyrite materials are related to the use of In, Ga, and Se, with In having received the largest attention because of its concurrent major use in consumer electronics. There are different estimates with regard to natural reserves and availability of In [202]. It is, however, unquestionable that In is very scarce in the Earth's crust compared to other elements. Since In and Ga in Cu(In,Ga)Se2 materials can be replaced by the ordered substitution of Zn and Sn yielding the quaternary or compound Cu$_2$ZnSn(S,Se)$_4$, (CZTS and CZTSe) considerable research has recently focused on this polycrystalline semiconducting material. This material also shows a direct band gap of between 1 and 1.5 eV depending on the S/Se content and is expected to possess very similar material properties to chalcopyrite compounds. Recently, photoconversion efficiencies larger than 10% have been demonstrated [209], although there are many open questions with regard to these absorber materials, device structure at the present. If the lessons learned and results achieved for chalcopyrite-based solar cells can be transferred to this new material system, highly efficient thin-film photovoltaics based on earth-abundant materials could present a strong option for a sustainable energy supply on the TW scale.

References

[1] Shay JL and Wernick JH (1975) *Ternary Chalcopyrite Semiconductors: Growth, Electronic Properties and Applications*. Oxford: Pergamon Press.
[2] Hahn H, Frank G, Klingler W, et al. (1953) Untersuchungen uber ternare chalkogenide.5. Uber einige ternare chalkogenide mit chalkopyritstruktur. *Zeitschrift Fur Anorganische Und Allgemeine Chemie* 271(3–4): 153–170.
[3] Migliorato P, Tell B, Shay JL, and Kasper HM (1974) Junction electroluminescence in CuInSe2. *Applied Physics Letters* 24: 227.
[4] Wagner S, Shay JL, Migliorato P, and Kasper HM (1974) CuInSe2/CdS heterojunction photovoltaic detectors. *Applied Physics Letters* 25: 434.
[5] Shay J (1975) Efficient CuInSe2/CdS solar cells. *Applied Physics Letters* 27(2): 89.
[6] Kazmerski L (1976) Thin-film CuInSe2/CdS heterojunction solar cells. *Applied Physics Letters* 29(4): 268–270.
[7] Mickelsen RA and Chen WS, presented at the 15th IEEE Photovoltaic Specialists Conference, Orlando, 1981 (unpublished).
[8] Mickelsen RA and Chen WS, presented at the 16th IEEE Specialists Conference, New York, 1982 (unpublished).
[9] Jackson P, Hariskos D, Lotter E, et al. (2011) New world record efficiency for Cu(In,Ga)Se2 thin-film solar cells beyond 20%. *Progress in Photovoltaics: Research and Applications* 19: 894–897.
[10] Sugimoto H, Yagioka T, Nagahashi M, et al. presented at the 37th IEEE Photovoltaic Specialists Confeence, Seattle, 2011 (unpublished).
[11] Rocket A and Birkmire RW (1991) CuInSe$_2$ for photovoltaic applications. *Journal of Applied Physics* 70: R81.
[12] Shafarman W and Stolt L (2003) Cu(In,Ga)Se$_2$ solar cells. In: Luque A and Hegedus S (eds.) *Handbook of Photovoltaic Science and Engineering*, pp. 567–616. West Sussex: John Wiley & Sons. ISBN: 0-471-49196-9.
[13] Schock HW (2004) Properties of Chalcopyrite-based materials and film deposition for thin-film solar cells. In: Hamakawa Y (ed.) *Thin-Film Solar Cells: Next Generation Photovoltaics and Its Applications*, pp. 163–182. Heidelberg, Germany: Springer-Verlag. ISBN: 3-540-43945.
[14] Singh UP and Patra SP (2010) Progress in polycrystalline thin-film Cu(In,Ga)Se$_2$ solar cells. *International Journal of Photoenergy* 2010: 468147. doi:10.1155/2010/468147.
[15] Niki S, Contreras M, Repins I, et al. (2010) CIGS absorbers and processes. *Progress in Photovoltaics: Research and Applications* 18(6): 453–466.
[16] Scheer R and Schock HW (2011) *Chalcogenide Photovoltaics: Physics, Technologies, and Thin Film Devices*. Weinheim, Germany: Wiley-VCH.

[17] Klenk R and Lux-Steiner MC (2006) Chalcopyrite based solar cells. In: Poortmans J and Arkhipov V (eds.) *Thin Film Solar Cells: Fabrication, Characterization and Applications*, pp. 237–275. West Sussex, UK: John Wiley and Sons Ltd. ISBN: 0-470-09126-6. doi:10.1002/0470091282.ch6
[18] Grimm HG and Sommerfeld A (1978) Über den Zusammenhang des Abschlusses der Elektronengruppen im Atom mit den chemischen Valenzzahlen. *Zeitschrift für Physikalische Chemie* 110: 17.
[19] Tomlins RD, Hill AE, and Pilkington RD (eds.) (1997) Ternary and multinary compounds. *Proceedings of the 11th International Conference on Ternary and Multinary Compounds*, ICTMC-11, University of Salford, Institute of Physics Series Number 152, 8–12 September 1997. Bristol, UK; Philadelphia, PA: Institute of Physics Publishing.
[20] Herberholz R, Rau U, Schock HW, *et al.* (1999) Phase segregation, Cu migration and junction formation in Cu(In, Ga)Se-2. *European Physical Journal-Applied Physics* 6(2): 131–139.
[21] Suri DK, Nagpal KC, and Chadha GK (1989) X-RAY study of $CuGaXIn_{1-x}Se_2$ solid-solutions. *Journal of Applied Crystallography* 22: 578.
[22] Ishizuka S, Sakurai K, Yamada A, *et al.* (2005) Progress in the Efficiency of Wide-Gap $Cu(In_{1-x}Ga_x)Se_2$ Solar Cells Using CIGSe Layers Grown in Water Vapor. *Japanese Journal of Applied Physics* 44: L679–682.
[23] Abou-Ras D, Caballero R, Kaufmann CA, *et al.* (2008) Impact of the Ga concentration on the microstructure of CuIn1−xGaxSe2. *Physica Status Solidi-Rapid Research Letters* 2(3): 135–137.
[24] Alonso MI, Wakita K, Pascual J, *et al.* (2001) Optical functions and electronic structure of CuInSe2, CuGaSe2, CuInS2, and CuGaS2. *Physical Review B* 63: 075203.
[25] Wei SH and Zunger A (1995) Band offsets and optical bowings of chalcopyrites And Zn-based II–VI alloys. *Journal of Applied Physics* 78(6): 3846–3856.
[26] Turcu M, Kotschau IM, and Rau U (2001) Band alignments in the Cu(In,Ga)(S,Se)(2) alloy system determined from deep-level defect energies. *Applied Physics a-Materials Science & Processing* 73(6): 769–772.
[27] Maeda T and Wada T (2010) Electronic structue and characteristics of chemical bonds in CuInSe2, CuGaSe2 and CuAlSe2. *Japanese Journal of Applied Physics* 49: 04DP07.
[28] Palm J, Probst, V, and Karg FH (2004) Second generation CIS solar modules. *Solar Energy* 77(6): 757–765.
[29] Schmid D, Ruckh M, and Schock HW (1996) Photoemission studies on Cu(In,Ga)Se-2 thin films and related binary selenides. *Applied Surface Science* 103(4): 409–429.
[30] Noufi R, Axton R, Herrington C, and Deb S (1984) Electronic properties versus composition of thin films of $CuInSe_2$. *Applied Physics Letters* 45: 668–670.
[31] Neumann H and Tomlinson RD (1990) Relation between electrical properties and composition in $CuInSe_2$ single crystals. *Solar Cells* 28: 301–313.
[32] Dirnstorfer I, Wagner M, Hofmann DM, *et al.* (1998) Characterization of CuIn(Ga)Se2 Thin Films. *Physica Status Solidi (a)* 168: 163.
[33] Caballero R, Kaufmann CA, Eisenbarth T, *et al.* (2009) The effect of NaF precursors on low temperature growth of CIGS thin film solar cells on polyimide substrates. *Physica Status Solidi a – Applications and Materials Science* 206(5): 1049–1053.
[34] Wei S (1999) Effects of Na on the electrical and structural properties of CuInSe2. *Journal of Applied Physics* 85(10): 7214.
[35] Niles DW, Al-Jassim M, and Ramanathan K (1999) Direct observation of Na and O impurities at grain surfaces of CuInSe2 thin films. *Journal of Vacuum Science and Technology A* 17: 291–296.
[36] Kronik L, Cahen D, and Schock HW (1998) Effects of sodium on polycrystalline Cu(In,Ga)Se-2 and its solar cell performance. *Advanced Materials* 10(1): 31–36.
[37] Cojocaru-Mirédin O, Choi P, Wuerz R, and Raabe D (2011) Atomic-scale distribution of impurities in CuInSe2-based thin-film solar cells. *Ultramicroscopy* 111(6): 552–556.
[38] Caballero R, Kaufmann CA, Eisenbarth T, *et al.* (2009) The influence of Na on low temperature growth of CIGS thin film solar cells on polyimide substrates. *Thin Solid Films* 517(7): 2187–2190.
[39] Möller HJ (1993) *Semiconductors for Solar Cells*: Norwood, MA: Artech House Publishers.
[40] Zhang SB, Wei SH, Zunger A, and Katayama-Yoshida H (1998) Defect physics of the CuInSe2 chalcopyrite semiconductor. *Physical Review B* 57(16): 9642–9656.
[41] Wei SH, Zhang SB, and Zunger A (1998) Effects of Ga addition to CuInSe2 on its electronic, structural, and defect properties. *Applied Physics Letters* 72(24): 3199–3201.
[42] Zhao YJ, Persson C, Lany S, and Zunger A (2004) Why can CuInSe2 be readily equilibrium-doped n-type but the wider-gap CuGaSe2 cannot? *Applied Physics Letters* 85(24): 5860–5862.
[43] Walter T, Herberholz R, Muller C, and Schock HW (1996) Determination of defect distributions from admittance measurements and application to Cu(In,Ga)Se-2 based heterojunctions. *Journal of Applied Physics* 80(8): 4411–4420.
[44] Heath J (2004) Bulk and metastable defects in CuIn1?xGaxSe2 thin films using drive-level capacitance profiling. *Journal of Applied Physics* 95(3): 1000.
[45] Heath J (2002) Effect of Ga content on defect states in CuIn1?xGaxSe2 photovoltaic devices. *Applied Physics Letters* 80(24): 4540.
[46] Eisenbarth T, Unold T, Caballero R, *et al.* (2010) Interpretation of admittance, capacitance-voltage, and current-voltage signatures in Cu(In,Ga)Se-2 thin film solar cells. *Journal of Applied Physics* 107(3): 034509.
[47] Igalson M and Zabierowski P (1998) Laplace-DLTS of Cu(In,Ga)Se-2-based devices. In: Tomlinson RD, Hill AE, and Pilkington RD (eds.) *Ternary and Multinary Compounds*, vol. 152, pp. 931–934.
[48] Wasim SM (1986). Transport properties of $CuInSe_2$. *Solar Cells* 16: 289–316.
[49] Siebentritt S, Igalson M, Persson C, and Lany S (2010) The electronic structure of chalcopyrites-bands, point defects and grain boundaries. *Progress in Photovoltaics* 18(6): 390–410.
[50] Repins IL, Stanbery BJ, Young DL, *et al.* (2006) Comparison of device performance and measured transport parameters in widely-varying Cu(In,Ga) (Se,S) solar cells. *Progress in Photovoltaics: Research and Applications* 14(1): 25–43.
[51] Unold T and Gutay L (2011) Photoluminescence of thin film solar cells. In: Abou-Ras D, Kirchatz T, Rau U (eds.) *Advanced Characterization of Thin Film Solar Cells*, pp. 151–175. Weinheim, Germany: Wiley.
[52] Siebentritt S (2006) Shallow defects in the wide gap chalcopyrite CuGaSe2. In: Siebentritt S and Rau U (eds.) *Wide-Gap Chalcopyrites*, vol. 86, pp. 113–156. Heidelberg, Germany: Springer-Verlag.
[53] Unold T, Enzenhofer T, Kaufmann CA, *et al.* (2006) Analysis of defects in coevaporated high-efficiency Cu(In,Ga)Se-2 solar cells. *Photovoltaic Energy Conversion, Conference Record of the 2006 IEEE 4th World Conference*.Waikoloa, HI, May 2006.
[54] Rau U, Schmitt M, Parisi J, *et al.* (1998) Persistent photoconductivity in Cu(In,Ga)Se-2 heterojunctions and thin films prepared by sequential deposition. *Applied Physics Letters* 73(2): 223–225.
[55] Igalson M, Cwil M, and Edoff M (2007) Metastabilities in the electrical characteristics of CIGS devices: Experimental results vs theoretical predictions. *Thin Solid Films* 515(15): 6142–6146.
[56] Eisenbarth T, Nichterwitz M, Caballero R, *et al.* (2011) Characterization of metastabilities in Cu(In,Ga)Se[sub 2] thin-film solar cells by capacitance and current-voltage spectroscopy. *Journal of Applied Physics* 110: 094506–094513.
[57] Ruberto MN and Rothwarf A (1987) Time-dependent open-circuit voltage in CuInSe2 solar cells: Theory and experiment. *Journal of Applied Physics* 61: 4662.
[58] Mack P, Walter T, Hariskos D, et al. presented at the 24th European Photovoltaic Solar Energy Conference, Hamburg, 2009 (unpublished).
[59] Cwil M, Igalson M, Zabierowski P, and Siebentritt S (2008) Charge and doping distributions by capacitance profiling in Cu(In, Ga)Se-2 solar cells. *Journal of Applied Physics* 103(6): 063701.
[60] Engelhardt F, Schmidt M, Meyer T, *et al.* (1998) Metastable electrical transport in Cu(In,Ga)Se-2 thin films and ZnO/CdS/Cu(In,Ga) Se-2 heterostructures. *Physics Letters A* 245(5): 489–493.
[61] Eisgruber IL, Granata JE, Sites JR, *et al.* (1998) Blue-photon modification of nonstandard diode barrier in $CuInSe_2$ solar cells. *Solar Energy Materials and Solar Cells* 53: 367.
[62] Igalson M, Bodegard M, and Stolt L (2003) Reversible changes of the fill factor in the ZnO/CdS/Cu(In,Ga)Se-2 solar cells. *Solar Energy Materials and Solar Cells* 80(2): 195–207.
[63] Lany S and Zunger A (2006) Light- and bias-induced metastabilities in Cu(In,Ga)Se-2 based solar cells caused by the (V-Se-V-Cu) vacancy complex. *Journal of Applied Physics* 100(11): 113725.

[64] Nishitani M, Negami T, Kohara N, and Wada T (1997) Analysis of transient photocurrents in Cu(In,Ga)Se$_2$ thin film solar cells. *Journal of Applied Physics* 82: 3572.
[65] Meyer T, Engelhardt F, Parisi, J, and Rau U (2002) Spectral dependence and Hall effect of persistent photoconductivity in polycrystalline Cu(In,Ga)Se-2 thin films. *Journal of Applied Physics* 91(8): 5093–5099.
[66] Dinca SA, Schiff EA, Egaas B, et al. (2009) Hole drift mobility measurements in polycrystalline CuInGaSe2. *Physical Review B* 80: 235201.
[67] Rau U, Taretto K, and Siebentritt S (2009) Grain boundaries in Cu(In, Ga)(Se, S)(2) thin-film solar cells. *Applied Physics A – Materials Science & Processing* 96(1): 221–234.
[68] Abou-Ras D, Schorr S, and Schock HW (2007) Grain-size distributions and grain boundaries of chalcopyrite-type thin films. *Journal of Applied Crystallography* 40: 841–848.
[69] Seto J (1975) The electrical properties of polycrystalline silicon films. *Journal of Applied Physics* 46(12): 5247.
[70] Visoly-Fisher I, Cohen SR, Ruzin A, and Cahen D (2004) How polycrystalline devices can outperform single-crystal ones: THin film CdTe/CdS solar cells. *Advanced Materials* 16: 879.
[71] Azulay D, Millo O, Balberg I, et al. (2007) Current routes in polycrystalline CuInSe2 and Cu(In,Ga)Se-2 films. *Solar Energy Materials and Solar Cells* 91(1): 85–90.
[72] Gloeckler M (2005) Grain-boundary recombination in Cu(In,Ga)Se2 solar cells. *Journal of Applied Physics* 98(11): 113704.
[73] Taretto K and Rau U (2008) Numerical simulation of carrier collection and recombination at grain boundaries in Cu(In,Ga)Se-2 solar cells. *Journal of Applied Physics* 103(9): 094523.
[74] Persson C and Zunger A (2003) Anomalous grain boundary physics in polycrystalline CuInSe2: The existence of a hole barrier. *Physical Review Letters* 91(26): 266401.
[75] Lei C (2010) Effects of solution-grown CdS on Cu(InGa)Se2 grain boundaries. *Journal of Applied Physics* 108(11): 114908.
[76] Abou-Ras D, Schaffer B, Schaffer M, et al. (in press) Direct insight into grain boundary reconstruction in polycrystalline Cu(In,Ga)Se 2 with atomic resolution. *Physical Review Letters*.
[77] Sadewasser S, Abou-Ras D, Azulay D, et al. (2011) Nanometer-scale electronic and microstructural properties of grain boundaries in Cu(In,Ga)Se(2). *Thin Solid Films* 519(21): 7341–7346.
[78] Abou-Ras D, Jahn U, Nichterwitz M, et al. (2010) Combined electron backscatter diffraction and cathodoluminescence measurements on CuInS2/Mo/glass stacks and CuInS2 thin-film solar cells. *Journal of Applied Physics* 107(1): 014311.
[79] Nichterwitz M, Abou-Ras D, Sakurai K, et al. (2009) Influence of grain boundaries on current collection in Cu(In,Ga)Se-2 thin-film solar cells. *Thin Solid Films* 517(7): 2554–2557.
[80] Kazmerski LL, Ayyagari MS, White FR, and Sanborn GA (1976) Growth and properties of vacuum-deposited cuInSe2 thin-films. *Journal of Vacuum Science & Technology* 13(1): 139–144.
[81] Gogol CA and Reagan SH (1983) A performance comparison of vacuum deposition monitors employing atomic absorption (AA) and electron impact emission spectroscoopy (EIES). *Journal of Vacuum Science & Technology A* 1: 252–256.
[82] Shafarman WN and Zhu J (2000) Effect of substrate temperature and depostion profile on evaporated Cu(InGa)Se2 films and devices. *Thin Solid Films* 361–362: 473–477.
[83] Mickelsen RA and Chen WS (1980) *High photocurrent polycrystalline thin-film CdS/CuInSe$_2$ solar cella. Applied Physics Letters* 36: 371–373.
[84] Repins I, Contreras M, Egaas B, et al. (2008) 19.9%-efficient ZnO/CdS/CuInGaSe$_2$ Solar Cell with 81.2% Fill Factor. *Progress in Photovoltaics: Research and Applications* 16: 235–239.
[85] Gabor A (1994) High-efficiency CuInxGa1-xSe2 solar cells made from (Inx,Ga1-x)2Se3 precursor films. *Applied Physics Letters* 65(2): 198.
[86] Gabor AM, Tuttle JR, Bode MH, et al. (1996) Band-gap engineering in Cu(In,Ga) Se2 thin films grown from (In,Ga)2Se3 precursors. *Solar Energy Materials and Solar Cells* 41–42: 247–260.
[87] Caballero R, Kaufmann CA, Efimova V, et al. (2012) Investigation of Cu(In,Ga)Se$_2$ thin-film formation during the multi-stage co-evaporation process. *Progress in Photovoltaics Research and Applications*. doi: 10.1002/pip.1233.
[88] Kessler F, Schmid D, Zweigart S, et al. (1994) CuInSe$_2$ formation from sequential deposition of In(Se):Cu:Se, pp. 684–652. *Proceedings of the 12th EU PVSEC*. Amsterdam, 1994.
[89] Klenk R, Walter T, Schock HW, and Cahen D (1993) A model for the successful growth of polycrystalline films of cuinse2 by multisource physical vacuum evaporation. *Advanced Materials* 5(2): 114–119.
[90] Wada T, Kohara N, Negami T, and Nishitani M (1997) Growth of CuInSe$_2$ crystals in Cu-rich Cu-In-Se thin films. *Journal of Materials Research* 12: 1456–1462.
[91] Kessler J, Chityuttakan C, Lu J, et al. (2003) Cu(In,Ga)Se$_2$ thin films grown with a Cu-poor/rich/poor sequence: Growth model and structural considerations. *Progress in Photovoltaics: Research and Applications* 11(5): 319–331.
[92] Barreau N, Painchaud T, Couzinié-Devy F, et al. (2010) Recrystallization of CIGSe layers grown by three-step processes: A model based on grain boundary migration. *Acta Materialia* 58(17): 5572–5577.
[93] Rodriguez-Alvarez H, Mainz R, Marsen B, et al. (2010) Recrystallization of Cu-In-S thin films studied *in situ* by energy-dispersive X-ray diffraction. *Journal of Applied Crystallography* 43: 1053–1061.
[94] Sakurai K, Hunger R, Scheer R, et al. (2004) *In situ* diagnostic methods for thin-film fabrication: Utilization of heat radiation and light scattering. *Progress in Photovoltaics* 12(2–3): 219–234.
[95] Hesse R, Caballero R, Abou-Ras D, et al. (2007) A reliable optical method for in-situ process control for deposition of Cu(In,Ga)Se$_2$ thin layers for photovoltaics – Art. no. 665108. In: VonRoedern B and Delahoy AE (eds.) *Photovoltaic Cell and Module Technologies*, vol. 6651, pp. 65108–65108.
[96] Repins I, Gomez N, Simpson L, and Joshi B (2005) *In situ* sensors for CIGS deposition and manufacture. *Materials Research Society Symposia Proceedings* 865: 499–510. Materials Research Society.
[97] Kessler F, Scholdstrom J, and Stolt L, presented at the 28th IEEE PVSEC, Anchorage, USA, 2000 (unpublished).
[98] Kaigawa R, Wada T, Bakehe S, and Klenk R (2006) Three-stage evaporation of Cu(In,Ga)S$_2$ solar cell absorber films without KCN treatment and Na control. *Thin Solid Films* 511–512: 430–433.
[99] Merdes S, Mainz R, Klaer J, et al. (2011) 12.6% efficient CdS/Cu(In,Ga)S(2)-based solar cell with an open circuit voltage of 879 mV prepared by a rapid thermal process. *Solar Energy Materials and Solar Cells* 95(3): 864–869.
[100] Stolt L, Hedstrom J, Kessler J, et al. (1993) Zno/Cds/Cuinse2 thin-film solar-cells with improved performance. *Applied Physics Letters* 62(6): 597–599.
[101] Dimmler B and Schock HW (1996) Scaling-up of CIS technology for thin-film solar modules. *Progress in Photovoltaics* 4(6): 425–433.
[102] Jackson P, Wurz R, Rau U, et al. (2007) High quality baseline for high efficiency, Cu(In1−x,Gax)Se2 solar cells. *Progress in Photovoltaics* 15(6): 507–519.
[103] Hibberd CJ, Chassaing E, Liu W, et al. (2010) Non-vacuum methods for formation of Cu(In,Ga)(Se,S)(2) thin film photovoltaic absorbers. *Progress in Photovoltaics* 18(6): 434–452.
[104] Hergert F, Jost S, Hock R, and Purwins M (2006) A crystallographic description of experimentally identified formation reactions of Cu(In,Ga)Se2. *Journal of Solid State Chemistry* 179(8): 2394–2415.
[105] Djordjevic J, Rudigier E, and Scheer R (2006) Real-time studies of phase transformations in Cu-In-Se-S thin films – 3: Selenization of Cu-In precursors. *Journal of Crystal Growth* 294(2): 218–230.
[106] Roussel O, Ramdani O, Chassaing E, et al. (2008) First stages of CuInSe2 electrodeposition from Cu(II)-In(III)-Se(IV) acidic solutions on polycrystalline mo films. *Journal of the Electrochemical Society* 155(2): D141–D147.
[107] Marudachalam M, Hichri H, Klenk R, et al. (1995) Preparation of homogeneous Cu(In,Ga)Se$_2$ films by selenization of metal precursors in H$_2$S atmosphere. *Applied Physics Letters* 67: 3978.
[108] Basol B and Kapur VK (1990) Deposition of CuInSe$_2$ films by a two-stage process utilizing E-beam evaporation. *IEEE Transactions on Electron Devices* 37: 418–421.

[109] Caballero R and Guillén C (2002) Comparative studies between Cu_Ga_Se and Cu_In_Se thin film systems. *Thin Solid Films* 403–404: 107–111.
[110] Kapur VK, Basol B, and Tseng E (1987) Low cost methods for the production of semiconductor films for CuInSe$_2$/CdS solar cells. *Solar Cells* 21: 65–70.
[111] Guillemoles JF, Cowache P, Lusson A, et al. (1996) One, step electrodeposition of CuInSe2: Improved structural, electronic, and photovoltaic properties by annealing under high selenium pressure. *Journal of Applied Physics* 79(9): 7293–7302.
[112] Kapur VK, Bansal A, Le P, and Asensio OI (2003) Non-vacuum processing of CuIn1−xGaxSe2 solar cells on rigid and flexible substrates using nanoparticle precursor inks. *Thin Solid Films* 431–432: 53–57.
[113] Guo Q, Ford GM, Hillhouse HW, and Agrawal R (2009) Sulfide nanocrystal inks for dense Cu(In(1−x)Ga(x))(S(1−y)Se(y))2 absorber films and their photovoltaic performance. *Nano Letters* 9: 3060.
[114] Mitzi DB, Yuan M, Liu W, et al. (2009) Hydrazine-based deposition route for device-quality CIGS films. *Thin Solid Films* 517(7): 2158–2162.
[115] Taunier S, Sicx-Kurdi J, Grand PP, et al. (2005) Cu(In,Ga)(S,Se)(2) solar cells and modules by electrodeposition. *Thin Solid Films* 480: 526–531.
[116] Basol BM, Pinarbasi M, Aksu S, et al. presented at the IEEE Photovoltaic Specialists Conference, 2009 (unpublished).
[117] Grindle S, Smith C, and Mittleman S (1979) Preparation and properties of CuInS$_2$ thin films produced by exposing sputtered Cu-In films to an H$_2$S atmosphere. *Applied Physics Letters* 35: 24–26.
[118] Chu T, Chu S, Lin S, and Yue J (1984) Large Grain Copper Indium Diselenide Films. *Journal of the Electrochemical Society* 131: 2182–2185.
[119] Mooney GD, Hermann AM, Tuttle JR, et al. (1991) Formation of CuInSe2 thin films by rapid thermal recrystallization. *Applied Physics Letters* 58: 678–2680.
[120] Siemer K, Klaer J, Luck I, et al. (2001) Efficient CuInS$_2$ solar cells from a rapid thermal process (RTP). *Solar Energy Materials and Solar Cells* 67(1–4): 159–166.
[121] Kulkarni SS, Koishiyev GT, Moutinho H, and Dhere NG (2009) Preparation and characterization of CuIn$_{1-x}$Ga$_x$Se$_{2-y}$S$_y$ thin film solar cells by rapid thermal processing. *Thin Solid Films* 517(7): 2121–2124.
[122] Hergert F, Hock R, Weber A, et al. (2005) In situ investigation of the formation of Cu(In,Ga)Se$_2$ from selenised metallic precursors by X-ray diffraction – The impact of gallium sodium and selenium excess. *Journal of Physics and Chemistry of Solids* 66: 1903–1907.
[123] Rodriguez-Alvarez H, Kotschau IM, and Schock HW (2008) Pressure-dependent real-time investigations on the rapid thermal sulfurization of Cu-In thin films. *Journal of Crystal Growth* 310(15): 3638–3644.
[124] Mainz R (2011) In situ analysis of elemental depth distributions in thin films by combined evaluation of synchrotron x-ray fluorescence and diffraction. *Journal of Applied Physics* 109(12): 123515.
[125] Weber A, Rodriguez-Alvarez H, Mainz R, et al. presented at the IEEE Photovoltaic Specialists Conference, Seattle, 2011 (unpublished).
[126] Kaufmann CA, Caballero R, Unold T, et al. (2009) Depth profiling of Cu(In,Ga)Se$_2$ thin films grown at low temperatures. *Solar Energy Materials and Solar Cells* 93(6–7): 859–863.
[127] Chirila A, Blösch P, Pianezzi F, et al. presented at the 26th EU PVSEC, Hamburg, 2011 (unpublished).
[128] Haarstrich J, Metzner H, Oertel M, et al. (2011) Increased homogeneity and open-circuit voltage of Cu(In,Ga)Se(2) solar cells due to higher deposition temperature. *Solar Energy Materials and Solar Cells* 95(3): 1028–1030.
[129] Contreras M, Mansfield LM, Egaas B, et al. presented at the 37th IEEE PVSEC, Seattle, USA, 2011 (unpublished).
[130] Nakada T and Shirakata S (2011) Impacts of pulsed-laser assisted deposition on CIGS thin films and solar cells. *Solar Energy Materials and Solar Cells* 95(6): 1463–1470.
[131] Li Z, Nishijima M, Yamada A, and Konagai M (2009) Growth of Cu(In,Ga)Se$_2$ thin films using ionization Ga source and application for solar cells. *Physica Status Solidi (c)* 5: 1273–1277.
[132] Caballero R, Izquierdo-Roca V, Fontane X, et al. (2010) Cu deficiency in multi-stage co-evaporated Cu(In,Ga)Se$_2$ for solar cells applications: Microstructure and Ga in-depth alloying. *Acta Materialia* 58(9): 3468–3476.
[133] Rissom T, Kaufmann CA, Caballero R, et al. (2012) Influence of the Se rate on high-temperature deposited CIGSe thin film solar cells. *Thin Solid Films*.
[134] Chaisitsak S, Yamada A, and Konagai M (2002) Preferred Orientation Control of Cu(In$_{1-x}$Ga$_x$)Se$_2$ ($x \approx 0.28$) Thin Films and Its Influence on Solar Cell Characteristics. *Japanese Journal of Applied Physics* 41: 507–513.
[135] Contreras M, Repins I, Metzger WB, et al. (2009) Se activity and its effect on Cu(In,Ga)Se2 photovoltaic thin films. *Physica Status Solidi A – Applications and Materials Science* 5: 1042–1048.
[136] Ishizuka S, Shibata H, Yamada A, et al. (2007) Growth of polycrystalline Cu(In,Ga)Se2 thin films using a radio frequency-cracked Se-radical beam source and application for photovoltaic devices. *Applied Physics Letters* 91: 041902.
[137] Puttnins S, Zachmann H, Rahm A, et al. presented at the 25th EU PVSEC, Valencia, Spain, 2010 (unpublished).
[138] Güttler D, Chirila A, Seyrling S, et al. presented at the Honolulu, USA, 2010 (unpublished).
[139] Rudmann D, Bremaud D, Dacunha A, et al. (2005) Sodium incorporation strategies for CIGS growth at different temperatures. *Thin Solid Films* 480-481: 55-60. doi: 10.1016/j.tsf.2004.11.071.
[140] Caballero R, Kaufmann CA, Eisenbarth T, et al. (2011) High efficiency low temperature grown Cu(In,Ga)Se(2) thin film solar cells on flexible substrates using NaF precursor layers. *Progress in Photovoltaics* 19(5): 547–551.
[141] Caballero R, Kaufmann CA, Eisenbarth T, et al. (2010) Influence of Na on Cu(In,Ga)Se-2 solar cells grown on polyimide substrates at low temperature: Impact on the Cu(In,Ga)Se-2/Mo interface. *Applied Physics Letters* 96(9): 092104.
[142] Ishizuka S, Yamada A, Fons P, and Niki S (2008) Flexible Cu(In,Ga)Se$_2$ solar cells fabricated using alkali-silicate glass thin layers as an alkjali source material. *Journal of Renewable and Sustainable Energy* 1: 013102.
[143] Yun J, Kim K, Kim M, et al. (2007) Fabrication of CIGS solar cells with a Na-doped Molayer on a Na-free substrate. *Thin Solid Films* 515(15): 5876–5879.
[144] Rockett A (2005) The effect of Na in polycrystalline and epitaxial single-crystal CuIn$_{1-x}$Ga$_x$Se$_2$. *Thin Solid Films* 480: 2–7.
[145] Seward TP and Vascott T (eds.) (2005) *High Temperature Glass Melt Property Database for Process Modeling*. Westerville, OH: The American Ceramic Society.
[146] Rau U and Schock HW (1999) Electronic properties of Cu(In,Ga)Se-2 heterojunction solar cells-recent achievements, current understanding, and future challenges. *Applied Physics A – Materials Science & Processing* 69(2): 131–147.
[147] Hedstrom J, Ohlsen H, Bodegard M, et al. (1993) Zno/Cds/Cu(IN,GA)Se2 thin-film solar-cells with improved performance, pp. 364–371. *Conference Record of the Twenty Third IEEE Photovoltaic Specialists Conference*. May 1993.
[148] Herz K, Kessler F, Wächter A, et al. (2002) Dielectric barriers for flexible CIGS solar modules. *Thin Solid Films* 403–404: 384–389.
[149] DuPont Electronic Technologies (2011) Product information, Kapton 100 HN Film, 25μm. http://www2.dupont.com/Kapton/en_US/assets/downloads/pdf/summaryofprop.pdf.
[150] Heraeus-Quarzglas GmbH & Co. KG (2011) Product information. http://basismaterial.heraeusquarzglas.de/media/webmedia_local/media/dokumente/QuartzBaseMaterials_semifinishedfusedsilica~1.pdf.
[151] Duran Group GmbH (2011) Product information. http://www.duran-group.com/en/aboutduran/duran-properties.html.
[152] Wuerz R, Eicke A, Kessler F, et al. (2011) Alternative sodium sources for Cu(In,Ga)Se2 thin-film solar cells on flexible substrates. *Thin Solid Films* 519(21): 7268–7271.
[153] Kessler F and Rudmann D (2004) Technological aspects of flexible CIGS solar cells and modules. *Solar Energy* 77(6): 685–695.
[154] Eisenbarth T, Caballero R, Kaufmann CA, et al. (in press) Impact of iron on defect concentrations and device performance for CuIn$_{(1-x)}$Ga$_x$Se$_2$. *Solar Cells on Stainless Steel*.
[155] Contreras M, Egaas B, Ramanathan K, et al. (1999) Progress toward 20% efficiency in Cu(In,Ga)Se2 polycrystalline thin-film solar cells. *Progress in Photovoltaics* 7: 311–316.
[156] Wuerz R, Eicke A, Frankenfeld M, et al. (2009) CIGS thin-film solar cells on steel substrates. *Thin Solid Films* 517(7): 2415–2418.
[157] Yagioka T and Nakada T (2009) Cd-free flexible Cu(In,Ga)Se2 thin film solar cells with ZnS(O,OH) buffer layers on Ti foils. *Applied Physics Express* 2: 072201.
[158] Kaufmann CA, Neisser A, Klenk R, and Scheer R (2005) Transfer of Cu(In,Ga)Se-2 thin film solar cells to flexible substrates using an in situ process control. *Thin Solid Films* 480: 515–519.

[159] Brémaud D, Rudmann D, Kaelin M, et al. (2007) Flexible Cu(In,Ga)Se2 on Al foils and the effects of Al during chemical bath deposition. *Thin Solid Films* 515(15): 5857–5861.
[160] Rechid J, Thyen R, Raitzig A, et al. presented at the 3rd World Conference on Photovoltaic Energy Conversion, Osaka, Japan, 2003 (unpublished).
[161] Nakada T, Kuraishi T, Inoue T, and Mise T, presented at the 35th IEEE PVSEC, Honolulu, USA, 2010 (unpublished).
[162] Chirilă A, Buecheler S, Pianezzi F, et al. (2011) Highly efficient Cu(In,Ga)Se2 solar cells grown on flexible polymer films. *Nature Materials* 10(11): 857–861.
[163] Kessler F, Herrmann D, and Powalla M (2005) Approaches to flexible CIGS thin-film solar cells. *Thin Solid Films* 480–481: 491–498.
[164] Stolwijk NA (2010) Fe diffusion in polycrystalline Cu(In,Ga)Se2 layers for thin-film solar cells. *Applied Physics Letters* 96(24): 244101.
[165] Kamikawa-Shimizu Y, Shimada S, Watanabe M, et al. (2009) Effects of Mo back contact thickness on the properties of CIGS solar cells. *Physica Status Solidi A – Applications and Materials Science* 206: 1063–1066.
[166] Scofield JH, Duda A, Albin D, et al. (1995) Sputtered molybdenum bilayer back contact for copper indium diselenide-based poylcrystalline thin-film solar cells. *Thin Solid Films* 260: 26–31.
[167] Al-Thani HA, Hasoon FS, Young M, et al. presented at the 29th IEEE Photovoltaic Specialists Conference, New Orleans, 2002 (unpublished).
[168] Shafarman W and Phillips JE (1996) Direct current-voltage measurements of the Mo/CuInSe2 contact on operating solar cells. *Proceedings of the 25th IEEE PV Specialists Conference*: Washington, USA, 13–17 May 1996, 917–919.
[169] Kohara N, Nishiwaki S, Hashimoto Y, et al. (2001) Electrical properties of the Cu(In,Ga)Se2/MoSe2/Mo structure. *Solar Energy Materials and Solar Cells* 67: 209–215.
[170] Russell PE, Jamjoum O, Ahrenkiel RK, and Kazmerski LL (1982) Properties of the Mo-CuInse2 interface. *Applied Physics Letters* 40(11): 995–997.
[171] Jaegermann W, Löher T, and Pettenkofer C (1996) Surface properties of chalcopyrite semiconductors. *Crystal Research and Crystal Technology* 31: 273.
[172] Orgassa K, Schock HW, and Werner JH (2003) Alternative back contact materials for thin film Cu(In,Ga)Se-2 solar cells. *Thin Solid Films* 431: 387–391.
[173] Shafarman WN and Stolt L (2003) Cu(InGa)Se2 solar cells. In: Luque A and Hegedus S (eds.) *Handbook of Photovoltaic Science and Engineering*, p. 567. West Sussex: John Wiley.
[174] Rietke PC and Bentjen S (1993) Deposition of cadmium sulfide films by decomposition of thiourea in basic solution. *Chemistry of Materials* 5: 4–53.
[175] Lehmann JI (2010) Oberflächenpräparation zur Untersuchung von elektronischen Korngrenzeneigenschaften in Cu(In,Ga)Se$_2$. Diploma Thesis, Freie Universität Berlin.
[176] Allsop N, Kauffmann CA, Neisser A, et al. presented at the Mater. Res. Soc. Symp.Proc., San Francisco, 2005 (unpublished).
[177] Buffière M, Harel S, Arzel L, et al. (2011) Fast chemical bath deposition of Zn(O,S) buffer layers for Cu(In,Ga)Se2 solar cells. *Thin Solid Films* 519(21): 7575–7578.
[178] Contreras MA, Nakada T, Hongo M, et al. presented at the 3rd WCPEC, Osaka, Japan, 2003 (unpublished).
[179] Couzinié-Devy F, Barreau N, and Kessler J (2009) Influence of absorber copper concentration on the Cu(In,Ga)Se2/(PVD)In2S3 and Cu(In,Ga)Se2/(CBD)CdS based solar cells performance. *Thin Solid Films* 517(7): 2407–2410.
[180] Engelhardt F, Bornemann L, Kontges M, et al. (1999) Cu(In,Ga)Se-2 solar cells with a ZnSe buffer layer: Interface characterization by quantum efficiency measurements. *Progress in Photovoltaics* 7(6): 423–436.
[181] Ernits K, Brémaud D, Buecheler S, et al. (2007) Characterisation of ultrasonically sprayed InxSy buffer layers for Cu(In,Ga)Se2 solar cells. *Thin Solid Films* 515(15): 6051–6054.
[182] Fischer C-H, Allsop NA, Gledhill SE, et al. (2011) The spray-ILGAR® (ion layer gas reaction) method for the deposition of thin semiconductor layers: Process and applications for thin film solar cells. *Solar Energy Materials and Solar Cells* 95(6): 1518–1526.
[183] Huang CH, Li SS, Shafarman WN, et al. (2001) Study of Cd-free buffer layers using Inx(OH,S)y on CIGS solar cells. *Solar Energy Materials and Solar Cells* 69(2): 131–137.
[184] Hariskos D, Menner R, Jackson P, et al. presented at the 26th EUPVSEC, Hamburg, Germany, 2011 (unpublished).
[185] Okamoto A, Minemoto T, and Takakura H (2011) Application of sputtered ZnO1-xSx buffer layers for Cu(In,Ga)Se2 solar cells. *Japanese Journal of Applied Physics* 50: 04DP10.
[186] Pistor P, Caballero R, Hariskos D, et al. (2009) Quality and stability of compound indium sulphide as source material for buffer layers in Cu(In,Ga)Se solar cells. *Solar Energy Materials and Solar Cells* 93(1): 148–152.
[187] Sáez-Araoz R, Ennaoui A, Kropp T, et al. (2008) Use of different Zn precursors for the deposition of Zn(S,O) buffer layers by chemical bath for chalcopyrite based Cd-free thin-film solar cells. *Physica Status Solidi (a)* 205(10): 2330–2334.
[188] Siebentritt S, Walk P, Fiedeler U, et al. (2004) MOCVD as a dry deposition method of ZnSe buffers for Cu(In,Ga)(S,Se)2 solar cells. *Progress in Photovoltaics: Research and Applications* 12(5): 333–338.
[189] Yakioka T and Nakada T (2009) Cd-Free Flexible Cl8In,Ga)Se$_2$ Thin Film solar Cells with ZnS(O,OH) Buffer Layers on Ti Foils. *Applied Physics Express* 2: 072201.
[190] Hariskos D, Spiering S, and Powalla M (2005) Buffer layers in Cu(In,Ga)Se2 solar cells and modules. *Thin Solid Films* 480–481: 99.
[191] Siebentritt S (2004) Alternative buffers for chalcopyrite solar cells. *Solar Energy* 77(6): 767–775.
[192] Naghavi N, Abou-Ras D, Allsop N, et al. (2010) Buffer layers and transparent conducting oxides for chalcopyrite Cu(In,Ga)(S,Se)(2) based thin film photovoltaics: Present status and current developments. *Progress in Photovoltaics* 18(6): 411–433.
[193] Orgassa K, Rau U, Nguyen Q, et al. (2002) Role of the CdS buffer layer as an active optical element in Cu(In,Ga)Se-2 thin-film solar cells. *Progress in Photovoltaics* 10(7): 457–463.
[194] Pettersson J, Platzer-Bjorkman C, and Edoff M (2009) Temperature-dependent current-voltage and light-soaking measurements on Cu(In,Ga)Se2 solar cells with ALD-Zn1-xMgx buffer layers. *Progress in Photovoltaics: Research and Applications* 17: 460–469.
[195] Ishizuka S, Sakurai K, Yamada A, et al. (2005) Fabrication of wide-gap Cu(In$_{1-x}$Ga$_x$)Se$_2$ thin film solar cells: A study on the correlation of cell performance with highly resistive i-ZnO layer thickness. *Solar Energy Materials and Solar Cells* 87: 541–548
[196] Olsen LC, Eschbach P, and Kundu S (2002) Role of buffer layers in CIS based solar cells, p. 652. *Proceedings of the 29th IEEE Photovoltaic Specialists Conference*. New Orleans, LA, 2002.
[197] Minemoto T (2001) Cu(In,Ga)Se2 solar cells with controlled conduction band offset of window/Cu(In,Ga)Se2 layers. *Journal of Applied Physics* 89(12): 8327.
[198] Niemegeers A, Burgelman M, Herberholz R, et al. (1998) Model for electronic transport in Cu(In,Ga)Se-2 solar cells. *Progress in Photovoltaics* 6(6): 407–421.
[199] Gloeckler M, Jenkins CR, and Sites JR, presented at the Mat. Res. Soc. Sympos., 2003 (unpublished).
[200] Fahrenbruch A and Bube RH (1983) *Fundamentals of Solar Cells: Photovoltaic Energy Conversion*. New York: Academic Press.
[201] Scheer R (2009) Activation energy of heterojunction diode currents in the limit of interface recombination. *Journal of Applied Physics* 105(10): 104505.
[202] Unold T and Schock HW (2011) Nonconventional (non-silicon-based) photovoltaic materials. In: Clarke DR and Fratzl P (eds.) *Annual Review of Materials Research*, vol. 41, pp. 297–321.
[203] Ohnesorge B (1998) Minority-carrier lifetime and efficiency of Cu(In,Ga)Se2 solar cells. *Applied Physics Letters* 73(9): 1224.
[204] Repins IL, Metzger WK, Perkins CL, et al. (2009) Measured Minority-Carrier Lifetime And CIGS Device Performance. *Proceedings of the 34th IEEE Photovoltaic Specialists Conference*, p. 978.
[205] Metzger WK (2008) Long lifetimes in high-efficiency Cu(In,Ga)Se2 solar cells. *Applied Physics Letters* 93(2). 022110.
[206] Schock HW, Rau U, Dullweber T, et al. presented at the EC PVSEC, Glasgow, Scotland, 2000 (unpublished).
[207] Turcu M, Pakma O, and Rau U (2002) Interdependence of absorber composition and recombination mechanism in Cu(In,Ga)(Se,S)(2) heterojunction solar cells. *Applied Physics Letters* 80(14): 2598–2600.
[208] Schultz C, Schüle M, Richter M, et al. presented at the 26th European Photovoltaic Solar Energy Conference, Hamburg, 2011 (unpublished).
[209] Barkhouse DAR, Gunawan O, Gokmen T, et al. (2011) *Device Characteristics of a 10.1% Hydrazine-Processed Cu2ZnSn(Se,S)4 Solar Cell Progress in Photovoltaics: Research and Applications*. Chichester, UK: Wiley.

1.19 Cadmium Telluride Photovoltaic Thin Film: CdTe

TA Gessert, National Renewable Energy Laboratory (NREL), Golden, CO, USA

Published by Elsevier Ltd.

1.19.1	Introduction	423
1.19.2	Brief History of CdTe PV Devices	423
1.19.3	Attempts Toward Initial Commercial Modules	424
1.19.4	Review of Present Commercial Industry/Device Designs	424
1.19.5	General CdTe Material Properties	426
1.19.6	Layer-Specific Process Description for Superstrate CdTe Devices	427
1.19.6.1	Superstrate Materials	427
1.19.6.2	TCO Layer	428
1.19.6.3	Buffer Layer	428
1.19.6.4	CdS Layer	429
1.19.6.5	CdTe Layer	430
1.19.6.6	$CdCl_2$ Activation	431
1.19.6.7	Back Contact	432
1.19.7	Where Is the Junction?	434
1.19.8	Considerations for Large-Scale Deployment	434
1.19.8.1	Reliability	435
1.19.8.2	Mineral Availability	436
1.19.8.3	Environmental	436
1.19.8.4	Energy-Payback Time	436
1.19.9	Conclusion	437
Acknowledgment		437
References		437

1.19.1 Introduction

Thin-film photovoltaic (PV) devices based on CdTe absorbers represent one of the fastest growing segments of all PV technologies [1, 2]. It is even more remarkable that most of this impact has occurred within the past few years. Much of the reason for this rapid development can be traced to two facts: (1) thin-film PV modules have been designed specifically to embody production advantages over historic PV products (i.e., wafer-based technologies) and (2) CdTe PV modules and/or production processes presently embody some advantages over other thin-film technologies.

In the following discussion, the development and present state of CdTe PV technology will be reviewed to describe advantages that have made this technology a dominant force in the PV market. Although much is understood regarding the physics and materials science of the thin-film CdTe device, this discussion will indicate that producing PV modules that are cost effective in present market(s) remains a complex technological undertaking. Furthermore, although current CdTe commercial technology demonstrates the lowest specific production cost of any PV technology (i.e., specific cost = cost/Watt), the discussion will also suggest additional improvements and further market penetration remain likely.

Finally, the discussion will indicate that as economic viability of CdTe PV products proceeds, the impacts of less-obvious considerations emerge. These include developing reliability that could extend beyond the warranty period (i.e., >25 years), the likelihood of large-scale mineral resource availability (i.e., Te), and issues of how CdTe PV sustainability compares to other base-load energy sources (i.e., energy-payback time and toxicity considerations).

1.19.2 Brief History of CdTe PV Devices

One of the first-noted uses of CdTe was for gamma and X-ray detectors, and it was through research related to these applications that much of the early material understanding was established [3]. Additionally, because the photoelectric absorption coefficient of CdTe is similar to that of normal skin tissue, several uses have been investigated for use in nuclear medicine [4, 5].

The first notable investigations of CdTe as a solar absorber were published by Vodakov and Naumov in 1960 and 1961 [6, 7]. Although few details are cited in these papers, devices with reported efficiencies up to ~6% were fabricated by diffusing semitransparent surface coatings into crystalline n-type-doped CdTe.

More detailed work was reported in 1963 by Cusano, who was seeking to understand the formation and operation of (what would eventually be called) the $Cu_{2-x}Te/CdS$ cell. In this work, Cusano substituted n-CdTe for the more typically used n-CdS to form $Cu_{2-x}Te/CdTe$ devices. Both thin-film and crystalline n-CdTe layers were used, and the process involved dipping the CdTe into a solution containing Cu ions [8].

Results of these studies provided considerable insight relating to the formation of the p-type $Cu_{2-x}Te$ layer during cell processing and indicated that the $Cu_{2-x}Te/CdTe$ device performs more like a heterojunction than a CdTe homojunction. This study also revealed several problems related to CdTe PV devices that remain today. Noteworthy of these were a close relationship between effects occurring at the CdTe contact electrodes and junction characteristics and the observation that the best II–VI devices almost always involved the use of Cu.

In the same year, Nicoll became one of the first to report on the use of close-space vapor transport (CSVT) for the deposition of CdTe [9]. During the next several years, measurements of the CdTe minority-carrier lifetimes indicated that the maximum lifetime for n-CdTe is about 10 ns, with even shorter lifetimes observed in p-CdTe [10–12]. Subsequent modeling indicated that efficiencies >10% would not be achieved for CdTe homojunction devices unless the minority-carrier lifetimes were longer than 100 ns.

This benchmark lifetime was an order of magnitude longer than that observed for the lowest doped, crystalline CdTe. Because the homojunction emitter would have to be heavily doped to reduce series resistance effects, most research efforts during about the last 40 years have been directed toward development of CdTe heterojunction devices. Recently, however, reports have emerged suggesting that crystalline homojunction CdTe-based devices may demonstrate a significant opportunity for multijunction concentrator PV devices [13].

In the CdTe heterojunction configuration, the choice for an appropriate heteroface material is limited by several considerations. For example, because of the near-optimum bandgap of CdTe, the heterojunction should be designed so that the majority of the absorption occurs within the CdTe bulk. Thus, the heteroface partner must act as a highly transparent, low-resistance window layer and not be responsible for carrier generation.

Because all known wide-bandgap, low-resistivity window materials are n-type, the CdTe layer must be p-type. The choice of window layer is further constrained in that it is preferable for it to have a small lattice mismatch with CdTe to avoid excessive interface recombination.

Finally, to promote long-term stability, the window material should be composed of elements that are slow to diffuse into CdTe, preferably with the cation from column II (e.g., Zn, Cd, and Hg). Although the considerations mentioned above provide a guide for the choice of the wide-bandgap heteroface window, a wide range of materials have been investigated, including CdS [14–16], ZnO [17], and ZnSe [18]. It is worth noting that the 5–6%-efficient CdS/CdTe devices fabricated by Bonnet in 1972 were not only the first CdS/CdTe devices reported but were also the first all-thin-film CdS/CdTe devices reported (i.e., gas-phase transport (GPT) was used to deposit thin films of both the CdS and CdTe layers).

Some of the other window materials may eventually demonstrate certain advantages over CdS. However, the most efficient cells to date have been produced using the CdS/CdTe configuration [19–21]. Additionally, because the CdS/CdTe configuration represents a three-element system (rather than four-element or more), it may produce fewer potential native defects and ultimately present fewer unforeseen industrial (production) problems and/or problems due to interdiffusion.

1.19.3 Attempts Toward Initial Commercial Modules

With the success of the all-thin-film CdS/CdTe device reported by Bonnet and Rabenhorst in 1972, many entrepreneurs who had previously worked to develop $Cu_{2-x}Te/CdS$ PV products began to consider if CdTe might demonstrate advantages compared to Cu_xS-based devices. **Table 1** highlights early attempts at CdTe commercial products. It has been assembled from a variety of sources, including reports, web sites, and personal communications, and is intended to be representative rather than exhaustive.

The table indicates that in the time period of *c*. 1975–85, several significant commercial endeavors were initiated to develop thin-film CdTe PV products. Many of the early attempts were based on a belief that chemical and/or atmospheric pressure processes were a more attractive commercialization avenue compared to the vacuum-sublimation processes used to produce the laboratory devices in the early 1970s. Although only the companies presently in commercial (or precommercial) production are using vacuum sublimation, several companies are now re-exploring potential advantages of nonvacuum CdTe deposition processes. For a more detailed discussion of the successes and difficulties that can be encountered during CdTe PV module commercialization, the reader is directed to Reference 22.

1.19.4 Review of Present Commercial Industry/Device Designs

Nearly all of the companies listed in **Table 1** have been involved in developing or producing thin-film CdTe devices configured in the superstrate design as shown in **Figure 1**. In the superstrate design, light enters through a transparent glass 'superstrate', through a transparent conducting oxide (TCO) layer(s), and through a CdS window layer. The light is then absorbed in the CdTe absorber layer.

Because the glass superstrate also provides the mechanical surface onto which all subsequent layers are deposited, the sequence of layer deposition is TCO, then CdS, then CdTe, and then back contact. Although the superstrate design is currently the most widely studied (e.g., the present world-record, thin-film CdTe device is a superstrate device) [19, 23], a device that is designed opposite to this (known as a substrate design) continues to attract both research and commercial interest.

Table 1 Historical and present commercial companies involved in CdTe PV. In some cases, several entries are listed indicating name transitions and/or involvements by different corporate entities

Approximate time period	Name	Location	CdTe absorber deposition
1975–1984	Photon Power, Inc.	El Paso, TX, USA	Chemical spraying
1984–1992	Photon Energy, Inc.	Golden, CO, USA	
1992–1997	Golden Photon, Inc.		
1977–1997?	Matsushita Corp.	Japan	Screen printing sublimation
1980–1984	Monosolar, Inc.	Santa Monica, CA, USA	Electrodeposition
1984–1999	BP Solar	London, UK	
1999–2002	BP/Solarex	Baltimore, MD, USA	
1980–1989	AMETEK	Harleysville, PA, USA	Electrodeposition
1994–2002	ANTEC GmbHAntec Solar Energy	Arnstadt, Germany	Vacuum sublimation
2002–present			
1990–1999	Solar Cells, Inc.	Toledo, OH, USA	Vacuum sublimation
1999–present	First Solar		
2003–2007	Solar Fields	Toledo, OH, USA	Nonvacuum sublimation
2007–present	Calyxo USA		
2006	Ziax Corp.	Arvada, CO, USA	Vacuum sublimation
2006–2008	Primestar Solar		
2008–present	Primestar GE Solar		
2006–present	Solexant Corp.	San Jose, CA, USA	Nonvacuum printing
2007–2009	AVA Solar Abound	Fort Collins, CO, USA	Vacuum sublimation
2009–present	Solar		
2008–present	Xunlight 26 Solar	Toledo, OH, USA	Sputtering
2008–present	SunPrint	Richmond, CA, USA	Nonvacuum printing
2008–present	Advanced Solar Power	Hangzhou, China	Vacuum sublimation
2007–present	WK Solar Group	Toledo, OH, USA	Vacuum sublimation
2010–present	Encore Solar	Fremont, CA, USA	Electrodeposition

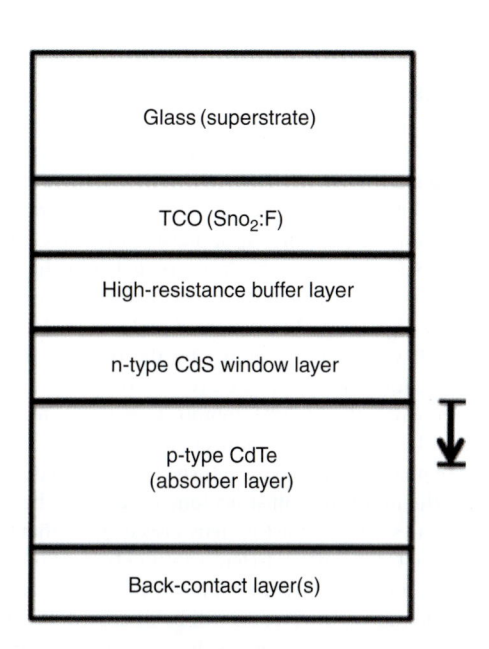

CdTe device structure:
- Glass (superstrate)
- TCO (SnO$_2$:F)
- High-resistance buffer layer
- n-type CdS window layer
- p-type CdTe (absorber layer)
- Back-contact layer(s)

Figure 1 Schematic diagram showing main functional components of typical thin-film CdTe PV solar cell device configured as a superstrate structure. Arrow on right indicates direction and approximate location of junction electric field.

Figure 2 SEM micrograph showing cross section of CdS/CdTe superstrate device produced at NREL. The layers have been color enhanced for clarity.

In the substrate design, the device is grown (typically) on a nontransparent substrate that is often either a Mo or a Mo-coated stainless steel foil. This results in a deposition sequence opposite to the substrate device (i.e., back contact, then CdTe, then CdS, then TCO, then encapsulation). Although the current reported maximum performance of substrate devices is significantly lower than high-performance superstrate devices (< 10% efficiency vs. ~17% efficiency, respectively) [24, 25], the substrate configuration has advantages that could be exploited in certain commercial products. These include applications requiring high specific power (i.e., W kg^{-1}), ability to produce flexible products (i.e., for aerospace and/or building-integrated PV (BIPV) markets), and/or envisioned use of roll-to-roll processing during module manufacture.

Figure 2 shows a scanning electron microscopy (SEM) cross section of a superstrate CdTe device produced at NREL. The figure has been graphically enhanced to more clearly delineate the various layers. This particular device was produced on barium-silicate glass (Corning 7059), an SnO$_2$:F TCO layer and an SnO$_2$ buffer layer (BL) that were produced by metal organic chemical vapor deposition (MOCVD), a CdS layer produced by chemical bath deposition (CBD), a CdTe layer produced by close-space sublimation (CSS), a dry CdCl$_2$ process, a chemical recontact etch step, and a graphite-paste contact.

1.19.5 General CdTe Material Properties

One reason many technologists believe CdTe PV devices embody industrial advantages is that the phase diagram of this material is very simple. The phase diagram shown in **Figure 3** illustrates that stoichiometric CdTe can exist only very near the 50/50% Cd/Te ratio. If the composition deviates from the 50/50% ratio during crystal growth, the CdTe material will phase separate into CdTe and Cd or Te – whichever has the greater composition. Because the vapor pressure of both Cd and Te are much higher than CdTe, these elemental regions will tend to re-evaporate before they can be incorporated into the growing crystal. If a sufficient Cd or Te overpressure exists, and/or if the rate of crystal growth exceeds the elemental evaporation rates, elemental inclusions can be incorporated. If the temperature is sufficiently high (i.e., >324 °C for Cd and >449 °C for Te), liquid elemental regions can reside on the surface of the crystal. The CdTe itself will melt, as shown by the outside of the overall curve, and is a function of off-stoichiometry. The highest melting point is for stoichiometric CdTe at ~1092 °C.

Although single-phase CdTe exists only very near the 50/50% composition, the material can sustain a Cd or a Te deficiency to a small extent. This off-stoichiometry can extend to a maximum value of about 5×10^{17} cm^{-3} before the Te or the Cd deficiency will spontaneously produce the separate Cd or Te phases indicated previously. Recalling that most materials have a density of atoms on the order of 1×10^{22} cm^{-3}, this means that the maximum off-stoichiometry that can be sustained in crystalline CdTe at thermodynamic equilibrium is only about 0.01%. Analysis of off-stoichiometry also suggests that for equilibrium conditions, temperatures greater than 600 °C can yield higher excess Te or Cd compared to temperatures below 500 °C [26]. Depending on the concentration of other defects, the excess Te or Cd can manifest in polycrystalline films to yield material with net acceptors or net donors, thereby assisting with various types of junction functionality. However, as will be discussed, the influence of the CdCl$_2$ treatment and Cu incorporation during contacting also has a significant impact on resultant electrical variations.

In addition to a relatively simple phase space, another important reason CdTe embodies production advantages is because CdTe demonstrates a property known as congruent sublimation and condensation. When a source of bulk CdTe is heated to a

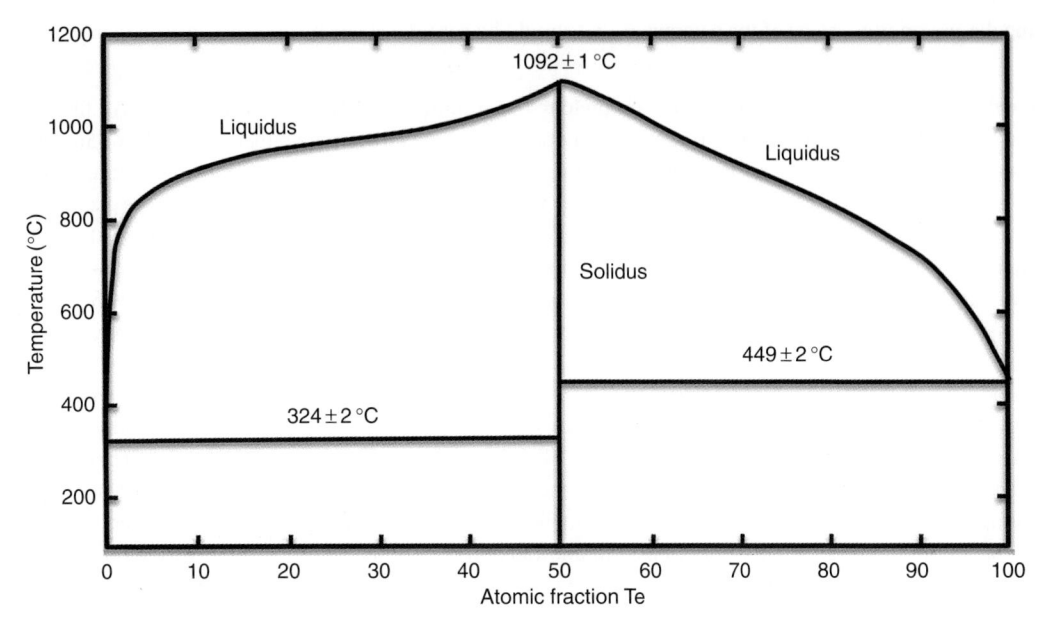

Figure 3 Phase diagram of CdTe. Reproduced from Zanio K (1978) *Cadmium Telluride, Vol. 13: Semiconductors and Semimetals*, pp. 164–186. New York: Academic Press, with permission.

temperature at which the CdTe surface sublimates into Cd and Te$_2$ gas, the Cd and Te gas-phase atoms evaporate at roughly the same rate (i.e., congruent sublimation). Although the vapor pressure for Cd is higher than that for Te$_2$ at any given temperature, Te$_2$ has two atoms, so the arrival rate of Te and Cd atoms at the surface will be very similar. Furthermore, when Cd and Te$_2$ vapors condense onto a (cooler) surface, they again do so at about the same rate (i.e., congruent condensation). These two similar processes enable a bulk source of stoichiometric CdTe to evaporate and condense into a film of nearly stoichiometric CdTe. If for some reason the arrival of Cd and Te at a growing film surface is not balanced, as noted above, the vapor pressure of Cd (or Te$_2$) above a pure Cd (or Te) surface is much higher than the vapor pressure of Cd or Te$_2$ above a CdTe surface. Thus, any depositing Cd or Te surface atoms that do not coordinate rapidly into the CdTe material will be re-evaporated from the surface, limiting the existence of Cd or Te secondary phases.

The previous discussion pertains to high-purity, crystalline CdTe formed under equilibrium conditions. However, for thin-film PV devices, the CdTe will be formed using less pure materials and ambients, and relatively nonequilibrium conditions. These differences can result in polycrystalline thin films that will contain numerous structural and impurity defects that can affect the material properties of the film. Luckily, because the kinetics of film growth for CdTe is fairly rapid, even high-rate film growth processes tend to retain much of the structural regularity that is observed for bulk crystalline materials.

Although CdTe is ambipolar (i.e., it can be doped both n-type and p-type), the material tends to self-compensate. This means if one attempts to incorporate acceptors by substituting group I dopants on the cation (Cd) site, or group V dopants on the anion (Te) site, a dopant concentration will be reached where the lattice will spontaneously create 'compensating' donors, with the result that the further change in net acceptor concentration is minimal [27].

Production of epitaxial CdTe films using molecular beam epitaxy (MBE) techniques can achieve n- and p-type doping into the mid 10^{18} cm^{-3} range using extrinsic dopants [28, 29]. For polycrystalline PV devices, the CdTe is typically deposited without extrinsic dopants added. The as-deposited CdTe is often believed to be p-type as a result of cadmium vacancies (V_{Cd}); however, the electrical resistance of as-deposited CdTe is very high, so the electrical properties of as-deposited polycrystalline thin films are not well established. Most device technologists only know that a working junction results if the CdTe is deposited onto an n-type heteroface layer, such as CdS, and a back contact is fabricated onto the CdTe. The conclusion is that the CdTe must have been, or have become, p-type. As we will see in the following discussion, for some CdTe deposition processes, it is possible that the as-deposited CdTe may be p-type, intrinsic, or even n-type, and it is the postdeposition processes (i.e., CdCl$_2$ and/or contacting with a Cu-containing layer) that establish the necessary p-type properties.

1.19.6 Layer-Specific Process Description for Superstrate CdTe Devices

1.19.6.1 Superstrate Materials

Thin-film CdTe PV devices typically are grown on a glass superstrate. At this time, nearly all published research on CdTe PV has been performed using barium-silicate glass (e.g., Corning 7059), borosilicate glass, or soda-lime float glass. Furthermore, there are presently no definitive studies that compare material and/or performance differences resulting from these different glass choices.

The following discussion notes some of the parameters that should be considered when choosing a glass superstrate for a CdTe PV device.

Temperature stability. Higher substrate temperatures are preferred to minimize the defect density in the CdTe film. In the case of commonly used soda-lime, float-glass substrates, it is essential to keep the processing temperatures below 550–580 °C to avoid mechanical failure due to the low strain and softening points, and to avoid altering the degree of temper of the as-fabricated glass. For some industrial processes, the temperature may be much lower to avoid even small distortions in the glass and/or limit loss of glass temper. For higher processing temperatures, borosilicate (and historically, barium silicate, Corning 7059) glass substrates have been used for laboratory devices to allow studies of material functionality at higher temperature. Because of the size of the potential market for thin-film CdTe PV device, many commercial glass companies are considering the use of other types of glass compositions that may demonstrate higher strain points compared to soda-lime glass or may embody other commercial advantages.

Coefficient of thermal expansion (CTE). A difference in the CTE between the substrate and the film can induce stress in the deposited layers following deposition and cooling. The stress gives rise to structural defects and can also affect the adhesion of the film(s). For these reasons, it is preferred to choose a glass with a CTE that matches closely that of the material(s) being deposited.

Glass composition and impurity diffusion. Because glass constituents can diffuse out from the glass at elevated processing temperatures and/or during long-term field deployment, the effect of mobile impurities from the glass on the device layers must be considered. For alkali glasses, impurities (e.g., sodium, potassium, and calcium) can diffuse into the films during processing. If impurity diffusion is found to negatively impact underlying device layers, additional diffusion-barrier layers, and/or glass compositions that mitigate these issues, may be required. Barrier layers may incorporate designs to reduce optical reflection, especially at non-normal incidence. It also remains possible that, as in copper indium gallium diselenide (CIGS) PV device technology, improved understanding of the CdTe material may indicate that certain types of alkali diffusion could be beneficial.

1.19.6.2 TCO Layer

Following deposition of any alkali diffusion-barrier layer(s), the next layer deposited onto the glass is the TCO layer. Because this layer provides a lateral conduction pathway for electrons from the n-type side of the device, it must be highly conductive. However, because incident light must pass through the TCO layer for subsequent absorption in the junction, it must also be highly transparent.

For many production CdTe technologies, fluorine-doped SnO_2 (SnO_2:F) has been the historical choice for the TCO layer. SnO_2:F-coated glass has been widely available for many years because of its use in low-emissivity (low-e) glass for residential and appliance applications (e.g., window glazing and heat-reflecting glass in oven windows). SnO_2:F is chemically inert, is not greatly affected by environmental moisture or diffusion from other materials in the PV device, and may provide a degree of protection from Na diffusion from soda-lime glass. Finally, SnO_2:F has sufficient stability in its electrical and optical properties at CdTe processing temperatures (> 600 °C).

Detriment of SnO_2:F is that it demonstrates lower visible transmission than does either indium tin oxide (ITO) or ZnO:Al and thus limits current generation. This is mainly because the maximum electron mobility of present commercial-grade SnO_2:F is lower than that in other TCOs (i.e., in the range of 20–25 $cm^2 V^{-1}$ s). This means that to achieve both low sheet resistance (typically ~15 Ω per square) and high transmission, higher carrier concentration must be used in the film (~$7 \times 10^{20} cm^{-3}$). This higher carrier concentration will produce more free-carrier absorption, limiting the transmitted near-infrared (NIR) light entering the PV device, thus limiting short-circuit current.

Many research groups are presently investigating avenues to improve the performance of SnO_2:F and/or develop alternative TCOs for CdTe devices [30]. For example, the present world-record, thin-film CdTe device uses a Cd_2SnO_4 TCO layer [19, 31, 32]. An alternative avenue to improve the transmission of TCOs for PV applications involves forming TCO alloys with higher dielectric permittivity [33]. Because the dielectric permittivity affects the plasma wavelength, this technique can yield a TCO with much less NIR absorption.

1.19.6.3 Buffer Layer

In most high-performance CdTe PV devices, a high-resistance oxide layer is placed between the TCO and the CdS layers. This layer is often called a buffer layer (BL) but has also been called a high-resistance transparent (HRT) layer. Many attributes have been ascribed to this layer, and it is not presently clear if all attributes manifest in all CdTe device processes, or if certain BL attributes assist only certain types of device designs and/or fabrication processes.

Suggested benefits include the following:

1. The BL allows thinner CdS layers to be used. One proposed reason for this is that the space charge on the n-type side of the junction can expand into the BL when the CdS becomes too thin to balance the charge needed to maintain the space-charge width in the p-type side of the junction. This enables the space charge in the p-CdTe region to remain sufficiently wide as the CdS

is thinned, thereby avoiding device functionality dominated by voltage-dependent collection (i.e., low fill factor due to loss of minority-carrier collection at high forward bias). A different explanation for BL allowing thinner CdS layers suggests that the BL reduces surface recombination at the CdS/TCO interface. Reduced recombination at this interface will impart less of a detriment to device performance as the use of thinner CdS layers positions this interface closer to the junction.
2. The BL provides tolerance to shunt (or short) paths from the back contact to the front contact. These pathways will be present if the CdTe layer contains cracks or pinholes that may form during CdTe deposition or during precontact treatments such as chemical etching.
3. Certain types of BL can allow higher temperatures or longer times to be used during the $CdCl_2$ treatment. It has been suggested this benefit may be more likely for a chemically active BL, such as Zn_2SnO_4 or related alloys.
4. A chemically active BL, such as Zn_2SnO_4 or related alloys, may consume some of the CdS layer, reducing the amount of (optically absorbing) CdS and producing instead a wider bandgap CdZnS material [19].

The particular choices of glass superstrate, TCO, BL, and CdS will significantly affect the amount of light that can enter the junction region of a thin-film CdTe PV device and thus will impact the device short-circuit current. **Figure 4** compares the quantum efficiency of the 16.7% CdTe device produced at NREL (J_{sc} = ~26 mA cm^{-2}, dotted quantum efficiency curve) to that of a historic commercial device (J_{sc} = ~19 mA cm^{-2}, solid curve).

The comparison reveals significant loss differences in both the NIR region (600–850 nm) and the UV region (300–600 nm). About one half of the ~3 mA cm^{-2} NIR loss is believed to be due to absorption in the (high-Fe) commercial glass (~1.5 mA cm^{-2}) and about half is believed to be due to the free-carrier absorption of commercial TCO (~1.5 mA cm^{-2}). For the NREL device shown, barium-silicate glass (Corning 7059) and a Cd_2SnO_4 TCO layer were used to minimize both these NIR losses. It should also be noted that the commercial TCO modeled for this figure (using Drude theory approximations) might actually suggest less NIR absorption compared to typical commercial SnO_2:F. The difference in UV loss between the commercial and NREL device (~4 mA cm^{-2} shown in the figure) is primarily due to the use of relatively thick layers of CdS in the commercial device (typically ~100–300 nm).

In the NREL device, a Zn_2SnO_4-alloy BL was used to allow a CdS layer that is typically thinned to ~70 nm thick. From this discussion, it is clear that additional performance benefits remain possible by further reduction of the CdS thickness. However, this will require improved understanding of the function(s) and optimization of specific BLs.

1.19.6.4 CdS Layer

Although the CdS layer is the n-type 'heteroface' partner of the CdS/CdTe device, for most device processes, the resulting electrical junction forms between the CdTe absorber layer and an intermixed CdSTe layer that forms during CdTe deposition. Because of this intermixing, the device is not generally considered a heterojunction – but instead a quasi-homojunction [34]. Although materials other than CdS have been tested for the heteroface partner layer, CdS has been found to yield the highest device performance. Moreover, and

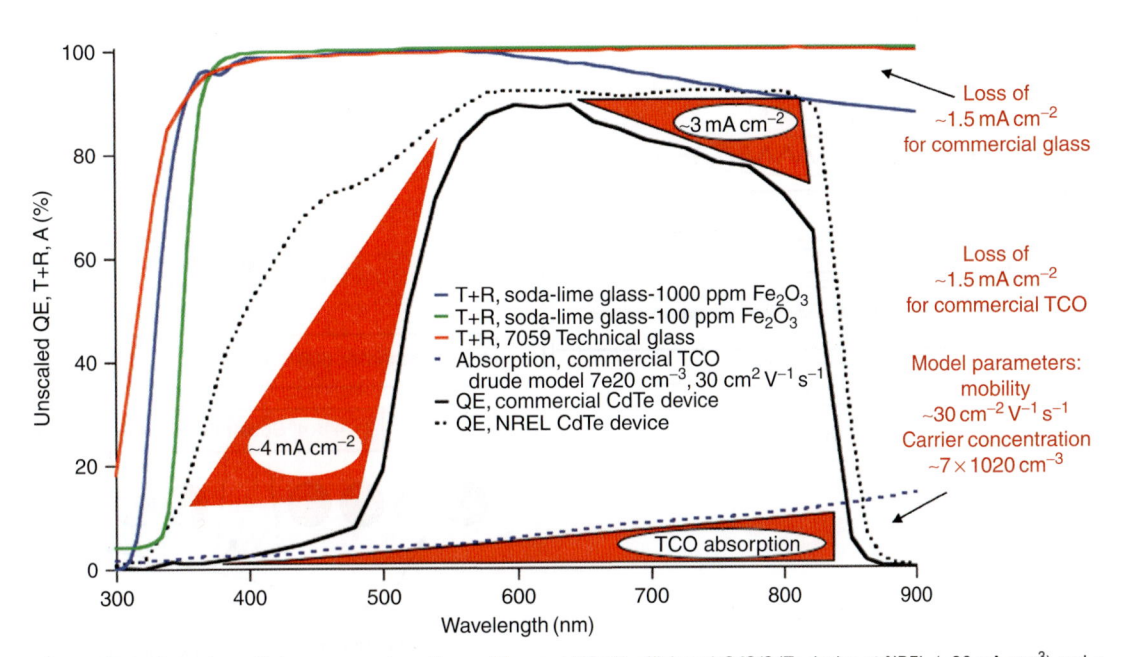

Figure 4 Comparison of quantum efficiency curves from the world-record (16.7% efficiency) CdS/CdTe device at NREL (~26 mA cm^{-3}) and a representative commercial CdS/CdTe device (~19 mA cm^{-3}). The triangles in red indicate the approximate amount of loss in each region. The figure also shows several different types of glass superstrates and a modeled absorption curve for a typical commercial TCO.

unlike the situation in CuInSe$_2$-alloy devices, because a much thicker Cd-containing layer still exists in the device (the CdTe layer!), there has been little motivation to eliminate the Cd from the heteroface layer based solely on perceived toxicity concerns.

Many different CdS deposition processes can be used for the CdTe device. The NREL world-record cell uses CBD [23]. However, sputter deposition, evaporation, and various forms of GPT (CSS, vapor-transport deposition (VTD), etc.) are also used by research and industry. When processes other than CBD are used, CdTe technologists have found that adding oxygen to the CdS deposition process appears to produce beneficial diffusion during the subsequent CdTe deposition process. In the case of sputter deposition of CdS, oxygen can also lead to the formation of a nanocrystalline CdS phase [35]. It is believed that quantum-confinement effects yield a wider bandgap for nanocrystalline CdS, leading to increased device short-circuit current.

1.19.6.5 CdTe Layer

A primary production advantage of CdTe, relative to other known thin-film absorber layers, is that it can be deposited very quickly (at rates >20 μm min^{-1}). This means that the length of the CdTe deposition zone in an in-line manufacturing tool (and related deposition hardware costs) can be much smaller compared to other thin-film PV technologies that require slower deposition rates.

A variety of deposition techniques have been used to deposit CdTe including the following: various forms of GPT (e.g., CSS and VTD), physical vapor deposition (PVD) (e.g., evaporation and sputtering), electrodeposition, screen printing, spray techniques, and printing. Assisted by its congruent sublimation/condensation properties, nearly all these techniques have yielded devices with efficiency >10%. The first method used to deposit CdTe films for 'high-efficiency' solar cell applications used a process in which a crystal of CdTe was heated to its sublimation point, and the vapor was transported by a gas and recondensed on a substrate [14]. **Figure 5** illustrates two laboratory-scale methods that are presently used for deposition of CdTe (and possibly CdS). A description of one commercial process is provided in Reference 36.

The important material differences for CdTe deposition techniques can be divided into the following two categories: (1) low-temperature growth (<425 °C) – small-grain material, n-type as-deposited, oriented films under stress; and (2) high-temperature growth (>500 °C) – large-grain material, slightly p-type as-deposited, lower inbuilt stress.

Higher CdTe growth temperature also yields significant interdiffusion between the CdTe and the underlying CdS layer. This leads to the formation of what is often called the CdSTe-alloy region (or CdSTe layer) naturally resulting from thermal diffusion between the CdS and CdTe layers. For devices formed at high temperature, the CdSTe-alloy region forms primarily during CdTe growth and is altered further during the CdCl$_2$ process (discussed below). If a low-temperature CdTe deposition process is used, the CdSTe-alloy region is typically established entirely during the CdCl$_2$ treatment [37]. Although it is known that most high-performance CdTe devices contain a CdSTe-alloy region, the function and preferred attributes of this region remain areas of active debate.

In addition to CdTe deposition temperature and CdCl$_2$ treatment, another important parameter affecting the CdSTe-alloy region is the amount of oxygen available within this region [38]. **Figure 6** shows that the amount of oxygen in the CdS layer alters the interdiffusion between the CdS and CdTe layers during the high-temperature CdTe deposition. In general, adding oxygen to the CdS layer reduces the

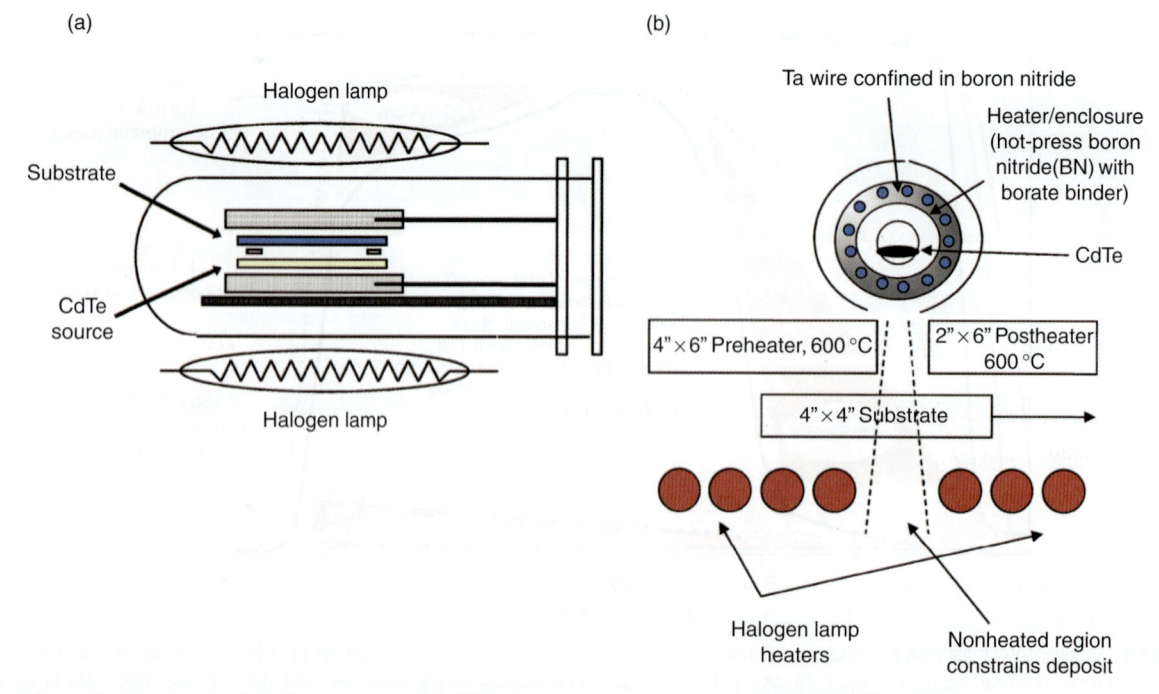

Figure 5 (a) Cross-sectional schematic of research-scale CSS system. (b) Cross section of research-scale GPT system.

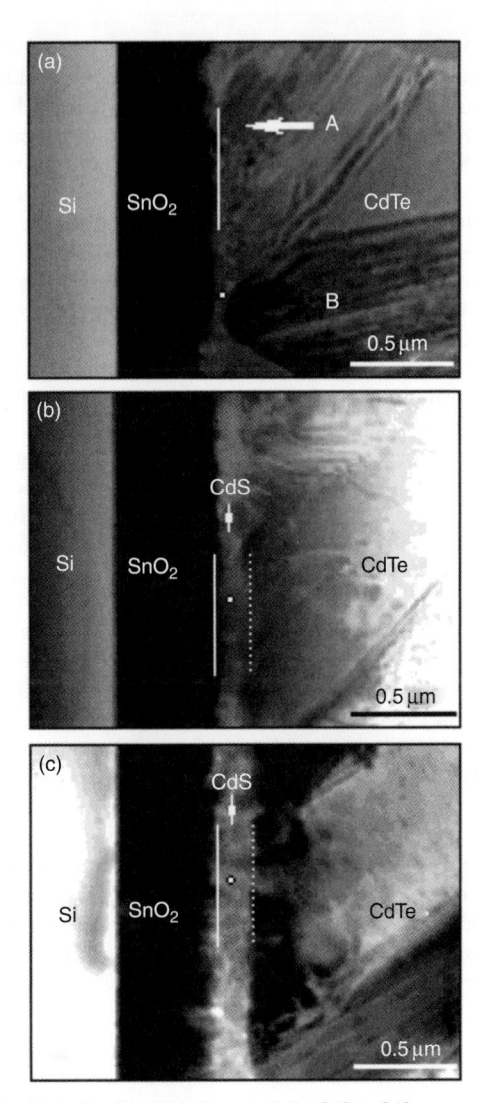

Figure 6 SEM cross section of CdS/CdTe device illustrating the effect of oxygen in the CdS on CdS consumption during CdTe deposition. (a) CSS-deposited CdS containing no oxygen. Note significant consumption of CdS. (b) CSS-deposited CdS that was postdeposition treated to incorporate oxygen. Note much less consumption of CdS. (c) CBD-deposited CdS. Note very little consumption of CdS. From Albin DS, Yan Y, and Al-Jassim MM (2002) The effect of oxygen on interface microstructure evolution in CdS/CdTe solar cells. *Progress in Photovoltaics: Research and Applications* 10: 309–322 [38].

amount of CdS consumed during the high-temperature CdTe deposition. The reduced CdS consumption not only limits the extent of the CdSTe alloy that forms on the CdTe side of the device but also appears to limit the amount of Te that diffuses into the CdS layer.

It has been suggested that the resulting moderation of the extent of the CdSTe thickness by oxygen limits the depth of the CdSTe/CdTe interface, which limits the depth of the quasi-homojunction [34, 39]. One possible explanation for these effects of oxygen is that oxygen acts as an isoelectronic substitutional defect for Te and/or S vacancies. The formation of these defects could limit diffusion and possibly reduce interface recombination. However, at this time, the effects of this diffusion on junction formation and ultimate cell performance are not well understood.

1.19.6.6 CdCl$_2$ Activation

Since about 1985, nearly all research and commercial thin-film CdTe PV devices have incorporated a CdCl$_2$ 'treatment' or 'activation step'. The incorporation of this step is one of the main reasons why so many different groups, using different CdTe deposition processes and temperatures, have been able to achieve conversion efficiencies greater than 10%. Many call the CdCl$_2$ process an 'equalizer' step because it results in CdTe polycrystalline thin-film material that demonstrates minority-carrier lifetimes that are similar and sufficiently high to enable good device performance.

For PVD CdTe (e.g., GPT, evaporated, and sputtered), the CdCl$_2$ process usually involves dipping or spraying a CdCl$_2$-saturated methanol or water solution onto the CdTe surface after deposition, followed by drying and annealing in an oxygen-containing ambient at ~400 °C for ~10 min. The CdCl$_2$ treatment can also be performed by combining the application and thermal steps into a CdCl$_2$ vapor process at ~400 °C (e.g., GPT, evaporation, and CVD). For solution-based CdTe deposition processes, chlorine can be included in the CdTe precursor with results similar to a postdeposition CdCl$_2$ treatment.

For small-grained CdTe (e.g., solution or low-temperature CdTe growth), the CdCl$_2$ process typically leads to complete recrystallization that produces larger polycrystalline grains [37]. Although for larger grained material (higher temperature CdTe growth), the CdCl$_2$ process generally does not lead to significant recrystallization, both small- and large-grained materials demonstrate higher minority-carrier lifetime after the CdCl$_2$ treatment. For large-grained material, the improvement is primarily due to passivation at grain boundaries [40].

The particular defect modifications associated with the CdCl$_2$ treatment continue to be debated [41]. In general, adding either excess Cd or Cl to CdTe generally results in the formation of donor defects. However, many technologists associate improved p-type CdTe material quality following the CdCl$_2$ treatment with the formation of what has become known as the 'Cl A-center', which is believed to be an acceptor level located ~150 meV above the valence band and ascribed to a Cl on Te-vacancy defect (Cl$_{Te}$) paired to a Cd-vacancy defect (V$_{Cd}$–Cl$_{Te}$) [3, 42, 43].

One artifact of the CdCl$_2$ process that is often not discussed relates to residuals left behind on the CdTe surface. It has been shown that, if the CdCl$_2$ process is wet (application of a saturated methanol or aqueous solution), residuals are either cadmium oxychlorides or oxytellurides [40], as shown in **Figure 7**. Removing these residuals will often occur during precontact chemical etching step(s) and is therefore not a major concern for wet contact processing. If, however, a dry contacting process is desired, sufficient removal of CdCl$_2$ residuals requires the use of a dry removal process (e.g., ion-beam or ion-etch processes) [40]. If a vapor process is used for the CdCl$_2$ process, the resulting residual is CdCl$_2$ that can be removed using a thermal precontact processing [44].

In addition to the CdCl$_2$ treatment affecting the electrical properties of the CdTe layer, it also alters CdSTe interdiffusion. **Figures 8(a)** and **8(b)** compare secondary ion-mass spectrometry (SIMS) of two CdS/CdTe devices that were deposited at two different CSS substrate temperatures. Both figures also show the sulfur (S) profile before and after a CdCl$_2$ process. By comparing these sulfur profiles, one notes that the extent of S diffusion from the CdS layer during the CdCl$_2$ treatment is much greater for the device shown in **Figure 8(a)** where the CdTe was deposited at lower temperature (i.e., 550 °C). Recalling that the amount of oxygen at the CdS/CdTe also affects the extent of the CdSTe layer, one notes that controlling the formation of the CdSTe layer requires (at least) controlling the CdTe temperature, the CdCl$_2$ temperature and time, and the amount of available oxygen. The interrelationship between these parameters begins to explain why developing a reproducible and cost-effective CdTe PV module process requires a deep understanding of the mechanisms at work and the ability to control these mechanisms.

The above description of how the CdCl$_2$ treatment affects CdSTe and CdTe material properties provides clues to how the treatment also affects device performance. **Figures 9(a)** and **9(b)** show the effect of the CdCl$_2$ treatment process on device performance as a function of CSS CdTe substrate temperature [39]. The figure shows that while higher CdTe deposition temperatures lead to improved device performance, the CdCl$_2$ process improves performance at all substrate temperatures. In this data set, a device process parameter (i.e., substrate temperature) was altered to yield a device that responds better to a given (wet) CdCl$_2$ treatment. However, depending on process constraints, the CdCl$_2$ treatment could also be varied to produce a higher performance for a given device process. Because these process alterations can be subtle, and are often done without full knowledge of what aspect of cell functionality is being altered, it may be difficult to know precisely how a specific CdCl$_2$ process parameter may be affecting junction performance.

1.19.6.7 Back Contact

For superstrate CdTe PV devices, the last step in device formation is fabrication of the back contact. Until recently (about 2000), most CdTe technologists believed the primary function of the back contact was to establish a low-resistance pathway for electrons to enter the CdTe layer during device operation. It was believed that the semiconductor junction properties (i.e., n-type and p-type regions, respective space-charge regions, and minority-carrier lifetimes) were established prior to contacting. However, more recent

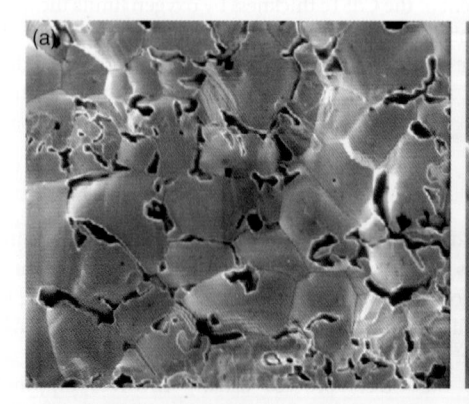

Figure 7 SEM micrographs of CdCl$_2$ oxychloride residuals from wet CdCl$_2$ processing treatment. (a) Low magnification. (b) Higher magnification. From Gessert TA, Romero MJ, Perkins CL, et al. (2001) Microscopic residuals on polycrystalline CdTe following wet CdCl2 treatment. *Materials Research Society Symposium Proceedings*, vol. 668, pp.H1.10.1–H1.10.6. Warrendale, PA: MRS [40].

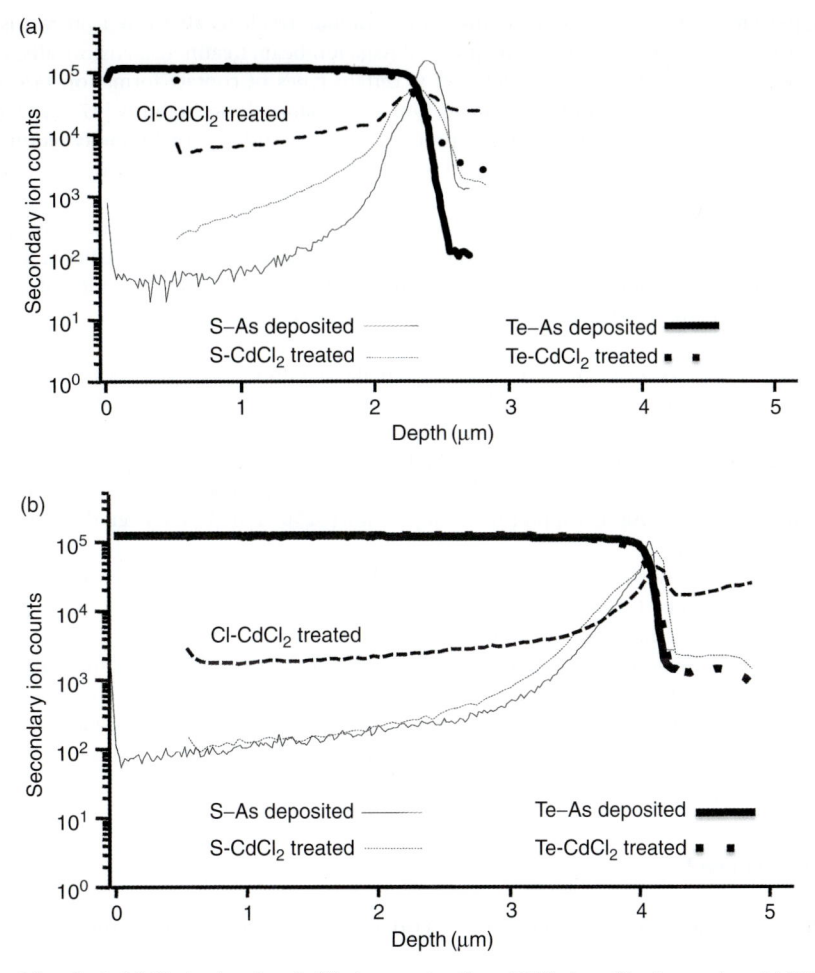

Figure 8 SIMS analysis of the effect of CdCl$_2$ treatment on S diffusion as a function of CdTe deposition temperature. (a) 550°C. (b) 600°C. Data from Dhere RG, Albin DS, Rose DH, *et al.* (1996) Intermixing at the CdS/CdTe interface and its effect on device performance. *Materials Research Society Symposium Proceedings*, vol. 426, pp. 361–366. Warrendale, PA: MRS [39].

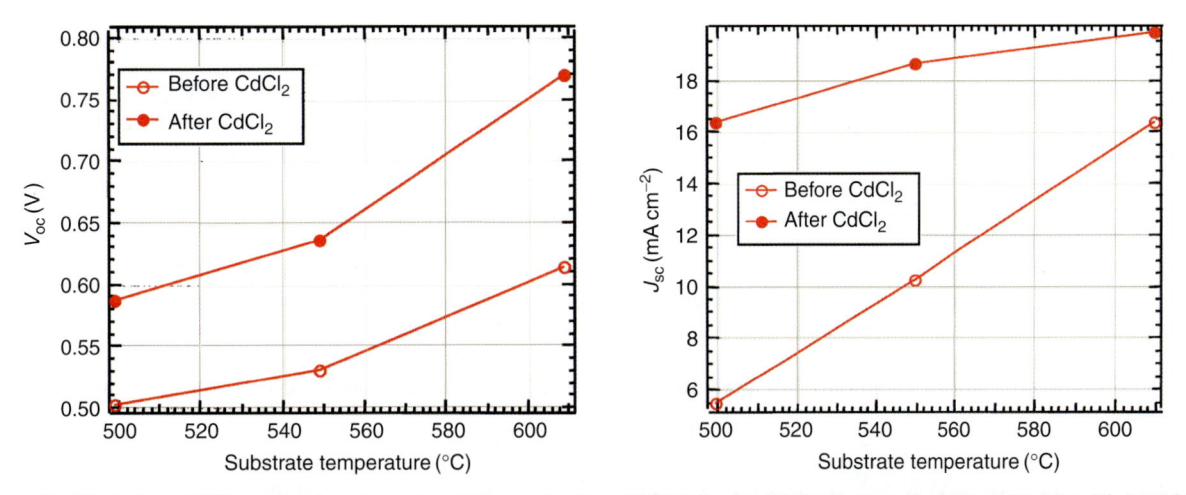

Figure 9 Effect of a wet CdCl$_2$ treatment on device J_{sc} and V_{oc} as a function of CSS CdTe substrate temperature. From Dhere RG, Albin DS, Rose DH, *et al.* (1996) Intermixing at the CdS/CdTe interface and its effect on device performance. *Materials Research Society Symposium Proceedings*, vol. 426, pp. 361–366. Warrendale, PA: MRS [39].

studies have shown that the back contact process not only provides a low-resistance current pathway but also significantly alters the electrical properties of the underlying CdTe layer, thereby significantly affecting junction functionality.

The first consideration in developing a back-contacting process is to determine if/how any residuals from the CdCl$_2$ process should be removed. Depending on how the CdCl$_2$ process was performed, this removal can be easy or difficult (i.e., removing CdCl$_2$

residual following a vapor process is easy, while removing Cd oxychloride residuals after a wet process is more difficult) [40]. Removal process options include thermal, chemical, and physical (e.g., ion-beam treatment). Historically, a chemical option was preferred because it often produces a Te-rich layer that assists certain types of contact formation [45, 46]. It has also been suggested that gettering of excess Cu by etch-formed Te inclusions can enhance device stability [47]. One also needs to consider that the process used to remove CdCl$_2$ residuals must also produce the CdTe surface stoichiometry required for specific contact functionality (i.e., a p-ZnTe contact interface requires a stoichiometric CdTe surface, whereas many other contact designs require a Te-rich surface layer).

For most processes used for PV devices, the as-deposited and/or CdCl$_2$-treated bulk CdTe layer is of insufficient electrical quality for effective junction operation. Specifically, depending on the CdTe source material used, the specifics of the CdTe deposition, and CdCl$_2$ treatment processes, the net acceptor density will be generally too low ($< 10^{-13}$ cm^{-3}) for optimal device operation, and/or the material may be n-type. Furthermore, even if the acceptor density is sufficiently high, the minority-carrier lifetime is generally too short (< 0.5 ns).

Most contacting processes utilize a contact interface layer (CIFL) that can diffuse one or more dopant species into the CdTe layer. Although Cu has been historically used for the active diffusing dopant species, other group I species (i.e., Au or Ag) or group V species (i.e., P, As, Sb, or Bi) have been found to demonstrate potential [3]. Although the precise defect formation that occurs during dopant diffusion remains debated, it is known that a successful diffusion alters the electrical properties of the underlying CdTe layer so that it becomes sufficiently p-type to establish a strong field (i.e., narrow space charge) in the ~0.5–1 μm of the device nearest to the CdS layer [48]. Furthermore, Cu diffusion at appropriate temperature (~250–350 °C) has been found to increase the lifetime of the CdTe layer [49].

In contrast to doping the CdTe layer from the contact and producing n–p junction functionality, an alternatively proposed contact design yields a low-resistance CdTe/contact interface while sustaining a CdTe layer that is electrically intrinsic and demonstrates a high minority-carrier lifetime (i.e., n–i–p junction functionality) [50]. Presently, the contacts for the highest performance devices produce p-type doping by adding a small amount of Cu as a CIFL and diffusing it into the CdTe layer at ~250–350 °C. Low CdTe/contact resistance can be assisted by narrowing the barrier that forms between the CIFL and CdTe layers. Typical CIFLs are thin layers of ZnTe:Cu, HgTe:Cu, CuTe, or (chemically formed) Te through which a thin layer (~1–2 nm) of pure Cu is diffused. On top of the CIFL is deposited metal(s) that reduces lateral resistivity and may also be chosen to limit moisture ingress and/or provide functionality to enhance stability [51, 52].

1.19.7 Where Is the Junction?

Having established a basic understanding of what each layer of a CdTe PV device does, a final question remains regarding where the semiconductor junction is actually located. We now know that the specific parameters of the CdS and CdTe deposition, combined with the parameters of the CdCl$_2$ treatment, affect the formation and extent of the CdSTe layer. Furthermore, we know that diffusion from the CIFL additionally alters the electrical properties of the CdTe, thereby altering the junction. However, we still have not discussed our present understanding of where the junction is.

To understand this better, one must also consider that when sulfur is diffused into the CdTe layer (forming a CdSTe interdiffused layer), the bandgap of the CdSTe alloy decreases relative to CdTe or CdS. This is called band bowing and is shown in **Figure 10(a)**. At a temperature of ~600 °C, depending on the stoichiometry of the CdSTe alloy, it can exist as single-phase hexagonal (Wurtzite, ~85–100% sulfur), single-phase cubic (Zincblende, 0 to ~15% sulfur), or a mixed phase CdSTe material (between ~15% and ~85% sulfur) [53]. During intermixing of the CdS and CdTe layers at the CdTe deposition temperature, it is believed that all three of these phases will be present in what has so far been described simply as the CdSTe layer. Many technologists believe that it is reasonable to assume the CdSTe layer will be primarily in the wurtzite phase (i.e., S rich) nearest to the CdS layer, primarily in the zincblende phase (Te-rich) nearest to the CdTe layer, and in the mixed phase between these two (primarily) single-phase endpoints. However, few reports exist that detail this region to this extent [34].

For the type of devices produced at NREL, we believe the electrical junction forms between the nonalloyed CdTe and a diffusion-formed zincblende CdSTe [34]. Analysis of the IR absorption characteristics of quantum efficiency data indicates the 'effective sulfur concentration' in the junction region is ~10%. This concentration is estimated by calculating the 'effective bandgap' from device quantum efficiency (~1.46 eV), while accounting for the known band bowing. This estimation process is shown graphically in **Figure 10(a)**. A schematic diagram and an associated field diagram are shown in **Figure 10(b)**.

1.19.8 Considerations for Large-Scale Deployment

The previous discussion suggests that thin-film CdTe PV modules are a viable option for large-scale, long-term, renewable electricity generation. This is because the specific 'cost' of these thin-film modules is (or is quickly becoming) less than the 'price' of delivering electricity in many parts of the world. Although economic viability is a necessary element for both continued production expansion and societal acceptance, the promise of thin-film PV as a source of 'sustainable' base energy requires additional issues to be considered. Even though a thorough treatment of any of the following topics is beyond the scope of this chapter, the following

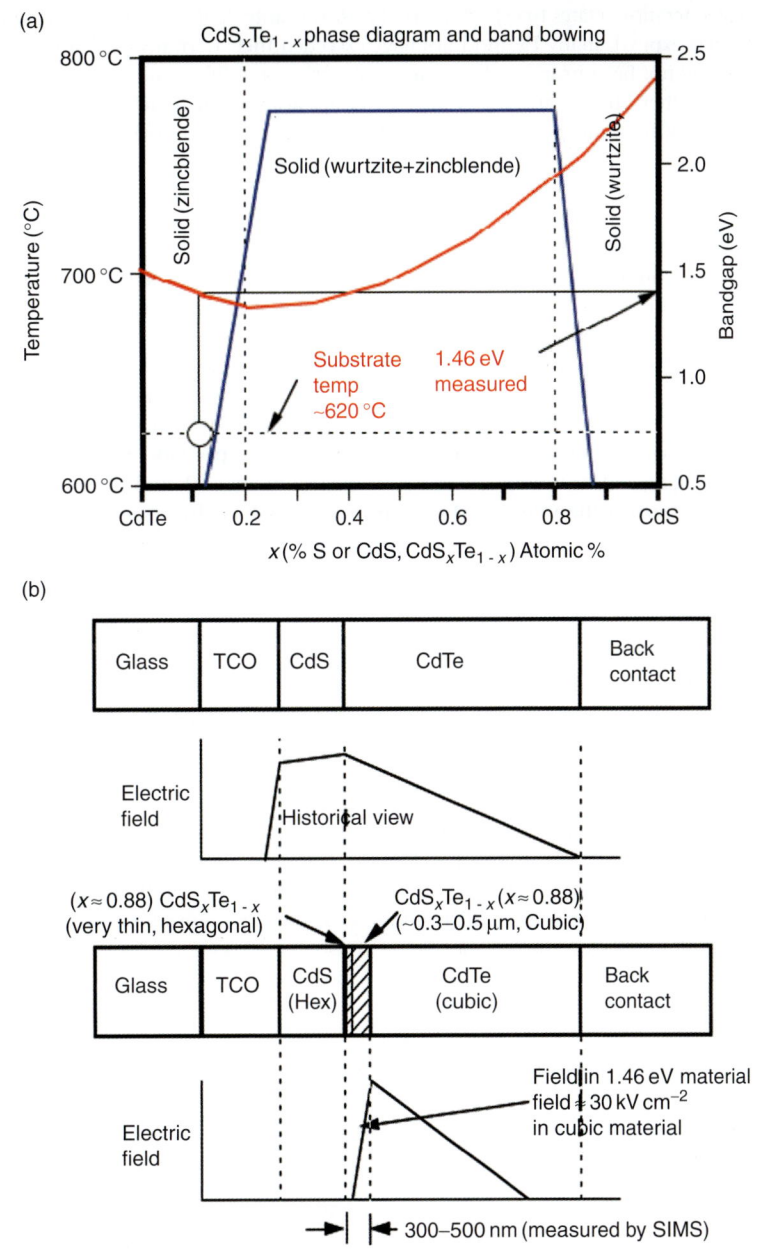

Figure 10 (a) Diagram illustrating the effect of band bowing and phase separation in the CdSTe layer. (b) Diagram illustrating the location of the junction in a CdS/CdTe PV device from a historic and more recent perspective.

discussion suggests why many believe these topics are rapidly becoming just as important as specific cost in the widespread establishment of any PV energy infrastructure.

1.19.8.1 Reliability

As any PV technology matures from the laboratory to commercial production, a point is reached when product reliability must be understood well enough to assign a product warranty. Presently, most thin-film CdTe PV module manufacturers desire to align with module warranties consistent with established PV alternatives (i.e., wafer-based Si). This level of reliability is typically consistent with the panel delivering at least 80% of its initial power after 25 years of field deployment. Assuming a constant exponential degradation, this equates to about 0.9% power loss per year. Because thin-film manufacturers need to ensure their products demonstrate reliability consistent with their warranty, developing techniques that can rapidly, accurately, and cost-effectively probe reliability expectations remains one of the more critical challenges for both public- and private-sector PV researchers.

Another evolving value consideration relates to expectations of post-warranty deployment. Like many older cars that are still on the road after their warranty has expired, many PV modules have exceeded their warranty period but remain usefully deployed. Although degraded modules may not be appropriate for many applications, modules with derated performance will continue to have significant value in many other off-grid and/or remote-power applications. It therefore seems reasonable to assume that designing CdTe module reliability for time periods exceeding the warranty could impart (marketing) advantages to new PV products.

1.19.8.2 Mineral Availability

As production of all types of PV technologies expands, there is increasing debate as to whether mineral availability will become a significant factor in module cost. This is especially true for present thin-film alternatives because each uses a mineral component that is perceived to be relatively scarce. The minerals most typically mentioned in this context are Ge (for amorphous Si devices), In (for CIGS devices), and Te (for CdTe PV devices). A direct answer in this debate is complicated because, like other (secondary) minerals that are considered 'scarce', most of these minerals are presently coprocessed along with other (primary) minerals.

Because of this interdependence, parameters that will influence Te availability include the following: (1) the amount of production of the primary ore; (2) concentration of the secondary mineral in the primary ore; (3) industry incentive to coprocess the secondary mineral (i.e., emerging and/or multiple markets for the secondary ore); and (4) environmental, governmental, or practical constraints related to extracting the mineral. The main message is that the business plan of anyone considering the establishment of a large-scale production facility for any PV technology should include thorough advisement from a reputable mineral geologist.

1.19.8.3 Environmental

It is well known that although PV modules do not produce toxic waste or greenhouse gas when operating, toxic products and/or by-products can be produced during the initial production and recycling phases of the PV module's life cycle. This waste is the primary component of what is often referred to as the 'total life-cycle ecotoxicity' of any PV technology. Although this ecotoxicity derives from many sources, much of it depends on the particular chemicals used to process subcomponents, as well as the burning of fossil fuels to mine, transport, or refine raw materials, or provide the electricity used to produce the modules.

Realizing that different module-production methods may use different amounts and types of chemicals, and that different countries use different amounts, types, and mixtures of fossil fuels to produce and deliver their electricity, it is easy to see how associating a given level of ecotoxicity with any particular PV technology involves significant assumptions of both production process and location. Furthermore, the energy mix will continue to evolve as more PV-derived electricity is used to fuel the production of PV modules (i.e., often called the 'breeder PV' energy-balance scenario). Nevertheless, reports are beginning to suggest some useful guidance for technology-dependent reduction in PV ecotoxicity [54–56].

For example, a primary source of ecotoxicity in glass-encapsulated, thin-film CdTe modules arises from the production of the glass. This suggests that significant opportunities may exist to reduce ecotoxicity (as well as to reduce the energy used to make the module) by developing module designs that incorporate either less glass or glass produced in such a way to generate less ecotoxicity.

1.19.8.4 Energy-Payback Time

The energy-payback time (EPBT) of a PV module is the amount of time a module must produce power to recover the energy it took to produce the module initially. Although assumptions vary among EPBT calculations, the energy to produce the module should be as inclusive as possible, accounting for everything from the energy needed to mine, transport, refine, produce, and deliver all module subcomponents to that required to deposit/assemble/package the module, deploy it, and eventually recycle the module at the end of its life.

Within this definition, if a particular module is expected to last for 25 years and it demonstrates an EPBT of 5 years, one can roughly expect to get about 5 times more energy out of the module than was used to produce it. Although this ratio of energy returned-to-invested sounds great, a 5-year EPBT may still be too long when one accounts for the production-growth scenarios that are presently occurring.

A 5-year EPBT might be consistent with the dominant PV technologies and efficiency levels of several years ago. In this case, as long as the PV module produced more energy in its expected lifetime (~15–25 years) than it took to produce the module, it was considered a net energy producer. In contrast, we presently have PV production technologies and module efficiencies that yield EPBTs of 2–5 years or less. An EPBT of 2 years would allow a module with a 25-year warranty to produce more than 10 times the original energy investment during its lifetime. Although this sounds both environmentally and financially attractive, a serious complication arises when the growth in PV production becomes so rapid that the expected doubling time of production rate becomes shorter than the EPBT. In this rapid-growth scenario, an energy balance at any given time during production expansion can be achieved only if the EPBT is equal to or less than the expected production doubling time. Otherwise, additional amounts of traditional energy resources (e.g., fossil fuels) may have to be supplied to provide the energy to sustain the rapid growth in PV production. Furthermore, if PV is to be a 'net energy producer' during this period of rapidly expanding production, the EPBT may need to be 'significantly less' than the production doubling time. Specifically, the 46% exponential growth in PV production observed during the past 10 years indicates that EPBTs need to be less than 2 years. Therefore, the primary question is, what is the EPBT for different PV technologies and specifically for thin-film CdTe PV technologies?

Recent reports have indicated that most thin-film technologies may have advantages over wafer Si in the EPBT criteria, with some thin-film PV module technologies (i.e., CdTe) demonstrating EPBTs of between 6 months and 1 year [54, 56].

1.19.9 Conclusion

This chapter has presented a technological description of components and process alternatives consistent with the present generation of thin-film CdTe PV devices. The chapter also suggests why this technology may embody considerable opportunity for becoming a significant part of future large-scale electricity production. However, even when economic requirements are met, the establishment of a sustainable energy-production infrastructure from CdTe technologies will require additional consideration of longer term issues. These include reliability, material availability, environmental, and energy-payback time.

Acknowledgments

The author wishes to thank R.G. Dhere, D.S. Albin, T.M. Barnes, and T.J. Coutts of NREL for assistance and thoughtful suggestions regarding the preparation of this chapter. Portions of this work were supported under DOE Contract No. DE-AC36-08-GO28308 to NREL.

References

[1] Mehata S (2011) PV news annual data collection result: 2010 cell, module production explodes past 20 GW. *PV News* 29(5), May.
[2] Coggeshall C and Margolis R. (2011) *Solar vision study*. U.S. Dept. of Energy Report (to be published).
[3] Zanio K (1978) *Cadmium Telluride, Vol. 13: Semiconductors and Semimetals*, pp. 164–186. New York: Academic Press.
[4] Meyer E, Martini M, and Sternberg J (1972) Measurement of disappearance rate of Se-75 sodium selenite in eye of rat by CdTe medical probe. *IEEE Transaction on Nuclear Science* 19: 237.
[5] Garcia DA, Entine G, and Tow DE (1974) Detection of small bone abscesses with a high-resolution cadmium telluride probe. *Journal of Nuclear Medicine* 15: 892.
[6] Vodakov YA, Lomakina GA, Naumov GP, and Maslakovets YP (1960) Properties of p–n junctions in cadmium telluride photocells. *Soviet Physics – Solid State* 2: 11.
[7] Naumov GP and Nikolaeva OV (1961) The efficiency of transformation of direct solar radiation energy into electric energy using a CdTe photocell. *Soviet Physics – Solid State* 3: 2718.
[8] Cusano DA (1963) CdTe solar cells and photovoltaic heterojunctions in II–IV compounds. *Solid-State Electronics* 6: 217.
[9] Nicoll FH (1963) The use of close spacing in chemical-transport systems for growing epitaxial layers of semiconductors. *Journal of the Electrochemical Society* 110: 1165.
[10] Cusano DA and Lorenz MR (1964) CdTe hole lifetime from the photovoltaic effect. *Solid State Communications* 2: 125.
[11] Artobolevskaya ES, Afanas'eva EA, Vodop'yanov LK, and Sushkov VP (1968) Photoelectromagnetic effect in cadmium telluride. *Soviet Physics – Semiconductors* 1: 1531.
[12] Cusano DA (1967) Thin film studies and electro-optical effects. In: Aven M and Prener JS (eds.) *Physics and Chemistry of II–VI Compounds*, ch. 14, pp. 709–766. Amsterdam: North-Holland Publishing Co.
[13] Carmody M, Mallick S, Margetis J, *et al.* (2010) Single-crystal II–VI on Si single junction and tandem solar cells. *Applied Physics Letters* 96: 153502.
[14] Bonnet D and Rabenhorst H (1972) New results on the development of thin film p-CdTe–n-CdS heterojunction solar cell. *Proceedings of the 9th IEEE PVSC*, pp. 129–132. Silver Springs, MD, USA.
[15] Yamaguchi K, Nakayama N, Matsumoto H, and Ikegami S (1977) CdS–CdTe solar cell prepared by vapor phase epitaxy. *Japanese Journal of Applied Physics* 16: 1203.
[16] Bube RH, Buch F, Fahrenbruch AL, *et al.* (1977) Photovoltaic energy-conversion with n-CdS–p-CdTe heterojunctions and other II–VI junctions. *IEEE Transactions on Electron Devices* ED-24: 487.
[17] Aranovich J, Golmayo D, Fahrenbruch AL, and Bube RH (1980) Photo-voltaic properties of ZnO–CdTe heterojunctions prepared by spray pyrolysis. *Journal of Applied Physics* 51: 4260.
[18] Bube RH, Fahrenbruch A, Aranovich J, *et al.* (1975) Applied research in II–VI compound materials for heterojunction solar cells. *NSF Report No. NSF/RANN/SE/AER-75-1679/75/4*.
[19] Wu X (2004) High efficiency polycrystalline CdTe thin-film solar cells. *Solar Energy* 77: 803–814.
[20] Bube RH (1988) CdTe junction phenomena. *Solar Cells* 23: 1.
[21] Chu TL (1988) Cadmium telluride solar cells. In: Coutts TJ and Meakin JD (eds.) *Current Topics in Photovoltaics*, ch. 3, vol. 3, pp. 235–300. New York: Academic Press.
[22] Braun GW and Skinner DE (2007) Experience scaling-up manufacturing of emerging photovoltaic technologies. *National Renewable Energy Laboratory Subcontract Report*, NREL/SR-640-39165, January.
[23] Rose DH, Hasoon FS, Dhere RG, *et al.* (1999) Fabrication procedures and process sensitivities for CdS/CdTe solar cells. *Progress in Photovoltaics: Research and Applications* 7: 331–340.
[24] Romeo N, Bosio A, and Canevari V (1992) Large crystalline grain CdTe thin films for photovoltaic application. *International Journal of Social Energy* 12: 183–186.
[25] Singh VP, McClure JC, Lush GB, *et al.* (1999) Thin film CdTe–CdS heterojunction solar cells on lightweight metal substrates. *Solar Energy Materials and Solar Cells* 59: 145–161.
[26] Greenberg JH (1996) P–T–X phase equilibrium and vapor pressure scanning of non-stoichiometry in CdTe. *Journal of Crystal Growth* 161: 1–11.
[27] Zunger A (2003) Practical doping principles. *Applied Physics Letters* 83(1): 57–59.
[28] Tatarenko S, Bassani F, Saminadayar K, *et al.* (1993) Indium doping of (001), (111), and (211) CdTe layers grown by molecular beam epitaxy. *Journal of Crystal Growth* 127: 318–322.
[29] Dhese KA, Devine P, Ashenford DE, *et al.* (1994) Photoluminescence and p-type conductivity in CdTe:N grown by molecular beam epitaxy. *Journal of Applied Physics* 76(9): 5423–5428.
[30] Dhere RG, Bonnet-Eymard M, Charlet E, *et al.* (2011) CdTe solar cell with industrial Al:ZnO on soda-lime glass. *Thin Solid Films* 519(21): 7142–7145.
[31] Coutts TJ, Young DL, and Li X (2000) Characterization of transparent conducting oxides. *Materials Research Society Bulletin* 25: 58–65.

[32] Wu X, Mulligan WP, and Coutts TJ (1996) Recent developments in RF sputtered cadmium stannate films. *Thin Solid Films* 286: 274–276.
[33] Gessert TA, Burst J, Li X, *et al.* (2011) Advantages of TCO thin films with controlled permittivity for thin film photovoltaic solar cell. *Thin Solid Films* 519(21): 7146–7148.
[34] Dhere RG, Zhang Y, Romero MJ, *et al.* (2008) Investigation of junction properties of CdS/CdTe solar cells and their correlation to device properties. *Proceedings of the 33rd IEEE PVSC*, Manuscript No. 279. San Diego, CA, USA, 11–16 May.
[35] Wu X, Dhere RG, Yan Y, *et al.* (2002) High efficiency polycrystalline CdTe thin-film solar cells with an oxygenated amorphous CdS (a-CdS:O) window layer. *Proceedings of the 29th IEEE PVSC*, pp. 531–535. New Orleans, LA, USA, 20–24 May.
[36] Powell RC, Dorer GL, Reiter NA, *et al.* (1999) US Patent 5,945,163, 13 August.
[37] Moutinho HR, Dhere RG, Al-Jassim MM, *et al.* (1999) Investigation of induced recrystallization and stress in close-spaced sublimated and radio-frequency magnetron sputtered CdTe thin films. *Journal of Vacuum Science & Technology A* 17(4): 1793–1798.
[38] Albin DS, Yan Y, and Al-Jassim MM (2002) The effect of oxygen on interface microstructure evolution in CdS/CdTe solar cells. *Progress in Photovoltaics: Research and Applications* 10: 309–322.
[39] Dhere RG, Albin DS, Rose DH, *et al.* (1996) Intermixing at the CdS/CdTe interface and its effect on device performance. *Materials Research Society Symposium Proceedings*, vol. 426, pp. 361–366. Warrendale, PA: MRS.
[40] Gessert TA, Romero MJ, Perkins CL, *et al.* (2001) Microscopic residuals on polycrystalline CdTe following wet $CdCl_2$ treatment. *Materials Research Society Symposium Proceedings*, vol. 668, pp.H1.10.1–H1.10.6. Warrendale, PA: MRS.
[41] Corwine C, Sites JR, Gessert TA, *et al.* (2005) CdTe photoluminescence: Comparison of solar-cell material with surface-modified single crystals. *Applied Physics Letters* 86: 221901.
[42] Halliday DP, Potter MDG, Boyle DS, and Durose K (2001) Photoluminescence characterization of ion implanted CdTe. *Materials Research Society Symposium Proceedings*, vol. 668, p. H1.8.1. Warrendale, PA: MRS.
[43] Valdna V, Hiie J, and Gavrilov A (2001) Defects in Cl-doped CdTe thin films. *Solid State Phenomena* 80: 155.
[44] Waters DM, Niles D, Gessert T, *et al.* (1988) Surface analysis of CdTe after various pre-contact treatment. *Proceedings of the 2nd World Conference on Photovoltaic Solar Energy Conversion*, p. 1031. Vienna, Austria. Luxembourg: European Commission.
[45] Li X, Niles DW, Hasoon FS, *et al.* (1999) Effect of nitric–phosphoric acid etches on materials properties and back-contact formation in CdTe-based solar cells. *Journal of Vacuum Science & Technology A* 17(3): 805–809.
[46] Levi D, Albin D, and King D (2000) Influence of surface composition on back-contact performance in CdTe/CdS PV devices. *Progress in Photovoltaics: Research and Applications* 8: 591–602.
[47] Albin DS, Demtsu SH, and McMahon TJ (2006) Film thickness and chemical processing effects on the stability of cadmium telluride solar cells. *Thin Solid Films* 515: 2659–2668.
[48] Gessert TA, Asher S, Johnston S, *et al.* (2006) Formation of ZnTe:Cu/Ti contacts at high temperature for CdS/CdTe devices. *Proceedings of the 4th World Conference on Photovoltaic Energy Conversion*, pp. 432–435. Waikoloa, Hawaii, 7–12 May.
[49] Gessert TA, Metzger WK, Dippo P, *et al.* (2009) Dependence of carrier lifetime on Cu-contacting temperature and ZnTe:Cu thickness in CdS/CdTe thin film solar cells. *Thin Solid Films* 517: 2370–2371.
[50] Sites J and Pan J (2007) Strategies to increase CdTe solar-cell voltage. *Thin Solid Films* 515: 6099–6102.
[51] Gessert TA, Perkins CL, Asher SE, *et al.* (2003) Study of ZnTe:Cu/metal interfaces in CdS/CdTe photovoltaic solar cells. *Materials Research Society Symposium Proceedings*, vol. 796, pp. 79–84. Warrendale, PA: MRS.
[52] Gessert TA, Asher S, Johnston S, *et al.* (2007) Analysis of CdS/CdTe devices incorporating a ZnTe:Cu/Ti contact. *Thin Solid Films* 515: 6103–6106.
[53] Nunoue S-Y, Hemmi T, and Kato E (1990) *Journal of the Electrochemical Society* 137(4): 1248–1251.
[54] Raugei M, Bargigli S, and Ulgiati S (2007) Life cycle assessment and energy pay-back time of advanced photovoltaic modules: CdTe and CIS compared to Poly-Si. *Energy* 32: 1310–1318.
[55] Fthenakis VM (2004) Life cycle impact analysis of cadmium in CdTe PV production. *Renewable and Sustainable Energy Reviews* 8: 303–334.
[56] Held M and Ilg R (2008) Life cycle assessment (LCA) of CdTe thin-film PV modules and material flow analysis (MFA) of cadmium within EU27. *Proceedings of the 23rd European Photovoltaic Solar Energy Conference*, pp. 2551–2557. Valencia, Spain, 1–5 September.

1.20 Plastic Solar Cells

L Sims, Konarka Technologies GmbH, Nürnberg, Germany; Universität Augsburg, Augsburg, Germany
H-J Egelhaaf, JA Hauch, FR Kogler, and R Steim, Konarka Technologies GmbH, Nürnberg, Germany

© 2012 Elsevier Ltd. All rights reserved.

1.20.1	**Introduction**	440
1.20.1.1	Why Solar Cells?	440
1.20.1.2	Why OSCs?	441
1.20.2	**Fundamentals**	442
1.20.2.1	Comparison of Inorganic Solar Cells and OSCs	442
1.20.2.1.1	Inorganic semiconductors	442
1.20.2.1.2	Organic semiconductors	442
1.20.2.1.3	Conduction mechanisms in organic semiconductors	444
1.20.2.1.4	Basic working principles of inorganic solar cells and OSCs	445
1.20.2.2	Solar Cell Device Architectures	448
1.20.2.2.1	Bilayer architecture	448
1.20.2.2.2	Blend architecture	449
1.20.2.3	Characteristic Values of a Solar Cell	449
1.20.2.3.1	*JV* curve under illumination	449
1.20.2.3.2	*JV* curve in the dark	449
1.20.2.3.3	External and internal quantum efficiency	450
1.20.3	**Materials for OSCs**	450
1.20.3.1	Active Materials for OSCs	450
1.20.3.1.1	Donor materials	451
1.20.3.1.2	Acceptor materials	452
1.20.3.2	Interfacial Materials	453
1.20.3.2.1	Choosing the right interfacial materials	453
1.20.3.2.2	Material types	455
1.20.3.3	Electrode Materials	456
1.20.3.3.1	Transparent electrodes	456
1.20.3.3.2	Opaque electrodes	456
1.20.4	**Driving Efficiency**	457
1.20.4.1	Preferable Properties of the Donor Molecule	457
1.20.4.2	Impact of Morphology	457
1.20.4.2.1	Influence of solvents on morphology	458
1.20.4.2.2	Influence of mixing ratio and concentration	459
1.20.4.2.3	Influence of annealing	459
1.20.4.2.4	Binary solvent systems	461
1.20.4.3	Improved Material Properties for Efficiency Increase	461
1.20.4.4	Effect of Interference in the Device	463
1.20.4.5	Solar Cell Architectures for Enhanced Device Performance	463
1.20.4.5.1	Tandem architecture	463
1.20.4.5.2	Nanostructured solar cells	464
1.20.4.5.3	Further device architectures	464
1.20.5	**Stability of OSCs**	465
1.20.5.1	Encapsulation	465
1.20.5.2	Electrodes	466
1.20.5.3	Interfacial Layers	467
1.20.5.4	Active Materials	468
1.20.5.5	Testing the Lifetime	469
1.20.6	**Production Methods**	470
1.20.6.1	Layer Deposition for Single Devices	470
1.20.6.2	Large-Scale Production Methods	472
1.20.7	**Summary and Outlook**	473
References		474
Further Reading		480

Glossary

Acceptor Molecule that mainly accepts electrons from another molecule (e.g., donor).
Bulk heterojunction or blend solar cell Solar cell where the active layer consists of a mixture of donor and acceptor materials.
Copolymer Macromolecule composed of two or more different repeating units, for example, A-B-A-B-A-B....
Donor Molecule that mainly donates electrons to another molecule (e.g., acceptor).
Organic molecule/polymer Molecule/polymer consisting mainly of carbon atoms.
Polymer Macromolecule composed of repeating monomer units, for example, A-A-A....
Roll-to-roll printing Low-cost printing technique also used for newspaper printing.

1.20.1 Introduction

1.20.1.1 Why Solar Cells?

The discussion about alternative energy sources has accelerated during the last decades and various technologies for harvesting energy have been demonstrated by research and already implemented by companies. One of the most promising technologies makes use of sunlight to generate electricity. The most charming feature of solar cells is that their source of energy, the sun, will always be available – at least as long as humans will be able to populate the earth. In 2008, the world's energy demand summed up to 5.32×10^{20} J and it is projected that it will increase to 8.12×10^{20} J in the year 2035 [1]. The sun delivers 2.7×10^{24} J every year when considering only the part of the sun's energy that reaches the earth's surface without being reflected or absorbed by the atmosphere or clouds [2]. Thus, only 0.02% of the sun's energy reaching our planet is enough to cover the annual demand of mankind. In 2009, the total capacity of grid-connected and off-grid photovoltaic installations was 24 GW. This delivers a fraction of less than 0.1% of the worldwide energy consumption and therefore the increase of the solar power portion is a logical consequence [3]. For this reason, solar cell development has been a very active effort for the past 50 years. Today the third generation (3G) of solar cells is in the development stage. A short overview of the three generations is presented by Bagnall and Boreland [4].

The first generation (1G) consists of single-junction solar cells made of mono- or polycrystalline silicon. About 90% of the current solar installations make use of these 1G devices [5]. The theoretical efficiency limit for these devices was calculated in 1961 by Shockley and Queisser to be about 30% [6]. The efficiencies reached in production are currently slightly below 20%. However, efficiencies of around 25% have been demonstrated for lab devices, which is near the theoretical limit [7]. Depending on the segments of the market, photovoltaics have already achieved cost-competitiveness or are close to achieving it. In off-grid applications, for example, it can be a cheaper alternative to diesel power. In grid-connected applications, the best photovoltaic prices are approaching 25¢ kWh^{-1} for sufficiently high incident solar radiation [8].

Second-generation (2G) solar cells attempt to reduce the costs of active materials by reducing the layer thickness, which is possible when materials that absorb the sunlight much more efficiently are used. Thus, they are commonly referred to as thin-film photovoltaic devices. Active materials for thin-film devices are, for example, amorphous silicon, $CuInS_2$, CdTe, and CdS. Typical laboratory and production efficiencies are around 10–19% and 7–12%, respectively. An actual problem of the thin-film technology is the formation of a uniform film on a large area. The various 2G technologies have the potential to decrease costs when compared with 1G, but due to material and production costs, the limit for the price per watt peak (€ W_p^{-1}) is expected to be higher than for third-generation solar cells. **Table 1** shows recent efficiencies for 1G and 2G solar cells and solar modules in laboratory and on the market.

Today further possibilities to reduce the costs of 1G and 2G solar devices are investigated and new paths are followed to gain energy from the sun. Among these third-generation techniques are the following four:

- In dye-sensitized solar cells, also called Grätzel cells, a dye which absorbs the photons is distributed over a porous material with a large surface area. Electrons which are excited upon absorption of photons are transferred from the dye to the porous substrate and further to one of the two electrodes of the cell. For the dye, new electrons are provided by an electrolyte which in turn takes the electrons from the other electrode. Actual efficiencies for laboratory devices reach 11%, while typical production efficiencies are around 5–6%. One issue of that technology which is currently being tackled by companies is the stability and related packaging problems [7, 13, 14].

Table 1 Comparison of efficiencies of cells in the laboratory (η lab) and modules on the market (η market)

Solar cell type	Technology	η lab (%)	η market (%)
Monocrystalline	1G	~25 [7]	~19 [9]
Polycrystalline		~20 [7]	~14 [10]
Amorphous	2G	~10 [7]	~7 [11]
CIGS		~19 [7]	~12 [12]

- In tandem solar cells, multiple devices are stacked on top of each other to enhance the absorption spectrum and consequently improve the power conversion efficiency. This possibility of efficiency improvement does not depend on a certain solar cell type but can be used with different photovoltaic technologies.
- Another concept utilizes concentrators which bundle the incident light, thus resulting in a higher incident intensity on the solar module. This allows for reducing the cell size without losses in the amount of absorbed photons. Expensive active materials and highly efficient tandem concepts become cost-efficient. Efficiencies beyond 40% have been reported for this technology. The disadvantages are mainly in the manufacture and installation complexity [15].
- In OSCs, light is absorbed by polymers or small molecules consisting mainly of carbon atoms. The best laboratory efficiencies in 2010 were around 8% [25, 57]. Commercial products reach efficiencies between 3% and 4%.

1.20.1.2 Why OSCs?

The foundation for OSCs – organic because they are composed mainly of carbon atoms – was the discovery and development of conductive organic polymers in 1974 which was awarded the Nobel Prize in Chemistry in 2000. The most remarkable aspect of this discovery by Alan J. Heeger, Alan G. MacDiarmid, and Hideki Shirakawa is that these conductive polymers "offer a unique combination of properties not available from any other known material" [16]. Polymers are a class of materials that everybody knows – and uses every day. In colloquial language, polymers are called plastic due to their property that objects made from them can be formed in every arbitrary way. Furthermore, polymers are among the most used materials today. They can be synthesized in laboratories and adapted to respective needs by chemical modifications. They are nontoxic and their production is low cost and energy efficient, which makes them an extremely attractive and widespread material class. While plastics have been used as insulating materials in the past, the discovery of conductivity in such materials has given rise to completely new technological developments. One of these new application possibilities are plastic solar cells. Apart from semiconducting polymers, small molecules can also serve as active materials in OSCs. One important difference between these two material classes besides the molecular structure consists in the deposition methods. Small molecules are generally deposited by thermal evaporation, which needs vacuum conditions and is currently rather slow and expensive, although roll-to-roll (R2R) processing is possible. Semiconducting polymers, however, can be chemically designed in a way that they are soluble in a wide range of organic solvents. Thus, they can be coated via fast and low-cost standard R2R printing techniques in ambient air at low temperature, which have been utilized by the printing industry for decades. Due to this large advantage, it is expected that the production costs for polymer solar cells will be below those for solar cells made out of small molecules or other photovoltaic technologies. The term OSCs in this chapter refers to polymeric OSCs unless otherwise stated. The semiconducting property of organic polymers is similar to that of silicon or other inorganic semiconductors under illumination. Electrons are excited from the ground state upon light illumination and charges exit the device via the electrodes – a current flow is generated.

In 2007, conventional solar cells consisting of poly- or monocrystalline silicon dominated with about 90% share in the market [5]. The energy payback time, that is, the operation time which is required to produce the exact amount of energy which was required for the entire production process, is around or below 2 years for 1G as well as 2G thin-film technologies for sufficiently high incident solar radiation [17, 18]. Solar cells made from organic materials offer the opportunity for even shorter energy payback times because of easily accessible raw materials, less energy-demanding purification steps of the raw materials, significantly lower material consumption, and the fast and easy R2R printing methods. The lower material consumption of OSCs is enabled by the much higher absorption of the organic materials at a given wavelength compared with inorganic materials, which allows for extremely thin films. For example, OSCs have active layer thicknesses of a few hundred nanometers, while 2G and 1G solar cells need a few micrometers and even over 100 µm, respectively [4]. Together with a better environmental sustainability, their light weight, flexibility, and the possibility of transparency in different colors, OSCs have a good chance to fill a gap in the market.

At the beginning of the twentieth century and in the 1950s, the first investigations on the conductivity of organic materials were performed; in the 1970s, OSCs with efficiencies of 10^{-5}% were produced [19–21]. Reasons for these low efficiencies were not only the used materials but rather the device structure – only one active layer was sandwiched between two electrodes. In the mid-1980s, Tang could increase the efficiency to around 1% by incorporating an additional active layer in the device stack, the so-called acceptor layer [22]. The acceptor layer accepts electrons from the first active layer, the donor. Depending on the point of view, one could also denote the electron-accepting material donor since it donates positively charged charge carriers, so-called holes, to the electron-donating material. However, the electron donor absorbs a broader spectrum of sunlight and hence more photons; thus, this layer produces and donates more charges and is therefore called donor. The introduction of the electron-accepting layer improved not only the current output but also all other parameters which determine the overall efficiency of a solar cell.

In the mid-1990s, the concept of blend solar cells was developed [23]. In contrast to a two-layer approach, the donor and the acceptor units are intermixed here, leading to a large interface area which is much more beneficial for the electron transport from the donor to the acceptor. The superiority of that concept is expressed in the efficiency evolution of OSCs which make use of the so-called bulk heterojunction architecture. The efficiency of this type of device has increased almost by a factor of 10 since 1995, and an efficiency of 8.3% on a 1 cm^2 single-junction device was demonstrated by the end of 2010 (**Figure 1**) [25]. In order to understand how OSCs work, it is important to understand the fundamental mechanisms of charge generation, separation, and transport in semiconductors. Moreover, it is important to know the limiting factors of OSCs to find new ways to increase their efficiency and stability.

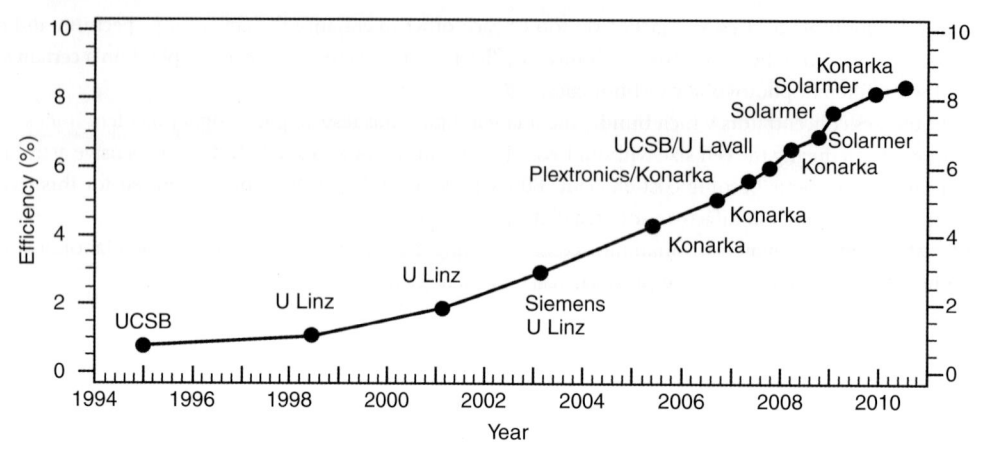

Figure 1 Efficiency evolution of OSCs (values from Reference 24).

1.20.2 Fundamentals

In this section, the fundamental concepts of organic semiconductor physics and solar cells are introduced. Most photovoltaic technologies on the market today consist of inorganic semiconductor materials, which have been intensively investigated for decades and are therefore fairly well understood. This section starts with a comparison of inorganic and organic semiconductors since the theory of organic semiconductors is partly based upon concepts developed for inorganic semiconductors. Subsequently, intra- and intermolecular conductivity and the working principle of a diode – a solar cell in the dark – are discussed. To understand how OSCs work, the fundamentals of charge generation, dissociation, and recombination are summarized.

1.20.2.1 Comparison of Inorganic Solar Cells and OSCs

Pauli's exclusion principle describes that two electrons, which belong to the particle group of fermions, cannot exist in the same state. Thus, at least one of the four quantum numbers which describe an electron has to be different compared with another electron's quantum numbers. This principle is fundamental and determines the structure of matter. The first two quantum numbers are the principal and orbital quantum numbers, which respectively describe the size and shape of the orbital, that is, the size of the area around the atom core where an electron can exist with a certain probability. The third and fourth numbers are the magnetic and spin quantum numbers, which describe the spatial orientation of the orbital and the spin orientation of the electron, respectively.

1.20.2.1.1 Inorganic semiconductors

The functionality of semiconductors can be depicted best by the energy band model. When two atoms A and B approach each other, wave functions of the same symmetry which describe the orbitals of the atoms, for example, the two 1s orbitals, will overlap. This overlap is described as an addition or subtraction of the wave functions $\psi_{A(1s)}$ and $\psi_{B(1s)}$, that is, $\psi_{A(1s)} + \psi_{B(1s)}$ and $\psi_{A(1s)} - \psi_{B(1s)}$, respectively. This linear combination results in two new wave functions, each describing a new orbital. The energetically more favorable orbital is named bonding, the other antibonding. In other words, the 1s orbitals split into two new orbitals. Approach of another atom leads to a further splitting. According to the number of atoms N, there exist N splittings. The large amount of typically 10^{23} atoms in a solid-state body leads to a high density of energy levels with distances in the range of 10^{-23} eV since the width of the arising energy band is in the range of some electron volts. Due to the very small differences of the energy levels, the energy change seems to be continuous, and when there are enough free states, electrons can move as if they were free. The highest energy band which is still occupied by electrons is called valence band (VB) and the following one conduction band (CB). In metals, the VB and the CB overlap; thus, conduction is always possible independent of the filling of the VB (**Figure 2(a)**). When there is no overlapping, conduction is still possible if there are enough free states in the VB. This can be the case for doped semiconductors (**Figure 2(b)**). For undoped semiconductors, the VB is totally filled up with electrons. However, the energy gap E_g between the VB and the CB is sufficiently small so that electrons can be excited into the CB by, for example, absorption of a photon (**Figure 2(c)**). In this case, a hole remains in the VB. This hole now is also considered to be a particle like an electron but with opposite sign and it is able to move by changing its position with the electrons of the VB. The resulting pair of the excited electron and its hole is named exciton, which plays a key role in charge generation. In insulators, the energy gap is too large and electrons cannot be excited into the CB (**Figure 2(d)**).

1.20.2.1.2 Organic semiconductors

The valence shell of the carbon atom is occupied by two s and two p electrons. Carbon atoms constituting π-conjugated organic compounds undergo sp^2 hybridization. In this case, the 2s, p$_x$, and p$_y$ orbitals form three equivalent, singly occupied sp^2 orbitals and a singly occupied p$_z$ orbital, which is perpendicular to the plane defined by the other three orbitals. The sp^2 orbitals are

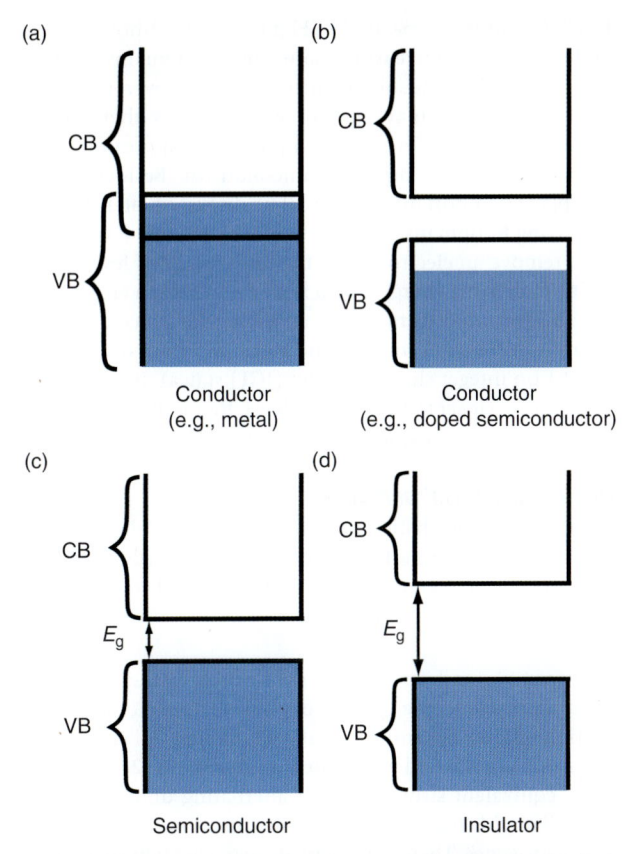

Figure 2 (a) Due to the overlapping of VB and CB in a metal, there are always enough free states for the electrons to move around. (b) A conductor is also present if there are enough free states in the VB. (c) For a semiconductor, the VB is filled up. The energy gap E_g is small enough so that the electrons can be excited into the CB by, for example, absorption of a photon. (d) For an insulator, the energy gap E_g is too large and cannot be overcome by the electrons.

employed in the formation of the σ bonds, which define the molecular framework. The overlap of the p_z orbitals of two covalently linked carbon atoms results in two molecular orbitals (MOs) with π symmetry, one of them having bonding character and the other one antibonding character (i.e., one is occupied, the other is not) (**Figure 3(a)**). The energetic splitting of the π-MOs is smaller than that of the σ-MOs, and the bonding and antibonding π-MOs are called highest occupied molecular orbitals (HOMOs) and

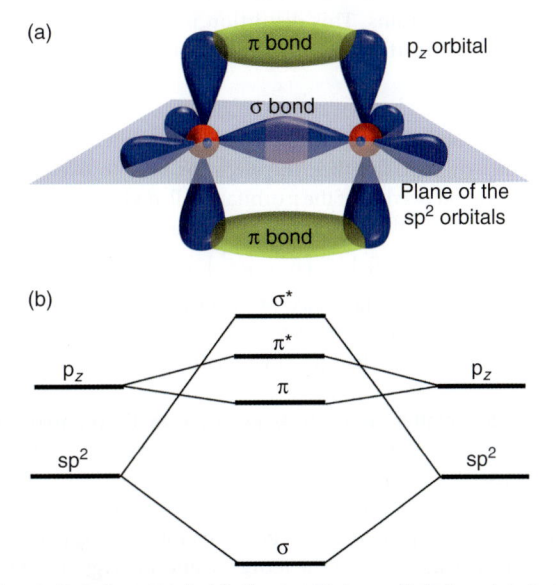

Figure 3 (a) The overlapping sp² orbitals constitute the σ bond while the p_z orbitals constitute the π bonds. (b) Splitting of the sp² and p_z orbitals into bonding (σ, π) and antibonding (σ*, π*) orbitals, respectively. The vertical distance indicates the energetic difference.

lowest unoccupied molecular orbitals (LUMOs), respectively (**Figure 3(b)**). Although the energy gap between HOMO and LUMO (often called the band gap) decreases with increasing chain length, it remains quite large (typically around 2 eV), even in infinitely long polymers [26]. This would lead to insulating properties. However, polymers are heavily doped by impurities with high electron affinities, for example, molecular oxygen, which makes them reasonably good p-type conductors. Furthermore, the HOMO–LUMO gap can also be overcome by a photon of appropriate wavelength. Therefore, HOMO and LUMO play a similar role like VB and CB of an inorganic semiconductor. Besides the HOMO–LUMO gap, the absolute positions of HOMO and LUMO also play an important role as will be discussed later. The energetic position of an MO can be referenced to the vacuum level by applying Koopmans' theorem [27]. The HOMO level is thus given by the ionization energy, that is, the energy which is needed to remove an electron from the fully occupied level into vacuum. Accordingly, the LUMO level is defined by the electron affinity, that is, the energy which is gained when an electron is attached to the neutral molecule from vacuum. It should be noted, however, that intra- and intermolecular relaxation processes following the removal or attachment of a charge may significantly decrease or increase the absolute values of ionization energies or electron affinities, respectively (see also Section 1.20.3.2.1 on integer charge transfer (ICT) states). In order to avoid ambiguities with respect to the ordering of energy levels, those which are closer to the vacuum level, that is, having smaller binding energies, are referred to as lying at a higher energy in this chapter. Within this nomenclature, the LUMO has a higher energy than the HOMO.

1.20.2.1.3 Conduction mechanisms in organic semiconductors

In this section, we differentiate between two conductivities, that is, the intramolecular and the intermolecular conduction. Since molecules can be arranged in different ways, the intermolecular conductivity strongly depends on the ordering of the molecules, while the intramolecular conductivity depends on the molecule's constitution and conformation of the polymer.

1.20.2.1.3(i) Intramolecular conduction

As mentioned above, the π bond between two carbon atoms is constituted by the electrons in the $2p_z$ atomic orbitals (AOs; **Figure 3(a)**). In aromatic compounds like benzene, the $2p_z$ AOs of all six carbon atoms overlap above and below the molecular plane, which leads to the delocalization of the π electrons over the whole ring. All six bonds have the same length of 139 pm, which lies in between the lengths of a single bond and an isolated double bond [28]. Consequently, in the VB formulation of the benzene molecule, there are two equivalent structures with alternating double and single bonds, which can be interconverted by simultaneously flipping all double bonds to the adjacent position. The true electronic structure may be conceived as a superposition of these two mesomeric states. There is no activation barrier between these states so that the π electrons may be considered as being perfectly mobile along the perimeter of the benzene molecule. The energy which is gained by this delocalization is called the resonance or delocalization energy. In linear π-conjugated systems, there is also an overlap of the $2p_z$ AOs of adjacent carbon atoms, which leads to a similar situation as in aromatic systems. However, although the formal single bonds are somewhat shorter and the formal double bonds are somewhat longer than the single and double bonds in ethane, respectively, there is no perfect delocalization as is the case in benzene (or, to put it in the VB picture, it is not possible to obtain an identical structure by simultaneously flipping all π bonds to the adjacent position). In other words, due to the large splitting of HOMO and LUMO, no unoccupied states are available for electron transport. However, if an electron is removed from the π electron system to produce a cation radical, the positive hole (i.e., the missing electron) can move along the chain, dragging with it the distortion of the molecular framework which is caused by the reduced bonding forces between the nuclei of the constituting carbon atoms. This distortion is also called polarization, and thus the quasiparticle consisting of the hole and its accompanying distortion is termed polaron.

1.20.2.1.3(ii) Intermolecular conduction

The charge transport between the polymer chains or molecules in organic solids is realized by thermally activated hopping in most cases. In order to move from one polymer chain to another, the electrons have to overcome the potential barrier between two molecules or polymers [29]. In the case of a good overlap of the π orbitals, called π–π stacking, the chance for electrons to jump from one molecule to another becomes larger, which is the reason for an increased mobility. The mobility μ of the charges, which is defined as the ratio of drift velocity v_d and the electric field E $\left(\vec{v_d} = \mu \vec{E}\right)$, depends critically on the molecular order in the organic solid. Within a single crystal, hydrogen bonds can be established or interactions due to van der Waals forces take place [30, 31]. In this case, μ can be up to $10^2 \, cm^2 \, V^{-1} \, s^{-1}$ and for polycrystals up to $10^{-1} \, cm^2 \, V^{-1} \, s^{-1}$ is possible [32]. When it comes to amorphous structures, a good overlap of the π orbitals and a sufficient polymer chain configuration can lead to mobilities similar to that of polycrystalline structures [33].

The low mobility of charges in disordered matter can be explained by a small overlap of the wave functions of the molecules' orbitals and a large energetic disorder of the transport levels. Two prominent models, the Marcus theory and the Miller–Abrahams model, are generally used to describe the hopping rates of charges in disordered molecular solids [34, 35]. The Marcus model calculates the jump rate from a preexponential attempt-to-jump frequency, which is given by the transfer integral of the overlapping wave functions, and a factor which accounts for the negative exponential dependency of the jump frequency on the energy difference of the two sites and on the reorganization energy. The Miller–Abrahams model accounts for the tunneling effect during hopping by a negative exponential dependency of the ratio of the distance of the two sites r_{ij} and the localization radius $1/\gamma$:

$$v_{ij} = v_0 e^{-\gamma r_{ij}} \begin{cases} e^{\frac{\Delta E_{ij}}{k_B T}} & \Delta E_{ij} > 0 \\ 1 & \Delta E_{ij} \leq 0 \end{cases} \qquad [1]$$

The localization radius describes the region around a site where the charge is located with a certain probability. The second term contains the energy difference of the two sites ΔE_{ij} and becomes 1 in the case where the final site has a lower energy than the starting site (i.e., farer away from vacuum) or if the energy difference is 0. Further, v_0, k_B, and T denote the maximum hopping rate, the Boltzmann constant, and the temperature, respectively. A macroscopic model for the mobility derived from the Miller–Abrahams hopping rate by Monte Carlo simulations is the Gaussian disorder or Bässler model [36]. It describes the dependence of the mobility on the width of the Gaussian distribution of the density of states, on the electric field, and on the temperature.

The temperature dependence can thereby be explained by the concept of transport energy. In disordered materials, the excited charges thermalize under steady-state conditions below the center of density of states of a Gaussian or exponential distribution. The center of charge density is shifted by $\sigma^2/k_B T$, where σ is the energetic width of the distribution. Around the transport energy, which lies in between the center of density of states and the center of charge density, hopping transport is possible. Charges that fall below this border are trapped in the tail of density of states and do not contribute to the current anymore. When the temperature is increased, the charges can reach energetically higher states. From these states, more downhill jumps to unoccupied neighboring states are possible and the overall hopping rate increases. When the temperature tends toward 0 K, the charge carriers occupy only the deepest states where they remain trapped. As the trapped charges do not recombine, they still contribute to the charge density.

1.20.2.1.4 Basic working principles of inorganic solar cells and OSCs

A diode is an electronic component which allows current to pass only in one direction. This direction is called the forward direction. The opposite direction in which current cannot flow is called the reverse direction. Classical diodes are used as rectifiers in order to convert an alternating current into a direct current. A solar cell is nothing less than a diode that produces current under illumination. To understand why such a device is able to produce current when using adequate materials, it is important to understand the working principle. The differences between inorganic and organic diodes under illumination will be explained, starting with the inorganic case.

At 0 K, every electron tries to occupy a state energetically as low as possible. Since electrons are fermions, every state can be occupied by only one electron; thus, one electron has to occupy a state with energy higher than the energy of every other state occupied by an electron. The energy of this state is called Fermi energy and the state is named Fermi level. For temperatures above 0 K, some electrons near the Fermi energy will be able to reach energetically higher states. The formerly sharp edge of the electron distribution – occupation probability 100% for states with energy equal to or below the Fermi energy and 0% for states above – becomes smoother. Now the Fermi level is the state of which the occupation probability is 50%. For a semiconductor, the Fermi level lies within the band gap which is possible since the occupation probability is only a theoretically calculated value. When two materials with different Fermi levels are brought into contact, the levels will start to align near the junction, which means that electrons will start to diffuse from the material with the higher to that with the lower Fermi level. As a consequence, an excess of negative charges builds up in the low-Fermi level material and a lack of negative charges remains in the high-Fermi level material. This results in a potential difference and an electric field is built up pointing in the opposite direction of the electron diffusion.

In the case of an inorganic diode, p- and n-doped semiconductors are brought into contact and a p–n junction is formed. The purpose of n-type doping is to create filled states near the semiconductor's CB lying within the band gap. This results in an elevation of the Fermi level and less energy is needed to lift electrons to the CB. For Si, this is typically achieved by the addition of group V elements such as P, As, or Sb. p-Doping can be explained analogously. Adding free states near the semiconductor's VB provides electrons a possibility to leave the VB resulting in an abundance of holes in the VB and a reduced Fermi level. For p-doping of Si, typically group III elements like B and Al are applied.

Thus electrons will diffuse from the n-doped to the p-doped region, leaving positively charged ions behind. In the same manner, positive holes diffuse from the p-doped into the n-doped region, leaving behind negatively charged ions. Upon encounter, electrons and holes recombine, resulting in the diffusion current. The positively charged immobile ions in the n-region and negatively charged immobile ions in the p-region build up an electric field, forcing mobile charges to move oppositely to the diffusion direction, causing a drift current. Once equilibrium is reached, diffusion and drift current add up to zero net current. The region of positively and negatively charged immobile ions is called depletion or space-charge region because there are no free charges left that could contribute to a current. If a positive voltage is applied to the p-doped region, the injected holes will recombine with the negatively charged ions and the same only with opposite sign will happen when a negative voltage is applied to the n-doped region. Since positively and negatively charged carriers are moving in opposite directions, they formally cross the p–n junction and a current flow is generated. When a bias voltage is applied and becomes large enough, every free ion body will recombine with a charge and the space-charge regions collapse whereby a normal current flow becomes possible. In the case of reverse bias, no charges will flow since they are repelled by the equally charged ions. This way a diode allows charge flow only in one direction.

The p–n junction allows the conversion of light into electric current. By the absorption of a photon, an electron can be excited into a higher electronic state, provided the energy of the photon matches the energy difference between these two states. So-called selection rules determine the intensity of this transition. Transitions between states of different spin multiplicities are strongly forbidden and are thus very weak. Transitions between states of the same multiplicity with good spatial overlap and appropriate symmetries are fully allowed and are thus very strong. In most organic dyes, the lowest energy absorption band corresponds to a transition from the singlet ground state S_0 to the first excited singlet state (S_1). For the majority of the polymers described in this chapter, this excitation can be described in good approximation by moving the electron from the HOMO to the LUMO. Transitions from S_0 to higher excited singlet states are also possible, albeit generally weaker. Further, each of the electronic states is coupled to molecular vibrations, involving those bonds whose strength is weakened by the excitation (mainly the bonds of the π-conjugated backbone). This leads to a manifold of vibronic states which build on the vibrational ground state of each electronic state. If the energy of the incident photon is larger than the energy difference of the vibrational ground states of S_0 and S_1, the electron will be excited into an excited vibrational state of S_1 and the molecule will reach the vibrational ground state of S_1 by dissipation of the excess energy to the environment (thermal relaxation).

After absorption of a photon and excitation of an electron from the VB into the CB in inorganic solar cells and from the HOMO into the LUMO for OSCs, respectively, the current generation process can be described by a three-event process: charge separation, charge transport, and charge extraction. In the following, the first and the latter will be discussed in more detail, while the second has been reviewed in detail in the previous section. Let us first look at charge separation. In an inorganic semiconductor, the resulting electron–hole pair is weakly bound and is called Wannier–Mott exciton. Its binding energy has the same magnitude as $k_B T$. In organic semiconductors, the exciton is strongly bound and is called Frenkel exciton [37]. The difference in binding energy comes from the different permittivities and can be estimated by the attracting Coulomb force:

$$F_c = \frac{q}{4\pi\varepsilon\varepsilon_0 r} \quad [2]$$

with q the charge, ε and ε_0 the permittivities of the material and the vacuum, respectively, and r the distance between the charges. A low permittivity of $\varepsilon \approx 3$ for organic materials leads to less screening of the charges' fields and thus a higher binding energy compared with inorganic materials [37–40]. For charges in an organic solid, located 1 nm apart from each other, the binding energy is around 0.3–0.5 eV.

Here the different working principles of an inorganic and an organic illuminated diode become clear. In inorganic materials, the space-charge region is able to separate the quasi-free Wannier–Mott excitons and to drive the electrons and holes into opposite directions toward the collecting electrodes, thus generating a current flow. Furthermore, the Wannier–Mott excitons can be separated over a large material thickness because the space-charge region and the diffusion length of the excitons are large.

In comparison with inorganic semiconductors, in organic semiconductors separation, transport, and extraction of charges are more difficult due to the properties of the organic material. No space-charge region is formed and a quite large amount of energy is needed to separate the strongly bound Frenkel excitons. Here a fundamental principle of physics can help: minimization of energy. If one provides the electron an energetically preferable state, that is, a state with lower energy, it will try to reach this state in order to minimize its energy. The excess energy that becomes available when the electron moves to the lower state can be used to split up the exciton. Such a lower state can be provided by adding a second semiconductor, the acceptor. The electron of the exciton, which was generated in the donor, can now move from the donor to the acceptor LUMO. However, before this transfer can take place, the exciton must diffuse to the donor–acceptor junction. In this connection, an additional hurdle must be cleared – the short lifetime of excitons of below 1 ns, which corresponds to a diffusion length of around 10 nm in a given material which in general is smaller than the thickness of the donor–acceptor layer [41–44]. This issue can be addressed by an increase in the interface area between the donor and the acceptor and will be discussed later. When the exciton has reached the junction, the electron transfer from the donor to the acceptor LUMO takes place in the femtosecond regime [45, 46]. Actually, current investigations show that for a significant number of excitons diffusion to the junction seems not to be necessary since the electron is excited directly into the LUMO of the acceptor. The timescale for this event is below 100 fs and is possible only for electrons excited within a few molecules away from the junction [47, 48]. After the two charges reside on the different materials, they still feel their mutual Coulomb attraction. However, their binding energy is much smaller compared with the binding energy of the exciton and they are called polaron pair now. Since the polaron pair is bound less strongly than the Frenkel exciton, the electric field resulting from the alignment of the different Fermi levels of the electrodes is sufficient to separate the pair with a certain probability. A model which describes polaron pair dissociation is the Onsager–Braun model [49, 50].

The second event is the transport of the charges and was described above. However, the recombination of charge carriers plays a very important counterpart to charge generation and the different mechanisms for recombination are summarized here. Since recombination determines how many charges reach the electrodes at a certain applied voltage, it influences a measure called fill factor (FF), which is important for the performance of the solar cell. Recombination can be of either geminate or nongeminate type. It is of geminate type when the excited electron falls back to the ground state and recombines with its original hole. This is called monomolecular recombination, and it can emit a photon; the process is then called fluorescence. Nongeminate recombination describes a situation where an electron transfers the excitation energy to another molecule and recombines there. It is called bimolecular recombination because at least two molecules must be involved in that process. Because fluorescence is not possible in this case, it is also called fluorescence quenching. The order of bimolecular recombination is determined by the number of participants and is 2 if two charges, an electron and a hole, are involved. It can also be 1 if the amount of one recombination partner is much larger than that of the other. In this case, only the amount of the underrepresented charge type reduces noticeably, while the other seems to be constant. An example is the recombination of electrons with, for example, traps which can occur in a vast amount in the material. The effective recombination R of electrons with holes depends, on the one hand, on the direct recombination rate and, on the other hand, on the probability of the participants to find each other. The former dominates in high-mobility semiconductors, while the latter is important for materials with low charge carrier mobilities. The effective rate R is derived by the Langevin theory and includes the charge carrier density n as well as the bimolecular Langevin recombination prefactor $\gamma = q/\varepsilon(\mu_e + \mu_h)$, with the mobilities of electrons μ_e and holes μ_h, the charge q, and the permittivity ε of the specified material [51, 52]. Since there are two general possibilities to bring the two semiconductors into contact, that is, either by a planar bilayer or by the bulk heterojunction approach, the chance for recombination of charge carriers can be different. Due to the large interface in the bulk heterojunction approach, that is, where p-type and n-type semiconductors are intermixed, the probability for recombination of a free charge carrier with a carrier of the other sort is larger. A combination of the Onsager–Braun model and a model developed by Sokel and Hughes describes the photocurrent behavior quite well [53–55].

During the last event, the charge extraction, recombination of free charges at the interface of the electrode and the organic semiconductor, can occur. Although the electric field provided by the different energy levels of the electrodes causes the charges to drift into the right direction, it cannot be excluded that some carriers travel to the wrong electrode. Here interfacial layers, sometimes called interface or intermediate layers, can help to reduce recombination. They can also adjust disadvantageous properties of electrodes and active materials which will be discussed later.

Some of the described processes are illustrated in **Figure 4**(a). **Figure 4**(b) shows a typical energy level diagram of an OSC. To keep the energy barrier small, the energy level of the next layer to which a charge shall move should always have a similar or even better a smaller or larger value depending on whether the charge is an electron or a hole.

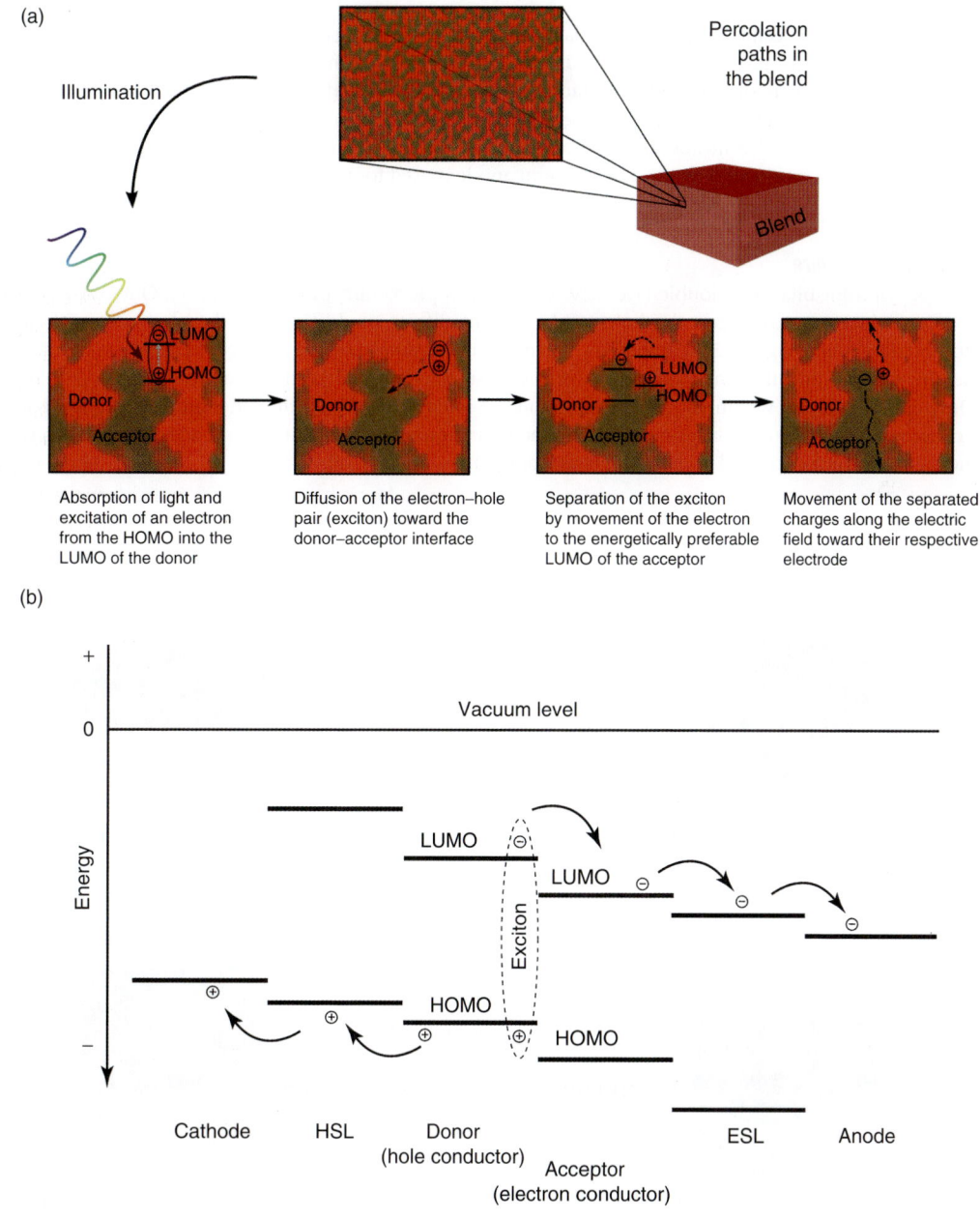

Figure 4 (a) Percolation pathways allow for separated charges to reach the anode and the cathode, respectively. (b) Typical energy level diagram of a solar cell with two interfacial layers: hole-selective layer (HSL) and electron-selective layer (ESL). The energy gradient guarantees that charges cannot easily move back to their original material.

Table 2 Comparison of inorganic and organic semiconductors

	Inorganic	Organic
Absorption	Weak → layer thicknesses some micrometers	Strong → layer thicknesses some nanometers
Excitons	Weakly bound, long diffusion length	Strongly bound, short diffusion length
Charge separation	Within the space-charge region	Near semiconductors' interface
Charge transport	Continuous	Hopping from site to site

Table 2 summarizes some differences of inorganic and organic semiconductors concerning current generation. As a result, different cell architectures can be of benefit. Two elementary architectures will be discussed in the next section.

1.20.2.2 Solar Cell Device Architectures

The minimum structure of a solar cell is electrode/active layer/electrode. Depending on the type of architecture and electrodes used for an OSC, it can be necessary to provide the cell with interfacial layers, either on one or on both sides of the active layer. The general structure in this case is therefore electrode/interfacial layer/active layer/interfacial layer/electrode (**Figure 5**).

Note that in this text the electrodes are described for the case of photovoltaic operation of the cell (i.e., for the fourth quadrant of the current–voltage (*IV*) curve), which means that the term cathode is used for the electrode that collects holes from the active layer – which is equivalent to emitting electrons – and the term anode is used for the electrode that collects the generated electrons (**Figure 4(b)**).

1.20.2.2.1 Bilayer architecture

The major advantage of using bilayer or double-layer devices is the low probability of recombination. Once the charge carriers are separated at the donor–acceptor interface, the holes and electrons diffuse or drift toward the electrodes without reaching a donor–acceptor interface again (**Figures 5(a)** and **5(b)**). The major disadvantage of this architecture is the small interface between the donor and the acceptor and the small ratio of exciton diffusion length and layer thicknesses required for sufficient light absorption. Only excitons created within about 10 nm around the interface can reach the junction and contribute to the current [41–44]. As a consequence of this small diffusion length, the active layer must be very thin and the absorption coefficient very high. Otherwise, one has to accept a decreased current generation potential.

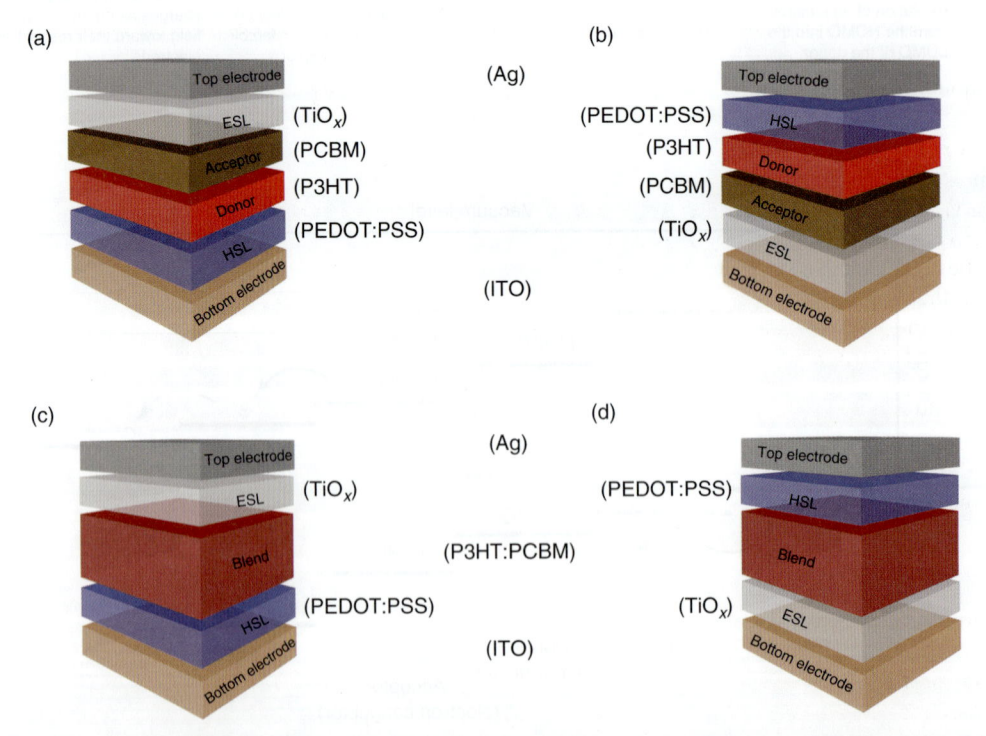

Figure 5 Typical bilayer and blend structure of OSC: (a) normal bilayer; (b) inverted bilayer; (c) normal blend; and (d) inverted blend. In general, illumination takes place through the bottom electrode which is transparent. The top electrode in most cases is not transparent. If the electrodes have appropriate properties, one or both interfacial layers can be omitted. Material examples are given in parentheses.

1.20.2.2.2 Blend architecture

The bulk heterojunction is the most widely used device architecture (**Figures 5(c)** and **5(d)**). Donor and acceptor materials are intermixed in the active layer, which results in a very large interface area between the two active components. This in turn allows the excitons to reach a donor–acceptor interface within their short diffusion length and charge carriers can be separated throughout the entire active layer. However, the two components must not be intermixed on a molecular level to guarantee percolation paths for charge transport to the corresponding electrode (**Figures 4(a)** and **4(b)**). Thus, a high-efficiency bulk heterojunction needs a certain extent of phase separation of polymer and fullerene, for which the product of exciton splitting and charge extraction reaches a maximum [56]. Because charge carriers are always in close contact with phases of the opposite sort, the loss of charge carriers by recombination is much higher than for the bilayer architecture. However, this is compensated by the fact that many more free charge carriers are generated in thicker devices, generally leading to higher currents. Therefore, blend solar cells will reach higher efficiencies than bilayer solar cells as long as no polymer semiconductor with a significantly increased diffusion length of excitons is found. In the case of bulk heterojunction solar cells, interfacial layers are used not only to adjust the energy levels but also to act as hole-blocking layers (HBLs) or hole-injection layers (HILs). The term HIL was adopted from the field of organic light-emitting diodes (OLEDs) where holes and electrons are not extracted but injected into the semiconductor layer. In this chapter, more general terms like ESL and HSL will be used, indicating that on the ESL side electrons and on the HSL side holes are extracted.

Up to January 2011, the highest reported efficiency for a polymer solar cell was demonstrated by the company Konarka. By utilizing the blend structure, they demonstrated a solar cell with 8.3% efficiency [25]. A comparable efficiency of 8.13% was reached by the company Solarmer [57].

1.20.2.3 Characteristic Values of a Solar Cell

There are three main characterization methods that determine the performance of a solar cell:

1. *IV* characteristics under illumination (*IV* light),
2. *IV* characteristics in the dark (*IV* dark), and
3. measurement of the external quantum efficiency (EQE).

Each method delivers different properties of the solar cell and the combination thereof gives a good overview of a device's performance. In order to account for different device areas, normally not the *IV* curves of solar cells but the current density–voltage (*JV*) curves are presented with the unit area mostly given in cm².

Laboratory measurements of solar cell characteristics are mostly performed with solar simulators or more generally with xenon or halogen lamp illumination. To allow for comparability, each laboratory measurement should be performed under air mass 1.5 global (AM1.5G) illumination [58]. The AM1.5G spectrum corresponds to the spectrum of sunlight after it has passed through the 1.5-fold air mass relative to normal incidence on the earth's atmosphere. This corresponds to an incident angle of 48° from zenith, including the photons which do not hit the solar cell directly but after scattering or reflection. The intensity is 100 mW cm^{-2}; cell temperature should be 25 °C.

1.20.2.3.1 JV curve under illumination

A typical *JV* curve is shown in **Figure 6**. The voltage where the *JV* curve crosses the *x*-axis and the current density is zero is called open-circuit voltage V_{OC}. At this voltage, the current flow injected by the applied bias equals the current output from the solar cell, resulting in zero net current. The theoretical limit of V_{OC} is always smaller than the energy difference between the LUMO of the acceptor and the HOMO of the donor.

At zero bias, the short-circuit current density J_{SC} or short-circuit current I_{SC} is measured. The maximum power output of the cell is obtained as the product of I_{mpp} and V_{mpp}, the current and voltage, respectively, at the maximum power point P_{mpp}. P_{mpp} is smaller than the product of V_{OC} and I_{SC} because of the diode shape. The ratio of P_{mpp} and $V_{OC} \times I_{SC}$ is called the FF and calculated by

$$\text{FF} = \frac{V_{mpp} \times I_{mpp}}{V_{OC} \times I_{SC}} \qquad [3]$$

The ratio between the maximum electrical output power and the sun's incident power P_{in} equates to the efficiency η and reads

$$\eta = \frac{P_{out}}{P_{in}} = \frac{V_{OC} \times I_{SC}}{P_{in}} \times \text{FF} \qquad [4]$$

These values are the most important and most presented values of a solar cell measured under illumination.

1.20.2.3.2 JV curve in the dark

Additional important values to characterize a solar cell are obtained from *JV* measurements in the dark (**Figure 6(a)**). In the ideal case, the current flow is zero in the reverse direction and the *JV* curve is parallel to the *x*-axis. In the equivalent circuit in **Figure 6(b)**, this corresponds to an infinitely high parallel resistance R_p. Smaller R_p values cause nonparallelity of the *JV* curve and a dark current or so-called leakage current is measured. Very good leakage currents for OSCs are typically smaller than 100 μA cm^{-2} [59]. The

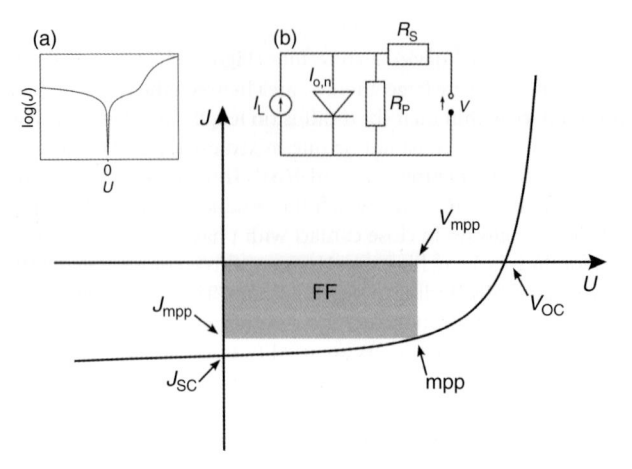

Figure 6 Typical JV curve under illumination. mpp is the maximum power point and FF is the ratio of $J_{mpp} \times V_{mpp}$ divided by $J_{SC} \times V_{OC}$. (a) Typical shape of a JV curve recorded in the dark shown on a semilogarithmic scale. (b) Equivalent circuit diagram of a solar cell. Compared with the equivalent circuit diagram of a diode, it is extended by the light-generated current I_L. I_0 denotes the saturation current in the reverse direction, n is the ideality factor, V is the source for the current I corresponding to I_L, and R_S and R_P denote the series and the parallel resistors, respectively.

leakage current not only is a measure for the stability of a solar cell but also determines to a major part the low light sensitivity, that is, the power output at illumination at, for example, 5000 lx and below. While W m^{-2} is a measure for the whole intensity of a light source, lux (or lx) accounts for the spectral sensitivity of the eye. For example, a sunny day has about 100 000 lx, while in the shadow one measures about 10 000 lx.

In the forward bias direction, the so-called injection current is an indicator for the loss of current due to unfavorable interfaces between the different layers or poor conductivity of the layers. A high injection current is therefore desirable. In the equivalent circuit diagram, the series resistance R_S is related to the injection current and should be as low as possible.

1.20.2.3.3 External and internal quantum efficiency

JV curves measured under illumination show the response of a device to the intensity integrated over the entire spectrum absorbed by the active materials. Often it is of interest to see how the response is to certain wavelengths. In this case, the EQE spectrum is a helpful quantity. It is defined as the number of extracted charges divided by the number of incident photons per wavelength interval. The integral over the EQE spectrum can thus be used to correct the J_{SC} measured for deviations of the spectrum of the sun simulator from the AM1.5G spectrum. If the EQE for a certain wavelength interval is unity, all incident photons of this interval are absorbed and every photon produces exactly one pair of charge carriers. For two different wavelength intervals, this means that the current and thus the power output of the solar cell will be the same if the EQE and the number of incident photons are equal. This is valid independently of the wavelength as long as it is shorter than the absorption edge. However, the energies of the photons with the shorter wavelengths are higher, thus leading to a higher input power and therefore lower power efficiency due to the constant current.

An EQE spectrum is typically obtained by illuminating the solar device with single wavelength intervals that are generated either by grating optics, which is, for example, used in UV–vis spectrometers, or by placing wavelength filters in front of the device. The J_{SC} is then measured as a function of wavelength and an EQE spectrum is obtained whose shape looks similar to the absorption spectrum. It can be an indicator for problems concerning charge separation or extraction when both spectra differ considerably from each other.

The internal quantum efficiency is defined as the number of extracted charge carriers per absorbed photon, thus considering only photons actually absorbed and not reflected or transmitted ones. As a consequence, the IQE is always higher than the EQE and a value of 100% describes perfect conversion and transport processes in the active layer.

1.20.3 Materials for OSCs

A typical OSC consists of two electrodes, the active layer, and interfacial layers. The most common materials are presented in the following subsections. The most important layer of the solar cell, the active layer, will be discussed first, followed by a description of interfacial and electrode materials.

1.20.3.1 Active Materials for OSCs

The active layer is the heart of any solar cell and plays a key role with respect to efficiency and stability. A high yield of photon absorption and conversion into electricity is mandatory in order to minimize the energy payback time. In addition, a high

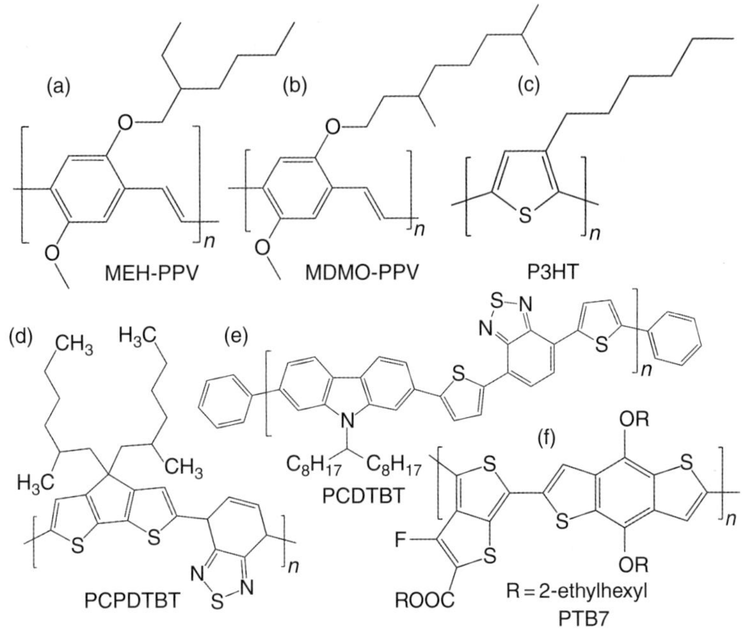

Figure 7 Different donor materials for plastic solar cells: (a) MEH-PPV; (b) MDMO-PPV; (c) P3HT; (d) PCPDTBT; (e) PCDTBT; and (f) PTB7.

absorption coefficient allows for thin layers and thus low material consumption, which additionally contributes to an advantageous cost–benefit calculation. A short energy payback time is especially important for short-lived applications such as battery chargers where a solar device must pay off within 1 or 2 years. A much longer lifetime and thus stability, however, is required for, for example, permanent rooftop installations.

In 1992, Sariciftci et al. investigated the charge transfer from the polymer poly[2-methoxy-5-(2'-ethyl-hexyloxy)-1,4-phenylene vinylene] (MEH-PPV; **Figure 7(a)**) to the buckminster-fullerene C_{60} (**Figure 8(a)**). They found that the charge transfer, occurring on the picosecond timescale, is more than 2 orders of magnitude faster than competing processes like radiative or nonradiative deactivation of the excitons, thus leading to quantum efficiencies of exciton splitting close to unity [46]. This investigation marks the starting point for an increasing interest in polymer-based OSCs with polymers as donors and fullerenes as acceptors [23].

Since a huge variety of different materials have been synthesized and investigated, only well-established and well-understood as well as high-potential materials with respect to efficiency will be described.

1.20.3.1.1 Donor materials

After MEH-PPV:C_{60}, the focus was on the material system poly[2-methoxy-5-(3',7'-dimethyloctyloxy)-1,4-phenylene vinylene]: phenyl-C_{61}-butyric-acid-methyl ester (MDMO-PPV:PCBM) due to its better processability (**Figures 7(b)** and **8(b)**). However, because of the large band gap of PPVs (e.g., 2.26 eV for MDMO-PPV), which allows only for absorption of high energetic photons, and the low mobilities, the maximum achieved efficiencies were only around 3% [66–69].

Undoubtedly, to date the most investigated polymer for OSCs is poly(3-hexylthiophene) (P3HT; **Figure 7(c)**). It exhibits some beneficial properties such as good compatibility with different interfacial materials and good environmental and thermal stability. The monomer consists of a thiophene ring with an n-hexyl tail at the 3-position, which is added for solubility reasons in different organic solvents. P3HT in conjunction with the acceptor PCBM constitutes the fruit fly of organic semiconductors used in a bulk heterojunction. A large amount of effort has been spent on improving this material system, and efficiencies of 4–5% have been reached [70–73]. Due to the relatively large optical band gap of P3HT and the high-lying frontier molecular orbitals (HOMO and LUMO), mediocre absorption and a relatively small V_{OC} limit the maximum possible efficiency.

Thus, the focus has shifted more recently to the development of low-band gap polymers with increased absorption and higher open-circuit voltages to further drive the efficiency of OSCs. These polymers make use of internal charge transfer from electron-rich to electron-poor domains within the p-type polymer chain. The alternating partially charged domains of the copolymer lead to a lower band gap, which results in a broader absorption of the solar spectrum and thus higher current densities [74, 75]. An example for such a low-band gap material is poly[2,1,3-benzothiadiazole-4,7-diyl[4,4-bis(2-ethylhexyl)-4H-cyclopenta[2,1-b:3,4-b']dithiophene-2,6-diyl]] (PCPDTBT; **Figure 7(d)**). With 1.46 eV, its band gap is much smaller compared with P3HT that has a band gap of 1.9 eV, leading to the opportunity of absorbing photons with a wavelength of up to 850 nm and an efficiency of 5.5% [61].

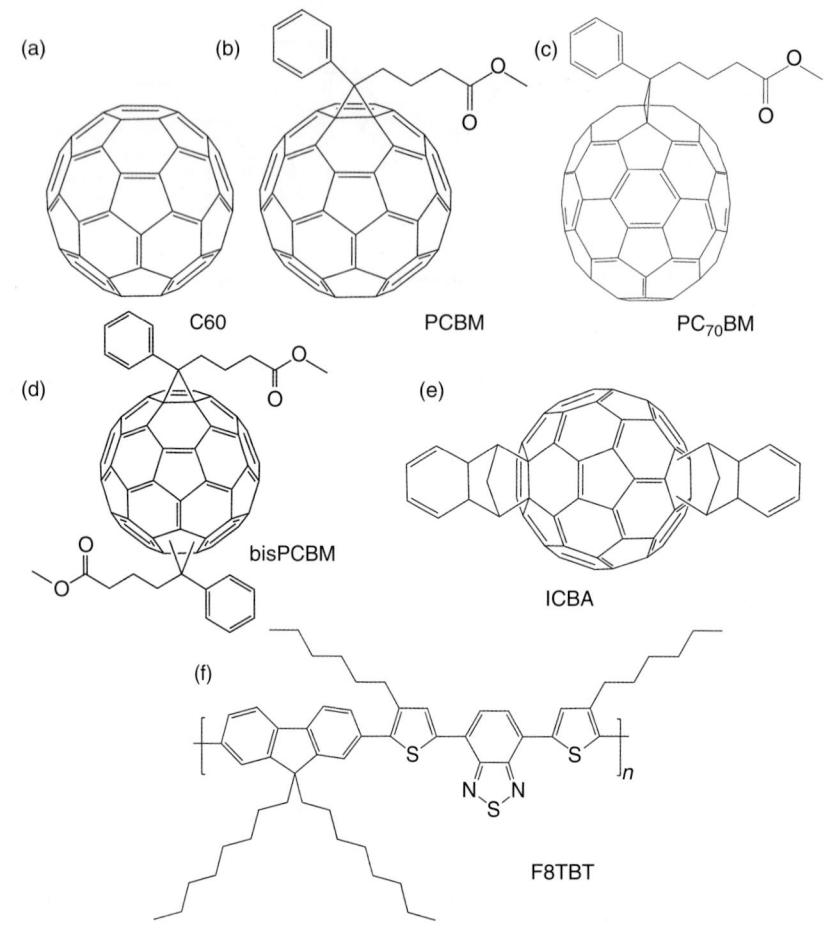

Figure 8 Different fullerene derivatives as acceptor materials for solar cells: (a) C_{60}; (b) PCBM; and (c) $PC_{70}BM$; (d) bisPCBM; and (e) ICBA. An acceptor polymer: (f) F8TBT.

The V_{OC} depends on the difference between the donor HOMO and the acceptor LUMO. Lowering the energy level of the HOMO thus increases the V_{OC}. Again a copolymer consisting of alternating electron-rich and electron-poor monomer units is used. Poly[N-9'-hepta-decanyl-2,7-carbazole-*alt*-5,5-(4',7'-di-2-thienyl-2',1',3'-benzothiadiazole) (PCDTBT; Figure 7(e)) has a LUMO of −3.6 eV and comprises a carbazole group, which ensures a low-lying HOMO of −5.5 eV. The band gap is 1.9 eV, which is as large as for P3HT, leading in turn to a decreased absorption of photons compared with PCPDTBT. However, the downshifted HOMO leads to an increase in V_{OC} and an efficiency of 6.1%. The flexibility in the synthesis can be used to reduce the band gap as a next step [75].

Among the most efficient polymers in 2010 was PTB7, a polymer of the alternating ester-substituted thieno[3,4-*b*]thiophene and benzodithiophene polymer (PTB) group. Besides an improved band gap of 1.6 eV, this polymer was further found to be stacked in the face-down conformation on the substrate supporting a good charge transport. Thus, a current density of 14.50 mA cm^{-2} and an efficiency of 7.4% were reached [63].

For commercial use, the stability of the active materials is of paramount importance as well. Some degradation mechanisms are attributed to the softness of the thin polymeric layers, which leads to instabilities of the ideal blend morphology. Krebs *et al.* have successfully attempted to increase the rigidity of the active layer by utilizing thermocleavable materials. In this concept, a polymer is equipped with thermally unstable side chains. During the coating process, these side chains provide for solubility, but are then removed by heat in the dried film [76–79]. Cross-linking is another possibility for increasing the stability and making layers insoluble [80, 81].

1.20.3.1.2 *Acceptor materials*

Fullerene derivatives are the most widely used acceptor materials for OSCs and the vast majority of scientific publications describes the use of PCBM. One related derivative is phenyl-C_{70}-butyric acid methyl ester ($PC_{70}BM$; Figure 8(c)). $PC_{70}BM$ has a lower band gap and is therefore able to absorb a broader spectrum of light, which in turn leads to improved current and efficiency. For solar cells consisting of MDMO-PPV and $PC_{70}BM$, a short-circuit current increase of 50% compared with PCBM has been reported [64].

So-called bis-adducts of C_{60} and C_{70} derivatives bear two solubilizing units on the fullerene core and have an energetically higher LUMO. This increases the efficiency of solar cells by increasing the V_{OC} ($HOMO_{donor}$ – $LUMO_{acceptor}$). Problems have been observed with charge transport, charge dissociation, or morphology for polymers or other fullerene derivatives with a higher-lying LUMO, and bis-adducts have a promising potential to overcome these problems [82, 83]. The LUMO of the PCBM bis-adduct (bisPCBM), for example, was found to be 0.1 eV higher than the PCBM LUMO, resulting in an increase of V_{OC} from 0.58 V for P3HT:PCBM to 0.73 V for P3HT:bisPCBM (Figure 8(d)). Consequently, an efficiency of 4.5% compared with 3.8% was achieved [84]. Another even more promising bis-adduct is bisindene-C_{60} (ICBA; Figure 8(e)). Here voltages of 0.84 V and efficiencies of 5.44–6.5% were achieved with P3HT as the donor material in the normal blend structure [65, 85]. For the inverted type, high efficiencies have been shown, too [86].

The stability of bis-adducts has not been investigated intensively until now. Generally, it is expected that a higher LUMO of the acceptor is more prone to oxidation. The benefit of the use of bis-adducts for commercial products is still open and needs to be investigated.

The good tunability of polymers has led to extensive research on polymers as donors, thus reaching IQE values near 100% [75]. Therefore, p-type materials with outstanding properties with respect to efficiency already exist. But polymers can be used not only as donors but also as acceptors. Comparably little research has been performed in this field. One of the best reported efficiencies is 1.8% for the polymer poly((9,9-dioctylfluorene)-2,7-diyl-alt-[4,7-bis(3-hexylthien-5-yl)-2,1,3-benzothiadiazole]-2′,2″-diyl) (F8TBT) blended with P3HT (Figure 8(f)) [87]. Since it has a similar absorption as P3HT, both polymers are not optimal partners. Due to the possibility of tuning the band gap of polymers, it is conceivable to create a polymer acting as acceptor with different absorption spectra compared with the donor, thus leading to an increase in overall absorption and current generation.

Table 3 gives an overview of cell performances comprising different donor and acceptor materials. However, the best active materials are useless if it is not possible to prevent charges from moving toward the wrong electrode and to reduce recombination at the interface with opposite charge carriers. Furthermore, the workfunctions (WFs) of the electrodes have to be aligned in order to avoid building up unfavorable space charges or a reduced V_{OC}. For these reasons, interfacial layers are needed, which are presented next.

1.20.3.2 Interfacial Materials

Interfacial materials serve a number of functions. They can block holes but conduct electrons or vice versa and thus determine the polarity of the device. They can be used to adjust the energy levels of the electrodes in order to ensure formation of an ohmic contact between the active layer and the electrodes to avoid electrical losses. They can be used to influence the interference of the incident light and therefore light harvesting. They can have an impact on the environmental stability of the device and also prohibit a chemical or physical reaction between the active layer and the electrode. Thus, interfacial layers are an important instrument to obtain optimal performance from the OSC.

1.20.3.2.1 Choosing the right interfacial materials

When organic semiconductors are brought in contact with metals or metal-like materials, the alignment of the Fermi levels with energy E_F can lead to the formation of an ohmic or a so-called Schottky contact. The formation of an ohmic contact is favorable since in this case band bending does not hinder charges to cross the junction. Therefore, a process called Fermi level pinning is desirable, which means that the Fermi level of the electrode material is pinned to a value near the HOMO or LUMO of the semiconductor. In this case, the WF value at the interface electrode/active layer is independent of the electrode's WF but depends solely on the semiconductor. In the case of semiconducting materials, the positions of HOMO and LUMO of the material are also important to decide whether it is an appropriate interfacial layer. To understand the contact formation of an organic semiconductor deposited on a conducting substrate, the ICT model was developed. It can help to estimate if a material with a certain Fermi level could serve as an interfacial layer [88].

Table 3 Device parameters for solar cells comprising different donor and acceptor materials

Active layer	J_{SC} (mA cm^{-2})	V_{OC} (V)	FF	Efficiency (%)	Reference
MDMO-PPV:PCBM[a]	5.25	0.83	0.60	3.3	[68]
P3HT:PCBM[a]	9.5	0.63	0.68	5.0	[71]
PCPDTBT:PC$_{70}$BM	16.2	0.62	0.55	5.5	[61]
PCDTBT:PC$_{70}$BM	10.6	0.88	0.66	6.1	[75]
PTB7:PC$_{70}$BM	14.5	0.74	0.69	7.4	[63]
P3HT:F8TBT	4.0	1.26		1.8	[87]
P3HT:bisPCBM	9.14	0.72	0.68	4.5	[84]
P3HT:PCBM[a]	9.5	0.68	0.63	5.0	[71]
P3HT:ICBA	10.61	0.84	0.73	6.5	[85]

[a] Illumination 80 mW cm^{-2}, otherwise 100 mW cm^{-2}.

The ICT model is valid for weak interactions of the molecule or polymer with the substrate. From an electronic point of view, this is described by little overlap of the wave functions of the interfacial material with the wave functions of the substrate. Establishing a conducting connection between a conjugated molecule or polymer and a substrate, for example, a metal, leads to an ICT either from the organics to the metal or vice versa. Due to the strong vibronic coupling in organic polymers, every additional or reduced charge will lead to an energetic relaxation which is achieved by geometrical relaxation. This leads to new energetic states called polarons, which are separated from the original LUMO and HOMO levels and appear within the formerly forbidden band gap. New states that are filled with holes and are close to the HOMO are called positive integer transfer states (ICT+). The energy of these states equals the energy needed to remove an electron adiabatically from the organic material and is denoted with E_{ICT+}. States which are close to the LUMO and occupied with electrons are called negative integer transfer states (ICT−). These have the energy E_{ICT-}, which is the energy gained by adiabatically adding an electron to this state. In both cases, the energies refer to adiabatic ionization processes, that is, those for which the final state has fully relaxed. The ICT model describes three different regimes:

1. $E_F < E_{ICT+}$, that is, E_F of the substrate is farther away from the vacuum level than E_{ICT+} of the polymer – electron transfer from ICT+ to the substrate and subsequent pinning of the substrate's Fermi level to ICT+ (**Figure 9(a)**);
2. $E_{ICT+} < E_F < E_{ICT-}$ – alignment of the vacuum levels is observed and E_F of the substrate remains unaltered (**Figure 9(b)**); and
3. $E_F > E_{ICT-}$ – electrons will be transferred to ICT−, leading to Fermi level pinning to ICT− (**Figure 9(c)**).

The model was confirmed experimentally with the polyfluorene derivative APFO-Green1. Deposition on different substrates with varying Fermi levels ranging from values smaller than E_{ICT+} to values larger than E_{ICT-} showed linear dependence of the polyfluorene/substrate WF within the regime $E_{ICT+} < E_F < E_{ICT-}$ with a slope of 1. Below or above this regime, the slope becomes 0 which indicates Fermi level pinning. The resulting graph is called mark of 'Zorro' (inset in **Figure 9**) [89]. With this knowledge, it is possible to make a promising preselection of interfacial materials.

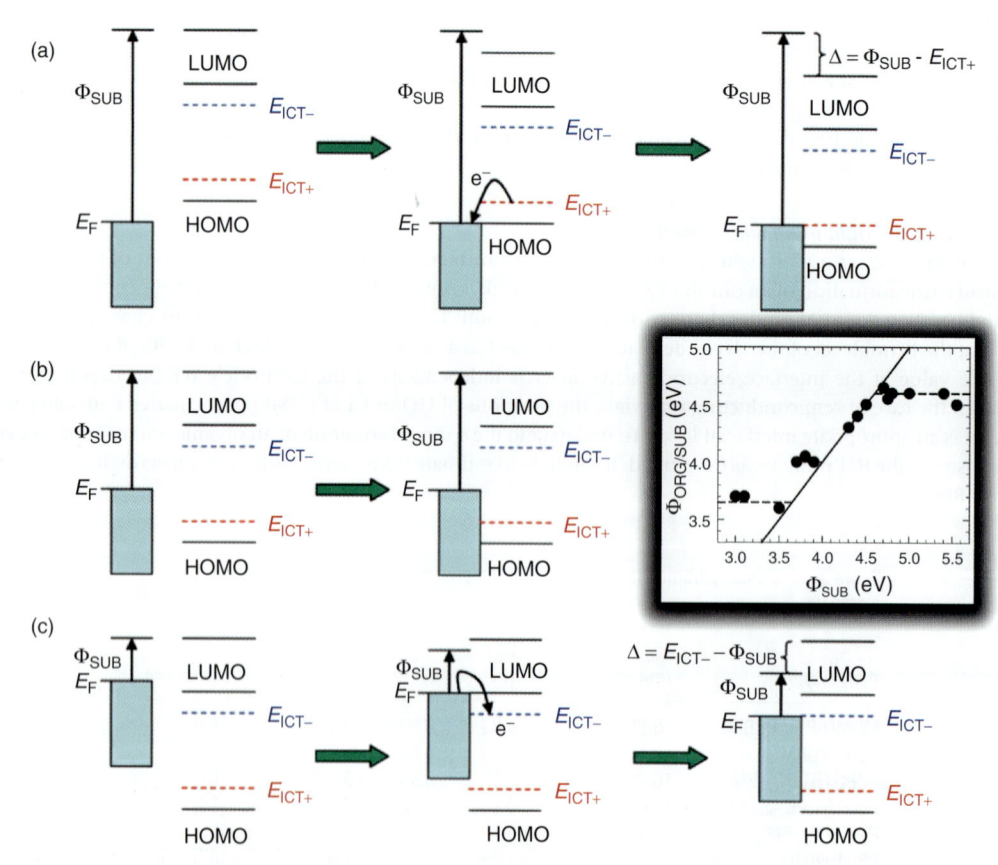

Figure 9 (a) $E_F < E_{ICT+}$: Fermi level pinning to ICT+. (b) $E_{ICT+} < E_F < E_{ICT-}$: no change of the substrate's Fermi level. (c) $E_F > E_{ICT-}$: Fermi level pinning to ICT−. Φ_{SUB} is the energy needed to remove an electron from the substrate. Inset: The plot of the WF at the junction APFO-Green1/substrate $\Phi_{ORG/SUB}$ vs. the pure substrate WF Φ_{SUB} for different substrates confirms the prediction of the ICT model. Copyright Wiley-VCH Verlag GmbH & Co. KGaA. Reproduced with permission from Braun S, Salaneck WR, and Fahlman M (2009) Energy-level alignment at organic/metal and organic/organic interfaces. *Advanced Materials* 21: 1450–1472 [89].

1.20.3.2.2 Material types

The most widely used material for the hole-selective electrode is poly(3,4-ethylenedioxythiophene):poly(styrenesulfonate) (PEDOT:PSS; **Figure 10**) [71, 85, 91–94]. Up to now, new types of PEDOT:PSS with improved properties have been developed constantly, and conductivities of above 900 S cm^{-1} have been reached [95]. Depending on which side of the active layer PEDOT:PSS is used, one obtains either the normal or the inverted device structure, that is, electrons are moving to the top or bottom electrode (**Figure 5**). Both architectures are comparable in efficiency. One reason for the somewhat lower current typically shown by the inverted architecture can be a vertical phase segregation of the blend layer, thus leading to slightly asymmetric conditions [96].

In general, there are two types of interfacial materials that can fulfill some or all of the required functions. Semiconducting interfacial layers, for example, show always nearly the same WF when deposited on different electrodes. Layers consisting of dipoles in contrast alter the WF of the electrode; thus, the value depends on the electrode and not on the interfacial layer.

Semiconducting interfacial materials can be of inorganic or organic nature. They are classified in p-type and n-type layers, depending on whether they conduct holes but block electrons or vice versa. This property is affected by the position of their VB and CB relative to the HOMO and LUMO of the active materials. Inorganic p-type materials are, for example, metal oxides such as V_2O_5, WO_3, and MoO_3. With respect to efficiency, it was shown that they are able to replace PEDOT:PSS (**Table 4**) [97–100].

As inorganic n-type contacts, TiO_x and ZnO can be used [86, 101, 102]. Also indium-doped zinc oxide (IZO) is possible. ZnO and IZO, for example, can be coated as nanoparticles [103]. PEDOT:PSS and sulfonated poly(diphenylamine) are organic p-type polymers [60, 104–107]. Examples for organic n-type materials are bathocuproine and BPhen [100, 108–110].

Altering of WFs through dipoles describes another approach for forming ohmic contacts between the electrodes and the active layer. In the simplest case, treatment with Brønsted acids leads to a protonation of indium tin oxide (ITO), the most frequently used transparent electrode for OSCs, and results in the accumulation of anions. This in turn leads to a dipole pointing away from the electrode's surface. The arrangement of molecules and charges results in an increase of the WF. Treatment by bases leads to dipoles pointing toward the surface of the electrode, thus decreasing the WF. Another approach to forming dipoles is by using either salts or self-assembled monolayers (SAMs) [111]. The most commonly used salt is lithium fluoride in the combination LiF/Al. In literature, a p-doping of the active material and a dipole pointing toward the active layer are discussed as operation methods of LiF [68]. Another salt that has been reported to give a reasonable device performance is Cs_2CO_3 [112, 113]. Applying SAMs by using *para*-substituted benzoic acids in between ZnO and Al had a strong impact on the resulting V_{OC} of the device consisting of ITO/PEDOT:PSS/P3HT:PCBM/ZnO/Al. The more negative the dipole was (pointing away from the electrode), the better was V_{OC}. For positive dipoles (pointing toward the electrode), V_{OC} decreased rapidly. The same was observed when Ag or Au were used as electrode [114].

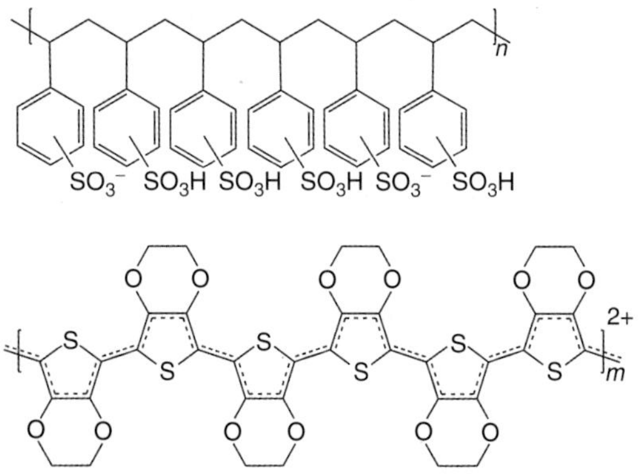

Figure 10 Chemical structure of PEDOT (bottom) and PSS (top).

Table 4 Performance of inverted solar cells with different hole-selective interfacial materials

Hole-selective contact	J_{SC} (mA cm^{-2})	V_{OC} (V)	FF	Efficiency (%)
ITO only	7.82	0.49	0.511	1.96
ITO/PEDOT:PSS	8.95	0.59	0.596	3.18
ITO/V_2O_5	8.83	0.59	0.591	3.10
ITO/MoO_x	8.94	0.50	0.619	3.33

Values from Reference 97.

Also for the application of SAMs at TiO$_x$/blend and ITO/blend interfaces, positive influences were reported when the right material was chosen [115–117].

With the aforementioned methods and materials, it has been shown that an adequate interface modification is possible; a more detailed description can be found elsewhere [118, 119]. Whether these materials are also suitable for mass production strongly depends on the stability of the applied materials when it comes to lifetime testing.

1.20.3.3 Electrode Materials

The optimum electrode has a very good conductivity and sheet resistance, is transparent, and is capable of forming an ohmic contact with the active layer materials, that is, possesses a Fermi level which is not in between the HOMO of the donor and the LUMO of the acceptor. Because the WF can be controlled quite well with the aid of interfacial materials, the major focus in electrode development today is on conductivity and transmission.

1.20.3.3.1 Transparent electrodes

At least one of the electrodes must have good transparency in order to yield a high illumination intensity of the active layer. ITO is up to now the most common transparent electrode. Depending on the substrate material, the transmittance of an ITO layer sputtered at high oxygen partial pressure can reach about 90% for wavelengths between 500 and 800 nm, which is the region where most polymers absorb. Furthermore, good-quality ITO layers deposited by sputtering can have a low sheet resistance and resistivity down to less than $10\,\Omega\,\square^{-1}$ and $1.2 \times 10^{-4}\,\Omega\,cm$, respectively, depending on the sputtering voltage, temperature, and oxygen partial pressure during sputtering [120–122]. A resistivity minimum is reached for a certain oxygen content. Below and above this amount, the resistivity increases rapidly. For high amounts, this behavior is explained as follows: with each oxygen vacancy, the number of charges in the CB is increased by two electrons to satisfy charge neutrality. As a consequence, the film becomes more metallic, which leads to a decreased sheet resistance concomitant with a decrease in transmission. Standard ITO-based transparent electrodes are currently probably the best trade-off between resistivity and transmission [123, 124]. ITO therefore is the preferred electrode material for electronic device production when transparency and conductivity are needed. Its WF is reported to lie between 4.4 and 4.8 eV, depending on the quality of the ITO, environmental conditions, and the measurement technique [125–127]. It is used mainly as the bottom electrode deposited as the first layer onto the substrate. Besides sputtering, there are also other processing methods like sol–gel, e-beam, and pulsed laser deposition [122, 123, 128]. The search for alternative transparent electrodes is mainly driven by the costs of ITO-based electrodes. Sputtering processes result in the highest quality ITO layers but require expensive vacuum steps. Moreover, indium is a rare material, which additionally adds to the costs of ITO.

Other metal oxides, for example, aluminum-doped zinc oxide (AZO), provide a low-cost alternative to ITO. The transmittance of AZO was shown to be similar to that of ITO, being around 90% for the visible spectrum. With a sheet resistance of $8-25\,\Omega\,\square^{-1}$, a resistivity of about $4 \times 10^{-4}\,\Omega\,cm$, and a WF of 4.5 eV, it is also comparable to ITO. A direct comparison of OSCs with either ITO or AZO as transparent conductive oxide (TCO) resulted in a similar performance [129–131].

The properties of fluorine tin oxide (FTO) are related to that of ITO, too. It has a transmittance of around 90% in the visible range, a sheet resistance of $12.5\,\Omega\,\square^{-1}$, and a resistivity of $5 \times 10^{-4}\,\Omega\,cm$. Due to its lower costs, it could also be a candidate for replacing ITO. A comparison of OSCs with P3HT:PCBM as active layer coated on ITO and FTO showed similar efficiencies, too [132, 133].

Besides aluminum, indium, and fluorine, other dopants for ZnO and SnO$_2$ like antimony, boron, or gallium are also possible, thus leading to a variety of possible TCOs. Stacking of TCOs and thin, transparent metal layers was shown to improve some of the properties required for TCO layers [134–136]. Again, stability is a decisive factor and needs to be addressed in addition to the time zero performance values.

Another approach which entirely omits the use of TCO materials is the so-called grid electrode. Here a metal grid, for instance, Ag, is deposited on a substrate and coated with a highly conductive polymer such as PEDOT:PSS. The support of a metal grid is required for large-area devices because the conductivity of PEDOT:PSS-type materials is not sufficient to transport charges over long distances without losses due to series resistance.

1.20.3.3.2 Opaque electrodes

In general, calcium, aluminum, silver, and gold are used as the opaque electrode. The WFs are around 2.9, 4.3, 5.0, and 5.1 eV, respectively [101, 137–139]. They are normally used as top electrodes and deposited by evaporation when cells are produced on a lab scale. For larger-scale production, silver is the preferred material due to the availability of silver inks [140].

Calcium has a WF that makes it suitable as the electron-selective contact. However, the low WF leads to an unstable behavior as soon as it comes in contact with water or oxygen. Therefore, it is not a suitable material for ambient processing and environmentally stable solar cells.

Aluminum has a higher but still rather low WF and is therefore often used in the normal cell structure as electron-collecting electrode, too. With aluminum, the highest reported efficiencies have been reached so far. It is more stable against oxidation and hydrolysis than Ca but still too reactive to obtain air-stable cells.

Silver and gold with their rather high WFs are mostly used as top contacts in the inverted structure. However, with an adequate interfacial layer that shifts the electrode WF, the application of, for example, silver as electron-collecting electrode is also possible

[103]. Compared with calcium and aluminum, both noble metals have the advantage of a high stability, thus leading to devices which are more robust toward environmental influences.

1.20.4 Driving Efficiency

The largest effort in research has been spent on improving the efficiency of OSCs. Various possibilities were explored to improve the J_{SC}, the V_{OC}, or the FF. This includes changes in morphology, absorption, mobility, energy level, molecular structure, and last but not least different device architectures.

1.20.4.1 Preferable Properties of the Donor Molecule

For P3HT as a model system of semicrystalline polymers, it was found that the primary structure can have a large influence on device performance. The key parameters are molecular weight, regioregularity, and polydispersity, that is, chain length distribution.

The polydispersity (PD) is defined by the ratio of the weight-average molar mass M_w and the number-average molar mass M_n as

$$\text{PD} = \frac{M_w}{M_n} \quad [5]$$

M_n describes the average mass of a randomly picked molecule and is equal to the total molar mass of the batch over the total number of molecules. M_w is the average molar mass one obtains when randomly picking not a whole molecule but a single monomer and looking at the mass of the polymer it belongs to. It is equal to the sum over the weight fraction of each molar mass times the molar mass itself. In the case of polymers having the same molar mass, M_n and M_w become equal, thus leading to PD = 1. However, for man-made polymers, this is never the case and PD is always larger than 1. It is suggested that a broader PD affects the material properties in a positive way [141].

The regioregularity of a polymer describes the orientation in which asymmetric monomers are connected with each other. Generally, three different possibilities exist to connect a pair of asymmetric monomers: head-to-tail (HT), tail-to-tail (TT), and head-to-head (HH). In the case of P3HT, head denotes the 2-position of 3-hexylthiophene and tail denotes the 5-position. It was shown that regioregularity increases the mobility significantly. P3HT with a 91% HT linkage showed field-effect mobilities in transistors (FET mobility) of up to $0.1\,\text{cm}^2\,\text{V}^{-1}\,\text{s}^{-1}$, while the values for polythiophenes with lower HT linkages of 86% were around $2 \times 10^{-4}\,\text{cm}^2\,\text{V}^{-1}\,\text{s}^{-1}$. X-ray studies revealed that the π–π-stacking direction was in the substrate plane for the first and perpendicular to it for the second case [142]. Thus, regioregular (RR) orientation enables a better π–π stacking (aggregation) and better charge transport between different molecules compared with the regiorandom (ReRa) orientation [33, 143]. Also for OSCs, similar results for the behavior of the mobility were observed [144, 145].

Apart from RR, the molecular weight can also shift the mobility by magnitudes. Kline et al. showed that an increase in M_n from 3200 to $36\,500\,\text{g}\,\text{mol}^{-1}$ also increases the mobility from 1.7×10^{-6} to $9.4 \times 10^{-3}\,\text{cm}^2\,\text{V}^{-1}\,\text{s}^{-1}$. In addition, atomic force microscopy (AFM) and X-ray diffraction (XRD) revealed a higher grade of crystallinity for low M_n polymers. Therefore, grain boundaries between the crystal structures are made responsible for the low mobility. Long polymer chains are less well defined in crystallinity and are therefore assumed to be good connectors between the highly ordered regions, thus enhancing the charge transfer between the crystalline domains [142, 143].

Schilinsky et al. investigated the influence of M_n on the performance of OSCs and found that the photocurrent is strongly molecular weight dependent. Besides an increase in current with increasing M_n, larger FF and V_{OC} were also observed. A significant efficiency increase took place for $M_n > 10\,000\,\text{g}\,\text{mol}^{-1}$. Efficiencies from slightly above 0% for a molecular weight of $2200\,\text{g}\,\text{mol}^{-1}$ to around 3% for $19\,000\,\text{g}\,\text{mol}^{-1}$ were observed. Further semi-theoretical calculations showed a good agreement between an increased series resistance and a lowered mobility [146].

Woo et al., however, critically discussed the above results [147]. They noticed that many of the studies were not conducted on optimized systems and different efficiencies were reported for similar P3HT molecular weights. Woo further argued that low M_n P3HT can also have advantageous properties compared with high M_n P3HT such as thermal stability. For annealing times above 300 min at 150 °C, a significant efficiency decrease was observed for high M_n P3HT, while the lower M_n P3HTs remained stable. An explanation could be that the higher crystallinity of the low M_n P3HT leads to a more stable orientation of the polymer stacking. For long polymer chains with less ordering, larger PCBM clusters can arise, thus dislocating the stacked polymers [147].

1.20.4.2 Impact of Morphology

Besides the properties of the donor which plays the role of the main absorbing and therefore main current-producing material, the interplay of donor and acceptor, that is, polymer and fullerene, is also very important. Pathways for electrons and holes are required in order to allow for the charges to reach the electrodes. In the case where donor and/or acceptor domains are too small, the separated charges are more likely to get in contact with charges of the other sort, and a higher recombination rate limits current generation. In the opposite case, that is, where the domain size exceeds the exciton diffusion length significantly, exciton splitting becomes the limiting factor and again current generation is decreased. Moreover, it is of paramount importance to generate domains which are continuous throughout the entire device, thus paving the way for charges to the electrodes. Last but not least, the enrichment of the donor near one electrode and of the acceptor near the other electrode can also play a role in decreasing recombination at the electrodes.

It was found that the alignment of the morphology is governed by different factors. These include the use of different solvents and coating conditions as well as postproduction treatment. Therefore, the knowledge of how to influence the morphology in a positive way is of crucial interest. Typical methods for morphology investigations include transmission electron microscopy (TEM), selected area electron diffraction (SAED), scanning electron microscopy (SEM), scanning probe microscopy (SPM), AFM, and electron tomography. The latter uses a series of 2D projections taken by TEM to visualize a 3D structure of the specimen. The main difference between TEM and electron tomography, on the one hand, and SEM, SPM, and AFM, on the other hand, is that the latter provide information about the surface of the investigated layer, while the former also inform about the lateral organization of thin-film samples.

1.20.4.2.1 Influence of solvents on morphology

Often active materials are soluble in not only one but several solvents. Typically used solvents are chlorobenzene (CBZ), o-dichlorobenzene (DCBZ), dichloromethane (DCM), orthoxylene (XY), and toluene (TOL). For solar cells consisting of MDMO-PPV and PCBM, it was found that under otherwise identical production conditions, the efficiency varied in a wide range when different solvents were used. Shaheen et al. [67] managed to increase the efficiency from 0.9% to 2.5% when using CBZ instead of TOL. The better solubility of PCBM in CBZ leads to a more homogeneous film and avoids aggregation of PCBM on the surface. A more than twofold J_{SC} improvement from 2.33 to 5.25 mA cm^{-2} was the main contribution to the efficiency improvement. The FF increased from 0.50 to 0.61, whereas V_{OC} remained unchanged. The large increase in current density was explained by smaller PCBM domains and improved polymer chain interactions of MDMO-PPV. On the one hand, larger aggregates of PCBM lead to a smaller mobility for electrons caused by larger voids between the domains, which lead to a higher hopping barrier for charges. On the other hand, larger interchain interactions improve the hole mobility in MDMO-PPV. The increased FF could be a result of the improved mobility as well as a result of a better interfacial contact of the smoother active layer to the electrode. A study comparing XY, CBZ, and DCBZ for solving MDMO-PPV:PCBM revealed that CBZ caused larger donor and acceptor domains than DCBZ but smaller ones than XY. Nevertheless, the best efficiency (~3%) was achieved with CBZ. This was explained by the large domains in the XY case, which led to a decreased exciton separation since the excitons could not reach a donor–acceptor interface within their lifetimes. Although a large interface between donor and acceptor is desirable, a too intimate mixing is expected to lead to increased recombination [148]. Similar results for phase separation were obtained by Martens et al. [149]. They found that PCBM domains are embedded in a matrix consisting of MDMO-PPV and PCBM. For TOL as solvent, the PCBM domains were larger than for CBZ. Further, the matrix contained more PCBM for CBZ (**Figures 11**(a) and **11**(b)).

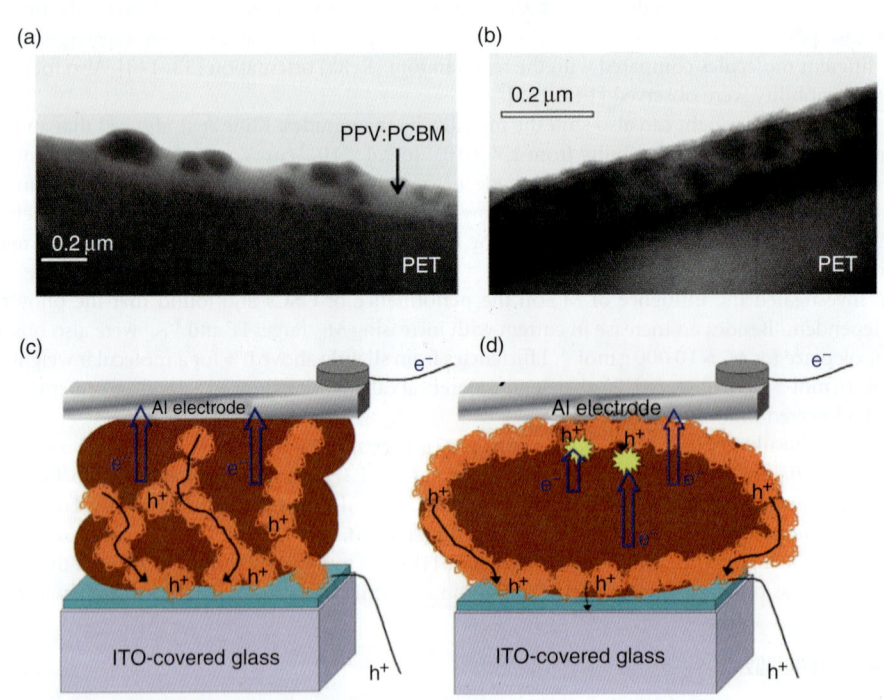

Figure 11 Cross-sectional TEM images of MDMO-PPV:PCBM films spin-coated on a PET substrate from TOL (a) and CBZ (b). The dark regions are the PCBM-rich regions. In the case of CBZ, the PCBM domains are smaller. Reprinted from Martens T, D'Haen J, Munters T, et al. (2003) Disclosure of the nanostructure of MDMO-PPV:PCBM bulk hetero-junction organic solar cells by a combination of SPM and TEM. *Synthetic Metals* 138: 243–247 [149], with permission from Elsevier. Schematic of (c) CBZ and (d) TOL cast MDMO-PPV:PCBM blend layers. In (c), holes and electrons find percolated pathways to reach the respective electrode. In (d), increased recombination occurs due to missing percolation. Reprinted from Hoppe H, Glatzel T, Niggemann M, et al. (2006) Efficiency limiting morphological factors of MDMO-PPV:PCBM plastic solar cells. *Thin Solid Films* 511–512: 587–592 [56], with permission from Elsevier.

Hoppe *et al.* observed another interesting behavior when casting MDMO-PPV-PCBM films from TOL. Larger domains of PCBM were covered by MDMO-PPV, thus forming a barrier for electrons migrating toward the anode [56]. Kelvin probe force microscopy measurements revealed a very homogeneous WF for the blend cast from CBZ. Under illumination, the WF was decreased around 300 meV. In the case of TOL, the WF was very inhomogeneous, and on top of morphological elevations caused by PCBM, it was increased around 200 meV. This was explained as follows: under illumination, electrons are excited and transferred from MDMO-PPV to PCBM. In the case of CBZ where PCBM has access to the surface, the elevated electron density in PCBM leads to an increase in its Fermi level. In the case of TOL where MDMO-PPV covers the PCBM domains, the same effect is observed and the reduced electron density in MDMO-PPV under illumination decreases the Fermi level. The situation is schematically depicted in **Figures 11(c)** and **11(d)**. Electrons must penetrate hole-rich domains to reach the cathode because the electron-extracting electrode is the top electrode in the normal geometry, thus leading to increased recombination.

1.20.4.2.2 Influence of mixing ratio and concentration

A decisive factor for efficiency optimization is the ratio of the donor and acceptor material in the active layer. The blending ratio cannot be varied at will since the desired phase segregation cannot be achieved with any ratio. For instance, the PCBM domain size in an MDMO-PPV:PCBM film spin-coated from CB stays almost constant, showing very homogeneous films in TEM images until the PCBM weight fraction reaches 70%. From this point, the domain size increases rapidly [149, 150]. In the case of MDMO-PPV:PCBM solar cells, a ratio of 1:4 was found to be adequate.

For solar cells consisting of P3HT:PCBM, ratios between 1:1 and 1:0.8 were found to give the best performing devices [70, 71, 151].

Table 5 gives an overview of different mixture ratios for various polymers. It is important to note that different materials can lead to different optimal blending ratios.

In addition to the mixing ratio, the absolute concentration also influences the phase segregation. An increase in the concentration at the same mixing ratio, for example, can lead to different extents of phase segregation. Thus, the concentration where the maximum absorption is reached may lead to an unfavorable phase segregation and hence decreased performance. For a constant ratio of 1:4 for MDMO-PPV:PCBM but different concentrations, Hoppe *et al.* observed larger PCBM domains with increasing concentration. After exceeding a certain concentration, the domains started to shrink. This was explained by a higher viscosity of the solution due to the high MDMO-PPV concentration and therefore differing drying conditions of the film [66, 156].

1.20.4.2.3 Influence of annealing

The optimum morphology of an active layer film is rarely obtained directly after coating from solution. For instance, film deposition via spin coating leads to very fast evaporation of the solvent, leaving behind a film which is not in thermal equilibrium. Equilibrium is reached by rearrangement of molecules, polymer chain segments, or entire polymer chains, which happens very slowly at room temperature conditions. However, the process of morphology change can be accelerated by the aid of thermal or solvent vapor annealing. Especially for P3HT:PCBM, a lot of research has been devoted to that topic, leading to interesting insights into morphology formation.

1.20.4.2.3(i) Thermal annealing

Thermal annealing describes the heating of the active layer after coating and solvent evaporation in order to alter the nanoscale structure. The annealing step can be applied either before or after deposition of the top electrode. However, often observations depend mainly on the thermal annealing process itself and are independent of pre- or postannealing. Further, in most cases, a preannealing step is performed since surface investigations of the active layer are possible only without electrode confinement on top. The impact of the thermal treatment is controlled via the annealing time and temperature. Yang *et al.* showed by TEM measurements that increasing the annealing time of MDMO-PPV:PCBM at 130 °C from 10 through 20 to 30 min leads to a strong growth of PCBM domains, thus causing phase segregation [150]. They showed further by SAED that these PCBM clusters were single crystals. The size of the crystals reached from the submicrometer scale after 10 min to several micrometers after 30 min annealing. Annealing at different temperatures revealed two different sorts of PCBM crystals. One sort was obtained at annealing temperatures above 80 °C and the other at temperatures below 80 °C. The latter was much thinner but had a larger lateral dimension. Since the

Table 5 Mixture ratios and corresponding efficiencies for MDMO-PPV and P3HT blended with PCBM

Material – blend ratio	J_{SC} (mA cm^{-2})	V_{OC} (V)	FF	Efficiency (%)	Reference
MDMO-PPV:PCBM – 1:4	5.25[a]	0.82	0.61	2.5	[67]
MDMO-PPV:PCBM – 1:4	5.0[a]	0.80	0.71	2.65	[152]
P3HT:PCBM – 1:4	15.9	0.56	0.47	3.8	[153]
P3HT:PCBM – 1:2	8.5[a]	0.55	0.60	3.5	[154]
P3HT:PCBM – 1:1	10.9	0.63	0.49	3.4	[155]
P3HT:PCBM – 1:0.8	11.1[a]	0.64	0.55	4.9	[70]
P3HT:PCBM – 1:0.8	9.5[a]	0.63	0.68	5.1	[71]

[a] Illumination 80 mW cm^{-2}, otherwise 100 mW cm^{-2}.

glass transition temperature (T_g) of MDMO-PPV is around 80 °C, they concluded that the PCBM diffusion benefits from a loose polymer matrix, while it was hampered by a more rigid one below 80 °C. Hoppe *et al.* found a similar behavior for MDMO-PPV: PCBM films cast from either TOL or CBZ by AFM investigations and could observe PCBM crystal growth at the expense of surrounding PCBM clusters by increasing the annealing time. Photoluminescence (PL) measurements confirmed the depletion of PCBM in the polymer matrix. The PL signal increased significantly after annealing, resulting from excitons that could not reach the interface of the active materials due to the large phase segregation which was also shown by other groups [157, 158].

For solar cells consisting of P3HT:PCBM, different annealing temperatures of 80, 105, and 155 °C resulted in a strong performance increase when the annealing time was not longer than 5 min [70]. In the optimal case of 155 °C and 5 min, the efficiency could be increased from 1.11% to around 4.9% due to improvements in FF and first and foremost J_{SC} (**Figures 12(a)** and **12(b)**). The authors suggest that crystallization of the polymer and thus a higher hole mobility is responsible for the improved performance. However, annealing times exceeding 5 min decreased the performance. By AFM, they observed an increasing root mean square height variation on the micron scale, but a smoother film at the submicron level, which indicates aggregation of PCBM clusters to larger domains responsible for the performance decrease, similar to the MDMO-PPV:PCBM case [70]. Related results of efficiency improvement were reported by Beal *et al.*, who observed an efficiency increase from 1.3% to 4%. Imaging the active layer during the annealing process at 150 °C by TEM revealed at the beginning a PCBM cluster size below 10 nm and an average nearest neighbor distance of 1.3 ± 0.6 nm (width of the P3HT matrix between two adjacent PCBM domains). After 12 min of annealing, the average area of the PCBM domains increased from 143 ± 44 to 350 ± 110 nm^2. In this connection, a smaller portion of excitons could reach the donor–acceptor interface and became separated. However, the average nearest neighbor distance did almost not change with 1.8 ± 0.8 nm, which means that separated electrons have to transit less frequently from one PCBM domain to another. As this transit is governed by nonconductive mechanisms such as hopping or tunneling, it results in an improvement of the fullerene mobility within the device [159].

van Bavel *et al.* gained insight into the 3D morphology of annealed P3HT:PCBM films by applying electron tomography. For PCBM contents of 40%, they found a homogeneous distribution of P3HT, with a crystallization degree of ~45%, over the entire layer thickness. This high degree of crystallization and the homogeneous distribution led to devices with efficiencies of around 3.3% compared with 1.3% before annealing. Again the performance boost resulted from an increased current density and FF, both caused by the improved morphology [160].

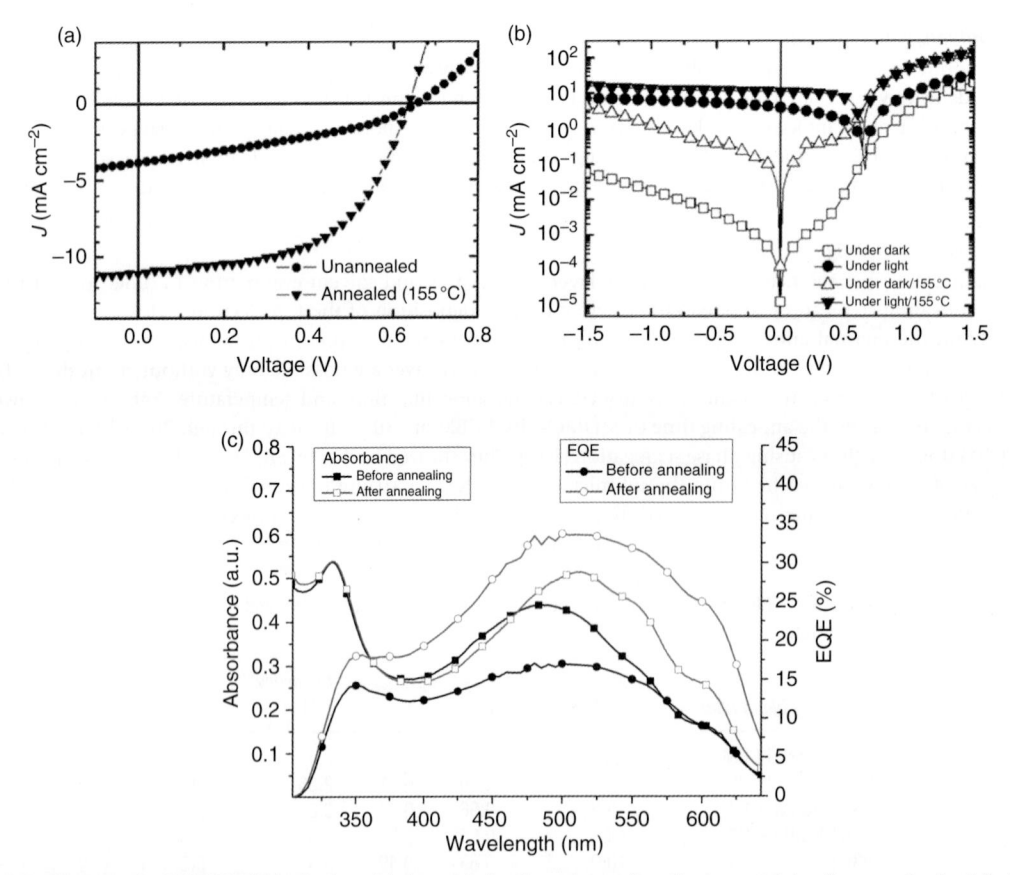

Figure 12 (a, b) *JV* curves of a P3HT:PCBM blend solar cell before and after thermal annealing. The increased J_{SC} after annealing is attributed to better hole mobility in P3HT due to crystallization. Reprinted with permission from Reyes-Reyes M, Kim K, and Carroll DL (2005) High-efficiency photovoltaic devices based on annealed poly(3-hexylthiophene) and 1-(3-methoxycarbonyl)-propyl-1-phenyl-(6,6)C$_{61}$ blends. *Applied Physics Letters* 87: 083506/1–3 [70]. Copyright 2005, American Institute of Physics. (c) Absorbance and EQE improve significantly after thermal annealing for 5 min at 105 °C.

Besides the improved charge transport, the increased efficiency also results from an improved absorption as was shown by Reyes-Reyes et al. [73]. Figure 12(c) shows the typical change of absorbance and EQE due to annealing.

In general, thermal treatments are performed utilizing a hot plate or an oven. However, other possibilities like pulsed laser or microwave annealing were also shown to have a similar impact on the devices as classical treatments [161, 162].

In conclusion, annealing is an effective way for improving the morphology and thus performance of OSCs. However, the optimum annealing conditions must be identified for each different active material combination.

1.20.4.2.3(ii) Solvent vapor annealing

Besides thermal annealing, solvent vapor annealing can also influence the morphology of the active layer. When active layers are exposed to solvent-rich atmospheres or if production conditions are altered in a way that the solvent evaporates sufficiently slowly, the system has more time to reach thermal equilibrium. Similar to thermal annealing, different grades of phase separation can be obtained with this technique, leading to improved performance.

Li et al. utilized the spin coating time t_s during preparation of the P3HT:PCBM layer to define a solvent annealing time t_a [163]. Both are connected in a way that an increase in t_s leads to a decrease in t_a and vice versa. By absorbance measurements, they found that the optical density is increased with increasing solvent annealing time. For a long t_s of 80 s and thus short t_a, an efficiency of only 1.17% was found for P3HT and PCBM as active materials. Efficiencies of 3.38% and 3.64% were obtained by increasing t_a and thus decreasing t_s to 50 and 20 s, respectively. The authors argue that a longer growth time of the active materials leads to an ordered and more crystalline structure of P3HT and PCBM, thus leading to similar effects as thermal annealing, that is, mainly an increase in J_{SC}. Zhao et al. performed solvent annealing by transferring P3HT:PCBM active layers spin-coated from CBZ to a jar filled with another organic solvent. By comparison of different solvents, it was concluded that solvents which dissolve both thiophene and fullerene work best. DCBZ was identified as the best solvent and the efficiency was further increased by a combination of solvent and thermal annealing [164].

1.20.4.2.4 Binary solvent systems

Another approach to influence morphology makes use of a binary solvent system for dissolution of the active materials where the second solvent can dissolve either only one component or both. It was reported that addition of a small amount of CBZ into the chloroform solution of poly(2,7-(9,9-dioctyl-fluorene)-alt-5,5-(4′,7′-di-2-thienyl-2′,1′,3′-benzothiadiazole)):PCBM leads to a finer phase separation and thus higher J_{SC}. Addition of, for example, XY or TOL in turn increased phase separation [165]. A similar observation of a more uniform blend film was made by Liang et al. when they investigated PTB7:PC$_{70}$BM films spin-coated from CBZ in combination with diiodoctane (DIO) instead of CBZ alone. Due to an improved charge separation, a remarkable efficiency increase from 3.92% to 7.40% could be achieved [63]. More complex approaches make use of three or even more solvents, and experiments to learn more about the requirements concerning the properties of additional solvents were performed [61, 165–167]. For example, Chen et al. found that addition of a solvent with a higher boiling point to CBZ for dissolution of P3HT:PCBM, for example, 1-chloronaphthalene, has a similar effect on morphology as described for solvent annealing. Because of the slower drying process, a better morphology is established, which results in an efficiency increase from 3.1% to 4.3% [168]. The addition of octanedithiol (ODT), a solvent that dissolves only one component but not the other, was investigated for the PCPDTBT:PC$_{70}$BM system. Since the solvent system becomes less attractive for one material, this component minimizes its surface energy by agglomeration. In the reported case, this led to an increase in electron mobility in PC$_{70}$BM, which was identified as the main contribution to the twofold efficiency increase from 2.8% to 5.5% [169].

The use of solvent mixtures in general is a promising alternative for production scenarios where postproduction treatment may become critical.

Besides the above-described morphology changes, the vertical phase segregation of donor and acceptor is also discussed. For polymer–polymer blend solar cells, it was shown that adequate segregation can have a positive impact on the device performance [170]. The same was observed for devices consisting of small molecules [171]. Also for polymer:fullerene solar cells, namely, P3HT:PCBM, there are several indications for an influence of vertical phase segregation on the performance. Thereby, all possibilities, an enrichment of PCBM or P3HT at the surface as well as a homogeneous distribution, were observed [159, 160, 172–176]. Probably this depends on the respective used solvents, substrates, and production methods. Xu et al. attributed the phase separation to an interaction of the components with the substrate due to their respective surface energies [175]. The vertical alignment is of interest because a PCBM-rich phase near the electron-selective and a P3HT-rich phase near the hole-selective contact can lead to improved performance since surface recombination, that is, the recombination at the active layer/electrode interface, is decreased.

1.20.4.3 Improved Material Properties for Efficiency Increase

The power conversion efficiency of semiconductors is limited due to their working mechanisms. The upper limit of the theoretical efficiency for inorganic p–n junction solar cells was estimated by Shockley and Queisser as the detailed balance limit in 1961 [6]. The theory is based on two major considerations: the first fundamental limitation lies in the energy which is required to excite an electron from the VB of the semiconductor to its CB. Only photons with energies larger than the band gap will contribute to current generation. Silicon, for example, has a band gap of 1.1 eV, but only half of the photons which reach the earth's surface possess an energy greater than 1.1 eV. This already limits the maximum efficiency to ~50%. Second, if photons with energies higher than the band gap are absorbed, the electrons will be excited to a state above the band gap and subsequently thermally relax to the CB. These thermal relaxation losses further decrease the theoretical power conversion efficiency. The V_{OC} is proportional to the band gap; thus, on the one hand, a high band gap is desirable for high voltages. On the other hand, high band gaps lead to a lower absorption, which in turn results in a lower current generation. Therefore, a trade-off has to be made between V_{OC} and J_{SC} and an optimum is found around 1.4 eV. Thus, the ultimate efficiency limited by the band gap and the solar spectrum is 48%. By estimating loss mechanisms under real conditions, Shockley and Queisser found a maximum theoretical efficiency of around 30% for inorganic single-junction solar cells [6].

For OSCs, it is generally observed that the V_{OC} correlates with the HOMO–LUMO difference of donor and acceptor. To separate the strongly bonded excitons in OSCs, a difference of at least 0.3 eV between the LUMOs of donor and acceptor is required. This decreases the HOMO–LUMO difference of donor and acceptor and thus the V_{OC}. Additionally, the observed V_{OC} in OSCs is normally about 0.3 V smaller than the HOMO–LUMO difference of donor and acceptor, which leads to a further reduction of V_{OC}. Charge transport losses (FF < 100%) and EQEs < 100% reduce the maximum theoretical efficiency value further. Despite these losses, calculations show that practical efficiencies larger than 10% are possible by assuming typical values for FF and EQE of 65% in each case, a donor with a band gap of 1.5 eV, and a donor–acceptor LUMO difference of 0.3 eV [177].

A general drawback of P3HT which has been the most commonly used donor within the last decade is the comparably high band gap of 1.9 eV, which leads to a maximum absorption wavelength of around 650 nm. Thus, P3HT absorbs only 22.4% of the incident photons. The maximum photon flux of the sun is reached at around 700 nm and is therefore out of reach for P3HT [178, 179].

The optimal material parameters for polymer donors can be obtained by utilizing a model developed in 2006 by Scharber *et al.* [177]. They studied the relation between the energy levels of a donor–acceptor blend by applying 26 different donor materials and derived the following correlation for the open-circuit voltage with PCBM as acceptor:

$$V_{OC} = \left(\frac{1}{e}\right)\left(|\text{HOMO}_{donor}| - |\text{LUMO}_{acceptor}|\right) - 0.3 \text{ V} \quad [6]$$

with e being the elementary charge, HOMO_{donor} the energy of the HOMO of the donor, and $\text{LUMO}_{acceptor}$ the energy of the LUMO of the acceptor. Together with the band gap and the LUMO of the donor, the maximum attainable efficiency $\eta = \text{FF}(J_{SC}V_{OC}/P_{in})$ for the polymer–PCBM system can be obtained. As a practical limit, an FF and EQE of 65% were chosen. The LUMO of PCBM was assumed to be −4.3 eV. In all these calculations, the contribution to J_{SC} from photons absorbed by the acceptor molecules was neglected. J_{SC} can be easily obtained by integrating the AM1.5G spectrum multiplied with the EQE spectrum. Plotting the efficiencies for various donor LUMOs and band gaps leads to a contour plot, with the donor band gap on the *x*-axis and the donor LUMO on the *y*-axis, as shown in **Figure 13**. Until now, this model is the main guide for potential estimations of donor materials and has been driving the search for novel donor polymers.

The practical ~10% efficiency limit of OSCs can be exceeded by decreasing recombination and increasing the charge carrier mobility.

Generally, an increase in the ultimate efficiency limit can be obtained by applying various methods like fluorescent downconversion of high-energy photons. Some fluorescent materials are capable of absorbing one high-energy photon and emitting several low-energy photons [180]. This is an interesting possibility since each photon with energy larger than the band

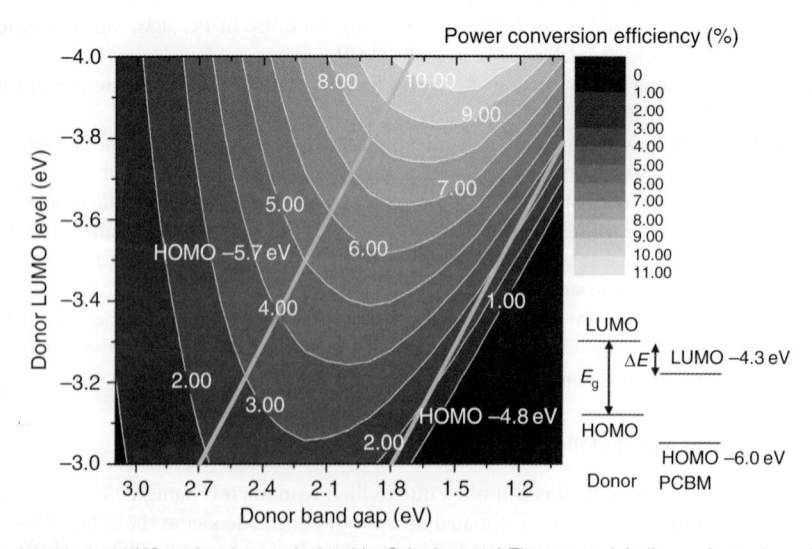

Figure 13 Contour plot of the donor LUMO vs. band gap calculated by Scharber *et al.* The two straight lines refer to donor HOMO levels of −5.7 and −4.8 eV. In addition, the LUMO and HOMO levels of PCBM are shown. Copyright Wiley-VCH Verlag GmbH & Co. KGaA. Reproduced with permission from Scharber MC, Mühlbacher D, Koppe M, *et al.* (2006) Design rules for donors in bulk-heterojunction solar cells – Towards 10% energy-conversion efficiency. *Advanced Materials* 18: 789–794 [177].

gap generates exactly one electron, independently of its energy. Also upconversion of low-energy photons can be a possibility [180]. Another method utilizes tandem solar cells, which will be discussed later in detail. In tandem devices, several solar cells with active layers which absorb in different wavelength regions are stacked. Similar considerations as for single-junction devices can be made to estimate optimal material properties [181]. For the same assumptions as for the single-junction cell, that is, FF and EQE 65%, acceptor LUMO −4.3 eV, further a fixed LUMO–LUMO difference of 0.3 eV for the two donor–acceptor systems, and an IQE of 85% for the bottom subcell, one obtains a contour plot similar to the one in **Figure 13**. The maximum achievable efficiency for this cell type under the given assumptions is calculated to be about 15%.

1.20.4.4 Effect of Interference in the Device

An easily controlled parameter that has a big influence on the efficiency is the thickness of the active layer. While a minimum thickness of the active layer is required for efficient light absorption, its maximum thickness is limited by the product of mobility and lifetime of the charge carriers. The thicknesses usually lie, not only for P3HT:PCBM but also for other donor:PCBM layers, in the range between 70 and 250 nm [23, 67, 92, 93, 96, 147, 160, 161, 174, 182–184]. Including interfacial and electrode layers, the thicknesses of OSCs are in the range of the wavelengths that can be absorbed. For opaque solar cells with a reflecting top electrode like evaporated silver, interference of the incident with the reflected electric field takes place. Since the interference pattern is sensitive to the refractive indices and the thicknesses of the different layers in the cell, the absorption by the active layer can also be influenced by variation of the parameters of the nonabsorbing layers. Thus, an improvement in efficiency can also be achieved by optimally adjusting properties of the nonabsorbing layers. However, a strong optical spacer effect which should lead to an interference maximum within the active layer and thus improved J_{SC} as described by Kim *et al.* seems to be rather unlikely [92, 185, 186].

1.20.4.5 Solar Cell Architectures for Enhanced Device Performance

1.20.4.5.1 Tandem architecture

Tandem solar cells, or more generally multijunction solar cells, attempt to improve the efficiency of solar cells by stacking of at least two active layer materials with different absorption properties. The overlap of the absorption spectra of the different materials should be as small as possible to allow for maximum absorption of the incident light. When the absorption properties of both materials are identical, the second active layer will contribute only little to current generation because most of the light has been absorbed already by the first one. Different types of tandem solar cells will be discussed in the following paragraphs.

1.20.4.5.1(i) Series-connected multijunction solar cells

The structure itself can be described as a serial connection of two single cells just the way two batteries are connected (**Figure 14(a)**). In between the two active layers of the two subcells, a layer is required that serves as an HSL for one subcell and as an ESL for the other subcell. This layer can be a combination of two single interfacial layers or a layer that inhibits both properties. It is termed recombination layer because holes of one active layer and electrons of the other active layer recombine here. The recombination layer is indeed one of the major challenges for solution-processed tandem solar cells. Other challenges are the availability of active materials with sufficiently different absorption spectra and the deposition of at least six layers on top of each other without damaging the previously deposited layers. Deposition of one layer on top of the other is possible only when the underlying layer is not dissolved by the solvent. This can be achieved either by cross-linking of the underlying layer or by the use of orthogonal solvents. Considering six layers which are coated on top of each other, the orthogonality approach becomes especially challenging.

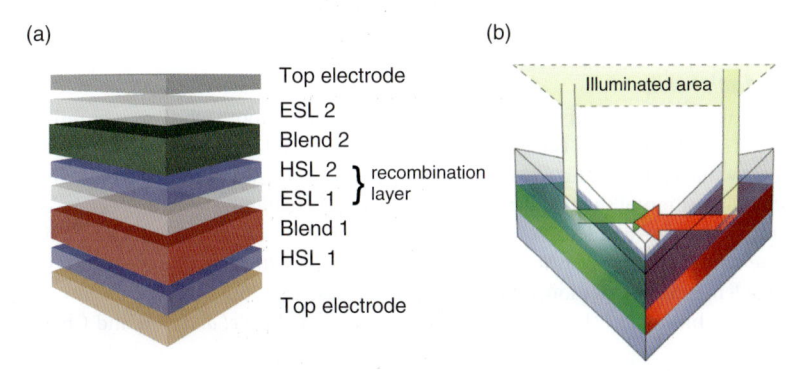

Figure 14 (a) Layer sequence of a tandem solar cell with serially connected subcells, resulting in higher voltages. (b) Structure of a folded tandem solar cell. The incident light is reflected toward the neighboring cell, which absorbs a different spectrum. Reprinted with permission from Tvingstedt K, Andersson V, Zhang F, and Inganas O (2007) Folded reflective tandem polymer solar cell double efficiency. *Applied Physics Letters* 91: 123514/1–3 [187]. Copyright 2007, American Institute of Physics.

Another key point which must be addressed in tandem solar cells is the optical and electrical matching of the two subcells. As expected, the serial connection results in a V_{OC} which is nearly the sum of the voltages of the single cells. Thus, $V_{OC} > 1$ V can be achieved which, in connection with a comparable good performance, is barely possible with single-junction devices. The serial connection also causes the same current to flow through both the subcells. Thus, unbalanced current generation in the subcells leads to performance losses [188]. A general problem is that the current through the tandem cell is smaller than that of the single subcells, which means that additional factors besides a balanced current of the single cells are important [101]. Since in most cases there is a (small) overlap of the absorption spectra of the two subcells, the thicknesses of the different active layers should be chosen carefully. Here and also in the case of single-junction solar cells, simulations can help to determine optimal layer thicknesses [185, 186, 189].

By using PCPDTBT:PCBM as the cell that was illuminated as the first cell (bottom cell) and P3HT:PC$_{70}$BM as the cell that was illuminated as the second cell (top cell), Kim et al. were able to produce a solar cell with an efficiency of 6.5% [101]. The characteristic values were $J_{SC} = 7.8$ mA cm^{-2}, $V_{OC} = 1.24$ V, and FF = 0.67. Obviously, the J_{SC} of the tandem cell was smaller than the short-circuit currents of the individual single cells (9.2 mA cm^{-2} for PCPDTBT and 10.8 mA cm^{-2} for P3HT). This behavior was explained by the fact that the tandem current is limited by the cell that delivers the smaller current within the tandem structure [181, 190]. In the present case, this was the P3HT:PC$_{70}$BM subcell that was chosen as the top cell, which led to a reduced current due to absorption losses caused by PCPDTBT:PCBM. Since the FF of a tandem cell is very close to that of the limiting subcells, this choice has the advantage that the tandem FF value was close to the higher value of the P3HT:PC$_{70}$BM subcell. Not only J_{SC} but also V_{OC} was slightly reduced compared with the sum of the single voltages (1.29 V). An explanation is that the excess charges from the subcell with the higher current cannot contribute to the photocurrent and therefore compensate for the built-in potential [188].

1.20.4.5.1(ii) Parallel-connected multijunction solar cells

For parallel tandem solar cells, similar requirements apply as for serial tandem cells. The architecture differs from that of the serial tandem cell in a way that the top cell is deposited as inverted cell. In this case, the challenge is to find material systems providing the same voltages. This is a much more difficult task than matching currents, because voltages are intrinsic properties of the material systems, whereas currents can be adjusted by thickness variation. When the voltages are different, residual currents flow, thus reducing the utilizable current. However, recently, a cell was presented by Sista et al. exhibiting the sum of the currents of the single cells without losses in voltage [191]. Here as active layers, P3HT:PC$_{70}$BM for the bottom and PSBTBT:PC$_{70}$BM for the top cell were used. A J_{SC} of 15.1 mA cm^{-2}, which is the exact sum of the subcells, was achieved (P3HT: 10.1 mA cm^{-2} and PSBTBT: 5.1 mA cm^{-2}). The resulting voltage amounted to 0.60 V (subcells: 0.58 and 0.60 V) and together with an FF of 0.525 (subcells: 0.60 and 0.395), an efficiency of 4.8% was reached.

1.20.4.5.1(iii) Folded tandem solar cells

Since some light will always be reflected instead of being absorbed, it is reasonable to try to use this reflected light again. The basic idea of folded tandem solar cells is to arrange cells in such a way that the reflected light of one cell hits another. This can be achieved by arranging the different layers at a certain angle (**Figure 14(b)**). Folded tandem solar cells do not have the classical tandem device structure but are generally discussed within this family because two different active layer materials are being used. Tvingstedt et al. increased the efficiency of such a folded tandem device in series connection from 2% to 3.7% by using alternating copolymers of fluorine (APFO-Green9 and APFO-3) as donors with PCBM as the acceptor. The maximum efficiency was reached at a folding angle of 70° relative to the plane (e.g., 20° relative to the surface normal) [187]. Besides serial connection, parallel connection is also possible for this cell type.

Higher power output from the same area is the most charming idea behind the tandem architecture. Efficiencies exceeding the theoretical maximum efficiency of single-junction devices are possible. However, more research especially with respect to orthogonal solution processing and recombination layers is required. The highest reported efficiencies in 2010 were 6.5% for tandems comprising active layers made from polymers and 8.3% for those made from small molecules [101, 192].

1.20.4.5.2 Nanostructured solar cells

Most of the devices described above make use of the blend instead of the bilayer approach. This is mainly based on the small exciton diffusion length in polymeric semiconductors. The so-called nanostructured solar cell architecture aims at increasing the interface between donor and acceptor while retaining the advantageous transport properties of the bilayer architecture (**Figure 15(a)**). The approach is as follows: after deposition of the first active layer, this layer is patterned with a structure of pillars on the nanometer scale (**Figure 15(b)**). On top of this structured active layer, the second active layer is deposited. The challenges with this method are to assemble a structure size with a spacing of twice the exciton diffusion length and to deposit the second active layer without dissolving the first one. Wiedemann et al. demonstrated a current increase of about 50% for an interface increase of about 70% compared with the unstructured bilayer [193]. Similar results were shown by Kim et al. [196] and Cheyns et al. [197].

1.20.4.5.3 Further device architectures

Besides tandem architecture, there is also another method to increase the voltage of a device. With so-called high-voltage devices, a series connection of nanomodules consisting of P3HT and PCBM, voltages up to 880 V were achieved (**Figure 15(c)**) [194]. A further advantage is that no transparent electrode is needed. However, a large disadvantage is that only very small active areas are

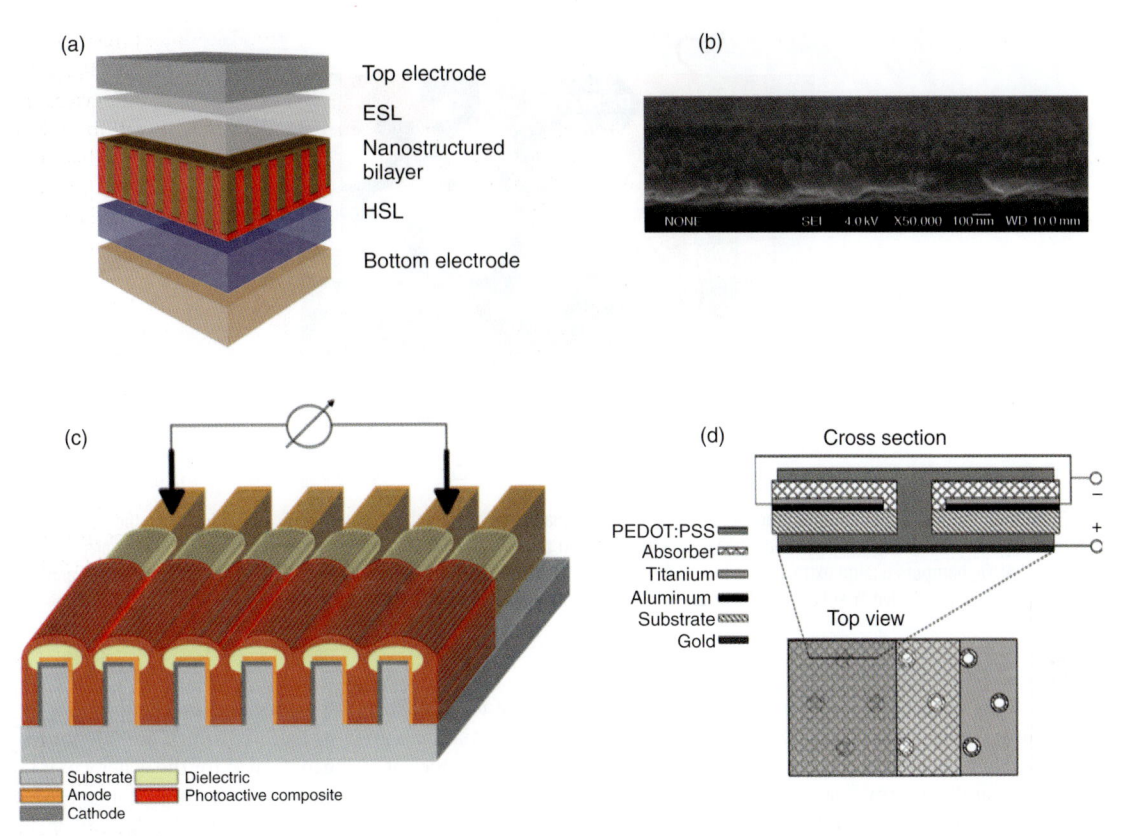

Figure 15 (a) Illustration of an ideal nanostructured solar cell in normal layer sequence. (b) Cross-sectional SEM image of a nanostructured P3HT layer. Reprinted with permission from Wiedemann W, Sims L, Abdellah A, et al. (2010) Nanostructured interfaces in polymer solar cells. *Applied Physics Letters* 96: 263109 [193]. Copyright 2010, American Institute of Physics. (c) Illustration of a high-voltage device. Copyright Wiley-VCH Verlag GmbH & Co. KGaA. Reproduced with permission from Niggemann M, Graf W, and Gombert A (2008) Realization of ultrahigh photovoltages with organic photovoltaic nanomodules. *Advanced Materials* 20: 4055–4060 [194]. (d) Cross section and top view of a wrap-through solar cell. Reprinted from Zimmermann B, Glatthaar M, Niggemann M, et al. (2007) ITO-free wrap through organic solar cells – A module concept for cost-efficient reel-to-reel production. *Solar Energy Materials and Solar Cells* 91: 374–378 [195]. Copyright 2007, with permission from Elsevier.

possible, which leads to very low currents. For applications where high voltages without high currents are needed, this cell type could be of interest.

Wrap-through devices are an interesting architecture that allows for the omission of the highly conductive transparent, and therefore expensive, electrodes [195]. Here both electrodes are arranged on the same side of the active layer, one on the top and the other on the bottom side of the flexible substrate, and the connection is established through vias which are drilled during device fabrication (**Figure 15(d)**). Both parallel connection for current increase and serial connection for voltage increase are possible with this architecture.

1.20.5 Stability of OSCs

Academic research has been mainly focusing on the efficiency increase with the techniques described in this chapter. Since OSCs are already entering the market, there has also been an increasing interest devoted to the stability of organic solar modules. Various factors affect the lifetime of OSCs and modules. Mechanical stability is especially important for flexible applications, which are one of the target markets for OSCs. While flexibility is not a major issue for the active layers due to their organic nature and thickness, it is an issue for, for example, the TCO materials which are susceptible to cracking upon bending. Another factor is the morphological stability of the active layer. Exposure to elevated temperatures can alter morphology and consequently charge generation and/or transport, thus affecting the efficiency. Water and oxygen are mainly responsible for the chemical instability of OSCs and are tackled by packaging cells and modules. **Figure 16** shows a schematic illustration of typical degradation processes in a blend solar cell.

1.20.5.1 Encapsulation

The stability of OSCs toward atmospheric constituents such as oxygen or water is limited, especially under illumination [199–201]. The most effective way of extending the lifetime of OSCs is by packaging them with barrier materials to keep oxygen and water out

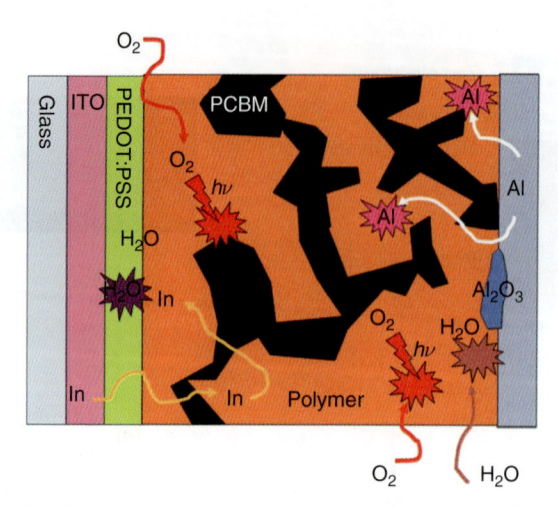

Figure 16 Schematic illustration of typical degradation processes taking place in a blend solar cell: In and Al can diffuse into the active layer. In combination with H$_2$O, PEDOT:PSS shows an acidic behavior and can harm the ITO layer; O$_2$ in the active layer can act as trap for electrons. Due to its isolating property, Al$_2$O$_3$ hampers charge extraction at the interface active layer/Al electrode. Reprinted from Jørgensen M, Norrman K, and Krebs FC (2008) Stability/degradation of polymer solar cells. *Solar Energy Materials and Solar Cells* 92: 686–714 [198]. Copyright 2008, with permission from Elsevier.

of the devices. Glass is typically used for inorganic solar modules due to its good transparency and excellent barrier properties toward water and oxygen. For flexible OSC modules, flexible packaging materials are also required which are inferior to glass in terms of transparency and barrier properties. Similar to OLEDs, maximum values of 10^{-6} g m^{-2} day^{-1} for the water vapor transmission rate (WVTR) and 10^{-3} g m^{-2} day^{-1} for the oxygen transmission rate (OTR) are required for lifetimes competitive to such conventionally packaged devices [202]. Typical barriers are thin films of transparent oxides like AlO$_x$ or SiO$_x$ that can be deposited by various methods like plasma-enhanced chemical vapor deposition, electron beam evaporation, or sputtering. These barriers reach permeation rates that are more than 1000 times lower than those of substrates like polyethylene terephthalate (PET) and polyethylene naphthalate (PEN), which are in the range of 10^0 to 10^2 g m^{-2} day^{-1} at about 38 °C and 90% relative humidity for both WVTR and OTR. The latter values satisfy requirements for food packaging or pharmaceutical industry but not for organic electronic devices [202]. A drawback of single-layer barriers is that they are prone to pinhole defects. Improvement has been demonstrated by multilayer concepts where organic and inorganic layers are alternating, thus decoupling the defects from each other [203, 204]. Dennler *et al.* increased the shelf lifetime of MDMO-PPV:PCBM solar cells (here efficiency over 50% of the starting value) from around 10 to 3000 h under dark, ambient air conditions by encapsulating them with layers of plasma-enhanced chemical vapor-deposited SiO$_x$ and a plasma-deposited organic material [202]. For P3HT:PCBM devices under dark, ambient air conditions a lifetime of 6000 h were reported [205]. In addition to water and oxygen barriers, a UV screener is required to protect the organic materials of the active layer from degradation and to avoid absorption losses due to yellowing of the polymeric barrier and substrate.

Another method of preventing oxygen and moisture from reacting with the OSC layers is to absorb them with scavenger materials, which can be used in addition to barrier materials [202].

1.20.5.2 Electrodes

Both cathode and anode are prone to degradation during storage and operation of the device. In most devices, ITO is used as transparent electrode. To produce ITO with low sheet resistances, high temperatures are required. For sputtering processes on flexible, polymeric substrates, such high temperatures are not possible, which results in higher sheet resistances. Therefore, Fahlman *et al.* substituted the single-layer system of ITO by the three-layer system ITO-Ag-ITO, thus reducing the sheet resistance below 16 Ω □$^{-1}$ while retaining transmission values above 80% at 550 nm [134]. This approach not only decreases the sheet resistance but also improves the mechanical stability because thinner layers are possible. By performing bending tests where the substrate is bent to a certain radius and stretched again, Lewis *et al.* showed that the resistance of ITO-Ag-ITO layers did not increase significantly, while pure ITO subjected to the same treatment showed a sevenfold increase in sheet resistance [135]. Similar results were obtained by Cho *et al.* when utilizing IZO-Ag-IZO instead of ITO-Ag-ITO [136].

In devices with normal structure, low WF metals like Ca or Al are generally used as anodes. They are rapidly hydrolyzed and/or oxidized under ambient conditions, leading to the formation of insulating layers. This takes place not only at the surface of the electrode but also at the interface semiconductor/Al as was shown by X-ray photoelectron spectroscopy (XPS) depth profiling [206]. Encapsulation as mentioned above can decrease the amount of oxygen and water that diffuses toward the device, but it is still necessary to have a top electrode that has at least a lifetime equal to that of the active layer. This makes silver or gold, at least from a stability point of view, interesting materials for the top electrodes.

1.20.5.3 Interfacial Layers

The most widely used interfacial material for hole collection is PEDOT:PSS [60, 104–106]. The material has an adequate WF to provide for a hole-selective contact, and promising efficiencies were demonstrated also with new-generation polymers [63]. The major disadvantages of PEDOT:PSS are its affinity toward water and its acidic nature, which can lead to a fast degradation of the TCO [207]. Further, Norrman *et al.* showed that reactions at the interface active layer/PEDOT:PSS due to oxygen exposure are the major cause of device failure for inverted devices. They performed XPS and time-of-flight secondary ion mass spectrometry (TOF-SIMS) measurements and detected a phase separation of PEDOT:PSS with a subsequent oxidation of PEDOT [176]. Because of these known drawbacks, alternative interfacial materials based on, for example, transition metal oxides were investigated recently [97, 208]. Yamanari *et al.* compared the stability of devices with PEDOT:PSS and MoO_x as interfacial layers and devices without interfacial layer with light beam-induced photocurrent (LBIC) measurements [206]. At the beginning, both the PEDOT:PSS and the MoO_x samples showed comparable efficiencies, while the devices without interfacial layer suffered from a lower V_{OC}. After 300 h storage in the dark under ambient air conditions, the local currents of PEDOT:PSS samples were significantly reduced. Further, a gradient in current density, decreasing from the middle to the rim of the substrate, was observed, and large regions with low currents were located over the whole sample (**Figure 17**). For the samples with MoO_x and those without interfacial layer, only some small points with reduced current and no gradient toward the rim were observed [206]. Another approach for prolonging the lifetime by choosing adequate HSLs makes use of mixtures of different metal oxide nanoparticles. Huang *et al.* demonstrated a 10% drop in efficiency after 1200 h storage under dark ambient conditions by applying a WO_3–V_2O_5 nanoparticle layer. Within the same time, the efficiency of a reference without this interfacial layer dropped by 50% [98].

Also on the electron-selective side, attempts to replace commonly used materials like LiF by introducing better protecting and less degrading materials have been made [103, 112, 209]. Lee *et al.* developed a solution-based sol–gel process for depositing a titanium suboxide layer (TiO_x) on top of the active layer of a solar cell in the normal structure. By applying photoluminescence measurements, they showed that TiO_x has a positive influence on device stability since it acts as a barrier layer. For devices stored in ambient air without a TiO_x layer, a 50% degradation was reached after 30 h, while devices with TiO_x showed a 20% drop after 130 h [209]. Krebs *et al.* demonstrated good stability of inverted devices with P3CT (not P3HT) and ZnO as active materials, PEDOT:PSS as the hole-selective contact, and ZnO as electron-selective interfacial layer [210]. Accelerated lifetime testing (ALT) in ambient air under AM1.5G illumination, 30 °C, and 35% relative humidity resulted in lifetimes of more than 500 h. The stability was significantly reduced to 100 h lifetime, however, when a UV filter with a cutoff at 400 nm was used. A similar behavior, that is, a

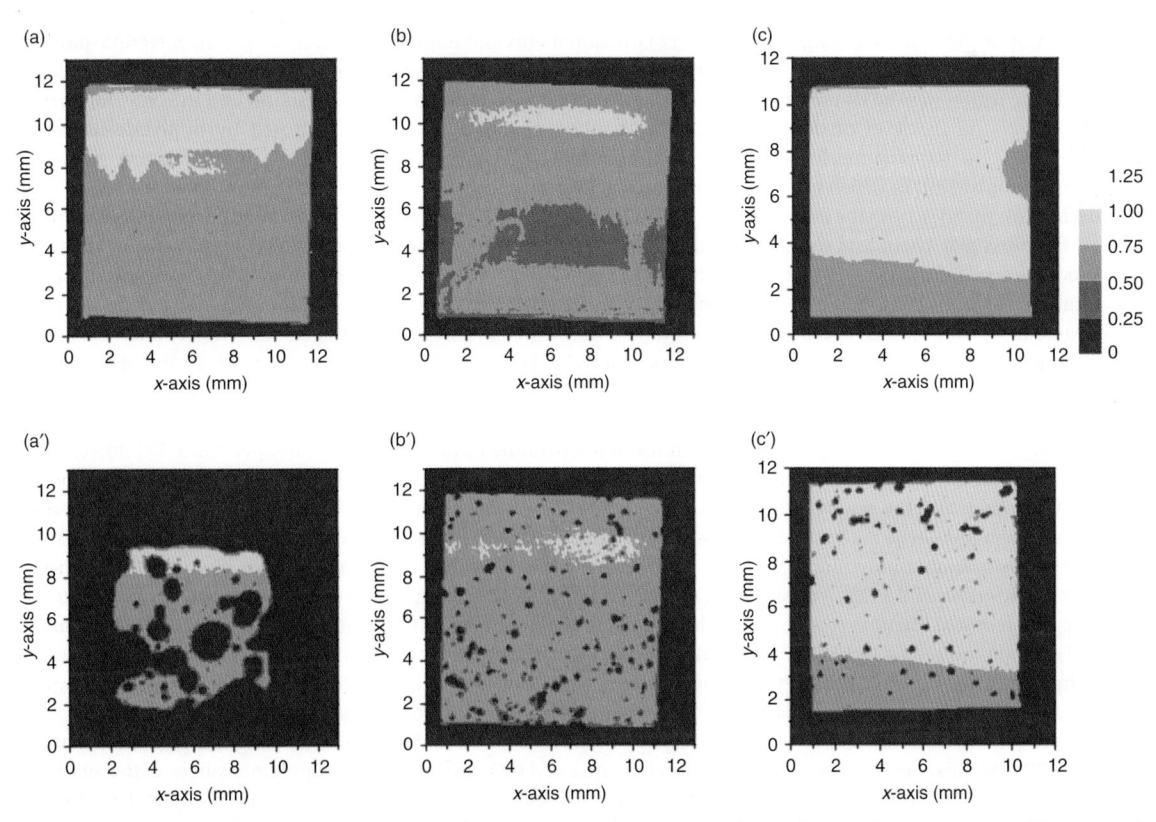

Figure 17 Light beam induced current (LBIC) images for fresh P3HT:PCBM solar cells with PEDOT:PSS (a), MoO_x (b), and without HSL (c). (a′–c′) show the devices with the respective layers after degradation for 300 h under dark, ambient air conditions. With permission from Yamanari T, Taima T, Sakai J, et al. (2010) Effect of buffer layers on stability of polymer-based organic solar cells. *Japanese Journal of Applied Physics* 49: 01AC02/1–4 [206].

drop in efficiency upon cutting UV light, was observed for P3HT:PCBM-based solar cells with TiO$_x$ as the electron-selective contact. This behavior is explained by dependence of the conductivity of TiO$_x$ and ZnO on UV illumination [113, 211].

Another approach toward an electron-selective interfacial layer that has a stabilizing effect on the solar cell was presented by Yang et al. OSCs with LiF, with Cs$_2$CO$_3$, and without additional ESL were compared. After gauging device stability in an inert atmosphere for 200 h, the cells were illuminated in air. They observed an increase in lifetime of around 33% for the Cs$_2$CO$_3$ devices compared with the cells with LiF. Compared with samples without buffer layer, it was even increased by about 73%. Guided by the results of investigations which showed that Cs$_2$CO$_3$ decomposes to CsO$_2$, CsO, and metallic Cs during evaporation, Yang et al. concluded that the reaction of this interfacial layer with immersive oxygen and moisture leads to shielding and scavenging properties and thus improved lifetime [112, 212].

1.20.5.4 Active Materials

While academia and industry have gained an understanding of how efficiency of OSCs can be increased, there is less knowledge about stability. Nevertheless, for conjugated polymers like PPV, there are known stability issues under illumination when water and oxygen are present, that is, photooxidation takes place and conjugation is interrupted when oxygen molecules bind to the vinyl bonds yielding carbonyl groups. This process starts with the transfer of the excitation energy from the singlet to the triplet state of the polymer (intersystem crossing) and the subsequent formation of extremely reactive singlet oxygen by energy transfer from the polymer triplet state to ground state oxygen [213, 214]. It was further shown for oligomers of phenylene vinylenes that the reaction rate with oxygen depends on the substituents of the polymer chain. Electron-donating groups speed up kinetics, while electron-withdrawing groups act as stabilizing agents [215].

Another degradation behavior was also observed in MDMO-PPV:PCBM devices. Degradation occurred in the dark under inert conditions and was accelerated at elevated temperatures or under illumination. This was explained with morphological changes in the semiconductor blend [216].

The superior lifetime of P3HT is explained by the absence of easily oxidizable groups [198]. In addition, P3HT shows a reversible and an irreversible part of degradation. Seemann et al. investigated inverted P3HT:PCBM solar cells with PEDOT:PSS and a silver grid as transparent top electrode and applied a computational model to give a phenomenological explanation of the experimental results. They found that without illumination the effect of oxygen is rather small but increases dramatically under illumination. The degradation was mainly observed in current density. Also the amount of oxygen present in the atmosphere had an impact on the degradation speed. By annealing for 5 min at 140 °C, the current could be partially recovered (**Figures 18(a)–18(d)**). With the help of charge extraction by linearly increasing voltage (CELIV) measurements and impedance spectroscopy, the reversible part could be explained with p-doping of the active layer by oxygen. p-Doping in turn leads to mobile holes and immobilized superoxide anions and a space-charge region in front of the electron-extracting electrode, which limits charge extraction and thus J_{SC}. The thickness of this region depends on the level of doping and on the applied bias that could be monitored by impedance spectroscopy. **Figure 18(e)** depicts the trapping mechanism of an electron at molecular oxygen dissolved in the layer. This process is reversible by thermal annealing at 140 °C, which provides the required activation energy to transfer the electron back to the HOMO of P3HT [217]. A mechanism that describes the irreversible degradation was proposed by Manceau et al. and considers photooxidation of the α-carbon of the hexyl side chain and the sulfur of the thiophene ring. The formed carbonyl and thioester groups trap electrons, which results in reduced charge carrier mobility [218, 219].

Less attention has been paid to the degradation of n-type materials. Chambon et al. illuminated C$_{60}$ and PCBM in air and followed degradation with infrared spectroscopy. Both fullerenes showed fast degradation of the C$_{60}$ moiety and PCBM exhibited additional changes in the carbonyl region [220]. Reese et al. studied P3HT:PCBM layers under exposure to air and light and found by calculations that the photooxidation of PCBM leads to a lower LUMO, which then acts as deep trap for electrons [221].

Approaches for stabilization of the active layer with respect to the different failure modes have been investigated. Physical degradation such as morphology change can be slow at room temperature but fast at elevated temperatures. Reinforcement of the active blend layers was addressed with thermocleavable or cross-linkable materials (see Section 1.20.3.1.1). Both methods lead to insoluble active layers, which can also be beneficial for some steps of solar cell fabrication [79, 222, 223]. For example, Bjerring et al. utilized a soluble polythiophene derivative for deposition of the active layer. Two subsequent heating steps removed the side chain and left behind an insoluble polythiophene with an increased glass transition temperature when compared with the soluble derivative [77]. Efficiencies of 1.5–2% were achieved with reasonably stable currents for 500 h in nitrogen and 1/3 sun illumination. However, the best reported lifetimes to date were achieved for active layers which make use of standard P3HT:PCBM blends [224].

Chemical degradation can be tackled by using improved semiconductors or by the addition of stabilizing agents. It was shown that adding fullerenes like C$_{60}$ or PCBM to PPV or thiophene polymers can have an antioxidant effect due to the scavenging property of fullerenes and thus can slow down degradation. Following this reasoning, Griffini et al. added multiwalled carbon nanotubes (MWCNTs) to P3HT and demonstrated an improved stability of the absorption under simulated sunlight degradation. In the case of MDMO-PPV:PCBM blends, the slower degradation was also explained by a quenching of the polymer singlet state, which leads to reduced population of the triplet state and consequently to suppressed sensitization of harmful singlet oxygen [199, 225, 226].

In summary, it was observed that the inverted solar cell architecture shows better stability compared with the normal one. This is mainly explained to result from the better stability of the used electrodes. Normal devices require the use of materials with smaller WFs, which are more prone to oxidation and hydrolysis. Inverted devices mostly use silver or gold electrodes which are air stable

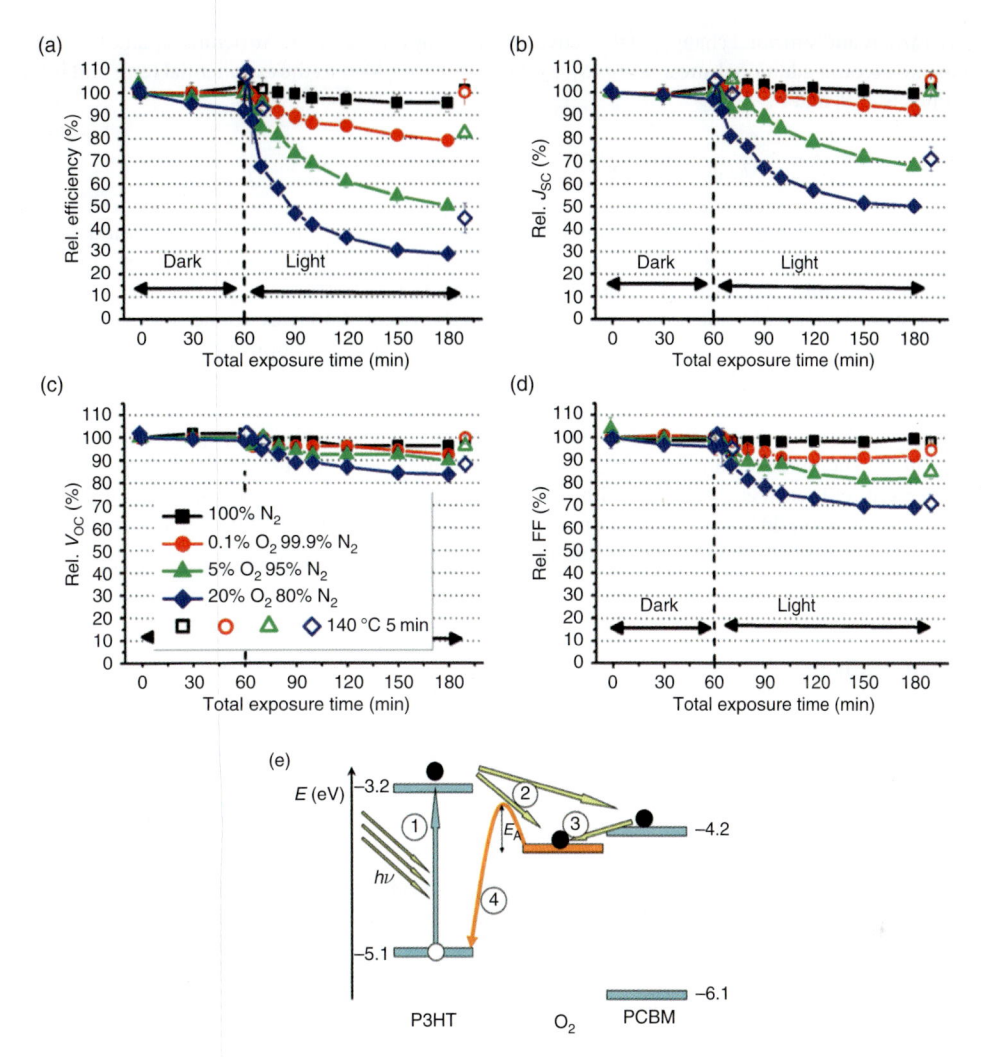

Figure 18 Temporal evolution of (a) efficiency, (b) J_{SC}, (c) V_{OC}, and (d) FF of P3HT:PCBM solar cells during exposure to different gas mixtures in the dark and under illumination (AM1.5). The open symbols denote annealing steps at 140 °C for 5 min under nitrogen atmosphere. (e) Effects of oxygen doping on the charge transfer dynamics in a P3HT:PCBM blend. After excitation of an electron (1), it is transferred to PCBM (2) and subsequently trapped by oxygen (3). The recombination (4) can take place only if enough energy is applied to overcome the activation energy E_A. This can be achieved by annealing the blend at 140 °C. The energy of the oxygen acceptor level is approximated. Reprinted from Seemann A, Sauermann T, Lungenschmied C, *et al.* (2010) Reversible and irreversible degradation of organic solar cell performance by oxygen. *Solar Energy*, Volume 85, Issue 6, June 2011, pp. 1238–1249. Copyright 2010, with permission from Elsevier.

[198, 211]. Additionally, the acidic PEDOT:PSS is not in contact with the TCO in the inverted structure, which also contributes to stability [206, 207].

1.20.5.5 Testing the Lifetime

Most scientific publications deal with laboratory or outdoor degradation, which is insufficient for devices with enhanced stability. The stability of inorganic PV devices is deduced from ALT protocols like the ones described in the IEC61646 standard or more elaborate multistress test programs. For OSCs, currently no such industry norms exist and test protocols are derived from protocols used in the display and consumer electronics industry. Typical testing conditions applied include elevated temperatures in the dark (e.g., 65 and 85 °C), temperature cycling, power cycling by variation of the applied voltage, damp heat (e.g., 85 °C, 85% relative humidity), illumination with various light sources (e.g., UV light, simulated sunlight), or mechanical testing (e.g., bending cycles). It is common to attempt to extract and extrapolate the stability by, for example, using the Arrhenius equation:

$$k_{\mathrm{deg}} = A e^{\frac{-E_a}{k_B T}} \qquad [7]$$

with k_{deg} the degradation constant, E_a the activation energy, k_B the Boltzmann constant, T the temperature, and A a constant depending on the degradation mechanisms and experimental conditions. This universal model is capable of describing the trapping behavior of charge carriers and structural changes of the active materials. By extending the Arrhenius equation to the Eyring model, it is possible to take into account additional stress factors $S_1, S_2, S_3,...$ that are added to the exponential term and influence the device via different parameters a, B, and C:

$$k_{\text{deg}} = AT^{a}\exp\left(\frac{-E_a}{k_BT} + \left(B_1 + \frac{C_1}{T}\right)S_1 + \cdots + S_2 + \cdots\right) \quad [8]$$

These additional stress factors comprise illumination intensity, applied bias, and so on. Schuller et al. found an acceleration factor $K = k_{\text{deg}}(T')/k_{\text{deg}}(T)$ of 10 for the decrease of the I_{SC} of MDMO-PPV:PCBM solar cells when the temperature during the aging test was increased by about 80 °C. For this specific case, they found linear kinetics $I_{SC}(t) = I_{SC}(0)(1 - k_{\text{deg}}t)$ and an activation energy of around $E_a = 350$ meV [227]. For P3HT:PCBM solar cells, an acceleration factor of 4.45 was found for ALT testing under AM1.5 (100 mW cm^{-2}) illumination at a temperature of 60 °C compared with working conditions of 25 °C [228]. A third model that is used is the inverse power model $k_{\text{deg}} = AV^{\gamma}$, where V designates the stress, for example, the applied bias, and A and γ product-specific parameters [227].

Hauch et al. compared the outdoor stability of OSCs with the lifetime of devices which were aged by illumination under 1 sun at 65 °C in the laboratory. The outdoor samples were placed on a rooftop at maximum power point conditions. Under these conditions, an increase in efficiency was observed within 14 months due to an FF increase. The ALT samples showed a similar increase in FF between 600 and 800 h of constant illumination, roughly indicating that this time under these ALT conditions is approximately equivalent to about 1 year of outdoor conditions [224].

1.20.6 Production Methods

New technologies naturally start on a small scale in laboratories and must be scaled up for industrial production. Some of the techniques are practicable only for batch production, while others have the ability to be scaled up for R2R processes.

1.20.6.1 Layer Deposition for Single Devices

Probably the most common method for the deposition of thin films for polymer solar cells is spin coating. Here the substrate is placed on a sample holder where it is fixed by vacuum suction. A small amount of the coating solution is applied onto the sample and the sample holder starts to rotate. Due to the centrifugal force, the solution is hurled from the substrate whereupon a thin, homogeneous layer remains (**Figure 19(a)**). Layer thicknesses from a few nanometers to some micrometers are possible, depending on the spinning speed, spinning time, acceleration, and solution viscosity. The formation of the film is also influenced by the vapor pressure during subsequent drying. The thickness can be estimated by the empirical formula $d = k\omega^{a}$, with ω the angular velocity and k and a as empirical constants [230]. Typical values of rotations per minute lie in the range 500–5000. One spinning cycle lasts around 30–120 s. Because the layer thickness can be controlled very precisely, it is a popular method in academia. Moreover, all layers but the electrodes can be coated that way. The major drawback, however, is the impossibility of upscaling and a quite inefficient material usage, since most of the solution is lost.

Dip coating is another technique used for the deposition of layers from solution. The substrate is dipped into a bath containing the solution of the desired material and is then removed perpendicularly at constant speed. Depending on the speed and the solution properties, a certain amount of the fluid will wet the surface of the sample. This amount is determined by the balance of forces at the stagnation point, which is a point near the area where substrate and solution surface cross. Here a part of the fluid branches off and does not follow the direction of the substrate anymore but follows the surface of the solution. Fast withdrawal speeds result in a thick layer and slow speeds in a thin layer (**Figure 19(b)**). Similar to spin coating, homogeneous layers can be prepared although not with the same quality. However, compared with spin coating, it is possible to upscale this technique and use it in R2R systems. The problems here are the large amount of material that is needed and the fact that the substrate is always coated from both sides.

Another method that is applicable to R2R processing is doctor blading where the substrate is placed below a knife. The gap between the knife and the sample, usually with a width of several to hundred micrometers, is then filled with solution and the knife is moved along the substrate (**Figure 19(c)**). Apart from material properties, the layer characteristics are guided mainly by three parameters: the temperature of solution and substrate carrier, the velocity of the blade, and the width of the gap between the blade and the substrate. Thicker layers are obtained with larger gaps and faster coating speeds. Coating temperature determines the evaporation of the solvent and the viscosity of the solution. Higher viscosity at lower temperature results in thicker layers. A rough estimate of the final film thickness, not taking into account parameters such as velocity and temperature, is given by $d = 1/2(w(c/\rho))$, with w the gap width, c the concentration of the solid in the solution, and ρ the final film density [230]. Compared with spin coating, the drying of the wet films lasts rather long, and it was observed that this can give rise to aggregation or crystallization of the coated material [231].

Spray coating is a method where the film is generated stepwise by casting droplets onto the substrate. The size of the droplets can be controlled via the gas pressure in the spray valve. Typical sizes of the droplets are microns to tens of microns. Multiple ways of film formation are possible. Depending on the formulation, the droplets may start to dry while still in the air or they may dry soon

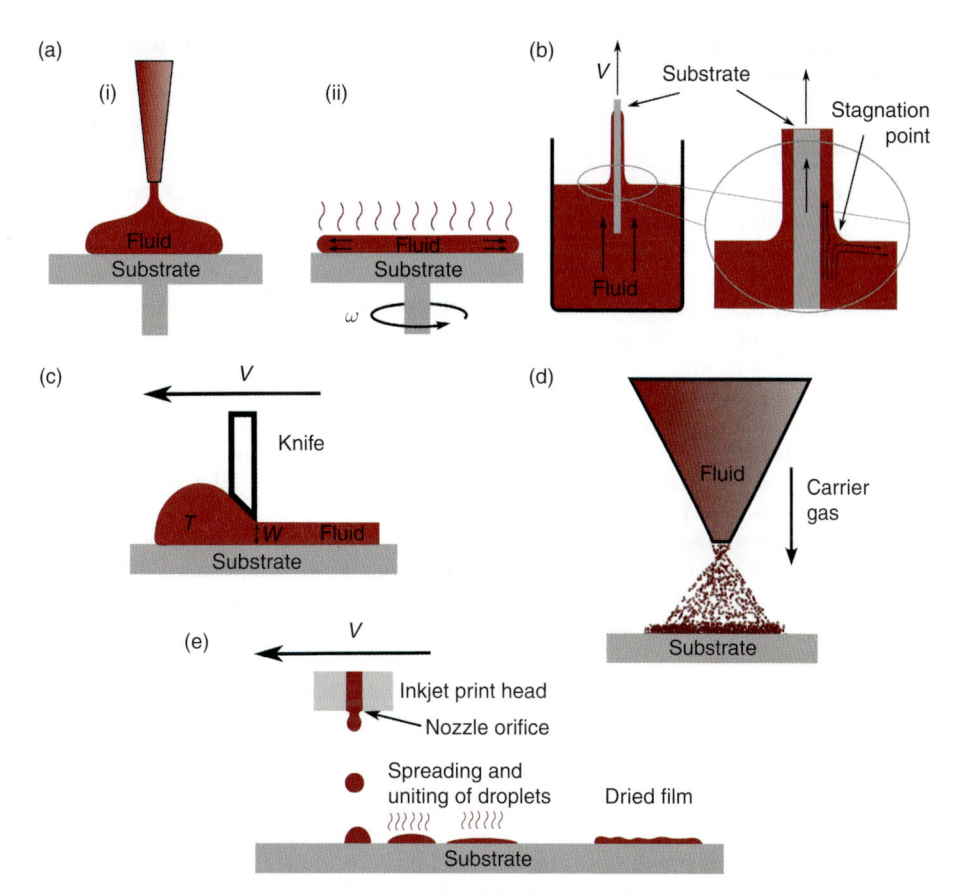

Figure 19 (a) Spin coating of thin layers: (i) Deposition of the fluid onto the substrate. (ii) The thickness is determined by the angular velocity ω, acceleration $d\omega/dt$, and vapor pressure. (b) For dip coating, the thickness of the deposited layer is determined by the withdrawal speed v. (c) During doctor blading, the layer thickness is determined by the blading speed v, the gap width w, and the solution temperature T. (d) By spray coating, single droplets, whose size is determined by the gas pressure, are deposited onto the substrate and combine with adjacent droplets. (e) With inkjet printing, patterning during film deposition is possible, which makes it an interesting layer deposition technology [229].

after hitting the substrate (**Figure 19(d)**). Due to these different types of film formation, a distinct morphology arises, which leads to a relatively high surface roughness when compared with spin coating. In general, spray coating is appropriate also for large-scale coating [229].

Inkjet printing is also a very attractive possibility for film deposition since it enables the production of patterned films, which makes the additional step of structuring obsolete. Resolutions of a few micrometers are possible due to droplet volumes in the picoliter regime [230]. The single droplets are ejected from the nozzle orifice and fall onto the substrate where they spread. A compact film is formed by affiliation of neighboring droplets (**Figure 19(e)**). The spread depends on the viscosity of the solution and can be altered by heating either the printing head or the reservoir. The film thickness is varied via the droplet size, which in turn is altered via the opening behavior of the nozzle orifice. It can be estimated by $d = N_d V_d(c/\rho)$, with N_d the number of droplets delivered per area, V_d the volume of a single droplet, c the solid concentration in the solution, and ρ the final film density [230]. Besides active and interfacial layers, the silver top electrode has also been demonstrated to be printable by utilizing a silver ink [229, 232]. Current limitations are only seen in the maximum printing speed.

TCO films are generally applied via sputtering processes where a target with the desired material is located above the substrate. A bombardment of particles, usually noble gas ions, leads to momentum exchange with the atoms of the target. After several momentum exchanges, the atoms will have a momentum pointing away from the target and toward the substrate. When the energy is high enough, they can leave the material. Typical energies for the ions are 30–50 eV. To ensure that the atoms can reach the sample surface where they condensate, high vacuum is needed. When chemical alteration of the atoms is wanted, a reaction gas, typically oxygen, can be added to the process gas, for example, argon [233]. During sputtering, alloys are not demixed unlike in the case of thermal evaporation, a method often applied for deposition of top electrodes. For thermal evaporation, the desired material, for example, Ca, Al, Ag, or Au, is placed in an evaporation boat consisting of a material with a high melting point. Then a voltage is applied causing a large current which in turn heats the boat and thus the material above its melting point. Typically, currents of 10–160 A are needed depending on the geometry of the evaporation chamber, the boat, and the type of material that shall be evaporated. The substrate is placed above the evaporation boat. Like in sputtering, a high vacuum is needed in order to guarantee that the evaporated material reaches the sample surface [234].

1.20.6.2 Large-Scale Production Methods

R2R production is a fast and cost-effective production method. All layers that are required for OSCs can be coated from solution at high speeds, apart from ITO and metal electrodes. To close this gap, the deposition of ITO from nanoparticle suspensions was demonstrated, while the use of metal inks is a general concept [229, 235, 236]. An important factor that determines the method of choice is the viscosity of the ink to be printed.

In 2008, Krebs presented fully R2R-produced polymer solar cells using slot-die coating and screen printing [237]. Slot-die coating allows for the coating of stripes and is appropriate for the production of serially connected solar cells (**Figure 20(a)**). The different layers can be easily coated with an offset to each other by moving the coating head perpendicular to the movement direction of the substrate. The thickness d of the coated layer depends on the flow rate f of the ink onto the substrate, the speed of the substrate S, the coating width w, the solid content c in the solution, and the density of the dried layer ρ and can be estimated as $d = (f/S_w) \times (c/\rho)$ [230]. With this method, Krebs deposited the active and interfacial layers as well as the silver top electrode. However, before depositing PEDOT:PSS and silver, both inks had to be diluted. Thus, this method is rather appropriate for solutions whose viscosity is not too high [237].

Screen printing is a method normally used for depositing inks with higher viscosities. Besides the silver top electrode, Krebs was also able to deposit PEDOT:PSS with this method [237]. Here the screen with the desired pattern is brought close to the substrate and filled with the ink. A squeegee presses the screen onto the sample and moves along the screen, thereby pushing the solution through the pattern of the screen (**Figure 20(b)**). By using a cylindrical screen with a squeegee inside the cylinder, it is possible to use screen printing together with the R2R technique. The thickness d of the dry film can be estimated as $d = V_{screen} k_p (c/\rho)$, where V_{screen} is the volume of the threads of the mask and thus determines the thickness of the emulsion. It is measured as volume of ink per area of open screen ($cm^3 \, m^{-2}$). In practice, the volume which is actually deposited onto the substrate differs from the theoretical volume and is accounted for by the pick-out ratio k_p. The solid material concentration in the ink is designated by c and the density of the dried film by ρ [230].

A method applicable for inks with lower viscosity is gravure coating. With this method, Ding et al. deposited the interfacial and the active layer, thus producing P3HT:PCBM solar cells with an efficiency of 1.68% [238]. Similar to screen printing with gravure coating, it is possible to deposit not only one-dimensional but also two-dimensional patterns. The coating roller (left one in **Figure 20(c)**) has thereby an engraved pattern and is partially inserted into an ink bath while the excess ink is removed by a knife.

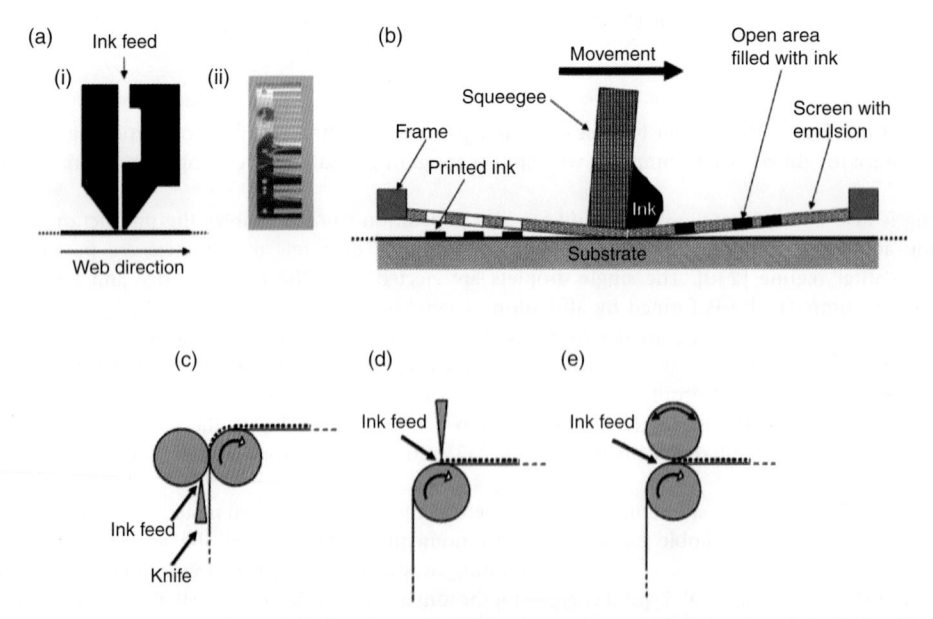

Figure 20 (a) Side view of a slot-die coater head (i). Distinct lines with defined size can be coated by using a mask that is fitted into the head (ii). (b) Screen printing: the squeegee presses the screen which is filled with the desired emulsion onto the substrate where the ink is deposited. (c) Gravure coating: one- and two-dimensional patterns are possible. The knife removes the excess ink. Further deposition methods that can be used with R2R are (d) knife-over-edge and (e) meniscus coating. Reprinted from Krebs FC (2009) Fabrication and processing of polymer solar cells: A review of printing and coating techniques. *Solar Energy Materials and Solar Cells* 93: 394–412 [230]. Copyright 2010, with permission from Elsevier.

Table 6 Overview of properties of different printing and coating techniques

Deposition method	Solution consumption	Speed	Roll-to-roll
Spin coating	Large		No
Doctor blading	Medium		Yes
Spray coating	Medium	Fast	Yes
Inkjet printing	Small	Medium	Yes
Slot-die coating	Small	Fast	Yes
Screen printing	Small	Fast	Yes
Knife-over-edge	Small	Fast	Yes
Meniscus	Small	Fast	Yes
Gravure	Small	Fast	Yes

Adapted from Krebs FC (2009) Fabrication and processing of polymer solar cells: A review of printing and coating techniques. *Solar Energy Materials and Solar Cells* 93: 394–412 [230].

Further methods that can be applied together with R2R production are knife-over-edge and meniscus coating [230]. Knife-over-edge is similar to doctor blading and the film thickness can be calculated via the same formula like for doctor blading (Figure 20(d)). For meniscus coating, the knife is replaced by a roller which meters the ink amount and controls the thickness via gap and rotation direction variation (Figure 20(e)). With these two methods, it is only possible to coat areas homogeneously and not to print patterns. Properties of the mentioned methods are summarized in Table 6.

1.20.7 Summary and Outlook

In the past few years, the number of publications on OSCs has risen almost exponentially and the public interest is growing [239]. In order to stabilize the CO_2 content in the atmosphere to a maximum value of 450 ppm, the German Advisory Council on Global Change deems it necessary to increase the solar energy fraction (including photovoltaic as well as solar thermal power plants) in primary energy use from below 1% as of today to around 25% in 2050 and greater than 60% in 2100 (Figure 21(a)). In this time frame a shift from crystalline silicon technologies toward thin-film solar cells, organic solar cells, and other new concepts is expected. In other words, renewable energies become more and more important and power generation by means of photovoltaic applications will play a key role [240].

The roadmap for organic photovoltaics set out by the Organic Electronics Association is divided into four terms. The first term includes the development and market start of modules for consumer electronics with efficiencies of 1–3% and lifetimes between 1 and 2 years. In the years 2012–15, outdoor and recreational applications shall be introduced, with efficiencies of 3–4% and lifetimes between 2 and 4 years. In the years 2015–18, the implementation of off-grid and building-integrated photovoltaic (BIPV) systems, for example, in windows, is aimed at. In the long term (2018–25), rooftop and grid-connected applications with efficiencies of 6–9% and lifetimes of 5–7 years are to follow (Figure 21(b)) [241]. The first goal of market introduction of OSCs has been achieved by Konarka in 2009 with a solar bag, appropriate for charging small electronic devices on the way [25]. Currently, the efficiencies projected in the roadmap are in agreement with what is available on the market, while the lifetimes have developed more positively than expected. Today's modules already have lifetimes between 3 and 5 years.

Besides the development of efficiency and lifetime, the cost development is also important. At the moment, calculations for P3HT:PCBM solar cells result in a price of around 8 € for the production of a solar module that delivers a maximum power output under standard conditions of 1 W at the peak of power (W_p). This is still high compared with inorganic counterparts (<2 € W_p^{-1}) [8, 241]. At this point in time, not the active material but the transparent ITO electrode constitutes the largest matter of expense and consumes around 87% of the production energy of the OSC [241, 242].

To get an idea of the minimum efficiency and lifetime that are required for an OSC plant to become competitive in the mainstream photovoltaic market, it is necessary to account for the costs of the module and the costs of the installation. Dennler *et al.* assumed a rooftop, residential photovoltaic installation with costs of the module and the installation of 50 and 70 € m^{-2}, respectively, a lifetime of the installation of 25 years, and an annual capacity of 1 MWh which is equivalent to a 1 kW_p plant assuming 1000 h at full sun. Under the assumption that the OSC modules of the plant can be replaced during the lifetime of the installation, efficiencies of 8% and 5% with module lifetimes of 7 and 9 years, respectively, are necessary to fall below the 3 € W_p^{-1} threshold [243]. A more interesting question is the price for the kWh in euro cents, which was calculated for modules with a lifetime of 5 years to be 25 and 10 euro cents per kWh, assuming efficiencies of around 4.5% and 12%, respectively [243].

The rising interest in OSC technologies is reflected not only by the number of publications on this topic but also by the wealth of published or granted patents in this field. In the past decade the number of patents concerning OSCs has increased significantly and distributes evenly over the United States, the European Union, and the Far East. This suggests that all over the world OSCs are seen as a promising technology for future energy production [241].

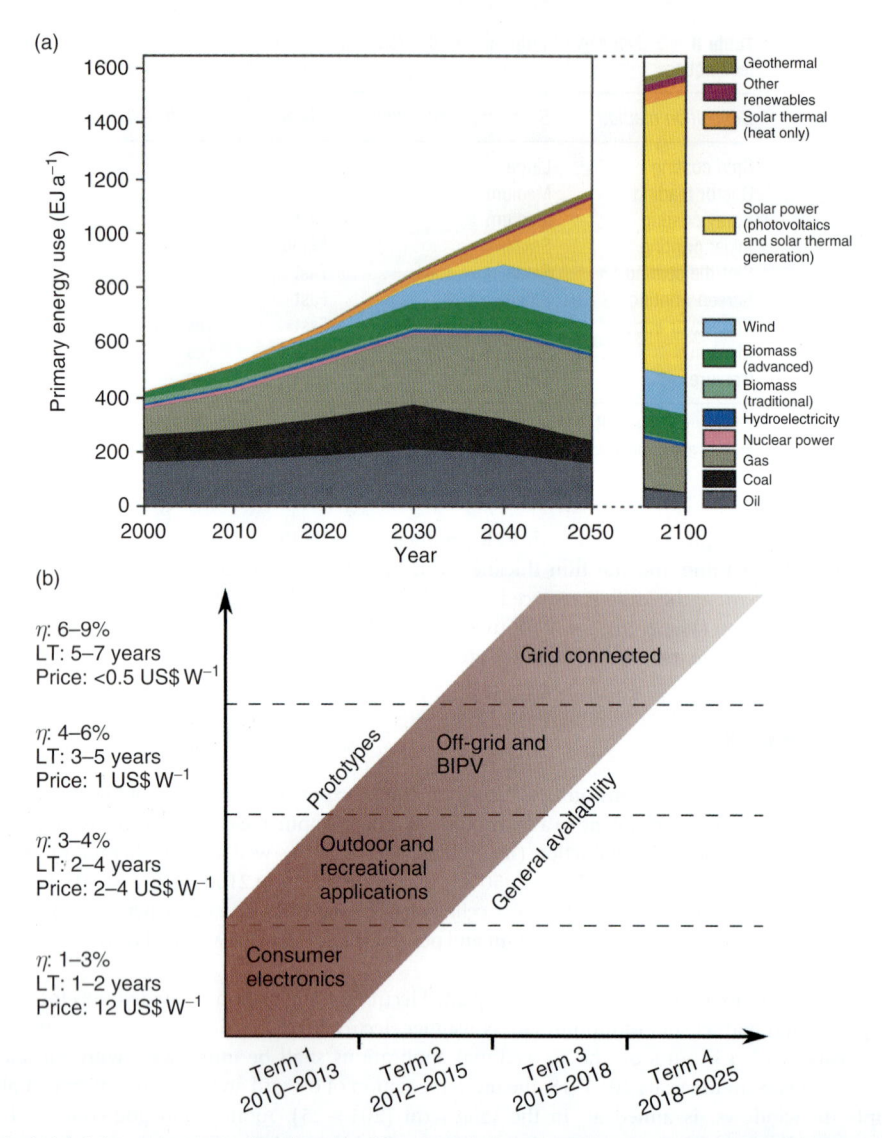

Figure 21 (a) Required global change in energy mix to keep the CO_2 content in the atmosphere below 450 ppm. With permission from the German Advisory Council on Global Change (WBGU) (2003) World in transition – Towards sustainable energy systems. *Summary for Policy-Makers.* Berlin, Germany: WBGU [240]. (b) Roadmap for organic photovoltaics (values from Reference 241). η, efficiency; LT, lifetime.

In summary, OSCs seem to have a bright future when looking at the development of the last decade concerning efficiencies and research effort (**Figure 1**). With power conversion efficiencies of larger than 8% in the laboratory, OSCs are in reach of efficiencies of inorganic thin-film technologies on the market (**Table 1**) [25, 63]. Together with the prospect of advantages such as light weight, flexibility, transparency, low material consumption, environmental sustainability, and low cost, organic photovoltaic technology has the potential to become a success story. However, the trough of disillusionment as predicted by the hype cycle is still imminent [244]. Thus, realistic expectations of the development of OSCs should take into account a decrease in interest followed by an increase again and a constant plateau of productivity.

To establish OSCs as an alternative solar energy source, their efficiency and lifetime have to be increased continuously. In order to achieve this, further understanding of degradation mechanisms and module and cell losses, the search for efficient and stable new materials, and the optimization of the manufacturing process are necessary.

References

[1] US Energy Information Administration (EIA). http://www.eia.gov/forecasts/ieo/index.cfm (accessed 2 November 2011).
[2] UNEP/GRID-Arendal. http://www.grida.no/publications/other/ipcc_tar/?src=/climate/ipcc_tar/wg1/041.htm#121 (accessed 2 November 2011).
[3] (2010) Renewable energy policy network for the 21st century. *Renewables 2010 – Global Status Report.* Paris: Deutsche Gesellschaft für Technische Zusammenarbeit (GTZ) GmbH. http://www.ren21.net/Portals/97/documents/GSR/REN21_GSR_2010_full_revised%20Sept2010.pdf (accessed 2 November 2011).

[4] Bagnall DM and Boreland M (2008) Photovoltaic technologies. *Energy Policy* 36: 4390–4396.
[5] PHOTON, Europe (2009) *Photon* 56–61. http://www.photon.de/presse/mitteilungen/ModultestFebruar2009.pdf (accessed 2 November 2011).
[6] Shockley W and Queisser HJ (1961) Detailed balance limit of efficiency of p–n junction solar cells. *Journal of Applied Physics* 32: 510–519.
[7] Green MA (2010) Solar cell efficiency tables (version 36). *Progress in Photovoltaics: Research and Applications* 18: 346–352.
[8] Solarbuzz. http://www.solarbuzz.com/ (accessed 2 November 2011).
[9] SunPower Corporation. http://us.sunpowercorp.com/homes/products-services/solar-panels/ (accessed 2 November 2011).
[10] Yingli Solar. http://www.yinglisolar.com/us/products/multicrystalline/ (accessed 2 November 2011).
[11] Solar AG. http://www.schottsolar.com/global/products/photovoltaics/schott-asi-107/ (accessed 2 November 2011).
[12] SoloPower. http://www.solopower.com/solopower-receives-sfx3-certifications.html (accessed 2 November 2011).
[13] Gonçalves LM, de Zea Bermudes V, Ribeiro HA, and Mendes AM (2008) Dye-sensitized solar cells: A safe bet for the future. *Energy & Environmental Science* 1: 655–667.
[14] Acrosol. http://acrosol.com/en/main/main.php# (accessed 2 November 2011).
[15] Fraunhofer-Institut. http://www.ise.fraunhofer.de/presse-und-medien/presseinformationen/presseinformationen-2009/weltrekord-41-1-wirkungsgrad-fuer-mehrfachsolarzellen-am-fraunhofer-ise/view?searchterm=41,1% (accessed 2 November 2011).
[16] Heeger AJ (2000) Semiconducting and metallic polymers: The fourth generation of polymeric materials. In: Grenthe I (ed.) *Nobel Lectures, Chemistry 1996–2000*, pp. 380–416. Singapore: World Scientific Publishing Co.
[17] Ito M, Kato K, Komoto K, *et al.* (2008) A comparative study on cost and life-cycle analysis for 100 MW very large-scale PV (VLS-PV) systems in deserts using m-Si, a-Si, CdTe, and CIS modules. *Progress in Photovoltaics: Research and Applications* 16: 17–30.
[18] Chopra KL, Paulson PD, and Dutta V (2004) Thin-film solar cells: An overview. *Progress in Photovoltaics: Research and Applications* 12: 69–92.
[19] Spanggaard H and Krebs FC (2004) A brief history of the development of organic and polymeric photovoltaics. *Solar Energy Materials and Solar Cells* 83: 125–146.
[20] Akamatu H, Inokuchi H, and Matsunaga Y (1954) Electrical conductivity of the perylene–bromine complex. *Nature* 173: 168–169.
[21] Chamberlain GA (1983) Organic solar cells: A review. *Solar Cells* 8: 47–83.
[22] Tang CW (1986) Two-layer organic photovoltaic cell. *Applied Physics Letters* 48: 183–185.
[23] Yu G, Gao J, Hummelen JC, *et al.* (1995) Polymer photovoltaic cells: Enhanced efficiencies via a network of internal donor–acceptor heterojunctions. *Science* 270: 1789–1791.
[24] Green MA (1993–2010) Solar cell efficiency tables (version 1-36). *Progress in Photovoltaics: Research and Applications* 1–18, diff. pages.
[25] Konarka Technologies, Inc. http://konarka.com/index.php/newsroom/press-release-list (accessed 2 November 2011).
[26] Gierschner J, Cornil J, and Egelhaaf H-J (2007) Optical bandgaps of *p*-conjugated organic materials at the polymer limit: Experiment and theory. *Advanced Materials* 19: 173–191.
[27] Koopmans T (1934) Über die Zuordnung von Wellenfunktionen und Eigenwerten zu den Einzelnen Elektronen Eines Atoms. *Physica* 1: 104–113.
[28] Kotz JC, Treichel PM, and Townsend JR (2010) *Chemistry and Chemical Reactivity*, 7th edn. Belmont, CA: Brooks/Cole.
[29] Dimitrakopoulos CD and Malenfant PRL (2002) Organic thin film transistors for large area electronics. *Advanced Materials* 14: 99–117.
[30] Kalinowski J, Stampor W, Marco PD, and Fattori V (1994) Electroabsorption study of excited states in hydrogen-bonding solids: Epindolidione and linear trans-quinacridone. *Chemical Physics* 182: 341–352.
[31] Rege PJF, Williams SA, and Therien MJ (1995) Direct evaluation of electronic coupling mediated by hydrogen bonds: Implications for biological electron transfer. *Science* 269: 1409–1412.
[32] Karl N (2003) Charge carrier transport in organic semiconductors. *Synthetic Metals* 133–134: 649–657.
[33] Sirringhaus H, Tessler N, and Friend RH (1998) Integrated optoelectronic devices based on conjugated polymers. *Science* 280: 1741–1744.
[34] Marcus RA and Sutin N (1985) Electron transfers in chemistry and biology. *Biochimica et Biophysica Acta* 811: 265–322.
[35] Miller A and Abrahams E (1960) Impurity conduction at low concentrations. *Physical Review* 120: 745–755.
[36] Bässler H (1993) Charge transport in disordered organic photoconductors – A Monte Carlo simulation study. *Physica Status Solidi B* 175: 15–56.
[37] Mihailetchi VD, van Duren JKJ, Blom PWM, *et al.* (2003) Electron transport in a methanofullerene. *Advanced Functional Materials* 13: 43–46.
[38] Garcia-Belmonte G, Munar A, Barea EM, *et al.* (2008) Charge carrier mobility and lifetime of organic bulk heterojunctions analyzed by impedance spectroscopy. *Organic Electronics* 9: 847–851.
[39] Scheidler M, Lemmer U, Kersting R, *et al.* (1996) Monte Carlo study of picosecond exciton relaxation and dissociation in poly(phenylenevinylene). *Physical Review B* 54: 5536–5554.
[40] Alvarado SF, Seidler PF, Lidzey DG, and Bradley DDC (1998) Direct determination of the exciton binding energy of conjugated polymers using a scanning tunneling microscope. *Physical Review Letters* 81: 1082–1085.
[41] Piris J, Dykstra TE, Bakulin AA, *et al.* (2009) Photogeneration and ultrafast dynamics of excitons and charges in P3HT/PCBM blends. *Journal of Physical Chemistry C* 113: 14500–14506.
[42] Shaw PE, Ruseckas A, and Samuel IDW (2008) Exciton diffusion measurements in poly(3-hexylthiophene). *Advanced Materials* 20: 3516–3520.
[43] Haugeneder A, Neges M, Kallinger C, *et al.* (1999) Exciton diffusion and dissociation in conjugated polymer/fullerene blends and heterostructures. *Physical Review B* 59: 15346–15351.
[44] Halls JJM, Pichler K, Friend RH, *et al.* (1996) Exciton diffusion and dissociation in a poly(*p*-phenylenevinylene)/C60 heterojunction photovoltaic cell. *Applied Physics Letters* 68: 2120–3121.
[45] Hwang I-W, Moses D, and Heeger AJ (2008) Photoinduced carrier generation in P3HT/PCBM bulk heterojunction materials. *Journal of Physical Chemistry C* 112: 4350–4354.
[46] Sariciftci NS, Smilowitz L, Heeger AJ, and Wudl F (1992) Photoinduced electron transfer from a conducting polymer to buckminsterfullerene. *Science* 258: 1474–1476.
[47] Guo J, Ohkita H, Benten H, and Ito S (2010) Charge generation and recombination dynamics in poly(3-hexylthiophene)/fullerene blend films with different regioregularities and morphologies. *Journal of the American Chemical Society* 132: 6154–6164.
[48] Howard IA, Mauer R, Meister M, and Laquai F (2010) Effect of morphology on ultrafast free carrier generation in polythiophene: Fullerene organic solar cells. *Journal of the American Chemical Society* 132: 14866–14876.
[49] Braun CL (1984) Electric field assisted dissociation of charge transfer states as a mechanism of photocarrier production. *Journal of Chemical Physics* 80: 4157–4161.
[50] Onsager L (1938) Initial recombination of ions. *Physical Review* 54: 554–557.
[51] Langevin P (1903) Recombinaison et mobilites des ions dans les gaz. *Annales de Chimie et de Physique* 28: 433–530.
[52] Pope M and Swenberg CE (1999) *Electronic Processes in Organic Crystals and Polymers*, 2nd edn. New York: Oxford University Press.
[53] Sokel R and Hughes RC (1982) Numerical analysis of transient photoconductivity in insulators. *Journal of Applied Physics* 53: 7414–7424.
[54] Mihailetchi VD, Koster LJA, Hummelen JC, and Blom PWM (2004) Photocurrent generation in polymer–fullerene bulk heterojunctions. *Physical Review Letters* 93: 216601/1–4.
[55] Limpinsel M, Wagenpfahl A, Mingebach M, *et al.* (2010) Photocurrent in bulk heterojunction solar cells. *Physical Review B* 81: 085203/1–6.
[56] Hoppe H, Glatzel T, Niggemann M, *et al.* (2006) Efficiency limiting morphological factors of MDMO-PPV:PCBM plastic solar cells. *Thin Solid Films* 511–512: 587–592.
[57] Solarmer Energy, Inc. http://solarmer.com/newsevents.php (accessed 2 November 2011).
[58] ASTM (2010) E927-10 standard specification for solar simulation for terrestrial photovoltaic testing. *ASTM International Report*. West Conshohocken, PA.
[59] Steim R, Choulis SA, Schilinsky P, *et al.* (2009) Formation and impact of hot spots on the performance of organic photovoltaic cells. *Applied Physics Letters* 94: 043304/1–3.
[60] Matsumoto F, Moriwaki K, Takao Y, and Ohno T (2008) Synthesis of thienyl analogues of PCBM and investigation of morphology of mixtures in P3HT. *Beilstein Journal of Organic Chemistry* 4: 33/1–6.
[61] Peet J, Kim JY, Coates NE, *et al.* (2007) Efficiency enhancement in low-bandgap polymer solar cells by processing with alkane dithiols. *Nature Materials* 6: 497–500.

[62] Blouin N, Michaud A, and Leclerc M (2007) A low-bandgap poly(2,7-carbazole) derivative for use in high-performance solar cells. *Advanced Materials* 19: 2295–2300.
[63] Liang Y, Xu Z, Xia J, et al. (2010) For the bright future – Bulk heterojunction polymer solar cells with power conversion efficiency of 7.4%. *Advanced Engineering Materials* 22: E135–E138.
[64] Wienk MM, Kroon JM, Verhees JH, et al. (2003) Efficient methano[70]fullerene/MDMO-PPV bulk heterojunction photovoltaic cells. *Angewandte Chemie International Edition* 42: 3371–3375.
[65] He Y, Chen H-Y, Hou J, and Li Y (2010) Indene-C 60 bisadduct: A new acceptor for high-performance polymer solar cells. *Journal of the American Chemical Society* 132: 1377–1382.
[66] Hoppe H, Egbe DAM, Mühlbacher D, and Sariciftci NS (2004) Photovoltaic action of conjugated polymer/fullerene bulk heterojunction solar cells using novel PPE-PPV copolymers. *Journal of Materials Chemistry* 14: 3462–3467.
[67] Shaheen SE, Brabec CJ, Sariciftci NS, et al. (2001) 2.5% Efficient organic solar cells. *Applied Physics Letters* 78: 841–843.
[68] Brabec CJ, Shaheen SE, Winder C, et al. (2002) Effect of LiF/metal electrodes on the performance of plastic solar cells. *Applied Physics Letters* 80: 1288–1290.
[69] Mihailetchi VD, Koster LJA, Blom PWM, et al. (2005) Compositional dependence of the performance of poly(p-phenylenevinylene): Methanofullerene bulk-heterojunction solar cells. *Advanced Functional Materials* 15: 795–801.
[70] Reyes-Reyes M, Kim K, and Carroll DL (2005) High-efficiency photovoltaic devices based on annealed poly(3-hexylthiophene) and 1-(3-methoxycarbonyl)-propyl-1-phenyl-(6,6)C$_{61}$ blends. *Applied Physics Letters* 87: 083506/1–3.
[71] Ma W, Cuiying Y, Xiong G, et al. (2005) Thermally stable, efficient polymer solar cells with nanoscale control of the interpenetrating network morphology. *Advanced Functional Materials* 15: 1617–1622.
[72] Kim Y, Cook S, Sachetan M, et al. (2006) A strong regioregularity effect in self-organizing conjugated polymer films and high-efficiency polythiophene: Fullerene solar cells. *Nature Materials* 5: 197–203.
[73] Reyes-Reyes M, Kim K, Dewald J, et al. (2005) Meso-structure formation for enhanced organic photovoltaic cells. *Organic Letters* 7: 5749–5752.
[74] Mullekom HAM, Vekemans JAJM, Havinga EE, and Meijer EW (2001) Developments in the chemistry and band gap engineering of donor–acceptor substituted conjugated polymers. *Materials Science and Engineering, R: Reports* 32: 1–40.
[75] Park SH, Roy A, Beaupré S, et al. (2009) Bulk heterojunction solar cells with internal quantum efficiency approaching 100%. *Nature Photonics* 3: 297–303.
[76] Bjerring M, Nielsen JS, Siu A, et al. (2008) An explanation for the high stability of polycarboxythiophenes in photovoltaic devices – A solid-state NMR dipolar recoupling study. *Solar Energy Materials and Solar Cells* 92: 772–784.
[77] Bjerring M, Nielsen JS, Nielsen NC, and Krebs FC (2007) Polythiophene by solution processing. *Macromolecules* 40: 6012–6013.
[78] Krebs FC and Spanggaard H (2005) Significant improvement of polymer solar cell stability. *Chemistry of Materials* 17: 5235–5237.
[79] Helgesen M and Krebs FC (2010) Photovoltaic performance of polymers based on dithienylthienopyrazines bearing thermocleavable benzoate esters. *Macromolecules* 43: 1253–1260.
[80] Drees M, Hoppe H, Windner C, et al. (2005) Stabilization of the nanomorphology of polymer–fullerene 'bulk-heterojunction' blends using a novel polymerizable fullerene derivative. *Journal of Materials Chemistry* 15: 5158–5163.
[81] Miyanishi S, Tajima K, and Hashimoto K (2009) Morphological stabilization of polymer photovoltaic cells by using cross-linkable poly(3-(5-hexenyl)thiophene). *Macromolecules* 42: 1610–1618.
[82] Kooistra FB (2007) Fullerenes for Organic Electronics. Dissertation. University of Groningen.
[83] Kooistra FB, Knol J, and Kastenberg F (2007) Increasing the open circuit voltage of bulk-heterojunction solar cells by raising the LUMO level of the acceptor. *Organic Letters* 9: 551–554.
[84] Lenes M, Wetzelaer G-JAH, Kooistra FB, et al. (2008) Fullerene bisadducts for enhanced open-circuit voltages and efficiencies in polymer solar cells. *Advanced Materials* 20: 2116–2119.
[85] Zhao G, He Y, and Li Y (2010) 6.5% Efficiency of polymer solar cells based on poly(3-hexylthiophene) and indene-C$_{60}$ bisadduct by device optimization. *Advanced Materials* 22: 4355–4358.
[86] Cheng Y-J, Hsieh C-H, He Y, et al. (2010) Combination of indene-C$_{60}$ bis-adduct and cross-linked fullerene interlayer leading to highly efficient inverted polymer solar cells. *Journal of the American Chemical Society* 132: 17381–17383.
[87] McNeill CR, Abrusci A, and Zaumseil J (2007) Dual electron donor/electron acceptor character of a conjugated polymer in efficient photovoltaic diodes. *Applied Physics Letters* 90: 193506/1–3.
[88] Fahlman M, Crispin A, Henze SKM, et al. (2007) Electronic structure of hybrid interfaces for polymer-based electronics. *Journal of Physics: Condensed Matter* 19: 183202/1–20.
[89] Braun S, Salaneck WR, and Fahlman M (2009) Energy-level alignment at organic/metal and organic/organic interfaces. *Advanced Materials* 21: 1450–1472.
[90] Nardes AM, Kemerink M, de Kok MM, et al. (2008) Conductivity, work function, and environmental stability of PEDOT:PSS thin films treated with sorbitol. *Organic Electronics* 9: 727–734.
[91] Li G, Shrotriya V, Huang J, et al. (2005) High-efficiency solution processable polymer photovoltaic cells by self-organization of polymer blends. *Nature Materials* 4: 864–868.
[92] Kim JY, Kim SH, Lee H-H, et al. (2006) New architecture for high-efficiency polymer photovoltaic cells using solution-based titanium oxide as an optical spacer. *Advanced Materials* 18: 572–576.
[93] Wang E, Wang L, Lan L, et al. (2008) High-performance polymer heterojunction solar cells of a polysilafluorene derivative. *Applied Physics Letters* 92: 03307/1–3.
[94] Reese MO, Morfa AJ, and White MS (2008) Pathways for the degradation of organic photovoltaic P3HT:PCBM based devices. *Solar Energy Materials and Solar Cells* 92: 746–752.
[95] Heraeus Precious Metal GmbH. http://www.cievios.com (accessed 2 November 2011).
[96] Waldauf C, Morana M, and Denk P (2006) Highly efficient inverted organic photovoltaics using solution based titanium oxide as electron selective contact. *Applied Physics Letters* 89: 233517/1–3.
[97] Shrotriya V, Li G, Yao Y, et al. (2006) Transition metal oxides as the buffer layer for polymer photovoltaic cells. *Applied Physics Letters* 88: 073508/1–3.
[98] Huang J-S, Chou C-Y, and Lin C-F (2010) Efficient and air-stable polymer photovoltaic devices with WO$_3$–V$_2$O$_5$ mixed oxides as anodic modification. *IEEE Electron Device Letters* 31: 332–334.
[99] Han S, Shin WS, Seo M, et al. (2009) Improving performance of organic solar cells using amorphous tungsten oxides as an interfacial buffer layer on transparent anodes. *Organic Electronics* 10: 791–797.
[100] Chan MY, Lee CS, Lai SL, et al. (2006) Efficient organic photovoltaic devices using a combination of exciton blocking layer and anodic buffer layer. *Journal of Applied Physics* 100: 094506/1–4.
[101] Kim JY, Lee K, Coates NE, et al. (2007) Efficient tandem polymer solar cells fabricated by all-solution processing. *Science* 317: 222–225.
[102] Verbakel F, Meskers SCJ, and Janssen RAJ (2006) Electronic memory effects in diodes from a zinc oxide nanoparticle–polystyrene hybrid material. *Applied Physics Letters* 89: 102103/1–3.
[103] Puetz A, Stubhan T, Reinhard M, et al. (2010) Organic solar cells incorporating buffer layers from indium doped zinc oxide nanoparticles. *Solar Energy Materials and Solar Cells*, doi: 10.1016/j.solmat.2010.09.020.
[104] Grczynski G, Kugler T, Keil M, et al. (2001) Photoelectron spectroscopy of thin films of PEDOT–PSS conjugated polymer blend: A mini-review and some new results. *Journal of Electron Spectroscopy and Related Phenomena* 121: 1–17.

[105] Moujoud A, Oh SH, Shin HS, and Kim HJ (2010) On the mechanism of conductivity enhancement and work function control in PEDOT:PSS film through UV-light treatment. *Physica Status Solidi A* 207: 1704–1707.
[106] Huang J, Miller PF, Wilson JS, et al. (2005) Investigation of the effects of doping and post-deposition treatments on the conductivity, morphology, and work function of poly (3,4-ethylenedioxythiophene)/poly(styrene sulfonate) films. *Advanced Functional Materials* 15: 290–296.
[107] Li C-Y, Wen T-C, Lee T-H, et al. (2009) An inverted polymer photovoltaic cell with increased air stability obtained by employing novel hole/electron collecting layers. *Journal of Materials Chemistry* 19: 1643–1647.
[108] Vogel M, Doka S, Breyer C, et al. (2006) On the function of a bathocuproine buffer layer in organic photovoltaic cells. *Applied Physics Letters* 89: 163501/1–3.
[109] Masumoto Y and Mori T (2008) Application of organic bathocuproine-based alloy film to organic light-emitting diodes. *Thin Solid Films* 516: 3350–3356.
[110] Olthof S, Meiss J, Lüssem B, et al. (2011) Photoelectron spectroscopy investigation of thin metal films employed as top contacts in transparent organic solar cells. *Thin Solid Films* 519: 1872–1875.
[111] Nüesch F and Rothberg LJ (1999) A photoelectron spectroscopy study on the indium tin oxide treatment by acids and bases. *Applied Physics Letters* 74: 880–882.
[112] Yang L, Xu H, Tian H, et al. (2010) Effect of cathode buffer layer on the stability of polymer bulk heterojunction solar cells. *Solar Energy Materials and Solar Cells* 94: 1831–1834.
[113] Steim R (2010) *The Impact of Interfaces on the Performance of Organic Photovoltaic Cells*. Karlsruhe, Germany: KIT Scientific Publishing.
[114] Yip H-L, Hau SK, Baek NS, et al. (2008) Polymer solar cells that use self-assembled-monolayer-modified ZnO/metals as cathodes. *Advanced Materials* 20: 2376–2382.
[115] Hau K, Yip H-L, and Acton O (2008) Interfacial modifications to improve inverted polymer solar cells. *Journal of Materials Chemistry* 18: 5113–5119.
[116] Kim JS, Park JH, Lee JH, et al. (2007) Control of the electrode work function and active layer morphology via surface modification of indium tin oxide for high efficiency organic photovoltaics. *Applied Physics Letters* 91: 112111/1–3.
[117] Khodabakhsh S, Sanderson BM, Nelson J, and Jones TS (2006) Using self-assembling dipole molecules to improve charge collection in molecular solar cells. *Advanced Functional Materials* 16: 95–100.
[118] Steim R, Kogler FR, and Brabec CJ (2010) Interface materials for organic solar cells. *Journal of Materials Chemistry* 20: 2499–2512.
[119] Chen L-M, Xu Z, Hong Z, and Yang Y (2010) Interface investigation and engineering – Achieving high performance polymer photovoltaic devices. *Journal of Materials Chemistry* 20: 2575–2598.
[120] Guillén C and Herrero J (2005) Comparison study of ITO thin films deposited by sputtering at room temperature onto polymer and glass substrates. *Thin Solid Films* 480–481: 129–132.
[121] Ishibashi S, Higuchi Y, Ota Y, and Nakamura K (1990) Low resistivity indium-tin oxide transparent conductive films. II. Effect of sputtering voltage on electrical property of films. *Journal of Vacuum Science and Technology A* 8: 1403–1406.
[122] Wang RX, Beling CD, Djurišić AB, et al. (2004) Properties of ITO thin films deposited on amorphous and crystalline substrates with e-beam evaporation. *Semiconductor Science and Technology* 19: 695–698.
[123] Kim H, Horwitz JS, Kushto GP, et al. (2001) Indium tin oxide thin films grown on flexible plastic substrates by pulsed-laser deposition for organic light-emitting diodes. *Applied Physics Letters* 79: 284–286.
[124] Kim Y-S, Park Y-C, Ansari SG, et al. (2003) Influence of O_2 admixture and sputtering pressure on the properties of ITO thin films deposited on PET substrate using RF reactive magnetron sputtering. *Surface and Coatings Technology* 173: 299–308.
[125] Yu HY, Feng XD, Grozea D, et al. (2001) Surface electronic structure of plasma treated indium tin oxides. *Applied Physics Letters* 78: 2595–2597.
[126] Schlaf R, Murata H, and Kafafi ZH (2001) Work function measurements on indium tin oxide films. *Journal of Electron Spectroscopy and Related Phenomena* 120: 149–154.
[127] Park Y, Choong V, Gao Y, et al. (1996) Work function of indium tin oxide transparent conductor measured by photoelectron spectroscopy. *Applied Physics Letters* 68: 2699–2701.
[128] Alam MJ and Cameron DC (2001) Characterization of transparent conductive ITO thin films deposited on titanium dioxide film by a sol–gel process. *Surface and Coatings Technology* 142–144: 776–780.
[129] Xu D, Deng Z, Xu Y, et al. (2005) An anode with aluminum doped on zinc oxide thin films for organic light emitting devices. *Physics Letters A* 346: 148–152.
[130] Schulze K, Maennig B, and Leo K (2007) Organic solar cells on indium tin oxide and aluminum doped zinc oxide anodes. *Applied Physics Letters* 91: 073521/1–3.
[131] Murdoch GB, Hinds S, Sargent EH, et al. (2009) Aluminum doped zinc oxide for organic photovoltaics. *Applied Physics Letters* 94: 213301/1–3.
[132] Kim H, Kushto GP, Auyeung RCY, and Piqué A (2008) Optimization of F-doped SnO_2 electrodes for organic photovoltaic devices. *Applied Physics A* 93: 521–526.
[133] Yang F and Forrest SR (2006) Organic solar cells using transparent SnO_2–F anodes. *Advanced Materials* 18: 2018–2022.
[134] Fahland M, Karlsson P, and Charton C (2001) Low resistivity transparent electrodes for displays on polymer substrates. *Thin Solid Films* 392: 334–337.
[135] Lewis J, Grego S, Chalamala B, et al. (2004) Highly flexible transparent electrodes for organic light-emitting diode-based displays. *Applied Physics Letters* 85: 3450–3452.
[136] Cho S-W, Jeong J-A, and Bae J-H (2008) Highly flexible, transparent, and low resistance indium zinc oxide–Ag–indium zinc oxide multilayer anode on polyethylene terephthalate substrate for flexible organic light-emitting diodes. *Thin Solid Films* 516: 7881–7885.
[137] Brown AR, Bradley DDC, Burroughes JH, et al. (1992) Poly(*p*-phenylenevinylene) light-emitting diodes: Enhanced electroluminescent efficiency through charge carrier confinement. *Applied Physics Letters* 61: 2793–2795.
[138] White MS, Olson DC, Shaheen SE, et al. (2006) Inverted bulk-heterojunction organic photovoltaic device using a solution-derived ZnO underlayer. *Applied Physics Letters* 89: 143517/1–3.
[139] Kim JS, Lägel B, Moons E, et al. (2003) Kelvin probe and ultraviolet photoemission measurements of indium tin oxide work function: A comparison. *Synthetic Metals* 111–112: 311–314.
[140] Krebs FC, Gevorgyan SA, and Alstrup J (2009) A roll-to-roll process to flexible polymer solar cells: Model studies, manufacture and operational stability studies. *Journal of Materials Chemistry* 19: 5442–5451.
[141] Kim YS, Lee Y, Lee W, et al. (2010) Effects of molecular weight and polydispersity of poly(3-hexylthiophene) in bulk heterojunction polymer solar cells. *Current Applied Physics* 10: 329–332.
[142] Zen A, Pflaum J, Hirschmann S, et al. (2004) Effect of molecular weight and annealing of poly(3-hexylthiopene)s on the performance of organic field-effect transistors. *Advanced Functional Materials* 14: 757–764.
[143] Kline RJ, McGehee MD, Kadnikova EN, et al. (2003) Controlling the field-effect mobility of regioregular polythiophene by changing the molecular weight. *Advanced Materials* 15: 1519–1522.
[144] Pivrikas A, Juška G, Österbacka R, et al. (2005) Langevin recombination and space-charge-perturbed current transients in regiorandom poly(3-hexylthiophene). *Physical Review B* 71: 125205/1–5.
[145] Ballantyne AM, Wilson JS, Nelson J, et al. (2006) TOF mobility measurements in pristine films of P3HT: Control of hole injection and influence of film thickness. *Proceedings of SPIE* 6334: 633408/1–11.
[146] Schilinsky P, Asawapirom U, Scherf U, et al. (2005) Influence of the molecular weight of poly(3-hexylthiophene) on the performance of bulk heterojunction solar cells. *Chemistry of Materials* 17: 2175–2180.
[147] Woo CH, Thompson C, Kim BJ, et al. (2008) The influence of poly(3-hexylthiophene) regioregularity on fullerene-composite solar cell performance. *Journal of the American Chemical Society* 130: 16324–16329.
[148] Rispens MT, Meetsma A, Rittberger R, et al. (2003) Influence of the solvent on the crystal structure of PCBM and the efficiency of MDMO-PPV:PCBM 'plastic' solar cells. *Chemical Communications* 2003: 2116–2118.

[149] Martens T, D'Haen J, Munters T, et al. (2003) Disclosure of the nanostructure of MDMO-PPV:PCBM bulk hetero-junction organic solar cells by a combination of SPM and TEM. *Synthetic Metals* 138: 243–247.
[150] Yang X, van Duren JKJ, Janssen RAJ, et al. (2004) Morphology and thermal stability of the active layer in poly(*p*-phenylenevinylene)/methanofullerene plastic photovoltaic devices. *Macromolecules* 37: 2151–2158.
[151] Chirvase D, Parisi J, Hummelen JC, and Dyakonov V (2004) Influence of nanomorphology on the photovoltaic action of polymer–fullerene composites. *Nanotechnology* 15: 1317–1323.
[152] Mozer AJ, Denk P, Scharber MC, et al. (2004) Novel regiospecific MDMO-PPV copolymer with improved charge transport for bulk heterojunction solar cells. *The Journal of Physical Chemistry B* 108: 5235–5242.
[153] Waldauf C, Schilinsky P, Hauch J, and Brabec CJ (2004) Material and device concepts for organic photovoltaics: Towards competitive efficiencies. *Thin Solid Films* 451–452: 503–507.
[154] Padinger F, Rittberger RS, and Sariciftci NS (2003) Effects of postproduction treatment on plastic solar cells. *Advanced Functional Materials* 13: 85–88.
[155] Al-Ibrahim M, Ambacher O, Sensfuss S, and Gobsch G (2005) Effects of solvent and annealing on the improved performance of solar cells based on poly(3-hexylthiophene):Fullerene. *Applied Physics Letters* 86: 201120.
[156] Kooistra FB, Mihailetchi VD, Popescu LM, et al. (2006) New C_{84} derivative and its application in a bulk heterojunction solar cell. *Chemistry of Materials* 18: 3068–3073.
[157] Hoppe H, Niggemann M, Winder C, et al. (2004) Nanoscale morphology of conjugated polymer/fullerene-based bulk-heterojunction solar cells. *Advanced Functional Materials* 14: 1005–1011.
[158] Nieuwendaal RC, Snyder CR, Kline RJ, et al. (2010) Measuring the extent of phase separation in poly-3-hexylthiophene/phenyl-C_{61}-butyric acid methyl ester photovoltaic blends with ^{1}H spin diffusion NMR spectroscopy. *Chemistry of Materials* 22: 2930–2936.
[159] Beal RM, Stavrinadis A, and Warner JH (2010) The molecular structure of polymer-fullerene composite solar cells and its influence on device performance. *Macromolecules* 43: 2343–2348.
[160] van Bavel SS, Bärenklau M, de With G, et al. (2010) P3HT/PCBM bulk heterojunction solar cells: Impact of blend composition and 3D morphology on device performance. *Advanced Functional Materials* 20: 1458–1463.
[161] Okraku EW, Gupta MC, and Wright KD (2010) Pulsed laser annealing of P3HT/PCBM organic solar cells. *Solar Energy Materials and Solar Cells* 94: 2013–2017.
[162] Ko C-J, Lin Y-K, and Chen F-C (2007) Microwave annealing of polymer photovoltaic devices. *Advanced Materials* 19: 3520–3523.
[163] Li G, Yao Y, Yang H, et al. (2007) 'Solvent annealing' effect in polymer solar cells based on poly(3-hexylthiophene) and methanofullerenes. *Advanced Functional Materials* 17: 1636–1644.
[164] Zhao Y, Guo X, Xie Z, et al. (2009) Solvent vapor-induced self assembly and its influence on optoelectronic conversion of poly(3-hexylthiophene): Methanofullerene bulk heterojunction photovoltaic cells. *Journal of Applied Polymer Science* 111: 1799–1804.
[165] Zhang F, Jespersen KG, Björström C, et al. (2006) Influence of solvent mixing on the morphology and performance of solar cells based on polyfluorene copolymer/fullerene blends. *Advanced Functional Materials* 16: 667–674.
[166] Yao Y, Hou J, Xu Z, et al. (2008) Effects of solvent mixtures on the nanoscale phase separation in polymer solar cells. *Advanced Functional Materials* 18: 1783–1789.
[167] Moulé AJ and Meerholz K (2008) Controlling morphology in polymer–fullerene mixtures. *Advanced Materials* 20: 240–245.
[168] Chen F-C, Tseng H-C, and Ko C-J (2008) Solvent mixtures for improving device efficiency of polymer photovoltaic devices. *Applied Physics Letters* 92: 103316.
[169] Hwang I-W, Cho S, and Kim JY (2008) Carrier generation and transport in bulk heterojunction films processed with 1,8-octanedithiol as a processing additive. *Journal of Applied Physics* 104: 33706.
[170] Arias AC, Corcoran N, and Banach M (2002) Vertically segregated polymer-blend photovoltaic thin-film structures through surface-mediated solution processing. *Applied Physics Letters* 80: 1695–1697.
[171] Rand BP, Xue J, Uchida S, and Forrest SR (2005) Mixed donor–acceptor molecular heterojunctions for photovoltaic applications. I. Material properties. *Journal of Applied Physics* 98: 124902.
[172] van Bavel SS, Sourty E, and de With G (2009) Three-dimensional nanoscale organization of bulk heterojunction polymer solar cells. *Nano Letters* 9: 507–513.
[173] Campoy-Quiles M, Ferenczi T, Agostinelli T, et al. (2008) Morphology evolution via self-organization and lateral and vertical diffusion in polymer: Fullerene solar cell blends. *Nature Materials* 7: 158–164.
[174] Gao D, Helander G, Wang Z-B, et al. (2010) C_{60}:LiF blocking layer for environmentally stable bulk heterojunction solar cells. *Advanced Materials* 22: 5404–5408.
[175] Xu Z, Chen L-M, Yang G, et al. (2009) Vertical phase separation in poly(3-hexylthiophene): Fullerene derivative blends and its advantage for inverted structure solar cells. *Advanced Functional Materials* 19: 1227–1234.
[176] Norrman K, Madsen MV, Gevorgyan SA, and Krebs FC (2010) Degradation patterns in water and oxygen of an inverted polymer solar cell. *Journal of the American Chemical Society* 132: 16883–16892.
[177] Scharber MC, Mühlbacher D, Koppe M, et al. (2006) Design rules for donors in bulk-heterojunction solar cells – Towards 10% energy-conversion efficiency. *Advanced Materials* 18: 789–794.
[178] Kroon R, Lenes M, Hummelen JC, et al. (2008) Small bandgap polymers for organic solar cells (polymer material development in the last 5 years). *Polymer Reviews* 48: 531–582.
[179] Smestad GP, Krebs FC, Lampert CM, et al. (2008) Reporting solar cell efficiencies in solar energy materials and solar cells. *Solar Energy Materials and Solar Cells* 92: 371–373.
[180] Paßlick C, Császár I, Henke B, et al. (2010) Advances in up- and down-converted fluorescence for high efficiency solar cells using rare-earth doped fluorozirconate-based glasses and glass ceramics. In: Tsakalakos L (ed.) *Proceedings of the SPIE 7772*, pp. 77720A–77720A-9. San Diego, CA, USA.
[181] Dennler G, Scharber MC, Ameri T, et al. (2008) Design rules for donors in bulk-heterojunction tandem solar cells – Towards 15% energy-conversion efficiency. *Advanced Materials* 20: 579–583.
[182] Slooff LH, Veenstra SC, Kroon JM, et al. (2007) Determining the internal quantum efficiency of highly efficient polymer solar cells through optical modeling. *Applied Physics Letters* 90: 143506/1–3.
[183] Zhang F, Mammo W, Andersson LM, et al. (2006) Low-bandgap alternating fluorene copolymer/methanofullerene heterojunctions in efficient near-infrared polymer solar cells. *Advanced Materials* 18: 2169–2173.
[184] Mühlbacher D, Scharber M, Morana M, et al. (2006) High photovoltaic performance of a low-bandgap polymer. *Advanced Materials* 18: 2884–2889.
[185] Andersson BV, Huang DM, Moulé AJ, and Inganäs O (2009) An optical spacer is no panacea for light collection in organic solar cells. *Applied Physics Letters* 94: 043301/1–3.
[186] Ameri T, Dennler G, Waldauf C, et al. (2008) Realization, characterization, and optical modeling of inverted bulk-heterojunction organic solar cells. *Applied Physics Letters* 103: 08506/1–6.
[187] Tvingstedt K, Andersson V, Zhang F, and Inganas O (2007) Folded reflective tandem polymer solar cell double efficiency. *Applied Physics Letters* 91: 123514/1–3.
[188] Hadipour A, de Boer B, Wildeman J, et al. (2006) Solution-processed organic tandem solar cells. *Advanced Functional Materials* 16: 1897–1903.
[189] Dennler G, Forberich K, Scharber MC, et al. (2007) Angle dependence of external and internal quantum efficiencies in bulk-heterojunction organic solar cells. *Applied Physics Letters* 102: 054516/1–7.
[190] Burdick J and Glatfelter T (1986) Spectral response and I–V measurements of tandem amorphous-silicon alloy solar cells. *Solar Cells* 18: 301–314.
[191] Sista S, Hong Z, Park M-H, et al. (2010) High-efficiency polymer tandem solar cells with three-terminal structure. *Advanced Materials* 22: E77–E80.
[192] Heliatek GmbH. http://heliatek.de/news-19 (accessed 2 November 2011).
[193] Wiedemann W, Sims L, Abdellah A, et al. (2010) Nanostructured interfaces in polymer solar cells. *Applied Physics Letters* 96: 263109.
[194] Niggemann M, Graf W, and Gombert A (2008) Realization of ultrahigh photovoltages with organic photovoltaic nanomodules. *Advanced Materials* 20: 4055–4060.

[195] Zimmermann B, Glatthaar M, Niggemann M, *et al.* (2007) ITO-free wrap through organic solar cells – A module concept for cost-efficient reel-to-reel production. *Solar Energy Materials and Solar Cells* 91: 374–378.
[196] Kim M-S, Kim J-S, Cho JC, *et al.* (2007) Flexible conjugated polymer photovoltaic cells with controlled heterojunctions fabricated using nanoimprint lithography. *Applied Physics Letters* 90: 123113/1–3.
[197] Cheyns D, Vasseur K, Rolin C, *et al.* (2008) Nanoimprinted semiconducting polymer films with 50 nm features and their application to organic heterojunction solar cells. *Nanotechnology* 19: 424016/1–6.
[198] Jørgensen M, Norrman K, and Krebs FC (2008) Stability/degradation of polymer solar cells. *Solar Energy Materials and Solar Cells* 92: 686–714.
[199] Neugebauer H, Brabec C, Hummelen JC, and Sariciftci NS (2000) Stability and photodegradation mechanisms of conjugated polymer/fullerene plastic solar cells. *Solar Energy Materials and Solar Cells* 61: 35–42.
[200] Hauch JA, Schilinsky P, Choulis SA, *et al.* (2008) The impact of water vapor transmission rate on the lifetime of flexible polymer solar cells. *Applied Physics Letters* 93: 103306/1–3.
[201] Zimmermann B, Würfel U, and Niggemann M (2009) Longterm stability of efficient inverted P3HT:PCBM solar cells. *Solar Energy Materials and Solar Cells* 93: 491–496.
[202] Dennler G, Lungenschmied C, Neugebauer H, and Sariciftci NS (2005) Flexible, conjugated polymer-fullerene-based bulk-heterojunction solar cells: Basics, encapsulation and integration. *Journal of Materials Research* 20: 3224–3233.
[203] Fahlteich J, Fahland M, Schönberger W, and Schiller N (2009) Permeation barrier properties of thin oxide films on flexible polymer substrates. *Thin Solid Films* 517: 3075–3080.
[204] Greener J, Ng KC, Vaeth KM, and Smith TM (2007) Moisture permeability through multilayered barrier films as applied to flexible OLED display. *Journal of Applied Polymer Science* 106: 3534–3542.
[205] Lungenschmied C, Dennler G, and Neugebauer H (2007) Flexible, long-lived, large-area, organic solar cells. *Solar Energy Materials and Solar Cells* 91: 379–384.
[206] Yamanari T, Taima T, Sakai J, *et al.* (2010) Effect of buffer layers on stability of polymer-based organic solar cells. *Japanese Journal of Applied Physics* 49: 01AC02/1–4.
[207] Kawano K, Pacios R, Poplavskyy D, *et al.* (2006) Degradation of organic solar cells due to air exposure. *Solar Energy Materials and Solar Cells* 90: 3520–3530.
[208] Liu F, Shao S, Guo X, *et al.* (2010) Efficient polymer photovoltaic cells using solution-processed MoO_3 as anode buffer layer. *Solar Energy Materials and Solar Cells* 94: 842–845.
[209] Lee K, Kim JY, Park SH, *et al.* (2007) Air-stable polymer electronic devices. *Advanced Materials* 19: 2445–2449.
[210] Krebs FC (2008) Air stable polymer photovoltaics based on a process free from vacuum steps and fullerenes. *Solar Energy Materials and Solar Cells* 92: 715–726.
[211] Kuwabara T, Nakayama T, Uozumi K, *et al.* (2008) Highly durable inverted-type organic solar cell using amorphous titanium oxide as electron collection electrode inserted between ITO and organic layer. *Solar Energy Materials and Solar Cells* 92: 1476–1482.
[212] Huang J, Xu Z, and Yang Y (2007) Low-work-function surface formed by solution-processed and thermally deposited nanoscale layers of cesium carbonate. *Advanced Functional Materials* 17: 1966–1973.
[213] Sutherland DGJ, Carlisle JA, Elliker P, *et al.* (1996) Photo-oxidation of electroluminescent polymers studied by core-level photoabsorption spectroscopy. *Applied Physics Letters* 68: 2046–2048.
[214] Scurlock RD, Wang B, Ogilby PR, *et al.* (1995) Singlet oxygen as a reactive intermediate in the photodegradation of an electroluminescent polymer. *Journal of the American Chemical Society* 117: 10194–10202.
[215] Dam N, Scurlock RD, Wang B, *et al.* (1999) Singlet oxygen as a reactive intermediate in the photodegradation of phenylenevinylene oligomers. *Chemistry of Materials* 11: 1302–1305.
[216] Padinger F, Fromherz T, Denk P, *et al.* (2001) Degradation of bulk heterojunction solar cells operated in an inert gas atmosphere: A systematic study. *Synthetic Metals* 121: 1605–1606.
[217] Seemann A, Sauermann T, Lungenschmied C, *et al.* (2010) Reversible and irreversible degradation of organic solar cell performance by oxygen. *Solar Energy* 85: 1238–1249.
[218] Manceau M, Gaume J, Rivaton A, *et al.* (2010) Further insights into photodegradation of poly(3-hexylthiophene) by means of X-ray photoelectron spectroscopy. *Thin Solid Films* 518: 7113–7118.
[219] Griffini G, Turri S, and Levi M (2010) Degradation and stabilization of poly(3-hexylthiophene) thin films for photovoltaic applications. *Polymer Bulletin* 10: 1–12.
[220] Chambon S, Rivaton A, Gardette J-L, and Firon M (2007) Photo- and thermal degradation of MDMO-PPV:PCBM blends. *Solar Energy Materials and Solar Cells* 91: 394–398.
[221] Reese MO, Nardes AM, Rupert BL, *et al.* (2010) Photoinduced degradation of polymer and polymer–fullerene active layers: Experiment and theory. *Advanced Functional Materials* 20: 3476–3483.
[222] Krebs FC and Norrman K (2007) Analysis of the failure mechanism for a stable organic photovoltaic during 10 000 h of testing. *Progress in Photovoltaics: Research and Applications* 15: 697–712.
[223] Norrman K and Krebs FC (2006) Lifetimes of organic photovoltaics: Using TOF-SIMS and $^{18}O_2$ isotopic labelling to characterise chemical degradation mechanisms. *Solar Energy Materials and Solar Cells* 90: 213–227.
[224] Hauch AJ, Schilinsky P, Choulis SA, *et al.* (2008) Flexible organic P3HT:PCBM bulk-heterojunction modules with more than 1 year outdoor lifetime. *Solar Energy Materials and Solar Cells* 92: 727–731.
[225] Sarkas HW, Kwan W, Flom SR, *et al.* (1996) Enhanced photooxidative stability of conjugated polymers via C_{60} doping. *The Journal of Physical Chemistry* 100: 5169–5171.
[226] Jipa S, Zaharescu T, Gigante B, *et al.* (2003) Chemiluminescence investigation of thermo-oxidative degradation of polyethylenes stabilized with fullerenes. *Polymer Degradation and Stability* 80: 209–216.
[227] Schuller S, Schilinsky P, Hauch J, and Brabec CJ (2004) Determination of the degradation constant of bulk heterojunction solar cells by accelerated lifetime measurements. *Applied Physics A* 79: 37–40.
[228] De Bettignies R, Leroy J, Firon M, and Sentein C (2006) Accelerated lifetime measurements of P3HT:PCBM solar cells. *Synthetic Metals* 156: 510–513.
[229] Hoth C (2009) Ink Formulations for Organic Photovoltaics and Their Processing with Printing and Coating Technologies. Dissertation, Carl von Ossietzky Universität Oldenburg.
[230] Krebs FC (2009) Fabrication and processing of polymer solar cells: A review of printing and coating techniques. *Solar Energy Materials and Solar Cells* 93: 394–412.
[231] Mens R, Adriaensens P, Lutsen L, *et al.* (2008) NMR study of the nanomorphology in thin films of polymer blends used in organic PV devices: MDMO-PPV/PCBM. *Journal of Polymer Science Part A: Polymer Chemistry* 46: 138–145.
[232] Hoth CN, Choulis SA, Schilinsky P, and Brabec CJ (2007) High photovoltage performance of inkjet printed polymer: Fullerene blends. *Advanced Materials* 19: 3973–3978.
[233] Martin PJ (1986) Ion-based methods for optical thin film deposition. *Journal of Materials Science* 21: 1–25.
[234] Sze ME (2002) *Semiconductor Devices: Physics and Technology*, 2nd edn. New York: Wiley.
[235] Hong S-J, Kim Y-H, and Han J-I (2008) Development of ultrafine indium tin oxide (ITO) nanoparticles for inkjet-printing by low-temperature synthetic method. *IEEE Transactions on Nanotechnology* 7: 172–176.
[236] Ding Z, An C, Li Q, *et al.* (2010) Preparation of ITO nanoparticles by liquid phase coprecipitation method. *Journal of Nanomaterials* 2010: 543601/1–5.
[237] Krebs FC (2009) Polymer solar cell modules prepared using roll-to-roll methods: Knife-over-edge coating, slot-die coating and screen printing. *Solar Energy Materials and Solar Cells* 93: 465–475.
[238] Ding JM, de la Fuente Vornbrock A, Ting C, and Subramanian V (2009) Patternable polymer bulk heterojunction photovoltaic cells on plastic by rotogravure printing. *Solar Energy Materials and Solar Cells* 93: 459–464.
[239] Thomson Reuters. http://www.isiknowledge.com (accessed 2 November 2011).
[240] German Advisory Council on Global Change (WBGU) (2003) World in transition – Towards sustainable energy systems. *Summary for Policy-Makers.* Berlin, Germany: WBGU.

[241] Nielsen DT, Cruickshank C, Foged S, *et al.* (2010) Business, market and intellectual property analysis of polymer solar cells. *Solar Energy Materials and Solar Cells* 94: 1553–1571.
[242] Espinosa N, García-Valverde R, Urbina A, and Krebs FC (2011) A life cycle analysis of polymer solar cell modules prepared using roll-to-roll methods under ambient conditions. *Solar Energy Materials and Solar Cells* 95: 1293–1302.
[243] Dennler G, Scharber MC, and Brabec CJ (2009) Polymer–fullerene bulk-heterojunction solar cells. *Advanced Materials* 21: 1323–1338.
[244] Fenn J and Raskino M (2008) *Mastering the Hype Cycle: How to Choose the Right Innovation at the Right Time*. Boston, MA: Harvard Business Press.

Further Reading

[1] Krebs FC (2010) *Polymeric Solar Cells*. Lancaster, PA: DEStech Publications Inc.
[2] Deibel C and Dyakonov V (2010) Polymer–fullerene bulk heterojunction solar cells. *Reports on Progress in Physics* 73: 096401/1–39.
[3] Liang Y and Yu L (2010) Development of semiconducting polymers for solar energy harvesting. *Polymer Reviews* 50: 454–473.
[4] Troshin PA, Hoppe H, Renz J, *et al.* (2009) Material solubility–photovoltaic performance relationship in the design of novel fullerene derivatives for bulk heterojunction solar cells. *Advanced Functional Materials* 19: 779–788.
[5] Dennler G and Brabec CJ (2008) *Organic Photovoltaics: Materials, Device Physics, and Manufacturing Technologies*. Weinheim, Germany: Wiley-VCH.

# 1.21 Mesoporous Dye-Sensitized Solar Cells

A Hagfeldt, UB Cappel, and G Boschloo, Uppsala University, Uppsala, Sweden
L Sun, KTH—Royal Institute of Technology, Stockholm, Sweden; Dalian University of Technology (DUT), Dalian, China
L Kloo, KTH—Royal Institute of Technology, Stockholm, Sweden
H Pettersson, Swerea IVF AB, Mölndal, Sweden
EA Gibson, University of Nottingham, Nottingham UK

© 2012 Elsevier Ltd.

1.21.1	Introduction	481
1.21.2	Mesoporous Dye-Sensitized Solar Cells	482
1.21.2.1	Overview of Current Status and Operational Principles	482
1.21.2.2	The Kinetic Model – Electron-Transfer Processes	484
1.21.2.2.1	Electron injection and excited state decay	485
1.21.2.2.2	Regeneration of the oxidized dyes	485
1.21.2.2.3	Electron transport through the mesoporous oxide film	485
1.21.2.2.4	Loss reactions	486
1.21.2.2.5	Transport of the redox mediator and reactions at the counter electrode	486
1.21.2.3	Basic Characterization of DSC Devices	487
1.21.2.3.1	Efficiency measurements	487
1.21.2.3.2	External and internal quantum efficiencies	488
1.21.2.3.3	Overview of the concept of a DSC toolbox	489
1.21.2.4	Development of Material Components and Devices	490
1.21.2.4.1	Mesoporous oxide working electrodes	490
1.21.2.4.2	Dyes	491
1.21.2.4.3	Electrolytes	492
1.21.2.4.4	Counter electrodes	492
1.21.2.4.5	Development of modules	492
1.21.3	Future Outlook	494
References		494

1.21.1 Introduction

The umbrella of solar energy conversion encompasses solar thermal, solar fuels, solar-to-electricity (photovoltaic (PV)) technology, and the great many subcategories below those. PVs, or solar cells, are advancing quickly, both with regard to industrialization and research. Globally, the total PV installation is around 40 giga Watts (GW), and an annual growth rate of 45% has been experienced over the recent years. Solar cell technologies can be divided into three generations. The first is an established technology such as crystalline silicon, the second includes the emerging thin-film technologies that have just entered the market, while the third generation covers future technologies that are not yet commercialized. A link for PV updates is www.solarbuzz.com, and our own contribution for a review of PV technologies with special emphasis on the materials science aspects is Reference 1.

When comparing different PV technologies, a figure of merit is the production cost per peak Watt of solar electricity produced. For the so-called second-generation thin-film solar cells, production costs down to and even below $1 W_{peak}^{-1} are reported. To be competitive with conventional energy sources for large-scale electricity production, new PV technologies need to aim at production costs below $0.5 W_{peak}^{-1}. To give an example, this means a cost of $70 m^{-2} at a module efficiency of 14%. The dye-sensitized solar cell (DSC) is a molecular solar cell technology that has the potential to achieve production costs below $0.5 W_{peak}^{-1}.

DSC is based on molecular- and nanometer-scale components. Record cell efficiencies of 12%, promising stability data and energy-efficient production methods, have been accomplished. In the present table of record solar cell efficiencies [2], in which the solar cell area must be at least 1 cm^2, the record is held by the Sharp company in Japan at 10.9% [3]. The record cell efficiencies for a DSC module is 9.9% achieved by Sony, Japan [4]. Key advantages of the DSC technology over others include the prospect of low investments and fabrication costs and a short energy-payback time (<1 year). DSCs can be designed with great flexibility in shape, color, and transparency. Because they are relatively easy to integrate into a range of different products, new commercial opportunities for niche applications have been made possible. Ultimately, the most important comparison of different energy sources is the cost in relation to energy production, e.g., the production cost per kWh. For DSC technology, it is advantageous to compare energy cost rather than cost per peak Watt since DSCs perform relatively better compared with other solar cell technologies under diffuse light conditions and at higher temperatures.

DSC research groups have been established around the world and the field is growing fast, which can be illustrated by the fact that about two or three research articles are being published every day. From a fundamental research perspective, we can conclude that the physical chemistry of several of the basic operations in the DSC device remains far from fully understood. The energetics and kinetics of many specific model and reference systems under controlled conditions have been carefully investigated. However, it is still not possible to predict accurately how a small change to the system – e.g., replacing one component or changing the electrolyte composition – will affect the DSC performance. Such investigations have demonstrated the sheer chemical complexity of DSCs, and the main challenge for future research is to understand and master this complexity, in particular, at the oxide-dye-electrolyte interface. A challenging but realizable goal for the present DSC technology is to achieve efficiencies above 15%. We have for many years known where the main losses in the state-of-the-art DSC device are: the potential drop in the regeneration process and the recombination loss between electrons in the TiO_2 and acceptor species in the electrolyte. With our breakthrough of using one-electron-transfer redox systems such as Co complexes, in combination with a dye that efficiently prevents the recombination loss, we may now have found the path to increase the efficiency significantly [5]. With the recent world record of 12.3 by Grätzel and co-workers [6] using Co complexes, the main direction of the research field is now to explore this path.

The industrial interest in DSCs is strong and several companies present encouraging results, in particular with regard to upscaling with world record minimodule efficiencies above 9% (Sony and Fujikura). In this context, we emphasize that world record efficiencies are not the same as stable efficiencies obtained after durability tests. The stable module efficiencies that are reported vary significantly in the literature and are difficult to judge. The best values listed in the literature are about 5%, although presentations at conferences report better results. Several companies are dedicated to setting up manufacturing pilot lines. G24i is a company based in Cardiff, Wales, that focuses on consumer electronics. On its website (www.g24i.com), such niche products are now for sale. Companies that sell material components, equipment, and consultancy services have increased and are growing.

There are several recent reviews on DSCs, and the reader is directed to these papers for further information [7–19]. In this chapter, we present the general concepts and principles of DSC, introduce the basic characterization methods, and overview materials and device development. This also means that the reference list gives more of a general summary of the field, including mainly books, review articles, and some original papers.

1.21.2 Mesoporous Dye-Sensitized Solar Cells

Attempts to develop mesoporous DSCs have been made before [9, 20–22] the breakthrough of O'Regan and Grätzel in 1991 [23]. The basic problem was the belief that only smooth semiconductor surfaces could be used. The light-harvesting efficiency (LHE) for a monomolecular layer of dye sensitizer is far less than 1% of the AM1.5 spectrum. Attempts to harvest more light by using multilayers of dyes were in general unsuccessful. Indications of the possibilities to increase the roughness of the semiconductor surface so that a larger number of dyes could be adsorbed directly to the surface and simultaneously be in direct contact with a redox electrolyte had also been reported before 1991. For example, Matsumura et al. [24] and Alonso et al. [25] used sintered ZnO electrodes to increase the efficiency of sensitization by rose bengal and related dyes. But the conversion yields from solar light to electricity remained well below 1% for these systems. Grätzel, Augustynski, and co-workers presented results on dye-sensitized fractal-type TiO_2 electrodes with high surface area in 1985 [26]. For DSC, there was thus an order-of-magnitude increase when O'Regan and Grätzel in 1991 reported efficiencies of 7–8% [23]. With regard to stability, a turnover number of 5×10^6 was measured for the ruthenium complex sensitizer. This was followed up by the introduction of the famous N3 dye, giving efficiencies around 10% [27]. For more than a decade, the ruthenium complex N3, $Ru(L_{bip})_2(NCS)_2$ with L_{bip} being a dicarboxylated bipyridyl ligand, its salt analog N719, and the so-called black dye $RuL_{ter}(NCS)_3$ with L being a terpyridyl ligand, were state-of-the-art sensitizers. Recently developed Ru complexes such as C101 show now higher performances both in terms of efficiency and stability [17, 28]. The molecular structures of N3, the black dye, and C101 are shown in **Figure 1**.

1.21.2.1 Overview of Current Status and Operational Principles

Since the initial work in the beginning of the 1990s, a wealth of DSC components and configurations have been developed. At present, several thousands of dyes have been investigated. Fewer, but certainly hundreds of electrolyte systems and mesoporous films with different morphologies and compositions have been studied and optimized. For DSCs at present, in the official table of world record efficiencies for solar cells, the record is held by the Sharp company in Japan at $10.9 \pm 0.3\%$ [2, 3]. A criterion to qualify for these tables is that the solar cell area is at least $1\,cm^2$. For smaller cells, conversion efficiencies above 12% have been reached using the so-called C101 sensitizer as the sensitizer and with Co complex-based electrolytes [6] (see Section 1.21.2.4.3).

A schematic of the interior of a DSC showing the principle of how the device operates is shown in **Figure 2**.

The typical configuration is as follows. At the heart of the device is the mesoporous oxide layer composed of a network of TiO_2 nanoparticles. These are deposited on a transparent conducting oxide (TCO) substrate and an Ohmic contact is formed between them during the sintering step, which also fuses together the nanoparticles to enable electronic conduction. The mesoporous film thickness is, typically, ca. 10 μm and the nanoparticle diameter is 10–30 nm giving a porosity of 50–60%. The mesoporous layer is deposited on a transparent conducting oxide on a glass or plastic substrate. A typical scanning electron microscopy (SEM) image of a mesoporous TiO_2 film is shown in **Figure 3**.

Attached to the surface of the nanocrystalline film is a monolayer of the charge-transfer dye.

Photoexcitation of the latter results in the injection of an electron into the conduction band of the oxide leaving the dye in its oxidized state. The dye is restored to its ground state by electron transfer from the electrolyte, usually an organic solvent containing

Figure 1 Molecular structures of N3, the black dye, and C101.

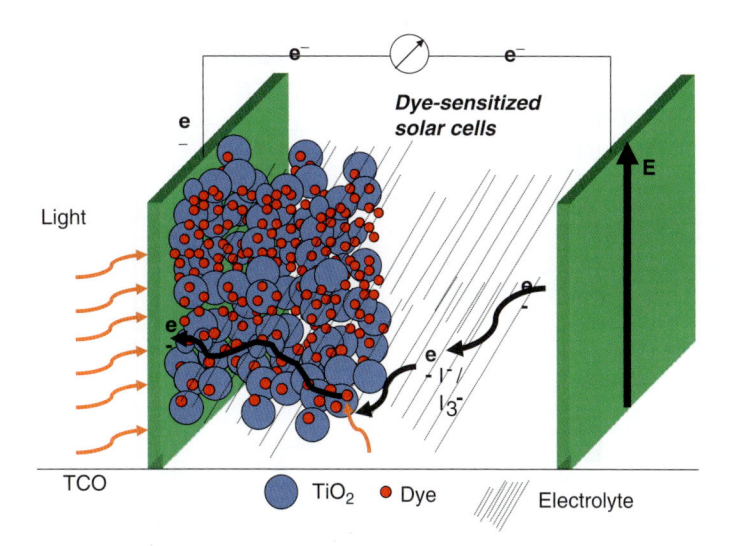

Figure 2 A schematic of the interior of a DSC showing the principle of how the device operates.

Figure 3 SEM picture of a typical mesoporous TiO_2 film.

the iodide–triiodide redox system. The regeneration of the sensitizer by iodide intercepts the recapture of the conduction band electron by the oxidized dye. The I_3^- ions formed by oxidation of I^- diffuse a short distance (<50 μm) through the electrolyte to the cathode, which is coated with a layer of catalytic platinum, where the regenerative cycle is completed by electron transfer to reduce I_3^- to I^-. For a DSC to be durable for more than 15 years outdoors, the turnover number required is 10^8. This is satisfied by the ruthenium complexes mentioned above.

The voltage generated under illumination corresponds to the difference between the electrochemical potential of the electron at the two contacts. For DSCs, this is generally the difference between the Fermi level of the mesoporous TiO_2 layer and the redox potential of the electrolyte. Overall, electric power is generated without permanent chemical transformation.

As mentioned above, a huge number of material components, dyes, mesoporous and nanostructured electrodes, electrolytes, and counter electrodes have been synthesized and developed for DSC applications. The material component variations of a DSC device are therefore endless. It is important to keep in mind that the description above, and the one below in the next section, of the conventional DSC device with a mesoporous TiO_2, a Ru complex sensitizer, I^-/I_3^- redox couple, and a platinized TCO counter electrode is only valid for this particular combination of material components. As soon as one of these components are modified or completely replaced by another component, the picture has changed; energetics and kinetics are different and need to be determined for the particular system at hand. To generalize a result in DSC research is therefore difficult and can many times be misleading.

1.21.2.2 The Kinetic Model – Electron-Transfer Processes

The basic electron-transfer processes in a DSC, as well as the potentials for a state-of-the-art device based on the N3 dye adsorbed on TiO_2 and I^-/I_3^- as redox couple in the electrolyte, are shown in **Figure 4**. The corresponding kinetic data for the different electron-transfer processes taking place at the oxide–dye–electrolyte interface are summarized in **Figure 5**.

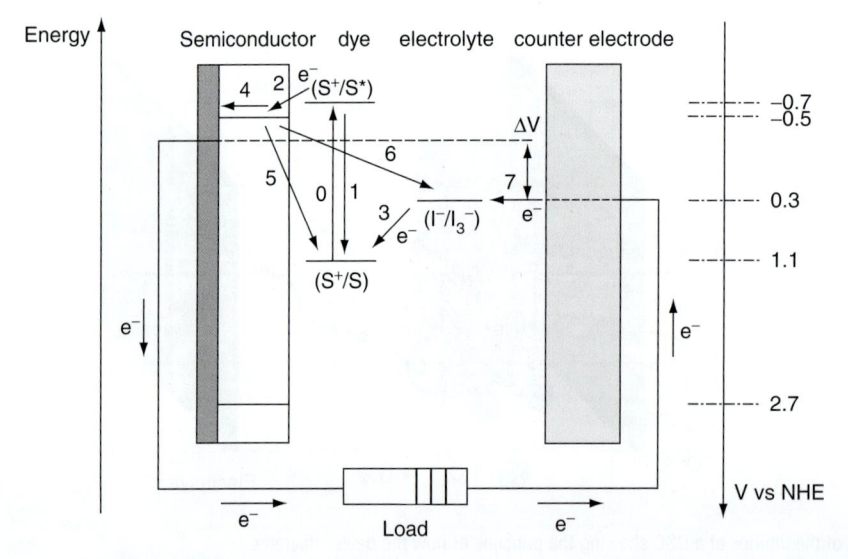

Figure 4 Simple energy-level diagram for a DSC. The basic electron-transfer processes are indicated by numbers (1–7). The potentials for a DSC based on the N3 dye, TiO_2, and the I^-/I_3^- redox couple are shown. Reprinted with permission from Hagfeldt A, Boschloo G, Sun L, et al. (2010) *Chemical Reviews* 110: 6595. American Chemical Society.

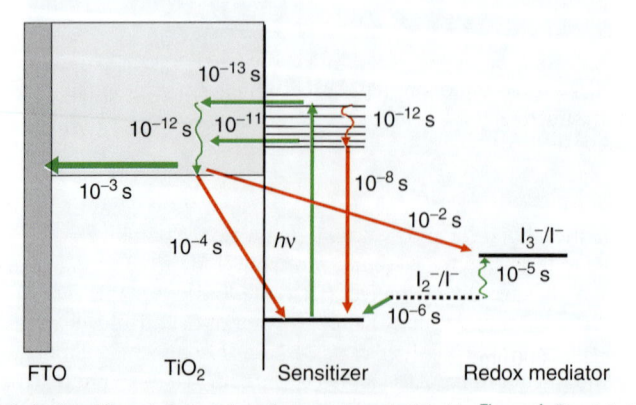

Figure 5 Summary of the kinetic data for the different electron-transfer processes depicted in **Figure 4**. Reprinted with permission from Hagfeldt A, Boschloo G, Sun L, et al. (2010) *Chemical Reviews* 110: 6595. American Chemical Society.

Besides the desired pathway of the electron-transfer processes (processes 2, 3, 4, and 7) described in **Figure 4**, the loss reactions 1, 5, and 6 are indicated. Reaction 2 is electron injection from the excited state of the dye to the semiconductor, 3 is regeneration of the oxidized dye by the electrolyte, 4 is electron transport through the mesoporous oxide layer, and 7 is the reduction of the electrolyte at the counter electrode. Reaction 1 is direct recombination of the excited dye reflected by the excited state lifetime. Recombination reactions of injected electrons in the TiO$_2$ with either oxidized dyes or with acceptors in the electrolyte are numbered 5 and 6, respectively. In principle, electron transfer to I$_3^-$ can occur either at the interface between the nanocrystalline oxide and the electrolyte or at areas of the TCO contact that are exposed to the electrolyte. In practice, the second route can be suppressed by using a compact blocking layer of oxide deposited on the anode by spray pyrolysis [29, 30]. Blocking layers are mandatory for DSCs that utilize one-electron redox systems or for cells using solid organic hole-conducting media [18].

1.21.2.2.1 Electron injection and excited state decay

One of the most astounding findings in DSC research is the ultrafast injection from the excited ruthenium complex in the TiO$_2$ conduction band. Although the detailed mechanism of this injection process is still under debate, it is generally accepted that a fast, femtosecond (fs) component is observed for these types of sensitizers, directly attached to an oxide surface [31–34]. This would then be one of the fastest chemical processes known to date. There is a debate for a second, slower, injection component on the picosecond (ps) timescale. The reason for this could, on the one hand, be due to an intersystem crossing of the excited dye from a singlet to a triplet state. The singlet state injects on the fs timescale, whereas the slower component arises from the relaxation time of the singlet to triplet transition and from a lower driving force in energy between the triplet state and the conduction band of the TiO$_2$ [34]. Another view of the slower component is that it is very sensitive to sample condition and originates from dye aggregates on the TiO$_2$ surface [33]. For DSC device performance, the timescales of the injection process should be compared with direct recombination from the excited state of the dye to the ground state. This is given by the excited state lifetime of the dye, which for typical ruthenium complexes used in DSC is 30–60 ns [8]. Thus, the injection process itself has not generally been considered to be a key factor limiting device performance. Koops *et al.* observed a much slower electron injection in a complete DSC device with a time constant of around 150 ps. This would then be slow enough for kinetic competition between electron injection and excited state decay of the dye, with potential implications for the overall DSC performance [35]. These results are debated since they are obtained with a single-photon counting technique that is a nondirect measurement of the injection process. A slower injection in the sub-ps time regime could be even more severe for organic dyes, for which the excited state decay time could be less than nanoseconds.

Therefore, research on the electron injection process will continue to be an important topic in DSC research and needs to be extended to other classes of sensitizers beside the ruthenium complexes.

1.21.2.2.2 Regeneration of the oxidized dyes

The interception of the oxidized dye by the electron donor, normally I$^-$, is crucial for obtaining good charge collection yields and long cycle life of the sensitizer. For a turnover number (cycle life of the sensitizer in the DSSC device) above 10^8 (which is required for a DSC lifetime of >15 years in outdoor conditions), the lifetime of the oxidized dye must be longer than 100 s if the regeneration time is 1 μs [36]. This is achieved by the best-performing ruthenium complexes such as C101.

A large number of sensitizers are efficiently regenerated by iodide, as is evident from their good solar cell performance. Most of these sensitizers have oxidation potentials that are similar to or more positive than that of the standard N3 sensitizer Ru(L$_{bip}$)$_2$(NCS)$_2$ (V^0_{redox} = +1.10 V vs. normal hydrogen electrode (NHE)). Because the redox potential of the iodide–triiodide electrolyte with organic solvent is about +0.35 V versus NHE, the driving force ΔG^0 for regeneration of N3 is 0.75 eV. It is of interest to estimate how much driving force is needed. Kuciauskas *et al.* [37] investigated regeneration kinetics of a series of Ru and Os complexes and found that Os(L$_{bip}$)$_2$(NCS)$_2$ with a ΔG^0 = 0.52 eV is not (or is very slowly) regenerated by iodide, while Os(L$_{bip}$)$_2$(CN)$_2$ (ΔG^0 = 0.82 eV) is regenerated. The black dye, RuL$_{ter}$(NCS)$_3$, with ΔG^0 = 0.60 eV, shows rapid regeneration [38]. Clifford *et al.* [39] studied regeneration in a series of Ru sensitizers and found that Ru(L$_{bip}$)$_2$Cl$_2$ with ΔG^0 = 0.46 eV gave slow regeneration (>100 μs), leading to a low regeneration efficiency. The results suggest that 0.5–0.6 eV driving force is needed for regeneration of Ru complex sensitizers in iodide–triiodide electrolyte. The need for such a large driving force is probably and outcome of the initial regeneration reaction, involving the I$^-$/I$_2^-$ redox couple, having a more positive potential than I$^-$/I$_3^-$ [40].

Fast regeneration kinetics are also found for the one-electron redox mediators. Cobalt(II)-bis[2,6-bis(1'-butylbenzimidazol-2'-yl)pyridine] (Co(dbbip)$_2^{2+}$) gave regeneration times of some microseconds and regeneration efficiencies of more than 0.9 [41, 42]. Ferrocene and phenothiazine gave rapid regeneration, while cobalt(II)-bis(4,4'-di-tert-butyl-2,2'-bipyridine) was slow [43]. Interestingly, mixtures of this Co complex with ferrocene and phenothiazine were efficient in DSCs, suggesting that a mix of redox mediators can be a viable approach in DSCs [43]. Very rapid dye regeneration was observed in the case of the solid-state DSCs (sDSCs) where the redox electrolyte is replaced by the solid hole conductor spiro-MeOTAD [44]. Bach *et al.* found that hole injection from the oxidized Ru(L$_{bip}$)$_2$(SCN)$_2$ dye to the spiro-MeOTAD proceeds over a broad timescale, ranging from less than 3 ps to a few nanoseconds [45].

Very recently, several papers have been published dealing with the regeneration of oxidized dyes with the iodide–triiodide electrolyte [40, 46, 47].

1.21.2.2.3 Electron transport through the mesoporous oxide film

The mesoporous semiconductor electrode consists of numerous interconnected nanocrystals. Because these particles are typically not electronically doped and surrounded by ions in the electrolyte, they will not have an internal electrical field and will not display any significant band bending. Electrons photoinjected into the nanoparticles from the dye molecules are charge-compensated by ions in the electrolyte. Photocurrent will be detected in the external circuit once the electrons are transferred into the conducting substrate. The gradient in electron concentration appears to be the main driving force for transport in the mesoporous oxide films – that is, electron transport occurs by diffusion [11,18, 48]. Because the electrons in the mesoporous electrode are charge-compensated by ions in the electrolyte, the diffusion processes of electrons and ions will be coupled through a weak electric field. This will affect transport of charge carriers. The measured electron diffusion can thus be described by an ambipolar diffusion model [49, 50].

In contrast to the notion that electron transport occurs by diffusion, it is observed that the electron transport depends on the incident light intensity, becoming more rapid at higher light intensities [51, 52]. This can be explained by a diffusion coefficient that is light intensity-dependent or, more correctly, dependent on the electron concentration and Fermi level in the TiO_2. The measured value of the diffusion coefficient is orders of magnitude lower than that determined for single-crystalline TiO_2 anatase ($0.4 \, cm^2 \, s^{-1}$) [53]. These observations are usually explained by using a multiple-trapping model [52, 54–57]. In this model, electrons are considered to be mostly trapped in localized states below the conduction band, from which they can escape by thermal activation. Experiments suggest that the density and energetic location of such traps is described by an exponentially decreasing tail of states below the conduction band [54, 56]. The origin of the electron traps remains obscure at present: they could correspond to trapping of electrons at defects in the bulk, grain boundaries, or surface regions of the mesoporous oxide or to Coulombic trapping due to local field effects through interaction of electrons with the polar TiO_2 crystal or with cations of the electrolyte [58–60].

1.21.2.2.4 Loss reactions

During their relatively slow transport through the mesoporous TiO_2 film, electrons are always within only a few nanometers distance of the oxide–electrolyte interface. Recombination of electrons with either oxidized dye molecules or acceptors in the electrolyte is therefore a possibility. The recombination of electrons with the oxidized dye molecules competes with the regeneration process, which usually occurs on a timescale of submicroseconds to microseconds. The kinetics of the back electron-transfer reaction from the conduction band to the oxidized sensitizer follow a multiexponential time law, occurring on a microsecond to millisecond timescale, depending on electron concentration in the semiconductor and, thus, the light intensity. The reasons suggested for the relatively slow rate of this recombination reaction are as follows: (1) weak electronic coupling between the electron in the solid and the Ru(III) center of the oxidized dye, (2) trapping of the injected electron in the TiO_2, and (3) the kinetic impediment due to the inverted Marcus region [61]. Application of a potential to the mesoporous TiO_2 electrode has a strong effect [62–65]. When the electron concentration in the TiO_2 particles is increased, a strong increase in the recombination kinetics is found. Under actual working conditions, the electron concentration in the TiO_2 particles is rather high and recombination kinetics may compete with dye regeneration.

Recombination of electrons in TiO_2 with acceptors in the electrolyte is, for the I^-/I_3^- redox system, generally considered to be an important loss reaction, in particular under working conditions of the DSC device when the electron concentration in the TiO_2 is high. The kinetics of this reaction are determined from voltage decay measurements and normally referred to as the electron lifetime. Lifetimes observed with the I^-/I_3^- system are very long (1–20 ms under 1 sun light intensity) compared with other redox systems used in DSCs, explaining the success of this redox couple. The mechanism for this recombination reaction remains unsettled but appears to be dominated by the electron trapping–detrapping mechanism in the TiO_2 [66]. Recently, a lot of attention has been drawn to the effects of the adsorbed dye on the recombination of TiO_2 electrons with electrolyte species. There are several reasons: first, adsorption of the dye can lead to changes in the conduction band edge of TiO_2 because of changes in surface charge. This will lead to a larger driving force for recombination. Second, dyes can either block or promote reduction of acceptor species in the electrolyte [67]. The size of the oxide particle, and thus the surface-to-volume ratio, is also expected to have a significant effect on electron lifetime [68, 69].

1.21.2.2.5 Transport of the redox mediator and reactions at the counter electrode

Transport of the redox mediator between the electrodes is mainly driven by diffusion. Typical redox electrolytes have a high conductivity and ionic strength so that the influence of the electric field and transport by migration is negligible. In viscous electrolytes such as ionic liquids, diffusion coefficients can be too low to maintain a sufficiently large flux of redox components, which can limit the photocurrent of the DSC [70].

In the case of the iodide–triiodide electrolyte, an alternative and more efficient type of charge transport can occur when high mediator concentrations are used: the Grotthuss mechanism. In this case, charge transport corresponds to the formation and cleavage of chemical bonds. In viscous electrolytes, such as ionic liquid-based electrolytes, this mechanism can contribute significantly to charge transport in the electrolyte [70–73]. In amorphous hole conductors that replace the electrolyte in sDSCs, charge transport takes place through hole hopping. In the most investigated molecular hole conductor for DSCs, spiro-MeOTAD, mobility is increased 10-fold by the addition of a Li salt [74]. Resistance, however, in the hole-transporting layer can be a problem in sDSCs.

At the counter electrode in standard DSCs, triiodide is reduced to iodide. The counter electrode must be catalytically active to ensure rapid reaction and low overpotential. Pt is a suitable catalyst as iodine (triiodide) dissociates to iodine atoms and iodide upon adsorption, enabling a rapid one-electron reduction. The charge-transfer reaction at the counter electrode leads to a series resistance in the DSC, the charge-transfer resistance R_{CT}. Ideally, R_{CT} should be $\leq 1 \, \Omega \, cm^2$ to avoid significant losses. A poor counter electrode will affect the current–voltage characteristics of the DSC by lowering the fill factor (FF).

1.21.2.3 Basic Characterization of DSC Devices

In this section, we describe the basic solar cell measurements – that is, the determination of solar-to-electrical energy conversion efficiency, η, and the quantum efficiency. As mentioned above, there are a huge number of material components and combinations which can be used to prepare a DSC device. To illustrate some results from basic efficiency measurements we have included a comparison between liquid and solid-state DSC [75]. The results are obtained for DSC devices which contained an organic sensitizer, D35, a liquid I^-/I_3^- electrolyte or a solid-state, spiro-MeOTAD, hole conductor. The molecular structures of D35 and spiro-MeOTAD are shown in **Figure 6**.

For the liquid cell, a platinized fluorine-doped tin oxide TCO substrate is used as counter electrode, and for the sDSC, an evaporated silver layer on top of the hole conductor is used. For the working electrode, 1.8 μm mesoporous TiO_2 films screen printed on dense TiO_2 blocking layers were used. The mesoporous TiO_2 films were treated with a $TiCl_4$ solution [76]. The electrolyte concentrations were 0.05 M I_2, 0.5 M LiI, and 0.5 M 4-tert-butyl pyridine (4TBP) in 3-methoxypropionitrile (MPN), while the spiro-MeOTAD solution used for spin coating consisted of 150 mg spiro-MeOTAD per milliliter of chlorobenzene with 15 mM LiTFSI and 60 mM 4TBP added.

1.21.2.3.1 Efficiency measurements

Current–voltage measurements (I–V measurements) under illumination are used to determine the efficiencies of solar cells. A lamp which simulates the AM1.5 solar spectrum is used for illumination and is calibrated to an intensity of $1000\,W\,m^{-2}$ for measurements at 1 sun intensity. A Newport solar simulator of class B was used for the results presented below. A voltage is then applied between the working and counter electrode of the solar cell and the current output is measured. The voltage range should include the voltage at which the current is 0 (the open-circuit voltage, V_{OC}) and 0 V at which the short-circuit current density (J_{SC}) is measured. The resulting current–voltage curve is usually referred to as an I–V curve. The conditions for measuring the current–voltage characteristics of a DSC device should be carefully checked. The I–V characteristics of DSC can be quite sensitive to scan rate, preconditioning of the scan (which potential is applied and for how long), as well as changes occurring after repeated scans – see, for example, discussions in Reference 75.

Measurements can also be carried out in the dark, and the measured data are accordingly called a 'dark current curve'. **Figure 7** shows an example of I–V curves under illumination and in the dark for the solid and the liquid-electrolyte cell with the D35 dye.

The efficiency of a solar cell, η, is given by

$$\eta = \frac{P_{max}}{P_{in}} = \frac{(J \times V)_{max}}{P_{in}} \quad [1]$$

where P_{in} is the illumination intensity and P_{max} is the maximum power output of the solar cell at this light intensity. To describe the efficiency of a solar cell in terms of V_{OC} and J_{SC}, a quantity called the fill factor (FF) is introduced, relating P_{max} to V_{OC} and J_{SC}:

$$FF = \frac{(J \times V)_{max}}{J_{SC} \times V_{OC}} \quad [2]$$

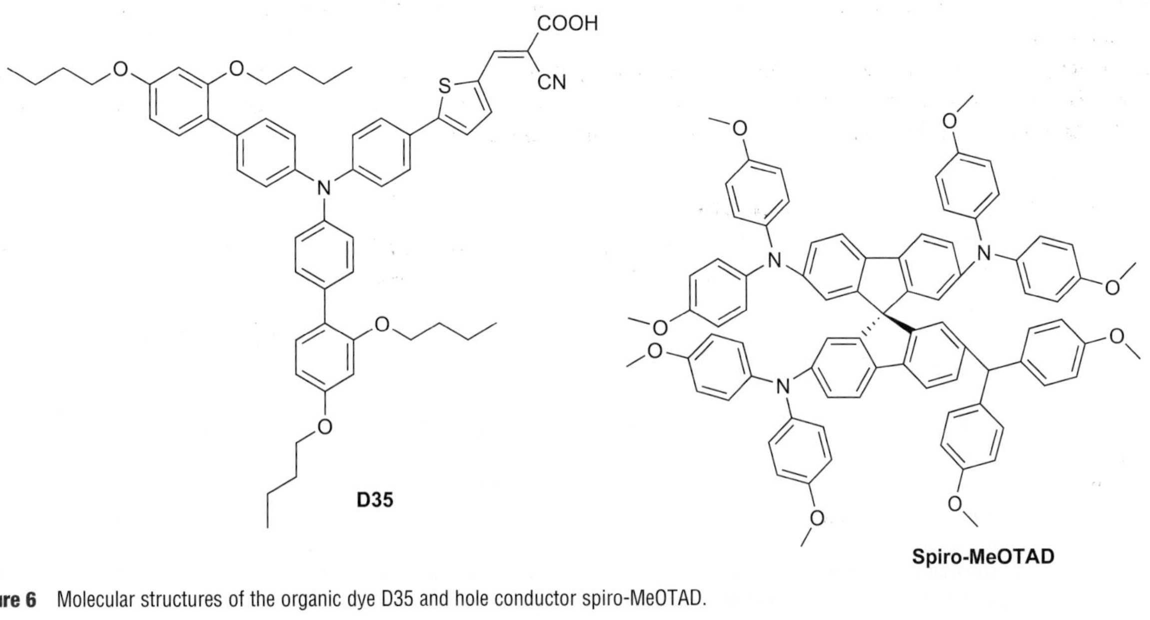

Figure 6 Molecular structures of the organic dye D35 and hole conductor spiro-MeOTAD.

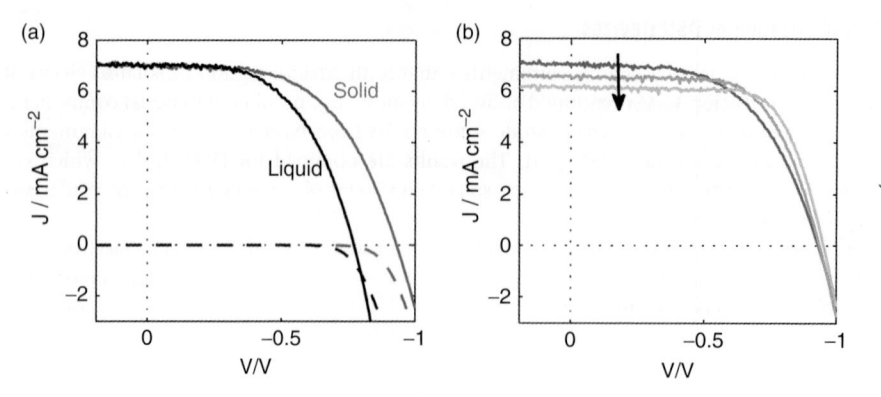

Figure 7 I–V curves of an sDSC (gray) and a liquid-electrolyte DSC (black) with D35 as sensitizer under 1 sun illumination (solid line) and in the dark (dashed line). Courtesy of Dr. Ute Cappel.

The efficiency can then be written as

$$\eta = \frac{J_{SC} \times V_{OC} \times FF}{P_{in}} \quad [3]$$

For the example in **Figure 7**, the efficiencies of the liquid DSC and sDSC were 2.9% and 3.6%, with V_{OC} of 0.77 V and 0.93 V, J_{SC} of 7.0 and 7.0 mA cm^{-2}, and FF of 0.54 and 0.55, respectively. Thus, the sDSC has a higher V_{OC} than the liquid-electrolyte DSC, which is the reason for the higher efficiency of the sDSC. It should be noted that the film thickness is only 1.8 μm, so the optical density of the film is relatively low, reducing the overall efficiency. What was also observed in Reference 75 is that in consecutive scans, the short-circuit current of the solid-state cell decreases, while the FF and the overall efficiency increase, demonstrating how care must be taken in measuring I–V curves for DSCs, in particular for sDSCs.

With regard to illumination of the DSC cell, the cells should be masked. A mask size that is 1 mm on each side bigger than the active area is recommended in Reference 77. Using thin TCO glass (~1 mm) and a device size of at least 5 × 5 mm is also recommended. This will reduce optical artefacts that can enhance or diminish the power conversion efficiency. To be qualified in the official table of world record efficiencies for PVs, the solar cell area must be at least 1 cm^2. For efficiency measurements of solar cells in general, we refer to Reference 78. For DSC specifically, we summarize the discussions above according to Reference 79.

1. The rate of change of the bias applied must be slow, and the IV curve should be scanned in both directions to determine if it is slow enough.
2. The efficiency depends on the premeasurement state. The temperature should be 25 °C, and there should be a bias light of one-sun at P_{max}. Procedures that approximate this can be used. It should be noted that V_{OC} or J_{SC} might not give the same results as preconditioning at P_{max}.
3. Light may penetrate from outside the defined area. The magnitude of this should be determined by looking at J_{SC} with or without an aperture.
4. The monochromatic quantum efficiency dependence on light intensity (see 1.21.2.3.2) may be nonlinear, and control measurements should be made at different light intensities to check this. It is recommended that quantum efficiency measurements should be done with bias light and preferably chopped monochromatic beam.

1.21.2.3.2 External and internal quantum efficiencies

The incident photon-to-current conversion efficiency (IPCE), sometimes also called the external quantum efficiency of the solar cell, describes how many of the incoming photons at one wavelength are converted to electrons:

$$\text{IPCE}(\lambda) = \frac{\text{Electrons out }(\lambda)}{\text{Incident photons }(\lambda)} = \frac{J_{SC}(\lambda)}{q\Phi(\lambda)} = \frac{hc}{q} \times \frac{J_{SC}(\lambda)}{\lambda P_{in}(\lambda)} = 1240 \frac{J_{SC}(\lambda)[\text{Å cm}^{-2}]}{\lambda[\text{nm}] \times P_{in}(\lambda)[\text{W cm}^{-2}]} \quad [4]$$

where J_{SC} is the short-circuit current density, Φ is the photon flux, P_{in} is the light intensity at a certain wavelength λ, q the elementary charge, and h and c are the Planck's constant and speed of light, respectively.

IPCEs are made by typically using a xenon or halogen lamp coupled to a monochromator. The photon flux of light incident on the samples is measured with a calibrated photodiode, and measurements are typically made at 10 or 20 nm wavelength intervals between 400 nm and the absorption threshold of the dye. Since DSCs are devices with relatively slow relaxation times, it is important to make sure that the measurement duration for a given wavelength is sufficient for the current to be stabilized (normally 5–10 s). If it is observed that IPCE depends on light intensity, then the measurements should be made with additional bias light to

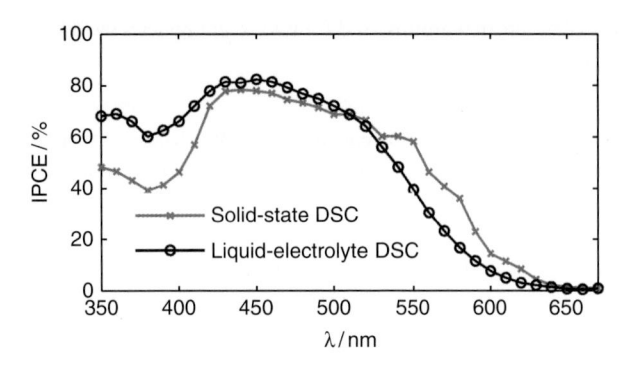

Figure 8 IPCE spectra of the sDSC and the liquid-electrolyte DSC with D35 as sensitizer. Courtesy of Dr. Ute Cappel.

ascertain that IPCE is determined at relevant light intensity conditions. The reasons for light intensity-dependent IPCE may be that the charge collection efficiency (process 4 in **Figure 4**) increases with light intensity due to faster electron transport, or that there are mass transport limitations in the electrolyte, decreasing IPCE with light intensity.

The magnitude of the IPCE spectrum depends on how much light is absorbed by the solar cell and how much of the absorbed light is converted to electrons, which are collected:

$$\text{IPCE}(\lambda) = \text{LHE}(\lambda) \times \varphi_{\text{inj}}(\lambda) \times \varphi_{\text{reg}} \times \eta_{\text{CC}}(\lambda) \quad [5]$$

Where LHE is equal to $1 - 10^{-A}$ with A being the absorbance of the film, φ_{inj} and φ_{reg} the quantum yields for electron injection and dye regeneration, respectively, and η_{CC} the charge collection efficiency.

IPCE spectra of the liquid DSC and sDSCs sensitized with D35 are shown in **Figure 8** [75].

The spectra are slightly different in shape, although the same TiO$_2$ thickness and the same dye were used. The spectrum of the sDSC is lower at around 380 nm and higher at the red edge of the spectrum than the spectrum of the liquid-electrolyte DSC. These differences can be explained with Equation [5]: at around 380 nm, spiro-MeOTAD absorbs strongly, decreasing the transmittance at this wavelength in the solid-state device compared with the liquid-electrolyte DSC and therefore decreasing the IPCE. LHE at the absorption maximum of D35 was close to 1 for the devices, resulting in IPCE maxima of 80%. However, at longer wavelengths, light harvesting was incomplete. In the sDSC, the reflecting back contact increased the light harvesting at these wavelengths and therefore also the IPCE.

The short-circuit current of a solar cell can be calculated by integrating over the product of the IPCE and the AM1.5 solar spectrum:

$$J_{\text{sc}} = \int \text{IPCE}(\lambda) q \phi_{\text{ph,AM1.5}}(\lambda) d\lambda \quad [6]$$

where $\varphi_{\text{ph,AM1.5}}$ is the photon flux in AM1.5 at wavelength λ. For the DSC presented in **Figure 8**, the integrated J_{SC} were determined to be 7.75 mA cm^{-2} for the sDSC and 7.4 mA cm^{-2} for the liquid-electrolyte cell. These currents are slightly higher than the currents determined in the *I–V* measurements. For the sDSC, this might be due to the fact that the IPCE measurement was carried out prior to the *I–V* measurements, so the analysis of the data must be checked according to the discussions above.

From a fundamental viewpoint, the so-called absorbed photon-to-current conversion efficiency (APCE) values provide further insight into the properties of the device. APCE (or internal quantum efficiency) shows how efficiently the numbers of absorbed photons are converted into current. APCE is obtained by dividing the IPCE number by the LHE (0–100%). The IUPAC name for LHE is 'absorptance'. Thus,

$$\text{APCE} = \frac{\text{IPCE}}{\text{LHE}} = \varphi_{\text{inj}}(\lambda) \times \varphi_{\text{reg}} \times \eta_{\text{CC}}(\lambda) \quad [7]$$

Quantitative *in situ* measurement of the LHE of complete devices is complicated because of light scattering by the mesoporous oxide film and light absorption by the other cell components. For fundamental studies, it is therefore advisable to use transparent mesoporous TiO$_2$ films. There are several descriptions of the procedures to obtain LHE in the literature, including on how to take into account scattering effects – see, for example, References 80–83.

1.21.2.3.3 Overview of the concept of a DSC toolbox

The dye-sensitized solar cell is a complex, highly cooperative system. To understand the precise working mechanism of the DSC and to optimize its performance, it is important to map the energetics of the different components and interfaces and the kinetics of the different electron-transfer reactions for complete DSC devices working under actual operating conditions. The so-called toolbox of characterization techniques is used to investigate the kinetics of different reactions in situ in DSC devices. These studies are particularly fruitful, as the interactions between different components can be studied. Toolbox methods are continuously being developed by several research groups, and for two recent reviews we refer to References 18 and 84. Examples of tool-box techniques are:

- Photovoltage and photocurrent as a function of light intensity
- Small-modulation photocurrent and photovoltage transients to investigate electron transport and recombination
- Steady-state, quantum efficiency measurements to determine injection efficiency, collection efficiency, and electron diffusion length
- Electron concentration measurements
- Determination of the internal potential (*quasi*-Fermi level) in the mesoporous electrode
- Photo-induced absorption spectroscopy to obtain information on recombination reactions and regeneration of the oxidized dye by the electrolyte.

A set of very powerful toolbox techniques is based on electrochemical impedance spectroscopy (EIS). The reader is referred to the works of Bisquert and co-workers on this topic, and as examples of references we propose References 84–86. In EIS, the potential applied to a system is perturbed by a small sine-wave modulation, and the resulting sinusoidal current response (amplitude and phase shift) is measured as a function of modulation frequency. The impedance is defined as the frequency domain ratio of the voltage to the current and is a complex number. For a resistor (R), the impedance is a real value, independent of modulation frequency, while capacitors (C) and inductors (L) yield an imaginary impedance with values that vary with frequency. The impedance spectrum of an actual system – that is, the impedance measured in a wide range of frequencies – can be described in terms of an equivalent circuit consisting of series- and parallel-connected elements R, C, L, and W, which is the Warburg element that describes diffusion processes. Using EIS, the following parameters can be obtained: series resistance, charge-transfer resistance of the counter electrode, diffusion resistance of the electrolyte, the resistance of electron transport and recombination in the semiconductor, and the chemical capacitance of the mesoporous electrode. One of the advantages of impedance spectroscopy is that it allows simultaneous characterization of electron transport in the mesoporous oxide and of recombination of the electrons from the oxide to the hole-conducting medium. The transport and interfacial transfer of electrons in the mesoporous oxide layer can be modeled using a distributed network of resistive and capacitive elements in the form of a finite transmission line.

1.21.2.4 Development of Material Components and Devices

Since the initial work in the beginning of the 1990s, a wealth of DSC components and configurations have been developed. Perhaps a key concept for the future success of DSC is 'diversity'. At present, several thousands of dyes have been investigated, as well as numerous types of mesoporous films with different morphologies and compositions. The last year has seen some very interesting breakthroughs in the use of alternative redox systems, and this field is now opened up after almost 20 years of I^-/I_3^- dominance. With such a diversity to explore, the DSC technology can be expected to progress rapidly, be it through design of new materials and combinations based on fundamental insights or by 'evolution' – that is, trial and error – or better, with the use of combinatorial approaches.

In the following sections, we briefly overview the development of the material components and devices in DSC and in general refer to the many recent reviews on these topics.

1.21.2.4.1 *Mesoporous oxide working electrodes*

The key to the breakthrough for DSCs in 1991 was the use of a mesoporous TiO_2 electrode with a high internal surface area to support the monolayer of a sensitizer. Typically, the increase of surface area by using mesoporous electrodes is about a factor of 1000 in DSCs. TiO_2 still gives the highest efficiencies, but many other metal oxide systems have been tested, such as ZnO, SnO_2, and Nb_2O_5. Besides these simple oxides, ternary oxides, such as $SrTiO_3$ and Zn_2SnO_4, have been investigated, as well as core–shell structures, such as ZnO-coated SnO_2. For recent reviews on the development of nanostructured metal oxide electrodes for DSC, the reader is referred to References 1, 18 and 87–90. During the last few years, large efforts have been made to optimize the morphology of the nanostructured electrode, and a large range of nanostructures has been tested from random assemblies of nanoparticles to organized arrays of nanotubes and single-crystalline nanorods. These studies are motivated by the expectation of an improved and directed charge transport along the rods and tubes and by an improved pore filling of hole conductor materials for sDSC. The general reviews for preparation techniques and structures are given, for example, by Chen *et al.* for TiO_2 [91] and Ozgur *et al.* for ZnO [92].

TiO_2 is a stable, nontoxic oxide that has a high refractive index ($n = 2.4$–2.5) and is widely used as a white pigment in paint, toothpaste, sunscreen, self-cleaning materials, and food (E171). Several crystal forms of TiO_2 occur naturally: rutile, anatase, and brookite. Rutile is thermodynamically the most stable form. Anatase is, however, the preferred structure in DSCs, because it has a larger band gap (3.2 vs. 3.0 eV for rutile) and a higher conduction band edge energy, E_c. This leads to a higher Fermi level and V_{OC} in DSCs for the same conduction band electron concentration.

For state-of-the-art DSCs, the employed architecture of the mesoporous TiO_2 electrode is as follows [Reference 18 and references therein]:

1. A TiO$_2$ blocking layer (thickness <50 nm), coating the fluorine doped tin oxide (FTO) plate to prevent contact between the redox mediator in the electrolyte and the FTO, prepared by chemical bath deposition, spray pyrolysis, or sputtering.
2. A light absorption layer consisting of <10 μm thick film of mesoporous TiO$_2$ with <20 nm particle size that provides a large surface area for sensitizer adsorption and good electron transport to the substrate.
3. A light scattering layer on the top of the mesoporous film, consisting of a <3 μm porous layer containing 400 nm-sized TiO$_2$ particles. Voids of similar size in a mesoporous film can also give effective light scattering.
4. An ultrathin overcoating of TiO$_2$ on the whole structure, deposited by means of chemical bath deposition (using aqueous TiCl$_4$), followed by heat treatment.

1.21.2.4.2 Dyes

As one of the crucial parts in DSCs, the photosensitizer should fulfill some of the following essential characteristics:

1. The absorption spectrum of the photosensitizer should cover the whole visible region and even the part of the near-infrared (NIR).
2. The photosensitizer should have anchoring groups (–COOH, –H$_2$PO$_3$, –SO$_3$H, etc.) to strongly bind the dye onto the semiconductor surface.
3. The excited state level of the photosensitizer should be higher in energy than the conduction band edge of n-type DSCs, so that an efficient electron-transfer process between the excited dye and conduction band of the semiconductor can take place. In contrast, for p-type DSCs, the highest occupied molecular orbital (HOMO) level of the photosensitizer should be at more positive potential than the valence band level of p-type semiconductor.
4. For dye regeneration, the oxidized state level of the photosensitizer must be more positive than the redox potential of electrolyte.
5. Unfavorable dye aggregation on the semiconductor surface should be avoided through optimization of the molecular structure of the dye or by addition of co-adsorbers that prevent aggregation. Dye aggregates can, however, be controlled (H and J aggregates), leading to an improved performance compared with a monomer dye layer as, for example, described in Reference 93.
6. The photosensitizer should be photostable, and electrochemical and thermal stability are also required.

Based on these requirements, many different photosensitizers, including metal complexes, porphyrins, phthalocyanines, and metal-free organic dyes, have been designed and applied to DSCs in the past decades. Ru complexes have since the early days given the best results.

Osmium and iron complexes and other classes of organometallic compounds such as phthalocyanines and porphyrins have also been developed. These dyes have recently been reviewed [18, 94]. Metal-free organic dyes are catching up, showing efficiencies close to 10% with the use of indoline dyes. Moreover, chemically robust organic dyes showing promising stability results have recently been developed by several groups. Organic dyes for DSCs have been reviewed in References 18 and 95.

During the last 2 to 3 years, the advent of heteroleptic ruthenium complexes furnished with an antenna function has taken the performance of the DSC to a new level (see Reference 18 and references therein). An example of these dyes is C101 (**Figure 1**). Compared with the classical N3, N719, and black dye, its extinction coefficient is higher and the spectral response is shifted to the red. Efficiencies above 12% have been reported [17]. The C101 sensitizer maintains, moreover, outstanding stability at efficiency levels more than 9% under light soaking at 60 °C for more than 1000 h [28]. This is achieved by the molecular engineering of the sensitizer, but also very importantly by the use of robust and nonvolatile electrolytes, such as ionic liquids and adequate sealing materials.

A common line of development for organic dyes in DSCs is to synthesize so-called D–π–A dyes that consist of an electron donor (D), a conjugated linker (π), and an electron acceptor (A). The idea behind this concept is that in such molecules, most of the electron density of the HOMO will be located on the donor, while most of the density of the lowest unoccupied molecular orbital (LUMO) will be located on the acceptor. The dyes therefore show intramolecular charge transfer from the donor to the acceptor upon excitation. For typical n-type dyes used in standard DSCs, the anchoring group is located close to or is even part of the acceptor. This ensures that the excited state of the dye is located closer to the TiO$_2$ surface than the hole remaining on the dye after electron injection. This should help to suppress recombination between electrons and oxidized dye molecules and make the hole easily accessible for the redox mediator, which is beneficial for regeneration. A variation of this theme is employed in p-type DSCs, which use a p-type semiconductor (NiO) as a photocathode [96–99]. In these DSCs, a hole is injected into the semiconductor and therefore the anchoring group will now be on the donor of the sensitizer, facilitating hole injection. A p-type DSC can be combined with the conventional n-type DSC into a tandem DSC device (see References 1 and 18 for recent reviews on these systems).

The donor, acceptor, and linker of the molecule can then be independently varied to tune the properties of the molecules [18]. Typically used donors are triphenylamine, indoline, or coumarin units. Examples of acceptors, which include anchoring groups, are cyanoacrylic acid and rhodanine-3-acetic acid. Another modification often made to organic dyes is to introduce alkyl chains to the linker or donor part of the molecule. These can prevent the formation of dye aggregates or inhibit electron and hole recombination by protecting the TiO$_2$ surface. An example of such a dye based on a triphenylamine donor is D35 (**Figure 6**) [100, 101], which has been successfully employed in both liquid-electrolyte and sDSCs.

1.21.2.4.3 Electrolytes

There are many demands on the electrolyte–hole-conducting material. They should be chemically stable; provide good charge transport properties; not dissolve the dye from the oxide surface or the oxide, counter electrode, and substrates; and be compatible with a suitable sealing material to avoid losses by evaporation or leakage. Several types of electrolyte–hole conductor materials have been developed over the years.

The standard redox electrolyte for DSC ever since the very start in 1991 now comprises the iodide–triiodide (I^-/I_3^-) redox couple in an organic solvent. It has good solubility and a suitable redox potential, and it provides rapid dye regeneration. A serious disadvantage of this redox mediator is that a significant part of the potential is lost in the regeneration of the oxidized dye due to intermediate reactions [40]. To develop DSCs with efficiencies significantly larger than 12%, our strategy was to use one-electron redox couples or hole conductors instead of I^-/I_3^-. Unfortunately, the use of one-electron mediators in DSC nearly always leads to strongly increased recombination between electrons in TiO_2 and the oxidized part of the redox couple, which seriously limits the solar cell efficiency. Recently, however, we obtained a breakthrough with cobalt polypyridine-based mediators in combination with the organic dye, D35. Careful matching of the steric bulk of the mediator and the dye molecules minimizes the recombination between electrons in TiO_2 and Co(III) species in the electrolyte and avoids mass transport limitations of the redox mediator. The organic sensitizer D35, equipped with bulky alkoxy groups, efficiently suppresses recombination, allowing the use of cobalt redox mediators with relatively small steric bulk. The best efficiency obtained for a DSC sensitized with D35 and employing a $[Co(bpy)_3]^{3+/2+}$-based electrolyte was 6.7% at full sunlight ($1000\,W\,m^{-2}$ AM1.5G illumination) [5], which is more than a doubling of previously published record efficiencies using similar cobalt-based mediators. We could thus show that the dye layer itself could efficiently suppress the recombination of electrons in the TiO_2 with oxidized species in the electrolyte opening up the possibilities to use alternative redox couples. With the recent world record of 12.3% using Co complexes by Grätzel and co-workers [6, 102], the main direction of the research field is now to explore this path. Interesting results are also currently presented using other redox systems such as organic redox couples [103, 104], ferrocenes [105], and Cu complexes [106].

Alternative redox systems have been developed over the years such as Br^-/Br_3^- [107, 108], $SCN^-/(SCN)_3^-$ [109–111], $SeCN^-/(SeCN)_3^-$ [109–111], and organic redox systems such as TEMPO [112]. For practical applications, it is preferable to use a low-volatility electrolyte system, simplifying production processes, encapsulation methods, and materials. Ionic liquids and gel electrolytes are also normally based on I^-/I_3^- [113, 114]. sDSC [115, 116] have developed quickly using the spiro-MeOTAD hole conductor with efficiencies above 5% and recently above 7% [117], but interesting results are also obtained with conducting polymers such as P3HT [118] and inorganic p-type semiconductors such as CuSCN [119, 120] and CuI [121, 122]. The electrolyte–hole conductor systems have recently been reviewed in Reference 18.

1.21.2.4.4 Counter electrodes

Counter electrodes for DSCs with iodide–triiodide electrolytes can be rather easily prepared by deposition of a thin catalytic layer of platinum onto a conducting glass substrate. Without platinum, conducting tin oxide (SnO_2:F) glass is a very poor counter electrode and has a very high charge-transfer resistance, $>10^6\,\Omega\,cm^2$, in a standard iodide–triiodide electrolyte [123]. Pt can be deposited using a range of methods such as electrodeposition, spray pyrolysis, sputtering, and vapor deposition. Best performance and long-term stability has been achieved with nanoscale Pt clusters prepared by thermal decomposition of platinum chloride compounds [124]. In this case, very low Pt loadings ($5\,\mu g\,cm^{-2}$) are needed so that the counter electrode remains transparent. Charge-transfer resistances of $<1\,\Omega\,cm^2$ can be achieved.

Alternative materials are, for example, carbon, which is suited as a catalyst for the reduction of triiodide [125] and provides good conductivity [126]. Films prepared on TCO substrates from carbon powders and carbon nanotubes showed good catalytic activity for I_3^- reduction as well as good conductivity [126–130]. Conducting polymers have been successfully developed, PEDOT doped with toluenesulfonate anions in particular [131–133]. Recently, metal (Co, W, Mo) sulfides have been identified as suitable catalysts for the I^-/I_3^- redox couple [134–136].

1.21.2.4.5 Development of modules

The manufacturing, reliability, performance, and stability of a DSC module are more complex compared with the test cell situation due to the larger size. Moreover, interconnected cells in a DSC module may interact through, for example, mismatched performance of the cells or unwanted mass transport of electrolyte between adjacent cells. The dominating DSC module designs can be divided into five categories [18] and is schematically shown in **Figure 9**. In the figure caption, the term 'sandwich' is used to define a device structure carrying the working and the counter electrodes on two substrates. The term 'monolithic' is used to define a device structure carrying the working and counter electrode on one and the same substrate. **Figure 10** is an example of a monolithic module prepared at Swerea IVF AB, Sweden. In the present table of record solar cell efficiencies, a DSC module efficiency of 9.9% is listed, achieved by Sony, Japan [2, 4].

As described above, there are many different DSC module designs, substrates, and manufacturing combinations. Our view is that it is still too early to identify a winning combination. Clearly, the monolithic concept offers a cost advantage because only one substrate is used. Likewise, the use of flexible substrates, polymers or metal foils, allow for rapid manufacturing using, for example, roll-to-toll processes. However, the highest module efficiencies have been obtained on glass-based sandwich modules. The performance of the described DSC module designs may be increased by improved device components – for example, TCO glass and dye, or closer packaging of cells, or a less inactive area. The latter can, for the designs utilizing current collectors or interconnects, be

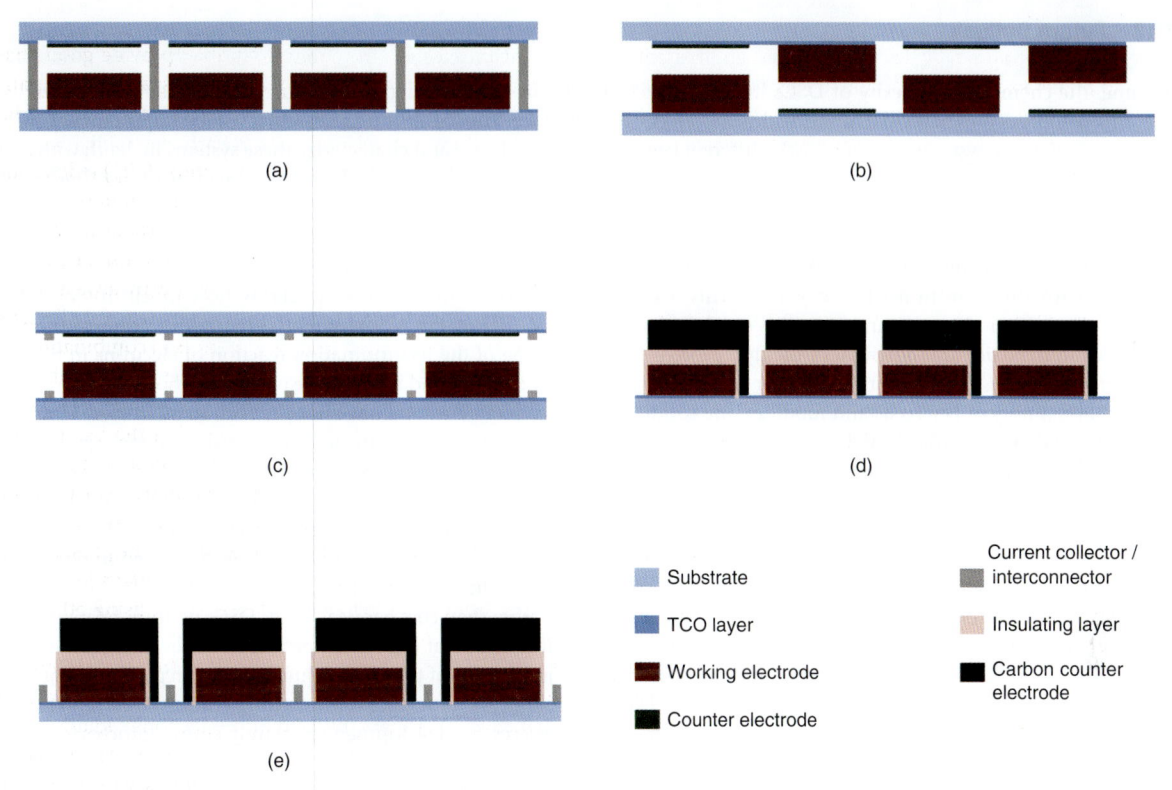

Figure 9 Schematic cross-sections of examples of constructions of the five categories of DSC modules: (a) sandwich Z-interconnection, (b) sandwich W-interconnection, (c) sandwich current collection, (d) monolithic serial connection, and (e) monolithic current collection. Each module consists of four working and counter electrodes. The proportions of the module layers and substrates are not drawn to scale but have been adjusted to illustrate the device constructions. Reprinted with permission from Hagfeldt A, Boschloo G, Sun L, et al. (2010) *Chemical Reviews* 110: 6595. American Chemical Society.

Figure 10 A 900 cm^2 demonstrator consisting of 12 parallel-connected modules that are connected in series. The cell width is 8 mm, and the amount of active area is 75%.

obtained by using an inert combination of electrical conductor and electrolyte. In recent years, various companies have reported such DSC systems. Unfortunately, the DSC technology is not so trivial that the highest module efficiency, the fastest production methods, or the lowest materials cost necessarily provides the best module solution. The big challenge is to produce reliable devices that are long-term stable to fulfill the requirements of the designed application. It may thus be that a winning combination springs from the most functional encapsulation method.

1.21.3 Future Outlook

With time, the chemical complexity of DSCs has become clear, and the main challenge for future research is to understand and master this complexity, in particular at the oxide–dye–electrolyte interface. Thus, for future research, it will be important to carefully select several reference systems that emphasize different key aspects of the device and characterize these systems in depth with all the different techniques we have at hand. From comparisons and modeling, we may then find a better generality of our fundamental understanding.

A challenging but realizable goal for the present DSC technology is to achieve efficiencies above 15%. The new one-electron-based redox couples may significantly lower the voltage drop between the redox system and the oxidized dye, thus pointing out the direction to reach above 15%. This will require electron-transfer studies to clarify how much driving force is needed in the regeneration step and how this can be optimized by tuning of the redox potential by modification of the redox complexes and the oxidation potential of the dye. Moreover, the blocking of the recombination reaction of electrons in the oxide with electrolyte species is an important task for further design of dye molecules and surface passivation methods.

Regarding stability of DSC cells and modules, the conditions for accelerated testing have not yet been standardized. Until now, 1000 h light soaking and 1000 h high-temperature storage tests have mainly been performed to compare materials and to show feasibility of the technology. As the technology advances, the outcome of accelerated testing will also be used to start calculating acceleration factors and estimating product life. Since this is not straightforward, intensified research and development is urgently required to define the procedures for relevant accelerated testing of dye-sensitized solar devices. Especially important is collecting outdoor test results from different locations and application-relevant conditions. The outcome needs to be related to results from accelerated testing to define the key tests for accelerated testing of DSC modules.

For the DSC technology, it is advantageous to compare energy cost rather than cost per peak Watt. DSCs perform relatively better compared with other solar cell technologies under diffuse light conditions and at higher temperatures. An overall goal for future research will thus be to collect data and develop models to make fair judgments of the DSC technology with regard to energy costs.

With the ever-increasing industrial development of the DSC technology, we anticipate some exciting years to come with possible introduction of niche applications such as consumer electronics and successful development of manufacturing processes.

References

[1] Gibson EL and Hagfeldt A (2011) Solar energy materials. In: Bruce DW, O'Hare D, and Walton RI (eds.) *Energy Materials*, ch. 3. Chichester, UK: Wiley.
[2] Green MA, Emery K, Hishikawa Y, and Warta W (2011) *Progress in Photovoltaics: Research and Applications* 19: 565–572.
[3] Koide N, Yamanaka R, and Katayama H (2009) Recent advances of dye-sensitized solar cells and integrated modules at SHARP. *MRS Proceedings* 1211: 1211-R12-02.
[4] Morooka M, Ogura R, Orihashi M, and Takenaka M (2009) Development of dye-sensitized solar cells for practical applications. *Electrochemistry* 77: 960–965.
[5] Feldt SM, Gibson EA, Gabrielsson E, et al. (2010) *Journal of the American Chemical Society* 132: 16714.
[6] Yella A, Lee H-W, Tsao HN, et al. (2011) *Science* 4: 629–634.
[7] Hagfeldt A and Grätzel M (1995) *Chemical Reviews* 95: 49.
[8] Hagfeldt A and Grätzel M (2000) *Accounts of Chemical Research* 33: 269.
[9] Grätzel M (2001) *Nature* 414: 338.
[10] Grätzel M (2005) *Inorganic Chemistry* 44: 6841.
[11] Ardo S and Meyer GJ (2009) *Chemical Society Reviews* 38: 115.
[12] Peter LM (2007) *The Journal of Physical Chemistry C* 111: 6601.
[13] Peter LM (2007) *Physical Chemistry Chemical Physics* 9: 2630.
[14] Bisquert J, Cahen D, Hodes G, et al. (2004) *The Journal of Physical Chemistry B* 108: 8106.
[15] O'Regan BC and Durrant J (2009) *Accounts of Chemical Research* 42: 1799.
[16] Kalyanasundaram K (2010) *Dye-Sensitized Solar Cells*, 1st edn. Lausanne, Switzerland: EPFL Press.
[17] Grätzel M (2009) *Accounts of Chemical Research* 42: 1788.
[18] Hagfeldt A, Boschloo G, Sun L, et al. (2010) *Chemical Reviews* 110: 6595.
[19] Meyer GJ (2010) *ACS Nano* 4: 4337.
[20] McEvoy AJ and Grätzel M (1994) *Solar Energy Materials and Solar Cells* 32: 221.
[21] Gerischer H and Tributsch H (1968) *Berichte Bunsenges Physical Chemistry* 72: 437.
[22] Gerischer H, Michel-Beyerle ME, Rebentrost F, and Tributsch H (1968) *Electrochimica Acta* 13: 1509.
[23] O'Regan B and Grätzel M (1991) *Nature* 353: 737.
[24] Matsumura M, Nomura Y, and Tsubomura H (1977) *Bulletin of the Chemical Society of Japan* 50: 2533.
[25] Alonso N, Beley M, Chartier P, and Ern V (1981) *Journal of Applied Physics* 16: 5.
[26] Desilvestro J, Grätzel M, Kavan L, et al. (1985) *Journal of the American Chemical Society* 107: 2988.
[27] Nazeeruddin MK, Kay A, Rodicio I, et al. (1993) *Journal of the American Chemical Society* 115: 6382.
[28] Kuang DB, Klein C, Ito S, et al. (2007) *Advanced Materials* 19: 1133.
[29] O'Regan B and Schwartz DT (1996) *Journal of Applied Physics* 80: 4749.
[30] Hamann TW, Jensen RA, Martinson ABF, et al. (2008) *Energy & Environmental Science* 1: 66.
[31] Asbury JB, Ellingson RJ, Ghosh HN, et al. (1999) *The Journal of Physical Chemistry B* 103: 3110.
[32] Ramakrishna G, Jose DA, Kumar DK, et al. (2005) *The Journal of Physical Chemistry B* 109: 15445.
[33] Kuang D, Ito S, Wenger B, et al. (2006) *Journal of the American Chemical Society* 128: 4146.
[34] Benkö G, Kallioinen J, Korppi-Tommola JEI, et al. (2002) *Journal of the American Chemical Society* 124: 489.
[35] Koops SE, O'Regan B, Barnes PRF, and Durrant JR (2009) *Journal of the American Chemical Society* 131: 4808.
[36] Wang P, Wenger B, Humphry-Baker R, et al. (2005) *Journal of the American Chemical Society* 127: 6850.
[37] Kuciauskas D, Freund MS, Gray HB, et al. (2001) *The Journal of Physical Chemistry B* 105: 392.

[38] Bauer C, Boschloo G, Mukhtar E, and Hagfeldt A (2002) *The Journal of Physical Chemistry B* 106: 12693.
[39] Clifford JN, Palomares E, Nazeeruddin MK, et al. (2007) *The Journal of Physical Chemistry C* 111: 6561.
[40] Boschloo G and Hagfeldt A (2009) *Accounts of Chemical Research* 42: 1819.
[41] Nusbaumer H, Moser J-E, Zakeeruddin SM, et al. (2001) *The Journal of Physical Chemistry B* 105: 10461.
[42] Nusbaumer H, Zakeeruddin SM, Moser J-E, and Grätzel M (2003) *Chemistry – A European Journal* 9: 3756.
[43] Cazzanti S, Caramori S, Argazzi R, et al. (2006) *Journal of the American Chemical Society* 128: 9996.
[44] Cappel UB, Smeigh AL, Plogmaker S, et al. (2011) *The Journal of Physical Chemistry C* 115: 4345.
[45] Bach U, Tachibana Y, Moser JE, et al. (1999) *Journal of the American Chemical Society* 121: 7445.
[46] Anderson AY, Barnes PRF, Durrant JR, and O'Regan BC (2011) *The Journal of Physical Chemistry C* 115: 2439.
[47] Rowley JG and Meyer GJ (2011) *The Journal of Physical Chemistry C* 115: 6156.
[48] Barnes PRF, Anderson AY, Durrant JR, and O'Regan BC (2011) *Physical Chemistry Chemical Physics* 13: 5798.
[49] Kopidakis N, Schiff EA, Park NG, et al. (2000) *The Journal of Physical Chemistry B* 104: 3930.
[50] Nistér D, Keis K, Lindquist S-E, and Hagfeldt A (2002) *Solar Energy Materials and Solar Cells* 73: 411.
[51] Cao F, Oskam G, and Searson PC (1996) *The Journal of Physical Chemistry* 100: 17021.
[52] Dloczik L, Ileperuma O, Lauermann I, et al. (1997) *The Journal of Physical Chemistry B* 101: 10281.
[53] Forro L, Chauvet O, Emin D, et al. (1994) *Journal of Applied Physics* 75: 633.
[54] van de Lagemaat J and Frank AJ (2000) *The Journal of Physical Chemistry B* 104: 4292.
[55] Bisquert J and Vikhrenko VS (2004) *The Journal of Physical Chemistry B* 108: 2313.
[56] Fisher AC, Peter LM, Ponomarev EA, et al. (2000) *The Journal of Physical Chemistry B* 104: 949.
[57] Bisquert J (2004) *The Journal of Physical Chemistry B* 108: 2323.
[58] Westermark K, Henningsson A, Rensmo H, et al. (2002) *Chemical Physics Letters* 285: 157.
[59] Peter LM (2009) *Accounts of Chemical Research* 42: 1839.
[60] Hendry E, Koeberg M, O'Regan BC, and Bonn M (2006) *Nano Letters* 6: 755.
[61] Moser JE and Grätzel M (1993) *Chemical Physics* 176: 493.
[62] Haque SA, Tachibana Y, Klug DR, and Durrant JR (1998) *The Journal of Physical Chemistry B* 102: 1745.
[63] Kuciauskas D, Freund MS, Gray HB, et al. (2001) *The Journal of Physical Chemistry B* 105: 392.
[64] O'Regan B, Moser J, Anderson M, and Grätzel M (1990) *The Journal of Physical Chemistry* 94: 8720.
[65] Yan SG and Hupp JT (1996) *The Journal of Physical Chemistry* 100: 6867.
[66] Peter LM (2007) *The Journal of Physical Chemistry C* 111: 6601.
[67] O'Regan BC and Durrant JR (2009) *Accounts of Chemical Research* 42: 1799.
[68] Zhu K, Kopidakis N, Neale NR, et al. (2006) *The Journal of Physical Chemistry B* 110: 25174.
[69] Nakade S, Saito Y, Kubo W, et al. (2003) *The Journal of Physical Chemistry B* 107: 8607.
[70] Papageorgiou N, Athanassov Y, Armand M, et al. (1996) *Journal of the Electrochemical Society* 143: 3099.
[71] Kawano R and Watanabe M (2005) *Chemical Communications* 16: 2107.
[72] Zistler M, Wachter P, Wasserscheid P, et al. (2006) *Electrochimica Acta* 52: 161.
[73] Yamanaka N, Kawano R, Kubo W, et al. (2007) *The Journal of Physical Chemistry B* 111: 4763.
[74] Snaith HJ and Grätzel M (2006) *Applied Physics Letters* 89: 262114.
[75] Cappel U Characterization of Organic Dyes for Solid-State Dye-Sensitized Solar Cells. PhD Thesis, Uppsala University.
[76] The TiCl$_4$ treatment leads to the deposition of an ultrapure TiO$_2$ shell (approximately 1 nm) on the mesoporous TiO$_2$ (which may contain impurities or have carbon residues at the surface). The procedure leads to increased dye adsorption, lowers the acceptor levels in TiO$_2$ in energy, which can improve the injection efficiency, and it improves electron lifetime significantly.
[77] Ito S, Murakami TN, Comte P, et al. (2008) *Thin Solid Films* 516: 4613.
[78] Emery KA (2011) Measurement and characterization of solar cells and modules. In: Luque A and Hegedus S (eds.) *Handbook of Photovoltaic Science and Engineering*, 2nd edn., ch. 18, pp. 797–840. W. Sussex, UK: Wiley.
[79] Correspondence with Keith Emery, National Renewable Energy Laboratory, Golden, Colorado, USA.
[80] Kubo W, Sakamoto A, Kitamura T, et al. (2004) *Journal of Photochemistry and Photobiology A* 164: 33.
[81] Halme J, Boschloo G, Hagfeldt A, and Lund P (2008) *The Journal of Physical Chemistry C* 112: 5623.
[82] Barnes PRF, Anderson AY, Koops SE, et al. (2009) *The Journal of Physical Chemistry C* 113: 1126.
[83] Tachibana Y, Hara K, Sayama K, and Arakawa H (2002) *Chemistry of Materials* 14: 2527.
[84] Hagfeldt A and Peter L (2010) Characterization and modeling of dye-sensitized solar cells: A toolbox approach. In: Kalyanasundaram K (ed.) *Dye-Sensitized Solar Cells*. Lausanne, Switzerland: EPFL Press.
[85] Bisquert J and Fabregat-Santiago F (2010) Impedance spectroscopy: A general introduction and application to dye-sensitized solar cells. In: Kalyanasundaram K (ed.) *Dye-Sensitized Solar Cells*. Lausanne, Switzerland: EPFL Press.
[86] Fabregat-Santiago F, Garcia-Belmonte G, Mora-Seró I, and Bisquert J (2011) *Physical Chemistry Chemical Physics* 13: 9083.
[87] Hamann TW, Jensen RA, Martinson ABF, et al. (2008) *Energy & Environmental Science* 1: 66.
[88] Pagliaro M, Palmisano G, Ciriminna R, and Loddo V (2009) *Energy & Environmental Science* 2: 838.
[89] Jose R, Thavasi V, and Ramakrishna S (2009) *Journal of the American Ceramic Society* 92: 289.
[90] Zhang QF, Dandeneau CS, Zhou XY, and Cao GZ (2009) *Advanced Materials* 21: 4087.
[91] Chen X and Mao SS (2007) *Chemical Reviews* 107: 2891.
[92] Ozgur U, Alivov YI, Liu C, et al. (2005) *Journal of Applied Physics* 98: 41301.
[93] Mann JR, Gannon MK, Fitzgibbons TC, et al. (2008) *The Journal of Physical Chemistry C* 112: 13057.
[94] Robertson N (2006) *Angewandte Chemie International Edition* 45: 2338.
[95] Mishra A, Fischer MKR, and Bauerle P (2009) *Angewandte Chemie International Edition* 48: 2474.
[96] He JJ, Lindstrom H, Hagfeldt A, and Lindquist SE (1999) *The Journal of Physical Chemistry B* 103: 8940–8943.
[97] Qin P, Zhu HJ, Edvinsson T, et al. (2008) *Journal of the American Chemical Society* 130: 8570–8571.
[98] Pleux LL, Smeigh AL, Gibson E, et al. (2011) *Energy & Environmental Science* 4: 2075.
[99] Odobel F, Pleux LL, Pellegrin Y, and Blart E (2010) *Accounts of Chemical Research* 43: 1063.
[100] Hagberg DP, Jiang X, Gabrielsson E, et al. (2009) *Journal of Materials Chemistry* 19: 7232.
[101] Jiang X, Marinado T, Gabrielsson E, et al. (2010) *The Journal of Physical Chemistry C* 114: 2799.
[102] Tsao HN, Yi C, Moehl T, et al. (2011) *ChemSusChem* 4: 591.
[103] Wang M, Chamberland N, Breau L, et al. (2010) *Nature Chemistry* 2: 385.
[104] Tian H, Yu Z, Hagfeldt A, et al. (2011) *Journal of the American Chemical Society* 133: 9413.
[105] Daeneke T, Kwon T-H, Holmes AB, et al. (2011) *Nature Chemistry* 3: 211.

[106] Bai Y, Yu Q, Cai N, et al. (2011) *Chemical Communications* 47: 4376.
[107] Ferrere S, Zaban A, and Gregg BA (1997) *The Journal of Physical Chemistry B* 101: 4490.
[108] Wang ZS, Sayama K, and Sugihara H (2005) *The Journal of Physical Chemistry B* 109: 22449.
[109] Oskam G, Bergeron BV, Meyer GJ, and Searson PC (2001) *The Journal of Physical Chemistry B* 105: 6867.
[110] Wang P, Zakeeruddin SM, Moser J-E, et al. (2004) *Journal of the American Chemical Society* 126: 7164.
[111] Bergeron BV, Marton A, Oskam G, and Meyer GJ (2005) *The Journal of Physical Chemistry B* 109: 937.
[112] Zhang Z, Chen P, Murakami TN, et al. (2008) *Advanced Functional Materials* 18: 341.
[113] Gorlov M and Kloo L (2008) *Dalton Transactions* 20: 2655.
[114] Li B, Wang LD, Kang BN, et al. (2006) *Solar Energy Materials and Solar Cells* 90: 549.
[115] Kruger J, Plass R, Cevey L, et al. (2001) *Applied Physics Letters* 79: 2085.
[116] Snaith HJ, Moule AJ, Klein C, et al. (2007) *Nano Letters* 7: 3372.
[117] Burschka J, Dualeh A, Kessler F, et al. (2011) *Journal of the American Chemical Society* 133: 18042.
[118] Jiang KJ, Manseki K, Yu YH, et al. (2009) *Advanced Functional Materials* 19: 2481.
[119] O'Regan B and Schwartz DT (1996) *Journal of Applied Physics* 80: 4749.
[120] Kumara G, Konno A, Senadeera GKR, et al. (2001) *Solar Energy Materials and Solar Cells* 69: 195.
[121] Tennakone K, Kumara G, Kumarasinghe AR, et al. (1995) *Semiconductor Science and Technology* 10: 1689.
[122] Meng QB, Takahashi K, Zhang XT, et al. (2003) *Langmuir* 19: 3572.
[123] Hauch A and Georg A (2001) *Electrochimica Acta* 46: 3457.
[124] Papageorgiou N, Maier WF, and Grätzel M (1997) *Journal of the Electrochemical Society* 144: 876.
[125] Kay A and Grätzel M (1996) *Solar Energy Materials and Solar Cells* 44: 99.
[126] Pettersson H, Gruszecki T, Bernhard R, et al. (2007) *Progress in Photovoltaics* 15: 113.
[127] Murakami TN, Ito S, Wang Q, et al. (2006) *Journal of the Electrochemical Society* 153: A2255.
[128] Ramasamy E, Lee WJ, Lee DY, and Song JS (2007) *Applied Physics Letters* 90: 173103.
[129] Imoto K, Takahashi K, Yamaguchi T, et al. (2003) *Solar Energy Materials and Solar Cells* 79: 459.
[130] Suzuki K, Yamaguchi M, Kumagai M, and Yanagida S (2003) *Chemistry Letters* 32: 28.
[131] Bay L, West K, Winther-Jensen B, and Jacobsen T (2006) *Solar Energy Materials and Solar Cells* 90: 341.
[132] Saito Y, Kitamura T, Wada Y, and Yanagida S (2002) *Chemistry Letters* 31: 1060.
[133] Saito Y, Kubo W, Kitamura T, et al. (2004) *Journal of Photochemistry and Photobiology A* 164: 153.
[134] Wang M, Anghel AM, Marsan B, et al. (2009) *Journal of the American Chemical Society* 131: 15976.
[135] Wu M, Lin X, Hagfeldt A, and Ma T (2011) *Chemical Communications* 47: 4535.
[136] Wu M, Lin X, Hagfeldt A, and Ma T (2011) *Angewandte Chemie International Edition* 50: 3520.

1.22 Multiple Junction Solar Cells

M Yamaguchi, Toyota Technological Institute, Tempaku, Nagoya, Japan

© 2012 Elsevier Ltd. All rights reserved.

1.22.1	Introduction	497
1.22.2	Key Issues for Realizing High-Efficiency MJ Solar Cells	498
1.22.2.1	Selection of Cell Materials and Improving Quality	498
1.22.2.2	Lattice Matching Between Cell Materials and Substrates	500
1.22.2.3	Effectiveness of Wide Bandgap Back-Surface-Field Layer	501
1.22.2.4	Low-Loss Tunnel Junction for Intercell Connection and Preventing Impurity Diffusion from Tunnel Junction	502
1.22.3	High-Efficiency InGaP/GaAs/Ge 3-Junction Solar Cells and their Space Applications	503
1.22.3.1	Development of High-Efficiency InGaP/GaAs/Ge 3-Junction Solar Cells	503
1.22.3.1.1	Wide bandgap tunnel junction	504
1.22.3.1.2	Heteroface structure Ge bottom cell	504
1.22.3.1.3	Precise lattice matching to Ge substrate	504
1.22.3.2	Radiation Resistance of InGaP-Based MJ Solar Cells	505
1.22.3.3	Space Applications of InGaP/GaAs/Ge 3-Junction Solar Cells	506
1.22.4	Low-Cost Potential of Concentrator MJ Solar Cell Modules and High-Efficiency Concentrator InGaP/GaAs/Ge 3-Junction Solar Cell Modules and Terrestrial Applications	506
1.22.5	Most Recent Results of MJ Cells	509
1.22.6	Future Directions	509
Acknowledgments		513
References		514

1.22.1 Introduction

Multi-junction (MJ, Tandem) solar cells are composed of multilayers with different bandgap energies; an example is shown in **Figure 1**. They have the potential for achieving high conversion efficiencies of over 50% and are promising for space and terrestrial applications due to their wide photo response. **Figure 2** shows theoretical conversion efficiencies of single-junction and MJ solar cells in comparison with experimentally realized efficiencies.

Tandem solar cells were proposed in 1955 by Jackson [1] and in 1960 by Wolf [2]. **Table 1** shows progress of the III–V compound MJ solar cell technologies. The MIT group [3] encouraged R&D of tandem cells based on their computer analysis. Although AlGaAs/GaAs tandem cells, including tunnel junctions and metal interconnectors, were developed in the early years, a high efficiency close to 20% was not obtained [4]. This is because of difficulties in making high-performance and stable tunnel junctions, and the defects related to the oxygen in the AlGaAs materials [5]. A double-hetero (DH) structure tunnel junction was found to be useful for preventing diffusion from the tunnel junction and improving the tunnel junction performance by the authors [6]. The authors demonstrated 20.2% efficiency AlGaAs/GaAs 2-junction cells [7]. An InGaP material for the top cell was proposed by the NREL group [8]. As a result of performance improvements in tunnel junction and top cell, over 30% efficiency has been obtained with InGaP/GaAs 2-junction cells by the authors [9].

InGaP/GaAs-based MJ solar cells have drawn increased attention for space applications because of the superior radiation resistance of InGaP top cells and materials, as has been discovered by the authors [10]; in addition, they also have the possibility of reaching high conversion efficiency of over 30%. In fact, the commercial satellite (HS 601HP) with 2-junction GaInP/GaAs-on-Ge solar cell arrays was launched in 1997 [11].

More recently, InGaP/GaAs-based MJ solar cells have drawn increased attention for terrestrial applications because concentrator operation of MJ cells has great potential of providing high-performance and low-cost solar cell modules. For concentrator applications, the cell contact grid structure has been designed in order to reduce the energy loss due to series resistance, and 38.9% (AM1.5G, 489 suns) efficiency has been demonstrated by Sharp [12]. Most recently, 41.6% efficiency has been reported with InGaP/GaAs/Ge 3-junction concentrator cells by Spectrolab [13]. In addition, the authors have realized high-efficiency and large-area (5445 cm^2) concentrator InGaP/InGaAs/Ge 3-junction solar cell modules of an outdoor efficiency of 31.5% [14] as a result of developing high-efficiency InGaP/InGaAs/Ge 3-junction cells, low-optical-loss Fresnel lens and homogenizers, and designing low-thermal-conductivity modules. Some companies including Sharp [15] have announced to commercialize InGaP/GaAs/Ge 3-junction concentrator cell modules for terrestrial use.

Liquid-phase epitaxy (LPE) was used to fabricate GaAs single-junction solar cells in the 1960s and 1970s because it produces high-quality epitaxial film and has a simple growth system. However, it is not as useful for devices that involve multilayers because of difficulty of control over layer thickness, doping, composition, and speed of throughput. Since 1977, metal-organic chemical vapor deposition (MOCVD) has been used to fabricate large-area, GaAs single-junction solar cells and recent MJ solar cells because it is capable of large-scale, large-area production and has good reproducibility and controllability. Molecular beam epitaxy (MBE) and

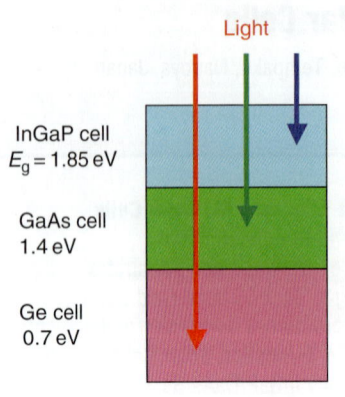

Figure 1 A schematic structure of a multilayer solar cell, illustrating that high-energy light is absorbed by the top cell (InGaP), medium energy by the middle cell (GaAs), and low energy by the bottom cell (Ge).

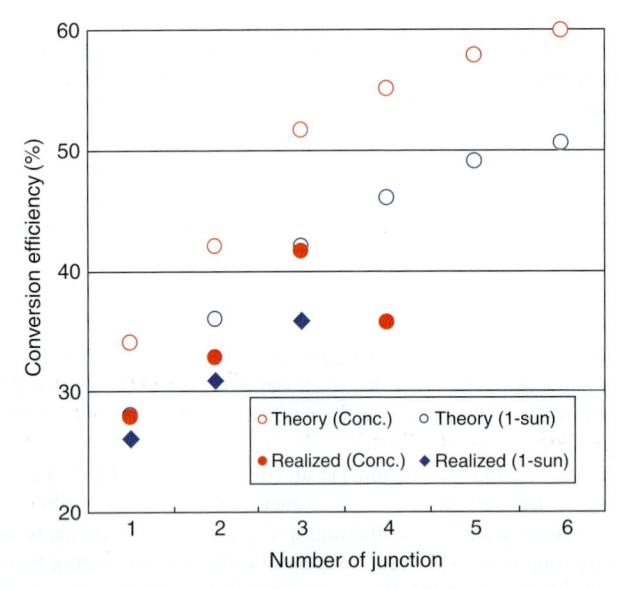

Figure 2 Theoretical conversion efficiencies of single-junction and multi-junction solar cells in comparison with experimentally realized efficiencies for 1-sun intensity and under concentration.

chemical beam epitaxy (CBE) have been used for laboratory stage's research and development of MJ solar cells because they provide excellent of monolayer abruptness and thickness due to the nature of beam. Especially, CBEs [16] are advantages of realizing new materials such as III–V-N materials and solar cells and novel multilayer structures such as quantum nanostructure solar cells.

1.22.2 Key Issues for Realizing High-Efficiency MJ Solar Cells

The key issues for realizing high-efficiency MJ tandem cells are discussed based on results obtained in our laboratory.

1.22.2.1 Selection of Cell Materials and Improving Quality

MJ cells with different bandgaps are stacked in tandem (see **Figure 1**) so that the cells cover a wide wavelength region from 300 to 1800 nm. Cell materials are selected by considering bandgap energies close to the optimal bandgap energy combination based on theoretical efficiency calculation, by considering lattice matching to substrates, and by less impurity problems such as high-concentration residual impurities and impurities acting as recombination centers. **Figure 3** shows minority-carrier diffusion length dependence of GaAs single-junction solar cell efficiency. It is clear that a high minority-carrier diffusion length, L (minority-carrier lifetime, $\tau = L^2/D$, where D is the minority-carrier diffusion coefficient) is substantially necessary to realize high-efficiency solar cells. **Figure 4** shows carrier concentration dependence of minority-carrier lifetime in p-type and n-type GaAs [17]. Minority-carrier lifetime τ depends on carrier concentration N of solar cell layers as expressed by

Table 1 Progress of the III–V compound multi-junction solar cell technologies

1955		*Jackson*
1960	*Proposal of multi-junction solar cell*	*Wolf*
1982	Efficiency calculation of tandem cells	MIT
1982	15.1% AlGaAs/GaAs 2-junction (2-J) cell	RTI
1987	Proposal of double-hetero structure tunnel junction for multi-junction interconnection	NTT
1987	20.2% AlGaAs/GaAs 2-J cell	NTT
1989	32.6% GaAs//GaSb concentrator 2-J cell (mechanical-stacked, 100 suns concentration)	Boeing
1990	Proposal of InGaP as top a cell material	NREL
1990	27.3% InGaP/GaAs 2-J cell	NREL
1996	30.3% InGaP/GaAs 2-J cell	Jpn. Energy
1997	Discovery of radiation resistance of InGaP top cell	Toyota Tech. Inst.
1997	33.3% InGaP/GaAs//InGaAs 3-J cell (mechanical-stacked)	Jpn. Energy, Sumitomo & Toyota Tech. Inst.
1997	Commercial satellite with 2-J cells	Hughes
2000	31.7% InGaP/InGaAs/Ge 3-J cell	Jpn. Energy
2003	37.4% InGaP/InGaAs/Ge 3-J cell (200 suns concentration)	Sharp
2004	38.9% InGaP/InGaAs/Ge 3-J cell (489 suns concentration)	Sharp & Toyota T.I.
2006	31.5% large-area (5445 cm^2) InGaP/InGaAs/Ge 3-J cell module (outdoor)	Daido Steel, Daido Metal, Sharp &Toyota T.I.
2006	40.7% InGaP/GaAs/Ge 3-J cell (236 suns concentration)	Spectrolab
2009	41.1% InGaP/InGaAs/Ge 3-J cell (454 suns concentration)	Fraunhofer ISE
2009	41.6% InGaP/InGaAs/Ge 3-J cell (364 suns concentration)	Spectrolab
2009	35.8% InGaP/GaAs/InGaAs 3-J cell (1 sun)	Sharp

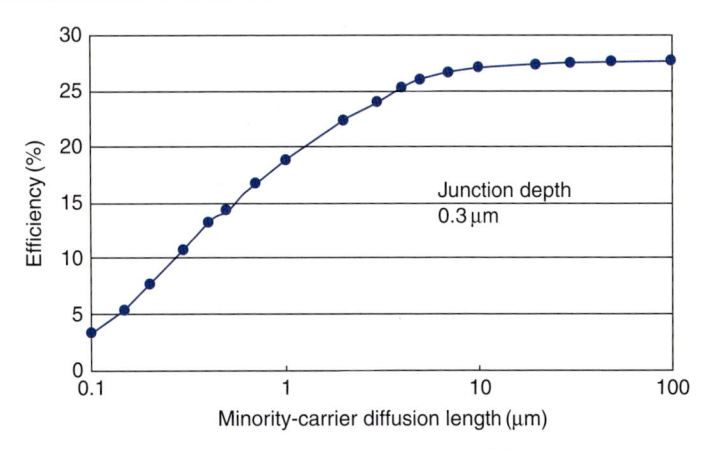

Figure 3 Minority-carrier diffusion length dependence of GaAs single-junction solar cell efficiency.

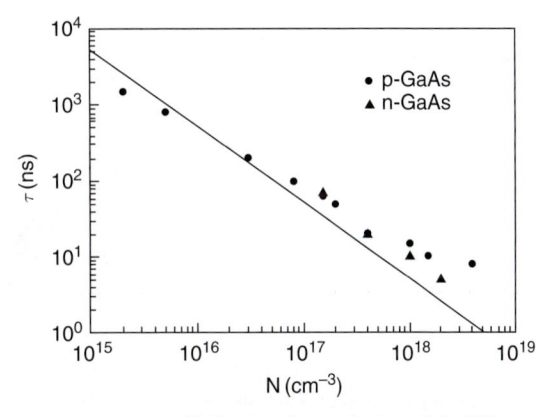

Figure 4 Carrier concentration dependence of minority-carrier lifetime in p-type and n-type GaAs [17].

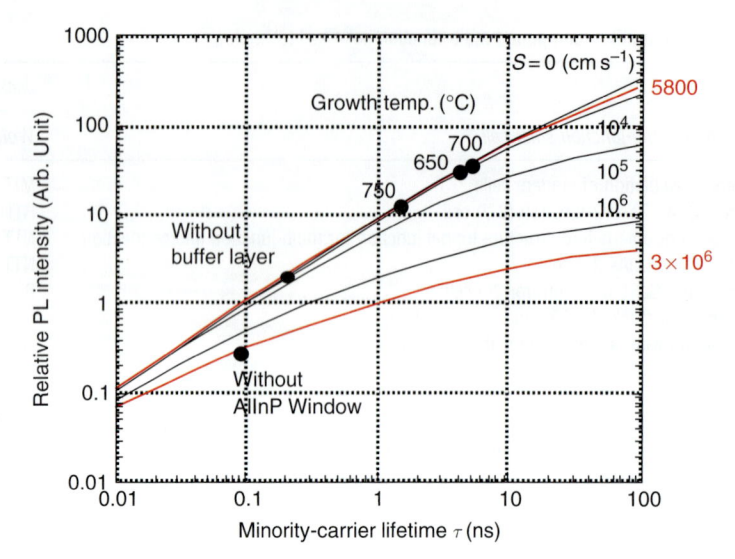

Figure 5 Changes in photoluminescence (PL) intensity of the solar cell active layer as a function of the minority-carrier lifetime in GaAs, grown by MOCVD and surface recombination velocity (S).

$$\tau = \frac{1}{BN} \qquad [1]$$

where B is the radiative recombination coefficient. Therefore, carrier concentration of cell layers must be optimized by considering minority-carrier lifetime, build-in potential and series resistance of p-n junction diodes.

Selection of cell materials, especially selection of top cell materials, is also important for high-efficiency tandem cells. It has been found by the authors [5] that an oxygen-related defect in the AlGaAs top cell materials acts as a recombination centre. As a top cell material lattice matched to GaAs or Ge substrates, InGaP has some advantages [8] such as lower interface recombination velocity, a lower oxygen-related defect, and a good window layer material compared to AlGaAs. The top cell characteristics depend on the minority-carrier lifetime in the top cell layers. **Figure 5** shows changes in photoluminescence (PL) intensity of the solar cell active layer as a function of the minority-carrier lifetime τ of the p-InGaP base layer grown by MOCVD and surface recombination velocity (S). The lowest S was obtained by introducing an AlInP window layer and the highest τ was obtained by introducing a buffer layer and optimizing the growth temperature. The best conversion efficiency of the InGaP single-junction cell was 18.5% [18].

1.22.2.2 Lattice Matching Between Cell Materials and Substrates

Lattice mismatching of cell materials to substrates should be decreased because miss-fit dislocations are generated in the upper cell layers due to lattice mismatch, which deteriorates cell efficiency. **Figure 6** shows calculated and experimental dislocation density

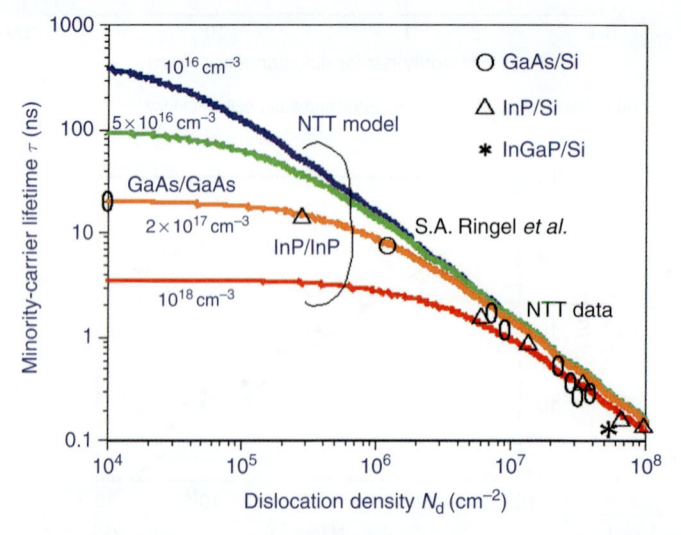

Figure 6 Calculated and experimental dislocation density dependence of minority-carrier lifetime in GaAs, InP, and InGaP. NTT model (eqn [2]), NTT data and Ringel's data refer to references 19–21, respectively.

dependence of minority-carrier lifetime in GaAs [19]. Dislocation density N_d dependence of minority-carrier lifetime τ is expressed by the following equation [19]:

$$\frac{1}{\tau} = \frac{1}{\tau_r} + \frac{1}{\tau_0} + \frac{\pi^3 DN_d}{4} \qquad [2]$$

where τ_r is radiative recombination lifetime, τ_0 is minority-carrier lifetime associated with recombination at other unknown defects, and D is the minority-carrier diffusion coefficient.

Application of InGaAs middle cell [22] lattice matched to Ge substrates has been demonstrated to increase open-circuit voltage (V_{oc}) due to lattice matching and short-circuit current density (J_{sc}) due to decrease in bandgap energy of the middle cell.

1.22.2.3 Effectiveness of Wide Bandgap Back-Surface-Field Layer

Figure 7 shows the surface recombination effect on short-circuit current density J_{sc} of $In_{0.14}Ga_{0.86}As$ homo-junction solar cells as a function of junction depth; an optimum (29 mA cm^{-2}) exists for surface recombination velocity of 10^4 cm s^{-1} and a junction depth of ~0.5 μm. Therefore, in order to improve efficiency drop attributed from front and rear surface, recombination formation of heteroface or DH structure is necessary. **Figure 8** shows changes in V_{oc} and J_{sc} of InGaP single-junction cells as a function of potential barrier ΔE. A wide bandgap back-surface-field (BSF) layer [22] is found to be most effective for confinement of minority carriers compared to highly doped BSF layers.

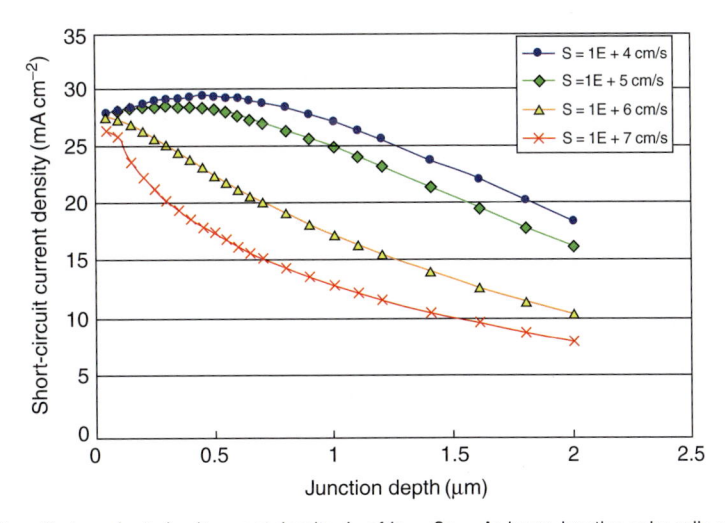

Figure 7 Surface recombination effect on short-circuit current density J_{sc} of $In_{0.14}Ga_{0.86}As$ homo-junction solar cells as a function of junction depth.

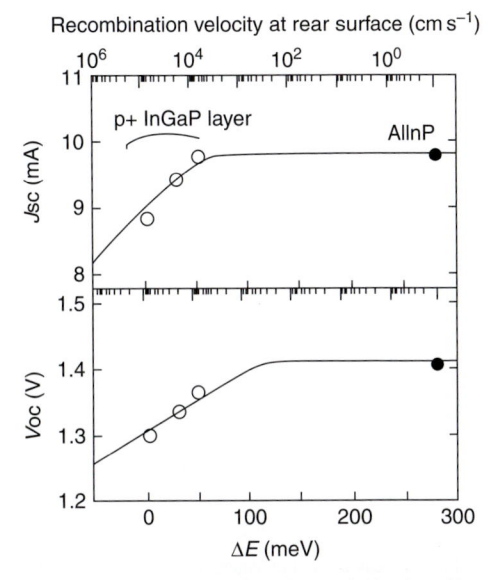

Figure 8 Changes in V_{oc} and J_{sc} of InGaP single-junction cells as a function of potential barrier ΔE.

1.22.2.4 Low-Loss Tunnel Junction for Intercell Connection and Preventing Impurity Diffusion from Tunnel Junction

Another important issue for realizing high-efficiency monolithic-cascade-type tandem cells is the achievement of optically and electrically low-loss interconnection of two or more cells. A degenerately doped tunnel junction is attractive because it involves only one extra step in the growth process. To minimize optical absorption and achieve higher J_{sc} for bottom cell as shown in **Figure 9**, formation of thin and wide bandgap tunnel junctions is necessary. However, the formation of a wide bandgap tunnel junction is very difficult because the tunneling current decreases exponentially with increase in bandgap energy.

In addition, impurity diffusion from a highly doped tunnel junction during overgrowth of the top cell increases the resistivity of the tunnel junction. As shown in **Figure 10**, a DH structure was found to be useful for preventing diffusion by the authors [6]. An InGaP tunnel junction has been for the first time tried for an InGaP/GaAs tandem cell in our work [9]. As p-type and n-type dopants Zn and Si were used, respectively. The peak tunneling current of the InGaP tunnel junction is found to increase from 5 mA cm^{-2} up to 2 A cm^{-2} by making a DH structure with AlInP barriers. Effective suppression of the Zn diffusion from the tunnel junction by the InGaP tunnel junction with the AlInP DH structure is thought to be attributed to the lower diffusion coefficient [23] for Zn in the wider bandgap energy materials such as the AlInP barrier layer and InGaP tunnel junction layer. Therefore, the InGaP tunnel junction has been observed to be very effective for obtaining high tunneling current, and the DH structure has also been confirmed to be useful for preventing diffusion.

Table 2 summarizes key issues of realizing super high-efficiency MJ solar cells.

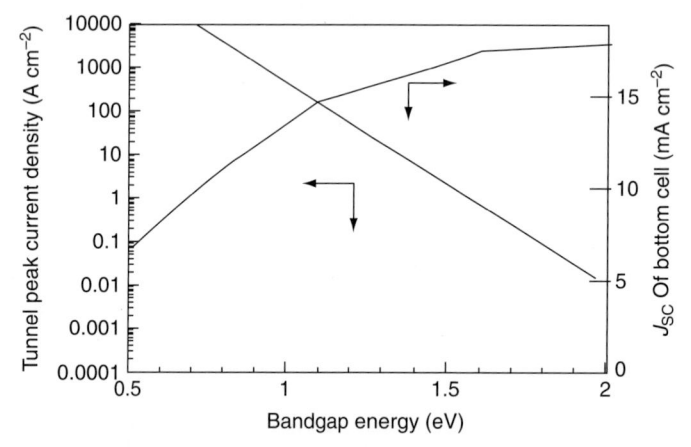

Figure 9 Calculated tunnel peak current density and short-circuit current density J_{sc} of GaAs bottom cell as a function of bandgap energy of tunnel junction.

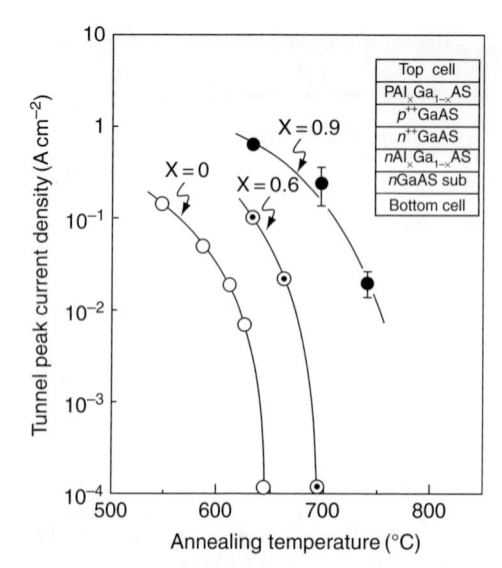

Figure 10 Annealing temperature dependence of tunnel peak current densities for double-hetero structure tunnel diodes. X is the Al mole fraction in Al$_x$Ga$_{1-x}$As barrier layers.

Table 2 Key issues for realizing super high-efficiency multi-junction solar cells

Key issue	Past	Present	Future
Top cell materials	AlGaAs	InGaP	AlInGaP
Third cell materials	None	Ge	InGaAsN, etc.
Substrate	GaAs	Ge	Si
Tunnel junction	DH-structure GaAs tunnel junction (TJ)	DH-structure InGaP TJ	DH-structure InGaP or GaAs TJ
Lattice matching	GaAs middle cell	InGaAs middle cell	(In)GaAs middle cell
Carrier confinement	InGaP-BSF	AlInP-BSF	Widegap-BSF; Quantum Dots (QDs)
Photon confinement	None	None	Bragg reflector, QDs, etc.
Others	None	Inverted Epi. (Epi. from top cell to bottom cell layers)	Inverted Epi.; Epitaxial lift off (peeled thin film off technique)

1.22.3 High-Efficiency InGaP/GaAs/Ge 3-Junction Solar Cells and their Space Applications

1.22.3.1 Development of High-Efficiency InGaP/GaAs/Ge 3-Junction Solar Cells

As one of the projects in the Sunshine Program in Japan, an R&D project for super high-efficiency MJ solar cells was started in 1990. Conversion efficiency of InGaP/GaAs-based MJ solar cells has been improved by the following technologies:

1. Selection and high-quality growth of InGaP as a top cell material.
2. Proposal of DH structure and wide bandgap tunnel junction for cell interconnection.
3. Precise lattice matching of InGaP top cell and InGaAs middle cell with Ge substrate.
4. Proposal of AlInP as a BSF layer for the InGaP top cell.
5. Proposal of InGaP-Ge heteroface structure bottom cell.

As a result of the above proposals and performance improvements, we have demonstrated a world-record efficiency (33.3% at 1-sun AM1.5G) of InGaP/GaAs/InGaAs 3-junction solar cells in 1997 [24]. The conversion efficiency of InGaP/(In)GaAs/Ge 3-junction solar cells has been improved to 31.7% (AM1.5G) [25]. A schematic illustration of the InGaP/(In)GaAs/Ge 3-junction solar cell and key technologies for improving conversion efficiency are shown in **Figure 11**.

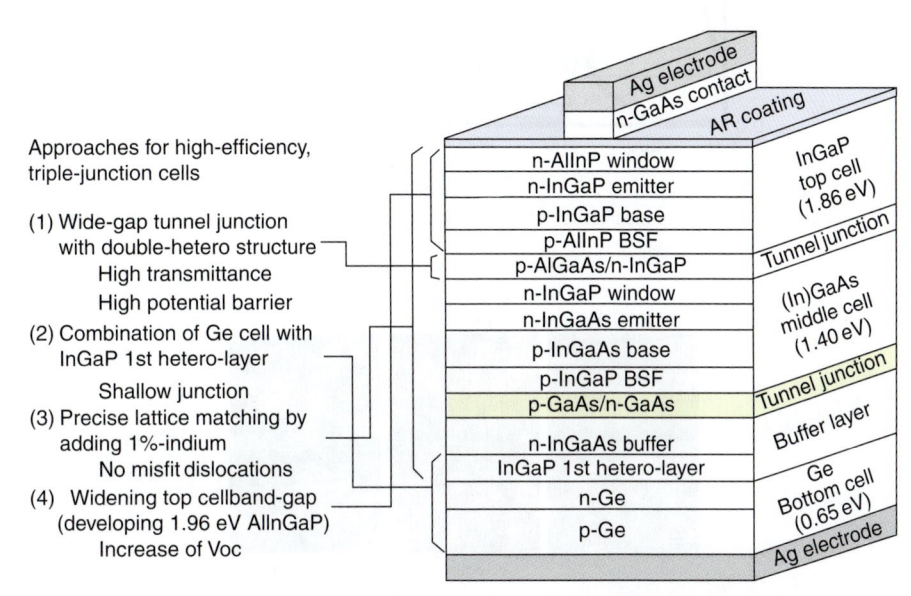

Figure 11 Schematic illustration of a 3-junction cell and approaches for improving the efficiency of the cell.

1.22.3.1.1 Wide bandgap tunnel junction

A wide bandgap tunnel junction, which consists of a DH structure p-Al(Ga)InP/p-AlGaAs/n-(Al)InGaP/n-Al(Ga)InP, increases the amount of incident light into the (In)GaAs middle cell and produces effective potential barriers for both minority carriers generated in the top and middle cells. Both V_{oc} and I_{sc} of the cells are improved by the wide bandgap tunnel junction without absorption and recombination losses [9]. It is difficult to obtain a high-tunneling peak current with wide gap tunnel junction, so thinning the depletion layer width by formation of a highly doped junction is quite necessary. Since impurity diffusion occurs during growth of the top cell [6], both carbon and silicon having a low-diffusion coefficient are used for p-type AlGaAs and n-type (Al)InGaP, respectively. Furthermore, the DH structure supposes to suppress impurity diffusion from the highly doped tunnel junction [23]. The second tunnel junction between the middle and bottom cells consists of p-InGaP/p-(In)GaAs/n-(In)GaAs/n-InGaP, which has a wider bandgap than the middle-cell materials.

1.22.3.1.2 Heteroface structure Ge bottom cell

InGaP/GaAs cell layers are grown on a p-type Ge substrate. A p–n junction is formed automatically during MOCVD growth by diffusion of the V-group atom from the first layer grown on the Ge substrate. So, the material of the first hetero layer is important for the performance of the Ge bottom cell. An InGaP layer is thought to be suitable as material for the first hetero layer, because phosphor has a lower-diffusion coefficient in Ge than arsenic and indium has a lower solubility in Ge than gallium. **Figure 12** shows the change in spectral response of the 3-junction cell by changing the first hetero growth layer on Ge from GaAs to InGaP. The quantum efficiency of the Ge bottom cell was improved by using the InGaP hetero-growth layer. In the case of the GaAs hetero-growth layer, the junction depth was measured to be around 1 μm. On the other hand, the thickness of the n-type layer produced by phosphor from the InGaP layer was 0.1 μm. An increase in Ge quantum efficiency was confirmed to be due to a reduction in junction depth.

1.22.3.1.3 Precise lattice matching to Ge substrate

Although the 0.08% lattice mismatch between GaAs and Ge is thought to be negligibly small, misfit dislocations are found to be generated in thick GaAs layers, which deteriorate cell performance. By adding about 1% indium into the InGaP/GaAs cell layers, all cell layers are lattice matched precisely to the Ge substrate. As a result, crosshatch pattern caused by misfit dislocations due to lattice mismatch disappeared in the surface morphology of the cell with 1% indium, as shown in **Figure 13**. The misfit dislocations were found to influence the V_{oc} of the cell and not the I_{sc}. V_{oc} was improved by eliminating misfit dislocations for the cell with 1% indium. In addition, wavelength of the absorption edge became longer and I_{sc} of both the top and middle cells increased by adding 1% indium.

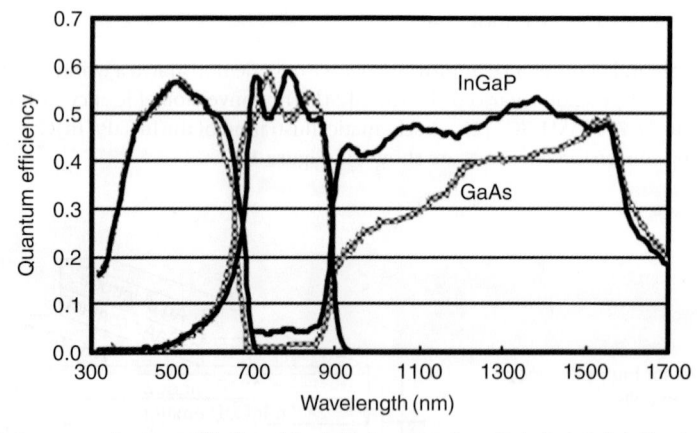

Figure 12 Change in the spectral response due to modification of the 1st hetero layer from GaAs to InGaP (without antireflection coating).

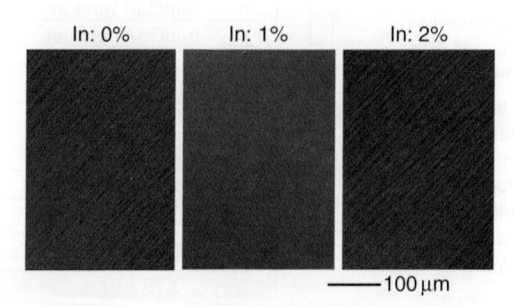

Figure 13 Surface morphology of InGaAs with various indium compositions grown on Ge.

1.22.3.2 Radiation Resistance of InGaP-Based MJ Solar Cells

Since radiation in space is severe, particularly in the Van Allen radiation belt, lattice defects are induced in semiconductors due to high-energy electron and proton irradiations, and the defects cause a decrease in the output power of solar cells. **Figure 14** shows effectiveness of radiation resistance and high conversion efficiency of space cells from the point view of power density (W m^{-2}) for space missions. Further improvements in conversion efficiency and radiation resistance of space cells are necessary for widespread applications of space missions. Recently, InGaP/GaAs-based MJ solar cells have drawn increased attention because of the possibility of high conversion efficiency of over 40% and radiation resistance. An AM0 efficiency of 29.2% has been demonstrated for an InGaP/InGaAs/Ge 3-junction cell (4 cm^2) [12].

Figure 15 shows the maximum power recovery due to light illumination of 100 mW cm^{-2} at various temperatures for 1-MeV electron-irradiated InGaP/GaAs tandem cells [10]. The ratios of maximum power after injection, P_I, to maximum power before irradiation, P_0, are shown as a function of injection time. Even at room temperature, photo injection-enhanced annealing of radiation damage to InGaP/GaAs tandem cells was observed. The recovery ratio increases with an increase in ambient temperature within the operating range for space use. Such a recovery is found to be attributed from damage recovery in the InGaP top cell layer [10]. Therefore, the results show that InGaP/GaAs tandem cells under device operation conditions have superior radiation-resistant properties.

Figure 16 shows deep level transient spectroscopy (DLTS) spectra of Trap H2 (Ev + 0.55 eV) for various injection times at 25 °C with an AM1.5 light intensity of 100 mA cm^{-2}. It is also found [26] by DLTS measurements that a major defect level H2 (Ev + 0.55 eV) recovers by forward bias or light illumination, that is, the signal decreases with prolonged light exposure. Moreover, the H2 center is confirmed to act as a recombination center by using the double carrier pulse DLTS method. The enhancement of defect annealing in InGaP top cell layer under minority-carrier injection conditions is thought to occur as a result of the nonradiative electron-hole recombination process [27] whose energy E_R enhances the defect motion. The thermal activation energy E_A (1.1 eV) of the defect is reduced to E_I (0.48–0.54 eV) by an amount E_R (0.56–0.62 eV). Thus, electronic energy from a recombination event can be channeled into the lattice vibration mode that drives the defect motion: $E_I = E_A - E_R$.

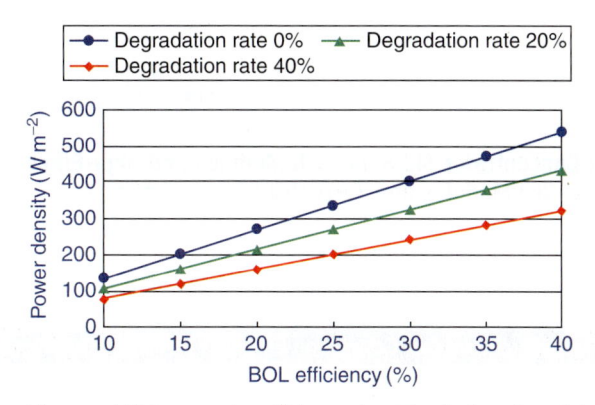

Figure 14 Effectiveness of radiation resistance and high conversion efficiency of space cells from the point view of power density (BOL = beginning of life).

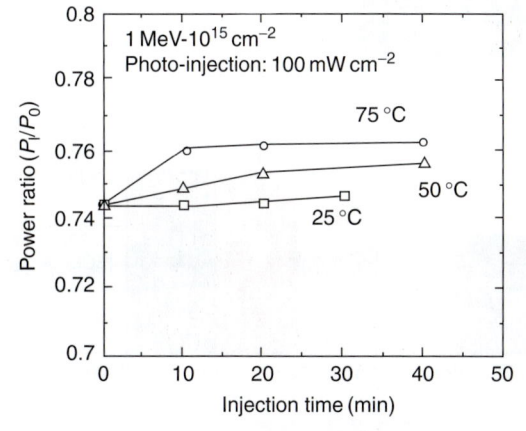

Figure 15 The maximum power recovery of the InGaP/GaAs tandem cell due to light illumination at various temperatures.

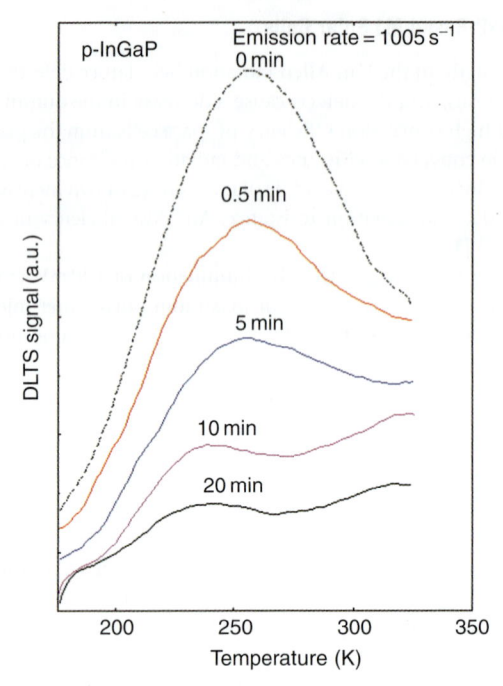

Figure 16 DLTS spectrum of Trap H2 (Ev + 0.55 eV) for various injection times at 25 °C with an injection density of 100 mA cm^{-2}.

1.22.3.3 Space Applications of InGaP/GaAs/Ge 3-Junction Solar Cells

Advanced technologies for high-efficiency cells and discovery of superior radiation resistance of InGaP-based materials are thought to contribute to industrialization of InGaP-based MJ space solar cells in Japan. **Figure 17** shows the Sharp space solar cell conversion efficiency heritage. Since 2002, InGaP/GaAs/Ge 3-junction solar cells have been commercialized for space use in Japan.

1.22.4 Low-Cost Potential of Concentrator MJ Solar Cell Modules and High-Efficiency Concentrator InGaP/GaAs/Ge 3-Junction Solar Cell Modules and Terrestrial Applications

Concentrator operation is very effective for cost reduction of solar cell modules and thus also of photovoltaic (PV) systems. **Figure 18** shows a configuration of a concentrator PV (CPV) system composed of a solar cell, optics, and tracker. Concentrator

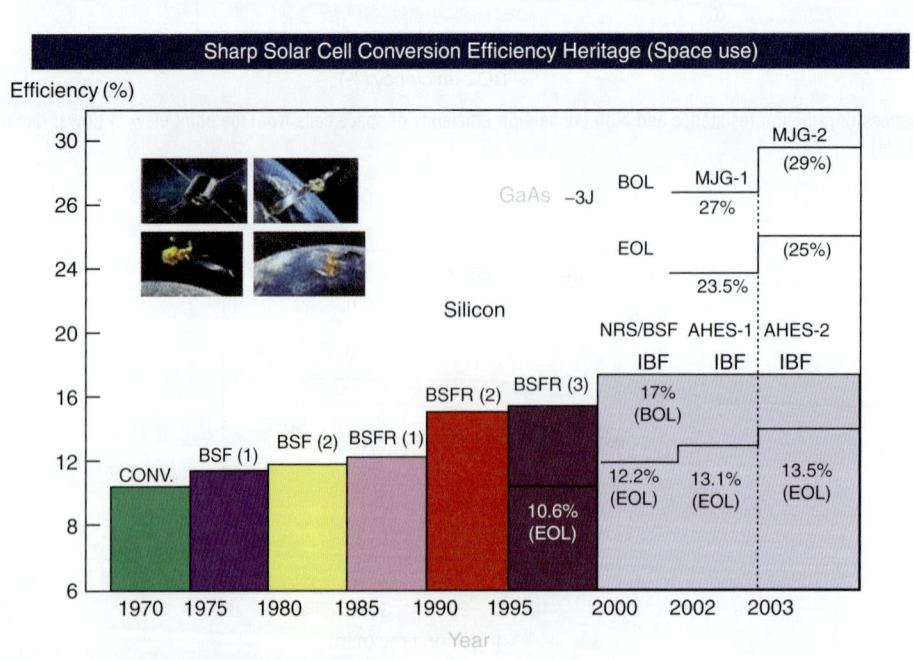

Figure 17 Sharp space solar cell conversion efficiency heritage.

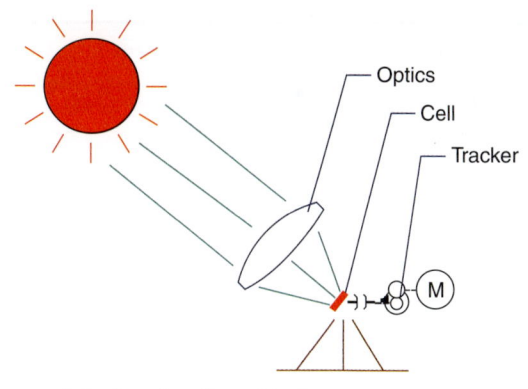

Figure 18 Configuration of PV system composed of solar cell, optics and tracker.

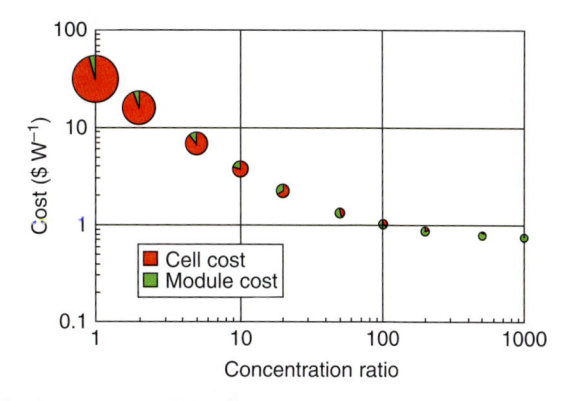

Figure 19 Summary of estimated cost for the concentrator PV systems vs. concentration ratio [28].

operation of the MJ cells is essential for economic viability of their terrestrial applications. Since CPV systems using MJ solar cells have great potential of cost reduction as shown in **Figure 19** [28], R&D on concentrator technologies including MJ cells was started in Japan.

In order to apply a high-efficiency MJ cell developed for 1-sun condition to a concentrator cell operating under ~500-sun condition, reduction in energy loss due to series resistance is the most important issue. Cell size was designed to be 7 × 7 mm considering the total current flow. Grid electrode pitching, height, and width were designed in order to reduce series resistance. **Figure 20** shows the fill factor (FF) of the cell with various grid pitchings under 250 suns. The grid electrode with 5 μm height and 5 μm width was made of Ag. Grid pitching influences lateral resistance between two grids (R_L) and total electrodes resistance (R_E). Series resistance of the cell (R_s), R_E, and R_L are also shown in **Figure 20**. R_E was measured directly after removing electrode from the cell by chemical etching. R_L was calculated by using the sheet resistance of window and emitter layers. Based on the data in **Figure 20**, the best grid pitching is determined to be 0.12 mm at this time. In order to reduce series resistance down to 0.01 Ω and obtain high FF under 500 suns, grid height should be increased twofold. High efficiency under < 500 suns can be obtained by an optimal grid design without modification of the cell layer.

For concentrator applications, the grid structure has been designed in order to reduce the energy loss due to series resistance as was shown in **Figure 20**. Most recently, we have successfully fabricated high-efficiency concentrator InGaP/InGaAs/Ge 3-junction solar cells designed for 500-sun application. The efficiencies by in-house measurements are 39.2 % at 200 suns and 38.9% at 489 suns as shown in **Figure 21** [12]. The solar simulator was equipped with both a Xe lamp and a halogen lamp and was adjusted for AM1.5G spectrum.

Concentrator InGaP/GaAs/Ge 3-junction solar cell modules have also been developed for terrestrial use [14]. A new concentrator optic is introduced, consisting of a nonimaging dome-shaped Fresnel lens, and a kaleidoscope homogenizer. The nonimaging Fresnel lens allows a wide acceptance half angle with keeping the same optical efficiency with minimum chromatic aberration. The homogenizer reshapes the concentrated light into the square solar cell aperture, and mixes rays to yield a uniform flux. Injection molding is capable of manufacturing thousands of lenses in a single day and by a single machine. The drawback of this method is the difficulty in creating precise prism angles and flat facets. The maximum efficiency was measured to be a little above 80%; the overall efficiency was 73%. After improvement of the process conditions, the averaged efficiency raised to 85.4%.

A new packaging structure for III–V concentrator solar cells is developed, applicable mainly to Fresnel lens concentrator modules but it may also be used in a dish concentrator systems. The solar cell used in the new receiver package is a specially developed III–V

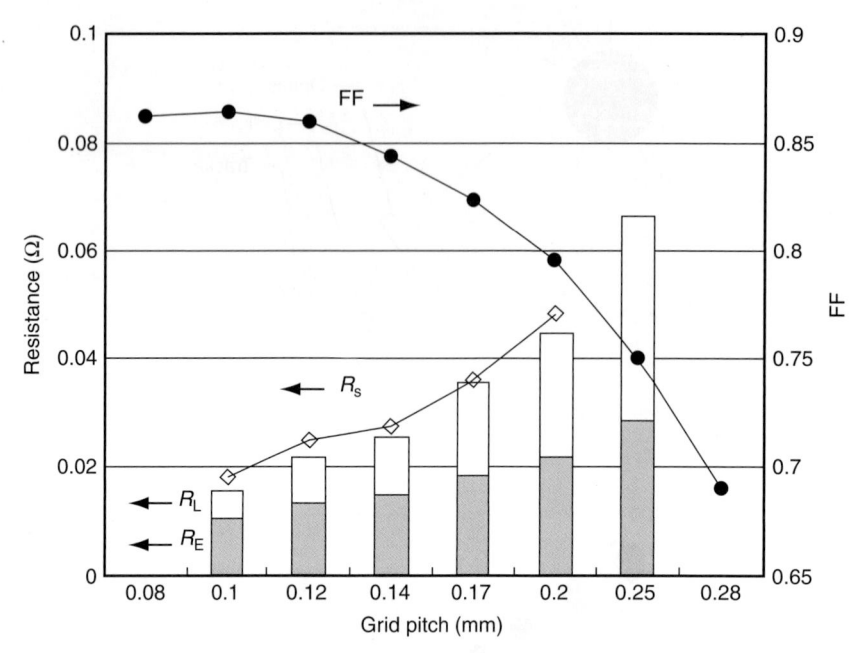

Figure 20 FF of the concentrator cells with various grids pitching under 250-sun light. Series resistance (R_s), lateral resistance (R_L), and total electrodes resistance (R_E) are also shown.

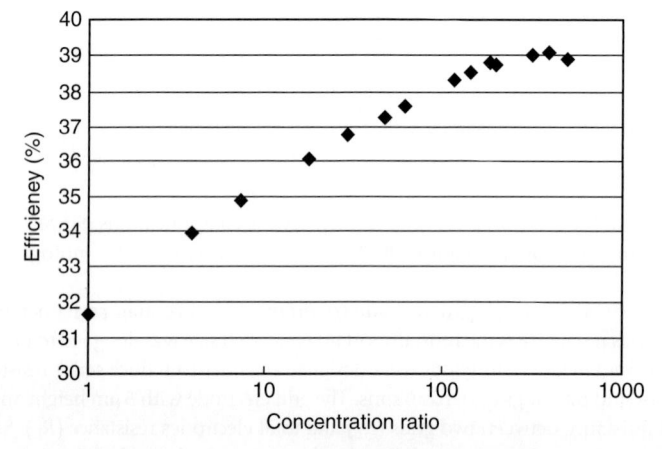

Figure 21 Efficiency of a high-efficiency InGaP/InGaAs/Ge 3-junction cell vs. number of suns [12].

3-junction concentrator solar cell. It is grown on a fragile Ge substrate with thickness of only 150 um. The overall size was 7 × 9 mm with 7 mm square aperture area.

In addition, the following technologies have been developed:

1. Super high-pressure and vacuum-free lamination of the solar cell that suppresses the temperature rise to 20 °C under 550 × geometrical concentration illumination of sunbeam.
2. Direct and voids-free soldering technologies of the fat metal ribbon to the solar cell, suppressing hot-spots and reducing the resistance, thereby allowing a current 400 times higher than normal nonconcentration operation to be passed with negligible voltage loss.
3. A new encapsulating polymer that survives exposure to high-concentration UV and heat cycles.
4. Beam-shaping technologies that illuminate the square aperture of the solar cell, from a round concentration spot.
5. Homogenizer technologies that give a uniform flux and prevent the conversion losses that stem from chromatic aberration and flux intensity distribution.

The concentrator module is designed with ease of assembly in mind. All the technologically complex components are packaged into a receiver so that a series of receivers and lenses can be assembled with standard tools, using local materials and workforce. The

Figure 22 Inside view of the 400 × concentrator module with 36 receivers connected in series.

concept is similar to the computer and automobile assembly industries, where key components are imported but the product assembled locally. It is anticipated that this approach will reduce the manufacturing cost of the module as shown in **Figure 22**.

The peak uncorrected efficiency for the 7056 cm^2 400 × module with 36 solar cells connected in series was 27.6%, measured in house. The peak uncorrected efficiencies for the same type of module with six solar cells connected in series and 1176 cm^2 area measured by Fraunhofer ISE and NREL were 27.4% and 24.9%, respectively. The 5445 cm^2 550 × modules have also demonstrated 27–28.9%, measured in house. **Table 3** summarizes the measured efficiency in three different sites.

New 400 × and 550 × (geometrical concentration ratio) modules are developed and show the highest efficiency in any types of PV as well as more than 20 years of accelerated lifetime. This achievement is due to new innovative concentrator technologies. The new concentrator system is expected to open a door to a new age of high-efficiency PV.

1.22.5 Most Recent Results of MJ Cells

Recently, more than 40% efficiency cells were reported by Fraunhofer ISE [29] and Spectrolab [30]. Concentrator 4-junction or 5-junction solar cells have great potential for realizing super high efficiency of over 50%. We have been studying concentrator MJ solar cells under the Japanese Innovative Photovoltaic R&D program started since fiscal year (FY) 2008 [31]. **Figure 23** shows an overview of NEDO's PV R&D Program. The Japanese Innovative Photovoltaics R&D Program has started in FY 2008 and the target in this program is to develop high-efficiency solar cells with conversion efficiency of more than 40% and low electricity cost of less than 7 JPY kWh^{-1} until 2050.

Most recently, world-record efficiency (35.8%) at 1 sun (AM1.5G) has been realized with inverted epitaxial grown InGaP/GaAs/InGaAs 3-junction cells by Sharp [32]. **Figure 24** shows the fabrication process of InGaP/GaAs/InGaAs 3-J solar cell by inverted epitaxial growth, and in **Figure 25** the I–V curve of this world-record efficiency InGaP/GaAs/InGaAs solar cell is depicted. **Figure 26** shows chronological improvements in conversion efficiencies of III–V compound MJ solar cells under 1-sun and concentrator conditions. Most recently, 42.1% efficiency under 230 suns has been obtained with InGaP/GaAs/InGaAs cell as shown in **Figure 27** [32].

1.22.6 Future Directions

MJ solar cells will be widely used in space because of their high conversion efficiency and better radiation resistance. In order to apply super high-efficiency cells widely, it is necessary to improve their conversion efficiency and reduce their cost. The new CPV

Table 3 Uncorrected peak efficiency measurement

Concentration	Area (cm^2)	Site	Ambient temperature (°C)	Uncorrected efficiency (%)	DNI (W m^{-2})
400 ×	7056	Inuyama, Japan, manufacturer	29	27.6	810
400 ×	7056	Toyohashi, Japan, independent	7	25.9	645
400 ×	1176	Fraunhofer ISE, Germany, independent	19	27.4	839
400 ×	1176	NREL, USA, independent	29	24.9	940
550 ×	5445	Inuyama, Japan, manufacturer	33	28.9	741
550 ×	5445	Toyohashi, Japan, independent	28	27	777

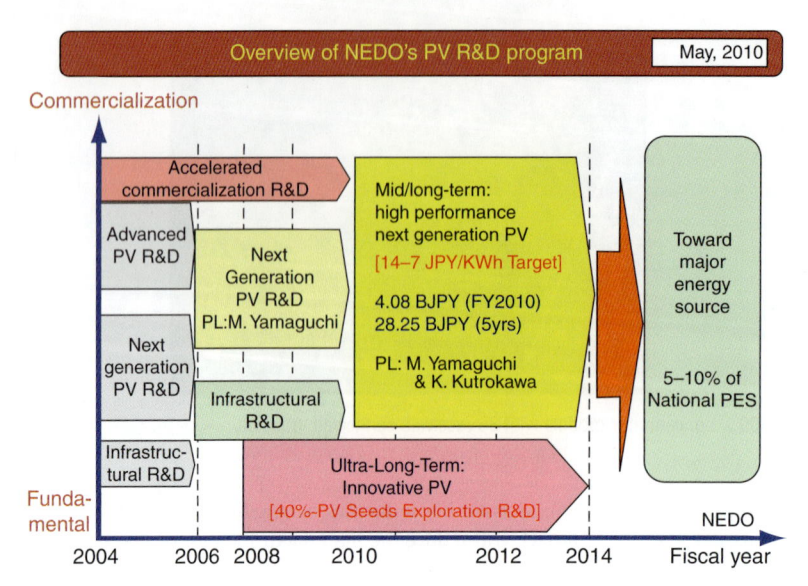

Figure 23 Overview of NEDO's PV R&D Program.

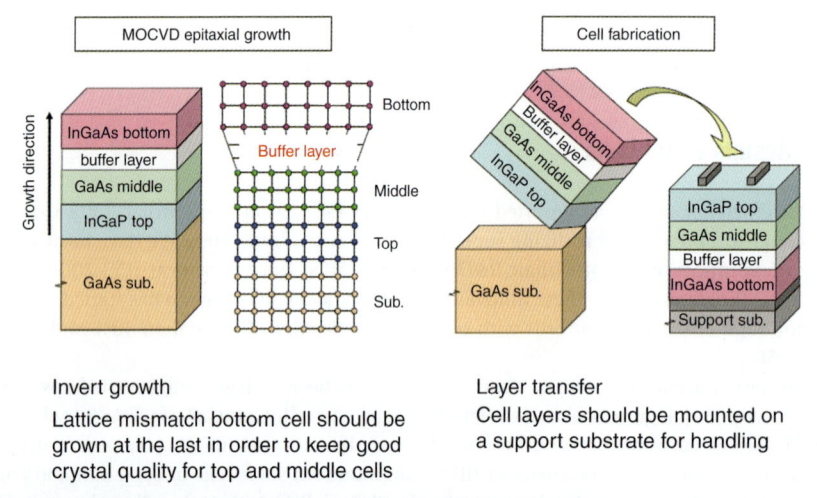

Figure 24 Fabrication process of InGaP/GaAs/InGaAs 3-J solar cell inverted epitaxial grown [29].

system with 2 times more annual power generation than the conventional crystalline silicon flat-plate system will open a new market for apartment or building rooftop applications. Another interesting application is what we call the tree planting PV and large-scale PV power plant applications.

Now, we are approaching 40% efficiency by developing concentrator MJ solar cells as shown in **Figure 28**. Concentrator 4-junction or 5-junction solar cells have great potential for realizing super high-efficiency of over 50% [33, 34]. Therefore, concentrator 3-junction and 4-junction solar cells have great potential for realizing super high efficiency of over 40%. As a 3-junction combination, InGaP/InGaAs/Ge cell on a Ge substrate will be widely used because this system has already been developed. The 4-junction combination of an $E_g = 2.0$ eV top cell, a GaAs second-layer cell, a material third-layer cell with an E_g of 1.05 eV, and a Ge bottom cell is lattice matched to Ge substrates and has a theoretical efficiency of about 42% under 1-sun AM0. This system has a potential efficiency of over 47% under 500-sun AM1.5 condition.

Since concentrator MJ and crystalline Si solar cells are expected to contribute to electricity cost reduction for widespread PV applications as shown in **Figure 29** [28], we would like to contribute to commercialization of CPV technologies as the third-generation PV technologies in addition to the first-generation crystalline Si PV and the second–generation, thin-film PV technologies. The scale of the CPV industry lags that of flat-plate PV by about one or two decades. It is expected, however, to make up this delay to the point where, in 2013, the cumulative installed capacity will lie in the region of several hundred MWp. R&D work has to be undertaken particularly in the area of large-scale production, that is, high throughput, to realize this ambition. Material consumption must also be reduced. A projection for future turnkey CPV system prices extrapolated from current prices is shown in

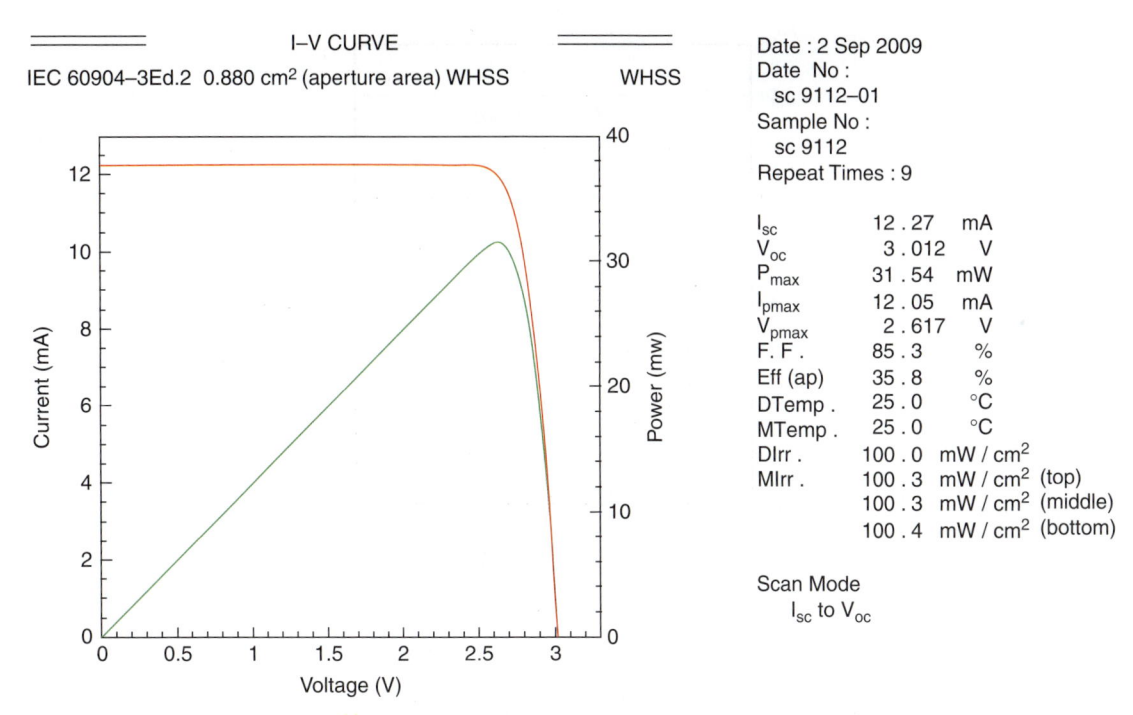

Figure 25 Current(I)–voltage(V) curve of world-record efficiency InGaP/GaAs/InGaAs measured by the AIST [29].

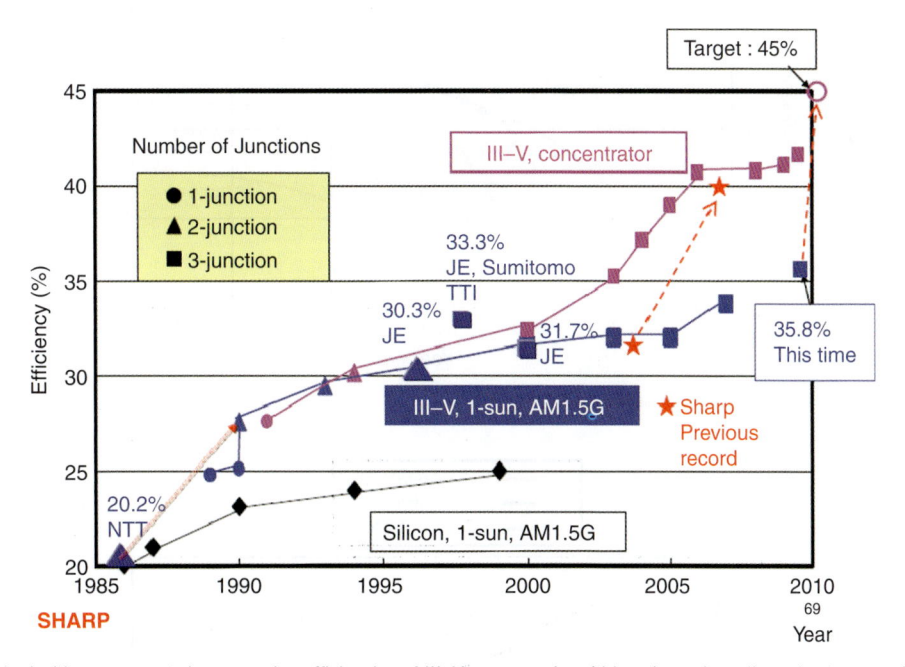

Figure 26 Chronological improvements in conversion efficiencies of III–V compound multi-junction solar cells under 1-sun and concentrator conditions [32].

Figure 30. This figure shows the expected yearly production of CPV systems (red) and the price of turnkey installed CPV systems in Euro/W_p (black) [35].

The most important R&D in CPV manufacturing will aim at [35]:

1. Improving the efficiency of mass-produced cells to the levels currently seen in the laboratory (over 26%) and to 35–45% efficiency in the longer term.
2. Improving optical elements (optical efficiency, lifetime, and product engineering).

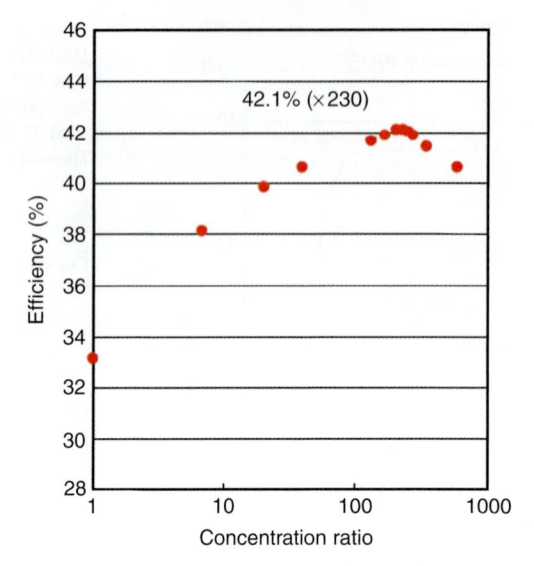

Figure 27 Concentration ration dependence of efficiency of a high-efficiency InGaP/GaAs/InGaAs 3-junction cell [32].

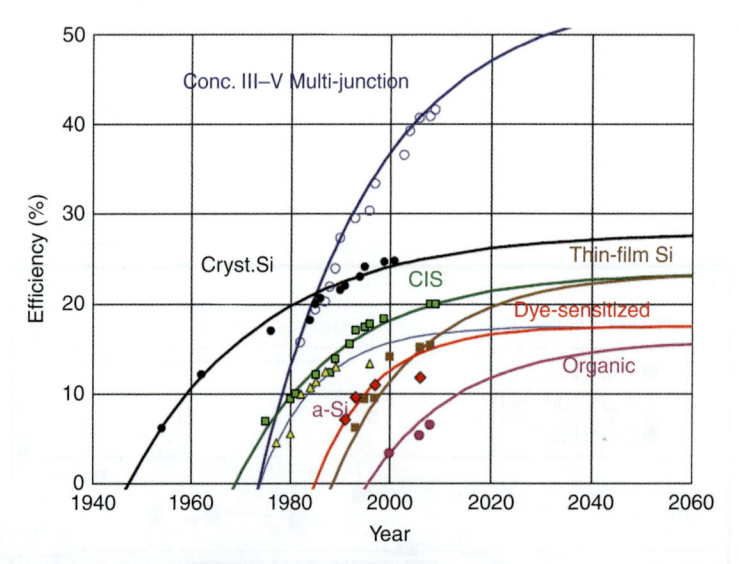

Figure 28 Future predictions of solar cell efficiencies [33, 34].

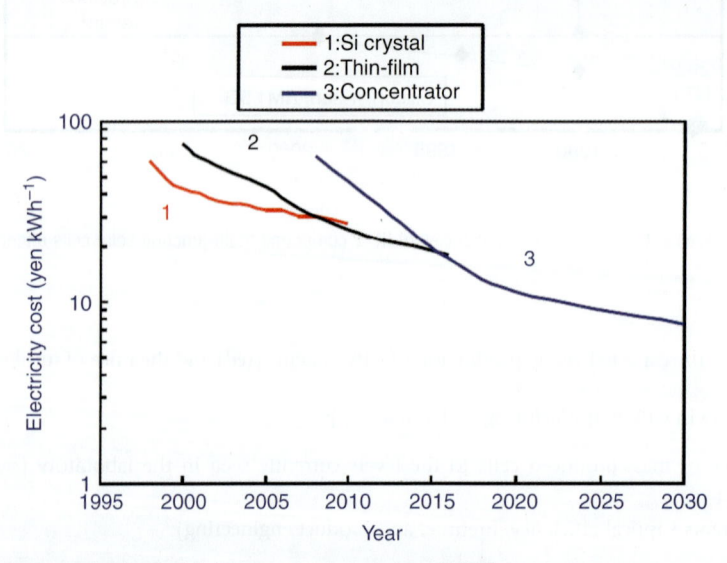

Figure 29 Scenario of electricity cost reduction by developing concentrator solar cells [28].

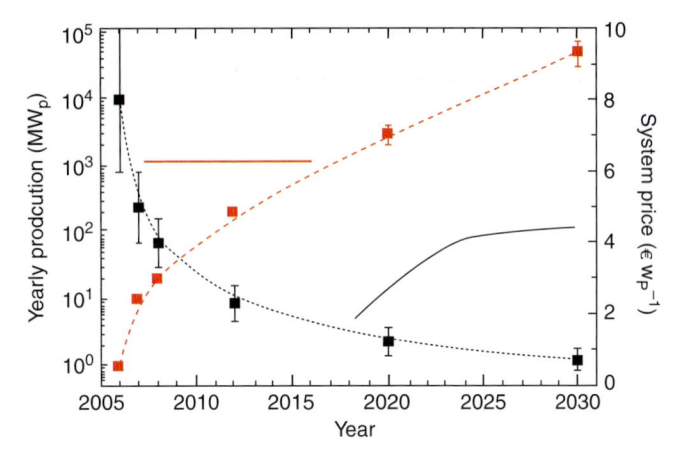

Figure 30 The expected yearly production of concentrator PV (CPV) systems (red) and the price of turnkey installed CPV systems in Euro/W$_p$ (black) [35].

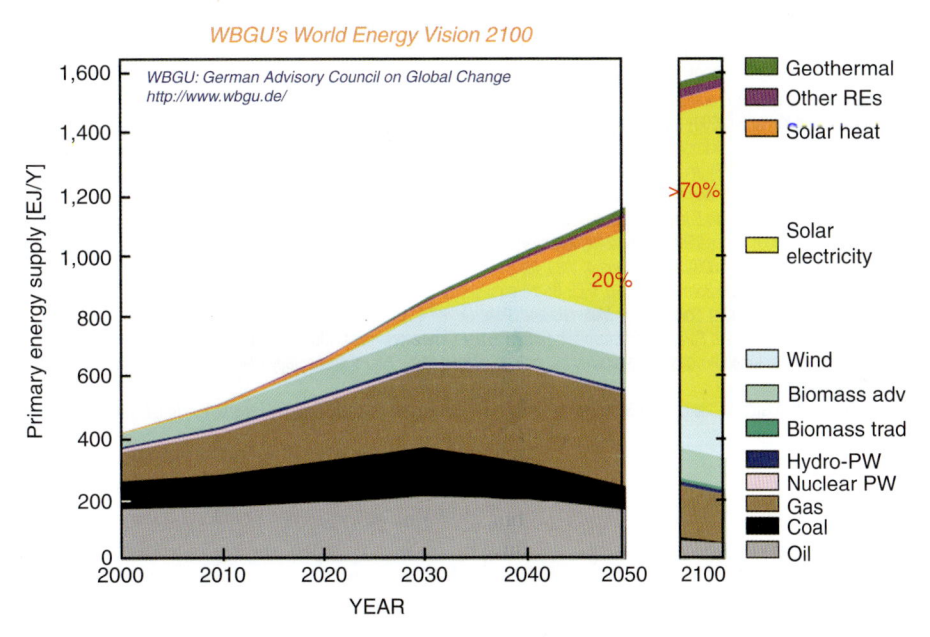

Figure 31 World Energy Vision 2100 presented by the German Council on Global Change [36].

3. Automated industrial module assembly (adjustment of elements, packaging, and sealing), high-throughput manufacturing with high yield, resulting in products with long lifetimes.
4. Construction of light, robust, and precise trackers for all outdoor climate conditions.
5. Set-up and monitoring of demonstration systems and large plants, in the range several hundred kWp (short term) to multi-MWp (medium term).
6. Techniques for guaranteeing the quality of products with intended lifetimes of over 20 years, development of standards, in-line testing, and recycling methods for the modules.

Figure 31 shows the World Energy Vision 2100 presented by the German Council on Global Change [36]. As a result of further development of higher efficiency, lower cost, and highly reliable solar cells, larger contribution to world energy by PV is expected, including concentrator MJ solar cells.

Acknowledgments

This work was supported by the New Energy and Industrial Technology Development Organization (NEDO) under the Ministry of Economy, Trade and Industry (METI). The author thanks members of Toyota Technological Institute, Sharp, Daido Steel, JAXA, JAEA, University of Tokyo, Meijo University, Kyushu University, and Miyazaki University for their collaboration and cooperation.

References

[1] Jackson ED (1955) *Transactions of the Conference on the Use of Solar Energy*, Vol. 5, p.122. Tucson: University of Arizona Press.
[2] Wolf M (1960) *Proceedings of the Institute of Radio Engineers* 48: 1246.
[3] Fan JCC, Tsaur B-Y, and Palm BJ (1982) *Proceedings of the 16th IEEE Photovoltaic Specialists Conference*, p. 692. New York: IEEE.
[4] Hutchby JA, Markunas RJ, and Bedair SM (1985) In: Ded SK (eds.) *Proceedings of the SPIE. "Photovoltaics"*, vol. 543, p. 543.
[5] Ando K, Amano C, Sugiura H, et al. (1987) *Japanese Journal of Applied Physics* 26: L266.
[6] Sugiura H, Amano C, Yamamoto A, and Yamaguchi M (1988) *Japanese Journal of Applied Physics* 27: 269.
[7] Amano C, Sugiura H, Yamamoto A, and Yamaguchi M (1987) *Applied Physics Letters* 51: 1998.
[8] Olson J, Kurtz S, and Kibbler K (1990) *Applied Physics Letters* 56: 623.
[9] Takamoto T, Ikeda E, Kurita H, et al. (1997) *Japanese Journal of Applied Physics* 36: 6215.
[10] Yamaguchi M, Okuda T, Taylor SJ, et al. (1997) *Applied Physics Letters* 70: 1566.
[11] Brown MR, Goldhammer LJ, Goodelle GS, et al. (1997) *Proceedings of the 26th IEEE Photovoltaic Specialists Conference*, p. 805. New York: IEEE.
[12] Takamoto T, Kaneiwa M, Imaizumi M, and Yamaguchi M (2005) *Progress in Photovoltaics* 13: 495.
[13] King RR, Law DC, Fetzer CM, et al. (2005) *Proceedings of the 20th European Photovoltaic Solar Energy Conference*, p. 118. Munich: WIP.
[14] Araki K, Uozumi H, Egami T, et al. (2005) *Progress in Photovoltaics* 13: 513.
[15] Tomita T (2006) *Proceedings of the 4th World Conference on Photovoltaic Energy Conversion*, p. 2450. New York: IEEE.
[16] Yamaguchi M, Warabisako T, and Sugiura H (1994) *Journal of Crystal Growth* 29: 136.
[17] Ahrenkiel RK, Keyes BM, Durbin SM, and Gray JL (1993) *Proceedings of the 23rd IEEE Photovoltaic Specialists Conference*, p. 42. New York: IEEE.
[18] Yang M-J, Yamaguchi M, Takamoto T, et al. (1997) *Solar Energy Materials and Solar Cell* 45: 331.
[19] Yamaguchi M and Amano C (1985) *Journal of Applied Physics* 58: 3601.
[20] Yamaguchi M, Ohmachi Y, Oh'hara T, et al. (2001) *Progress in Photovoltaics* 9: 191.
[21] Ringel SA, Sieg RM, Ting S, et al. (1998) *Proceedings of the 2nd World Conference on Photovoltaic Solar Energy Conversion*, p.3594. European Commission.
[22] Takamoto T, Agui T, Kamimura K, et al. (2003) *Proceedings of the 3rd World Conference on Photovoltaic Energy Conversion*, p. 581. Osaka: WCPEC-3.
[23] Takamoto T, Yamaguchi M, Ikeda E, et al. (1999) *Journal of Applied Physics* 85: 1481.
[24] Takamoto T, Ikeda E, Agui T, et al. (1997) *Proceedings of the 26th IEEE Photovoltaic Specialists Conference*, p. 1031. New York: IEEE.
[25] Takamoto T, Agui T, Ikeda T, and Kurita E (2000) *Proceedings of the 28th IEEE Photovoltaic Specialists Conference*, p. 976. New York: IEEE.
[26] Khan A, Yamaguchi M, Bourgoin JC, and Takamoto T (2000) *Applied Physics Letters* 76: 2559.
[27] Lang DV, Kimerling LC, and Leung SY (1976) *Journal of Applied Physics* 47: 3587.
[28] Yamaguchi M (2003) *Solar Energy Materials and Solar Cells* 75: 261.
[29] Bett AW, et al. (2009) *Proceedings of the 24th European Photovoltaic Solar Energy Conference*, p. 1. WIP.
[30] King RR, Boca A, Hong W, et al. (2009) *Proceedings of the 24th European Photovoltaic Solar Energy Conference*, p. 55. Munich: WIP.
[31] Yamaguchi M, Ohshita Y, Kojima N, et al. (2009) *Proceedings of the 24th European Photovoltaic Solar Energy Conference*, p. 218. WIP.
[32] Takamoto T, et al. (2010) *Proceedings of the 35th IEEE PVSC*. IEEE (to be published).
[33] Goetzberger A, Luther J, and Willeke G (2002) *Solar Energy Materials and Solar Cells* 74: 1.
[34] Yamaguchi M (2004) *Proceedings of the 19th European Photovoltaic Solar Energy Conference*, pp. l. Munich: WIP.
[35] EC (2007) A strategic research agenda for photovoltaic solar energy technology. *Report of the EU PV Technology Platform*. http://www.eupvplatform.org/fileadmin/Documents/PVPT_SRA_Complete_070604.pdf
[36] WBGU (German Advisory Council on Global Change) (2003) *World in Transition – Towards Sustainable Energy Systems*. London: Earthsan. ISBN 1-85383-882-9. http://www.wbgu.de/

1.23 Application of Micro- and Nanotechnology in Photovoltaics

L Tsakalakos, General Electric – Global Research Center, New York, NY, USA

© 2012 Elsevier Ltd. All rights reserved.

1.23.1	Introduction	515
1.23.2	Application of Micro and Nanotechnologies to Conventional PV	517
1.23.2.1	Improved Performance	518
1.23.2.1.1	Upconversion	518
1.23.2.1.2	Downconversion	519
1.23.2.1.3	Antireflective layers	520
1.23.2.2	Process Improvements	521
1.23.2.2.1	Thin films by nanoparticles	522
1.23.2.2.2	Lift-off of thin films	522
1.23.3	Nanoarchitectures	523
1.23.3.1	Nanocomposites	523
1.23.3.2	Nano/Microwires	524
1.23.4	Quantum Structures	525
1.23.4.1	Multi-Exciton Generation	525
1.23.4.1.1	Sensitized SCs	526
1.23.4.1.2	Carbon nanotubes	526
1.23.4.1.3	Quantum dots	526
1.23.4.2	Hot Carriers	526
1.23.4.2.1	Quantum dots	526
1.23.4.3	Intermediate Bands	527
1.23.4.3.1	Quantum wells	527
1.23.4.3.2	Quantum dots	527
1.23.4.4	Plasmonics	527
1.23.5	Outlook	528
1.23.6	Conclusions	529
References		529

1.23.1 Introduction

Solar photovoltaics (PVs) is widely considered to be one of the leading class of renewable energy technologies as the mix of energy-producing technologies evolves from primarily carbon-based sources to a more balanced distribution [1]. As has been noted in prior chapters, the PV market has grown tremendously in the last decade with steady expansion expected in the coming decade. Key terrestrial markets are utility-scale power plants (flat-plate or concentrator configurations), commercial rooftops, and residential rooftops (on-grid or off-grid). PV modules typically comprise a semiconducting PV device that is packaged in a construction typically consisting of one or two glass sheets and/or a polymer backsheet, with encapsulation used to protect the solar cells. Electrical cables are used to connect multiple panels together to form large area strings that ultimately connect to inverters and the load of interest.

The majority of PV modules today (ca. 80–85%) are based on silicon technology. These have the benefit of a well-established Si technological base, materials abundance, and the ability to produce in large-scale processes. The typical power conversion efficiency (PCE or η) of Si PV modules is 14–16%, with some higher-cost technologies achieving 18–19%. The costs of Si PV technology are relatively high (ca. US$1.10–2 $(W_p)^{-1}$) compared with other renewable energy technologies as well as other PV technologies, yet have been reduced in the last few years due to economic and supply-side factors. The second largest technology segment in the PV industry today is based on thin films [2]. These are primarily thin-film (1–5 μm), CdTe-based modules that are monolithically deposited and integrated on low-cost glass substrates. This allows for achievement of the lowest-cost PV technology available on the market at under US$0.8 $(W_p)^{-1}$. Another emerging thin-film PV material system is the $Cu(In,Ga)(Se,S)_2$ (CIGS) class of absorber materials. Record CdTe cells have achieved a PCE of 17.1% with production modules at the ~11–12% level, whereas CIGS record cells have achieved 20.3% with modules at the 12–14% level [3].

There are three primary metrics that are of importance to PVs: (1) cost, (2) PCE, and (3) stability. The first and third are somewhat beyond the scope of this chapter, yet very critical to deployment of PVs. Within PCE, there are second-level performance parameters that are considered, namely, short-circuit current density (J_{SC}), open-circuit voltage (V_{OC}), fill factor (FF), series resistance (R_s), and shunt resistance (R_{sh}). The PCE is defined as:

$$\eta = \frac{J_{SC} \times V_{OC} \times FF}{P_{in}} \quad [1]$$

where P_{in} is the input solar power, which is $1000 \, W \, m^{-2}$ for the standard terrestrial AM1.5 solar spectrum [4]. The key challenge with PV cells is to simultaneously increase J_{SC} and V_{OC}, while minimizing extrinsic losses such as shunts and energy barriers that reduce FF.

In addition to extrinsic loss mechanisms such as grain boundary and contact recombination, and parasitic absorption in front contact/electrode layers, there are two fundamental loss mechanisms that limit the performance of solar cells [5]. The first is thermalization of high-energy photons that are excited by photons of energy higher than the band gap (**Figure 1**). These photons lose energy by emission of photons (heat) and hence lead to a loss of energy. The second fundamental loss mechanism is loss of photons below the energy band gap of the semiconductor due to lack of absorption. This can account for a significant fraction of energy loss (ca. 30–40%) depending on the band gap of the solar absorber materials used. These two basic loss mechanisms lead to a detailed balance limit (assuming unity quantum efficiency (QE)) for a single band gap solar cell of ~33%, as was first calculated by Shockley and Queisser [6]. This leads to an optimum band gap for the AM1.5 terrestrial solar spectrum of ~1.45 eV (**Figure 2**).

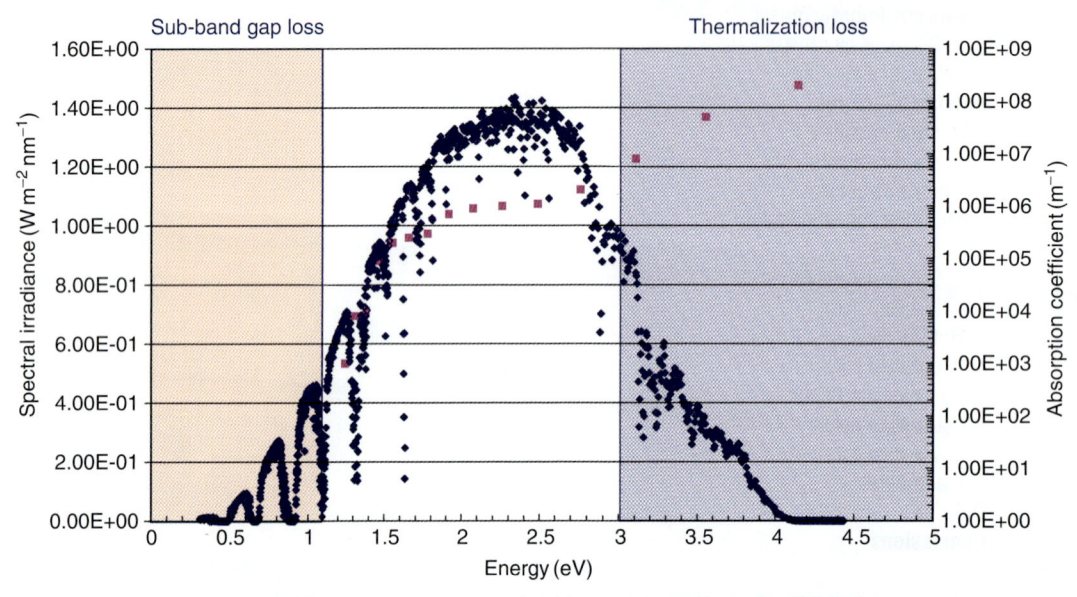

Figure 1 Fundamental loss mechanisms in silicon solar cells at low- and high-photon energies as related to the AM1.5 solar spectrum.

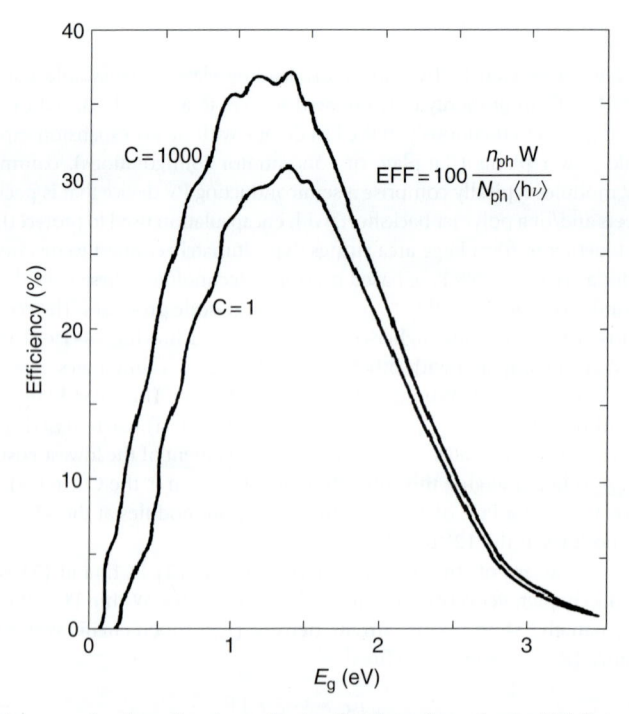

Figure 2 Detailed balance limit efficiency as a function of band gap showing that the optimum for the AM1.5 spectrum is ~1.45 eV at 1 sun leading to ~31% PCE, and ~37% PCE at 1000 suns [7].

To date, the record for a single junction has been achieved by direct band gap GaAs solar cells at ~27.6% [8], whereas indirect band gap Si solar cells have achieved a record laboratory cell efficiency of 25% [3].

This begs the question of what PCE is required in a solar PV module technology. Before providing a possible answer to this question, note that this specifically refers to PV module efficiency and not solar cell efficiency. Note that in most technologies, the module efficiency is 2–3% lower in absolute terms than the solar cells from which the module is constructed, though some module technologies are 5–10% lower in absolute efficiency than the corresponding record laboratory solar cell efficiency reported in the literature. Within this context, the answer to the initial question is dependent on the particular application, but there is a minimum value of ~10% that has emerged in recent years. If the application is space-constrained (e.g., residential rooftops or extraterrestrial applications), then it may be beneficial to pay more for a higher-efficiency technology, such as high-performance silicon in the 16–19% module efficiency range or for space application the use of III–V technologies that are orders of magnitude more expensive. For applications with a lesser constraint of space, it is of interest to achieve as low a levelized cost of electricity (LCOE); hence, a combination of efficiency and module cost will be required to achieve the desired goals, which are typically in the range of US$0.15 to US$0.25 kWh^{-1} depending on location (solar insolation). Of course, lower LCOE is required to compete with conventional power sources (ca. US$0.05 kWh^{-1}–US$0.15 kWh^{-1}). It is in such utility-scale and large-scale commercial rooftop applications that medium efficiency (ca. 10–16%), yet, low-cost module technologies such as CdTe (and CIGS) thin-films or lower-cost polycrystalline silicon module technologies are more important.

It must be noted that cost is a significant driver in the solar industry. Indeed, efficiency is a parameter that impacts costs at the module and system level. Costs that must be considered include the capital expenditure (CAPEX), the overall module bill-of-materials (BOM) cost (US$ m^{-2}), the module manufacturing cost (US$ (W$_p$)$^{-1}$), total installed system cost (US$ (W$_p$)$^{-1}$), and ultimately the LCOE discussed above. Indeed, one cannot consider cost without considering efficiency and vice versa. Hence, as has been pointed out by Green [5], there is a strong need to produce module technologies that are both low cost, that is, with cost structure similar to thin films, yet with efficiency that is truly breakthrough (ca. 20–40%), the so-called Third Generation or Generation III PV technology (**Figure 3**). Such PV technologies simply do not exist today and would truly revolutionize the PV industry, leading to wide-scale adoption of PV technologies.

While efficiency and cost are widely discussed, another significant parameter for PV module technologies is the stability of the module performance. A related parameter is reliability, which is related to complete failure of the module by a number of mechanisms; however, stability is related to the rate of degradation of the module performance with time. Stability can in fact be a critical parameter in determining the success of a PV technology. If a high-efficiency module degrades in performance very quickly, then the value of this technology is lesser since it may become difficult to predict the power output (and hence financial payback) of the system as a whole. The scientific mechanisms that impact stability are indeed often not well understood for many technologies. While this topic will not be discussed in detail, it should be a factor that must be considered in more detail by the research community as new solar cell technologies, such as those based on micro- and nanotechnology, are developed.

1.23.2 Application of Micro and Nanotechnologies to Conventional PV

Within the framework of the solar efficiency–cost landscape, as shown in **Figure 3**, there is a strong need to develop Generation III PV technologies with breakthrough efficiency and low cost. However, there are opportunities to apply new technologies such as

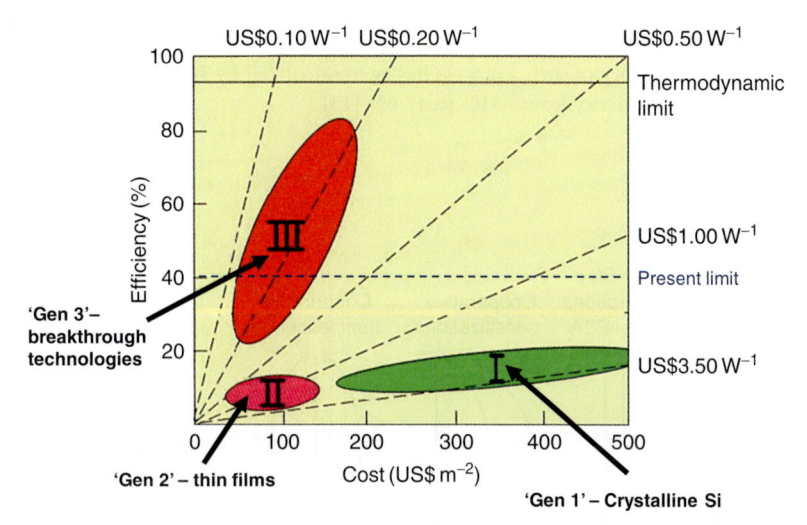

Figure 3 Solar cell landscape as defined by M. Green showing the desire to develop Generation III technologies with high efficiency and low costs, as compared to Generation I (silicon) and Generation II (thin films) [5]. Reproduced with permission from Green MA (2003) *Third Generation Photovoltaics: Advanced Solar Energy Conversion*. Berlin, Germany: Springer Science+Business Media, Figure 1.2.

nanotechnology to conventional solar technologies in the Generation I and Generation II categories. Silicon continues to be the dominant solar material in the market (ca. 80–85% in 2011) and will not be fully replaced in the near future, whereas CdTe thin films make up approximately 15–20% of the 2011 market with the remainder based on emerging CIGS modules and amorphous silicon (a-Si) thin films for certain applications. Micro- and nanotechnologies can be applied for several purposes, the main reasons being to increase the PCE of the technology or to improve the processing of conventional PV modules for reduced costs, yield, and related manufacturing targets. Several examples of such approaches will be described below.

1.23.2.1 Improved Performance

We first discuss various approaches to improve the performance of conventional solar cells. The general strategy here is to improve the performance by overcoming various intrinsic or extrinsic losses in the device. In the former case, this may include undesired reflection losses, parasitic absorption in various device layers/films, or recombination losses at grain boundaries, contacts, or in the bulk of the absorber volume. In the latter case, this include mechanisms to reduce thermalization loss of carriers excited by high-energy photons, or to allow absorption of portions of the solar spectrum that are below the band gap of the absorbing semiconductor (we implicitly assume conventional conversion mechanisms are operable for Generation I and II devices).

Since we are dealing with established solar module technologies, the obvious question is how much of a gain is relevant, followed by what type of gain we can expect. In other words, what solar cell parameters can be impacted by various enhancement mechanisms? With regard to efficiency gains, it is noted that absolute efficiency of ~0.25% or greater can have significant cost and market impact for a particular technology. Depending on the starting efficiency of the technology, this could correspond to a gain of approximately 1%, 2%, 3%, or even higher in relative terms. Of course, the gain mechanism typically comes with some added cost that should be less than the relative gain. Each technology should be evaluated on its own terms to determine whether the gain is worth the cost of introducing the gain mechanism. Interestingly, most of the gain mechanisms to be discussed below lead to a gain in the J_{SC} of the PV cell/module. This is important to understand because for some technologies it is well known that the main challenge is in fact not the J_{SC} but rather the V_{OC} (or in some cases FF). This is indeed well known in the case of CdTe thin-film technologies [9]. We stress here that the performance enhancement mechanisms we are referring to are based on external, typically optically active, films that by their nature would not affect V_{OC}. Parameters that affect V_{OC} are generally directly related to the inherent device structure and, hence, would require detailed device engineering, in addition to efforts at defect passivation. We begin the discussion with efforts to improve intrinsic losses by shifting photons either up or down in energy to a region of the solar cell spectral response curve that is maximal.

1.23.2.1.1 Upconversion

As the name implies, upconversion (UC) involves the conversion of low-energy photons to high-energy photons. Put another way, long-wavelength photons are converted to shorter-wavelength photons. For most PV technologies, this implies that infrared (IR) photons are being converted to photons in the near-IR or visible range. For example, the band gap of Si is at ~1100 nm, whereas the peak EQE for Si solar cells typically lies in the range of 550–900 nm. Therefore, it would be most useful to convert photons in the range of 1100–1800 nm to the aforementioned regime, preferably in a broadband manner.

UC is necessarily a multiphoton process [10, 11]. To first order, two photons are utilized in sequential order by initial excitation of a ground-state electron to an intermediate state followed by subsequent excitation by another low-energy photon to a further energy level at twice or higher the energy of the photons (**Figure 4**). Relaxation back to the ground state yields a single high-energy photon that can be absorbed by the active layer to produce electron–hole pairs. As is evident, this process has an inherent maximum luminescent quantum yield (LQY) of 50%. Furthermore, this must be achieved over a broadband utilizing unpolarized, diffused light from the sun. The theoretical efficiency of such a process has been calculated by Trupke *et al.* and it was shown to provide an increase in the detailed balance limit efficiency from ~31% to 47.6% [13].

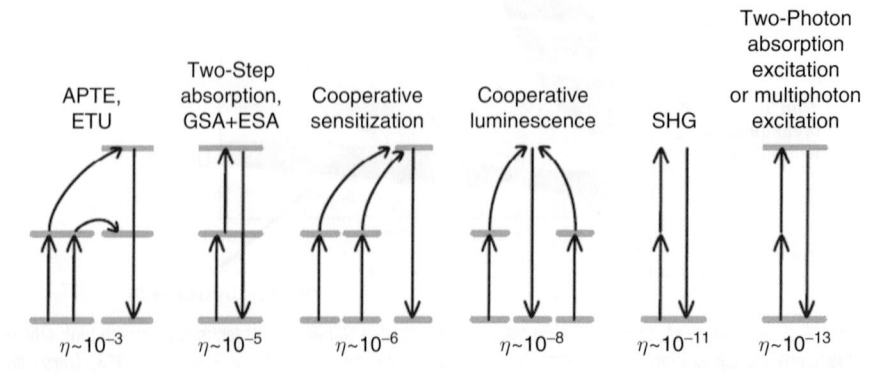

Figure 4 Mechanisms of upconversion [12].

There are several other UC mechanisms that have been described in the literature. For example, the energy transfer upconversion (ETU) mechanisms involved simultaneous absorption of two photons followed by energy transfer to two separate adjacent states with subsequent relaxation from the higher energy state. Alternatively, both carriers can resonantly transfer to the same high-energy state, the so-called cooperative sensitization mechanism. Cooperative luminescence occurs via virtual states and hence has a relatively low LQY, whereas second harmonic generation (SHG) also is based on virtual states obtained at extremely high intensities, $\sim 10^{13}$ W m^{-2} [12].

Various micro- and nanoparticle types have been reported in the literature with measurable UC. Wang et al. synthesized upconverting nanoparticles of various compositions and showed that doping of nanoparticles of complex composition such as NaYF$_4$:Yb/Er can control both the phase of the material as well as the size of the particles [14]. The nanoparticles were embedded in a polydimethylsiloxane (PDMS) polymer matrix and UC was observed. However, these were not applied to solar cells. De Wild et al. applied a powder of β-NaYF$_4$:Yb^{3+} (18%) Er^{3+} (2%) embedded in poly(methyl methacrylate) (PMMA) to the back of an a-Si device [15]. Upon application of a 980 nm laser (10 mW) to the device, a gain in photocurrent of 10 µA cm^{-2} was measured. This shows that it is possible to apply UC to a thin-film device, though more research is needed to improve this gain. Similarly, Fischer et al. demonstrated UC in a Si solar cell using trivalent erbium-doped sodium yttrium fluoride [16]. An UC gain of 5.1% was measured under monochromatic irradiance of 1880 W m^{-2} at 1523 nm. This led to an EQE gain of 0.34% at an irradiance of 1090 W m^{-2} at 1522 nm. Again, this shows that UC is possible, though more work is required to develop materials with suitable UC efficiency, as well as new methods of device integration.

Interestingly, recent reports have focused on the use of molecular-based UC. These are typically complex organic molecules in which UC is demonstrated in solution, or in limited examples in a polymer matrix. Schmidt and co-workers demonstrated the mechanism of triplet–triple annihilation upconversion (TTA-UC) in a bimolecular system of palladium porphyrin and a polycyclic aromatic hydrocarbon [17]. Through a rigorous analysis, it was shown that the efficiency of this UC mechanism is not 11% as has been surmised in prior literature, but as high as 60% theoretically, and they demonstrated a TTA-UC efficiency of up to 40%. While this was not applied to a solar cell, it shows the potential to apply such an UC mechanism to solar cells, especially those that show a poor near-IR response such as a-Si and dye sensitized solar cells. A similar mechanism was also demonstrated by Castellano and co-workers [18].

1.23.2.1.2 Downconversion

The above discussion has highlighted the fact that more basic research is required to implement UC in solar cells. Perhaps, a mechanism that is slightly more mature from a materials perspective is so-called downconversion (DC). The standard mechanism described in the literature as DC or quantum splitting is the emission of more than one long-wavelength photon per absorbed higher-energy photon. A related spectral DC mechanism is based on photoluminescence (PL), that is, a single low-energy photon emitted per absorbed higher-energy photon. This is also typically referred to in the literature as downshifting (DS). Examples of spectral DC as applied to solar PVs are described below.

1.23.2.1.2(i) Conversion

DC is typically based on mechanisms of quantum cutting. This requires a band structure that contains one or more intermediate levels, such that electrons excited into relatively high-energy states relax to one or more of these intermediate states, thus producing more than one lower energy photon. A band diagram illustrating this basic mechanism, which is also referred to as quantum cutting, is shown in **Figure 5**. This mechanism inherently has an LQY associated with it of greater than 100%, and theoretically up to 200%. DC was first proposed in 1953 by Dexter [20], and experimentally demonstrated in the 1970s by Piper et al. [21]. Most work has focused on DC from very high-energy photons (<200 nm) that are useful in fluorescent lighting applications. Indeed, LQYs higher than 190% have been shown excitations high in the conduction band of semiconducting materials such as ZnS [22]. However, another major approach to DC is to utilize rare-earth based compounds, particularly those in the lanthanide series. Due to the electronic structure of trivalent lanthanides, such as Pr, Er, and Yb, that is based on filling of [Xe]4f^{n}5s^{2}5p^6, there are multiple energy levels associated with these ions that give rise to multiple transitions. Transition metal ions can be added to serve as sensitizers, thus both improving photon absorption (oscillator levels in these ions are low and lead to low absorption coefficients) and providing additional energy levels via resonant energy transfer [10].

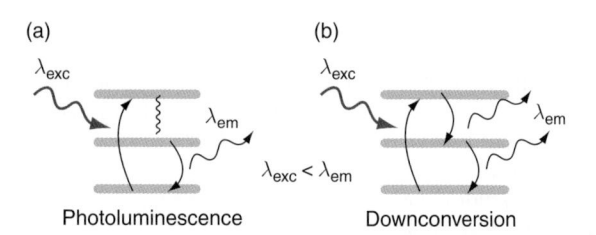

Figure 5 Simplified band diagram for (a) photoluminescence/downshifting and (b) for quantum cutting/downconversion [19].

Application of DC to solar cells is quite a challenging problem. While up to 40% of the available solar energy is available above the band gap, the photon energy required to achieve high QY as noted above is limited in the solar spectrum. Often it is necessary to concentrate. The theoretical efficiency of DC was analyzed by Trupke *et al.* [19], who showed that the detailed balance efficiency can increase from ~31% to ~39%. However, as shown below, the experimental demonstration of downconverting materials that are of relevance to the solar spectrum is quite limited, and experimental LQY values are very low. The application of micro- and nanoparticles to DC is also discussed.

As noted above, several lanthanide-based phosphor compositions have been shown to yield DC with spectral feature that are relevant to solar PV cells. Meijerink and co-workers have shown that $YF_3:Nd^{3+}$, Yb^{3+} can achieve spectral conversion of photons at 360 nm through a quantum cutting mechanism, which is a very promising development [23]. The LQY was found to be ~140% at low temperature. However, the LQY was found to be lower at room temperature. Loureiro *et al.* demonstrated DC in nanoparticles based on $SrAl_{12}O_{19}:Pr$, Mg [24]. The impact of surface states was also found to be critical in achieving a high LQY. There have been experiments to also demonstrate DC using quantum dot (QD) semiconductors. Among the first to explore this were Van Sark and co-workers [25], who showed gains in Si solar cells using a QD layer with spectral conversion.

1.23.2.1.2(ii) Shifting

Luminescent DS is a related mechanism that involves the emission of one lower energy photon for each absorbed high-energy photon. This involved energy loss subsequent to the initial photon absorption event due to a Stokes shift followed by emission of the lower energy photon. Therefore, DC is limited to an LQY of no greater than unity, and it does not contribute to the fundamental limiting efficiency gain for a solar cell. Therefore, its practical application is to alleviate parasitic losses associated with layers in a solar cell that lead to a drop in EQE at short wavelengths. This can be related to say window layers, as in the case of CdTe, or perhaps highly doped emitter layers in Si.

As in the case of DC, lanthanide-doped phosphors have been extensively studied for DC and luminescence in many applications. Perhaps the most successful example is the work of Hong and Kawano, who showed that it is possible to achieve a relative gain of up to 5% on CdTe solar cells based on this material [26]. This work also highlights the potential limitation of such materials, namely, that the absorption coefficient for such ions in wide-band gap host lattices is very low (ca. 1–100 cm^{-1}), and hence very thick crystals were required to achieve such gains. Practical implementation without a thinner layer that can be readily integrated will be quite limited. Recently, it was shown by Klampaftis and Richards that it is possible to achieve gains in Si solar cells using DS phosphors, with relative gains of ~0.2% [27, 28]. A cautionary note is provided, in that great care must be taken to demonstrate gains on solar cells, as thermal and optical phenomena that are not related to DS (or DC) can easily manifest in gains that are not truly due to these mechanisms.

QDs have also been applied to solar cells as a means of improving efficiency via DS. Svrek *et al.* demonstrated gains in IQE with Si QDs embedded in a dielectric matrix applied to a silicon solar cell [29]. The absolute gain in efficiency obtained was ~0.4%, and it was estimated that an absolute gain of up to 1.4% is possible, assuming a DS LQY of 100%.

1.23.2.1.3 Antireflective layers

Another mechanism to improve the performance of solar cells is to impart an antireflection coating (ARC), layer or film. Reflection losses related to the refractive index contrast between the source medium, typically air, and the medium into which the photons are entering. To first order, this reflection loss is described by the following equation:

$$R = \left[\frac{n_1 - n_2}{n_1 + n_2}\right]^2 \quad [2]$$

where n_1 is the refractive index of the first medium and n_2 the refractive index of the medium into which light is entering. The ultimate goal of an AR layer is to reduce the refractive index contrast between air and the medium into which light is entering. This can be applied as a single layer with an intermediate index or as a layer that provides a graded refractive index from air to the underlying substrate. In the case of solar cells, this may include glass, semiconductor materials (such as Si, GaAs, etc.), and/or polymers such as ethyl vinyl acetate (EVA). Nanotechnology has been applied to solar application of AR layers quite extensively. Several examples are shown below.

One of the best examples of this is the use of nanoporous films to provide a refractive index between that of air and glass. This is typically formed in silicon oxide (silica) films fabricated by a sol–gel method [30]. These films have been formed on glass substrates and have shown relative efficiency gains as high as 2.65% on silicon solar cells.

Nanoporous films represent a route to achieving an AR effect by use of random nanostructures in a solid film. Another approach is to provide a more controlled gradient in effective refractive index. This is best exemplified by work on the so-called moth-eye effect, first observed by Clapham and Hutley in the early 1970s [31]. It was found that the retina of a moth is black due to a microstructuring of the retina with protrusions that are graded in their profile, which tend to gradually match the index of the substrate and hence provide very low reflection loss. Reflections of 1% of less are possible with such an approach. Various top–down methods have been applied for the formation of such structures, including techniques such as interference lithography [32]. These microstructured approaches have led to successful demonstrations of an AR effect, though their applicability to PV remains to be seen.

A related approach to the moth-eye effect is to use nanostructured protrusions on a surface to provide enhanced AR effect. While these approaches can improve efficiency by decreasing reflectance, at the nanoscale it is also possible to

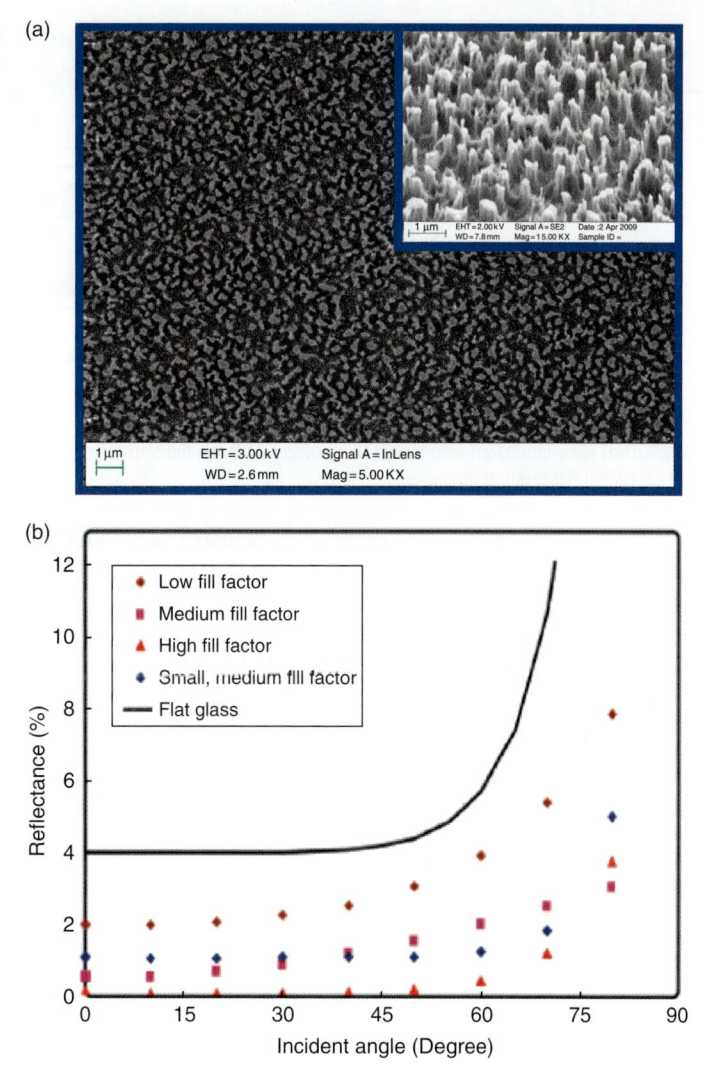

Figure 6 (a) Scanning electron microscopy image of an ODAR layer and (b) modeled reflectance as a function of angle for various geometries showing an improvement over all angles. Adapted from Tsakalakos L, Dalakos G, Brewer J, Zalyubovskiy S GE Global Research, unpublished.

improve the angular response of the surface relative to a planar surface. Therefore, such a structure can provide both an increase in efficiency as well as an increase in energy yield of the module due to improved capture of light throughout the course of the day. We term this type of a nanotextured pillar/rod surface an omnidirectional antireflective (ODAR) layer. **Figure 6** shows an example of such an ODAR layer as well as the improvement in reflectance with angle compared with a planar surface. This was initially explored by Hadobas *et al.* in dry etched nanostructures formed on Si wafers after interference lithography [33]. It was shown that the reflectance can be reduced to levels as low as ~1% on silicon wafers using such nanomachined Si structures. More manufacturable approaches have also been demonstrated using processes such as electroless metal-assisted etching, chemical vapor deposition (CVD), nanosphere lithography coupled with dry etching, and related methods. **Figure 7** shows the effective absorption of silicon nanowire (SiNW) films formed by wet etching and CVD processes. It is evident that there is a significant gain in light capture by use of such a nanostructured surface, particularly in Si where the absorption depth is long. It can also be useful for direct band gap semiconductors that have high refractive indices leading to relatively high inherent reflection losses. Indeed, the area of ODARs remains an active area of research within the applied physics and PV community, offering the potential for rapid efficiency gains.

1.23.2.2 Process Improvements

One of the most mature areas for application of nanotechnology to PV is the use of nanostructures to enable new, improved processing methods that are also lower cost. There are multiple processes that can potentially be impacted across various PV material systems. Some approaches have already begun to find large-scale application at the commercial scale. Before providing some examples, a brief description of the major PV processes is provided.

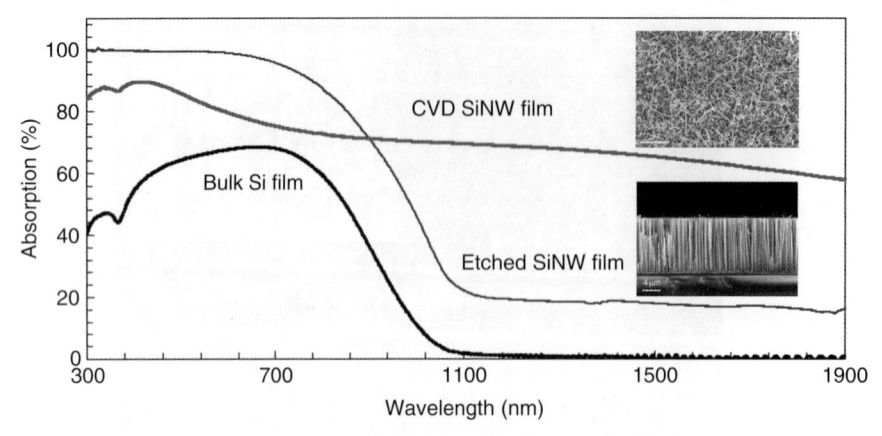

Figure 7 Optical reflectance of SiNW ODAR films compared with planar Si, showing a broadband improvement in performance. Adapted from Tsakalakos L, Brewer J, Fronheiser J GE Global Research, unpublished.

Silicon technologies are typically based on mining of Si-containing materials (e.g., sand), a refining processes to remove impurities and oxygen, and a crystal pulling process such as the Czochralski process for single crystals or zone melting for polycrystalline boules. The boules are then cut, typically with a wire saw that leads to significant materials loss (though kerfless methods are being explored), and the cells are then processed to add the p–n junction (e.g., diffusion from doped silicate glasses), a back contact via screen printing, passivation/AR layers (e.g., Si_xN_y), and front metallization grid contacts by screen printing [34].

Thin-film technologies are processed in a very different fashion. Here, the goal is to deposit a thin (typically < 5 μm) film on a low-cost substrate. The material is usually a direct band gap semiconductor which allows for maximal light absorption at these thicknesses. CdTe, which classically is a superstrate configuration (sunny side is through original growth substrate), is processed at temperatures of between 450 °C and 650 °C using a closed-space sublimation process on glass that has been precoated with transparent conducting oxide layers. Since these are monolithically integrated modules, the deposition processes are typically interposed by laser scribing processes, and finished with a back contact metallization process [35]. Other thin-film materials, such as CIGS, may be deposited by one of many methods, including sputtering (reactive or co-sputter), co-evaporation, ion-assisted deposition, and related vacuum processes. Sometimes, these are followed by a selenization (or sulfurization) process [36]. As opposed to CdTe, CIGS is a substrate configuration (sunny side is opposite to growth substrate), so a metal back contact such as Mo is first applied to the substrate (glass, metal, or polymer). It is also possible to deposit CIGS by electrodeposition of the constituent metals, followed by selenization, for example, as developed by SoloPower, Inc. [37]. Finally, III–V-based technologies are fabricated almost exclusively by metal–organic chemical vapor deposition (MOCVD) processes on high-cost GaAs or Ge single-crystal wafers. Some examples of how micro/nanotechnology is enabling novel processes are now discussed.

1.23.2.2.1 Thin films by nanoparticles

Perhaps the best example of how nanotechnology is impacting PV modules is in the processing of thin films. In particular, research and development in the processing of CIGS thin films has become quite intensive in recent years. Mitzi and co-workers have demonstrated the solution-based processing of CIGS using nanoparticle inks reaching impressive efficiencies, that is, ~12% [38]. This was achieved by processing nanoparticles of the constituent metals into a thin film by spin-casting or slot-die coating, followed by a selenization process. Alternatively, it is possible to directly form nanoparticles of the required composition and simply sinter the film once deposited. Nanoparticle sintering has also been used to form films of the emerging earth-abundant material Cu_2ZnSnS_4 (CZTS) [39]. The best example of commercial success with a nanoparticle approach is by Nanosolar, Inc., which is in production of CIGS modules based on this method [40].

Another example of successful implementation of nanoparticles-based inks is the application of silicon nanoparticles. Here, silicon particles may be formed by vapour-phase or laser-based approaches. Care must be taken when processing these particles since they typically contain a thin silicon oxide layer. While it is possible to process full solar cells based on Si with these particles [41], to date, the most success has been with the application of selective emitters to Si solar cells. This has been pioneered by Innovalight, Inc., who provides a full process to single- and multicrystalline-based cell manufacturers. Application of the selective emitter yields absolute efficiency improvements of up to 1% [42].

1.23.2.2.2 Lift-off of thin films

Another approach to forming high-quality thin films is to grow epitaxial absorber layers on a high-quality, typically high-cost substrate, and then transfer them to a lower-cost receptor substrate. It is necessary to reuse the substrates for additional film growth in order to achieve low-cost modules.

This lift-off processing route has been most successfully applied to high-efficiency GaAs solar cells. In this process, an ultrathin film of AlAs (ca. 1–10 nm) is first deposited on the growth substrate, followed by deposition of the p–n diode-based solar cells. Owing to the ~10^6 contrast in etch rates between AlAs and GaAs in certain acid solutions, one can readily peel off a fully or partially finished solar cell from a substrate. This so-called epitaxial lift-off (ELO) approach was proposed in the early 1980s with some success at the level of small solar cells [43]. There is a renewed interest in this technology, and recently a world record (28.1%) single-junction, thin-film, and flexible solar cell was demonstrated by Alta Devices, Inc [8].

Lift-off technology was also applied to silicon solar cells. Here the Si film must be removed from the growth substrate in a very different fashion. The best example of this is the so-called Smart-Cut® process [44]. A partially processed Si wafer is bombarded with high-energy hydrogen and/or helium ions that are deposited at a particular depth of interest. The ions locally damage the Si crystal, which allows the upper layer to be fractured from the growth substrate by thermal processing or by crack initiation/Si solar cells with efficiency as high as 11.2% have been demonstrated by such an approach [45].

1.23.3 Nanoarchitectures

So far, we have discussed the application of micro/nanostructures and nano-related processes to form convention solar cells. There are also significant efforts in the PV community to create novel solar cell structures that are based on micro- and/or nanostructures. The ability to refashion materials at the nanoscale creates several opportunities to create distinct advantages for PV [46].

One of these advantages is that one can control light in new ways [47]. This was described above in the case of ODAR layers, for example. The use of nanoparticle arrays or nanowire films can create strong improvements in light trapping and absorption. Most importantly, this can be achieved without the use of an additional ARC, and there is a possibility to create an improvement over the full solar spectrum.

Electrically, the use of nanostructures can create not only new mechanisms of charge separation (see below) but also would allow for an improved charge collection via transport of charge carriers to interfaces that are very close to the solid volume in which photoexcited carriers are generated. Here we describe two classes of nanostructured solar cells that are under investigation and that have shown promising results.

1.23.3.1 Nanocomposites

The fashioning of bulk nanocomposites is one major approach to improving charge collection in solar cells. This has been applied to both inorganic and organic solar cells. Among the first class of solar cells to be demonstrated with such a structure was the extremely thin absorber (ETA) solar cell. This concept was first developed as early as 1998 by Siebentritt *et al.* [48]. The idea is to sandwich a very thin absorber film (i.e., 10–100 nm) such as CuInS$_2$ between a nanostructured template layer that also acts as a charge carrier and a transparent conductor of opposite doping on the top side (**Figure 8**). For example, a nanostructured n-type TiO$_2$

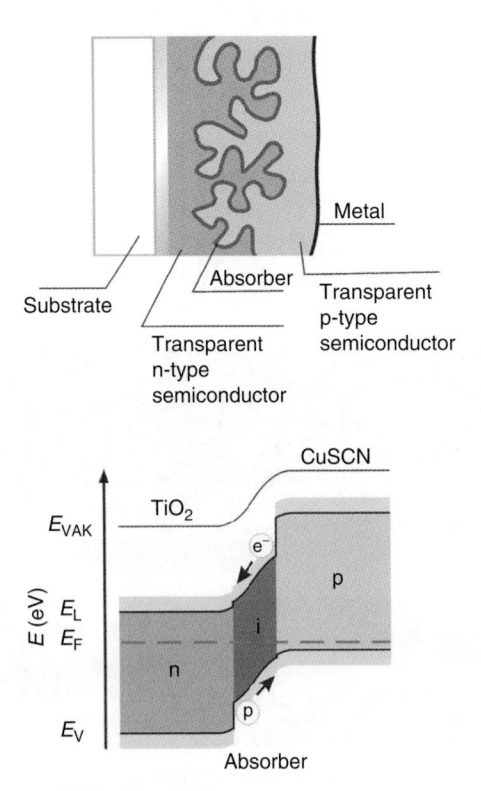

Figure 8 Schematic of an extremely thin-absorber (ETA) solar cell [49].

conductor can be formed on a substrate by screen printing or spray pyrolysis of nanoparticles [49]. CIS is then deposited by an ion layer gas deposition (ILGAR) process, followed by electrodeposition of a transparent p-type CuSCN layer. Early work yielded relatively low performance; however, subsequent work showed that it is possible to obtain solar cells with efficiency as high as 5% by using a modified nanocomposite approach based on a nanostructured stack of $TiO_2/In_2S_3/CuInS_2$ [50].

The concept of a nanocomposite has also been extensively applied to organic photovoltaics (OPVs). Since it is well known that excitons have a very short diffusion length in organic semiconductors, the strategy adopted by many researchers is to create a very high surface area charge separation junction that is randomly interleaved. This is typically referred to as a bulk heterojunction (BHJ) device and has shown efficiency that is on the order of 6% and led to significant advances in the OPV field [51]. One challenge with such a concept has been that the two semiconductor layers (typically both organic or a hybrid) are interleaved which can create shunts. This has necessitated the development of electron blocking layers to minimize shunting. Such structures can also benefit from the use of nanocylinders that help to create a thick layer of one subcomponent on top of the BHJ region [52].

1.23.3.2 Nano/Microwires

A class of nanostructured solar cells that has gained significant interest in recent years is based on micro/nanowires or pillars. These have been shown in Si [53], CdTe [54], a-Si [55], and III–V materials, such as InP and GaAs [56]. Recent work (by this author) has shown that these architectures, when applied to high-efficiency materials such as GaAs, have the potential for >20% PCE, with experimental devices having achieved efficiency of >10%. The benefits of such architectures include the separation of light absorption from charge transport by allowing for lateral extraction of charge from the pillar structure [57] (**Figure 9**), as well as improved optical absorption through extreme light trapping in these structures that is also omnidirectional [58, 59].

Nanowire/pillar approaches also offer potential for improvements in the performance of polymer-based solar cells. It is well known that the so-called excitonic PV cells require dimensions less that 10 nm for effective charge separation due to the low transport lengths in polymer semiconductors [60]. Active efforts for developing templates for such approaches are underway [61].

Silicon has been the most widely studied micro/nanowire material for PV application. This is because Si is the second most earth-abundant material and most dominant in the PV industry, yet the cost remains relatively high compared with thin films. If one can develop a thin-film Si device that uses less Si yet has equivalent efficiency to a polycrystalline PV cell (14–16%), this would have a dramatic impact on the market. Efforts to reengineer Si solar cells at the micro- or nanoscale have focused exactly on this point. There have been two major approaches to forming Si devices, the first being the use of CVD to grow Si wires on low-cost substrates

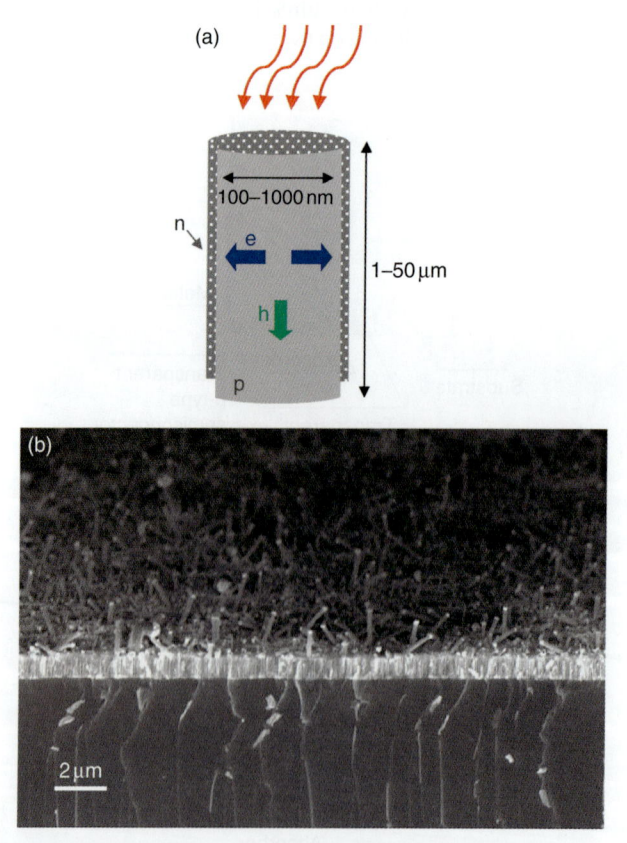

Figure 9 (a) Schematic of the operation of a nanowire solar cell (not drawn to scale) and (b) cross-sectional scanning electronic micrograph of templated SINWs.

[53] and the second being the wet or dry etching of Si wires into prefabricated Si films or substrates [59, 62]. The former has obvious processing advantages since it involves direct deposition as opposed to a subtractive process, whereas the latter has yielded better performance. A modified approach has recently been to deposit Si microwires on single-crystal Si wafers and then transfer them to another substrate while reusing the wafers for subsequent growth [63].

Initial devices reported in the 2005–07 time frame obtained efficiencies in the range of 0.1–1.3% [53, 62, 64]. A significant challenge was the development of severe shunting that lead to poor performance of the solar cells. It also became clear that control of the diameter of the wire is important, since a too small diameter leads to fully depleted wires and greater susceptibility to surface recombination. More recently, efforts have been made to produce devices based on prepatterned pillar arrays. Such devices have yield efficiencies in the range of 6–9% [63, 65, 66], whereas a-Si-based devices achieved efficiency of 6–11% [55, 67].

A related approach has been to implement wire morphologies in III–V material systems. These systems are typically direct band gap, so the benefit here is not directly related to light trapping, rather, it solves problems associated with defects in III–V systems by allowing improved charge collection, particularly for carriers generated near the top surface of the micro/nanostructure. Furthermore, one can implement the III–V device without the use of an ARC, which is required in III–V modules due to the high refractive index of these materials. Finally, by using nanostructure, it may be possible to fabricate high-efficiency III–V devices on low-cost substrates, which is not possible today. This is enabled by micro/nanopillars because the surfaces are available for both charge extraction and passivation, whereas polycrystalline III–V films have yielded relatively low PV performance since the grain boundaries are generally regions of high recombination velocity [68].

Initial work on III–V nanowire solar cells produced devices with efficiency of less than 1% [69]. This was attributed to the fact that (1) the wires were fabricated by molecular beam epitaxy (MBE) rather than by MOCVD, which is not a conformal process, (2) due to this fact it was not possible to fully coat the p–n junction around the nanowires, and (3) Zn was used as a dopant and was found to be diffused throughout the device structure, thus impacting the p–n doping profile. A GaAs device based on randomly grown MOCVD-produced nanowires yielded an efficiency of 1.65% [70], whereas patterned MOCVD-produced GaAs nanowire solar cells showed an efficiency as high as 2.54% [71]. In this case, it was shown that the use of a TCO with such a device can lead to losses due to the poor contact quality. InP nanowire arrays were also applied to solar cells and showed an efficiency of ~3% [56]. GaAs micro/nanopillar solar cells were also characterized in detail by Tsakalakos et al., with the goal of understanding the impact of higher junction area on the PV device performance parameters [72]. It was shown that while the FF and V_{OC} do decrease with increased junction area, it is not expected to be a significant loss factor and can be counterbalanced by an increase in J_{SC} by improved antireflection or light-trapping effects. Stable devices with active area efficiency as high as ~11% were demonstrated in GaAs substrates. This shows that indeed the concept of using known high-efficiency PV materials in a novel nano- or microstructured format is viable.

1.23.4 Quantum Structures

Nanostructures also enable the implementation of new materials and device physics in solar cells. Many examples of this in the scientific literature are emerging. Quantum nanostructures have the potential to provide improved electrical performance through better mobility, improved optical absorption, as well as new energy conversion mechanisms through novel band structures and device structures. For example, QDs are being proposed as a way to create multijunctions by using quantum confinement in Si QDs as a function of size [73]. QDs are also being utilized as a possible method to implement intermediate band (IB) solar cells [74]. The field of multi-exciton generation (MEG), in which more than one electron–hole pair is generated per incident photon to improve efficiency, takes advantage of quantum confinement effects to improve the MEG process. This is being explored in QDs using optical characterization methods [75], and more recent work has shown the potential to apply MEG to electrically contacted one-dimensional carbon nanotube (CNT) devices [76]. Colloidal QDs (PbSe) have been used in a Schottky junction configuration with a high short-circuit current density level of >20 mA cm^{-2} [77]. These concepts hold great promise in future PV module concepts. An account of these major quantum-related PV approaches/mechanisms will be provided below.

1.23.4.1 Multi-Exciton Generation

MEG is an example of the use of quantum confinement to produce a fundamentally novel conversion mechanism. Here the goal is to increase the number of electron–hole pairs generated per given incident photon. This is akin to the well-known impact ionization mechanisms known in bulk solid-state devices such as avalanche photodiodes. In QDs, impact ionization, or now MEG, which is an inverse Auger process, becomes enhanced due to selection rules [78]. Furthermore, it is well known that in a quantum confined system, the density of states of phonon modes becomes limited, which has the effect of both limiting thermal transport as well as reducing thermalization of hot carriers. This further promotes the multiplication factor for MEG as compared with bulk crystals. As a result, the limiting efficiency for PV conversion increases from ~31% to ~45%, and the optimal band gap is shifted from ~1.45 to ~0.95 eV.

While the mechanism for MEG is conceptually straightforward, there are many practical challenges that must be considered in order for it to be useful. The most important aspect is the fact that the carriers must be effectively extracted from the absorbing MEG medium with minimal recombination. This points to the fact that the role of both bulk recombination centers and surface states is relatively unexplored in systems that can produce MEG. In complex systems, it is not clear how charge will effectively be extracted without recombination losses. Finally, it is challenging to consider how reasonable FFs can be achieved with such devices. Nevertheless, there are recent works that show promise in both demonstrating the MEG mechanism and illuminate possible paths for practical implementation.

1.23.4.1.1 Sensitized SCs
Recently, Parkinson and co-workers showed that it is possible to obtain MEG in a complex absorber system [79]. The device was based on a PbS QDs bonded to titania surfaces measured in an electrochemical setup. Quantum yields as high as 180% were measured for high-energy photon excitation, which proves that it is possible to achieve MEG in a complicated device structure.

1.23.4.1.2 Carbon nanotubes
In a quite different approach to implementing MEG, it has been recently shown that it is possible to achieve MEG in electrically contacted single nanostructures such as CNTs [76]. A single nanotube field-effect transistor device was configured in a split-gate configuration such that the CNT can be electrostatically doped to form a p–n junction. Below a temperature of 90K, it was observed that as the devices were illuminated with higher intensity and higher photon energy, that discrete current steps were displayed in the current–voltage characteristics (constant gate voltage, source-drain voltage sweep). Furthermore, it was shown that the magnitude of the voltage steps decreases with increasing CNT diameter, which is evidence that indeed quantum confinement of the band structure is occurring, leading to higher band gap energy E_{11} transition with finer diameter. The results clearly showed evidence of multiple electron–hole pair creation in these devices. However, for practical application, there are many challenges that would need to be addressed. These include the creation of large-scale parallel arrays of CNTs with the same band gap that also can be electrostatically or chemically doped to form a p–n junction. Also, the impact of the lateral electric field on the observed MEG process is not clear. More experiments and theory are required, but this points to a possible fruitful path to practical implementation of MEG in the future.

1.23.4.1.3 Quantum dots
Much of the early experimental work on MEG has been performed by Nozik and co-workers [80] and Klimov and co-workers [81] with QD assemblies. Experiments based on optical absorption studies have been performed, which have shown evidence of MEG. These are typically based on QDs in solution. There has been some controversy in regard to such measurements, since they tend to be very sensitive to experimental factors such as the dielectric constant of the solution, laser power, the optical methods and analyses used to evaluate this effect, and so on [82]. Nevertheless, recent data suggest that indeed MEG does occur in these systems, but it is not as efficient as has been reported. Furthermore, attempts to fabricate QD-based MEG devices have to date not yielded an MEG effect [83, 84], though QD solar cells based on a Schottky contact have produced devices with promising efficiency of ~6% [85].

1.23.4.2 Hot Carriers
Another emerging high-efficiency concept based on novel energy conversion mechanisms is the hot carrier solar cell (HCSC). As has been described above, charge carriers that are excited to states above the conduction band edge typically relax back to the edge via emission of photons, the so-called thermalization process. This leads to significant loss in the energy of the system through heat, which is of course one of the main fundamental loss mechanisms leading to the detailed balance or Shockley–Queisser (SQ) efficiency limit. If one could extract these high-energy charge carriers prior to thermalization, the efficiency of the solar cell would significantly increase, both in the theoretical limit and practically. It has been estimated that a HCSC increases the SQ limit to ~55% for AM0 irradiation [86].

There are some significant practical challenges to making a HCSC. The most important has to do with the timescale for thermalization. This is typically in the femtosecond time frame, which requires that the distribution of hot carriers be extracted in less than that time. This therefore necessitates the use of nanostructures that provide a charge-separating interface in very close proximity to the absorbing volume. Much attention has naturally focused on QDs as a result [87]. Furthermore, the interface must possess a band structure that can readily accept this energy distribution without the carriers losing energy upon transfer from the absorbing medium to the contact. Much attention has been focused on the development of the so-called energy-selective filter contacts that indeed can achieve this charge transfer without energy loss, though the exact structure and practical implementation of such a contact remains elusive [88].

1.23.4.2.1 Quantum dots
Until recently, there has been no experimental confirmation of hot carrier extraction from a semiconductor. However, Zhu and co-workers have recently reported the demonstration of such an effect using time-resolved SHG experiments of a PbSe QD layer assembled on a single-crystal titania surface [89]. This was possible because of the favorable band structure alignment between the quantized PbSe nanoparticles and the high-band gap titania. It was further shown, again through femtosecond optical measurements, that indeed there is a phonon recoil that occurs as the hot electron population leaves the QDs and enters the titania conductor. This is quite a remarkable result, and shows that it is indeed possible to extract hot carriers, though again there is significantly more research required to achieve practical implementation of an HCSC.

1.23.4.3 Intermediate Bands

Another so-called Generation III high-efficiency PV concept is the intermediate band solar cell (IBSC). Here the idea is to create a solid-state device that can effectively absorb low-energy photons not absorbed by the active material by introduction of a band of certain width within the band gap, as opposed to UC that is a purely optical mechanism for harnessing sub-band gap absorption. It has been shown theoretically that an IBSC can increase the limiting efficiency of the solar cell from 31% up to 63% for a device with a fundamental band gap of 1.93 eV and an intermediate band gap of ~0.7 eV [90].

Like the hot carrier effect, a functional IBSC device has only been demonstrated in the last 5 years. The reason why it is challenging is that the requirements for excited state lifetimes are very stringent, such that the carriers excited to the IB can be further excited to the conduction band by a second photon. If this does not occur, the charge carriers will immediately recombine. IBSCs have been attempted in several classes of nanostructures, including quantum wells (QWs) and QDs.

1.23.4.3.1 Quantum wells

Quantum well (QW) solar cells have been studied for over a decade, with perhaps the first work performed by Barnham and co-workers [91]. By using a strain balancing layer within the multiquantum well (MQW) stack, it was shown that a higher J_{SC} can be obtained by improving the sub-band gap EQE response of the device. While this did not prove that an IB is present, it was a first step toward such an approach. Subsequent work showed that it is possible to obtain an enhanced V_{OC} also in QW solar cells by taking advantage of Bragg reflectors that improve photon recycling [92]. These cells are particularly interesting as possible replacements for multijunction solar cells in concentrator PV systems.

1.23.4.3.2 Quantum dots

QD-based solar cells have to date shown the most promise as an implementation of IBSCs. This is a promising approach because an assembly of QDs embedded in a higher band gap matrix at relatively high packing density is able to form a collection of overlapping minibands that lead to a net effective IB structure [93]. Marti *et al.* were among the first to demonstrate IB to conduction band transitions in QD system fabricated in InAs multi-QDs embedded in a p–i–n GaAs device structure [94]. Efforts to demonstrate QD-based IBSCs have also focused on solution-based processing [95]. It was shown that valence band to IB and IB to conduction band transitions are possible within the same device by using highly mismatched alloys (HMAs) of GaN_xAs_{1-x} [96]. This was achieved in a III–V device structure and by combining J–V, QE, and light emission measurements. An HMA-based IBSC device was also demonstrated in ZnTe:O by Wang *et al.* [97]. Such devices show promising results, though much work remains to obtain performance that is competitive with conventional III–V PV devices. Key challenges include the formation of defects within the QD layers, doping, charge extraction, and limited absorption of the QD assemblies that require a very high density and thickness (which in turn leads to more extended defects and hence recombination).

1.23.4.4 Plasmonics

Another proposed mechanism to obtain improved PVs that also relies on the use of nanostructures is plasmonics [98]. A plasmon is a collective oscillation of the electron/Fermi sea within a metallic material, which is known to lead to varying resonance features in optical spectra, particularly as the size of a metallic nanoparticle is changed. This effect is referred to as localized surface plasmon resonance (LSPR), whereas one can also excite a traveling surface plasmon wave on a metal surface, often termed surface plasmon resonance (SPR). One of the important features of an SPR/LSPR is that the oscillation of the plasmons creates high electric fields in the near-surface region of the metal, and if the metal is a particle, one can obtain quite high electric field strengths in the vicinity or corners or edges of particles [99]. Ensembles of particles or holes in a film can lead to intriguing optical transmission spectra due to excitation of SPR [100], which can also be related to enhance scattering.

This latter effect was exploited by Green and co-workers [101], and Yu and co-workers [102] who showed that by placing random ensembles of particles on the surface of a solar cell it is possible to obtain an improved J_{SC}. Enhancement in the photocurrent in the range of 2–8 times was measured for bulk Si solar cells. This is exactly the region where the absorption coefficient is particularly low for Si due to the indirect band gap. The Ag particles showed that it is also possible to improve electroluminescence, as well as the promise of reducing the thickness of Si required. Concurrently, it was shown that Au nanoparticles improve the photocurrent of Si and a-Si solar cells in the short-wavelength portion of the spectrum, that is, below 500 nm. It was shown that this is directly related to the extinction coefficient of the particle arrays as a function of the mean particle size. It became clear, however, that the plasmonic particles act simply as a forward scattering layer, akin to an antireflection layer, and hence the density of particle must be finely controlled so that a significant back scattering loss does not occur as coverage becomes large [103].

One early idea for using nanoparticles, nanorods, nanotetrapods, and related structures as plasmonic enhancement features was to place them in the vicinity of the p–n junction such that the locally high electrical fields lead to improved absorption and charge carrier generation within the region of the junction [104]. While this has been attempted, there are many challenges with achieving a gain by such a mechanism. Since the plasmonic particles are typically Au or Ag, care must be taken so that the particles does neither shunt the junction nor create a space charge region that alters the function of the junction. Due to these facts, application of such a concept to an inorganic PV device has not been successful. It may be possible, however, to apply such particles within a dye-sensitized solar cell and achieve a performance gain [105].

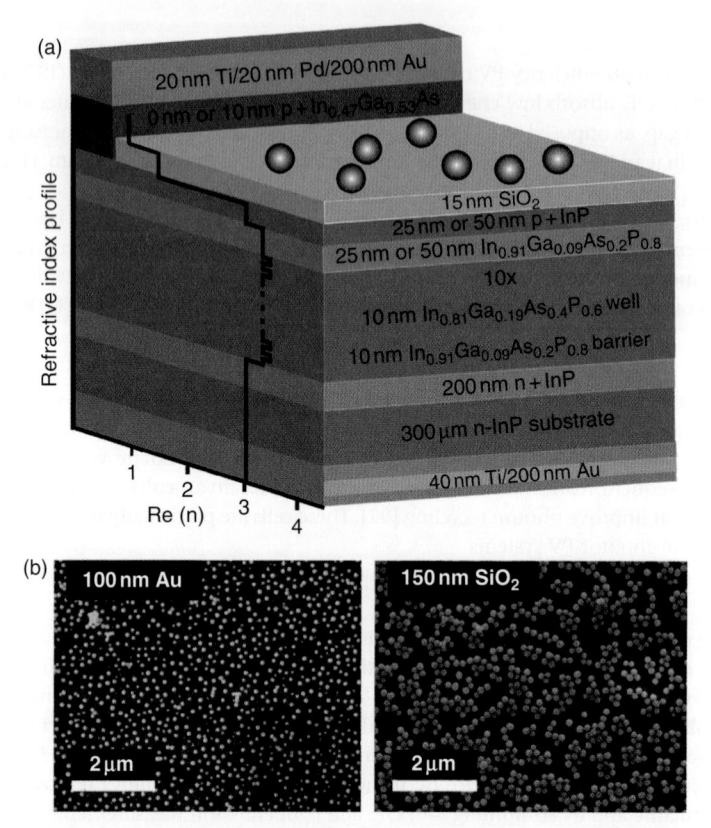

Figure 10 The use of plasmonic features to convert solar radiation to thin-film waveguide modes for ultrathin QW solar cells; (a) schematic device structure and (b) scanning electron microscopy images of Au and silica nanoparticles on the surface of a QW device [107].

Another use of plasmonics for enhanced PV devices has been the development of ordered plasmonic structures that can both focus energy to a particular location and do so with a predetermined wavelength. Essentially, the concept is to create an array of plasmonic antennas that emit light at a portion of the spectral response curve of the solar cell that is most optimum [106]. This is akin to a plasmonic metamaterial structure. To date, numerous simulations have shown the potential for such an approach, though more work is required to show a promising experimental improvement in device performance.

Plasmonic structures have also been proposed as a means to improve both the performance and materials utilization of solar cells. The concept is to utilize plasmonic features on the surface of an ultrathin absorber layer such that the incoming light can be converted to thin-film waveguide modes (**Figure 10**). This has been proposed by both Atwater and Polman [108] and Yu and co-workers [107], who calculated that it is possible to obtain J_{SC} increases on the order of 26%, while it reduces the amount of active material by 10–100 times. The latter group has indeed demonstrated this approach for III–V QW devices, with improvement in efficiency of up to 17%.

1.23.5 Outlook

The use of micro- and nanotechnologies in solar energy conversion has gained strong interest from the broader PV community. While there is much enthusiasm, this must be tempered also by the reality that there are many unknowns when applying new concepts to this field. However, it is apparent that the application of micro/nanotechnology to existing or conventional PV cells is the first area that will have an impact in a market sense. Companies such as Nanosolar and Solexant, Inc., are already actively commercializing or even producing solar modules containing thin-film active layers manufactured by solution processes using nanoparticle inks. The application of up- or downconverters, or ODAR layers, may have an impact in the near future on thin films or even Si module technologies. Many of the potential challenges with such approaches have already been discussed, but obtaining clear performance gains at low cost will be critical.

In the longer term, it is expected that novel device architectures will be introduced to the market. Concepts such as wire/pillar-based devices are actively being pursued by several companies. It can be expected that in the long run, devices based on Generation III concepts such as MEG, IBSC, and HCSCs will achieve performance levels that are competitive with conventional technologies. Clearly, significant basic research is required to harness the potential of these novel conversion mechanisms, including fundamental physics, materials science, and device physics research. If one can pursue such a high efficiency with truly low-cost technology, the use of solar energy would be truly revolutionized and significant market adoption would occur.

It has been noted above that cost is an important factor in considering new PV technologies. While clearly some concepts are too advanced for active consideration of cost, it is certainly useful to begin to assess this question with regard to maturing technologies. The question of cost is closely linked to manufacturing technology and to materials. With regard to materials, it is important that the elements used are (1) earth-abundant to the extent possible, (2) nontoxic, and (3) form crystal structures that have the right band gap and defect structure so that they are amenable to flexible manufacturing approaches. As for manufacturing, these materials should also be processable at low temperatures, and to the extent, possible to evaporate or sublime congruently so that minimal control of stoichiometry is required, if they are binary or more complex compositions. Processes should be chosen that are inherently low cost, both in operation and in CAPEX. These include sputtering, closed-space sublimation, and solution-based deposition, among others. Higher-cost processes should yield significantly higher performance from the device.

1.23.6 Conclusions

In summary, micro- and nanotechnologies are under intense research and development for application to solar energy conversion. These implementations manifest themselves in several strategies. The most immediate impact is by application of nanoparticles to low-cost processing of conventional thin films in the form of cast or coated inks that are subsequently sintered. Various nanostructured coatings are also being developed to improve light collection by the PV module via an antireflection effect. In the medium term, there are multiple efforts to create novel nano- or microstructured architectures, though employing conventional device physics or conversion mechanisms. These are exemplified by the ETA cell, wire-based solar cells, and BHJ OPVs. Finally, longer-term basic research is focused on application of novel conversion mechanisms and quantum structures for ultrahigh efficiency. Examples include MEG, HCSC, and IBs. Each of the above approaches is presented with potential performance and/or cost benefits, as well as in some cases substantial fundamental physics, chemistry, materials, or device challenges. In some respects, the PV industry of today is like the computing industry of the late 1950s and 1960s in that there are many technologies under rapid development. Silicon is the incumbent technology with thin films growing. Given the degree of innovation in technology and science, one can be cautiously optimistic that micro- and nanotechnologies will begin to make a meaningful impact in the solar energy industry in the second half of this decade, if not before. Significant efforts in research and development of advanced micro/nanotechnologies for solar energy are required and should be sustained in order to help make solar energy one of the primary, if not the primary, sources of energy generation in the world [109, 110].

References

[1] Tollefson J (2011) How green is my future? *Nature* 473: 134–135.
[2] Shah A, Torres P, Tscharner R, *et al.* (1999) Photovoltaic technology: The case for thin-film solar cells. *Science* 285: 692.
[3] Green MA, Emery K, Hishikawa Y, and Warta W (2011) Solar cell efficiency tables (version 37). *Progress in Photovoltaics: Research and Applications* 19: 84–92.
[4] [Online] National Renewable Energy Laboratory http://rredc.nrel.gov/solar/spectra/am1.5/.
[5] Green MA (2003) *Third Generation Photovoltaics: Advanced Solar Energy Conversion*. Berlin, Germany: Springer Science+Business Media.
[6] Queisser W and Shockley HJ (1961) Detailed balance limit of efficiency of p-n junction solar cells. *Journal of Applied Physics* 32: 510.
[7] Henry CH (1980) Limiting efficiencies of ideal single and multiple energy gap terrestrial solar cells. *Journal of Applied Physics* 51: 4494–4500.
[8] Kayes BM, Nie H, Twist R, *et al.* (2011) 27.6% conversion efficiency, a new record for single-junction solar cells under 1 sun illumination. *Proceedings of the 37th IEEE Photovoltaics Specialist Conference*. Seattle, WA: IEEE.
[9] Basol BM (1990) Thin film CdTe solar cells: A review. *21st IEEE Photovoltaic Specialists Conference* 1: 588.
[10] van Sark WGJHM, Meijerink A, Schropp REI, *et al.* (2005) Enhancing solar cell efficiency by using spectral converters. *Solar Energy Materials and Solar Cells* 87: 395.
[11] Shalav A, Richards BS, and Green MA (2005) Application of NaYF$_4$:Er^{3+} up-converting phosphors for enhanced near-infrared silicon solar cell response. *Applied Physics Letters* 86: 013505.
[12] Strumpel C, McCann M, and Beaucarne G (2007) Modifying the solar spectrum to enhance silicon solar cell efficiency: An overview of available materials. *Solar Energy Materials and Solar Cells* 91: 238.
[13] Trupke T, Green M, and Würfel P (2002) Improving solar cell efficiencies by up-conversion of sub-band-gap light. *Journal of Applied Physics* 92: 4117.
[14] Wang F, Han Yu, Lim CS, *et al.* (2010) Simultaneous phase and size control of upconversion nanocrystals through lanthanide doping. *Nature* 463: 1061–1065.
[15] De Wild J, Rath JK, Meijerink A, *et al.* (2010) Enhanced near-infrared response of a-Si:H solar cells with β-NaYF$_4$:Yb^{3+} (18%), Er^{3+} (2%) upconversion phosphors. *Solar Energy Materials and Solar Cells* 94: 2395–2398.
[16] Fischer S, *et al.* (2010) *Journal of Applied Physics* 108(4): 044912–044912-11.
[17] Cheng YY, Fückel B, Roberts DA, *et al.* (eds.) (2010) Molecular approaches to third generation photovoltaics: Photochemical up-conversion. Loucas Tsakalakos. *Proceedings of the SPIE*, San Diego, CA, USA. Next Generation (Nano) Photonic and Cell Technologies for Solar Energy Conversion. vol. 7772, pp.777207–777207-10.
[18] Singh-Rachforda TN and Castellano FN (2010) Photon upconversion based on sensitized triplet–triplet annihilation. *Coordination Chemistry Reviews* 254(21–22): 2560–2573.
[19] Trupke T, Green M, and Würfel P (2002) Improving solar cell efficiencies by down-conversion of high energy photons. *Journal of Applied Physics* 92: 1668.
[20] Dexter DL (1953) A theory of sensitized luminescence in solids. *Journal of Chemical Physics* 21: 836–850.
[21] Piper WW, DeLuca JA, and Ham FS (1974) Cascade fluorescent decay in Pr^{3+}-doped fluorides: Achievement of a quantum yield greater than unity for emission of visible light. *Journal of Luminescence* 8: 344.
[22] Wegh RT, Donker H, Oskam KD, and Meijerink A (1999) Visible quantum cutting in LiGdF$_4$:Eu^{3+} through down conversion. *Science* 283: 663–666.
[23] Meijer J-M, Aarts L, Bryan M, *et al.* Downconversion for solar cells in YF$_3$:Nd^{3+}, Yb^{3+}.
[24] Loureiro SM, Setlur A, Heward W, *et al.* (2005) First observation of quantum splitting behavior in nanocrystalline SrAl$_{12}$O$_{19}$:Pr, Mg phosphor. *Chemistry of Materials* 17: 3108–3113.
[25] Sark WGJHM, *et al.* (2004) Modeling improvement of spectral response of solar cells by deployment of spectral converters containing semiconductor nanocrystals. *Semiconductors* 38: 962–969.

[26] Hong BC and Kawano K (2003) PL and PLE studies of KMgF$_3$:Sm crystal and the effect of its wavelength conversion on CdS/CdTe solar cell. *Solar Energy Materials and Solar Cells* 80: 417–432.

[27] Klampaftis E, Ross D, McIntosh KR, and Richards BS (2009) Enhancing the performance of solar cells via luminescent down-shifting of the incident spectrum. *Solar Energy Materials and Solar Cells* 93: 1182–1194.

[28] Klampaftis E and Richards BS (2011) Improvement in multi-crystalline silicon solar cell efficiency via addition of luminescent material to EVA encapsulation layer. *Progress in Photovoltaics: Research and Applications* 19: 345–351.

[29] Švrček V, Slaoui A, and Muller J-C (2004) Silicon nanocrystals as light converter for solar cells. *Thin Solid Films* 451–452: 384–388.

[30] Ballif C, Dicker J, Borchert D, and Hofmann T (2004) Solar glass with industrial porous SiO$_2$ antireflection coating: Measurements of photovoltaic module properties improvement and modelling of yearly energy yield gain. *Solar Energy Materials and Solar Cells* 82: 331–344.

[31] Clapham PB and Hutley MC (1973) Reduction of lens reflexion by the 'moth eye' principle. *Nature* 244: 281–282.

[32] Aydin C, Zaslavsky A, Sonek GJ, and Goldstein J (2002) Reduction of reflection losses in ZnGeP$_2$ using motheye antireflection surface relief structures. *Applied Physics Letters* 80: 2242.

[33] Hadobas K, Kirsch S, Carl A, et al. (2000) Reflection properties of arrayed silicon surfaces. *Nanotechnology* 11: 161–164.

[34] Alsema EA and de Wild-Scholten MJ (2006) Environmental impacts of crystalline silicon photovoltaic module production. *13th CIRP International Conference on Life Cycle Engineering*. Leuven, Belgium, 31 May–2 June.

[35] Birkmire RW (2008) Pathways to improved performance and processing of CdTe and CuInSe$_2$ based modules. *33rd Photovoltaic Specialists Conference*. pp. 1–6. IEEE.

[36] Britt J, Wiedeman S, Beck M, and Albright S (2003) Process development for CIGS based thin film photovoltaic modules. Global Solar Energy, Inc. Golden, CO: National Renewable Energy Laboratory. http://www.nrel.gov/docs/fy03osti/33651.pdf.NREL/SR-520-33651

[37] Basol B (2010) Commercialization of high efficiency low cost CIGS technology based on electroplating. SoloPower, Inc., NREL, http://www1.eere.energy.gov/solar/pdfs/48590.pdf. NREL/SR-520-48590.

[38] Liu W, Mitzi DB, Yuan M, et al. (2010) 12% efficiency CuIn(Se, S)$_2$ photovoltaic device prepared using a hydrazine solution process. *Chemistry of Materials* 22: 1010–1014.

[39] Guo Q, Hillhouse HW, and Agrawal R (2009) Synthesis of Cu$_2$ZnSnS$_4$ nanocrystal ink and its use for solar cells. *Journal of the American Chemical Society* 131: 11672–11673.

[40] Sager BM, Yu D, and Robinson MR (2007) Coated Nanoparticles and Quantum Dots for Solution-Based Fabrication of Photovoltaic Cells. U.S. Patent 7,306,823, 11 December 2007, B2.

[41] Liu G, et al. (2011) Silicon Inks for Thin Film Solar Cell Formation, Corresponding Methods and Solar Cell Structures. U.S. Patent 20,110,120,537, 26 May 2011.

[42] Antoniadis H, Jiang F, Shan W, Liu Y (2010) All screen printed mass produced silicon ink selective emitter solar cells. *35th IEEE Photovoltaic Specialists Conference (PVSC)*. Honolulu, HI: IEEE.

[43] Yablonovitch E, et al. (1987) Extreme selectivity in the lift-off of epitaxial GaAs films. *Applied Physics Letters* 51: 2222–2224.

[44] Aspar B, et al. (1999) Smart-cut(R) process using metallic bonding: Application to transfer of Si, GaAs, InP thin films. *Electronics Letters* 35: 1024–1025.

[45] Lin Z-M and Chang C-H (2011) Structure design for single crystalline film Si solar cells. *Thin Solid Films* 519(15): 5118–5121.

[46] Tsakalakos L (2008) Nanostructures for photovoltaics. *Materials Science and Engineering R: Reports* 62: 175–189.

[47] Atwater HA (2011) Bending light to our will. *MRS Bulletin* 36: 57–62.

[48] Siebentritt S, Ernst K, Fischer Ch-H, et al. *Proceedings of the 14th*.

[49] Kaiser I, Ernst K, Fischer Ch-H, et al. (2001) The eta-solar cell with CuInS$_2$: A photovoltaic cell concept using an extremely thin absorber (eta). *Solar Energy Materials and Solar Cells* 67: 89–96.

[50] Nanu M, Schoonman J, and Goossens A (2005) Nanocomposite three-dimensional solar cells obtained by chemical spray deposition. *Nano Letters* 5: 1716.

[51] Park SH, Roy A, Beaupré S, et al. (2009) Bulk heterojunction solar cells with internal quantum efficiency approaching 100%. *Nature Photonics* 3: 297–302.

[52] Luo L, Lin C-J, Tsai C-Y, et al. (2010) Effects of aggregation and electron injection on photovoltaic performance of porphyrin-based solar cells with oligo(phenylethynyl) links inside TiO$_2$ and Al$_2$O$_3$ nanotube arrays. *Physical Chemistry Chemical Physics* 12: 1064–1071.

[53] Tsakalakos L, Balch J, Fronheiser J, et al. (2007) Silicon nanowire solar cells. *Applied Physics Letters* 91: 233117.

[54] Fan Z, et al. (2009) Three-dimensional nanopillar-array photovoltaics on low-cost and flexible substrates. *Nature Materials* 8: 348.

[55] Zhu J, Hsu C-M, Yu Z, et al. (2010) Nanodome solar cells with efficient light management and self-cleaning. *Nano Letters* 10: 1979–1984.

[56] Goto H et al. (2009) Growth of core-shell InP nanowires for photovoltaic application by selective-area metal organic vapor phase epitaxy. *Applied Physics Express* 2: 035004.

[57] Kayes BM, et al. (2005) Comparison of the device physics principles of planar and radial p-n junction nanorod solar cells. *Journal of Applied Physics* 97: 114302.

[58] Kelzenberg MD, Boettcher SW, Petykiewicz JA, et al. (2010) Enhanced absorption and carrier collection in Si wire arrays for photovoltaic applications. *Nature Materials* 9: 239–244.

[59] Tsakalakos L, Balch J, Fronheiser J, et al. (2007) Strong broadband optical absorption in silicon nanowire films. *Journal of Nanophotonics* 1: 013552.

[60] Yu G, et al. (1995) *Science* 270: 1789–1791.

[61] Gowrishankar V, et al. (2008) Exciton harvesting, charge transfer, and charge-carrier transport in amorphous-silicon nanopillar/polymer hybrid solar cells. *Journal of Applied Physics* 103: 064511-1-8.

[62] Peng KQ, et al. (2005) Aligned single-crystalline Si nanowire arrays for photovoltaic applications. *Small* 1: 1062–1067.

[63] Kelzenberg MD, Turner-Evans DB, Putnam MC, et al. (2011) High-performance Si microwire photovoltaics. *Energy and Environmental Science* 4: 866–871.

[64] Tsakalakos L, Tsakalakos L, Balch J, et al. (2008) Silicon nanowire solar cells: Device physics, fabrication, and optoelectronic properties. *23rd European Photovoltaic Solar Energy Conference*. 1AP.1.3.

[65] Yang E and Garnett P (2010) Light trapping in Silicon nanowire solar cells. *Nano Letters* 10: 1082–1087.

[66] Yoon HP, Yuwen YuA, Kendrick CE, et al. (2010) Enhanced conversion efficiencies for pillar array solar cells fabricated from crystalline silicon with short minority carrier diffusion lengths. *Applied Physics Letters* 96: 213503.

[67] Naughton MJ, Kempa K, Ren ZF, et al. (2010) Efficient nanocoax-based solar cells. 4: 181–183.

[68] Heller A (1981) Chemical control of surface and grain boundary recombination in semiconductors. *Photoeffects at Semiconductor-Electrolyte Interfaces* 146: 57–77, ACS Symposium Series.

[69] Czaban JA, Thompson DA, and LaPierre RR (2009) GaAs core-shell nanowires for photovoltaic applications. *Nano Letters* 9(1): 148–154.

[70] Cirlin G, Bouravleuv A, Soshnikov I, et al. (2009) Photovoltaic properties of p-doped GaAs nanowire arrays grown on n-type GaAs(111)B substrate. *Nanoscale Research Letters* 5: 360–363.

[71] Mariani G, Wong PS, Katzenmeyer AM, et al. (2011) Patterned radial GaAs nanopillar solar cells. *Nano Letters* 11: 2490–2494.

[72] Tsakalakos L, Balch JE, Byun AT, et al. (2010) High efficiency III-V micro/nano-pillar solar cells: Bulk devices & growth on metal foils. *25th European Photovoltaic Solar Energy Conference and Exhibition/5th World Conference on Photovoltaic Energy Conversion*. pp. 274–279. Valencia, Spain.

[73] Green MA, et al. All-silicon tandem cells based on 'artificial' semiconductor synthesised using silicon quantum dots in a dielectric matrix. *Proceedings of the 20th European Photovoltaic Solar Energy Conference and Exhibition*. p. 3, Barcelona, Spain.

[74] Marti A, et al. (2006) Production of photocurrent due to intermediate-to-conduction-band transitions: A demonstration of a key operating principle of the intermediate-band solar cell. *Physical Review Letters* 97: 247701.

[75] Nozik AJ (2008) Multiple exciton generation in semiconductor quantum dots. *Chemical Physics Letters* 457: 3–11.

[76] Gabor NM, et al. Extremely efficient multiple electron-hole pair generation in carbon nanotube photodiodes. *Science* 325(5946): 1367–1371.

[77] Luther JM (2008) Schottky solar cells based on colloidal nanocrystal films. *Nano Letters* 8(10): 3488–3492.

[78] Nozik AJ (2010) Nanoscience and nanostructures for photovoltaics and solar fuels. *Nano Letters* 10: 2735–2741.
[79] Sambur JB, Novet T, and Parkinson BA (2010) Multiple exciton collection in a sensitized photovoltaic system. *Science* 330(6000): 63–66.
[80] Nozik AJ, et al. (2006) Third generation solar photon conversion: Multiple exciton generation in semiconductor quantum dots. *Polymeric Materials: Science and Engineering* 95: 161.
[81] Schaller RD, Agranovich VM, Klimov VI (2005) High-efficiency carrier multiplication through direct photogeneration of multi-excitons via virtual single-exciton states. *Nature Physics* 1: 189–194.
[82] Trinh, MT et al. (2008) In spite of recent doubts carrier multiplication does occur in PbSe nanocrystals. *Nano Letters* 8: 1713–1718.
[83] Luther, JM, et al. (2010) Stability assessment on a 3% bilayer PbS/ZnO quantum dot heterojunction solar cell. *Advanced Materials* 22: 3704–3707.
[84] Nozik, AJ, et al. (2010) Semiconductor quantum dots and quantum dot arrays and applications of multiple exciton generation to third-generation photovoltaic solar cells. *Chemical Reviews* 110: 6873–6890.
[85] Luther, JM, et al. (2008) Schottky solar cells based on colloidal nanocrystal films. *Nano Letters* 5.
[86] Wurfel P (1997) Solar energy conversion with hot electrons from impact ionization. *Solar Energy Materials and Solar Cells* 46: 43–52.
[87] König, D, et al. (2010) Hot carrier solar cells: Principles, materials and design. *Physica E* 42: 2862–2866.
[88] Yagi, S, Oshima, R and Okada, Y (2009) Evaluation of selective energy contact for hot carrier solar cells based on III–V semiconductors. *34th IEEE Photovoltaic Specialists Conference (PVSC).* pp. 000530–000533, IEEE.
[89] Tisdale WA, Williams KJ, Timp BA, et al. (2010) Hot-electron transfer from semiconductor nanocrystals. *Science* 328(5985): 1543–1547.
[90] Cuadra L, Martí A, and Luque A (2004) Present status of intermediate band solar cell research. *Thin Solid Films* 451–452: 593–599.
[91] Ekins-Daukes NJ, Barnham KWJ, Connolly JP, et al. (1999) Strain-balanced GaAsP/InGaAs quantum well solar cells. *Applied Physics Letters* 75: 4195.
[92] Johnson D, et al. (2007) Observation of photon recycling in strain-balanced quantum well solar cells. *Applied Physics Letters* 90: 213505.
[93] Shao Q, Balandin AA, Fedoseyev AI, and Turowski M (2007) Intermediate-band solar cells based on quantum dot supracrystals. *Applied Physics Letters* 91: 163503.
[94] Marti A, Antolin E, Stanley CR, et al. (2006) Production of photocurrent due to intermediate-to-conduction-band transitions: A demonstration of a key operating principle of the intermedia. *Physical Review Letters* 97: 247701.
[95] Raffaelle RP, Castro SL, Hepp AF, and Bailey SG (2002) Quantum dot solar cells. *Progress in Photovoltaics: Research and Applications* 10: 433–439.
[96] Loipez N, Reichertz LA, Yu KM, et al. (2011) Engineering the electronic band structure for multiband solar cells. *Physical Review Letters* 106: 028701.
[97] Wang OW, Lin, AS, and Phillips JD (2009) Intermediate-band photovoltaic solar cell based on ZnTe. *Applied Physics Letters* 95: 011103.
[98] Maier SA and Atwater HA (2005) Plasmonics: Localization and guiding of electromagnetic energy in metal/dielectric structures. *Journal of Applied Physics* 98: 011101.
[99] Haes AJ, Zou S, Schatz GC, and Van Duyne RP (2004) A nanoscale optical biosensor: The long range distance dependence of the localized surface plasmon resonance of noble metal nanoparticles. *Journal of Physical Chemistry B* 108: 109–116.
[100] Drolo AQ, Gordon R, Leathem B, and Kavanagh KL (2004) Surface plasmon sensor based on the enhanced light transmission through arrays of nanoholes in gold films. *Langmuir* 20: 4813–4815.
[101] Pillai S, Catchpole KR, Trupke T, and Green MA (2007) Surface plasmon enhanced silicon solar cells. *Journal of Applied Physics* 101: 093105.
[102] Derkacs D, Lim SH, Matheu P, et al. (2006) Improved performance of amorphous silicon solar cells via scattering from surface plasmon polaritons in nearby metallic nanoparticles. *Applied Physics Letters* 89: 093103.
[103] Matheu P, Lim SH, Derkacs D, et al. (2008) Metal and dielectric nanoparticle scattering for improved optical absorption in photovoltaic devices. *Applied Physics Letters* 93: 113108.
[104] Atwater HA and Polman A (2010) Plasmonics for improved photovoltaic devices. *Nature Materials* 9: 205–213.
[105] Qi J, Dang X, Hammond PT, and Belcher AM (2011) Highly efficient plasmon-enhanced dye-sensitized solar cells through metal@oxide core–shell nanostructure. *ACS Nano*.
[106] Alici KB, Ozbay E, and Tsakalakos L (eds.) (2010) Photonic metamaterial absorber designs for infrared solar-cell. *Next Generation (Nano) Photonic and Cell Technologies for Solar Energy Conversion.* vol. 7772, pp. 77721B–77721B-3. San Diego, CA: SPIE.
[107] Derkacs D, Chen WV, Matheu PM, et al. (2008) Nanoparticle-induced light scattering for improved performance of quantum-well solar cells. *Applied Physics Letters* 93: 091107.
[108] Polman HA and Albert A (2010) Plasmonics for improved photovoltaic devices. *Nature Materials* 9: 205–213.
[109] Richards, BS and McIntosh KR (2007) Overcoming the poor short wavelength spectral response of CdS/CdTe photovoltaic modules via luminescence down-shifting: Ray-tracing simulations. *Progress in Photovoltaics* 15: 27–34.
[110] Mukherjee S, Sudarsan V, Vatsa RK, and Tyagi AK (2009) Luminescence studies on lanthanide ions (Eu^{3+}, Dy^{3+} and Tb^{3+}) doped YAG:Ce nano-phosphors. *Journal of Luminescence* 129: 69–72.

1.24 Upconversion

TW Schmidt and MJY Tayebjee, The University of Sydney, Sydney, NSW, Australia

© 2012 Elsevier Ltd. All rights reserved.

1.24.1	Introduction	533
1.24.2	Single Threshold Solar Cells	534
1.24.3	Upconversion-Assisted Solar Cells: Equivalent Circuits	535
1.24.4	Solar Concentration	538
1.24.5	Definition of Upconversion Efficiency	538
1.24.5.1	Monochromatic Optical Efficiency	539
1.24.5.2	Photoelectrical Efficiency	540
1.24.6	Practical Implementation	540
1.24.6.1	Rare Earths	540
1.24.6.1.1	Spectroscopy of rare-earth ions	540
1.24.6.1.2	Upconversion with rare earths	540
1.24.6.2	Upconversion with Organic Molecules	541
1.24.6.2.1	Molecular photophysics	542
1.24.6.2.2	Photochemical upconversion	543
1.24.6.2.3	Annihilation statistics	543
1.24.6.2.4	Experimentally achieved high efficiency	543
1.24.6.3	Comparison between Organics and Rare Earths	546
1.24.7	Prospects	546
References		547
Further Reading		548

Glossary

Centrosymmetric Characterized by being symmetric with respect to inversion through the center.
Rare earths The *f*-block lanthanoid elements, and in some cases scandium and yttrium.
Shockley–Queisser limit The limiting energy conversion efficiency of a single threshold solar cell under 1 sun.
Triplet–triplet annihilation A bimolecular reaction between two triplet states to yield one excited state and one ground state.
Upconversion The conversion of a stream of lower energy photons into one of a higher energy.
Upconvertor A device capable of upconversion.

1.24.1 Introduction

Upconversion (UC) is a general term used to describe the conversion of a stream of low-energy photons to a stream of higher-energy photons, the 'up' here referring to energy. There are various ways in which this may be achieved. For instance, a high-peak-power laser pulse propagating through a noncentrosymmetric medium may induce a second-order response in the polarization of the material. Since the square of a sinusoidal wave may be written in terms of one of twice the frequency, second harmonic light can be emitted by the polarized medium. This second harmonic generation (SHG) is widely used in laser applications [1]. Where two light pulses of different frequencies interact in a similar medium to that which exhibits SHG, light at the sum and difference of the two frequencies may be produced. Sum-frequency generation (SFG) is exploited in solid-state tunable lasers and also in ultrafast luminescence experiments.

The UC phenomena on which we will concentrate in this chapter are incoherent phenomena, described in terms of the absorption of multiple photons rather than the nonlinear response of a medium to an intense, coherent pulse of light. In such a way, it is hoped that UC will become efficient under $mW\,cm^{-2}$ illumination, comparable to unconcentrated solar radiation. The recovery of subband gap light in a single threshold photovoltaic device by UC promises to increase solar energy conversion efficiencies, especially in high-band gap devices such as amorphous silicon and organic solar cells.

In this chapter, we revise the theory of single-junction solar cells and extend the treatment to cells enhanced with an upconvertor. The limiting efficiencies are established for various cases, with several different equivalent circuits considered. Following, the two leading technologies are reviewed, and their future application is considered.

1.24.2 Single Threshold Solar Cells

Single threshold solar cells are photovoltaic energy conversion devices comprised of a material transparent to photons of energy below the threshold E_g, corresponding to the band gap in the case of a semiconductor. Here we utilize equations based on a master equation model of the absorber, as described by Tayebjee *et al.* [2]. This differs from the usual treatment in the form of the emission rate, where stimulated emission is held to be negligible. As discussed by Hirst and Ekins-Daukes [3], this approximation is found to be applicable for realistic band gaps, where the voltage of the solar cell differs from the E_g by many times, k_BT.

The ideal current–voltage characteristic is given by the following [2]:

$$I = e[k - k' \exp((eV - E_g)/k_BT)] \quad [1]$$

where k is the rate of absorption of photons by the absorber and k' is the rate of emission of photons. The absorption rate is given by

$$k = \frac{\sigma}{hc} \int_0^{hc/E_g} \lambda F_\lambda^\odot \, d\lambda \quad [2]$$

where σ is the (step-function) cross section of the absorber and $F_\lambda^\odot$ is the solar spectral irradiance in Jm^{-2} nm^{-1} s^{-1} at wavelength λ. In all that follows, we utilize the solar spectrum as defined by ASTM G173-03 [4]. The rate of photon emission by the absorber is given by

$$k' = \frac{\sigma}{4\pi^2 c^2 \hbar^3} \int_{E_g}^{\infty} E^2 \exp(-(E - E_g)/k_BT) dE$$

$$= \frac{\sigma}{4\pi^2 c^2} \left(\frac{k_BT}{\hbar}\right)^3 \left[\left(\frac{E_g}{k_BT}\right)^2 + 2\left(\frac{E_g}{k_BT}\right) + 2\right] \quad [3]$$

where emission is assumed to take place over only one hemisphere by a Lambertian surface. Equation [1] is used to obtain the maximum power of a solar cell of given band gap under solar radiation. This is plotted in **Figure 1** for an operating temperature of 300 K. As can be seen, the maximum possible energy conversion efficiency for unconcentrated sunlight is 33.7% at a band gap of 1.34 eV. This number is higher than the 32.9% derived by Brown and Green [5] who used a slightly different solar spectrum, but is identical to that found by Hanna and Nozik [6]. This maximum single threshold efficiency is widely termed the Shockley–Queisser limit, for the authors of the original derivation [7]. To understand this number, we should revise some of the following assumptions made in deriving eqn [1]:

- All absorption takes place at a planar surface with step-function absorptivity. All photons with energy above E_g are absorbed and those below E_g pass through.
- Carriers are thermalized to the lattice temperature, 300 K, with respect to the operating voltage, V.
- There is infinite carrier mobility, no shunting, and no series resistance.
- All recombination is radiative.

The contributions of the various efficiency losses have been recently reinvestigated by Hirst and Ekins-Daukes (see Chapter 1.15) [3]. They elegantly plotted the contributions as a function of band gap, which is reproduced in **Figure 2**. Immediately clear is that the

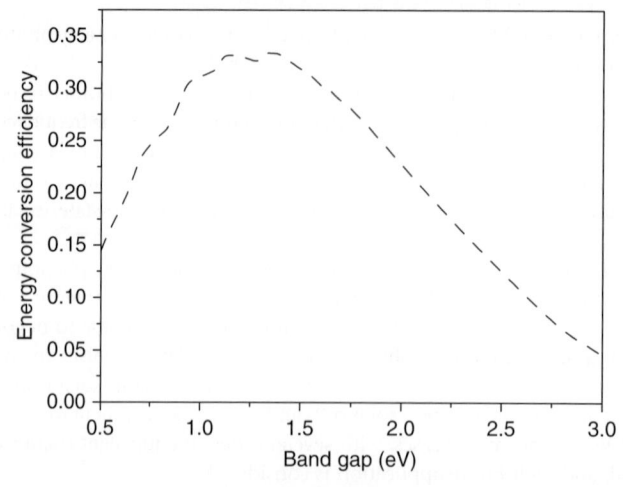

Figure 1 The energy conversion efficiency limit for a single threshold photovoltaic device operating at 300 K under 1 sun (ASTM G173-03), as a function of the absorption threshold (band gap).

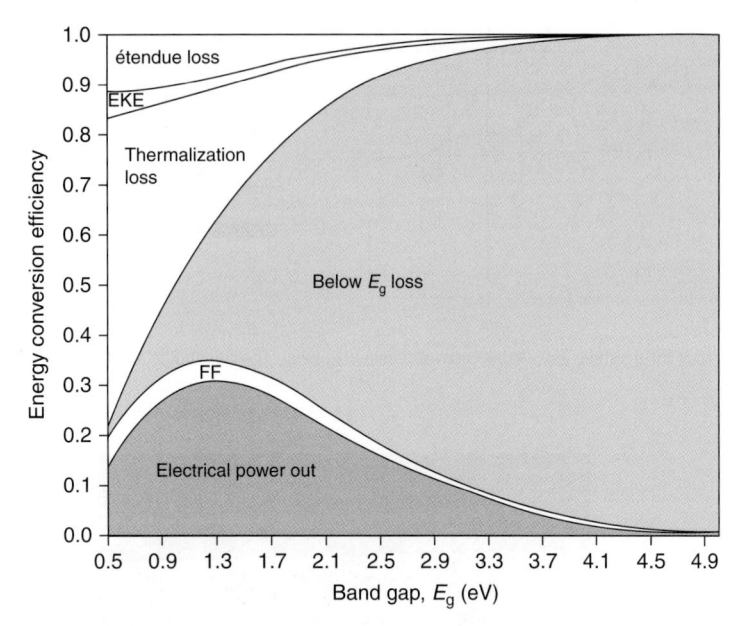

Figure 2 Energy apportioning as a function of band gap for a cell illuminated by a 6000 K blackbody sun. All energy received from the sun is accounted for. EKE and FF stand for electron kinetic energy and fill factor losses, respectively. Maximum efficiency is shown to be 0.31 for a band gap of 1.32 eV. Adapted from Hirst LC and Ekins-Daukes NJ (2010) *Progress in Photovoltaics: Research and Applications* 19: 286–293 [3].

major loss for cells with a band gap above about 1.3 eV is 'below E_g loss'; that is, a large proportion of incoming energy with $h\nu < E_g$ passes through the cell without being absorbed. It is this loss mechanism that is addressed with intermediate band solar cells and UC, the latter being the focus of this chapter.

1.24.3 Upconversion-Assisted Solar Cells: Equivalent Circuits

Trupke, Green, Würfel (TGW), and co-workers considered a general upconverting device with two lower energy thresholds that conspire to upconvert to a higher energy threshold [8]. This offers the greatest flexibility, with the AM1.5G spectrum affording an energy conversion efficiency exceeding 50% [9]. Their highest efficiency was obtained with an upper threshold of 2.00 eV, with lower thresholds of 0.94 and 1.40 eV. An intermediate thermalization of 0.34 eV enhances the efficiency considerably.

However, UC systems under current consideration for implementation in solar devices do so from a single lower energy threshold. Two excitations created at this lower threshold then interact to populate a higher level, bringing about UC. As such, in the following we only consider such systems which, due to decreased flexibility, are not as efficient as multiple threshold devices such as those considered by TGW [8, 9]. Indeed, the devices that follow are similar in spirit to the molecular intermediate band device put forward by Ekins-Daukes and Schmidt [10]. Calculations are all performed with $T = 300$ K, using the AM1.5G spectrum (as defined by ASTM G173-03), except in calculations under concentrated sunlight, where only the direct component is used (AM1.5D).

A commonly used approach to calculating limiting efficiencies of solar cell configurations beyond the single threshold device is to invoke the equivalent circuit. A simple device that recovers the 'below E_g loss' as identified by Hirst and Ekins-Daukes [3] is to place two lower-band gap solar cells in series behind the higher-band gap top cell, as illustrated in **Figure 3**. In this configuration, the working voltage of the top device is V and that of the lower-band gap devices is, by symmetry, $V/2$. The currents are drawn together and thus add. The I–V characteristic is given by

$$I = e[k_b - k_b' \exp((eV - E_b)/k_BT) + k_r - k_r' \exp((eV/2 - E_r)/k_BT)] \quad [4]$$

where the subscripts refer to the lower threshold cell (r, red) and the higher threshold cell (b, blue), respectively. E_b and E_r are the thresholds of the cells. The kinetic parameters are given by

$$k_b = \frac{\sigma}{hc} \int_0^{hc/E_b} \lambda F_\lambda^\odot \, d\lambda \quad [5]$$

$$k_r = \frac{\sigma}{2hc} \int_{hc/E_b}^{hc/E_r} \lambda F_\lambda^\odot \, d\lambda \quad [6]$$

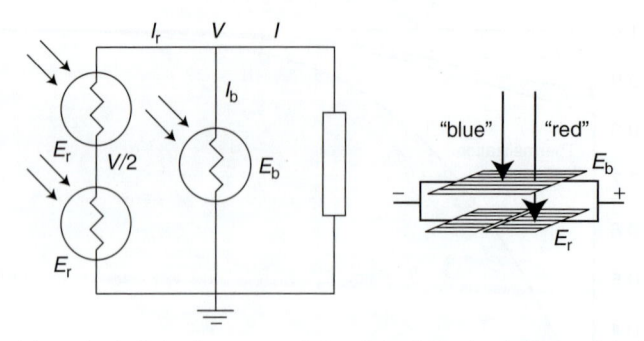

Figure 3 (Left) The equivalent circuit for a simple device that recovers 'below E_g loss'. The thresholds are E_r (red) and E_b (blue).

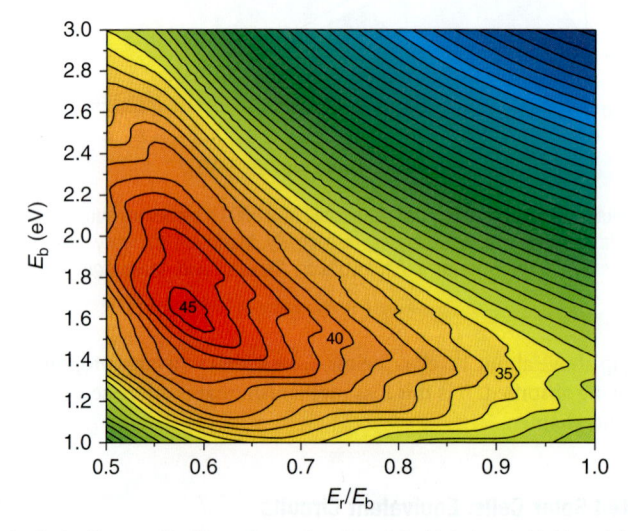

Figure 4 The limiting efficiency for the device illustrated in **Figure 3**, as a function of the high threshold, E_b, and the ratio E_r/E_b. The highest efficiency is over 45%, with thresholds of 1.63 and 0.96 eV.

and

$$k'_b = \frac{\sigma}{4\pi^2 c^2}\left(\frac{k_B T}{\hbar}\right)^3\left[\left(\frac{E_b}{k_B T}\right)^2 + 2\left(\frac{E_b}{k_B T}\right) + 2\right] \quad [7]$$

$$k'_r = \frac{\sigma}{8\pi^2 c^2}\left(\frac{k_B T}{\hbar}\right)^3\left[\left(\frac{E_r}{k_B T}\right)^2 + 2\left(\frac{E_r}{k_B T}\right) + 2\right] \quad [8]$$

The emission and absorption rates of the lower-threshold cells contain an additional factor of 2 in the denominator as a result of their being half the size of the high-threshold cell.

The energy conversion efficiency of this device is shown in **Figure 4**. The peak is over 45% at a large band gap of about 1.63 eV. For this configuration, the optimal smaller band gap is about 0.59 that of the large one, 0.96 eV. The left-hand edge of the plot is equivalent to the symmetric molecular intermediate device described by Ekins-Daukes and Schmidt [10], while the right-hand edge is equivalent to **Figure 1**. This is not quite equivalent to an UC-assisted solar device. The difference can be shown by considering particle flux. Let the absorbed photon flux in the top cell be ϕ_b and that in each bottom cell be ϕ_r. The emission from these cells is $\phi'_b(V)$ and $\phi'_r(V)$. It holds that

$$I = e(\phi_b + \phi_r - \phi'_b(V) - \phi'_r(V/2)) \quad [9]$$

Now consider the situation where the two low-band gap cells pump a light-emitting diode that illuminates the rear of a bifacial top cell of the same band gap (**Figure 5**), as analyzed by Trupke et al. [8]. The incoming upconverted flux is ϕ_{uc}. Now,

$$I = e(\phi_b + \phi_{uc} - 2\phi'_b(V)) \quad [10]$$

The emission from the top cell is doubled to take account of the bifacial emission. In the absence of any external input, the UC circuit likewise gives

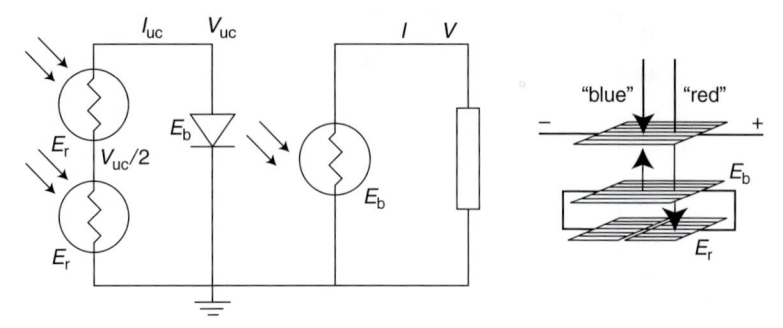

Figure 5 The equivalent circuit for an UC-assisted solar cell that uses two low-threshold (E_r) cells to pump a light-emitting diode of threshold E_b. A top cell with threshold E_b receives solar and upconverted photon flux.

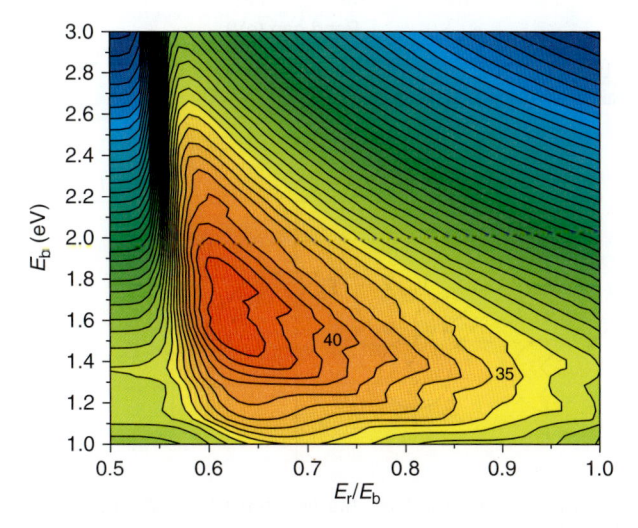

Figure 6 The limiting efficiency for the device illustrated in **Figure 5**, as a function of the high threshold, E_b, and the ratio E_r/E_b. The highest efficiency is over 43%. If E_r is below about $0.58 E_b$, the light-emitting diode cannot be operated and the efficiency crashes.

$$\phi_{uc} - \phi'_b(V) = \phi_r - \phi'_r(V/2) \quad [11]$$

where $\phi_{uc} = \phi'_b(V_{uc})$, since it is made of the same material as the top cell. Substitution of ϕ_{uc} into eqn [10] yields

$$I = e(\phi_b + \phi_r - \phi'_b(V) - \phi'_r(V_{uc}/2)) \quad [12]$$

Now, if $V_{uc} = V$, then the top cell is operating under equivalent conditions to the first circuit (**Figure 3** and eqn [10]). But now the left-hand side of eqn [11] is 0, and the right-hand side cannot be satisfied at an arbitrary voltage set by the top cell. As such, the upconverting equivalent circuit is not as efficient as the electrically coupled circuit in **Figure 3**. In order to drive the emitting diode, the voltage V_{uc} must be held higher than V, which is set to extract photogenerated carriers as current. As such, the amount of light radiated from the red cells, $\phi'_r(V_{uc})$, is higher than in the case of **Figure 3**, and consequently the losses are higher. The efficiency plot for the circuit in **Figure 5** is given in **Figure 6**. It is broadly similar to **Figure 4**, but there are important differences. The peak conversion efficiency, of just below 44%, is near 1.6 eV for the high-band gap cell, with the lower band gap 0.62 times that value, at 1.0 eV. The efficiency of the optimized upconverting cell is compared with the single threshold cell (**Figure 7**). Immediately clear is the potential gain in efficiency for higher-band gap cells with $E_g \sim 2$ eV. While the peak upconverting cell has $E_g \sim 1.6$ eV, those with higher band gaps stand to double their efficiency with an upconverting layer.

A third situation is illustrated in **Figure 8**. Here, the low-threshold cells are placed in parallel, but are connected to a circuit element that combines voltage by dumping half of the incoming current to ground (booster convertor). One might imagine an Auger device in which electrons are injected into an intermediate band thereon undergoing Auger 'ionization' whereby one electron is placed into the valence band and another into the conduction band. Electrons entering in the reverse fashion undergo impact ionization to bring about two intermediate band electrons. In this circuit, the low-threshold cells are held at voltage $V_{uc}/2$, passing current I_{uc}. The emitting diode is held at V_{uc} and thus the relevant circuit elements are under identical conditions as in **Figure 5**. It is thus intuitive that the device in **Figure 8** will convert energy with the same efficiency. An Auger upconvertor is a satisfying analogy for the energy transfer upconversion (ETU) and triplet–triplet annihilation (TTA) UC mechanisms, which are described below.

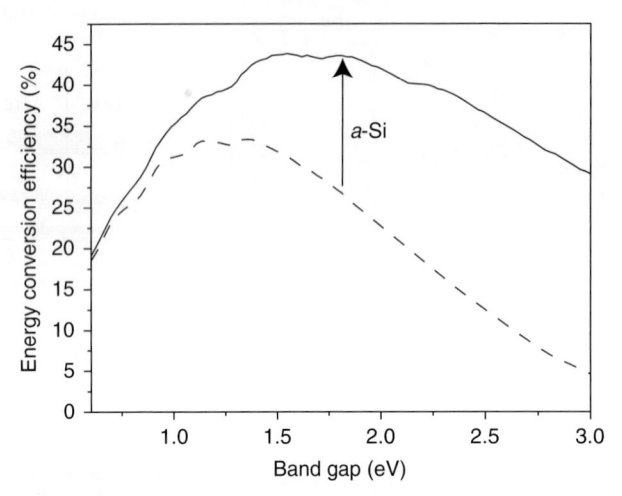

Figure 7 The limiting efficiency for an UC-assisted solar cell with an optimized single lower threshold. The dashed curve illustrates the single threshold limit. As indicated, a-Si cells stand to gain in efficiency by application of UC.

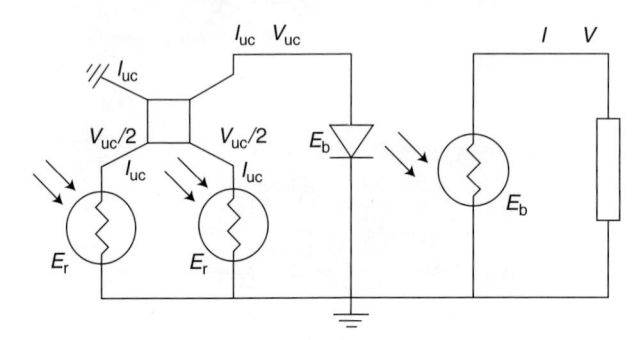

Figure 8 The equivalent circuit for an UC-assisted solar cell that uses two low-threshold (E_r) cells in parallel to pump a booster convertor that drives a light-emitting diode of threshold E_b. A top cell with threshold E_b receives solar and upconverted photon flux.

1.24.4 Solar Concentration

Highly efficient photovoltaic devices, while expensive, are of great interest to concentrator photovoltaics. In a practical sense, too, UC is much more efficient under solar concentration. The calculations performed above are repeated with

$$k_b = \frac{\sigma}{hc} \int_0^{hc/E_b} \lambda CF_\lambda^\odot d\lambda \qquad [13]$$

$$k_r = \frac{\sigma}{2hc} \int_{hc/E_b}^{hc/E_r} \lambda CF_\lambda^\odot d\lambda \qquad [14]$$

where C is the solar concentration factor, which cannot exceed about 46 200 for our Sun. The emission rate constants are unchanged by concentration.

The limiting efficiencies of the devices illustrated in **Figure 5** are plotted under various degrees of solar concentration in **Figure 9**. Since the AM1.5G spectrum is bluer than the direct spectrum (AM1.5D), at some band gaps the unconcentrated efficiency exceeds the efficiency under 10-fold solar concentration. Under full concentration, the limiting efficiency exceeds 50% for a very broad range of band gaps, spanning germanium to organic solar cells, as indicated by the dashed line.

1.24.5 Definition of Upconversion Efficiency

In order that various implementations of UC can be compared, it is useful to define various measurements of efficiency. Indeed, much confusion persists due to a factor of 2 arising from there being needed two photons of low energy light to produce one photon of higher energy light. There are generally two ways to measure the efficiency of an UC device: from optical or electrical measurements. The definitions put forth by Fischer *et al.* are adapted in the following [11] and are listed for reference in **Table 1**.

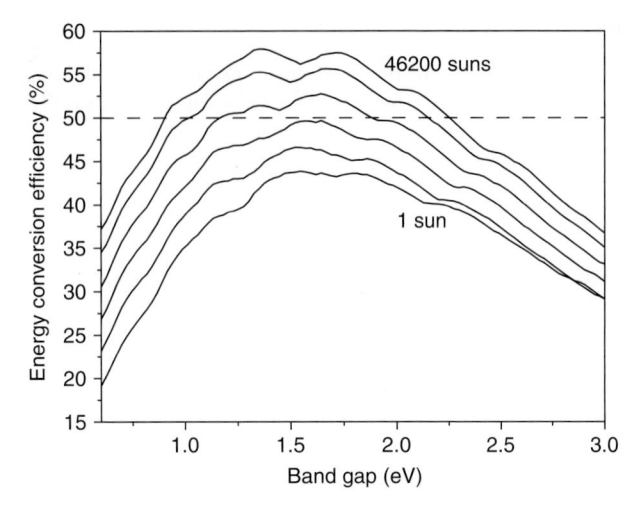

Figure 9 The limiting efficiency for the UC-assisted solar cell illustrated in **Figure 5**, with an optimized single lower threshold under solar concentration. From least to most efficient at a band gap of 1.5 eV is 1 sun, 10 suns, 100 suns, 1000 suns, 10 000 suns, and 46 200 suns (full concentration). The unconcentrated curve exceeds 10-fold concentration at high band gaps due to blue light being scattered out of the AM1.5D spectrum by the atmosphere.

Table 1 Definitions of symbols used frequently in this chapter

Symbol	Name	Units
k_B	Boltzmann constant	$J\,K^{-1}$
T	Temperature	K
$h = 2\pi\hbar$	Plank's constant	$J\,s$
c	Speed of light in vacuum	$m\,s^{-1}$
ϵ	Molar extinction coefficient	$M^{-1}\,cm^{-1}$
N_A	Avogadro constant	
$\eta_{UC,spectral}$	Spectral upconversion efficiency	nm^{-1}
η_{UC}	Upconversion efficiency	
$\bar{\eta}_{UC}$	Normalized upconversion efficiency	$cm^2\,W^{-1}$
$\bar{\eta}_{UC}^{\odot}$	Solar upconversion efficiency	

1.24.5.1 Monochromatic Optical Efficiency

The spectral UC efficiency is the spectral density of UC efficiency measured in nm^{-1}:

$$\eta_{UC,spectral}(\lambda_{inc}, \lambda_{UC}, I) = \frac{F_\lambda^{UC}(\lambda_{UC}, I)}{I} \frac{\lambda_{UC}}{\lambda_{inc}} \quad [15]$$

where λ_{UC} and λ_{inc} are upconverted and incident wavelengths, respectively, and I is the incident intensity. The spectral radiative emittance of the upconverted light flux is given by F_λ^{UC}. Importantly, $\eta_{UC,spectral}$ is a particle efficiency, not an energy efficiency.

The integrated UC efficiency is the integral over $\eta_{UC,spectral}$:

$$\eta_{UC}(\lambda_{inc}, I) = \int \eta_{UC,spectral} d\lambda_{UC} \quad [16]$$

This quantity has a maximum value of 0.5; that is, maximally one photon is emitted for every two incident.

The normalized UC efficiency is the integrated optical UC efficiency divided by the incident intensity, thus

$$\bar{\eta}_{UC}(\lambda_{inc}, I) = \frac{\eta_{UC}(\lambda_{inc}, I)}{I} \quad [17]$$

A convenient unit is $cm^2\,W^{-1}$. Such a measurement implies a linearity between incident power and efficiency, which is the case for quadratic processes such as low-power two-photon UC.

To properly compare different UC systems for the purpose considered here, we introduce the solar UC efficiency, $\bar{\eta}_{UC}^{\odot}$:

$$\bar{\eta}_{UC}^{\odot} = \bar{\eta}_{UC} \int_{\lambda_b}^{\lambda_r} F_\lambda^{\odot} d\lambda \quad [18]$$

where the limits on the integral are chosen to span the absorption range of the UC material.

1.24.5.2 Photoelectrical Efficiency

The external quantum efficiency (EQE) of a device is the flux of electrons extracted from the solar cell under operating conditions divided by the flux of photons incident on the solar cell. The EQE of the UC solar cell device is $EQE_{UC}(\lambda_{inc}, I)$, whereby it is assumed that the unadorned device would have a negligible response in the range of λ_{inc} chosen.

The normalized EQE_{UC}, $\overline{EQE}_{UC}(\lambda_{inc}, I)$, in $cm^2 W^{-1}$, is the EQE_{UC} per unit illumination. As above, the implied linear relationship is due to the quadratic response of efficiency at low incident power.

1.24.6 Practical Implementation

1.24.6.1 Rare Earths

Rare earths is the name given to the f-block lanthanoid elements, and in some cases scandium and yttrium. On the whole, they are not particularly rare, with cerium being the top 30th most abundant element in the Earth's crust. Contrastingly, promethium's longest-living isotope has a half-life of about 3 days, and thus has a natural abundance of 0. The lanthanoids are mostly characterized as those elements with a partially filled 4f shell. In nature, the elements are found as trivalent cations (except for cerium and europium), with a xenon-like core and a number of 4f electrons. The f-orbitals formally possess $3\hbar$ angular momentum, and thus the various ways of filling electrons in the seven available f-orbitals bring about a manifold of electronic states.

1.24.6.1.1 Spectroscopy of rare-earth ions

Because the 4f electrons are buried within the cation, even in condensed media, the ions behave *quasi*-atomically. As such, the electronic states are labeled $^{2S+1}L_J$, where S is the electronic spin multiplicity, L is the orbital angular momentum ($S = 0$, $P = 1$, $D = 2$, $F = 3$, $G = 4$, $H = 5$, $I = 6...$), and J is the total electronic angular momentum.

Several rare earths are utilized in optical applications. Notably, neodymium is introduced into host lattices such as yttrium aluminum garnet ($Y_3Al_5O_{12}$) or yttrium lithium fluoride to produce lasing media such as Nd:YAG and Nd:YLF. Population inversion is brought about by absorption by yttrium in the lattice, with the energy transferred to Nd^{3+}, which then undergoes $^4F_{3/2} \rightarrow {}^4I_{11/2}$ emission with a lifetime of 230 μS. This rather long lifetime reflects the fact that f-f transitions are parity (Laporte) forbidden. In the dipole approximation, only transitions between 'gerade' (symmetric with respect to inversion) and 'ungerade' (antisymmetric with respect to inversion) states are allowed. Since all f electrons are of ungerade symmetry, the transitions are weak.

Erbium in its trivalent cationic state possesses 11 f electrons, which are placed into the seven available orbitals, such that three remain with parallel, unpaired spins. The total spin angular momentum of 3/2 may be projected onto the laboratory z-axis in four ways (+3/2, +1/2, −1/2, −3/2) and thus the configuration is known as a quartet. The lowest energy state is that with maximum L, so if the unpaired spins are in $l = -3, -2$, and -1, the orbital angular momentum is $6\hbar$, denoted as I. Spin–orbital coupling splits the quartet I state into the four components, ^4I_J, $J = 15/2, 13/2, 11/2,$ and $9/2$, with the $J = 15/2$ being the overall ground state. The electronic energy-level structure of Er^{3+} is shown in **Figure 10**.

In crystalline media, the $J = 15/2$ level is actually split into eight sublevels, and the $J = 13/2$ into seven sublevels. In silica, this broadens the $^4I_{15/2} \leftarrow {}^4I_{13/2}$ absorption (emission) spectrum, centered at 1530 nm (1580 nm), by 50 nm. Population inversion in this transition may be achieved by pumping erbium-doped silica at 980 nm, bringing about an amplifying medium of use in telecommunication fibers.

1.24.6.1.2 Upconversion with rare earths

The history of rare-earth UC has been reviewed by Auzel [12]. In 1959, Bloembergen proposed that sequential absorption of infrared photons by rare-earth ions could bring about luminescence at shorter wavelengths [13]. This idea underpinned a proposed

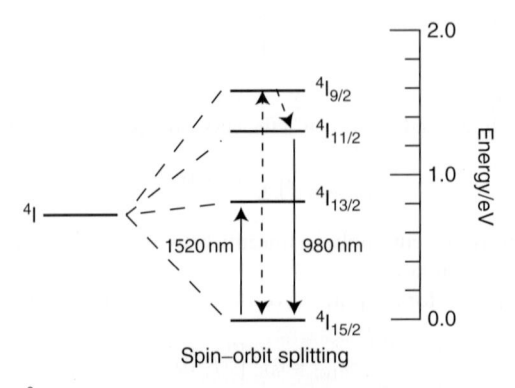

Figure 10 The energy-level structure of the Er^{3+} cation. Ions energized by absorption of 0.8 eV (1530 nm) photons interact to produce one ion at 1.55 eV, which decays to 1.26 eV. Light is subsequently emitted at 980 nm.

infrared quantum counter. However, such ground-state absorption followed by excited-state absorption (GSA-ESA) is inefficient except under high pumping intensities. It was realized by Auzel in the 1960s that energy could be transferred between two excited ions, to bring about a ground-state ion and a doubly excited ion, which could then luminesce at a shorter wavelength than that used to prepare the states [14]. This mechanism was named by Auzel as APTE, for "addition de photon par transferts d'energie." However, ETU is the most widely applied term now. In erbium, ETU takes place between ions prepared in $^4I_{13/2}$ by 1530 nm light, to bring about an excited ion in $^4I_{11/2}$, which emits at 980 nm (**Figure 10**). The excited ion is actually initially placed in the $^4I_{9/2}$ state, but this rapidly decays into the nearby $^4I_{11/2}$ state.

The rate, W, of ETU may be derived from Fermi's golden rule:

$$W = \frac{2\pi}{\hbar} |\langle f|\hat{H}|i\rangle|^2 \rho \qquad [19]$$

where f and i represent the initial and final states and ρ is the final density of states. The matrix element may be expanded:

$$\langle f|\hat{H}|i\rangle = \int \psi_D^0 \psi_A^{\ddagger} \hat{H} \psi_D^{\dagger} \psi_A^{\dagger} d\tau \qquad [20]$$

where 0, †, and ‡, respectively, indicate wave functions of the ground, first excited, and second excited states of the donor, D, and the acceptor A. Since the initial and final states differ by the movement of two electrons, the one-electron operators within $\hat{H}$ do not contribute, and only the two-electron Coulombic repulsion term applies. When this interaction is well described by the dipole–dipole interaction of transition densities, the transfer process is of the Förster type [15], which decays as R^{-6}, where R is the distance between excited ions. For the UC to be efficient, the ETU rate must exceed the natural decay lifetime of the $^4I_{13/2}$ state erbium ions. The nonradiative decay (NRD) of these ions is greatly affected by the phonon energy of the host lattice. A lower phonon energy brings about a necessarily higher-order process for the lattice to accept the 0.8 eV of the $^4I_{13/2}$ state ions. Since higher-order processes are generally less probable, the lifetime is enhanced in low phonon energy lattices such as sodium yttrium fluoride. The phonon energies are still lower for chloride, bromide, and iodide analogs. However, there are indications that chloride performs the most favorably [16]. Though bromide and iodide engender lower phonon energies, they also have narrower excitation spectra since the larger halides have smaller anionic field strengths, resulting in smaller Stark splitting. The increased UC performance of the chlorides implies the ideal host should have not only a low phonon energy but also a large excitation spectrum.

The application of rare earths to spectral modification for the purpose of improving solar efficiencies was recently reviewed by van der Ende *et al.* [17]. In the following, we describe some of the attempts at photovoltaic application of rare-earth UC.

The first reported use of rare earths to enhance photovoltaic energy conversion was in 1996 by Gibart, Auzel, and co-workers (GAGZ) [18]. They invoked a Yb^{3+}/Er^{3+} UC system on a high-quality GaAs cell. When the 0.039 cm^2 cell was illuminated by 1 W of monochromatic radiation (256 kW m^{-2}) at 1.391 μm, a 2.5% power efficiency was obtained. The $\bar{\eta}_{UC}$ is estimated at 0.0005 cm^2 W^{-1}. Such intensity in the absorption band of Er^{3+} corresponds to about 10 000 suns.

In 2007, Shalav, Richards, and Green (SRG) applied Er^{3+}-doped NaYF$_4$ phosphors to crystalline Si double-sided buried contact solar cells [19]. At low irradiation powers, they observed a slope of 2 on the bilogarithmic plot of photocurrent against irradiation, which is expected where the UC mechanism is operating inefficiently. Upon saturation of efficiency, the slope turns over to unity. However, at their highest level of irradiation the slope was 1.57, indicating that the system was operating far from maximum efficiency. The maximum EQE measured was 3.4% at 6 mW 1523 nm excitation using their second prototype device with 20% erbium doping. Under 46 200 suns, the authors calculate that the luminescence quantum efficiency (equivalent to η_{UC} as defined above) of their upconvertor would be less than 3.5%, corresponding to an efficiency of $\bar{\eta}_{UC}$ = 0.0003 cm^2 W^{-1}, similar to that of GAGZ. The energy efficiency enhancement, $\Delta\eta$, was 0.008.

A recent report by Fischer *et al.* [11] employs a similar phosphor to SRG [19]. However, these authors reported an UC quantum efficiency of 5.1% under 1880 W m^{-2} monochromatic irradiation at 1523 nm, $\bar{\eta}_{UC}$ = 0.27 cm^2 W^{-1}. The AM1.5G spectrum integrates to 23.7 W m^{-2} in the 1480–1580 nm region, the absorption range of the phosphor. As such, the radiation level is conservatively estimated to be about 70 suns. The EQE was 0.34% under 1090 W m^{-2} at 1522 nm. However, as estimated by SRG [19], even with fully efficient UC, δ_η would not exceed 0.024. This reflects the narrowness of the absorption band of Er^{3+}, which accounts for only 2.4% of the energy in the AM1.5G spectrum. A recent attempt to sensitize an erbium-based upconvertor over a broader spectral range using lead sulfide quantum dots is promising: the improvement in photocurrent detected by the combination of the upconvertor and the PbS quantum dots being 60% better than without them [20]. However, the evidence for a contribution from the PbS in the EQE curve is not striking, and the PbS particles may also directly absorb a portion of the upconverted light. Recently, β-NaYF$_4$:Yb^{3+} (18%) and Er^{3+} (2%) UC phosphors have been applied to a-Si:H solar cells by de Wild and co-workers [21, 22]. Here, Yb^{3+} is excited at 980 nm with subsequent energy transfer to Er^{3+}. The upconvertor achieved an efficiency of 0.0005 under about 1.2 W cm^{-2}, equating to $\bar{\eta}_{UC}$ = 0.0004 cm^2 W^{-1}.

1.24.6.2 Upconversion with Organic Molecules

In nature, light is harvested using organic molecules, which possess broad and tunable absorption spectra. An emerging UC technology using triplet states of organic molecules, while yet to be applied to photovoltaics, shows great promise.

Triplet–triplet annihilation upconversion (TTA-UC) has been demonstrated to operate in the visible and near-infrared spectrum, with sensitizer molecules continuously tunable across the spectrum. To date, numerous systems have been demonstrated, with UC

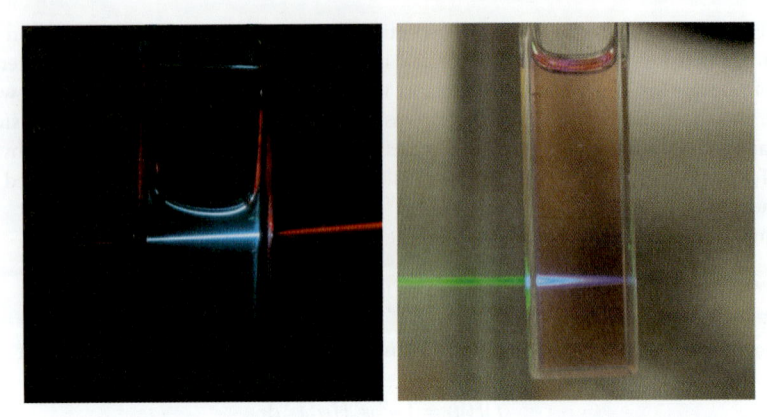

Figure 11 Red to blue, and green to blue UC achieved by TTA in organic molecules. © Y. Y. Cheng (The University of Sydney).

margins as high as 0.94 eV, and from as deep in the infrared as 1.49 eV [23, 24]. Spectacular examples are shown in **Figure 11**. An understanding of TTA is aided by a revision of molecular photophysics as set out below.

1.24.6.2.1 Molecular photophysics

Figure 12 is a depiction of the Jablonski diagram on which molecular states, rather than electronic energy levels, are set out with the vertical direction indicating the molecular energy, and the horizontal direction used only for organizational purposes. The occupation of electronic energy levels is illustrated schematically beside each level. The levels are labeled by their spin multiplicity, $2S + 1$, where S is the total electronic spin. As such, singlet states, $S = 0$ ($2S + 1 = 1$), are written as S_n, where 'S' stands for 'singlet'. Similarly, the triplet states and quintet states, if relevant, are T_n and Q_n, respectively. The 0 subscript is reserved for the global ground state. Excitation from S_0 to S_n is responsible for the optical absorption spectrum of a molecule. Following absorption, the vibrational energy is normally thermalized with the surroundings on a few picosecond timescale. From the vibrationally thermalized S_n levels, emission of light may occur back to S_0 in the form of fluorescence on the picosecond–nanosecond timescale. Normally, internal conversion (IC) from $S_{n>1}$ is faster than fluorescence. IC is an isoenergetic coupling between a higher electronic state and highly vibrationally excited levels of a lower electronic state. As such, within picoseconds following photon absorption, the molecule will be poised to emit fluorescence from the lowest vibrational levels of the S_1 state. This is the essence of Kasha's law. The fluorescence yield will be less than unity if IC can occur from S_1 to S_0 faster than the fluorescence lifetime or if intersystem crossing (ISC) to triplet levels is operative.

ISC, all other things being equal, is roughly a million times slower than IC. However, the energy gap law states that these nonadiabatic phenomena are exponentially dependent on the energy gap between the electronic states involved (an excellent example of the energy gap law in operation is compiled in figure 9 in Reference 19). As such, if a triplet state is just below S_1, then ISC may be dominant. Inclusion of heavy atoms will amplify the effect by reducing the legitimacy of the spin quantum number through spin–orbit coupling. Once a molecule has 'intersystem crossed' to the triplet manifold, it may phosphoresce from the bottom of the T_1 level on the microsecond timescale, or undergo reverse ISC back to S_0. Both of these processes are formally forbidden if spin is considered a good quantum number.

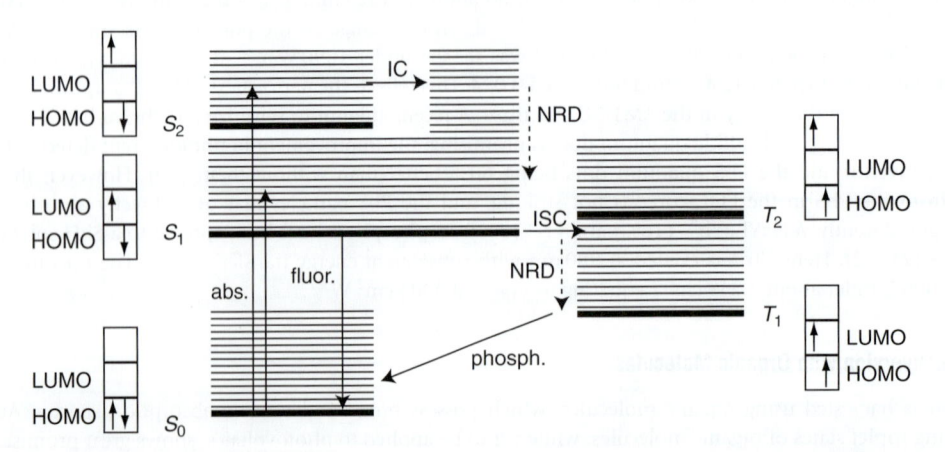

Figure 12 The Jablonski diagram, showing molecular states of importance in molecular photophysics, and indicative orbital occupancies. The key photophysical processes of absorption (abs.), fluorescence (flour.), phosphorescence (phosph.), IC, ISC, and NRD are indicated.

1.24.6.2.2 Photochemical upconversion

UC due to TTA following triplet energy transfer (TET) has been developed in recent years principally by the groups of Baluschev in Mainz and Castellano in Ohio [25, 26] with important contributions from our group in Sydney and Monguzzi and his colleagues in Milan [27–29]. The basic scheme is illustrated in **Figure 13**. Sensitizer molecules are promoted from the S_0 ground state to S_1 by absorbing (relatively) low-energy photons ($h\nu_1$). ISC results in a nonadiabatic transition to the long-lived T_1 triplet state, satisfying the energy sacrifice requirements set out by TGW [8, 9]. Subsequent TET to emitter molecules (in excess) produces a population of emitter triplets which then undergo TTA to produce $S_1 \rightarrow S_0$ emission at a higher energy than the photons absorbed ($h\nu_2$). TTA can only occur from the singlet complex, where the triplet spins cancel. This forms with 1/9 probability, the other 8/9 being triplet and quintet complexes. (There are nine states arising from the tensor product of two triplet states. These are comprised of one singlet, three triplets, and five quintets. As such, the probability of forming the singlet is statistically 1/9.) Importantly, and unlike SHG and other nonlinear optical processes, this is a completely incoherent optical process that can be effected by sunlight. Prior to 2010, the highest UC quantum efficiencies reported in the literature were by Baluschev and co-workers at ≈0.08 [31] with Castellano's group having approached 0.11 [32]. It was widely believed, and explicitly stated by some, that the limiting efficiency for UC by TTA is $\eta_{UC} = 0.055$, as only 1/9 encounter complexes of two triplets statistically yield the singlet required for subsequent emission of a photon. However, placing a 0.055 limit on the annihilation efficiency implicitly assumes that triplet and quintet encounter complexes quench to produce ground-state emitter molecules, a mechanism which is not established. In the following, it is demonstrated that there exists no statistical upper limit to photochemical UC by TTA at all. In so doing, we put forward this technology as a possibility to improve the efficiency of single threshold solar cells with large band gaps.

1.24.6.2.3 Annihilation statistics

To be cost-effective, an upconvertor must attain a certain (high) efficiency. In the case of TTA as the UC process, the underlying mechanism is described in terms of the complex formation between two emitter molecules in an excited triplet state, T_1 [33–36]. As a consequence of the tensor product of the initial spin states of the molecules, the encounter complex can be of singlet, triplet, or quintet multiplicity (**Figure 14**) [33–36].

From the multiplicities of the spin states, the complex formation probabilities are statistically weighted in the ratio 1:3:5 [33–36]. Only the singlet complex (1 in 9) dissociates to the S_1 state and yields the desired upconverted fluorescence. An important question is whether these statistics limit the efficiency of the TTA-UC process and thereby fundamentally constrain its applicability to solar cells. In the following, we define the probability that one S_1 emitter state is formed for each T_1 state quenched by TTA (i.e., in the absence of first-order decay processes) as η_{conv}. The highest possible value of η_{UC} is thus η_{conv}.

The simplest spin-statistical value of $\eta_{conv} = 0.055$ can be rebuked by considering that the quintet encounter complex will normally dissociate back into the two initial triplet molecules [36, 37], there being no lower states of quintet multiplicity. Given that the triplet encounter complex can produce a higher excited triplet state (e.g., T_2), in the same manner as the singlet complex produces the S_1 emitter, and that these states usually undergo fast relaxation to T_1, we arrive at a limit of $\eta_{conv} = 0.2$. If one entertains the possibility that the quintet complex can decay into one T_1 and one S_0 emitter, then the associated limit is $\eta_{conv} = 0.1$. As is shown below, there is no spin-statistical limitation on TTA-UC efficiency, provided that the electronic structure of the emitter is chosen carefully.

1.24.6.2.4 Experimentally achieved high efficiency

To test the limits to the efficiencies of TTA-UC, a comparison was made by Cheng et al. [27] between the prompt fluorescence yield, where emitters are excited to S_1 directly, and the delayed fluorescence yield, where emitters are placed in S_1 through sensitized TTA. In the experiment, the authors used a palladium porphyrin (PQ$_4$Pd) as the sensitizer and rubrene as the emitter [27].

Figure 15 shows a two-dimensional plot of delayed fluorescence as a function of time after a 670 nm laser pulse. Considering that the excitation is performed using a femtosecond laser, and the emission occurs many microseconds later, it is clear that the UC is achieved incoherently. For comparison, the inset shows a time-correlated single photon counting (TCSPC) trace of prompt

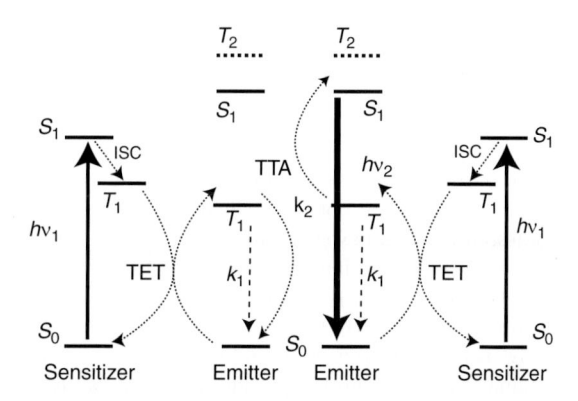

Figure 13 The molecular states and interactions involved in UC by TTA. Redrawn from Cheng YY, Fückel B, Khoury T, *et al.* (2010) Kinetic analysis of photochemical upconversion by triplet-triplet annihilation: Beyond any statistical limit. *Journal of Physical Chemistry Letters* 1(12): 1795–1799.

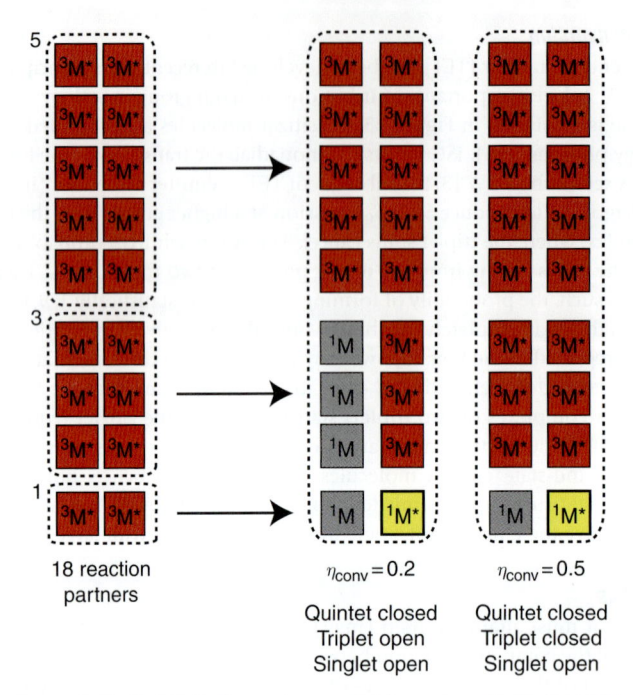

Figure 14 If 18 triplet emitter molecules react, 10 will statistically couple as a quintet complex, with 6 in the triplet configuration and only 1 pair coupling as a singlet. Assuming the quintet channel only returns triplets to the reaction mixture, if the triplet channel is open then five triplets are burned for the production of one photon, $\eta_{UC} = 0.2$. If the triplet channel is closed due to there being an accessible T_2 state, then $\eta_{UC} = 0.5$.

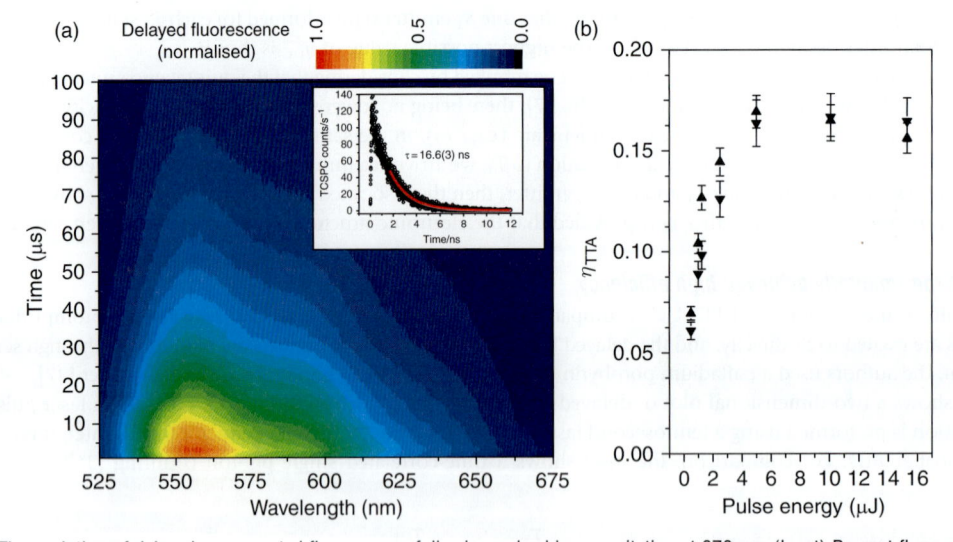

Figure 15 (a) The evolution of delayed, upconverted fluorescence following pulsed laser excitation at 670 nm. (Inset) Prompt fluorescence following 525 nm excitation. (b) Annihilation yields, η_{TTA}, as a function of pulse energy. Adapted from Cheng YY, Khoury T, Clady RGCR, *et al.* (2010) *Physical Chemistry Chemical Physics* 12: 66–71 [27].

fluorescence following 525 nm excitation of the rubrene emitter. Comparison of the prompt and delayed fluorescence intensity shows that annihilation efficiencies $\eta_{TTA} > 0.055$ can be obtained, where $\eta_{UC} = \eta_{TTA}\Phi_F$, Φ_F being the fluorescence yield. In the presently described experiment, the fluorescence quantum yield of the emitter is an internal reference [27]. The best results indicate an annihilation efficiency of $\eta_{TTA} \sim 0.16$. However, these integrated decays include the many emitter triplet states that decay by first-order, unimolecular means. As such, while the value $\eta_{TTA} > 0.15$ represents an experimentally attained annihilation efficiency, it neither does represent the actual upper limit for this system nor the highest instantaneously attainable annihilation efficiency. To determine these factors, kinetic data were analyzed in terms of mixed first- and second-order kinetics [28].

The delayed fluorescence solely originates from S_1 emitters produced by TTA. As such, its intensity I_F is proportional to the square of the concentration of emitter triplets, $[^3M^*]^2$, in the solution. Since TTA occurs on a many microsecond timescale, it can be treated independently of the emitter triplet concentration buildup [38]. The buildup illustrated on the left of **Figure 15** is one

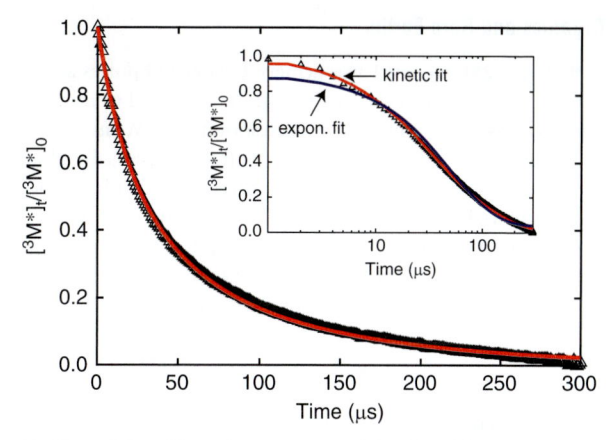

Figure 16 The normalized triplet decay kinetics as inferred from the square root of the delayed fluorescence signal. As can be seen, eqn [22] produces a fit to the data superior to a single exponential, revealing the importance of the second-order TTA kinetics, particularly at early times where the concentration of triplets is highest. Redrawn from Cheng YY, Fückel B, Khoury T, et al. (2010) Kinetic analysis of photochemical upconversion by triplet-triplet annihilation: Beyond any statistical limit. *Journal of Physical Chemistry Letters* 1(12): 1795–1799.

of the slowest observed, and is shown to illustrate the kinetics. The highest efficiency experiments are associated with a much faster submicrosecond buildup. For the time dependence of the concentration of emitter triplet molecules $[^3M^*]_t$, one can write [34, 36, 39]

$$\frac{d\sqrt{I_F(t)}}{dt} \propto \frac{d[^3M^*]_t}{dt} = -k_1[^3M^*]_t - k_2[^3M^*]_t^2 \quad [21]$$

where the first-order decay component k_1 is a combination of the intrinsic phosphorescent and NRD of the triplet emitter, and other *quasi* first-order quenching processes. The second-order component, k_2, originates from the triplet quenching of the TTA process including all bimolecular pathways according to **Figure 14**.

The analytical solution to [21] is given by [36]

$$\frac{[^3M^*]_t}{[^3M^*]_0} = \frac{1-\beta}{\exp(k_1 t) - \beta} \quad [22]$$

with $\beta = \alpha/(k_1 + \alpha)$ and α being the product of the TTA rate constant and the initial triplet concentration $\alpha = k_2 [^3M^*]_0$. As pointed out by Bachilo and Weisman [36], β represents the initial fraction of decay that occurs in second-order TTA kinetics. **Figure 16** shows the excellent fit of eqn [21] to the date, from which we obtain β and thus can determine the proportions of first- and second-order decay, respectively, f_1 and f_2. By integrating eqn [21]

$$f_1 = -[^3M^*]_0^{-1} \int_0^\infty k_1[^3M^*]_t dt = \frac{\beta - 1}{\beta} \ln(1-\beta) \quad [23]$$

and likewise

$$f_2 = -[^3M^*]_0^{-1} \int_0^\infty k_2[^3M^*]_t^2 dt = 1 - \frac{\beta - 1}{\beta} \ln(1-\beta) \quad [24]$$

Hence, one can calculate the efficiency of bimolecular quenching of triplets to yield S_1 emitter states $\eta_{conv} = \eta_{TTA}/f_2$.

The results of Cheng et al. [28] show that, over a range of observed annihilation efficiencies, η_{TTA} and the proportion of triplets undergoing second-order decay, f_2, is proportional. The kinetic experiments reveal that emitter triplet states that undergo second-order decay produce S_1 states with roughly 30% of the quantum efficiency of direct excitation at 525 nm. This value of $\eta_{conv} = 0.3$ not only exceeds 0.055 but also comfortably exceeds the 0.2 limit imposed where the triplet channel is in operation. Moreover, the initial annihilation efficiency observed immediately following the laser pulse exceeds 0.2 within the experimental uncertainty.

The quantity η_{conv} is directly related to the underlying TTA mechanism as depicted in **Figure 14**. Thus, in the current system, the conversion efficiency of encounter complexes to excited singlets exceeds the limit calculated assuming that the triplet channel is open, $\eta_{conv} = 20\%$. The operation of the triplet channel crucially depends on the energies of the product molecules.

It is known that the energy of the rubrene T_2 state exceeds the energy of its S_1 state by 87 meV in toluene [40]. Indeed, for rubrene the energies of the T_1 and T_2 states are about 1.15 and 2.38 eV above the ground state, respectively [40]. That is, the formation of a T_2 rubrene state from two T_1 states is endothermic by 74 meV, while the S_1 state is exothermic by 12 meV. The high η_{conv} values found in the above analysis are attributed to the inaccessibility of the T_2 state. Hence, it is proposed that emitter molecules with still larger $T_2 - S_1$ energy gaps than rubrene can yield η_{conv} values of up to 0.5. Indeed, when the excitation energy of the emitter T_2 state exceeds double that of its T_1 state, the amount of radiationless decay via the triplet channel is reduced.

1.24.6.3 Comparison between Organics and Rare Earths

In efficiency experiments by Cheng et al. [27, 28], $\eta_{UC} = 0.1$ was achieved using 1 μJ pulses at 1 kHz. As the authors explain, since the triplets decay within about 30 μs, a power 30 times this (30 mW) would be required to reach an equivalent *quasi*-steady-state triplet concentration. Since the spot illuminated was about 1 mm^2, this corresponds to 3 W cm^{-2}, or 300 suns if the light were distributed across the absorption band of the sensitizer. The normalized efficiency for this process is therefore $\bar{\eta}_{UC} = 0.033$ cm^2 W^{-1}. Despite the high reported efficiencies, this system is not as efficient as Fischer and co-workers' phosphor, which achieved 0.27 cm^2 W^{-1} [11]. Baluschev et al. report an external quantum yield of 0.04 with excitation intensity of <1 W cm^{-2}. This gives ≥0.04 cm^2 W^{-1}; but it is important to note that in this case the excitation source was the Sun itself [31]. Estimating their excitation bandwidth to be 40 nm gives 200-fold solar concentration. An earlier experiment by Baluschev and co-workers achieved only about $\eta_{UC} = 0.01$ at 10 W cm^{-2} [41].

However, the bimolecular TTA rate constant (k_2 above) for rubrene is a paltry, 1×10^8 M^{-1} s^{-1}. The upper limit on this rate is

$$k_2^{max} = \frac{k_d}{9\eta_{conv}} \qquad [25]$$

where k_d is the diffusion limited bimolecular rate constant (~10^{10} M^{-1} s^{-1}). Where $\eta_{conv} = 0.055$, the rate at which triplets are removed from the solution is twice the diffusion limit, since two triplets are removed per collision. For highly efficient systems, where η_{conv} approaches 0.5, the limit is $2/9k_d$. The diffusion limit may be approximated by the Stokes–Einstein relation which gives

$$k_d = 10^3 \frac{8k_B T}{3\eta} N_A \qquad [26]$$

in M^{-1} s^{-1}, where η is the viscosity of the solvent. For a solvent of viscosity 0.59 cP, such as toluene (5.9×10^{-4} Pas), this gives $k_d \approx 1.1 \times 10^{10}$ M^{-1} s^{-1}. In this case, for efficient upconvertors, $k_2^{max} \approx 2.4 \times 10^9$ M^{-1} s^{-1}.

Rates approaching this limit are observed for some molecules, and in these cases the $\bar{\eta}_{UC}$ will be higher. Castellano's group measured $\eta_{UC} = 0.0753$ using boron dipyrromethene chromophores [33]. This was achieved at a power density of 0.1162 W cm^{-2} giving $\bar{\eta}_{UC} = 0.648$ cm^2 W^{-1}. This excitation density is equivalent to about 14 suns across the 640–580 nm excitation bandwidth.

However, a fairer comparison for the purposes of this chapter is the UC efficiency per sun, where the solar intensity is gauged by integrating over the excitation band of the sensitizer. In this way, absorbers with narrow spectra, such as rare earths, are penalized. The $\eta_{UC} = 0.051$ result of Fischer et al. was achieved at about 70 suns. Thus, $\eta_{UC}^{\odot} = 7 \times 10^{-4}$. The result of Cheng et al. of $\eta_{UC} = 0.1$ was achieved at 300 suns, so $\eta_{UC}^e = 4 \times 10^{-4}$, a similar result. But, converting the pulsed experiments of Cheng into results for continuous light is fraught with difficulties, as will be discussed below. However, by far the best result under continuous light is that from Castellano's group, $\eta_{UC}^{\odot} = 0.0054$, an order of magnitude ahead of the others. Part of the reason for this is likely due to favorable annihilation kinetics. The annihilation rate constant is the critical factor, along with η_{conv}, in determining the UC efficiency. Increasing the value of this parameter is the subject of present research.

1.24.7 Prospects

Having obtained kinetic parameters for the rubrene system as described above, one can calculate the efficiency of an upconverting device under sunlight. An upconvertor may be treated as a simple steady-state system. In contrast to eqn [21], under continuous sunlight irradiation there is an equilibrium of the emitter triplet buildup and decay, that is, the concentration of emitter molecules in particular states ([^1M], [$^3M^*$]) is constant. Due to the fast ISC in the sensitizer and the rapid TET to the emitter, the buildup of the triplet emitter concentration can be expressed as a first-order behavior depending on the photon flux rate [38] by the sun k_ϕ and the (constant) concentration of ground-state sensitizer molecules:

$$\frac{d[^3M^*]t}{dt} = 0 = k_\phi[S] - k_1[^3M^*] - k_2[^3M^*]^2 \qquad [27]$$

The creation rate of triplets is assumed to be independent of the concentration of emitters. This is reasonable so long as the ground-state population of emitters is always significantly higher than the sensitizer population. The above equation is a simple quadratic, thus

$$[^3M^*] = \frac{-k + \sqrt{k_1^2 + 4k_2 k_\phi[S]}}{2k_2} \qquad [28]$$

The proportion of triplet emitter molecules decaying via TTA is thus determined:

$$f_2 = \frac{k_2[^3M^*]}{k_1 + k_2[^3M^*]} \qquad [29]$$

For the purposes of modeling, we consider an upconverting material with identical properties to the rubrene system above. In combination with the photon flux density F_λ of the AM1.5G solar spectrum in the relevant wavelength range, the sensitizer molecules produce $k_\phi = \int F_\lambda(\lambda)\sigma(\lambda)d\lambda = 4$ s^{-1}, where $\sigma(\lambda) = 1000\ln(10)\epsilon(\lambda)/N_A$. The measured value of $k_2 \approx 1.0 \times 10^8$ M^{-1} s^{-1} is in agreement with a previous study [43], as is $k_1 \approx 1.0 \times 10^4$ s^{-1}. If the sensitizer concentration of the upconvertor is set at [M] = 10^{-3} M,

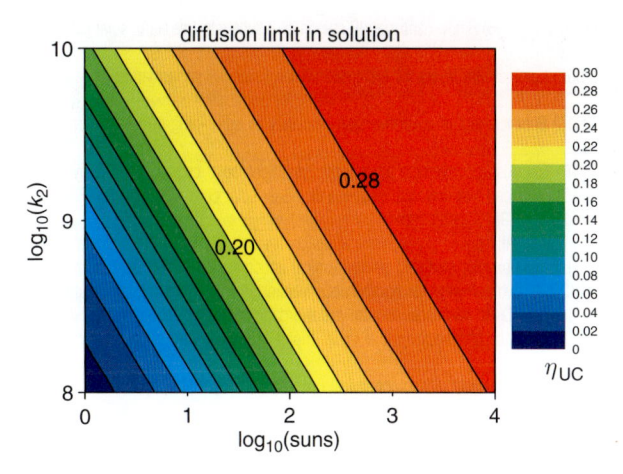

Figure 17 The performance of an $\eta_{conv} = 0.3$ upconvertor as a function of solar concentration and second-order rate constant.

as experimentally utilized, with these parameters, eqn [29] results in $f_2 = 0.4\%$. Accounting for the conversion efficiency $\eta_{conv} = 0.3$ extracted above for our system, one arrives at $\eta_{UC} = 0.0012$ under 1 sun ($\eta_{UC}^{\odot} = 0.0012$), which is about five times lower than Castellano's measurement [33], but higher than the estimate made above for the same system. This discrepancy, a factor of 4, is partly due to the fact that a saturating ultrafast laser pulse can place only a maximum of half the population in the excited state, providing that the electronic state decoheres on a faster time-scale than the excitation pulse. A nanosecond laser pulse would slowly feed population from S_0 to S_1 to T_1, and thus total population transfer would be possible and higher efficiencies would be observed.

The performance can be significantly improved. Prolonging the emitter triplet lifetime by an order of magnitude would increase f_2 to 23% leading to a maximum of 7% annihilation efficiency. Increasing the product $k_2 k_\phi [S]$ by the three possible means also boosts the efficiency. Increasing k_2 to $10^9 \, M^{-1} \, s^{-1}$ yields $\eta_{UC}^{\odot} = 0.01$.

In **Figure 17**, the performance of an $\eta_{conv} = 0.3$ upconvertor is plotted as a function of solar concentration and second-order rate constant, k_2, for a sensitizer concentration of 0.01 M, achievable in a dense medium. Unsurprisingly, increasing the solar concentration boosts the efficiency up to the maximum at 10 000 suns. The excitation rate k_ϕ can also be increased a few times by a broader sensitizer absorption range. However, pushing the second-order rate constant toward $2k_d/9\eta_{conv}$ has an equally dramatic effect. Still higher rate constants may be realized in condensed media where the triplet exciton diffuses, rather than the molecular carrier. Higher values for η_{conv} would clearly improve the upconvertor as well.

Considering such an improved performance, instantly the applicability of TTA for solar cell improvement is clear. The application of upconverting materials based on TTA for solar cells depends crucially on several parameters which will be steadily improved in the coming years. At present, the technology is under threshold for application, but this situation should be revised when the issues discussed above are addressed.

References

[1] Shen Y (2003) *The Principles of Nonlinear Optics*. Hoboken, NJ: Wiley Classics Library, Wiley-Interscience.
[2] Tayebjee MJY, Hirst LC, Ekins-Daukes NJ, and Schmidt TW (2010) The efficiency limit of solar cells with molecular absorbers: A master equation approach. *Journal of Applied Physics* 108(12): 124506.
[3] Hirst LC and Ekins-Daukes NJ (2010) Fundamental losses in solar cells. *Progress in Photovoltaics: Research and Applications* 19(3): 286–293.
[4] ASTM standard G173 standard tables for reference solar spectral irradiances: Direct normal and hemispherical on 37° tilted surface. http://rredc.nrel.gov/solar/spectra/am1.5/.
[5] Brown AS and Green MA (2002) Detailed balance limit for the series constrained two terminal tandem solar cell. *Physica E* 14: 96–100.
[6] Hanna MC and Nozik AJ (2006) Solar conversion efficiency of photovoltaic and photoelectrolysis cells with carrier multiplication absorbers. *Journal of Applied Physics* 100: 074510.
[7] Shockley W and Queisser HJ (1961) Detailed balance limit of efficiency of p-n junction solar cells. *Journal of Applied Physics* 32(3): 510–519.
[8] Trupke T, Green MA, and Würfel P (2002) Improving solar cell efficiencies by up-conversion of sub-band-gap light. *Journal of Applied Physics* 92(7): 4117–4122.
[9] Trupke T, Shalav A, Richards BS, *et al.* (2006) Efficiency enhancement of solar cells by luminescent up-conversion of sunlight. *Solar Energy Materials and Solar Cells* 90: 3327–3338.
[10] Ekins-Daukes NJ and Schmidt TW (2008) A molecular approach to the intermediate band solar cell: The symmetric case. *Applied Physics Letters* 93(6): 063507.
[11] Fischer S, Goldschmidt JC, Löper P, *et al.* (2010) Enhancement of silicon solar cell efficiency by upconversion: Optical and electrical characterization. *Journal of Applied Physics* 108: 044912.
[12] Auzel F (2004) Upconversion and anti-stokes processes with f and d ions in solids. *Chemical Reviews* 104(1): 139.
[13] Bloembergen N (1959) Solid state infrared quantum counters. *Physical Review Letters* 2: 84–85.
[14] Auzel F (1973) Materials and devices using double-pumped-phosphors with energy transfer. *Proceedings of the IEEE* 61, 758–786.
[15] Förster T (1948) Zwischenmolekulare energiewanderung und fluoreszenz. *Annalen der Physik* 437: 55.
[16] Gamelin D and Güdel H (2001) Upconversion processes in transition metal and rare earth metal systems. *Topics in Current Chemistry* 214: 1–56.
[17] van der Ende BM, Aarts L, and Meijerink A (2009) Lanthanide ions as spectral converters for solar cells. *Physical Chemistry Chemical Physics* 11: 11081–11095.

[18] Gibart P, Auzel F, Guillaume J-C, and Zahraman K (1996) Below band-gap IR response of substrate-free GaAs solar cells using two-photon up-conversion. *Japanese Journal of Applied Physics* 35(8): 4401–4402.
[19] Shalav A, Richards BS, and Green MA (2007) Luminescent layers for enhanced silicon solar cell performance: Up-conversion. *Solar Energy Materials and Solar Cells* 91(9): 829–842.
[20] Pan A, del Cañizo C, Cánovas E, et al. (2010) Enhancement of up-conversion efficiency by combining rare earth-dopedphosphors with PbS quantum dots. *Solar Energy Materials and Solar Cells* 94: 1923–1926.
[21] de Wild J, Meijerink A, Rath JK, et al. (2010) Towards upconversion for amorphous silicon solar cells. *Solar Energy Materials and Solar Cells* 94: 1919–1922.
[22] de Wild J, Rath JK, Meijerink A, et al. (2010) Enhanced near-infrared response of a-Si:H solar cells with beta-NaYF(4):Yb(3+) (18%), Er(3+) (2%) upconversion phosphors. *Solar Energy Materials and Solar Cells* 94: 2395–2398.
[23] Cheng Y, Fückel B, Khoury T, et al. (2011) Entropically driven photochemical upconversion. *Journal of Physics and Chemistry* 115(6): 1047–1053.
[24] Fückel B, Roberts D, Cheng Y, et al. (2011) Singlet oxygen mediated photochemical upconversion of NIR light. *Journal of Physical Chemistry Letters* 2(9): 966–971.
[25] Baluschev S, Yakutkin V, Wegner G, et al. (2007) Two pathways for photon upconversion in model organic compound systems. *Journal of Applied Physics* 101(2): 023101.
[26] Kozlov DV and Castellano FN (2004) Anti-stokes delayed fluorescence from metal-organic bichromophores. *Chemistry Communications* 24: 2860–2861.
[27] Cheng YY, Khoury T, Clady RGCR, et al. (2010) On the efficiency limit of triplet-triplet annihilation for photochemical upconversion. *Physical Chemistry Chemical Physics* 12: 66–71.
[28] Cheng YY, Fückel B, Khoury T, et al. (2010) Kinetic analysis of photochemical upconversion by triplet-triplet annihilation: Beyond any statistical limit. *Journal of Physical Chemistry Letters* 1(12): 1795–1799.
[29] Monguzzi A, Tubino R, and Meinardi F (2009) Multicomponent polymeric film for red to green low power sensitized up-conversion. *Journal of Physical Chemistry A* 113: 1171–1174.
[30] Trupke T, Green MA, and Würfel P (2002) Improving solar cell efficiencies by up-conversion of sub-band-gap light. *Journal of Applied Physics* 92(7): 4117–4122.
[31] Baluschev S, Yakutkin V, Miteva T, et al. (2007) Blue-green upconversion: Noncoherent excitation by nir light. *Angewandte Chemie International Edition* 46(40): 7693–7696.
[32] Singh-Rachford TN, Haefele A, Ziessel R, and Castellano FN (2008) Boron dipyrromethene chromophores: Next generation triplet acceptors/annihilators for low power upconversion schemes. *Journal of the American Chemical Society* 130(48): 16164–16165.
[33] Charlton JL, Dabestani R, and Saltiel J (1983) Role of triplet triplet annihilation in anthracene dimerization. *Journal of the American Chemical Society* 105(11): 3473–3476.
[34] Saltiel J and Atwater B (1988) *Advances in Photochemistry*. New York: Wiley.
[35] McLean AJ and Truscott TG (1990) Efficiency of triplet-photosensitized singlet oxygen generation in benzene. *Journal of the Chemical Society, Faraday Transactions* 86(14): 2671–2672.
[36] Bachilo SM and Weisman RB (2000) Determination of triplet quantum yields from triplettriplet annihilation fluorescence. *Journal of Physical Chemistry A* 104(33): 7711–7714.
[37] Levin PP, Costa SMB, Nunes TG, et al. (2003) Kinetics of triplet-triplet annihilation of tetraphenylporphyrin in liquid and frozen films of decanol on the external surface of zeolite. fast probe diffusion in monolayers and polycrystals. *Journal of Physical Chemistry A* 107(3): 328–336.
[38] Auckett JE, Cheng YY, Khoury T, et al. (2009) Efficient up-conversion by triplet-triplet annihilation. *Journal of Physics: Conference Series* 185: 012002.
[39] Singh-Rachford TN and Castellano FN (2009) Low power visible-to-UV upconversion. *Journal of Physical Chemistry A* 113(20): 5912–5917.
[40] Lewitzka F and Löhmannsröben HG (1986) Investigation of triplet tetracene and triplet rubrene in solution. *Zeitschrift für Physikalische Chemie Neue Folge* 150: 69–86.
[41] Baluschev S, Miteva T, Yakutkin V, et al. (2006) Up-conversion fluorescence: Noncoherent excitation by sunlight. *Physical Review Letters* 97(14): 143903.
[42] Singh-Rachford TN, Haefele A, Ziesseland R, and Castellano FN (2008) Boron dipyrromethene chromophores: Next generation triplet acceptors/annihilators for low power upconversion schemes. *Journal of the American Chemical Society* 130: 1616416165.
[43] Herkstroeter WG and Merkel PB (1981) The triplet state energies of rubrene and diphenylisobenzofuran. *Journal of Photochemistry* 16: 331–341.

Further Reading

Auzel F (2004) Upconversion and anti-stokes processes with f and d ions in solids. *Chemical Reviews* 104: 139.
Singh-Rachford TN and Castellano FN (2010) Photon upconversion based on sensitized triplet-triplet annihilation. *Coordination Chemistry Reviews* 254: 2560.
Green MA (2006) *Third Generation Photovoltaics: Advanced Solar Energy Conversion*. New York: Springer.
Conibeer GJ (2007) Third generation photovoltaics. *Materials Today* 10: 42.

1.25 Downconversion

MJY Tayebjee and TW Schmidt, The University of Sydney, Sydney, NSW, Australia
G Conibeer, University of New South Wales, Sydney, NSW, Australia

© 2012 Elsevier Ltd. All rights reserved.

1.25.1	Introduction	549
1.25.2	Equivalent Circuits	550
1.25.3	Practical Applications	554
1.25.3.1	QC in Rare-Earth Materials	555
1.25.3.2	MEG in Semiconductor Nanostructures	557
1.25.3.3	SF in Organic Materials	559
1.25.4	Prospects	560
References		560

Glossary
Carrier multiplication The generation of two low-energy charge carriers from one high-energy charge carrier.
Downconversion The conversion of a high-energy photon into two or more low-energy photons.
Downconverter A device capable of downconversion.
Exciton fission A general term for the generation of two or more low-energy excitons from one high-energy exciton.

Multiple exciton generation Exciton fission within a semiconductor nanostructured system.
Quantum cutting Exciton fission within a rare-earth ion.
Shockley–Queisser limit The limiting energy conversion efficiency of a single threshold solar cell under one sun.
Singlet fission Exciton fission within an organic molecular system. The initial exciton is in a singlet state, which then undergoes fission into two correlated triplet states.

1.25.1 Introduction

As explained in Chapter 1.24.2, and in detail in Chapter 1.14, one of the principal efficiency losses of all single threshold solar cells is that the energy absorbed in excess of the threshold is converted to heat. This mechanism accounts for the greater part of energy losses in solar cells with lower thresholds such as crystalline silicon. A strategy to counter this loss mechanism is to absorb photons well in excess of the threshold, and reradiate this energy with two photons at or above threshold. In this way, the current of the cell is increased with no penalty to operating voltage. This process is known as downconversion.

In this chapter we will consider the case where a photon with energy greater than an upper threshold, $E > E_b$, is converted into two or more photons with energy greater than a lower threshold, $E > E_r$. These photons are optically coupled to a single threshold solar cell (STSC), allowing for a reduction in the thermalization losses. In practice, this may be achieved via exciton fission (EF) processes: multiple exciton generation (MEG), singlet fission (SF), or quantum cutting (QC). (We will adhere to popular definitions. EF will be used a general term for the generation of two or more low energy excitons from one high energy exciton. The term MEG will be reserved for inorganic semiconductor nanostructures; SF will refer to an organic molecule in an excited singlet state and a molecule in the ground state evolving into two molecules in lower energy triplet states; QC will refer to rare-earth ion systems that undergo EF.) In this chapter, we also consider carrier multiplication (CM), where, instead of multiple photon generation, an absorber directly creates multiple charge carriers from a single absorbed photon.

Apart from increasing the efficiency of a solar cell, one might wish to protect a solar cell from damaging effects of higher energy photons. Organic cells are the only current solar technology which are constructed from materials that are abundant enough to scale up power generation to terawatt scales [1]. They, however, suffer from photostability issues. A downconverter placed at the front of these devices would play the dual role of increasing the photon flux and reduce degradation due to the absorption of high-energy photons. Furthermore, compared to tandem devices, which require current matching [2], downconversion and CM solar cells do not suffer from this restriction.

Before we proceed, be careful to note the difference between downconversion and downshifting. Downconversion does not conserve exciton number. Downshifting, on the other hand, is a linear process that alters the illumination spectrum such that its overlap with a device's incident photon conversion efficiency (IPCE) curve is maximized. In this chapter, we establish the efficiency limits of downconversion-assisted STSCs and solar cells with absorbers that undergo CM. Different practical approaches, implementations, and developments within the field will then be discussed.

1.25.2 Equivalent Circuits

The details of the efficiency limits of STSCs have been covered briefly in Chapter 1.24.2, and Reference 3. Further details of the following derivation are given in Reference 4. In keeping with the preceding chapter, we will use the STSC current–voltage characteristic [5]

$$\frac{I}{e} = k_r - k_r' \exp\left(\frac{(eV_c - E_r)}{k_B T}\right) \qquad [1]$$

for a cell operating at a voltage V_c, where e, k_B, and $T = 300\,\text{K}$ are the elementary charge, Boltzmann's constant, and operating temperature, respectively. The rate of absorption, $k_r = k_S(E_r, \infty, 1)$, from the highest occupied molecular orbital (HOMO) to the lowest unoccupied molecular orbital (LUMO), with energy difference E_r, is

$$k_S(E_1, E_2, \sigma) = \frac{\sigma}{hc} \int_{hc/E_2}^{hc/E_1} \lambda F_\lambda^\odot \, d\lambda \qquad [2]$$

where σ is the step-function cross section of the absorber and $F_\lambda^\odot$ is the solar spectrum irradiance in J m^{-2} nm^{-1} s^{-1} at a wavelength λ. Planck's constant and the speed of light in a vacuum are denoted h and c, respectively. This rate is countered by the rate of emission k_r' into a medium with refractive index n, where

$$\begin{aligned}
k_A(E_1, n, \sigma) &= \frac{\sigma n^2}{4\pi^2 c^2} \int_{E_1}^{\infty} E^2 \exp\left(\frac{-(E - E_1)}{k_B T}\right) \\
&= \frac{\sigma n^2}{4\pi^2 c^2} \left(\frac{k_B T}{\hbar}\right)^3 \left[\left(\frac{E_1}{k_B T}\right)^2 + 2\left(\frac{E_1}{k_B T}\right) + 2\right] \\
&\approx \frac{\sigma n^2 k_B T}{4\pi^2 c^2 \hbar^3} E_1^2
\end{aligned} \qquad [3]$$

The rate of stimulated emission can be ignored given the low irradiance and the fact that $E_m \gg k_B T$ [3]. As such, the lower order terms in E_1 can also be omitted.

We will consider three devices and establish their energy conversion efficiency limits. **Figure 1** shows their equivalent circuits and architectures. Device **A** consists of two photocells with respective band gaps of E_r and E_b. The CM process is provided by a direct current (DC) transformer (Buck converter) that doubles the current and halves the voltage. In practice, of course, the process would be provided by the absorber within a single photocell. Devices **B** and **C** are luminescent downconverters which have the same equivalent circuits. These are optically coupled to an STSC. The difference arises from the overall device architecture: **B** is placed at the rear of the STSC, whereas **C** is placed at the front. As we shall see, this gives rise to different absorption spectra.

In **A**, we must match the outgoing current of the cell, r, with twice the Buck converter's incoming current:

$$\begin{aligned}
\frac{I_A}{e} &= k_r - k_r' \exp\left(\frac{(eV_c - E_r)}{k_B T}\right) \\
&= 2\left(k_b - k_b' \exp\left(\frac{2eV_c - E_b}{k_B T}\right)\right)
\end{aligned} \qquad [4]$$

When considering **B** and **C**, the operating voltage of the downconverters, V_d, differs from that of the STSC, V_c. The current passing through the downconverters is determined by equating the currents passing through each photocell:

$$\begin{aligned}
\frac{I_B}{e} = \frac{I_C}{e} &= k_b - k_b' \exp\left(\frac{(2eV_d - E_b)}{k_B T}\right) \\
&= k_r' \exp\left(\frac{(2eV_d - E_r)}{k_B T}\right) - (k_r + \phi(V_c)/2)
\end{aligned} \qquad [5]$$

The photon flux passing from the STSC to the downconverter is denoted $\phi(V_c)$ and is equally partitioned between the two identical light-emitting diodes (LEDs). The forms of the downconverted flux, k_d, are shown in **Table 1** for **B** and **C**. The I–V characteristic of the STSC assisted by luminescent downconversion is given by

$$\frac{I_c}{e} = k_c + k_d - k_c' \exp\left(\frac{(eV_c - E_r)}{k_B T}\right) \qquad [6]$$

We are now in a position to calculate the efficiency of each device

$$\eta = \frac{P_{\max}}{\int_0^\infty F_\lambda^\odot \, d\lambda} \qquad [7]$$

where $P_{\max}$ is the maximum power point obtained from $I_A V_c$ for **A** and $I_c V_c$ for **B** and **C**.

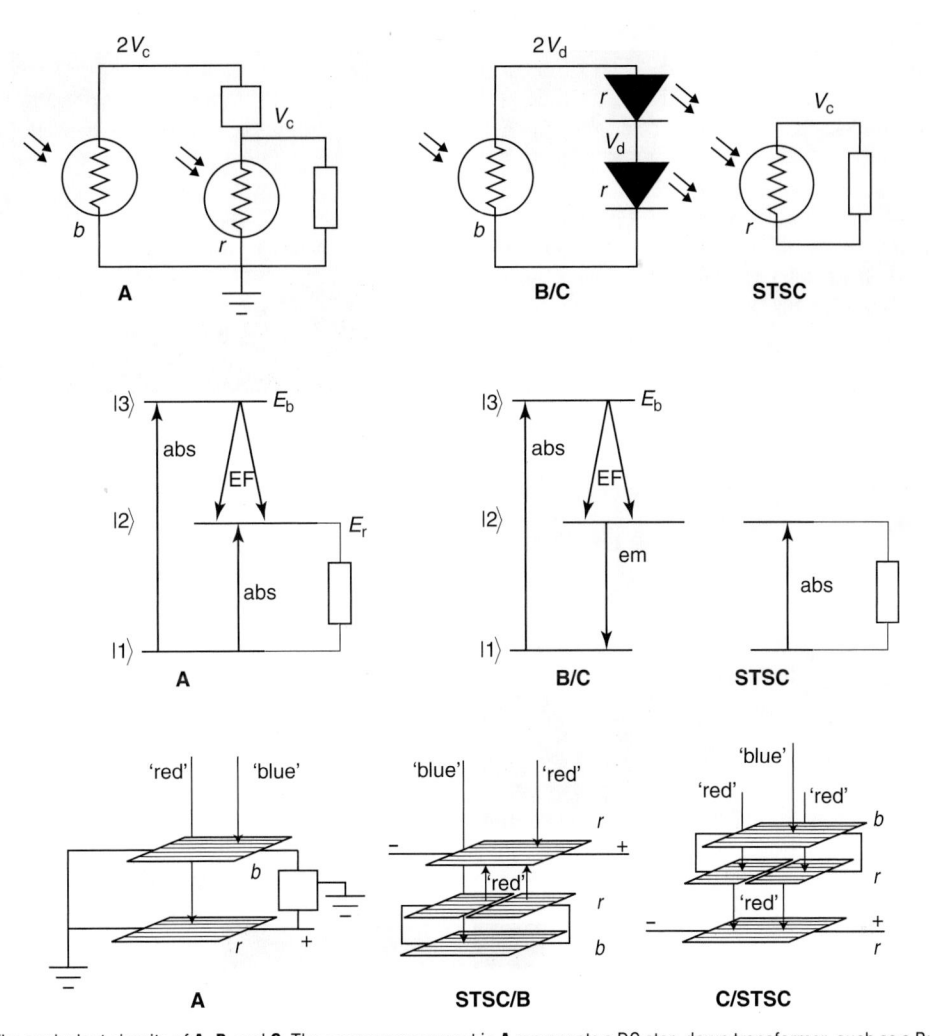

Figure 1 (Top) The equivalent circuits of **A**, **B**, and **C**. The square component in **A** represents a DC step-down transformer, such as a Buck converter with an operating efficiency of 100% that links a higher threshold photocell, b, to a lower threshold photocell, r. The luminescent circuits, **B** and **C**, consist of a high-threshold photocell, b, and two lower threshold LEDs, r, which drive an STSC. (Middle) Generalized energy-level diagram of the three devices. The labels |1>, |2>, and |3> will be used to describe systems undergoing EF. Absorptive and emissive transitions are, respectively, labeled abs and em. (Bottom) Schematics of the device architectures.

Table 1 Parameter values for the three devices considered

Parameter	A	B	C
k_r	$k_S(E_r, E_b, 1)$	0	$k_S(E_r, E_b, 1/2)$
k_r'	$k_A(E_r, 1, 1)$	$k_A(E_r, n_r, 1/2)$	$k_A\left(E_r, \sqrt{1+n_r^2}, 1/2\right)$
k_b	$k_S(E_b, \infty, 1)$	$k_S(E_b, \infty, 1)$	$k_S(E_b, \infty, 1)$
k_b'	$k_A(E_b, 1, 1)$	$k_A(E_b, n_r, 1)$	$k_A\left(E_b, \sqrt{1+n_r^2}, 1\right)$
k_d		$2k_r' \exp((eV_d - E_r)/k_B T)$	$F(2k_r' \exp((eV_d - E_r)/k_B T) + k_b' \exp((2eV_d - E_b)/k_B T))$
k_c		$k_S(E_r, E_b, 1)$	0
k_c'		$k_A\left(E_r, \sqrt{1+n_r^2}, 1\right)$	$k_A(E_r, n_r, 1)$
ϕ		$Fk_c' \exp((eV_c - E_r)/k_B T)$	$k_c' \exp((eV_c - E_r)/k_B T)$

Note that an internal refractive index, n_r, of 3.6 was chosen for **B** and **C** in order to compare with Reference 6. The fraction, $f = n_r^2/(1+n_r^2)$, denotes the fraction of photon flux that is directed into the device by virtue of its internal refractive index.

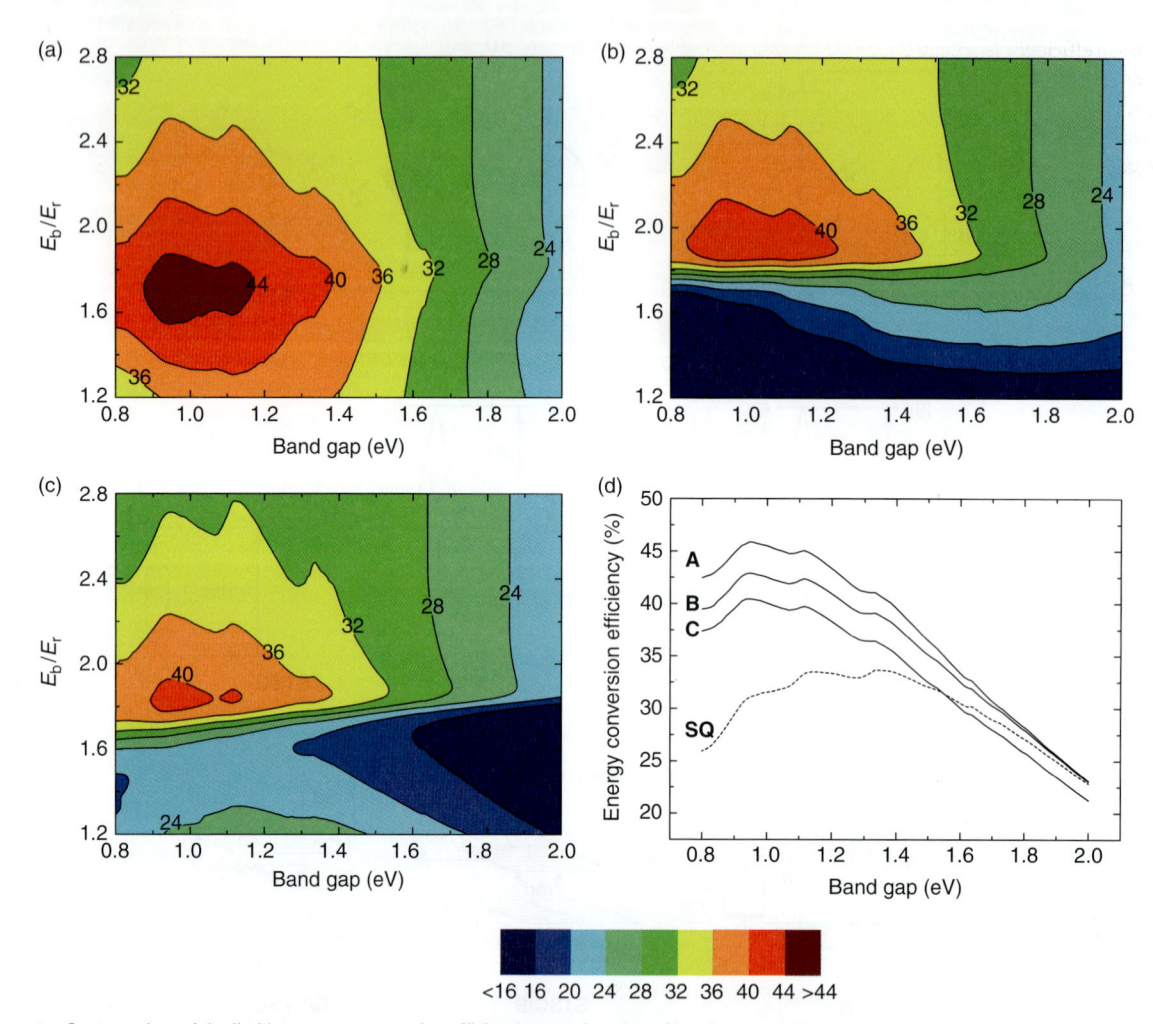

Figure 2 Contour plots of the limiting energy conversion efficiencies as a function of band gap and the ratio E_b/E_r for (a) **A**, (b) **B**, and (c) **C** under the AM1.5G spectrum [7]. (d) The maximum energy conversion efficiencies for each device. The SQ is shown for reference.

Figure 2 summarizes the energy conversion efficiencies of devices **A**, **B**, and **C**, under AM1.5G illumination, and their global maxima (45.9%, 42.9%, and 38.9%, respectively) are shown in **Table 2**. The three devices have energy conversion efficiency limits that are significantly greater than the the Shockley–Quesser limit of 33.7% under AM1.5G illumination. In all three cases, the greatest

Table 2 The maximum efficiency for devices operating under 6000 K black body and AM1.5G illumination

Device	6000 K black body η (%)	E_b/E_r	AM1.5G [7] η (%)	E_b/E_r
A	42.6 (39.6)	1.73	45.9 (41.9)	1.72
B	40.3 (39.6)	1.93	42.9 (41.9)	1.91
C	37.9 (36.8)	1.89	40.5 (38.9)	1.87
STSC	31.1	–	33.7	–

In all cases, the optimal values of E_r were 1.05 and 0.95 eV, for a device operating under black body and AM1.5G illumination, respectively. The values for an unassisted STSC are shown for comparison, with optimal band gaps of 1.30 and 1.34 eV, respectively. The values in parentheses denote the cases where the restriction $E_b/E_r = 2.0$ has been applied. Again, $n_r = 3.6$ was used for **B** and **C**.

conversion efficiency is obtained when the ratio $E_b/E_r < 2$. We can equivalently say that the sum of the enthalpies of the two low-energy excitons is greater than the enthalpy of the high-energy exciton. As such, the process is endothermic and must be driven by entropy.

This is best understood from a statistical thermodynamic viewpoint. Given a system of N absorbers and the vector $\mathbf{p}$ containing normalized state occupancies p_1, p_2, and p_3, respectively, for $|1\rangle$, $|2\rangle$, and $|3\rangle$ (see middle of **Figure 1**), the total number of microstates in the system is

$$\Omega(\mathbf{p}) = \binom{N}{p_1 N}\binom{N}{p_2 N}\binom{N}{p_3 N} \qquad [8]$$

where the definition of the binomial coefficient, $\binom{n}{k} = n!/[k!(n-k)!]$, is used. The EF process involves a change in the number of microstates:

$$\Delta_f \Omega(\mathbf{p}) = \Omega_f(\mathbf{p}) - \Omega_i(\mathbf{p})$$
$$= \binom{N}{p_1 N - 1}\binom{N}{p_2 N + 2}\binom{N}{p_3 N - 1} - \binom{N}{p_1 N}\binom{N}{p_2 N}\binom{N}{p_3 N} \qquad [9]$$

The entropy generated in the EF process is $\Delta_f S = k_b \ln(\Delta_f \Omega)$:

$$\Delta_f S(\mathbf{p}) = k_B \ln\left[\frac{p_1 N p_3 N(N - p_2 N)(N - p_2 N - 1)}{(N - p_1 N + 1)(p_2 N + 1)(p_2 N + 1)(N - p_3 N + 1)}\right]$$

As $N \to \infty$, collecting all the terms in N^4,

$$= k_B \ln\left[\frac{p_1 p_2 (p_2 - 1)^2}{p_2^2 (1 - p_1)(1 - p_3)}\right] \qquad [10]$$

Examining the above equation, we can see that as p_1 or p_3 approaches unity, the process becomes infinitely entropically favorable. This is also shown in **Figure 3**, where the value of $\Delta_f S$ is plotted on a ternary diagram as a function of $\mathbf{p}$. Horizontal lines correspond to iso-p_2 values, which are symmetric over the occupancies of p_1 and p_3. EF corresponds to movement vertically up the diagram. As such, entropy generation is maximized at the point (1/2, 0, 1/2). At the point (1/3, 1/3, 1/3), the EF process is at an entropic equilibrium ($\Delta_f S = 0$). Note that in the devices of interest the very large majority of the carrier population is in $|1\rangle$, that is, the bottom right corner of the diagram.

Of course, the component values of $\mathbf{p}$ and therefore $\Delta_f S$ depend on the operating voltage of the device. The voltage of the device is a measure of the free energy (chemical potential) within each state of the system, thus, under steady-state conditions in **A**:

$$p_1 = \frac{1}{Z_A} \qquad [11]$$

$$p_2 = \frac{1}{Z_A}\exp\left(\frac{eV_c - E_r}{k_B T}\right) \qquad [12]$$

$$p_3 = \frac{1}{Z_A}\exp\left(\frac{2eV_c - E_b}{k_B T}\right) \qquad [13]$$

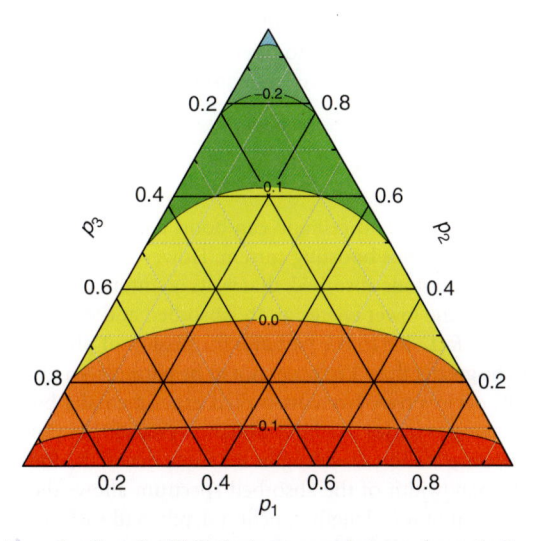

Figure 3 Ternary contour plot of $T\Delta_f S$ in eV as a function of $\mathbf{p}$. EF (fusion) corresponds to moving vertically up (down) the plot. Since $|T\Delta_f S| \to \infty$ as any component of $\mathbf{p}$ approaches unity, the vertices of the plot have been truncated. Here $T=300$ K.

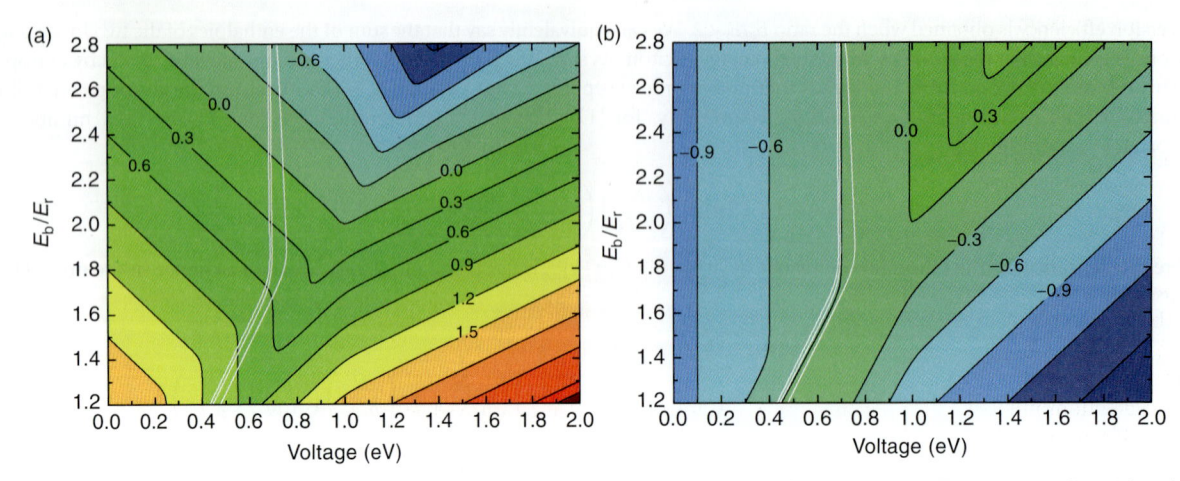

Figure 4 The value of (a) $T\Delta_f S$ and (b) $\Delta_f G$ in eV as a function of voltage and E_b/E_r for **A**, **B**, and **C**, where $E_r = 1$ eV. The white lines from left to right correspond to the operating voltage (at the maximum power point) of **A**, **C**, and **B**.

The partition function of the entire system is

$$Z_A = \left(1 + \exp\left(\frac{eV_c - E_r}{k_B T}\right) + \exp\left(\frac{2eV_c - E_b}{k_B T}\right)\right) \quad [14]$$

We can establish similar equations for **B** and **C**:

$$p_1 = \frac{1}{Z} \quad [15]$$

$$p_2 = \frac{1}{Z}\exp\left(\frac{eV_d - E_r}{k_B T}\right) \quad [16]$$

$$p_3 = \frac{1}{Z}\exp\left(\frac{2eV_d - E_b}{k_B T}\right) \quad [17]$$

$$Z = \left(1 + \exp\left(\frac{eV_d - E_r}{k_B T}\right) + \exp\left(\frac{2eV_d - E_b}{k_B T}\right)\right) \quad [18]$$

Figure 4 shows the changes in free energy, $\Delta_f G$, and entropy, $\Delta_f S$, associated with the EF process for **A**, **B**, and **C** as a function of operating voltage and E_b/E_r, where $E_r = 1$ eV. The white lines from right to left show the voltages of **A**, **C**, and **B** when operating at the maximum power point. We note that the ratio E_b/E_r can be lowered without lowering the operating voltage since EF becomes more entropically favorable. As such, EF is an endothermic process. This effectively means that a greater portion of the solar spectrum can be absorbed into states that undergo EF, increasing the photocurrent without penalizing the device voltage. This result is clarified in **Figure 4(b)**, where isoenergetic contours are almost parallel to operating voltages. In practice, this is probably only realizable in organic chromophores, since endothermic SF has been observed as a dominant relaxation pathway (cf. Section 1.25.3.3).

1.25.3 Practical Applications

A downconverter must be placed in front of a standard cell and can boost current by converting a UV photon to more than one photon just above the band gap of the solar cell, thus boosting current. However, the downconverter does require that more lower energy photons are emitted than high-energy photons absorbed, that is, its quantum yield (QY) must be greater than 1. Hence, there must be at least as many photons emitted at the lower energy as are absorbed at the higher, or else the DC layer will decrease the number of photons absorbed by the cell. In fact, due to the partial transmission of photons from a low refractive index in air to a higher one in the DC layer, the QY must be greater than 1 in order not to be parasitic – a QY of about 1 for a refractive index of 3.6 – similar to that for a Si solar cell [8]. DC devices have been attempted experimentally but so far an overall QY > 1 has not been achieved, resulting in a downshifting of energies in, for example, Si nanocrystals [9] or porous silicon [10], which nonetheless can give a useful enhancement in spectral response at short wavelengths for some materials, due to better absorption of the downshifted photons. This effective narrowing of the bandwidth of the absorbed spectrum allows the solar cell design to be optimized with respect to absorption coefficient as a function of wavelength, junction depth, and surface recombination [11]. Similarly, luminescent downshifting layers based on luminescent dyes have been demonstrated to boost the short wavelength response of CdTe cells in which short wavelengths are usually attenuated in the CdS window layer [12]. True downconversion or QC, as first suggested by

Dexter [13], requires absorption of a short wavelength photon and reemission of at least two photons of about twice the wavelength. In turn, this requires an appropriately located intermediate energy halfway between the excited state and the ground state. Most work has focused on lanthanide materials because of their varied and discrete energy levels.

1.25.3.1 QC in Rare-Earth Materials

The unique properties of rare-earth ions lend themselves to QC applications. A recent review by Zhang and Huang [14] detailed rare-earth ion QC phosphors, and the development of these systems has largely been inspired by applications in the lighting industry or in electronic displays. Nevertheless, in light of their rich energy-level structure, the promise of rare-earth ion systems for use in downconverters has been recognized and remains an active area of research [15].

The spectroscopy of rare-earth ions was discussed briefly in Chapter 1.24.6.1. Radiative electronic transitions in rare-earth ions are 'quasi'-atomic due to the tight binding of 4f electrons. Unlike molecular systems, electronic states are denoted by term symbols of the form $^{2S+1}L_J$. Here the spin multiplicity is $S = e_{u/2}$, where e_u is the number of unpaired electrons with the same spin. The total orbital quantum number $L = \sum_{n=1}^{e_u} |m_\ell|$, where m_ℓ is the magnetic orbital quantum number of a unpaired electron; in the case of rare-earth ions $m_\ell = -3, -2, -1, 0, 1, 2, 3$, as the highest energy electrons exist in the 4f orbital. By convention, the value of L is denoted with a letter ($S = 0, P = 1, D = 2, F = 3, G = 4, H = 5, I = 6 \ldots$). The total angular momentum quantum number takes values in the range $|L-S| \leq J \leq L+S$ in integer steps, where $J = L+S$ corresponds to the lowest energy state.

There are several possible mechanisms for QC, which have been discussed by Wegh et al. [16], and are summarized in **Figure 5**. Rare-earth ions exist as pairs of sensitizers and emitters. The trivalent ytterbium cation (Yb^{3+}) was suggested as an emitter in QC systems in 1957 by Dexter [13]. This is particularly applicable to solar cells since the $Yb^{3+} \sim 1.24\,eV\ ^2F_{5/2} \rightarrow 2F_{7/2}$ transition could be used in conjunction with a crystalline silicon ($E_r \sim 1.1\,eV$) STSC. Luminescent QYs greater than unity were actually achieved in a Tb^{3+}–Yb^{3+} couple in 2005 [17]. Several other trivalent cationic rare-earth couples have been suggested, and they are summarized in **Figure 6**.

Praseodymium (Pr^{3+}) is a good choice because of its widely dispersed energy levels well matched for photon cutting [27] (see **Figure 7**). The $^3P_2$, $^1I_0$, and P_0 levels at between 440 and 490 nm can absorb blue photons which can then radiatively recombine via the $^1G_4$ level at 1010 nm – at just greater than twice this wavelength, thus emitting two photons at just above the silicon band gap, although nonradiative recombination via the other levels at longer wavelengths than $^1G_4$ is also likely. Experiments indicating such photon cutting have been carried out on Pr^{3+} embedded in various phosphors [28, 29], and also for other lanthanide-doped materials [25, 30]. Transition metals with their partially screened 'd' shell electrons also have partially discrete levels and work on photon cutting in transition metal-doped materials has also been carried out [31, 32].

An alternative approach is to absorb a short wavelength photon high up in the conduction band of various semiconductors. There is then the possibility of an impact ionization event (i.e., reverse Auger recombination) in which the high-energy electron excites an additional electron to the conduction band, thus creating two or more electron–hole pairs at the band gap energy [32]. Luminescent recombination of these electron–hole pairs is then usually enhanced by choice of an appropriate doping level within the band gap and an increased number of photons emitted. The QY of such impact ionization depends on the energy of the initial photon and is reduced by nonradiative thermalization and recombination. QYs greater than 2 have been achieved in some

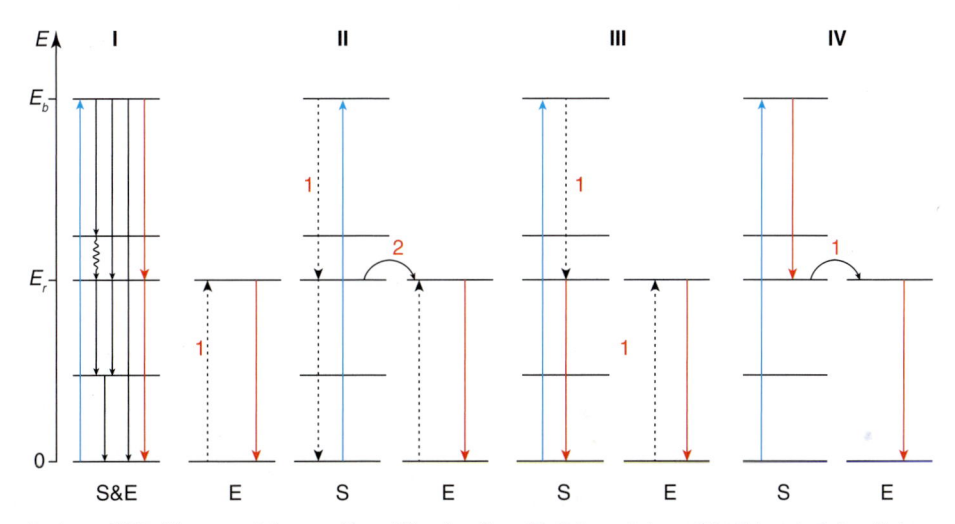

Figure 5 The mechanisms of QC with rare-earth ion sensitizers (S) and emitters (E). Scheme **I** shows QC within a single ion. **II** shows a two-step energy transfer process, where part energy from an excited sensitizer is transferred to an emitter by cross-relaxation. The emitter returns to the ground state through radiative recombination. The sensitizer then transfers the remainder to a second emitter, which also radiatively returns to the ground state. **III** and **IV** both show QC with only one energy step, that is, the sensitizer also emits one of the lower energy photons. Redrawn and adapted from Wegh RT, Donker H, Oskam KD, and Meijerink A (1999) Visible quantum cutting in LiGdF$_4$:Eu^{3+} through downconversion. *Science* 283(5402): 663–666 [16].

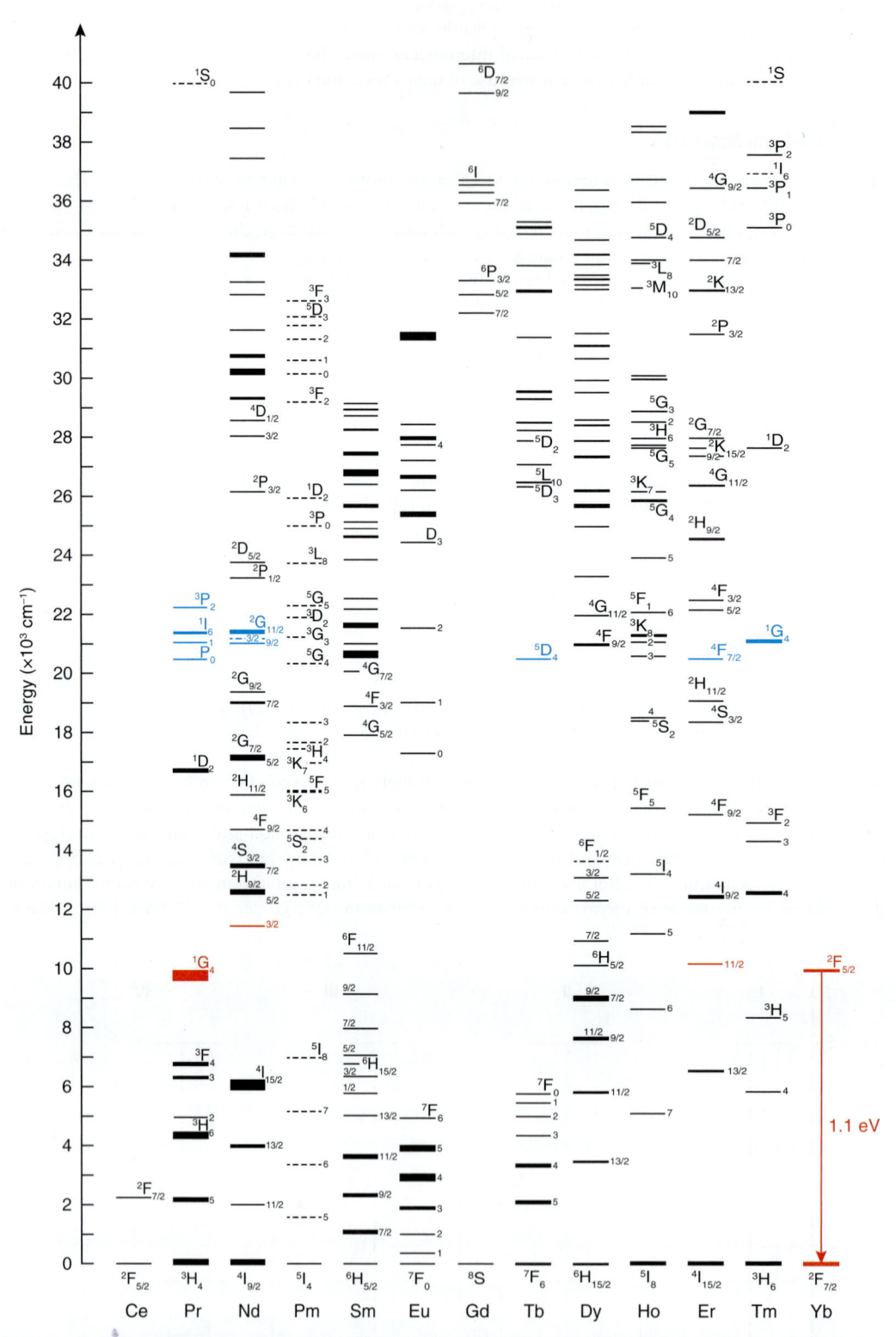

Figure 6 Dieke diagram showing the excited-state energies of trivalent rare-earth cations. Excited states that can be used for downconversion are shown in color: blue and red, respectively, represent the upper and lower excited states involved in QC. We consider rare earth couples where the emitter is Yb^{3+} in the $^2F_{7/2}$ state. To date, this includes coupling with Pr^{3+} [15, 18, 19], Nd^{3+} [20], Tb^{3+} [18, 21, 22], Er^{3+} [23, 24], or Tm^{3+} [18] sensitizers. An extension of this diagram for energies greater than 40×10^3 cm^{-1} has been provided by Wegh et al. [25]. Reproduced and adapted from Dieke GH and Crosswhite HM (1963) The spectra of the doubly and triply ionized rare earths. *Applied Optics* 2(7): 675–686 [26].

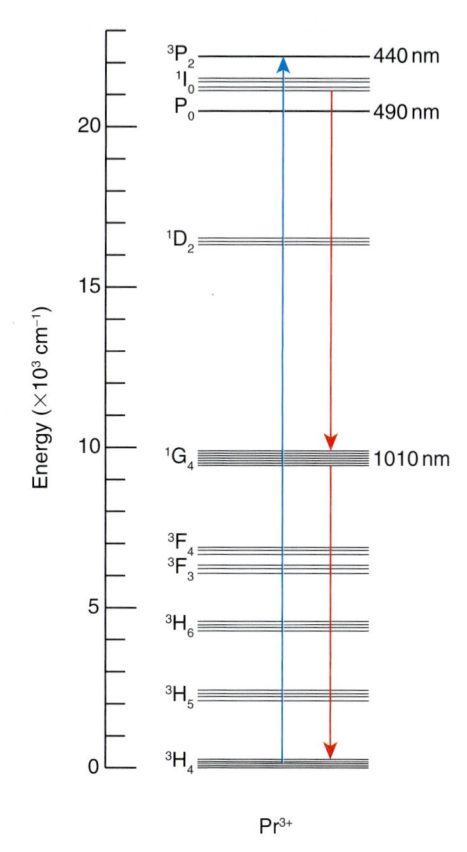

Figure 7 Energy levels for Pr^{3+} based on data from Reference 27 and extracted detail from **Figure 6**. Also shown is the possible photon-cutting mechanism for a photon absorbed around 450 nm and emitted as two photons via the $^1G_4$ level.

materials, usually based on wide band gap oxides (at least 5 eV) doped with lanthanide or transition metal atoms, but with incident photon energies of at least twice or thrice the band gap [30, 31]. QYs up to about 1.20–1.40 have also been achieved with the relatively narrow gap (3.4 eV) ZnS doped with Zn, Cu, or Ag, but only with photons in excess of 20 eV [32].

However, at the incident photon energies required for this impact ionization, there are almost no photons in the solar spectrum. Also, the efficiency of the impact ionization mechanism is very low. Hence, these are not good materials for downconversion for solar cells. But, in some materials based on quantum dot (QD) arrays, this efficiency can be increased dramatically such that several excitons can be generated from one incident high-energy photon.

1.25.3.2 MEG in Semiconductor Nanostructures

MEG is a process whereby a high-energy electron–hole pair in a nanostructured inorganic semiconductor undergoes impact ionization, yielding two lower energy excitons (see **Figure 8**). Quantum confinement is a key concept for EF, since bulk semiconductors usually require $E_b/E_r = 4-6$ due to (1) the conservation of carrier momentum and (2) extremely short hot carrier lifetimes as a result of rapid electron–phonon interactions [33–36]. Nanostructured materials, on the other hand, lend themselves to EF because

- electron–hole pairs are correlated, giving rise to excitons rather than free carriers [2];
- exciton cooling is slowed due to the discretization of electronic states [37];
- momentum is no longer a good quantum number, and thus does not need to be conserved [37]; and
- Auger processes (such as EF) are enhanced due to the increased Coulomb interaction between electrons and holes [2]

In the previous section, we suggested that EF could proceed even if $E_b/E_r < 2$. However, theoretical calculations of PbSe, CdSe, and InAs structures with quantum confinement suggest that MEG will only be appreciably observed when $E_b/E_r \geq 2.2$ [38, 39]. In practice, time-resolved spectroscopy of lead sulfide, selenide, and telluride QDs has shown MEG thresholds in the range $E_b/E_r = 2.7-3.0$ [40–43]. More precisely, the efficiency of MEG has been defined in terms of the QY at a given photon energy, $h\nu$ [44]:

$$QY = \left(\frac{h\nu}{E_r} - 1\right)\eta_{EHPM} \quad [19]$$

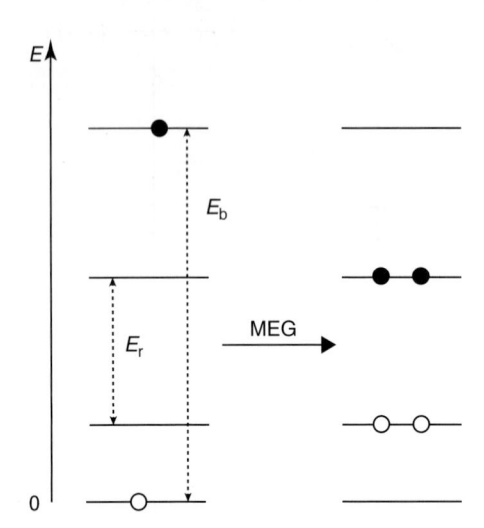

Figure 8 The creation of two excitons via MEG. MEG will occur in QD systems, where a band structure describes electronic states. Closed and open circles represent electrons in the conduction band and holes in the valence band, respectively.

Table 3 The MEG efficiency for a number of bulk QD and single-walled carbon nanotube (SWCNT) samples, as analyzed by Beard [45]

Sample	η_{EHPM}	References
Bulk Ge	0.3	[46]
Bulk Si	0.4	[47]
Bulk PbSe	0.2	[48]
Bulk PbS	0.3	[48]
PbSe QDs	0.4	[49, 50]
InP QDs	0.9	[51]
SWCNTs	0.7	[52]

The quantity η_{EHPM} is the electron–hole pair multiplication efficiency and is defined as the minimum energy required to produce an electron–hole pair, divided by the actual energy required. Very recently, Beard [45] quantified η_{EHPM} for a number of experimental results, which are tabulated in **Table 3**. Much higher values are obtained in confined structures, suggesting that quantum confinement is indeed a promising method for the promotion of EF. It should be noted, however, that there is still significant disagreement among researchers about the QY that can be obtained from such systems. For instance, some report a QY $\gg$ 1 in PbS and PbSe, while other investigations suggest that QY < 1.25 (see Reference 44 and references therein). These differences have chiefly been attributed to surface effects or charge delocalization, and a better understanding of these will stimulate further research into the field [45].

For a MEG material to be used directly as a DC with an STSC, a few conditions are required. The MEG QDs would need to have an appropriate band gap to illuminate a solar cell – for a Si STSC, Si QDs would be appropriate, and MEG has been shown in well-passivated Si QDs [41]. But, much more challenging would be the need for a high luminescent efficiency of the multiple excitons such that there would be a net QY greater than unity. However, it is not yet clear whether such a luminescent efficiency from these materials is feasible. The currently observable rate of MEG and subsequent Auger decay processes back to a single exciton at about 200 ps [41, 45], and the long radiative lifetimes of these materials, at about 10 ns, would make efficient multiple photon emission unlikely.

An alternative approach is to directly incorporate the MEG QDs in a solar cell in order to boost the current in the device through direct CM. Several attempts have been made to do this, which until recently have not successfully shown an increase in current. However, very recent results have shown a PbSe QD solar cell device with QYs greater than 1 for 3.5 eV illumination [53]. This very significant result demonstrates the feasibility of the approach and further significant improvement is likely to follow.

1.25.3.3 SF in Organic Materials

SF can occur in molecular crystals, thin films, aggregates, dimers, or polymers. An excited single-state organic chromophore undergoes fission with a nearby chromophore in the ground state giving rise to two triplet chromophores, as shown in **Figure 9**. These triplets may either undergo phosphorescence or spatial separation and be directly injected into the external circuit. A key advantage of using molecular systems is that triplet states are generally long lived due to the spin-forbidden transition to the ground singlet state. It is important to note, however, that the SF process does not violate spin conservation: the two triplets produced will be correlated such that their tensor product is a singlet state.

Since phosphorence is a slow spin-forbidden transition, these organic molecules are more suited to CM than downconversion since the yields would be too low. Alternatively, the system could be altered by the addition of a highly phosphorescent species, as shown in **Figure 10**. Sensitizers that undergo SF transfer their excited state energy to emitter molecules via triplet energy transfer (TET). In practice, the TET process would be exothermic; however, entropy could also be exploited by having a large emitter-to-sensitizer ratio. Unfortunately, to date, phosphorescent yields have not exceeded 50% - any gain from SF would be squandered.

SF first appeared in peer-reviewed literature in 1965, when Singh and coworkers [54] suggested that it occurred in anthracene. Further evidence of SF in other polyacene structures, including anthracene [55, 56], tetracene [56–61], and pentacene [59, 62–65], has also been shown. Investigations into other conjugated oligomer and polymer systems have also shown evidence of SF (see, for instance, the review by Smith and Michl [66]). Examining the body of literature, SF was initially avidly studied in the 1970s, before interest lapsed. We have experienced renewed interest over the last decade in light of the development of novel, efficient, photovoltaic devices.

Many authors have introduced their studies with the requirements for efficient SF, and invariably state the restriction $E_b \geq 2E_r$, in spite of some of the earliest observations of SF occurring in systems where this was not the case (for instance, SF in anthracene is highly endothermic [55]). The fact that SF is nevertheless a dominant relaxation process cannot be explained by thermal activation alone. A far more viable explanation is that entropy is acting as a driving force for the process, and the simple derivation given in Chapter **1.25.2** displays this. Very recently, Jadhav and coworkers [67] have demonstrated a working solar cell containing the singlet fissile organic compound, tetracene (Tc). The Tc/copper phtalocyanine/C_{60} device displays SF with an efficiency of $71 \pm 18\%$.

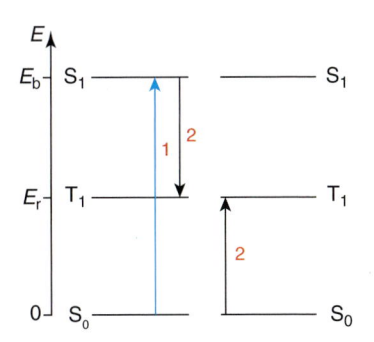

Figure 9 The creation of two excitons via SF. SF proceeds in molecular systems where electronic states are described by molecular orbitals. The first process (1) represents the absorption transition $S_1 \leftarrow S_0$, and the second (2) represents SF.

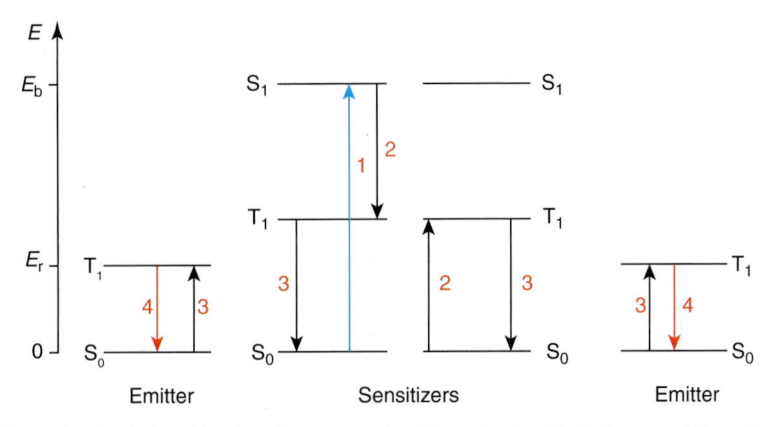

Figure 10 SF within sensitizer molecules, followed by phosphorescence of emitter molecules. The first process (1) represents the absorption transition $S_1 \leftarrow S_0$, and the second (2) represents SF. Process (3) is TET which leaves emitters in an excited triplet state from which they return to the ground state by phosphorescing (4).

While there is an extremely wide body of experimental studies with evidence of SF in organic materials, a fundamental and universal understanding of the mechanism is still an active area of research. In their review, Smith and Michl [66] presented quantum mechanical formalisms for SF by direct coupling and through a charge transfer state. Greyson *et al.* [68, 69] proposed SF mechanisms using density matrix theory and density functional theory. Zimmerman *et al.* [70] used *ab initio* molecular orbital calculations to show that SF proceeds in pentacene via a dark state.

1.25.4 Prospects

Chapter **1.24** dealt with the prospects of upconversion. One of the major obstacles for the realization of a working upconverter is the fact that it is an unfavourable process from an entropic standpoint. An enthalpic sacrifice is required in order for upconversion to be exergonic. By contrast, downconversion and carrier multiplication involves the creation of two (quasi-) particles from one (quasi-) particle: an entropically favourable process. That is, an exergonic reaction proceeds even where there is a gain in enthalpy. Therefore downconversion may prove to be more effective than upconversion at circumventing the energy conversion efficiency limits associated with conventional photovoltaic devices.

A further advantage of a luminescent downconverter is that it can be added to the front face of existing photovoltaic installations. This is especially advantageous when they are used to enhance an organic device as these often suffer from degradation due to photo-activated reactions with high energy photons. A luminescent downconverter can play the dual role of decreasing the number of such photons, while increasing the photon number, and therefore the current of the device. While downconversion technology is still currently in its infancy, the sheer extent of research can allow us to be optimistic about the realization of these devices in the near future.

References

[1] Grätzel M (2009) Recent advances in sensitized mesoscopic solar cells. *Accounts of Chemical Research* 42(11): 1788–1798.
[2] Nozik AJ (2010) Nanoscience and nanostructures for photovoltaics and solar fuels. *Nano Letters* 10(8): 2735–2741.
[3] Hirst LC and Ekins-Daukes NJ (2010) Fundamental losses in solar cells. *Progress in Photovoltaics: Research and Applications* 19(3): 286–293.
[4] Tayebjee MJY and Schmidt TW (submitted) Entropy recycling in exciton fission solar cells. *Physical Review Letters*.
[5] Tayebjee MJY, Hirst LC, Ekins-Daukes NJ, and Schmidt TW (2010) The efficiency limit of solar cells with molecular absorbers: A master equation approach. *Journal of Applied Physics* 108(11): 124506.
[6] Trupke T, Green MA, and Würfel P (2002) Improving solar cell efficiencies by down-conversion of high-energy photons. *Journal of Applied Physics* 92(3): 1668–1674.
[7] ASTM (2008) *Astm Standard G173 Standard Tables for Reference Solar Spectral Irradiances: Direct Normal and Hemispherical on 37° Tilted Surface.* ASTM G173. West Conshohocken, PA: ASTM.
[8] Würfel P (2005) *The Physics of Solar Cells.* Weinheim, Germany: Wiley.
[9] González-Diaz B, Guerrero-Lemus R, Haro-González P, *et al.* (2006) Down-conversion properties of luminescent silicon nanostructures formed and passivated in HNO$_3$-based solutions. *Thin Solid Films* 511: 473–477.
[10] Švrček V, Slaoui A, and Muller JC (2004) Silicon nanocrystals as light converter for solar cells. *Thin Solid Films* 451: 384–388.
[11] Strümpel C, McCann M, Beaucarne G, *et al.* (2007) Modifying the solar spectrum to enhance silicon solar cell efficiency – An overview of available materials. *Solar Energy Materials and Solar Cells* 91(4): 238–249.
[12] Klampaftis E, Ross D, McIntosh KR, and Richards BS (2009) Enhancing the performance of solar cells via luminescent down-shifting of the incident spectrum: A review. *Solar Energy Materials and Solar Cells* 93(8): 1182–1194.
[13] Dexter DL (1957) Possibility of luminescent quantum yields greater than unity. *Physical Review* 108(3): 630–633.
[14] Zhang QY and Huang XY (2010) Recent progress in quantum cutting phosphors. *Progress in Materials Science* 55(5): 353–427.
[15] van der Ende BM, Aarts L, and Meijerink A (2009) Near-infrared quantum cutting for photovoltaics. *Advanced Materials* 21(30): 3073–3077.
[16] Wegh RT, Donker H, Oskam KD, and Meijerink A (1999) Visible quantum cutting in LiGdF$_4$:Eu^{3+} through downconversion. *Science* 283(5402): 663–666.
[17] Vergeer P, Vlugt TJH, Kox MHF, *et al.* (2005) Quantum cutting by cooperative energy transfer in Yb$_x$Y$_{1-x}$PO$_4$:Tb^{3+}. *Physical Review B* 71(1): 014119.
[18] Zhang QY, Yang GF, and Jiang ZH (2007) Cooperative downconversion in GdAl$_3$(BO$_3$)$_4$:RE^{3+},Yb^{3+} (RE = Pr, Tb, and Tm). *Applied Physics Letters* 91(5): 051903.
[19] Aarts L, van der Ende BM, Reid MF, and Meijerink A (2010) Downconversion for solar cells in YF$_3$:Pr^{3+}, Yb^{3+}. *Spectroscopy Letters* 43(5): 373–381.
[20] Meijer JM, Aarts L, van der Ende BM, *et al.* (2010) Downconversion for solar cells in YF$_3$:Nd^{3+}, Yb^{3+}. *Physical Review B* 81(3): 035107.
[21] Zhang QY, Yang CH, Jiang ZH, and Ji XH (2007) Concentration-dependent near-infrared quantum cutting in GdBO$_3$:Tb^{3+},Yb^{3+} nanophosphors. *Applied Physics Letters* 90(6): 061914.
[22] Zhang QY, Yang CH, and Pan YX (2007) Cooperative quantum cutting in one-dimensional (Yb$_x$Gd$_{1-x}$)Al$_3$(BO$_3$)$_4$:Tb^{3+} nanorods. *Applied Physics Letters* 90(2): 021107.
[23] Aarts L, van der Ende BM, and Meijerink A (2009) Downconversion for solar cells in NaYF$_4$:Er, Yb. *Journal of Applied Physics* 106(2): 023522.
[24] Aarts L, Jaeqx S, van der Ende BM, and Meijerink A (2011) Downconversion for the Er^{3+}, Yb^{3+} couple in KPb$_2$Cl$_5$-a low-phonon frequency host. *Journal of Luminescence* 131(4): 608–613.
[25] Wegh RT, Meijerink A, Lamminmaki RJ, and Holsa J (2000) Extending Dieke's diagram. *Journal of Luminescence* 87–9: 1002–1004.
[26] Dieke GH and Crosswhite HM (1963) The spectra of the doubly and triply ionized rare earths. *Applied Optics* 2(7): 675–686.
[27] Dieke GH (1968) *Spectra and Energy Levels of Rare Earth Ions in Crystals.* New York: Wiley.
[28] Meijerink A, Wegh R, Vergeer P, and Vlugt T (2006) Photon management with lanthanides. *Optical Materials* 28(6–7): 575–581.
[29] Piper WW, Ham FS, and Deluca JA (1974) YF-Pr^{3+}, a phosphor with a quantum efficiency greater than one for emission of visible light. *Bulletin of the American Physical Society* 19(3): 257–258.
[30] Michels JJ, Huskens J, and Reinhoudt DN (2002) Noncovalent binding of sensitizers for lanthanide(III) luminescence in an EDTA-bis(beta-cyclodextrin) ligand. *Journal of the American Chemical Society* 124(9): 2056–2064.
[31] Ilmas ER and Savikhina TI (1970). Investigation of luminescence excitation processes in some oxygen-dominated compounds by 3 to 21 eV photons. *Journal of Luminescence* 1–2: 702–715.
[32] Berkowitz JK and Olsen JA (1991) Investigation of luminescent materials under ultraviolet excitation energies from 5 to 25 eV. *Journal of Luminescence* 50(2): 111–121.

[33] Werner JH, Kolodinski S, and Queisser HJ (1994) Novel optimization principles and efficiency limits for semiconductor solar cells. *Physical Review Letters* 72(24): 3851.
[34] Nozik AJ (2001) Spectroscopy and hot electron relaxation dynamics in semiconductor quantum wells and quantum dots. *Annual Review of Physical Chemistry* 52: 193–231.
[35] Nozik AJ (2002) Quantum dot solar cells. *Physica E: Low-Dimensional Systems and Nanostructures* 14(1–2): 115–120.
[36] Nozik AJ (2009) Nanophotonics: Making the most of photons. *Nature Nanotechnology* 4(9): 548–549.
[37] Nozik AJ, Beard MC, Luther JM, et al. (2010) Semiconductor quantum dots and quantum dots arrays and applications of multiple exciton generation to third-generation photovoltaic solar cells. *Chemical Reviews* 110(11): 6873–6890.
[38] Franceschetti A, An JM, and Zunger A (2006) Impact ionization can explain carrier multiplication in PbSe quantum dots. *Nano Letters* 6(10): 2191–2195.
[39] Rabani E and Baer R (2008) Distribution of multiexciton generation rates in CdSe and InAs nanocrystals. *Nano Letters* 8(12): 4488–4492.
[40] Ellingson RJ, Beard MC, Johnson JC, et al. (2005) Highly efficient multiple exciton generation in colloidal PbSe and PbS quantum dots. *Nano Letters* 5(5): 865–871.
[41] Nozik AJ (2008) Multiple exciton generation in semiconductor quantum dots. *Chemical Physics Letters* 457(1–3): 3–11.
[42] Schaller RD and Klimov VI (2004) High efficiency carrier multiplication in PbSe nanocrystals: Implications for solar energy conversion. *Physical Review Letters* 92(18): 186601-1–186601-4.
[43] Schaller RD, Agranovich VM, and Klimov VI (2005) High-efficiency carrier multiplication through direct photogeneration of multi-excitons via virtual single-exciton states. *Nature Physics* 1(3): 189–194.
[44] Beard MC, Midgett AG, Hanna MC, et al. (2010) Comparing multiple exciton generation in quantum dots to impact ionization in bulk semiconductors: Implications for enhancement of solar energy conversion. *Nanon Letters* 10(8): 3019–3027.
[45] Beard MC (2011) Multiple exciton generation in semiconductor quantum dots. *Journal of Physical Chemistry Letters* 2(11): 1282–1288.
[46] Koc S (1957) The quantum efficiency of the photo-electric effect in germanium for the 0.32 μ wavelength region. *Czechoslovak Journal of Physics* 7(1): 91–95.
[47] Kolodinski S, Werner JH, Wittchen JH, and Queisser HJ (1993) Quantum efficiencies exceeding unity due to impact ionization in silicon solar-cells. *Applied Physics Letters* 63(17): 2405–2407.
[48] Pijpers JJH, Ulbricht R, Tielrooij KJ, et al. (2009) Assessment of carrier-multiplication efficiency in bulk PbSe and PbS. *Nature Physics* 5(11): 811–814.
[49] Beard MC, Knutsen KP, Yu PR, et al. (2007) Multiple exciton generation in colloidal silicon nanocrystals. *Nano Letters* 7(8): 2506–2512.
[50] Midgett AG, Hillhouse HW, Huges BK, et al. (2010) Flowing versus static conditions for measuring multiple exciton generation in PbSe quantum dots. *Journal of Physical Chemistry C* 114(41): 17486–17500.
[51] Stubbs SK, Hardman SJO, Graham DM, et al. (2010) Efficient carrier multiplication in InP nanoparticles. *Physical Review B* 81(8): 081303.
[52] Wang SJ, Khafizov M, Tu XM, et al. (2010) Multiple exciton generation in single-walled carbon nanotubes. *Nano Letters* 10(7): 2381–2386.
[53] Semonin OE, Luther JM, Choi S, et al. (2011) Peak External Photocurrent Quantum Efficiency Exceeding 100% via MEG in a Quantum Dot Solar Cell. *Science* 334(16): 1530–1533.
[54] Singh S, Jones WJ, Siebrand W, et al. (1965) Laser generation of excitons and fluorescence in anthracene crystals. *Journal of Chemical Physics* 42(1): 330–342.
[55] Klein G, Voltz R, and Schott M (1972) Magnetic field effect on prompt fluorescence in anthracene: Evidence for singlet fission. *Chemical Physics Letters* 16(2): 340–344.
[56] Klein G, Voltz R, and Schott M (1973) Singlet exciton fission in anthracene and tetracene at 77K. *Chemical Physics Letters* 19(3): 391–394.
[57] Yarmus L, Rosenthal J, and Chopp M (1972) EPR of triplet excitons in tetracene crystalsspin polarization and the role of singlet fission. *Chemical Physics Letters* 16(3): 477–481.
[58] Müller AM, Avlasevich YS, Müllen K, and Bardeen CJ (2006) Evidence for exciton fission and fusion in a covalently linked tetracene dimer. *Chemical Physics Letters* 421(4–6): 518–522.
[59] Thorsmølle VK, Averitt RD, Demsar J, et al. (2009) Morphology effectively controls singlet-triplet exciton relaxation and charge transport in organic semiconductors. *Physical Review Letters* 102(1): 017401.
[60] Burdett JJ, Muller AM, Gosztola D, and Bardeen CJ (2010) Excited state dynamics in solid and monomeric tetracene: The roles of superradiance and exciton fission. *Journal of Chemical Physics* 133(14): 144506.
[61] Grumstrup EM, Johnson JC, and Damrauer NH (2010) Enhanced triplet formation in polycrystalline tetracene films by femtosecond optical-pulse shaping. *Physical Review Letters* 105(25): 257403.
[62] Jundt C, Klein G, Sipp B, et al. (1995) Exciton dynamics in pentacene thin films studied by pump-probe spectroscopy. *Chemical Physics Letters* 241(1–2): 84–88.
[63] Marciniak H, Fiebig M, Huth M, et al. (2007) Ultrafast exciton relaxation in microcrystalline pentacene films. *Physical Review Letters* 99(17): 176402.
[64] Johnson JC, Reilly TH, Kanarr AC, and van de Lagemaat J (2009) The ultrafast photophysics of pentacene coupled to surface plasmon active nanohole films. *The Journal of Physical Chemistry C* 113(16): 6871–6877.
[65] Wilson MWB, Rao A, Clark J, et al. (2011) Ultrafast dynamics of exciton fission in polycrystalline pentacene. *Journal of the American Chemical Society* 133(31): 11830–11833.
[66] Smith MB and Michl J (2010) Singlet fission. *Chemical Reviews* 110(11): 6891–6936.
[67] Jadhav PJ, Mohanty A, Sussman J, et al. (2011) Singlet exciton fission in nanostructured organic solar cells. *Nano Letters* 11(4): 1495–1498.
[68] Greyson EC, Vura-Weis J, Michl J, and Ratner MA (2010) Maximizing singlet fission in organic dimers: Theoretical investigation of triplet yield in the regime of localized excitation and fast coherent electron transfer. *The Journal of Physical Chemistry B* 114(45): 14168–14177.
[69] Greyson EC, Stepp BR, Chen XD, et al. (2010) Singlet exciton fission for solar cell applications energy aspects of interchromophore coupling. *Journal of Physical Chemistry B* 114(45): 14223–14232.
[70] Zimmerman PM, Zhang ZY, and Musgrave CB (2010) Singlet fission in pentacene through multi-exciton quantum states. *Nature Chemistry* 2(8): 648–652.

1.26 Down-Shifting of the Incident Light for Photovoltaic Applications

Y Jestin, Advanced Photonics and Photovoltaics Group, Bruno Kessler Foundation, Trento, Italy

© 2012 Elsevier Ltd. All rights reserved.

1.26.1	Introduction	563
1.26.2	The Down-Shifting Concept	565
1.26.3	Luminescent Down-Shifters Applied for Solar Cells	567
1.26.3.1	Silicon-Based Solar Cells	567
1.26.3.2	Gallium Arsenide-Based Devices	568
1.26.3.3	Cadmium-Based Solar Cells	568
1.26.3.4	Organic-Based Solar Cells	569
1.26.3.5	Critical Parameters	569
1.26.3.5.1	Incident spectra	569
1.26.3.5.2	Antireflective coating	570
1.26.3.5.3	Surface recombination	570
1.26.4	Simulation Approach – Modeling of the Spectral Response	571
1.26.4.1	Limit for the Efficiency	571
1.26.4.2	Modeling of the Spectral Response	572
1.26.5	Rare Earth-Based Down-Shifting Layers	573
1.26.5.1	Radiative and Nonradiative Transitions	574
1.26.5.2	Energy Transfer	574
1.26.5.3	Efficiency of Rare Earth Ions in Down-Shifting Layers	574
1.26.6	Quantum Dots-Based Down-Shifting Layers	575
1.26.6.1	Quantum Size Effects	576
1.26.6.2	Efficiency of Quantum Dots in Down-Shifting Layers	576
1.26.7	Organic Dyes-Based Down-Shifting Layers	578
1.26.7.1	Optical Properties	578
1.26.7.2	Efficiency of Organic Dyes in Down-Shifting Layers	579
1.26.8	Commercial Applications and Patents	580
1.26.8.1	Patents and Down-Shifting Technology	580
1.26.8.2	Commercial Applications	581
1.26.9	Conclusions	582
Acknowledgment		583
References		583

1.26.1 Introduction

As a clean renewable energy conversion technology, solar photovoltaics are nowadays brought to the forefront of 'green economy'. Indeed, the global market of photovoltaic electricity has increased by 7.2 GW in 2009 reaching a total capacity of 22 GW worldwide [1], with commercial module efficiencies of around 20%. This leads to the search for new development with respect to device design and new materials, as well as new concepts to increase the overall efficiency. Fundamental spectral losses limit the theoretical maximum efficiency to $\eta = 31\%$ for a single-junction Si solar cell with a band gap $E_g = 1.1$ eV, whereas the best experimental value of $\eta = 25\%$ has been measured in laboratories under the global AM1.5 spectrum [2]. This difference between the experimental and the theoretical value can be explained by different loss mechanisms dependent on the fabrication process itself and intrinsic properties of the raw materials used in fabrication.

There are basically two major loss mechanisms limiting the efficiency of solar cells, which can be explained by a simple observation of the solar spectrum represented in **Figure 1**. The solar spectrum can be divided into three different zones corresponding, respectively, to (1) the high-energy or low-wavelength part of the spectrum, (2) the more intense part of the spectrum, and (3) the infrared part of the spectrum. In the first zone, high-energy photons, that is, with energy higher than the band gap E_g, induce thermal losses: in this case, photons are lost via nonradiative relaxation of the excited electrons toward the conduction band in the form of heat. In the third zone low-energy photons, also called sub-band gap photons, that is, with energy lower than the band gap E_g of the semiconducting material, induce transparency losses: in most of these cases, the active material is not able to absorb the photon energy.

Different concepts and ideas are currently being investigated to overcome these fundamental limits of solar cells [3]. Research and development in this area generally aims to improve the characteristics of the solar cells and thus to provide higher efficiency and lower costs. The third generation of solar cells tends to include nonsemiconductor technologies (e.g., polymer-based solar cells [4]), quantum dot technologies [5], tandem/multijunction cells [6], intermediate band gap cells [7], hot carrier cells [8], dye sensitized

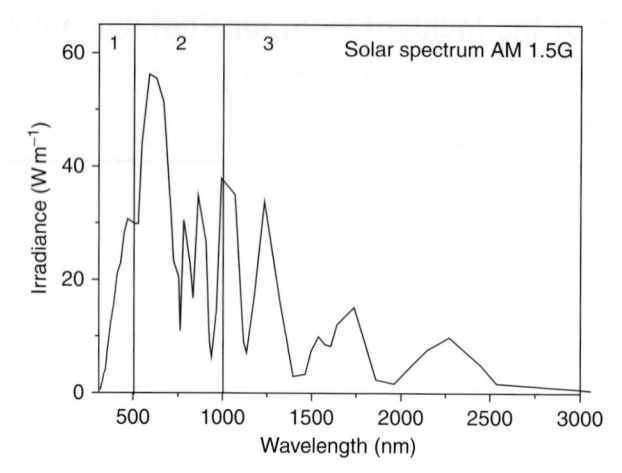

Figure 1 Representation of the air mass 1.5G solar spectrum.

solar cells [9] and up- and down-conversion technologies [10]. Besides these concepts, there are two relatively simple-principle approaches to achieve more efficient utilization of the short-wavelength part of the solar spectrum. The first is to improve the electronic properties of existing devices by using very narrow junctions or low doping levels [11], which is not so simple to implement and too expensive for use in production. A second approach is the application of passive luminescence conversion layers on solar cells. This approach can be divided into two physical processes: down-conversion (including down-shifting) and up-conversion. These phenomena are an intrinsic property of a certain class of materials, like quantum dots, rare earth ions, or organic complexes.

Down-conversion and down-shifting of the layers located on the front side of solar cells can be used to make a better utilization of the short-wavelength part of the solar spectrum. The down-conversion results in the generation of more than one lower-energy photon with energy higher than E_g being generated by high-energy photons with energy higher than $2E_g$. The down-shifting process is quite similar to down-conversion except that the external quantum efficiency of the down-shifting process is less than unity. Up-conversion layers located on the rear of a bifacial cell can be used to absorb the low-energy photons transmitted by the cell and re-emit photons above the band gap of the cell. In both cases, the solar cell and the converter are electronically isolated from each other. This chapter will concentrate on the down-shifting process.

The application of luminescent materials to overcome the poor blue response of solar cells was first described by Hovel et al. [11] in the late 1970s in the area of luminescent solar concentrators technology. In the paper, they demonstrated experimentally the potential of the method in different photovoltaic devices. Even though the efficiencies of the solar cells used in the late 1970s were worse than that of solar cells used today, the method can still be effective to enhance the performance of solar cells. Later, simulations by Richards and McIntosh [12] predicted that when applied to CdS/CdTe solar cells, organic luminescent down-shifter layers could result in an increase in conversion efficiency from $\eta = 9.6\%$ to $\eta = 11.2\%$, which corresponds to an enhancement in efficiency of nearly 17%.

The influence of the luminescent down-shifting layer on photovoltaic devices can be described by the measurement of the quantum efficiency (QE) with and without the layer. Two types of quantum efficiency are often considered: (1) the external quantum efficiency (EQE), defined as the ratio of the number of electron–hole pairs generated to the number of photons hitting the device surface. The EQE also gives information on the current that a given cell will produce when illuminated by a particular wavelength. If integrated over the whole solar spectrum, one can evaluate the current obtained outside the device when exposed to the solar spectrum; (2) the internal quantum efficiency (IQE), defined as the ratio of the number of electron–hole pairs generated to the number of photons hitting the device surface and absorbed by the cell (i.e., after the reflected and transmitted light has been lost). By measuring the reflection and transmission of a device, the EQE curve can be corrected to obtain the IQE of the device. Typical curves of EQE and IQE are presented in **Figure 2** for a basic c-Si solar cell. In this case, it is fairly clear that such devices are not fully efficient in the short-wavelength region of the solar spectrum (i.e., the Ultra Violet and blue region). Furthermore, the IQE is always larger than the EQE. A low IQE indicates that the active layer of the solar cell is unable to make good use of the photons. A low EQE with respect to the IQE indicates that additional loss mechanisms exist, for example, reflection, absorption, and/or emitter recombination.

An advantage of the luminescent down-shifting concept is that the luminescence down-shifter is only optically coupled to the solar cell. This down-shifter mainly shifts the photons from the blue- to the red region. The mechanisms of down-shifting will be discussed in the following section, followed by a description of simulation tools to model and predict the spectral response of solar cells. Then, a review of different solar cells will be presented in order to identify the best candidate for application of a down-shifting layer. Thereafter, the physical properties and efficiency of a large number of down-shifting species will be reviewed and compared as applied to different photovoltaic materials. Finally, commercial applications and the filed patents will be highlighted.

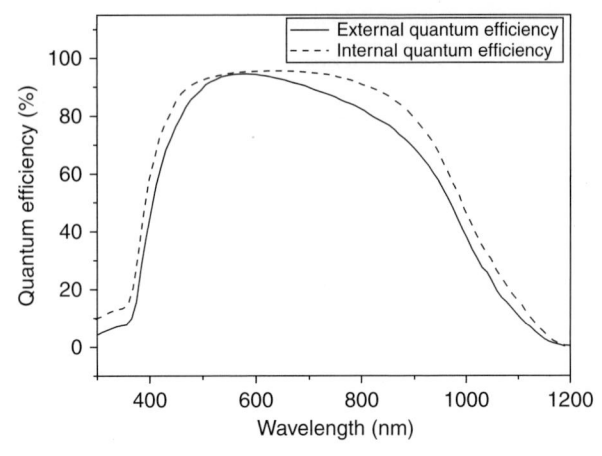

Figure 2 Typical curves of external quantum efficiency (solid line) and internal quantum efficiency (dash line) for a basic c-Si solar cell.

1.26.2 The Down-Shifting Concept

The concept of luminescent down-shifting has emerged in the late 1970s in the area of luminescent solar concentrators [13, 14] and was first reported by Hovel *et al.* [11]. The idea was to apply a transparent glass or plastic plate doped with fluorescent dyes on top of a solar cell in order to absorb a fraction of the solar spectrum and re-emit it at a more favorable wavelength for the solar cell. The first attempts made on silicon-based devices have shown a significant increase in the amount of generated electrical energy. The interest in this kind of approach has grown, as it has a number of advantages over the third-generation concepts [3] that could combine high-efficiency performance with low-cost production [15].

The mechanism of luminescent down-shifting can be seen as a photon-conversion process similar to up-conversion [16–18] and down-conversion [10, 19]. Indeed, the down-shifting process does not differ significantly from down-conversion; down-conversion that occurs with an EQE below 100% can be referred to as a luminescent down-shifting process.

A typical schematic representation of a photovoltaic down-shifting-based device is presented in **Figure 3**. It is made up of four separate layers. The active material is located on the front surface of the device and is electronically isolated from the solar cell by an insulator layer, that is, the coupling between the active medium and the solar cell is purely radiative. A perfect mirror is located on the rear surface of the device to provide high internal surface reflectance for all angles of incidence of light. A large number of materials can be used as down-shifter for all types of existing solar cells, but they have to respect the following: (1) the EQE cannot exceed unity; (2) the absorption band has to be wide enough to cover the region where the EQE of the cell is low (UV–blue region in silicon-based solar cells as can be seen in **Figure 2**); (3) the absorption coefficient has to be high; (4) the emission band has to cover a spectral band where the EQE of the cell is the best (red region in silicon-based solar cells as can be seen in **Figure 2**); (5) the energy difference between the absorption band and the emission band (Stokes' shift) has to be large enough to avoid the reabsorption phenomenon of the emitted photons.

The down-shifter consists of a material with a certain band gap E_g in which an intermediate level is located between the lowest and the highest energy level (in the case of a down-converter, the intermediate level will be located in the center of the band gap). In the case of a semiconducting down-shifter, the band gap energy corresponds to the difference between the conduction and the valence band; in the case of an organic complex down-shifter, the band gap energy corresponds to the difference between the highest occupied molecular orbital (HOMO) and the lowest unoccupied molecular orbital (LUMO). **Figure 4** represents the schematic energy diagram of a solar cell in combination with a down-shifter. The process of down-shifting, or absorption of incident high-energy photons and re-emission at lower energies that are more favorable for the solar cell, can be achieved with every three-level systems. The absorption of a high-energy photon leads to an electronic transition from the lowest level to the highest

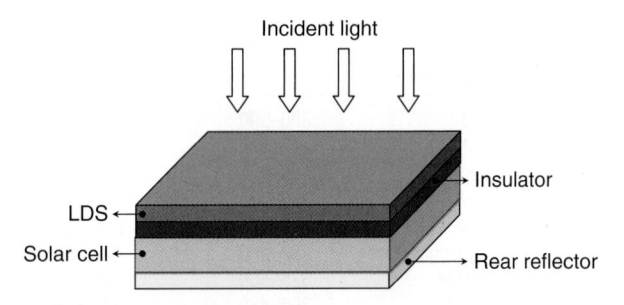

Figure 3 Schematic reprentation of a photovoltaic down-shifting-based device.

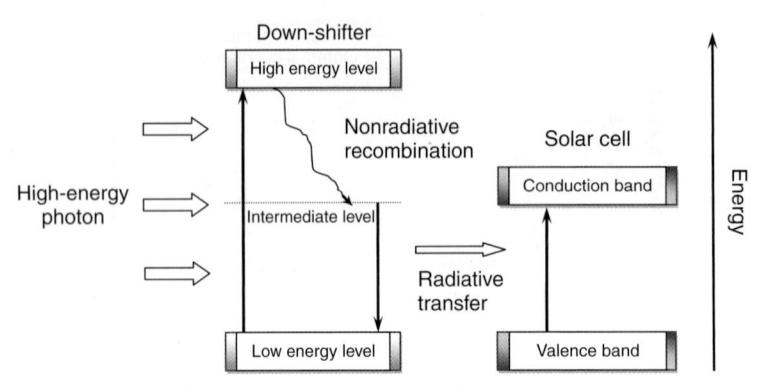

Figure 4 Schematic energy diagram of a solar cell in combination with a down-shifter.

excited level. A first and fast nonradiative recombination generally takes place between the highest excited level and the intermediate level; the emission of one lower-energy photon is accompanied by the radiative recombination of the electron from the intermediate level to the lowest level. As a result of the luminescent process, a part of the incident photons is shifted to a longer wavelength before reaching the active photovoltaic material of the device. The result is an increase in electron–hole pairs generation leading to an improvement in the EQE and the short-circuit current of the device. The two other electrical characteristic parameters of the device, namely, the open-circuit voltage and the fill factor, will not change significantly, as the electronic properties of the semiconducting material or the resistance of the device remains unchanged.

A number of down-shifting species for different kinds of solar cells have been reported in the literature and are presented in **Table 1**. The absorption range and emission peak are reported for wafer-based Si devices. As can be seen in **Table 1**, three main categories of down-shifting species can be listed: (1) semiconducting quantum dots; (2) rare earth complexes; and (3) organic dyes.

The rich and unique energy level structure of rare earth complexes arising from the 4f inner shell configuration gives a variety of options for efficient down-shifting. They generally exhibit a high luminescent quantum efficiency but have narrow absorption peaks with low absorption coefficients; therefore, high concentrations are required, leading to increased cost of the device [28]. Rare earth down-shifting species will be reviewed in Section 1.26.5. Absorption and emission bands of semiconducting quantum dots can easily be tuned by their size; as a result of quantum confinement [29], they exhibit large absorption and high emission intensity at a good stability [30]. On the other hand, the overlap of the absorption and the emission band can lead to significant reabsorption losses [31]. Semiconducting quantum dots will be discussed in detail in Section 1.26.6. Organic luminescent dyes exhibit near-unity luminescence quantum efficiency, and have been demonstrated to be stable for many years in a polymethylmethacrylate (PMMA) host incorporating a UV absorber [32]. On the other hand, they exhibit narrow absorption bands, and significant reabsorption losses occur in solid host matrices [33]. Organic dyes for down-shifting will be detailed in Section 1.26.7.

Loss mechanisms have been described in detail for down-conversion systems by Trupke *et al.* [19]. From a geometrical point of view, and considering that the down-shifting layer is located on the front surface of the cell, we can assume that similar behavior is exhibited by a down-conversion and a down-shifting layer. In this case, one might expect that only half of the luminescence emitted by the down-shifter contributes to the photocurrent of the solar cell, because only this contribution is emitted into the direction of the solar cell. This assumption is valid if the refractive index of the material, which is emitting hemispherically, is $n = 1$. For large refractive indexes like $n = 3.6$ for silicon or GaAs solar cells, this statement is not correct. Further details will be given in Section 1.26.4.

The physical and chemical properties of the host matrix containing the down-shifting species can also play an important role in the performance of the device. As can be seen in **Table 1**, the suitable host material can include different types of polymers or glasses. According to the design of the cell, the down-shifting emitter can be located in the encapsulation system [23, 27, 34], but also in dielectric thin films used to enhance the performances of photovoltaic devices [20, 35, 36]. If the down-shifting emitter is incorporated in the encapsulating system, the material host has to satisfy some specific requirements: (1) achieve and maintain

Table 1 Down-shifting elements with their absorption and emission range

Luminescent material	Host material	Absorption range (nm)	Emission range (nm)	Reference
Silicon nanocrystals	SiO$_2$	300–500	700–900	[20]
(CdSe)ZnS quantum dots	PMMA	220–620	470–620	[21]
CdSe quantum dots	Plastic	425–625	575–650	[22]
Eu(dbm)$_3$Phen	PVA	250–325	600–630	[23]
Eu(tfc)$_3$-EABP	EVA	280–460	600–630	[24]
Ag	Phosphate glass	250–450	400–700	[25]
Sumipex 652	PMMA	375–500	475–650	[26]
Lumogen 570	PMMA	300–450	375–600	[27]

maximum optical coupling between the solar cell and the incident solar radiation in a given spectral region, that is, an optical transmission of 90% as well as low scattering with losses less than 5% after 30 years of use [37]; (2) achieve and maintain reliable electrical isolation of the solar cell circuit elements from both the operational and the safety points of view during the useful life of the module. Potentials above ground may exceed 1000 V; (3) provide and maintain physical isolation of the solar cell and circuit components from exposure to hazardous or degrading environmental factors; (4) provide an optimum environment for the dissolution of luminescent species. If located in a dielectric thin film, some additional requirements are to be fulfilled, too: (1) the refractive index of the host matrix should be close to $n = 1.5$ as commercially available photovoltaic modules are optimized to perform under glass or PMMA encapsulation; this is in fact to minimize front surface reflection [38]; (2) the film will have to be compatible with the surface passivation of the solar cell [36].

1.26.3 Luminescent Down-Shifters Applied for Solar Cells

Solar cells are composed of various semiconducting materials [2, 39–43] of which silicon actually represents 95% of the worldwide production [44]. Semiconductors are materials that become electrically conductive when supplied with light or heat. This phenomenon is described by the photoelectric effect, which consists in the release of positive and negative charge carriers in a solid state when light strikes the surface of the material. Three physical and fundamental steps are common to each type of solar cell independently of the semiconducting material: (1) Photons coming from the sun hit the solar cell and are absorbed by the semiconducting material; (2) Electrons are knocked loose from the atoms in the semiconductor material, allowing them to flow through the material to produce electricity; and (3) An array of solar cells converts solar energy into a usable amount of direct current.

A number of solar cells electrically connected to each other and mounted in a support structure or frame is called a photovoltaic module, and a distinction between the module and the solar cell has to be made, as the performances may differ from one to the other [2]. The current produced is directly dependent on how much light strikes the module. So, herein is the interest of down-shifting solar cells, trying to increase the quantity of light that can be used by the semiconducting material and thus increase the quantity of electricity produced.

In the remaining part of this section, a review of the principal characteristics of different and most common types of solar cells that can be used with down-shifting species is presented: namely, silicon-, gallium arsenide-, cadmium-, and organic-based solar cells.

1.26.3.1 Silicon-Based Solar Cells

One can distinguish three silicon-based solar cell types according to the crystalline phase of the silicon: monocrystalline, polycrystalline, and amorphous. To produce a monocrystalline silicon cell (c-Si), pure semiconducting material is necessary. This production process guarantees a relatively high level of efficiency [45]. The production of polycrystalline cells (mc-Si) is more cost-efficient, but the defects present in the crystal as a result of the production process lead to less efficient solar cells [46]. Fabrication of amorphous or thin-layer cells involves the deposition of a silicon thin film on a glass or another substrate material. With a low production cost, its efficiency is much lower than that of the other two cell types [47].

The EQEs of the three silicon-based cell types are shown in **Figure 5**. The most important difference is located in the short-wavelength region (i.e., $\lambda \leq 500$ nm) where the luminescent down-shifter will have to absorb efficiently. In the visible region, the cells exhibit high EQE, where the luminescent down-shifter will re-emit the light. Depending on the different types of silicon material used for the fabrication of the cell, the effect of the down-shifter will give different results on the performance of the device. Indeed, with maximum efficiencies of, respectively, 20.4% (mc-Si), 10.5% (a-Si), and 25% (c-Si), the down-shifter should be more efficient on mc-Si and a-Si solar cells than on c-Si.

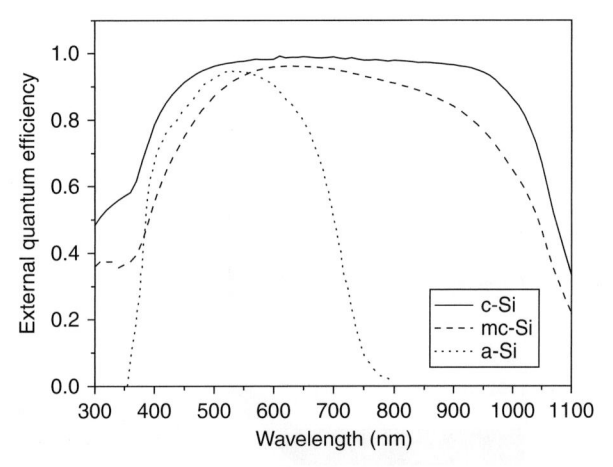

Figure 5 External quantum efficiency of C-Si [45]-, mc-Si [46]-, and a-Si [47]-based solar cells.

1.26.3.2 Gallium Arsenide-Based Devices

Gallium arsenide-based multijunction solar cells are the most efficient solar cells to date, reaching the record efficiency of 42.3% with a triple-junction metamorphic cell [48]. They were originally developed for special applications such as satellites and space investigation. Their high efficiency comes from the possibility to grow three or more junctions for the same cell. Furthermore, the high quality of the direct III–V semiconductors obtained by the metalorganic chemical vapor deposition technique contributes to their high efficiency. A triple-junction cell may consist of the deposition of three layers of GaInP, GaInAs, and Ge, respectively. As can be seen in **Figure 6**, each type of semiconductor has a characteristic band gap energy leading to efficient light absorption in a specific wavelength range. Here the three contributions observed are the contributions of the three layers GaInP/GaInAs/Ge of the cell. Materials are carefully chosen to absorb nearly the entire solar spectrum. The first experiments with incorporation of down-shifting species in GaAs-based solar cells were conducted by Hovel et al. [11] in the late 1970s, but the rare documentation present on this topic shows that more recent work has not focused on this technology. Indeed, as presented in **Figure 6**, for a triple junction using the inverted metamorphic multijunction solar cell architecture there is very little room for any improvement, given the very good response of this cell at short wavelength [49].

1.26.3.3 Cadmium-Based Solar Cells

Owing to its low cost and high efficiency, the heterojunction of cadmium telluride with cadmium selenide (CdS/CdTe) has attracted considerable attention [50–52]. With an energy band gap of 1.5 eV, CdTe has been identified as having a band gap perfectly matching with the distribution of photons of the solar spectrum. Its high absorption coefficient is larger than 10^3 cm^{-1} in the visible region [53]. The typical structure of the CdS/CdTe device is presented in **Figure 7**, and is composed of five different layers: (1) the glass substrate; (2) a transparent and conducting oxide (TCO) which acts as a front contact; (3) a CdS film which is the so-called window layer; (4) a CdTe film which is the absorber layer made on top of CdS; (5) the metal back contact on top of the CdTe layer. Nevertheless, the high band gap energy (2.41 eV) of the CdS window layer results in the fact that lights at wavelength below 514 nm

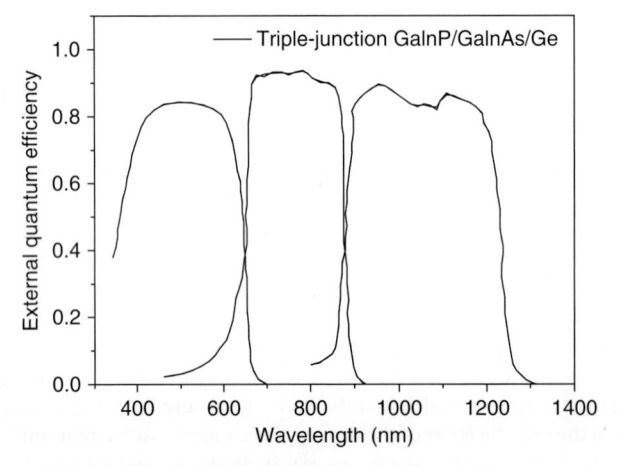

Figure 6 External quantum efficiency of a triple junction GaInP/GaInAs/Ge

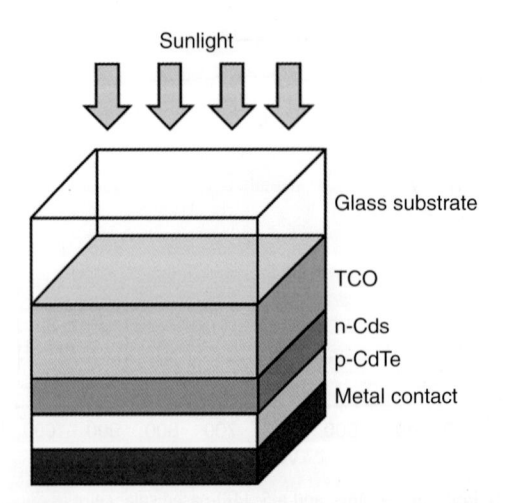

Figure 7 Typical structure of the CdS/CdTe device.

will be absorbed in the CdS layer. On this basis, Cadmium-based solar cells appear to be the most promising candidate for the implementation of a luminescent down-shifter. Indeed, assuming a quantum efficiency equal to 1 for the down-shifter, an increase of efficiency of 40% has been predicted [54].

1.26.3.4 Organic-Based Solar Cells

Research on the photovoltaic effect in organic solar cells began in the late 1950s when several groups measured the photo-electromotive forces of various organic semiconductors on inorganic substrates [55, 56]. One can distinguish two types of organic solar cells: the organic bulk heterojunction solar cell [4, 57] and the dye sensitized solar cell [42, 58]. Organic solar cells differ a lot from silicon-based solar cells. Normally, silicon acts as the source of photoelectrons, as well as providing the electric field to separate the charges and create a current. In the case of organic solar cells, the semiconducting element (polymers or titanium oxide nanoparticles) is only used for charge transport, and the photoelectrons are provided by an organic dye material or fullerene-based material.

According to the shape of the EQE spectrum [4, 59], organic-based solar cells could be a good candidate for the utilization of down-shifting species. However, only few papers exist on the topic. This could be explained by the fact that the technology of organic solar cells has not reached its maturity. Indeed, significant progress is made each year always pushing the limits of efficiency [2, 60]. However, light-converter species have been introduced as a protection layer in dye sensitized solar cells, as the major loss is caused by the degradation of dye and electrolyte owing to high-energy photons [61, 62].

1.26.3.5 Critical Parameters

When considering the critical parameters that influence the performance of down-shifting solar cells, we may pin down three essential factors: (1) the energy distribution of the incident spectra; (2) the presence or not of an antireflecting coating on the front face of the solar cell; and (3) the surface recombination. In the following part, the performance variations of the cells are explained on the basis of the three essential factors cited above.

1.26.3.5.1 Incident spectra

The solar spectrum changes throughout the day and with location, making the down-shifter efficiency dependent of the spectral energy distribution [63, 64]. Using two different solar spectra, differences in efficiency measurements as large as 10% have been demonstrated in a Si-based cell using a fluorescent dye as down-shifter [64]. Indeed, without using standard reference spectra, the author has estimated the efficiency of the down-shifter considering two different solar spectra under two different atmospheric conditions: (1) the first one under excellent atmospheric conditions with a power density of 950 W m^{-2}, (2) the second one under diffuse atmospheric conditions with a power density of 250 W m^{-2}. Under excellent atmospheric conditions, around 13.5% of the incident energy fits in a wavelength range going from 300 to 475 nm corresponding to the active absorption wavelength range of the down-shifter. This proportion is much higher, that is, 22.5%, under diffuse atmospheric conditions, thus making in this case the down-shifter much more efficient for the solar cell.

Thus, standard reference spectra have been defined to allow the performance comparison of photovoltaic devices from different manufacturers and research laboratories. The use of different kinds of reference spectra for efficiency measurement can be found in the literature: (1) the air mass zero spectrum referred to as AM0 is the standard spectrum for space application; (2) the air mass 1.5 global spectrum referred to as AM1.5G was designed for flat plate modules; (3) the air mass 1.5 direct spectrum referred to as AM1.5D is usually used for solar concentrator work; (4) the air mass 1.5 diffused spectrum referred to as AM1.5Diff, blue-shifted with respect to the global and direct ones, makes reference to a cloudy weather. It is defined as AM1.5Diff = AM1.5G − AM1.5D (5) the xenon lamps, which produce a bright white light that closely mimics natural daylight. Table 2 shows the power density of each standard spectrum with the proportion of blue light in the 300–475 nm-wavelength region. As can be seen, a down-shifter can be estimated to be efficient under the AM1.5Diff spectrum with 34.7% of 'blue light' included in his spectrum [54], and inefficient under the AM1.5D spectrum with 12.5% of 'blue light' included in his spectrum [44].

Table 2 Power density of each standard spectrum with the proportion of blue light in the 300–475 nm-wavelength region

Solar conditions	Power density (W m^{-2})	Spectral proportion useful for down-shifters (%)	Reference
AM0	1366.1	17.3	[11]
AM1.5G	1000	14.5	[12]
AM1.5D	900	12.5	[54]
AM1.5Diff	100	34.7	[63]

1.26.3.5.2 Antireflective coating

Photovoltaic modules suffer from reduced conversion efficiency even before the sun's light reaches the solar cell. Under illumination, light is reflected at the interface between the module and the air, thus reducing the quantity of light absorbed by the solar cell. Antireflection coatings consist of a thin layer of dielectric material, with a specially chosen thickness and refractive index such that interference effects in the coating cause the wave reflected from the top surface of the antireflection coating to be out-of-phase with the wave reflected from the semiconductor surface. These out-of-phase reflected waves destructively interfere with one another, resulting in zero net reflected energy.

The thickness of the antireflective coating is chosen such that the wavelength in the dielectric material is one-quarter the wavelength of the incoming wave. Although the reflection for a given thickness, index of refraction, and wavelength can be reduced to zero, the refractive index is dependent on the wavelength, so zero reflection occurs only at a single wavelength. Usually for photovoltaic applications, the refractive index and thickness are chosen so as to minimize reflection for a wavelength of 600 nm. This wavelength is chosen because it is close to the peak power of the solar spectrum. However, by adding more than one antireflection layer on the cell, the reflectivity can be reduced over a wide range of wavelengths, although this may be too expensive for most commercial solar cells.

Antireflection coatings on solar cells thus play an important role in the efficiency of the luminescent down-shifter. Indeed, the presence of an antireflective coating can have negative effects on the down-shifter efficiency, making the cell less efficient. However, it can have a major influence on the performance of the cell with respect to the down-shifter itself. For typical glass panels, depending on the time of the day, 4–15% of the incoming light is lost through reflection and thus is not available to generate electricity. Applying an antireflective coating to the glass cover of the module will reduce these reflections and increase the module's output power. Current commercial photovoltaic technologies convert 10–20% of the incoming light to electricity. The same module with a suitable antireflective coating can deliver an additional 0.3–0.6% power conversion.

1.26.3.5.3 Surface recombination

Any defect or impurities within or at the surface of a semiconductor promote recombination. As the surface of a solar cell represents a severe disruption of the crystal lattice, it is a site of particularly high recombination. In this case, a localized region of low carrier concentration causes carriers from the surrounding regions (i.e., high-concentration regions) to flow into that, thereby increasing the surface recombination. Thus, the surface recombination rate is limited by the rate at which minority carriers move toward the surface. A parameter called the 'surface recombination velocity', in units of cm s^{-1}, is used to specify the recombination at a surface. In a surface with no recombination, the movement of carriers toward the surface is zero. In a surface with infinitely fast recombination, the movement of carriers toward the surface is limited by the maximum velocity they can attain, and for most semiconductors this value is on the order of 10^7 cm s^{-1}.

Surface recombination can have a major impact both on the short-circuit current and on the open-circuit voltage of a solar cell. Indeed, high recombination rates at the top surface have a particularly detrimental impact on the short-circuit current in the solar cell, as well as on the IQE. In **Figure 8**, the IQE of a silicon-based solar cell is shown with a surface recombination velocity varying from 10^4 to 10^6 cm s^{-1}, thus highlighting that the IQE for wavelengths lower than 450 nm, that is, the spectral region where the down-shifter has to be active, depends strongly on the surface recombination velocity [20].

Lowering the high top-surface recombination can be typically accomplished by reducing the number of dangling bonds at the top surface by growing a passivating layer on the top surface [65, 66].

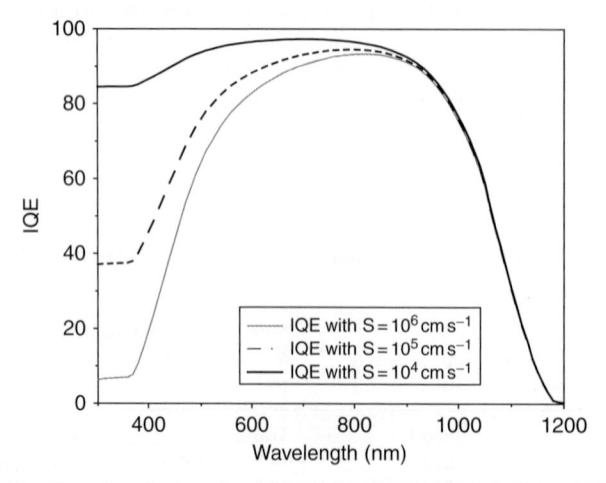

Figure 8 Internal quantum efficiency of a silicon-based solar cell with a surface recombination velocity varying from 10^4 to 10^6 cm s^{-1} [20].

1.26.4 Simulation Approach – Modeling of the Spectral Response

A common practice in science and engineering is to make an equivalent model of a device or system so as to better analyze and predict its performance. It is a challenge to develop an equivalent circuit for a down-shifting solar cell and provide the cell output characterization using a computer program. The fundamental electrical parameters of a solar cell are defined as: (1) the short-circuit current, I_{sc}, (2) the open-circuit voltage, V_{oc}, (3) the maximum power, P_m, and (4) the fill factor, FF. This simple model is then generalized to take into account series and shunt resistive losses and recombination losses.

To create a model of the performance of a down-shifting solar cell, a mathematical description and the effect the environment has on the transmitted spectrum must be determined. Once the mathematical descriptions of the various components are combined, then the model can be used to evaluate the performance and electrical parameters of a theoretical solar cell without the necessity of fabricating it. A particular emphasis on the theoretical limit of efficiency of down-shifting solar cells will be placed in the following section in order to identify the best candidate for down-shifting. Then, one method consisting in the modeling of the spectral response will be detailed.

1.26.4.1 Limit for the Efficiency

Considered to be one of the most significant contributions in the field of solar cells, Shockley and Queisser [67] have determined the Shockley–Queisser limit or detailed balance limit, which refers to the maximum theoretical efficiency of a solar cell using a p–n junction. This fundamental limit places the maximum solar conversion efficiency around 31%, assuming a p–n junction band gap of 1.1 eV. Trupke et al. [19] have determined an upper theoretical limit for the efficiency of a down-shifting solar cell as a function of its band gap by using detailed balance calculations. The proposed model was not developed exclusively for down-shifting solar cells, but for a mixture of the down-shifting and down-conversion processes, the down-shifting process being a particular configuration of the down-conversion process as previously seen in Section 1.26.2. The model has later been improved by Badescu et al. [68]. For this model, the schematic representation of the solar cell in combination with a down-shifting layer is presented in **Figure 3**. In this case, the down-shifter is described as a three-level system: (1) the absorption of a high-energy photon leading to an electronic transition from the lowest level to the highest excited level representing a band-to-band transition, (2) a two-step recombination of the electron between the conduction band and an intermediate level and between the intermediate level and the valence band, accompanied by the emission of a lower-energy photon. These three types of transitions may be seen as three independent two-band systems with individual electrochemical potentials. As can be seen in **Figure 9**, the whole down-shifting system may be represented by an equivalent circuit consisting of three fictitious solar cells connected in series [68]. The two solar cells C3 and C4 represent the intermediate transitions, whereas the band-to-band transitions are represented by C2. Finally, C1 represents the real solar cell.

The efficiency of the solar cell/down-shifter system is calculated as the ratio of the electrical power of the solar cell C1 to the incident power. The solar cell power is determined from the current–voltage (I–V) curve of the cell C1, which, according to an approach introduced by Shockley and Queisser [67], is calculated as the difference between the absorbed photon current and the emitted photon current. Details on the photon current emitted by a solar cell, and described by a generalization of Kirchhoff's law, can be found in the literature [19, 69].

The results obtained by Trupke et al. and Badescu et al. are presented in **Table 3** and compared with the Shockley limit for a solar cell with a refractive index of 3.6. In both cases, the ideal band gap is found to be around 1.1 eV, which is the band gap of silicon, and with efficiency limits of 38.6% or 26%, respectively, thus highlighting the interest in down-shifting solar cell for the improvement of the efficiency. The quite large difference observed in the results obtained by Trupke et al. and Badescu et al. essentially owes to the different approximations made in the calculation.

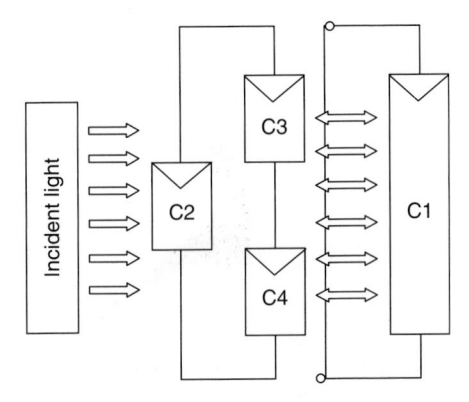

Figure 9 Schematic representation of an equivalent circuit consisting of three fictitious solar cells connected in series.

Table 3 Efficiency limits calculated by Turpke et al. and Badescu et al., and compared with the Shockley limit for a solar cell with a refractive index of 3.6

Refractive index of the cell	Ideal band gap (eV)	Limit on efficiency (%)	Reference
3.6	1.05	38.6	[19]
3.6	1.05	26	[68]
3.6	1.1	22	[67]

1.26.4.2 Modeling of the Spectral Response

Among the available solar cell-modeling programs, PC 1D, developed by the University of New South Wales in Australia, which allows the simulation of solar cells in 1 dimension, seems to be the most commonly used [20, 70, 71]. This program written for personal computers is intended to solve the fully coupled nonlinear equations for the quasi-one-dimensional transport of electrons and holes in crystalline semiconductor devices, with emphasis on photovoltaic devices. Its success is based on its speed, user interface, and continual updates to the latest models.

One simple approach to evaluate the input parameters to include in the PC 1D program has been proposed by Van Sark [22, 70] and consists in the modification of the incident solar spectrum and its introduction as input data for the solar cell simulation model. In this case, the incident spectrum, converted into the amount of photons per wavelength $\Phi_s(\lambda)$, is modified by the absorption of photons in the down-shifting layer. The amount of absorbed photons in the down-shifting layer $\Phi_a(\lambda)$ is determined from the absorption spectrum of the down-shifting species. This absorbed amount is then subtracted from the incident spectrum: $\Phi_{sa}(\lambda) = \Phi_s(\lambda) - \Phi_a(\lambda)$. As seen in the previous section, down-shifting species will re-emit at a red-shifted wavelength. The amount of emitted photons $\Phi_e(\lambda)$ is calculated from the emission spectrum of the down-shifter, which can be determined by the help of the SCOUT program [72, 73], thus permitting to optimize the shape of the luminescent bands.

To this end, the quantum efficiency of the down-shifter has to be taken into account, as well as the fact that owing to the isotropic emission of the down-shifting species, only a part of the emitted photons will be used by the solar cell. In this case, one can calculate the photoluminescence emission patterns for different angles from 0 to 90° for both light emitted into the solar cell and emitted into the air. Integration of the emission patterns over the solid angles gives the fraction of light emitted into the solar cell [20, 74]. **Figure 10** represents the angular dependence of the integrated photoluminescence intensity emitted from the luminescent down-shifter layer into the air (blue) and into the solar cell (red). The intensity is represented in arbitrary units.

The amount of emitted photons is then added to the already modified spectrum: $\Phi_{sae}(\lambda) = \Phi_s(\lambda) - \Phi_a(\lambda) + \Phi_e(\lambda)$. The resulting spectrum then serves as input data for the solar cell simulation model. The absorption of photons can be calculated using the Lambert–Beer equation: the photon flux density $\Phi(x,\lambda)$ after passing a distance x in a film with an absorption coefficient $\alpha(\lambda)$ is reduced by a factor $\exp[-\alpha(\lambda)x]$ which can be written as follows:

$$\Phi(x,\lambda) = \Phi^0(\lambda) \cdot \exp[-\alpha(\lambda)x]$$

where $\Phi^0(\lambda)$ is the incident photon flux density. The absorption coefficient can be measured from the absorption spectra of the luminescent down-shifter and depends on the concentration of down-shifting species in the host material and the thickness of the host material. In **Figure 11** is presented the modified AM1.5G spectrum for a luminescent down-shifting layer of TiO_2 nanoparticles doped with europium ions. The fraction of light absorbed and re-emitted by the down-shifting layer is also depicted [74].

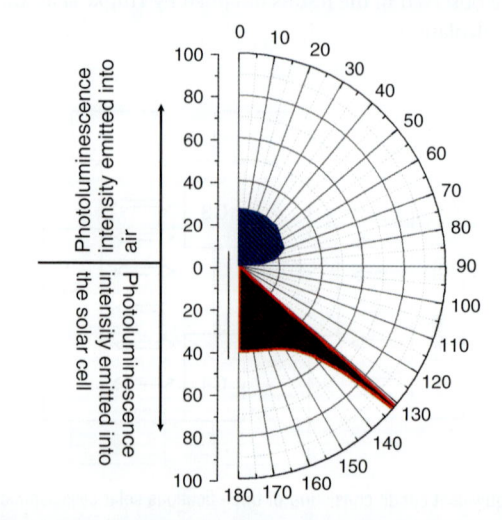

Figure 10 Angular dependence of the integrated photoluminescence intensity emitted from the luminescent down-shifter layer into the air (blue) and into the solar cell (red). The intensity is represented in arbitrary units.

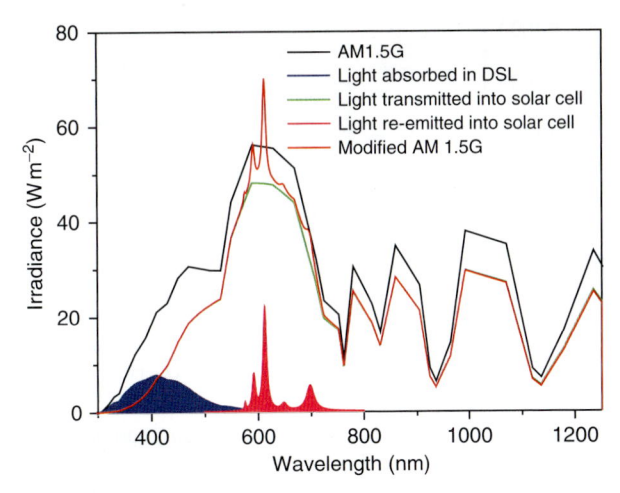

Figure 11 Modified AM1.5G spectrum for a luminescent down-shifting layer of TiO$_2$ nanoparticles doped with europium ions. The fraction of light absorbed and re-emitted by the down-shifting layer is also depicted.

Table 4 Results of efficiency simulation obtained on different solar cells

Solar cell	Luminescent material	Host material	Performance difference (%)	Illuminating spectrum	Reference
mc-Si	Silicon nanocrystals	SiO$_2$	−0.5	AM1.5G	[20]
CdS/CdTe	Lumogen-F (570 + 083 + 240)	PMMA	+ 17	AM1.5G	[12]
mc-Si	CdSe quantum dots	Plastic	+ 28.6	AM1.5d	[63]
			+ 9.6	AM1.5G	
			+ 6.3	AM1.5D	
mc-Si	Lumogen-F (570 + 083 + 240 + 300)	PMMA	+ 0.3	AM1.5G	[75]
a-Si	Quantum dots	Plastic	0	AM1.5G	[22]
mc-Si	Eu^{3+}	TiO$_2$ amorphous	+ 0.4	AM1.5G	[74]
	nc-Si/Eu^{3+}	SiO$_2$	−1.8		

In **Table 4** are presented the simulated results of efficiency obtained on different solar cells. The large disparity in values shows, for example, that for silicon-based devices the influence of a luminescent down-shifter is low as compared to CdS/CdTe-based devices. Furthermore, it is important to note that the results are dependent on the input parameters introduced in the simulation program; they are usually chosen as close as possible to the experimental ones of the fabricated solar cells. However, the optimum parameters of experimental solar cells have changed over the years, making solar cells always more and more efficient. Input parameters such as cell thickness, doping rate, depth of the p–n junction, bulk recombination lifetime, surface recombination, and surface reflection owing to the presence or not of an antireflective coating can have a significant effect on the down-shifter efficiency, thus making the direct comparison of down-shifting solar cells difficult.

1.26.5 Rare Earth-Based Down-Shifting Layers

Lanthanides are usually known as rare earth elements. The potential applications of these elements are various; indeed, owing to an incompletely filled 4f shell, each rare earth element can be characterized by a unique and particular luminescence spectrum [76]. Their use in converting photons to a different, more useful wavelength is well known from a wide range of applications like fluorescent tubes, lasers, and optical amplifiers [77–79]. Rare earth ions have the electronic configuration $4f^n$–$5s^2$–$5p^6$ where n varies from 0 to 14. For luminescent applications, the rare earth is usually in a mostly stable ionized state, and, in most of the cases, with an oxidation degree of +3. The position of the energy levels and the possible electronic transitions responsible for the luminescence depend only barely on the host material in which the rare earth element is incorporated. This is because of the optically active 4f orbital being well shielded from the host environment by the outer-filled 5s and 5p orbitals.

The energy levels of trivalent rare earth ions are presented in **Figure 12** in the so-called Dieke diagram [76]. As can be seen, the rich and unique energy level structure gives a variety of options for efficient down-shifting. The two essential types of transitions, that is, radiative and nonradiative, induced by the excitation of the rare earth ion will be presented in the following section. Then, the rules of energy transfer between rare earth ions will be explained, in order to fully understand the physical process permitting the use of rare earth ions as down-shifing species for solar cells.

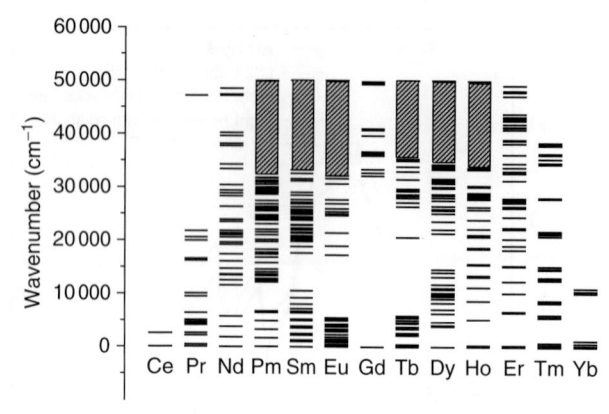

Figure 12 Energy levels of the 4f^n configurations of the trivalent rare earth ions [76]. Closely spaced levels are depicted as bands.

1.26.5.1 Radiative and Nonradiative Transitions

Under illumination, rare earth elements can absorb the incident radiation and pass its electrons from a ground state energy level to an excited state energy level. Once in its excited state, the electron can return to its initial state by two processes: a radiative transition or a nonradiative transition, that is, a transition with or without the emission of radiation, respectively. Radiative and nonradiative transitions compete with each other, which can significantly decrease the quantum efficiency of the rare earth emission. Energy can be dissipated via the emission of 'phonons', which are quantized vibrational modes of the lattice surrounding the rare earth ion. This process is known as 'multiphonon emission'. When the energy difference between two energy levels is smaller than 5 times the phonon energy, nonradiative relaxation will dominate over radiative decay. The excitation energy can then be lost by simultaneous emission of a number of phonons. As presented in Section 1.26.3, the down-shifting process involves both a radiative and a nonradiative mechanism.

In order to determine whether a particular transition is allowed or not for a particular rare earth ion, certain selection rules have been formulated with the help of the classical and quantum theory. Some 50 years ago, Judd and Ofelt established a theory permitting the calculation of the radiative emission lifetime and branching ratio intensities of transitions between the 4f^n multiplets [80, 81]. This formalism is based on an analysis of room temperature absorption spectra, with the assumption that all the Stark sublevels of each multiplet are equally populated. The method usually gives fairly good results.

1.26.5.2 Energy Transfer

The down-shifting process can take place within a single type of dopant ion, or it can involve energy transfer between two or more types of ions co-doped within the same host material. Several types of energy transfer processes between two rare earth ions can occur, especially in highly doped materials. The dominant mechanism behind this is usually the dipole–dipole resonant interaction between closely located ions. As the strength of the dipole–dipole interaction rapidly decreases with increasing distance between the ions, its overall importance depends strongly on the doping concentration, the host material, and the tendency of ions to form clusters.

As can be seen in the Dieke diagram presented in **Figure 12**, the relative positioning of the rare earth energy levels offers excellent opportunities for the design of materials that take advantage of the resonant energy transfer. As seen in Section 1.26.5.1, energy transfer can be divided into two categories: radiative and nonradiative resonant transitions. Nonresonant energy transfer between co-doped ions can also be possible via a multiphonon-assisted mechanism or via cooperative or accretive processes in the absence of a resonant intermediate level. The cooperative mechanism involves the mediation of a virtual energy level, whereas the accretive mechanism involves a virtual energy level for one of the ions with the lower-energy excited state. If the energy loss of the donor ion is larger than the energy gain of the acceptor ion, the excess energy can be taken away by one or several phonons.

The most efficient energy transfer processes involve resonance between the donor and the acceptor transition and are observed when there is a special overlap between the emission band of the donor ion and the absorption band of the acceptor ion [82]. In this case, He *et al.* [82] have shown that an efficient energy transfer between Cerium and Terbium ions can take place. As can be seen on the energy-level diagram of Cerium and Terbium ions presented in **Figure 13**, after UV-excitation of the 5d energy level of Ce^{3+}, a part of the energy relaxes to the $^2F_{7/2}$ level by radiative transition, while another part of the energy is transferred to the ^5H_j levels of Tb^{3+} ions by phonon-assisted electric dipole–dipole interaction followed by rapid relaxation to the $^5D_3$ and $^5D_4$ levels, resulting in a luminescent band centered around 545 nm.

This co-doping technique can be efficient in taking advantage of the higher absorption coefficient in the UV region of some rare earth ions [83] in order to increase the luminescent quantum efficiency of the emitting ion in the visible range.

1.26.5.3 Efficiency of Rare Earth Ions in Down-Shifting Layers

Rare earth ions exhibit high luminescent quantum efficiency but have extremely low absorption coefficients [84]. Nevertheless, an improvement of the absorption coefficient can be realized by increasing the thickness of the down-shifting layer and the concentration of rare earth ions in the down-shifting layer. However, too high a rare earth concentration will lead to an effect of

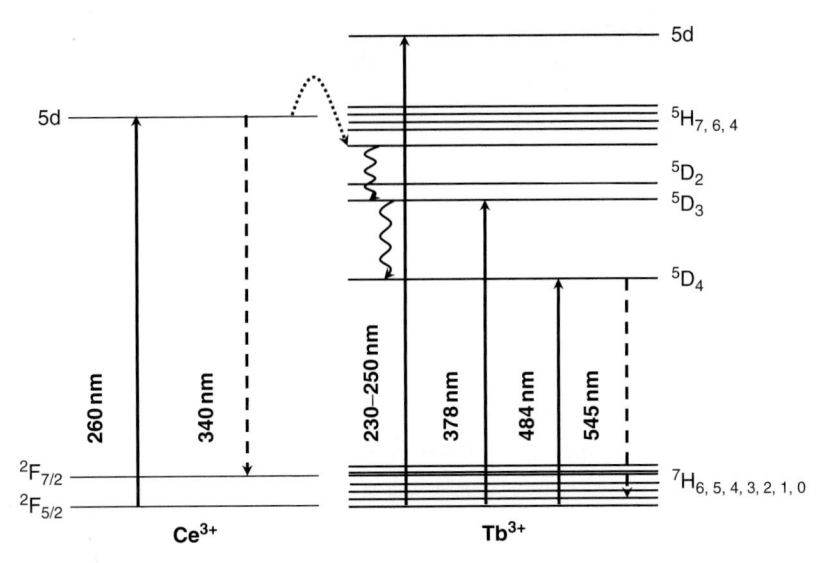

Figure 13 Energy level diagram of Cerium and Terbium ions and energy transfer [82].

Table 5 Performance results of different rare earth-based luminescent down-shifters

Solar cell	Rare earth ion	Host material	Performance difference (%)	Illuminating spectrum	Reference
c-Si	Eu^{3+} Phenantroline	ORMOSIL	+18	AM1.5	[86]
a-Si	Tb^{3+} Bipyridine		+8		
a-Si	Eu^{2+}	CaF_2	+50	AM1.5	[87]
mc-Si	Eu^{3+}	Bycor glass	−2–3	Undefined	
CdS/CdTe	Sm3+	$KMgF_3$	+5	AM1.5	[88]
DSSC	Dy^{3+}	$LaVO_4$	+23	Undefined	[61]
c-Si	Eu3+	PVA	+2.8	AM1.5G	[23]
c-Si	Eu^{3+}	SiO_2	+9.5	AM1.5	[89]

clustering [85], and the energy transfer processes will dramatically decrease the luminescent efficiency. The use of a sensitizer or antenna constituted by rare earth organic complexes ensures a separation between the absorption and emission bands required to obtain large Stokes' shift and to avoid self-absorption losses; the excited states of the emitting ion are efficiently populated by resonant energy transfer from the optically excited organic antenna [23].

Rare earth-based luminescent down-shifters have been investigated by several research groups. A number of experimental attempts have been reported in the literature and are presented in **Table 5**. As can be seen, the efficiency of rare earth-based down-shifters varies a lot depending on the solar cell used. Indeed, a significant enhancement in performance can be observed in dye sensitized solar cells and a-Si-based solar cells, making this kind of solar cells more sensitive to the application of a rare earth-based luminescent down-shifting layer.

On the basis of the experimental attempts found in the literature, europium ions appear to be the best candidate for efficient down-shifting. The Dieke diagram of europium ions presents many absorption lines in the UV spectral range and intense emission lines in the red spectral range. In **Figure 14** is presented the absorption spectrum of an organic europium complex with an absorption band centered at 310 nm with no absorption in the visible range. The emission band of europium complexes consists of a main line at 612 nm related to the $^5D_0$–$^7F_2$ transition and appears to be quite independent of the host material or the sensitizer [24].

1.26.6 Quantum Dots-Based Down-Shifting Layers

A quantum dot is a small semiconductor crystal with very peculiar properties. The exact size and shape of the crystal determine many of its properties. The terms 'quantum dots' and 'nanocrystals' are often used to describe the same system; but they are not synonymous. The term 'nanocrystal' describes the size of a small crystal, from 1 to 999 nm, whereas the term 'quantum dots' hints at quantum mechanical changes in the electronic structure of a system. Moreover, the wave functions of electrons in a quantum dot are confined in three dimensions, which leads to the quantum size effects to which the dot owes its name.

Quantum dots are small devices that can be described as 'droplets' of free electrons containing anything from a single electron to a collection of several thousands. Many people refer to quantum dots as 'artificial' atoms. This comparison highlights two properties of a quantum dot: (1) the relatively small number of electrons in the dot and (2) the many body effects by which the properties of

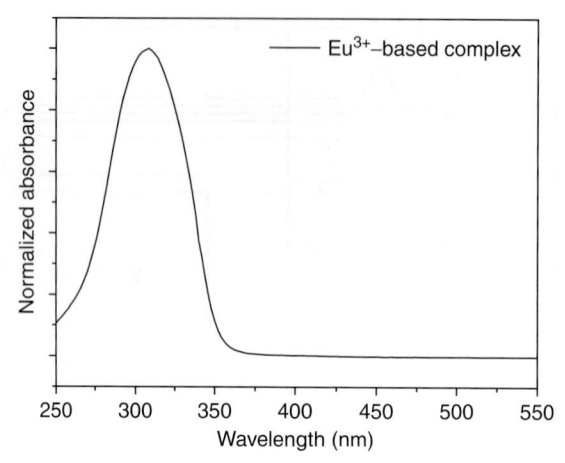

Figure 14 Absorption spectrum of an organic europium-based complex with an absorption band centered at 310 nm and no absorption in the visible range.

the dot could be dramatically changed by adding just one electron. This analogy can be extended by saying that two or more quantum dots might form an 'artificial molecule'. Their typical dimensions range from nanometers to a few microns, and their size, shape, and interactions can be precisely controlled through the use of advanced nanofabrication technology. The physics of quantum dots shows many parallels with the behavior of naturally occurring quantum systems in atomic and nuclear physics. It is appropriate that, owing to their quantum confinement effects but also to their excellent dispersion ability in polymers films, semiconductor nanocrystals or quantum dots have been proposed as an attractive candidate for the fabrication of down-shifting layers applied to solar cells [22, 90].

Quantum dots were first proposed by Chatten *et al.* [91] for use in luminescent concentrators to replace organic dye molecules. In this case, the interest is to take advantage of the emission properties of the quantum dots, which can be tuned by their size, resulting from quantum confinement [29]. The advantages of quantum dots with respect to organic dye molecules are their high brightness, stability, and quantum efficiency [92]. In the following sections, quantum size effects in down-shifting solar cells will be explained, as well as their effect on solar cell efficiency once embedded in a solar cell.

1.26.6.1 Quantum Size Effects

Quantum size effect occurs in particles with a size below ~10 nm and is at the origin of modifications of optical properties like wavelength shifts in absorption and emission. The reasons for these changes are governed by quantum mechanical rules. As a consequence, quantum dots emissions are usually much narrower and more symmetric than typical emissions from dyes or fluorophors.

Semiconductors are characterized by two primary bands of energy: a valence band and a conduction band, separated by an energy range for which no levels are present, known as the 'energy band gap'. The energetic width of this band gap indicates many of the electrical and optical properties of the semiconductor. Indeed, it is this amount of energy that is absorbed, in order to promote the electron from the valence band to the conduction band, and subsequently emitted when the electron relaxes directly from the conduction band back to the valence band. When sufficient energy has been supplied to the semiconducting material, the electrons that have been promoted to the conduction band may subsequently be made to move under the influence of an electric field.

As can be seen in **Figure 15**, the size reduction from a bulk semiconductor to quantum dots leads to a degeneracy of the energy levels; the width of the 'new' band gap is directly proportional to the size and size distribution of the quantum dots. One can easily think that by choosing the quantum dots size, it becomes possible to tune the optical and electrical response of the material. In **Figure 16** are presented the absorption properties of silicon quantum dots as a function of wavelength for three different quantum dot sizes. Silicon quantum dots were prepared by thermal annealing at 1000 °C of a 100 nm silicon-rich oxide film deposited by plasma-enhanced chemical vapor deposition. The samples showed strong absorption below 450 nm. The shape of the absorption bands is similar to that of bulk silicon, although the characteristic peaks and shoulders are slightly blurred out owing to disorders and quantum size effects. In addition, it is possible to observe a blue shift of the absorption bands with the decreasing size of the quantum dots. The inset presents the photoluminescence bands, centered at ~800–850 nm, showing a shift to shorter wavelengths for smaller quantum dots [20].

1.26.6.2 Efficiency of Quantum Dots in Down-Shifting Layers

One of the main advantages of using quantum dots as down-shifting species in solar cells is that the threshold can be tuned by the choice of the dot diameter, and that the red shift of absorption and luminescence is related to the distribution of dot sizes. Furthermore, the photoluminescence emission generally exhibits a fairly high efficiency. In **Table 6** preliminary simulation results

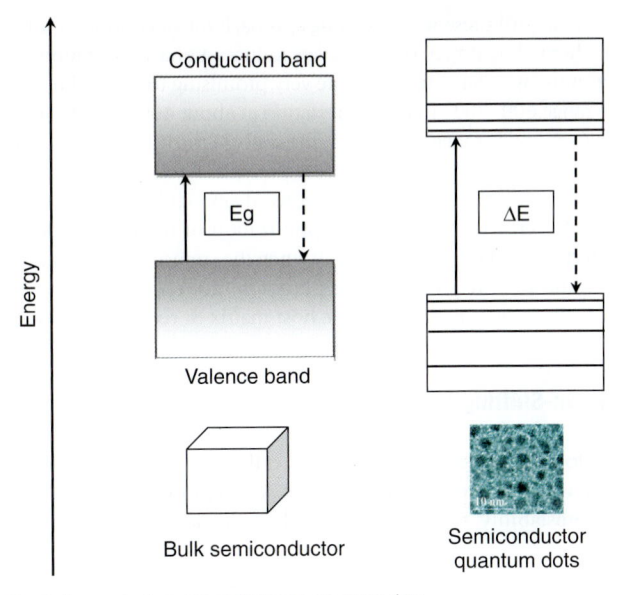

Figure 15 Degeneracy of the energy levels from a bulk semiconductor to quantum dots.

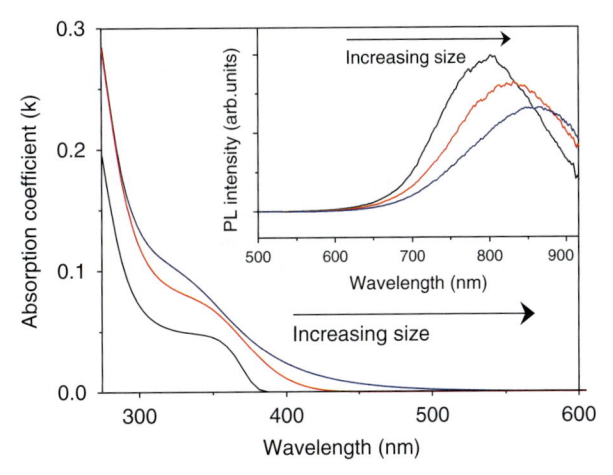

Figure 16 Absorption and emission properties of silicon quantum dots as a function of wavelength for three different quantum dots sizes.

Table 6 Performance results of different quantum dots-based luminescent down-shifters

Solar cell	Quantum dots	Host material	Performance difference (%)	Illuminating spectrum	Reference
c-Si	Silicon quantum dots	SiO$_2$	No improvement	AM1.5G	[20]
		Glass	+0.4	AM1.5	[93]
mc-Si	CdSe	Ideal plastic	+9.6	AM1.5G	[63]
			+6.3	AM1.5D	
			+28.6	AM1.5d	
CIS	CdS	ILGAR-ZnO/Zn(OH)$_2$	+3	AM1.5	[94]
a-Si	Ideal quantum dots	Ideal plastic	No improvement	AM1.5G	[90]

reported by Van Sark are shown, demonstrating the great capacity of quantum dots as down-shifting species [63, 70]. Using modeled spectra for four typical days throughout the year, performance enhancement in terms of short-circuit increase has been investigated. The simulation shows that for a cloudy winter day, a maximum short-circuit increase of 22.9% can be established. Moreover, during a clear winter day, a minimum short-circuit increase of 6.9% can be observed.

In **Table 6** are summarized the performance differences reported in the literature obtained after incorporation of quantum dots in solar cells. As seen in the previous section, the efficiency of the down-shifter is strongly dependent of the efficiency of the cell at low wavelengths. Nevertheless, Jestin et al. [20] present a promising approach for silicon-based solar cells, consisting in the deposition of SiOx or SiNx thin-film layers. The thermal treatment of such layers induces a phase separation Si/SiO$_2$ or Si/SiN, and the growth of silicon quantum dots into an amorphous layer. Such materials are very promising for several reasons: (1) silicon nanocrystals exhibit high luminescence properties in the range 600–800 nm under excitation at about 400 nm; (2) SiO$_2$ and SiN layers playing the role of host materials are highly transparent over a wide range of wavelengths; and (3) the host material can be used as surface passivation and antireflective coating. In this case, the Si/SiO$_2$ or Si/SiN layer has to be very thick to optimize the absorption in the UV–blue region of the solar spectrum and to produce very narrow interference fringes to avoid any significant reflection losses in the spectral region where the silicon solar cell has a large IQE. Nevertheless, despite the optimization of the layer thickness, it has been shown that silicon quantum dots can have a positive effect on the EQE of the cell only when the surface recombination velocity is in excess of 10^5 cm s^{-1}. A better use of this phenomenon would then require a higher photoluminescence efficiency of the dots, which can be obtained through an increase in the density of silicon quantum dots in the host matrix or reduction of defects.

1.26.7 Organic Dyes-Based Down-Shifting Layers

The organic dyes incorporated as down-shifting species for solar cells presently are the most studied material for efficiency enhancement [12, 26, 75]. Their use was first proposed by Hovel et al. [11] in the late 1970s. At that time, available fluorescent organic dyes exhibited very poor photostability, typically lasting only a few days under solar illumination before photobleaching occurred.

Organic dyes are characterized by their ability to absorb or emit light in the visible range. The specificity of dyes is that they can be applied to different substrates from a liquid in which they are completely or at least partially soluble. Furthermore, dyes must possess a specific affinity to a given substrate. Relationship between the absorption–emission properties and the molecular structure of organic dyes has long been a subject of great interest to both theoretical and organic chemists, and as a consequence, a significant number of publications on this subject have appeared in the scientific literature since Witt first proposed his theory of chromophores and auxochromic groups more than a century ago [95]. Indeed, Witt provided a basis for understanding the relation between color and structure of the molecule. According to his color theory, a dye is made up of two essential kinds of parts: chromophores and auxochromes. He designated the groups that produce color as chromophores. Presence of at least one such group is essential to produce a color in an organic compound, and a molecule containing such a group is called a 'chromogen'. Witt also observed that certain organic groups, though not producing color themselves, are able to intensify the color when present in a molecule together with a chromophore. These are called 'auxochromes'. Like many theories, the Witt theory has also been replaced by modern electronic theory, claiming that it is the resonance stabilization of excited states that is responsible for the absorption in the UV–visible region. The energy required to promote an electron from the HOMO to the LUMO of the molecule depends upon the environment of the electron; sigma bond electrons are, for example, firmly held, and very high energy is necessary to promote them. On the contrary, pi electrons are less firmly held and require less energy to be excited. Electrons belonging to conjugated systems require even less energy. The advent of quantum theory has greatly accelerated progress in this field, and the eventual development of quantitative methods for spectroscopic predictions has proved to be of considerable practical value in the search for new dyes. Nowadays, chemists are in a position to predict the absorption and emission spectra of any conjugated molecules, however complex, if not with high precision, at least with some confidence as to the general appearance of the spectrum relative to some model chromogen.

1.26.7.1 Optical Properties

The optical properties of organic dyes thus depend on the transitions involved and can be fine-tuned by elaborate design strategies if the structure–property relationship is known for the given class of dye [96]. The emission of organic dyes typically originates either from an optical transition delocalized over the whole chromophore (in this case, because of their resonant emission, the dyes are referred to as resonant dyes) or from intramolecular charge transfer transitions (in this case, the dyes are referred to as charge transfer dyes). The majority of commercially available dyes like rhodamine [97] are resonant dyes characterized by slightly structured narrow absorption and emission bands, high molar absorption coefficients, and relatively high quantum yields. The spectral overlap of the absorption and the emission band favors cross talk between different dye molecules. Their Stokes' shift is not sensitive to the host matrix.

In **Figure 17** are presented the chemical structure, and the absorption and emission bands of rhodamine 6G obtained from the PhotochemCAD package developed by J. Linsey. This program allows rapid comparison of spectra and enables one to do a variety of relevant calculations [98]. As can be seen, the absorption peak is centered on 530 nm with a Full width at half maximum (FWHM) of 31 nm; the emission band is centered on 552 nm with a FWHM of 57 nm; and the Stokes' shift is about 22 nm.

In contrast, charge transfer dyes such as coumarins [11], have well-separated, broader, and structureless absorption and emission bands, with large Stokes' shift dependent on the matrix polarity. Their molar absorption coefficients, and in most of the cases also their fluorescence quantum yields, are generally smaller than those of dyes with a resonant emission. In **Figure 18** are presented the chemical structure, and the absorption and emission bands of coumarin 30 obtained from the photochemCAD package [98]. As can be seen, the absorption peak is centered on 408 nm with a FWHM of 57 nm and the emission band is centered on 477 nm with a FWHM of 70 nm. The Stokes' shift is larger than in the case of the rhodamine 6G and is about 69 nm.

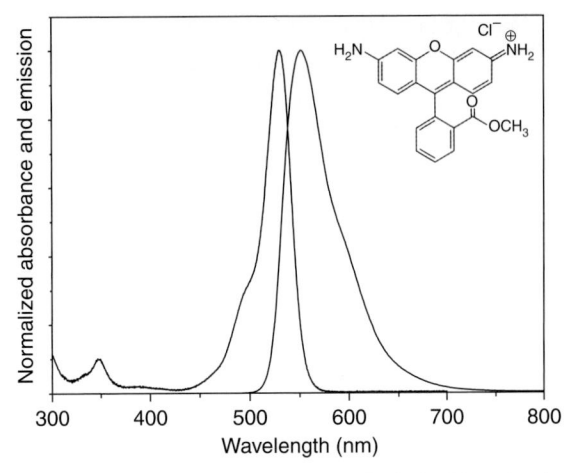

Figure 17 Chemical structure, and absorption and emission bands of rhodamine 6G, obtained from the photochemCAD package.

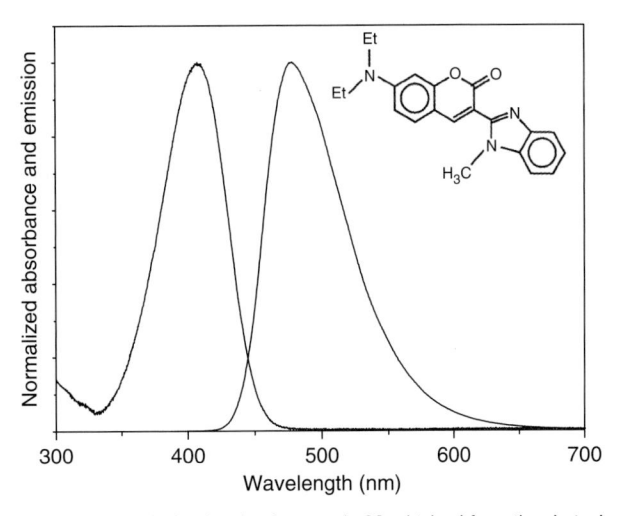

Figure 18 Chemical structure, and absorption and emission bands of coumarin 30, obtained from the photochemCAD package.

With such optical properties, both rhodamine and coumarine seem to be good candidates as down-shifting species for solar cells.

1.26.7.2 Efficiency of Organic Dyes in Down-Shifting Layers

The organic dyes reported in **Table 7** as luminescent down-shifting layers have been chosen basically for their widespread availability on the chemical market. BASF is in fact one of the main providers of organic dyes like lumogen and rhodamine 6G. In order to determine how the performance of solar cells will be altered by the application of a luminescent down-shifter organic dye, Richards and McIntosh [12] performed preliminary simulations on CdS/CdTe solar cells. The solar cell efficiency was determined as a function of the number of dyes and the individual dye concentration. Their model employs well-known optical equations to track the position, direction, wavelength, and intensity of each ray as it passes through the host material. In this case, the addition of a further coversheet on top of the cell without luminescent dyes induces a decrease in the ray intensity owing to external reflection at the front surface, absorption in the host material, and imperfect reflection at the internal surfaces. The results indicate that by incorporation of a dye, a significant increase of 17% in the cell efficiency can be realized for photovoltaic devices that exhibit poor IQE at low wavelengths [12].

It is important to state here that there are two possibilities for increasing the range of wavelengths that a dye absorbs: (1) The optical density of the dye can be increased; however, this only results in a slight increase in the number of longer-wavelength photons absorbed. (2) It is possible to combine multiple dyes into a single coversheet in order to achieve wideband absorption [12]. Dye mixtures are typically selected starting with the ultraviolet and then adding dyes that exhibit longer-wavelength absorption and emission spectra.

Table 7 Performance results of different organic dye-based luminescent down-shifters

Solar cell	Organic dye	Host material	Performance difference (%)	Illuminating spectrum	Reference
c-Si	Rhodamine 6G	PMMA	+48	Xe Lamp	[97]
mc-Si	Sumipex 652	PMMA	+2.7	AM1.5G	[26]
	Lumogen-F (Violet570 + Yellow083)	PMMA	+0.3		[75]
GaAs	Coumarine 540	PMMA	+3	AM1.5	[11]
	Rhodamine 6G				
CdS/CdTe	Lumogen-F (Yellow083)	PMMA	+33	AM1.5D	[54]
	Lumogen-F (Violet570 + Yellow083 + Orange240)	PMMA	+17	AM1.5G	[12]
DSSC	Lumogen	PMMA	No improvement	AM1.5G	[99]
Polymer	Coumarine	PMMA	+0.7	AM1.5G	[99]

On the basis of the experimental attempts found in the literature, organic dyes appear to be a more efficient candidate for efficiency enhancement of solar cells as compared to rare earth ions and quantum dots. Nevertheless, further experiments have to be performed on high-efficiency solar cells in order to have an idea of the real improvement that organic dye down-shifters could bring on solar cells. A further interest that can be found in organic dyes, in addition to the efficiency enhancement of photovoltaics modules, is the coloration of the modules for their integration in urban environments. Indeed, owing to the intrinsic properties of photoactive materials and antireflective coatings, solar cells result to be matt dark. However, any coloration of the surface of the antireflective coating immediately lowers the energy conversion efficiency. A compromise is to change the refractive index and the thickness of the antireflection film. Solar cells colored brown, gold, and green have been reported in the literature [100], but this coloration induced by a modification of the antireflective coating leads to additional losses of efficiency in the modules. Nevertheless, the incorporation of red-colored organic dyes increases the efficiency of the cell, and their coloration could facilitate their incorporation in urban environments in addition to the efficiency enhancement.

1.26.8 Commercial Applications and Patents

Nowadays, many companies are starting to invest in solar projects, and Canon, Applied Materials, and Sharp are among the largest patent holders in solar photovoltaic panels, although they have no products in the field today. By contrast, many of the world's biggest producers of solar panels hold relatively few patents on the technology. This was one conclusion of a report by the Cleantech Group analyzing US patents in solar technology [101]. The report analyzes trends in the US solar patents by company and technology. With more than 100 manufacturers of solar cells all over the world, going from China (SunTech Power, Solarfun Power, etc.) to USA (First Solar, Solec International Inc, Spectrawatt Inc, etc.) but also France, Israel, Switzerland, and Italy, predictions made by First Solar, which is the world's largest supplier of photovoltaic panels, indicate that US demand for solar photovoltaic could double in 2011 to 2 GW.

Substantial progress and great discoveries have been made since the late 1970s, when the traditional solar cell applications were at remote locations where utility power was unavailable. In the late 1980s, solar energy began to be routinely used for providing site-specific energy for urban and suburban homes, offices, and buildings. Solar systems have now become a very important source of energy and provide for the increasing needs of energy as one of the cheapest and best way to generate electricity.

Thus, cheap solutions to increase the efficiency of solar modules by even 1% can be of great interest. On the basis of the good results obtained on down-shifting solar cells [12, 23, 54, 63, 89], the concept of down-shifting technology seems to be a good way for future commercial application. By implementing this new technology and manufacturing processes to further improve the efficiency figures, manufacturers could begin to reduce the average module-manufacturing cost and dramatically shift the market for entire multibillion-dollar solar energy plants.

1.26.8.1 Patents and Down-Shifting Technology

An observation of the filed patent applications over time shows that down-shifting solar cells have attracted the interest of companies for possible commercial application more than 20 years ago when Garlick [102, 103] had a few patent applications filed. Then, since 2008 the number has largely increased thanks to the help of nanotechnologies; this may be correlated with the expansion of silicon solar cells implementation. **Table 8** provides an insight into the location, date, and owners where priority patent application filings have been made. This provides information not just on the countries of origin of the applicant but also on the countries where the research is carried out. These regions may be qualified as the motors for innovation in the photovoltaics field based on crystalline silicon, namely, United States, Japan, and Europe. As can be seen in **Table 8**, the most common down-shifting species are fluorescent organic dyes, as considerable progress in terms of photostability has been made in recent

Table 8 Location, date, and owners of priority patent applications filed

Date	Solar cell	Down-shifing species	Inventor	Assignee	Reference
April 1986	GaAs	ZnSe	G.F.J. Garlick	Hughes aircraft company (USA)	[102]
December 1987	GaAs	ZnSe	G.F.J. Garlick	Spectrolab Inc (USA)	[103]
November 2009	Not specified	Organic dye	T. Miteva et al.	Sony corporation (Japan)	[104]
December 1986	Not specified	Organic dyes	I. Bronstein-bonte et al.	Polaroid Corp. (USA)	[105]
November 2010	All semiconducting materials	Combination of organic dyes or inorganic materials	D. Hollars	Miasole (USA)	[106]
July 2010	Inorganic materials	Organic dyes	A. Boehm et al.	BASF (Germany)	[107]

years. Furthermore, owing to the high quantum efficiency, large absorption coefficient, ease of processing, and relatively low cost, their incorporation as down-shifting species has become a viable and promising solution.

Boehm et al. described the incorporation of a luminescent dye in the encapsulation element made of a low-iron glass material and/or a plastic material such as a transparent polymer like PMMA or ethylene tetrafluoroethylene (ETFE). The photovoltaic cell may comprise one or more inorganic and/or organic semiconductor materials including, at least, CdS, CdTe, Si, InP, GaAs, Cu_2S, and Copper Indium Gallium Diselenide [107]. This patent is based on the theoretical considerations made by Richards and McIntosh [12] demonstrating by ray-tracing simulation the benefit of a certain class of organic dyes on CdS/CdTe-based solar cells. In this case, it is interesting to note that the owners have protected their invention including a large quantity of materials both for the solar cell and the down-shifter. The down-shifter can indeed be a luminescent organic dye like the rhodamine or coumarine presented in Section 1.26.7, but also an inorganic luminescent material based on rare earth ions, or semiconducting quantum dots. To this date, it seems that no experimental data referring to the patent are available and no commercial application has been found.

In his patent, Garlick [102] describes a more specific process for the fabrication and incorporation of down-shifting species of zinc selenide in GaAs- or AlGaAs-based solar cells. The invention is largely described in Reference [108]. The inventor claims to coat on the upper or sunlight-receiving surface of a GaAs or AlGaAs solar cell a fluorescent zinc selenide substrate and an antireflective coating. A commercially available nonfluorescent zinc selenide substrate is initially chosen and then processed to convert it into a highly stable fluorescent material of good optical quality, transparency, and fluorescence. Adhesively bonded to a GaAs or GaAlAs solar cell, the down-shifter substrate should protect the solar cell from ultraviolet radiation damage and also serves as a protective cover against proton radiation damage. The preparation process of the fluorescent zinc selenide substrate is also described. The initial substrate is treated by a physicochemical process at a selected elevated temperature such as the interaction of ZnSe with a chlorine-containing hydrogen selenide gas. Till date, no commercial application of the invention has been found.

1.26.8.2 Commercial Applications

A low-cost photovoltaic cell is intended to produce electrical energy at a price competitive with those of traditional energy sources. This alternative to the conventional electricity and the related fossil fuel dependence has to provide clean distributed power. First Solar Inc. recently announced that it has reduced its manufacturing cost for solar modules to US$0.98 W^{-1} [109], thus breaking the $1-per-watt price barrier, which the industry has been striving for in recent years. With the aim of always lowering the price per watt, down-shifting solar cells have proved to be an alternative solution to increasing solar cell efficiency at low cost, as the technology seems mature enough to be commercialized. The numerous patents found in the literature demonstrate the vast interest of companies in this field. Nevertheless, few companies have directly incorporated down-shifting technology in their products.

An alternative can be found in luminescent solar concentration technologies [110]. Indeed, companies like Covalent Solar try to launch on the market luminescent solar concentrators taking advantage of the down-shifting process and including organic dyes in polymer sheets. They propose a module innovation that combines the beneficial features of existing, disparate product solutions without their attendant drawbacks. By utilizing a unique optical collection technique based on waveguides, they enable the reduction in expensive semiconductor components, possible with optical concentration, without the requirement for tracking and cooling subsystems, in a thin-film module-type configuration. By increasing power conversion efficiency without high cost of manufacturing, the power output of each solar panel increases as compared to thin-film modules, thus reducing installation, maintenance, and overall system cost [111]. The luminescent solar concentrator uses organic dye materials embedded in a flat-plate waveguide. The fundamental efficiency limit of the luminescent solar concentrator is improved by controlling the orientation of dye molecules using a liquid crystalline host. In this case, it is an increase in the trapping efficiency that permits the increase of the overall efficiency of the luminescent solar concentrator by 16% by aligning the dipole moment of the dye molecules perpendicular to the waveguide.

1.26.9 Conclusions

Various down-shifting species for different types of solar cells have been reviewed in this chapter, showing the great interest of the scientific community in this field of research. The significant investments in renewable energies made by local governments all over the world demonstrate the strategic importance of replacing fossil energies by green energies. As a result of possible performance enhancement of solar cells, but also cost reductions in energy production, down-shifting technology seems to be a viable solution. Its mechanism, which can be seen as a photon conversion process similar to up-conversion and down-conversion but with an EQE below 100%, has first been applied on solar cells by Hovel *et al.* [11] in the late 1970s. It is the band gap energy difference between the HOMO and LUMO that determines the characteristics of a down-shifting species. The process of down-shifting, or absorption of incident high-energy photons and re-emission at lower energy more favorable for the solar cell, then becomes available in every three-level system. The quite simple geometry of the cells is a large advantage, as only a few modifications of the original fabrication process of standard solar cells have to be made. Solar cells, for which the entire production is dominated (up to 95%) by silicon, are made of inorganic and/or organic semiconducting material, which have the characteristic of becoming electrically conductive when supplied with light or heat. A review of the most common solar cells, namely, silicon-, gallium arsenide-, Cadmium-, and organic-based solar cells, has been presented in order to identify the best candidates for down-shifting applications. All these solar cells present different characteristics at high energy, and it has been demonstrated that solar cells with low EQE in the UV region of the solar spectrum are more influenced by the down-shifting. Furthermore, different parameters playing an important role in the cell efficiency have been identified. Indeed, parameters like surface recombination induced by the semiconducting material, the presence or not of an antireflective coating, and the energy distribution of the incident spectra are some of the fundamental parameters that have to be presented for the direct comparison of the down-shifter efficiency. A more systematic report of the results would simplify the comparison between down-shifters. Furthermore, the comparison of the down-shifting solar cells should always be done making reference to a control sample. This analysis has permitted us to conclude that cadmium-based solar cells can be considered as the most promising devices for down-shifting applications.

An important theoretical analysis of efficiency limits for all kinds of solar cells has been demonstrated and has permitted us to evaluate the efficiency of down-shifting species for solar cell performance enhancement. The works published by Trupke *et al.* [19] have first managed to estimate the theoretical maximum power efficiency of an ideal down-shifting solar cell to be 38.6%, which represents an increase of more than 40% with respect to the theoretical maximum power efficiency of classic solar cells. Powerful simulation programs like PC 1D developed by the University of New South Wales, Australia, now permit in a simple way the simulation of the performance of numerous different types of solar cells. After a modification of the solar spectrum induced by the absorption and emission of the down-shifting species, efficiency and electrical parameters of down-shifting solar cells have been simulated by different research groups, which has permitted the validation of the method for efficiency enhancement of solar cells.

The three most promising elements for down-shifting have been reviewed. Indeed, most of the literature existing on this argument is concentrated on rare earth ions, quantum dots, and organic dyes. Rare earth elements or lanthanides are well known from a wide range of applications to convert photons to different, more useful wavelengths. By a simple analysis of absorption spectra, radiative and nonradiative emissions can be used to explain the various peaks on the basis of the Judd–Ofelt theory. By studying the possible energy transfer processes occurring between neighboring rare earth ions, it is possible to associate them in order to increase the absorption or emission properties of the system. It is their association with organic elements that may make them the most attractive for down-shifting applications. Quantum dots, or small semiconductor crystals, have very interesting properties. Their main characteristic as down-shifting elements for solar cells is that their emission properties can be tuned by their size as a result of quantum confinement. It is because of the quantum size effect that modifications of optical properties like wavelength shifts in absorption and emission can be observed. Their efficiency in down-shifting solar cells has been estimated by simulation, which has permitted us to confirm them as good candidates for down-shifting applications. The most promising approach for silicon solar cells may consist in the deposition of SiOx and SiNx thin-film layers and the thermal treatment of such layers inducing a phase separation Si/SiO$_2$ or Si/SiN, and the growth of silicon quantum dots into an amorphous layer. Indeed, silicon nanocrystals exhibit high luminescence properties in the range 600–800 nm under excitation at about 400 nm; SiO$_2$ and SiN layers playing the role of host materials are highly transparent over a wide range of wavelengths; and the host material can be used for surface passivation and as antireflective coating. Organic dyes as down-shifting species for solar cells is today the most studied material for efficiency enhancement. Organic dyes are characterized by their ability to absorb or emit light in the visible range. The numerous research works in the industry of dyes have allowed the synthesis of a lot of different complex molecules absorbing and emitting in a large range of the visible spectrum. Owing to the maturity of its technology, organic dyes may be the most probable elements, in terms of fabrication cost versus efficiency, that can be introduced in down-shifting solar cells. Furthermore, when used in luminescent solar concentrators they could provide a better integration in the urban environment.

With considerable budgets that have been allocated over many years to the development of alternative energy sources, significant progress and comprehension of the physical phenomena in down-shifting solar cells has been achieved. An observation of the filed patent applications over time has permitted us to correlate its growth with the expansion of the silicon solar cell implementation. The introduction on the market of down-shifting technology for solar cells is still in its infancy and, despite the growth of filing patent applications, very few companies are actually selling such modules. In this case, two important explanations may be offered: the technology is not yet ready to guarantee a good utilization of the solar panels, or the cost of incorporation of down-shifting is still too significant, resulting in an increase of the price of the produced amount of electrical energy (watts).

Nevertheless, in recent years, a new very significant growth of the market for polymer-based solar cells has been observed. Indeed, organic solar cells, mainly owing to their still too low efficiency, are not yet able to compete with silicon cells for the mass production of electricity, but down-shifting technologies could, in this case, bring significant improvement on polymer-based solar cells.

Acknowledgment

This work has been partially supported by EU 7th framework program through the project LIMA.

References

[1] Mints P (2010) European photovoltaic industry association (EPIA), market installed 7.2GW of PV in 2009. *Renewable Energy Focus* 11: 14–17.
[2] Green MA, Emery K, Hishikawa Y, and Warta W (2010) Solar cell efficiency tables (version 35). *Progress in Photovoltaics: Research and Applications* 18: 144–150.
[3] Green MA (2003) *Third Generation Photovoltaics: Advanced Solar Energy Conversion*. Springer Verlag, Berlin.
[4] Park SH, Roy A, Beaupré S, et al. (2009) Bulk heterojunction solar cells with internal quantum efficiency approaching 100%. *Nature Photonics* 3: 297–303.
[5] Nozik AJ (2002) Quantum dot solar cells. *Physica E* 14: 115–120.
[6] Yamaguchi M, Takamoto T, Araki K, and Ekins-Daukes N (2005) Multi-junction III–V solar cells: Current status and future potential. *Solar Energy* 79: 78–85.
[7] Luque A and Marti A (1997) Increasing the efficiency of ideal solar cells by photon induced transitions at intermediate levels. *Physical Review Letters* 78: 5014–5017.
[8] Takeda Y, Ito T, Motohiro T, et al. (2009) Hot carrier solar cells operating under practical conditions. *Journal of Applied Physics* 105: 074905-1–074905-10.
[9] Grätzel M (2003) Dye-sensitized solar cells. *Journal of Photochemistry and Photobiology C: Photochemistry Reviews* 4: 145–153.
[10] Richards BS (2006) Enhancing the performance of silicon solar cells via the application of passive luminescence conversion layers. *Solar Energy Materials and Solar Cells* 90: 2329–2337.
[11] Hovel HJ, Hogdson RT, and Woodall JM (1979) The effect of fluorescent wavelength shifting on solar cell spectral response. *Solar Energy Materials* 2: 19–29.
[12] Richards BS and McIntosh KR (2007) Overcoming the poor short wavelength spectral response of CdS/CdTe photovoltaic modules via luminescence down-shifting: Ray-tracing simulations. *Progress in Photovoltaics* 15: 27–34.
[13] Goetzberger A and Greubel W (1977) Solar energy conversion with fluorescent collectors. *Applied Physics* 14: 123–139.
[14] Hermann AM (1982) Luminescent solar concentrator: A review. *Solar Energy* 29: 323–329.
[15] Green MA (2001) Third generation photovoltaics: Ultra-high conversion efficiency at low cost. *Progress in Photovoltaics: Research and Applications* 9: 123–135.
[16] Shalav A, Richards BS, and Green MA (2007) Luminescent layers for enhanced silicon solar cell performance: Up-conversion. *Solar Energy Materials & Solar Cells* 91: 829–842.
[17] Richards BS and Shalav A (2007) Enhancing the near-infrared spectral response of silicon optoelectronic devices via up-conversion. *IEEE Transactions on Electron Devices* 54: 2679–2684.
[18] Trupke T, Green MA, and Würfel P (2002) Improving solar cell efficiencies by up-conversion of sub-band-gap light. *Journal of Applied Physics* 92: 4117–4122.
[19] Trupke T, Green MA, and Wurfel P (2002) Improving solar cell efficiencies by down-conversion of high-energy photons. *Journal of Applied Physics* 92: 1668–1674.
[20] Jestin Y, Pucker G, Ghulinyan M, et al. (2010) Silicon solar cells with nano-crystalline silicon down shifter: Experiment and modeling. *Proceedings of SPIE – Optics and Photonics*, 7772, San Diego, CA, USA. August 1–5.
[21] Mutlugun E, Soganci IM, and Demir HV (2008) Photovoltaic nanocrystal scintillators hybridized on Si solar cells for enhanced conversion efficiency in UV. *Optics Express* 16: 3537–3545.
[22] van Sark WGJHM, Meijerink A, Schropp REI, et al. (2005) Enhancing solar cell efficiency by using spectral converters. *Solar Energy Materials and Solar Cells* 87: 395–409.
[23] Le Donne A, Acciarri M, Narducci D, et al. (2009) Encapsulating Eu^{3+} complex doped layers to improve Si-based solar cell efficiency. *Progress in Photovoltaics: Research and Applications* 17: 519–525.
[24] Le Donne A, Dilda M, Crippa M, et al. (2011) Rare earth organic complexes as down-shifters to improve Si-based solar cell efficiency. *Optical Materials* 33: 1012–1014.
[25] Zakhidov RA and Koifman AI (1994) Solar cell with a protecting coating. *Applied Energy Solutions* 30: 22–25.
[26] Maruyama T, Enomoto A, and Shirasawa K (2000) Solar cell module colored with fluorescent plate. *Solar Energy Materials and Solar Cells* 64: 269–278.
[27] McIntosh KR, Lau G, Cotsell JN, et al. (2009) Increase in external quantum efficiency of encapsulated silicon solar cells from a luminescent down-shifting layer. *Progress in Photovoltaics: Research and Applications* 17: 191–197.
[28] van der Ende BM, Aarts L, and Meijerink A (2009) Lanthanide ions as spectral converters for solar cells. *Physical Chemistry Chemical Physics* 11: 11081–11095.
[29] Alivisatos AP (1996) Perspectives on the physical chemistry of semiconductor nanocrystals. *The Journal of Physical Chemistry* 100: 13226–13239.
[30] Sanderson K (2009) Special report: Quantum dots go large. *Nature* 459: 760–761.
[31] Rowan BC, Wilson LR, and Richards BS (2008) Advanced material concepts for luminescent solar concentrators. *IEEE Journal of Selected Topics in Quantum Electronics* 14: 1312–1322.
[32] Earp AA, Smith GB, Franklin J, and Swift P (2004) Optimisation of a three-colour luminescent solar concentrator daylighting system. *Solar Energy Materials and Solar Cells* 84: 411–426.
[33] Sah RE and Baur G (1980) Influence of the solvent matrix on the overlapping of the absorption and emission bands of solute fluorescent dyes. *Applied Physics* 23: 369–372.
[34] Czanderna AW and Pern FJ (1996) Encapsulation of PV modules using ethylene vinyl acetate copolymer as a pottant: A critical review. *Solar Energy Materials & Solar Cells* 43: 101–181.
[35] Marchionna S, Meinardi F, Acciarri M, et al. (2006) Photovoltaic quantum efficiency enhancement by light harvesting of organo-lanthanide complexes. *Journal of Luminescence* 118: 325–329.
[36] Richards BS (2004) Comparison of TiO_2 and other dielectric coatings for buried contact solar cells: A review. *Progress in Photovoltaics: Research and Applications* 12: 253–281.
[37] Cuddihy E, Coulbert C, Gupta A, and Liang R (1986) Flate-plate solar array project, final report. JPL publication 86-31. Pasadena.
[38] Gee JM, Schubert WK, Tardy HL, et al. (1994) The effect of encapsulation on the reflectance of photovoltaic modules using textured multicrystalline-silicon solar cells. *Proceedings of IEEE, First WCPEC*. pp. 1555–1558. Hawaii, USA. December 5–9.
[39] Woodall JM and Hovel HJ (1990) High efficiency $Ga_{1-x}Al_xAs$-GaAs solar cells. *Solar Cells* 29: 167–172.
[40] Schmidtke J (2010) Commercial status of thin-film photovoltaic devices and materials. *Optics Express* 18: 477–486.
[41] Rose DH, Hasoon FS, Dhere RG, et al. (1999) Process sensitivities for CdS/CdTe solar cells. *Progress in Photovoltaics: Research and Applications* 7: 331–340.
[42] O'Regan B and Grätzel M (1991) A low-cost, high-efficiency solar cell based on dye-sensitized colloidal TiO_2 films. *Nature* 353: 737–740.

[43] Yu G, Gao J, Hummelen JC, *et al.* (1995) Polymer photovoltaic cells: Enhanced efficiencies via a network of internal donor-acceptor heterojunctions. *Science* 270: 1789–1791.
[44] Fath P, Keller S, Winter P, *et al.* (2009) Status and perspective of crystalline silicon solar cell production. *Proceedings of 34th IEEE Photovoltaic Specialists Conference*, June 7–12, Philadelphia. pp. 002471–002476.
[45] Zhao J, Wang A, Green MA, and Ferrazza F (1998) Novel 19.8% efficient 'honeycomb' textured multicrystalline and 24.4% monocrystalline silicon solar cells. *Applied Physics Letters* 73: 1991–1993.
[46] Schultz O, Glunz S, and Willeke G (2004) Multicrystalline silicon solar cells exceeding 20% efficiency. *Progress in Photovoltaics: Research and Applications* 12: 553–558.
[47] Bergmann R, Rinke T, Berge C, *et al.* (2002) Advances in monocrystalline Si thin-film solar cells by layer transfer. *Solar Energy Materials and Solar Cells* 74: 213–218.
[48] Wojtczuk S, Chiu P, Zhang X, *et al.* (2010) InGaP/GaAs/InGaAs concentrators using Bi-facial epigrowth. 35th IEEE PVSC. pp. 001259–001264, Honolulu, HI, June, 20–25.
[49] Stan M, Aiken D, Cho B, *et al.* (2008) Very high efficiency triple junction solar cells grown by MOVPE. *Journal of Crystal Growth* 310: 5204–5208.
[50] Jenny DA and Bube RH (1954) Semiconducting cadmium telluride. *Physical Review* 96: 1190–1191.
[51] Morales-Acevedo A (2006) Thin film CdS/CdTe solar cells: Research perspectives. *Solar Energy* 80: 675–681.
[52] Wu X, Keane JC, Dhere RG, *et al.* (2001) 16.5% efficient CdS/CdTe polycrystalline thin-film solar cell. *Proceedings of 17th European Photovoltaic Solar Energy Conference*. pp. 995–1000. Munich, Germany. October 22–26.
[53] Vigil-Galan O, Marin E, Sastre Hernandez J, *et al.* (2007) A study of the optical absorption in CdTe by photoacoustic spectroscopy. *Journal of Materials Science* 42: 7176–7179.
[54] Maruyama T and Kitamura R (2001) Transformations of the wavelength of the light incident upon solar cells. *Solar Energy Materials and Solar Cells* 69: 207–216.
[55] Gutmann F and Lyons LE (1967) *Organic Semiconductors*. ch. 8, p. 516. New York: Wiley.
[56] Chamberlain GA (1983) Organic solar cells: A review. *Solar Cells* 8: 47–83.
[57] Kim JY, Lee K, Coates NE, *et al.* (2007) Efficient tandem polymer solar cells fabricated by all-solution processing. *Science* 317: 222–225.
[58] Cahen D, Hodes G, Gratzel M, *et al.* (2000) Nature of photovoltaic action in dye-sensitized solar cells. *Journal of Physical Chemistry B* 104(9): 2053–2059.
[59] Hardin BE, Yum JH, Hoke ET, *et al.* (2010) High excitation transfer efficiency from energy relay dyes in dye-sensitized solar cells. *Nano Letters* 10: 3077–3083.
[60] Green MA, Emery K, Hishikawa Y, and Warta W (2009) Solar cell efficiency tables (version 34). *Progress in Photovoltaics: Research and Applications* 17: 320–326.
[61] Liu J, Yao Q, and Lia Y (2006) Effect of downconvertion luminescence film in dye-sensitized solar cells. *Applied Physics Letters* 88: 1731191–1731193.
[62] Kim HJ, Song JS, and Kim SS (2004) Efficiency enhancement of solar cell by down-conversion effect of Eu^{3+} doped LiGdF4. *Journal of the Korean Physical Society* 45: 609–613.
[63] van Sark WGJHM (2005) Enhancement of solar cells performance by employing planar spectral converter. *Applied Physics Letters* 87: 1511171–1511173.
[64] Sarti D, Le Poull F, and Gravisse P (1981) Transformation du rayonnement solaire par fluorescence: Application a l'encapsulation des cellules. *Solar Cells* 4: 25–35.
[65] Yablonovitch E, Allara DL, Chang CC, *et al.* (1986) Unusually low surface recombination velocity on silicon and germanium surfaces. *Physical Review Letters* 57: 249–252.
[66] Kerr MJ, Schmidt J, Cuevas A, and Bultman JH (2001) Surface recombination velocity of phosphorus-diffused silicon solar cell emitters passivated with plasma enhanced chemical vapor deposited silicon nitride and thermal silicon oxide. *Journal of Applied Physics* 89: 3821–3826.
[67] Shockley W and Queisser HJ (1961) Detailed balance limit of efficiency of p-n junction solar cells. *Journal of Applied Physics* 32: 510–519.
[68] Badescu V, De Vos A, Badescu AM, and Szymanska A (2007) Improved model for solar cells with down-conversion and down-shifting of high-energy photons. *Journal of Physics D: Applied Physics* 40: 341–352.
[69] Trupke T, Daub E, and Wurfel P (1998) Absorptivity of silicon solar cells obtained from Luminescence. *Solar Energy Materials & Solar Cells* 53: 103–114.
[70] van Sark WGJHM (2008) Simulating performance of solar cells with spectral downshifting layers. *Thin Solid Films* 516: 6808–6812.
[71] Basore PA and Clugston DA (1996) PC1D version 4 for windows: From analysis to design. *Proceedings of 25th IEEE PVSC*, pp. 211–214, Washington, DC. May 13–17.
[72] Thiess M (2009) SCOUT 2.3 software, Aachen, Germany.
[73] Venturello A, Ricciardi C, Giorgis F, *et al.* (2006) Controlled light emission from dye-impregnated porous silicon microcavities. *Journal of Non-Crystalline Solids* 352: 1230–1233.
[74] Jestin Y, Pucker G, Ghulinyan M, and Laidani N (2010) Down-shifter based silicon solar cells: Modeling of the spectral response. *E-MRS 2010 Spring Meeting*. Strasbourg, France, 7–11 June.
[75] McIntosh KR and Richards BS (2006) Increased mc-Si module efficiency using fluorescent organic dyes: A ray-tracing study. *Proceedings of IEEE 4th World Conference on Photovoltaic Energy Conversion*. pp.2, 2108–2111. Hawaii, USA. May 7–12.
[76] Dieke GH and Crosswhite HM (1963) The spectra of the doubly and triply ionized rare earths. *Applied Optics* 2: 675–686.
[77] Smets BMJ (1987) Phosphors based on rare-earths, a new era in fluorescent lighting. *Materials Chemistry and Physics* 16: 283–299.
[78] Geusic FE, Marcos HM, and Van Uitert LG (1964) Laser oscillation in Nd-doped Yttrium Aluminum, Yttrium Gallium and Gadolinium garnets. *Applied Physics Letters* 4: 182–184.
[79] Jestin Y, Armellini C, Chiappini A, *et al.* (2007) Low-loss optical Er^{3+}-activated glass-ceramics planar waveguides fabricated by bottom-up approach. *Applied Physics Letters* 91: 719091–719093.
[80] Judd B (1962) Optical absorption intensities of rare-earth ions. *Physical Review* 127: 750–761.
[81] Ofelt G (1962) Intensities of crystal spectra of rare-earth ions. *Journal of Chemical Physics* 37: 511–513.
[82] He DB, Yu CL, Cheng JM, *et al.* (2010) A novel Ce^{3+}/Tb^{3+} codoped phosphate glass as down-shifting materials for enhancing efficiency of solar cells. *Chinese Physics Letters* 27: 1142081–1142084.
[83] Loh E (1967) Ultraviolet absorption spectra of Ce^{3+} in alkaline-earth fluorides. *Physical Review* 154: 270–276.
[84] Strumpel C, McCann M, Beaucarne G, *et al.* (2007) Modifying the solar spectrum to enhance silicon solar cell efficiency: An overview of available materials. *Solar Energy Materials & Solar Cells* 91: 238–249.
[85] Nazarov AN, Tiagulskyi SI, Tyagulskyy IP, *et al.* (2010) The effect of rare-earth clustering on charge trapping and electroluminescence in rare-earth implanted metal-oxide-semiconductors light-emitting devices. *Journal of Applied Physics* 107: 1231121–12311214.
[86] Jin T, Inoue S, Machida K, and Adachi G (1997) Photovoltaic cell characteristics of hybrid silicon devices with lanthanide complex phosphor-coating film. *Journal of the Electrochemical Society* 144: 4054–4058.
[87] Kawano K, Hashimoto N, and Nakata R (1997) Effects on solar cell efficiency of fluorescence of rare-earth ions. *Materials Science Forum* 239–241: 311–314.
[88] Hong BC and Kawano K (2003) PL and PLE studies of $KMgF_3$:Sm crystal and the effect of its wavelength conversion on CdS/CdTe solar cell. *Solar Energy Materials and Solar Cells* 80: 417–432.
[89] Cheng Z, Pan L, Su F, *et al.* (2009) Eu^{3+} doped silica film as luminescent down-shifting layer for crystalline Si solar cells. *Surface Review and Letters* 16: 669–673.
[90] van Sark WGJHM, Meijerink A, Schropp REI, *et al.* (2004) Modeling improvement of spectral response of solar cells by deployment of spectral converters containing semiconductor nanocrystals. *Semiconductors* 38: 962–969.
[91] Chatten AJ, Barnham KWJ, Buxton BF, *et al.* (2003) A new approach to modeling quantum dot concentrators. *Solar Energy Materials and Solar Cells* 75: 362–371.
[92] Bruchez M, Jr., Moronne M, Gin P, *et al.* (1998) Semiconductor nanocrystals as fluorescent biological labels. *Science* 281: 2013–2016.
[93] Švrcek V, Slaoui A, and Muller J-C (2004) Silicon nanocrystals as light converter for solar cells. *Thin Solid Films* 451–452: 384–388.
[94] Muffler HJ, Bar M, Lauermann I, *et al.* (2006) Colloid attachment by ILGAR-layers: Creating fluorescing layers to increase quantum efficiency of solar cells. *Solar Energy Materials & Solar Cells* 90: 3143–3150.
[95] Witt O (1876) Zur kenntniss des baues und der bildung farbender kohlenstoffverbindungen. *Berichte der deutschen Chemischen Gesellschaft* A9: 522.
[96] Mason WT (1999) *Fluorescent and Luminescent Probes for Biological Activity*, 2nd edn., London, UK: Academic Press.
[97] Mansour AF (2003) On enhancing the efficiency of solar cells and extending their performance life. *Polymer Testing* 22: 491–495.

[98] Du H, Fuh RA, Li J, *et al.* (1998) PhotochemCAD: A computer-aided design and research tool in photochemistry. *Photochemistry and Photobiology* 68: 141–142.
[99] Slooff LH, Kinderman R, Burgers AR, *et al.* (2007) Efficiency enhancement of solar cells by application of a polymer coating containing a luminescent dye. *Journal of Solar Energy Engineering* 129: 272–276.
[100] Ishikawa N, Yamashita H, Goda S, *et al.* (1994) PV modules, using color solar cells, designed for buildings. *Proceedings of the First World Conference on Photovoltaic Energy Conversion.* pp. 977–978. Hawaii, USA. December 5–9.
[101] Cleantech energy patent landscape annual report. http://www.foley.com/files/tbl_s31Publications/FileUpload137/6147/CleantechReportExecSummary2009.pdf
[102] Garlick GFJ (1986) Solar Energy Converter Employing a Fluorescent Wavelength Shifter. US Patent 4,584,328. Hughes Aircraft Company.
[103] Garlick GFJ (1987) Process for Fabricating a Solar Energy Converter Employing a Fluorescent Wavelength Shifter. US Patent 4,710,254. Spectrolab Inc.
[104] Miteva T, Nelles G, Balouchev S, and Yakutkin V (2009) Device for Modifying the Wavelength Spectrum of Light. US Patent 0,290,211. Sony Corporation (last accessed 21 September 2011).
[105] Bronstein-Bonte I and Fischer AB (1986) Photovoltaic Cell. US Patent 4,629,821. Polaroid Corporation.
[106] Hollars D (2010) Photovoltaic Device with a Luminescent Down-Shifting Material. US Patent 0,294,339. Miasole.
[107] Boehm A, Grimm A, and Richards BS (2010) Photovoltaic Modules with Improved Quantum Efficiency. US Patent 0,186,801. BASF.
[108] Walsh D and Shing YH (1980) ZnSe solar spectrum converter for GaAs solar cells. *Proceeding of IEEE 14th Photovoltaic Specialists Conference.* pp. 476–477. San Diego, CA, USA. January 7–10.
[109] First solar, First solar overview. http://www.firstsolar.com/Downloads/pdf/FastFacts_PHX_NA.pdf (last accessed 22 September 2011).
[110] van Sark WGJHM, Barnham KWJ, Slooff LH, *et al.* (2008) Luminescent solar concentrators – a review of recent results. *Optics Express* 16: 21773–21792.
[111] Mulder CL, Reusswig PD, Velázquez AM, *et al.* (2010) Dye alignment in luminescent solar concentrators: I. Vertical alignment for improved waveguide coupling. *Optics Express* 18: 79–90.

1.27 Luminescent Solar Concentrator

JC Goldschmidt, Fraunhofer Institute for Solar Energy Systems ISE, Freiburg, Germany

© 2012 Elsevier Ltd. All rights reserved.

1.27.1	Introduction	587
1.27.2	Theory of Luminescent Solar Concentrators	588
1.27.2.1	The Factors that Determine the Efficiency of Luminescent Concentrator Systems	588
1.27.2.2	Thermodynamic Efficiency Limits	589
1.27.2.3	Thermodynamic Models of the Luminescent Concentrator	590
1.27.2.4	Ray Tracing Simulations of Luminescent Concentrators	592
1.27.3	Materials for Luminescent Solar Concentrators	593
1.27.3.1	Organic Dyes	593
1.27.3.2	Inorganic Luminescent Materials	594
1.27.4	Luminescent Solar Concentrator System Designs and Achieved Results	594
1.27.4.1	System Designs	594
1.27.4.2	Achieved System Efficiencies	595
1.27.5	The Future Development of Luminescent Solar Concentrators	596
1.27.5.1	Extending the Used Spectral Range into the IR	596
1.27.5.2	Controlling Escape Cone Losses	596
1.27.5.2.1	Photonic structures for increased efficiencies	596
1.27.5.2.2	Controlling the angular emission	598
1.27.6	Conclusion	599
Acknowledgments		599
References		599

1.27.1 Introduction

In a luminescent collector, a luminescent material embedded in a transparent matrix absorbs sunlight and emits radiation at a different wavelength than the incident one. Total internal reflection traps most of the emitted light and guides it to the edges of the collector (**Figure 1**). This underlying principle was first used in scintillation counters [1, 2]. A geometric concentration is achieved if the area of the edges is smaller than the illuminated front surface of the collector, that is, when the area from which light is collected is larger than the area from which light is emitted.

When solar cells are optically coupled to the edges, they can convert the guided light into electricity. The application to concentrate solar radiation onto a solar cell was proposed in the late 1970s [3, 4]. If the solar cell is illuminated with a higher intensity than it would be in direct sunlight, a real concentration is achieved. For real concentration, high geometric concentration, as well as high collection efficiency, is necessary. Probably, the most outstanding feature of luminescent solar concentrators is their ability to concentrate both direct and diffuse radiation. This ability is a great advantage for the application of luminescent concentrators in temperate climates, such as in middle Europe, or in indoor applications with relatively high fractions of diffuse radiation. Additionally, luminescent concentrators do not require tracking systems that follow the path of the sun, in contrast to concentrator systems that use lenses or mirrors in combination with trackers. This facilitates, for instance, the integration of luminescent concentrators in buildings.

Luminescent concentrators were investigated intensively in the early 1980s, for example, [5, 6]. Research at that time aimed at cutting costs by using the concentrator to reduce the need for expensive solar cells. However, several problems led to reduced research interest. First, the used organic dyes had only relatively narrow absorption bands. Second, although the organic dyes showed high quantum efficiencies, defined as the ratio between absorbed and emitted photons, above 95% in the visible range of the spectrum, quantum efficiencies remained at 50% and lower in the infrared (IR) because of fundamental physical reasons. Furthermore, the dyes that were sensitive in the IR were unstable under long-term illumination. Reabsorption of the emitted light due to overlapping absorption and emission spectra further reduced efficiencies [5]. A fundamental problem was the escape cone of the internal reflection, which caused losses of at least 26%. Finally, efficient solar cells of which the spectral response matched the emission spectra of the dyes were hardly available.

After more than 20 years of progress in the development of solar cells and luminescent materials, and with new concepts, several groups such as those of References 7–25 are currently reinvestigating the potential of luminescent concentrators. High efficiencies have been achieved [19, 25, 26] and there has also been considerable progress in the understanding and theoretical description, for example, [22, 24, 26–28]. However, efficiencies are still too low and system sizes too small for a commercial application.

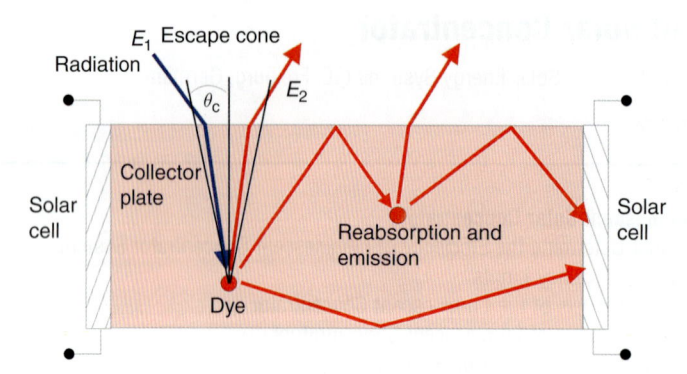

Figure 1 Principle of a luminescent concentrator. A luminescent material (dye) in a matrix absorbs incoming sunlight (E_1) and emits radiation with a different energy (E_2). Total internal reflection traps most of the emitted light and guides it to solar cells optically coupled to the edges. Emitted light that impinges on the internal surface with an angle steeper than the critical angle θ_c is lost due to the escape cone of total internal reflection. A part of the emitted light is also reabsorbed, which can be followed by reemission.

The concept of luminescent concentrators has been given many different names; among them are fluorescent collectors [4], quantum-dot solar concentrator [20–22, 29], and organic solar concentrator [30]. In this work, I will use the term 'luminescent concentrator' for the overall concept. For clarity, 'luminescent collector' will refer to the collector plate without attached solar cells and 'luminescent concentrator system' will refer to a system constructed from a collector plate with solar cells attached.

In Section 1.27.2, I will give an overview of the theoretical understanding on luminescent concentrator. I will start with identifying the factors that determine luminescent concentrator system efficiencies. I will then shortly review theoretical models and simulation approaches.

In principle, all kinds of luminescent materials can be used in a luminescent concentrator: fluorescent materials that show a Stokes shift of the emission to longer wavelengths; phosphorescent materials; upconverters that emit one high-energy photon after the absorption of at least two low-energy photons; and quantum-cutting materials that emit two low-energy photons after the absorption of one high-energy photon. In Section 1.27.3, I will review which materials are investigated for their application in luminescent concentrators.

Many different system configurations have been proposed for luminescent concentrators. Variations include deposition of the luminescent material in a film on a transparent slab [31], stacking of different luminescent collectors [4], cylindrical collectors [32], solar cells coupled to the bottom of the collector [13, 15], and many more. The most important system configurations and results of their experimental investigation will be presented in Section 1.27.4. In Section 1.27.5, I will discuss the possibilities for the future research on luminescent concentrators.

1.27.2 Theory of Luminescent Solar Concentrators

1.27.2.1 The Factors that Determine the Efficiency of Luminescent Concentrator Systems

Several factors determine the efficiency of a luminescent concentrator system. Most of these factors are wavelength dependent. By integrating over the respective relevant spectrum, a description of the overall system efficiency with a set of efficiencies for individual processes is possible [33, 34]. Following their representation, the important parameters are the following:

$\eta_{\text{trans,front}}$ transmission of the front surface with respect to the solar spectrum
η_{abs} absorption efficiency of the luminescent material due to its absorption spectrum with respect to the transmitted solar spectrum
QE   Quantum efficiency of the luminescent material
η_{Stoke} 'Stokes efficiency'; $(1 - \eta_{\text{Stoke}})$ is the energy loss due to the Stokes shift
η_{trap} fraction of the emitted light that is trapped by total internal reflection
η_{reabs} efficiency of light guiding limited by self-absorption of luminescent material; $(1-\eta_{\text{reabs}})$ is the energy loss due to reabsorption
η_{mat} 'matrix efficiency'; $(1 - \eta_{\text{mat}})$ is the loss caused by scattering or absorption in the matrix
η_{tref} efficiency of light guiding by total internal reflection
η_{coup} efficiency of the optical coupling of solar cell and luminescent collector
η_{cell} efficiency of the solar cell under illumination with the edge emission of the luminescent collector

The overall system efficiency η_{system} can be calculated from the single parameters via

$$\eta_{\text{system}} = \eta_{\text{trans}} \eta_{\text{abs}} \text{QE} \eta_{\text{Stoke}} \eta_{\text{trap}} \eta_{\text{reabs}} \eta_{\text{mat}} \eta_{\text{tref}} \eta_{\text{coup}} \eta_{\text{cell}} \quad [1]$$

Several aspects are of importance for the different efficiencies:

- The transmission of the front surface is determined by its reflection $R(\lambda_{inc})$, where λ_{inc} is the incident wavelength. This is usually the Fresnel reflection, which is

$$R(\lambda) = \left(\frac{n(\lambda_{inc})-1}{n(\lambda_{inc})+1}\right)^2 \qquad [2]$$

  for normal incidence and the surface between a medium with refractive index of 1 and a medium with refractive index $n(\lambda_{inc})$. The reflection of typical materials is in the range of 4% for one surface. Special layers or structures applied to the front can decrease or increase reflection. Interestingly, an antireflection coating that reduces the Fresnel reflection does not affect the total internal reflection. This can be understood by considering that total internal reflection is an effect strongly linked to refraction. Total internal reflection occurs when the light from inside the high-index material impinges on the surface with an angle sufficiently shallow that the light would be refracted back into the medium again. As the antireflection coating does not change the refraction, total internal reflection is not affected either.
- The absorption spectrum $Abs(\lambda_{inc})$ determines the absorption efficiency. A large fraction of the solar spectrum is lost, because many luminescent materials absorb only a narrow spectral region. The absorption range of typical fluorescent organic dyes is only about 200 nm in width.
- The quantum efficiency QE of the luminescent material is defined as the ratio of the number of emitted photons to the number of the absorbed photons. For organic dyes, the luminescent quantum efficiency can exceed 95%.
- The energy of the emitted photons is usually different from the energy of the absorbed photons. For most luminescent materials, a Stokes shift to lower energy occurs. This means that the emitted photons possess less energy than the absorbed ones. Therefore, the wavelength of the emitted photons λ_{emit} is different from the wavelength of the incident photons λ_{inc}. As we will see in Section 1.27.2.2, this Stokes shift is of critical importance to the ability of the luminescent concentrator to concentrate light.
- The luminescent material emits light isotropically in a first approximation. All light that impinges on the internal surface with an angle smaller than the critical angle $\theta_c(\lambda_{emit})$ leaves the collector and is lost (**Figure 1**). The critical angle is given by

$$\theta_c(\lambda) = \arcsin\left(\frac{1}{n(\lambda_{emit})}\right) \qquad [3]$$

  This effect is also called the escape cone of total internal reflection. The light that impinges with greater angles is totally internally reflected. Integration gives a fraction

$$\eta_{trap}(\lambda) = \sqrt{1-n(\lambda_{emit})^{-2}} \qquad [4]$$

  of the emitted photon flux that is trapped in the collector [35]. For polymethyl methacrylate (PMMA) with $n = 1.5$, this results in a trapped fraction of around 74%, which means that a fraction of 26% is lost after every emission process. The 26% ratio accounts for the losses through both surfaces. An attached mirror does not change this number, as with a mirror the light leaves the collector through the front surface after being reflected.
- The absorption spectrum and the emission spectrum overlap. For principal reasons, absorption must be possible in the spectral region where emission occurs. Therefore, part of the emitted light is reabsorbed. Again, the energy loss due to a quantum efficiency smaller than 1 occurs, and again radiation is lost into the escape cone.
- Realistic matrix materials are not perfectly transparent. They absorb light and they scatter light, so it leaves the collector.
- Total internal reflection is a loss-free process. However, the surface of the luminescent collector is not perfect. Minor roughness at the surface causes light to leave the collector, because locally the light hits the uneven surface with a steep angle. Fingerprints and scratches can seriously harm the efficiency of light guiding.
- The luminescent collector and the solar cell have to be optically coupled. Otherwise, reflection losses occur at the interface between collector and air and again at the interface between air and solar cell. However, the optical coupling can also cause losses: light can be scattered away from the solar cell or parasitic absorption can occur.
- Finally, the solar cell has to convert the radiation it receives from the collector into electricity. Again, a whole set of parameters determine this process, ranging from reflection and transparency losses to thermalization and electrical losses.

This description is not very relevant for actually calculating the efficiency of luminescent concentrator systems, because some of the involved efficiencies are neither easy to calculate nor directly accessible by measurement. Nevertheless, this description illustrates very well the effects that affect the efficiency of luminescent concentrator systems.

1.27.2.2 Thermodynamic Efficiency Limits

The ability to as well concentrate diffuse radiation sets the luminescent concentrator apart from all other types of concentrators. Systems utilizing only geometrical optics cannot concentrate diffuse light. For a discussion of this difference, the concept of étendue and its links with entropy are very helpful. For light incident from a cone, with θ_{inc} being half of the opening angle, and a flat, not tilted illuminated area A_{inc}, the étendue ε can be calculated to be

$$\varepsilon = \pi \sin^2 \theta_{inc} A_{inc} \qquad [5]$$

From the definition and this result, the étendue can be understood as a measure of how 'spread out' a light beam is in terms of angular divergence and illuminated or emitting area. The étendue can be calculated for an emitted beam as well. In this case, the area of the emitting surface and the opening angle of the emission cone must be applied in the above relation.

The étendue is closely linked to entropy. If an optical system increases the étendue, entropy is generated. Following Markvart in Reference 36, if ε_{inc} is the étendue of the incident beam and ε_{emit} the étendue of the emitted beam, the entropy per photon σ that is generated is

$$\sigma = k_B \ln \frac{\varepsilon_{emit}}{\varepsilon_{inc}} \qquad [6]$$

with k_B is the Boltzmann constant. A conservative system does not generate entropy, so in a conservative system, the étendue is constant. If there are no other sources of entropy, the étendue cannot be reduced, because the entropy cannot decrease. That is, any concentration with geometrical optics that decreases the illuminated area must increase the angular divergence. Because for diffuse radiation, angular divergence is already at its maximum, diffuse radiation cannot be concentrated with a system using only geometrical optics.

As a luminescent concentrator is able to concentrate diffuse radiation, there must be another source of entropy. This source of entropy can be found in the Stokes shift. The dissipation of part of the excitation energy as heat generates entropy and leads to photon emission at longer wavelengths. Therefore, the extent of the Stokes shift determines the maximum concentration that is achievable with a luminescent concentrator.

This relationship between Stokes shift and concentration has been theoretically described in Reference 37. The theoretical model considers two distinct photon fields: one that is incident on the luminescent collector and one that is emitted from the collector. The entropy change $\Delta\sigma_1$ associated with the loss of a photon from the incident Bose field is

$$\Delta\sigma_1 = -k_B \ln\left(1 + \frac{8\pi n^2 v_{inc}^2}{c^2 F_{p,v,inc}}\right) \qquad [7]$$

where $F_{p,v,inc}$ is the flux of photons (i.e., photons per unit time) per unit area, per unit bandwidth, and per 4π solid angle of the incident field. The other parameters are the frequency of the photon v_{inc}, the speed of light c, and the refractive index n [37].

The emission of a photon with the frequency v_{emit} increases the entropy of the emitted field. Additionally, due to the Stokes shift, the energy $h(v_{inc} - v_{emit})$ is dissipated as heat at the ambient temperature T. The entropy generated from these two processes is

$$\Delta\sigma_2 = k_B \ln\left(1 + \frac{8\pi n^2 v_{emit}^2}{c^2 F_{p,v,emit}}\right) + \frac{h(v_{inc} - v_{emit})}{T} \qquad [8]$$

with the parameters defined for the emission field corresponding to the parameters of the incident field.

According to the second law of thermodynamics, it must hold

$$\Delta\sigma_1 + \Delta\sigma_2 \geq 0 \qquad [9]$$

In the argument of the logarithm in eqns [7] and [8], the '1' can be neglected under illumination with sunlight and for frequencies in the visible spectral range. With this approximation and the eqns [7]–[9], the concentration ratio C can be calculated to be

$$C := \frac{F_{p,v,emit}}{F_{p,v,inc}} \leq \frac{v_{emit}^2}{v_{inc}^2} \exp\left(\frac{h(v_{inc} - v_{emit})}{k_B T}\right) \qquad [10]$$

Figure 2 illustrates these results. The maximum possible concentration has been calculated with eqn [10] for three different wavelengths of the incident light. It becomes obvious that from an entropic point of view, higher concentrations can be achieved for shorter wavelengths than for longer wavelengths. For short wavelengths, the maximum concentration is very high and constitutes no practical limit. For longer wavelengths, however, a sufficiently large Stokes shift is necessary in order to avoid limitations for principal reasons.

The fact that there is a maximum concentration has one more consequence: when the maximum concentration is reached, increasing the collector area will not increase the output at the edges of the concentrator. Already before the maximum concentration is reached, increasing the collector area of a large concentrator will not increase the output in the same way as increasing the area of smaller collector. As a consequence, the light collection efficiency of luminescent collectors decreases with increasing size.

1.27.2.3 Thermodynamic Models of the Luminescent Concentrator

The picture of an incident and an emitted light field that was introduced by Yablonovitch in Reference 37 has been subsequently developed into a thermodynamic model of luminescent concentrators, for example, [20–22, 29, 38]. These models were successfully used to describe luminescent concentrators based on luminescent quantum dots. At a microscopic level, further developments

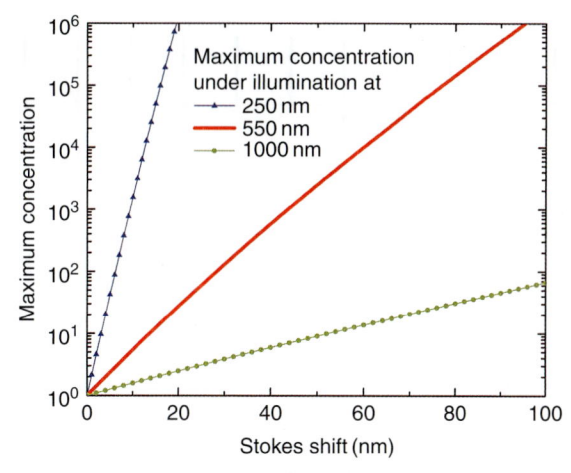

Figure 2 Illustration of the maximum concentration from an entropic point of view. For short wavelengths, very high concentrations are theoretically possible. For longer wavelengths, a large Stokes shift is necessary to avoid limitations.

were presented in Reference 39. At this point, I would like to present a phenomenological thermodynamic model, which brings together the main ideas from different theoretical discussions and offers valuable insight into the working principles of luminescent concentrators.

If one considers a conventional luminescent collector with dye molecules embedded in a transparent matrix, the incident light field with the intensity B_{inc} excites the ensemble of luminescent molecules in the collector out of equilibrium with the ambient temperature T. Because of the fast thermal equilibration among the vibrational substates of the electronically excited state, the electrons cool down very fast to the ambient temperature. But as the molecule remains nonetheless in an electronically excited state, the electrons have a chemical potential $\mu > 0$, just as in an illuminated semiconductor. The chemical potential is a measure of how many luminescent molecules are excited. The emission of the ensemble of the luminescent molecules is described by the generalized Planck's law [37, 40]. The number of emitted photons per time, per area, per unit solid angle, and per frequency interval $B_{p,\nu,\text{emit}}(\nu_{\text{emit}}, T, \mu)$ is

$$B_{p,\nu,\text{emit}}(\nu_{\text{emit}}, T, \mu) = \frac{2\nu_{\text{emit}}^2 n^2}{c^2} a(\nu_{\text{emit}}) \frac{1}{\exp\left(\frac{h\nu_{\text{emit}} - \mu}{k_B T}\right) - 1} \quad [11]$$

where $a(\nu_{\text{emit}})$ is the absorption coefficient, which is equal to the emission coefficient following Kirchhoff's law.

Part of the emitted light is lost due to the escape cone of total internal reflection, but most of the light is trapped and guided in the collector to its edges. As a consequence, the molecules are illuminated by not only the incident field but also the emitted and trapped light. The higher the combined intensity B_{int} is at a point of the collector, the higher is the chemical potential, and in turn also the emission of light. The chemical potential is not constant throughout the collector. For instance, close to the front surface, the chemical potential is higher because the luminescent molecules are excited from the full incident field. Further away from the surface, part of the incident light has been absorbed and therefore intensity is lower (**Figure 3**).

This picture can explain why there is a maximum possible concentration. The larger the collector is, the more the photons from the incident field are collected. Thus, the intensity of the trapped light field that travels toward the edges also increases. This increases the chemical potential, and consequently the emission of light as well. The maximum concentration is reached when the chemical potential has become so high that the emitted light lost in the escape cone equals the incident field. The limit obtained from this consideration is stricter than the limit presented in eqn [10] [37].

The link of the maximum concentration with the Stokes shift and the problem of reabsorption can be understood considering a simple model system that features an absorption region and an emission region (see **Figure 4**) [13]. The absorption coefficient α_{abs} in the absorption region is much higher than that in the emission region with an absorption coefficient α_{emit}.

As said before, the absorption and emissions coefficients are equal as described by Kirchhoff's law. In spite of $\alpha_{\text{abs}} > \alpha_{\text{emit}}$, the emission in the emission region is much larger than that in the absorption region because of the energy dependency of the generalized Planck's law, which states that in this regime, the emission at lower energies is considerably more likely than that at higher energies. Hence, the larger the Stokes shift, that is, the bigger the energy difference $E_2 - E_1$, the less frequent the emission in the absorption range 'relative' to the emission in the emission range. With less light being emitted in the absorption range, reabsorption becomes less likely. Because each reabsorption and reemission again causes escape cone losses, with less reabsorption, the escape cone losses are reduced as well. Less escape cone losses mean that a higher internally guided field and a higher chemical potential are possible until the emitted light lost in the escape cone equals the incident field. As a consequence, a higher maximum concentration is possible.

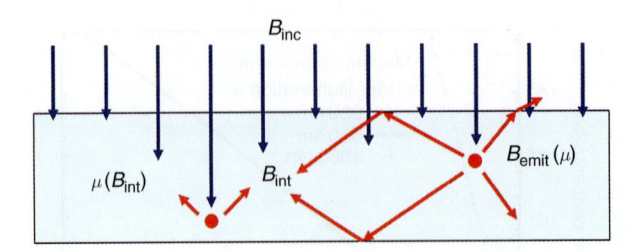

Figure 3 Illustration of the main ideas of the thermodynamic model. Incident radiation with the intensity B_{inc} excites the ensemble of luminescent molecules in the luminescent collector. The fraction of excited molecules is described by the chemical potential μ of the molecule ensemble. The luminescent molecules emit radiation with the intensity B_{emit}, which depends on the chemical potential. The trapped fraction of the emitted light and the incident light combines to the internal intensity B_{int}. This internal intensity again determines the chemical potential. As the internal intensity is not constant throughout the collector, the chemical potential varies as well.

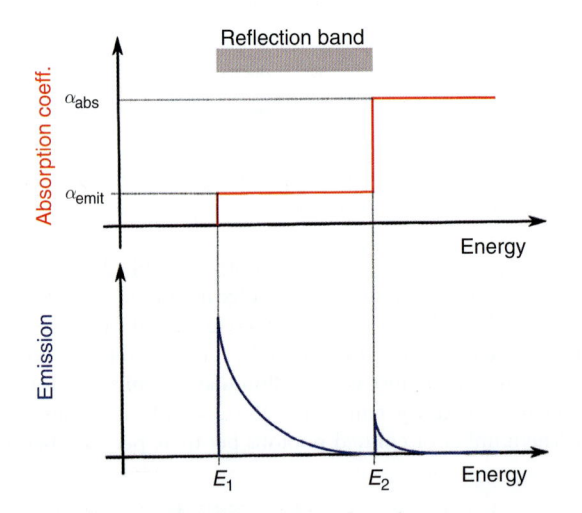

Figure 4 Idealized model of the absorption and emission characteristics of a luminescent concentrator [13]. In the absorption region, the absorption coefficient α_{abs} is high, while in the emission region, the coefficient α_{emit} is much smaller. Following Kirchhoff's law, the emission coefficient equals the absorption coefficient. Nevertheless, emission in the emission region is much higher, because the generalized Planck's law favors emissions at lower energies. A band-stop reflection filter that reflects in the emission region can increase efficiency and the maximum possible concentration considerably.

Because absorption and emission are linked by Kirchhoff's law, it is not possible to eliminate reabsorption entirely. Additionally, without reabsorption, the excitation of the molecules would be completely independent of the emitted light. This would allow for an infinite concentration, which is a clear contradiction of the second law of thermodynamics. However, it is possible to reduce the escape cone losses and therefore to increase the maximum possible concentration with the addition of a band-stop filter. The band-stop filter should reflect in the emission range but should transmit in the absorption range. The desirable reflection band is sketched in **Figure 4**. Like this, only the small amount of light emitted in the absorption region can be subjected to escape cone losses. Again, this means that a higher internally guided field and a higher chemical potential are possible until the emitted light lost in the escape cone equals the incident field. In Reference 13 it was shown that the maximum efficiency of a luminescent concentrator system with such a band-stop filter equals the Shockley–Queisser limit of a solar cell with a bandgap similar to that of the cutoff wavelength E_2 of the band-stop filter.

1.27.2.4 Ray Tracing Simulations of Luminescent Concentrators

For complex geometries with different materials, imperfect surfaces, scattering, etc., most thermodynamic models were not sufficient. Therefore, several works have investigated luminescent concentrators using Monte Carlo methods and ray tracing. One of the first works is the dissertation of Heidler [41]. Heidler modeled absorption of the dye, isotropic emission, total internal reflection, and reabsorption. The model was even capable of simulating a diffuse-back reflector and stack configurations. Simulated collection efficiencies exceeded experimental data by 15% on average due to the idealized conditions of the model. However, good agreement between the simulated and measured edge emission spectrum was achieved. Recently, new attempts for simulating luminescent concentrators have been made [13, 14, 42–45]. Kennedy et al. [43, 44] use a simple model describing absorption of the dye, emission, total internal reflection, and reabsorption to calculate the relative J_{sc} of solar cells coupled to one edge of the collector and to predict the emitted spectrum leaving at the bottom of the collector. The J_{sc} values were overestimated by about 10%, but again the emitted spectra agreed well with predictions. Burgers *et al.* [45] used a quite similar model. He determined relevant parameters, such as the dye concentration or the quantum efficiency, by fitting the model to measured data. He also included mirrors at the collector edges. With his model, he achieved good agreement between external quantum efficiency (EQE) measurements and the simulation-based predictions; a review was presented in Reference 8. In References 13 and 14, a highly idealized model was presented, which for the first time included a photonic structure. This idealized model has then been further developed by Prönneke *et al.* [46] to describe more realistic systems [46]. In References 26 and 47, a model was presented that was tested against spectrally resolved experimental data, such as reflection and transmission spectra as well was the emission spectra from different surfaces of the collector. The shape of the photoluminescence spectrum and the angular distribution of the emitted light proved to be very important input parameters. With the model it was also possible to reproduce the angular distribution of the light leaving the collector at the edges. In References 26 and 48, the effect of a dependence of the photoluminescence spectrum on the excitation wavelength was investigated. In Reference 48, the impact of reabsorption was examined. It was found that reduced reabsorption due to a larger Stokes shift can overcompensate a lower quantum efficiency of the absorption/emission process in respect of the overall system efficiency.

1.27.3 Materials for Luminescent Solar Concentrators

1.27.3.1 Organic Dyes

Organic dyes were the dominant luminescent material in the first research campaign in the 1980s [5, 6, 31, 33, 49–52]. They were applied both distributed in a transparent matrix material and as a thin layer on a transparent slab of material. The research in that time resulted in luminescent dyes with high luminescent quantum efficiencies above 95% and good stability. **Figure 5** shows a photograph of a selection of luminescent concentrator materials produced during that time. Today, these luminescent dyes are commercially available and therefore also used in recent works [16, 18, 19, 53, 54]. Until now, the highest reported efficiencies [19, 25] were reached with systems based on organic dyes.

However, high quantum efficiency is achieved only in the visible range of the spectrum, while efficiency remains low in the IR. In Reference 33, it is shown that these low quantum efficiencies have fundamental reasons that are difficult to overcome. The main reason is that the energy difference between the excited electronic states moves closer to the energy of vibrational transitions within the molecule, which facilitates nonradiative transitions. Nevertheless, also in recent works, organic dyes are being developed that extend the efficiently used spectral range to longer wavelength. For example, in Reference 55, the synthesis of a dye based on a perylene perinone is described, which extends the absorption wavelength range by more than 50 nm in comparison to the perylene-based dye Lumogen Red 305, which is very frequently used in luminescent concentrators. This extended absorption allows for the collection of potentially 25% more photons at a reasonable luminescent quantum yield and photostability.

Another problem of the organic dyes is the large overlap between absorption and emission spectra. This results in reabsorption and reemission with the associated losses. Research has therefore been conducted to increase the Stokes shift of the organic dyes. One option is to use energy transfer from one absorbing dye to another emitting dye [30, 56]. In Reference 57, hybrid dyes were investigated, which were composed of organic antenna and inorganic emitting ions to achieve large Stokes Shifts. Another option is to use phosphorescence instead of fluorescence [30]. Phosphorescence is associated with a larger Stokes shift, but also with lower quantum efficiency. There have also been attempts to increase overall efficiency by bringing metal nanoparticles close to the dyes, in order to increase absorption and luminescence due to plasmonic resonances [58, 59].

Figure 5 A selection of luminescent concentrator materials based on organic dyes that were produced during the first research campaign in the 1980s at Fraunhofer ISE [5, 6, 33, 49, 51] that are still among the most efficient luminescent concentrator materials. The luminescent collectors consist of PMMA doped with organic dyes produced from BASF. The used dyes are perylene derivates. The precise chemical structures, however, were not published by BASF.

1.27.3.2 Inorganic Luminescent Materials

Because of the instability of organic materials, especially under ultraviolet radiation, inorganic materials have been investigated as well. Promising inorganic materials are glasses and glass ceramics doped with rare-earth ions like Nd^{3+} and Yb^{3+}, or other metal ions like Cr^{3+} [60–63]. The advantages to these approaches are high stability and a high refraction index of the glasses, which increases the trapped fraction of light. One big disadvantage is the narrow absorption bands of the luminescent materials. Additionally, these material systems turned out to be quite complex and costly to fabricate.

With the development of nanotechnology, luminescent nanocrystalline quantum dots (NQDs) have become of interest for luminescent concentrators. The most frequently used materials are CdS, CdSe, and ZnS quantum dots [20, 21, 64–68]. One big advantage of the NQDs is that absorption and emission properties can be tuned by the size and composition of the nanocrystals. Additionally, the NQD features a broad absorption range. However, the achieved quantum efficiencies are lower than those of organic dyes, especially if the NQDs are incorporated into polymer matrixes. In addition, the low Stokes shift presently prohibits reaching high efficiencies; NQDs with larger Stokes shifts are under development (nanorods [68] and type II heteronanocrystals [69]), thus potentially leading to high light collection efficiencies. There are also hybrid approaches; for example, in Reference 70, Er-doped WO_6 nanocrystals in composite telluride glasses are investigated.

1.27.4 Luminescent Solar Concentrator System Designs and Achieved Results

1.27.4.1 System Designs

Many system designs have been proposed for efficient and economic luminescent concentrator systems. Probably, the most fundamental one was the concept to stack several collector plates [4]. With different dyes in each plate, different parts of the spectrum can be utilized (see **Figure 6**). At each luminescent collector, a solar cell can be attached, which is optimized for the spectrum emitted from the collector. With this spectrum splitting, high efficiencies can be achieved in principle. The stack design with the matched solar cells at the edges provides a high degree of freedom for cell interconnection. Therefore, there is no forced series connection like in tandem cell concepts, which causes current limitation problems. Additionally, no tunnel diodes are necessary.

Figure 6 shows mirrors at some of the edges of the collector plate as well. If some edges are not covered with solar cells, but with reflectors, the geometric concentration is increased. This can be beneficial for the costs of the luminescent concentrator system, as solar cells are usually the most expensive component of the system. However, the reflection on mirrors is not free of losses. Therefore, it should be kept to a minimum and the emitted light should reach the solar cells with as few reflections on mirrors as possible. For this purpose, an isosceles and rectangular triangular shape of the luminescent collector is beneficial [4]. With solar cells at the hypotenuse and the two other sides covered with mirrors, only two reflections are necessary at most until the emitted light hits a solar cell.

A reflector underneath the collector increases the collection efficiency as well. It reflects transmitted light back into the collector and creates a second chance for absorption. When a white reflector instead of a mirror is used, light can also be scattered and redirected toward the solar cells. For both reflectors underneath the collector and mirrors at the edges, it is beneficial to maintain an air gap between collector and reflector. In this configuration, the reflection of the reflector comes on top of total internal reflection. However, with an air gap, the diffuse reflector does not change the direction of light emitted into the escape cone to directions that are subject to total internal reflection. The reason for this is that due to refraction, the light that leaves the collector is already

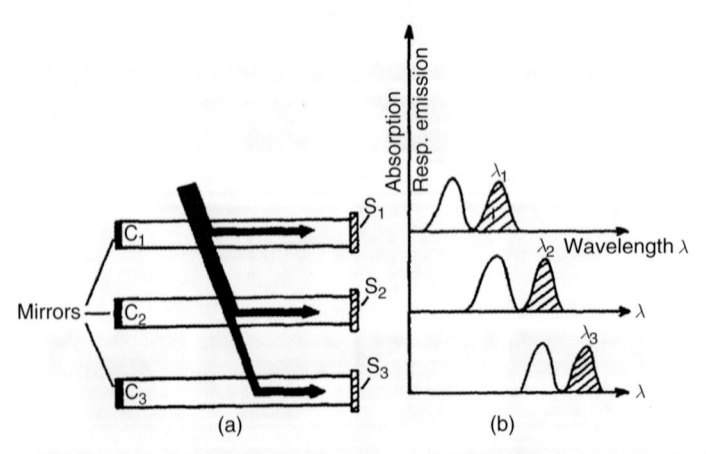

Figure 6 Concept of stacked luminescent concentrators, as presented in Reference 4. (a) The different collectors C_1–C_3 are connected with different solar cells S_1–S_3. In each collector, a different dye is incorporated. The absorption and emission (shaded) spectra of the different dyes are shown in (b). With a proper alignment of the absorption and emission properties, the recycling of photons lost from one collector to another collector is possible. It is important that an air gap between the different collectors is maintained so that each spectral range of light is guided in one collector by total internal reflection and does not get lost in adjacent collectors.

distributed over a complete hemisphere, even before it hits the diffuse reflector. This is not changed by diffuse reflection. So consequently, when the light enters the collector again, it is refracted into exactly the angles of the escape cone.

Another idea to increase the geometric concentration was proposed in Reference 71. The angular range of the edge emission of the luminescent concentrator is limited by the critical angle of total internal reflection. Therefore, a further concentration is possible until the divergence reaches the full hemisphere. Compound parabolic concentrators, which are attached to the edges, are one possibility for this purpose.

As mentioned before, no luminescent materials that are active in the IR while showing high quantum efficiency, high stability, and broad absorption have been developed so far. Therefore, a range of designs were proposed to utilize the IR radiation. One option could be to place a cheap solar cell underneath the collector that utilizes IR radiation [15]. The IR light transmitted through the collector could be used as well by a thermal collector. It was also suggested to use an upconverter to convert the transmitted radiation into light that could be collected by the luminescent collector [34]. The transmitted light can also be used to grow plants in a greenhouse [51]. A complex geometry for building integrated PV was also presented by Chatten et al. in Reference 72, where a luminescent concentrator is integrated into a blind system. Finally, the application of luminescent concentrators is also discussed in the context of day lighting, for example, [73], where only the light collection properties are used and no solar cells are involved.

1.27.4.2 Achieved System Efficiencies

Many materials have been investigated for their potential use in luminescent concentrators. However, the number of luminescent concentrator systems consisting of luminescent collectors with attached solar cells that were tested under standard testing conditions used for solar cells remained relatively small. The highest efficiencies have been reached based on the combination of different organic dyes. Already in the first research campaign in the 1980s, Wittwer et al. [51] achieved a conversion efficiency of 4% with a system that combined two 3 mm-thick plates with different dyes in one stack with GaAs solar cells attached to the edges. The system was 40 cm × 40 cm in size and therefore quite large, so the achieved efficiency can be considered a very good result. The geometric concentration ratio, that is, the ratio of the illuminated collector area to the solar-cell area, was 16.7. The system produced around 3 times more energy than that the solar cells would have produced if they had been placed directly in the sun.

The highest reported efficiency was achieved by Slooff et al. [19]. In this work, four GaAs were attached to a 5 cm × 5 cm luminescent collector with a thickness of 5 mm. The collector consisted of PMMA. The collector contained two dyes, 0.01 wt.% Lumogen F Red 305 (Red305) from BASF (a perylene) and 0.003 wt.% Fluorescence Yellow CRS040 (CRS040) from Radiant Color (a coumarine). At the bottom of the collector, a diffuse reflector was placed. With this configuration, a system efficiency of 7.1% was achieved. The geometric concentration of this system was 2.5.

While both described systems used two different dyes, only one type of solar cell was used, therefore not fully exploiting the possibilities of spectrum splitting described in the previous section. In References 26 and 74, a system was investigated that used as well different types of solar cells, made of GaInP and GaAs. GaInP solar cells have a bandgap of 1.85 eV, which corresponds to a wavelength of 670 nm. The typical open-circuit voltage (V_{OC}) of a GaInP solar cell is in the region above 1300 mV. The bandgap of GaAs is at 1.43 eV and the typical V_{OC} is above 1000 mV. The dimensions of the used collector plates were 5 cm × 5 cm × 0.5 cm. One plate contained a dye active in the spectral region of 400–550 nm. It was used to illuminate the GaInP solar cells. The second collector plate contained a dye active between 550 and 650 nm. This one was used to illuminate the GaAs solar cells. To each of the plates, two solar cells were optically coupled with silicone to adjoining edges. In front of the remaining two edges of each collector plate, white reflectors made from polytetrafluoroethylene (PTFE) were placed. In this configuration, the geometric concentration defined as the ratio of the luminescent collector area to the area of the used solar cells is 2.5 as well. At the bottom of the system, a diffuse reflector was placed. Overall, a system efficiency of 6.9% was achieved. **Figure 7** shows the EQE of the two subsystems.

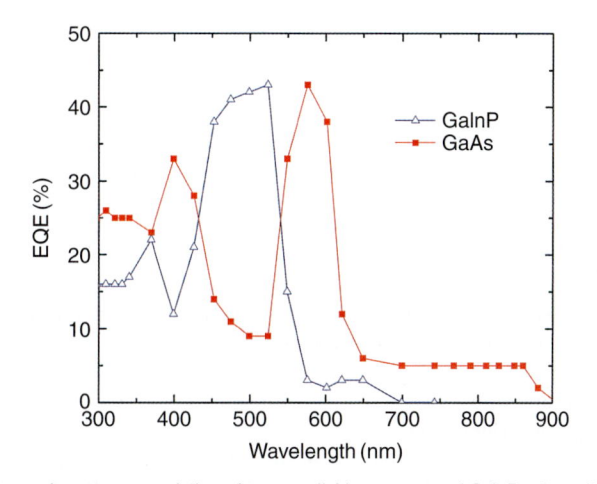

Figure 7 EQE measurements of the two subsystems, consisting of two parallel interconnected GaInP solar cells and two parallel interconnected GaAs solar cells, respectively, coupled to two different luminescent collector plates. The two systems together cover a wide spectral range.

In all the works [19, 26, 74], it was found that the bottom reflector contributed significantly to the overall system efficiency. This can be seen as well in **Figure 7**, where an EQE of more than 5% is visible at wavelengths longer than the active region of the dyes, which ends at about 650 nm. This effect is expected to decrease for bigger systems.

1.27.5 The Future Development of Luminescent Solar Concentrators

The main task for the future development of luminescent concentrators is to increase system efficiencies based on cheap materials in reasonably sized systems. When this task is solved successfully, the integration into applications can be undertaken. To increase system efficiencies, there are two main topics:

- Extending the used spectral range into the IR
- Controlling escape cone losses

1.27.5.1 Extending the Used Spectral Range into the IR

From the EQE measurement presented in **Figure 7**, it is obvious that in the active region of the dyes, the systems reach already quite high quantum efficiencies of approximately 45%. As the used solar cells also deliver high voltages and show high fill factors, the main reason for the low overall efficiency is that only the visible part of the spectrum is used. If one reached a 45% quantum efficiency also in the range from 650 to 1050 nm, one could expect an extra current density of around 12 mA cm^{-2}. When the luminescent material emits in the region between 1050 and 1125 nm, the emitted light could be used by a silicon solar cell, which reaches a maximum power point voltage of around 580 mV. The extra silicon solar-cell luminescent concentrator system then would have an efficiency of nearly 7%, which would result in an overall system efficiency of close to 14%. Even with only silicon solar cells attached, which would result in approximately half the efficiency for the higher energy photons because of the lower voltage of the silicon solar cells, an overall system efficiency of 10% appears to be feasible. However, these are all highly hypothetical cases, which require a lot of material development for near-infrared (NIR) luminescent materials. The concepts presented in Section 1.27.3, especially the use of hybrid materials [57, 70] and the use of luminescent semiconductor quantum dots, might be able to achieve this task. However, the already achieved progress in these fields still remains to be demonstrated at a system level.

1.27.5.2 Controlling Escape Cone Losses

Besides the losses due to an incomplete utilization of the full solar spectrum, the escape cone of total internal reflection is the most important loss mechanism. The loss of around 26% does occur not only once but also after every reabsorption and reemission, as already introduced in Section 1.27.2.1. To reduce the escape cone losses, one can identify two different strategies: first, reabsorption can be reduced to reduce the number of emission events. The different approaches in the development of luminescent materials with low reabsorption were already discussed in Section 1.27.3. The second approach is to control the path of the light in the luminescent collector. In this field, arguably, the biggest progress has been made in the last years.

1.27.5.2.1 Photonic structures for increased efficiencies

The Stokes shift between absorption and emission opens the opportunity to reduce escape cone losses significantly: a selective reflector, which transmits all the light in the absorption range of the luminescent material and reflects the emitted light, would trap nearly all the emitted light inside the collector [75]. The concept is illustrated in **Figure 8**.

In Reference 12, hot mirrors were proposed to serve as selective reflectors and, in Reference 13, photonic structures. A possible realization of such a selective reflector is a so-called rugate filter. It features a continuously varying refractive index profile that results in a single reflection peak. However, some unwanted side lobes remain. Optimized rugate filters [76] show only one single reflection peak for a certain wavelength and almost no other reflections. In Reference 25, it was shown that overall system efficiencies of luminescent concentrator systems can be increased with the help of such an optimized filter. The investigated system used a 5 cm × 10 cm, 5-mm-thick luminescent collector of PMMA doped with an organic dye. One GaInP solar cell was coupled to one short edge with silicone. The solar cell had an active area of 5 mm × 49 mm. Hence, the ratio of illuminated luminescent concentrator area and solar-cell area constitutes a geometric concentration ratio of 20 ×. The solar cell had an efficiency of 16.7% under AM1.5G illumination. White PTFE served as bottom reflector and also as reflector at the edges, which were not covered by solar cells. The used photonic structure was produced by the company mso-jena by ion-assisted deposition (IAD) and was tuned for high reflection in the emission range of the organic dye (see **Figure 9**). Without this structure, the system had an efficiency of 2.6 ± 0.1% in reference to the 50 cm^2 area of the system. The structure increased the efficiency to 3.1 ± 0.1%, which constitutes an efficiency increase of around 20% relative. **Figure 10** shows the result from a light beam-induced current (LBIC) scan of the system, illustrating how the light collection efficiency is increased over most of the luminescent collector area. With the achieved efficiency of 3.1% and the concentration ratio of 20, the realized luminescent concentrator produces about 3.7 times more energy than the GaInP solar cell had produced on its own.

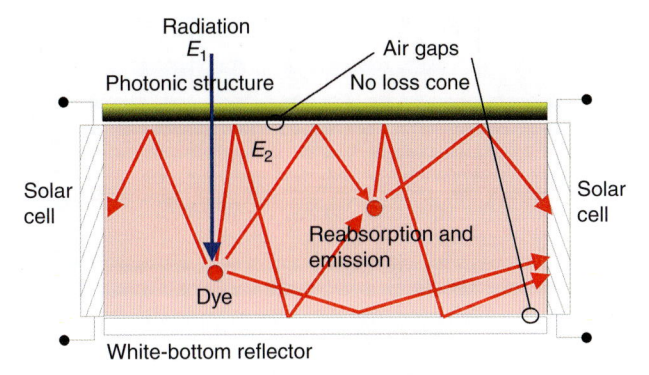

Figure 8 A selective reflector, realized as a photonic structure, reduces the escape cone losses. The photonic structure acts as a band-stop reflection filter. It allows light in the absorption range of the dyes to enter the collectors but reflects light in the emission range.

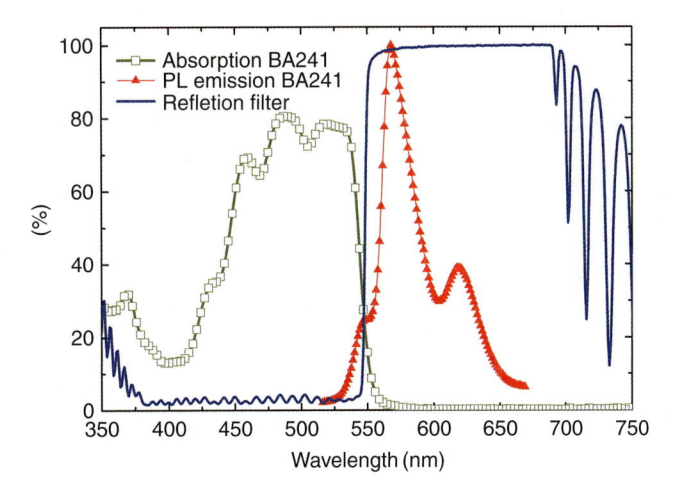

Figure 9 Reflection spectrum of the used photonic structure and the absorption and photoluminescence of the luminescent concentrator the filter was designed for. The reflection of the structure very nicely fits the emission peak of the dye in the concentrator.

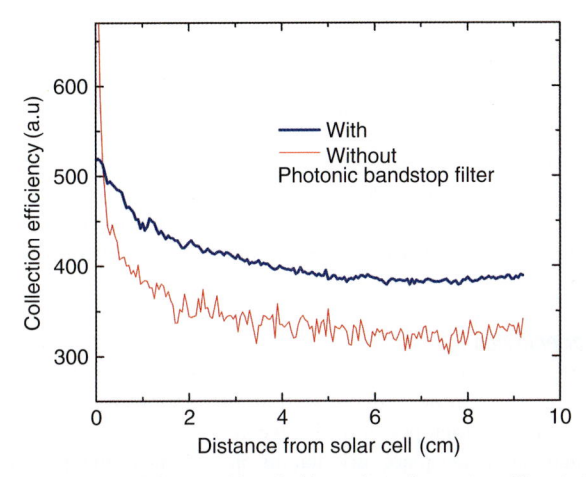

Figure 10 Averaged linescans in x-direction from an LBIC scan with and without photonic structure. Close to the solar cell, the efficiency is lower with the photonic structure, because it reduces the effectiveness of the bottom reflector for small distances. Over most of the luminescent concentrator, however, collection efficiency is significantly higher with a photonic structure, resulting in a relative efficiency increase of 20%.

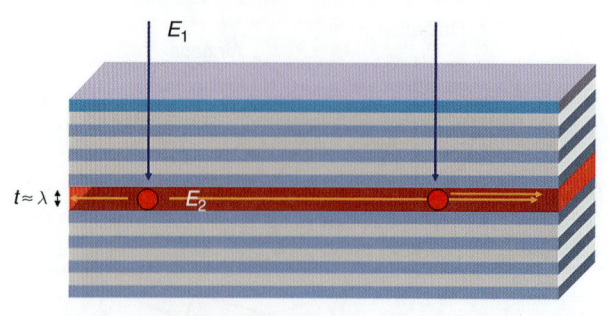

Figure 11 Conceptual sketch of a 'Nano-Fluko'. A very thin layer of luminescent material with thickness t in the range of wavelength λ of the emitted light is placed between two photonic structures, for example, Bragg stacks. The photonic structures transmit light in the absorption range of the luminescent material with an energy E_1. They are reflective in the emission region (E_2) of the luminescent material. Because the layer with the luminescent material is so thin, the photonic structures suppress the emission into unfavorable directions.

The observed efficiency increase of 20% can be already considered as a great success since it shows that photonic structures reduce the escape cone losses significantly. However, the used filter is a multilayer system and therefore costly to produce. Three-dimensional (3D) photonic structures are a potential alternative to the presented multilayer systems. A special three-dimensional photonic structure is the opal. The opal has the advantage that it can be produced by a dip-coating process utilizing self-organization of monodisperse PMMA beads [77]. This is a potentially low-cost process that could be applied on large-area concentrators. However, the achieved quality of opaline films is still too low to achieve optical properties that allow for an increase in efficiency.

Another, probably more promising options are chiral nematic (cholesteric) liquid crystals that act as spectrally selective mirrors. In Reference 78, such chiral nematic liquid crystals were applied onto luminescent collectors, with a small air gap in between. It was observed that the highest output is achieved using a scattering background and cholesteric mirror, with a reflection band significantly redshifted (similar to 150 nm) from the emission peak of the luminescent dye. The use of an air gap results in light bending away from the waveguide surface normal and, consequently, a redshift of the cholesteric mirrors is required. Also, the importance of considering the angular dependence of the spectrally selective mirrors was analyzed in Reference 79. Overall, up to 35% more emitted light exits the luminescent collector edge after application of the cholesteric mirror.

However, even with a photonic structure, light emitted into the escape cone is more frequently subject to loss events. Because it is emitted into a steep angle with respect to the front surface, it has a very long effective path until it reaches a solar cell and therefore suffers more from path length-dependent losses. Hence, it would be very beneficial to suppress emission into these unfavorable directions completely. This should as well be possible with the help of photonic structures. Already the very first works on photonic crystals of Bykov [80] and Yablonovitch [81] dealt with influencing emission with photonic structures. Many papers discussed the possibilities subsequently [82–87]. For influencing the emission of the dye successfully, it is necessary that the photonic structures are very close to the emission process or that the luminescent material is incorporated into the photonic structures. For the luminescent concentrator systems, this means that one has to go from the macroscopic design of the presented systems to a system design in the nanoscale. Possible realizations of such a system denoted 'Nano-Fluko' were suggested in Reference 88. One possible realization consists of a very thin layer of luminescent material between two photonic structures, for example, rugate filters or Bragg stacks (**Figure 11**). In such a configuration, the emission of the light would be restricted to a plane parallel to the photonic structure. Galli *et al.* [89, 90] showed that the emission of Er^{3+} can be strongly enhanced if it is incorporated in a photonic crystal waveguide and that efficient waveguiding occurs. Therefore, there is first experimental evidence that such a system can work, and it is an interesting approach to apply this concept to luminescent concentrators.

However, several layers with the same dye will be needed to achieve sufficient absorption. As the guided light is constraint to very thin layers, high intensities will occur in these layers. Because of thermodynamic limit for the achievable concentration depending on the Stokes shift of the used dye, one question is which system sizes can be achieved using this approach until the thermodynamic limit reduces efficiency.

1.27.5.2.2 *Controlling the angular emission*

An alternative to selective reflectors is to modify the emission characteristic of the dyes in such a way that emission occurs predominantly in favorable directions. This can be achieved with an orientation of dye molecules that show a distinct angular characteristic in their emissions depending on their position. The dye molecules can be aligned accordingly with the help of liquid crystals [17, 91–93]. The dye alignment has to take place such that the optical transition dipole of the luminescent material (the dye molecule) is oriented along the luminescent collector surface normal, directing the maximum possible proportion of luminescence into waveguide modes. In Reference 91, it is reported that up to 30% more light is emitted from the edge of a luminescent collector due to the dye alignment.

1.27.6 Conclusion

Luminescent solar concentrators have the fascinating ability to concentrate both direct and diffuse radiation. This ability is directly related to the Stokes shift that occurs between absorption of incoming light and the subsequent emission. Up to now, system efficiencies of around 7% have been achieved. The efficiency potential that could be achieved based on commercially attractive materials such as silicon solar cells is in the range of 10%. To achieve this goal, further progress in the development of luminescent materials that cover the visible and the near-IR range of the solar spectrum, showing high luminescent quantum efficiencies and low reabsorption, is necessary. Furthermore, current progress in the research on photonic structures needs to be exploited for its application in luminescent concentrator systems.

With continuously falling prices for the production of solar cells, however, the cost advantages, which can be achieved by using cheap concentrators such as luminescent collectors, decrease. Hence, it is unlikely that luminescent concentrators will play an important role for rooftop or power-plant applications. Nevertheless, the unique optical appearance of luminescent concentrators, the possibilities to achieve transparency and to combine different colors, the 'invisibility' of solar cells integrated into the frames of modules, etc. offer unique design possibilities and might open the way for luminescent concentrators into building integrated photovoltaics and also into the power supply of small appliances and portable consumer electronics. Therefore, they could help to spread photovoltaics into fields that are not accessible by conventional solar-cell module technology.

Acknowledgments

Some of the presented work was supported by the German Research Foundation within the Nanosun (PAK88) project. I would like to thank all colleagues at Fraunhofer ISE that are or have been involved in the research on luminescent solar concentrators, especially Marius Peters, Armin Zastrow, Volker Wittwer, and Adolf Goetzberger.

References

[1] Shurcliff WA and Jones RC (1949) The trapping of fluorescent light produced within objects of high geometrical symmetry. *Journal of the Optical Society of America* 39(11): 912–916.
[2] Birks JB (1964) *The Theory and Practice of Scintillation Counting*. London: Pergamon.
[3] Weber WH and Lambe J (1976) Luminescent greenhouse collector for solar radiation. *Applied Optics* 15(10): 2299–2300.
[4] Goetzberger A and Greubel W (1977) Solar energy conversion with fluorescent collectors. *Applied Physics* 14: 123–139.
[5] Wittwer V, Heidler K, Zastrow A, and Goetzberger A (1981) Theory of fluorescent planar concentrators and experimental results. *Journal of Luminescence* 24/25: 873–876.
[6] Seybold G and Wagenblast G (1989) New perylene and violanthrone dyestuffs for fluorescent collectors. *Dyes and Pigments* 11: 303–317.
[7] van Roosmalen JAM (2004) Molecular-based concepts in PV towards full spectrum utilization. *Semiconductors* 38(8): 970–975.
[8] van Sark WGJHM, Barnham KWJ, Slooff LH, *et al.* (2008) Luminescent solar concentrators – A review of recent results. *Optics Express* 16(26): 21773–21792.
[9] Luque A, Martí A, Bett AW, *et al.* (2005) FULLSPECTRUM: A new PV wave of more efficient use of solar spectrum. *Solar Energy Materials and Solar Cells* 87(1–4): 467–479.
[10] Goldschmidt JC, Glunz SW, Gombert A, and Willeke G (2006) Advanced fluorescent concentrators. In: Poortmans J, Ossenbrink H, Dunlop E, and Helm P (eds.) *Proceedings of the 21st European Photovoltaic Solar Energy Conference*, pp. 107–110. Dresden, Germany.
[11] Richards BS and Shalav A (2005) The role of polymers in the luminescence conversion of sunlight for enhanced solar cell performance. *Synthetic Metals* 154: 61–64.
[12] Richards BS, Shalav A, and Corkish R (2004) A low escape-cone-loss luminescent solar concentrator. In: Hoffmann W, *et al.* (eds.) *Proceedings of the 19th European Photovoltaic Solar Energy Conference*, pp. 113–116. Paris, France.
[13] Rau U, Einsele F, and Glaeser GC (2005) Efficiency limits of photovoltaic fluorescent collectors. *Applied Physics Letters* 87(17): 171101-1–3.
[14] Glaeser GC and Rau U (2006) Collection and conversion properties of photovoltaic fluorescent collectors with photonic band stop fillers. In: Gombert A (ed.) *Proceedings of SPIE*, pp. 143–153. Bellingham, WA: SPIE Press.
[15] Goldschmidt JC, Peters M, Löper P, *et al.* (2007) Advanced fluorescent concentrator system design. In: Willecke G, Ossenbrink H, and Helm P (eds.) *Proceedings of the 22nd European Photovoltaic Solar Energy Conference*, pp. 608–612. Milan, Italy.
[16] Danos L, Kittidachachan P, Meyer TJJ, *et al.* (2006) Characterisation of fluorescent collectors based on solid, liquid and Langmuir Blodgett (LB) films. In: Poortmans J, Ossenbrink H, Dunlop E, and Helm P (eds.) *Proceedings of the 21st European Photovoltaic Solar Energy Conference*, pp. 443–446. Dresden, Germany.
[17] Debije MG, Broer DJ, and Bastiaansen CWM (2007) Effect of dye alignment on the output of a luminescent solar concentrator. In: Willecke G, Ossenbrink H, and Helm P (eds.) *Proceedings of the 22nd European Photovoltaic Solar Energy Conference*, pp. 87–89. Milan, Italy.
[18] Slooff LH, Budel T, Burgers AR, *et al.* (2007) The luminescent concentrator: Stability issues. In: Willecke G, Ossenbrink H, and Helm P (eds.) *Proceedings of the 22nd European Photovoltaic Solar Energy Conference*, pp. 584–588. Milan, Italy.
[19] Slooff LH, Bende EE, Burgers AR, *et al.* (2008) A luminescent solar concentrator with 7.1% power conversion efficiency. *Physica Status Solidi—Rapid Research Letters* 2(6): 257–259.
[20] Chatten AJ, Barnham KWJ, Buxton BF, *et al.* (2003) The quantum dot concentrator: Theory and results. In: Kurokawa K, *et al.* (eds.) *Proceedings of the 3rd World Conference on Photovoltaic Energy Conversion*, pp. 2657–2660. Osaka, Japan.
[21] Chatten AJ, Barnham KWJ, Buxton BF, *et al.* (2001) Novel quantum dot concentrators. In: McNelis B, Palz W, Ossenbrink H, and Helm P (eds.) *Proceedings of the 17th European Photovoltaic Solar Energy Conference*, pp. 200–203. Munich, Germany.
[22] Chatten AJ, Barnham KWJ, Buxton BF, and Ekins-Daukes NJ (2003) A new approach to modelling quantum dot concentrators. *Solar Energy Materials and Solar Cells* 75(3–4): 363–371.
[23] Goldschmidt JC, Peters M, Prönneke L, *et al.* (2008) Theoretical and experimental analysis of photonic structures for fluorescent concentrators with increased efficiencies. *Physica Status Solidi A* 205(12): 2811–2821.
[24] Peters M, Goldschmidt JC, Löper P, *et al.* (2009) The effect of photonic structures on the light guiding efficiency of fluorescent concentrators. *Journal of Applied Physics* 105: 014909.
[25] Goldschmidt JC, Peters M, Bösch A, *et al.* (2009) Increasing the efficiency of fluorescent concentrator systems. *Solar Energy Materials and Solar Cells* 93: 176–182.

[26] Goldschmidt JC (2009) *Novel Solar Cell Concepts*, p. 273. München: Verlag Dr. Hut.
[27] Peters M, Goldschmidt JC, Löper P, *et al.* (2010) Spectrally-selective photonic structures for PV applications. *Energies* 3(2): 171–193.
[28] Peters IM (2009) Photonic concepts for solar cells. In: *Faculty of Mathematics and Physics*, p. 202. Freiburg, Germany: Universität Freiburg.
[29] Barnham K, Marques JL, Hassard J, and O' Brien P (2000) Quantum-dot concentrator and thermodynamic model for the global redshift. *Applied Physics Letters* 76(9): 1197–1199.
[30] Currie MJ, Mapel JK, Heidel TD, *et al.* (2008) High-efficiency organic solar concentrators for photovoltaics. *Science* 321: 226–228.
[31] Viehmann W and Frost RL (1979) Thin film waveshifter coatings for fluorescent radiation converters. *Nuclear Instruments and Methods* 167: 405–415.
[32] Bose R, Farrell DJ, Pardo-Sanchez C, *et al.* (2009) Luminescent solar concentrators: Cylindrical design. In: Sinke W, Ossenbrink H, and Helm P (eds.) *Proceedings of the 24th European Photovoltaic Solar Energy Conference*, pp. 359–362. Hamburg, Germany.
[33] Zastrow A (1981) Physikalische Analyse der Energieverlustmechanismen im Fluoreszenzkollektor. In: *Fakultät für Physik*, p. 209. Freiburg: Albert-Ludwigs-Universität Freiburg.
[34] Goetzberger A (2009) Fluorescent solar energy concentrators: Principle and present state of development. In: Petrova-Koch V, Hezel R, and Goetzberger A (eds.) *High-Efficient Low-Cost Photovoltaics: Recent Developments*, pp. 159–176. Berlin: Springer-Verlag GmbH.
[35] Keil G (1969) Radiance amplification by a fluorescence radiation converter. *Journal of Applied Physics* 40(9): 3544–3547.
[36] Markvart T (2008) Solar cell as a heat engine: Energy–entropy analysis of photovoltaic conversion. *Physica Status Solidi A* 205(12): 2752–2756.
[37] Yablonovitch E (1980) Thermodynamics of the fluorescent planar concentrator. *Journal of the Optical Society of America* 70(11): 1362–1363.
[38] Chatten AJ, Farrell DJ, Büchtemann A, and Barnham KWJ (2006) Thermodynamic modelling of luminescent solar concentrators. In: Poortmans J, Ossenbrink H, Dunlop E, and Helm P (eds.) *Proceedings of the 21st European Photovoltaic Solar Energy Conference*, pp. 315–320. Dresden, Germany.
[39] Scudo PF, Abbondanza L, Fusco R, and Caccianotti L (2009) Spectral converters and luminescent solar concentrators. *Solar Energy Materials and Solar Cells* 94(7): 1241–1246.
[40] Würfel P (1995) *Physik der Solarzellen [Physics of Solar Cells]*. Heidelberg, Germany: Spektrum Akademischer Verlag.
[41] Heidler K (1982) *Wirkungsgraduntersuchungen zur Solarenergiekonversion mit Fluoreszenzkollektoren, in Fakultät für Physik*, p. 135. Freiburg, Germany: Universität Freiburg.
[42] Gallagher SJ, Eames PC, and Norton B (2004) Quantum dot concentrator behaviour, predicted using a ray trace approach. *International Journal of Ambient Energy* 25(1): 47–56.
[43] Kennedy M, Dunne M, McCormack SJ, *et al.* (2008) Multiple dye luminescent solar concentrators and comparison with Monte-Carlo ray-trace predictions. In: Lincot D, Ossenbrink H, and Helm P (eds.) *Proceedings of the 23rd European Photovoltaic Solar Energy Conference*, pp. 390–393. Valencia, Spain.
[44] Kennedy M, Chatten AJ, Farrell DJ, *et al.* (2008) Luminescent solar concentrators: A comparison of thermodynamic modelling and ray-trace modelling predictions. In: Lincot D, Ossenbrink H, and Helm P (eds.) *Proceedings of the 23rd European Photovoltaic Solar Energy Conference*, pp. 334–337. Valencia, Spain.
[45] Burgers AR, Slooff LH, Kinderman R, and van Roosmalen JAM (2005) Modelling of luminescent concentrators by ray-tracing. In: Palz W, Ossenbrink H, and Helm P (eds.) *Proceedings of the 20th European Photovoltaic Solar Energy Conference*, pp. 394–397. Barcelona, Spain.
[46] Prönneke L, Gläser G, Uslu Y, and Rau U (2009) Measurement and simulation of enhanced photovoltaic system with fluorescent collectors. In: Sinke W, Ossenbrink H, and Helm P (eds.) *Proceedings of the 24th European Photovoltaic Solar Energy Conference*, pp. 385–387. Hamburg, Germany.
[47] Bendig M, Hanika J, Dammertz H, *et al.* (2008) Simulation of fluorescent concentrators. In: Parker S and Reshetov A (eds.) *IEEE/EG Symposium on Interactive Ray Tracing*, pp. 93–98. Los Angeles, CA, USA.
[48] Wilson LR, Rowan BC, Robertson N, *et al.* (2010) Characterization and reduction of reabsorption losses in luminescent solar concentrators. *Applied Optics* 49(9): 1651–1661.
[49] Zastrow A, Heidler K, Sah RE, *et al.* (1980) On the conversion of solar radiation with fluorescent planar concentrators. In: Palz W (ed.) *Proceedings of the 3rd European Photovoltaic Solar Energy Conference*, Cannes, France, pp. 413–417. Dordrecht, The Netherlands: Springer.
[50] Sah RE (1981) Stokes shift of fluorescent dyes in the doped polymer matrix. *Journal of Luminescence* 24/25: 869–872.
[51] Wittwer V, Stahl W, and Goetzberger A (1984) Fluorescent planar concentrators. *Solar Energy Materials* 11: 187–197.
[52] Mugnier J, Dordet Y, Pouget J, *et al.* (1987) Performances of fluorescent solar concentrators doped with a new dye (benzoxazinone derivative). *Solar Energy Materials* 15: 65–75.
[53] Reisfeld R, Shamrakov D, and Jorgensen C (1994) Photostable solar concentrators based on fluorescent glass films. *Solar Energy Materials and Solar Cells* 33: 417–427.
[54] Hammam M, El-Mansy MK, El-Bashir SM, and El-Shaarawy MG (2007) Performance evaluation of thin-film solar concentrators for greenhouse applications. *Desalination* 209: 244–250.
[55] Debije MG, Verbunt PPC, Nadkarni PJ, *et al.* (2011) Promising fluorescent dye for solar energy conversion based on a perylene perinone. *Applied Optics* 50(2): 163–169.
[56] Calzaferri G (2005) Light-harvesting host-guest antenna materials for thin film solar cells. In: Kenny R, Dunlop E, and Luque A (eds.) *Proceedings of the Fullspectrum Meeting*. Ispra, Italy, pp. 157–166.
[57] Wu WX, Wang TX, Wang X, *et al.* (2010) Hybrid solar concentrator with zero self-absorption loss. *Solar Energy* 84(12): 2140–2145.
[58] Wilson HR (1987) Fluorescent dyes interacting with small silver particles; a system extending the spectral range of fluorescent solar concentrators. *Solar Energy Materials* 16: 223–234.
[59] Hinsch A, Zastrow A, and Wittwer V (1990) Sol–gel glasses: A new material for solar fluorescent planar concentrators? *Solar Energy Materials* 21: 151–164.
[60] Reisfeld R and Kalisky Y (1981) Nd^{3+} and Yb^{3+} germanate and tellurite glasses for fluorescent solar energy collectors. *Chemical Physics Letters* 80(1): 178–183.
[61] Reisfeld R (1984) Fluorescence and nonradiative relaxations of rare earths in amorphous media on high surface area supports: A review. *Journal of the Electrochemical Society: Solid-State Science and Technology* 131(6): 1360–1364.
[62] Andrews LJ, McCollum BC, and Lempicki A (1981) Luminescent solar collectors based on fluorescent glasses. *Journal of Luminescence* 24/25: 877–880.
[63] Neuroth N and Haspel R (1987) Glasses for luminescent solar concentrators. *Solar Energy Materials* 16: 235–242.
[64] Schüler A, Python M, Valle del Olmo M, and de Chambrier E (2006) Quantum dot containing nanocomposite thin films for photoluminescent solar concentrators. *Solar Energy* 81: 1159–1165.
[65] Reda SM (2008) Synthesis and optical properties of CdS quantum dots embedded in silica matrix thin films and their applications as luminescent solar concentrators. *Acta Materialia* 56: 259–264.
[66] Gallagher SJ, Norton B, and Eames PC (2007) Quantum dot solar concentrators: Electrical conversion efficiencies and comparative concentrating factors of fabricated devices. *Solar Energy* 81: 813–821.
[67] Wang CH, Shcherbatyuk G, Inman R, *et al.* (2010) Efficiency improvement by near infrared quantum dots for luminescent solar concentrators. In: Tsakalakos L (ed.) *Next Generation*, p. 77720G. Bellingham: Spie-Int Soc Optical Engineering.
[68] Bomm J, Buechtemann A, Chatten AJ, *et al.* (2011) Fabrication and full characterization of state-of-the-art quantum dot luminescent solar concentrators. *Solar Energy Materials and Solar Cells* 95(8): 2087–2094.
[69] van Sark WGJHM, de Mello Donega C, and Schropp REI (2010) Towards quantum dot solar concentrators using thin film solar cells. In: De Santi GF, Ossenbrink H, and Helm P (eds.) *25th European Photovoltaic Solar Energy Conference*, pp. 289–292. Munich, Germany: WIP-Renewable Energies.
[70] Balaji S, Misra D, and Debnath R (2011) Enhanced green emission from Er_2WO_6 nanocrystals embedded composite tellurite glasses. *Journal of Fluorescence* 21(3): 1053–1060.
[71] Goetzberger A and Schirmer O (1979) Second stage concentration with tapers for fluorescent solar collectors. *Applied Physics* 19: 53–58.
[72] Chatten AJ, Farrell DJ, Bose R, *et al.* (2011) Luminescent and geometric concentrators for building integrated photovoltaics. In: Swanson RM, *et al.* (eds.) *37th IEEE Photovoltaic Specialist Conference*. Seattle, WA, USA.

[73] Chen W, Abdul-Rahman H, and Rao SP (2010) Development and testing of a fluorescent fiber solar concentrator for remote daylighting. *Journal of Energy Engineering* 136(3): 76–86.
[74] Goldschmidt JC, Peters M, Dimroth F, *et al.* (2009) Developing large and efficient fluorescent concentrator systems. In: Sinte W, Ossenbrink H, and Helm P (eds.) *Proceedings of the 24th European Photovoltaic Solar Energy Conference*, pp. 207–212. Hamburg, Germany.
[75] Smestad G, Ries H, Winston R, and Yablonovitch E (1990) The thermodynamic limit of light concentrators. *Solar Energy Materials* 21: 99–111.
[76] Southwell WH (1989) Using apodization functions to reduce sidelobes in rugate filters. *Applied Optics* 28(23): 5091–5094.
[77] Jiang P, Bertone JF, Hwang KS, and Colvin VL (1999) Single-crystal colloidal multilayers of controlled thickness. *Chemistry of Materials* 11(8): 2132–2140.
[78] Debije MG, Van MP, Verbunt PPC, *et al.* (2010) Effect on the output of a luminescent solar concentrator on application of organic wavelength-selective mirrors. *Applied Optics* 49(4): 745–751.
[79] de Boer DKG (2010) Optimizing wavelength-selective filters for Luminescent Solar Concentrators. In: Wehrspohn RB and Gombert A (eds.) *Photonics for Solar Energy Systems III*, p. 77250Q. Bellingham: Spie-Int Soc Optical Engineering.
[80] Bykov VP (1972) Spontaneous emission in a periodic structure. *Soviet Physics JETP* 35: 269.
[81] Yablonovitch E (1987) Inhibited spontaneous emission in solid-state physics and electronics. *Physical Review Letters* 58(20): 2059–2062.
[82] Kweon G and Lawandy NM (1995) Quantum electrodynamics in photonic crystals. *Optics Communications* 118: 388–411.
[83] Vats N, John S, and Busch K (2002) Theory of fluorescence in photonic crystals. *Physical Review A* 65(043808): 1–13.
[84] Schriemer HP, van Driel HM, Koenderink AF, and Vos WL (2000) Modified spontaneous emission spectra of laser dye in inverse opal photonic crystals. *Physical Review A* 63(011801): 1–4.
[85] Nair RV, Vijaya R, Kuroda K, and Sakoda K (2007) Emission studies on photonic crystals fabricated using dyed polystyrene colloids. *Journal of Applied Physics* 102: 123106.
[86] Chigrin DN (2009) Spatial distribution of the emission intensity in a photonic crystal: Self-interference of Bloch eigenwaves. *Physical Review A* 79(033829): 1–9.
[87] Busch K, von Freymann G, Linden S, *et al.* (2007) Periodic nanostructures for photonics. *Physics Reports* 444(3–6): 101–202.
[88] Goldschmidt JC, Peters M, Gutmann J, *et al.* (2010) Increasing fluorescent concentrator light collection efficiency by restricting the angular emission characteristics of the incorporated luminescent material – The 'nano-fluko' concept. In: Wehrspohn RB and Gombert A (eds.) *Conference on Photonics for Solar Energy Systems III*, 77250S. Bellingham, WA: SPIE Press.
[89] Galli M, Gerace D, Politi A, *et al.* (2006) Direct evidence of light confinement and emission enhancement in active silicon-on-insulator slot waveguides. *Applied Physics Letters* 89(241114): 241114/1–3.
[90] Galli M, Politi A, Belotti M, *et al.* (2006) Strong enhancement of Er3+ emission at room temperature in silicon-on-insulator photonic crystal waveguides. *Applied Physics Letters* 88(251114): 251114/1–3.
[91] Verbunt PPC, Kaiser A, Hermans K, *et al.* (2009) Controlling light emission in luminescent solar concentrators through use of dye molecules aligned in a planar manner by liquid crystals. *Advanced Functional Materials* 19(17): 2714–2719.
[92] MacQueen RW, Cheng YY, Clady R, and Schmidt TW (2010) Towards an aligned luminophore solar concentrator. *Optics Express* 18(13): A161–A166.
[93] Mulder CL, Reusswig PD, Beyler AP, *et al.* (2010) Dye alignment in luminescent solar concentrators: II. Horizontal alignment for energy harvesting in linear polarizers. *Optics Express* 18(9): A91–A99.

1.28 Thermophotovoltaics

J van der Heide, imec vzw, Leuven, Belgium

© 2012 Elsevier Ltd. All rights reserved.

1.28.1	Introduction	603
1.28.2	Thermophotovoltaic System	604
1.28.2.1	Heat Source	605
1.28.2.2	Selective Emitter	605
1.28.2.3	Filter	607
1.28.2.4	Thermophotovoltaic Cells	608
1.28.3	TPV Cells	608
1.28.3.1	Introduction	608
1.28.3.2	Possible Materials	608
1.28.3.3	TPV Cells Based on GaSb	608
1.28.3.4	TPV Cells Based on InGaAs/InP	610
1.28.3.5	TPV Cells on InGaSb Substrates	610
1.28.3.6	Low-Band Gap TPV Cells Based on InAsSbP	611
1.28.3.7	Germanium-Based Cells	611
1.28.4	TPV Concepts	612
1.28.4.1	Solar Thermophotovoltaic	612
1.28.4.2	Micron-Gap ThermoPhotoVoltaics	613
1.28.4.3	Radioisotope Thermophotovoltaics	613
1.28.5	TPV Systems	614
1.28.5.1	Introduction	614
1.28.5.2	Midnight Sun	614
1.28.5.3	TPV Prototype System Built by PSI	615
1.28.6	TPV Market Potential	616
1.28.7	Summary and Outlook	616
References		617

Glossary

Combined heat and power (CHP) Systems where power is generated together with heat. Examples are the generation of electricity by means of TPV or Stirling engines in a residential heating system.

Photon In physics, a photon is considered as the basic unit of light and all other forms of electromagnetic radiation and is in photovoltaic systems absorbed by the semiconductor and converted into electricity.

Photovoltaics Technology with which electric power is generated by the conversion of solar radiation into electricity by using semiconductors that exhibit the photovoltaic effect.

Selective emitter Material which has a specific emission spectrum when heated up. The emission spectrum depends on the material itself or on its structure.

Thermophotovoltaics Technology which directly transfers heat radiation into electricity with the use of photovoltaic receiver cells.

1.28.1 Introduction

In photovoltaic systems, electricity is generated from photons that are incident on the surface of the photovoltaic receiver cell. For photovoltaic systems, these photons are emitted by the sun, which can be considered as a heat source at a very large distance with a surface temperature of about 6000K. Analogous to this process, it is also possible to convert the light emitted by another heat source. Because the heat source is the basic source of energy for this kind of photovoltaic technology, the system is typically called 'thermophotovoltaic' where 'thermo' refers to the heat source. The photovoltaics part refers then to the principle that the heat source also emits 'photons' from which electricity, or alternatively 'voltaics', is generated by the receiver cells. Thermophotovoltaics is often abbreviated as TPV, which will also be used in this chapter.

TPV energy conversion has a number of attractive features, including fuel versatility (nuclear, fossil, biomass, etc.), noiseless, low maintenance since no moving parts are used, light weight, high power density, and cogeneration of heat and power. TPV could potentially be used for distributed power, combined heat and power (CHP), or for the generation of electricity out of waste heat in glass [1] or other high-temperature industries.

Next to the heat source and the receiver cells also extra elements to increase the overall energy conversion efficiency are used in typical TPV systems. Instead of direct illumination of the TPV cell by the heat source, which would lead to an unwanted heating up of the cell because of large amount of sub-band gap photons, a selective emitter is used to transform the near blackbody irradiation to a spectrum which is more suited to the receiver cell. In Section 1.28.2.2, an overview of different types of selective emitters is given.

Where a selective emitter already converts the incoming energy to a spectrum which better matches the absorbance of the receiver cells, still many sub-band gap photons will reach the cell surface. By using a selective filter or a back-surface mirror, or a combination, these sub-band gap photons can be reflected back to the heat source. An overview of different filter technologies is given in Section 1.28.2.3.

Because of the heat source being different from the sun, a different spectrum is incident on the cell surface than in the case of solar photovoltaics. The lower temperature of the heat source (typically about 1200 °C), compared to the temperature of the sun's surface, will cause a shift in the emission spectrum toward longer wavelengths as a consequence of Wien's displacement law. This shift requires the use of a low-band gap semiconductor as receiver cell in order to absorb the low-energetic photons. Typical semiconductors used as absorber in TPV systems are germanium or semiconductors based on III–V compounds containing gallium (Ga) and antimonide (Sb). In Section 1.28.3, an overview of the different receiver cell materials is given.

Next to the shift toward longer wavelengths, the relatively small distance between the heat source and receiver cell will result in a much higher incident spectral density and thus generated current compared to classical photovoltaic systems. Where, on the one hand, this requires optimized front- and rear-contact structures, this also leads to a potentially very high output power per unit area.

Comparing TPV to PV, in which an incident energy density of $0.1\,\text{W}\,\text{cm}^{-2}$ (AM1.5G) is standard, in TPV energy densities in the range of 5–$30\,\text{W}\,\text{cm}^{-2}$ are received by a traditional TPV system. This means that for a given electrical output power, a much smaller TPV system is required which also makes the technology more practical and usable for mobile devices. Because sunlight is not used in TPV systems, this technology is not limited to availability of sunlight and electricity can be generated on the user's demand.

Besides TPV systems based on a combustion heat source, also alternative heat sources are possible. An example is a TPV system where electricity is generated from heat emitted by an isotope. This technology is called 'radioisotope thermophotovoltaics' (RTPVs) and can be used for energy supply in deep space missions. For near-sun space missions, it is also possible to use the high intensity, concentrated, sunlight to heat up a selective emitter around which TPV cells have been placed [2]. This system is called solar thermophotovoltaic (STPV) and can also be applied on earth as an alternative to terrestrial concentrated photovoltaic systems. An overview of different technologies based on TPV is given in Section 1.28.4.

In Section 1.28.5, two different TPV systems are described in more detail followed by an overview of the potential market in Section 1.28.6. This chapter is finalized by a short summary and some conclusions.

1.28.2 Thermophotovoltaic System

A standard TPV system consists of four different parts. In **Figure 1**, a schematic overview of a typical TPV system is shown. The source of the system is the heat source, which can be a hot surface (metal plate or melt), an industrial system for glass or steel fabrication or a burner in a residential heating system. In order to optimize the emitted spectrum of the burner for the used TPV cell, a selective emitter is used which is heated by the burner and has a typical emission spectrum. Examples of well-known selective emitters are, for example, Er_2O_3, Yb_2O_3 or photonic crystals based on tungsten.

To further increase the system efficiency, it is possible to filter and reflect the sub-band gap photons back to the emitter using a filter (not shown in **Figure 1**). The TPV system is completed with the TPV cell, which is a photovoltaic cell which absorbs the incoming photons and out of which electricity can be extracted. In this section, each of the different elements in a TPV system is explained in more detail.

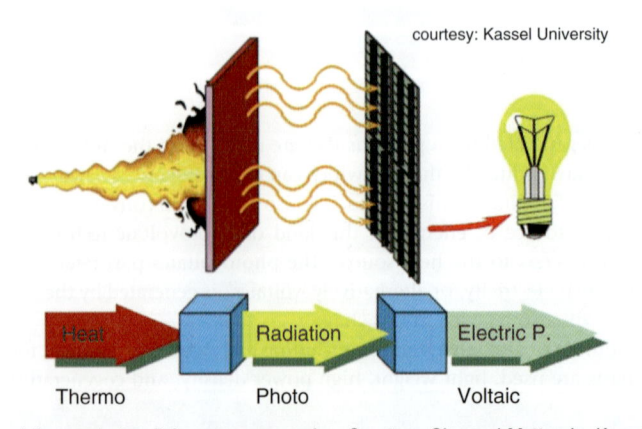

Figure 1 Schematic representation of thermophotovoltaic energy conversion. Courtesy: Giovanni Mattarolo, Kassel University.

1.28.2.1 Heat Source

In principle, every heat source having an operational temperature above 1000 °C can be used in TPV systems. Because of this, a lot of different types of heat sources can be used in TPV systems varying from combustion flames, radiative isotopes (RTPV), and concentrated sunlight (STPV). Most heat sources used in TPV systems are based on combustion systems to reach a sufficiently high temperature. This is very important since, according to Stefan–Boltzmann law, emitted power scales with temperature to the fourth power as can be seen in eqn [1].

$$P = A\varepsilon\sigma T^4 \quad [1]$$

Here P is the total emitter power (W), A is the surface area (m^2), ε the emissivity, σ is Stefan–Boltzmann constant ($5.670\,400 \times 10^{-8}$ Js^{-1}m^{-2}K^{-4}), and T is the temperature (K). In **Figure 2**, the relationship between the blackbody temperature and spectral energy density is shown, according to Planck's law. Here the strong relationship of the emitted power and temperature is clearly visible as the peak height reduces with decreasing temperature.

The temperature of the heat source also causes a shift in the spectrum toward longer wavelengths, which can also be seen in **Figure 2**. This effect is described by the Wien displacement law which is given by

$$\lambda_{\max} = \frac{b}{T} \quad [2]$$

Where $\lambda_{\max}$ is the peak wavelength in meter, T the temperature of the blackbody (K), and b is the constant of proportionality, called Wien's displacement constant, and is equal to 2.898×10^{-3} mK. As a consequence, a blackbody temperature of 1811K should be reached to have a peak in the emitted spectrum at 1600 nm which is needed for most types of TPV receivers. Since in most applications this is a too high temperature, the use of a selective emitter is necessary to reach high conversion efficiencies.

At the Institut für Solare Energieversorgungstechnik (ISET, Kassel, Germany) [3], research has been done on the development of a high-temperature recuperative burner. Two concepts have been developed; a premixed combustion where air and fuel are mixed first and burned later and a not premixed combustion where air and fuel are burned simultaneously. Where a premixed combustion gives a better combustion control, it has a higher risk because of the presence of the already premixed solution together with the risk of backfire and an explosion when too large quantities of the premixed reactants are available. The not premixed solution does not have these risks but will have high temperature peaks.

A very important factor in optimizing the burners is however the reduction of NO$_x$ emission. Where a high temperature leads to a more efficient burner, it also creates problems in NO$_x$ emission. These problems can be solved by limiting the temperature to 1300 °C which can be realized easier with the premixed combustion because of the better temperature control.

1.28.2.2 Selective Emitter

As described in the previous section, the emission spectrum of a heat source is strongly dependent on the temperature. Since typical heat sources have a temperature in the range of 1000 °C and 1500 °C and because the receiver cells will only absorb photons which have energy above the band gap, only a small part of the emitted radiation can be converted into electricity. In order to enhance the system efficiency, the use of a selective emitter is very important. The role of this selective emitter is to absorb the incoming heat and

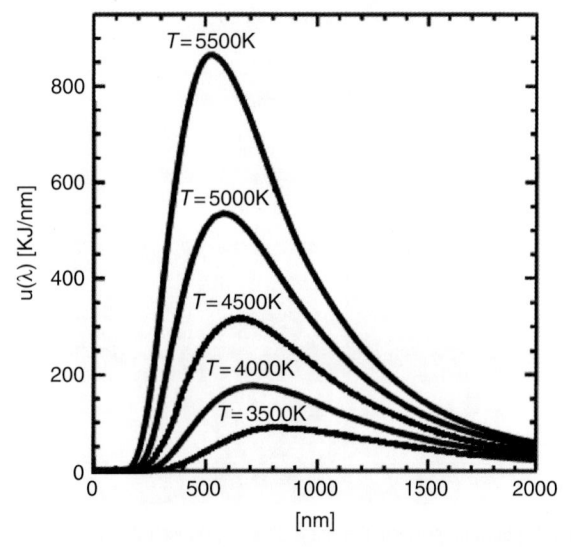

Figure 2 Graph showing Wien's law of radiation. Source: http://en.wikipedia.org/wiki/Wien%27s_displacement_law.

emit an emission spectrum adapted to the receiver sensitivity. This means that selective emission is needed with the photon energy in a narrow band just above the band gap of the photocell's material.

A method to obtain selective emission is the use of photonic crystals which are structured materials where the refractive index is modulated in one, two, or three dimensions. Tungsten (W) can be chosen [4] as substrate because of its high melting temperature and its optical and structural properties. Selective emitters based on tungsten always require an oxide-free environment to prevent oxidation during heating up of the emitter. A method to solve this issue is the integration of the tungsten emitter in a closed chamber filled with Argon. The emittance of a single crystal can be modified by applying a periodic pattern of cavities in the substrate. These cavities can be thought of as a cylindrical metallic waveguide, characterized by a unique dispersion relationship resulting in an increase of the emittance at certain wavelengths.

Another way is the use of emitters made from rare earth oxides like Yb_2O_3 and Er_2O_3. The rare earth material exists as single- and double-charged ions when combined with other atoms (like oxygen) at solid-state densities. The 4f valence electrons of these ions, which account for absorption and emission of radiation, lie in orbits inside the outer 5s and 5p electron shells. As a result, the 5s and 5p electrons shield the 4f electrons from neighboring ions. Thus, the rare earth ions at solid-state densities behave nearly like isolated atoms and emit radiation in narrow bands, rather than in a continuous gray body fashion. This phenomenon goes together with nonradiative processes for the 4f levels, such as collisions with the host atoms, which compete with the radiative de-excitations. However, due to the symmetry of the host crystal, this nonradiative process is reduced. It is known from the literature [5] that the emissivity of a selective emitter is independent from the temperature in case there is no temperature gradient across the sample.

The emission band of Yb_2O_3 has a peak at 1.1 eV ($\lambda \approx 1000$ nm), which corresponds to the band gap of silicon, Er_2O_3 has a peak at ≈ 0.8 eV ($\lambda \approx 1500$ nm), which makes it most suited to be used together with a Ge or GaSb receiver cell. The first practical selective emitter was developed by Nelson et al. [6] consisting out of a 'rug' of fibers of Yb_2O_3 fixed in a ceramic substrate above which the fuel was burned such that the Yb_2O_3 fibers were heated and start to emit its selective spectrum.

A second approach was developed by Holmquist [7], which was a selective emitter also based on Yb_2O_3 using a replication process. A rayon felt mat of fibers was first coated with ytterbium nitrate, followed by a reaction with ammonia to form the hydroxide, which coated the rayon fibers. Finally, the mat was heated in oxygen to create the oxide. As a consequence of the substantial shrinkage, the heating schedule was crucial to avoid cracking.

Bitnar et al. [8] reported in 2002 on the production of incandescent mantle emitters made from Yb_2O_3 and Er_2O_3, which were fabricated using the method of Auer [9] where an Y_2O_3 mantle was chemically coated with Yb_2O_3 and Er_2O_3 layers. Therefore, the mantle was immersed into an Er_2O_3/alcohol and afterwards an Yb_2O_3/alcohol solution and the alcohol was burned by enkindling the mantle after every dip. An Er_2O_3 emitter of approximately 50 cm^2 is shown in **Figure 3**.

Unfortunately, the mantle structure suffered from a high mechanical fragility, which can be solved by using a novel Yb_2O_3 foam ceramic emitter which is mechanically more stable. Its thermal stability was tested at a maximum operation temperature in a gas burner of 1500 °C. The structure is porous for the flame gas. The selectivity of the foam ceramic emitter is 10%, which is about a factor of 2 lower than the selectivity of the mantle. In addition, the novel foam ceramic structure has the advantage that similar porous ceramics are already industrially used as filters for metal production, such that these emitters can be manufactured

Figure 3 The Er_2O_3 emitter shines during the burnout process. Courtesy: Bitnar B, Durisch W, Mayor J-C, et al. (2002) Characterisation of rare earth selective emitters for thermophotovoltaic applications. *Solar Energy Materials and Solar Cells* 73: 221–234 [8].

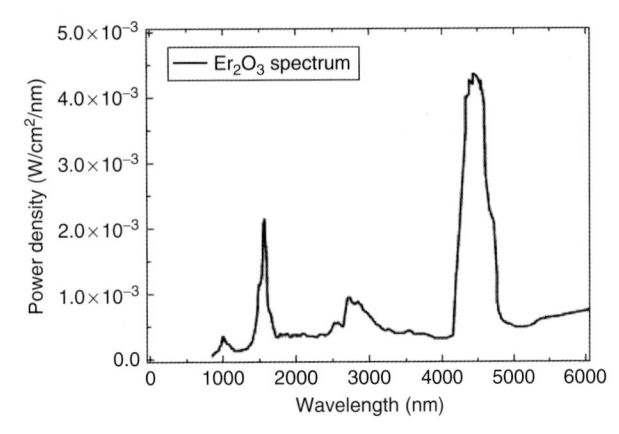

Figure 4 Spectrum of an Er$_2$O$_3$-selective emitter heated by a butane burner at 1407 °C. Courtesy: Holmquist GA (1995) TPV power source development for an unmanned undersea vehicle. *Proceedings of the First NREL/TPV Conference.* pp. 308–314 [7].

cost-effectively. Furthermore, the emitter structure is compatible to the porous burner technology, which is currently under development for use in future heating systems. This may make the application of TPV systems with this technology even more attractive.

Although the approach presented by Bitnar looks promising, in 2005 Tobler *et al.* [10] showed that the approach presented by Bitnar suffered from a low thermal shock resistance of pure oxides. They therefore suggest the use of a thermal shock-resistant body and applying a coating of rare earth oxides. Materials like graphite or SiC are often commonly used for high-temperature applications where extreme thermal shock resistance is required. However, the very high emission of the substrate itself counteracts the selective emission of the rare earth coatings since these are mainly transparent for the substrate's radiation. One of the main issues is the effective shielding of this substrate's high emission and, in return, the desired selective emission of the coatings, combined with a good long-term stability. Tobler *et al.* also suggest the use of slurry and plasma spray-coated selective Er$_2$O$_3$ emitters on MoSi$_2$ substrates, which allows the usage of these emitters in an oxidizing atmosphere at < 1900 °C and eliminates the thermal shock failure of the substrate as well as of the coating. A thin Pt intermediate layer, being able to shield the strong substrate radiation and promoting the selective emission of the rare earth oxide coating, has been reported auspicious for further tests by Tobler *et al.* as conclusion.

The spectrum emitted by an Er$_2$O$_3$-selective emitter is given in **Figure** 4. The emitter was mounted on a tubeless butane burner with a nominal thermal input power P_{in} of 1.35 kW. The emitter had a cylindrical shape and was fixed with ceramic rings to a metal rod above the burner. The burner was mounted onto a conventional transportable liquid butane cylinder.

A selective emission band with a maximum radiation power of 2.1 W cm^{-2} nm^{-1} at 1500 nm dominates the emission spectrum. The peaks in emission at 2800 and 4500 nm correspond to emission lines of the butane flame, where the first most likely corresponds to the O–H bonds of water and the second to CO$_2$.

Selective emitters fabricated by coating the emitting material on a nonporous and nontransparent substrate do not show these emission lines. Since only photons with energy above the band gap of the semiconductor will be absorbed, the photons in the large peak will not be absorbed by the TPV cell and will only heat the cell itself. Therefore, it is important to place a filter between the selective emitter and the receiver cells. In the subsequent section, some examples of these filters will be given.

1.28.2.3 Filter

Particularly for a broad-band radiation, many of the emitted photons have energies that are lower than the band gap of the converter and are as such unusable by the converter. To ensure high system efficiency, it is important to send these photons back to the radiator, thereby conserving heat and permitting less fuel to be used to achieve the required radiator temperature. This can be achieved in a variety of ways including plasma filters, dielectric stacks, back-surface reflectors, and resonant antennae arrays. Each of these solutions has strengths and weaknesses and the best performance may be achieved by a combination of a back-surface reflector with an antireflective coating and a filter. An ideal filter makes a large difference to the system efficiency but does not affect the power density, which is only influenced by the usage of above band gap photons.

In the literature, several types of filters are presented. Rahmlow *et al.* [11] present results on Sb$_2$Se$_3$/YF$_3$ front-surface tandem filters, which are glued to the cell to give good optical properties. Although these filters give a good spectral control, resulting in conversion efficiency for single-module TPV cells which exceed 20%, the authors mention that the used Sb$_2$Se$_3$ undergoes a phase transition at 90 °C which results in high near infrared (NIR) absorption. They suggest the use of two alternative high-index materials which offer higher thermal stability. These materials are Sb$_2$S$_3$ and GaTe where the latter has proven to be the most promising material with which they have realized a filter together with YF$_3$. Other examples of filters are the use of a dual-layer SiO$_2$/SiN$_x$ layer, which acts as surface passivation and antireflective coating together. Quartz glass can also be used as a simple selective filter since it blocks photons with a wavelength longer than 4 μm.

1.28.2.4 Thermophotovoltaic Cells

The TPV cell is the device in the system which will directly transfer the incoming photons into electricity using photovoltaic energy conversion. The different types of photon source require modifications on the used semiconductor and the cell design, compared to the traditional solar PV cell. The requirement to absorb as many photons as possible necessitates the use of a semiconductor having a low band gap. In the literature [12], TPV cells that are based on Ge, Si, GaInSb, InGaAs/InP, GaSb and InGaAsSb/GaSb, and InAsSbP/InAs fabricated by liquid phase epitaxy (LPE), metal organic chemical vapor deposition (MOCVD), molecular beam epitaxy (MBE), and diffusion methods can be found. In Section 1.28.3, an overview of the different cell structures on each of the substrate materials is given.

The majority of the cells presented in the literature use GaSb, InGaAs, or other low-band gap III–V-type semiconductors. Where, on the one hand, these III–V cells will initially deliver cells with high energy conversion efficiency, on the other hand, these cells will be expensive, due to the high substrate price.

Alternatives are the use of cheaper type IV semiconductors like silicon or germanium having a band gap of 1.1 and 0.66 eV, respectively. The high band gap of silicon leads to the fact that not many photons will be absorbed but the very low price of the silicon cell reduces the cost advantage when only small powers need to be generated by the cells. Germanium is well suited to be used as substrate for TPV cells since it has a low band gap and it is also a relatively low-cost material compared to the other low-band gap semiconductors.

1.28.3 TPV Cells

1.28.3.1 Introduction

In the literature, no clear experiment can be found that can be denoted as the first TPV concept; however, the invention of Dr. Henry H. Kolm at MIT's Lincoln Laboratory (Lexington, MA) in 1960 can be considered as the first elementary TPV system [13]. The system consisted of a Coleman camping lantern using an incandescent gas mantle as emitter. A silicon solar cell was used as receiver. The system had a potential efficiency of 5–10%, and the prototype showed a potential output power of 1 W.

Also other results on TPV research were presented using receiver cells that were based on group IV semiconductors like silicon and germanium [14]. Later, Fraas [15] and co-workers introduced GaAs/GaSb tandem solar cells exhibiting a record 35% concentrated solar conversion efficiency [16]. The introduction of photovoltaic devices based on GaSb also influenced the TPV development in later years. In the 1980s in the United States, TPV research introduced TPV cells based on low-band gap III–V materials like InGaAs.

The progress on III–V cell development renewed the interest in TPV, where most research concerned the semiconductors InGaAs and InGaAsSb grown by MOCVD or MBE. The research was directed on the realization of an InP substrate grown on InGaAs TPV cell where the focus was on the reduction of the band gap from 0.73 to 0.5 eV [17, 18], which was the optimal value for their application. The reduction of the band gap, however, leads to a lattice mismatch between the active layer and the InP substrate. In addition, considerable effort has been devoted to the characterization of the alloys, the development of reduced band gap devices, and to novel concepts like the tunnel junction scheme used by Wilt *et al.* in their mini-modules [2].

Despite the progress obtained in these multicomponent alloys, the only commercially manufactured TPV system is the Midnight Sun®, manufactured by JX Crystals Inc. This system employs the binary semiconductor GaSb, which has a band gap of 0.7 eV. The Midnight Sun® will be explained in more detail in Section 1.28.5.2.

Further research focuses on the reduction of the cell cost by using low-cost, low-band gap semiconductors like silicon and germanium [19], which became possible due to the improved substrate quality. In Section 1.28.3.7 more details will be given on the development of TPV cells on germanium substrates.

In this section, an overview of TPV cells based on different types of semiconductors will be given. First, an overview of different types of suited materials will be given followed by a more detailed overview of cell concepts and technologies grouped per semiconductor.

1.28.3.2 Possible Materials

In **Figure 5** the relationship between band gaps and lattice constants is given for semiconductors that are typically used in (thermo) photovoltaic systems. Semiconductors within the band gap range of $E_g = 0.5$–0.75 eV, which corresponds to Ge (0.66 eV), GaSb (0.73 eV)/InGaAsSb/GaSb (0.5–0.6 eV), and $In_{0.53}Ga_{0.47}As$ (0.74 eV), are the most suitable for TPV receiver application. It is also possible to create TPV cells based on polycrystalline InGaSb (0.5–0.6 eV) which can be considered as low-cost III–V alternative and single-crystal InAsSbP (0.39 eV) which is a substrate material with a low band gap.

1.28.3.3 TPV Cells Based on GaSb

The introduction of GaSb photovoltaic cells started with their use as high efficiency bottom cell for mechanically stacked concentrator GaAs/GaSb tandems and was published by Fraas *et al.* in 1990 [15]. Efficiencies above 30% were reported for this stack and it was shown that the GaSb PV cell was well suited for this application. These GaSb cells were made using simple zinc diffusion into tellurium-doped single-crystal GaSb wafers, so no expensive epitaxial growth of semiconductor layers was needed. GaSb has a band gap of 0.72 eV, which makes it a semiconductor that can also act as receiver cell in TPV systems because of the

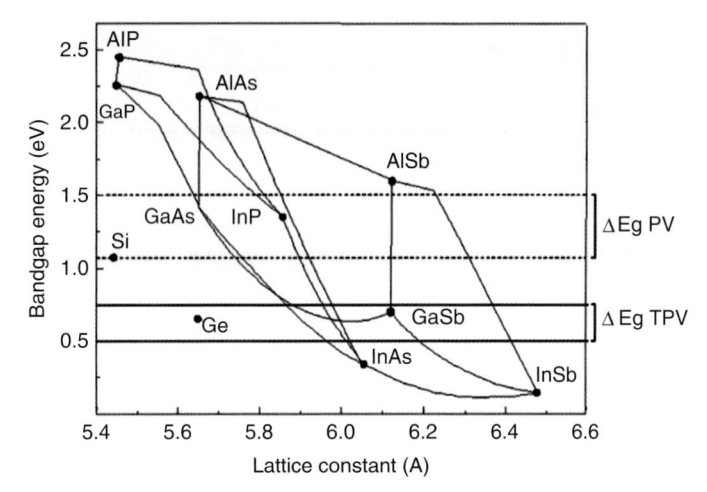

Figure 5 Relationship between the band gap of Ge, Si, and III–V compounds and their solid solutions and the lattice constant of these materials. ΔE_g PV and ΔE_g TPV – ranges of the single-junction cell band gaps optimal for solar PV and TPV applications, correspondingly [20].

similarity with concentrator PV. TPV is working with a high power density output of more than 50 W cm^{-2}, which corresponds to a concentration of about 500 suns, comparable to standard values of concentration in typical concentrator PV systems.

Later, more results based on GaSb were presented by several groups, like the Ioffe Institute in St. Petersburg, Russia [21], Fraunhofer ISE [22], and JX Crystals [23]. Because of the low-surface recombination rate of p-type GaSb high-quality TPV cells can easily be fabricated by a simple Zn diffusion technique without a lattice-matched AlGaAsSb window layer, using the pseudo-closed-box diffusion technique. With this technique, Zn is diffused from a Zn vapor in a graphite box closed tightly by screws. Mixtures of zinc and antimony, zinc and gallium, or zinc–gallium–antimony can be used as diffusion sources. The resulting diffusion process and diffusion profile strongly depends on the diffusion temperature and time, so by optimizing these parameters, the optimal emitter profile can be obtained.

At Fraunhofer ISE, GaSb has been developed using Zn diffusion and with the use of epitaxial growth. They showed an improvement of the device performance by the use of a strong built-in electrical field (up to 8 kV cm^{-1}) in the p-type emitter due to a specific steep Zn diffusion profile. The large electrical field reduces the impact of surface recombination causing a higher generated current and voltage. GaSb cells with internal quantum efficiency above 90% and a V_{oc} larger than 0.5 V at current densities above 3 A cm^{-2} have been reported [23].

Fraunhofer ISE reported results on epitaxial GaSb TPV cells. Analogous to GaAs cells, where an AlGaAs window layer and back-surface field results in a better cell performance, the same can be done in TPV cells based on GaSb. Such cells consist of MOCVD-grown AlGaAsSb/GaSb heterostructures where AlGaAsSb (0.72–0.9 eV) acts as a window layer. Several epitaxial growth technologies like LPE, MBE, and MOCVD can be used, giving a big variety for cell processing. A TPV cell with a highly doped GaSb layer and a lattice-matched AlGaAsSb used for passivation shows comparable quantum efficiencies as the diffused GaSb cells, but give an extra increase in V_{oc} because of a reduced dark current in the device. The authors conclude that an AlGaAsSb layer indeed improves the surface of GaSb in a similar manner as AlGaAs passivates GaAs [23].

At Ioffe further optimizations were done on a stand-alone GaSb cell, using a two-stage diffusion process on Te-doped GaSb. In the first stage, a shallow p–n junction is formed by exposure to Zn. During the second stage, a deeper emitter is formed by an additional spatially selective diffusion process to reduce the current leakages under the contact grid fingers (see **Figure 6**). The precise thickness of the p-GaSb layer can be fine-tuned by a combination of oxidation and selective etching.

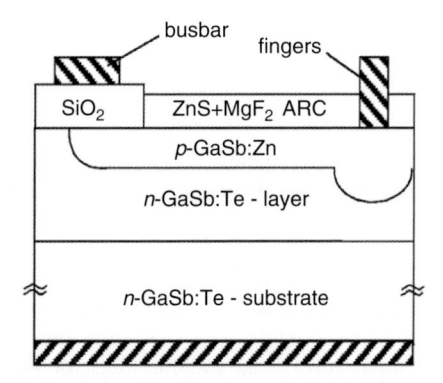

Figure 6 Cross section of epitaxial GaSb cell fabricated by two-stage Zn diffusion method [19].

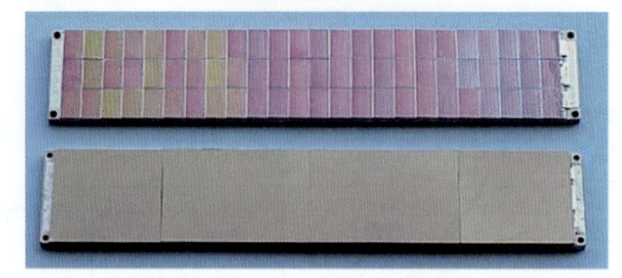

Figure 7 GaSb cells are shingle mounted on a circuit measuring 5 cm by 26 cm. The photos show a shingled circuit and a circuit covered with planar filter covers [23].

The thickness of the emitter limits the maximum obtainable photocurrent in the cell. Because the thickness of the p-region is between 0.15 and 0.3 µm, the need for a second deep selective diffusion step becomes clear. The authors conclude [19], based on more precise investigation of the photocurrent generated by the GaSb cells, that the optimal p–n junction depth of about 0.25 µm ensures an increase in the photocurrent density up to 30 mA cm^{-2} under sunlight with AM0 spectrum cut-off at λ < 900 nm which mimics the shift toward longer wavelengths in the spectrum emitted by a heat source in a typical TPV system.

JX Crystals also produced TPV cells based on GaSb substrates created by a low-cost diffusion process [24]. Also, modules were created consisting of interconnected GaSb cell covered with a planar filter (see **Figure 7**). The modules were used to convert the heat emitted by in-house developed radiant burners for the use as stand-alone TPV systems in remote areas or as heater in the first commercial product based on TPV technology, the Midnight Sun®. In Section 1.28.5.2, more details are given about this application.

1.28.3.4 TPV Cells Based on InGaAs/InP

Lattice-matched In$_{0.53}$Ga$_{0.47}$As grown on InP was developed initially for fabrication of infrared photodetectors. Because of the low band gap, InGaAs can also be used as bottom cell in mechanically stacked solar cells, with GaAs as top cell, or monolithic, having an InP top cell. Also InGaAs can be grown using LPE or MOCVD and excellent results have been presented on cells produced with a simultaneous Zn and p-diffusion onto the LPE-grown InGaAs layer [25].

InGaAs cells are also used to create monolithic interconnected modules (MIMs) for TPV applications. For the fabrication of these modules, InGaAs layers are grown on semi-insulating InP substrates after which the structure is divided into individual subcells which are subsequently interconnected in series. The semi-insulating substrate has two advantages: first of all it provides an electrical isolation for the components cells and also near perfect optical transparency for sub-band gap photons. The fact that InP is insulating and not electrically active, allows a direct bonding of the substrate to a heat sink without concern for electrical isolation. The second advantage is that the series interconnection will also provide a high voltage with a low current which reduces the Joule losses and will thus cause an increase of the power output at high illumination intensities. The last advantage allows the introduction of an infrared mirror deposited on the back contact of the InP substrate to improve the optical confinement in the module.

Optical confinement realized by a highly reflective rear-surface act in two different ways. First of all it reflects the sub-band gap photons back to the emitter to avoid the unwanted heating up of the TPV cell. Besides that it also creates a longer optical path length for the other photons to have a higher probability for absorption by the TPV cell.

By changing the composition of InGaAs, it is possible to change between lattice-matched and lattice-mismatched configurations. It allows also variations in band gap between 0.55 and 0.6 eV, so optimizations as function of the incoming spectrum can be done by changing the InGaAs properties. InGaAs can also be used as center cell in a lattice-matched InAs$_{0.32}$P$_{0.68}$(0.96eV)/In$_{0.68}$Ga$_{0.32}$As (0.6eV)/InAs$_{0.32}$P$_{0.68}$ double heterostructure, grown lattice-mismatched on an InP substrate where the InAsP acts a step-graded buffer [25].

1.28.3.5 TPV Cells on InGaSb Substrates

In the literature, results are reported on the use of polycrystalline GaInSb substrates [26–28] as substrate material for TPV cells. InGaSb has a band gap of 0.5–0.6 eV which makes it of special interest for TPV applications. These cells were introduced as low-cost alternative because only ternary bulk substrates are needed in which an emitter could easily be formed by Zn diffusion, so no expensive epitaxial steps are required.

The formation of the emitter is comparable to that in GaSb, but requires a lower temperature since the presence of InSb strongly enlarges the diffusion depth of Zn in the material. With cells processed on InGaSb, very low V_{oc} values of 0.12 V were obtained, which is caused by leakage at the surface combined with a loss of V_{oc} in the bulk due to the polycrystalline material. Although the proposed cells demonstrate a high photocurrent, the low voltage and thus fill factor need to be improved to act as a competitor for other low-cost TPV substrate materials.

1.28.3.6 Low-Band Gap TPV Cells Based on InAsSbP

InAsSbP can be a useful material as receiver cell in TPV system because of its low band gap of 0.39 eV. TPV cells based on this material were fabricated by Fraunhofer ISE together with the companies AstroPower and Rensselaer Polytechnic Institute (RPI) who grew an epitaxial n-InAsSbP cell on top of an n-InAs single crystal. An emitter (p-type InAsSbP) is formed by diffusion.

The external quantum efficiency (EQE) measurements showed a spectral sensitivity up to 3500 nm, because of the low band gap, which makes the material specially suited for low-temperature TPV applications. The authors [26] conclude that the decrease of the band gap inevitably caused a reduction of the voltage such that a trade-off between the increasing current and falling voltage must be found. The measured V_{oc} of 0.1 V limits the application of these cells in TPV systems. Also for this type of cell, the V_{oc} is limited because of surface leakage, because a V_{oc} of 0.2 V is expected for cells based on a semiconductor with this band gap.

At Ioffe, also a process for the fabrication of InAsSbP is developed [29], but in contrast to the process developed by Fraunhofer, wherein an emitter is realized by Zn diffusion. A patterned SiN_x or SiO_2 dielectric layer on the top surface was used as a diffusion mask, so that the junction was formed only within the designated illumination area, which allows reducing current leakages. The presented spectral response results show a reduction of the photosensitivity in the long wavelength range which is probably explained by not sufficient diffusion length for the photogenerated holes in the epitaxial base layer.

1.28.3.7 Germanium-Based Cells

Germanium has a band gap of 0.66 eV, which is too low to be applied as stand-alone receiver cell for photovoltaic applications. Because of the low band gap, it was one of the first materials proposed as receiver cell in TPV applications in the 1960s. Because of the poor material quality it was not possible to fabricate good performing TPV systems based on germanium. During the last two decades, the renewed interest for germanium as substrate or bottom cell in monolithic or mechanically multijunction solar cells also renewed the interest for germanium as receiver cell in TPV systems. The availability of high-quality germanium substrates with a large substrate size at a relatively low cost compared to other low-band gap semiconductors opens the pathway to low-cost TPV systems.

There are several ways to fabricate a photovoltaic cell based on germanium. First results were reported [30] on (Al)GaAs/Ge tandem cells for the use in solar arrays. In this process, a single-junction cell is created by the epitaxial growth of a p-(Al)GaAs layer on top of an n-type Ge substrate. During the growth, a p–n junction is formed in the germanium due to in-diffusion of Ga and As in the germanium substrate. Later [31], results were presented where oxide layers, grown with an optimized growth process, are used as surface passivation on n^+pp^+Ge (In,As) diffused cells. As an alternative, also a germanium cell can be created by the epitaxial growth of n-type GaInP layers on p-type germanium substrates by MOCVD. Due to in-diffusion, an InGaP/n-Ge/p-Ge is created in which the InGaP acts as a front-surface passivation which results in a higher V_{oc} for these kinds of cells.

At the third world conference on photovoltaics in 2003, two new cell concepts based on germanium substrates without the need of expensive epitaxial growth were proposed. Andreev *et al.* [32] presented results on a germanium TPV cell where the p–n junction was realized by diffusion of Zn from the vapor phase in a pseudo-closed box. The fabricated cells had also an optimized MgF_2/ZnS antireflective coating. Although the fabricated cells showed a high short-circuit current, the obtained V_{oc} was lower than cells made from GaSb, which in part can be explained by the difference in intrinsic carrier concentration (n_i) between the two different types of semiconductors. It must be noted that the V_{oc} is inversely proportional to $\ln(n_i^2)$ and given the fact that $n_i(Ge) = 2.0 \times 10^{13}$ cm^{-3} and $n_i(GaSb) = 1.5 \times 10^{12}$ cm^{-3}, the difference can be explained. Besides the intrinsic difference in V_{oc} caused by the difference in n_i, also a poor passivation of the front-surface results in an extra reduction of the V_{oc}.

To solve this issue, cells were fabricated with a thin (0.1 µm) window layer of GaAs. To avoid the use of expensive epitaxial growth by means of MOCVD, here the more cost-efficient LPE technique was used to grow the GaAs layer combined with an additional Zn diffusion process. The benefit of using the low-temperature LPE process is that the unwanted diffusion of Ga and As in germanium is avoided. Efficiencies of higher than 13% under the cut-off (AM0, $\lambda < 900$ nm) have been achieved in PV cells with the GaAs window layer at photocurrent densities of 3–25 A cm^{-2} which was at that time the highest among those measured in these conditions.

Andreev also presented results on germanium cells passivated with MOCVD-grown and Zn-diffused p-GaAs/p-Ge/n-Ge, where the inevitable process of diffusion of Ga and As during the GaAs growth is used to form the emitter in the n-type germanium substrate. The fabricated cells showed an excellent passivation resulting in the highest reported V_{oc} for a germanium TPV cell of 0.42–0.43 V at 10 A cm^{-2}.

Nagashima *et al.* [33] were the first one to propose a fully rear-contact TPV cell based on germanium. The use of back-contact cells further increases the cell efficiency because of a reduction of resistive and shadowing losses. However, a back-contacted cell requires a high bulk lifetime and low-surface recombination velocities. The authors propose a back-contact cell design based on a p-type germanium substrate with a floating emitter structure for a better front-surface passivation and an SiN_x front- and rear-surface passivation. The interdigitated rear contacts are separately contacted by metal bus bars isolated with a polyimide. Best cell results under AM1.5G light are 6.01% having a V_{oc} of 197 mV and a J_{sc} of 52.8 mA cm^{-2} with a fill factor of 57.8%. No results for a TPV relevant spectrum were presented in the paper.

In 2004, IMEC proposed a low-cost TPV cell based on germanium where the emitter is created by diffusion from a spin-on dopant source [34] and an innovate front-surface passivation process was developed by amorphous silicon deposited by plasma-enhanced chemical vapor deposition (PECVD). Because in the process only Si-like processing steps are used, without any

Figure 8 Photograph of a 4 inch germanium substrate with a specifically engineered front-surface structure.

expensive epitaxial growth, the proposed Ge TPV cells are a cost-efficient alternative to the cells based on III–V materials. Further optimizations on the cell concept at IMEC focused on an improvement of the optical confinement by introducing laser-fired contacts (LFCs) which resulted in an excellent EQE up to 90% at wavelength ranges relevant for TPV [35]. A record Ge PV cell efficiency, measured by Fraunhofer CalLab, was reported of 7.9% with a V_{oc} of 264.1 mV, a J_{sc} of 43.2 mA cm^{-2}, and an FF of 69.4%, for a cell fabricated with an Al back-surface field which shows a poor reflectance in the TPV relevant wavelength range. A large increase of the EQE at long wavelengths can be obtained with the application of a highly reflective rear contact. This improvement shows the potential for these cells in TPV applications.

Currently, research is ongoing to further reduce the cost of germanium TPV cell by fabricating cells on germanium substrates with a specifically engineered surface finish which has a higher roughness compared to the 'epi-ready' substrates used in the previous research. This is possible since no epitaxial growth is needed in the process developed at IMEC. First results even show an increase in EQE at long wavelengths because of a better optical confinement. In **Figure 8** a photograph of a germanium TPV cell with a specifically engineered front-surface structure is shown.

1.28.4 TPV Concepts

1.28.4.1 Solar Thermophotovoltaic

An STPV system is based on a principle of conversion of concentrated solar energy into radiation by heating an intermediate photon emitter with subsequent photovoltaic conversion of this radiation in low-band gap photo-converters. In the STPV system, concentrated solar radiation is thus absorbed and reemitted as a thermal radiation before illumination of the TPV cells. Essential advantage of such a system, compared to conventional ones, is the possibility to choose emitter material with selective emission spectrum and to use sub-band gap photons owing to recycling process. The theoretically [19] estimated values of the STPV efficiency are in a wide interval from 30% to 70%, depending on the approach used. For ideal system elements, maximal theoretical efficiency was found to be about 85% which is identical to the efficiency of an unlimited stack of tandem cells. In practice, the expected efficiency of STPV converters is 30–35%.

A STPV system consists of a sun tracker, concentrator, and an STPV module as shown in **Figure 9**. One of the most important parts of the STPV system is the concentrator itself. Because of the use of a high-temperature emitter, the solar concentration ratio needs to be as high as possible to obtain high emitter temperature values. The maximum achievable concentration ratio on earth can be 46 164 suns, determined by the aperture angle of the sun, this value cannot be reached in STPV systems since expensive optics will be needed. Therefore, cost-effective Fresnel lenses will be used in STPV systems. A Fresnel lens based on two-stage sunlight concentrator system was developed for TPV systems, consisting of a 0.36 m^2 Fresnel lens together with a secondary quartz concave–convex lens which gives a total concentration ratio of 4600 suns.

In STPV systems, the sunlight is concentrated on an emitter, which is made of a refractory metal like tungsten because the emissivity of tungsten matches the used TPV cells. The emitter needs to be protected from oxidation by placing it in a quartz tube, filled with an inert gas. The emitter can be made in a cylindrical shape with a sealed bottom such that the TPV cells can be placed around the emitter.

In the STPV system developed at Ioffe Psysico-Technical Institute [35], TPV cells were fabricated from GaSb cells. The cells are mounted on a BeO ceramic plate which is water-cooled to prevent heating up of the cells because in a TPV generator the cells operate at high current densities and are placed close to the heat source. BeO is well suited for this application since it has an electrical resistivity of more than 1×10^{14} Ω cm with the best thermal conductivity of 250 W (m K)$^{-1}$ and it has thermal expansion coefficient of 6×10^{-6} K^{-1} which matches with the thermal expansion coefficient of GaSb. By means of ray-tracing it is also possible to calculate the optimal cavity structure to reach the highest possible energy conversion efficiency [36].

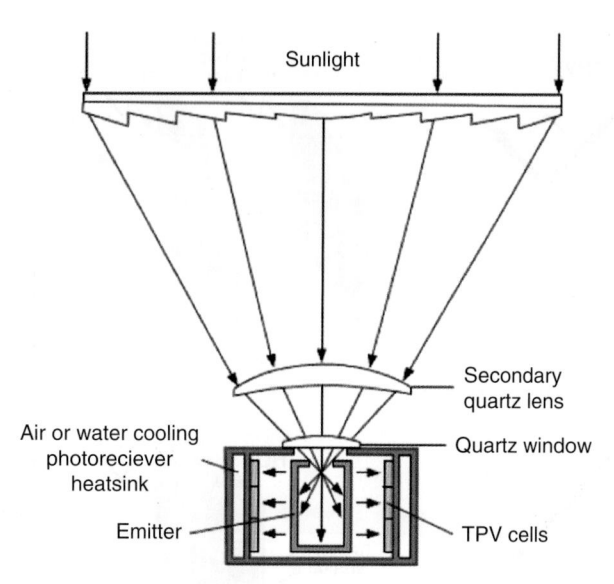

Figure 9 Concept of an STPV system with a Fresnel lens as primary concentrator.

A module of three 1×1 cm^2 GaSb cells has been measured in the STPV setup resulting in a total output power of 0.762 W by a total incident irradiation density of about 770 W cm^{-2}. Higher values can be expected for higher irradiation densities, the use of a larger emitter and the application of optical confinement or the use of tandem TPV cells based on InGaAsSb alloys. The use of a selective emitter, like 2D- or 3D-texturized tungsten may lead to the increase in emissivity in the desired wavelength region. All these approaches should ensure an STPV system efficiency increase of up to 30% and higher.

1.28.4.2 Micron-Gap ThermoPhotoVoltaics

Micron-gap ThermoPhotoVoltaics (MTPVs) was introduced by DiMatteo et al. in 2003 [37] and is based on the concept that in far-field TPV, the radiative heat transfer is limited by the density of states in vacuum to σT^4. A simple solution to increase the heat transfer significantly is to reduce the distance between the emitter and the TPV receiver cell to a submicron range. This allows the energy to 'evanescently couple' or tunnel directly to the TPV receiver cell. The large increase of heat transfer creates a potentially large gain in electrical output power density.

In **Figure 10**, the concept of MTPV is schematically shown. The transfer of heat between two surfaces is analogous to the transfer of light between two prisms with a spacing which is much less than the wavelength of the incident light. The enhancement is limited to n^2 of the lowest index of refraction material and will thus depend on the wavelength-dependent nature of the material.

Because of the very close spacing between the heat source and the cell, the requirements are different compared to far-field TPV. First of all, because of the large energy transfers, large currents will be generated in the cell which requires TPV cells with a high current carrying density. Because of the low spacing, the surface of the TPV cell must be flat, so no extending contacts can be present on the system. The authors present three possible cell designs to solve this issue: a gridless design, a design with recessed front contacts, and an inverted design with interdigitated contacts. There is an increase in photogenerated current visible because of the MTPV effect, but side effects as series and shunt resistance and diode temperature make it impossible to determine the actual enhancement of the photogenerated current.

To ensure a constant spacing between the heater and the cell, tubular spacers are used which are designed to minify the heat transfer along the spacers. Analysis shows that the use of spacers results in a final reduction of the parasitic conductive heat flow to less than 3% of the total heat transferred. The application of a back-surface reflector will also improve the cell results as sub-band gap photons will be reflected back to the emitter.

The technology looks very promising because of the high amount of transferred energy and the potential high energy conversion efficiency, but the more complex cell technology together with the strict requirements for its mechanical stability will be a challenge for this technology.

1.28.4.3 Radioisotope Thermophotovoltaics

RTPVs can be seen as an alternative technology for other energy-generating technologies in deep space missions, like radioisotope thermoelectric generators (RTGs), or Stirling radioisotope generator (SRG), where classical PV technologies cannot be used because of a lack of usable sunlight. Where RTG shows an excellent reliability, the technology is quite heavy and shows a low efficiency which leads to an increased cost. SRG has typically a higher efficiency; however, a redundant system is required because of the lower reliability which results in a low mass-specific power.

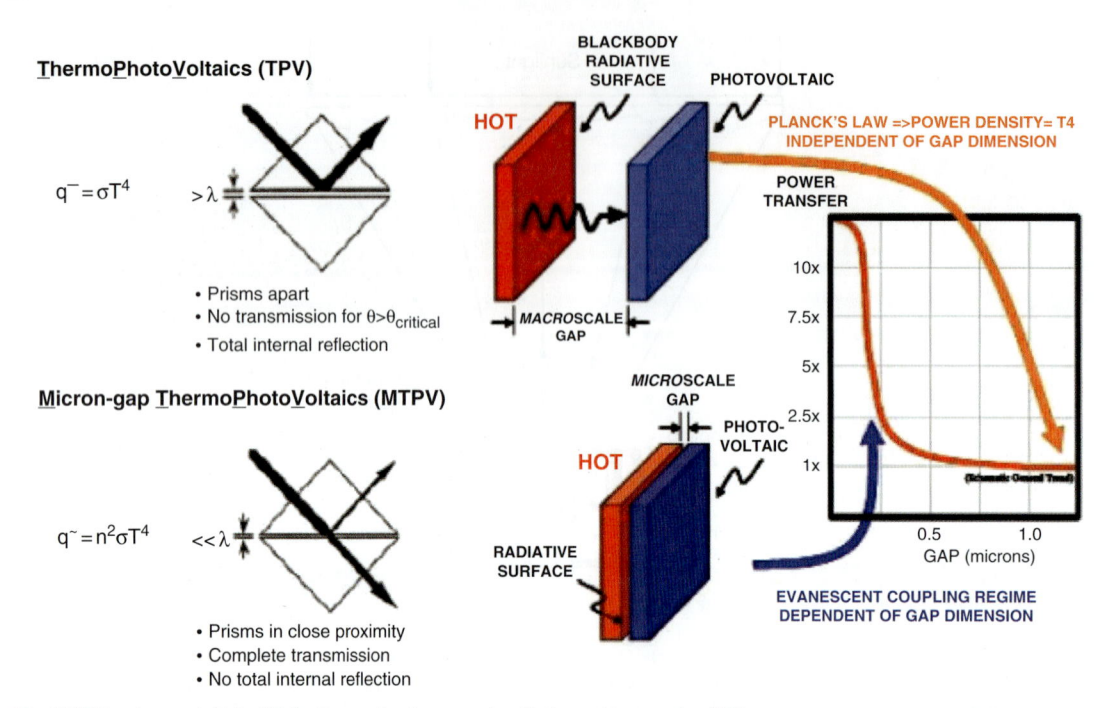

Figure 10 MTPV background. Potential for large gains in power density from close spacing [38].

The use of TPV for energy production in near-deep space missions could be a good alternative because it is a static system, so influence of vibrations is small. The unproven longevity is a serious challenge for RTPV for the use in near-deep space missions. An important concern is the possible contamination of the TPV optical surfaces by material evaporating from the hot surfaces; also the operation at temperatures of more than 50 °C for an expected mission life of 14 years will have an impact on the longevity.

The heat source in RTPV is a so-called general purpose heat source (GPHS) which is a stackable, compact unit designed to deliver over 600 °C. Convertible photons are transmitted through a tandem filter and converted into electricity by low-band gap (0.6 eV) InGaAs MIMs. For this application, only TPV cells based on III–V semiconductors can be used because of the necessity for radiation hardness. Experimental results demonstrated a ~18% convertor efficiency including housing thermal losses. By means of neutron radiation tests, the degradation of the MIM, the filter, and other components have been tested. The results [2] show 20% degradation in the MIM efficiency after a 14-year mission which is comparable to the 14% degradation of an RTG. An improvement of the filters could reduce the degradation in efficiency.

1.28.5 TPV Systems

1.28.5.1 Introduction

In the literature, several prototype TPV systems can be found [39]. Scotto *et al.* [40] developed a prototype of a portable diesel-fuel-fired TPV system for military applications. The system delivered 500 W DC with 8% system efficiency using GaSb cells together with an SiC ceramic emitter. A heat recuperation system was also installed to recover heat from the hot exhaust gasses.

TPV can also be integrated in a hybrid car where a compressed natural gas-fuelled TPV generator is used to recharge the battery pack that feeds the electric motor of the car. This system was introduced by the Western Washington University in 1997 and was called 'Viking 29' [41]. Important features of this system were its low noise, the small size, and low weight compared to standard combustion engines.

In the subsequent sections, two important systems are described in more detail. First the Midnight Sun®, developed by JX Crystals, followed by a TPV system based on Si cells for the integration in residential heating systems introduced by the Paul Scherrer Institute (PSI).

1.28.5.2 Midnight Sun

The Midnight Sun® [42] was the first commercial TPV unit developed by JX Crystals [43] and was introduced in 1999. The Midnight Sun® is a propane-fuelled TPV indoor stove using GaSb TPV cells. A photo and schematic design of the stove is shown in **Figure 11**.

The system has a total electrical and thermal output power of 100 W and 7.3 kW, respectively, giving a system efficiency of 2%. The unit uses a flow through an SiC screen emitter which is heated up to 1200 °C together with a dielectric filter and uses air to cool

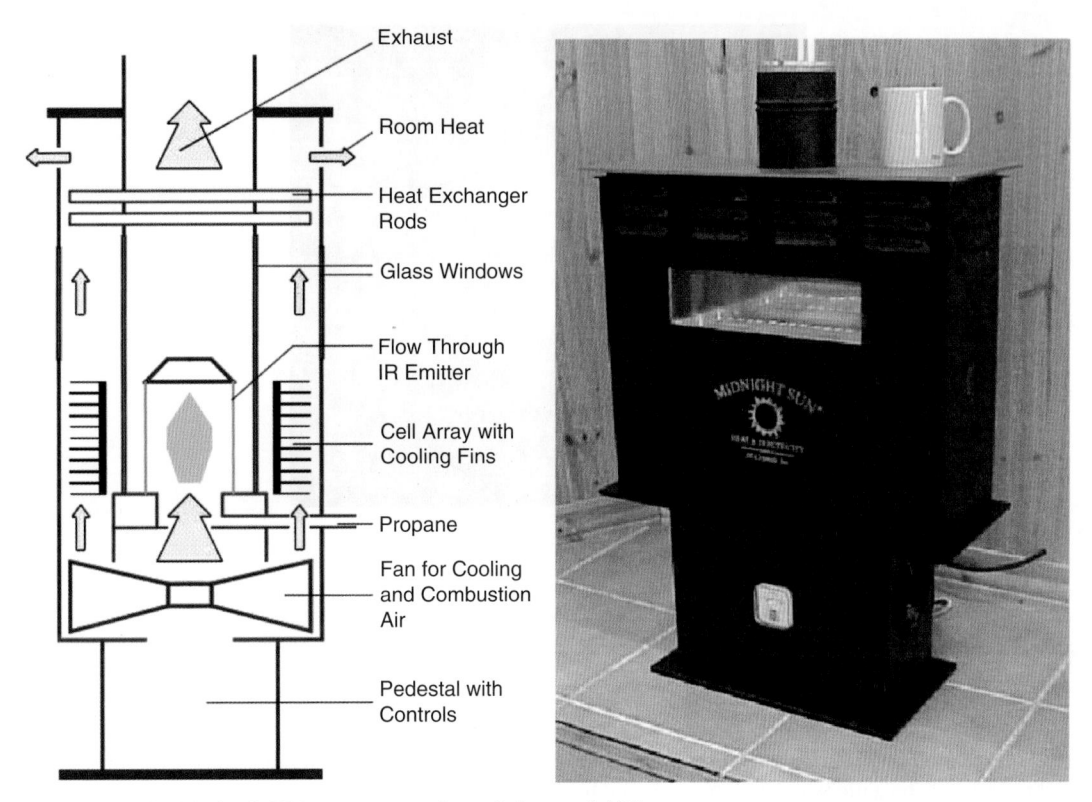

Figure 11 JX Crystals' Midnight Sun® TPV stove cross section and photograph [42].

the system. The system is self-powered and takes 20 W from its electrical output power for the air circulation fans, combustion blower, and thermostat control system.

The benefit of the system is the fact that no grid connection is needed and that there is no additional electricity cost for operation. That allows that the system can work independent in remote buildings, caravans, and mobile homes. The Midnight Sun® is the first commercial available system on the market. It was designed to be cost-efficient, so therefore the total electrical efficiency is quite low due to the lack of a recuperator and a poor view factor.

JX Crystals also developed new prototypes based on the Midnight Sun® which did have recuperation and a better design giving efficiencies of 10%; however, only demonstrators were built.

1.28.5.3 TPV Prototype System Built by PSI

At the PSI, a prototype TPV system has been developed for the use in residential heating systems [44–46]. Including TPV cells in these systems makes it possible to have the system run independently from the grid. Typically, an electrical power of about 150 W is necessary to supply sufficient electricity to run a 20 kW$_{th}$ gas heating system. PSI used commercially available components to keep the system cost low. Commercial silicon solar cells were provided by the University of New South Wales (UNSW) and were used together with an Yb$_2$O$_3$-selective emitter. This Yb$_2$O$_3$-based emitter is well suited for the use together with TPV cells based on silicon since it has an emission band which is matched very well to the band gap of silicon.

A 1.2–2.0 kW butane burner was used which heated up a selective Yb$_2$O$_3$ mantle emitter. In **Figure 12**, a photographic image of the system is shown. To protect the silicon photocells from hot exhaust gasses, a surrounding quartz tube was placed around the burner. The cells were mounted on a water-cooled metal block to avoid any unwanted heating of the cells. The best obtained result with this prototype was a total electrical output power of 47.8 W with a thermal input power of 1.98 kW which results in a gas-to-electricity power efficiency of 2.4%. A total short-circuit current of 7.8 A together with an open circuit voltage of 8.1 V with a fill factor of 75% was measured.

The importance of this prototype is that it aims for a low-cost system to be integrated in a domestic application, with a large potential market (see Section 1.28.6). To reach the first goal, TPV cells based on silicon were used. Although this has an impact on the system efficiency because of the poor absorbance of low-energetic photons by silicon because of its band gap of 1.1 eV, it also has a very low cost. To enter the residential burner market, the cost per watt is of utmost importance. When the goal is to make the system self-supporting, about 100 W is needed to be generated by the TPV cell array. Given the total input power of 2 kW, a total gas-to-electricity efficiency of 5% is required. This might be a challenge when only using Si PV cells, but using low-cost, low-band gap TPV cells, this goal can definitely be reached.

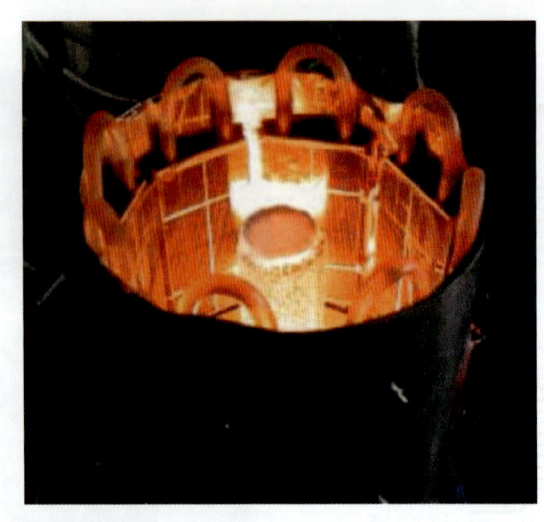

Figure 12 Image of the TPV prototype system built at PSI. The Yb_2O_3 mantle emitter [50].

1.28.6 TPV Market Potential

Because TPV is a technology which only requires a heat source with a sufficiently high temperature, it can be applied in many different technologies. A straightforward application would be the waste heat recovery in high-temperature industries like the glass or steel industry, but also integration in domestic heating systems would be a potential application.

A group at Canmet in Ottawa, Canada, proposed [47] a prototype where GaSb cells are integrated in a residential heating system for stand-alone operation. TPV is well suited for this application since it contains no moving parts and is thus noiseless and robust. When TPV cells are integrated in the burner chamber, part of the heat produced by the burner is directly converted into electricity which can be used by the burner system for operation of pumps and electronics. Because only heat is required by the TPV cell, also no restrictions need to be taken into account regarding the fuel.

An important challenge will be to produce enough power with the cells to have the heating system self-supporting. To make this system commercially attractive, it is also important to limit the extra cost of the integration of the cells in the boiler. The application of low-cost TPV technology is required to fulfill this requirement. There is however a huge market potential, given the total amount of installed residential heating systems in the world. The United Kingdom is market leader for domestic boiler systems with a total volume of 1.7 million units in 2007 [48], worldwide over 10 million units were sold in 2007.

Looking to the recovery of waste heat in industry, mainly high-temperature industries are of interest. Examples of high-temperature industries are the glass and steel industries. Taking the market in the United Kingdom in 1990 [49], a total amount of about 50 PJ yr^{-1} is lost as waste heat. Taking the Japanese waste heat market in 2007, yearly about 24 PJ is lost as waste heat from a solid substance of more than 1000 °C. The biggest contribution in this number is the steel and iron industry where yearly about 20 PJ is lost as waste heat, but also in the petroleum and transportation high-temperature waste heat is available.

An example for waste heat recovery in industry with TPV cell is during continuous casting of steel plates. These plates have an initial temperature of 1500 °C and are cooled down to a temperature for cutting of 1000 °C. When TPV cells are placed above the metal plates during the cooling process, electricity can be generated from the heat emitted by the plate. A first-order calculation shows a potential power output of 440 kW for a 50 m^2 slab.

These two examples already show the enormous market potential for TPV. It will however be very important to develop a low-cost and robust solution which is easy to integrate to enter the consumer market. To implement TPV in the industry for waste heat recovery, a low-cost per watt needs to be realized without a too large impact on the industrial systems.

1.28.7 Summary and Outlook

TPV is an elegant technology in which electricity is generated from radiation from a heat source. The working principle is comparable to classical photovoltaic systems, but the short distance between heat source and the receiver cell compared to the distance to the sun and the relative low temperature create special requirements for the TPV receiver cell. Where the former results in a high current density which will be generated in the cell, the latter requires a receiver cell with a low band gap. Given a typical burner temperature of about 1000 °C, the optimal band gap range is between 0.5 and 0.7 eV. The lower the band gap, the more photons will be absorbed, but the inevitable reduction of the V_{oc} and thus cell performance requires a balance between these two parameters.

A TPV system does not only contain a heat source and receiver cell, although only these two elements are required. To improve the efficiency, a selective emitter is placed between the heat source and the cell such that the emitted energy is converted in such a way that a larger part of the energy can be converted into electricity. Typical examples of selective emitters are SiC, oxides of rare earth materials like Er_2O_3 or Yb_2O_3, or photonic crystals. To avoid the unwanted heating up of the TPV receiver cell, the sub-band gap photons can be filtered out and returned to the emitter by using a selective filter or a back-surface mirror.

Given the fact that a simple TPV system consists of four different parts (heat source, selective emitter, filter, and TPV cell), this also shows the complexity of TPV research. Although many research institutes were or are involved in TPV research, most of them were always focusing of one single aspect of a TPV system. This results in just a few commercially applicable systems where up to now only some demonstrators were built. Given the huge market potential of TPV for the recovery of waste heat, the next step would be to corporate with the industry to develop a TPV system which can easily be integrated in existing industrial systems as a next step in green technology.

References

[1] Bauer T, Forbes I, Penlington R, and Pearsall N (2003) The potential of thermophotovoltaic heat recovery for the glass industry. *Proceedings of the Fifth Conference Thermophotovoltaic Generation of Electricity.* Rome, Italy, 16–19 September 2002, vol. 653, pp. 101–110

[2] Wilt D, Chubb D, Wolford D, et al. (2006) Thermophotovoltaics for space power applications. *Seventh Conference on Thermophotovoltaic Generation of Electricity, AIP Conference Proceedings.* Madrid, Spain, 25–27 September 2006, vol. 890, pp. 335–345.

[3] Mattarolo G (2005) High temperature recuperative burner. *First Conference on Thermophotovoltaics: Science to Business.* Slide 7–8.

[4] Sai H, Kamikawa T, Kanamori Y, et al. (2004) Thermophotovoltaic generation with microstructured tungsten selective emitters. *Sixth Conference on Thermophotovoltaic Generation of Electricity, AIP Conference Proceedings.* Freiburg, Germany, 14–16 June 2004, vol. 738, pp. 206–214.

[5] Torsello G, Lomascolo M, Licciulli DD, Tundo S, et al. (2004) The origin of highly efficient selective emission in rare-earth oxides for thermophotovoltaic applications. *Nature Materials* 3: 632.

[6] Nelson RE (1994) Thermophotovoltaic emitter development. *Proceedings of the First NREL/TPV Conference.* Copper Mountain, CO, USA, pp. 80–98.

[7] Holmquist GA (1995) TPV power source development for an unmanned undersea vehicle. *Proceedings of the First NREL/TPV Conference.* Copper Mountain, CO, USA, pp. 308–314.

[8] Bitnar B, Durisch W, Mayor J-C, et al. (2002) Characterisation of rare earth selective emitters for thermophotovoltaic applications. *Solar Energy Materials and Solar Cells* 73: 221–234.

[9] Johnstone SJ (1915) The rare earth industry. In: Martin G (ed.) *Manuals of Chemical Technology II.* London, UK: Crosby Lockwood and Son.

[10] Tobler WJ and Durisch W (2005) A selective rare-earth emitter concept for solar thermophotovoltaics. *Proceedings of the Twentieth European Photovoltaic Conference and Exhibition.* Barcelona, Spain, 6–10 June 2005, pp. 398–401.

[11] Rahmlow T, Jr., Depoy D, Fourspring DM, et al. (2006) Development of front surface spectral control filters with greater temperature stability for thermophotovoltaic energy conversion. *Proceedings of the Seventh Conference on Thermophotovoltaic Generation of Electricity, AIP Conference Proceedings.* Madrid, Spain, 25–27 September 2006, vol. 890, pp. 59–67.

[12] van der Heide J (2009) Cost-Efficient Thermophotovoltaic Cells Based on Germanium. PhD Thesis, Katholieke Universiteit Leuven.

[13] Chubb D (2007) *Fundamentals of Thermophotovoltaic Energy Conversion.* Elsevier.

[14] Guazzoni G and Matthews M (2004) A retrospective of four decades of military interest in thermophotovoltaics. *Sixth Conference on Thermophotovoltaic Generation of Electricity, AIP Conference Proceedings.* Freiburg, Germany, 14–16 June 2004, vol. 738, pp. 3–12.

[15] Fraas LM, Avery JE, Sundaram VS, et al. (1990) Over 35% efficient GaAs/GaSb stacked concentrator cell assemblies for terrestrial applications. *Proceedings of the 21st IEEE PV Specialists Conference.* Kissimmee, FL, USA, pp. 190–195.

[16] Nelson R (2003) A brief history of thermophotovoltaic development. *Semiconductor Science and Technology* 18: S141–S143.

[17] Wanlass MV, Carapella JJ, Duda A, et al. (1998) High-performance 0.6-eV, $Ga_{0.32}In_{0.68}As/InAs_{0.32}P_{0.68}$ thermophotovoltaic converters and monolithically interconnected modules. *The Fourth NREL Conference on Thermophotovoltaic Generation of Electricity,* Denver, CO, USA, 11–14 October 1998, pp. 132–141.

[18] Fatemi NS, Wilt DM, Hoffman RW, Jr. et al. (1998) High performance, lattice-mismatched InGaAs/InP monolithic interconnected modules (MIM). *The Fourth NREL Conference on Thermophotovoltaic Generation of Electricity.* Denver, CO, USA, 11–14 October 1998.

[19] Andreev VM, Khvostikov VP, Rumyantsev VD, et al. (2005) Thermophotovoltaic converters with solar powered high temperature emitters. *Proceedings of the Twentieth European Photovoltaic Solar Energy Conference,* Barcelona, Spain, 6–10 June 2005.

[20] Andreev VM and Khvostikov VP Solar Thermophotovoltaic Convertors. Ioffe Institute.

[21] Rumyantsev VD, Khvostikov VP, Sorokina SV, et al. (1999) V generator based on metallic emitter and 1–5 Amp GaSb cells. *AIP Conference Proceedings.* vol. 460, pp. 384–393.

[22] Bett AW and Sulima OV (2003) GaSb photovoltaic cells for applications in TPV generators. *Semiconductor Science and Technology* 18: S184–S190.

[23] Fraas LM, Ballantyne R, Samara J, and Seal M (1994) A thermophotovoltaic energy generator using GaSb cells with a hydrocarbon burner. *First World Conference on Thermophotovoltaic Energy Conversion.* Copper Mountain, CO, USA, pp. 1713–1716.

[24] Fraas L, Avery J, and Huang H (2002) Thermophotovoltaics: Heat and electric power from low bandgap 'solar' cells around gas fired radiant tube burners. *29th Conference Record IEEE Photovoltaic Specialists Conference.* New Orleans, LA, 17 May 2002, vol. 29, pp. 1553–1556.

[25] Hitchcock C, Gutmann R, Borrego J, et al. (1999) Antimonide-based devices for thermophotovoltaic applications electron devices. *IEEE Transactions* 46: 2154–2161.

[26] Sulima OV, Bett A, Mauk M, et al. (2003) Diffusion of Zn in TPV materials: GaSb, InGaSb, InGaAsSb and InAsSbP. *Fifth Conference on Thermophotovoltaic Generation of Electricity, AIP Conference Proceedings.* Rome, Italy, 16–19 September 2002, vol. 653, pp. 402–413.

[27] Sulima O, Bett A, Mauk MG, et al. (2003) GaSb-, InGaAsSb-, InGaSb-, InAsSbP- and Ge-TPV cells for low-temperature TPV applications. *Fifth Conference on Thermophotovoltaic Generation of Electricity, AIP Conference Proceedings.* Rome, Italy, 16–19 September 2002, vol. 653, pp. 434–441.

[28] Dutta PS, Borrego JM, Ehsani H, et al. (2003) GaSb and $Ga_{1-x}In_xSb$ thermophotovoltaic cells using diffused junction technology in bulk substrates. *Fifth Conference on Thermophotovoltaic Generation of Electricity, AIP Conference Proceedings.* Rome, Italy, 16–19 September 2002, vol. 653, pp. 392–340.

[29] Khvostikov VP, Khostikov OA, Oliva EV, et al. (2002) Zinc-diffused InAsSbP/InAs and Ge TPV cells. *Conference Record of the Twenty-Ninth IEEE Photovoltaic Specialists Conference.* New Orleans, LA, 17 May 2002, pp. 943–946.

[30] Tobin SP, Vernon SM, Bajgar C, et al. (1988) High efficiency GaAs/Ge monolithic tandem solar cells. *Conference Record of the Twentieth IEEE PVSC.* Las Vegas, NV, USA, 26–30 September 1988, pp. 405–410.

[31] Mircea F, Maria F, Bailey SG, et al. (1997) Front surface engineering of high efficiency Si solar cells and Ge TPV cells. *Conference Record of the Twenty-Sixth IEEE PVSC.* Anaheim, CA, USA, 29 September–3 October 1997, pp. 73–79.

[32] Andreev V, Khvostikov V, Khvostikova O, *et al.* (2003) Low-bandgap PV and thermophotovoltaic cells. *The Third World Conference on Photovoltaic Energy Conversion.* Osaka, Japan, 12–16 May 2003.
[33] Nagashima T, Okumura K, Murata K, and Yamaguchi M (2003) A germanium back-contact type cell for thermophotovoltaic applications. *The Third World Conference on Photovoltaic Energy Conversion.* Osaka, Japan, 12–16 May 2003.
[34] Posthuma N, van der Heide J, Flamand G, and Poortmans J (2004) Development of low cost germanium photovoltaic cells for application in TPV using spin on diffusants. *The Sixth Conference on Thermophotovoltaic Generation of Electricity, AIP Conference Proceedings.* Freiburg, Germany, 14–16 June 2004, vol. 738, pp. 337–344.
[35] van der Heide J, Posthuma N, Flamand G, *et al.* (2009) Cost-efficient thermophotovoltaic cells based on germanium substrates. *Solar Energy Materials and Solar Cells* 93: 1810–1816.
[36] Datas A and Algora C (2009) Analytical model of solar thermophotovoltaic systems with cylindrical symmetry: Ray tracing approach. *Progress in Photovoltaics: Research and Applications* 17(8): 526–541.
[37] DiMatteo RS, Greiff P, Finberg SL, *et al.* (2003) Micron-gap ThermoPhotoVoltaics (MTPV). *AIP Conference Proceedings.* Rome, Italy, 16–19 September 2002, vol. 653, pp. 232–240.
[38] DiMatteo R, Greiff P, Seltzer D, *et al.* (2004) Micron-gap ThermalPhotoVoltaics (MTPV). *The Sixth Conference on Thermophotovoltaic Generation of Electricity, AIP Conference Proceedings.* Freiburg, Germany, 14–16 June 2004, vol. 738, pp. 42–51.
[39] Coutts TJ (2001) An overview of thermophotovoltaic generation of electricity. *Solar Energy Materials and Solar Cells* 66: 443–452.
[40] Scotto MV and DeBellis L (1999) Diesel burner development for 500W portable thermophotovoltaic generator, American flame research 1999. *Fall International Symposium.* San Francisco, CA, USA.
[41] Christ S and Seal M (1997) Viking 29 – A Thermophotovoltaic Hybrid Vehicle Designed and Built at Western Washington University. DOI: 10.4271/972650.
[42] Fraas LM, Avery JE, Huang HX, and Martinelli RU (2003) Thermophotovoltaic system configurations and spectral control. *Semiconductor Science and Technology* 18: S165–S173.
[43] http://www.jxcrystals.com/(last accessed 19 October 2011).
[44] Schubnell M, Benz P, and Major JC (1998) Design of a residential heating system. *Solar Energy Materials and Solar Cells* 52: 1–9.
[45] Bitnar B, Mayor J, Durisch W, *et al.* (2003) Record electricity-to-gas power efficiency of a silicon solar cell based TPV system. *AIP Conference Proceedings.* Freiburg, Germany, 14–16 June 2004, vol. 653, pp. 18–28.
[46] Bitnar B, Durisch W, Mayor J, *et al.* (2001) Development of a small TPV prototype system with an efficiency >2%. *Proceedings of the Seventeenth European Photovoltaic Solar Energy Conference and Exhibition.* Munich, Germany, 22–26 October 2001, pp. 33–36.
[47] Qiu K and Hayden ACS (2004) A novel integrated TPV power generation system based on a cascaded radiant burner. *Proceedings of the Sixth Conference on Thermophotovotaic Generation of Electricity.* Freiburg, Germany, 14–16 June 2004, pp. 105–113.
[48] http://www.bsria.co.uk/news/2006/ (last accessed 19 October 2011).
[49] Bauer T, Forbes I, and Pearsall N (2004) The potential of thermo-photovoltaic heat recovery for the UK industry. *International Journal of Ambient Energy* 25(1): 19–25.
[50] Bitnar B (2003) Silicon, germanium, and silicon/germanium photocells for thermophotovoltaics applications. *Semiconductor Science Technology* 18: S221–S227.

1.29 Intermediate Band Solar Cells

E Antolín, A Martí, and A Luque, Universidad Politécnica de Madrid, Madrid, Spain

© 2012 Elsevier Ltd. All rights reserved.

1.29.1	Introduction	619
1.29.2	Theoretical Model of the Intermediate Band Solar Cell	619
1.29.3	The Impurity-Based Approach or 'Bulk IBSC'	624
1.29.4	The QD-IBSC	628
1.29.4.1	The Use of QDs for Implementing an IBSC	628
1.29.4.2	QD-IBSC Prototypes	630
1.29.4.3	Proof of the Concept	631
1.29.4.4	Strategies to Boost the Efficiency of the QD-IBSC	632
1.29.4.4.1	Improved InAs/GaAs QDs	633
1.29.4.4.2	Non-Stranski–Krastanov QDs	635
1.29.5	Summary	635
Acknowledgments		637
References		637

1.29.1 Introduction

The efficiency of solar cells has experienced a notable increase in the past decades. The conventional photovoltaic (PV) technology, based on single-gap semiconductor devices, has achieved record conversion efficiencies of 29% in operation under concentrated sunlight [1]. However, the room for improvement of this technology is limited. The fundamental principles of photoconversion applied in single-gap cells are subject to an absolute efficiency limit, the Shockley–Queisser (SQ) limit, of 40.7% (calculated for an ideal single-gap cell under maximum sunlight concentration [2, 3]). If it is desired to achieve a substantial increase in the efficiency of PV energy conversion, novel devices not subject to the SQ limit are required. Such alternative technologies are usually known as 'third-generation solar cells' and some researchers have proposed that their implementation could prompt a breakthrough in PV electricity cost reduction and be the seed for a massive solar energy production [4–7].

The most developed third-generation approach at the moment is the multijunction solar cell (MJSC). A MJSC is a device that combines several single-gap cells of different semiconductor materials. Using the MJSC technology, it has become recently possible to fabricate devices that exceed in practice the SQ limit (the current record is 43.5% for a triple-junction GaInP/GaAs/GaInNAs cell operated at 400× sunlight concentration) [1]. Other alternatives have been proposed with the aim of achieving similar or even higher efficiencies, accompanied by potential advantages such as a more compact design, lower manufacture cost, higher tolerance toward changes in the solar spectrum, and so on. One of these proposals is the subject of the present review: the intermediate band solar cell (IBSC) [8]. It has an ideal efficiency limit of 63.2%, the same that of the current-matched triple-junction solar cell. A few years ago, it was just a theoretical concept. Now, several research groups around the world aim to materialize the concept on real devices.

To understand the potential of the IBSC concept, it is useful to discuss first the intrinsic limitation of conventional solar cells. The efficiency of single-gap solar cells is fundamentally limited by the fact that they only harness a portion of the solar spectrum. A conventional solar cell is made of a semiconductor material, characterized by a bandgap of forbidden energies of width E_G. In principle, the optical energy of a solar photon can be absorbed by an electron at the valence band (VB), which will use that energy to promote to the conduction band (CB), creating an electron–hole pair. However, not all photons from the solar spectrum are suitable for that process. A photon of energy equal to E_G can generate a VB → CB electronic transition, but a photon of lower energy cannot, and it will not be absorbed in the semiconductor. A photon of energy greater than E_G can be absorbed in an electronic transition, but its excess energy with respect to E_G will be lost. Since the electronic states within the bands form a continuum, the produced carriers will easily migrate to lower energy states, transferring the energy excess to the lattice in the form of heat (phonon emission). In any conventional semiconductor, carriers will relax by this 'thermalization' process to the bandgap edges in sub-picoseconds time and the remaining collectable energy from a photon of energy greater than E_G will be the same as in the case of a photon of energy equal to E_G. We face then a trade-off: if we choose a semiconductor of high E_G, such as GaAs, few photons will be absorbed, whereas if a low-bandgap material as Ge is chosen, we will absorb more photons, but a greater part of their energy will be lost to heat.

1.29.2 Theoretical Model of the Intermediate Band Solar Cell

The IBSC concept is based on the use of an absorbing material characterized by the existence of an isolated electronic band, the so-called intermediate band (IB), between the CB and VB [8]. As depicted in **Figure 1**, the IB divides the main bandgap (E_G) into two sub-bandgaps, referred to as E_L, the smallest one, and E_H, the largest one. An electron–hole pair can be generated in this material by two mechanisms: absorption of one photon in a conventional VB → CB transition (labeled (3) in **Figure 1**) or absorption of two

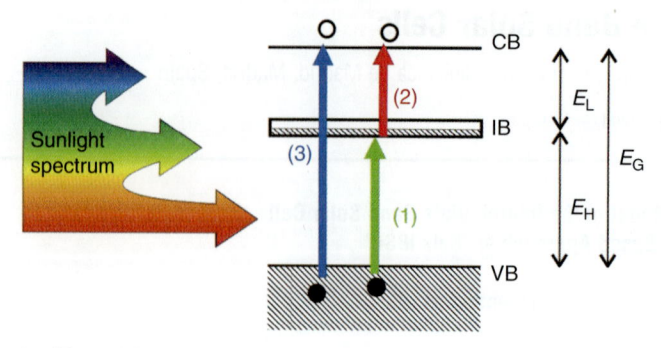

Figure 1 Simplified band diagram of an IB material showing the three possible optical transitions that allow a better exploitation of the solar spectrum in the case of a single-gap solar cell.

sub-bandgap photons through the IB-mediated transitions labeled (1) and (2). We have represented the IB in the upper half of E_G (E_L is identified with the IB–CB gap). This arrangement will be maintained throughout our description, but it is an arbitrary choice. Conceptually, it would make no difference to presume that the IB is located in the lower half of E_G. In this respect, it can be only anticipated that in the general case, the IB should not coincide with E_G's midpoint so that three distinct absorption thresholds are produced.

The potential of the IBSC relays on the production of extra photocurrent by the simultaneous absorption of photons in the two sub-bandgap transitions. In order to surpass the single-gap efficiency limit, it is necessary that the increase in photocurrent is not counteracted by a reduction of the output voltage. This can be achieved if the electronic populations associated with the IB, the CB, and the VB are each described by the respective quasi-Fermi levels ε_{FIB}, ε_{Fe}, and ε_{Fh}, to be defined below. In addition, two layers of conventional semiconductor of opposite doping, usually called p-emitter and n-emitter, have to be attached on either side of the IB material to block the direct flow of carriers from the IB to the metal contacts. For simplification, we shall assume in the following description that the emitters have a zero width and do not absorb light.

Figure 2 shows the band diagram of an ideal IB material in two situations. Under equilibrium (**Figure 2(a)**), the electronic population in all bands is described by a Fermi-level ε_F. When the semiconductor is illuminated (**Figure 2(b)**) with photons of suitable energy, electrons are excited from the VB to the CB, from the VB to the IB, and from the IB to the CB, at a rate g_{VC}, g_{VI}, and g_{IC}, respectively. The system will tend to recover equilibrium and the excited carriers will recombine at the respective rates r_{CV}, r_{IV}, and r_{CI}, which will depend on the generation rates, as well as on the boundary constraints of the system (e.g., on the amount of each type of carrier that is allowed to exit the IB material). The balance populations of electrons at the CB, holes at the VB and IB carriers in the IB material are now described by the respective quasi-Fermi levels ε_{FIB}, ε_{Fe}, and ε_{Fh}.

In the IBSC model, the (quasi-)Fermi level concept maintains the two-fold physical meaning, thermodynamical and statistical, that it has in common semiconductor science. From a quantum-statistical point of view, it is the energy at which the probability of occupation by the carriers of an electronic gas is ½. States of higher (lower) energy will have an occupation probability lower (higher) than ½, following the Fermi–Dirac distribution. In this context, it is important to recall that in the IBSC model, the creation of an electron–hole pair from the absorption of sub-bandgap photons does not imply the simultaneous absorption of two photons by a single electron in the VB, a rather unlikely three particle collision mechanism. The generation is produced by the confluence of a VB → IB and an IB → CB transitions. Therefore, it is preferred that ε_{FIB} crosses the IB in order to maximize sub-bandgap absorption: if the IB is semi-filled, it has enough electrons to promote to the CB and enough unoccupied states to receive electrons from the VB. In principle, the position of ε_{FIB} can be adjusted by the generation and recombination rates. But to make it independent of the operation conditions, the ideal model assumes that ε_F is pinned to the IB under equilibrium (using n- or p-doping if necessary) and that the IB has a sufficient density of states so that ε_{FIB} remains clamped to it under illumination, as depicted in **Figure 2**.

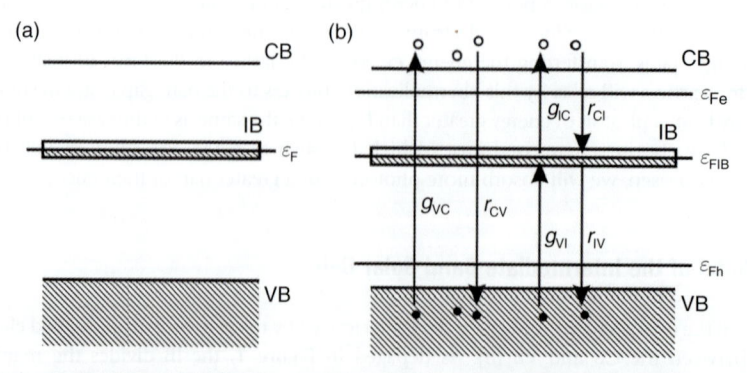

Figure 2 Simplified band diagrams of an IB material: (a) under equilibrium and (b) under illumination with photons of appropriate energy to generate electronic transitions between any pair of bands.

From the point of view of thermodynamics, the (quasi-)Fermi level is the electrochemical potential of the carrier ensemble, that is, the amount of free energy that is gained or lost by the system when a carrier is added to or removed from it. We refer here to the 'Gibbs free energy', the thermodynamic potential that measures the 'useful' energy (which can be entirely transformed into work) obtainable from a system at a constant temperature and pressure. In our context, to define the electrochemical potential, it is assumed that the carrier ensemble is in thermal equilibrium with the semiconductor lattice, or in other words, that carriers with an excess of kinetic energy have thermalized instantaneously.

The definition of three quasi-Fermi levels in the IB material has important implications. This means that each band contains an electronic gas and carrier relaxation between any pair of bands (recombination) is a much slower process than carrier relaxation within the bands (thermalization). In addition, when three quasi-Fermi levels are defined, the promotion of electrons, for example, from the IB to the CB at a rate g_{IC}, implies that the free energy of the system increases at a rate $g_{IC} \times (\varepsilon_{Fe} - \varepsilon_{FIB})$. As it is well known, the laws of thermodynamics restrict the ways by which the useful energy of a system can be increased. For instance, it can be demonstrated [9, 10] that the thermal energy of the lattice is used to promote a carrier from the IB to the CB, augmenting the total free energy of the system, violates the second law of thermodynamics. Thermal IB → CB generation can of course take place, but to comply with thermodynamics, the electrochemical potential of CB electrons thermally promoted from the IB has to be set to $\varepsilon_{Fe} \leq \varepsilon_{FIB}$ and there is no possible net gain in free energy but even loss. That is not the case when IB → CB transitions take place because photons from a source hotter than the cell are absorbed. The later consideration, which might appear rather abstract in the way it has been expounded, is indeed the cornerstone of the prediction of a high voltage, and hence a high efficiency, for the ideal IBSC.

For simplification, we shall assume that the quasi-Fermi levels are constant through the IB material. The following quasi-Fermi splits can be defined, which according to our argumentation, should be nonzero in an IB material under certain illumination conditions and boundary constrains of the carrier ensembles

$$\mu_{CV} \equiv \varepsilon_{Fe} - \varepsilon_{Fh}$$
$$\mu_{CI} \equiv \varepsilon_{Fe} - \varepsilon_{FIB}$$
$$\mu_{IV} \equiv \varepsilon_{FIB} - \varepsilon_{Fh} \qquad [1]$$

They are related by the equation

$$\mu_{CV} = \mu_{CI} + \mu_{IV} \qquad [2]$$

The emitters play an important role in the way carriers and useful energy are extracted from the IBSC. **Figure 3** illustrates the complete structure of an IBSC including the emitters and the corresponding band diagram under equilibrium, as well as when the cell is illuminated and connected to an external load. As the emitters are located between the IB material and the metal contacts, they define the boundary constrains of the carrier ensembles in the IB material. They act as selective contacts: the n-emitter only allows the transport of electrons, setting their quasi-Fermi level ε_{Fe} to match that of electrons at the adjacent metal contact (ε_{Fn}) and the p-emitter only allows the transport of holes, setting their quasi-Fermi level ε_{Fh} to match that of electrons at the adjacent metal contact (ε_{Fp}). When the IBSC is under operation, electrons from the CB leave the solar cell through the n-contact, their free energy is used at the external load, and they return to the cell as low-energy carriers through the p-contact (in other words, VB holes leave the cell through the p-contact). The power (P) that the cell delivers by means of the electron flux can be expressed as

$$P = \dot{n}(\varepsilon_{Fn} - \varepsilon_{Fp}) = \dot{n}(\varepsilon_{Fe} - \varepsilon_{Fh}) = \dot{n}\mu_{CV} \qquad [3]$$

where $\dot{n}$ is the rate at which carriers are transferred. This power, P, has to equal the electrical power consumed at the external load, which can be expressed as

$$P = JV \qquad [4]$$

where V is the voltage drop generated at the load and J is the photocurrent delivered by the cell, that is, $J = q\dot{n}$, q being the electron charge. From eqns [3] and [4], it is deduced that

$$V = \mu_{CV/q} = \frac{\mu_{CI} + \mu_{IV}}{e} \qquad [5]$$

We shall denote the net generation rates between the bands of the IB material as

$$\dot{n}_{CV}(\mu_{CV}) \equiv g_{VC} - r_{CV}(\mu_{CV})$$
$$\dot{n}_{IC}(\mu_{CI}) \equiv g_{IC} - r_{CI}(\mu_{CI})$$
$$\dot{n}_{VI}(\mu_{IV}) \equiv g_{VI} - r_{IV}(\mu_{IV}) \qquad [6]$$

As the emitters prevent that carriers are extracted directly from the IB, the net generation across both sub-bandgap transitions must be equal

$$\dot{n}_{IC}(\mu_{CI}) = \dot{n}_{VI}(\mu_{IV}) \qquad [7]$$

Therefore, the total current extracted from the device can be expressed as

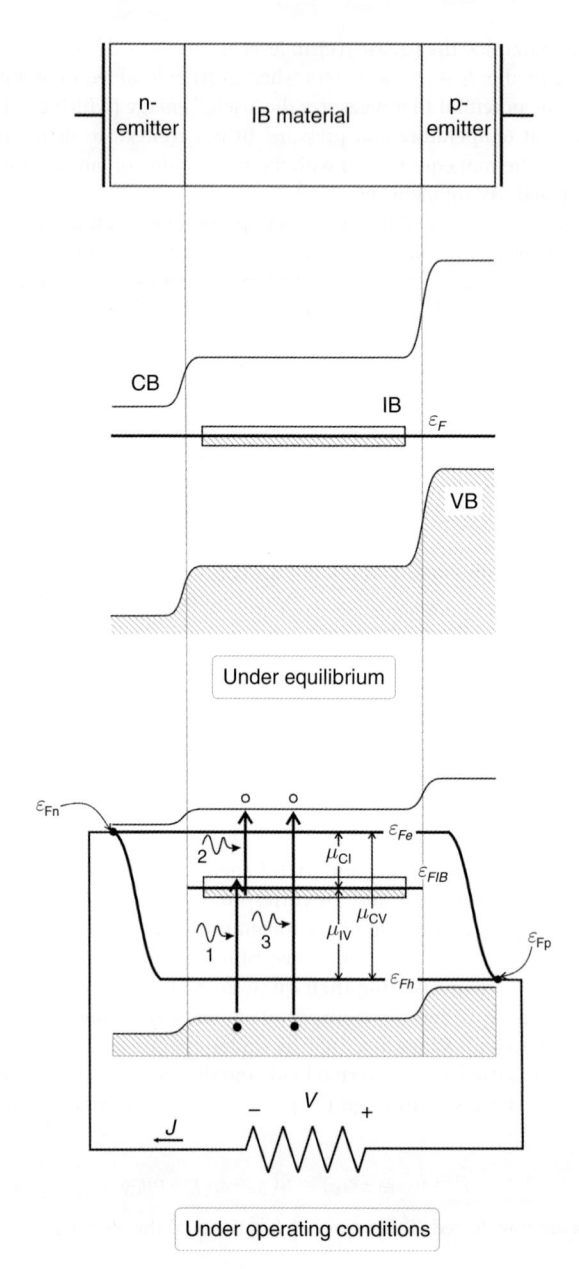

Figure 3 Structure of an IBSC (top) and corresponding band diagrams under equilibrium (middle) and under illumination and positive bias (bottom).

$$J = q[\dot{n}_{VC}(\mu_{CV}) + \dot{n}_{IV}(\mu_{IV})] \quad [8]$$

Equations [5] and [8], together with conditions [2] and [7], determine the current–voltage characteristic of an ideal IBSC. Based on those expressions, we can compare now the potential of the ideal IBSC to the potential of the ideal single-gap solar cell. Let us take as an example a single-gap cell and an IBSC with the same E_G. The band diagram of the single-gap cell would be as depicted in **Figure 3**, without IB (and without ε_{FIB}). The J–V characteristic would be given by

$$J^{sg} = q\dot{n}_{VC}^{sg}(\mu_{CV}^{sg})$$
$$V^{sg} = \frac{\mu_{CV}^{sg}}{e} \quad [9]$$

We have used the symbols $\dot{n}_{VC}^{sg}$ and μ_{CV}^{sg} to remark that those magnitudes cannot be directly identified with the magnitudes $\dot{n}_{VC}$ and μ_{CV} of the IBSC (even in the case that only photons with energy $\geq E_G$ reach both cells). But some absolute limits can be defined for the two cells. In both cases, the maximum V (the open-circuit voltage (V_{OC})) is limited by E_G. If the cells were operated at a voltage exceeding E_G, then their electronic populations would be inverted (the electron occupation in the lower CB states would exceed the electron occupation in the upper VB states). In this case, the semiconductors would be unable to absorb photons; on the contrary, stimulated photon emission would be released. On the other hand, the current that each device can produce is

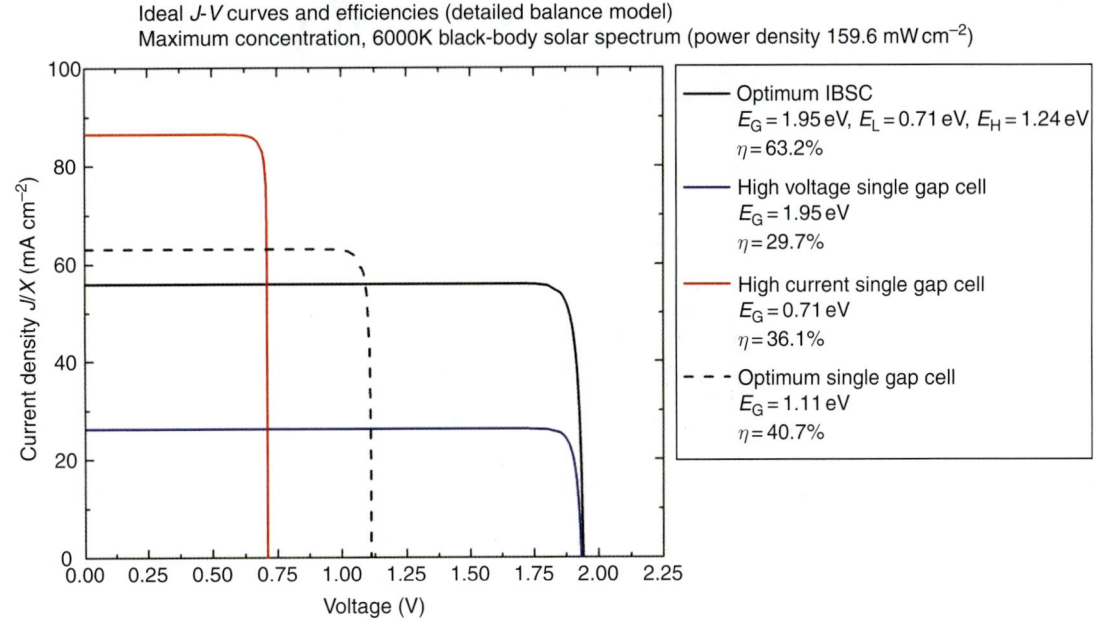

Figure 4 Ideal current–voltage characteristics (under maximum sunlight concentration). The current density is expressed as current per unit of concentrator area (i.e., current per exploited solar flux area). The bandgap configuration and ideal efficiency (η) for each curve are given in the legend. The solid black curve corresponds to an IBSC of optimized bandgaps E_G, E_H, and E_L. It is compared with a single-gap cell with gap equal to the lowest gap of the optimized IBSC (0.71 eV, red curve) and a single-gap cell with gap equal to the highest gap of the optimized IBSC (1.95 eV, blue curve). The dashed black curve corresponds to the optimized single-gap cell ($E_G = 1.11$ eV).

limited by the number of photons that it absorbs. For the single-gap cell to achieve a current as high as that produced by the IBSC, it would be necessary to reduce E_G. But in that case, its voltage would be decreased. This trade-off between current and voltage for the single-gap cell is indeed another way of seeing the trade-off between absorption and thermalization that we had already mentioned above.

We see that the IBSC design breaks the trade-off between current and voltage of the single-gap cell: an IBSC can deliver a high current by exploiting sub-bandgap absorption, while it preserves a high output voltage not limited by the sub-bandgap absorption thresholds. This is illustrated in **Figure 4**. The plot shows the current–voltage curve of an ideal IBSC with bandgaps $E_G = 1.95$, $E_H = 1.24$, and $E_L = 0.71$ eV under maximum concentration ($X = 46\,050$ suns; the solar spectrum is approximated by the black-body spectrum at 6000 K). It is compared with the curves of three ideal single-gap cells, with E_G of 0.71, 1.95, and 1.11 eV, under the same conditions. The curves have been calculated using the detailed balance model [2, 3, 8] and the legend gives the corresponding efficiency. The bandgap values chosen for the IBSC are optimized; they give the absolute efficiency limit of the IBSC under maximal concentration, 63.2%. In the case of the single-gap cell, $E_G = 1.11$ eV is the optimal gap under the same conditions. Its choice results in the SQ efficiency limit of 40.7%.

So far, we have summarized the fundamental principles of the IBSC theoretical model. We will now briefly discuss some properties that are required in an IBSC prototype in order to achieve proper IBSC operation. References are given where these aspects have been discussed in detail.

- The preservation of a high output voltage is possible only if both μ_{CI} and μ_{IV} are positive under illumination, that is, if the IBSC absorbs photons in VB $\to$ IB transitions and in IB $\to$ CB transitions. If there is absorption only in, say, VB $\to$ IB transitions, then $\mu_{CI} \leq 0$ and V_{OC} is limited by E_H (the cell is subjected to the single-gap efficiency limit for E_H [9, 10]). As we have said before, thermal generation from the IB to the CB cannot help in this respect.

- To maximize sub-bandgap absorption, ε_{FIB} has to be pinned to the IB. The minimum IB density of states required depends on the illumination conditions for which the IBSC prototype is designed (in particular, the concentration level). For example, it has been calculated that if the IBSC is implemented using quantum dots (QDs), a dot density of 10^{17} cm^{-3} provides a clamping of ε_{FIB} at the IB within 1 kT when the cell is operated up to 1000 suns [12].

- To make consistent our argumentation regarding voltage preservation, the fact that ε_{FIB} crosses the IB must not prompt stimulated photon emission. If the upper and lower energy levels of the IB are designated by E_{IBH} and E_{IBL}, then we have $\mu_{CI} < E_C - E_{IBH}$ and $\mu_{IV} < E_{IBL} - E_V$, where E_C and E_V are the CB minimum and VB maximum energy levels [13]. Therefore, there is a limitation to the quasi-Fermi level splits that can be tolerated in relation to the IB bandwidth. For the example studied in Reference 13, it was estimated that the IB width can be ≤ 700 meV for one-sun operation and ≤ 100 meV for

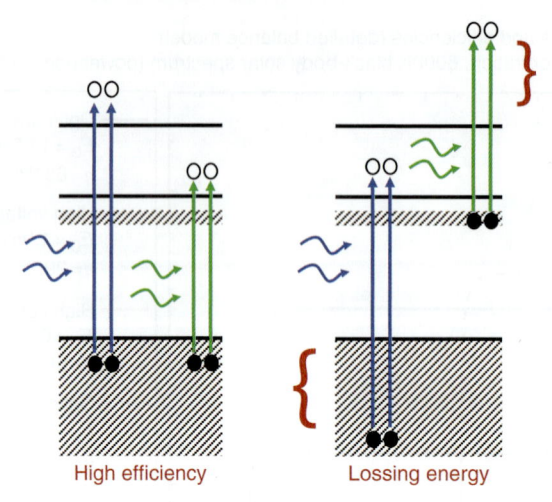

Figure 5 In an IB material, photons of certain energy range could in principle be absorbed in different electronic transitions. The diagram on the left shows the case where photons are absorbed over the largest bandgap with energy smaller than the photon energy. The diagram on the right corresponds to the less favorable case where photons are absorbed over bandgaps of energy lower as possible and a greater part of the photon energy is lost by thermalization.

operation under maximum concentration. On the other hand, the mobility of IB carriers will typically have a positive dependence on the IB width (the carrier effective mass is proportional to the inverse of the band curvature at its extremes), and therefore, an IBSC with a relatively wide IB can homogenize better its carrier population in case illumination is too inhomogeneous throughout the device [14] (very high mobilities in the IB are not required because this band is not connected to the external contacts).

- According to thermodynamics, the work delivered in an energy conversion process is maximized when the process is reversible. In this case, the highest degree of reversibility in the optical–electrochemical energy conversion corresponds to the case where carriers in any band can only recombine by emitting a photon (exactly the same case in a single-gap solar cell). The ideal curves plotted in **Figure 4** have been calculated assuming that there are no nonradiative recombination mechanisms, such as Auger or Shockley–Read–Hall (SRH) recombination.

The relative strength and spectral dependence of the three transitions within the IB material are a sensitive aspect of the IBSC design. It is quite intuitive that the efficiency of the device would sink if part of the energy of the photons gets lost because they are absorbed in a transition of energy lower than possible (e.g., if photons with energy enough to be absorbed in an VB → CB transition are absorbed in an VB → IB transition; see **Figure 5**). The most certain way to achieve optimal performance in an IBSC (at least when the bandgaps are optimized) would be to ensure the selectivity of the absorption coefficients (α_{VC}, α_{VI}, and α_{IC}) associated, respectively, to the VB → CB, VB → IB, and IB → CB transitions. This means that α_{IC} should be zero in the range where α_{VI} is nonzero (photon energies $\geq E_H$) and α_{VI} should behave analogously with respect to α_{VC} (Note that also from a thermodynamic point of view this condition should lead to the highest efficiencies, since it maximizes the reversibility of the process. When a photon is absorbed in a high energy transition, it can be re-emitted and recycled inside the material using the same transition [15]) (see **Figure 6**). Absolute selectivity of the absorption coefficients has been assumed to compute the ideal IBSC J–V curve of **Figure 4**. But it seems difficult to achieve such a complete selectivity in a real IB material. A probably more feasible approach is to engineer an IB material with $\alpha_{IC} \ll \alpha_{VI} \ll \alpha_{VC}$. It has been proven that this configuration would also lead to optimal efficiencies in the idealized case of an infinitely thick IBSC [16] and also in the more realistic approach where light confinement techniques assist the weaker transitions [17].

1.29.3 The Impurity-Based Approach or 'Bulk IBSC'

It is not new at all that an atom of a foreign species can introduce discrete levels in the bandgap of a semiconductor, sometimes quite distant from the CB and VB (the so-called 'deep levels' (DL)). The fact that some impurity sites in semiconductors allow sub-bandgap light absorption is routinely used to characterize them. It seems then quite logical to propose that a bulk IB material could be synthesized by doping a semiconductor material with appropriate DL impurities. Actually, the investigation on this subject is older than the IBSC concept itself.

The use of DL impurities to generate sub-bandgap photocurrent and enhance the efficiency of solar cells was first proposed in a pioneering work by M. Wolf [18]. He called the impurity-doped device multitransition solar cell (MTSC). Two years later, H. Grimmeiss and coworkers tested the idea empirically on Zn-doped GaP p–n junctions [19]. Originally, they had fabricated those

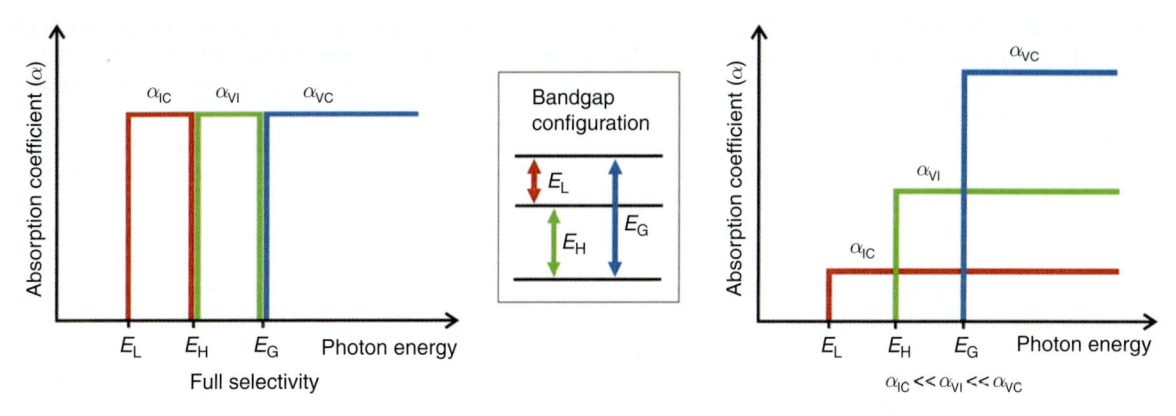

Figure 6 Diagrams showing the two possible absorption coefficient spectral distributions that result in an efficient photon sorting in the IBSC. α_{XY} represents the absorption coefficient associated to transitions between bands X and Y. The diagram on the left shows the ideal case of full selectivity and the one on the right the step distribution.

devices to study their electroluminescence (EL) at a time when the basis of present light-emitting diode (LED) technology was being established [20]. **Figure 7** shows the photocurrent (PC) spectra that they measured on GaP:Zn p–n junctions, compared to the DL energy distribution that they had identified in the same devices through luminescence experiments. It can be seen that there is a contribution to the PC from sub-bandgap photon absorption ($E < E_G$[GaP] = 2.25 eV). Most importantly, from the dependence of the PC on the temperature, the authors concluded that the sub-bandgap generation mechanism most probably included two-photon absorption [19]. That was probably the first empirical demonstration of a two-photon effect in a doped semiconductor [21] and they realized its importance in relation to Wolf's work, but unfortunately, the research was soon abandoned. The efficiencies obtained were lower than those of reference samples. Actually, it could not had been otherwise if they had stuck by Wolf's original MTSC proposal, since it failed at one point: he did not reckon the importance of implementing selective contacts (free of intermediate energy levels) in order to enable voltage preservation. His work was prior to the publication of the SQ detailed balance model for a solar cell [2].

When the implementation of a bulk IB material using DL impurities is discussed, it is interesting to reflect on the fact that intermediate states are supposed to form a 'band'. This is not included, at least not explicitly, in Wolf's MTSC or other more recent proposals as the impurity photovoltaic (IPV) cell [22]. The term 'band' in the IBSC description does not refer to conduction properties of the collection of intermediate states. As we have seen, the IB in principle does not need to carry any current. The significance of the term 'band' in the IBSC is related to the assumption that the intermediate states should not act as SRH recombination centers (it is sometimes understood that the use of the term 'band' is related to the definition of a third quasi-Fermi level in the IBSC model. The definition of a quasi-Fermi level only refers to the way carriers are distributed. In fact,

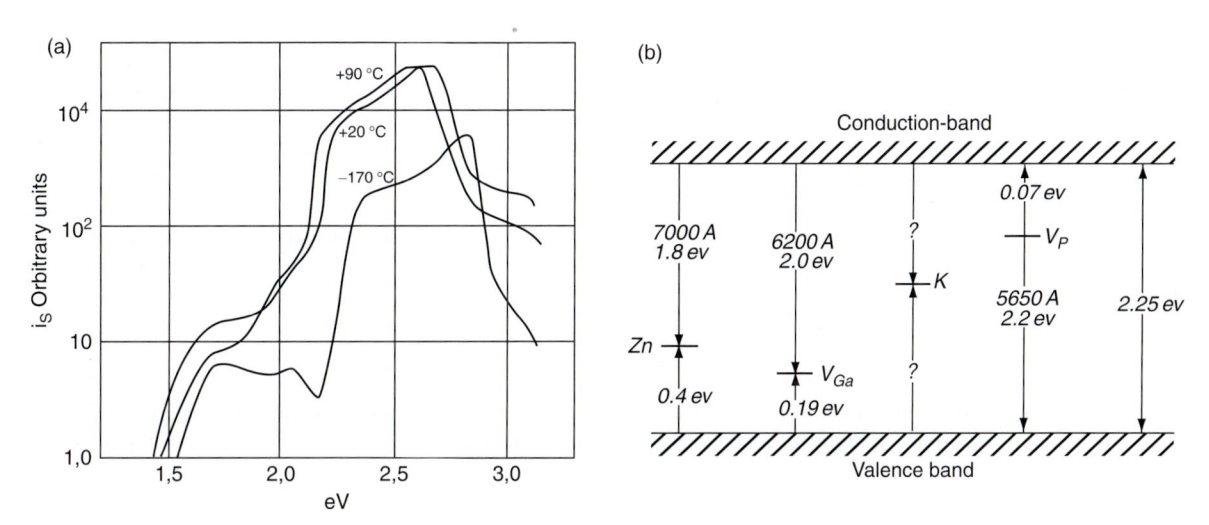

Figure 7 (a) The plot shows PC measured on Zn-doped GaP p–n junctions. Extracted from Grimmeiss HG, Kischio W, and Koelmans H (1962) p–n-junction photovoltaic effect in zinc-doped GaP. *Solid-State Electronics* 5: 155–159 [19] (b) Shows the DLs identified by the same authors through luminescence measurements on Zn-doped GaP p–n junctions. Extracted from Grimmeiss HG and Koelmans H (1961) Analysis of p–n luminescence in Zn-Doped GaP. *Physical Review* 123: 1939 [20]. The PC spectra in (a) reveal sub-bandgap absorption. From the comparison to Figure (b) the absorption could be produced by transitions mediated by the DLs introduced by Zn impurity sites and Ga vacancies.

Shockley's original model also introduces a third quasi-Fermi level to model nonradiative recombination in the presence of traps [23, 24]) [23]. This is a crucial issue for the successful implementation of IBSC devices and there is especial cause for concern when the use of DL impurities is considered: it is well known that isolated DLs act as 'carrier traps', promoting nonradiative relaxation of electrons through multiphonon emission [25].

In the first stages of the theoretical discussion on the IBSC model, it was intuitively postulated that a dominant radiative behavior could be achieved if the intermediate states form a delocalized band similar to the conventional CB and VB of a semiconductor. This intuition has been recently justified by the theoretical model expounded in Reference 26. In that work, it is concluded that SRH recombination can be suppressed in a semiconductor containing DLs if the concentration of impurities is as high as to allow charge delocalization among them.

To understand this problem and envisage possible ways to skip it, it has been necessary to review the fundamentals of nonradiative recombination (NRR) physics from the point of view of the underlying microscopic mechanisms [25, 27-29], rather than from the point of view of carrier statistics [24, 30], which is the aspect usually studied in PV contexts. The main question to be answered regarding NRR mechanisms is to which particle or particles can be transferred the energy of a CB electron if it is not to a photon. In the case of materials highly doped with conventional, shallow level dopants (or materials under high injection), there is a significant probability that the energy lost by a de-excited electron is transferred to other electrons (Auger process). But in the general case, phonons are the only particles that can absorb that energy. Because of the low energy of lattice phonons compared to the bandgap, it would be required that many phonons are emitted. The probability that so many phonons are emitted simultaneously is too low to justify the empirical NRR occurrence. In some cases, the process is facilitated by the existence of a collection of closely spaced electronic states within the bandgap (the best example would be surface recombination) and a cascade emission of phonons can be assumed [28]. Contrarily, in the case of interest for us, bulk semiconductors presenting isolated deep levels, cascade mechanisms do not apply and we face a more complex process, the so-called Lattice Relaxation Multiple-Phonon Emission (MPE) mechanism [25].

The origin of the MPE mechanism lies in the different nature of the levels introduced by impurities and the electronic states that form the semiconductor bands. Electrons in the bands are characterized by Bloch functions extending across the whole crystal, while electrons in deep traps are characterized, when the traps are sparse, by localized wavefunctions. If a transition is produced from an electron in, say, the CB to the localized state at the impurity, there is a big swift charge movement. The charge that was formerly distributed across the whole crystal becomes suddenly closely packed around the impurity. This change displaces the impurity, which starts vibrating heavily in order to recover equilibrium. That answers our original question: the electron energy is absorbed in a vibration that cannot be described in terms of the common lattice phonons; it occurs through a 'breathing mode' of the excited impurity coupled to the lattice. The main point to be remarked here is that the vibration is released by the displacement (in real space) of the impurity as a consequence of changing its charge distribution or, if preferred, the electrostatic potential to which it is subjected. Subsequently, the violent vibration induced in the impurity is damped to its thermal value not by a simultaneous, but by a successive emission of phonons through ordinary phonon-electron interaction. The number of phonons delivered to complete the transition is the so-called Huang-Rhys factor [29], which usually lies in the range of 10 or 12. The capture of a hole can be described in the same way through the production of a breathing mode and subsequent multiphonon emission.

The NRR suppression model [26] is based on the statement that, since the premise for the MPE is the localization of the impurity wavefunctions, this process can be prevented if we are able to extend those wavefunctions and that this can be achieved by increasing the density of traps. By doing so, a localization-delocalization transition can be reached which is analogous to the classical insulator-metal transition described by Mott [31]. The Mott transition is produced because increasing the impurity density N_T (in the classical description, shallow level impurities) increases the electrical screening that any of the single impurities experiences when it is charged. For a given critical density, $N_{T,crit}$, the screening should be so strong as to counteract the Coulomb potential produced by a localized charge. Then, an extended state is produced with an eigenfunction that is shared among all impurities. In other words, for densities above $N_{T,crit}$, the impurities are close enough as to experience interaction and their levels split into bands.

When the delocalization has occurred, any transition from the CB to the impurity band does not involve a large charge movement and cannot release a breathing mode vibration on the impurity. For the recombination to take place, the energy of the de-excited electron has to be transferred to a photon. The model predicts that the suppression of NRR occurs for $N_{T,crit} = 5.9 \times 10^{19}$ cm^{-3} (at 300 K and assuming that ε_{FIB} crosses the IB). That is, then, the minimal impurity density required to fabricate a proper bulk IB material. It is important to note that for a not half-filled IB, the critical density will be different. Alternatively, in Reference 26, an estimation for $N_{T,crit}$ based on the Anderson's transition model [32] is presented which results in a slightly higher value ($1-2 \times 10^{20}$ cm^{-3}).

Let us now see how this delocalization transition will impact the recombination statistics. According to the classical SRH theory of trap-assisted recombination, in a semiconductor out of equilibrium where Δn represents the excess of electrons or holes with respect to their equilibrium concentrations (n_0 and p_0, respectively) the carrier lifetime τ is given by the expression [24, 30]:

$$\tau = \tau_{p0} \frac{(n_0 + n_1 + \Delta n)}{(n_0 + p_0 + \Delta n)} + \tau_{n0} \frac{(p_0 + P_1 + \Delta n)}{(n_0 + p_0 + \Delta n)} \qquad [10]$$

where n_1 and p_1 stand for the number of electrons in the CB and holes in the VB, respectively, when the occupation of the trap levels is ½. The parameters τ_{p0} and τ_{n0} (usually referred to as the SRH minority carrier lifetimes) are independent of the injection and doping levels. They depend on the density of traps (N_t) and their capture cross-sections (σ_n and σ_p) through the expression

$$\frac{1}{\tau_{p0}} = N_t \sigma_P \langle v_p^{th} \rangle \quad \text{and} \quad \frac{1}{\tau_{n0}} = N_t \sigma_n \langle v_n^{th} \rangle \qquad [11]$$

where $\langle v^{th} \rangle$ stands for the averaged thermal velocity of electrons or holes in their respective bands. Expression [10] can be simplified for certain injection and doping levels. For instance, in a heavily n-doped sample ($n_0 \gg p_0$), where all traps are filled ($n_0 \gg n_1$) and under low injection ($n_0 \gg \Delta n$), τ equals the minority carrier lifetime τ_{p0}. For a sufficiently high injection, $\tau = \tau_{p0} + \tau_{n0}$ in any sample ($\Delta n \gg n_0, n_1, p_0, p_1$).

It has been commonly assumed that the capture cross-section of the traps is independent of their concentration and, consequently, that the lifetimes given by eqn [11] decrease linearly with increasing N_t. Within this context, the model of the delocalization transition introduces the novelty of considering a concentration dependent $\sigma_{n,p}(N_t)$ and, in particular, that the capture cross-sections will decrease if a sufficiently high N_t is reached. Therefore, it is expected to observe an increase of the SRH lifetime as the impurity concentration reaches the critical value $\sim 10^{20}$ cm^{-3}.

The lifetime raise at the transition point is expected to be quite abrupt (in homogenously doped samples) because the assumption of constant $\sigma_{n,p}$ has proven to be extremely accurate in the DL concentration range usually explored. The solubility of deep level impurities (e.g., transition metals) is low in common semiconductors and samples contaminated with DLs, unintentionally or even intentionally, rarely are able to reach 10^{18} cm^{-3} without forming clusters. However, it is difficult to extract conclusions about the actual lifetime related to impurity assisted recombination. In the context ultrafast electronic device development, semiconductor samples are often implanted with DL at very high doses, but the damage produced to the crystalline lattice impacts and even determines the final carrier lifetime (see, e.g., [33]). One of the main challenges of the current work on the bulk IBSC is to achieve an ultrahigh DL concentration while keeping a crystalline quality high enough as to allow and make observable the predicted delocalization transition or, in other words, the formation of an IB.

A first experimental observation of a partial lifetime recovery in a bulk IBSC material has recently been obtained in Si samples that were heavily doped with Ti. The samples were prepared [34] by heavy ion implantation (with densities above 10^{21} cm^{-3}) followed by a pulsed laser melting process that restores crystal quality. Ti produces deep levels in silicon and leads to strong recombination [35–37] and is thus known to be a minority carrier lifetime killer. The effective lifetime has been measured by the quasi-steady photoconductance technique and longer lifetimes have been found for the samples with the higher Ti doses [38]. However, in this first study, the lifetime recovery is still small and much more research needs to be done.

Apart from the problem of NRR, it is also important to study which combinations of impurities and host materials can lead to the most suitable band diagrams for IBSc implementation. *Ab initio* quantum mechanical calculations have been performed by Tablero, Wahnón, Palacios, and others, to assess whether the substitution of certain host semiconductor atoms by certain impurity atoms would give rise to an isolated IB or, to the contrary, the states introduced by the impurities would overlap with the CB and the VB. In this respect, it has been found, for example, that Ti-substituted GaAs or GaP could be suitable IB material candidates [39–41], in addition to Sc-, V-, or Cr-substituted GaP [42], Ti-substituted CuGaS$_2$ [43], or Cr-substituted ZnS [44].

The insertion of V as impurity in In-thiospinels has also been theoretically proposed [45]. In this case, V-substituted In$_2$S$_3$ with high V concentration (V$_2$In$_{14}$S$_{24}$) could be prepared by solvo-thermal synthesis and experimental evidence of sub-bandgap absorption has been reported [46] (see **Figure 8**(a)). Following a different approach, Yu *et al.* have synthesized II-VI oxide semiconductors [48] and GaNAsP quaternary alloys [49]. Those materials belong to the so-called highly mismatched alloys (HMAs) and they are expected to exhibit an IB due to the interaction of localized impurity states with CB continuum states by

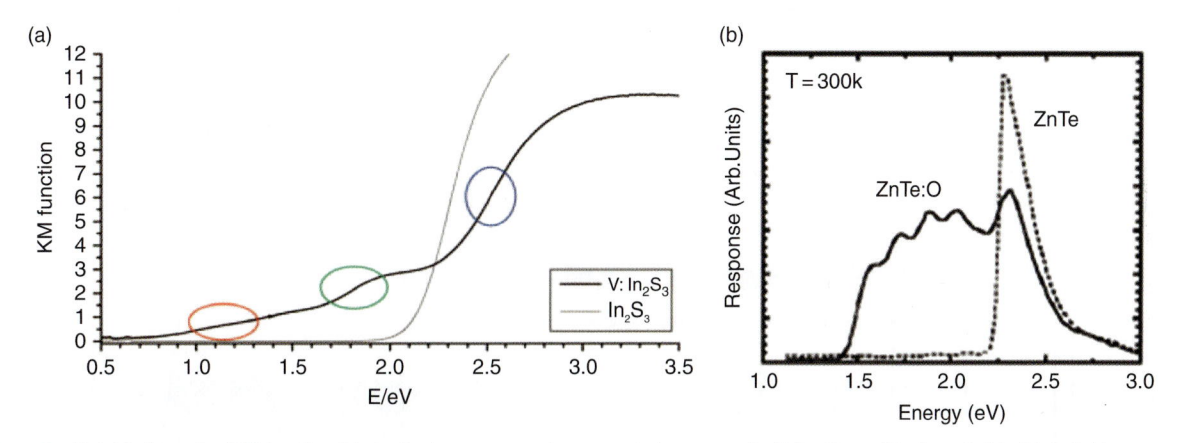

Figure 8 Plot (a) shows the K-M function (absorption) measurements versus photon energy for V$_2$In$_{14}$S$_{24}$ and In$_2$S$_3$ materials fabricated by solvothermal synthesis. The red circle is associated with transitions from the IB to the CB, the green one to transitions from the VB to the IB, and the blue one to transitions from the VB to the CB. Extracted from Lucena R, Aguilera I, Palacios P, *et al.* (2008) Synthesis and spectral properties of Nanocrystalline V-substituted In$_2$S$_3$, a novel material for more efficient use of solar radiation. *Chemistry of Materials* 20: 5125–5127 [46]. Plot (b) shows the photoresponse of a ZnTe:O based IBSC compared with a ZnTe reference cell. Extracted from Wang W, Lin AS, and Phillips JD (2009) Intermediate-band photovoltaic solar cell based on ZnTe:O. *Applied Physics Letters* 95: 011103 [47].

the band anticrossing effect [50]. In this case, it has also been possible for the authors to show the existence of an IB through optical characterization (photoreflectance measurements). Finally, Phillips *et al.* have also shown promising results with ZnTe:O material [47] (see **Figure 8(b)**).

1.29.4 The QD-IBSC

1.29.4.1 The Use of QDs for Implementing an IBSC

The use of QDs arrays for the implementation of IB materials was proposed in Reference 51. As it is well known, QDs are semiconductor crystals of such a reduced size (typically in the order of nanometers) that their electronic properties resemble those of single atoms, that is, they exhibit discrete energy levels instead of the continuous bands that characterize bulk crystals [52–54]. If they are embedded in a material (host or barrier material) of wider bandgap, three-dimensional (3D) confining potentials are created for electrons, for holes, or for both carriers, depending on the respective electronic affinities of QD and barrier materials. The number and energy of the discrete energy levels that appear in the confining potential is determined by the QD size and the carrier-effective masses. In the simplest case of an infinite band-offset between barrier and dot and assuming a QD with the shape of a rectangular box, the energy of the confined levels is given by

$$E_{n_x,n_y,n_z} = \frac{\hbar^2 \pi^2}{2m^*}\left(\frac{n_x^2}{L_x^2} + \frac{n_y^2}{L_y^2} + \frac{n_z^2}{L_z^2}\right) \quad [12]$$

where $\hbar$ is the reduced Plank's constant; m^* is the carrier effective mass; L_x, L_y, and L_z are the box lengths; and $n_{x,y,z} = 1, 2, 3 \ldots$ are the quantum numbers. In principle, confining potentials in the CB are preferred for the implementation of a QD-IBSC, because the effective mass of electrons is typically smaller than that of holes, and therefore, the number of excited levels that appear is lower. As depicted in **Figure 9(b)**, the IB is formed in this case by the ground states of electrons in the QDs.

To fabricate the QD-IBSC, the QD array has to be sandwiched between an n-emitter and a p-emitter (see **Figure 9(a)**). When the IB material is implemented with QDs, the Fermi level can be located at the IB using δ-doping [55]. This means that a shallow dopant species is introduced in a concentration equal to the density of dots, resulting in the semi-occupation of the ground states (these states can host two electrons due to spin degeneracy). **Figure 9(c)** shows the simplified band diagram of a QD-IBSC under

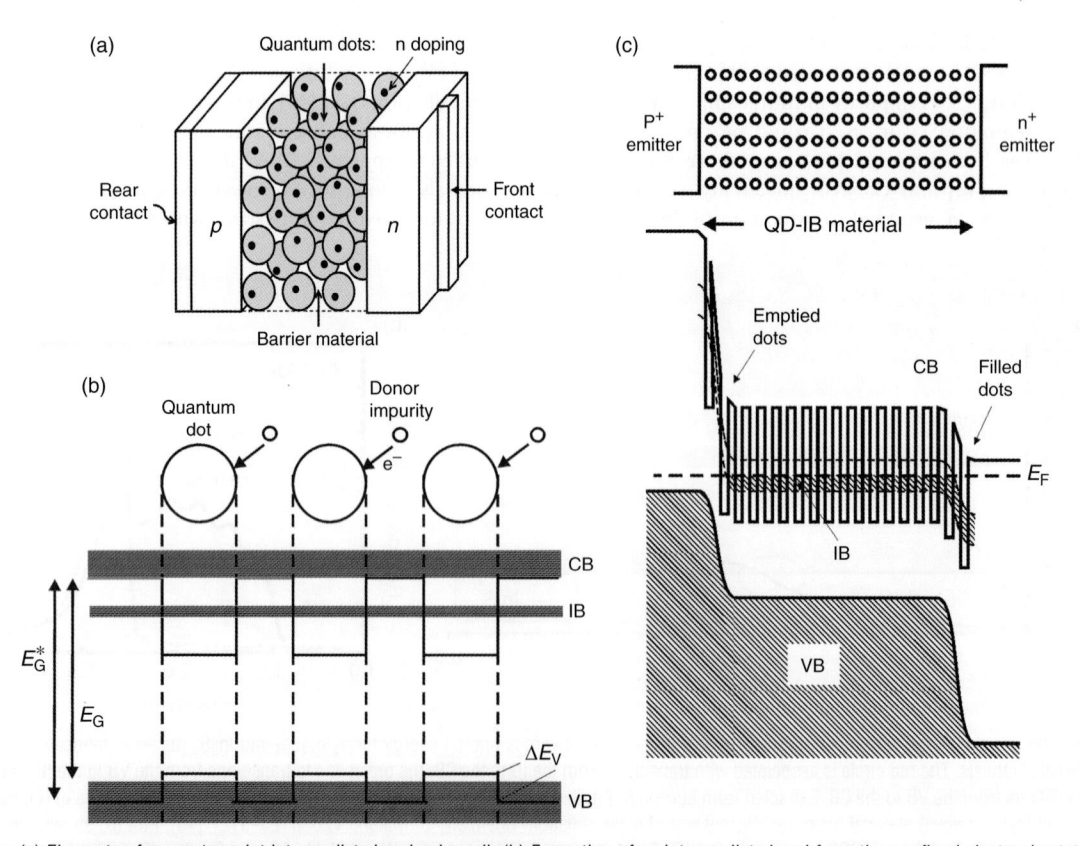

Figure 9 (a) Elements of a quantum-dot intermediate band solar cell. (b) Formation of an intermediate band from the confined electronic states in an array of quantum dots. (c) Simplified energy band diagram of a QD-IBSC in equilibrium.

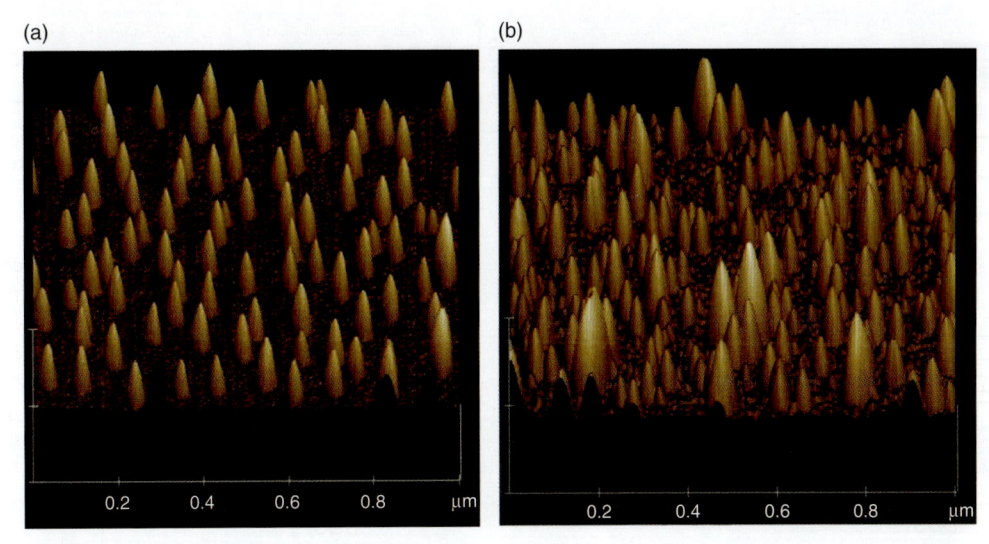

Figure 10 AFM images of two InAs/GaAs QD layers grown by MBE. The growth conditions applied in sample (a) have allowed the achievement of high size uniformity, contrarily to the case of sample (b). The vertical dimension is overestimated in the pictures (the dot's height is actually smaller than the base). When the QDs are buried with a GaAs layer, their morphology typically changes. These pictures are a courtesy of the University of Glasgow.

equilibrium. Using δ-doping, it is, in principle, possible that most QDs are semi-filled with electrons, except those located at the extremes of the IB material, which are embedded in the space charge region (SCR).

Most of the QD-IBSCs that have been fabricated to the moment use InAs as dot material and GaAs as host material [56–64]. InAs and GaAs present a relatively large difference in lattice constant. When an InAs layer is epitaxially deposited on a GaAs layer QDs form spontaneously (self-assemble) because islanding allows some elastic relaxation of the strain induced by lattice mismatch [65]. In particular, the growth takes place in the Stranski–Krastanov mode [66], which means that a part of the InAs material forms a thin layer (the so-called 'wetting layer' (WL)) and the 3D islands grow on top of it. **Figure 10** shows atomic force microscope (AFM) images of uncapped InAs QDs grown on GaAs by this method using molecular beam epitaxy (MBE). The successive deposition of In(Ga)As and GaAs layers has been widely used since the middle 1990s to fabricate QD arrays. It has been shown that the islands can be coherently strained (i.e., no dislocations) and pretty uniform in size [67]. The fabrication of In(Ga)As/GaAs QD arrays is now widely used to implement infrared (IR) detectors [68] and lasers [69, 70]. Of course, there are limitations to the size and morphology of QDs that can be grown, as we will discuss later in Section 1.29.4.4.

The InAs/GaAs QD material system is not optimal for the implementation of an IBSC. The gap of GaAs is 1.42 eV, much lower than the IBSC optimum according to the ideal models. Furthermore, the effective gap (E_G^*) of the QD material is reduced by the offset between the VB maxima of InAs and GaAs (see **Figure 9(b)**). This material system has been chosen for the implementation of the first QD-IBSC prototypes mainly because there is a wide previous experience in its fabrication.

It is interesting to review why QDs, not quantum wells (QW), are proposed to implement IBSCs. A QW is a thin layer of material where confinement only takes place in the growth dimension. It is easier to fabricate, since strain fields to not play such a relevant role as for QDs. It is known that in both cases band-to-band recombination (of confined electrons with confined holes, also called 'excitonic' recombination) is of dominant radiative nature. But in the case of a QD, the density of states is δ-like, as illustrated by eqn [12], while in a QW the lack of confinement in the transversal dimensions leads to the formation of continuous sub-bands.

In a QD there are gaps with zero density of states that separate the levels from each other and also from the continuous states of the bulk semiconductor bands (see **Figure 11**). If these gaps are larger than the energy of optical phonons, carrier relaxation from one state to a lower state by interaction with a single phonon is ruled out due to energy non-conservation. Therefore, the relaxation times for excited carriers to the fall to the ground-state should be much larger than in the case of QWs (see **Figure 11**). This phenomenon, usually called *phonon-bottleneck effect* (PBE) [71–73], can be used to prevent fast thermalization of carriers from the CB to the IB as required in the IBSC context. In the case of self-assembled InGaAs/GaAs QDs relaxation times ranging from 1 ns to 10 ps have been reported [74]. However, several works (see [75] for a literature review) point out that in real QDs at room temperature some mechanisms can appear that introduce paths for fast relaxation, such as inelastic multi-phonon and second-order electron–phonon processes [76, 77], coupling to defect states [78], coupling to the 2D states of the WL [79], electron–electron scattering [80, 81], and very importantly, electron–hole scattering [82, 83]. In fact, the results obtained in InAs/GaAs QD-IBSCs that we will discuss later in this Chapter show that the relaxation/escape of carriers between CB and IB are too strong to achieve proper IBSC behavior at room temperature.

With respect to the absorption properties of QDs, it has been shown that QDs enable the absorption of photons both in excitonic and intra-band transitions (see **Figure 11**). It is of particular importance for photovoltaic applications that in the case of

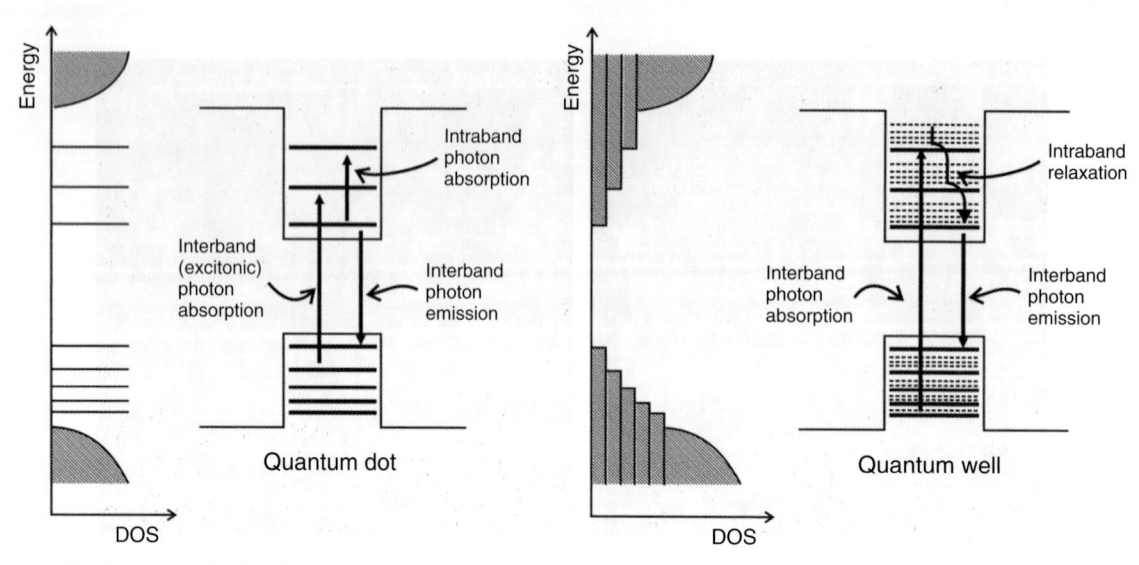

Figure 11 Density of states (DOS) and band structure of a QD (left) and a QW (right). Some of the numerous possible transitions are shown. It is remarked the fact that optical intraband transitions under normal incidence are allowed for electrons confined in the QD, but not for electrons confined in the QW, and also that fast relaxation of confined electrons has a higher probability in the QW.

electronic intra-band transitions light can be also absorbed in normal incidence [84–86], and not only when it propagates parallel to the growth plane, as it is the case of QWs [87]. However, it must be taken into account that the density of dots is rather low when compared to the atomic density of bulk semiconductors (in current In(Ga)As/GaAs QD arrays it is typically $\leq 10^{17}$ cm^{-3}). Then, the resulting volumetric absorption coefficient in the transitions only allowed inside the dots can be low and selective light trapping techniques may be required for the implementation of IBSCs of really high efficiency.

1.29.4.2 QD-IBSC Prototypes

Figure 12 shows some examples of QD-IBSC structured designed and fabricated by University of Glasgow/IES-Universidad Politécnica de Madrid [63, 64, 88–95]. The structure depicted in **Figure 12(a)** is an older one, which includes a GaAs n-emitter, a GaAs p-emitter, and Si δ-doping for half-filling the QDs as explained above. It contains a QD stack of 10 layers. Attempts to grow more layers failed due to strain build-up and emitter degradation [90]. Another problem observed while the structure shown in **Figure 12(a)** was studied was that the whole QD stack was immersed in the SCR of the junction [88]. Under these circumstances, only the QDs of a few layers will be semi-filled with electrons (the ones for which the Fermi level crosses the electron ground states), while the rest will be either completely full or empty. According to the ideal IBSC theory, full QDs are ineffective for VB–IB photon absorption processes and the empty ones are ineffective for photon absorptions that should cause transitions from the IB to the CB. In addition, tunneling of carriers from the QD confined states to the CB is possible in this structure, which makes voltage preservation impossible (this will be further discussed in the next section). These problems can be solved by inserting a thin, conventional n-layer adjacent to the p-emitter and a thin p-layer next to the n-emitter to sustain the built-in field [12]. This kind of layers are called 'field damping layers' (FDLs) and the way to optimize their design for a certain QD-IBSC structure has been expounded in detail in Reference 96. The structure in **Figure 12(b)** includes FDLs.

Finally, the third possibility shown in **Figure 12(c)** has thicker GaAs spacers between the QD layers (84 vs. 10 nm). This possibility constitutes an alternative solution to the tunneling problem [94]. A second motivation for the insertion of thick spacers in the QD-IBSC structure is to allow the dilution of the strain produced by the deposition of a QD layer before the next layer is grown. This is expected to avoid the formation of defects by inelastic strain relaxation, improving the general material quality, and preventing the emitter degradation found in our previous batches. Hence, it seems that it is possible to grow a high number of QD layers using this new approach, without the need of implementing strain compensation growth techniques.

Some QD-IBSC designs reported in the literature implement strain compensation strategies in order to avoid strain built-up effects. They consist in using as spacer material GaNAs [59] or GaAsP [57, 58, 60]. The lattice constant of the alloy is smaller than that of InAs, so that the averaged lattice constant of the InAs QD layer + spacer system is similar to the GaAs substrate lattice constant [97]. Although the application of strain compensation methods has been very useful in some cases to increase the VB–IB sub-bandgap absorption, it may compromise other aspects of the QD-IBSC performance, in particular the always problematic split between IB and CB. The use of GaNAs reduces the E_L gap [59]. In Reference 60, it is noted that the conditions needed to achieve strict strain-balance using GaAsP in thin spacers (< 20 nm) also leads to a narrower E_L gap.

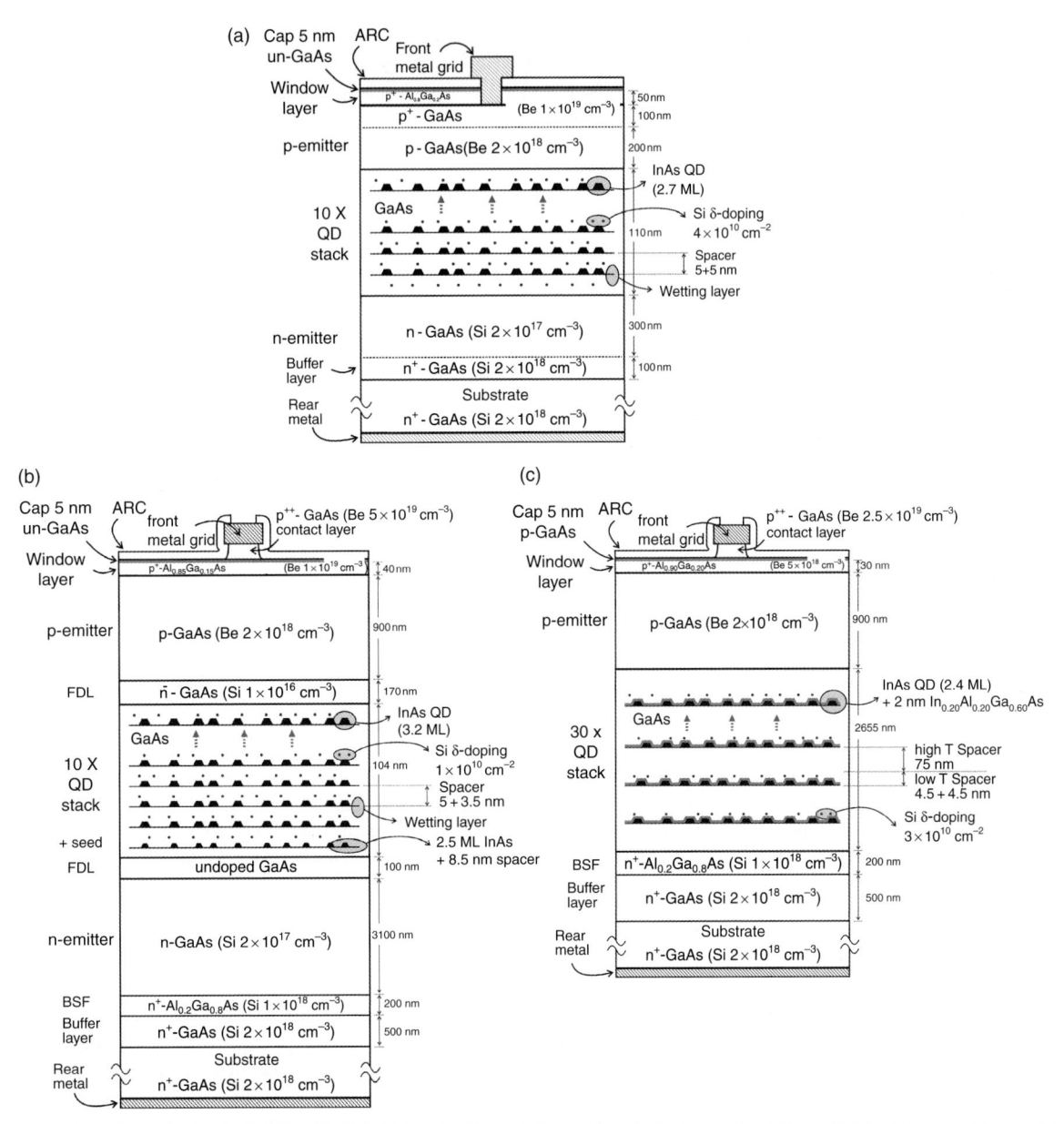

Figure 12 Evolution during the last years of the InAs/GaAs QD-IBSC prototypes fabricated by University of Glasgow/IES – Universidad Politécnica de Madrid. The first sample in (a) has a simple structure with 10 QD layers separated by thin spacers. In (b), field dumping layers were introduced to put the QD stack in a flat band region. Another possibility is to use thicker GaAs spacers as shown in (c). In this last structure, the number of layers could be increased to 30 because the thicker spacer dilutes the strain.

1.29.4.3 Proof of the Concept

The quantum efficiency (QE) of the very early QD-IBSC devices already showed the production of photocurrent for below bandgap energy photons (**Figure 13**). However, this result does not necessarily mean that they are behaving according to the IBSC model. It is possible that the monochromatic photons used in the QE measurement are only absorbed in one sub-bandgap transition, and that the photocurrent is extracted because carriers escape (thermally or by tunnel) to the other band instead of undergoing a second photon absorption. In particular, in the case of InAs/GaAs QDs it was expected that the IB-CB optical transition could be supplanted by thermal escape, since the E_L gap is so small in this structures (more details about this problem are given in the next section). As discussed when presenting the IBSC model, under that situation the principle of voltage preservation cannot be achieved, which states that the output voltage of an IBSC is limited by the wider bandgap E_G, and not by the sub-bandgaps E_L or E_H. The QD-IBSC prototype behaves then just as a solar cell with tailored bandgap and is subjected to the Shockley-Queisser limit.

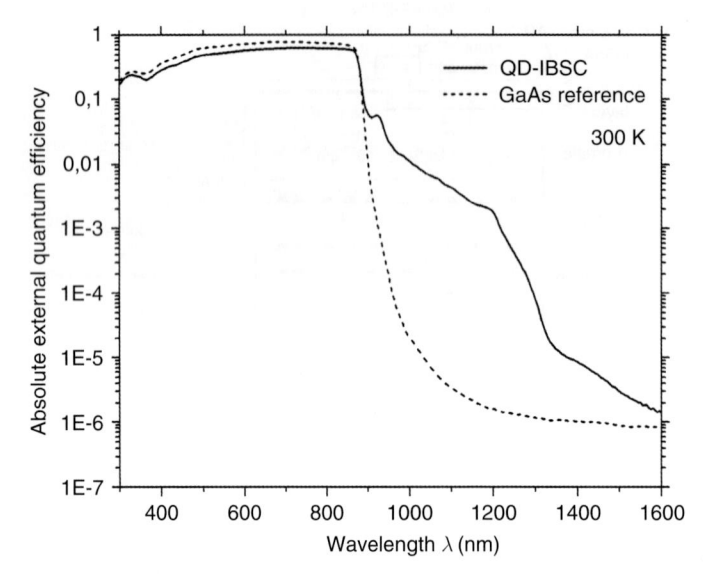

Figure 13 Example comparing the quantum efficiency of a quantum dot InAs/GaAs solar cell and a GaAs single-gap control cell. Extracted from Antolín E, Martí A, Stanley CR, et al. (2008) Low temperature characterization of the photocurrent produced by two-photon transitions in a quantum dot intermediate band solar cell. *Thin Solid Films* 516: 6919–6923 [92].

It was necessary to define and perform two proof-of-concept experiments to clarify whether InAs/GaAs QDs have the potential to fulfill the IBSC principles. Both were conducted at low temperatures and showed a positive result after optimization of the QD stack and QD-IBSC design. Now the goal is to improve the quality of IB materials to achieve similar properties at room temperature.

The first experiment aimed to proof unambiguously that the QD-IBSC is capable to produce photocurrent due to "two sub-bandgap photon absorption", that is, electron–hole pairs generated by the confluence of the absorption of one sub-bandgap photon in a VB → IB transition and the absorption of another sub-bandgap photon in an IB → CB transition. In the demonstrative experiment the QD-IBSC prototype was illuminated with two light sources: one of them (the primary source) with variable photon energies between E_H and E_G, the other (the secondary source) with fixed photon energies between E_L and E_H. To distinguish the photocurrent produced by any of them or by their confluence, the secondary source was frequency modulated while the primary (see **Figure 14**). Also, the photocurrent was extracted under short-circuit conditions to discard photoconductive effects. A representative result of this experiment is given in **Figure 14**. Further details can be found in References [89, 91, 92].

The second experiment showed that properly designed QD-IBSCs are capable of achieving an open-circuit voltage (V_{OC}) that surpasses the energy (divided by the electron charge) of the sub-bandgap photons that it absorbs. This constitutes a measurable confirmation of the voltage preservation principle of the IBSC model. **Figure 15** shows results of this experiment when applied to two different QD-IBSC prototypes (from [95]): plot **Figure 15(b)** corresponds to the prototype depicted in **Figure 12(a)** and plot **Figure 15(c)** corresponds to **Figure 12(c)**. Finally, **Figure 15(a)** shows the behavior of a GaAs reference cell. In the case of the reference cell, the V_{OC} (black circles) increases as the temperature is lowered, approaching E_G (solid black line). The QD-IBSC in **Figure 15(b)** shows proper IBSC voltage preservation, since its V_{OC} also approaches E_G although E_H is much lower (red line). The values of E_H have been extracted from QE measurements and they are not plotted for lower temperatures because the sub-bandgap QE is suppressed. This fact is in itself a demonstration that thermal escape from the IB to the CB has been suppressed. The QD-IBSC prototype in **Figure 15(c)** does not behave as a proper IBSC even at the lowest temperatures, since its V_{OC} is limited by the position of the IB. This problem has been explained by the existence of tunneling mechanisms that let carrier escape from the IB to the CB independently of the temperature.

1.29.4.4 Strategies to Boost the Efficiency of the QD-IBSC

In this section, we will review the limitations found in the InAs/GaAs QD system for implementation of a QD-IBSC. We will also review the strategies that are being explored in order to achieve a QD-IBSC capable of operating with high efficiency at room temperature.

First, the gap of GaAs, 1.4 eV, is too low to fabricate a very efficient IBSC. A gap of about 2 eV would be required. But this is not the only limiting factor. Most of the problems of the InAs/GaAs-based IBSC are strain related. The QD synthesis is based on the Stranski–Krastanov (S-K) growth mode, in which nano-islands nucleate on top of a thin WL with certain critical thickness [65]. This process is triggered by the elastic relaxation of the strain that appears between the two materials, which have a large lattice mismatch. However, as depicted in **Figure 16**, the band diagram is severely affected by the presence of strain. The InAs gap is blue-shifted from 0.36 to ~0.7 eV, and the sub-gaps become extremely asymmetric: E_H is typically over 1 eV, while E_L is in the range of 0.2 eV. This makes that the electron populations of CB and IB (i.e., ε_{Fe} and ε_{FIB}) cannot be split at room temperature. The situation is worsened because the

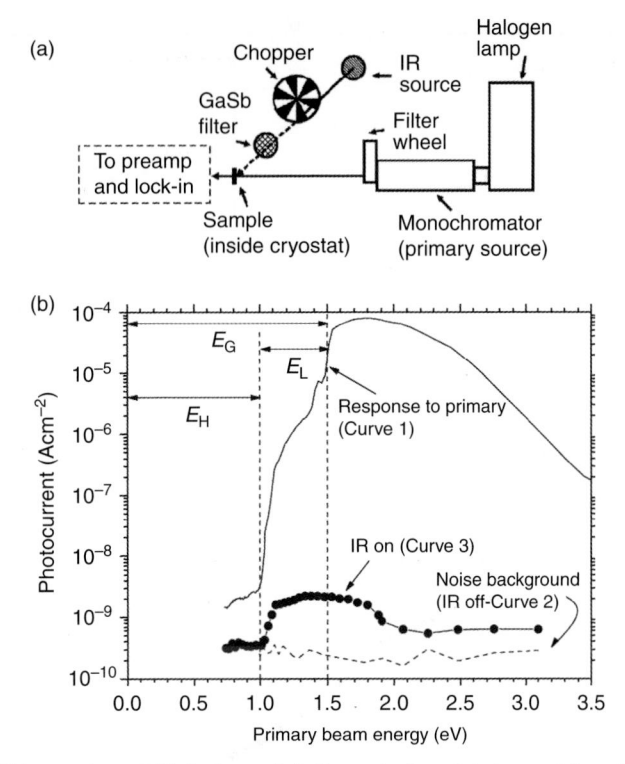

Figure 14 (a) Modified quantum efficiency setup suitable to demonstrate the production of photocurrent from the absorption of two below bandgap energy photons. (b) Results of the measurement showing the photocurrent produced in the QD-IBSC samples as a function of the energy of the photons of the primary light source. Curve 1 (response to primary) represents the photocurrent produced when pumping with the chopped primary source only (cell biased at −1.5 V, T = 4.2 K). Curve 2 (noise background) is the photocurrent measured when the IR source is off while the chopper, located in front of the of the IR source, is kept spinning (cell biased at 0 V, T = 36 K). Curve 3 (IR on) is the photo-generated current when the IR source is turned on and chopped (cell biased at 0 V, T = 36 K). Extracted from Martí A, Antolin E, Stanley CR, et al. (2006) Production of photocurrent due to intermediate-to-conduction-band transitions: A demonstration of a key operating principle of the intermediate-band solar cell. *Physical Review Letters* 97: 247701–247704 [89].

strain also induces a degradation of the shape of the dots, which tend to have a very wide base and small height. This shape results in a high number of extra confined states for electrons. We have identified that this situation reduces the absorption in intraband (IB → CB) transitions [98] and enhances the thermal connection between IB and CB [99, 100]. Besides, the existence of a WL also degrades the QD material properties because it contributes to a fast nonradiative relaxation of carriers from the CB to the IB [99].

The fact that the quasi-Fermi levels ε_{Fe} and ε_{FIB} cannot be split at room temperature is a fundamental drawback of present QD-IBSC prototypes. It explains why voltage preservation could be realized only for the moment at low temperatures [95].

With these considerations in mind, there are two possible strategies for the development of the QD-IBSC. One is to continue using the III-V S-K approach, but with introducing important variations in the QD material system. To maintain the S-K approach means most likely to keep fighting the effects of strain with techniques as reported in References 57–60. The second strategy is to move away from the InAs/GaAs QD family toward a completely different set of materials. We will give some examples of these two approaches in the following two subsections.

1.29.4.4.1 Improved InAs/GaAs QDs

One possibility to enlarge the IB–CB gap in order to reduce thermal escape and improve optical absorption is the capping of the InAs QDs with a thin InAlGaAs strain relief layer [94]. It has been demonstrated in the context of QD lasers and LEDs that the use of InGaAs or InAlGaAs SRLs is an effective method to red-shift E_H [101–105]. It has been proposed that this red-shift is produced by an increase in the effective height/size of the QDs in the presence of an SRL [102–104] and also that the reduction of the local strain in the QDs may avoid, to some extent, the blue-shifting of the InAs bandgap energy [101, 105]. However, for the QD-IBSC application, the red-shift of E_H alone is not a solution if E_L is not increased at the same time. For example, if an InGaAs SRL was applied, the SRL would form a QW adjacent to the dots. The E_H gap would be reduced due to strain relief, but the effective value of E_L would not be as much increased, since the presence of the InGaAs QW would lower the effective CB minimum. To avoid this possibility, in the samples it is necessary to produce a quaternary SRL where the $In_x(Al_yGa_{1-y})_{1-x}As$ composition has been tuned to achieve a negligible CB offset with respect to GaAs [106].

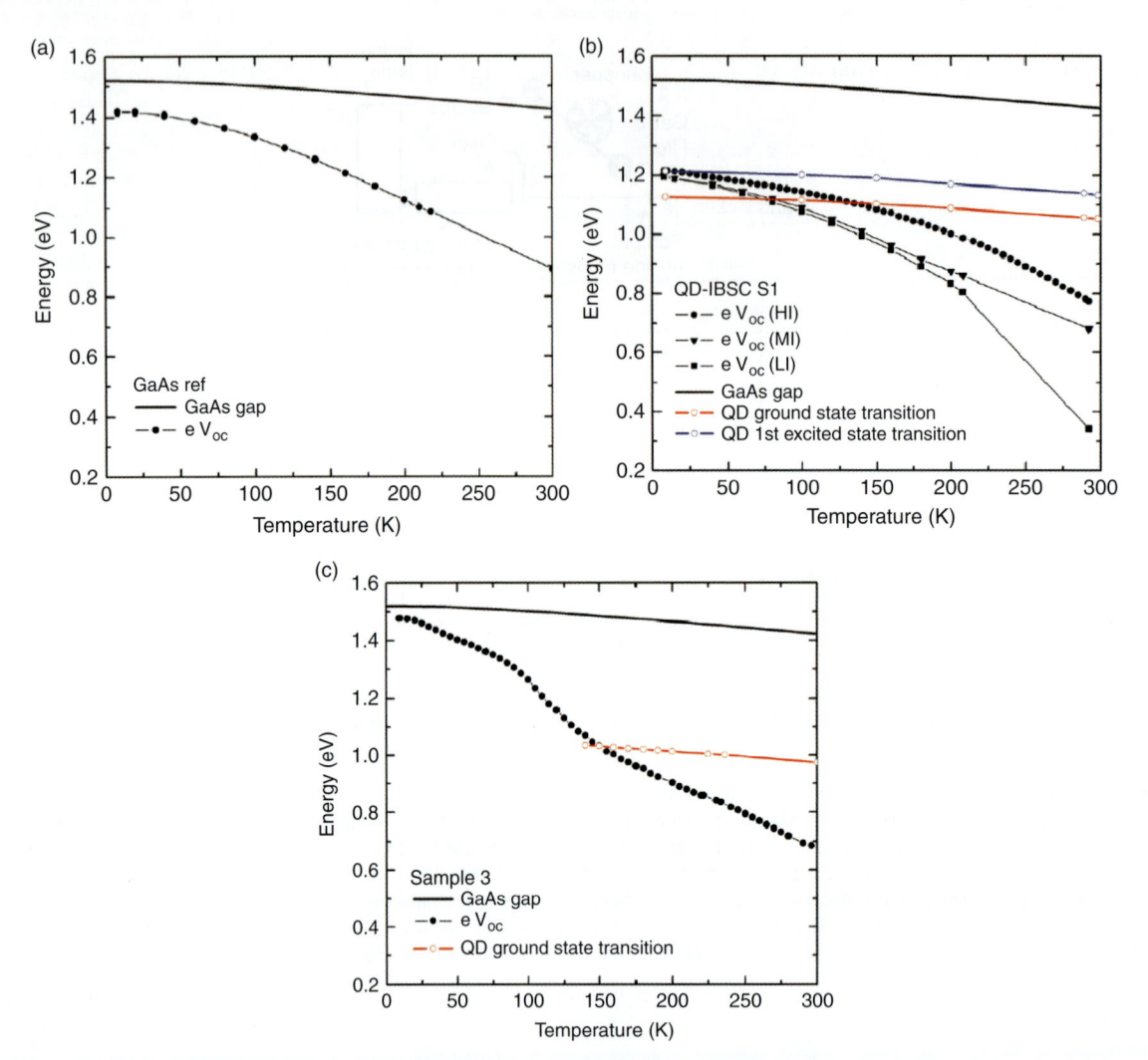

Figure 15 Comparison between open-circuit voltage (filled black dots) and location of the intermediate band energy levels (blue and red lines) at different temperatures for: (a) a GaAs reference cell, (b) QD-IBSC in which thermal and tunnel escape from the IB to the CB is not effectively suppressed and (c) QD-IBSC in which thermal and tunnel escape from the IB to the CB is effectively suppressed. The GaAs bandgap connected line is shown for reference.

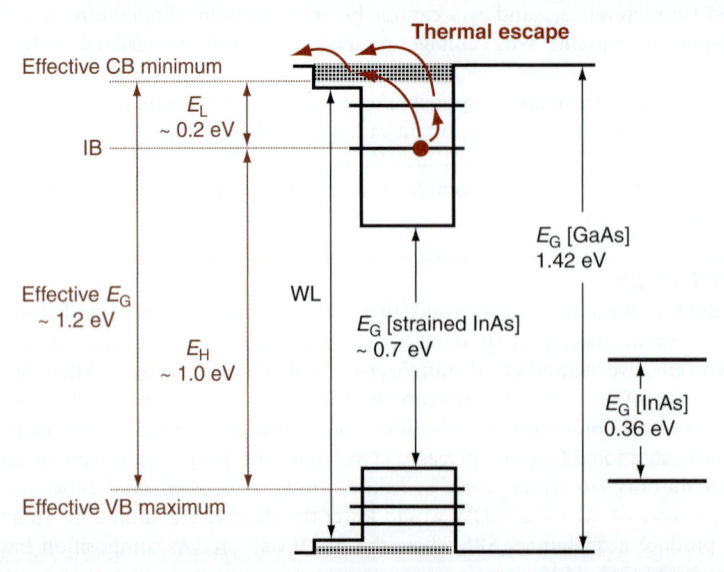

Figure 16 Simplified InAs/GaAs QD band diagram including the effects of strain and the WL. On the left are shown the corresponding effective bandgaps of an IBSC fabricated with that QD material system. On the right is included the band diagram of bulk (unstrained) InAs for comparison.

In Reference 94, QD-IBSCs have been fabricated using this capping technique and it was possible to estimate the thermal escape activation energy, E_A, from the thermal dependence of sub-bandgap QE. An enhancement of E_A indicates that the thermal carrier escape is weaker. It was found that $E_A = 224$ meV in samples with InAlGaAs capping, to be compared with 115 meV for the samples where QDs are directly buried in GaAs. The increase of more than 100 meV in E_A was related to the following observed changes in the electronic configuration: (1) the red-shift of the VB–IB gap, (2) the augmentation of the energy difference between the QD ground-state transition and the first transition involving excited states, and (3) the blue-shift of the WL absorption edge (due to the substitution of In atoms in the WL by Al atoms). The values for (1) and (2) are 0.974 eV and 101 meV in the samples with SRLs.

Although these results are encouraging from the point of view of the electrical problem, it is doubtful that the InAlGaAs capping can introduce notable room of improvement with respect to the optical problem, that is, the weak absorption between IB and CB. **Figure 17** presents high magnification TEM images of the InAlGaAs-capped QDs compared to QDs directly capped with GaAs. The dimensions of a significant number of QDs were measured on those images, leading to the histograms and the average values for width and height that can be seen at the bottom of the figure. The conclusion is that the aspect ratio has been improved because the height has been increased, but the base has not been reduced. According to theoretical modeling [98], the intraband transitions in these QDs are stronger between adjacent confined levels. Therefore, it would be boosted if we could split more confined levels, which would require a reduction of the base. Further experiments are needed in order to see whether a lower InAs content could lead to smaller dots with a similar aspect ratio.

Other modifications of the classical InAs/GaAs QDs are also being considered to improve the band diagram enlarging the separation between IB and CB. One example is to add N to the dot and substitute the GaAs host by a wider gap material (GaInP or AlGaAs) as proposed in Reference 107.

1.29.4.4.2 Non-Stranski–Krastanov QDs

In this section, we will present a different family of epitaxial QD materials, the lead salt QD materials, which are synthesized by a completely different technique than the S-K method. In this case, the QD and host materials have closely matched lattice parameters. Both have the same face-centered cubic symmetry, but the bonding configuration is different: lead salts crystallize in the sixfold coordinated rocksalt lattice and the host materials in the fourfold coordinated zincblende lattice. This lattice-type mismatch results in a large miscibility gap, that is, for a range of synthesis temperatures, lead salt QDs precipitate in the host zincblende material.

The most studied IV-VI/II-VI QD material system is PbTe/CdTe. The QDs are typically synthesized in a two-step method: first, a PbTe/CdTe multilayer stack is epitaxially grown, and second, the material is annealed to make the QDs precipitate [108]. In this approach the size of the dots is determined by the thickness of the PbTe layers grown. Diameters as small as 5 nm and areal densities over 10^{11} cm^{-2} can be achieved from a 1 nm PbTe epitaxial layer [109]. It has been demonstrated that PbTe/CdTe QDs are WL-free and can have highly centrosymmetric shapes (almost spherical) [108], they have atomically sharp interfaces [110] and they are strongly luminescent up to over 400K [110–112]. **Figure 18** illustrates how a QD-IBSC would be produced using this method.

The main advantage of this system is that the lack of strain between the QD and the host eliminates the problems illustrated in **Figure 16** for the InAs/GaAs QD system. Thus, the QD material gap is not blue-shifted. This, together with the possibility of growing small, centrosymmetric QDs (aspect ratio ~ 1) [108, 110–112], is expected to provide an advantageous band diagram for IBSC implementation: E_H and E_L can be maximized, while the number of undesired extra confined states can be minimized.

In a more optimized design, it has been proposed that PbTe QDs could be embedded in a $Cd_{1-x}Mg_xTe$ alloy to fabricate a high efficiency IBSC [113]. It has been calculated an efficiency limit of 60.7% for $Cd_{0.7}Mg_{0.3}Te$ as host material under maximum concentration. The reason to add Mg to the host material is twofold. On the one hand, it increases the host gap, making it approach 2 eV, which increases the detailed balance efficiency limit of the IBSC. On the other hand, it improves the lattice-matching between QD and host (see **Figure 19**). Other possibilities include embedding PbSe dots in a CdSe or ZnTe matrix, or embedding PbS QDs in a $CdS_{1-x}Se_x$ or $ZnSe_{1-x}Te_x$ host. The three families are marked by the red boxes on **Figure 19**.

1.29.5 Summary

The operation of the IBSC is first reviewed in this chapter. The principles of two-photon sub-bandgap photocurrent and voltage preservation are explained, showing how they lead to the theoretical efficiency limit of 63.2%. The two possible implementations of the IBSC, using impurity doping and QDs, are presented. In both cases, multiple references are given for different theoretical and experimental works where IB materials and devices have been tested. It is explained how it is expected to mitigate nonradiative recombination in impurity-doped IB materials by increasing the impurity density. With regard to the QD implementation, the design and properties of to-date fabricated prototypes are described, as well as the proof-of-concept experiments that have allowed the demonstration of the principles of two-photon sub-bandgap photocurrent and voltage preservation at low temperatures. The reasons why those experiments are not successful at room temperature using InAs/GaAs QDs have been analyzed and some alternative QD materials have been proposed.

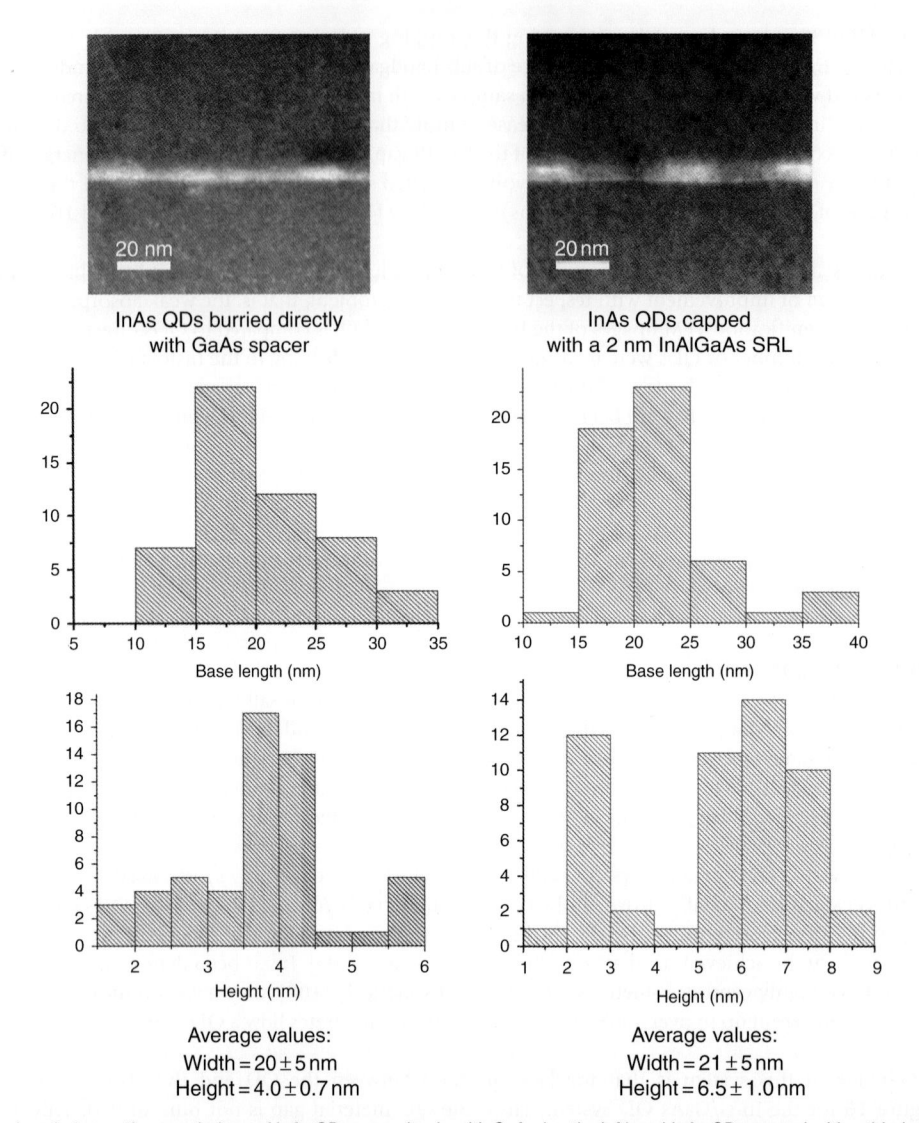

Figure 17 Comparison between the morphology of InAs QDs capped only with GaAs (on the left) and InAs QDs capped with a thin InAlGaAs layer before depositing the GaAs spacer (on the right). In both cases, the QDs are formed by depositing 2.4 ML of InAs under the same conditions. The top images have been obtained by high angular annular dark field scanning transmission electron microscopy (HAADF-TEM), a technique which is suitable for extracting reasonably accurate QD dimensions. The histograms show the occurrence of QDs dimensions in nm for the two samples and the corresponding average values and standard deviations are given below. The images and morphological data are a courtesy of Tersa Ben and Sergio I. Molina, University of Cádiz.

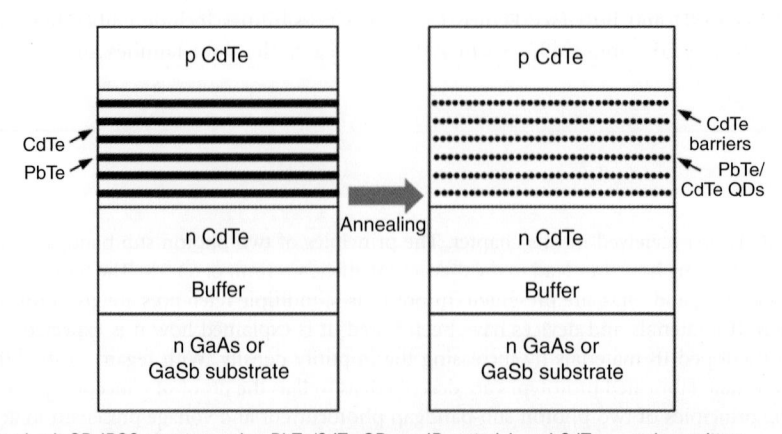

Figure 18 Example of a lead salt QD-IBSC structure using PbTe/CdTe QDs as IB material, and CdTe p- and n-emitters.

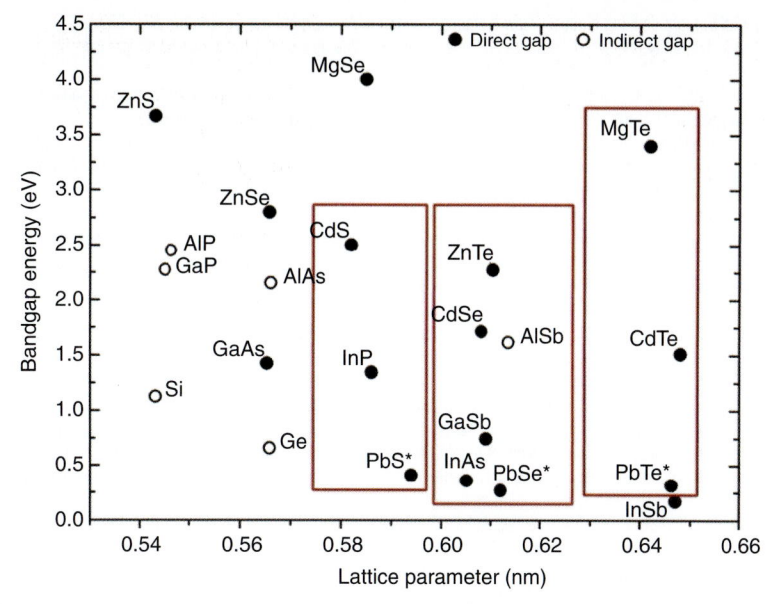

Figure 19 Bandgap vs. lattice parameter map, including most used binary compounds of the III-V, II-VI, and VI-VI families, and the diamond-like semiconductors Si-Ge. All values correspond to the zincblende structure, except those marked with *, which correspond to the rocksalt crystal structure.

Acknowledgments

This work was funded by the European Commission under the project Ibpower (Contract 211640). The authors are indebted to collaborators in their research group for assistance and fruitful discussion: P. G. Linares, I. Ramiro, E. López, E. Hernández, I. Artacho, C. Tablero, D. Fuertes-Marrón, M. J. Méndes, A. Mellor, and I. Tobías. C. R. Stanley and C. D. Farmer (University of Glasgow, UK) are acknowledged for the growth and processing of many samples discussed here, and S. I. Molina and T. Ben (Universidad de Cádiz, Spain) for TEM characterization. E. A. is grateful to Prof. J. Phillips and the University of Michigan for hosting her during part of the duration of this work.

References

[1] Green MA, Emery K, Hishikawa Y, et al. (2011) Solar cell efficiency tables (version 38). *Progress in Photovoltaics: Research and Applications* 19: 565–572.
[2] Shockley W and Queisser HJ (1961) Detailed balance limit of efficiency of p-n junction solar cells. *Journal of Applied Physics* 32: 510–519.
[3] Araújo GL and Martí A (1994) Absolute limiting efficiencies for photovoltaic energy conversion. *Solar Energy Materials & Solar Cells* 33: 213–240.
[4] Luque A and Martí A (2008) Ultra-high efficiency solar cells: The path for mass penetration of solar electricity. *Electronic Letters* 44: 943–945.
[5] Luque A and Martí A (2003) Non-conventional photovoltaic technology: A need to reach goals. In: Martí A and Luque A (eds.) *Next Generation Photovoltaics: High Efficiency through Full Spectrum Utilization*, pp. 1–18. Bristol, UK: Institute of Physics Publishing.
[6] Green MA (2001) Third generation photovoltaics: Ultra-high conversion efficiency at low cost. *Progress in Photovoltaics: Research and Applications* 9: 123–135.
[7] Lewis NS, Crabtree G, Nozik AJ, et al. (2005) Basic research needs for solar energy utilization. *Report of the Basic Energy Sciences Workshop on Solar Energy Utilization*. The Office of Science, US Department of Energy.
[8] Luque A and Martí A (1997) Increasing the efficiency of ideal solar cells by photon induced transitions at intermediate levels. *Physical Review Letters* 78: 5014–5017.
[9] Luque A, Martí A, and Cuadra L (2001) Thermodynamic consistency of sub-bandgap absorbing solar cell proposals. *IEEE Transactions on Electron Devices* 48: 2118–2124.
[10] Luque A, Martí A, and Cuadra L (2002) Thermodynamics of solar energy conversion in novel structures. *Physica E* 14: 107–114.
[11] Luque A (1989) *Solar Cells and Optics for Photovoltaic Concentration, Non-Imagining Optics and Static Concentration*. Bristol, UK: Adam Hilguer.
[12] Martí A, Cuadra L, and Luque A (2001) Quantum dot analysis of the space charge region of intermediate band solar cell. In: McConnell RD, and Kapur VK (eds.) *Proceedings of the 199th Electrochemical Society Meeting*, pp. 46–60. Pennington, NJ: The Electrochemical Society.
[13] Cuadra L, Martí A, and Luque A (2000) Modeling of the absorption coefficients of the intermediate band solar cell. In: *Proceedings of the 16th European Photovoltaic Solar Energy Conference*, pp. 15–21. Glasgow, UK. London: James and James.
[14] Martí A, Cuadra L, and Luque A (2002) Quasi drift-diffusion model for the quantum dot intermediate band solar cell. *IEEE Transactions Electron Devices* 49: 1632–1639.
[15] Martí A, Cuadra L, and Luque A (2003) Intermediate band solar cells. In: Martí A and Luque A (eds.) *Next Generation Photovoltaics: High Efficiency through Full Spectrum Utilization*, pp. 140–162. Bristol, UK: Institute of Physics Publishing.
[16] Cuadra L, Martí A, and Luque A (2004) Influence of the overlap between the absorption coefficients on the efficiency of the intermediate band solar cell. *IEEE Transactions Electron Devices* 51: 1002–1007.
[17] Martí A, Antolín E, Cánovas E, et al. (2008) Light management issues in intermediate band solar cells. In: *MRS Proceedings, Spring Meeting 2008*, vol. 1101E, pp. KK06-02. San Francisco, CA: Materials Research Society.
[18] Wolf M (1960) Limitations and possibilities for improvements of photovoltaic solar energy converters. Part I. Considerations for earth's surface operation. *Proceedings of IRE* 48: 1246–1263.
[19] Grimmeiss HG, Kischio W, and Koelmans H (1962) p-n-junction photovoltaic effect in zinc-doped GaP. *Solid-State Electronics* 5: 155–159.
[20] Grimmeiss HG and Koelmans H (1961) Analysis of p-n luminescence in Zn-Doped GaP. *Physical Review* 123: 1939.

[21] Grimmeiss HG and Allen JW (2006) Light emitting diodes – How it started. *Journal of Non-Crystalline Solids* 352: 871–880.
[22] Green AM (2001) Multiple band and impurity photovoltaic solar cells: General theory and comparison to tandem cells. *Progress in Photovoltaics: Research and Applications* 9: 137–144.
[23] Martí A, Cuadra L, López N, and Luque A (2004) Intermediate band solar cells: comparison with Shockley–Read–Hall recombination. *Semiconductors* 38: 985–987.
[24] Shockley W and Read WT (1952) Statistics of the recombination of holes and electrons. *Physical Review* 87: 835–842.
[25] Lang DV and Henry CH (1975) Nonradiative recombination at deep levels in GaAs and GaP by Lattice-relaxation multiphonon emission. *Physical Review Letters* 35: 1525.
[26] Luque A, Martí A, Antolín E, and Tablero C (2006) Intermediate bands versus levels in non-radiative recombination. *Physica B: Condensed Matter* 382: 320–327.
[27] Seitz F (1939) An interpretation of crystal luminescence. *Transactions of the Faraday Society* 35: 74–84.
[28] Lax M (1960) Cascade capture of electrons in solids. *Physical Review B* 119: 1502.
[29] Huang K and Rhys A (1950) Theory of light absorption and non-radiative transitions in F-centres. *Proceedings of the Royal Society of London Series A-Mathematical and Physical Sciences* 204: 406–423.
[30] Hall RN (1952) Electron-hole recombination in germanium. *Physical Review* 87: 387.
[31] Mott NF (1968) Metal-insulator transition. *Reviews of Modern Physics* 40: 677–683.
[32] Anderson PW (1958) Absence of diffusion in certain random lattices. *Physical Review* 109: 1492.
[33] Doany FE, Grischkowsky D, and Chi CC (1987) Carrier lifetime versus ion-implantation dose in silicon on sapphire. *Applied Physics Letters* 50: 460.
[34] Olea J, Toledano-Luque M, Pastor D, *et al.* (2008) Titanium doped silicon layers with very high concentration. *Journal of Applied Physics* 104: 016105.
[35] Chen JW, Milnes AG, and Rohatgi A (1979) Titanium in Silicon as a deep level impurity. *Solid-State Electronics* 22: 801–808.
[36] Rohatgi A, Davis JR, Hopkins RH, *et al.* (1980) Effect of titanium, copper and iron on silicon solar cells. *Solid-State Electronics* 23: 415–422.
[37] Wang AC and Sah CT (1984) Complete electrical characterization of recombination properties of Titanium in Silicon. *Journal of Applied Physics* 56: 1021–1031.
[38] Antolín E, Martí A, Olea J, *et al.* (2009) Lifetime recovery in ultrahighly titanium-doped silicon for the implementation of an intermediate band material. *Applied Physics Letters* 94: 042115.
[39] Wahnón P and Tablero C (2002) Ab-initio electronic structure calculations for metallic intermediate band formation in photovoltaic materials. *Physical Review B* 65: 1–10.
[40] Tablero C and Wahnón P (2003) Analysis of metallic intermediate-band formation in photovoltaic materials. *Applied Physics Letters* 82: 151–153.
[41] Tablero C (2005) Optoelectronics properties of Ti-substituted GaP. *Journal of Chemical Physics* 123: 184703.
[42] Tablero C (2005) Survey of intermediate band material candidates. *Solid State Communications* 133: 97–101.
[43] Palacios P, Sánchez K, Conesa JC, and Wahnón P (2006) First principles calculation of isolated intermediate bands formation in a transition metal-doped chalcopyrite-type semiconductor. *Physica Status Solidi (a)* 203: 1395–1401.
[44] Tablero C (2006) Electronic and magnetic properties of ZnS doped with Cr. *Physical Review B* 74: 195203.
[45] Palacios P, Aguilera I, Sanchez K, *et al.* (2008) Transition-metal-substituted Indium Thiospinels as novel intermediate-band materials: Prediction and understanding of their electronic properties. *Physical Review Letters* 101: 46403–464034.
[46] Lucena R, Aguilera I, Palacios P, *et al.* (2008) Synthesis and spectral properties of Nanocrystalline V-substituted In$_2$S$_3$, a novel material for more efficient use of solar radiation. *Chemistry of Materials* 20: 5125–5127.
[47] Wang W, Lin AS, and Phillips JD (2009) Intermediate-band photovoltaic solar cell based on ZnTe:O. *Applied Physics Letters* 95: 011103.
[48] Yu KM, Walukiewicz W, Wu J, *et al.* (2003) Diluted II-VI oxide semiconductors with multiple band gaps. *Physical Review Letters* 91: 246403–246404.
[49] Yu KM, Walukiewicz W, Ager JW, *et al.* (2006) Multiband GaNAsP quaternary alloys. *Applied Physics Letters* 88: 92110–921103.
[50] Walukiewicz W, Shan W, Yu KM, *et al.* (2000) Interaction of localized electronic states with the conduction band: Band anticrossing in II-VI semiconductor ternaries. *Physical Review Letters* 85: 1552–1555.
[51] Martí A, Cuadra L, and Luque A (2000) Quantum dot intermediate band solar cell. In: *Conference Record of the 28th IEEE Photovoltaics Specialists Conference*, pp. 940–943. Anchorage, Alaska. New York: IEEE and the Electron Devices Society.
[52] Bimberg D, Grundmann M, and Ledentsov NN (1999) *Quantum Dot Heterostructures*. Chichester, UK: Wiley.
[53] Sugawara M (1999) *Self-Assembled InGaAs/GaAs Quantum Dots Vol. 60: Semiconductors and Semimetals*. San Diego, CA: Academic Press.
[54] Wang ZM (2008) *Self-Assembled Quantum Dots*. New York: Springer.
[55] Martí A, Cuadra L, and Luque A (2001) Partial filling of a quantum dot intermediate band for solar cells. *IEEE Transactions Electron Devices* 48: 2394–2399.
[56] Martí A, López N, Antolín E, *et al.* (2006) Novel semiconductor solar cell structures: The quantum dot intermediate band solar cell. *Thin Solid Films* 511–512: 638–644.
[57] Hubbard SM, Cress CD, Bailey CG, *et al.* (2008) Effect of strain compensation on quantum dot enhanced GaAs solar cells. *Applied Physics Letters* 92: 123512.
[58] Laghumavarapu RB, El-Emawy M, Nuntawong N, *et al.* (2007) Improved device performance of InAs/GaAs quantum dot solar cells with strain compensation layers. *Applied Physics Letters* 91: 243115.
[59] Oshima R, Takata A, and Okada Y (2008) Strain-compensated InAs/GaNAs quantum dots for use in high-efficiency solar cells. *Applied Physics Letters* 93: 083111.
[60] Popescu V, Bester G, Hanna MC, *et al.* (2008) Theoretical and experimental examination of the intermediate-band concept for strain-balanced (In,Ga)As/Ga(As,P) quantum dot solar cells. *Physical Review B* 78: 205321.
[61] Blokhin SA, Sakharov AV, Nadtochy AM, *et al.* (2009) AlGaAs/GaAs photovoltaic cells with InGaAs quantum dot arrays. *Physics and Semiconductor Technique* 43: 537–542.
[62] Hubbard SM, Bailey CG, Cress CD, *et al.* Short circuit current enhancement of GaAs solar cells using strain compensated InAs quantum dots. In: *Conference Record of the 33rd IEEE Photovoltaic Specialists Conference*, pp. 1–6. San Diego, CA. New York: IEEE and Electron Devices Society.
[63] Luque A, Martí A, López N, *et al.* (2005) Experimental analysis of the quasi-Fermi level split in quantum dot intermediate-band solar cells. *Applied Physics Letters* 87: 83505–835053.
[64] Luque A, Martí A, Stanley C, *et al.* (2004) General equivalent circuit for intermediate band devices: Potentials, currents and electroluminescence. *Journal of Applied Physics* 96: 903–909.
[65] Leonard D and Krishnamurthy M (1993) Direct formation of quantum-sized dots from uniform coherent islands of InGaAs on GaAs surfaces. *Applied Physics Letters* 63: 3203.
[66] Stranski IN and Krastanov LV (1939) Akademie der Wissenschaften und der Literatur in Mainz. *Abhandlungen der Mathematisch-Naturwissenschaftlichen Klasse* 146: 797.
[67] Solomon GS, Trezza JA, Marshall AF, and Harris JJS (1996) Vertically aligned and electronically coupled growth induced InAs Islands in GaAs. *Physical Review Letters* 76: 952.
[68] Steiner T (2004) *Semiconductor Nanostructures for Optoelectronic Applications*, ch. 3. Boston, MA; London, UK: Artech House, Inc.
[69] Ledentsov NN, Grundmann M, Heinrichsdorff F, *et al.* (2000) Quantum-dot heterostructure lasers. *IEEE Journal of Selected Topics in Quantum Electronics* 6: 439–451.
[70] Grundmann M (2000) The present status of quantum dot lasers. *Physica E* 5: 167–184.
[71] Bockelmann U and Bastard G (1990) Phonon scattering and energy relaxation in two-, one- and zero-dimensional electron gasses. *Physical Review B* 42: 8947–8951.
[72] Benisty H, Sotomayor-Torres CM, and Weisbuch C (1991) Intrinsic mechanism for the poor luminescence properties of quantum-box systems. *Physical Review B* 44: 10945–10947.
[73] Benisty H (1995) Reduced electron-phonon relaxation in quantum-box systems: Theoretical analysis. *Physical Review B* 51: 13281–13293.
[74] Mukai K, Ohtsuka N, Shoji H, and Sugawara M (1996) Phonon bottleneck in self-formed In$_x$Ga$_{1-x}$As/GaAs quantum dots by electroluminescence and time-resolved photoluminescence. *Physical Review B* 54: R5243–R5246.
[75] Nozik AJ (2001) Spectroscopy and hot electron relaxation dynamics in semiconductor quantum wells and dots. *Annual Review of Physical Chemistry* 52: 193–231.
[76] Heitz R, Veit M, Ledentsov NN, *et al.* (1997) Energy relaxation by multiphonon processes in InAs/GaAs quantum dots. *Physical Review B* 56: 10435–10445.
[77] Inoshita T and Sakaki H (1992) Electron relaxation in a quantum dot: Significance of multiphonon processes. *Physical Review B* 46: 7260–7263.
[78] Li X-Q and Arakawa Y (1997) Ultrafast energy relaxation in quantum dots through defect states: A lattice-relaxation approach. *Physical Review B* 56: 10423–10427.

[79] Toda Y, Moriwaki O, Nishioka M, and Arakawa Y (1999) Efficient carrier relaxation mechanism in InGaAs/GaAs self-assembled quantum dots based on the existence of continuum states. *Physical Review Letters* 82: 4114–4117.
[80] Bockelmann U and Egeler T (1992) Electron relaxation in quantum dots by means of Auger processes. *Physical Review B* 46: 15574–15577.
[81] Fekete D, Dery H, Rudra A, and Kapon E (2006) Temperature dependence of the coupling between n-type δ-doping region and quantum dot assemblies. *Journal of Applied Physics* 99: 034304.
[82] Vurgaftman I and Singh J (1994) Effect of spectral broadening and electron-hole scattering on carrier relaxation in GaAs quantum dots. *Applied Physics Letters* 64: 232–234.
[83] Sosnowski TS, Norris TB, Jiang H, et al. (1998) Rapid carrier relaxation in In0.4Ga0.6As/GaAs quantum dots characterized by differential transmission spectroscopy. *Physical Review B* 57: R9423.
[84] Li SS and Xia JB (1997) Intraband optical absorption in semiconductor coupled quantum dots. *Physical Review B* 55: 15434–15437.
[85] Phillips J, Kamath K, Zhou X, et al. (1997) Intersubband absorption and photoluminescence in Si-doped self-organized InAs/GaAlAs quantum dots. *Journal of Vacuum Science & Technology B* 16: 1243–1346.
[86] Pan D, Zeng YP, Kong MY, et al. (1996) Normal incident infrared absorption from InGaAs/GaAs quantum dot superlattice. *Electronics Letters* 32: 1726–1727.
[87] Loehr JP and Manasreh MO (1993) Theoretical modeling of the intersubband transitions in III-V semiconductor multiple quantum wells. In: Manasreh MO (ed.) *Semiconductor Quantum Wells and Superlattices for Long-Wavelength Infrared Detectors.* Boston, MA; London, UK: Artech House.
[88] Luque A, Martí A, López N, et al. (2006) Operation of the intermediate band solar cell under nonideal space charge region conditions and half filling of the intermediate band. *Journal of Applied Physics* 99: 9.
[89] Martí A, Antolín E, Stanley CR, et al. (2006) Production of photocurrent due to intermediate-to-conduction-band transitions: A demonstration of a key operating principle of the intermediate-band solar cell. *Physical Review Letters* 97: 247701.
[90] Martí A, López N, Antolín E, et al. (2007) Emitter degradation in quantum dot intermediate band solar cells. *Applied Physics Letters* 90: 233510.
[91] Antolín E, Martí A, Linares PG, et al. (2008) Demonstration and analysis of the photocurrent produced by absorption of two sub-bandgap photons in a quantum dot intermediate band solar cell. In: *23rd European Photovoltaic Solar Energy Conference*, pp. 5–10. Valencia, Spain. WIP - Renewable Energies.
[92] Antolín E, Martí A, Stanley CR, et al. (2008) Low temperature characterization of the photocurrent produced by two-photon transitions in a quantum dot intermediate band solar cell. *Thin Solid Films* 516: 6919–6923.
[93] Cánovas E, Martí A, López N, et al. (2008) Application of the photoreflectance technique to the characterization of quantum dot intermediate band materials for solar cells. *Thin Solid Films* 516: 6943–6947.
[94] Antolín E, Martí A, Farmer CD, et al. (2010) Reducing carrier escape in the InAs/GaAs quantum dot intermediate band solar cell. *Journal of Applied Physics* 108: 064513.
[95] Antolín E, Martí A, Linares PG, et al. (2010) Advances in quantum dot intermediate band solar cells. In: *Photovoltaic Specialists Conference (PVSC), 2010 35th IEEE*, pp. 65–70. Honolulu, Hawaii. New York: IEEE and the Electron Devices Society.
[96] Martí A, Antolín E, Cánovas E, et al. (2007) Elements of the design and analysis of quantum-dot intermediate band solar cells. *Thin Solid Films* 516: 6716–6722.
[97] Ekins-Daukes NJ, Kawaguchi K, and Zhang J (2002) Strain-balanced criteria for multiple quantum well structures and its signature in X-ray rocking curves. *Crystal Growth & Design* 2: 287–292.
[98] Luque A, Martí A, Antolín E, and García-Linares P (2010) Intraband absorption for normal illumination in quantum dot intermediate band solar cells. *Solar Energy Materials and Solar Cells* 94: 2032–2035.
[99] Antolín E, Martí A, Farmer CD, et al. (2010) Reducing carrier escape in the InAs/GaAs quantum dot intermediate band solar cell. *Journal of Applied Physics* 108: 064513.
[100] Luque A, Martí A, Antolín E, et al. (2011) Radiative thermal escape in intermediate band quantum dot solar cells. *AIP Advances* 1: 0225125.
[101] Ustinov VM, Maleev NA, Zhukov AE, et al. (1999) InAs/InGaAs quantum dot structures on GaAs substrates emitting at 1.3 μm. *Applied Physics Letters* 74: 2815–2817.
[102] Ustinov VM, Zhukov AE, Kovsh AR, et al. (2000) Long-wavelength emission from self-organized InAs quantum dots on GaAs substrates. *Microelectronics Journal* 31: 1–7.
[103] Maximov MV, Tsatsul'nikov AF, Volovik BV, et al. (2000) Tuning quantum dot properties by activated phase separation of an InGa(Al)As alloy grown on InAs stressors. *Physical Review B* 62: 16671–16680.
[104] Nishi K, Saito H, Sugou S, and Jeong-Sik L (1999) A narrow photoluminescence linewidth of 21 meV at 1.35 μm from strain-reduced InAs quantum dots. *Applied Physics Letters* 74: 1111–1113.
[105] Tatebayashi J, Nishioka M, and Arakawa Y (2001) Over 1.5 μm light emission from InAs quantum dots embedded in InGaAs strain-reducing layer grown by metalorganic chemical vapor deposition. *Applied Physics Letters* 78: 3469–3471.
[106] Linares PG, Farmer CD, Antolín E, et al. (2010) In$_x$(Ga$_y$Al$_{1-y}$)$_{1-x}$As quaternary alloys for quantum dot intermediate band solar cells. *Energy Procedia* 2: 133–141.
[107] Linares PG, Martí A, Antolín E, and Luque A (2011) III-V compound semiconductor screening for implementing quantum dot intermediate band solar cells. *Journal of Applied Physics* 109: 014313.
[108] Heiss W, Groiss H, Kaufmann E, et al. (2006) Centrosymmetric PbTe/CdTe quantum dots coherently embedded by epitaxial precipitation. *Applied Physics Letters* 88: 192109.
[109] Groiss H, Kaufmann E, Springholz G, et al. (2007) Size control and midinfrared emission of epitaxial PbTe/CdTe quantum dot precipitates grown by molecular beam epitaxy. *Applied Physics Letters* 91: 222106.
[110] Heiss W, Groiss H, Kaufmann E, et al. (2007) Quantum dots with coherent interfaces between rocksalt-PbTe and zincblende-CdTe. *Journal of Applied Physics* 101: 081723.
[111] Koike K, Harada H, Itakura T, et al. (2007) Photoluminscence characterization of PbTe/CdTe quantum dots grown by lattice-type mismatched epitaxy. *Journal of Crystal Growth* 301–302: 722–725.
[112] Schwarzl T, Kaufmann E, Springholz G, et al. (2008) Temperature-dependent midinfrared photoluminescence of epitaxial PbTe/CdTe quantum dots and calculation of the corresponding transition energy. *Physical Review B* 78: 165320–165329.
[113] Antolín E, Martí A, and Luque A (2011) The lead salt quantum dot intermediate band solar cell. In: *37th IEEE Photovoltaic Specialists Conference.* Seattle, WA, USA.

1.30 Plasmonics for Photovoltaics

S Pillai and MA Green, The University of New South Wales, Sydney, NSW, Australia

© 2012 Elsevier Ltd. All rights reserved.

1.30.1	Introduction	641
1.30.2	Background	642
1.30.3	Surface Plasmons	642
1.30.3.1	General	642
1.30.3.1.1	Surface plasmon polaritons	643
1.30.3.1.2	Localized surface plasmons	643
1.30.3.2	Scattering Mechanism	644
1.30.3.3	Effect of Size	644
1.30.3.4	Effect of Shape	645
1.30.3.5	Effect of Material Properties	646
1.30.3.6	Effect of Dielectric Medium	646
1.30.3.7	Effect of Surface Coverage	647
1.30.3.8	Nanoparticle Location	648
1.30.3.8.1	Particles on the front	648
1.30.3.8.2	Particles on the rear	649
1.30.3.8.3	Particles embedded in the absorbing layer	650
1.30.3.8.4	Particles on a spacer layer	650
1.30.4	Nanoparticle Fabrication	651
1.30.5	Applications of Plasmonics in PV	652
1.30.6	Potential of Plasmonics for Third-Generation Solar Cells	653
1.30.7	Future Outlook	654
1.30.8	Conclusion	655
Acknowledgments		655
References		655

Glossary

Nanoparticles Particle sizes less than 500 mm.
Plasmons Oscillation of conduction band electrons in metal.
Spacer layer A dielectric layer used on solar cells for surface passivation or a layer that isolates the absorber layer from air.

1.30.1 Introduction

Photovoltaics (PV) or solar electricity is one of the most promising sustainable energy options of the future with virtually zero greenhouse gas emissions. It is one of the fastest growing sectors of electrical generation industry with a growth rate exceeding 30–40% per annum. The efficiency is increasing as a result of better understanding of the conversion limiting factors and innovations provided by fabrication technology and materials research. Silicon (Si) has dominated research in this area due to its dominance in the microelectronics sector together with a greater understanding of the technology. Since its inception, PV research has been oriented toward overcoming the high costs associated with Si solar cells. Cost reductions from both increased manufacturing volume, and improved technology are expected to continue to drive down cell prices over the coming two decades to a level where the cells can provide competitively priced electricity on a large scale and achieve grid parity.

The efficiency of single-junction solar cells are limited by the various loss mechanisms of solar cells, as shown in **Figure 1**, and has been limited to a maximum of 31%, which is the well-known Shockley–Queisser limit [1]. With the development of technology and fabrication methods, immense progress has been made with reducing intrinsic losses within a cell; however, fabricating cells approaching these limits still remains a major challenge mainly because of the two main losses – sub-band gap transmission losses and thermalization losses which together can account for 50% of the total losses.

Thin-film solar cells have the advantage of using lesser active material thereby potentially driving the cost down and for the same reason a shorter energy payback time. They offer additional advantages of efficient carrier collection while using materials with low diffusion lengths. Penetration of low-cost non-Si materials like CdTe and potentially CIGS into the thin-film PV market is also providing necessary impetus to the PV market to achieve grid parity and compete with fossil fuels. However, the major challenge for thin-film solar cells is reduced efficiency due to transmission losses since the thickness of the optimal photoactive material is likely to be much less than the absorption length of the semiconductor material, particularly when using potentially very expensive metals

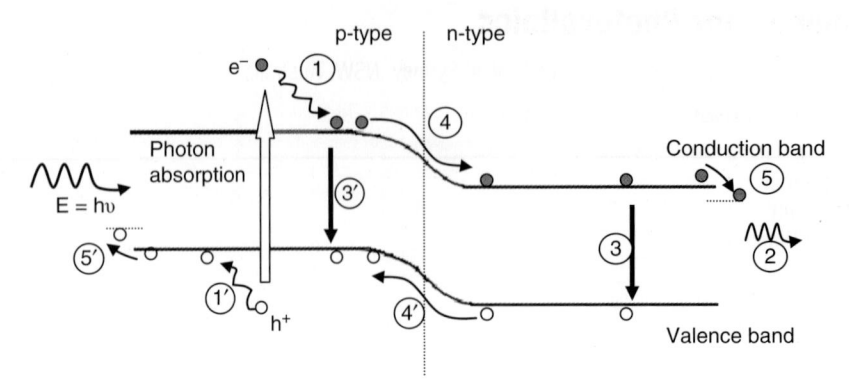

Figure 1 Loss mechanisms in a standard solar cell: (1) thermalization losses, (2) transmission losses, (3) recombination losses, (4) junction losses, and (5) contact losses.

such as Te and In. Hence, thin-film solar cells based on these elements and also Si due to its lower absorption coefficient require mechanisms for absorption enhancement.

In this chapter, one such light management technique is discussed, which makes use of the unique optical properties of metals on the nanoscale. The interest triggered in this area over the last decade has been so extensive that it has evolved into a new field of science called 'Plasmonics', which opens up a whole new capability of light matter interaction on the nanoscale. The application of plasmonics in the field of PV has been recent, but the potential is immense. In this chapter, an attempt will be made to give the reader a brief perspective of the mechanism, fabrication techniques, and some design considerations that have evolved over the last few years following the incorporation of plasmonics into solar cells particularly into Si solar cells.

1.30.2 Background

Si is an indirect band gap material and, hence, a weak absorber of light; therefore, the Si layer has to be quite thick for the material to be able to absorb most of the incident light over the full spectrum. Greater understanding of the material properties in the early 1980s led to the findings that due to the high refractive index of Si, randomizing the light to an oblique inclination in such a way as to increase the total internal reflection within the layer could facilitate light trapping [2, 3]. This light-trapping technique has the potential of increasing the optical path length by $4n^2$, where n is the refractive index of the material. This for Si would mean that the cell would appear 50 times thicker than the geometrical thickness of the cell. Hence, light trapping provides the potential to reduce the thickness of the cell.

Thick, wafer-based cells employ surface texturing as a means to enhance the optical path length of long-wavelength radiation. However, the feature sizes of these textures can be up to 10 μm, which are not feasible and realizable on thin-film structures that are as thin as 1–2 μm. Thin-film amorphous silica (a-Si) grown on nano-textured transparent conducting oxide (TCO) substrates like Asahi U-type glasses are being used as a means to avoid texturing the thin film directly [4]. But the increased surface area of the absorbing layer due to these features can substantially increase recombination losses. Though in practice it has been experimentally proven to be very difficult to reduce recombination losses beyond a certain limit, theoretically energy conversion efficiency of above 24% even for 1 μm cells can be achieved [5]. This highlights the need to incorporate better light-trapping mechanisms that do not increase recombination losses in thin-film solar cells to extract the full potential of the cells. Hence, novel wavelength-scale light-trapping techniques are needed to enhance the efficiency of thin-film solar cells. Plasmonics is one such technique that involves trapping light inside the cell by exciting surface plasmons (SPs) on metallic nanostructures. New photonic and plasmonic structures offer the as yet unrealized potential to take the absorption enhancement factor far beyond $4n^2$ or Yablonovitch limit with proper design due to nanoscale field confinement [6].

Plasmonics provide a simple and efficient way of increasing the efficiency of solar cells without significantly adding to the cost of cell fabrication. The optical properties of this layer are electrically decoupled from the cell; hence, they do not affect the cell properties or necessitate any major modification to the device fabrication process. They can be tuned and optimized independently at the final stage of device fabrication. Additionally, no recombination losses are introduced and it can be incorporated into any semiconductor substrate.

1.30.3 Surface Plasmons

1.30.3.1 General

Metals for PV applications are used mainly to provide low-resistance electrical contacts for solar cells, connecting them to the external circuit or as a backside reflector/contact. Because of their large free-electron density, metals make good conductors. However, for the same reason they can act as good recombination centers as well, which results in recombination in the metal-contacted region – a major loss mechanism in solar cells. Hence, great attention has been paid to metal contacts in the fabrication of solar cells in order to optimize the metal area to minimize recombination, shading, and contact resistance losses. How can metal nanoparticles then improve absorption in solar cells?

1.30.3.1.1 Surface plasmon polaritons

Metal nanoparticles have optical properties that are totally different from the bulk. SPs are the coherent oscillations of conduction electrons in thin metal films. SPs occur at the interfaces between metals and dielectrics where the real part of the dielectric function (Re(ε)) of these layers have opposite signs. This requirement is accomplished in the infrared to visible region for metals, where metals have negative Re(ε). These oscillations are accompanied by a transverse and longitudinal electromagnetic field, which has its maximum at the surface $z = 0$, decays exponentially, and disappears at $z = \infty$ [7]. This field that is perpendicular to the surface is said to be evanescent or near-field in nature, and decays exponentially with distance from the interface. Re(ε) < 0 occurs where a material is strongly absorbing; this strong absorption is responsible for the high reflectivity of metals. A schematic representation of the SP is shown in **Figure 2**. Its properties depend on the film thickness and the dielectric medium on both sides of the film.

Surface plasmon polaritons (SPPs, propagating plasmons) have a larger momentum for a given frequency than the incident photons, which prevents power from propagating away from the surface or in other words the propagation is nonradiative. For the same reason, there is a momentum mismatch between the photons and SPs; hence, to generate SPPs using light, the momentum mismatch between light and SPPs must be bridged, that is, both the frequency and wave vector of the incident light must be matched. The frequency-dependent SP wave vector (also called the SP dispersion relation) is given by [7].

$$k_{spp} = k_0 \sqrt{\frac{\varepsilon_m \varepsilon_d}{\varepsilon_m + \varepsilon_d}} \quad [1]$$

where the free-space wave vector $k_0 = \omega/c$, ε_d is the dielectric function of the adjacent medium, and ε_m is the dielectric function of the metal.

The change in momentum required for the coupling of photons to the SPs is provided by surface roughness or external means like prism coupling or attenuated total reflection (ATR) by increasing the wave vector of the incident electromagnetic radiation to match it with that of the SPs. It is beyond the scope of this chapter to describe these approaches, and we recommend additional reading for interested readers [7–9]. However, it would be worth noting here that surface roughness can excite SPPs, which could be an important loss mechanism due to lossy modes. This could have implications in the design of metal contacts/back-side reflectors for solar cells.

1.30.3.1.2 Localized surface plasmons

In contrast to SPPs, localized surface plasmons (LSPs) are oscillations of the electrons in confined geometries smaller than the wavelength of light, such as small metal particles or voids in metallic structures. Movement of the conduction electrons upon excitation with incident light leads to a build up of polarization charges on the particle surface, as shown in **Figure 3**. This acts as a restoring force, allowing a resonance to occur at a particular frequency, which is termed the localized surface plasmon resonance (LSPR) frequency ω_{sp} to distinguish it from bulk resonances and resonance on metal surfaces. The LSPR is predominantly dipolar in nature for small particles where $r \ll \lambda$ (where r is the radius of the particle and λ is the wavelength of the light). However, it has been shown that for Ag particles and light of visible wavelengths, higher-order multipoles can be neglected to a good approximation even for particle diameters as high as ~100 nm [10].

The surface roughness provided by sub-wavelength ($r \ll \lambda$) particles or voids that generate SPs locally can provide the additional momentum for the coupling of incident light to the SP. The LSPs can therefore be excited with light of appropriate frequency irrespective of the excitation light wave vector [11]. For the same reason, LSPs can also effectively decay with light emission/scattering, which is being exploited for PV applications. This is also used for applications like improving efficiency of light-emitting diodes [12–14]. Hence, metal nanoparticles for experimental work require no additional setup for SP excitation.

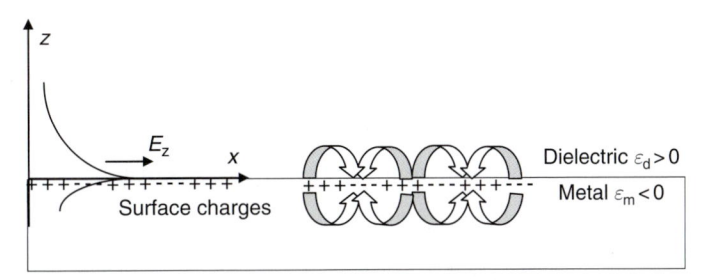

Figure 2 Schematic representation of a propagating plasmon at the interface of a metal and dielectric with the electromagnetic field at its maximum along the surface (x-axis, $z = 0$) and decaying exponentially at $z = \infty$.

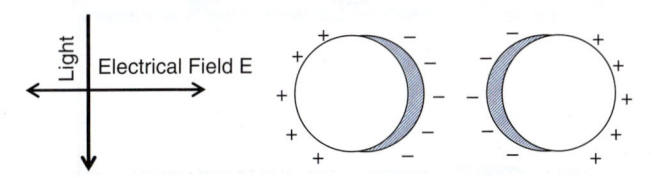

Figure 3 Schematic representation of an LSP for a normally incident light exciting a horizontal electric dipole.

The polarization of the sphere due to the presence of an external field can be calculated by applying boundary conditions and is given by the following equation:

$$\alpha = 4\pi_0 \varepsilon R^3 \frac{\varepsilon_m - \varepsilon_d}{\varepsilon_m + 2\varepsilon_d} \quad [2]$$

where the relative permittivity of the metal particle is $\varepsilon_m = \varepsilon'_m + i\varepsilon''_m$ given by $\varepsilon_m = \varepsilon'_m + i\varepsilon''_m$. The real part describes the polarizability, whereas the imaginary part gives the energy dissipation in the metal. Equation [2] $\varepsilon_m' = -2\varepsilon_d$ implies that very strong interaction occurs with the incident field when $\varepsilon_m = -2\varepsilon_d$ and $|\varepsilon_m + 2\varepsilon_d|$ = minimum. This occurs when $\varepsilon_m' = -2\varepsilon_d$ and $\varepsilon_m'' = 0$. The corresponding SP resonance frequency approaches

$$\omega_{sp} = \frac{\omega_p}{\sqrt{1 + 2\varepsilon_d}} \quad [3]$$

Therefore, the resonance occurs at $\omega_{sp} = \omega_p/\sqrt{3}$ for a metal sphere in vacuum, where $\varepsilon_d = 1$. The LSPR frequency is dependent on the size, shape, material properties, and the effect of the dielectric medium around the nanoparticles [15] and gives metal nanoparticles its strong and well-defined color. They determine the position and width of the plasmon resonance. Due to the confinement of the SP to the metal nanoparticles, excitation of SPs can result in selective photon absorption, scattering, and a giant enhancement of the local electric field in the close vicinity of the metal nanoparticles. Hence, varying these parameters offers tunability of the resonance position to engineer plasmonic structures to target weakly absorbing regimes of various types of solar cells. Therefore, the optical characteristics of metal nanoparticles are clearly different from those of SPPs and have been reviewed elsewhere [11]. We will discuss each effect in more detail in the following sections.

The resonant interaction between oscillating electrons and electromagnetic field of light gives rise to its unique optical properties, which have been exploited for centuries in luster pottery and stained glasses for the resulting colorful appearance. One of the best examples is that of the Lycurgus Cup from Roman times, which owes its unique property of appearing green in reflected light and red in transmitted light due to Au and Ag nanoparticles embedded in it.

1.30.3.2 Scattering Mechanism

The strong optical scattering (far-field) associated with SP excitation along with local-field enhancement are taken into advantage for increasing light trapping and therefore absorption in PV cells. However, for solid-state PV devices, the improved performance is attributed to the scattering process of the plasmonic structures as the near-field is limited to only a few tens of nanometers.

The metal nanoparticles are considered to be dipoles accepting the incoming radiation and scattering it at large angles. In the process, a fraction of the light is lost into air and the rest are coupled into the semiconductor layer. The scattering is preferential to the semiconductor. The high refractive index (or high polarizability) of the absorbing layer (i.e., for Si the refractive index is ~ 3.5) leads to a high density of available photonic modes; hence, most of the scattered light is coupled into Si, that is, $f_{subs} \gg f_{air}$, where f_{subs} is the fraction of light scattered into the substrate and f_{air} is the fraction of light scattered into air. The scattering process is at its maximum at resonance. The large angular distribution of the scattering process ensures that most of the incident light is outside the escape cone facilitating total internal reflection and thereby is totally trapped and absorbed. The coupling is most efficient when the dipole is as close to the semiconductor as possible. A schematic representation of the scattering process is shown in **Figure 4**. For particles on the rear, the principle is the same, but the mode of excitation of the plasmons is different leading to an enhanced scattering cross-section.

For efficient light trapping using plasmons, Q_{scat} (i.e., the normalized scattering cross-section) must be large and f_{subs} must be enhanced together with low Q_{abs}. The size, shape, material, dielectric environment, and distance of the particles from the substrate all play an important role in the scattering properties of these nanoparticles, hence leading to some important design considerations for solar cells. We will discuss each of them in more detail in the following sections.

1.30.3.3 Effect of Size

The extinction of the particles is defined as the sum of the scattering and absorption and is a measure of the interaction of the incident radiation with the metal nanoparticles. For small particles in the quasi-static limit, the scattering and absorption cross-sections are given by Bohren [16].

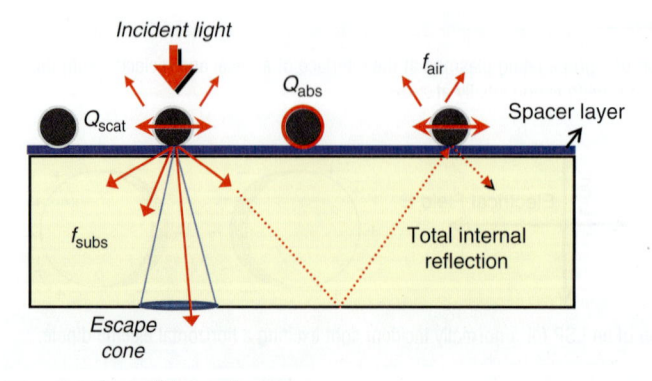

Figure 4 Schematic of the scattering process for particles on the front.

$$C_{abs} = \frac{2\pi}{\lambda} \text{Im}[\alpha] \quad [4]$$

$$C_{scat} = \frac{1}{6\pi}\left(\frac{2\pi}{\lambda}\right)^4 |\alpha|^2 \quad [5]$$

Here α is the polarizability of the particle, given by

$$\alpha = 3V \frac{(\varepsilon - 1)}{(\varepsilon + 2)} \quad [6]$$

where V is the volume of the particle and ε is the permittivity of the metal. The normalized scattering cross-section Q_{scat} is given by $Q_{scat} = C_{scat}/\pi r^2$, where πr^2 is the geometric cross-section of the particle. Away from the plasma frequency, the field lines are only slightly affected. But near the surface plasmon resonance, light may interact with the particle over a cross-sectional area larger than the geometric cross-section of the particle because the polarizability of the particle becomes very high in this frequency range, as discussed in more detail elsewhere [17]. For the same reason, the scattering is the maximum at resonance.

Scattering and absorption coexist in metal nanoparticles; however, one may dominate the other, which is determined by the size of the nanoparticles. For smaller nanoparticles (i.e., ~50 nm and less), absorption is the more dominant phenomenon, whereas for larger nanoparticles (i.e., ≥50 nm), scattering is a more dominant process. As the size increases, the scattering process increases significantly due to its dependence on r^6 (where r is the radius of the nanoparticle, as $V \propto r^3$), as can be derived by substituting eqn [6] into eqn [5]. The strong dependence of the scattering cross-section on the size of the particles makes it necessary that the size of the particles be optimized for the desired application. It is this scattering property that is taken advantage of for the application of light trapping in solid-state PV devices. Beyond certain limits, however, increasing the particle size results in increased retardation effects (due to inhomogeneous polarization) and higher-order multipole excitation modes, which decrease the efficiency of the scattering process.

The size of the particles affects only the scattering efficiency of the nanoparticles: the larger the size, the greater the scattering, and not the resonance position. This is consistent with the electrostatic theory and has been demonstrated by the work of Stuart et al. [18]. Reports of tuning plasmon resonance by changing the size is therefore attributed to change in the shape or aspect ratio of the particles as well [19] (i.e., valid for particles deposited by self-assembly technique), which is discussed in the Section 1.30.4.

1.30.3.4 Effect of Shape

The effect of shape of metal nanoparticles on the plasmon resonance frequency was studied by Mock et al. [20]. A change in the aspect ratio can also affect the shape of the nanoparticles, which in turn can tune the position of the resonance. A higher aspect ratio (i.e., ratio of maximum horizontal length to that of maximum vertical length) lowers the resonant frequency [21].

The shape of the particle can not only influence the resonance position but can also affect the coupling efficiency. Finite-difference time-domain calculations of the scattering from Ag particles of different shapes under normal incidence show that the f_{subs} of hemispheres and cylinders is more than that of spherical particles, as shown in **Figure 5(a)** [22]. This is attributed to enhanced near-field coupling due to its close proximity to the substrate when compared to a spherical geometry. For spherical particles, there is relatively weak coupling with the substrate due to the reduced surface area in contact, and for the same reason lifting the particle above the Si surface (i.e., increasing the spacer layer thickness) has minimum impact for spherical particles [23].

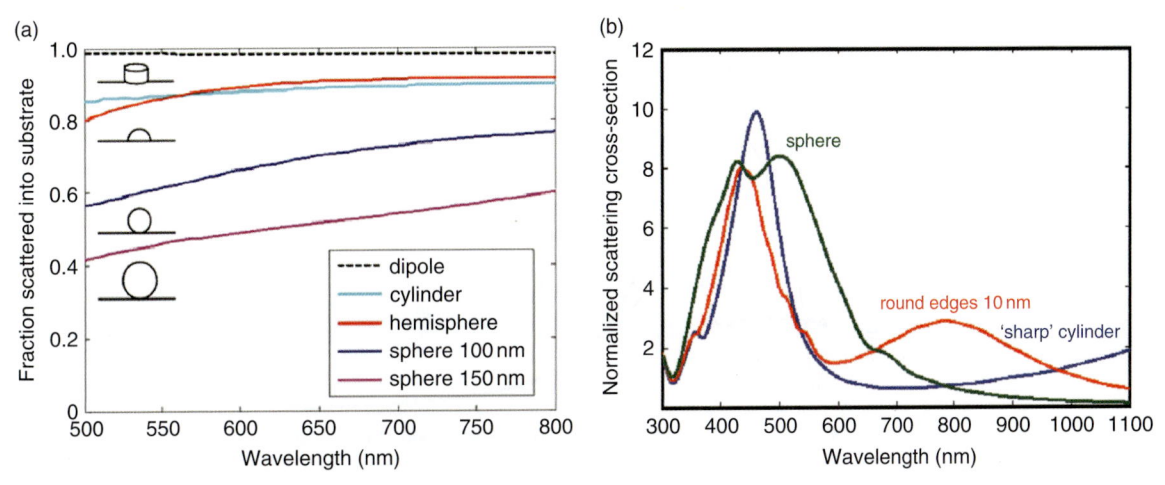

Figure 5 (a) Fraction scattered into substrate for each of the geometry. Reprinted with permission from Catchpole KR and Polman A (2008) Design principles for particle plasmon enhanced solar cells. *Applied Physics Letters* 93: 191113 © 2008 American Institute of Physics [22]. (b) Normalized scattering cross-section for different shaped particles (sphere, disk, hemisphere). Reprinted with permission from Spinelli P, van Lare C, Verhagen E, and Polman A (2011) Controlling Fano lineshapes in plasmon-mediated light coupling into a substrate. *Optics Express* 19: 303 © 2011 Optical Society of America [24].

However, for hemispheres or disk-shaped particles, this would be close to the interface, increasing the coupling as well as the depolarization effects due to increased surface area in contact with the substrate. The dipole resonance is strongly redshifted when the shape is changed from a sphere to a cylinder due to substrate effects, as shown in **Figure 5(b)** [24]. For the same reason, lifting the nanoparticles of this shape above the substrate (i.e., increasing the spacer layer thickness) can cause significant blueshifting of the resonance due to the change in the dielectric environment. The dipolar resonance resides at the particle–substrate interface; hence, is more sensitive to the substrate index and couples effectively to the underlying modes. However, the quadrupolar peak in the short-wavelength region is situated at the particle–air interface and least affected by the substrate as seen in **Figure 5(b)** [24]. This is the reason why higher-order modes cannot couple to waveguide modes.

1.30.3.5 Effect of Material Properties

The particle material also affects the resonance frequency. For Si solar cells, the most common plasmonic metals used are Ag, Au, and Cu. For metals like Au and Cu, the absorption band lies in the visible region, whereas for Ag the corresponding transition is in the UV region at ~310 nm, leading to a highly dispersive dielectric function at optical frequencies on excitation with light [15]. This means that for a particle size corresponding to the same mass thickness of Au and Ag deposited, Au nanoparticles have a lower frequency resonance than Ag nanoparticles as is clearly seen in **Figure 6** showing the normalized scattering cross-section for 150 nm diameter particles in air using Mie theory. Recently, it has been proposed that Al could be a good candidate for a-Si solar cells since it supports excitation of LSPs above and below a narrow interband transition range centered around 1.5 eV [25].

The radiative efficiency (i.e., ratio of the scattering to the extinction) is an important parameter for plasmonic metals as it forms the basis for the scattering effect. Associated with metals are the parasitic losses, which need to be minimal as scattering and absorption coexist. Of the different plasmonic metals in consideration, it has been found that Ag is the metal with the lowest absorption and highest radiative efficiency, making it the most popular choice for plasmonic applications. Alloying the two metals in different ratios can yield resonances in between the resonances of the pure Au and Ag particles [26]. The resonance can also be tuned using nanoshells that have a dielectric as the core and a metal as the shell [27]. This reduces potential parasitic absorption in the metal.

Highly doped semiconductors and metal oxides can also show plasmon effects, but because of the lower number of free charge carriers, their resonance is mostly in the infrared, hence not beneficial for Si PV applications.

1.30.3.6 Effect of Dielectric Medium

SPs are known to be very sensitive to the refractive index of the dielectric medium within the penetration depth of the evanescent field. This forms the basis of plasmon application in biosensors as a sensing transduction mechanism [28]. The dielectric layer above and below the particles also strongly influences the coupling of the radiation modes. This has important implications in PV due to the different types of dielectrics used such as passivation layers, anti-reflection coatings, and so on.

The presence of a substrate can cause a redshift of the plasma resonance wavelength of the metal particles, and the peak can be further redshifted by completely surrounding or embedding the particle with a dielectric medium [20, 21, 29–32]. The electrons in this case sense the presence of boundaries and modify their collective oscillation accordingly by depolarizing interaction with the adjacent medium, thereby redshifting the resonance. From the surface plasma frequency given by eqn [3], it can be clearly seen that by varying ε_d the SP frequency can be tuned and that increasing the permittivity of the medium leads to a redshift of the plasmon resonance. For a simple case, the permittivity of the medium ε_d can be taken as the averaged dielectric of the substrate and the surrounding medium and can be written as $\varepsilon_d = \varepsilon_{av} = (\varepsilon_{sub} + \varepsilon_{ext})/2$ [33]. This equation is valid for thick substrates but has been used here in a general context to help understand the effect of dielectric overcoating.

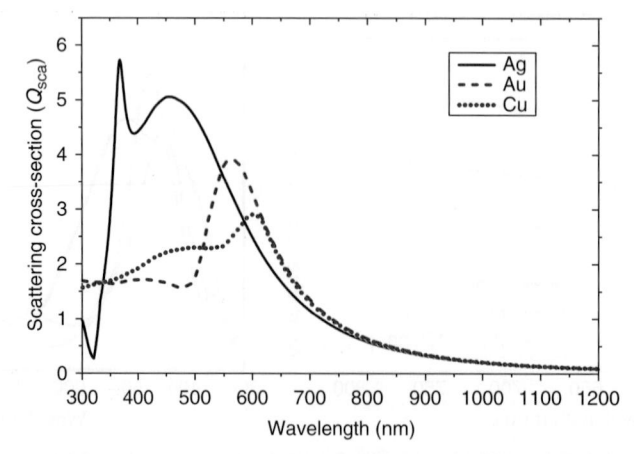

Figure 6 Normalized scattering cross-section for 150 nm Ag, Au, and Cu diameter nanoparticles in air showing the position of the relative scattering peaks.

Substrate effects form an important part of studying the plasmonic effect for solar cell application. For PV applications, the dielectric medium around the nanoparticles act in three ways:

1. It allows spectral tunability of the resonance position in the electromagnetic spectrum. The effect of the substrate on the SPs has been studied by many groups and the redshifting of the plasmon resonance wavelength with increasing refractive index of the substrate is well known [29, 34, 35]. The absorption coefficient of semiconductor materials drops close to their band gap; hence, shifting the resonance and therefore scattering closer to the band gap of the semiconductor materials helps absorbing more light by way of light trapping. A higher refractive index medium like Si tends to redshift the resonance due to depolarization effects.
2. It changes the angular spectrum of the scattered light, resulting in an asymmetric scattering profile with preferential scattering into the high refractive index material. This is because the scattering is influenced by the increased density of the optical modes in the semiconductor as is the case with Si, which is a high refractive index material. This ensures that more of the scattered light goes into the active semiconductor layer and trapped by total internal reflection. Furthermore, overcoating of the metal particles on a substrate can also change the resonance and scattering profile due to the effect of the dielectric layer.
3. The dielectric layer or spacer layer is critical for solar cells as it serves as a surface passivation layer both in the front and rear of the cell. However, it has been seen that the scattering cross-section will also be modified depending on the thickness of the spacer layer [36], due to changes in the electric field driving the resonance. The driving field increases with spacer layer thickness for particles located on the front, illuminated surface of the cell, whereas for particles on the rear, there is a strong asymmetry. This will be discussed in more detail in Section 1.30.3.8.4.

Mie calculations [37] show the observed redshifting of the normalized scattering cross-section Q_{scat} (i.e., normalized to the geometric cross-section) for 150 nm diameter Ag nanoparticles totally embedded in a dielectric medium in increasing order of refractive index 1 (air), 1.4 (SiO_2), and 3.5 (Si), as shown in **Figure 7**. The dipole wavelength can be shifted from around 450 nm in air to beyond 1200 nm using Si and is an effective means of achieving spectral tunability using SPs. This has also been achieved experimentally with shifts reported by varying the refractive index of the underlayer. For example, the shift observed was 200 nm as a result of varying the underlayer from SiO_2 to TiO_2 for > 100 nm diameter particles on the rear of Si solar cells [35]. A higher refractive index medium not only increases the redshift but also extends the tunable range of the plasmon resonance. A wide tunability in the range of 506–1310 nm was achieved by either overcoating or sandwiching silver islands with different dielectrics [33].

1.30.3.7 Effect of Surface Coverage

The effect of nanoparticle coverage is another important but less understood area of work. Apart from the substrate, size/shape, and dielectric environment effects, the interparticle effects can also play a role in affecting the overall response from the scattering layer. At present, the effect of nanoparticle surface coverage is one area where no experimental results have been established and is limited to numerical simulation findings. Lack of nanofabrication techniques with full control over the particles' parameters has been a constraint; but hopefully this will be overcome with newer techniques available in future. However, achieving an interparticle spacing of < 25 nm would still be a challenge. The optimal coverage of the nanoparticles would depend on the normalized scattering cross-section Q_{scat} of the nanoparticles – this means that if Q_{scat} is 5%, 20% coverage of the nanoparticles would be enough to scatter all the incoming light. However, losses due to outcoupling and interparticles' effects have to be accounted for as well.

Plasmonic nanoparticles with optimal distribution and diameters for different species of nanoparticles – nanospheres and nanoshells – have been studied theoretically for broadband harvesting of the solar spectrum [38]. In this study, it was found that

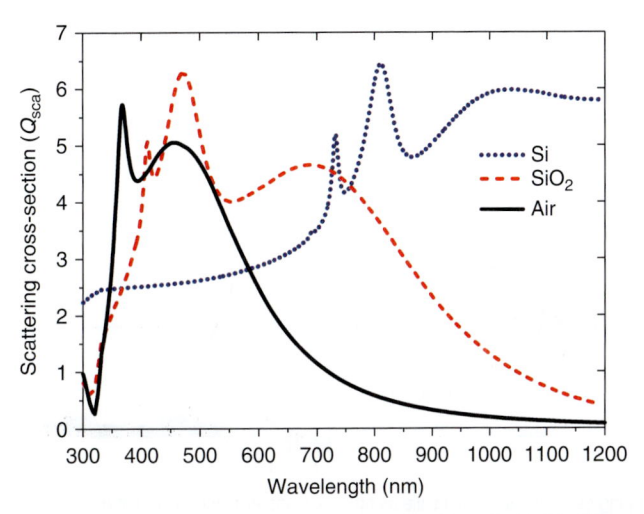

Figure 7 Normalized scattering cross-section for a 150 nm diameter spherical Ag nanoparticle embedded in different dielectric mediums: Si, SiO_2, and air.

30% coverage of 150 nm diameter Ag colloids on glass substrate could scatter 571.5 W m^{-2} out of an available 578 W m^{-2} of the visible spectrum. Optical periodic arrays of 150 nm high metal nanoparticles with a square base have been reported to provide maximum enhancement for a period spacing of 400 nm and particle diameter of 200 nm for particles on the rear [39]. As the particle size is increased, the resonance wavelength is redshifted, but larger period spacings are necessary to provide at least one diffraction mode propagating outside the escape cone in Si for long-wavelength light where light trapping is critical. However, if the grating pitch is increased beyond 400 nm, the nanoparticle coverage reduces to less than 20%, which can affect the light-trapping properties due to lesser interaction of light with the nanoparticles. Another optimization study comparing the size and coverage of spherical nanoparticles shows an inverse relationship between the two for particles on the front: 33% coverage for 60 nm diameter particles and 11% coverage for 160 nm diameter particles, provided the maximum enhancements for a-Si:H solar cells [40].

An interesting study used particle swarm optimization (i.e., inspired by the social behavior of insects) of nanoplasmonic arrays to achieve broadband absorption in the entire visible range. It follows that if the Fourier spectrum of a plasmonic array is almost flat, a large number of spatial frequencies are available. Unlike a periodic array, the nanoparticle clusters are inhomogeneously distributed so that photonic grating modes can be excited at many different wavelengths, giving rise to enhancement effects over a broad spectral range. Additionally, closely packed clusters resulted in higher field enhancement and stronger wave localization. The resulting structure had a particle density of 32 μm^{-2} [41].

1.30.3.8 Nanoparticle Location

As previously mentioned, the size and shape of the nanoparticles together with the dielectric medium around the nanoparticles and the metal properties determine the resonance position and scattering properties of the plasmons. In addition, the location of the metal nanoparticles is an important parameter that needs to be considered when designing a solar cell. Here we discuss the advantages and disadvantages of having nanoparticles on the front, rear, or embedded in the matrix, as shown in **Figure 8**. The effect of a spacer layer thickness, or in other words, the location of the metal nanoparticles from the absorbing layer, is also critical in determining the fraction of the coupled radiation into the substrate (f_{subs}).

1.30.3.8.1 Particles on the front

In this case, the particles are placed on the side of the device facing the incident light, as shown in **Figure 8**. The scattering mechanism for this geometry is as described in Section 1.30.3.2. The scattering of light by excitation of SPs can improve efficiency in two ways – by light trapping and by providing an anti-reflection effect as well [19, 42, 43], which is attributed to the preferential scattering property described earlier. Most reported solar cell absorption enhancements are for particles on the front [19, 35, 44, 45]. However, recent studies have led to a greater understanding of the scattering mechanisms and identified the drawbacks of this geometry [46, 47].

Metal nanoparticles normally are more absorbing in the shorter wavelength (UV regime) regions. For this geometry, any potential absorption in the metal cannot be avoided and can compromise absorption in the cell. Second, this leads to a suppression of light absorption in the regions below the resonance wavelength [48]. This effect is due to a phaseshift between the transmitted and scattered light of the nanoparticles leading to destructive interference below the resonance wavelength often referred to as Fano resonance effect [49]. In this region, the metal nanoparticles would be highly reflective, thereby compensating for the scattered light in the sub-resonance wavelength regime. This would mean that any attempt to redshift the resonance to target weakly absorbing long-wavelength photons would have a detrimental effect on the absorption of strongly absorbing photons below the resonance wavelength. Above resonance, the particles coupling light into the substrate are in phase and there is enhancement, which is largest for the nanoparticles corresponding to 16 nm mass thickness of Ag – the largest size nanoparticles of those compared. The effect of suppression in the visible region is clearly evident for these particles (blue circles), as shown in **Figure 9**. From the literature, it appears that spherical shape particles might be best suited for front-located nanoparticles for the efficient coupling of dipolar-like resonance of a sphere [23]. Introduction of a dielectric spacer layer between particles of other shapes can yield a blueshifted dipole resonance, but at the cost of coupling.

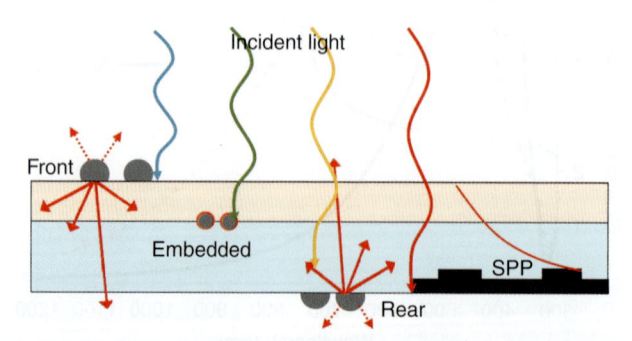

Figure 8 Schematic of the light-trapping geometries of solar cells using SPs: front, embedded, and rear case. The rear case can be scattering by LSPs or coupling to light using propagating plasmons.

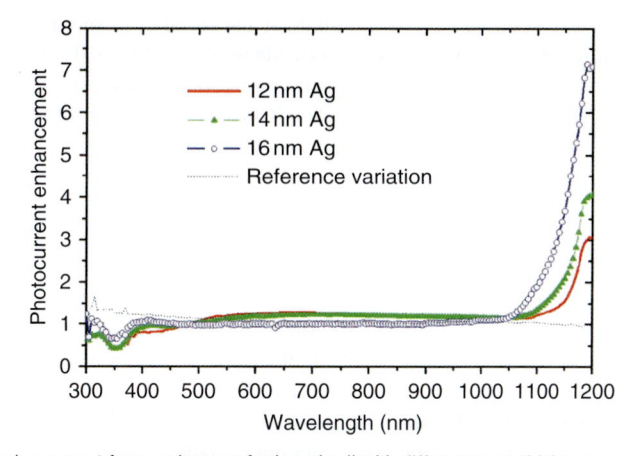

Figure 9 Measured photocurrent enhancement from a planar wafer-based cell with different mass thicknesses of Ag (corresponding to different size nanoparticles) on the front showing the effect of size. The effect of suppression (enhancement < 1) in the visible spectrum as particles size increases is clearly seen. Reproduced with permission from Pillai S, Catchpole KR, Trupke T, and Green MA (2007) Surface plasmon enhanced silicon solar cells. *Journal of Applied Physics* 101: 093105 © 2007 American Institute of Physics [19].

1.30.3.8.2 Particles on the rear

In this case, the metal nanoparticles are placed on the side opposite the illuminated face of the solar cell. The excitation of the nanoparticles in this case is by the light that is transmitted by the cell or, in other words, the light that is not absorbed but would otherwise be lost from the cell. Hence, no loss mechanisms come into play. By having particles on the rear, any potential absorption in the metal can be ruled out, as UV is absorbed in the cell. Additionally, the suppression of absorption due to interference effects is avoided allowing tunability of the resonance position over the entire region of interest. This effect is clearly evident from the results shown in **Figure 10** from front and rear depositions on a 2 μm poly-Si cell on glass. This geometry also allows for separate optimization of the anti-reflection layer on the front and plasmonic light-trapping layer at the rear of the cell. However, this geometry requires the solar cell to be bifacial at the time of deposition of the nanoparticles. Following the deposition of the particles, it can be combined with conventional back reflectors like paint or metal reflector to utilize light to its full extent. Enhanced photocurrent from rear-located Ag nanoparticles has been demonstrated for a 2 μm-thick poly-Si on glass cell and for 20 μm-thick microcrystalline Si solar cells [36, 47]. A further boost in the current was demonstrated with the use of paint and a detached reflector [47, 50].

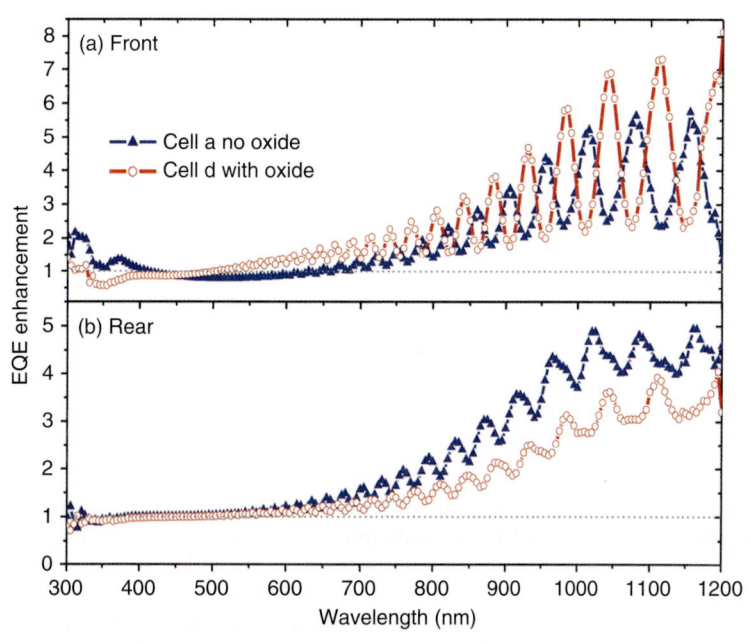

Figure 10 Measured photocurrent enhancements from 2 μm poly-Si solar cells with Ag metal nanoparticles on the (a) front and (b) rear of the cell. The effect of using 20 nm SiO$_2$ spacer layer for front and rear deposited nanoparticles is also shown. Reproduced with permission from Pillai S, Beck FJ, Catchpole KR, *et al.* (2011) The effect of dielectric spacer thickness on surface plasmon enhanced solar cells for front and rear side depositions. *Journal of Applied Physics* 109(7): 073105 © 2011 American Institute of Physics [46].

SPPs have recently been used as a way to increase photocurrent in an a-Si:H cell by incorporating nanostructured metal as a back contact [51]. Typically, SPPs are more difficult to couple in the outside world, and they also suffer from large losses due to field penetration into the metal. The nanostructured metal provides the necessary momentum break for the propagating SPs to couple to incident light and propagate in the plane of the semiconductor layer. In this case, a normally incident wave can be converted into a laterally propagating wave potentially absorbed in the semiconductor layer. The propagation length of the SPP on a planar metal surface is given by [7, 14].

$$\delta_{SPP} = \lambda_0 \frac{(\varepsilon'_m)^2}{2\pi\varepsilon''_m} \left(\frac{\varepsilon'_m + \varepsilon_d}{\varepsilon'_m} \varepsilon d \right)^{3/2} \quad [7]$$

which uses the complex permittivity of the metal ($\varepsilon_m = \varepsilon'_m + i\varepsilon''_m$) and where λ_0 is the free-space wavelength. From eqn [7], the propagation length is maximal when the real part of the relative permittivity of the metal is large (negative) and the imaginary part is small, that is, the absorption in the metal is small. More details on the experimental results using SPP is found in Section 1.30.5.

1.30.3.8.3 Particles embedded in the absorbing layer

Metal nanoparticles can be embedded in a medium if the metal does not degrade the performance of the cell. For solid-state devices like Si, this could have serious implications as the regions around the metal nanoparticles could act as strong recombination centers and decrease cell performance, as has been observed [52]. Moreover, high-temperature treatments during the fabrication process can affect the metal properties and precursor nanoparticle shape. Organic materials and metals exhibit good processing compatibility, and, hence, can be easily incorporated into the absorber matrix unlike solid-state devices. However, it may be necessary to isolate direct contact of the metal nanoparticles with the semiconductor layer using a dielectric layer to prevent exciton quenching through dipole–dipole interaction and charge trapping [53]. In the embedded particle case, the energy transfer between the metal nanoparticles and semiconductor can be due to enhanced electromagnetic field (near-field), scattering (far-field) effects, photo-emission, or a combination of two or more of these processes.

Nanoparticles buried in the material effectively act like small antennae, capturing and amplifying the incident light. If the semiconductor is placed close to the nanoparticle near-field, it can result in direct carrier generation [54]. This is because the nonradiative field in the vicinity of a metal nanoparticle is many times stronger than the field radiated from a dipole. Following this effect, 5 nm diameter Ag nanoclusters were used to enhance absorption in organic tandem thin-film solar cells [55]. The fact that 5 nm diameter particles are in the absorption size range rather than the scattering and that the enhancement exists far from the SP resonance wavelength validates the presence of near-field effects. For embedded nanoparticles where near-field effects are taken into advantage, the particle size can be small (i.e., 5–20 nm range). Such particles have a size in the range where ohmic damping dominates; hence, it would be more beneficial for materials with high absorption/charge separation rate (i.e., <10 fs which is the typical plasmon decay rate), but lower diffusion length as in organic solar cells as seen before, dye-sensitized solar cells [56], or some direct band gap materials. This calls for the use of larger nanoparticles where scattered power becomes comparable to the power absorbed by the metallic nanoparticles, leading to enhanced optical absorption in the surrounding absorbing medium minimizing any absorption in the metal nanosphere itself [53].

SP excitation of metal nanoparticles is also capable of resulting in emission of an electron directly in a preferential direction if the particles are placed inside an oriented electrical field. Direct injection of electrons has been attributed to the increase in photocurrent at the interface of an indium tin oxide (ITO) and ZnPc–Schottky junction using Ag metal clusters [57]. Similar reasons are given for enhancements observed from a-Si solar cells beyond 800 nm – a regime where a-Si does not directly absorb [58]. In this case, embedded particles have been utilized for a-Si cells where no high-temperature processing is involved following the incorporation of the metal, and the metal nanoparticles can be in the vicinity of the active layer.

1.30.3.8.4 Particles on a spacer layer

For Si solar cells, the surface can represent the largest possible disturbance of the crystal lattice due to nonsaturated or dangling bonds allowing energy states in the band gap. This can result in a recombination process via defect levels or surface states by a two-step recombination process best explained by the Shockley–Read–Hall theory, resulting in the loss of light-generated current and reduction in cell efficiency. SiO_2 and Si_3N_4 are known to provide good surface passivation and are thus extensively used on Si wafers – their effects are discussed in detail by Aberle [59]. They act by creating a new interface within the wafer. For monocrystalline Si cells, it is imperative that a thin layer of dielectric like SiO_2 or Si_3N_4 be deposited on the Si to reduce surface recombination and improve the electrical properties of the device.

The normalized decay rate outside the metal surface into each mode is zero at cutoff, but increases rapidly above the cutoff and then decreases thereafter. This suggests the need for an optimum spacer layer. Ford and Weber found that the decay rate is dependent on the overlap of the near-field of the dipole and the fields of the mode, so as the thickness of the spacer layer is increased above cutoff, there is good match between the dipolar and mode field due to mode field localization [60]. However, a further increase in the spacer layer thickness resulted in poor match of the dipolar fields due to the dissipation of the mode in the layer. Similar observations were noted by Soller et al. [61] for metal particles on Si waveguide structures. They found that when the mode is just above the cutoff, a large portion of the power carried by the mode is outside the Si layer, and hence, there is more interaction between the particle and the waveguide mode [61]. However, for a dipole that scatters light rather than fluoresces, the presence of nearby interfaces can also strongly affect the scattering cross-section and result in an angularly dependent scattering cross-section, which has been discussed in Reference 62. The waveguide can affect the scattering cross-section either by changing the dipole polarization or by changing the local driving field. The local driving field E_d is a superposition of the incident field and the back-reflected field from the interface, which is given by

$$E_d = K(\theta_{in})E_{in} \qquad [8]$$

and the corresponding dipole moment is given by

$$\rho = \varepsilon_0 \alpha E_d \qquad [9]$$

where E_{in} is the incident field and $K(\theta_{in})$ represents the linear transformation that is dependent on the geometry – position of the dipole and angle of incidence – and α represents the effective polarizability that includes the effect of the back-reflected field from the interface on radiative damping [63]. In the quasi-static limit, the dipole moment is proportional to the driving field E_d such that the scattered power Q_{scat} is proportional to $|E_d|^2$ [16]. Thus, the scattering cross-section is enhanced when the local field due to the waveguide is high and can increase absorption in semiconductor substrates. Hence, the effect of the spacer layer is an important parameter that needs to be considered while designing a plasmonic solar cell.

However, there is a trade-off between the benefits of increased scattering and reductions in the coupling efficiency as the particle is moved further away from the Si substrate [36]. A study on the effect of spacer layer thickness on the electrical quantum efficiency of a thin-film Si solar cell on glass shows a strong asymmetry in the response for particles in the front and rear, as also shown in **Figure 10** [46]. This is attributed to the effect of the driving field, which is predominant for front-located particles. For particles on the front, a dielectric thickness of 20–30 nm would be the minimum needed to provide good surface passivation without compromising for the coupling of SP into the underlying modes. On the rear, particles directly on Si (no spacer layer) provide the largest external quantum efficiency (EQE) enhancements due to enhanced scattering cross-sections and high-coupling efficiencies [47]. The results necessitate that the design considerations for a plasmonic solar cell be considered separately for the front and rear deposited particles.

1.30.4 Nanoparticle Fabrication

With developing technology, the challenges of fabrication and imaging of particles and features are being overcome, making it a lot easier and realizable in the nanoscale. Photolithography is popularly used in PV research to create features in the micron scale, for example, in electrical contacts. It is an expensive process, and the feature sizes in this case are limited by the diffraction limit of light. For PV applications, it is essential that the deposition techniques are scalable and economical for them to be viable. The impact of cost of incorporating a monolayer of metal to the device would hence be dominated by the fabrication process rather than by the cost of the deposited material. This section will cover some of the most popular deposition techniques used for plasmonics studies for PV applications (e.g., self-assembly, template deposition, colloidal deposition, nanoimprinting) being used and the challenges faced by each.

The self-assembly technique of nanoparticle fabrication is one of the oldest, simplest, and cheapest deposition techniques. The most widely used process for PV research is thermal evaporation of an ultrathin-layer metal (also termed the mass thickness) followed by annealing at low temperatures. The annealing process causes the metal to coalesce due to surface tension forces to form metal islands, as shown in **Figure 11(a)**. Hence, the surface properties are important for the island formation even for the same semiconductor material. The size/shape of the particles can be varied by changing the mass thickness of the deposited metal layer as detailed in Reference 19. This method requires minimal sample preparation, can be easily adapted to automated operation, and can

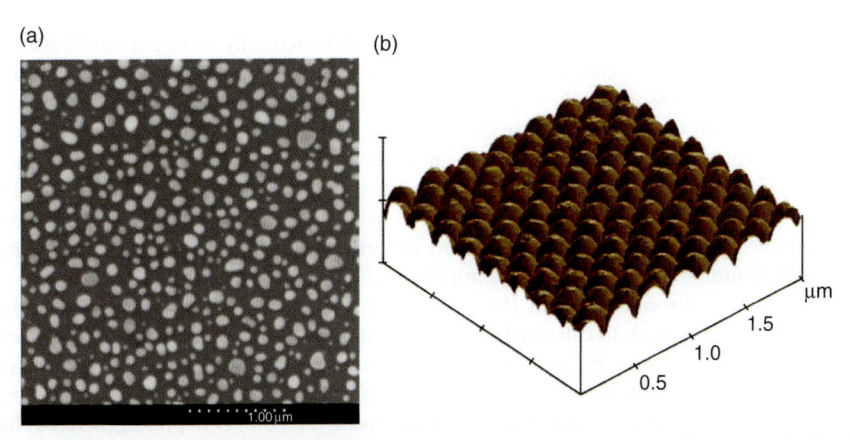

Figure 11 (a) Scanning electron microscopy (SEM) image of self-assembled Ag nanoparticles showing different size distributions. (b) Atomic force microscopy (AFM) image of a PDMS stamp used for nanoimprinting showing a uniform array of features.

be scaled up to production levels [64]. Nanoparticles fabricated in this manner show a broad resonance due to a varying distribution of particle sizes especially for larger mass thicknesses. This could be potentially advantageous for thin solar cell applications as the scattering would be over a wider wavelength regime thereby providing light trapping across the weakly absorbing regions of the electromagnetic spectrum. Though the resonance tunability from this fabrication technique is quite repeatable for the same substrates, the disadvantage of this method is obviously the noncontrollability of the particle size/shape and distribution. This form of deposition has been the most widely reported method for increased photocurrent from Si devices [18, 19, 35, 65].

Template deposition makes use of a template as an evaporation mask to deposit the nanoparticles, the feature dimension and coverage being dependent on the template properties. Anodized aluminum oxide (AAO) templates have been used to deposit dense and sparse metal nanoparticles on GaAs substrates, and an 8% increase in the short-circuit current density was reported [44]. This involves a two-step anodization process of aluminum sheets and the hole diameters are changed by controlling the etching time, whereas the particle height is varied by the deposition thickness; more details on this method can be found in Reference 66.

Colloidal deposition allows the use of prefabricated uniform size/shape of nanoparticles to be deposited onto cells by spin coating or dip coating techniques. It is a simple wet chemical process and easily caters for large area depositions needed for PV cells. But here again, the process is dependent on the surface condition resulting in a sparse, dense, or clustered distribution of nanoparticles. Schaadt et al. reported photocurrent enhancements using Au colloidal particles on Si photodetectors [45]. A similar study using Au colloids of 100 nm particles on a-Si solar cells gave an enhancement of 2.8% [42]. For solid-state devices, this process has the same disadvantage as the self-assembly technique in terms of controlling the particle distribution. Hence, other fabrication techniques that give more control over the particle parameters are being studied.

Nanoimprinting offers an inexpensive and scalable imprinting technique for nano- and micro-size features that could be easily adopted into standard solar cell production. It makes use of a prefabricated mask usually made by expensive lithographic processes like electron beam lithography, and the features are transferred onto a hard or soft stamp, normally polydimethylsiloxane (PDMS), as seen in **Figure 11(b)**. A thick sol–gel based resist is applied by spin coating over the substrate. The wafer is placed parallel to the stamp, at a distance. The stamp is attached by vacuum to a plate with grooves, which are sequentially pressurized to contact the resist-coated wafer. The sol–gel reacts at room temperature to form a solid. The grooves are then sequentially evacuated, which results in a smooth release of the stamp from the imprinted patterns. The stamps can be used for over 2000 sol–gel imprints without observed pattern degradation [51]. Unlike the self-assembly technique, this method enables control over the particle size, shape, and coverage and could also be used on large area and nonplanar substrates. The feature sizes in this case are limited by the mask.

1.30.5 Applications of Plasmonics in PV

Si solar cells are known to absorb the short-wavelength photons quite strongly; however, the absorption coefficient drops closer to the band gap of Si. Hence, light trapping is more critical, particularly at longer wavelengths. This can be achieved by redshifting of resonance that leads to an increase in scattering cross-section at longer wavelengths, which would be beneficial for increasing the absorption of Si solar cells because of the indirect band gap of Si. The effectiveness of the light trapping provided by the metal nanoparticles is assessed by a comparison between the current collection (i.e, using spectral response measurements) and optical absorptance, before and after the deposition on the same cell. Based on the cell design and material, the near-field, scattering (far-field), or direct charge generation effects are exploited for solar cell applications, some of which have been discussed above.

Metal nanoparticles have been used since the golden days in luster pottery and stained glass. One of the best examples is the Lycurgus Cup, already mentioned, from the Roman times that has Au and Ag nanoparticles embedded in it, appearing green in reflected light and red in transmitted light. Wood suspected a case of electrical resonance in minute metal nanoparticles as early as 1902 [67], Ritchie observed increased energy losses from thin metal foils in 1957 [68], and following this there have been many studies that lead to increased understanding of the mechanisms involved, that is, assigning them to LSPRs and lossy propagating plasmons that cannot couple to incident light.

The mechanisms and design considerations involving SPs have evolved dramatically in the field of PV over the last decade; some of which have already been discussed in the earlier sections. One of the earliest works in related area is by Stuart et al. where they reported an 18-fold enhancement in absorption from photodetectors using SPs at 800 nm from a 160 nm-thick Si-on-insulator device [18]. Subsequently, plasmonic enhancements were reported from 1.25, 2, and 300 μm Si cells in the visible as well as near the band gap of Si with photocurrent enhancements of 33%, 29%, and 16%, respectively, from 150 to 300 nm-size particles deposited by a self-assembly technique [13, 19, 47]. Scattering from the nanoparticles and coupling into the underlying Si waveguide modes is the mechanism attributed to these enhancements. Many other studies of decorating metal nanoparticles on inorganic devices like Si, GaAs, and a-Si have attributed photocurrent enhancements to this effect [35, 42, 44, 45, 69]. The results are all promising, considering that they could be further improved through optimization.

Organic materials have a low absorption length (i.e., ∼100 nm) and a low exciton diffusion length. Embedding metal nanostructures near the active interface leads to enhanced optical fields near the junction that results in more excitons being created within an exciton diffusion length away from the active interface [53]. One of the earliest reports of enhancement of PV conversion efficiency from organic solar cells was using Au, Ag, and Cu metal clusters at an ITO–copper phthalocyanine interface [70]. The intention of this work was to use the electrical field enhancement to increase the number of photogenerated charge carriers that was successfully achieved with a maximum enhancement of a factor of 2.7 using Cu clusters. Similar enhancements were also reported for CdSe/Si heterostructures [71] and organic bulk heterojunction cells [72]. Some other interesting results from organic solar cells

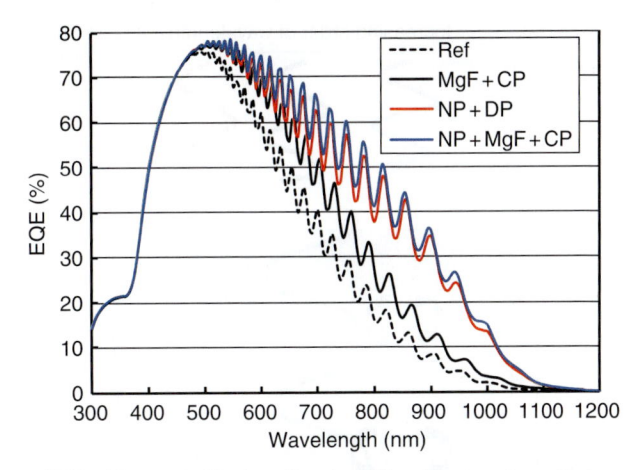

Figure 12 External quantum efficiency (EQE) of 2 μm poly-Si solar cells using different back-surface reflector combinations – bare case with no BSR (Ref), MgF$_2$ and paint (MgF + CP), Ag nanoparticles with detached paint where air is the buffer layer (NP + DP), and nanoparticles with MgF$_2$ and paint (NP + MgF + CP). From Ouyang Z, Zhao X, Varlamov S, et al. (2011) Nanoparticle-enhanced light trapping in thin-film silicon solar cells. *Progress in Photovoltaics* DOI 10.1002/pip.1135 © 2011 John Wiley & Sons [50].

have already been discussed in earlier sections. Like organic solar cells with plasmons, dye-sensitized solar cells are another class of cells that permit incorporation of the metal nanoparticles in the matrix. Dye-sensitized solar cells work on the principle of fast charge injection from a dye molecule into the conduction band of a large band gap semiconductor like TiO$_2$ instead of generating e–h pairs as in the case of semiconductors. Dye molecules sensitized with Au nanodisks lead to plasmonically enhanced charge injection from the dyes into the TiO$_2$, which was attributed to a combination of near-field and far-field effects [56].

Plasmon-enhanced conversion efficiencies have also been reported for III–V semiconductors. A 13.3% increase in short-circuit current (i.e., 2.64–2.99 mA) and a 15.3% increase in energy conversion efficiency (i.e., 19.6%–22.6%) are obtained for a three-junction InGaP/InGaAs/Ge tandem solar cells where 2 nm Au nanoclusters have been incorporated [73].

Recently, there have been reports of using SP excitations in metallic nanovoids for improving the efficiency of solar cells. These metallic nanovoids or 'anti-nanoparticles' as they are called are known to possess different plasmonic modes when compared to metallic nanoaparticles [74]. Large area substrates of Ag nanovoids are electrochemically templated through self-assembled colloidal spheres, and organic solar cells are fabricated on top. In this case, the near-field enhancement in the nanovoid along with the scattering from the nanovoid lattice has been used to improve the overall performance of organic solar cells by a factor of 4 [75].

SPP waveguide-based solar cells have been proposed as a novel way of improving the efficiency of solar cells [76]. Nanostructured metal fabricated by substrate conformal imprint lithography was used as a plasmonic back reflector on ultrathin-film n-i-p a-Si:H solar cells and an ~ 26% enhanced photocurrent was reported [51]. The enhancement is attributed to coupling of incident free-space radiation to SPP waveguide modes. At shorter wavelengths (i.e., 350–700 nm) close to the SPP resonance, the modes are lossy; however, having it at the back eliminates that problem. At longer wavelengths, the propagation lengths can be large as can be seen from eqn [7], which is attributed to the enhancement observed. Silver is known to be the metal with the lowest losses with 10–100 μm propagation lengths in the visible but increasing to as large as 1 mm in the near-IR range [14]. However, a large propagation length comes with a decreased optical confinement, hence requires optimization of design parameters [49].

The use of SPs along with conventional backside reflectors like paint or metal reflectors is also being investigated as a means of improving the performance of cells further. The use of a second light-trapping medium gives the light that has potentially escaped from the cell or the fraction coupled out of the metal nanoparticles, multiple opportunities to be redirected back to the cell. This also provides multiple opportunities for the SPs to be excited. Increased photocurrent has been reported with the use of paint either detached (such as air as buffer medium) or with a dielectric medium like MgF$_2$ ($n = 1.4$), as shown in **Figure 12** [50]. A 44% increase in the short-circuit current density was measured with Ag nanoparticles at the rear of a 2 μm-thick poly-Si cell overcoated with 350 nm MgF$_2$ and paint as a diffuse reflector.

The use of plasmons on the rear of high-efficiency cells with front textures are also being considered as a means of achieving broadband absorption. While front textures of solar cells target the visible to near-IR regions of the electromagnetic spectrum using rear-located plasmons with scattering peak tuned to near-band gap of Si, could be used to achieve light trapping over the entire spectrum of interest when used in conjunction with textures and metal reflectors [77].

1.30.6 Potential of Plasmonics for Third-Generation Solar Cells

The third-generation concept of solar cells has evolved as a way to address the high cost and low efficiency of the first- and second-generation solar cells and is regarded as the future of solar cells [78]. Third-generation approaches provide the potential to

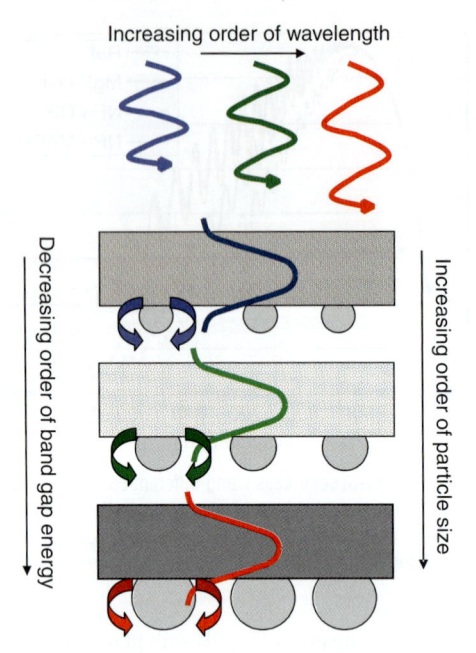

Figure 13 Schematic of a wavelength-dependent light-trapping tandem solar cell structure with size-tunable metal nanoparticles on the rear.

go above the Shockley–Queisser limit of 31% for a single-junction solar cell. They work by tackling one or both of the two major loss mechanisms of solar cells, that is, (1) sub-band gap and (2) thermalization losses, as shown in **Figure 1**. One such idea is the concept of using tandem structures to target the different parts of the spectrum by arranging the cells in decreasing order of band gap. Band gap-engineered structures can be fabricated using quantum-dot structures, where the band gap tunability is possible by tuning the size of the nanocrystals.

Low-dimensional structures like quantum-dot or quantum-well structures have poor optical and electrical properties; hence, enhancing photocurrent in these devices can be quite challenging. The thickness of these devices could be within the near-field of the metal nanoparticles; hence, the increased photonic density of states around the nanoparticles could possibly be exploited for increasing the efficiency from quantum dots that have a short carrier transport distance. SPs can also provide wavelength-dependent light trapping for tandem cell applications [79, 80]. A schematic of a wavelength-dependent light-trapping structure using size-tunable metal nanoparticles on the rear is shown in **Figure 13**.

The enhanced electric field around the SPs has the potential to aid nonlinear processes like upconversion, one of the important aspects being looked into for the third-generation solar cells [81, 82]. In the upconversion process, two or more below band gap photons are usually absorbed into the luminescent material emitting photon with higher energy that can then be absorbed. If the luminescent material is situated in the vicinity of the enhanced electric field, the process is likely to be enhanced manyfold. Enhancement of upconversion luminescence of erbium-doped Al_2O_3 has been reported by placing it near silver-island films of varying sizes. A maximum enhancement of 220 times was seen at 520 nm [83]. To date, the reported increases in power from the upconversion process is modest; however, SPs can potentially increase this value by manyfold contributing to an overall increased cell efficiency. Additionally, scattering properties of the plasmons can be utilized to 'amplify' the upconverted photons for absorption in the semiconductor material. Like SPs, the luminescent material is electrically isolated from the cell and can be easily deposited on the rear of the device structure.

1.30.7 Future Outlook

Over the last decade, there has been a rapid increase in the research on plasmonics for solar cell applications. This stems from the recent advances in nanofabrication, characterization, and simulation tools. Though optimization of the structures is still to be achieved, full-wave electromagnetic simulation software along with powerful computer hardware is proving to be a useful optimization tool for researchers. Parasitic absorption losses in the metal would be a limiting factor, and more work needs to be done on how this can be reduced through proper design. Unlike other optoelectronic applications, for solar cells, it is necessary that the optimization is compatible with low-cost processing and scalable techniques. It is expected that the barriers of large-area nanofabrication would soon be overcome with developing technology and the massive interest plasmonics has attracted recently. Plasmonics permits considerable reduction in the physical thickness of solar PV absorber layers and allows for new options for solar cell design. The adaptability of this technology onto any semiconductor material without degrading the performance of cells makes it even more attractive. Tunability of light scattering makes plasmonics suitable for 'hybrid' light-trapping structures in wafer-based cells. However, the promise of plasmonics clearly lies in (1) the potential of using ultrathin low-quality materials that can contribute effectively to cost-effective and efficient solar cells for the future and (2) the material-independent application that allows its diverse use in different solar cell structures/technologies including but not limited to Si-based, organic, dye-sensitized, III–V solar cells, and quantum-dot and quantum-well based cells.

1.30.8 Conclusion

Plasmonics has changed the way light can be harvested for solar cell applications. This light-trapping approach based on scattering by particles clearly allows amplifying the interaction between light and matter. The rapid advancement in fabrication and characterization techniques for nanoscale particles and the increased understanding of mechanisms behind the enhancement process is leading the way to the realization of a mature technology. What makes this area very attractive to researchers is the ability of light to interact with particles that are much smaller than the wavelength of light, and this consequently opens avenues to modify and manipulate the local light fields to suit various applications. This is particularly interesting as the trend is toward high-performance miniature devices – as the saying goes "The science of small is all set to make big".

Acknowledgments

S Pillai would like to acknowledge the support of the Australian Solar Institute for this work. The valuable contribution of past and present researchers at UNSW and their collaborators who have worked with the authors are also acknowledged.

References

[1] Shockley W and Queisser H (1961) Detailed balance limit of efficiency of p-n junction solar cells. *Journal of Applied Physics* 32(3): 510.
[2] Yablonovitch E (1982) Statistical ray optics. *Journal of the Optical Society of America A* 72: 899.
[3] Campbell P and Green MA (1987) Light trapping properties of pyramidally textured surfaces. *Journal of Applied Physics* 62(1): 243.
[4] Müller J, Rech B, Springer J, and Vanecek M (2004) TCO and light trapping in silicon thin film solar cells. *Solar Energy* 77(6): 917.
[5] Green MA (1999) Limiting efficiency of bulk and thin-film silicon solar cells in the presence of surface recombination. *Progress in Photovoltaics* 7(4): 327.
[6] Yu Z, Raman A, and Fan S (2010) Fundamental limit of nanophotonic light-trapping in solar cells. *Proceedings of the National Academy of Sciences of the United States of America* 107(41): 17491.
[7] Raether H (1988) *Surface Plasmons on Smooth and Rough Surface and on Gratings*. Berlin, Germany: Springer.
[8] Kretschmann E (1971) Die Bestimmung optischer Konstanten von Metallen durch Anregung von Oberflächenplasmaschwingungen. *Zeitschrift für Physik* 241(4): 313.
[9] Otto A (1968) Excitation of nonradiative surface plasma waves in silver by the method of frustrated total reflection. *Zeitschrift für Physik* 216(4): 398.
[10] Meier M and Wokaun A (1985) Enhanced fields on rough surfaces: dipolar interactions among particles of sizes exceeding the Rayleigh limit. *Journal of the Optical Society of America B* 2(6): 931.
[11] Zayats AV and Smolyaninov II (2003) Near-field Photonics: Surface plasmon polaritons and localized surface plasmons. *Journal of Optics A: Pure and Applied Optics* 5: S16.
[12] Moreland J, Adams A, and Hansma PK (1982) Efficiency of light emission from surface plasmons. *Physical Review B* 25(4): 2297.
[13] Pillai S, Catchpole KR, Trupke T, et al. (2006) Enhanced emission from Si-based light-emitting diodes using surface plasmons. *Applied Physics Letters* 88: 161102.
[14] Barnes WL, Dereux A, and Ebbesen TW (2003) Surface plasmon subwavelength optics. *Nature* 424: 824.
[15] Kreibig U and Vollmer M (1995) *Optical Properties of Metal Clusters*. New York: Wiley.
[16] Bohren CF and Huffman DR (1983) *Absorption and Scattering of Light by Small Particles*. New York: Wiley-Interscience.
[17] Bohren CF (1983) How can a particle absorb more than the light incident on it? *American Journal of Physics* 51(4): 323.
[18] Stuart HR and Hall DG (1998) Island size effects in nanoparticle enhanced photodetectors. *Applied Physics Letters* 73(26): 3815.
[19] Pillai S, Catchpole KR, Trupke T, and Green MA (2007) Surface plasmon enhanced silicon solar cells. *Journal of Applied Physics* 101: 093105.
[20] Mock JJ, Smith DR, and Shultz S (2003) Local Refractive Index Dependence of Plasmon resosnance spectra from individual nanoparticles. *Nano Letters* 3(4): 485.
[21] Kuwata H, Tamarua H, Esumi K, and Miyano K (2003) Resonant light scattering from metal nanoparticles: Practical analysis beyond Rayleigh approximation. *Applied Physics Letters* 83(22): 4625.
[22] Catchpole KR and Polman A (2008) Design principles for particle plasmon enhanced solar cells. *Applied Physics Letters* 93: 191113.
[23] Hägglund C, Zäch M, Petersson G, and Kasemo B (2008) Electromagnetic coupling of light into a silicon solar cell by nanodisk plasmons. *Applied Physics Letters* 92: 053110.
[24] Spinelli P, van Lare C, Verhagen E, and Polman A (2011) Controlling Fano lineshapes in plasmon-mediated light coupling into a substrate. *Optics Express* 19: 303.
[25] Temple TL and Bagnall DM (2011) Optical properties of gold and aluminium nanoparticles for silicon solar cell applications. *Journal of Applied Physics* 109: 084343.
[26] Baba K, Okuno T, and Miyagi M (1993) Silver-gold compound metal island films prepared by using a two step evaporation method. *Applied Physics Letters* 62(5): 437.
[27] Oldenburg SJ, Averitt RD, Westcott SL, and Halas NJ (1998) Nanoengineering of optical resonances. *Chemical Physics Letters* 288: 243.
[28] Kabashin AV, Evans P, Pastkovsky S, et al. (2009) Plasmonic nanorod metamaterials for biosensing. *Nature Materials* 8: 867.
[29] Royer P, Goudonnet JP, Warmack RJ, and Ferrel TL (1987) Substrate effects on surface-plasmon spectra in metal-island films. *Physical Review B* 35(8): 3753.
[30] Xu G, Tazawa M, Jin P, and Nakao S (2005) Surface plasmon resonance of sputtered Ag films: substrate and mass thickness dependence. *Applied Physics A* 80: 1535.
[31] Bijeon JL, Royer P, Goudonnet JP, et al. (1987) Effects of silicon substrate on surface plasmon spectra in silver island films. *Thin Solid Films* 155: L1.
[32] Kelly ML, Coronado E, Zhao LL, and Schatz GC (2003) The optical properties of metal nanoparticles: The influence of size, shape, and dielectric environment. *The Journal of Physical Chemistry. B* 107: 668.
[33] Xu G, Tazawa M, Jin P, et al. (2003) Wavelength tuning of surface plasmon resonance using dielectric layers silver island films. *Applied Physics Letters* 82(22): 3811.
[34] Malinsky MD, Kelly KL, Schatz GC, and Van Duyne RP (2001) Nanosphere lithography: Effect of substrate on the localized surface plasmon resonance spectrum of silver nanoparticles. *The Journal of Physical Chemistry B* 105: 2343.
[35] Beck FJ, Polman A, and Catchpole KR (2009) Tunable light trapping for solar cells using localized surface plasmons. *Journal of Applied Physics* 105: 114310.
[36] Beck FJ, Mokkapati S, Polman A, and Catchpole KR (2010) Asymmetry in photocurrent enhancement by plasmonic nanoparticle arrays located on the front or on the rear of solar cells. *Applied Physics Letters* 96: 033113.
[37] http://www.philiplaven.com/mieplot.htm.

[38] Cole JR and Halas NJ (2006) Optimized plasmonic nanoparticle distributions for solar spectrum harvesting. *Applied Physics Letters* 89: 153120.
[39] Mokkapati S, Beck FJ, Polman A, and Catchpole KR (2009) Designing periodic arrays of metal nanoparticles for light-trapping applications in solar cells. *Applied Physics Letters* 95: 053115.
[40] Akimov YA, Koh WS, and Ostrikov K (2009) Enhancement of optical absorption in thin-film solar cells through the excitation of higher-order nanoparticle plasmon modes. *Optics Express* 17(12): 1015.
[41] Forestiere C, Donelli M, Walsh GF, *et al.* (2010) Particle-swarm optimization of broadband nanoplasmonic arrays. *Optics Letters* 35(2): 133.
[42] Matheu P, Lim SH, Derkacs D, *et al.* (2008) Metal and dielectric nanoparticle scattering for improved optical absorption in photovoltaic devices. *Applied Physics Letters* 93: 113108.
[43] Stuart HR and Hall DG (1996) Absorption Enhancement in Silicon-on-insulator waveguides using metal island films. *Applied Physics Letters* 69(16): 2327.
[44] Nakayama K, Tanabe K, and Atwater HA (2008) Plasmonic nanoparticle enhanced light absorption in GaAs solar cells. *Applied Physics Letters* 93: 121904.
[45] Schaadt DM, Feng B, and Yu ET (2005) Enhanced semiconductor optical absorption via surface plasmon excitation in metal nanoparticles. *Applied Physics Letters* 86: 063106.
[46] Pillai S, Beck FJ, Catchpole KR, *et al.* (2011) The effect of dielectric spacer thickness on surface plasmon enhanced solar cells for front and rear side depositions. *Journal of Applied Physics* 109(7): 073105.
[47] Ouyang Z, Pillai S, Beck F, *et al.* (2010) Effective light trapping in polycrystalline silicon thin-film solar cells by means of rear localised surface plasmons. *Applied Physics Letters* 96: 261109.
[48] Lim SH, Mar W, Matheu P, *et al.* (2007) Photocurrent spectroscopy of optical absorption enhancement in silicon photodiodes via scattering from surface plasmon polaritons in gold nanoparticles. *Journal of Applied Physics* 101: 104309.
[49] Atwater H and Polman A (2010) Plasmonics for improved photovoltaic devices. *Nature Materials* 9: 205.
[50] Ouyang Z, Zhao X, Varlamov S, *et al.* (2011) Nanoparticle-enhanced light trapping in thin-film silicon solar cells. *Progress in Photovoltaics* DOI: 10.1002/pip.1135.
[51] Ferry VE, Verschuuren MA, Hongbo BT, *et al.* (2009) Improved red-response in thin film a-Si:H solar cells with soft-imprinted plasmonic back reflectors. *Applied Physics Letters* 95(18): 183503.
[52] Moulin E, Sukmanowski J, Luo P, *et al.* (2008) Improved light absorption in thin-film silicon solar cells by integration of silver nanoparticles. *Journal of Non-Crystalline Solids* 354: 2488.
[53] Lee J-Y and Peumans P (2010) The origin of enhanced optical absorption in solar cells with metal nanoparticles embedded in the active layer. *Optics Express* 18(10): 10078.
[54] Kirkengen M, Bergli J, and Galperin YM (2007) Direct generation of charge carriers in c-Si solar cells due to embedded nanoparticles. *Journal of Applied Physics* 102: 093713.
[55] Rand BP, Peumans P, and Forrest SR (2004) Long-range absorption enhancement in organic tandem thin-film solar cells containing silver nanoclusters. *Journal of Applied Physics* 96(12): 7519.
[56] Hägglund C, Zäch M, and Kasemo B (2008) Enhanced charge carrier generation in dye sensitized solar cells by nanoparticle plasmons. *Applied Physics Letters* 92: 013113.
[57] Westphalen W, Kreibig U, Rostalski J, *et al.* (2000) Metal cluster enhanced organic solar cells. *Solar Energy Materials and Solar Cells* 61: 97.
[58] Moulin E, Luo P, Pieters B, *et al.* (2009) Photoresponse enhancement in the near infrared wavelength range of ultrathin amorphous silicon photosensitive devices by integration of silver nanoparticles. *Applied Physics Letters* 95(3): 033505.
[59] Aberle AG (2004) *Crystalline Silicon Solar Cells: Advanced Surface Passivation and Analysis.* Sydney, Australia: Centre for Photovoltaic Engineering, UNSW.
[60] Ford GW and Weber WH (1984) Electromagnetic interactions of molecules with metal surfaces. *Physics Reports* 113(4): 195.
[61] Soller BJ and Hall DG (2001) Energy transfer at optical frequencies to silicon-based waveguiding structures. *Journal of the Optical Society of America A* 18(10): 2577.
[62] Catchpole KR and Pillai S (2006) Absorption enhancement due to scattering by dipoles into silicon waveguides. *Journal of Applied Physics* 100: 044504.
[63] Mertz J (2000) Radiative absorption, fluorescence, and scattering of a classical dipole near a lossless interface: a unified description. *Journal of the Optical Society of America B* 17(11): 1906.
[64] Gupta R, Dyer MJ, and Weimer WA (2002) Preparation and characterization of surface plasmon resonance tunable gold and silver films. *Journal of Applied Physics* 92(9): 5264.
[65] Temple TL, Mahanama GDK, Reehal HS, and Bagnall DM (2009) Influence of localized surface plasmon excitation in silver nanoparticles on the performance of silicon solar cells. *Solar Energy Materials and Solar Cells* 93(11): 1978.
[66] Sander MS and Tan LS (2003) Nanoparticle arrays on surfaces fabricated using anodic alumina films as templates. *Advanced Functional Materials* 13(5): 393.
[67] Wood RW (1902) A suspected case of the electrical resonance of minute metal particles for light-waves. A new type of absorption. *Proceedings of the Physical Society London* 18: 166.
[68] Ritchie RH (1957) Plasma losses by fast electrons in thin films. *Physical Review* 106(5): 874.
[69] Derkacs D, Lim SH, Matheu P, *et al.* (2006) Improved performance of amorphous silicon solar cells via scattering from surface plasmon polaritons in nearby metallic nanoparticles. *Applied Physics Letters* 89: 093103.
[70] Stenzel O, Stendal A, Voigtsberger K, and von Borczyskowski C (1995) Enhancement of the photovoltaic conversion efficiency of copper phthalocyanine thin film devices by incorporation of metal clusters. *Solar Energy Materials and Solar Cells* 37: 337.
[71] Konda RB, Mundle R, Mustafa H, *et al.* (2007) Surface plasmon excitation via Au nanoparticles in n-CdSe/p-Si heterojunction diodes. *Applied Physics Letters* 91: 191111.
[72] Morfa AJ, Rowlen KL, Rowlen KL, Reilly TH III, *et al.* (2008) Plasmon-enhanced solar energy conversion in organic bulk heterojunction photovoltaics. *Applied Physics Letters* 92: 013504.
[73] Yang MD, Liu YK, Shen JL, *et al.* (2008) Improvement of conversion efficiency for multijunction solar cells by incorporation of Au nanoclusters. *Optics Express* 16(20): 15754.
[74] Cole RM, Baumberg JJ, Garcia de Abajo FJ, *et al.* (2007) Understanding Plasmons in Nanoscale Voids. *Nano Letters* 7(7): 2094.
[75] Lal NN, Soares BF, Sinha JK, *et al.* (2011) Enhancing solar cells with localized plasmons in nanovoids. *Optics Express* 19(12): 11256.
[76] Ferry VE, Sweatlock LA, Pacifici D, and Atwater HA (2008) Plasmonic Nanostructure Design for Efficient Light Coupling into Solar Cells. *Nano Letters* 8(12): 4391.
[77] Yang Y, Pillai S, Ho-Baillie A, *et al.* (2011) Enhanced light trapping for high efficiency crystalline solar cells by the application of rear surface plasmons. *Journal of Applied Physics*.
[78] Green MA (2003) *Third Generation Photovoltaics.* Berlin, Germany: Springer.
[79] Pillai S and Green MA (2010) Plasmonics for photovoltaic applications. *Solar Energy Materials and Solar Cells* 94(9): 1481.
[80] Pillai S, Perez-Wurfl I, Conibeer GJ, and Green MA (2011) Surface plasmons for improving the performance of quantum dot structures for third generation solar cell applications. *Physica Status Solidi (C)* 8(1): 181.
[81] Shalav A, Richards BS, and Green MA (2007) Luminescent layers for enhanced silicon solar cell performance: Up-conversion. *Solar Energy Materials and Solar Cells* 91: 829.
[82] de Wild J, Meijerink A, Rath JK, van Sark WGJHM, and Schropp REI (2011) Upconverter solar cells: materials and applications. *Energy Environmental Science*, doi: 10.1039/C1EE01659H.
[83] Aisaka T, Fujii M, and Hayashi S (2008) Enhancement of upconversion luminescence of Er doped Al_2O_3 films by Ag island films. *Applied Physics Letters* 92: 132105.

1.31 Artificial Leaves: Towards Bio-Inspired Solar Energy Converters

A Pandit and RN Frese, VU University Amsterdam, Amsterdam, The Netherlands

© 2012 Elsevier Ltd. All rights reserved.

1.31.1	The Design of Natural Photosynthesis	657
1.31.1.1	Photosynthetic Light-Harvesting Antennae	658
1.31.1.2	Photosynthetic RCs	659
1.31.1.3	Supramolecular Organization	660
1.31.1.3.1	Supercomplexes	660
1.31.1.3.2	Supramolecular complexes	661
1.31.1.3.3	Membranes	661
1.31.1.3.4	Light harvesting and charge transport in purple bacteria	661
1.31.2	Design Principles of Natural Photosynthesis	663
1.31.2.1	Photon Absorption, Excitation Energy Transfer, and Electron Transfer	663
1.31.2.1.1	Photon absorption	663
1.31.2.1.2	Excitation energy transfer	664
1.31.2.1.3	Electron transfer	664
1.31.2.2	Photochemical Thermodynamics of Energy Storage	664
1.31.3	The Design of an Artificial Leaf	666
1.31.3.1	Interfacing Proteins onto Solid-State Surfaces	666
1.31.3.2	Protein Maquettes for Artificial Photosynthesis	667
1.31.3.3	Bio-Inspired Self-assembled Artificial Antennae	669
1.31.3.3.1	Chlorosome-based, light-harvesting antennae	669
1.31.3.4	Bio-Inspired DA Constructs	670
1.31.3.4.1	Self-assembled DA constructs	672
1.31.4	Outlook: The Construction of a Fuel-Producing Solar Cell	674
References		675
Further reading		677

Glossary

ATP Adenosine-5′-triphosphate, a nucleotide used in cells as a coenzyme and energy carrier.

(Bacterio) pheophytin A (bacterio) chlorophyll from which the central magnesium atom has been removed.

Carbohydrates Literally 'hydrates of carbon', chemical compounds that act as the primary biological means of storing or consuming energy; other forms being via fat and protein. Relatively complex carbohydrates are known as 'polysaccharides'.

Carotenoid Tetraterpenoid organic pigment; carotenoids are divided into xanthophylls (containing oxygen) and carotenes (purely hydrocarbons).

Chlorophyll (Chl) Green photosynthetic pigment found in plants, algae, and cyanobacteria.

Chloroplast Organelles found in plant cells and eukaryotic algae that conduct photosynthesis. Chloroplasts capture light energy from the sun to produce the free energy stored in ATP and NADPH.

Exciton (photosynthetic) Electronically excited state of a pigment molecule in a photosynthetic system. Depending on various parameters, the degree of exciton delocalization can vary from one pigment to many pigment molecules.

NADPH Nicotinamide adenine dinucleotide phosphate, used as reducing power for biosynthetic reactions in photosynthesis.

Porphyrin Pigment consisting of a heterocyclic macrocycle made from four pyrrole subunits. If one of the three pyrrole subunits is reduced to pyrroline, chlorine is produced, the ring structure found in chlorophyll.

Quinone (photosynthetic) Mobile, lipid-soluble carriers that shuttle electrons and protons between protein complexes embedded in the membrane.

1.31.1 The Design of Natural Photosynthesis

Photosynthetic organisms are ubiquitous on the surface of the Earth and, in fact, responsible for the development and sustenance of all life on the planet. They all use the same basic pattern whereby light energy from the sun is initially absorbed and concentrated by an antenna system, then transferred to a reaction center (RC) where charge separation takes place, followed by reactions that convert the captured light energy into a chemical form. Photosynthesis can be divided into oxygenic photosynthesis, carried out by

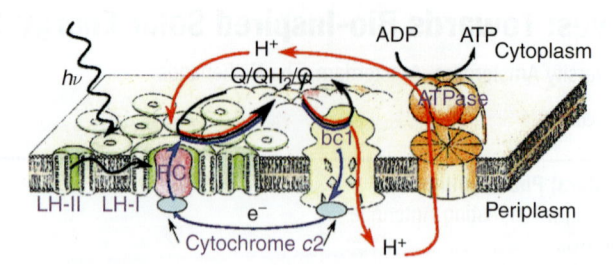

Figure 1 Schematic view of the purple bacterial photosynthetic membrane. Several components transform the incoming energy of photons. LH2 and LH1 are LHCs that absorb light and transfer excited-state energy among intra- and intercomplex bound pigments. The terminal acceptor is the RC, which is completely encircled by the LH1 complex. There the excited-state energy induced ETs among cofactors until two electrons reside on the terminal acceptor, which is a quinone molecule. This molecule becomes double protonated upon which it exits the complex into the lipid phase of the membrane, diffusing toward a proton-translocating pump, the bc1 complex. A small protein cytochrome $c2$ shuttles between the bc1 complex and the RC to re-reduce the primary electron donor, thus closing the circuit. When protons are actively transported back from the periplasm to the cytoplasm through the ATP synthase complex, the energy is chemically stored as ATP. Reproduced from Figure 1 in Hu XC, Damjanovic A, Ritz T, and Schulten K (1998) Architecture and mechanism of the light-harvesting apparatus of purple bacteria. *Proceedings of the National Academy of Sciences of the United States of America* 95: 5935–5941 [1], with permission of National Academy of Sciences USA.

cyanobacteria, algae, and plants that produce oxygen, and nonoxygenic photosynthesis, carried out by purple, green sulfur, and heliobacteria. Oxygenic organisms harness solar energy to extract the H^+ and e^- from H_2O, required for CO_2 fixation. Nonoxygenic organisms cannot generate the necessary oxidizing potential to oxidize H_2O and therefore extract H^+ and e^- from alternative substrates. Under normal conditions, both processes use the derived H^+ and e^- for synthesis of adenosine triphosphate (ATP), nicotinamide adenine dinucleotide phosphate (NADPH) oxidase, and ultimately CO_2 fixation, and to produce carbohydrates such as starch and glycogen, which can be considered to be H^+ and e^- 'stores' that can be used for the CO_2 neutral production of fuels; see **Figure 1** for a schematic representation of nonoxygenic photosynthesis. The factory where the photosynthetic process takes place is the cell, or a specialized compartment within the cell. Each reaction is carried out by specific proteins or complexes of proteins that often bind functional molecules for light absorption, redox chemistry, and charge transfer. Proteins are nanometric-sized biopolymers of specific shape and function, and are dynamically organized within, associated with, a lipid membrane. Membranes allow the compartmentalization of the various reactions and are especially important for ATP formation, which is driven by the electrochemical gradient formed by the protons that are pumped across the membrane and enable the synthesis of ATP during controlled back transfer through the ATP synthase enzyme.

1.31.1.1 Photosynthetic Light-Harvesting Antennae

Natural light-harvesting antenna complexes (LHCs) are complexes of proteins that are organized to collect and deliver light excited-state energy to the RC where charge separation takes place [2]. They permit an organism to increase greatly the absorption cross section for light without having to build an entire RC and associated electron-transfer (ET) system for each pigment, which would be very costly in terms of biosynthesis and cellular resources. The intensity of sunlight is dilute so that any given pigment molecule absorbs at most a few photons per second. By incorporating many pigments into a single antenna unit and creating supramolecular assemblies of antenna units, large photosynthetic membrane surfaces are covered, ensuring that photons striking any spot on the surface will be absorbed. The antenna units are interconnected to carry light energy through exciton migration over long distances to the RCs. They surround the RCs, optimizing the energy-transfer efficiency by multiple antenna–RC connections. Photosynthetic organisms are equipped with a light-harvesting antenna containing the pigments (bacterio) chlorophylls ((B)Chl), carotenoids (Cars), or phycobilins. While they share their function of funneling the excitation energy into the RC, there is a large variety in the antenna structures and macro-organization of different species.

Most organisms have antenna systems that are embedded in the photosynthetic membrane, but green sulfur bacteria and cyanobacteria contain aggregated antenna structures that are associated with the membrane. Green sulfur bacteria contain antennae built from large 3D tubular aggregates of self-assembled (B)Chls with small amounts of Cars and quinones, contained in specialized vesicles called chlorosomes [3] (see **Figure 2**). The energy harvested by these chlorosomes is transferred via a protein called the Fenna–Mathews–Olson (FMO) complex to the membrane-bound RC. The light-harvesting antenna of green sulfur bacteria is designed to operate at extremely low light intensities and therefore is extremely large compared to the antennae of other species. This is the only species in which the antenna structures are self-assembled from pigment molecules without the aid of a protein environment. Cyanobacteria use rod-like antenna structures called phycobilisomes [5], containing protein assemblies in which the proteins have prosthetic groups of linear pyrroles, the phycobilin pigments. The phycobilisomes are associated with the photosynthetic membranes and transfer their excitation energy to two photosystems that are embedded in the membrane: photosystem 1 (PS1) and photosystem 2 (PS2) that contain the RCs. This is the only species in which its antenna pigments are covalently bound to proteins.

Structure–function features are summarized here that are shared among different species. Tightly coupled (B)Chls allow efficient energy transfer via excitonic interactions. The combination of Cars in van der Waals contact with the (B)Chls allows efficient and rapid energy transfer from the Cars (absorbing in the blue-green region of the solar spectrum) to the (B)Chls that absorb in the red

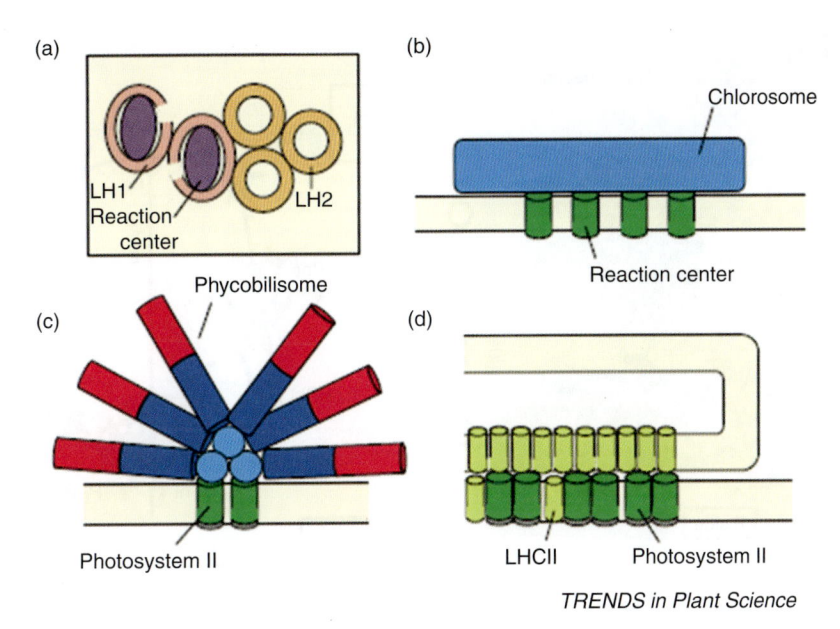

Figure 2 Schematic view of the organization of antenna–RC complexes of different organisms: (a) light-harvesting complex 2 (LH2) and light-harvesting complex 1–RC (LH1–RC) complexes of purple nonsulfur bacteria, (b) chlorosome antenna of green sulfur bacteria, (c) phycobilisome antenna of cyanobacteria, and (d) light-harvesting complex II (LHCII) antenna attached to photosystem 2 in plants. Reproduced from Figure 2 in Mullineaux CW (2005) Function and evolution of grana. *Trends in Plant Science* 10: 521–525 [4], with permission of Elsevier Science B.V.

or infrared region, covering a larger part of the solar spectrum. The Cars also protect the organism from photo-oxidative damage by rapidly quenching potentially harmful (B)Chl triplet states that can produce singlet oxygen. Pigment–protein and pigment–pigment interactions within the antennae broaden the lowest excited-state absorption spectrum (increasing the cross section for light absorption) and tune the absorption maxima of the different pigments, resulting in light energy transfer to the 'reddest' pigment with the lowest excited-state energy. The arrangements of the antenna complexes are such that light energy can migrate among the complexes via Förster energy transfer and that the antennae surround the RC so that light energy migration is funneled into the RCs from different sites.

1.31.1.2 Photosynthetic RCs

RCs are complexes of proteins with embedded cofactors that act simultaneously as chromophores, redox groups, and ET factors; see Reference 6 and **Figure 3** for a detailed description of the structural and functional characteristics of RCs. In RCs, the excited-state energy generated by photon absorption is utilized for the release of electrons after which energy back transfer has become impossible. ETs are directional among the cofactors and are accompanied by a loss of free energy that ensures a fast-forward and slow-backward transfer rate. The primary electron donor and the terminal acceptor are separated in space close to either side of a membrane where they are coupled to other proteins or molecules via redox chemistry; at that point, the energy is stored [8].

As such, RCs can carry out the primary photochemical reactions without the need of LHCs discussed in the previous section. While Nature has developed a large variety of LHCs among the species [9], RCs have remained surprisingly homologous throughout billions of years of evolution. This may be a reflection of the much more stringent design principles for ET compared to energy transfer, for instance, the distance dependency of the rates. All RCs contain dimers of proteins that covalently link the cofactors. Attached to the protein dimers are other proteins enabling redox chemistry via again other proteins or redox molecules. Differentiations between the species regarding the RCs are the type of chromophores used, the wavelengths of absorption, the redox potential between first electron donor and final acceptor, and the redox reactions leading to re-reduction of the primary donor and the re-oxidation of the terminal acceptor [10].

In **Figure 4**, the redox potentials of the components active in ETs within the four types of RCs are depicted. Two types are found in anoxygenic photosynthesis, which are the evolutionary precursors of the other two oxygenic types. The latter are part of the photosystem 1 and 2 supercomplexes (PS1 and PS2) that are coupled systems allowing the formation of NADPH. When the need for NADPH is low, PS1 and PS2 can become uncoupled and ATP is produced by cyclic electron transport, similar to the process in purple bacterial RCs.

As can be seen in **Figure 4**, there is a common theme among all types of RCs regarding the redox potential generated after the initial electron donors (P870, P680, P700, or P840) have been excited (indicated by P*). Light energy is used to promote the primary electron donors to a redox state that is more negative than the subsequent electron acceptors, thus promoting electrochemically downhill ETs. A most striking difference between the primary donor of photosystem 2 and that of the other RCs is the extremely large redox potential of P680, +1.2 V versus standard hydrogen electrode; it can oxidize water into protons and oxygen [12].

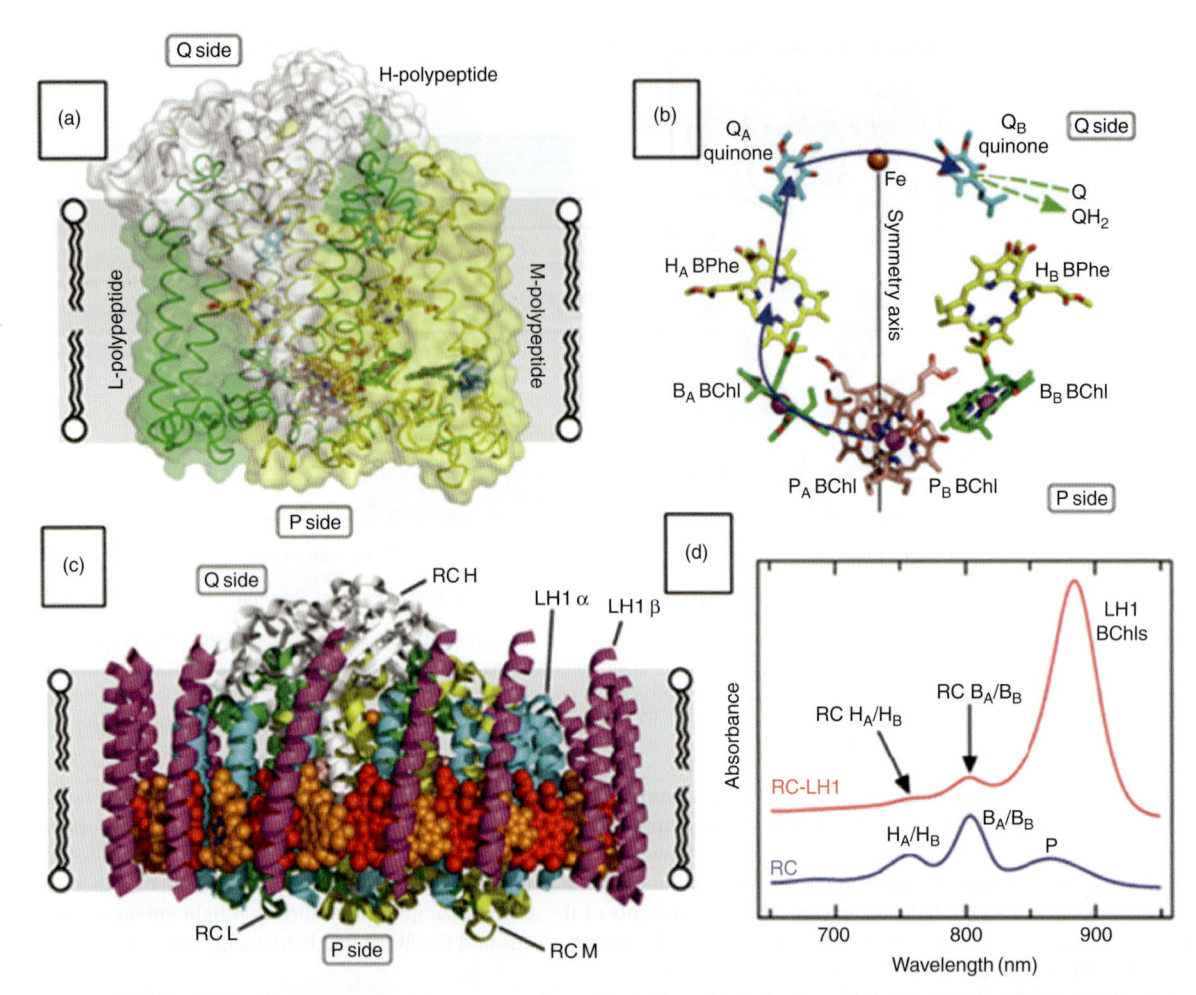

Figure 3 (a) Overall structure. The protein surface shown as a semitransparent object with the backbone fold of the H, L, and M polypeptides shown as white, green, and yellow tubes, respectively. The approximate position of the membrane is shown as a gray box, with the primary donor side (P side) and quinone side (Q side) of the RC labeled. The embedded cofactors are shown as sticks, with the Car (bottom left) shown with teal carbons. (b) Enlarged view of the BChl, BPhe, and quinone cofactors, color coded as in (a) with oxygens in red, nitrogens in blue, and Fe and Mg atoms in brown or magenta spheres. Membrane-spanning ET starts from the primary donor pair of BChls (P_A/P_B – pink carbons) and proceeds via the B_A BChl (green carbons), H_A BPhe (yellow carbons), and Q_A ubiquinone (cyan carbons). Electrons are passed on to the dissociable Q_B ubiquinone (cyan carbons), which can exchange with exogenous ubiquinone. The B_B BChl and H_B BPhe do not participate in ET. For clarity, the large hydrocarbon side chains of the BChl, BPhe, and quinone cofactors are not shown. (c) Structure of the RC–LH1 complex from *Rhodopseudomonas palustris* [7]; Protein DataBank (PDB) entry 1PYH – resolution 0.48 nm. The central RC, colored as for (a) and viewed from the same direction, is surrounded by concentric cylinders of multiple copies of α (cyan ribbons) and β (magenta ribbons) polypeptides, sandwiching a ring of BChls (colored alternately red and orange). (d) Absorbance spectra of the *Rhodobacter sphaeroides* RC and the *Rhodopseudomonas acidophila* RC–LH1, showing band attributions. Note the real contribution of the RC pigments to the absorbance of RC–LH1 complexes can be viewed in the RC–LH1 spectrum at 800 and 750 nm (Ba/Bb and Ha/Hb pigments, respectively). Structure and pigment organization in the photosynthetic RC of purple bacteria. Courtesy of Prof. Michael Jones, Sheffield University.

In fact, only P680 possesses a redox potential higher than the constituent Chl molecules [13]. The high redox potential of P680 is most likely a result of an intricate combination of various protein–Chl interactions such as hydrogen bonds, protein charges, and dielectric shielding [14]. As will be discussed in Section 1.31.4, the utilization of photon energy to split water into protons and oxygen has yet to be accomplished by a man-made catalyst. In fact, since protons can be redirected to form molecular hydrogen or other energy-rich compounds, PS2 mimics can be regarded as the Holy Grail in artificial photosynthesis.

1.31.1.3 Supramolecular Organization

1.31.1.3.1 Supercomplexes

As discussed in the previous sections, photosynthesis combines complexes of proteins for light-absorbing and ETs in combination with charge carriers and proton pumps. The RCs are always associated with some specific LHCs forming an RC–LHC core complex, a unit very well capable of performing primary photochemistry. But because of the dim- or low-light conditions within their environment, almost all species also synthesize extra LHCs that surround the core complexes [9]. In plants, PS1 [15] and PS2

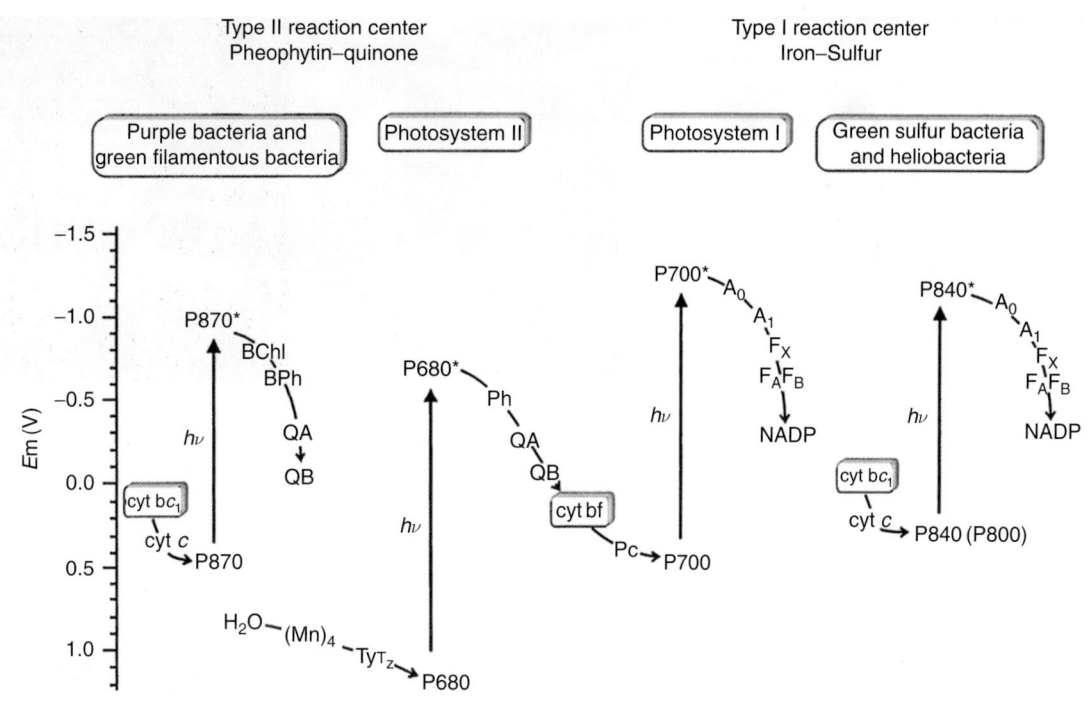

Figure 4 Diagrams of ET chains within the four types of RCs found in photosynthesis. The left axis shows the approximate redox potentials of the cofactors. The initial electron donors are indicated by their wavelength of absorption P870, P680, P700, and P840. Reprinted from Figure 3 in Hillier W and Babcock GT (2001) Photosynthetic reaction centers. *Plant Physiology* 125: 33–37 [11], with permission of American Society of Plant Physiologists.

[16] are large photosystems consisting of RCs linked to a variable set of LHCs. In purple bacteria, the core complex is an RC surrounded by an LHC consisting of a ring of proteins [7]. This core complex can form dimers with another, similar, core complex, which in turn may be surrounded by other smaller ring-like LHCs [17].

1.31.1.3.2 Supramolecular complexes
Recent advances in electron microscopy [18] and atomic force microscopy [19] have shown the existence of a distinct spatial organization of the photosynthetic components within the membranes. In plants, PS1 and PS2 are well separated in different membranous compartments accompanied by cytochrome *b6f* and ATP synthase complexes, respectively [20]. Among the purple bacteria, a large variety have been found in domain formation of RC–LHC core complexes and the peripheral LHCs [21]. Moreover, the supramolecular organization has been found to be dependent on the light conditions [22]. Most strikingly, the photosynthetic membranes are heavily packed with RCs and LHCs, much like a 2D crystal, which places much strain on diffusive processes [23]. While distinct supramolecular organizations exist, there is no underlying structure holding the components in place. Therefore, a thermodynamic model has been derived showing that entropy can be a driving force for domain formation of RCs and LHCs (see Reference 24 and **Figure 5**). Due to heavy packing, the clustering of larger photosystems, separated from the smaller LHCs, enhances the volume that can be occupied by the LHCs such that the total entropy is actually maximized. This effect has been shown for colloidal particles before and may be generalized for the nanometric-sized protein complexes as well. The more fluid domain of smaller LHCs may also enable diffusive pathways necessary for self-repair and adaptability. The model predicts how different supramolecular organizations may be inferred by specific tuning the size and shape of the components. Due to packing, also the ultrastructure of the entire photosynthetic membrane can be predicted from the same self-organizing principles [24].

1.31.1.3.3 Membranes
The membrane in which the photosynthetic complexes primarily reside is a two-dimensional (2D) structure and can be regarded as a monolayer film of energy-transducing nanometric components. Photosynthetic species enhance their photosynthetic volume by folding the membranes in three dimensions (see **Figure 6**). Plant membranes containing PS2 are layered close to each other [20]; purple bacterial membranes may be folded similarly or form small spheres, budded off from a linear membrane [25]. Whether or not there exists functionality from interacting complexes embedded in different membranes has to be established.

1.31.1.3.4 Light harvesting and charge transport in purple bacteria
To illustrate how the different components work together as a solar energy converter, we describe here how natural photosynthesis proceeds in one of the most simple and well-characterized photosynthetic systems: the photosynthetic machinery of purple nonsulfur bacteria.

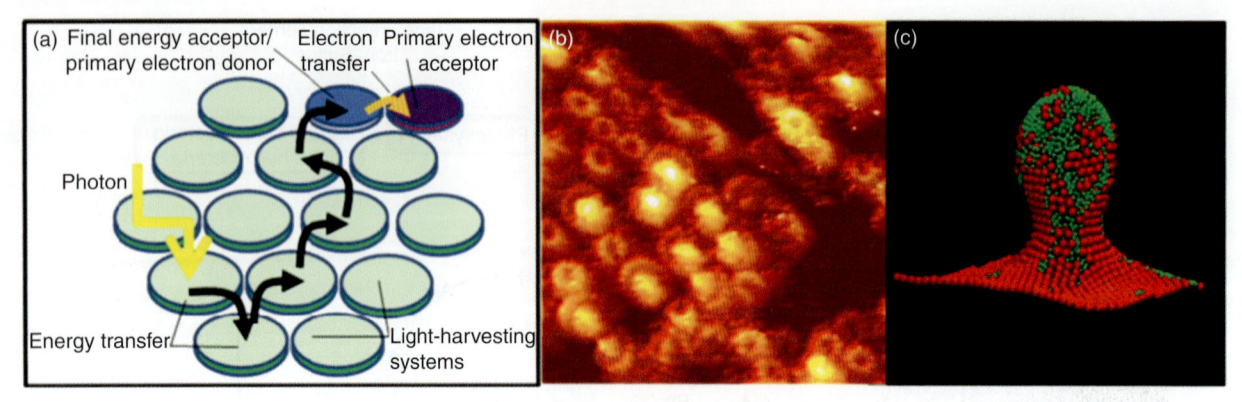

Figure 5 (a) Schematic representation of a photosynthetic membrane as proposed by L. Duysens in the 1950s (Leiden, The Netherlands). A membrane consists of many light-absorbing components, also named pigments that also transfer the energy among them. The target is an RC where this energy triggers a series of ET events starting off at a special site, the primary donor. (b) Image of protein complexes embedded within a bacterial photosynthetic membrane obtained by atomic force microscopy by Bahatyrova and co-workers (Enschede, the Netherlands). In this particular membrane, RC–LH1 complexes form dimeric supercomplexes, which in turn are arranged in rows. Adapted from Figure 1 in Bahatyrova S, Frese RN, Siebert CA, et al. (2004) The native architecture of a photosynthetic membrane. *Nature* 430: 1058–1062 [17], with permission of Nature Publishing Group. (c) Result of coarse-grained modeling of the photosynthetic membrane based on colloidal theory by Frese et al. [24]. A 2D lattice, occupied equally with dimeric RC–LH1 and RC–LH2 complexes, is equilibrated by a Monte Carlo method. Energy minimization is based only on differences in size and shape of the two components. Besides the two different domains as observed in the AFM images, the model also predicts the correct shape of the entire membrane. Various subsequent realizations show the green domain to be highly fluid, while the red domain remains rigid. Adapted from Figure 6d in Frese RN, Pamies JC, Olsen JD, et al. (2008) Protein shape and crowding drive domain formation and curvature in biological membranes. *Biophysical Journal* 94: 640–647 [24], with permission of Biophysical Society, USA.

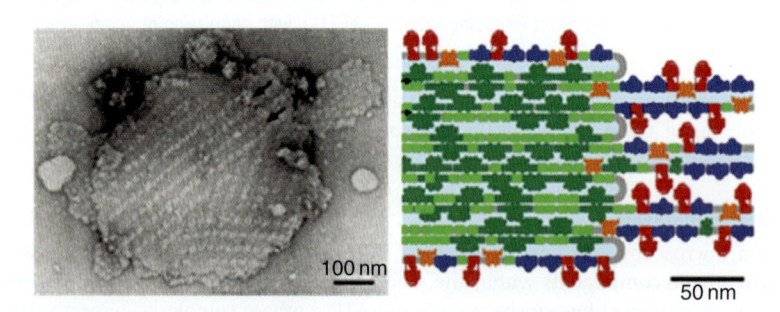

Figure 6 Electron micrograph of grana membranes that primarily contain the PS2 complexes (left panel) that are indicated in green in the schematic picture on the right panel. PS1 is indicated in blue, ATP synthase in red, and b6f complexes in orange. Adapted from Figures 7 and 9 in Dekker JP and Boekema EJ (2005) Supramolecular organization of thylakoid membrane proteins in green plants. *Biochimica et Biophysica Acta—Bioenergetics* 1706: 12–39 [20], with permission of Elsevier Science B.V.

The process starts with capture of light in the peripheral light-harvesting antennae, called LH2. The LH2 are ring-shaped protein oligomers that contain a ring of eight or nine BChl *a* monomers, called B800, and a second ring of eight or nine BChl *a* dimers, called B850 [26, 27] (see **Figure 7**). The pigment names are based on their lowest excited-state absorption maximum. In addition, the LHs contain Cars that are located in van der Waals contact with the BChls, allowing efficient and rapid energy transfer [28]. Excitations of the B800 BChls are localized on a single chromophore and move by Förster-type electronic energy transfer (EET) to the B850 BChls in ~0.7 ps [30]. In contrast, the B850 BChls are strongly coupled. This gives rise to excitonic interactions that distribute excitations across several chromophores of the B850 ring with an intraring 'hopping time' of ~100 fs. The energy is transferred from the peripheral LH2 complexes to the core antenna complexes, called LH1, in ~3 ps [31]. The larger core antennae are elliptical-shaped oligomers and contain Cars and a ring of 15 or 16 BChl *a* dimers, called B875. The B875 BChls are also strongly coupled and their arrangement is homologous to the B850 BChls in LH2 [7, 32].

The LH1 ellipse surrounds the bacterial RC and energy transfer from the B875 BChls into the RC takes place in ~35 ps [31]. The bacterial RCs organize the pigments into two parallel ET pathways, termed the A side and the B side. However, the RC only utilizes the A-side cofactors for ET. In the RC, light is absorbed by two BChl molecules called the 'special pair' or P870. Once the special pair absorbs a photon, it ejects an electron, which is transferred via another molecule of BChl to a bacteriopheophytin (BPheo). This induces the initial charge separation $P^{(+)}BPheo^{(-)}$ in ~3 ps. To prevent charge recombination in this state, the electron is transferred from $BPheo^{(-)}$ to a quinone, called Q_A at the A side, in ~200 ps and subsequently to a quinone at the B side, called Q_B, in ~200 μs. While the Q_A is tightly bound to the RC, the Q_B is loosely associated and can easily detach. Two electrons are required to fully reduce Q_B to Q_BH_2 by taking up two protons. The reduced quinone Q_BH_2 diffuses through the membrane to another protein complex

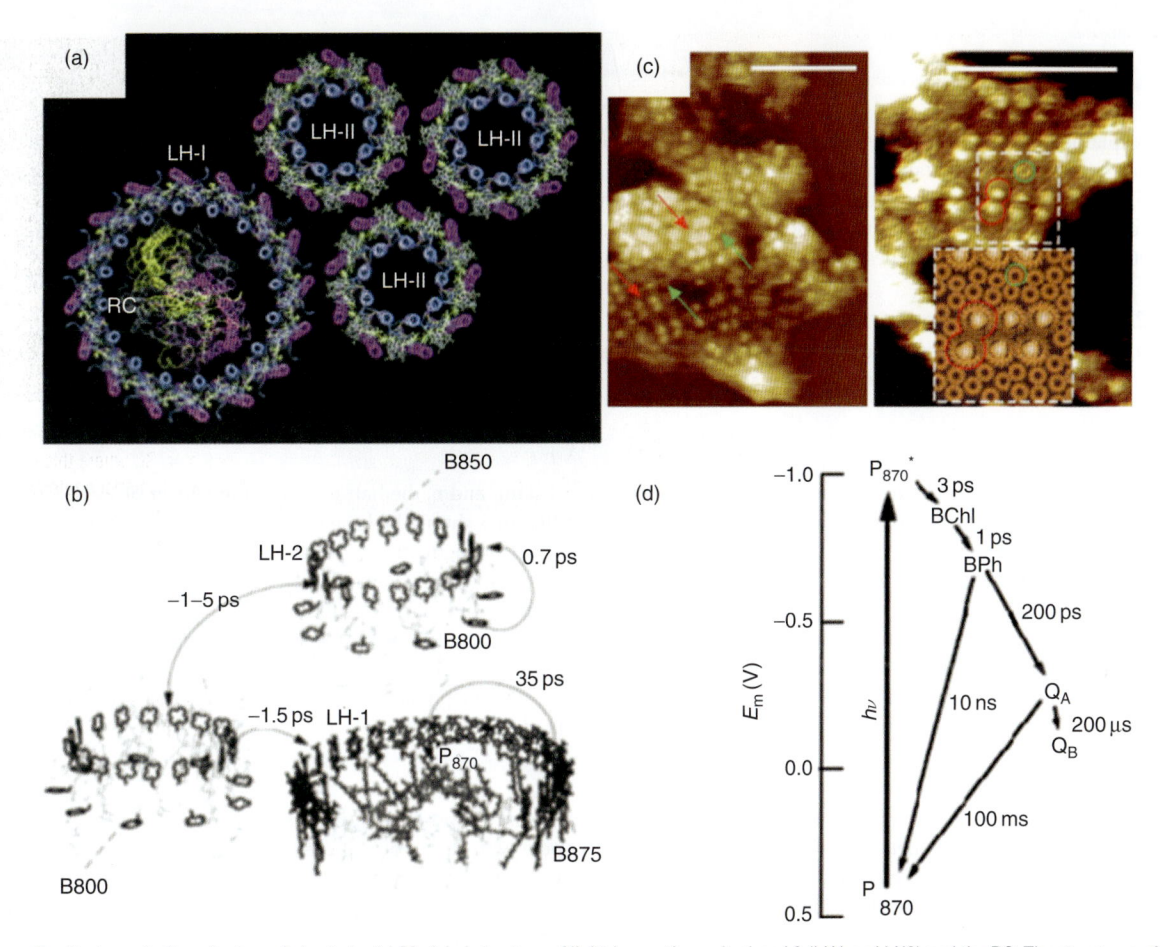

Figure 7 Photosynthetic unit of purple bacteria. (a) Modeled structure of light-harvesting units 1 and 2 (LH1 and LH2) and the RC. The structures of LH2 and the RC are from the crystal structures, and LH1 is simulated by analogy to LH2. Adapted from Figure 5 in Hu XC, Damjanovic A, Ritz T, and Schulten K (1998) Architecture and mechanism of the light-harvesting apparatus of purple bacteria. *Proceedings of the National Academy of Sciences of the United States of America* 95: 5935–5941 [1], with permission of National Academy of Sciences. (b) Dynamics of energy-transfer processes between bacteriochlorophylls B850 and B800 in LH2, B875 in LH1, and the special pair P870 in the RC. Adapted from Figure 1 in Yang M, Agarwal R, and Fleming GR (2001) The mechanism of energy transfer in the antenna of photosynthetic purple bacteria. *Journal of Photochemistry and Photobiology* 142: 107–119 [29], with permission of Elsevier Science B.V. (c) AFM image of arrangement of LH2–RC (highlighted in green) and LH1–RC (red) complexes in the bacterial membrane. The bright spots are the LH1–RC complex and the inset in the second panel is a model using the known crystal structures to reproduce the image. Adapted from Figure 1 in Bahatyrova S, Frese RN, Siebert CA, *et al.* (2004) The native architecture of a photosynthetic membrane. *Nature* 430: 1058–1062 [17], with permission of Nature Publishing Group. (d) Energies and timescales of ET within the RC. Adapted from Figure 6.3 in Blankenship RE (2002) *Molecular Mechanisms of Photosynthesis*. Oxford, UK: Blackwell Science Ltd [2], with permission.

(cytochrome $bc1$ complex) where it is oxidized. In the process, the reducing power of the Q_BH_2 is used to pump protons across the membrane (see also **Figure 1**). The generated electrochemical gradient is used to drive synthesis of ATP by the membrane-bound F0F1–ATPase protein, converting the captured light energy into a chemical form.

1.31.2 Design Principles of Natural Photosynthesis

From an engineer's perspective, the underlying physical chemical and physical principles of energy and ET processes in photosynthetic units can be described by a defined set of length and energy scales that may be used as guidelines for the design of a so-called artificial leaf. An excellent overview of these engineering guidelines is presented in the work of Noy and Dutton [33, 34].

1.31.2.1 Photon Absorption, Excitation Energy Transfer, and Electron Transfer

1.31.2.1.1 Photon absorption

The first length scale is connected with the rate of photon absorption K_{abs} and the following definition is taken from Reference 33. The absorption cross section σ depends on the photon energy E and on the flux of photons in the spectrum of solar irradiance $\phi(E)$. In addition, there is an energetic threshold E_{min}, set according to the driving force of the charge separation reaction so that

$$K_{\text{abs}} = \int_{E_{\min}}^{\infty} \phi(E)\sigma'(E)dE \qquad [1]$$

As explained by Noy et al. [33], a rough estimate of the amount of incident solar photons ($\varphi_{\text{total}} = 4 \times 10^{21}$ photons s^{-1} m^{-2}) is obtained by integrating the standard reference solar spectral irradiance at Air Mass 1.5 (ASTM G-173-03). Using this value, K_{abs} can be defined as $K_{\text{abs}} = 40r^2$, with r being the radius of the absorbing molecule in Å. Typically, r for a single Chl molecule is ~0.03 nm and the maximal photon absorption rate for a single pigment is therefore ~4 s^{-1} under standard solar irradiance conditions. Hereby, 30–300 absorber molecules are needed in a photosynthetic unit to obtain biological catalysis rates of 10^2–10^4 s^{-1}.

1.31.2.1.2 Excitation energy transfer

The second length scale is associated with excitation energy transfer. The excitation energy is transferred primarily via dipole–dipole Coulomb interactions in a Förster mechanism according to

$$k_{\text{EET}} = k_{\text{f}} \left(\frac{r_0}{r}\right)^6 \qquad [2]$$

with k_{EET} being the excitation energy transfer rate, k_{f} the radiative constant, and r_0 the half-radius of the Förster process. Since the length scale of exciton migration in the antenna is large, the exciton lifetimes should be long enough to allow for photons striking any part of the antenna to reach the RC. Typical r_0 values for photosynthetic pigments are 5–10 nm.

Once excitons are trapped in the RC, the process of charge separation should take place faster compared to back transfer to the antenna units. This is achieved by a relatively large antenna–RC distance (~2 nm) versus a short distance for the redox pigments in the RC. Furthermore, surrounding of the RCs by assemblies of antenna pigments gives a spatial arrangement in which energy transfer is optimized by multiple entries to the RC. The combination of constraints (spatial distance between antenna–RC and multiple entries to the RC) is achieved by circular-like arrangements of antenna pigments around the RCs, with a 'cordon sanitaire' zone (see Noy et al. [33]) of ~2 nm around the RC where no antenna pigments occur.

1.31.2.1.3 Electron transfer

The third length scale is connected to the ET processes. In the RC, electron transport via multiple steps is necessary because transfer across the membrane in a single step would be too slow to compete with decay of the excited state to the ground state and dissipation of the energy into useless heat. If the electron and the hole can be further separated before charge recombination occurs, the electronic coupling and therefore the rate constant for recombination is drastically reduced. The use of multiple cofactors separated by an edge-to-edge distance less than 0.6 nm ensures a rapid tunneling time of ~10 ps or less for every step. The dependence of the rates of ET reactions within covalently linked donor–acceptor (DA) molecules on the free energy of reaction and the electronic interaction between the donor and the acceptor are described well by theory. Equation [3] shows how the ET rate k_{ET} depends on these quantities:

$$k_{\text{ET}} = \frac{2\pi}{\hbar} V_{\text{DA}}^2 \left(\frac{1}{(4\pi\lambda kT)^{1/2}}\right) e^{-(\Delta G_0 + \lambda)^2 / 4\lambda kT} \qquad [3]$$

where ΔG_0 is the free energy of reaction, V_{DA} the electronic coupling between the donor and the acceptor, and λ the total energy of the nuclear reorganization (structural change) within the donor, the acceptor, and the solvent required for the reaction to occur. One of the key features of eqn [3] is that it predicts that the rate of an ET reaction will slow down when the free energy of reaction becomes very large. This is the so-called 'inverted Marcus region', which has been proven experimentally [35, 36]. This fact has proven critical to the design of long-lived charge separation systems. The total reorganization energy λ is usually divided into contributions from nuclear motions within the donor and acceptor molecules λ_{i} and solvent molecules λ_{s}. The value of λ_{i} may be calculated from the force constants for all the molecular vibrations in both the reactant and the product, while λ_{s} can be determined by application of the dielectric continuum model of a solvent.

1.31.2.2 Photochemical Thermodynamics of Energy Storage

The photosynthetic apparatus is connected to the steady-state network of catalytic conversion reactions in the organism that is continuously dissipating energy. If there is a shortage at one spot, it can be smoothly compensated from other dynamic reservoirs in the network.

The storage and downstream utilization can be described as a single-step conversion of solar energy into Gibbs free energy. In its simplest form, the photosynthetic solar cell is a heat engine that produces charge separation (see **Figure 8**). Inside the engine, a molecular absorber is excited that produces charge separation. There are three basic conversion processes in the primary mechanism of the photosynthetic solar cell [38]:

1. Excitation of a molecular absorber (Chl) with rate g
2. Energy conversion by charge separation with rate I into an electron and hole in dynamic equilibrium with the absorber
3. Back reaction with rate $1/\tau$ from the excited Chl state into the ground state

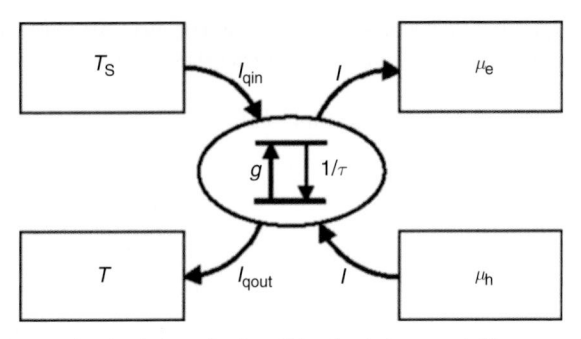

Figure 8 The solar energy converter as heat engine. In photosynthesis, a Chl molecule is connected to a reservoir at ambient temperature $T \sim 300$ K, and emitting heat flow I_{qout} is excited due to the heat flow I_{qin} from the solar reservoir at temperature $T = 5800$ K with a rate g to an excited state separated by an energy hv from the ground state. The excited Chl state either decays with loss rate $1/\tau$ or produces an electron–hole pair with net charge separation rate I and free energy $\Delta\mu = \mu_e - \mu_h$. Adapted from Figure 5 in Markvart T and Landsberg PT (2002) Thermodynamics and reciprocity of solar energy conversion. *Physica E* 14: 71–77 [37], with permission of Elsevier Science B.V.

The importance of a tight connection between energy conversion and energy storage was noted at an early stage [39]. First, excitation of a molecular Chl absorber in exchange with the field of solar irradiation leads to a difference in chemical potential:

$$\Delta\mu_{abs} = hv_0 + k_B T \ln\left(\frac{[\text{Chl}]^*}{[\text{Chl}]}\right) \quad [4]$$

with $[\text{Chl}]^*$ and $[\text{Chl}]$ being the populations of the excited and the ground state of the absorber, respectively. In the dark, the excited and the ground states are in equilibrium and $\Delta\mu_{abs} = 0$, leading to $[\text{Chl}]^*/[\text{Chl}] = \exp(-hv_0/k_B T)$, that is, the Boltzmann distribution. For Chl a in a plant, $hv_0 = 1.8$ eV. The upper limit at the absorber stage is $\eta = 1 - 4T/3T_S = 93\%$ efficiency due to entropic losses originating from the different temperatures of the incoming radiation and of the heat reservoir.

A photovoltaic solar cell produces electricity, while a photosynthetic RC produces a photochemical steady state with a voltage over the membrane and charge separation in dynamic equilibrium with the absorber. When the light is switched on and the absorber is coupled to a storage reservoir, a steady state is produced, where the formation of the excited state is balanced by its decay due to the limited life time and the net flow of energy into the charge–separated (CT) state. The quantity

$$\Delta\mu_{e-h} = e\Delta\psi + k_B T \ln\left(\frac{p'q'}{p_0'q_0'}\right) \quad [5]$$

represents the difference in chemical potential or free energy produced by light-induced charge separation and contains an electronic and a photochemical term that measures the probabilities $p'q'$ of electron and hole occupation of the acceptor and donor states in the light relative to the concentration $p_0'q_0'$ in the dark and is proportional to the temperature [37].

Biochemically, it is very difficult to maintain a membrane potential, which is rapidly converted in a ΔpH that is used to produce ATP, an intermediate energy carrier. When a storage reservoir is connected to the absorber, energy flows can be forwarded from the absorber into the reserve and backwarded from the reserve back into the absorber, where it can be emitted. In this way, assimilation has to compete against depletion of the reserve by backward reaction coupled with radiative loss in the absorber. The entire system has to operate linearly and close to the thermodynamic limit to minimize losses. The net production rate of charge separation and energy extraction can be described by the solar cell equation:

$$I = I_f - I_b \left[\exp\left(\frac{\Delta\mu}{k_B T}\right) - 1\right] \quad [6]$$

with I_f and I_b being the forward and backward reaction rates, respectively. Equation [6] is the equivalent of the Shockley equation for a solar cell, in which I_f and I_b would be the light-generated and dark saturation current, respectively [37].

The energy storage from an elementary steady-state process can be generalized according to the equation

$$\Delta\mu_{st} = \Delta\mu_{max} + k_B T \ln(\delta) \quad [7]$$

Here, the first factor is due to the kinetics of the steady state, while δ measures the thermodynamic activity of the trap. In order to favor the forward reaction over the backward process, the energy of the combined products is lower than that for the excited state by at least $k_B T \ln(\delta)$. The maximum power is generated for $\delta \sim k_B T/\mu_{max}$, a compromise between a high conversion efficiency and a high storage efficiency. For plant photosystems I and II under operational conditions, $\Delta\mu_{st} \sim 1.2$ eV and $\Delta\mu_{max} \sim 1.3$ eV.

Equation [7] can be generalized to storage processes further downstream and longer timescales, where the entire system is in Boltzmann equilibrium with the initial excited state. $\Delta\mu_{st}$ should be sufficiently low to maintain the steady state against back reactions and represents the work that can be obtained, for example, from sugar or biomass.

When the solar radiation is interrupted, the unavoidable back reaction causes gradual depletion of the accumulated energy. For instance, a plant in the dark produces a small flux of photons (luminescence) from its reserve that was stored during illumination periods. This leads to a generalized expression for the thermodynamic limit of energy storage in a steady-state reserve at all time and length scales, starting from the initial free energy stored in the solar energy assimilation $h\nu_0$, according to

$$\Delta\mu_{st}(t) = h\nu_0 - k_B T \ln\left(\frac{t}{\tau}\right) \qquad [8]$$

with t being the storage time.

The highest yields and efficiencies are attainable when energy is used as soon as it is assimilated, avoiding intermediate storage, for instance, by generating and using electricity, by running nanoscale catalytic converters directly from the photoconverter and storing the energy in a redox couple, by coupling a chemical cycle directly to a photoconverter like in the chloroplast, by connecting the chloroplast directly to respiration like in the plant, or by using light-driven cell factories for production of food and chemical feedstock.

1.31.3 The Design of an Artificial Leaf

What is an artificial leaf? The answer depends on the focus point that one has when talking about a leaf. Is a leaf a high surface area for the capture of photons? Or is it a natural design of a light energy to fuel converter? Or perhaps, is it an example of high-density-packed nanomachines that capture and utilize light energy?

The term 'artificial leaf' was introduced by Gratzel in 1991 [40] describing a new generation of solar cells, in which a Chl-mimicking sensitizer is bound as a monomolecular coating on the surface of a TiO_2 membrane. Upon light absorption, the sensitizer is excited and ejects an electron in the TiO_2 conduction band. Here, we like to expand the definition and point out that the main feature of a leaf lies in its biological nature. It represents Nature's approach toward light energy utilization. It features self-assembly, self-repair, and adaptability. Furthermore, a leaf constitutes different, well-defined nanometric systems, each of them precisely tuned to carry out a specific task and to interrelate with each other. As such, the most prominent feature of how a leaf utilizes light energy is the supramolecular functioning of the several building blocks.

The artificial leaf represents a different approach toward (photosynthesis) solar energy conversion compared to bio-based fuel production where natural or genetically modified organisms are used in an agricultural fashion. An artificial leaf is a device where biological material may well be entirely absent. At the same time, it has to feature some of the crucial aspects of natural photosynthesis. Minimally, this is the self-assembly of building blocks into a functional supramolecular network that operates on fine-tuned length and timescales constrained by physical rules.

The hypothetical device constitutes three aspects of photosynthesis: (1) light capture, (2) charge separation and ET, and (3) catalysis. The first two cover also the main aspects of photovoltaics. In photosynthesis though, ETs can trigger the splitting of water into oxygen and protons, the cycling of electrons, or the generation of proton-motive force. Artificial photosynthesis research targets all these aspects of natural photosynthesis and can be separated into two main approaches: bio-based systems and bio-inspired synthetic systems. The first approach utilizes integrated biological components, isolated via biochemistry techniques from living organisms. The latter approach mimics the biological systems by means of synthetic chemistry or surface physics. For both lines of research, there is a necessity to interconnect compounds or systems with conducting material in order to extract electrons and re-reduce the primary electron donor. In other words, the photovoltaic aspect of the artificial leaf constitutes the primary mode of operation and has to be solved for any artificial photosynthetic design.

1.31.3.1 Interfacing Proteins onto Solid-State Surfaces

Biology may serve as a template for a bottom-up approach in nanotechnology [41]. Ever since the discovery of the protein, it has been recognized that biological function is carried out starting from the nanoscale to higher length scales. At the nanoscale, matter has several properties that are different from larger scales, notably large reactive surfaces and a molecular thermodynamic regime. In biology, these properties lead to dynamic properties of the systems, allowing rapid response to changing impulses from the outside world. Measuring or utilizing environmental impulses that interact with biology in a technological fashion may utilize biological components [42]. Such devices have been constructed, most famously the electrochemical blood glucose test strips for diabetes [43]. Here, for an artificial leaf harboring features as in a biological cell but which is not a (synthetic) biological cell itself, adaptability implies nanometric components that are embedded within a flexible matrix. To date, proteins or protein complexes are the only compounds known that may provide this adaptability outside a cell. And for solar energy uses, photosynthetic proteins are the first to be utilized.

Early research on interfacing photosynthetic proteins and conducting surfaces concentrated on the purple bacterial RC since it has been the best characterized photosynthetic complex [44]. The RC encompasses the key features sought after in an artificial leaf: a self-assembling and high-pigment-density nanometric structure, with a near-unity quantum yield of directional energy and electron-transferring capability. Likewise, LHCs enhance the absorption cross section considerably with only minimal energy losses [9]. Ongoing photosynthesis research elucidates to more and more detail how pigments are organized by the proteins to accomplish these feats [45, 46]. Fine-tuning includes the mutual orientation and distances of cofactors within degrees and angstroms relative to each other, leading to very precise energy-transfer and ET reactions. While the research on protein functionality transferred into a device may have started (and perhaps still is) a proof-of-principle type of investigation, it will be hard to find any other matrix that can arrange light-active molecules with such precision [34]. In this section, we will present an overview of the investigations on the interfacing of protein complexes and conducting material.

The first attempts to derive electric currents from purple bacterial RCs *in vitro* were reported around 30 years ago [47]. These experiments utilized RCs embedded within a membrane that separated two aqueous compartments containing electron carriers similar to those used by the organism: cytochrome *c* in one compartment and short-chain (i.e., water-soluble) quinones in the other. These measurements showed the possibility of utilizing isolated RCs to generate a photocurrent, but the currents obtained were low, with a peak value less than a $pA\,cm^{-2}$. Much higher light-induced currents were subsequently obtained with bacterial RCs adhered onto a conducting surface immersed in a liquid and under potentiostatic control [48]. The surface functions as an electrode, with an extrinsic electric potential applied between the surface and a counter electrode. The potential can, in principle, be used to drive electrons in either direction between the RCs and the surface, and to control the redox state of both the RC chromophores and extrinsic charge carriers. Charge carriers such as cyt-c and water-soluble quinones have been used to shuttle electrons between the RCs and the electrode(s). This method was used by Katz [49] to derive currents up to $80\,nA\,cm^{-2}$ using a functionalized surface with special linkers that connected with the terminal electron acceptor, Q_B, site of the RC. Work by Trammell *et al.* [50] also indicated that the RC can be linked to a surface with either the P or the Q side facing the electrode, with photo-induced electron tunneling being proposed to occur between either P or QB and the surface. A large body of research focused on the bacterial RC alone, with special linkers adhered to surfaces serving as electrodes (see **Figure 9(a)**). The surfaces were functionalized with a self-assembled monolayer (SAM) of molecules and a variety of redox mediators were employed (for review, see Reference 52, 53). Similar light-induced electrochemistry experiments have also been reported on RCs surrounded by the LH1 LHC [54, 55]. An enormous increase in photocurrent has been reported after an electrode with linked RCs was exposed to a solution of water-soluble protein cytochrome *c*2 (see Reference 51 and **Figure 9(b)**). This finding indicated that this relatively small protein interspersed between the RCs and the electrode surface to form an electron relay that enhanced ETs for nonfavorable oriented RCs.

RCs and RC–LH1 complexes also adhere onto a gold surface in the absence of any engineered linkers onto the proteins and SAMs covering the surface. Bacterial photosynthetic membranes can also be functionally adhered onto a conducting surface [56]. Such design may be favorable, since the membrane provides a matrix allowing diffusive processes to occur, necessary for self-organization and adaptability.

More recently, electric currents have been derived from protein complexes from oxygenic photosynthetic organisms, such as Photosystem 1 (PS1) or Photosystem 2 (PS2) adhered onto metal electrodes [57–60]. A fully functional photocell has been constructed using spinach PS1 or bacterial RCs, sandwiched between two electrodes [61]. Although the energy conversion of this cell proved to be low, it did show the possibility to construct a photovoltaic device using photosynthetic components. All these designs discussed here can be characterized as proof of principle showing the applicability of biological material for solar energy devices. The highest light-induced current densities obtained were on the order of $10–100\,\mu A\,cm^{-2}$ [58], still a factor of 100 lower compared to a Grätzel cell [62]. Likely, the rate-limiting step in all these cases is electron tunneling from the RCs to the surface. On the other hand, some designs showed to be functional while exposed to air, a major advantage in solar energy conversion, especially when combined with a water-splitting catalyst.

On a final note, we stress here that a protein is a structured polymer. The usage of polymers as matrices for light-active molecules is a large research field [63] and research pushing the limit on utilizing biological material may well be leading the way for improving synthetic solar energy materials.

1.31.3.2 Protein Maquettes for Artificial Photosynthesis

Artificial proteins connect bio-based and bio-inspired solar energy converters. The protein matrix is used, and in fact indispensable, to fine-tune position and orientation of pigments, to create directional ET pathways, and to provide a proper scaffold for catalytic reactions, all of which processes have been characterized in great detail in natural proteins. In 1987, Ho and Degrado [64] programmed peptides to assemble into an amphiphilic four-helix bundle protein through hydrophobic interactions by imposing an alternating pattern of hydrophilic and hydrophobic helix-forming residues. Using histidines as ligands, self-assembled four-helix bundles were designed to bind heme cofactors, introducing the elementary design of an artificial photosynthetic pigment–protein complex [65]. For selective incorporation of electron-donor and electron-acceptor cofactors, a family of four-helix bundle peptides was designed with distinct hydrophilic and hydrophobic domains along the length of the helices, allowing light-induced ET along the helices across a surface between polar and nonpolar media [66]. The four-helix bundle families show the advantage of bottom-up approach, in which synthetic peptides are step-by-step assembled into more complex structures. Alternatively, a top-down approach uses natural proteins as templates, stripping down their complexity to create a minimal functional design. Back in the 1980s, it was found that the LH1 antenna complex of purple bacteria could be reconstituted from isolated antenna peptides and pigments and this process turned out to be reversible and controlled by its thermodynamic parameters [67–69]. By mutational approaches, the minimal requirements for self-assembly into subunits and into a ring-shaped complex were evaluated [70–73]. Absorption, fluorescence, and circular dichroism spectroscopy on reassembled LH1 antenna systems verified that pigment and antenna polypeptides were assembled together into functional antenna complexes with excitonic pigment–pigment and structural pigment–protein interactions.

Its reversible assembly makes the purple bacterial antenna complex very accessible for substitution with synthetic components to create an artificial antenna. Based on LH1 polypeptides, a minimal polypeptide unit was designed that is capable of intermediate self-assembly into subunits and binding of pigments [74] (see **Figure 10**); LHCs have been reassembled from natural polypeptides and Zn BChls [75], and zinc porphyrins were immobilized on a surface by assembly of the pigments with synthetic peptides that contained LH1 polypeptide sequences [76].

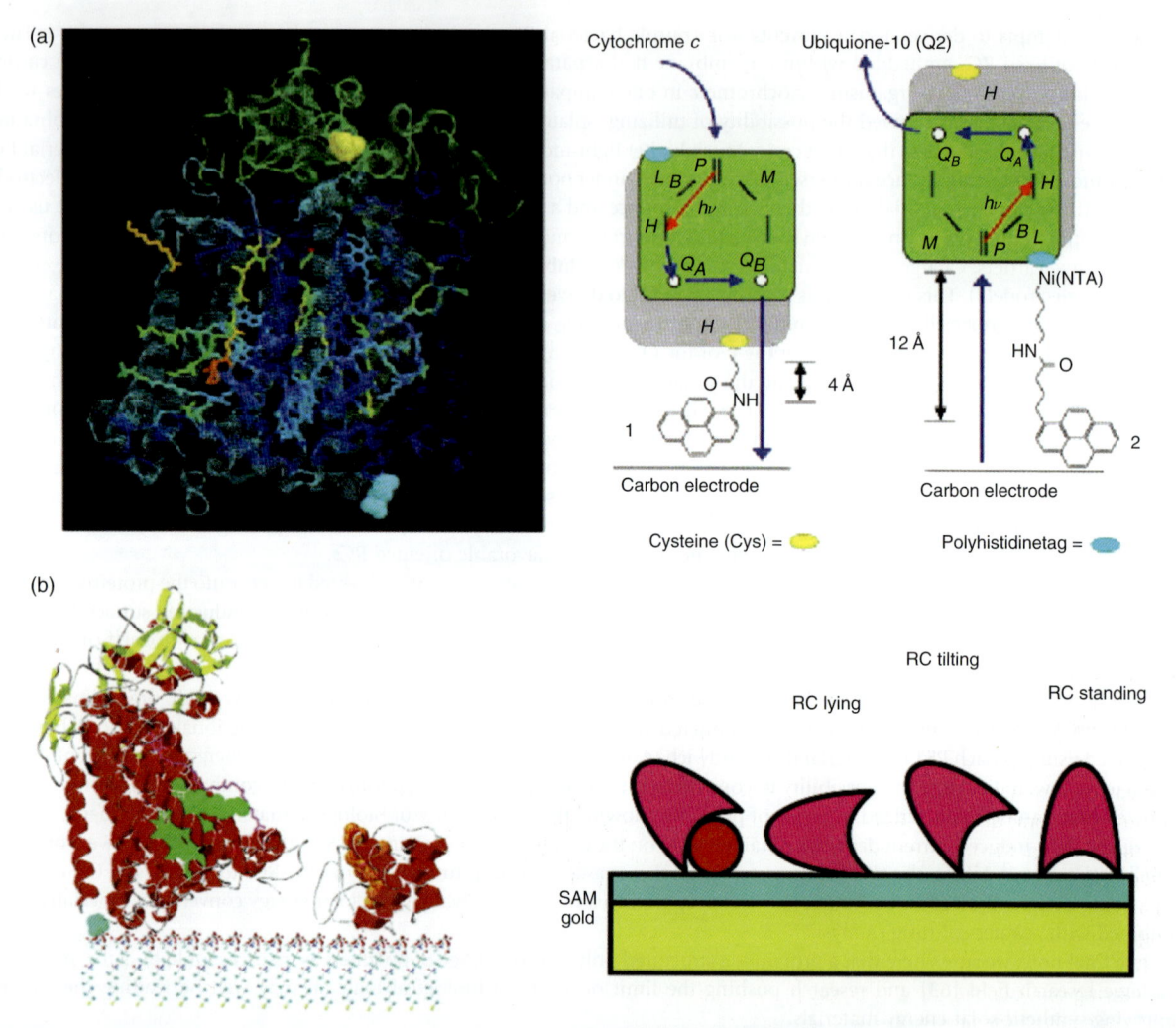

Figure 9 (a) Schematic presentation showing two possible ways of RC binding and ET pathways between RC and electrode. P, primary electron donor (special pair); B, monomeric bacteriochlorophyll; H, BPheo; Q_A and Q_B primary and secondary electron acceptors (quinones), respectively. The structure of the bifunctional linkers used for binding to carbon electrodes is labeled 1 and 2. Adapted from Figure 1B in Trammell SA, Spano A, Price R, and Lebedev N (2006) Effect of protein orientation on electron transfer between photosynthetic reaction centers and carbon electrodes. *Biosensors and Bioelectronics* 21: 1023–1028 [50], with permission of Elsevier Science B.V. (b) Molecular wiring RCs via cytochrome *c*2 complexes onto a SAM-covered electrode. Proteins: red (helices) and yellow (strands); his-tag: blue; pigments: green and orange. Inset shows the possible RC (red) orientation relative to SAM (blue) surface and the main orientation of which a molecular relay via cytochrome *c*2 (brown) enhances electron-tunneling rates. Adapted from Figure 1 in Lebedev N, Trammell SA, Spano A, *et al.* (2006) Conductive wiring of immobilized photosynthetic reaction center to electrode by cytochrome c. *Journal of the American Chemical Society* 128: 12044–12045 [51], with permission of American Chemical Society, USA.

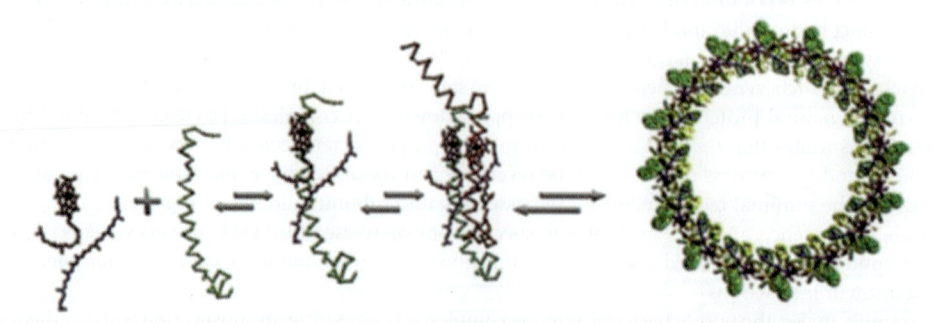

Figure 10 Reversible self-assembly of the purple bacterial LH1 antenna ring from isolated pigments and polypeptides.

The impact of the protein matrix on the pigment properties and vice versa have been investigated in great detail in numerous studies. Recent nuclear magnetic resonance (NMR) studies showed how mechanistic pigment–protein interactions are translated into subtle electronic perturbations [77–80]. The protein matrix induces pigment structural deformations that can create electronic polarization, and

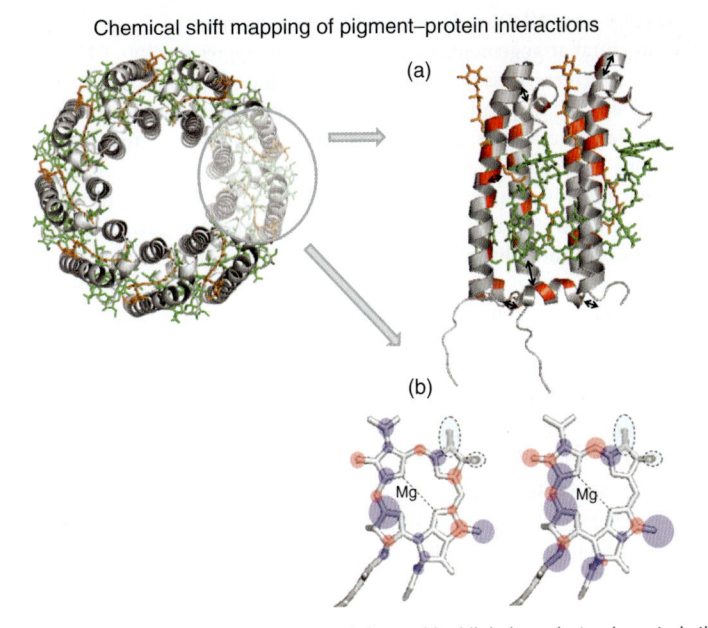

Figure 11 Pigment–protein interactions in the light-harvesting antenna of *Rps. acidophila* induce electronic perturbations that may tune the light-harvesting function. (a) Displacements in the protein backbone structure (colored in red) correlate with pigment–protein and protein–protein interactions. (b) The BChl electronic structures compared to free BChl in solution show perturbations induced by the protein matrix. Partial charges are drawn as spheres in red (positive) and blue (negative).

pigment–pigment distances are fine-tuned by balancing forces in the pigment–protein complex. This is illustrated in **Figure 11**. Since the structure–electronic details are revealed hereon an atomic scale, these features could in principle be rebuilt in artificial constructs.

Summarizing, the LH antenna polypeptides position and fine-tune the interpigment distances with nanometric precision and induce oligomerization into ring-shaped structures, controlling the functionality on length scales ranging from subnanometer distances to supramolecular scales. All of these features are ready for adaptation in artificial photo-antenna devices through programmed self-assembly of protein building blocks.

The design of photosynthetic RC protein mimics for light-driven electron transport is a more challenging task. Through protein engineering of a cytochrome *b*, artificial proteins that mimic the ET from a light-activated chlorine to a bound quinone molecule were constructed by Hay *et al.* [81]. A quinone-binding site was engineered into the *Escherichia coli* cytochrome *b*(562) by introducing a cysteine within the hydrophobic interior of the protein and reconstituting its heme-binding site with a Zn-chlorine. More recently, bacterioferritin (cytochrome *b*1 from *E. coli*) was used as a scaffold [82]. The heme was replaced with Zn chlorine and the diiron-binding sites were replaced by two manganese ions. Upon illumination, the bound Zn chlorines initiate ET followed by oxidation of the manganese center, possibly via an inherent tyrosine residue. This novel artificial RC potentially mimics the assembly of a water oxidation center, heading toward the design of a water-splitting artificial RC.

1.31.3.3 Bio-Inspired Self-assembled Artificial Antennae

The photosynthetic apparatus consists of self-assemblies that bridge length scales from fine-tuned subnanometer distances between connecting chromophores to the macroscopic scales of supramolecular aggregates. This allows the incoming light energy to migrate over long distances to the RC and to separate charge and transport charges to the catalytic sites. A major challenge in artificial photosynthesis is to develop functional components that equivalently self-organize themselves into an interconnected system.

This section will focus on the self-assembly of artificial antenna pigments to create antennae that transport light energy over long distances. In the subsequent section, artificial RC constructs are described that can create spatially separated CT states or transport holes and charges for directed charge injection into a solid surface. We limit the discussion to noncovalent assembled antennae, but it is stressed that significant progress has also been made toward the synthesis of bio-inspired covalent antenna structures [83, 84]. For instance, various dendrimer type of antennae have been constructed based on polyphenylene [85], porphyrin, or phthalocyanine [86] building blocks. Inspired by the oligomeric structures of purple bacterial antenna systems that allow for efficient excitation energy transfer (EET) between the protein-bound BChls, different types of cyclic porphyrin wheels have been designed as artificial light-harvesting antennae that allow for efficient EET between the porphyrins [87, 88].

1.31.3.3.1 Chlorosome-based, light-harvesting antennae

In contrast to the antenna apparatus of all other photosynthetic organisms, chlorosome antennae of green photosynthetic bacteria contain rod-shaped oligomers of BChl *c*/*d*/*e* molecules that self-aggregate without assistance of a protein scaffold. This fact was discovered in the early 1990s by the notion that chlorosome preparations compared with those of artificial pigment aggregates had striking similar spectroscopic properties [89]. A few years later, a model study applying resonance Raman and a cross-polarization magic-angle-spinning (CP-MAS) solid-state NMR study proved that also the structural organization of the pigment assemblies in chlorosomes was similar to the structural arrangements of *in vitro* pigment aggregates [90, 91].

The chlorosome self-organized structures possess characteristic redshifted Q_y absorption of the oligomerized BChls. Their structural functional features have been the inspiration for self-assembled artificial antennae. In chlorosomes, the self-assemblies are stabilized by C=O···H-O···Mg interactions between the 3^1 hydroxy group, the 13 carbonyl groups, and the central magnesium, and by π-π interactions between the tetrapyrrole macrocycles [92]. Starting from biological material, that is, Chl *a* isolated from natural photosynthetic organisms, metal complexes of 3^1-hydroxy-13^1-oxo-chlorins lacking the 13^2-COOCH$_3$ group were synthesized as model compounds by chemical modification. In particular, Zn chlorines were synthesized with various side-chain patterns, which self-assembled into oligomers with different degrees of redshifted Q_y absorption [93].

The efficiency of chlorosomal-based antennae depends on their excitation energy-transfer dynamics and exciton delocalization properties. These properties have been determined for different species of natural chlorosomes as well as for artificial pigment aggregates. EET between BChls in natural chlorosomes was estimated to be 4–6 ps [94, 95]. Based on two-pulse, photon-echo and transient absorption techniques, delocalization over 2–3 pigments was estimated for the species *Chlorobium tepidum* and over 10–12 pigments for *Chloroflexus aurantiacus* [96]. For artificial Zn-chlorine aggregates coaggregated with an energy trap, similar delocalization over 10–15 pigments was found [97]. Exciton theory calculations on chlorosomal model aggregates showed that the excitation energy transport occurs along helical trajectories, which reflects the presence of the macroscopic chirality in the tubular aggregates [98].

In the last years, there have been several breakthroughs in resolving the pigment-packing structure in natural and artificial chlorosome-like assemblies. Single-crystal X-ray diffraction of BChl *c* mimics showed extended BChl stacks that are packed by hydrophobic interactions, with weak interactions between carbonyl groups and the central Zn atom [99]. Recently, the chlorosome BChl aggregate structure was revealed of a triple mutant of the green sulfur bacteria *Chlorobaculum tepidum*, by a combination of solid-state NMR, cryo-electron microscopy (cryo-EM), and biological mutagenesis [100] (**Figures 12** and **13**). The absence of a methyl group at C-20 in the triple mutant and of side-chain heterogeneity and the very limited stereochemical heterogeneity at position 3^1 in the BChl *d* pigments provided very high-resolution MAS solid-state NMR data. Combining the NMR results with cryo-EM data that revealed a helical arrangement of Chl stacks, for the first time the molecular and supramolecular structure of a chlorosome was solved together. Combining solid-state NMR with X-ray diffraction techniques, the molecular packing structure in Zn-chlorine aggregates could be obtained without isotope labeling of compounds by similar methodologies [101]. The approach now allows for fast screening of new compounds in terms of the novel supramolecular structures with altered light-harvesting properties.

Zn porphyrin assemblies have been used for photosensitization of TiO$_2$ and SnO$_2$. Self-assembling chlorosome-mimicking porphyrin stacks were used to photosensitize wide-band-gap semiconductors with a 2.2% incident photon to charge separation efficiency [102]. In bilayers of porphyrin derivatives and a TiO$_2$ surface, exciton lengths up to 20 nm were observed for nematic layers at room temperature conditions [103], showing that it is possible to realize long exciton diffusion lengths by varying the design of porphyrin derivatives with different stacking tendencies.

Similar to chlorosome aggregates, the organic dye perylene tetracarboxylic acid bisimide (PBI) can assemble into supramolecular structures, directed by altering hydrogen bonding, metal–ligand interactions, and π-π stacking interactions. This way, structures such as squares, rosettes, and extended fibrous assemblies have been obtained in solution and at interfaces [104]. PBIs have favorable properties for applications in semiconductor solar cells, such as intense photoluminescence and n-type semiconductivity. Additional chromophores can be attached at the imide groups to induce energy and ET processes upon photoexcitation. Chen *et al.* [105] recently describe a trialkylphenyl-functionalized PBI, which formed extended fluorescent aggregates in nonpolar solvent and possesses liquid crystalline properties. The dye aggregates contained strong electronic coupling and charge-transfer interaction. Nanowires of this dye are considered ideal candidates for further investigations as n-type semiconducting materials.

1.31.3.4 Bio-Inspired DA Constructs

In the late 1970s, the first DA dyads were constructed based on porphyrin–quinone (P–Q) systems. In the P–Q system, the covalently linked porphyrin and quinone function as the electron-donor chromophore and the electron acceptor, respectively

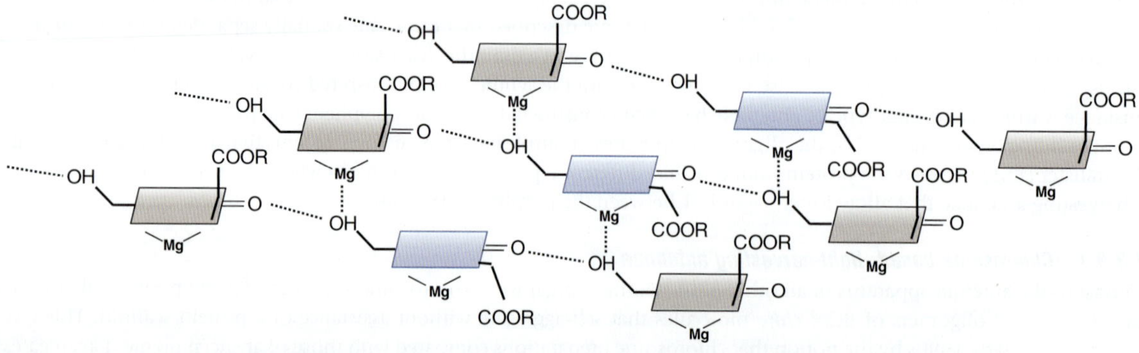

Figure 12 Syn–anti stacking of BChls in the triple bchQRU mutant of *Chlorobium tepidum* chlorosomes.

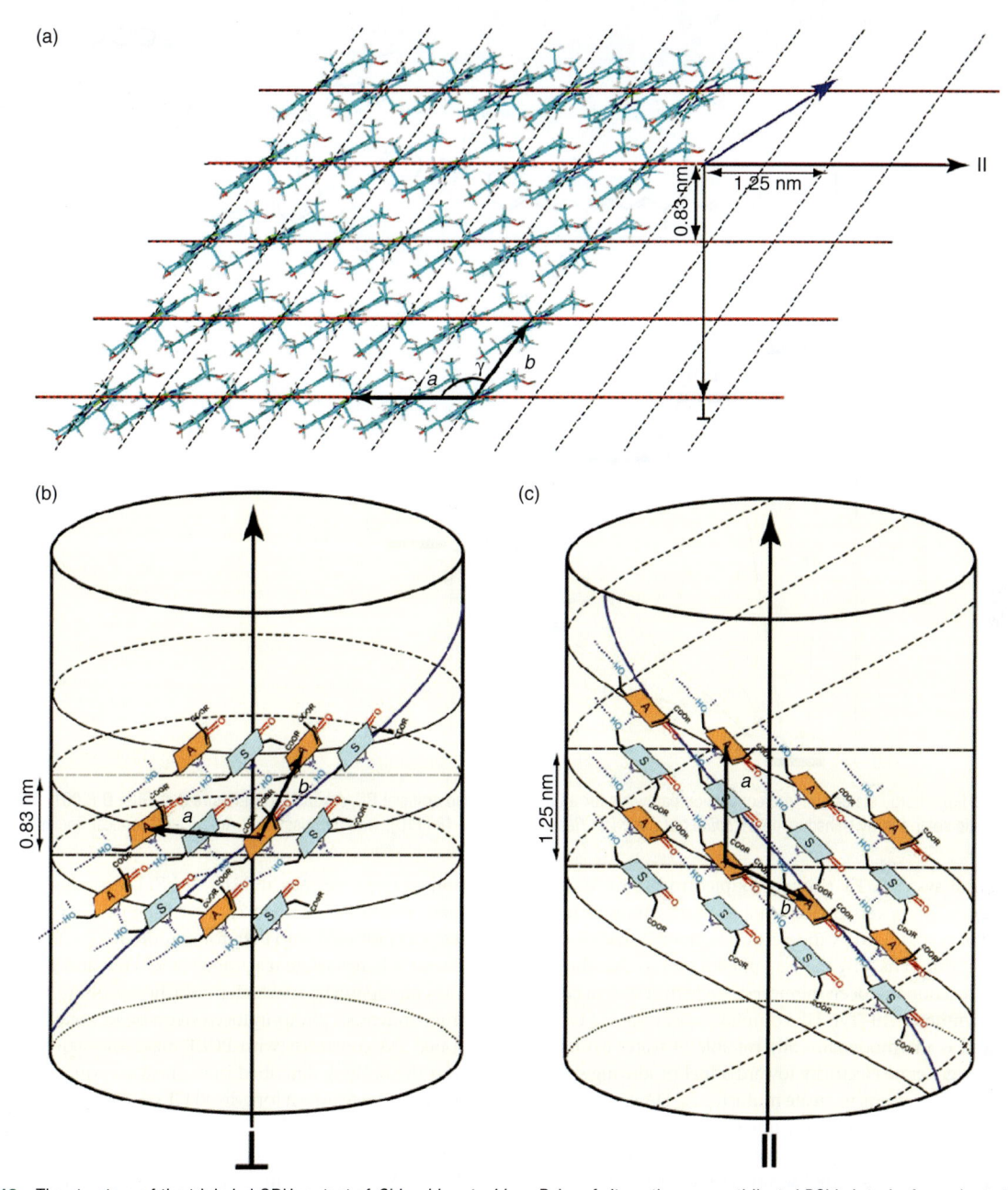

Figure 13 The structure of the triple bchQRU mutant of *Chlorobium tepidum*. Pairs of alternating syn–anti-ligated BChl *d* stacks form sheets that self-assemble into coaxial tubes. (a) Syn–anti arrays with the stacks indicated by red lines. (b and c) The H-bond helices that connect BChl stacks via the carbonyls are shown in blue and are right handed in (b) and left handed in (c). Adapted from Figure 5 in Ganapathy S, Oostergetel GT, Wawrzyniak PK, et al. (2009) Alternating syn–anti bacteriochlorophylls form concentric helical nanotubes in chlorosomes. *Proceedings of the National Academy of Sciences of the United States of America* 106: 8525–8530 [100], with permission of National Academy of Sciences.

[106]. While these simple DA systems could elucidate basic photochemical principles, they were unable to maintain long CT P$^+$–Q$^-$, with typical values of a few hundred picoseconds or less in solution before charge recombination takes place to the ground state. The CT state lifetimes were significantly improved by introduction of a third building block in a Car–P–Q triad, in which a porphyrin (P) is linked to a Car electron donor on one side and to a quinone (Q) electron acceptor on the other side [107]. Upon photoexcitation of the porphyrin in the triad, the first excited singlet-state Car–P*–Q decays via a two-step ET process, leading to the formation of a Car$^+$–P–Q$^-$ CT state that decays on a microsecond timescale. The triad contains three basic properties that mimic the functional design of natural RCs. First, a long-lived CT state is created via multielectron steps. Second, the structure allows the CT state to be spatially well separated. Third, coupling between the building blocks is weak and the first step endergonic so that charge recombination is slow [108]. The special properties of fullerene (C$_{60}$) and its capability to uptake several electrons have led to various DA dyads, triads, and more complex systems that include fullerene–porphyrin building blocks (see **Figure 14**) [108, 109].

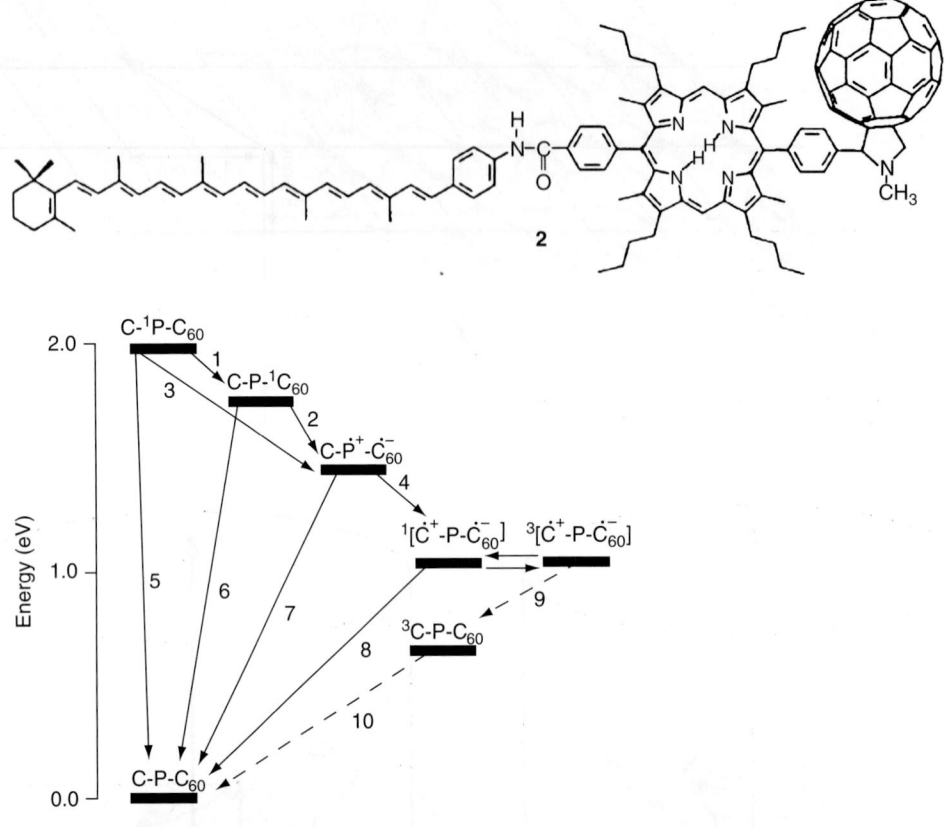

Figure 14 High-energy states and interconversion pathways for a Car–P–C$_{60}$ triad artificial RC. Adapted from Figure 2 in Gust D (2001) Mimicking photosynthetic solar energy transduction. *Accounts of Chemical Research* 34: 40–48 [110], with permission of American Chemical Society.

In natural systems, ET is often coupled to proton motions in proton-coupled electron transfer (PCET), avoiding high-energy intermediates by concerted electron and proton transfer reactions. In plant photosystem II (PS2), a tyrosine called Tyr$_Z$ is a redox mediator that is oxidized by the electron donor P$^{\bullet+}$. The oxidation step likely is combined with the protonation of a hydrogen-bonded histidine residue (His$^+$) by the Tyr$_Z$ phenol OH so that the combined, chemically reversible reactions His => His$^+$ and Tyr$_Z^+$ => Tyr$_Z^{\bullet}$ occur. The reaction has been mimicked in a hybrid system composed of TiO$_2$ nanoparticles to which photochemically active mimics of the photosynthetic Chl–Tyr–His complex were attached [111]. The construct undergoes photo-induced stepwise ET coupled to proton motion and is thermodynamically capable of water oxidation. Bio-inspired DA constructs with PCET make the step from photovoltaics that generate electricity toward a fuel-producing solar cell, which is the outlook described in the next section.

Despite many efforts to create multistep ET DA constructs, their performance in creating a long-lived CT state is still low compared to natural RCs. In alternative constructs, the special photophysical properties of ruthenium (Ru) dyes are used rather than porphyrins. After light excitation, Ru rapidly decays to the triplet state, with minimal losses from the (nanosecond) decay to the ground state. The long-lived (approximately millisecond) triplet state is used to create a CT state. As we will see in the next section, promising design for photoelectrochemical fuel cells use Ru-sensitized TiO$_2$ as an anode. Another approach totally opposed to the concept of multielectron steps is to create dyads that operate in the so-called 'inverted Marcus region', where the rate of an ET reaction will slow down when the free energy of reaction becomes very large, as can be deduced from eqn [3] (Section 1.31.2.1), and it is theoretically possible to create long charge separation lifetimes without loss of energy [112]. The boundary conditions for such 'inverted region' dyads is that they should have low reorganization energy (using short spacers between the donor and acceptor units) and that the charge separation energy should be lower than the triplet excited state. The latter prevents the CT state to decay rapidly to the triplet excited state in the Marcus normal region and decays to the ground state in the Marcus inverted region. An example of such a dyad is given by 9-mesityl-10-methylacridinium ion (Acr$^+$–Mes), in which an electron-donor moiety (mesityl group) is directly connected at the 9 position of the acridinium ion [112]. The dyads can be further developed to form self-assembled DA constructs that are linked by covalent and noncovalent bonds, combining 'nonnatural' design for charge separation with bio-inspired approaches for supramolecular assembly.

1.31.3.4.1 Self-assembled DA constructs

Different self-assembly strategies have been put forward using π-stacking interactions between small covalent building blocks based on perylene and naphthalene diimides (PDIs and NDIs) and porphyrin-based molecules. Wasielewski [113] has demonstrated the emergent behavior of self-assembled synthetic light-harvesting antenna structures that induce self-assembly of a functional special pair of five PDI molecules undergoing ultrafast, quantitative charge separation. The formed DA self-assemblies can be modified to assemble into higher organized stacks with controlled DA geometry, creating efficient charge transport along molecular wires.

Self-assembled DA triads having a primary and a secondary donor attached to PDI imide nitrogen atoms had an average distance between the two radical ions that was much larger than in their monomeric building blocks (3.1 vs. 2.3 nm), demonstrating that electron hopping through the π-stacked PDI molecules is fast enough to compete with the charge recombination time of 40 ns [114].

A remaining challenge in those systems is to induce unidirected transport of charge, efficiently coupled to a surface. In bilayer and bulk n/p heterojunction organic solar cells, electron-transporting materials are arranged via conductive materials, while hole-transporting materials need efficient charge separation at very large electron DA interfaces. For this purpose, Matile *et al.* [115–117] have developed supramolecular n/p heterojunctions with oriented multicolored antiparallel redox gradients, called OMARG-SHJs, that mimic Nature in capturing as much light as possible and quickly funnel electrons and holes in opposite directions. The self-assemblies include 3D zipper architectures, positioned on a surface, of NDIs attached to *p*-oligophenyl (POP) or *p*-oligophenylethynyl (OPE) chromophores. The NDIs build up redox gradients for electron transport, while the POP/OPE DA systems create hole transport in the opposite direction (**Figure 15**).

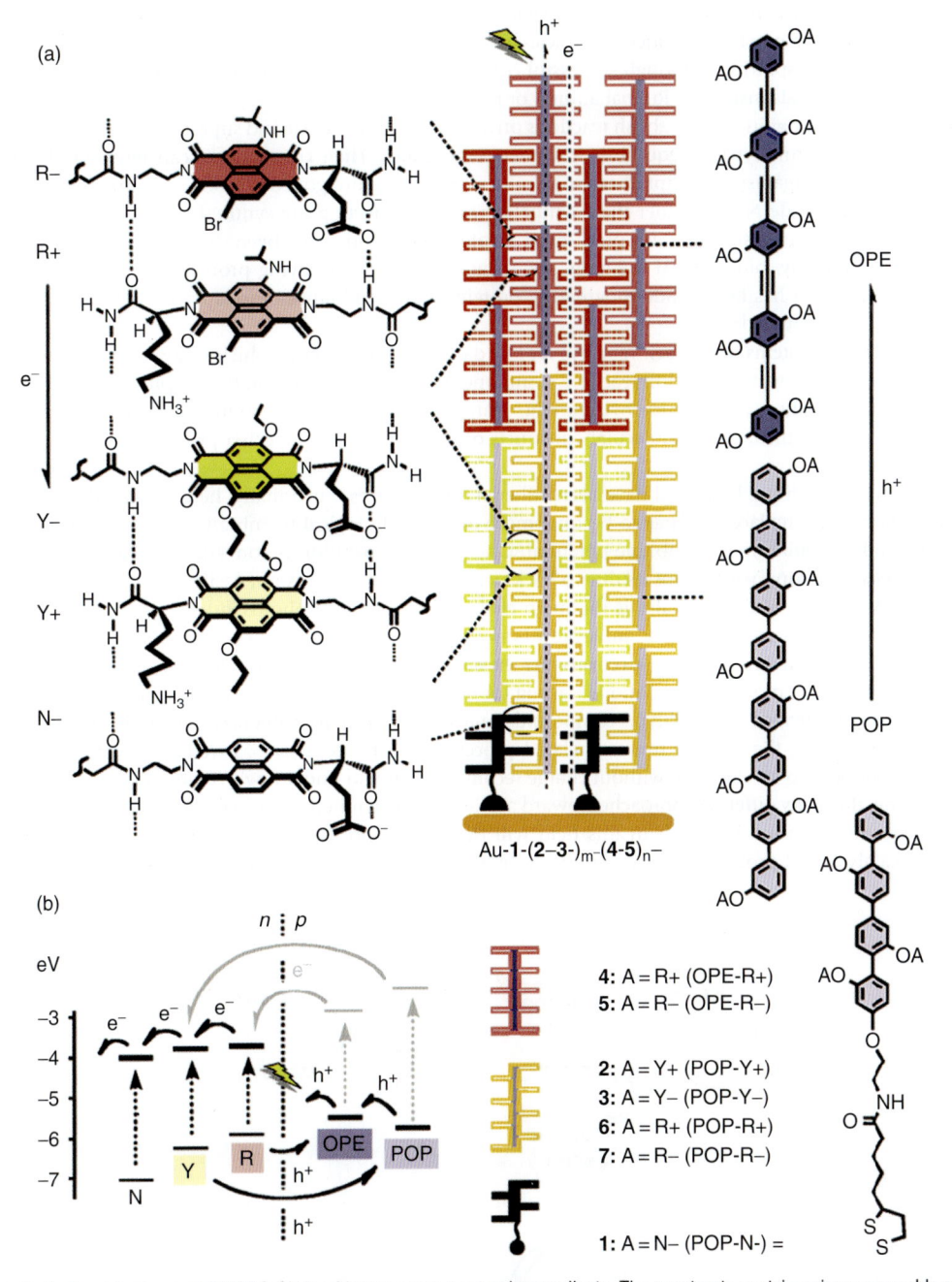

Figure 15 Hypothetical architectures of OMARG-SHJs with two-component redox gradients. The constructs contain a zipper assembly of stacks of red NDI electron donors along strings of OPE hole acceptors on top of yellow NDI electron acceptors along POP hole donors. By inducing gradients along both the electron- and hole-transporting pathways, photo-induced charge separation over very long distances is achieved. Adapted from Figure 1 in Sakai N, Bhosale R, Emery D, *et al.* Supramolecular n/p-heterojunction photosystems with antiparallel redox gradients in electron- and hole-transporting pathways. *Journal of the American Chemical Society* 132: 6923–6925 [116], with permission of American Chemical Society.

1.31.4 Outlook: The Construction of a Fuel-Producing Solar Cell

The final goal in creating artificial leaves is to build a fuel-producing solar cell as depicted in the scheme in **Figure 16**. For this aim, natural photosynthesis serves as a blueprint for clean hydrogen production. We described here in various sections the different materials that are being used as a starting point for the construction of an artificial leaf. Where one material is ready to use, the photosynthetic proteins, and research focuses on the integration within artificial devices, others are synthesized and tested for function, like the synthetic dyads and triads. Yet others are merely on the drawing board, the synthetic proteins. In any case, all research directions are facing major challenges of which we list here the most important ones.

Although the principal products of photosynthesis in plants and bacteria are carbohydrates, certain algae and cyanobacteria can produce hydrogen directly from water using sunlight, thus providing a basis for the creation of suitable artificial systems. Yet, considerable challenges need to be overcome in mimicking the functioning of natural photosynthetic systems for a water-splitting and hydrogen-producing device. In Nature, biological systems operate at ambient temperatures and neutral pH and evidently are built from earth-abundant materials. Considerable research effort is directed into constructing synthetic compounds that can catalyze light-activated water splitting. Although successful compounds have been presented, the major hurdle to overcome is to utilize earth-abundant materials instead of Ru, palladium, or platinum.

Proteins use molecular recognition to establish reactions on a nanoscale. Molecular and supramolecular assemblies are not fixed but flexible and exist in thermodynamic equilibria and metastable states. Their components can reversibly be dissociated and reassembled, permitting an organism to adapt to external influences such as sunlight conditions. Nanometric building blocks such as proteins do not exist outside Nature, other than synthetic proteins. Directing the synthesis of proteins, natural or synthetic, outside a cell is still an elaborate task, but after a proof-of-principle demonstration has been shown for its usefulness, technological progress is expected. Currently, biochemical methods are easily applied and purifying proteins outside organisms is a routine procedure. Although progress has been made in adhering proteins and membranes onto surfaces, light activation and catalytic machineries have not been coupled yet.

Furthermore, biological systems feature self-repair to replace damaged components, which is how they cope with photodamage by reactive side products of the water oxidation reaction. Component replacement, but also the coupling of reaction output to input of various components, requires a dynamic environment. Nanopatterned surfaces accompanied with chemical activation for specific binding may direct artificial supramolecular constructs of photosynthetic and other proteins. But likely such designs will not incorporate dynamics.

Membranes do ensure such flexibility and have been adhered onto surfaces functionally; here, the durability of the material or else the cost-effectiveness for replacement has to become more detailed. Biological membranes form a natural barrier for charge carriers (protons) and can build up a membrane potential. Once charge separation is converted into a membrane potential, the energy is stored in electrical form without losses due to back transfer, a feature that is not easily mimicked in an artificial device.

In general, energy storage on all timescales is the main challenge for artificial photosynthesis. It has proven very difficult to design a water-splitting catalyst because of the multiple ETs necessary (and thus the storage of electrons during these transfers). Synthetic compounds that can transfer two electrons per excitation may be a solution to this problem. Similarly, synthetic compounds will need to store molecular excitations waiting for demand of charge-transfer compounds. The major challenge will be the coupling of light-activated and catalytic compounds and the removal of bottlenecks in both reactions ensuring small recombination losses. Tuning the rates of two nonrelated processes will be necessary as well as the fast electron relay of the light-activated compound into an electrode without charge recombination and under low overpotential.

While at this time, the many different approaches toward artificial photosynthetic solar cells still focus on the different materials that could be used, the main breakthrough in this field will be proof-of-principle design incorporating light-absorbing units, coupled to redox catalysts and proton pumps or proton-to-hydrogen converters. A main theme within these designs will be the

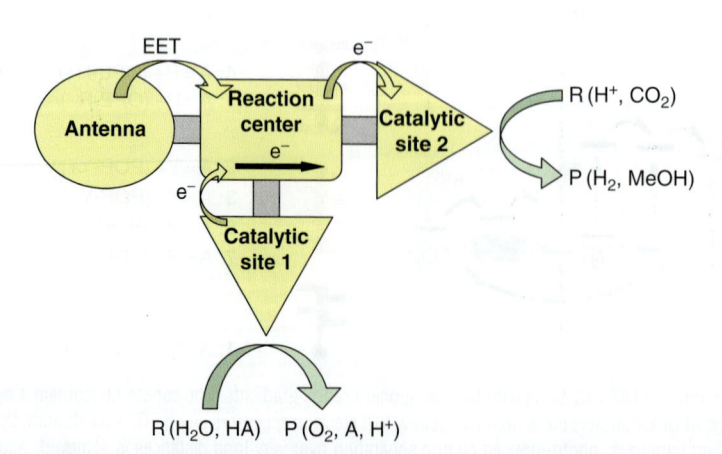

Figure 16 Schematic picture of an integrated artificial device for production of hydrogen and methanol.

utilization of a larger part of the solar spectrum than is used by natural photosynthesis, for instance, one part driving water splitting and another proton pumping or hydrogen production. It is likely that only at that stage, when all units have become interconnected, the true functioning of components will become apparent. As many research collaborations are aiming at just that, tremendous progress in this field is expected between now and 2015.

References

[1] Hu XC, Damjanovic A, Ritz T, and Schulten K (1998) Architecture and mechanism of the light-harvesting apparatus of purple bacteria. *Proceedings of the National Academy of Sciences of the United States of America* 95: 5935–5941.
[2] Blankenship RE (2002) *Molecular Mechanisms of Photosynthesis*. Oxford, UK: Blackwell Science Ltd.
[3] Oostergetel GT, van Amerongen H, and Boekema EJ The chlorosome: A prototype for efficient light harvesting in photosynthesis. *Photosynthesis Research* 104: 245–255.
[4] Mullineaux CW (2005) Function and evolution of grana. *Trends in Plant Science* 10: 521–525.
[5] Su HN, Xie BB, Zhang XY, et al. The supramolecular architecture, function, and regulation of thylakoid membranes in red algae: An overview. *Photosynthesis Research* 106: 73–87.
[6] Deisenhofer J, Epp O, Sinning I, and Michel H (1995) Crystallographic refinement at 2.3-angstrom resolution and refined model of the photosynthetic reaction-center from *Rhodopseudomonas viridis*. *Journal of Molecular Biology* 246: 429–457.
[7] Roszak AW, Howard TD, Southall J, et al. (2003) Crystal structure of the RC–LH1 core complex from *Rhodopseudomonas palustris*. *Science* 302: 1969–1972.
[8] Zinth W and Wachtveitl J (2005) The first picoseconds in bacterial photosynthesis – Ultrafast electron transfer for the efficient conversion of light energy. *ChemPhysChem* 6: 871–880.
[9] Vangrondelle R, Dekker JP, Gillbro T, and Sundstrom V (1994) Energy-transfer and trapping in photosynthesis. *Biochimica et Biophysica Acta—Bioenergetics* 1187: 1–65.
[10] Heathcote P, Fyfe PK, and Jones MR (2002) Reaction centres: The structure and evolution of biological solar power. *Trends in Biochemical Sciences* 27: 79–87.
[11] Hillier W and Babcock GT (2001) Photosynthetic reaction centers. *Plant Physiology* 125: 33–37.
[12] Yachandra VK, Sauer K, and Klein MP (1996) Manganese cluster in photosynthesis: Where plants oxidize water to dioxygen. *Chemical Reviews* 96: 2927–2950.
[13] Barber J and Archer MD (2001) P680, the primary electron donor of photosystem II. *Journal of Photochemistry and Photobiology A: Chemistry* 142: 97–106.
[14] Ishikita H, Loll B, Biesiadka J, et al. (2005) Redox potentials of chlorophylls in the photosystem II reaction center. *Biochemistry* 44: 4118–4124.
[15] Jordan P, Fromme P, Witt HT, et al. (2001) Three-dimensional structure of cyanobacterial photosystem I at 2.5 angstrom resolution. *Nature* 411: 909–917.
[16] Zouni A, Witt HT, Kern J, et al. (2001) Crystal structure of photosystem II from *Synechococcus elongatus* at 3.8 angstrom resolution. *Nature* 409: 739–743.
[17] Bahatyrova S, Frese RN, Siebert CA, et al. (2004) The native architecture of a photosynthetic membrane. *Nature* 430: 1058–1062.
[18] Frank J (2002) Single-particle imaging of macromolecules by cryo-electron microscopy. *Annual Review of Biophysics and Biomolecular Structure* 31: 303–319.
[19] Muller DJ and Dufrene YF (2008) Atomic force microscopy as a multifunctional molecular toolbox in nanobiotechnology. *Nature Nanotechnology* 3: 261–269.
[20] Dekker JP and Boekema EJ (2005) Supramolecular organization of thylakoid membrane proteins in green plants. *Biochimica et Biophysica Acta—Bioenergetics* 1706: 12–39.
[21] Sturgis JN and Niederman RA (2008) Atomic force microscopy reveals multiple patterns of antenna organization in purple bacteria: Implications for energy transduction mechanisms and membrane modeling. *Photosynthesis Research* 95: 269–278.
[22] Scheuring S and Sturgis JN (2005) Chromatic adaptation of photosynthetic membranes. *Science* 309: 484–487.
[23] Kirchhoff H, Haferkamp S, Allen JF, et al. (2008) Protein diffusion and macromolecular crowding in thylakoid membranes. *Plant Physiology* 146: 1571–1578.
[24] Frese RN, Pamies JC, Olsen JD, et al. (2008) Protein shape and crowding drive domain formation and curvature in biological membranes. *Biophysical Journal* 94: 640–647.
[25] Frese RN, Siebert CA, Niederman RA, et al. (2004) The long-range organization of a native photosynthetic membrane. *Proceedings of the National Academy of Sciences of the United States of America* 101: 17994–17999.
[26] Koepke J, Hu XC, Muenke C, et al. (1996) The crystal structure of the light-harvesting complex II (B800–850) from *Rhodospirillum molischianum*. *Structure* 4: 581–597.
[27] Papiz MZ, Prince SM, Howard T, et al. (2003) The structure and thermal motion of the B800–850 LH2 complex from *Rps. acidophila* at 2.0 (A)over-circle resolution and 100 K: New structural features and functionally relevant motions. *Journal of Molecular Biology* 326: 1523–1538.
[28] Sundstrom V, Pullerits T, and van Grondelle R (1999) Photosynthetic light-harvesting: Reconciling dynamics and structure of purple bacterial LH2 reveals function of photosynthetic unit. *Journal of Physical Chemistry B* 103: 2327–2346.
[29] Yang M, Agarwal R, and Fleming GR (2001) The mechanism of energy transfer in the antenna of photosynthetic purple bacteria. *Journal of Photochemistry and Photobiology* 142: 107–119.
[30] van Grondelle R and Novoderezhkin V (2001) Dynamics of excitation energy transfer in the LH1 and LH2 light-harvesting complexes of photosynthetic bacteria. *Biochemistry* 40: 15057–15068.
[31] Fleming GR and Vangrondelle R (1997) Femtosecond spectroscopy of photosynthetic light-harvesting systems. *Current Opinion in Structural Biology* 7: 738–748.
[32] Hu XC, Ritz T, Damjanovic A, et al. (2002) Photosynthetic apparatus of purple bacteria. *Quarterly Reviews of Biophysics* 35: 1–62.
[33] Noy D, Moser CC, and Dutton PL (2006) Design and engineering of photosynthetic light-harvesting and electron transfer using length, time, and energy scales. *Biochimica et Biophysica Acta—Bioenergetics* 1757: 90–105.
[34] Noy D (2008) Natural photosystems from an engineer's perspective: Length, time, and energy scales of charge and energy transfer. *Photosynthesis Research* 95: 23–35.
[35] Miller JR, Calcaterra LT, and Closs GL (1984) Intramolecular long-distance electron-transfer in radical-anions – The effects of free-energy and solvent on the reaction-rates. *Journal of the American Chemical Society* 106: 3047–3049.
[36] Wasielewski MR, Niemczyk MP, Svec WA, and Pewitt EB (1985) Dependence of rate constants for photoinduced charge separation and dark charge recombination on the free-energy of reaction in restricted-distance porphyrin quinone molecules. *Journal of the American Chemical Society* 107: 1080–1082.
[37] Markvart T and Landsberg PT (2002) Thermodynamics and reciprocity of solar energy conversion. *Physica E* 14: 71–77.
[38] Boeker E and van Grondelle R (1999) *Environmental Physics*. Chichester, NY: Wiley.
[39] Ross RT and Calvin M (1967) Thermodynamics of light emission and free-energy storage in photosynthesis. *Biophysical Journal* 7: 595–614.
[40] Gratzel M (1991) The artificial leaf, molecular photovoltaics achieve efficient generation of electricity from sunlight. *Coordination Chemistry Reviews* 111: 167–174.
[41] Mavroidis C, Dubey A, and Yarmush ML (2004) Molecular machines. *Annual Review of Biomedical Engineering* 6: 363–395.
[42] Sarikaya M, Tamerler C, Jen AKY, et al. (2003) Molecular biomimetics: Nanotechnology through biology. *Nature Materials* 2: 577–585.
[43] Defronzo RA, Tobin JD, and Andres R (1979) Glucose clamp technique – Method for quantifying insulin-secretion and resistance. *American Journal of Physiology* 237: E214–E223.
[44] Okamura MY, Paddock ML, Graige MS, and Feher G (2000) Proton and electron transfer in bacterial reaction centers. *Biochimica et Biophysica Acta—Bioenergetics* 1458: 148–163.
[45] Read EL, Lee H, and Fleming GR (2009) Photon echo studies of photosynthetic light harvesting. *Photosynthesis Research* 101: 233–243.
[46] van Grondelle R and Novoderezhkin VI (2006) Energy transfer in photosynthesis: Experimental insights and quantitative models. *Physical Chemistry Chemical Physics* 8: 793–807.

[47] Schonfeld M, Montal M, and Feher G (1979) Functional reconstitution of photosynthetic reaction centers in planar lipid bilayers. *Proceedings of the National Academy of Sciences of the United States of America* 76: 6351–6355.
[48] Janzen AF and Seibert M (1980) Photoelectrochemical conversion using reaction-center electrodes. *Nature* 286: 584–585.
[49] Katz E (1994) Application of bifunctional reagents for immobilization of proteins on a carbon electrode surface – Oriented immobilization of photosynthetic reaction centers. *Journal of Electroanalytical Chemistry* 365: 157–164.
[50] Trammell SA, Spano A, Price R, and Lebedev N (2006) Effect of protein orientation on electron transfer between photosynthetic reaction centers and carbon electrodes. *Biosensors and Bioelectronics* 21: 1023–1028.
[51] Lebedev N, Trammell SA, Spano A, et al. (2006) Conductive wiring of immobilized photosynthetic reaction center to electrode by cytochrome c. *Journal of the American Chemical Society* 128: 12044–12045.
[52] Lu YD, Xu JJ, Liu BH, and Kong JL (2007) Photosynthetic reaction center functionalized nano-composite films: Effective strategies for probing and exploiting the photo-induced electron transfer of photosensitive membrane protein. *Biosensors and Bioelectronics* 22: 1173–1185.
[53] Trammell SA, Griva I, Spano A, et al. (2007) Effects of distance and driving force on photoinduced electron transfer between photosynthetic reaction centers and gold electrodes. *Journal of Physical Chemistry C* 111: 17122–17130.
[54] Suemori Y, Nagata M, Nakamura Y, et al. (2006) Self-assembled monolayer of light-harvesting core complexes of photosynthetic bacteria on an amino-terminated ITO electrode. *Photosynthesis Research* 90: 17–21.
[55] Kondo M, Nakamura Y, Fujii K, et al. (2007) Self-assembled monolayer of light-harvesting core complexes from photosynthetic bacteria on a gold electrode modified with alkanethiols. *Biomacromolecules* 8: 2457–2463.
[56] Magis GJ, den Hollander MJ, Onderwaater WG, et al. (2010) Light harvesting, energy transfer and electron cycling of a native photosynthetic membrane adsorbed onto a gold surface. *Biochimica et Biophysica Acta—Biomembranes* 1798: 637–645.
[57] Maly J, Masojidek J, Masci A, et al. (2005) Direct mediatorless electron transport between the monolayer of photosystem II and poly (mercapto-p-benzoquinone) modified gold electrode-new design of biosensor for herbicide detection. *Biosensors and Bioelectronics* 21: 923–932.
[58] Badura A, Esper B, Ataka K, et al. (2006) Light-driven water splitting for (bio-)hydrogen production: Photosystem 2 as the central part of a bioelectrochemical device. *Photochemistry and Photobiology* 82: 1385–1390.
[59] Ciobanu M, Kincaid HA, Lo V, et al. (2007) Electrochemistry and photoelectrochemistry of photosystem I adsorbed on hydroxyl-terminated monolayers. *Journal of Electroanalytical Chemistry* 599: 72–78.
[60] Terasaki N, Yamamoto N, Tamada K, et al. (2007) Bio-photo sensor: Cyanobacterial photosystem I coupled with transistor via molecular wire. *Biochimica et Biophysica Acta—Bioenergetics* 1767: 653–659.
[61] Das R, Kiley PJ, Segal M, et al. (2004) Integration of photosynthetic protein molecular complexes in solid-state electronic devices. *Nano Letters* 4: 1079–1083.
[62] Sauvage F, Chen DH, Comte P, et al. (2010) Dye-sensitized solar cells employing a single film of mesoporous TiO$_2$ beads achieve power conversion efficiencies over 10%. *ACS Nano* 4: 4420–4425.
[63] Park C, Yoon J, and Thomas EL (2003) Enabling nanotechnology with self assembled block copolymer patterns. *Polymer* 44: 6725–6760.
[64] Ho SP and Degrado WF (1987) Design of a 4-helix bundle protein – Synthesis of peptides which self-associate into a helical protein. *Journal of the American Chemical Society* 109: 6751–6758.
[65] Choma CT, Lear JD, Nelson MJ, et al. (1994) Design of a heme-binding 4-helix bundle. *Journal of the American Chemical Society* 116: 856–865.
[66] Ye SX, Discher BM, Strzalka J, et al. (2005) Amphiphilic four-helix bundle peptides designed for light-induced electron transfer across a soft interface. *Nano Letters* 5: 1658–1667.
[67] Pandit A, Ma HR, van Stokkum IHM, et al. (2002) Time-resolved dissociation of the light-harvesting 1 complex of *Rhodospirillum rubrum*, studied by infrared laser temperature jump. *Biochemistry* 41: 15115–15120.
[68] Pandit A, Visschers RW, van Stokkum IHM, et al. (2001) Oligomerization of light-harvesting I antenna peptides of *Rhodospirillum rubrum*. *Biochemistry* 40: 12913–12924.
[69] Pandit A, van Stokkum IHM, Georgakopoulou S, et al. (2003) Investigations of intermediates appearing in the reassociation of the light-harvesting 1 complex of *Rhodospirillum rubrum*. *Photosynthesis Research* 75: 235–248.
[70] Todd JB, Recchia PA, Parkes-Loach PS, et al. (1999) Minimal requirements for *in vitro* reconstitution of the structural subunit of light-harvesting complexes of photosynthetic bacteria. *Photosynthesis Research* 62: 85–98.
[71] Loach PA, Parkesloach PS, Davis CM, and Heller BA (1994) Probing protein structural requirements for formation of the core light-harvesting complex of photosynthetic bacteria using hybrid reconstitution methodology. *Photosynthesis Research* 40: 231–245.
[72] Todd JB, Parkes-Loach PS, Leykam JF, and Loach PA (1998) *In vitro* reconstitution of the core and peripheral light-harvesting complexes of *Rhodospirillum molischianum* from separately isolated components. *Biochemistry* 37: 17458–17468.
[73] Parkes-Loach PS, Majeed AP, Law CJ, and Loach PA (2004) Interactions stabilizing the structure of the core light-harvesting complex (LHL) of photosynthetic bacteria and its subunit (B820). *Biochemistry* 43: 7003–7016.
[74] Noy D and Dutton PL (2006) Design of a minimal polypeptide unit for bacteriochlorophyll binding and self-assembly based on photosynthetic bacterial light-harvesting proteins. *Biochemistry* 45: 2103–2113.
[75] Nagata M, Nango M, Kashiwada A, et al. (2003) Construction of photosynthetic antenna complex using light-harvesting polypeptide-alpha from photosynthetic bacteria, R. rubrum with zinc substituted bacteriochlorophyll alpha. *Chemistry Letters* 32: 216–217.
[76] Ochiai T, Nagata M, Shimoyama K, et al. (1441) Immobilization of porphyrin derivatives with a defined distance and orientation onto a gold electrode using synthetic light-harvesting alpha-helix hydrophobic polypeptides. *Langmuir* 26: 14419–14422.
[77] Pandit A, Buda F, van Gammeren AJ, et al. (2010) Selective chemical shift assignment of bacteriochlorophyll a in uniformly [C-13-N-15]-labeled light-harvesting 1 complexes by solid-state NMR in ultrahigh magnetic field. *Journal of Physical Chemistry B* 114: 6207–6215.
[78] Pandit A, Wawrzyniak PK, van Gammeren AJ, et al. Nuclear magnetic resonance secondary shifts of a light-harvesting 2 complex reveal local backbone perturbations induced by its higher-order interactions. *Biochemistry* 49: 478–486.
[79] Alia A, Wawrzyniak PK, Janssen GJ, et al. (2009) Differential charge polarization of axial histidines in bacterial reaction centers balances the asymmetry of the special pair. *Journal of the American Chemical Society* 131: 9626–9627.
[80] Wawrzyniak PK, Alia A, Schaap RG, et al. (2008) Protein-induced geometric constraints and charge transfer in bacteriochlorophyll–histidine complexes in LH2. *Physical Chemistry Chemical Physics* 10: 6971–6978.
[81] Hay S, Wallace BB, Smith TA, et al. (2004) Protein engineering of cytochrome b(562) for quinone binding and light-induced electrons transfer. *Proceedings of the National Academy of Sciences of the United States of America* 101: 17675–17680.
[82] Conlan B, Cox N, Su J-H, et al. (2009) Photo-catalytic oxidation of a di-nuclear manganese centre in an engineered bacterioferritin 'reaction centre'. *Biochimica et Biophysica Acta* 1787: 1112–1121.
[83] Chu CC and Bassani DM (2008) Challenges and opportunities for photochemists on the verge of solar energy conversion. *Photochemical & Photobiological Sciences* 7: 521–530.
[84] Balzani V, Credi A, and Venturi M (2008) Molecular machines working on surfaces and at interfaces. *ChemPhysChem* 9: 202–220.
[85] Bauer RE, Grimsdale AC, and Mullen K (2005) Functionalised polyphenylene dendrimers and their applications. *Functional Molecular Nanostructures*, pp. 253–286. Berlin, Germany: Springer.
[86] Li WS and Aida T (2009) Dendrimer porphyrins and phthalocyanines. *Chemical Reviews* 109: 6047–6076.

[87] Nakamura Y, Aratani N, and Osuka A (2007) Cyclic porphyrin arrays as artificial photosynthetic antenna: Synthesis and excitation energy transfer. *Chemical Society Reviews* 36: 831–845.
[88] Aratani N, Kim D, and Osuka A (2009) Discrete cyclic porphyrin arrays as artificial light-harvesting antenna. *Accounts of Chemical Research* 42: 1922–1934.
[89] Holzwarth AR, Griebenow K, and Schaffner K (1992) Chlorosomes, photosynthetic antennae with novel self-organized pigment structures. *Journal of Photochemistry and Photobiology A: Chemistry* 65: 61–71.
[90] Tamiaki H (1996) Supramolecular structure in extramembranous antennae of green photosynthetic bacteria. *Coordination Chemistry Reviews* 148: 183–197.
[91] Balaban TS, Holzwarth AR, Schaffner K, et al. (1995) CP-MAS C-13-NMR dipolar correlation spectroscopy of C-13-enriched chlorosomes and isolated bacteriochlorophyll-c aggregates of *Chlorobium tepidum* – The self-organization of pigments is the main structural feature of chlorosomes. *Biochemistry* 34: 15259–15266.
[92] Miyatake T and Tamiaki H (2005) Self-aggregates of bacteriochlorophylls-c, d and e in a light-harvesting antenna system of green photosynthetic bacteria: Effect of stereochemistry at the chiral 3-(1-hydroxyethyl) group on the supramolecular arrangement of chlorophyllous pigments. *Journal of Photochemistry and Photobiology C: Photochemistry Reviews* 6: 89–107.
[93] Balaban TS, Tamiaki H, and Holzwarth AR (2005) Chlorins programmed for self-assembly. *Supermolecular Dye Chemistry*, pp. 1–38. Berlin, Germany: Springer.
[94] Psencik J, Polivka T, Nemec P, et al. (1998) Fast energy transfer and exciton dynamics in chlorosomes of the green sulfur bacterium *Chlorobium tepidum*. *The Journal of Physical Chemistry A* 102: 4392–4398.
[95] Steensgaard DB, van Walree CA, Permentier H, et al. (2000) Fast energy transfer between BChl d and BChl c in chlorosomes of the green sulfur bacterium *Chlorobium limicola*. *Biochimica et Biophysica Acta – Bioenergetics* 1457: 71–80.
[96] Prokhorenko VI, Steensgaard DB, and Holzwarth AF (2000) Exciton dynamics in the chlorosomal antennae of the green bacteria *Chloroflexus aurantiacus* and *Chlorobium tepidum*. *Biophysical Journal* 79: 2105–2120.
[97] Prokhorenko VI, Holzwarth AR, Muller MG, et al. (2002) Energy transfer in supramolecular artificial antennae units of synthetic zinc chlorins and co-aggregated energy traps. A time-resolved fluorescence study. *Journal of Physical Chemistry B* 106: 5761–5768.
[98] Prokhorenko VI, Steensgaard DB, and Holzwarth AR (2003) Exciton theory for supramolecular chlorosomal aggregates: 1. Aggregate size dependence of the linear spectra. *Biophysical Journal* 85: 3173–3186.
[99] Jochum T, Reddy CM, Eichhofer A, et al. (2008) The supramolecular organization of self-assembling chlorosomal bacteriochlorophyll c, d, or e mimics. *Proceedings of the National Academy of Sciences of the United States of America* 105: 12736–12741.
[100] Ganapathy S, Oostergetel GT, Wawrzyniak PK, et al. (2009) Alternating syn–anti bacteriochlorophylls form concentric helical nanotubes in chlorosomes. *Proceedings of the National Academy of Sciences of the United States of America* 106: 8525–8530.
[101] Ganapathy S, Sengupta S, Wawrzyniak PK, et al. (2009) Zinc chlorins for artificial light-harvesting self-assemble into antiparallel stacks forming a microcrystalline solid-state material. *Proceedings of the National Academy of Sciences of the United States of America* 106: 11472–11477.
[102] Huijser A, Marek PL, Savenije TJ, et al. (2007) Photosensitization of TiO_2 and SnO_2 by artificial self-assembling mimics of the natural chlorosomal bacteriochlorophylls. *Journal of Physical Chemistry C* 111: 11726–11733.
[103] Siebbeles LDA, Huijser A, and Savenije TJ (2009) Effects of molecular organization on exciton diffusion in thin films of bioinspired light-harvesting molecules. *Journal of Materials Chemistry* 19: 6067–6072.
[104] Wurthner F (2004) Perylene bisimide dyes as versatile building blocks for functional supramolecular architectures. *Chemical Communications* (14): 1564–1579.
[105] Chen ZJ, Stepanenko V, Dehm V, et al. (2007) Photoluminescence and conductivity of self-assembled pi–pi stacks of perylene bisimide dyes. *Chemistry – A European Journal* 13: 436–449.
[106] Gust D and Moore TA (1989) Mimicking photosynthesis. *Science* 244: 35–41.
[107] Moore TA, Gust D, Mathis P, et al. (1984) Photodriven charge separation in a carotenoporphyrin quinone triad. *Nature* 307: 630–632.
[108] Gust D, Moore TA, and Moore AL (2009) Solar fuels via artificial photosynthesis. *Accounts of Chemical Research* 42: 1890–1898.
[109] Imahori H (2007) Creation of fullerene-based artificial photosynthetic systems. *Bulletin of the Chemical Society of Japan* 80: 621–636.
[110] Gust D (2001) Mimicking photosynthetic solar energy transduction. *Accounts of Chemical Research* 34: 40–48.
[111] Moore GF, Hambourger M, Gervaldo M, et al. (2008) A bioinspired construct that mimics the proton coupled electron transfer between P680(center dot)+ and the Tyr(z)–His190 pair of photosystem II. *Journal of the American Chemical Society* 130: 10466–10467.
[112] Fukuzumi S (2008) Development of bioinspired artificial photosynthetic systems. *Physical Chemistry Chemical Physics* 10: 2283–2297.
[113] Wasielewski MR (2009) Self-assembly strategies for integrating light harvesting and charge separation in artificial photosynthetic systems. *Accounts of Chemical Research* 42: 1910–1921.
[114] Bullock JE, Carmieli R, Mickley SM, et al. (2009) Photoinitiated charge transport through pi-stacked electron conduits in supramolecular ordered assemblies of donor–acceptor triads. *Journal of the American Chemical Society* 131: 11919–11929.
[115] Bhosale R, Misek J, Sakai N, and Matile S Supramolecular n/p-heterojunction photosystems with oriented multicolored antiparallel redox gradients (OMARG-SHJs). *Chemical Society Reviews* 39: 138–149.
[116] Sakai N, Bhosale R, Emery D, et al. Supramolecular n/p-heterojunction photosystems with antiparallel redox gradients in electron- and hole-transporting pathways. *Journal of the American Chemical Society* 132: 6923.
[117] Bhosale R, Bhosale S, Bollot G, et al. (2007) Synthetic multifunctional nanoarchitecture in lipid bilayers: Ion channels, sensors, and photosystems. *Bulletin of the Chemical Society of Japan* 80: 1044–1057.

Further reading

Blankenship RE, Tiede DM, Barber J, et al. (2011) Comparing photosynthetic and photovoltaic efficiencies and recognizing the potential for improvement. *Science* 332: 805, DOI: 10.1126/science.1200165.
Regalado A (2010) Reinventing the leaf: Artificial photosynthesis to create clean fuel. *Scientific American Magazine* (2010).
Blankenship RE (2002) *Molecular Mechanisms of Photosynthesis*. Oxford, UK: Blackwell Science Ltd.
Collings AF and Critchley C (2006) *Artificial Photosynthesis: From Basic Biology to Industrial Application*. Weinheim, Germany: Wiley-VCH Verlag GmbH & Co. KGaA, ISBN: 9783527606740, DOI: 10.1002/3527606742.
Pandit A, de Groot HJM, and Holzwarth A (2006) *Harnessing Solar Energy for the Production of Clean Fuels*. Leiden, The Netherlands: Leiden University, ISBN 978-90-9023907-1.

1.32 Design and Components of Photovoltaic Systems

WGJHM van Sark, Utrecht University, Utrecht, The Netherlands

© 2012 Elsevier Ltd.

1.32.1	**Introduction**	679
1.32.2	**PV Cells and Modules**	680
1.32.2.1	Solar Cells	680
1.32.2.1.1	Irradiance-dependent solar cell performance	681
1.32.2.1.2	Modules	684
1.32.3	**Balance of System**	685
1.32.3.1	Inverters	685
1.32.3.2	Mounting Structures	686
1.32.3.3	Batteries	687
1.32.3.4	Charge Regulators	687
1.32.4	**PV System Design**	687
1.32.4.1	Hybrid Solar–Diesel System for Mandhoo Island	687
1.32.4.1.1	Hybrid design	688
1.32.4.1.2	Realization	689
1.32.4.1.3	Evaluation	690
1.32.4.1.4	Conclusion	690
1.32.4.2	100 MW PV Plant in Abu Dhabi Desert Area	690
1.32.4.2.1	Introduction	690
1.32.4.2.2	Methodology	691
1.32.4.2.3	Scenarios	692
1.32.4.2.4	Assumptions	692
1.32.4.2.5	System performance	692
1.32.4.2.6	Financial results	693
1.32.4.2.7	Environmental results	694
1.32.4.2.8	Conclusions	694
1.32.5	**Conclusions**	694
References		695

1.32.1 Introduction

In general, two types of photovoltaic (PV) solar energy systems exist: grid-connected and stand-alone (**Figure 1**). Grid-connected PV systems consist of one or more PV modules, one or several inverters to convert direct current (DC) PV power into alternating current (AC), cabling, and a mounting structure and are connected to the conventional electricity grid via the inverter [1]. Grid-connected PV system sizes range from ~50 Wp (one module) via small scale (0.5–4 kWp) for private homeowners, to medium scale (4–100 kWp), to large scale (0.1–100 MWp), while very large scale PV (VLS-PV) systems may range above 1 GWp [2]. Additional components to the modules that together form a PV system are denoted balance of system (BOS) components.

Stand-alone systems consist of one or a few PV modules, a battery for electrical storage, cabling, mounting structure, and a charge controller. As the output of the PV panel varies with the solar intensity and temperature, the charge controller is needed to condition the DC output and deliver it to the batteries. Stand-alone systems are usually designed to meet a specific load, for instance in solar home systems (SHSs); a few modules provide power to charge a battery during the day, and some lighting appliances and radio or television set can be powered in the evening [3]. Other applications are rural central power plants (mini grids), power supply for communication, lighting, cathodic protection, water pumps, and buoys.

PV modules or panels are built from several solar cells and range from about 0.024 (1 crystalline silicon cell of $156 \times 156 \text{ mm}^2$) to 2 m^2 in size, depending on the application possibilities and marketability as judged by various manufacturers. Building-integrated PV (BIPV) and power plant applications usually require the larger size, whereas for rural electrification projects, the smaller size suffices. The rated power, that is, the power generated by the PV module under standard test conditions (STCs) of 1000 W m^{-2} solar intensity at air mass (AM) 1.5 global spectrum and 25 °C module temperature, depends on the area of the module and is usually denoted as Watt-peak or Wp. At 15% efficiency, typical rated powers range from 3.65 (0.024 m^2) to 350 Wp (2 m^2). Panels are usually connected to form a solar array, to reach typical sizes of 3–4 kWp for individual houses.

System performance depends on the conversion efficiency of all components, of which the PV module has the most influence. For both PV modules and inverters, efficiency curves as a function of irradiance should be used to determine the efficiency of the whole system, while other losses should also be taken into account. For system design purposes, that is, to estimate the annual

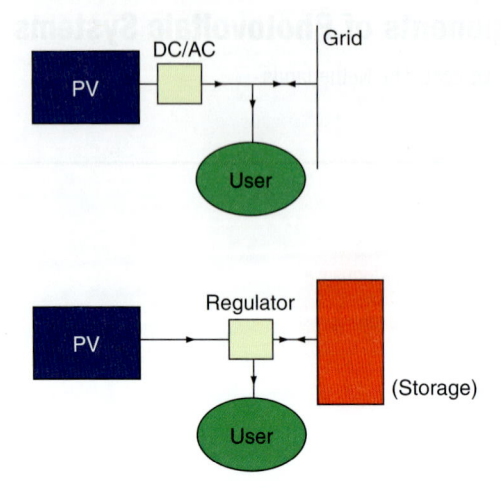

Figure 1 Grid-connected (top) and stand-alone (bottom) PV systems.

amount of generated energy per installed capacity, irradiation and temperature data are needed on an hourly basis. By convoluting these data sets with efficiency curves for modules and inverters, one can determine the expected annual yield.

In the following, panels and BOS components are discussed, with a focus on the performance of cells and modules; various loss factors in grid-connected systems are briefly described. Finally, two case studies that illustrate PV system design will be presented: a hybrid system on the Maldivian island Mandhoo and a large system in Abu Dhabi.

1.32.2 PV Cells and Modules

1.32.2.1 Solar Cells

The performance of a solar cell, the building block of solar panels, is characterized by four general parameters [4], which are derived from the current–voltage characteristic (I–V) measured under STCs, see also **Figure 2**: open-circuit voltage V_{oc}, short-circuit current I_{sc}, fill factor FF, and energy conversion efficiency η. The latter is calculated from

$$\eta = \frac{P_{max}}{AP_{in}} = \frac{V_{mpp}I_{mpp}}{AP_{in}} = \frac{V_{oc}I_{sc}FF}{AP_{in}} \qquad [1]$$

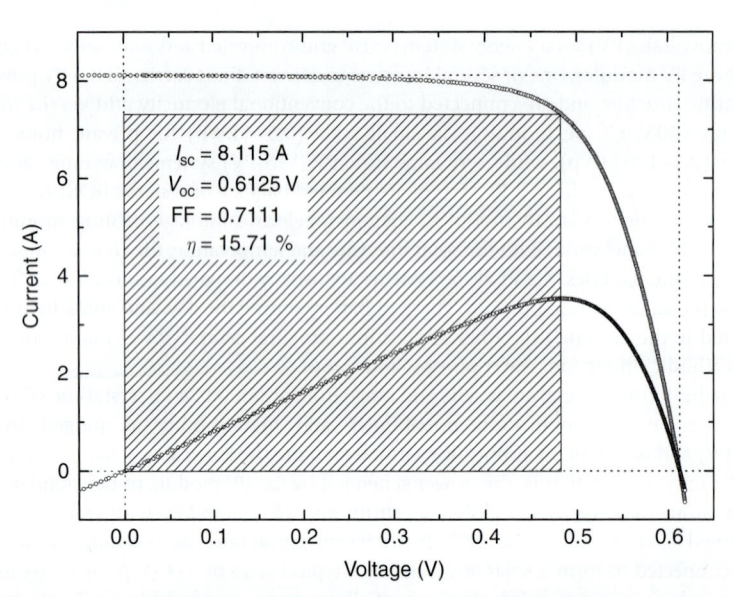

Figure 2 I–V characteristics of a 156 × 156 mm² crystalline silicon solar cell measured at STC. Performance parameters are I_{sc} = 8.115 A; V_{oc} = 0.6125 V, and η = 15.71%. The fill factor is a measure of the squareness of the I–V characteristics and is defined as FF = $V_{mpp}I_{mpp}/V_{oc}I_{sc}$ and equals FF = 0.7111. In other words, 71.11% of the area (0.0) to (V_{oc}, I_{sc}) is filled. From van Sark WGJHM (2007) Teaching the relation between solar cell efficiency and annual energy yield. *European Journal of Physics* 28: 415–427 [5].

where P_{max} is the maximum generated power, A the cell area, and P_{in} the incident power (=1000 W m^{-2} at STC). The maximum power P_{max} is given by $P_{max} = V_{mpp}I_{mpp}$, where V_{mpp} and I_{mpp} are the voltage and current, respectively, at the maximum power point (MPP). The fill factor is thus defined as FF = $V_{mpp}I_{mpp}/V_{oc}I_{sc}$.

In order to make an estimate of the irradiation dependence of the efficiency, van Sark has developed a method [5] (see also below) starting with the general expression for the current–voltage characteristic, which reflects the fact that a solar cell is a single-junction diode [4]:

$$I = I_L - I_{01}\left(\exp\frac{qV'}{kT} - 1\right) - I_{0n}\left(\exp\frac{qV'}{nkT} - 1\right) - \frac{V'}{R_{sh}}$$
$$V' = V + IR_{se} \quad [2]$$

in which I_L is the photocurrent, I_{01} and I_{0n} are diode saturation currents for the diodes with ideality factor 1 and n, respectively, V' is the effective voltage, R_{se} and R_{sh} represent series and parallel (shunt) resistances, respectively, k is Boltzmann's constant (1.38×10^{-23} J K^{-1}), T is the temperature (K), and q is the elementary charge (1.602×10^{-19} C). At room temperature, kT/q equals 25.67 mV and is also denoted as the thermal voltage V_{th}.

For an ideal single junction, eqn [2] is simplified to include one diode (with $n = 1$), zero series resistance, and infinite shunt resistance. Then, V_{oc} and I_{sc} are given by

$$V_{oc} = \frac{kT}{q}\ln\left(\frac{I_L}{I_0} + 1\right)$$
$$I_{sc} = I_L \quad [3]$$

Normal operating conditions of PV systems are rarely STC. Depending on geographical location, season, and time of the day, full sun conditions or (partly) overcast skies will prevail. Incident spectra also differ as a function of longitude and time of day from AM1 to about AM10. Under full sun, the temperature of the module can be much larger than 25 °C, reaching values between 60 and 80 °C. This lowers the efficiency, as the open-circuit voltage and, to a lesser extent, the fill factor are dependent on temperature. This is usually parameterized by the use of temperature coefficients dV_{oc}/dT and dFF/dT. The values differ for different solar cell materials, but in general are negative. A small positive temperature coefficient dJ_{sc}/dT of the short-circuit current may be present.

Lower irradiances not only lower the power output of the solar cell (**Figure 3**) but also affect its efficiency, depending on series resistance. Many cells with appreciable series resistance show a maximum efficiency at irradiances lower than 1000 W m^{-2}, peaking between 100 and 500 W m^{-2} [6]; see also **Figure** 4. A shunt resistance has an influence especially at irradiances < 100 W m^{-2} [7]. If indoor irradiation conditions prevail ($\ll$ 100 W m^{-2}), the performance drop will be much more dramatic. In case measured I–V curves as in **Figure** 3 are not available, a simple STC method to calculate irradiance-dependent efficiencies for cells with high shunt values can be used, which was developed by van Sark et al. [5, 8, 9].

1.32.2.1.1 Irradiance-dependent solar cell performance
1.32.2.1.1(i) Empirical three-parameter method

When I–V characteristics are available that have been measured at irradiance values other than STC, it is possible to fit the parameters of an empirical-derived relation between efficiency and irradiance. **Figure** 3 shows I–V characteristics of a crystalline

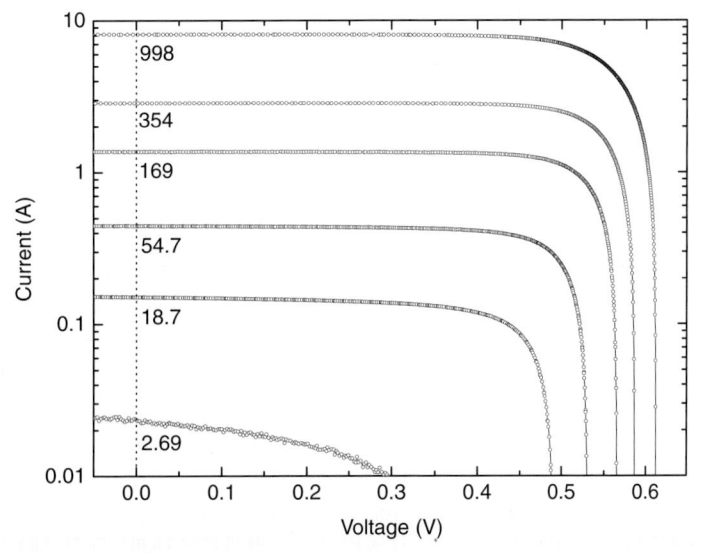

Figure 3 I–V characteristics of a 156 × 156 mm² solar cell measured at various irradiance values, that is, 2.69, 18.7, 54.7, 169, 354, and 998 W m^{-2}. From van Sark WGJHM (2007) Teaching the relation between solar cell efficiency and annual energy yield. *European Journal of Physics* 28: 415–427 [5].

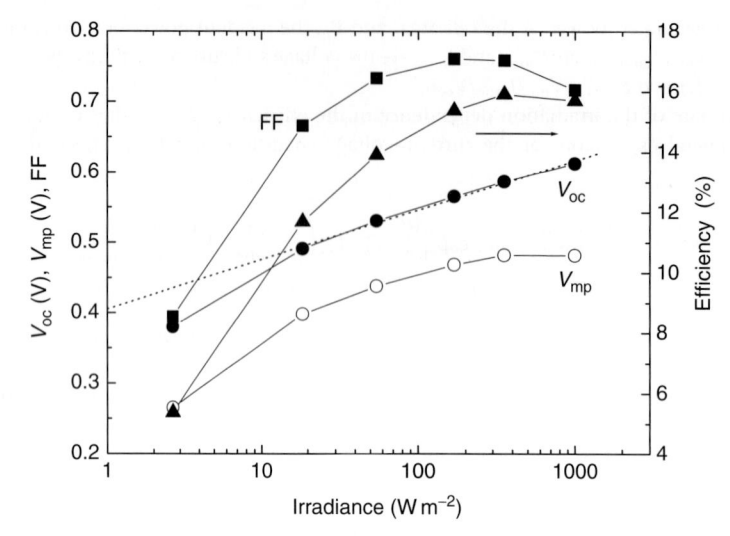

Figure 4 Performance parameters as a function of irradiance, derived from the data in **Figure 2**. The dotted line illustrates a single logarithmic dependence of the open-circuit voltage. From van Sark WGJHM (2007) Teaching the relation between solar cell efficiency and annual energy yield. *European Journal of Physics* 28: 415–427 [5].

silicon (c-Si) cell for various irradiance values. The efficiency values determined from these curves are fitted using a three-parameter equation proposed by Beyer *et al.* [10]:

$$\eta(G) = a_1 + a_2 G + a_3 \ln(G) \quad [4]$$

Figure 5 shows the fit results, the parameters are $a_1 = 0.214 \pm 0.004$, $a_2 = -0.060 \pm 0.007$, and $a_3 = 0.0265 \pm 0.0010$, when G is taken in kW m^{-2}. The parameters for another cell made from multicrystalline silicon (mc-Si) are $a_1 = 0.197 \pm 0.004$, $a_2 = -0.051 \pm 0.006$, and $a_3 = 0.0269 \pm 0.0011$.

During analysis, however, it was found that at very low irradiance intensities, negative efficiencies can also result using eqn [4]. Therefore, Reich *et al.* modified the original phenomenological equation by including another parameter (a_4) in the logarithmic part to avoid negative efficiencies and improve fitting accuracy at low (< 1 W m^{-2}) light intensities [8] that prevail indoors [9]:

$$\eta(G) = a_1 + a_2 G + a_3 \ln(a_4 + G) \quad [5]$$

For outdoor energy yield determination, the three-parameter eqn [4] suffices.

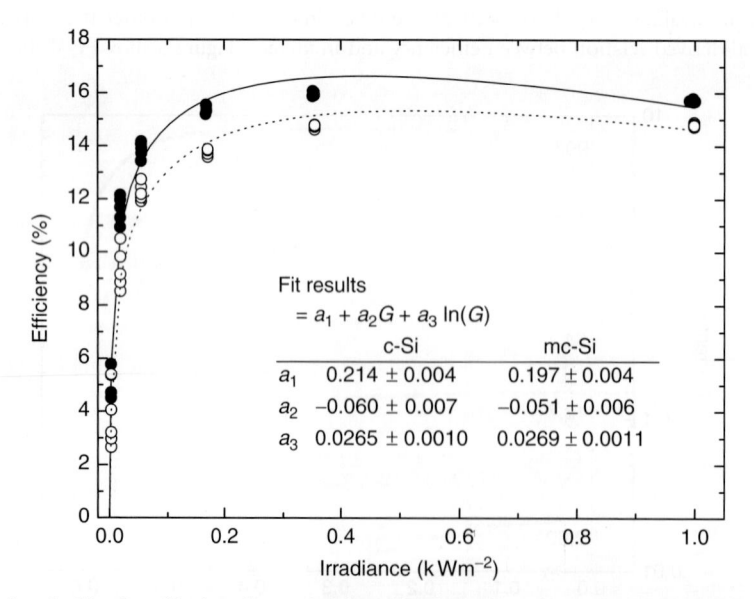

Figure 5 Measured efficiencies of c-Si and mc-Si solar cells as a function of irradiance. For c-Si, the fit shows a maximum efficiency of 16.64% at 0.45 kW m^{-2}, while the measured efficiency at 1 kW m^{-2} (STC) is 15.47%. For mc-Si, the fit shows a maximum efficiency of 15.32% at 0.525 kW m^{-2}, while the measured efficiency at 1 kW m^{-2} (STC) is 14.80%. From van Sark WGJHM (2007) Teaching the relation between solar cell efficiency and annual energy yield. *European Journal of Physics* 28: 415–427 [5].

1.32.2.1.1(ii) STC method

In order to make an estimate of the irradiation dependence of the efficiency, the simplified expression for the current–voltage characteristic, eqn [3], is used as the starting point. Green has derived an empirical relation between fill factor FF_0 and normalized open-circuit voltage v_{oc}, defined as $v_{oc} = V_{oc}(q/kT)$, for zero series resistance and infinite shunt resistance [4]:

$$FF_0 = \frac{v_{oc} - \ln(v_{oc} + 0.72)}{v_{oc} + 1} \qquad [6]$$

Fill factor loss due to series resistance R_s can then be represented by

$$FF = FF_0(1 - r_s) \qquad [7]$$

where r_s is the normalized series resistance given as $r_s = R_s/R_{CH}$. The characteristic resistance R_{CH} is defined as $R_{CH} = V_{oc}/I_{sc}$.

Equations [6] and [7] have been thoroughly validated and are found to be accurate for $v_{oc} > 10$ and $r_s < 0.4$ [4].

Similarly, shunt resistance effects can be estimated using

$$FF = FF_0 \left[1 - \frac{(v_{oc} + 0.7)}{v_{oc}} \frac{FF_0}{r_{sh}} \right] \qquad [8]$$

in which $r_{sh} = R_{sh}/R_{CH}$ is the normalized shunt resistance. This equation is accurate for $v_{oc} > 10$ and $r_{sh} > 2.5$ [4]. The combined effect of series and shunt resistance can be represented by eqn [8] if FF_0 is replaced by FF as given in eqn [7]:

$$FF = FF_0(1 - r_s) \left[1 - \frac{(v_{oc} + 0.7)}{v_{oc}} \frac{FF_0(1 - r_s)}{r_{sh}} \right] \qquad [9]$$

In the following, we will denote all variables as a function of irradiance level G, for example, $V_{oc}(G)$, $J_{sc}(G)$, $FF(G)$, and $\eta(G)$, while only certain variables are assumed constant.

We assume further that performance parameters V_{oc}, J_{sc}, FF, and η are available at a certain irradiance level G_0, that is, $V_{oc}(G_0)$, $J_{sc}(G_0)$, $FF(G_0)$, and $\eta(G_0)$. This level does not necessarily have to be $1000\,W\,m^{-2}$, only a known value is needed for the analysis; of course, this is usually the STC value. We further assume that the I–V characteristics can be described by an idealized one-diode model, eqn [3]. The normalized open-circuit voltage and characteristic resistance are calculated first: $v_{oc}(G_0)$ and $R_{CH}(G_0)$. Further, under the assumption that $I_L(G) = I_{sc}(G)$, the current ratio $I_L(G_0)/I_0(G_0)$ at irradiance level G_0 is calculated using eqn [3] followed by $FF_0(G_0)$ with eqn [6]. Taking into account only series resistance losses, $R_s(G_0)$ and $R_{CH}(G_0)$ are calculated using eqn [7]. Shunt resistance losses are expected to be important only at very low irradiance levels and are not included here. We further assume that both I_0 and R_s are not dependent on G. In the series resistance R_s, many components are lumped together, such as the series resistance from the metal grid, the contact resistance, and the emitter and base resistances, which generally are dependent on the injection level in the cell. However, for the sake of simplicity, we neglect irradiance dependence of R_s. Second, we assume that the short-circuit current is linearly dependent on G: $I_{sc}(G) = aG$. It is not necessary to know the constant a; we only use its linear dependence.

Figure 6 shows the results of this procedure for the c-Si cell of **Figure 2**. Comparing this method with the three-parameter fit method, it is clear that reasonable agreement is achieved over the whole range of interest down to $\sim 50\,W\,m^{-2}$. Thus, using only STC parameters will introduce small errors in calculating annual energy yield, at least smaller errors than using a constant efficiency over the whole range [5].

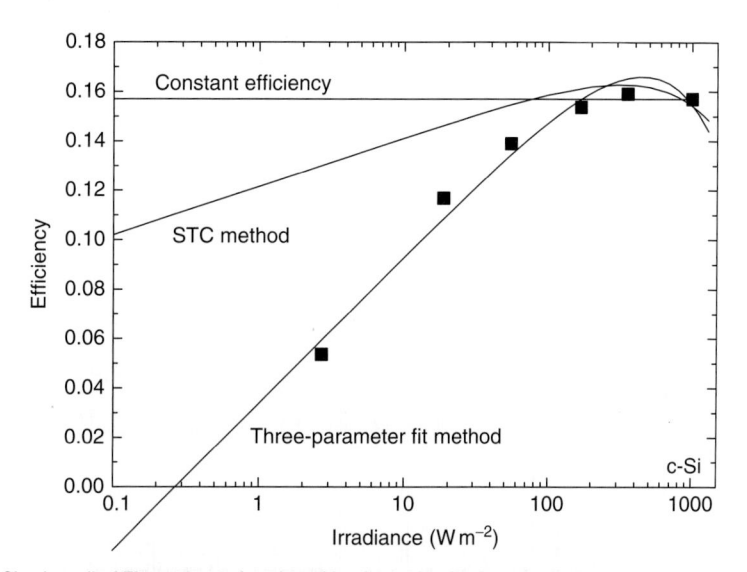

Figure 6 Efficiency of the c-Si solar cell of **Figure 2** as a function of irradiance for the three methods used; constant efficiency, three-parameter fit method, and STC method. From van Sark WGJHM (2007) Teaching the relation between solar cell efficiency and annual energy yield. *European Journal of Physics* 28: 415–427 [5].

With the method outlined above, we have calculated the irradiance-dependent behavior of the efficiency for various record efficiency cells [9, 11], see **Figure 7**. We have used the STC data for the 24.7% c-Si cell by University of New South Wales (UNSW), the 20.3% mc-Si cell by Fraunhofer-Institut für Solare Energiesysteme (FhG-ISE), the 9.5% a-Si:H cell by Neuchatel, the 18.8% CIGS cell by National Renewable Energy Laboratory (NREL), the 16.5% CdTe by NREL, the 10.4% dye-sensitized cell by Sharp, and the 3% polymer cell by Sharp, as reported in the 2009 record tables [11]. Clearly, all efficiencies show irradiance-dependent behavior. Some suffer from high series resistance values as evidenced from the drop in efficiency at high irradiance values.

1.32.2.1.2 Modules

Cells are assembled together in order to deliver the required currents and voltages. For example, 36 identical solar cells with characteristics as shown in **Figure 2** are mounted together in series in a solar panel, see **Figure 8**; note that a small edge area and intercell area are present. This panel would deliver a total power of 137.5 Wp at STC at an MPP current of 7.333 A and an MPP voltage of about 17.35 V. The total cell area is 0.876 m^2. However, the panel area is larger and depends on the arrangement of the cells, for example, in a 4 by 9 way (rectangular module, **Figure 8**) or in a 6 by 6 way (square module). Now, using an intercell distance of 1 cm and a module edge width of 2 cm, as most modules are framed, the area of the rectangular module would be 1.058 m^2. The area of the square module is somewhat smaller at 1.053 m^2. Thus, as the area of the module is 20.7% larger than the total area of the cells, the module efficiency is 17.2% lower than the cell efficiency, which is only due to the extra needed area of the module or, in absolute terms, the 'module' efficiency is 13.0%. Using nonidentical cells, the module efficiency further suffers from mismatch loss; this is usually minimized by manufacturers by selecting cells from the same efficiency class. After cells are made, they are tested and divided into efficiency classes of 0.1% width. The above module having an efficiency of 13% is built from cells from the efficiency class 15.65–15.75%.

A 72-cell module in a 6 by 12 configuration (275.1 Wp, with the cells of **Figure 2**) would be 2.075 m^2 in size, with a total cell area of 1.75 m^2, leading to a panel efficiency of 13.27%. If the intercell and edge sizes are halved, the 36-cell module would have an efficiency of 14.27% and the 72-cell module 14.41%. Clearly, these 'dead' areas in the module should be minimized.

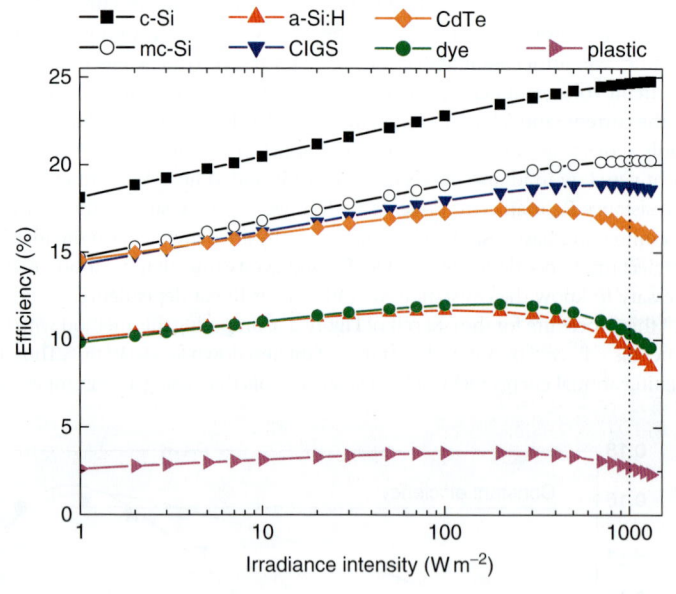

Figure 7 Efficiency of selected record efficiency solar cells [11] as a function of irradiance calculated with the STC method. Figure compiled from data presented in reference Reich NH, van Sark WGJHM, and Turkenburg WC (2011) Charge yield potential of indoor-operated solar cells incorporated into Product Integrated Photovoltaic (PIPV). *Renewable Energy* 36: 642–647 [9].

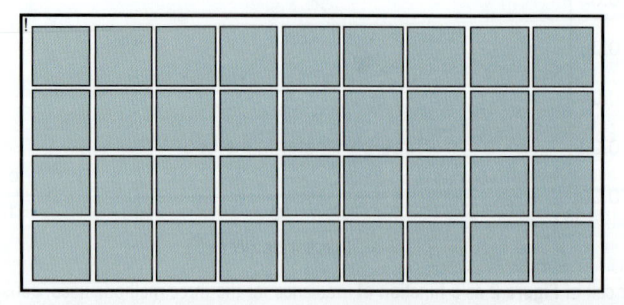

Figure 8 Schematic layout of a PV module with 36 solar cells in a 4 × 9 arrangement. Note the small but significant intercell and edge areas. From van Sark WGJHM (2007) Teaching the relation between solar cell efficiency and annual energy yield. *European Journal of Physics* 28: 415–427 [5].

Table 1 Examples of currently available PV modules

Manufacturer	Type	Solar cell type	Rated power (Wp)	Short-circuit current (A)	Open-circuit voltage (V)	Size (mm × mm)	Cells per module
Sunpower	SPR-327NE-WHT-D	Mono-Si	327	6.46	64.9	1559 × 1046	96
Solon	SOLON Black 280.17 (290)	Mono-Si	290	8.59	44.23	1973 × 993	72
Q-Cells	Q.Pro 250 G2	Poly-Si	250	8.58	37.72	1670 × 1000	60
Kaneka	U-EA120	a-Si	120	2.6	71	1210 × 1008	106
Sanyo	HIT-N240SE10	a-Si/c-Si	240	5.85	52.4	1580 × 798	72
Solar Frontier	SF150-L	CIS	150	2.1	110	1257 × 977	170
First Solar	FS-385	CdTe	85	1.98	61	1200 × 600	
Konarka	Power plastic 720	Thin-film organic	9.1	1.413	11.3	1553 × 340	20

Source: Photon.info module database www.photon.info/photon_site_db_solarmodule_en.photon (accessed 31 October 2011) [12].

A vast amount of different modules are or were available now or in the past. A module database maintained by Photon now lists nearly 40 000 different types of modules [12]. A few examples of current modules are listed in **Table 1**.

The present PV module market is dominated by modules made from wafer-based mono- or multicrystalline silicon at a market share of 80% [13]. Commercial monocrystalline silicon module efficiencies are between 14% and 20% and polycrystalline modules between 12% and 17%. The market share of thin-film modules presently is 16–20%, but is increasing fast [13].

1.32.3 Balance of System

1.32.3.1 Inverters

Inverters are designed to perform two main functions: (1) MPP tracking and (2) DC–AC conversion. As can be seen from **Figure 2**, the power generated by a PV cell (or module) is maximum at a certain voltage and current: the MPP. As the I–V characteristics depend on the irradiation intensity, the MPP also varies. An MPP tracker should constantly ensure that a PV module is at its MPP; this is realized by power electronic circuits, in which pulse-width modulation techniques are employed with a feedback loop to sense PV output power upon changing the voltage over the module or system until maximum power is reached [14, 15]. Here also DC–DC converters (buck–boost, boost–buck) are used: low-power inverters use metal-oxide-semiconductor field-effect transistor (MOSFET) thyristors in high-power applications, and typical efficiencies are 98% [15]. DC–AC conversion can be achieved on the basis of square wave, sine or modified sine wave, or pulse-width modulated inverters [15]. Inverter capacities may range from 500 W to 1 MW and deliver an AC output that has a waveform very close to a pure sinusoidal 50 or 60 Hz one.

Similar to PV modules, the inverter efficiency is given for its design operating power; however, the operation of inverters is usually at partial load. Therefore, it is desirable to have a high and flat efficiency curve over a wide range of partial loads.

The efficiency, η_{inv}, of the inverter is defined by

$$\eta_{inv} = \frac{P_{AC}}{P_{DC}} = \frac{P_{DC} - P_{loss}}{P_{DC}} \qquad [10]$$

where P_{DC}, P_{AC}, and $P_{loss}P_{DC}$ are the instantaneous DC power, AC power, and power loss, respectively [16].

The power losses in a solar inverter consist of a constant and a load-dependent part and are not constant. As an example, **Figure 9** shows the efficiency of some inverters as a function of per unit (pu) value of the DC power [16]. The nominal power varies between 2 and 1000 kW. For all inverters, the efficiency is high and constant between 20% and 100% of the rated power. At lower levels, the efficiency decreases suddenly. Thus, for cloudy conditions, inverters with high rated powers will operate with relatively low efficiency.

In order to determine PV system performance, it is clearly necessary to take the inverter efficiency over the whole operating range into account. This is the reason for the establishment of the European inverter efficiency value η_{Euro}, which is an efficiency number weighted for the Central European climate [17]. It is defined as follows:

$$\eta_{Euro} = 0.03\eta_{5\%} + 0.06\eta_{10\%} + 0.13\eta_{20\%} + 0.1\eta_{30\%} + 0.48\eta_{50\%} + 0.2\eta_{100\%} \qquad [11]$$

European efficiency values can be very high. In **Figure 10**, results from the market study in The Netherlands show that the European efficiency values depend on the size of the inverter and can be >97% for inverters larger than 5 kW [18].

A simple mathematical function has been proposed that describes the efficiency curve of any solar inverter with very good accuracy [16]:

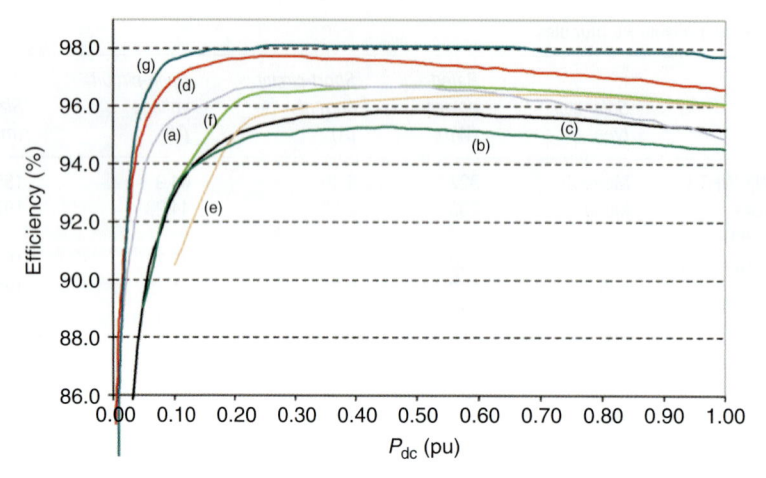

Figure 9 The efficiency of various solar inverters as a function of the pu DC power. (a) Solar Konzept, 2 kW; (b) Sunways, 3.6 kW; (c) SMA, 5 kW; (d) SMA, 11 kW; (e) Satcon, 50 kW; (f) Satcon, 100 kW; (g) Siemens, 1000 kVA. Source: Demoulias C (2010) A new simple analytical method for calculating the optimum inverter size in grid-connected PV plants. *Electric Power Systems Research* 80: 1197–1204, copyright (2010) with permission from Elsevier [16].

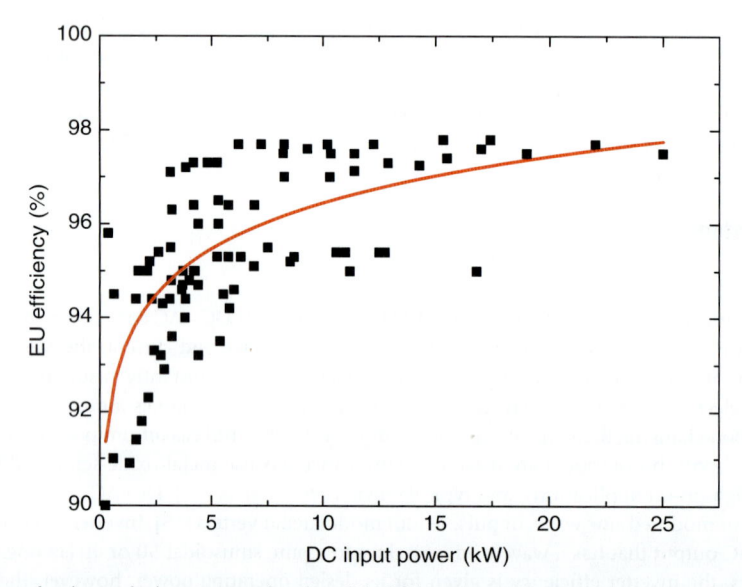

Figure 10 European efficiency of various solar inverters as a function of the DC input power. Source: Data from van Sark WGJHM, Muizebelt P, Cace J (2011) PV market in The Netherlands (in Dutch). Utrecht, The Netherlands: Stichting Monitoring Zonnestroom [18].

$$\eta_{inv}(P_{DC,pu}) = A + BP_{DC,pu} + \frac{C}{P_{DC,pu}} \quad [12]$$

in which $P_{DC,pu}$ is the pu value of the DC power. The parameters A, B, and C can be determined by fitting the curves as shown in **Figure 9**. For instance, for the Siemens 1000 kVA inverter, the parameters are $A = 98.78 \pm 0.12$, $B = -0.87 \pm 0.05$, and $C = -0.105 \pm 0.004$ [16].

When sizing a grid-connected PV system, the inverter capacity is to be matched with the PV array. Optimal PV system performance can usually be achieved by using an inverter with a capacity that is between 70% and 90% of the rating of the PV array. This obviously depends on the inverter efficiency curve and the climate characteristics.

Other requirements that utilities and standards prescribe are that acceptable levels of harmonic distortion should be achieved, that is, the voltage and current output waveforms should be of a certain quality. Further, there should be no emissions of electrical noise, as it could interfere with television or radio reception. Finally, in case of a grid failure, inverters should automatically switch off.

1.32.3.2 Mounting Structures

Mounting structures should be designed to hold the PV modules in place, and they should withstand heavy wind loads, for instance, on top of roofs as building-added PV (BAPV). For BIPV, these structures are designed to be building elements in which the PV modules are integrated. Examples are façade elements, roofing tiles, noise barriers, outdoor lighting systems, and (road) warning signs. The cost should be low, and in fact in BIPV, the cost of these elements can already be lower than marble or glazed façades. Also, mutual shading by modules should be avoided, and for maintenance, if at all necessary, easy access to the modules should be possible.

1.32.3.3 Batteries

In stand-alone systems, PV electricity is stored in rechargeable batteries; charging and discharging are regulated with the charge controller. The most commonly used battery is the lead-acid battery, although nickel-cadmium batteries are also used. Charging and discharging of batteries are unfortunately not reversible. Operation temperature and the rate of charge and discharge affect the performance and lifetime of a battery. The overall efficiency of charging and discharging is about 90% [15]. Usually slow discharge rates lead to longer lifetimes, while at low temperatures, discharge rates can decrease considerably. A sealed lead-acid battery avoids problems of spillage of the electrolyte and requires less maintenance.

1.32.3.4 Charge Regulators

Charge regulators are needed in stand-alone systems to regulate the flow of electricity between PV modules, battery, and loads. They are designed to determine the battery's state of charge (SOC) and protect the battery from overcharge or excessive discharge. PV modules operate at an approximately constant voltage under normal operating conditions, and an MPP tracker is not necessary. However, charge regulators may also contain an MPP tracker, and they use DC–DC converters to maintain a certain required system voltage; this however may be less cost-effective.

1.32.4 PV System Design

The size of a PV system may depend on the application for which it is intended. This certainly holds for stand-alone, or hybrid systems, where, for example, diesel generators are supplemented with a PV and battery system to provide electricity for remote or rural communities. For grid-connected PV systems available and suitable roof area usually determine at least the maximum size of a PV system, and cost the actual installed size. In all cases, an accurate prediction of the amount of annually generated electricity is needed to assess the feasibility of a system. The energy yield depends on the type of PV modules (i.e., their efficiency curve, as shown in **Figure 5**), the efficiency curve of the inverter (e.g., as shown in **Figure 9**), the meteorological conditions, and the orientation (south) and tilt angle of the modules. The annual energy yield nowadays can be modeled by a large selection of commercial software that differ in the level of sophistication, that is, from basic and quick assessment to full 3D simulations.

Energy losses in grid-connected PV systems that should further be taken into account are [19, 20] (1) irradiation losses such as spectral loss, reflection loss, shading loss, and soiling loss; (2) system losses such as deviating module power specifications, low irradiance losses, temperature effects, DC cable losses, various mismatch losses, static and dynamic MPP tracking losses, and inverter DC/AC and inverter control losses. Note that some of these losses are already reflected in the efficiency curves of the PV module and the inverter itself. Losses have been reduced from ~40% in the 1990s [19] to ~10% at present [20].

In the following, we present two case studies that we performed as examples of various issues that are encountered during the system design: (1) a hybrid PV–diesel system for an isolated island and (2) a large-scale PV power plant in a desert area.

1.32.4.1 Hybrid Solar–Diesel System for Mandhoo Island

A grid-connected PV–diesel hybrid system has been designed and installed at one of the outer islands of the Maldives [21]. Demonstration of a working hybrid PV–diesel system with storage backup was identified as crucial for raising awareness and building up know-how among the Maldivians. Therefore, a pilot hybrid PV–diesel system was designed for one of the islands. After reviewing a number of islands and assessing their suitability for installing such a system, the island of Mandhoo was selected. The system is expected to serve as an interesting learning experience for the Maldivians before setting up similar installations in future in other islands. In the design phase, the HOMER simulation tool has been extensively used in order to compare and optimize the electrical demand to the electrical energy that the system is able to supply on an hourly basis [22].

Mandhoo island is located about 100 km southwest of the capital Malé in the South Ari Atoll at 3°41″ N, 72°42″ E. The annual average temperature on the island is around 30 °C year-round, with a minor variation of a few degrees. The relative humidity levels are around 70–80%. The island is inhabited by about 40 families (250 persons in 2005) that are all connected to the island grid. The PV system is planned to operate in conjunction with the existing diesel power generating systems on the island, whereby the PV system in principle provides power during the day and the diesel systems during the evening and night.

The island has two diesel generators (G1 of 31 kW and G2 of 21.6 kW capacity, see **Figure 11**). Electricity is metered and sold to the households and the commercial clients at a rate (2005) of 4.5 Rf (US$ 0.35) kWh^{-1}. Another important electrical load is the streetlight in the island during nighttime. The generators are used alternately, and a manual switch is used to change the load from one to the other generator. The small diesel engine G2 runs during the day, meeting a demand that is around 6–8 kW, and the large diesel G1 is switched on around 18:00 hours to serve the peak load of about 16 kW during the evenings, with incidental peaks above 20 kW, and a nighttime demand of 12 kW. It is switched off at 06:00 hours.

Based on the gathered information, a load curve was derived. Electricity supplied by the generators amounted to 75 555 kWh in 2005, with an average of 207 kWh day^{-1}. Logged data enabled to determine the efficiency curves of both generators, as depicted in **Figure 12**. As a result, the existing system could be well-modeled using the HOMER software: electricity cost was calculated to be 0.342 US$ kWh^{-1}, using as assumptions a diesel fuel cost of 0.5 US$ l^{-1}, an interest rate of 12%, and a project lifetime of 15 years.

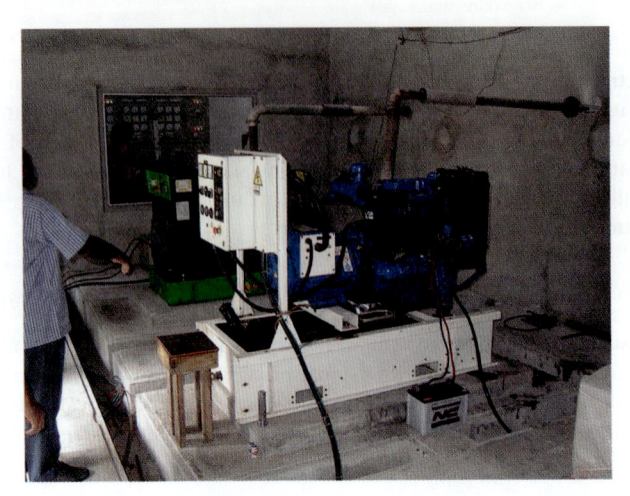

Figure 11 Existing diesel sets in Mandhoo: back 31 kW, front 22 kW. Reprinted from van Sark WGJHM, Lysen EH, Cocard D, *et al.* (2006) The first PV-diesel hybrid system in the Maldives installed at Mandhoo island. In: Poortmans J, Ossenbrink H, Dunlop E, and Helm P (eds.) *Proceedings of the 21st European Photovoltaic Solar Energy Conference*, pp. 3039–3043. Munich, Germany: WIP-Renewable Energies, with permission from WIP-Renewable Energies [21].

1.32.4.1.1 Hybrid design

1.32.4.1.1(i) Considerations

Integrating the PV system with battery backup in the current island grid was considered as a suitable way to introduce renewable electricity supply, as PV/battery systems are simply add-ons to the existing infrastructure. The system should be as simple and sturdy as possible and easy to operate for the present operator. Therefore, it was decided to go for an independent PV–battery system, that is, either the PV system or one of the diesel generators provides electricity to the distribution system. This is to be implemented through a manual switch-over between the two systems, in the same way it is being done at present, with a manual switch-over between the two diesel generators in the morning and in the evening. Synchronization was not opted for, given the added complexity and the need to add synchronization units for the diesel generators as well.

The way the operator of the power station operates the system has been integrated into the simulations of the PV–diesel system. The underlying constraints for designing the system are as follows:

- one should not expect to introduce too many changes in the operator's habits;
- both diesel generators should be turned off during a certain period of the day so that the surrounding population may feel ('hear') the difference once the PV system is installed;
- both diesel generators should be kept in operating conditions throughout the year (theoretically, one genset is sufficient to meet the load, but maintenance requires that they will be used alternatively); and
- the PV system should ideally be placed nearby the power house in order to minimize the transmission losses as well as to facilitate the maintenance of the entire system.

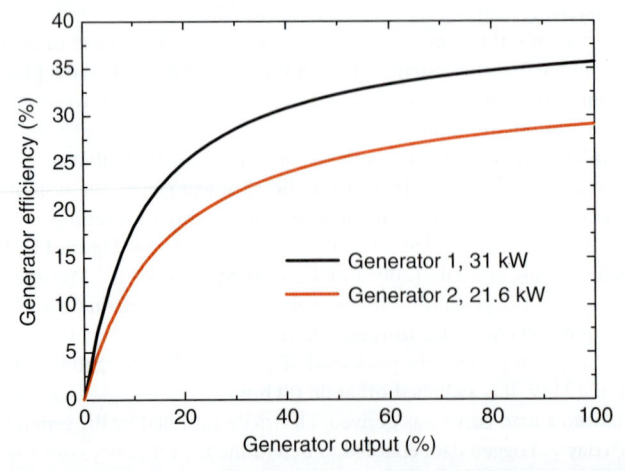

Figure 12 Generator efficiency as a function of relative output. Reprinted from van Sark WGJHM, Lysen EH, Cocard D, *et al.* (2006) The first PV-diesel hybrid system in the Maldives installed at Mandhoo island. In: Poortmans J, Ossenbrink H, Dunlop E, and Helm P (eds.) *Proceedings of the 21st European Photovoltaic Solar Energy Conference*, pp. 3039–3043. Munich, Germany: WIP-Renewable Energies, with permission from WIP-Renewable Energies [21].

The PV system should supply power to the network during daytime, from 07:00 until 18:00 hours, with the objective of avoiding the use of a diesel generator during that period and reducing the dependence on fossil fuel. As the PV system would operate during sunshine hours, the size of the storage batteries can be minimized, thus reducing the battery investment and replacement costs. On an average day, the battery will start feeding the network (through the inverter) and with higher solar radiation, the PV panel gradually takes over the load and also starts recharging the battery when extra power is available. On cloudy days, this may not be the case; then the battery will have to supply most of the load throughout the day. The HOMER model runs showed that on certain days, the battery is not able to meet the demand because it will reach a depth of discharge below 50% around midday. The operator will be instructed to switch on the diesel engines by midday on cloudy days. He will be guided by a simple indicator showing the SOC of the battery. On a normal sunny day, the operator makes a manual switch-over to one of the diesel generators at 18:00 hours. The same switch will reverse the energy flow in the converter, thereby starting to recharge the batteries. The batteries should be fully charged again before 07:00 hours of the next day. As an example of HOMER simulation results, **Figure 13** shows monthly averaged demand and supply curves.

1.32.4.1.1(ii) PV system

On the basis of local inspections and analysis with the HOMER model, the following design specifications were found to be optimal for a solar penetration of about 25%: PV capacity of 12 kWp, battery capacity of 108 kWh (50 batteries, 360 Ah, 6 V), and 12 kWp converter. The solar regime was taken from data measured (2003–05) at Hulhulé airport that is about 100 km away from Mandhoo. The average daily irradiance is 5.03 kWh m^{-2} day^{-1}, providing 1650 kWh kWp^{-1}.

In the ideal case, the PV panels should be located near the power station, but the site is not ideal as it is shaded by trees in the afternoon. Therefore, a street between the school and the health center, running from east–northeast to west–southwest, was selected. This location is partly shaded by trees, but only in the early morning and late afternoon. The PV panels are mounted on a self-standing elevated roof-like structure that is designed to withstand winds of up to 20 m s^{-1}. The structure is equipped with two gutters to lead the rain away from the edges of the panels. People are able to walk or bicycle easily below the structure.

Given the need to concentrate on the maintenance and the physical switch-over between PV and diesel generators in the powerhouse itself, it was decided to have the batteries and the converter installed in the powerhouse. This implies a long (200 m) DC connection between the PV panels and the rest of the system, which results in some DC transmission losses. The converter should be able to withstand the daily manual switch-over of the load, without voltage surges on the network.

The system was to be equipped with a monitoring system, which can be read from the Ministry of Environment, Energy and Water (MEEW) office in Malé. This is presently the case with the monitoring of weather data from three masts in the country: each data-logger sends a daily e-mail to the Malé office at 24:00 hours with the data recorded that day. In a similar manner, the monitoring system is to transmit the required 10-min average data, thus allowing to properly monitor the PV–diesel system. The monitoring system is located in the powerhouse and monitors the solar radiation (based on a global radiation pyranometer), the DC voltage and current from the PV panel to the batteries, the DC voltage and current to or from the battery bank, the DC voltage and current to or from the converter, and the outgoing AC power (three phases).

1.32.4.1.2 Realization

In a first mission to the Maldives in December 2004, the island of Mandhoo was visited and data were taken. Also, preliminary HOMER simulations were performed. During a second mission in February and March 2005, a final system design was defined together with Maldivian partners, based on acquired data of the daily load and commercially available PV and converter components. A 1-day visit to Mandhoo together with Maldivian partners marked a vital step in the introduction of the PV–diesel

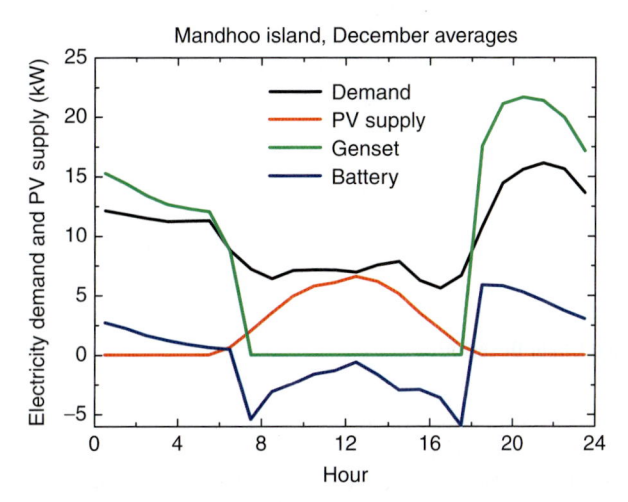

Figure 13 Daily demand and supply curves for Mandhoo in December. During this month, the PV system meets the full demand at noon, the rest being supplied by the batteries that are fully charged during night by the generator. Reprinted from van Sark WGJHM, Lysen EH, Cocard D, *et al.* (2006) The first PV-diesel hybrid system in the Maldives installed at Mandhoo island. In: Poortmans J, Ossenbrink H, Dunlop E, and Helm P (eds.) *Proceedings of the 21st European Photovoltaic Solar Energy Conference*, pp. 3039–3043. Munich, Germany: WIP-Renewable Energies, with permission from WIP-Renewable Energies [21].

Figure 14 PV system at Mandhoo. Reprinted from van Sark WGJHM, Lysen EH, Cocard D, *et al.* (2006) The first PV-diesel hybrid system in the Maldives installed at Mandhoo island. In: Poortmans J, Ossenbrink H, Dunlop E, and Helm P (eds.) *Proceedings of the 21st European Photovoltaic Solar Energy Conference*, pp. 3039–3043. Munich, Germany: WIP-Renewable Energies, with permission from WIP-Renewable Energies [21].

system in the island. The Maldivian partners had organized a meeting with all inhabitants of the island, during which a detailed presentation was made about the PV–diesel hybrid system in Dhivehi, the Maldivian language. The inhabitants unanimously voted in favor of the installation of the system.

In the months thereafter, a tender document was sent to well-known European solar system providers, inviting them to submit proposals with price quotations. Just after summer, a supplier was selected, and shipments to Malé were planned for November. In December, local workers constructed the steel support structure, and after transport of PV panels and converter to Mandhoo, installation of the PV system was carried out around Christmas and finalized on 31 December 2005. **Figure 14** shows a photograph of the finalized PV system. The structure was erected on the planned site, between the school and the Mandhoo Health Center. This will thereby serve the double purpose of providing shelter against rain or sunshine for those waiting in line for the Health Post and at the same time be of educational value for the children and teachers of the school. The installed system consists of PV capacity 12.8 kWp (160 pieces, 80 Wp. 12 V, BP), battery capacity 54 kWp (120 pieces OPzS solar 450, 450AhC120), and converter 20 kW (2 pieces, 10 kVA, Ainelec Energy Bay).

1.32.4.1.3 Evaluation

During the final mission in December 2005, it was found that the daily load of the island had substantially increased as a result of an additional air-conditioned communication center. The estimate for the daily consumption as used in the HOMER modeling exercise therefore had to be revised and was increased to 275 kWh day^{-1} (100 375 kWh yr^{-1}). Also, as the actual PV system is somewhat different from the optimum system simulated in Section 1.32.4.1.1, new HOMER runs were required. As the actual electricity consumption is expected to increase in the coming years, a few runs were made with a future value of 350 kWh day^{-1} (127 750 kWh yr^{-1}) to analyze the effect this higher consumption will have on the behavior of the PV–diesel system. Results show that in both cases, the most convenient solution for the operator is to let the generator G1 run longer in the morning, that is, until 07:00 hours for the load of 275 kWh day^{-1} or until 08:00 hours for the future load of 350 kWh day^{-1}. On cloudy days, the small generator G2 should be switched on, and this should perhaps be done every week for a few hours in order to prevent corrosion of the engine.

1.32.4.1.4 Conclusion

The first grid-connected PV system in the Maldives was successfully designed and realized. Care was taken to train MEEW employees in using the HOMER program for future developments. Also, it was found imperative to meet with the local community and to discuss the proposed system. Load curves and efficiency curves of diesel generators are indispensable in determining the most optimum configuration, as well as actual measurements of the solar regime. Finally, one has to take into account future electricity demand growth.

1.32.4.2 100 MW PV Plant in Abu Dhabi Desert Area

1.32.4.2.1 Introduction

Abu Dhabi can be identified as a place with large potential for electricity production from solar energy at competitive cost. Therefore, a study of the design of a conceptual 100 MW PV system was undertaken taking into account local climatic and geographic conditions as well as field experiences in system construction in other regions such as Germany and Spain. The focus of this study was on the economical feasibility, but also technical and environmental issues were addressed [23].

Abu Dhabi is the largest emirate of the United Arab Emirates. The emirate covers 67 340 km^2 and has a population of over 1.6 million in 2008 [24]. The Emirate of Abu Dhabi is located in the Persian Gulf and shares borders with the Kingdom of Saudi Arabia to the west and south and Oman to the east. Desert dominates Abu Dhabi's terrain, covering over 70% of its land area, where large amounts of sunshine [25] are available for electricity generation. Rapidly increasing electricity demand and environmental pressure stimulates the thought of development of future energy demand in a sustainable way in Abu Dhabi.

The electricity sector operates on a single buyer model, with the core player Abu Dhabi Water and Electricity Company (ADWEC) buying electricity from generators and selling electricity to distribution companies. Two electricity tariff models are used: a standard and a nonstandard electricity tariff. The majority of end customers including domestic customers are connected to the low-voltage distribution network and pay a standard (flat rate) electricity tariff, which includes government subsidy. Due to variations in subsidy, different standard tariffs in the range of 3 (0.6 euroct kWh^{-1}) to 15 fils kWh^{-1} (3 euroct kWh^{-1}) result (2009 level: 1 fil = 0.2 euroct). The reason for the very low electricity tariff is that the majority of existing power generation plants run on cheap natural gas. Nevertheless, peak electricity cost can amount to 16 euroct kWh^{-1}. As rapid growth in electricity consumption is foreseen in combination with limits in natural gas supply, Abu Dhabi has high ambitions to turn itself into a global energy center that would create high-quality jobs even after its oil runs out. With new coal and oil generation plants being built – where the electricity production cost is increasing to 75 fils kWh^{-1} – solar electricity could become cost-competitive.

1.32.4.2.2 Methodology

In this study, the RETScreen Clean Energy Project Analysis Software [26] was used to facilitate processing of the collected data and perform analysis on electricity production, economics, and CO_2 emission reduction. RETScreen is based on five standard analysis processes, of which energy generation, financial analysis, and GHG emission analysis are core perspectives in our study.

The Emirate of Abu Dhabi is characterized as a subtropical climate combined with arid weather due to large imposing desert areas. The clearness index for Abu Dhabi is high, the annual average being 0.58 (varying between 0.54 and 0.65) [25, 27]. The annual average daily global horizontal solar radiation in Abu Dhabi is 5.97 kWh m^{-2} day^{-1}; average daily solar radiation at a 20° tilted plane toward the south is 6.32 kWh m^{-2} day^{-1} [27]. The monthly variation is shown in **Figure 15**, illustrating that winter and summer differences are small; this leads to a flat power generation curve throughout the year taking into account that the high temperature in summer (**Figure 15**) reduces solar conversion efficiency. Average wind speeds vary between 3 and 4 m s^{-1} (at 10 m height) over the year.

Two PV technologies were selected: a wafer-based crystalline silicon (c-Si, Solarfun, 13.4% STC efficiency) and a thin-film technology (CdTe, First Solar, 10.1% STC efficiency). RETScreen calculates annual energy production using a sophisticated PV model, in which inverter and various other losses are also accounted for [26].

The conceptual 100 MW PV system is built from PV modules connected to several inverters. Depending on the specific modules (c-Si and CdTe) and inverters, a specific yield can be expected. A system layout is shown in **Figure 16**. The 100 MW PV plant consists of 100 subsystems of 1 MW each. Each subsystem converts DC electricity from two 500 kW PV arrays to 20 kV AC electricity through a SMA Sunny Central 1000 MV medium voltage station [28], which contains two identical high-efficiency inverters and a medium voltage transformer. In the case of c-Si modules, we integrated 196 subsystems into the 100 MW PV plant, with each pair connected to a Sunny Central 1000 MV substation. The Sunny Central 1000 MV substation (colored pink in **Figure 16**) is located in between each 1.02 MW subsystem in order to minimize wiring distance and complexity. The Sunny Central 1000 MV substation converts DC electricity from the 1.02 MW solar field to AC electricity with medium voltage of 20 kV, which then is fed into the 220 kV transmission grid through a 20 kV/220 kV transformer. The entire system demands an area of 1.65 km^2 and consists of 100 Sunny Central 1000 MV stations and 501 760 c-Si modules of 200 Wp. For CdTe modules of 72.5 Wp each, in total 1 380 000 modules are used in 200 sets of 500.25 kWp array units each. The total area is 2.09 km^2.

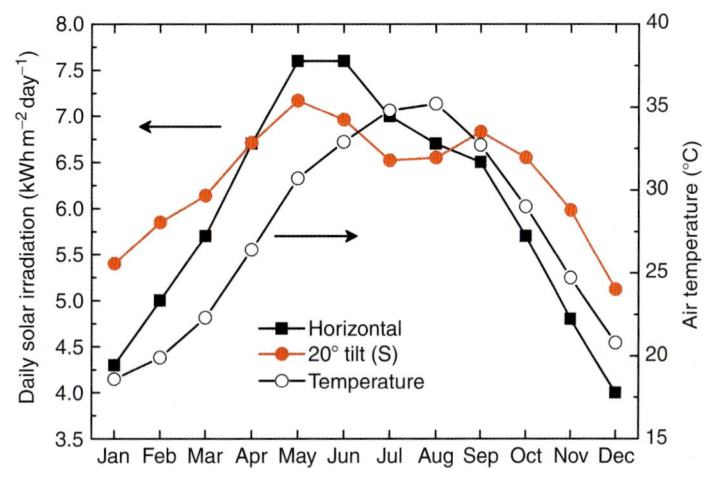

Figure 15 Monthly variation of daily solar irradiation in the horizontal plane and for a 20° tilted plane toward the south (left axis). Monthly variation of air temperature (right axis). Reprinted from Zhang C, van Sark WGJHM, and van Schalkwijk M (2010) Technical configuration, economic feasibility and environmental impacts of a 100 MW solar PV plant in desert areas in the Abu Dhabi Emirate. In: Sayigh A (ed.) *Proceedings of the World Renewable Energy Congress XI*, pp. 1056–1061. Brighton, UK: WREN, with permission from WREN [23].

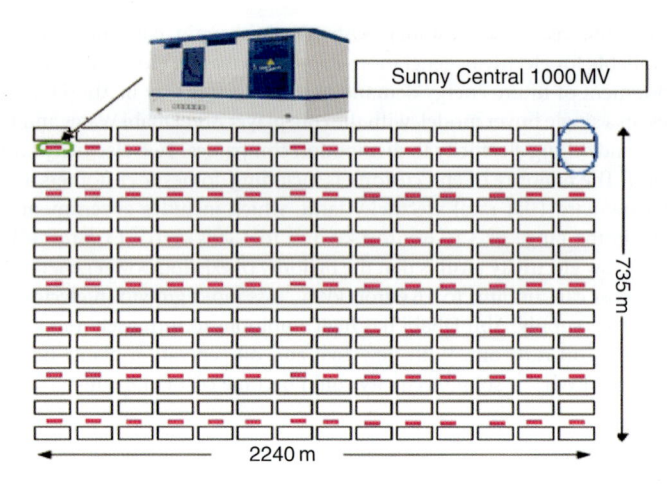

Figure 16 PV system layout. Reprinted from Zhang C, van Sark WGJHM, and van Schalkwijk M (2010) Technical configuration, economic feasibility and environmental impacts of a 100 MW solar PV plant in desert areas in the Abu Dhabi Emirate. In: Sayigh A (ed.) *Proceedings of the World Renewable Energy Congress XI*, pp. 1056–1061. Brighton, UK: WREN, with permission from WREN [23].

The profitability is determined using cost–benefit analysis; both net present value (NPV) and the payback period (PBP) are calculated. The simple PBP follows from dividing the initial investment (I) by the annual net benefit (B–C). Alternatively, the internal rate of return (IRR) reveals the discount rate at which the NPV is equal to zero.

1.32.4.2.3 Scenarios

In this study, three scenarios are established to compare economic feasibility of the 100 MW PV plant. Common parameters are inflation and discount rate, both at 10%, a project lifetime of 25 years, and a debt ratio of 70% at a debt period of 20 years at 10% interest. 'Scenario 1' presumes that feed-in-tariff (FiT) schemes similar to those in Germany are established by the Abu Dhabi government in order to accelerate deployment of renewable energy, cope with climate change, and create new economic growth sectors apart from the oil sector. The FiT rate is set fixed at 300 euro MWh^{-1} for a large-scale ground-based solar PV plant and remains constant for 25 years. Under 'scenario 2', the assumption is made based on increasing stress on shortage of natural gas supply. In this case, many gas-based generation plants are retrofitted to oil-based plants. The consequence is a sharp jump in generation cost from less than 20 to 75 fils kWh^{-1}. In these circumstances, electricity generated by PV plant is sold at a peak rate of 75 fils kWh^{-1} (150 euro MWh^{-1}) at the first year of generation. From year 1 on, an annual decrease of 10% is adopted. 'Scenario 3' takes into account the possibility of water production coupled with electricity production of the PV plant. Despite the low (mainly winter) precipitation of 100 mm each year in the deserts of Abu Dhabi, a large volume of rainwater collection is possible taking into account the potential rainwater catchment area of about 0.7 (c-Si) or 0.9 (CdTe) km^2. Using a project lifetime of 25 years and a rainwater efficiency of 75%, 52.5 million liters rainwater can be collected for c-Si (for CdTe 67.5 million liters).

1.32.4.2.4 Assumptions

The initial cost of the 100 MW plant was estimated on combining 1 MW blocks at costs regularly encountered in Spain (for systems designed in 2009). Module and support structure cost is assumed similar, and inverter cost is based on a quotation from SMA. Construction cost is adapted to local level, while engineering and training cost is 20% larger due to lack of experience in Abu Dhabi. In summary, the total initial cost for the 100 MW PV plant based on c-Si modules was 376.5 million euro, of which 56% is spent on modules. Total initial cost for the 100 MW PV plant based on CdTe modules was 360 million euro, of which 48% is spent on modules. The operation and maintenance (O&M) cost is estimated by averaging a few reported values in the range of 0.084–0.22% of the initial cost [8, 9], resulting in 0.11% of initial cost for the c-Si case and 0.12% for the CdTe case.

Regarding environmental impact of the 100 MW PV plant in Abu Dhabi, the focus was on greenhouse gas emissions (GHGs) determined by life cycle analysis (LCA) and the energy payback time (EPBT), using data of existing studies [29]. The LCA GHG emissions are 30–45 and 19–25 g CO$_2$ equiv. kWh^{-1} for c-Si and CdTe, respectively. Using corrections considering module efficiency, cell thickness, system performance, and electricity mix, we found a GHG emission factor for the used c-Si (CdTe) modules of 422 (59) kg CO$_2$ equiv. m^{-2} and a cumulative energy consumption of 3813 (1070) MJ m^{-2}. For the BOS (inverter, support structures, and cabling), these values are 17 (18) kg CO$_2$ equiv. m^{-2} and 543 (647) MJ m^{-2}, respectively.

1.32.4.2.5 System performance

Running the RETScreen energy model yields the following results. The 100 MW PV plant will deliver 177 GWh electricity annually for the c-Si case and 182 GWh electricity for the CdTe case without considering module degradation. The capacity factor for the c-Si case is 20.2% and a slightly higher value of 20.8% is found for the CdTe case. Finally, a performance ratio of 76.8% is calculated for the c-Si case and 79.0% for the CdTe case.

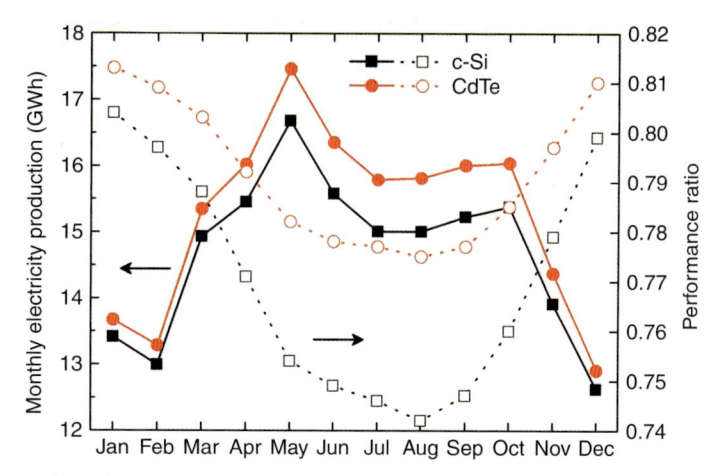

Figure 17 Monthly electricity production and performance ratio for c-Si and CdTe modules. Reprinted from Zhang C, van Sark WGJHM, and van Schalkwijk M (2010) Technical configuration, economic feasibility and environmental impacts of a 100 MW solar PV plant in desert areas in the Abu Dhabi Emirate. In: Sayigh A (ed.) *Proceedings of the World Renewable Energy Congress XI*, pp. 1056–1061. Brighton, UK: WREN, with permission from WREN [23].

Monthly electricity output is shown in **Figure 17**. For both technology cases, maximum electricity production occurs in May (16.7 GWh for c-Si and 17.5 GWh for CdTe) and minimum electricity production occurs in December (15.0 GWh for c-Si and 15.8 GWh for CdTe) when the solar radiation is at the lowest point. Despite the low performance ratio due to increasing temperature from June to September, more electricity is produced in summer, which matches very well with peak power demand due to substantial cooling load in those hot months. The highest performance ratio in both cases occurs in January: 80.4% for c-Si and 81.3% for CdTe. Due to high temperatures in August, the performance ratio decreases to a minimum: 74.3% for c-Si and 77.5% for CdTe.

For the calculation of total generated amount of electricity over the whole lifetime, we assumed that 90% power output at the end of 10 years and 80% power output at the end of 25 years lifetime is guaranteed. The calculated lifetime electricity output for the c-Si plant amounts to 3932 GWh, that is, 157.3 GWh on average per year. For the CdTe plant, the total electricity output is predicted to be 4047 GWh, that is, 161.9 GWh on average per year.

1.32.4.2.6 Financial results

Table 2 summarizes the general financial results of the three scenarios for both the c-Si and the CdSe technology cases. With constant FiT of 300 euro MWh^{-1} for 25 years assumed under scenario 1, the PV plant is economically attractive, with high IRR and low equity payback time (5 years) for both technologies. Electricity production costs for c-Si are 276.2 euro MWh^{-1} (257.2 euro MWh^{-1} for CdTe). The NPV of the c-Si project is about 35 million euro. For CdTe, the NPV is nearly double that of c-Si at 65.2 million euro. For both technologies, scenario 2 shows better IRR and NPV. A different approach is used under scenario 3 to calculate rainwater net profit rate in order to meet minimum cutoff IRR of a company, that is, 12% in our case. Therefore, the results only show minimum requirement for a project to be considered. Under this scenario, the electricity is sold at a tariff of 150 euro MWh^{-1}, constant for 25 years. Bottled rainwater is collected from the solar plant and sold with a net profit of 17 eurocent l^{-1}, with consideration of 10% inflation rate. Under these assumptions, the IRR on company's equity is 12.3% (c-Si) and 12.7% (CdTe). Electricity production cost stands at 125.3 (c-Si) and 124.1 euro MWh^{-1} (CdTe). Equity payback time is 11.2 (c-Si) and 10.6 years (CdTe). B–C ratio and debt payback capacity are fairly low.

Figure 18 shows yearly cumulative cash flow throughout the lifetime of the PV plant under the three scenarios for both technologies, showing that technology differences are small. For c-Si, in scenario 1, positive cash flow starts before year 6.

Table 2 Summary of financial results for both technologies and the three scenarios used, compiled from data in reference 23

Financial viability	c-Si technology			CdTe technology		
	Scenario 1	Scenario 2	Scenario 3	Scenario 1	Scenario 2	Scenario 3
After-tax IRR – equity (%)	14.9	16.8	12.3	19.2	18.4	12.7
Equity payback (years)	5.7	9.8	11.2	4.7	8.8	10.6
NPV (million euro)	35.2	168.9	36.5	65.2	202.9	39.4
Benefit–cost (B–C) ratio	1.3	2.5	1.3	1.6	2.9	1.4
Debt service coverage	1.7	0.9	1.2	1.8	1.0	1.2
Energy production cost (euro MWh^{-1})	276.2	106.1	125.3	257.2	99.3	124.1

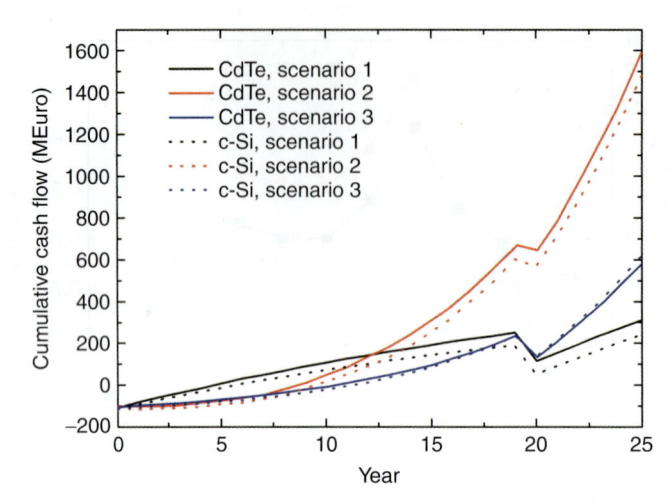

Figure 18 Cumulative cash flow under three scenarios for c-Si (dotted lines) and CdTe (solid lines). Reprinted from Zhang C, van Sark WGJHM, and van Schalkwijk M (2010) Technical configuration, economic feasibility and environmental impacts of a 100 MW solar PV plant in desert areas in the Abu Dhabi Emirate. In: Sayigh A (ed.) *Proceedings of the World Renewable Energy Congress XI*, pp. 1056–1061. Brighton, UK: WREN, with permission from WREN [23].

Periodic costs take place in year 20 due to replacement of inverters, which explains the sharp drop in year 20. End-of-life cumulative cash flow peaks at about 250 million euro. Yearly cash flow is nearly tripled after year 20 when the debt is paid up. In case of scenario 2, positive cash flow starts much later compared with scenario 1 due to the fact that electricity export rate is low at the early phase of the project and escalates gradually. Periodic costs take place in year 20 because of replacement of inverters, but the cost is less compared with substantial cash inflows cumulated in the later phase of the project. End-of-life cumulative cash flow peaks at about 1500 million euro. In scenario 3, positive cash flow happens after year 11. Periodic costs take place in year 20 because of replacement of inverters, which covers a big proportion of cumulative cash in that year. End-of-life cumulative cash flow peaks at about 620 million euro. For CdTe, similar observations can be made.

1.32.4.2.7 Environmental results

In our study, we conducted a rough estimation of GHG emission and EPBT of the conceptual PV plant. Input values are taken from the available literature with correction to some extent. From our rough estimation of GHG emissions and EPBT, we find that the potential for GHG emission reduction is significant. It is possible to reduce GHG emissions by 64 653 t yr^{-1} if c-Si modules are used; 76 983 t yr^{-1} for CdTe. Since the production process of CdTe modules is less energy-intensive than that of c-Si, the EPBT is 1.2 years for CdTe and 2.35 years for c-Si.

1.32.4.2.8 Conclusions

From this study [23], it was concluded that solar PV technology is very promising in Abu Dhabi. A 100 MW PV project can deliver substantial electricity for meeting the peak electricity demand locally and make some contribution to relieve cooling load stress in the summer season. However, as the current electricity tariff is low, financial incentives are needed. An FiT of 150 euro MWh^{-1} (scenario 2) would be economically viable. Note that this study was performed in 2009; since then, PV module prices have been decreased by >50%. Together with an expected increase of the peak electricity tariff to 15 ct kWh^{-1}, deployment of PV may be attractive with a low or even without a financial incentive.

The low cost of CdTe modules, their increasing efficiency, less energy-intensive production process, and the extreme hot climate in Abu Dhabi cause CdTe modules to be the best choice in terms of energetic performance, economic viability, and environmental impact, irrespective of the scenario considered.

1.32.5 Conclusions

In this chapter, various PV system components are described, with a focus on their individual performance. In grid-connected systems, PV modules are connected to the inverter, which converts DC PV power to AC, which is fed directly into the grid. In properly designed stand-alone systems, an additional charge controller and battery ensure that power is available at all times. PV module efficiency depends on the solar irradiation intensity and on temperature, and different types of modules differ in their specific efficiency behavior. Similarly, inverter efficiency depends on the percentage of maximum capacity at which they are operated. PV system design should include both PV and inverter efficiency curves and also other system losses. Finally, two case study examples are presented that show more details of the PV system design.

References

[1] Eltawil MA and Zhao Z (2010) Grid-connected photovoltaic power systems: Technical and potential problems – A review. *Renewable and Sustainable Energy Reviews* 14: 112–129.
[2] Komoto K, Ito M, van der Vleuten P, *et al.* (eds.) (2009) *Very Large Scale Photovoltaic Systems: Socio-Economic, Financial, Technical and Environmental Aspects.* London, UK: Earthscan.
[3] Nieuwenhout FDJ, van Dijk A, Lasschuit PE, *et al.* (2001) Experience with solar home systems in developing countries: A review. *Progress in Photovoltaics: Research and Applications* 9: 455–474.
[4] Green MA (1982) *Solar Cells; Operating Principles Technology and Systems Application.* Englewood Cliffs, NJ: Prentice-Hall.
[5] van Sark WGJHM (2007) Teaching the relation between solar cell efficiency and annual energy yield. *European Journal of Physics* 28: 415–427.
[6] Marion B (2002) A method for modeling the current-voltage curve of a PV module for outdoor conditions. *Progress in Photovoltaics: Research and Applications* 10: 205–214.
[7] Grunov P, Lust S, Sauter D, *et al.* (2004) Weak light performance and annual energy yields of PV modules and systems as a result of the basic parameter set of industrial solar cells. In: Hoffmann W, Bal J-L, Ossenbrink H, *et al.* (eds.) *Proceedings of the Nineteenth European Photovoltaic Solar Energy Conference*, pp. 2190–2193. Munich, Germany: WIP.
[8] Reich NH, van Sark WGJHM, Alsema EA, *et al.* (2009) Crystalline silicon cell performance at low light intensities. *Solar Energy Materials & Solar Cells* 93: 1471–1481.
[9] Reich NH, van Sark WGJHM, and Turkenburg WC (2011) Charge yield potential of indoor-operated solar cells incorporated into Product Integrated Photovoltaic (PIPV). *Renewable Energy* 36: 642–647.
[10] Beyer HG, Betcke J, Drews A, *et al.* (2004) Identification of a general model for the MPP performance of PV-modules for the application in a procedure for the performance check of grid connected systems. In: Hoffmann W, Bal J-L, Ossenbrink H, *et al.* (eds.) *Proceedings of the 19th European Photovoltaic Solar Energy Conference*, pp. 3073–3076. Munich, Germany: WIP.
[11] Green MA, Emery K, King DL, *et al.* (2009) Solar cell efficiency tables (version 33). *Progress in Photovoltaics: Research and Applications* 17: 85–94.
[12] Photon.info Module Database www.photon.info/photon_site_db_solarmodule_en.photon (accessed 31 October 2011).
[13] Jäger-Waldau A (2011) PV Status Report 2011. Research, Solar Cell Production and Market Implementation of Photovoltaics, European Commission, DG Joint Research Centre, Institute for Energy, Renewable Energy Unit.
[14] Krauter S (2006) *Solar Electric Power Generation-Photovoltaic Energy Systems.* Berlin, Germany: Springer-Verlag.
[15] Messenger RA and Ventre J (2010) *Photovoltaic Systems Engineering*, 3rd edn. New York: CRC Press.
[16] Demoulias C (2010) A new simple analytical method for calculating the optimum inverter size in grid-connected PV plants. *Electric Power Systems Research* 80: 1197–1204.
[17] Bletterie B, Bründlinger R, and Lauss G (2011) On the characterisation of PV inverters' efficiency – Introduction to the concept of achievable efficiency. *Progress in Photovoltaics: Research and Applications* 19: 423–435.
[18] van Sark WGJHM, Muizebelt P, and Cace J (2011) PV market in The Netherlands (in Dutch). Utrecht, The Netherlands: Stichting Monitoring Zonnestroom.
[19] Reinders AHME, van Dijk VAP, Wiemken E, and Turkenburg WC (1999) Technical and economic analysis of grid-connected PV systems by means of simulation. *Progress in Photovoltaics: Research and Applications* 7: 71–82.
[20] Reich NH, Mueller B, Armbruster A, *et al.* (2012) Performance ratio revisited: Are PR > 90% realistic? *Progress in Photovoltaics* 20 (in press).
[21] van Sark WGJHM, Lysen EH, Cocard D, *et al.* (2006) The first PV-diesel hybrid system in the Maldives installed at Mandhoo island. In: Poortmans J, Ossenbrink H, Dunlop E, and Helm P (eds.) *Proceedings of the 21st European Photovoltaic Solar Energy Conference*, pp. 3039–3043. Munich, Germany: WIP-Renewable Energies.
[22] Lambert T, Gilman P, and Lilienthal P (2006) Micropower system modeling with HOMER. In: Farret FA and Simões MG (eds.) *Integration of Alternative Sources of Energy*, pp. 379–418. New York: Wiley.
[23] Zhang C, van Sark WGJHM, and van Schalkwijk M (2010) Technical configuration, economic feasibility and environmental impacts of a 100 MW solar PV plant in desert areas in the Abu Dhabi Emirate. In: Sayigh A (ed.) *Proceedings of the World Renewable Energy Congress XI*, pp. 1056–1061. Brighton, UK: WREN.
[24] Abu Dhabi Tourism Authority http://www.visitabudhabi.ae/en/about.abudhabi.aspx (accessed 23 February 2012).
[25] Islam MD, Kubo I, Ohadi M, and Alili AA (2009) Measurement of solar energy radiation in Abu Dhabi, UAE. *Applied Energy* 86: 511–515.
[26] Natural Resources Canada (2005) *Clean Energy Project Analysis-RETScreen® Engineering & Cases Textbook.* http://www.retscreen.net. (accessed 23 February 2012).
[27] NASA Surface Meteorology and Solar Energy Data Set http://eosweb.larc.nasa.gov/sse/. (accessed 23 February 2012).
[28] SMA Solar Technology http://www.sma.de (accessed 23 February 2012).
[29] Fthenakis V and Alsema EA (2006) Photovoltaics energy payback times, greenhouse gas emissions and external costs: 2004–early 2005 status. *Progress in Photovoltaics* 14: 275–280.

1.33 BIPV in Architecture and Urban Planning

TH Reijenga, BEARiD Architecten, Rotterdam, The Netherlands
HF Kaan, TNO Energy, Comfort and Indoor Quality, Delft, The Netherlands

© 2012 Elsevier Ltd. All rights reserved.

1.33.1	**Introduction**	697
1.33.1.1	Building Integration of Photovoltaics Will Be the Future	697
1.33.1.2	Definition of Building Integration	698
1.33.2	**Photovoltaics in the Urban Planning Process**	699
1.33.2.1	Planning for Renewables	699
1.33.2.2	Site Layout and Solar Access	699
1.33.2.3	Successful Implementation	699
1.33.2.4	Long-Term Operation	699
1.33.3	**Steps in the Design Process with BIPV**	700
1.33.3.1	Urban Planning – Related Design Aspects	700
1.33.3.1.1	Orientation and angle	700
1.33.3.1.2	Distance between buildings	700
1.33.3.1.3	Trees	701
1.33.3.1.4	Zoning	701
1.33.3.1.5	Reflection	701
1.33.3.2	Practical Rules for Integration	701
1.33.3.3	Step-by-Step Design	702
1.33.3.3.1	Solar design	702
1.33.3.3.2	Module placement and shadowing	702
1.33.3.3.3	Space required for balance of systems and interconnections	702
1.33.3.4	Design Process: Strategic Planning	702
1.33.4	**BIPV in Architecture**	703
1.33.4.1	Architectural Functions of PV Modules	703
1.33.4.1.1	Roof-integrated PV	703
1.33.4.1.2	Façade-integrated PV	704
1.33.4.1.3	PV in building components	704
1.33.4.1.4	PV art in structures	704
1.33.4.2	PV Integrated as Roofing Louvres, Façades, and Shading Devices	705
1.33.4.3	Architectural Criteria for Well-Integrated Systems	705
1.33.4.4	Integration of PV Modules in Architecture	706
1.33.5	**Concluding Remarks**	706
References		707
Further Reading		707

1.33.1 Introduction

1.33.1.1 Building Integration of Photovoltaics Will Be the Future

Solar systems become an integral part of our society and thus our environment. In various Western countries, and also in Asian countries like Japan, Malaysia, and China, examples can be seen of large quantities of photovoltaics (PVs), incorporated in urban areas. There are large incentives for principals to ask for buildings with integrated PVs, and for urban planners and architects to incorporate PVs into their design. Some countries like France and China will give extra financial incentives for building-integrated photovoltaic (BIPV) systems.

The government's role in promoting and supporting sustainable energy (PV systems) strongly influences the extent to which these systems are used in buildings. The high interest in PV in Germany, for instance, is a result of the policy of the German government with regards to PV and renewable energy in general. In countries with less government intervention, the power utilities play a bigger role. Even without financial support, the government can encourage sustainable energy, for example, by demanding better performance for buildings. By introducing certain energy performance goals, like in the Dutch building code, sustainable energy and solar energy PV systems might be considered.

A large part of the future PV market will be associated with building applications, especially in Europe, Japan, and China where the population density is high and the land is valuable. The scale of building integration is increasing and goes up to over 11 MWp for a building (mainly exhibition or factory halls). In areas with less population, it will be possible to find land for ground-mounted PV structures.

New products are emerging, yet need further development to fully meet the architectural needs of sustainable buildings. Architects therefore need to start thinking about this new Smart Solar Architecture. This chapter is intended to stimulate this thinking. The second section focuses on planning aspects of large-scale PV applications. The third section deals with steps in the design process with BIPV and the third section goes into BIPV in architecture.

1.33.1.2 Definition of Building Integration

It is not easy to formulate a sound definition of BIPV. It not only concerns the physical integration of a PV system into a building, but it also covers the overall image of the PV system in the building. For the architect, the esthetic aspect, rather than the physical integration, is the main reason for talking about building integration. The optimal situation is a physically and aesthetically well-integrated BIPV system. In fact, many examples of physical integration show a lack of esthetic integration. Visual analysis of PV systems in buildings shows that the look of a poorly designed building does not improve, simply by adding a well-designed PV system. On the other hand, a well-designed building with a nicely integrated PV system will be accepted by everybody.

Building-integrated, grid-connected PV systems have the following advantages:

- There is no additional requirement for land.
- The cost of the PV wall, and up to a certain point the roof, can be offset against the cost of the building element it replaces.
- Power is generated on-site and replaces electricity that would otherwise be purchased at commercial rates.
- Connecting to the grid means that the high cost of storage is avoided and security of supply is ensured.

In addition, architecturally elegant, well-integrated systems will increase market acceptance, and BIPV systems provide building owners with a highly visible public expression of their environmental commitment.

The way people deal with PVs in architecture differs from country to country. This depends on the scale, culture, and type of financing for building projects. In countries such as Denmark, The Netherlands, and the United Kingdom, where public housing is very common, serial production is strongly emphasized in housing projects. Professionals such as housing associations, project developers, and architects implement the housing construction process, in which the main opportunities are for PV roof integration in single-family terraced houses and for façade and roof integration in apartment buildings (**Figure 1**).

Of course, there are also many countries where the government or professional, nonprofit housing associations have little influence on house building. In those countries, the process of developing and building houses is mainly a private initiative. Integration of PV systems in buildings can be carried out by professionals but, on the smaller scale of a single-family house, the motivation must mainly come from the private owner. In general, most BIPV systems are found in buildings in which building professionals are involved. Consequently, in countries where there is little professional involvement in large-scale housing projects, PV can be found in the first place on commercial and industrial buildings. With these types of buildings, PV systems are integrated both into façades and roofs. In addition, there is a significant market for private homeowners who buy small-scale (less than 500 Wp) PV systems and mount them somewhere on their house. However, as these systems are seldom architecturally integrated in the building design, we consider these applications as building-added PV (BAPV) systems rather than BIPV systems.

The aim of integrating PV systems into buildings clearly is to reduce the requirement for land and to reduce the costs [1]. This could be the cost of the support construction and the cost of building elements, such as cladding elements. It is more efficient to integrate a PV system when constructing or renovating the building, rather than mounting it afterwards.

Figure 1 The project in Etten-Leur has an ongoing PV roof that connects the detached houses. Each house has its own inverters and monitoring system. Photograph © Ronald Schlund Bodien.

1.33.2 Photovoltaics in the Urban Planning Process

In the framework of an EU-supported project 'PV Upscale' an inventory was made of the lessons learnt from urban areas all over the world where large numbers of PV systems have been installed (this section is largely based on Munro [2]). The lessons learnt are divided into the four main stages of developing an urban area:

1. *National and regional policy formation and strategies*. These set the context in which urban planners create plans for specific urban areas and developments.
2. *Site layout and initial design*. This stage is critical for maximizing the possibilities for installing renewable.
3. *Implementation – from design to construction*. Good sharing of information and team work are critical at this stage.
4. *Occupation – when the real success or otherwise of a project can be seen*. It is all too easy to ignore PV systems once they are installed, but this risks reduction in energy output.

1.33.2.1 Planning for Renewables

In the majority of cities that have installed significant amounts of renewable energy infrastructure over the last 10 years, the local municipal government has had a key role in stimulating projects. When it comes to installation of large amounts of PV, these cities tend to have several important factors in common:

- a strong local political commitment to the environment and sustainability;
- the presence of municipal departments or offices dedicated to the environment, sustainability, or renewable energy;
- obligations that some or all buildings include renewable energy;
- information provision about the possibilities of renewable energy;
- challenging development sites that have inspired ambitious renewable energy projects.

1.33.2.2 Site Layout and Solar Access

As a solar technology, the success of PV is highly depending on the solar orientation and shading. Consequently, the planning conditions for PV have to be determined in a very early stage of the urban planning process. Experience has shown that the decision for applying PV on a larger scale is taken relatively late in the urban planning process, when the site layout has been fixed. As a consequence, the site may have become less suitable or even almost not suitable for large-scale application of PV. When a municipality or other decision maker wants to have PV applied in a new urban plan, he should take care that solar energy is considered during the design process.

1.33.2.3 Successful Implementation

The following elements are important for the successful implementation of PVs within the urban renewal and development process:

- *Enthusiasm*. There has to be some enthusiasm for renewable energy in the design team or the project will not result in the hoped for emission reduction. If there is no one championing the inclusion of PV, it risks being dropped from the design or will be poorly integrated.
- *Technical knowledge*. This will be needed by the system designers and by the rest of the project team.
- *Inclusion in the work plan of the entire project team*. As designing a BIPV project is based on an integrated design and construction process, all team members have to be involved from the beginning: architect, structural engineer, electrical engineer, and construction company. Installation of a PV system will affect all members of the team, not just the PV installer.
- *Time*. The implementation of renewable energy projects has to fit within the construction time schedule or there will be delays and extra costs.
- *Transmission links*. A connection to the local electricity network will be needed. The local utility should be informed of the possibility of any forms of embedded generation at the earliest possible stage.
- *Finance*. Can the costs come out of the existing budget? If not, can money be raised from external funding sources or innovative financing?

Good communication between the different members of the project team is also important. Architects and engineers can appear to speak different languages at the best of times. The problem can be even worse when dealing with a technology that is new to some members of the team. Clear communication between the members of the team on what they hope PV can offer and the information they need should be discussed at an early stage in the project.

1.33.2.4 Long-Term Operation

PV systems should have a long lifetime successfully producing electricity at, or close to, their original output level for at least 20 years. However, experience has shown that while most PV systems reliably supply power for many years, poor implementation, erratic maintenance, or a lack of forward thinking can lead to loss of performance in the longer term. Experience from around Europe shows that when large numbers of small PV systems are installed on buildings in urban areas and then left for ordinary building occupants to operate with no professional support, there are risks that poor performance may not be picked up. This situation contrasts with one where an individual decision to purchase and install a PV system has been made. In this case, the occupants can be expected to have some understanding of the system, the quantity of electricity expected to be produced, the guarantees available, and contact information for the supplier in the event of problems. Nonetheless, issues may still arise in later years if the house is sold on, and the PV system remains installed on the house. The alternative approach of offering a high feed-in tariff for PV-generated electricity avoids many problems by providing an incentive to maintain the system.

The various factors that should be considered during the planning and project design stage because they will impact on long-term performance are as follows:

- The importance of good design and forward planning
- The system performance needs to be checkable
- The completed systems should be handed over to the eventual occupants in full working order, commissioned, and grid connected
- It is important to look ahead to consider practical and affordable arrangements for maintenance.

1.33.3 Steps in the Design Process with BIPV

1.33.3.1 Urban Planning – Related Design Aspects

The aim of integrating PV systems into buildings is to reduce costs and to optimize the scarce ground in urban areas. To generate maximum power from building-integrated systems, certain urban planning and architectural aspects have to be taken into account.

The main starting point is the maximum power that can be generated by a system. The primary hindrances can be the (partly) shadowing of a system by other buildings or objects, and the nonoptimum orientation relative to the sun. Reflection can also be a problem for the surrounding buildings.

1.33.3.1.1 Orientation and angle
The amount of irradiance depends on the latitude. The maximum irradiance corresponds to surfaces, tilted at an angle equal to about the latitude minus 10°. For instance at a latitude of 52° N, good results (>90% of maximum irradiance) can be achieved by orienting the modules between southeast and southwest, with system angles between 30° and 50° from the horizontal. Orientations between east and southeast, and between southwest and west, are fairly reasonable with system angles between 10° and 30° from horizontal. The irradiance will be reduced by around 15% of the maximum.

Flat-roof systems with very low angles (between 5° and 10°) can be a good solution for difficult orientations (as example, see **Figure 2**).

1.33.3.1.2 Distance between buildings
Shadowing is a critical issue for BIPV. In general, designs in which the PV modules are shaded for much of the year should be avoided. For low-rise areas, the problem is easy to solve. The distance between individual houses can be accounted for in designing BIPV. For mixed height neighborhoods, it will be more difficult. A high-rise apartment building in a low-rise neighborhood can cause a lot of unwanted shading.

The density of an area is also of high influence. In high-density areas (cities), the distances between buildings are often so small that there is significant shadowing throughout a large part of the year.

Figure 2 A large-scale application of PV systems for flat roofs. This is a sporting center in Wageningen. Picture © BEARiD Architecten, Tjerk Reijenga.

As a general note, it is worth mentioning that façade systems (vertical) are more sensitive to shading and need longer distances from other buildings than tilted systems (roofs). Horizontal systems have a lower irradiance, as previously mentioned, but will be the best solutions for avoiding shadow. Only neighborhoods with a mixture of low- and high-rise buildings might be unsuitable for horizontal systems.

1.33.3.1.3 Trees

Greening the area around buildings makes the area look very attractive and the microclimate more comfortable for the inhabitants. However, the shadowing effect of trees is very important, as the trees will be very dense during the summer. Even during the winter, when trees lose their leaves, the branches give too much shade.

The aspect of growth is sometimes underestimated. Planning for the future growth of trees is very important and must be done carefully to avoid problems a few years after the building has been completed or the PV system has been installed.

Solutions can be to

- only plant trees on the north side of buildings,
- plant only small trees up to two-stories high,
- prune trees annually to keep them small.

1.33.3.1.4 Zoning

In future, a special solar zoning will be needed in urban areas with PV systems. The borders of building areas can be clearly marked on three-dimensional maps to prevent future problems. The amount of sunlight can also be determined on these maps.

1.33.3.1.5 Reflection

Although not a major problem, under certain circumstances, reflection can occur. In low-rise buildings, there are no significant problems, but in mixed low- and high-rise areas residents in high-rise buildings may experience some annoying reflections if all the surrounding houses have (glass-covered) PV modules. The fact that there are certain distances between buildings (for shadowing) may eliminate most of the potential problems.

1.33.3.2 Practical Rules for Integration

There are a few important rules for integrating modules into buildings. These rules concern the functioning and maintenance of the system, for example:

1. shadow is not allowed on the module,
2. ventilation, that is, cooling, is required at the back of the modules (less important for thin film amorphous silicon, compared to crystalline silicon),
3. make it easy to mount and remove a module,
4. ensure that the module stays clean or can be cleaned,
5. make easy and reliable electrical connections,
6. ensure that wiring is sun and weatherproof.

Ad 1. As previously mentioned, even partial shadow on the modules will decrease the energy output. Profiled mounting constructions, in particular like awnings, can produce shadows along the edge of the adjacent module that will result in loss of efficiency. Note, for example, the shade in the left part of **Figure 2**.

Ad 2. Modules with crystalline silicon cells have a higher output when the temperature is lower. With ventilation at the back of the module, it is possible to keep the temperature low and avoid a decreasing output. However, thin-film amorphous silicon reacts differently. The higher temperature does not influence the efficiency as much as crystalline silicon. This also holds for other thin film technologies, such as cadmium telluride.

Ad 3. Although the lifetime of modules is proven to be over 20 years, it is better to know how to remove a single module in the middle of the installation without removing the whole system. Electrical connections should also be 'plug and play'. Easy electrical connections are needed for fast installation and for easy replacement of modules. Depending on the local safety regulations, precautionary measures should be taken, for example, using lifelines or moveable safety ladders.

Ad 4. The surface of the modules should be clean. Tilted modules will be automatically cleaned by rain in most regions. Modules mounted at low angles can be treated chemically, which makes the surface smooth and makes cleaning with rain easier. In dry areas, cleaning should be part of the regular maintenance schedule.

Ad 5. Protect wiring against the weather. Rain is not the main problem, though all connections must be waterproof. Long-term influence from water should be avoided. Protection against sun and UV light is needed to ensure that the insulation of the wiring is not deteriorated. Depending on the area, wiring may also need to be protected from small gnawing animals.

1.33.3.3 Step-by-Step Design

A PV system consists of a number of modules with solar cells, an inverter, batteries, or, in most cases, a connection to the grid. A single house with a small installation can be connected through the existing electricity meter. The electricity that is produced will be used primarily in the house. Any surplus will be fed into the grid and the meter will spin backwards. However, not every utility company will allow this and in some cases a second meter is installed. This often happens with larger systems (more than 2 or 3 kWp). Larger systems or combined systems that are maintained by the utilities are connected directly to the grid.

1.33.3.3.1 *Solar design*

To design with PVs the first set of questions are "Why do I want to integrate PV into the building?" and "Is PV needed for general energy supply, to make the building more independent, or to make a statement about the building's inhabitants?"

Large systems will be used for general energy supply. This means that large surfaces can be treated in an architectural way. Different types of modules, shapes, colors, and textures can be used to design the look of the building.

The main issues for a more independent building are the efficiency of the system and the generated yearly output. The size of the PV system will depend on this and the designer has to allow for a certain number of modules. The designer will probably design the building around the integrated system, otherwise the system will be something that is connected, but not integrated, into the building.

1.33.3.3.2 *Module placement and shadowing*

The first step in the design process will be to look at the number of modules, their dimensions, and the total dimensions of the system. All these aspects have to be integrated into the roof or façade. Shadowing of the modules is important. A module that is partly shaded will lose more efficiency than expected. Since all cells of all modules within a string are electrically mounted in series, one shaded cell will lower the current output of the complete string. Furthermore, the power dissipation in the shaded cell may cause too high cell temperatures. For that reason, modules contain one or more bypass diodes that create a current bypass for the shaded cell and for its neighboring cells. Very often a bypass diode covers 18 cells, and as a consequence, one shaded cell causes the power loss of totally 18 cells (N. van der Borg, private communication, 2011).

1.33.3.3.3 *Space required for balance of systems and interconnections*

The modules have junction boxes at the back that are connected by cables to the inverters. Space is also required for a junction box at the back. Together with the ventilation required at the back of the module, this means a gap between 20 and 50 mm (depending on the size of the junction box) between the back of the module and the mounting surface that can be used for both functions.

Space is also required for the inverters. For better efficiency, the best place for these inverters is near the modules. Inverters should be placed in a dry place, possibly inside the building. An AC cable has to be fed from the inverters into the grid via the meter.

Safety switches are required near the inverters in order to work on the PV system safely. Space for a second utility meter may be required near the first meter, unless a double meter can be used.

1.33.3.4 Design Process: Strategic Planning

A few procedural steps may be necessary to ensure that the PV system is successfully integrated into the design. A common rule is to integrate the PV system into the building process without disturbing that process.

Step 1: The first step is consultation with the authorities about local regulations, building permits, and the electrical connection to the grid.
Step 2: The second step is to consult the utility company about the grid connection, electrical diagrams, and the metering system.
Step 3: The third step is the internal meeting with all building partners. A kick-off meeting very early in the process may be useful to discuss the entire integrated PV system with the building contractor, the roofing company, the electrician, and the PV supplier.

There are many unique issues to resolve in installing BIPV. The main points in this meeting concern the responsibilities of each party in the building process. Who is responsible for the waterproofing of the roof – the roofing company or the PV installer? Who is responsible for electrical safety – the electrician or the PV installer? Who is responsible for safety on the site – the general contractor or the PV installer? All these aspects must be clearly defined and noted in advance.

Many PV suppliers offer turnkey contracts. This is easy for clients because they receive a complete working system for their money. However, the client is then responsible for the coordination between PV supplier and building contractor. Placing all responsibilities with the building contractor means an extra surcharge of perhap. 10% on the cost of the PV system. A good solution is to make the building contractor (general contractor) responsible for the PV system and negotiate a special fee for coordination and use of equipment (scaffolds and crane) from the building contractor.

1.33.4 BIPV in Architecture

This section aims to explain some basic thoughts about PV to nondesigners, from an architectural and design point of view.

Note: All specified power of PV systems is the power under standard test conditions and tilt which may be larger than the power delivered when installed in nonoptimum orientation required by the BIPV application.

1.33.4.1 Architectural Functions of PV Modules

For architects, the application of PV systems must be part of a whole (holistic) approach. A high-quality PV system can provide a substantial part of the building's energy needs if the building has been designed in the right way. However, the energy consumption for heating, ventilation, and air conditioning (HVAC), lighting, and occupant-related activities in an average house exceeds largely the possible energy production of a BIPV system. Therefore, the building should be designed and engineered in such a way that the building-related energy consumption will be substantially lower than in a conventionally designed building.

In a holistic approach, integrating a PV system not only means replacing a building material, thus physically integrating the PV system, but also aesthetically integrating it into the design. The integration also takes over other functions of the building's skin. Mounted on a sloped roof, profile systems mean that PV modules can be part of the watertight skin. As this is a solution which is debatable from the technical point of view, the system can also be mounted above an impermeable roof foil, thereby protecting the foil against UV light and direct sun. This extends the life span of the foil. This kind of system is also available for flat roofs. The Powerlight Company from Berkeley, CA (USA), introduced a PV system into the market that is glued on expanded polystyrene (XPS) insulation material. This type of warm roof construction (construction on the warm side of the insulation) system is very well suited to renovating large flat roofs.

A distinction can be made between literally integration of PV in the building skin (PV as a cladding element or integrated into the roof) and integration of PV in building components (awnings, shading devices, etc.) (see examples in **Figure 3**).

1.33.4.1.1 Roof-integrated PV

A PV system can be integrated into the roof in several ways. One choice is for the integrated system to be part of the external skin and therefore be part of an impermeable layer in the construction. In the early days of BIPV (1990s), several building projects were constructed on the basis of this principle. The other choice for roof mounting the PV system is above the impermeable layer. This is a more secure option but also not without some risk, as the impermeable layer has to be pierced in order to mount the system on the roof. Using PV modules as roof covering reduces the amount of building materials needed, which is very favorable for a sustainable building and can help reduce costs.

In addition to covering the complete roof with modules, there are also many products for small-scale use, for example, PV shingles and tiles. The small scale of these products (from 2 cells on a tile to around 20 cells on a look-alike tile) makes them very convenient for use in existing buildings or as do-it-yourself products.

(Semi)Transparent PV modules used as roofing materials serve as water and sun barriers and also transmit daylight. In glass-covered areas, such as sunrooms and atriums, sun protection on the roof is necessary in order to avoid overheating in summer. Transparent PV modules have the solar cells mounted between two transparent layers (mostly glass), while a certain distance has been kept between the different cells. The PV cells absorb 70–80% of the sun radiation. The space between the cells transmits enough diffused daylight to

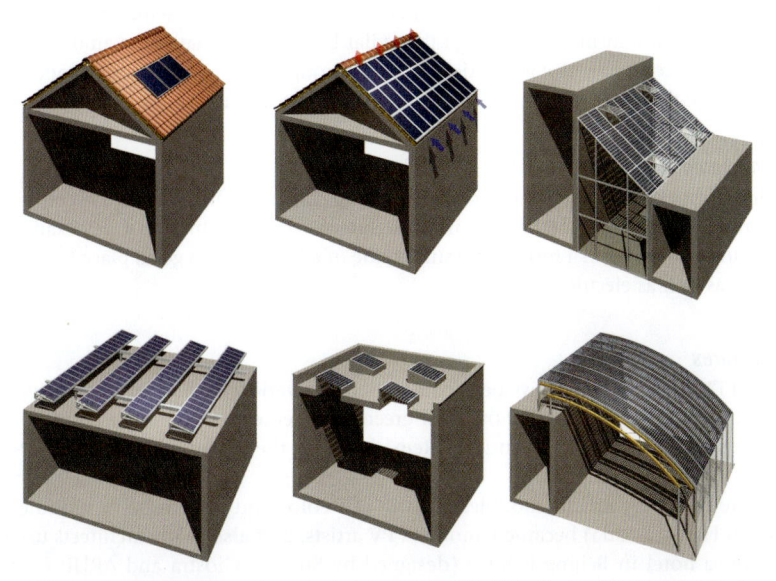

Figure 3 Pictures of different BIPV applications. Pictures from the training CD for IEA PVPS Task 7 [3]. Figure © Mart van der Laan.

Figure 4 PVT façade at RES UK in Kings Langley (UK). Photograph © Henk Kaan.

achieve a pleasant lighting level in the area. In order to increase the usage of daylight in the workplaces, transparent PV modules have been used instead of glass.

Of course, PV cells convert sunlight into electricity (with typical efficiencies of 6–20%) with the remainder of the solar energy being converted into heat. This residual heat can also be used to warm the building, for example, by designing an air cavity underneath the PV modules, through which warm air (heated by PV modules) is flowing. This hybrid collector provides warm air to the heating system in the home, which in this case, makes it a cost-effective use of the collector.

A relatively new application of PV combined with a thermal system is PVT: a PV module mounted on a solar thermal module. The residual heat is used to heat the water (or other liquid) in the thermal system. A demonstration project, which was financially supported by the European Commission, can be seen at the head offices of RES UK in Kings Langley, north of London (UK) (see **Figure 4**).

At the Netherlands Energy Research Foundation (ECN) in Petten (NL), Building 42 has a conservatory with 43 kWp BP solar roof-integrated transparent laminates that reduce light and sun transmission by around 70% as compared to glass. The conservatory therefore acts as a big parasol over the offices, protecting them from the sun while still providing enough daylight.

1.33.4.1.2 Façade-integrated PV

Façades are basically constructed using *in situ* bricklaying or concrete constructions, prefab elements, or structural metal façades that are mounted in place. Concrete constructions form the structural layer and are covered with insulation and a protective cladding. This cladding can be wood, metal sheets, panels, glass, or PV modules. For luxury office buildings, which often have expensive cladding, cladding with PV modules is not more expensive than other commonly used materials, for example, natural stone and expensive special glass. This cladding costs around $1500 m^{-2}, which is considerably larger than the cost of the PV module today.

Structural glazing or structural façades are constructed using highly developed profile systems, which can be filled with all types of sheeting, such as glass or frameless PV modules.

The development of transparent modules has gone further in the last 10 years. In the semi-transparent modules from the 1990s, the space between cells and the light transmission through the tedlar back foil stipulated the amount of light that came through. Starting with the Sunways cells, a complete new generation of light-through cells have been developed like Schott ASI Glass and Suntech MSK's light-thru and see-thru cells that can be used in roofs and structural façades.

1.33.4.1.3 PV in building components

Façades are very suitable for all types of sunshading devices, louvres and canopies. There is a logical combination between shading a building in summer and producing electricity at the same time. Architects recognize this and many examples of PV shading systems can be seen around the world. A terrace with a roof on the sunny side of a building is a good place for BIPV systems thus providing shade, protection from rain, as well as electricity.

1.33.4.1.4 PV art in structures

Freestanding applications of PV power systems have been constructed in a variety of more or less creative designs. Well known are solar sails that are landmarks for companies and show their green involvement. Many other types of freestanding construction designs to support PV power systems have been constructed. Remarkable are the constructions that show PV as a flower and in some cases track the sun.

On the small scale, there are many artistic modules both in cell color and pattern or in module form. Artists like Jürgen Claus (Germany) and Sarah Hall (Canada) became famous as PV artists, and also many architects use PV systems in an artistic way. The façade of the JingYa hotel in Beijing is huge (designed by Simone Giostra and ARUP for Greenpix). It is in fact a gigantic 2200 m^2 billboard with 2292 modules that collect the energy to lite the light-emitting diode (LED) billboard at night.

1.33.4.2 PV Integrated as Roofing Louvres, Façades, and Shading Devices

The designer may well use building elements such as canopies and shading systems to integrate PV systems, but will need to look in detail at shading and PV technology to understand the details of how to design this PV integration. One of the first things that the designer will discover is the fact that an efficient PV system is not automatically a good shading system. In general, a PV system on fixed louvres will need a certain mutual distance between the louvres to prevent shading of the cells, which may provide insufficient shading at a lower sun angle in spring and fall.

Heat load and daylight control systems can be combined with the integration of PV systems. Moreover, when the designer studies these aspects in detail, he or she will discover that PV systems can also be part of the thermal envelope or thermal system. Another example is the refurbishment of Building 31 of ECN in Petten (NL). In this project, the PV system is integrated into a louver system that supports the 35 kWp Shell Solar modules to keep out the summer heat and give less glare, and improve daylight conditions inside. To prevent shading of the modules by the upper louver, the dimensions of the louvers have to be almost twice the size of the modules.

Orientation is a major design issue for (green) buildings. The heat load of a building, the need for shading, and the design of façades all depend on the orientation. Orientation is also important for PV systems. Façade systems might be suitable in certain countries, especially at a northern (above 50° N) or a southern (below 50° S) latitude. When shading of the façade cannot be prevented, and for the countries in between these latitudes, sloped surfaces facing the sun or even horizontal surfaces might be more suitable. The designer's final choice will be based on orientation, amount of total annual (sun)light on the PV module, shading from surrounding buildings, and the aesthetics of the design. An important issue for the designer is to appreciate the blue, gray, or black cells and to become familiar with finding integration opportunities in the first draft design. Ideally, a PV system should not be added to a building but designed as part of the building.

1.33.4.3 Architectural Criteria for Well-Integrated Systems

In order to decide whether BIPV systems are well integrated, we need to distinguish between the following:

- Technical quality of the integration of the BIPV system, that is, the technical aspects of PV, cables, and inverters,
- *Building quality of the BIPV system.* Here we look for the quality of the integration of the system as a building element (part of the roof or the façade that is replaced by modules). The module and its integration must meet typical building standards, such as an impermeable layer or a structure strong enough to withstand wind or snow loads,
- *Aesthetic quality of the BIPV system.* This is the least scientific and most subjective part of judging BIPV systems. But the reality is that architecturally elegant, well-integrated systems will increase market acceptance.

Both the technical and building qualities of the PV system have been considered as preconditions. All installations in a building must function correctly.

Esthetic quality is not a precondition. The discussion of architectural values is very broad. The average architect is not yet convinced of the 'beauty' of a PV system on the building he/she designs. Some architectural journals [4] have criticized PV projects in, for example, the 250 kWp project in Sloten, Amsterdam (NL), and the 1.3 MWp project in Nieuwland, Amersfoort (NL), which are considered by many architects involved in PV projects as shining examples of good integration [5]. All the more reason this chapter shows some appealing examples and critically judges PV products.

Manufacturers of building elements and products may have a different view on the esthetics of PV. The Monier (Lafarge Braas) PV 700 roof tile system is a good example of how manufacturers look at their product. This system can be placed invisibly in between the flat Monier Stonewold tiles.

However, in product advertisements, the manufacturer has chosen tiles with contrasting colors instead of harmonious colors, thus ignoring the fact that integration, in most situations, should be discreet. After commercial introduction, the system was prepared for use with a standard roofing tile. This corrugated tile is an even bigger contrast to the flat PV elements. Technically speaking, this high-quality product has been integrated. Aesthetically, however, the product has not been integrated because of the contrast. Therefore, the architect, building inspectors, and clients might reject a PV system incorporating this product.

How can we discuss whether a BIPV system is well integrated? A group of architects within the IEA PV Power Systems (PVPS) Task 7 workgroup discussed this subject and came up with several criteria for judging the esthetic qualities of BIPV projects.

The criteria formulated by the IEA PVPS Task 7 workgroup for evaluating the esthetic quality of BIPV systems are as follows:

- natural integration,
- designs that are architecturally pleasing,
- good composition of colors and materials,
- dimensions that fit the gridula (gridula is not a common word outside architectural vocabulary; it denotes the grid that is used for the design that is a (sometimes hidden) part of the building), harmony, composition,
- PV systems that match the context of the building,
- well-engineered design,
- use of innovative design.

These architectural criteria need to be explained particularly to nonarchitects and manufacturers developing PV systems for integration into roofs and façades, who often believe that their systems fit perfectly.

- *Natural integration.* This means that the PV system seems to form a logical part of the building. The system adds the finishing touch to the building. The PV system does not have to be that obvious. In renovation situations, the result should look as though the PV system was there before the renovation.
- *Architecturally pleasing.* The design has to be architecturally pleasing. The building should look attractive and the PV system should noticeably improve the design. This is a very subjective issue, but there is no doubt that people find some buildings more pleasing than others.
- *Good composition of colors and materials.* The color and texture of the PV system should be consistent with the other materials.
- *Fit the gridula, harmony, and composition.* The dimensions of the PV system should match the dimensions of the building. This will determine the dimensions of the modules and the building grid lines used (grid = modular system of lines and dimensions used to structure the building, and should not be mixed up with the electrical grid).
- *Matching the context of the building.* The entire appearance of the building should be consistent with the PV system used. In a historic building, a tile-type system will look better than large modules. A high-tech PV system, however, would fit better in a high-tech building.
- *Well engineered.* This does not concern the waterproofing or reliability of the construction. However, it does concern the elegance of the details. Did the designers pay attention to detail? Has the amount of material been minimized? These considerations will determine the influence of the working details.
- *Innovative design.* PV systems have been used in many ways but there are still countless new ways to be developed. This is all the more reason to consider this criterion as well.

1.33.4.4 Integration of PV Modules in Architecture

The above section has discussed in brief the architectural criteria for judging a PV system as such. The following section focuses on the way in which these systems can be integrated into the architectural concept of the building.

The integration of PV systems in architecture can be divided into five categories:

1. Applied invisibly
2. Added to the design
3. Adding to the architectural image
4. Determining architectural image
5. Leading to new architectural concepts.

These categories have been classified according to the increasing extent of architectural integration. However, a project does not necessarily have to be of a lesser quality just because PV modules have been applied invisibly. A visible PV system is not always appropriate, especially in renovation projects with historic architectural styles. The challenge for architects, however, is to integrate PV modules into buildings properly. PV modules are new building materials that offer new designing options. Applying PV modules in architecture should therefore lead to new designs. In some of the selected projects, the design was based on this principle.

1. *Applied invisibly.* The PV system has been incorporated invisibly (and is therefore not architecturally 'disturbing'). The PV system harmonizes with the total project. An example is the Maryland project in the United States, where the architect tried to integrate PV modules into the design invisibly. This solution was chosen because the entire project concerned historic architecture. A modern high-tech PV module look would not be appropriate for this architectural style.
2. *Added to the design.* The PV system is added to the design. Building integration is not really used here, but this does not necessarily mean that architectural integration is also lacking. The 'added' PV system is not always visible either.
3. *The PV system adds to the architectural image.* The PV system has been integrated beautifully into the total design of the building, without changing the project's image. In other words, the contextual integration is very good.
4. *The PV system determines the architectural image.* The PV system has been integrated into the design in a remarkable and beautiful way and plays an important role in the total image of the building.
5. *PV system leads to new architectural concepts.* Using PV modules, possibly in combination with other types of solar energy, leads to new designs and new architecture. The integration of PV modules was considered on a conceptual level, which gives the project extra value.

1.33.5 Concluding Remarks

Building integration aims to reduce costs and minimize the requirement for land. To increase market acceptance it is important to show architecturally elegant, well-integrated systems. Moreover, building owners can show their environmental commitment with highly visible BIPV systems.

This means that there is a large potential for BIPV in the built environment. The main factors for successful integration are suitable buildings, (i.e., suitable orientation and lack of shadow) and a reason for building integration. For newly constructed sustainable buildings, BIPV will be part of the energy strategy. However, for existing buildings there must be a valid reason for integrating PV systems. Building renovation, including the roof and façade, often provides an opportune time for selecting BIPV.

The building or renovation process plays an important role in the success of BIPV. Can the building owner benefit from BIPV? If so, the owner will be willing to implement PV systems in the building plans. The architect or designer needs to have a good basic knowledge of BIPV and be able to integrate PV into the design. If architects do not understand the basics of PV, they will make mistakes that eventually have to be resolved during the installation process. The worst cases involve mistakes that cannot be resolved at the end of the building process and that result in a lower efficiency and quality of the PV system.

Is the utility company willing to cooperate? If not, the building owner will probably try to avoid difficulties in an already complex construction process.

The architect or designer should use all visible opportunities to integrate PV into the design in a highly esthetic way. The important issues are the architectural function of a PV module (replacing other building elements) and the visible aspects of modules, such as the dimensions, mounting system, form, and color of cells, back sheet, and frames.

To recognize these aspects, criteria have been formulated for judging building integration of PV. These criteria are useful for manufacturers and technicians who are involved with building integration from the engineering and technical aspects of the building process. However, it is the task and responsibility of the individual architect to adapt the criteria to his or her own esthetic standards.

References

[1] Pitts AC, Tregenza PR, and Coutts R (2000) Daylight, shading and the use of building integrated PV. *Proceedings of the Sixteenth European Photovoltaic Solar Energy Conversion Conference*, 1902–1905.

[2] Munro D (2009) Planning for urban-scale photovoltaic systems. In: Gaiddon, B, Kaan, H, and Munro, D (eds.) *Photovoltaics in the Urban Environment: Lessons Learnt from Large-Scale Projects*, pp. 5–20. London, UK: Earthscan.

[3] International Energy Agency (IEA) Photovoltaic Power Systems Task 7 'Building Integration of Photovoltaics', 1996–2001. CD ROM: 'Education and training material for architects', 2002.

[4] Wortmann A (1999) Sustainability on trial. Architecture and ecology. *ARCHIS Magazin*, February, p.8.

[5] Gaiddon, B, Kaan, H, and Munro, D (eds.) (2009) *Photovoltaics in the Urban Environment: Lessons Learnt from Large Scale Projects*. London, UK: Earthscan.

Further Reading

Hagemann I (2002) *Gebäudeintegrierte Photovoltaik*. Köln, Germany: Verlag Rudolf Müller.

Kaan H and Reijenga T (2004) Photovoltaics in an architectural context. *Progress in Photovoltaics* 12(6): 395–408.

Lloyd Jones D, Hattersley L, Ager R, and Koyama A (2000) *Photovoltaics in Buildings – BIPV Projects*. London, UK: ETSU, DTI.

Bonvin J, Roecker C, Affolter P, and Muller A (1997) *Proceedings of the Fourteenth European Photovoltaic Solar Energy Conversion Conference*. Barcelona, Spain, pp. 889–892.

Prasad D and Snow M (2002) *Designing with Solar Power: A Source Book for Building Integrated Photovoltaics (BIPV)*. Sydney, Australia: Images Publishing.

Schoen T, Prasad D, Toggweiler P, and Eiffert P (1998) Building with photovoltaics: The challenge for task VII of the IEA PV power systems program. *Proceedings of the Second World Conference Photovoltaic Solar Energy Conversion*. Vienna, pp. 2447–2451.

Strong S (1997) Photovoltaics in the built environment: A design guide for architects and engineers. DOE/GO-10097-436. Golden, CO: NREL.

1.34 Product-Integrated Photovoltaics

AHME Reinders, Delft University of Technology, Delft, The Netherlands; University of Twente, Enschede, The Netherlands
WGJHM van Sark, Utrecht University, Utrecht, The Netherlands

© 2012 Elsevier Ltd. All rights reserved.

1.34.1	**Introduction**	709
1.34.1.1	What Is PIPV?	709
1.34.1.2	The Structure of This Chapter	711
1.34.2	**Overview of Existing PIPV**	711
1.34.2.1	The Early Days of PIPV	711
1.34.2.1.1	Consumer products with integrated PV	711
1.34.2.2	Lighting Products with Integrated PV	712
1.34.2.3	Business-to-Business Applications with Integrated PV	712
1.34.2.4	Recreational Products with Integrated PV	713
1.34.2.5	Vehicles and Transportation	714
1.34.2.6	Arts	714
1.34.3	**Designing Products with Integrated PV**	716
1.34.3.1	Area Constraints in Design	716
1.34.3.2	Design Processes and PIPV	716
1.34.4	**Technical Aspects of PIPV**	717
1.34.4.1	PV Cells	717
1.34.4.2	Irradiance and Solar Cell Performance	720
1.34.4.2.1	Outdoor irradiance in relation to solar cell performance	720
1.34.4.2.2	Indoor irradiance	721
1.34.4.2.3	Solar cell performance at indoor irradiance	721
1.34.4.3	Rechargeable Batteries	722
1.34.5	**System Design and Energy Balance**	723
1.34.5.1	Irradiance	724
1.34.5.2	PV Power Conversion	724
1.34.5.3	Electronic Conversions	724
1.34.5.4	Efficiency of the Storage Device	724
1.34.5.5	Power Consumption	724
1.34.6	**Costs of PIPV**	725
1.34.7	**Environmental Aspects of PIPV**	725
1.34.8	**Human Factors of PIPV**	727
1.34.9	**Design and Manufacturing of PIPV**	728
1.34.10	**Outlook on PIPV and Conclusions**	730
References		730
Further Reading		732

1.34.1 Introduction

1.34.1.1 What Is PIPV?

Since the beginning of this century, product-integrated photovoltaics (PIPV) has become a new research field within photovoltaics (PV). Because of its recent emergence, this PIPV research field is still being developed and as such not all topics have been fully explored. For instance, a sound generic definition of PIPV does not exist yet. This is a somewhat surprising, because PIPV, in fact, already exists since the 1970s by the introduction of the solar-powered pocket calculator, while at the same time it is a considerable market. In 2006, 5% of the annual global shipments of PV that were in the segment of consumer products equaled a nominal power of 80 MWp of PV cells (Maycock P (2008), personal communication) (see **Figure 1**). This number has been steadily growing over the years and is still increasing.

However, the category 'consumer products' does not reflect all possible applications of PIPV. From an evaluation of studies that paid attention to the definition of PIPV [1–4], it can be summarized that PIPV meets the following criteria:

1. PV technology should be integrated in the product, that is, it should be positioned on the surfaces of the product.
2. The energy generated by the PV cells is used for the functioning of the product.
3. Users directly interact with the product in different scenarios of use.
4. Energy can be temporarily stored in a battery or other storage medium.

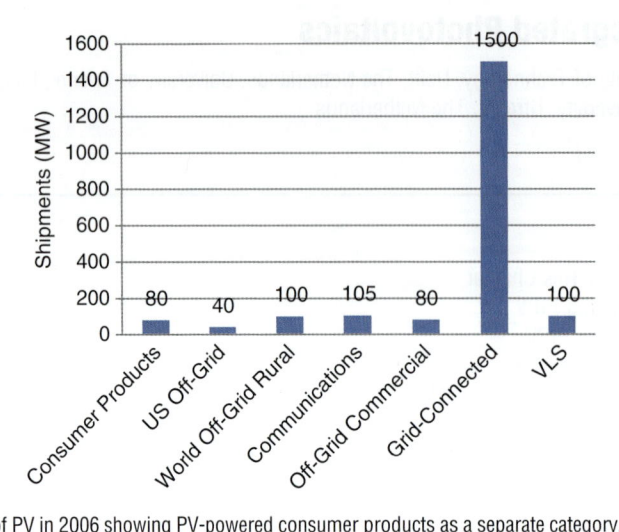

Figure 1 Annual global shipments of PV in 2006 showing PV-powered consumer products as a separate category. Source: Maycock P (2008), personal communication by Reinders, A.

5. The product is applied in a terrestrial setting.
6. Often, the product has mobile or portable features.

Due to aspect 5, the earthly application of PIPV, PV power supply for satellites and robots for the exploration of planets, will not be evaluated in this chapter. Adding to this, building-integrated photovoltaic (BIPV) is not considered either to be a large-scale version of PIPV since usually BIPV does not meet criteria 2 and 3, that is, electricity generated by BIPV is fed into the grid and a strong user interaction does not exist (yet) with grid-connected PV systems.

The main difference between PV systems and PIPV is that PIPV comprises product parts like casings as well as PV system components. And while the basic function of PV systems is to generate power, the functionality of PIPV is embedded in a product context. That is to say, PIPV provides functions that require electricity, for instance, lighting, sound, or transportation. Moreover, users can interact with PIPV by scenarios of use; that is, users impose load patterns on PIPV and they can affect the frequency at which solar cells are exposed to irradiance sources. Finally, products usually have a shorter lifetime than energy systems. Consumer products will be used for a few years, whereas PV systems are meant to survive life spans of at least 20 years without dramatic failure.

For the above-mentioned reasons, we consider PIPV with its specific generic features, as represented in **Figure 2**, as a separate category in the broad spectrum of PV applications.

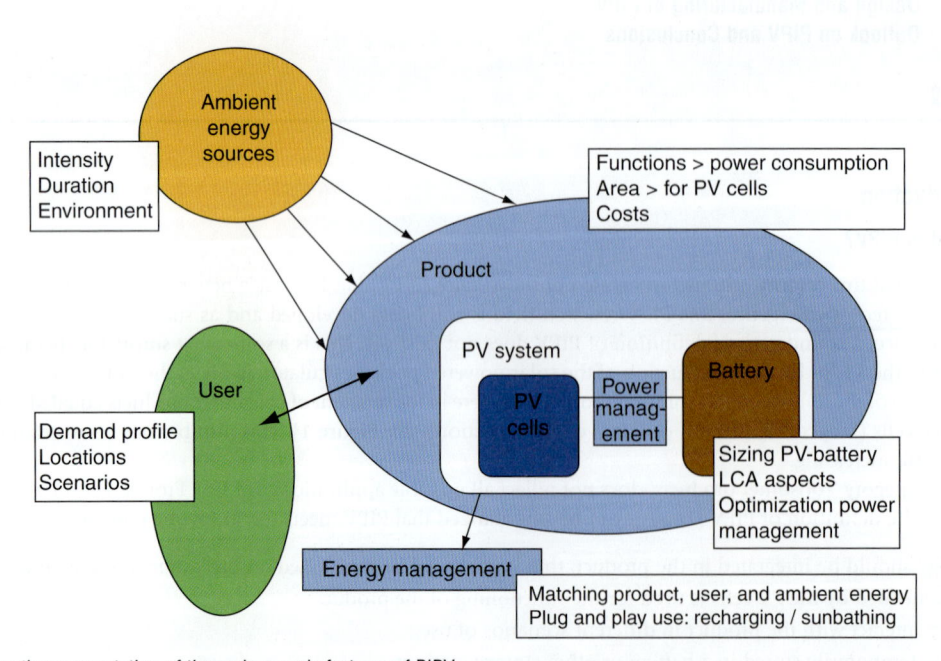

Figure 2 Schematic representation of the main generic features of PIPV.

1.34.1.2 The Structure of This Chapter

This chapter will present the following issues regarding PIPV. To start, in Section 1.34.2 we will give an overview of the existing solar-powered products. Next, the design of PIPV will be presented from the context of design processes (Section 1.34.3). Thereafter, we will discuss the technical aspects (Section 1.34.4), system design and the energy balance (Section 1.34.5), costs (Section 1.34.6), environmental aspects (Section 1.34.7), human factors (Section 1.34.8), and design and manufacturing (Section 1.34.9). Finally, we will end this chapter with an outlook on the future of PIPV and our conclusions (Section 1.34.10).

1.34.2 Overview of Existing PIPV

1.34.2.1 The Early Days of PIPV

In the 1950s, PV solar cells were developed at Bell Telephone Laboratories in the United States with the purpose to apply them in products that lacked permanent electricity supply from the mains. The solar cells were called silicon solar energy converters commonly known as the Bell Solar Battery [5]. Furnas [6] reported that "The Bell Telephone Laboratories have recently applied their findings in the transistor art to making a photovoltaic cell for power purposes. {....} and exposed to the sun, a potential of a few volts is obtained and the electrical energy so produced can be used directly or stored up in a conventional storage battery. {....} The Bell System is now experimenting with these devices for supplying current for telephone repeaters in a test circuit in Georgia. As to cost, one radio company has produced a power pack using this type of photoelectric cell for one of its small transistorized radios." The *Journal of the Franklin Institute* has mentioned already in Reference 7 that "these (*solar*) batteries can be used as power supplies for low-power portable radio and similar equipment." Expectations regarding the applicability of PV cells in products were high; Sillcox [8] reports on predictions by researchers of New York University "that small household appliances like toasters, heaters or mixers using the sun's energy might be in fairly widespread use within the next five years (i.e., 1960)." These predictions have not become reality, because at that time the costs of silicon PV cells were about $200 per Watt for high-efficiency cells [9] – where 12% was considered a high efficiency – and the costs of a dry cell to operate a radio for about 100 h would be less than a dollar [6]. Therefore, it was believed that the solar battery could be an economical source for all except the most special purposes. As such, by the end of the 1950s, silicon PV solar cells were applied as a power supply for satellites [10]. The Vanguard TV-4 test satellite launched on 17 March 1960 was the first satellite ever equipped with a solar power system, and it announced a new area of space technology with solar-powered satellites. It took about 20 years until interest in PIPV resumed again by the introduction of the first solar-powered calculators in 1978; the Royal Solar 1, Teal Photon, see **Figure 3** and the Sharp EL-8028.

1.34.2.1.1 Consumer products with integrated PV

Probably, the solar-powered pocket calculator has been the most apparent application of PV in commercially available consumer products in our daily lives during the past 30 years. Japanese manufacturers are leading in this field together with the production of PV-powered wrist watches with advanced electronic features.

Nowadays, we can commercially purchase PV-powered radios, solar-powered MP3 players, PV headsets, and automated lawn mowers. PV solar cells are widely applied in chargers used in cell phones and portable consumer electronics. These chargers are sometimes designed as a separate product solely meant to charge batteries in small electronic handhelds, sometimes they are

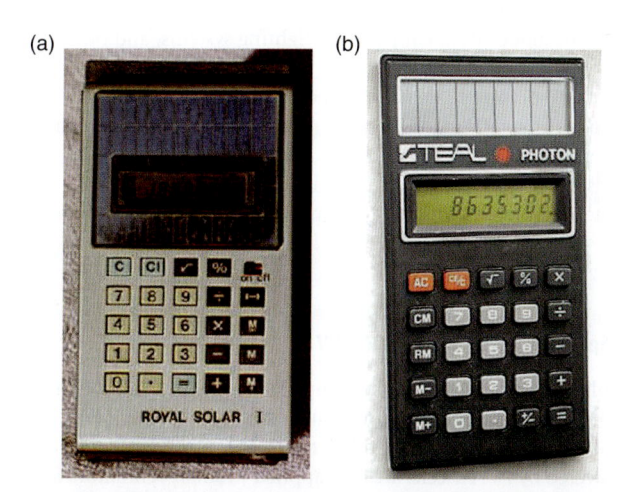

Figure 3 The first solar-powered pocket calculators appeared during the late 1970s on the market. Shown here are (a) the Royal Solar 1 and (b) the Teal Photon. Source: Vintage Calculators. http://www.vintagecalculators.com/ (accessed 23 October 2010) [11]. Courtesy of Nigel Tout & Guy Ball.

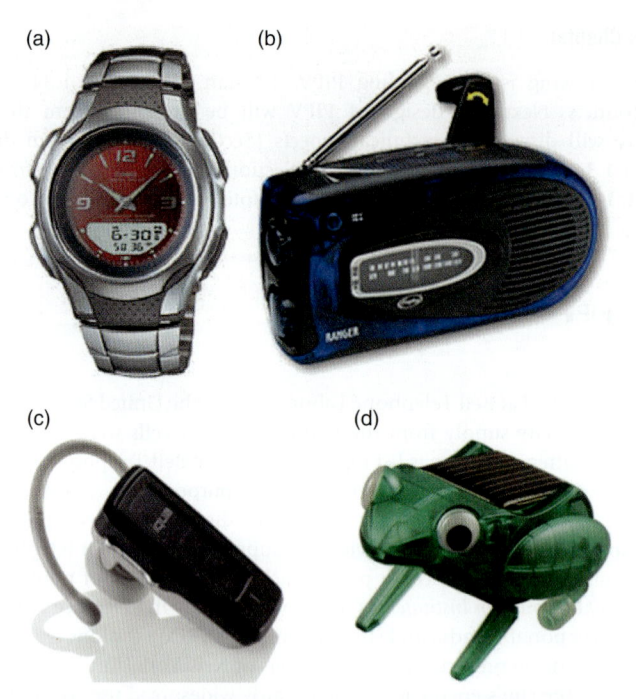

Figure 4 Examples of PIPV consumer products. (a) Solar-powered wrist watch by Casio. (b) Freeplay PV-powered radio. (c) Iqua 603 Sun bluetooth headset with integrated PV. (d) PV toy resembling a frog.

integrated in a handbag, backpack, or bicycle bag, allowing charging of small devices in the bag while being carried around outdoors exposed to sunlight.

Toys with integrated PV cells are rather common; they include small animals or cars that can move once exposed to light. Toys such as do-it-yourself (DIY) kits for the construction of PV-powered toy houses function sometimes as educational demonstration materials.

An interesting product concept for a PV-powered computer mouse had been explored in great detail and has been prototyped and tested in the framework of the Dutch SYN-Energy project [12–16]. Unfortunately, this product is not commercially available yet.

The nominal power of solar cells in the category 'consumer products' typically ranges from 0.001 W up to about 10 W (see **Figure 4**). The added value of PIPV in this category is portable energy supply. Some products have been designed for indoor use under artificial light conditions.

1.34.2.2 Lighting Products with Integrated PV

Since the mid-1990s, the emergence of energy-efficient light sources such as fluorescent lamps and light-emitting diodes (LEDs) in combination with PV technology resulted in numerous self-powered lighting products such as flash lights, ambient lights, lamps for bicycles, garden lights, pavement lights, indoor desk lamps, street lighting systems, and other products for lighting of public spaces [66, 78, 79].

In particular, in the past few years PV-powered lamps have been developed for markets at the bottom of the pyramid (BOP) in developing countries, fulfilling a need for an affordable, healthy, and clean alternative for candles, kerosene lamps, or fluorescent lamps that are powered by rechargeable car batteries [17–19].

The nominal power of solar cells in the category 'lighting products' typically ranges from 1 W up to about 100 W (see **Figure 5**). The added values of PIPV in this category are portable energy supply or remote lighting services. Some products have been designed for indoor use, wherein the energy is collected during daytime from sunlight either outdoors or indoors directly behind a glass window.

1.34.2.3 Business-to-Business Applications with Integrated PV

Since the 1990s, PIPV has been applied in business-to-business applications such as traffic control systems, traffic lights, and parking meters. Roth and Steinhueser [20] published an interesting status overview of PV energy supply in devices and small systems showing the technical and financial feasibility of PV in this market segment. Nowadays, public trash bins with automated control of trash collection are successfully powered by PV. PV cells are also applied in small ventilators for boats and cars that can be operated in stationary situations. In products for telecommunication, security, and environmental monitoring, PV systems can serve as an autonomous energy source. PV cells can be well integrated in surfaces of business-to-business products.

Figure 5 Examples of PIPV lighting products. (a) Garden light. (b) Ambient light corona. (c) Indoor table lamp by IKEA. (d) Street light for public spaces.

Figure 6 Examples of PIPV business-to-business products. (a) Parking meter in New York City. (b) Automated trash bin Big Belly.

The nominal power of solar cells in the category 'business-to-business applications' typically ranges from 10 W up to about 200 W (see **Figure 6**). The added value of PIPV in this category is automated operation of devices. Most products have been designed for outdoor use.

1.34.2.4 Recreational Products with Integrated PV

In this category, the following products can be found: PV-powered caravans and campers, solar-powered tents, solar-powered fountains, solar-powered pond equipment, and PV products for water sports. The nominal power of solar cells in the category 'recreational products' typically ranges from 50 W up to about 500 W (see **Figure 7**). The added value of PIPV in this category is mobile and remote energy supply. The products have been designed for outdoor use. At present, PIPV in recreational products is at the edge of financial viability; depending on the price developments of PV technology, this market segment might grow in the forthcoming decade.

Figure 7 Examples of PIPV recreational products: a conceptual design of a solar-powered tent.

1.34.2.5 Vehicles and Transportation

In the category 'vehicles and transportation', the following subcategories can be distinguished: bikes, boats, cars, and planes.

The nominal power of solar cells in the category 'vehicles and transportation' typically ranges from 200 W up to about 1500 W for electric cars, and several tens of kilowatts for planes (see **Figures 8–10**). The added value of PIPV in this category is mobile energy supply. The products have been designed for outdoor use only. Most of these PV applications are still in the demonstration phase.

PIPV in bikes is mainly meant to provide auxiliary power for navigation equipment and to charge batteries in the drive train. This application is not commercially available yet; however, at present, lead users are developing their own solutions for PIPV in bikes [23].

PV-powered boats can serve several different purposes: transportation of groups of people, recreation, research, and to participate in a contest called the Fryslan Solar Challenge. Gorter *et al.* [24] evaluated all PV-powered boats that have been developed. A typical PV-powered boat with a length of 7 m has a power of 1000 W and a 1 kWh battery; it can reach a speed of 10 km h^{-1} by electric propulsion in the water. Because of many environmental advantages and the high exposure of boats to sunlight, this application of PIPV seems promising.

A well-known example of a PV-powered vehicle is the golf cart. At present, Toyota explores the integration of solar cells in the roof of the Prius hybrid car. Adding to this, the World Solar Challenge that takes place every 2 years in Australia can be considered as an important incubator for future innovations of solar-powered electric vehicles. The required power of about 1500 W in combination with the costs of high-efficient solar cells and high-performance batteries are too high to expect commercial availability of PV-powered passenger cars on the short run.

Projects that aim at the realization of PV-powered air crafts such as Solar Impulse [22] have a highly innovative character [65]. The combination of lightweight constructions and a high power demand in the order of tens of kilowatts yields beautiful solutions, as shown in **Figure 10**.

1.34.2.6 Arts

The category 'arts' comprises products with decorative features and artistic objectives, for instance, PV jewellery, art for public spaces, and indoor art like a PV-powered chandelier (see **Figure 11**). In this field, the imaginary world merges with the possibilities provided by the PV technology and its aesthetic appeal. The PV power and the location of use can vary considerably in this category.

Figure 8 Examples of PIPV boats. (a) Recreational PV-powered boat, Aequus 7.0. (b) PV-powered ferry, Navette du Millenaire.

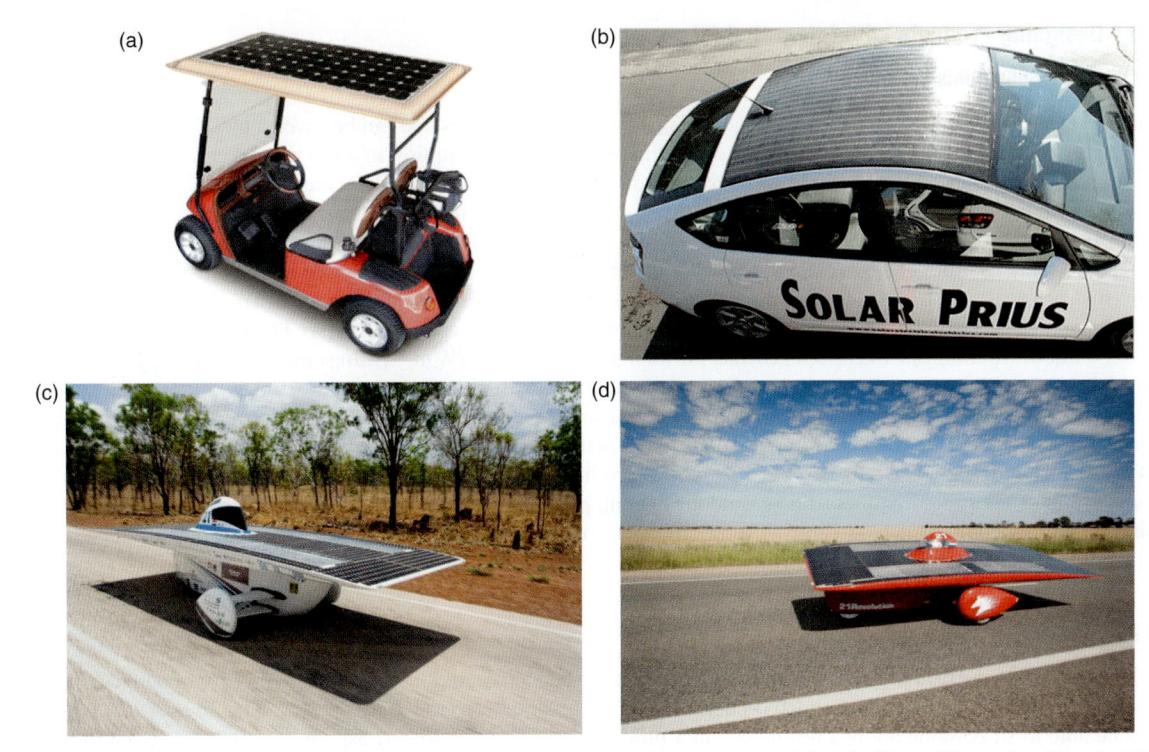

Figure 9 Examples of PIPV cars. (a) Golf cart. (b) Toyota Prius with PV roof. (c) Solar racing car of the Solar Team of University of Twente (2007). (d) Solar car of the Solar Team of University of Twente (2009). Courtesy: Solar Team (2010).

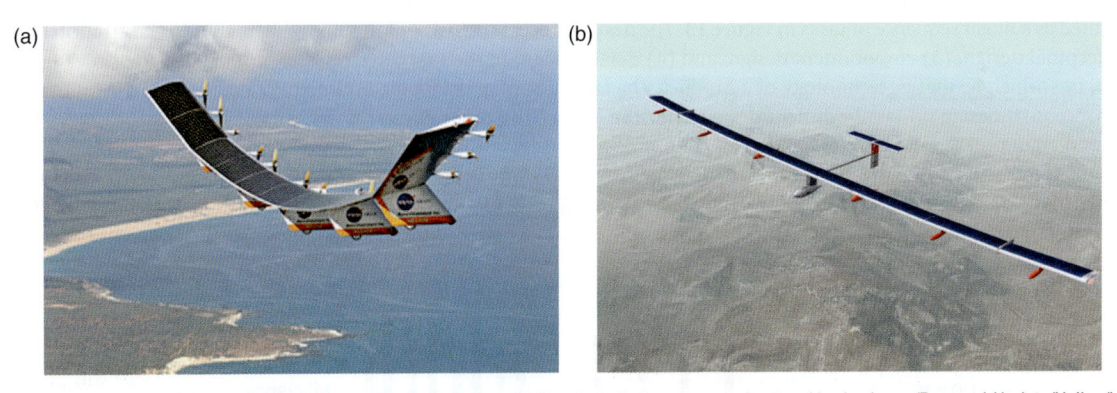

Figure 10 Examples of PIPV planes. (a) The Helios aircraft. Source: Helios. http://www.nasa.gov/centers/dryden/news/ResearchUpdate/Helios/index.html (accessed November 2010) [21]. (b) The solar impulse aircraft. Source: Impulse. http://www.solarimpulse.com/ (accessed November 2010) [22].

Figure 11 Examples of PIPV art. (a) The Brain in Graz (Austria). (b) The Sun Monument in Zahar (Kroatia) [25]. (c) A PV-powered chandelier [26], Photo: Bas Helbers, Virtue of Blue.

1.34.3 Designing Products with Integrated PV

1.34.3.1 Area Constraints in Design

A dominant factor in the design of PIPV is the required area on products surfaces that can be covered by solar cells. The typical area of solar cells in PIPV is determined by a trade-off of the internal power consumption of a product, its characteristic run time that results from the user behavior, the available area on the product, the PV technology applied, the storage capacity, and the irradiance conditions in the product's surrounding. For instance, in the case of PV-powered consumer products that are used indoors, area is constrained by the geometries of consumer products, which indirectly implies a very low internal power requirement of these products that can range from 0.005 mW up to a few Watts. Under indoor irradiance conditions of 10 W m^{-2}, c-Si PV cells perform with an efficiency of 10% or less. Assuming a run time similar to the charging time of batteries, an area of solar cells of 5×10^{-6} up to several square meters is required to meet the internal power requirement of these products (see **Figure 12**).

Under outdoor conditions, PV cells can generate power in the range of 120 W m^{-2} (using amorphous silicon) up to 270 W m^{-2} (using high-efficient III–V PV technologies) under STCs (which means standard test conditions that comprise an irradiance of 1000 W m^{-2}, an AM1.5 solar spectrum, and an ambient temperature of 25 °C). **Figure 12** gives an overview of the required solar cells area to meet the internal power consumption of products in the range from 0.005 mW up to 1000 W. It can be seen that an area of 5.4 m^2 of high-efficient solar cells is needed to meet a product's internal power consumption of 1000 W. PIPV that is used outdoors can meet the power requirements of outdoor lighting products, vehicles – such as cars, boats, and lightweight planes – portable accommodation – such as campers, caravans, and tents – and business-to-business applications – such as parking machines, traffic control, and public information displays.

1.34.3.2 Design Processes and PIPV

Only a few authors in the field of PIPV have discussed issues in the integration of PIPV from the perspective of designers and design processes. Here, we refer to studies by Randall [2], Kan *et al.* [68], Veefkind [80], Geelen *et al.* [27], and Reinders *et al.* (2009) [28, 29, 77]. To be able to successfully apply a technology in a product context, the following aspects should be included in the design process: (1) human factors such as ergonomics and customers' experiences with a product, (2) design and styling that fits to customers' lifestyles, (3) appropriate marketing of a product, and (4) societal aspects such as regulations and legislation. Product designers perceive each of these topics evenly decisive for the final success of a product. Hence, if these topics are required for a successful consumer product, they should be applied to products with integrated PV cells as well. As such, Randall [2] and Reinders *et al.* (2009) [28, 29, 77] agree on the applicability of generic engineering design processes [30] for the development of PIPV, represented as a linear sequence of tasks in **Figure 13**. The design process consists of four phases, namely, (1) clarification of the task, (2) conceptual design, (3) embodiment design, and (4) detail design. In the first three phases, product designers seek to optimize the working principle, that is, technology of a product. The last three phases involve optimizing the layout and form of a product. Thus, conceptual design and embodiment design form the connecting link between a technology – such as PV solar cells – and design and ergonomics, on the other hand [31].

Reinders and van Houten [31] mentioned that to foster innovation in PIPV during the design process, creativity and an integrated view are required. In this scope, innovation is not just a matter of implementing advanced technology in existing products but particularly a matter of sensing new opportunities that are created by new technology such as PV technology. To foster

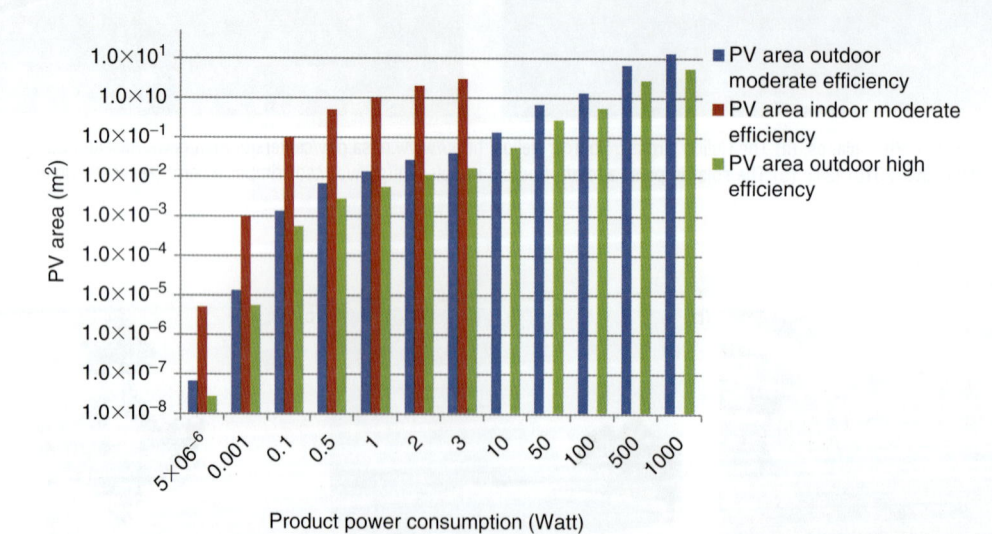

Figure 12 Area of PV solar cells required to meet the internal power consumption of products assuming an equal run time and charging time of batteries of 3 h under stationary conditions. Figures are based on an indoor irradiance of 10 W m^{-2} with 10% efficient c-Si cells (red bars), an outdoor irradiance of 500 W m^{-2} with 15% efficient c-Si cells (blue bars), and an outdoor irradiance of 800 W m^{-2} with 23% efficient III–V cells (green bars).

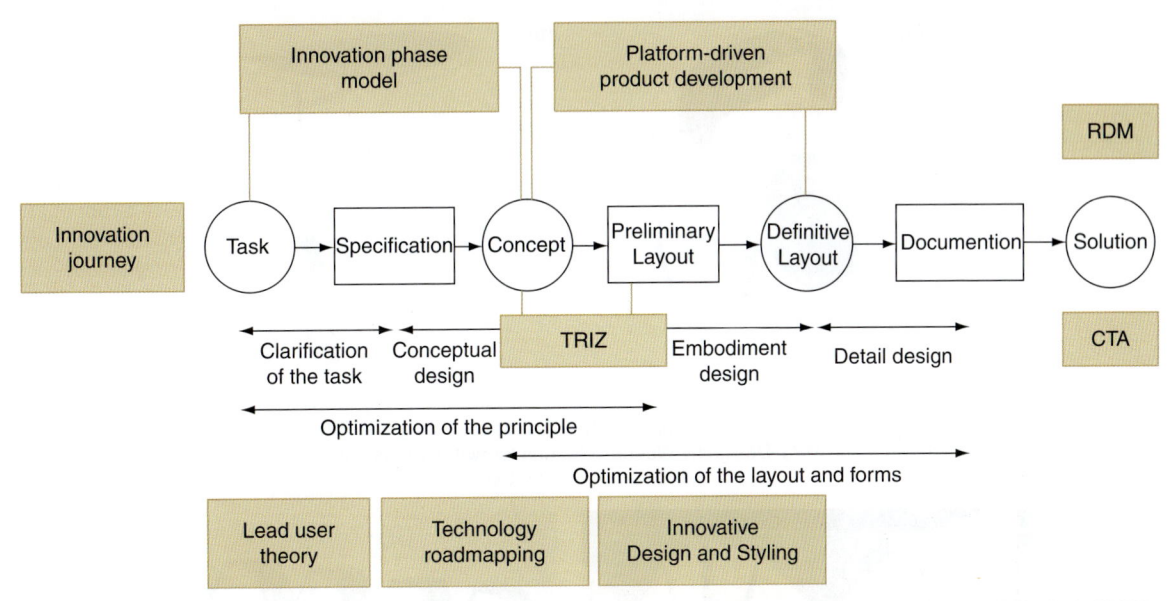

Figure 13 Linear design process in relation to innovation methods (brown boxes) that can be applied to innovate products in the field of PIPV.

innovation during a linear design process, several innovative design methods can be applied (indicated by brown boxes in **Figure 13**). These methods are the innovation phase model, lead user studies, platform-driven product development, risk diagnosing methodology (RDM), technology road mapping, TRIZ (a Russian acronym meaning 'theory of inventive problem solving'), innovative design and styling, innovation journey, and constructive technology assessment (CTA). From 2005 till 2010, Reinders conducted several case studies with the approach shown in **Figure 13**. A few resulting products are shown in **Figure 14**. The results show that the use of carefully chosen and applied industrial design methods can help to better integrate PV technology in products and can lead to surprising solutions.

1.34.4 Technical Aspects of PIPV

1.34.4.1 PV Cells

The efficiency of a PV solar cell is an important variable in the design of PIPV, because it determines the power that can be produced. The efficiency depends on the PV material and technology of the cell and the intensity of irradiance that impinges on a PV cell surface. In addition, the temperature of the PV cell and the spectral distribution of the light affect the efficiency.

If a solar cell is illuminated, a photocurrent I_{ph} is generated. This photocurrent is in most cases linearly related to the intensity of irradiance. Because of the semiconductor materials in the PV cell, the electric behavior of a PV cell can be represented by a current source in parallel with two diodes, D_1 and D_2. A series resistance, R_s, and a parallel resistance, R_{sh}, add to this electric circuit, as shown in **Figure 15**.

The electric behavior or current–voltage characteristic (I–V curve) of a PV cell is described by:

$$I = I_{ph} - I_{s1}\left(e^{\frac{q(V+IR_s)}{n_1 kT}} - 1\right) - I_{s2}\left(e^{\frac{q(V+IR_s)}{n_2 kT}} - 1\right) - \frac{V+IR_s}{R_{sh}} \quad [1]$$

Here I_{s1} and I_{s2} are the saturation currents of the two diodes and n_1 and n_2 are the quality factors of the two diodes. In general, n_1 will not deviate much from 1, and usually $n_2 = 2$ if no imperfections occur. V is the voltage over the circuit, T is the temperature, and k is the Boltzmann constant. **Figure 16** shows the I–V curve of a solar cell at a certain irradiation. It crosses the y-axis in the open-circuit voltage, V_{oc}, and the x-axis in the short-circuit current, I_{sc}.

In **Figure 16**, it is shown that the I–V curve of a PV cell has one point that delivers maximum power. This point is called maximum power point, P_{mpp}, and is characterized by V_{mpp} and I_{mpp}. This maximum power point is used to determine the efficiency, η:

$$\eta = \frac{I_{mp} V_{mp}}{AG} \quad [2]$$

Here, AG is the optical power falling onto the solar cell, with A the solar cell area and G the irradiance. Please note that from the two-diode model it follows that if the operational voltage, V, of the cell deviates from the maximum power point settings, the efficiency will drop accordingly.

718   Applications

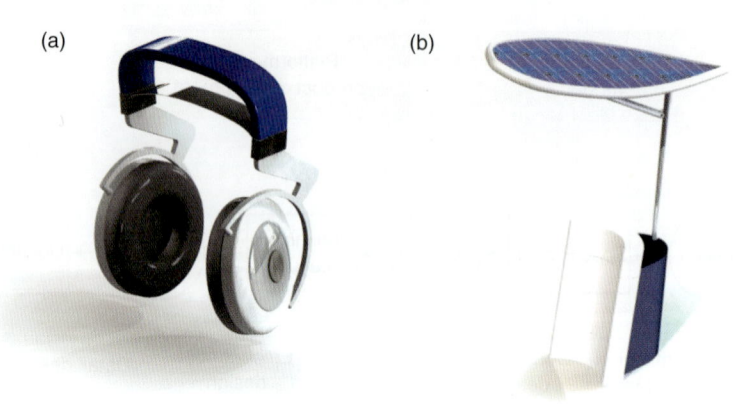

(a) Artist's rendering of a PV-powered headphone with integrated FM radio and MP3. Design by Weeda and Prinsen.

(b) Artist's rendering of a PV-powered cooling unit for water sportsmen. Design by Doorn and Everlo.

(c) Artist's rendering of a sunshade made from flexible PV foil with integrated LEDs by Bos and Hartman. Artist impression of use during night.

(d) Artist's rendering of PV-powered bricks that emit LED light, by Jong and de Beurs.

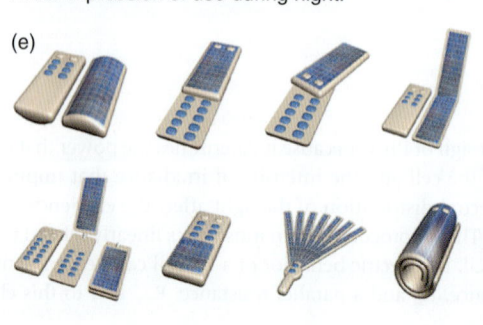

(e) Geometric design variations of a PV-powered remote control by Heeres and Kerkhoffs.

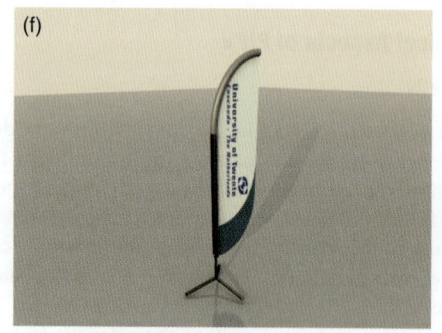

(f) Artist's rendering of a PV-powered beach flag by Groen and Verduijn.

Figure 14 Conceptual products with integrated PV systems resulting from case studies on innovative design of PIPV [28, 29].

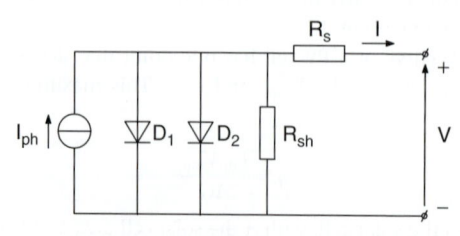

Figure 15 Equivalent circuit of a solar cell represented in the two-diode model.

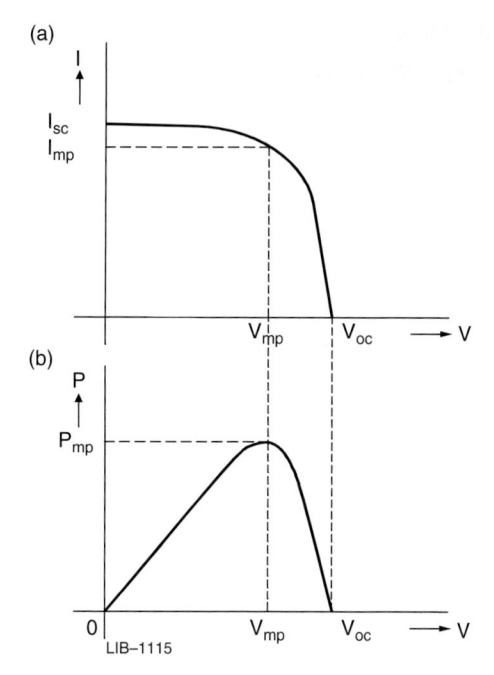

Figure 16 (a) The current–voltage characteristic of a solar cell. (b) The power–voltage characteristic of a solar cell.

Single values of efficiencies of solar cells are usually efficiencies at STC conditions, η_{STC}, which means that the value is measured at so-called STCs, which represent $1000\,W\,m^{-2}$ irradiance, AM1.5 spectrum, and 25 °C cell temperature.

PV cells are made from several different PV technologies based on semiconductor materials. These materials yield various efficiencies. The most well-known solar cell technology is the single-crystal silicon wafer-based solar cell, indicated by c-Si. It has improved significantly in the past 30 years, and today, it is the dominant solar cell technology. Crystalline silicon solar cell technology represents also multicrystalline silicon solar cells, indicated by m-Si. Both c-Si and m-Si are the so-called first-generation solar cells.

Besides this, second-generation solar cells have been developed with the intention to find a cheaper alternative for crystalline solar cell technology by using less material. For this reason, they are called thin-film solar cells. Several semiconductor materials allow for the production of thin films, namely, copper indium gallium diselenide ($CuInGaSe_2$), abbreviated to CIGS; cadmium telluride, CdTe; hydrogenated amorphous silicon (a-Si:H); and thin-film polycrystalline silicon (f-Si). Thin-film PV cells can also be made from organic materials. In the first place, dye-sensitized cells (DSCs) consist of titanium oxide nanocrystals covered with organic molecules. Second, polymer organic solar cells are made from conducting polymers. A third group of solar cells is made from compounds of the elements Ga, As, In, P, and Al. The entire group is called III–V technology, and the specific cells are named after their compounds, for instance, GaAs, GaInP, or InP. These PV cells have been developed for space applications because of their high efficiency. They are also increasingly being applied in terrestrial concentrator systems. **Table 1** shows typical efficiencies for the above-mentioned PV technologies.

Table 1 Characteristic efficiencies and spectral response range of several PV technologies

Type of PV cell	Record lab cells, η_{STC} (%)	Commercially available, η_{STC} (%)	Spectral range (nm)
c-Si	25	14–17	350–1200
	24.2		
m-Si	20.4	14–16	350–1200
a-Si	12.5	8–10	300–800
Nano-, micro- or poly-Si	16.5	11–13	300–800
CIGS	20.3	12–17	300–1200
CdTe	16.7	10.7	350–850
III–V three junction	43.5 (under 300 suns)	27–30	300–1250
III–V single junction, thin film	26	21–23	300–1000
DSC	11.1	8–10	300–800
Polymer	8	3–5	300–800

Adapted from Kan SY (2006) SYN-Energy in solar cell use for consumer products and indoor applications. Final Report 014-28-213, NWO/NOVEM. Delft, The Netherlands: Technical University of Delft [1], updated with Kazmerski L (2010) *Best Research Cell Efficiencies*. Golden, CO: NREL [32].

1.34.4.2 Irradiance and Solar Cell Performance

1.34.4.2.1 Outdoor irradiance in relation to solar cell performance

Irradiance, G, is the power density of light expressed in $W\,m^{-2}$. In daytime, outdoor irradiance is predominantly determined by sunlight. In **Figure 17**, the spectral distribution of the sunlight falling onto the earth surface is shown. This spectrum resembles the spectrum of a black body with a temperature of 5700K and is determined by the path length of the sunlight through the atmosphere (the air mass, AM): AM0 is the extraterrestrial spectrum. The various 'dips' in the spectra arise because of absorption in the atmosphere, among others by water vapor. In addition, the spectrum is being influenced by scattering taking place in the atmosphere.

The efficiency of a solar cell depends on the spectral composition of the light. Therefore, the efficiency is being defined at a standard spectrum. This is the AM1.5 standard spectrum for terrestrial applications and the AM0 standard spectrum for space travel applications. For terrestrial PV solar cells, STCs represent an irradiance of $1000\,W\,m^{-2}$, a spectrum AM1.5, and a cell temperature of $25\,°C$.

Figure 18 shows the measured efficiency curves in the maximum power point for c-Si and m-Si solar cells [33]. It can be seen that the efficiency steeply drops with respect to the STC efficiency with decreasing irradiance, which is confirmed by the two-diode model.

The sensitivity of each solar cell strongly depends on the wavelength of the light falling onto the solar cell. The sensitivity as a function of wavelength is called the spectral response (expressed in $((A\,m^{-2})/W\,m^{-2}))$ or in $(A\,W^{-1}))$ and is quantified by measuring the short-circuit current occurring at illumination with a monochromatic light beam. **Table 1** shows a range of spectral response of different cell technologies, which is determined by the band gap of the semiconductor material and the charge generation and recombination processes that internally take place in a solar cell. **Figure 19** shows the spectral response curves of samples of a-Si and c-Si under an AM1.5 spectrum by Reich et al. [34, 40].

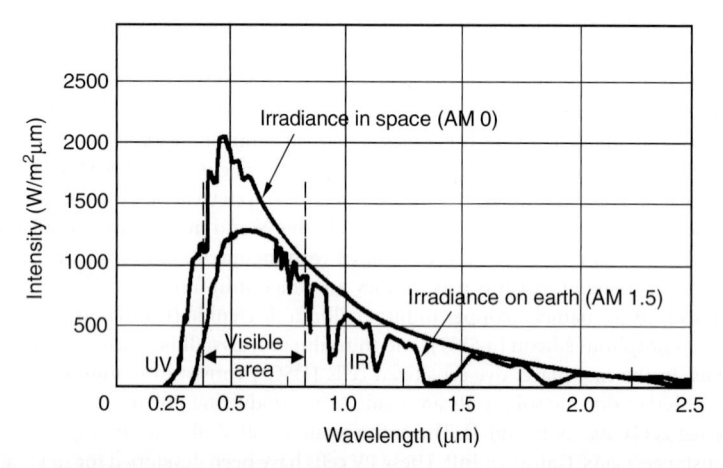

Figure 17 The wavelength-dependent AM0 and AM1.5 spectra of sunlight.

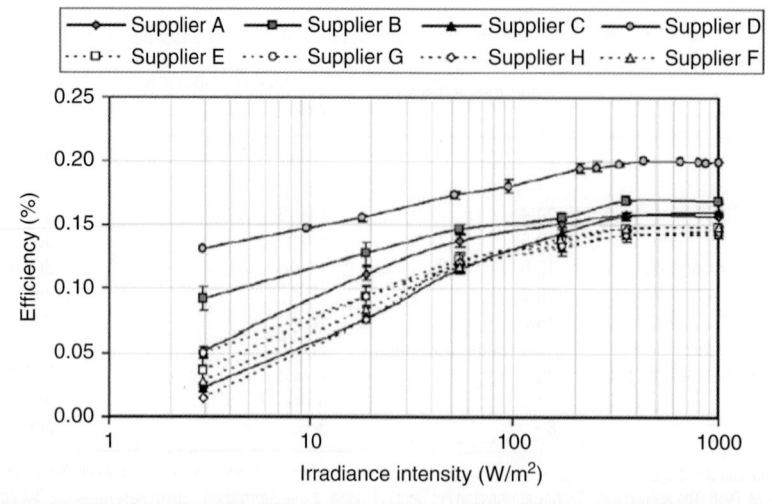

Figure 18 Measured irradiance intensity-dependent efficiencies of various Si solar cells by Reich et al. [15]. Measurements at $1000\,W\,m^{-2}$ reflect STCs below $1000\,W\,m^{-2}$, the intensity of the AM1.5 is linearly reduced.

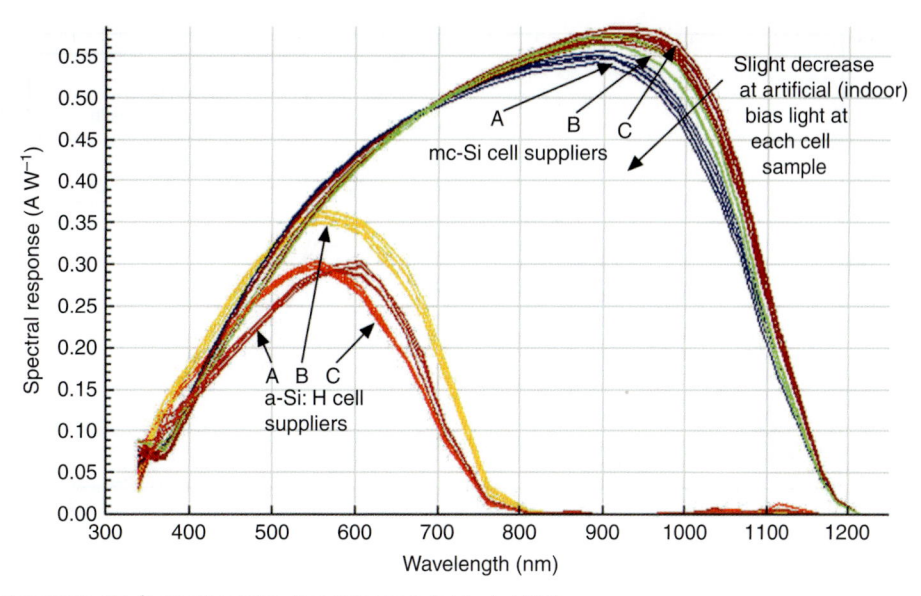

Figure 19 Spectral response of a-Si samples and m-Si samples from Reich *et al.* [40].

1.34.4.2.2 Indoor irradiance

Indoor irradiance usually consists of a mixture of sunlight that enters a building through windows and skylights, and artificial light originating from different light sources, such as incandescent lamps, fluorescent lamps, and LEDs.

Müller [35] has conducted an extensive research on the measurement of indoor irradiance. She reports that though indoor irradiance can exceed $500\,W\,m^{-2}$, the basic orders of magnitude typically are about 1–$10\,W\,m^{-2}$ with worst-case scenarios in the winter without the use of artificial light in the range of $0.1\,W\,m^{-2}$. For surfaces orientated to the window, the solar radiation will contribute most, and for surfaces orientated to the electric light, the latter will contribute most of the radiation. These features can be important concerning the dominating spectral distribution of irradiance that can be converted to electricity by PV solar cells. Namely, the spectral range of irradiance from sunlight is from 300 up to 4000 nm, whereas the spectral distributions of artificial light are more narrow. For instance, artificial light emitted by incandescent lamps has a spectral range of 350 up to 2500 nm, by LEDs from 400 up to 800 nm, and by fluorescent lamps from 300 up to 750 nm [37]. In **Figure 20**, measured spectra of incandescent light sources and fluorescent lamps are shown.

1.34.4.2.3 Solar cell performance at indoor irradiance

Several studies have been devoted to solar cell performance under weak light or indoor irradiance conditions. These studies were conducted by Randall [2], Randall and Jacot [14], Reich *et al.* [34], Girish [38], Gong *et al.* [39], and Reich *et al.* [40].

Here we would like to refer to the most recent study in this field by Müller [35, 71–73], who has simulated and measured the performance of different PV materials for different spectral distributions in order to identify maximum efficiencies and the optimum technology under the specific light spectra (**Figure 21**) [35].

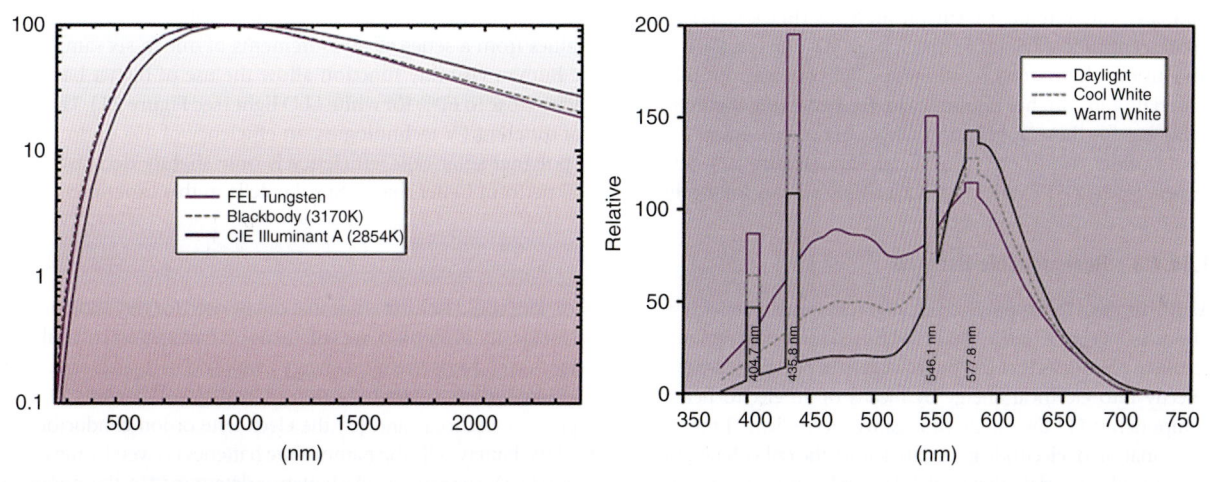

Figure 20 Spectra of incandescent lamps and typical fluorescent lamps from Ryer [37].

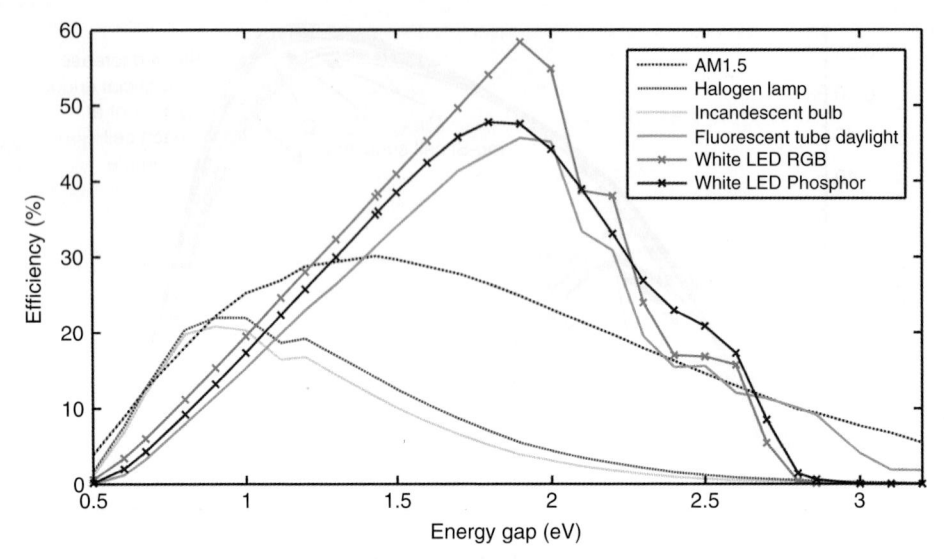

Figure 21 Calculated efficiencies for PV cells as a function of their band gaps for different radiation sources [35].

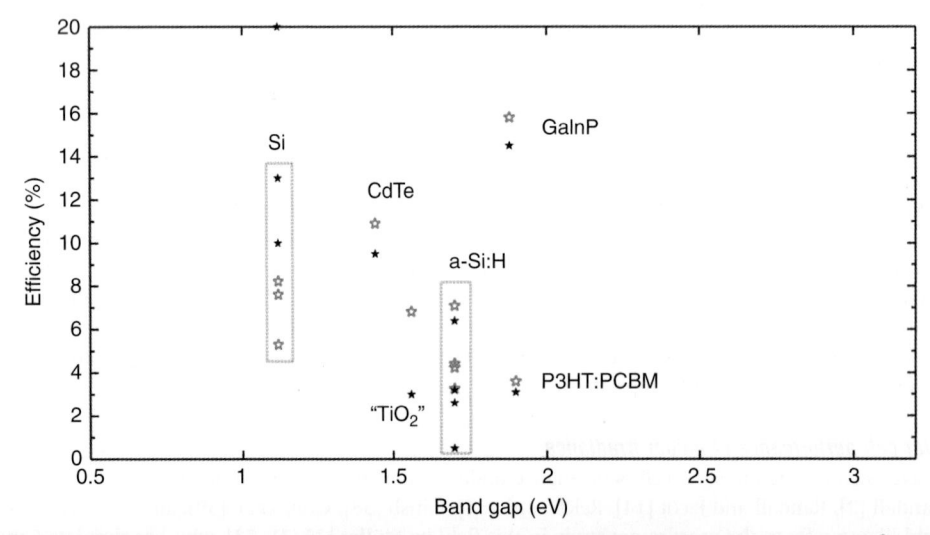

Figure 22 Measured efficiencies of a series of measurements of different sample groups at STC (solid symbol) and at 9.1 W m^{-2} OSRAM Lumilux 840 W fluorescent tube daylight lamps, 25 ± 2 °C (open symbol). Here TiO$_2$ stands for DSCs and P3HT:PCBM for polymer solar cells [35].

Although the measured devices were far from their ideal efficiency, all devices were within the theoretical predictions. **Figure 22** compares measurement results from STCs (black stars) to the results from measurements at 9.1 W m^{-2} OSRAM Lumilux 840 W fluorescent tube daylight lamps, 25 ± 2 °C. The results are average values from a series of measurements of one to six samples. In conclusion, the narrow band indoor light sources optimized for the human visibility function allow the use of higher band gap materials and a higher photon yield, thus enabling theoretical efficiencies close to 60% for white LED light (see **Figure 21**). The ideal band gap for these application ranges between 1.9 and 2 eV [35]. For different PV technologies, an efficiency of 4% up to 16% is found under conditions of artificial light (**Figure 22**). Surprisingly, polymer solar cells' efficiency is only slightly decreased with respect to their STC efficiency. Crystalline silicon solar cells in general perform better than a-Si solar cells in this experiment.

1.34.4.3 Rechargeable Batteries

A PIPV product that is powered by solar cells needs an energy storage device. This could be a capacitor that can be used for very short periods of storage [41] or a battery that can be used for longer periods of energy storage. In this section, we will focus on batteries, in particular on secondary batteries that can be recharged. In principle, a battery is a device that converts chemical energy contained in its active materials directly into electrical energy by means of an electrochemical oxidation–reduction (redox) reaction. A battery cell consists of three components: (1) the anode or negative electrode, (2) the cathode or positive electrode, and (3) the electrolyte or ion conductor. The combination of electrode materials defines the cell voltage and capacity of the battery cell. The name of the batteries is given by the anode and cathode materials, that is, nickel metal hydride (anode MH, cathode NiOOH). The capacity of a battery is determined by the amount of active materials in the cell and is expressed as the total quantity of electricity involved in the electrochemical reaction in terms of coulombs or ampere-hours. In **Table 2**, characteristic specifications are given for cells of different rechargeable batteries that are applied in PIPV.

Table 2 Practical specifications of cells of different rechargeable batteries that can be applied in PIPV

Battery type	Nominal cell voltage (V)	Specific energy (Wh kg^{-1})	Energy density (Wh l^{-1})	Cycle life, 20% fading (cycles)	Efficiency (%)
Sulfuric lead–acid	2.0	30–50	80–90	200–500	85
Nickel–cadmium	1.2	35–80	100	1500	80–95
Nickel metal hydride	1.2	75–120	240	300–500	
Lithium ion	4.1	110–160	400–500	500–1000	95–98
Lithium/manganese dioxide	3.0	100–135	265–350	300–500 2000	

Part of data adopted from Flipsen SFJ [42] and Kan [36].

1.34.5 System Design and Energy Balance

PV system design in a product context is a rather complex task because of the interdisciplinary character of product development, as discussed in Section 1.34.3. System design not only concerns an appropriate energy balance of the system components but also addresses issues related to manufacturability, costs, safety, operating temperatures, and environmental aspects.

Finally, the integration of PV systems in products should result in customer benefits like

1. a better functionality, increased comfort, or autonomy of a product
2. less dependency from the electricity grid
3. smaller batteries
4. fewer user interaction for recharging batteries [3].

Figure 23 aims to represents system design during product development of PIPV, by showing the relationships between the user, the product, and the integrated PV system and indicators that might be relevant for the decision making in the conceptual design stage.

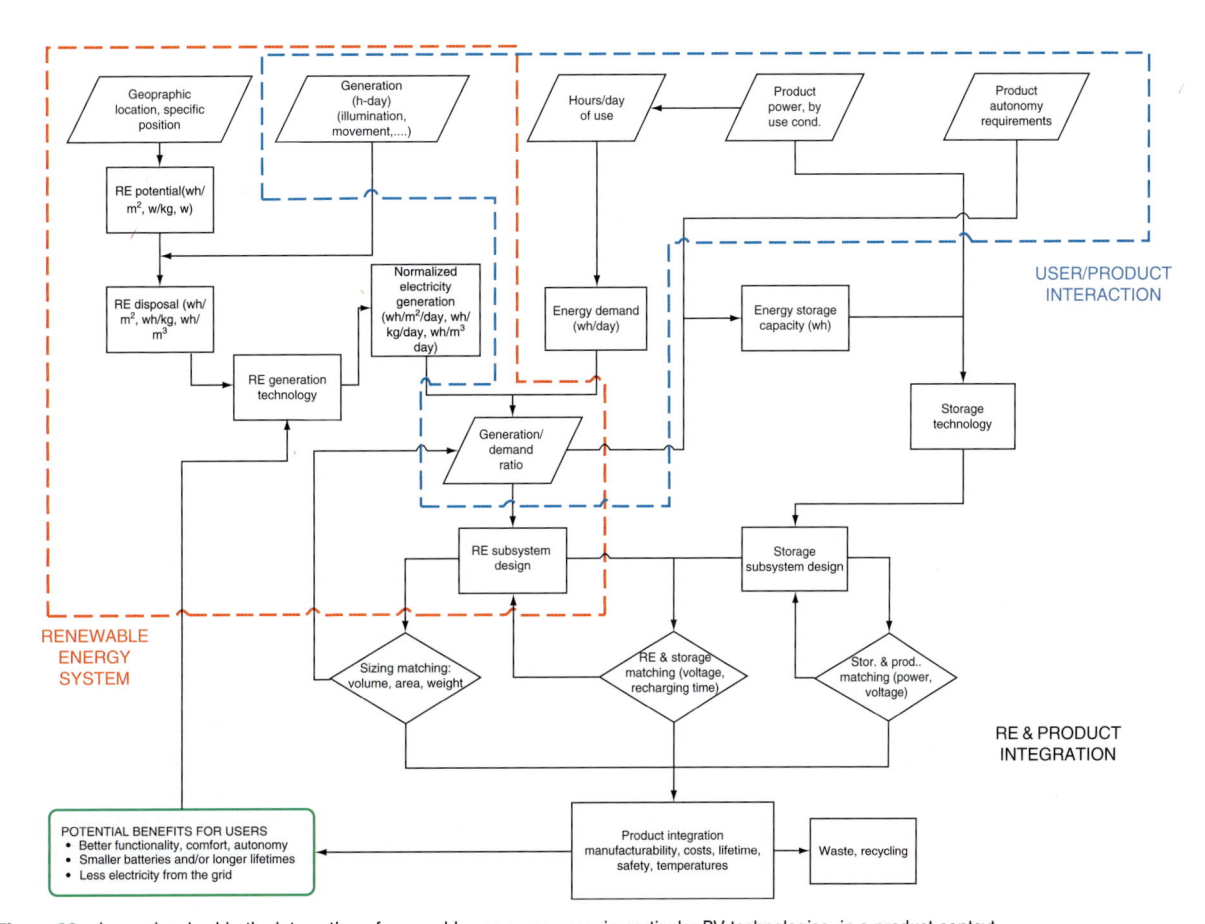

Figure 23 Issues involved in the integration of renewable energy sources, in particular PV technologies, in a product context.

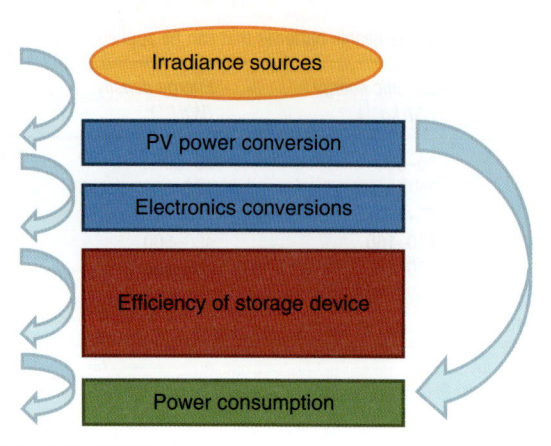

Figure 24 Flow scheme showing the energy chain of PIPV.

These indicators will be related to energy matching, final weight of the product, area required, volume, customer benefits, costs of the product, and safety and environmental indicators. Apart from this, it should be possible to produce a product with existing manufacturing technologies.

Within this vast context, the energy balance of a certain combination of PV system components, product, and user can be estimated, using the flow scheme shown in **Figure 24**. Next, we will give some guidelines for estimations of the energy balance of a PIPV.

1.34.5.1 Irradiance

Irradiance can be measured on locations of expected use of a PIPV. On the other hand, it might be convenient to simulate irradiance during the design process: Reinders [43], Reich *et al.* [15, 44, 75], and Tiwari and Reinders [45] developed different methods to determine irradiance in CAD tools. Moreover, at present the widely used design environment 3D Studio Max comprises a module with the established Perez model for irradiance simulation.

1.34.5.2 PV Power Conversion

The conversion of irradiance, G, should – at least – include the irradiance dependency of the efficiency, η_{PV}, of solar cells. In a certain period of time, the energy E_{PV} that can be produced by the solar cells is given by

$$E_{PV} = \int G(t) \times \eta_{PV}(G) dt \qquad [3]$$

1.34.5.3 Electronic Conversions

Power electronics in the device have a certain conversion efficiency that should be taken along in the estimates of the energy balance, in particular in low-power devices.

1.34.5.4 Efficiency of the Storage Device

The efficiency of a battery in a PIPV is affected by the charging patterns of the PV cells [69, 70]. Therefore, Gibson and Kelly [46] recommend determining the solar energy to charge conversion efficiency and to optimize it. This efficiency is given by

$$\eta_{PV-CC}(\%) = \frac{\text{average voltage (V)} \times \text{charge increase (Ah)}}{G(W\,m^{-2}) \times PV\text{ area }(m^2) \times \text{time interval (s)}} \qquad [4]$$

1.34.5.5 Power Consumption

A reliable estimate of the power consumption of future users of PIPVs can be based on questionnaires and a quantitative insight of the power required for the different functions of a PIPV. The variability between user behavior can be used to set a minimum and maximum value for the area of PV cells needed to fulfill the energy demand of the future users, as indicated in **Figure 23**.

1.34.6 Costs of PIPV

Studies on the costs of PIPV that are publicly available are rare. Since electricity produced by solar cells is internally consumed in the product, common cost indicators in the field of solar energy such as 'levelized costs of electricity' (LCOE) do not apply to PIPV. However, cost calculations of PIPV should comply with generally acceptable approaches toward cost estimates of product manufacturing, purchase costs, and costs of ownership. Costs of PIPV should also refer to the functions provided by the product.

One study [18] regards costs of ownership of PV-powered LED lamp and compares these findings with different options for lighting in a BOP market in Cambodia [76]. (In economics, the BOP is the largest, but poorest socioeconomic consumer group. In global terms, this is the 2.5 billion people who live on less than $2.50 per day.) It is shown here as an illustration for cost calculations of PIPV that refer to the products' function, namely, providing light.

A PV-LED product consists of one or more LEDs, a rechargeable battery, and a small PV module. The LED lamp itself is embedded in a luminaire, which often has an aesthetically pleasing appearance. A small PV panel of typical 1 Wp could provide enough electricity for 3–4 h of lighting by a 1 W LED in most of the developing countries. The retail price of a small PV-powered LED lamp, including a rechargeable battery of up to 10 Wh, would be in the order of $12 up to $16. Compared with PV lanterns with compact fluorescent lamps (CFLs) – which cost about $60–80 – an LED lamp is reasonably cheap. However, compared with a kerosene lamp of $1, it is still a relatively high investment for poor families. After purchase, operating costs determine the costs of ownership of a certain option for lighting. Costs of operation comprise replacements of spare parts and costs of energy to power light, such as electricity for grid-connected (GC) lighting and fuel for kerosene lamps. **Figure 25** presents for several lighting options the costs of ownership. It shows that grid-connected lighting is the cheapest option with $0.04 per 1000 lux-hours, but because access to the electricity often lacks, autonomous options for lighting have to be used. **Figure 25** shows that kerosene lamps have very high costs of ownership of $12.00 per 1000 lux-hours, mainly due to fuel consumption. Halogen flashlights with costs of $3.40 per 1000 lux-hours require frequent replacement of primary batteries. The costs of ownership of a rental lamp (called Proseed) comprising a 1 W LED and a rechargeable battery are mainly due to the rental costs. A 1 W PV-LED lamp is the cheapest option of two PV-powered lamps, as shown in **Figure 25**. With costs of ownership of $0.22 per 1000 lux-hours, it is the cheapest option for autonomous lighting available.

1.34.7 Environmental Aspects of PIPV

Environmental aspects of products with integrated PV cells have not been evaluated extensively so far. As such, information about characteristic environmental indicators such as the embodied energy, the energy payback time, and CO_2 emissions of PiPV is not available. These environmental aspects can be determined by a life-cycle analysis (LCA). LCA is the process of evaluating the potential effects that a product, process, or service has on the environment over the entire period of its life cycle. The International Organization for Standardization (ISO) has defined LCA as "a compilation and evaluation of the inputs, outputs and the potential environmental impacts of a product system throughout its lifecycle" [47]. The technical framework for LCA is illustrated in **Figure 26**.

PV lighting products can deliver a high quality of service in developing countries according to recent studies [19]. In general, it is assumed that PV lighting products have a better environmental profile than alternative lighting services. Though LCA data for PV cells seem to converge [48], still many uncertainties exist regarding the modeling of batteries in LCA studies [49, 50] due to variable charging regimes, lack of accurate data of materials used in batteries, and difficulties to estimate the energy required for several production processes for batteries. Maybe for this reason, LCAs of PIPV have not been widely explored [51–53]. Even the number of life-cycle analyses of a product that resembles PIPV, for instance, stand-alone PV systems, is rather limited. In 2000, three studies

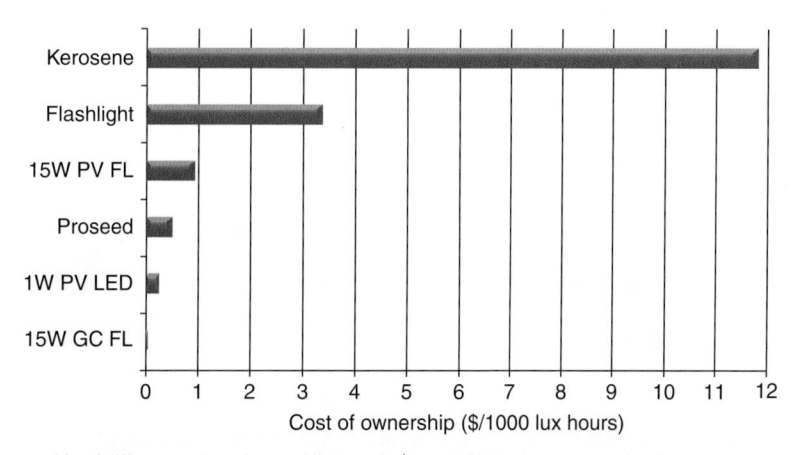

Figure 25 The costs of ownership of different options for rural lighting in $ per 1000 lux-hours assuming 3 h of lighting each day. Data are taken from Cambodia [18].

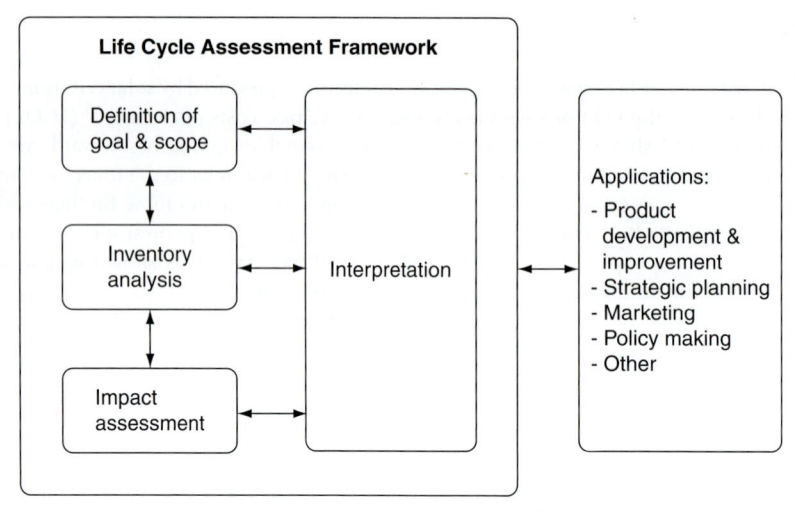

Figure 26 Framework for LCA from ISO [47].

have been executed [54–56] on small stand-alone PV systems leading to characteristic values for the CO_2 emissions and energy payback time of solar home systems (SHSs) of 49 Wp in Indonesia. The studies also covered a critical assessment of the selection of functional units of autonomous PV systems in developing countries. Relatively, recently, Celik *et al.* [57], Garcia-Valverde *et al.* [58], and Kaldellis *et al.* [59] published results of life-cycle assessments of stand-alone PV systems of, respectively, 12 kWp in Turkey, a 4.2 kWp stand-alone PV system in Spain, and stand-alone and grid-connected PV systems in Greece. All LCA studies about autonomous PV systems agree upon the fact that PV modules and batteries both contribute significantly to the environmental profile and the embodied energy of these systems.

To learn more about the potential environmental impact of small PV lighting products in South East Asia, Durlinger *et al.* [51, 52] executed a comparative LCA on these products. The results are shown in this section as an illustration of the application of LCA on PIPV. The LCA study was executed using software of Simapro with the EcoInvent v2.0 database [60] and the ReCiPe method [61, 62].

One of the products that was evaluated was a small PV lighting product powered by a 0.7 Wp a-Si solar panel. The product comprises two NiCd 2000 mAh AA-type batteries. Light is generated by six LEDs, delivering 42 lumens. It is assumed that the LEDs have a lifetime of 20 000 h of operation. The maximum daily operation time is 3.5 h and the lifetime of the entire product is considered to be 10 years.

For this product, most of the environmental impacts, as shown in **Figure 27**, can be attributed to production of the components, due to electricity used for the manufacturing of the PV panel and the printed wiring board, or materials used in the battery. In this case, the batteries contribute 23%, the solar panel 24%, and the printed circuit board with the LEDs 33% to damage to human health in the manufacturing phase. During the use phase, no processes take place; therefore, this phase has hardly any impact. An important contributor to impacts during the disposal phase is the disposal of the batteries.

The small PV lighting product was compared with an SHS. It was found that, in particular, the lead from the lead–acid battery in the SHS contributes significantly to the impacts on human health and ecosystems quality.

An important conclusion of the study of Durlinger is that solar PV lighting products have a lower environmental impact than conventional lighting solutions in developing countries, such as lighting services from kerosene lamps and powered by car batteries

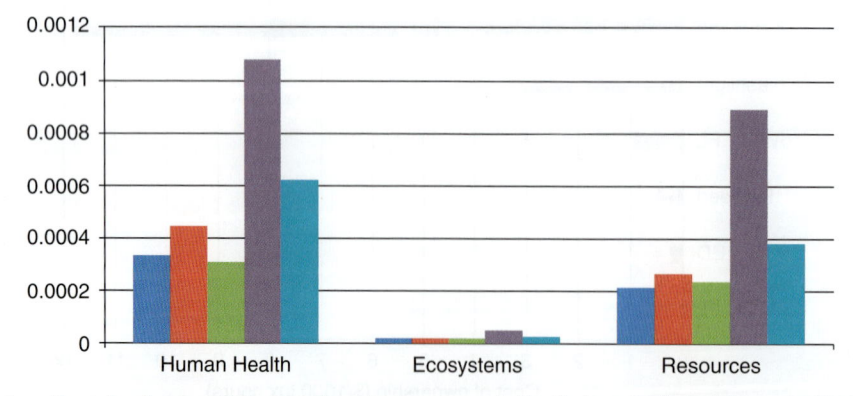

Figure 27 Normalized results per functional unit in endpoint impact categories, excluding the kerosene lamp, linear scale (World normalization). Small PV lighting system 1 (blue bars), small PV lighting system 2 (red bars), SHS (green bars), battery charged at station and CFL (purple bars), and grid connection and CFL (turquoise bars).

(see **Figure 27**). The environmental profile of small-size PV lighting products can be improved by 10% up to 50% by recycling of the batteries. From an evaluation of the accuracy of an LCA of PV lighting products, it can be concluded that impacts of these PV lighting products are lower or comparable to those of lighting by compact fluorescent lights powered by electricity from the grid in the South East Asian context. As such, they offer an environmentally beneficial lighting service for off-grid households. Although the results seem optimistic, there are some uncertainties in certain aspects of the inventory due to the relatively large impact of the battery (in relation to its disposal scenario) and the printed circuit board. An important conclusion of the study is that the environmental profile of solar lighting products can be improved by adequate battery waste management.

1.34.8 Human Factors of PIPV

Users' perception and users' experiences with PIPV are decisive in the adoption process toward these new innovative products. User perception refers not only to the perception of the real functioning of PIPV but also to more qualitative aspects such as the visual appeal of PIPV and the emotional reactions to PIPV. Despite this, only limited information is available about user studies regarding PIPV. We assume that for user studies on PIPV, existing methods such as interview techniques, observation, and participatory evaluations could be appropriate means to get insight in the user's reactions toward PIPV. The stage in which users should become involved should be as early as possible, preferably before or during the product development process to be able to implement the users' wishes as effectively as possible in the list of requirements of the product design. In the end, this will lead to a better acceptance of the final PV-powered product.

In this section, one of the few user studies available [44], which focused on an evaluation of a prototype of a PC computer mouse, will be presented as an illustration of the assessment of users' perspectives.

User tests with the PC computer mouse Sole Mio, as shown in **Figure 28**, were carried out during the period September–December 2007 at Delft University of Technology, University of Twente, Utrecht University, as well as at the KNMI by Reich *et al.* [44]. In total, 14 people used the mouse for several weeks in their daily practice, some doing a short test (5–6 weeks), others a longer test (10–12 weeks).

Users received instructions regarding the use of the mouse in advance. Each user kept a log to provide insight into their behavior and experiences. Halfway through the test and at the end, the logs served as a basis for an interview with each user to extract further relevant information. At the end of the test, a collective interview was held with all users at one location to extract further information regarding the interaction between the users themselves. The results of the user tests are listed as follows [44].

1. User assessment of the overall design
    Almost all users found the mouse rather big and poorly ergonomically adapted to the shape of the hand. The shape of the mouse (especially the width and height) clearly needs redesign.
    About half of the users liked the transparent cover as it gave a clear view of the solar cell. Some users liked to give advices about technical improvements of the mouse. A few users considered the PV-powered mouse as an ideal means to create awareness about sustainable energy.
2. Overall user expectations
    Most users did not have a clear idea about what to expect when they started the test. Everybody participated enthusiastically and pursued their own charging tactics.
    Across the whole test population, the varied performance of the mice clearly had a negative impact on the overall valuation of the concept. Still, the majority of users had faith in the product and believed that the problems related to the prototype stage of the Sole Mio device could be solved.

Figure 28 The prototype of the Sole Mio PV computer mouse that has been evaluated.

3. Sunbathing

The test period happened to be in the darker part of the year: a real challenge for the mice's performance. Therefore, to charge the batteries of the Sole Mio, it was necessary to expose the solar cell in the product to a higher irradiance. This was done by so-called sunbathing, which actually implies the positioning of the mouse in the window sill. Positive judgments regarding sunbathing were especially related to the fact that the mouse performed well when treated well. However, users differed in their tolerance. A charging tactic followed by virtually all users (independently from each other and without having been instructed to do so) was to place the mouse in the window at the end of each working day. When left there over the weekend, this led to flawless operation of the mouse for quite sometime.

Negative judgments regarding sunbathing were particularly related to the unreliability of the mouse after sunbathing. In some cases, the mouse was insufficiently charged, even after placing it on a brightly illuminated window sill for entire weekends.

4. User feedback on charging signal

Two users indicated that it was unclear to them whether the signal indicated that charging was taking place or that charging was required. The LED signal functioned quite differently across the test mice, ranging from almost continuously blinking (and still being able to use the mouse for days) to hardly ever blinking (and flawless operation as well).

Most users preferred the indicator to be as simple and energy-efficient as possible. One user would also like to have seen the impact charging had on the battery status.

5. User willingness to buy a Sole Mio

Based on this test and on interviews held earlier in the project to identify user needs, two relevant types of customers were distinguished:

- A group appreciating a PV mouse but preferring reliable, wired mice that are as cheap as possible
- A group that seriously considers buying a PV mouse that would cost about €10 extra.

Many users indicated to be willing to spend a total of approximately €50 for a Sole Mio mouse. Whether test users would actually purchase the Sole Mio, if it was available, could not be tested.

1.34.9 Design and Manufacturing of PIPV

Opportunities of the integration of PV technology in the final design of a product that can be manufactured partly depend, on the one hand, on the visual appearance of PV cells in the context of the product design and, on the other hand, on the possibility to shape and form PV cells and to attach them to the product. Roth and Steinhueser [20], Gorter et al. [24], Kan [36], Reinders and Akkerman [63], and researchers in the Europen PV-Accept project [64] have addressed these issues.

For PV cells characteristic, visual features of different PV technologies and possibilities to shape and form them have been shown in **Table 3**. It can be found that visual appeal, flexibility, and the number of possible operations vary considerably among the different technologies. Coloring is possible for c-Si and m-Si technologies, although it will affect the efficiency. For other solar cells, the use of colored glass sheets or colored plastics as a cover could bring in more variations with respect to their dark brown and grayish colors. a-Si and CIGS can be produced with customized patterns, and c-Si and m-Si can be decorated by grid designs that are different from the common H-pattern. Newly developed back-contact cells may be more appealing from a visual perspective.

PV cells or series of PV cells can be attached on product surfaces in the following ways:

1. Attachment on a surface and covering with a glass sheet or a plastic sheet
2. Attachment on a surface and covering with resin, for instance, epoxy resin
3. Lamination in between plastic sheets and next attachment on a surface
4. Encapsulation in fiber-reinforced plastic and next attachment on a surface.

The fourth option has the advantage of preshaping a series of PV cells into a mold that is injected with the fluid plastic, the so-called injection molding.

The selection of glass or plastics – such as epoxies, fluorides, polyolefins, and silcons – that could be applied for the protection of solar cells in products is based on variables like transparency, transmittance, service temperature, thermal expansion coefficient, glass temperature costs, weight, and expected lifetime in relation to the product's expected lifetime. Due to the last reason, we assume that for PIPV in consumer products, less stringent criteria are set to UV stability and impact resistance compared with PIPV in business-to-business products that must be able to endure harsh outdoor environments for many years.

Though less visible, the selection of a battery influences considerably the final design of a product regarding shaping, flexibility, costs, maintenance, and operating temperatures of the product. **Table 4** lists these design variables for a number of battery technologies that are frequently applied in PIPV.

Table 3 Design aspects of different PV technologies

Type of PV cell	Maturity	Color/surface/other	Typical area (mm)	Typical thickness (μm)	Flexibility of cell	Operations on cells during design and manufacturing
c-Si	Highly commercially available	Blue, dark-gray, or black/smooth surface with silver grid patterns on top/cells can be colored (gold, orange, pink, red, green, silver) by variable Si_3N_4 layer/decorative grid patterns possible	156 × 156	>180 to 220	Low	Bending only to a limited extent; laser cutting; heating; injection transfer molding in plastics; lamination in plastics
m-Si	Highly commercially available	Shiny blue, dark blue/shiny grains, smooth surface with silver grid patterns on top/cells can be colored (gold, orange, pink, red, green, silver) by variable Si_3N_4 layer/decorative grid patterns possible	156 × 156	>180 to 220	Low	Bending only to a limited extent; laser cutting; heating; injection transfer molding in plastics; lamination in plastics
a-Si	Commercially available	Dark brown or black/smooth surface with light lines/cell interconnects/patterned deposition is possible	Customizable from 10 × 10 to 1000 × 2000	<1	High	Bending; lamination in plastics; deposition on curved surfaces; cutting not possible
CIGS	Commercially available	Gray or black/smooth surface with light lines/cell interconnects/patterned screen printing is possible	Customizable from 10 × 10 to 1000 × 2000	1–3	High	Bending; lamination in plastics; deposition on curved surfaces; cutting not possible
CdTe	Highly commercially available	Brownish/smooth	Customizable from 10 × 10 to 1000 × 2000	1–3	Low	Heating
III–V three junction	Mainly available for space applications, concentrators	Black/smooth	40 × 80 80 × 80	140–200	Low	Connection to ceramics
III–V single junction, thin film	Commercially available for terrestrial applications	Black/smooth	40 × 80 80 × 80	5	High	Bending; heating; injection transfer molding in plastics; lamination in plastics
DSC	Available	Red or brown/transparent and smooth/cells can be colored by dye molecules	Customizable	1–10	High	Bending; lamination in plastics
Polymer	Limitedly available	Orange, red, or brown/smooth	Long strips, customizable	<1	High	Bending; lamination in plastics

Part of data adapted from Kan [36] and extended with manufacturing data.

Table 4 Design aspects of different battery technologies

Battery type	Shape	Flexible	Safety/ environmental	Operating temperature (°C)	Maintenance	Specific costs (€ Wh^{-1})
Sulfuric lead–acid	Cubic	Fluid	Hazard of shock/ release of gas	−20 to 60	3–6 months	0.50
Nickel–cadmium	Cylindrical	No	Toxic	−40 to 60	30–60 days	3.00
Nickel metal hydride	Cylindrical	No		−20 to 60	60–90 days	3.80
Lithium ion	Cylindrical, prismatic and pouch cells	Yes	Flammable	−20 to 45	Not necessary	9.50
Lithium/ manganese dioxide	Cylindrical, prismatic, and pouch cells	Yes		0–45	Not necessary	19.00

Part of data adapted from Kan [36] and Flipsen [42].

1.34.10 Outlook on PIPV and Conclusions

Because of the fact that the research field on PIPV has emerged only recently, it can be understood that from the review of the existing literature on PIPV, it follows that still many relevant issues regarding PIPV have not been addressed thoroughly. To foster innovation in PIPV, the following information should become available through research:

- Energy-efficient management of PIPV–battery systems
- Methodologies for cost calculations of PV technology in a product context
- Environmental aspects of PV technology in products
- Manufacturing of integrated PV in products
- The application of PIPV in combination with other renewable energy sources
- Users' experiences with PIPV in different product categories.

All the examples of PIPV products shown in Section 1.34.2 show that PIPV can be applied well in different product categories and various markets. With the steep decrease of prices of conventional PV technologies, such as c-Si, the emergence of low-cost PV technologies such as polymer solar cells and a slight decrease of the power demand of products induced by technological advances, PIPV might become a respectable widely applied energy source. For instance, PIPV might become common in public lighting products and other urban furniture in public spaces. We also expect that the market of PV-powered LED lamps in BOP markets might grow in the forthcoming years. In this chapter, it was shown that PIPV can offer energy to products with a wide range of power demand. Therefore, we believe that PIPV will be further developed in the field of microenergy harvesting, that is, for sensors and security, and that it will be applied more often in boats and cars.

References

[1] Kan SY (2006) SYN-Energy in solar cell use for consumer products and indoor applications. Final Report 014-28-213, NWO/NOVEM. Delft, The Netherlands: Technical University of Delft.
[2] Randall JF (2006) *Designing Indoor Solar Products: Photovoltaic Technologies for AES, 2005*. London: Wiley.
[3] Reinders A (2002) Options for photovoltaic solar energy systems in portable products. *Proceedings of the TMCE*. pp. 25–38. Wuhan, PR China, ISBN: 7-5609-2682-7.
[4] Timmerman MB (2008) Review of Existing Knowledge of Product Integrated PV for Industrial Design Engineers. Internal Research Paper, Master of Sustainable Energy Technology, University of Twente.
[5] Prince MB (1955) Silicon solar energy converters. *Journal of Applied Physics* 26: 68–74.
[6] Furnas CC (1957) The uses of solar energy. *Solar Energy* 1: 68–74.
[7] Anonymous (1955) Improvements in solar battery. *Journal of the Franklin Institute* 260(1), 87–88.
[8] Sillcox LK (1955) Fuels of the future. *Journal of the Franklin Institute* 259(3): 183–195.
[9] Prince MB (1959) The photovoltaic solar energy converter. *Solar Energy* 3: 35.
[10] Zahl HA and Ziegler HK (1960) Power sources for satellites and space vehicles. *Solar Energy* 4: 32–38.
[11] Vintage Calculators. http://www.vintagecalculators.com/ (accessed 23 October 2010).
[12] Alsema EA, Elzen B, Reich NH, et al. (2005) Towards an optimized design method for PV-powered consumer and professional applications: The SYN-Energy project. *Proceedings of 20th European Photovoltaic Solar Energy Conference*. pp. 1981–1984. Barcelona, Spain.
[13] Reich NH, Netten MP, Veefkind M, et al. (2007) A solar powered wireless computer mouse: Design, assembly and preliminary testing of 15 prototypes. *Proceedings of 22nd European Photovoltaic Solar Energy Conference*. pp. 2842–2845. Milan, Italy.
[14] Reich NH, van Sark WGHM, Alsema EA, et al. (2008) A CAD based simulation tool to estimate energy balances of device integrated PV systems under indoor irradiation conditions. *Proceedings of 23rd European Photovoltaic Solar Energy Conference*. pp. 3338–3343. Valencia, Spain.
[15] Reich NH, Veefkind M, van Sark WGHM, et al. (2009) A solar powered wireless computer mouse: Industrial design concepts. *Solar Energy* 83: 202–210.

[16] Veefkind M, Reich NH, Elzen B, et al. (2006) The design of a solar powered consumer product, a case study. *Proceedings of Going Green – Care Innovation 2006*. Vienna, Austria, *International Journal of Automation Austria* p. 3.6.4.
[17] Avato P, Bopp G, Cabraal A, et al. (2009) Investigations and tests of LED-based PV-powered lanterns. *Proceedings of 24th European Photovoltaic Solar Energy Conference*. pp. 3967–3976. Hamburg, Germany.
[18] Gooijer H, de Reinders AHME, and Schreuder DA (2008) Solar powered LED lighting: Human factors of low cost lighting for developing countries. *Proceedings of 23rd European Photovoltaic Solar Energy Conference*. pp. 3361–3366. Valencia, Spain.
[19] Reiche K, Grüner R,, Attigah B, et al. (2010) What a difference can a PicoPV system make? Early findings on small photovoltaic systems: An emerging low-cost energy technology for developing countries. Report. Eschborn, Germany: Duetsche Gesellschaft fur Technische Zusammenarbeit. http://www2.gtz.de/dokumente/bib-2010/gtz2010-0210en-picopv-system.pdf.
[20] Roth W and Steinhueser A (1997) *Photovoltaische Energieversorgung von Geraeten und Kleinsystemen, OTTI: Technologie-Kolleg*. Freiburg, Germany: Fraunhofer Institut Solare Energiesysteme (ISE).
[21] Helios. http://www.nasa.gov/centers/dryden/news/ResearchUpdate/Helios/index.html (accessed November 2010).
[22] Impulse. http://www.solarimpulse.com/ (accessed November 2010).
[23] Bikes PV. http://www.solarpoweredbike.com/ (accessed 23 November 2010).
[24] Gorter T, Voerman EJ, Joore P, et al. (2010) PV-boats: Design issues in the realization of PV powered boats. *Proceedings of 25th European Photovoltaic Solar Energy Conference*. pp. 4920–4927. Valencia, Spain.
[25] Moor D (2008) Works of art: A possibility to improve BIPV. *Proceedings of 23rd European Photovoltaic Solar Energy Conference*. pp. 3486–3487. Valencia, Spain.
[26] Virtue of Blue. http://www.blainsouthern.com/exhibitions/2011/jeroen-verhoeven-the-curious-image/images/40-virtue-of-blue-2010 (accessed 5 July 2011).
[27] Geelen D, Kan SY, and Brezet H (2008) Photovoltaics for product designers: How to design a photovoltaic solar energy powered consumer product. *Proceedings of 23rd European Photovoltaic Solar Energy Conference*. pp. 3329–3333. Valencia, Spain.
[28] Reinders AHME and de Boer A (2008) Product-integrated PV: Innovative design methods for PV-powered products. *Proceedings of 23rd European Photovoltaic Solar Energy Conference*. pp. 3321–3324. Valencia, Spain.
[29] Reinders A, de Boer A, de Winter A, and Haverlag M (2009) Designing PV powered LED products: Sensing new opportunities for advanced technologies. *Proceedings of 34th IEEE PVSC*. pp. 415–420. Philadelphia, PA, USA.
[30] Pahl G and Beitz W (1998) *Engineering Design: A Systematic Approach*. Berlin, Germany: Springer, ISBN: 3-540-19917-9.
[31] Reinders AHME and van Houten FJAM (2006) Industrial design methods for product integrated PEM fuel cells. *Proceedings of the NHA*. Los Angeles, USA.
[32] Kazmerski L (2010) *Best Research Cell Efficiencies*. Golden, NREL, Colorado, USA.
[33] Reich NH, van Sark WGHM, Reinders AHME, and de Wit H (2009) Using CAD software to simulate PV energy yield: Predicting the charge yield of solar cells incorporated into a PV powered consumer product under 3D-irradiation conditions. *Proceedings of 34th IEEE PVSC*. pp. 1291–1296. Philadelphia, PA, USA.
[34] Reich NH, Sark WGJHM, van Alsema EA, et al. (2005) Weak light performance and spectral response of different solar cell types. In: Palz W, Ossenbrink H, and Helm P (eds.) *Proceedings of the 20th European Photovoltaic Solar Energy Conference*. pp. 2120–2123. Munich, Germany: WIP-Renewable Energies.
[35] Müller M (2010) Regenerative Mikroenergiesysteme am Beispiel von Photovoltaik in Gebäuden. PhD Thesis. Osnabrück, Germany: Der Andere Verlag.
[36] Kan SY (2006) Energy Matching: Key towards the Design of Sustainable Powered Products. PhD Thesis, Technical University of Delft, Design for Sustainability Program, 201 p. ISBN: 978-90-5155-030-6.
[37] Ryer A (1997) *The Light Measurement Handbook*. Newburyport, MA: International Light, Inc. ISBN: 0-9658356-9-3.
[38] Girish TE (2006) Some suggestions for photovoltaic power generation using artificial light illumination. *Solar Energy Materials and Solar Cells* 90: 2569–2571.
[39] Gong C, Posthuma N, Dross F, et al. (2008) Comparison of n- and p-type high efficiency silicon solar cell performance under low illumination conditions. *Proceedings of 33rd IEEE PVSC*. pp. 1–4. San Diego, CA, USA.
[40] Reich NH, van Sark WGHM, Alsema EA, et al. (2009) Crystalline silicon cell performance at low light intensities. *Solar Energy Materials and Solar Cells* 93: 1471–1481.
[41] Kan SY, Verwaal M, and Broekhuizen H (2006) The use of battery-capacitor combinations in photovoltaic powered products short communication. *Journal of Power Sources* 162: 971–974.
[42] Flipsen SFJ (2006) Power sources compared: The ultimate truth? *Journal of Power Sources* 162: 927–934.
[43] Reinders AHME (2007) A design method to assess the accessibility of light of PV cells in an arbitrary geometry by means of ambient occlusion. *Proceedings of 22nd European Photovoltaic Solar Energy Conference*. pp. 2737–2739. Milan, Italy.
[44] Reich NH, Elzen B, Netten MP, et al. (2008) Practical experiences with the PV powered computer mouse 'Sole-Mio'. *Proceedings of 23rd European Photovoltaic Solar Energy Conference*. pp. 3121–3125. Valencia, Spain.
[45] Tiwari A and Reinders A (2009) Modeling of irradiance in a CAD environment for the design of PV powered products. *Proceedings of PVSEC-19*. Kolkata, India.
[46] Gibson TL and Kelly NA (2010) Solar photovoltaic charging of lithium-ion batteries. *Journal of Power Sources* 195: 3928–3932.
[47] International Organization for Standardization (2006) *ISO 14040:2006 Environmental Management – Life Cycle Assessment – Principles and Framework*. Geneva, Switzerland: International Organization for Standardization.
[48] Fhtenakis VM and Kim HC (2011) Photovoltaics: Life-cycle analyses. *Solar Energy* 85: 1609–1628.
[49] Rydh CJ and Sanden BA (2005) Energy analysis of batteries in photovoltaic systems. Part I: Performance and energy requirements. *Energy Conversion and Management* 46: 1957–1979.
[50] Rydh CJ and Sanden BA (2005) Energy analysis of batteries in photovoltaic systems. Part II: Energy return factors and overall battery efficiencies. *Energy Conversion and Management* 46: 1980–2000.
[51] Durlinger B, Reinders A, and Toxopeus M (2010) Environmental benefits of PV powered lighting products for rural areas in South East Asia: A life cycle analysis with geographic allocation. *Proceedings of 35th IEEE PVSC*. pp. 2353–2357. Hawaii, USA.
[52] Durlinger B, Reinders A, and Toxopeus M (2010) Life cycle assessment of solar powered lighting products for rural areas in South East Asia. *Proceedings of 25th EU PVSEC*. pp. 3917–3925. Valencia, Spain.
[53] Reich NH, Veefkind M, Alsema EA, et al. (2006) Industrial design of a PV powered consumer application: Case study of a solar powered wireless computer mouse. In: Poortmans J, Ossenbrink H, Dunlop E, and Helm P (eds.) *Proceedings of the 21st European Photovoltaic Solar Energy Conference*. pp. 2306–2311. Munich, Germany: WIP-Renewable Energies.
[54] Alsema EA (2000) Environmental life cycle assessment of solar home systems. Report No. E2000–15. Utrecht, The Netherlands: Utrecht University, Department of Science Technology and Society.
[55] Reinders A and Alsema E (2000) Environmental life cycle assessment of solar home systems and other rural electrification and lighting systems. Report. Utrecht, The Netherlands: Utrecht University.
[56] Kets A (2000) Functional Units in the Life Cycle Assessment of Solar Home Systems. MSc Thesis. Study Environmental Sciences, Utrecht University.
[57] Celik AN, Muneer T, and Clarke P (2008) Optimal sizing and life cycle assessment of residential photovoltaic energy systems with battery storage. *Progress in Photovoltaics: Research and Applications* 16: 69–85.
[58] Garcia-Valverde R, Miguel A, Martinez-Bejar R, and Urbina A (2009) Life cycle assessment study of a 4.2 kWp stand-alone photovoltaic system. *Solar Energy* 83: 1434–1445.
[59] Kaldellis JK, Zafirakis D, and Kondili E (2010) Energy pay-back period analysis of stand-alone photovoltaic systems. *Renewable Energy* 35: 1444–1454.
[60] Frischknecht R and Jungbluth N (2007) Overview and methodology: Ecoinvent data v2.0. Report. Dübendorf, Switzerland: Ecoinvent Centre.

[61] Goedkoop M, Heijungs R, Huijbregts M, *et al.* (2009) ReCiPe 2008, Part I: Characterisation. Report. The Hague, The Netherlands: Ministry of Housing, Spatial Planning and the Environment.
[62] Wegener Sleeswijk A, van Oers L, Guinee J, *et al.* (2008) Normalisation in product life cycle assessment: An LCA of the global and European economic systems in the year 2000. *Science of the Total Environment* 390: 227–240.
[63] Reinders AHME and Akkerman R (2005) Design, production and materials of PV powered consumer products: The case of mass production. *Proceedings of 20th European Photovoltaic Solar Energy Conference*. pp. 2196–2199. Barcelona, Spain.
[64] PV-Accept (2005) Final Report EU PVACCEPT/IPS-2000-0090. Hermannsdörfer I and Rüb C (eds.).
[65] Cendagorta-Galarza M, Friend E, Rodriguez J, *et al.* (2009) Development of a solar plane prototype. *Proceedings of 24th European Photovoltaic Solar Energy Conference*. pp. 4360–4362. Hamburg, Germany.
[66] Gorter T, Reinders AHME, Pascarella F, *et al.* (2009) LED/PV lighting systems for commercial buildings: Design of a sustainable LED/PV symbiotic system. *Proceedings of 24th European Photovoltaic Solar Energy Conference*. pp. 4250–4255. Hamburg, Germany.
[67] Kan SY and Strijk R (2006) Towards a more efficient energy use in photovoltaic powered products: Short communication. *Journal of Power Sources* 162: 954–958.
[68] Kan SY, van Beers S, and Brezet JC (2004) Towards mature design of PV powered products. *Proceedings of EuroSun 2004*. vol. 3, pp. 3-206–3-215. Freiburg, Germany.
[69] Kan SY and Verwaal M (2007) Figure of matching algorithm for analysing and quantifying the matching of battery: Capacitor combinations in photovoltaic powered products. *25th International Power Source Symposium*. pp. 1–12. Bath, UK.
[70] Kan SY, Verwaal M, Veefkind M, *et al.* (2007) Lessons learned: Power supply and battery choosing process for the photovoltaic powered wireless mouse. *25th International Power Source Symposium*. pp. 1–9. Bath, UK.
[71] Müller M, Hildebrand H, Walker WD, and Reindl LM (2009) Simulations and measurements for indoor photovoltaic devices. *Proceedings of 24th European Photovoltaic Solar Energy Conference*. pp. 4363–4367. Hamburg, Germany.
[72] Müller M, Wienold J, Walker WD, and Reindl LM (2009) Characterization of indoor photovoltaic devices and light. *Proceedings of 34th IEEE Photovoltaic Specialist Conference*. pp. 738–743. Philadelphia, PA: IEEE.
[73] Müller M, Würfel U, and Zimmermann B (2010) Photovoltaics in micro energy harvesting. In: Mateu L, Pollak M, and Spies P (Hrg.) *Handbook of Energy Harvesting Power Supplies and Applications*. Stanford, CA: Pan Stanford Publishing, ISBN: 978-981-4241-86-1.
[74] Randall JF and Jacot J (2003) Is AM1.5 applicable in practice? Modelling eight photovoltaic materials with respect to light intensity and two spectra. *Renewable Energy* 28: 1851–1864.
[75] Reich NH, van Sark WGHM, Turkenburg WC, and Sinke WC (2010) Using CAD software to simulate PV energy yield: The case of product integrated photovoltaic operated under indoor irradiation. *Solar Energy* 84: 1526–1537.
[76] Reinders A, de Gooijer H, and Diehl JC (2007) How participatory product design and micro-entrepreneurship favor the dissemination of photovoltaic systems in Cambodia. *17th PVSEC*. Fukuoka, Japan.
[77] Reinders AHME (2008) Product-integrated PV applications: How industrial design methods yield innovative PV powered products. *Proceedings of 33rd IEEE PVSC*. pp. 1–4. San Diego, CA, USA.
[78] Reinders A, de Boer A, de Winter A, and Haverlag M (2009) Designing PV powered LED products: Integration of PV technology in innovative products. *Proceedings of 24th European Photovoltaic Solar Energy Conference*. pp. 3179–3183. Hamburg, Germany.
[79] Scognamiglio A, Cancro C, Formisano F, *et al.* (2007) Optimization of the lighting photovoltaic component Stapelia. *Proceedings of 22nd European Photovoltaic Solar Energy Conference*. pp. 3317–3322. Milan, Italy.
[80] Veefkind M (2003) Industrial design and PV-power, challenges and barriers. *Proceedings of the ISES Solar World Congress 2003: Solar Energy for a Sustainable Future*. Göteborg, Sweden: ISES.

Further Reading

[1] Kan SY (2003) PV powered mobility and mobile/wireless product design. *Proceedings of the ISES Solar World Congress 2003: Solar Energy for a Sustainable Future*. Göteborg, Sweden: ISES.
[2] Kan SY, Silvester S, and Brezet JC (2004) Design applications of combined photovoltaic and energy storage units as supplies in mobile/wireless products. *Proceedings of the TMCE 2004*. pp. 309–318. Lausanne, Switzerland.
[3] Kan SY and Silvester S (2004) Synergy in a smart photovoltaic (PV) battery: SYN-ENERGY. *Journal of Sustainable Product Design* 3: 29–43.
[4] Miguet F and Groleau D (2002) A daylight simulation tool for urban and architectural spaces: Application to transmitted direct and diffuse light through glazing. *Building and Environment* 37: 833–843.
[5] Reich NH (2010) On the Design of Product Integrated Photovoltaic Systems. PhD Thesis, 123 p. Utrecht University, Department of Science, Technology and Society, ISBN: 978-90-8672-043-9.
[6] Veefkind MJ, Flipsen SFJ, and Broekhuizen HF (2004) Gathering data on the energy to be harvested with portable consumer products, methods and equipment. *Eurosun 2004: The 5th ISES Europe Solar Conference*. pp. 3-379–3-385. Freiburg, Germany: PSE GmbH.

1.35 Very Large-Scale Photovoltaic Systems

T Ehara and K Komoto, Mizuho Information & Research Institute, Tokyo, Japan
P van der Vleuten, Free Energy Consulting, Eindhoven, The Netherlands

© 2012 Elsevier Ltd. All rights reserved.

1.35.1	What is Very Large-Scale Photovoltaic System?	733
1.35.1.1	Definition of Very Large-Scale Photovoltaic	733
1.35.1.2	Multibenefit Approach	733
1.35.1.3	Deployment Strategies	734
1.35.2	Evaluation of the VLS-PV from Various Aspects	734
1.35.2.1	Energy Potential	734
1.35.2.2	Economics of VLS-PV	736
1.35.2.2.1	Generation cost of VLS-PV	736
1.35.2.2.2	Impact of capital costs	737
1.35.2.3	Technologies for VLS-PV	737
1.35.2.4	Environmental Aspects	737
1.35.2.4.1	Lifecycle Analysis	737
1.35.2.4.2	Ecological impacts	738
1.35.3	Progress in VLS-PV	739
1.35.3.1	VLS-PV as a Dream	739
1.35.3.2	Dream to Reality	739
1.35.3.3	Emerging New Initiatives in MENA Regions	739
1.35.4	Future for the VLS-PV	741
1.35.4.1	Sustainability Issues	741
1.35.4.2	VLS-PV Visions and Roadmap	743
1.35.5	Conclusion	743
References		744

1.35.1 What is Very Large-Scale Photovoltaic System?

1.35.1.1 Definition of Very Large-Scale Photovoltaic

The concept of 'A very large-scale photovoltaic (VLS-PV)' system was first presented by the International Energy Agency Photovoltaic Power Systems Programme (IEA-PVPS) Task 8 working group in 1999 [1]. According to the group, VLS-PV is defined as "a PV system ranging from 10 MW up to several gigawatts (0.1–20 km^2 total area) consisting of one plant or an aggregation of multiple units operating in harmony and distributed in the same district" [2].

The features of the concept are not only the scale of the PV plant. The basic idea is to install a VLS-PV system in a desert region where solar irradiation is abundant. Since the output from PV from a unit of system is dependent on solar energy radiated on the PV surface, application in the most solar resource-rich regions would improve the economy of the project substantially. In addition, it is worth noting that most of the desert areas are hard to utilize effectively for other purposes; hence, it will not compete with other land use objectives such as agriculture and grazing. **Figure 1** shows a conceptual VLS-PV system.

1.35.1.2 Multibenefit Approach

A VLS-PV project is also expected to foster the community development of the region where the plant is constructed. VLS-PV development would create a sustainable market for solar electricity as well as PV system components and installations. It will generate new jobs in this field and hence create a very unique community.

Desalination of the water using the generated electricity from VLS-PV is also within the scope of the VLS-PV concept. Desalinated water could be used for agricultural, industrial, and municipal purposes. In arid areas, production of water that can be used for drinking or irrigation would be greatly appreciated. Agriculture is often the largest economic sector in developing regions where the population continues to increase; therefore, VLS-PV could be an attractive option for those regions. Salt accumulation and associated desertification in the arid and semiarid region is a serious problem. With the VLS-PV, agricultural water can be obtained from ground sources through solar pumps, or from seawater through a desalination plant driven by the solar energy. A reverse osmosis (RO) system may be the promising technology for desalination. It would also be possible to recycle treated water from municipal sewage.

As is discussed above, VLS-PV concept pursues multibenefits from the various perspectives. The expected benefits presented by the IEA-PVPS Task 8 group are summarized in **Table 1**.

Figure 1 Conceptual image of a VLS-PV system in the desert area [2].

Table 1 Various benefits of VLS-PV [2]

Economic benefits	Introducing a solid strategy for the introduction of VLS-PV solar electricity generation will create a large and sustainable local market for solar panels and other system components and materials, including installation and maintenance. In addition, Clean Development Mechanism (CDM) credits will be generated. The generated electricity can be distributed in the local market as well as in the export market and the CDM credits can be sold in the international market.
Social benefits	The sustainable local market that will be created by the adoption of a solid long-term strategy for solar electricity generation allows for national and international investments in local production of solar panels, solar cells, silicon materials, and other basic materials such as glass, metals, and concrete. This will create significant additional employment in desert regions. For the introduction of state-of-the-art technology, international cooperation and technology transfer will be needed.
Security of energy supply	Because a lot of sunshine is and will always be available in desert regions, this is the most secure source of energy and sunshine is basically available to everybody. Because the components and systems for converting sunshine into electricity will become cheaper with technology evolution, very large as well as very small systems will become cost-effective in the near future.
Environmental issues	For reducing the effects of climate change, international agreements for reducing greenhouse gas emissions have been and will be concluded. By generating solar electricity instead of conventional electricity, greenhouse gas emissions will be significantly reduced.
Peace/poverty alleviation	The abundant availability of solar energy (sunshine) in desert regions provides fair access by everybody to affordable and sustainable energy solutions. This is an important condition for preventing wars over energy. Moreover, the availability of solar electricity will stimulate economic development in desert regions.
International recognition	By the introduction of a sustainable energy strategy based on solar electricity, an example will be created that will generate international recognition and this example will be followed by many other countries.

1.35.1.3 Deployment Strategies

As for the deployment strategies, the IEA-PVPS Task 8 group has proposed a very unique approach. **Figure 2** illustrates the proposed deployment steps for the sustainable growth of VLS-PV: the Solar Pyramid. As an initial stage, start-up VLS-PV plants as well as PV module manufacturing facilities are constructed. After installing the start-up VLS-PV plant, a part of the solar-generated power supply is supplied to the PV module factory. The PV module produced in the facilities will be used to enlarge the VLS-PV capacity. This 'step-by-step' approach has many advantages not only from an environment but also from an economic point of view. For example, the PV owner may be able to enjoy the benefits of 'experience curve' developments. The cost of PV would be reduced as the manufacturing process improves and scales up. Another advantage is risk management. Starting from relatively smaller capacity would reduce the risk of the project.

Since there are no PV systems operating more than 20 years in the desert area, preliminary operation and the careful monitoring of the system performance in the start-up stage would enhance the system reliability.

1.35.2 Evaluation of the VLS-PV from Various Aspects

1.35.2.1 Energy Potential

One of the characteristics of solar energy is its relatively low energy density. In order to have multi-megawatt or gigawatt scale of VLS-PV, naturally, the land requirement associated with the plants would be considerable. However, fortunately, the dry desert area

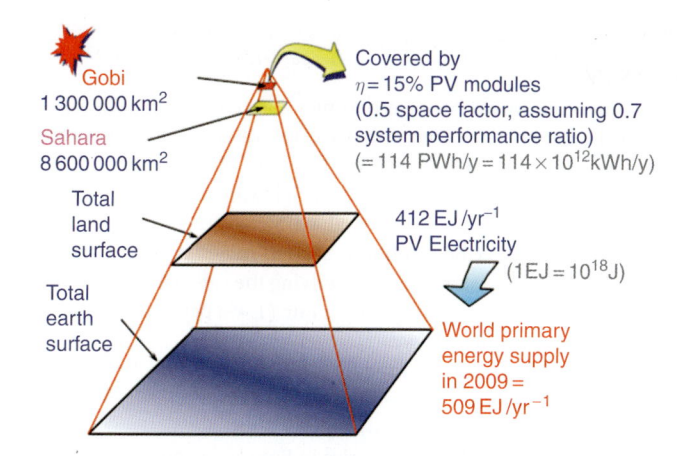

Figure 2 Solar pyramid.

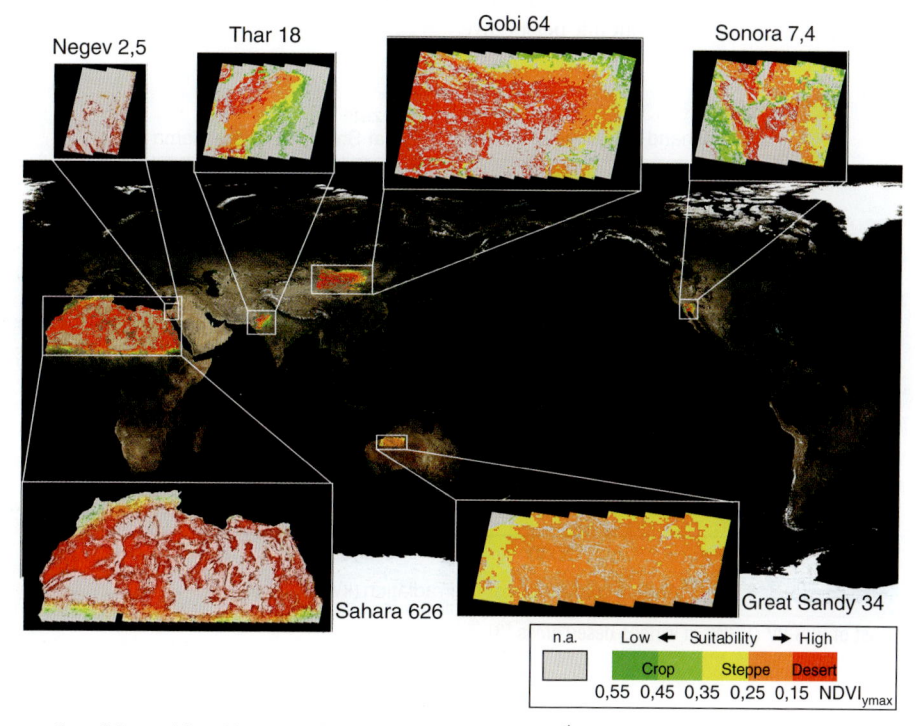

Figure 3 Annual generation of the world's arid areas by PV resource analysis (PWh yr^{-1}) [3].

on earth is abundant. It covers approximately one-third of the total land surface of the earth. According to the simplified calculation in the IEA-PVPS study, 4% of those desert areas would be sufficient to provide global energy needs [2].

In reality, however, not all desert areas are suitable for the VLS-PV application. Specifically, geometry and hardness of the ground are important from the point of view of stable installation. From these perspectives, a gravel desert is preferred over a sand dune desert for the VLS-PV application. **Figure 3** shows the evaluation of suitability of desert areas by using satellite image analysis. The analyzed deserts include the Gobi, Sahara, Great Sandy, Thar, Sonora, and Negev deserts. The total areas for these deserts represent half of the global desert area and 10% of the global land surface.

The gray areas of the map in **Figure 3** represent the unsuitable areas for VLS-PV application, while colored areas stand for suitable areas. The red color indicates that the land is arid with less vegetation (preferable for VLS-PV application); on the other hand, green color illustrates relatively higher vegetation (less-suitable for VLS-PV application).

According to the analysis, the potential PV power generation from all suitable areas is estimated to be 752 petawatt hours (PWh) or 2707 EJ, which is equivalent to approximately 5 times the world's annual energy consumption in 2010. The results indicate that the Sahara desert has the highest potential with 626 PWh, which is more than 80% of overall potential in the desert. The analysis above strongly justifies the VLS-PV concept at least from energy resource point of view [3].

1.35.2.2 Economics of VLS-PV

1.35.2.2.1 Generation cost of VLS-PV

Another interesting issue for people involved would be the economics and related financial aspects of VLS-PV. Although there are many aspects in this regard, one of the parameters commonly used to evaluate the economics of power plants is the so-called generation cost. Generation cost comprises the overall costs during the whole lifetime, both initial cost and running cost, divided by the total generated power. **Figure 4** illustrates the generation costs in eight different desert regions, namely, Gobi Sainshand, Gobi Huhhot, Negev, Sonoran, Sahara-Ouarzazate, Great Sandy, and Sahara-Nema. The economics of VLS-PV in each desert area varies since those are strongly influenced by regional specific conditions such as material costs, transportation, and labor cost as well as annual solar irradiation. The other parameters or assumptions underlying the calculation include the exchange rate (¥120 = US$1), the interest rate (3%), the salvage value rate (10%), the property tax rate (1.4% per year), the overhead expense rate (5% per year), and the lifetime of the system (PV: 30 years, inverters: 15 years).

Clearly, the generation cost is heavily influenced by the module price of the system. As indicated in **Figure 4**, the generation cost of the VLS-PV system is approximately 18–22 ¢ kWh^{-1} at a PV module price of 4 US$ W^{-1}, while the generation cost can be reduced to the range of 7–9 ¢ kWh^{-1} if the module price goes down to 1 US$ W^{-1}.

Figure 5 shows the historical change in average PV module price in Europe. As presented in the figure, the average price reaches 1.2 € W^{-1} in 2011 from 4.2 € W^{-1} in 2000 due to the continuous effort of the PV industry and drastic market expansion. This dramatic module cost reduction has strengthened the competitiveness of VLS-PV substantially. Taken into consideration the current trends of increasing cost of fossil fuels, the analysis clearly indicates that VLS-PV is becoming one of the promising technologies for utility-scale power generation even from an economic perspective.

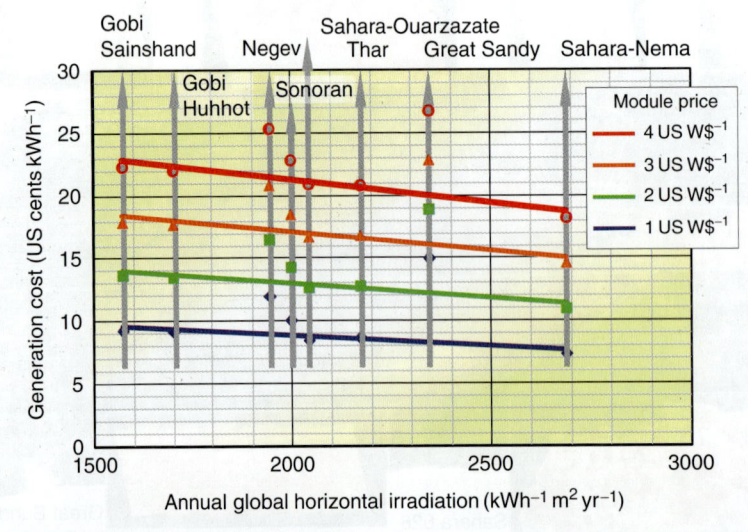

Figure 4 Generation cost of VLS-PV (1 GW) in various desert areas [3].

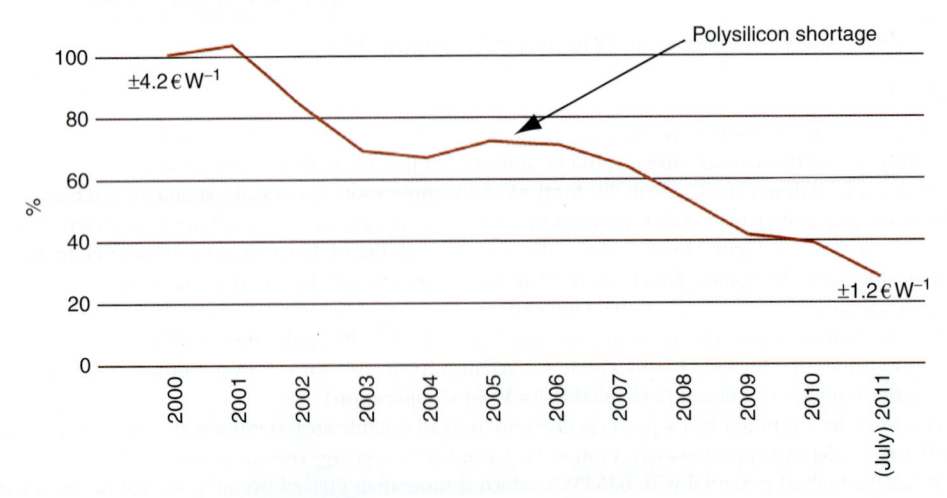

Figure 5 Change in average PV module price in Europe [4].

1.35.2.2.2 Impact of capital costs

VLS-PV projects are highly capital-intensive in general; therefore, access to the financial sector will be the key to success in this business. It should be kept in mind that the economics of the VLS-PV projects would also be strongly influenced by the capital cost and hence availability of an appropriate financial scheme.

As for the financing scheme, there are mainly three factors that affect the economics of the project. A first factor is the ownership of the project. The financial structure would be completely different if the plant is owned by utility as its own asset or by private entity within a portfolio of assets. Public–private partnership (PPP) is also an alternative for the ownership that would have a completely different structure.

The second factor is the market value of the power generated from VLS-PV. The value of the electricity can be regarded as electricity alone, but there is an opportunity that the environmental value is also added to the electricity market price, say the emission reduction credit.

A third factor is the support mechanism from central or local government. There are several supporting mechanisms already put in place in the market such as tax incentives, feed-in tariffs, and market-based incentives.

Taking the capital costs into account, the cost analysis presented in **Figure 4** would be changed to some extent. According to the IEA-PVPS Task 8 group analysis, the generation cost of VLS-PV would increase to around 30 ¢ kWh^{-1} in the case of 4 US\$ W^{-1} as PV module price and to 12 ¢ kWh^{-1} if the module cost is reduced to 1US\$ W^{-1}, if the capital cost were included (0.75% of total investment costs was assumed [3]). As such, development of a favorable financial scheme is essential for accelerating further VLS-PV developments.

1.35.2.3 Technologies for VLS-PV

There are several PV cell and module technologies available for VLS-PV application at present. Crystalline silicon wafer-based technologies are the major technologies widely used in the current market. The efficiency of the silicon cells have reached more than 20%, meaning that 20% of total solar energy radiated on the PV panel is converted into electric energy. The cost of the crystalline silicon cell has been diminished as the thickness of the cells becomes thinner and the efficiencies improve.

Another technology is thin-film modules. The production cost of thin-film cells is lower compared to crystalline silicon cells. There are several types of commercially available thin-film modules, namely, amorphous silicon (a-Si), copper indium selenide (CIS), copper indium gallium selenide (CIGS), and cadmium telluride (CdTe). It should be noted that the lower production cost of thin-film modules will not necessarily improve the economics of the overall project since lower efficiencies of the modules would lead to higher balance-of-system (BOS) cost.

The III–V compound semiconductors (multijunction gallium arsenide types) are also an option mainly for the concentrator type of application. The concentrator application uses an optical concentrator to focus light onto the cells. A tracking system is required to direct the cells precisely toward the Sun. The efficiency is approximately 30%, while 40% has been reached in laboratories.

Those are well-proven technologies and widely available in the current market. However, one of the uncertainties of VLS-PV is the long-term reliability of the systems. Since there are no VLS-PV systems operating more than 20 years in the desert, the reliability of the system might be a concern especially for the financial sectors.

The investors must wait at least 20–30 years to see the actual performance of the project throughout its lifetime; however, the risk can be minimized through applying careful design in the initial stage. Regarding the detailed technological design specially designed for more reliable systems in the desert, technical guidelines for the VLS-PV system will be published in 2012 by the IEA-PVPS Task 8 group.

1.35.2.4 Environmental Aspects

1.35.2.4.1 Lifecycle Analysis

PV in general emits no greenhouse gas during its operation. This environmental feature is one of the strong reasons why PV attracts public attention today. Nevertheless, energy is certainly consumed and associated greenhouse gas emission occurs during production or transportation of the system. The concept of lifecycle analysis (LCA) is applied to evaluate the environmental burden of all processes from production of PV to decommission and disposal of the system.

Figure 6 illustrates the energy payback time (EPBT) of VLS-PV with various types of PV module. The EPBT represents years required for VLS-PV to generate the same amount of energy consumed in its lifecycle process. The assumptions underlying the analysis include the following:

- System capacity: 1 GW
- Location of the site: Hohhot in the Gobi desert in Inner Mongolia, China
- Horizontal global irradiation: 1702 kWh $m^{-2} yr^{-1}$
- Tilted angle (30°) annual irradiation: 2017 kWh $m^{-2} yr^{-1}$
- Annual ambient temperature: 5.8 °C
- Electrical equipment: manufactured in Japan and transported to the site by cargo ship
- Foundation and steel structure: manufactured in China
- Lifetime of the system: 30 years (inverters 15 years)
- Decommission: Transported to a wrecking yard and transported for reclamation.

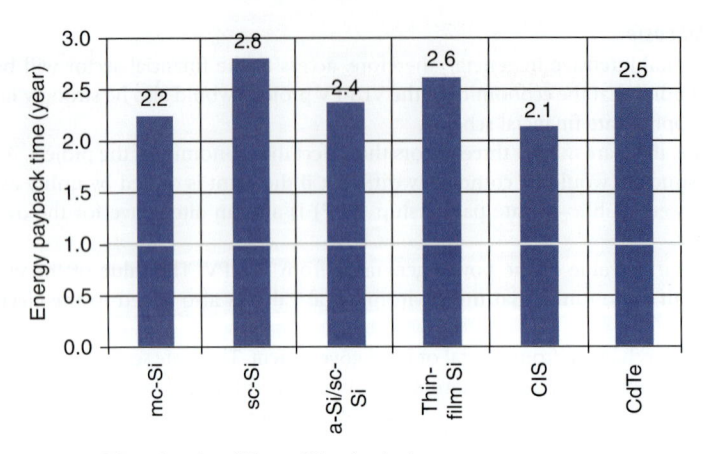

Figure 6 EPBT (year) of VLS-PV systems [3] made using different PV technologies.

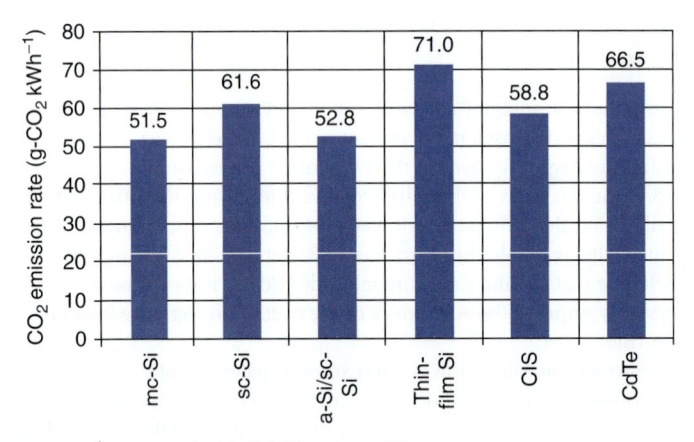

Figure 7 CO$_2$-equivalent emission (g kWh^{-1}) associated with VLS-PV systems [3].

As is shown in the figure, the EPBTs are in the range of 2.1–2.8 years. That is to say that VLS-PV can produce more than 10 times the amount of energy that is consumed during its 20–30 years of lifecycle. As such, it is obvious that VLS-PV can contribute to reduction in energy consumption as well as greenhouse gas emission considerably.

Figure 7 indicates the CO$_2$-equivalent emission per unit of electricity output (g kWh^{-1}) of the VLS-PV systems. Although the result is not comparable with other studies because of the difference in base assumptions, a similar LCA study for conventional fossil fuel power plant indicates that the CO$_2$ emission per unit of electricity output is at the magnitude 500 g kWh^{-1} for liquid natural gas (LNG)-based power plants to 1000 g kWh^{-1} for coal-fired power plants in Japan.

1.35.2.4.2 Ecological impacts

Another measure to evaluate the environmental impact introduced in this chapter is an ecological footprint (EF). According to the Global Footprint Network, the EF is defined as "a resource accounting tool used by governments, businesses, educational institutions and NGOs to answer a specific resource question: How much of the biological capacity of the planet is required by a given human activity or population?" [5].

The EF is measured in units of global hectares (gha) and is normalized to the area-weighted average productivity of biologically productive area. The criteria of the ecological footprint analysis (EFA) is called biological capacity (BC). The BC is the ability of an ecosystem to produce useful biological materials and to absorb carbon dioxide emissions; therefore, by definition, EF should be kept lower than BC so as to be sustainable. According to the latest analysis, the world's EF today is almost 1.5 times higher than BC.

Then, to what extent VLS-PV can contribute to reduce global and regional EF? In order to answer the question, the impact of VLS-PV on the ecological footprint was analyzed. It is expected that VLS-PV would have positive effects on both EF and BC since VLS-PV can

- reduce the CO$_2$ emissions by substituting existing electricity power generation, thus reducing the EF in the area of question, and
- increase BC through a regional development of the project area.

As shown in **Figure 8**, a 100 GW VLS-PV development could reduce the EF per capita from 12.5 to 11.9 gha per capita, while a 1000 GW of VLS-PV project can achieve 6.4 gha per capita, well below the BC in China. From the global point of view, 10 000 GW VLS-PV is required to keep the EF within the BC.

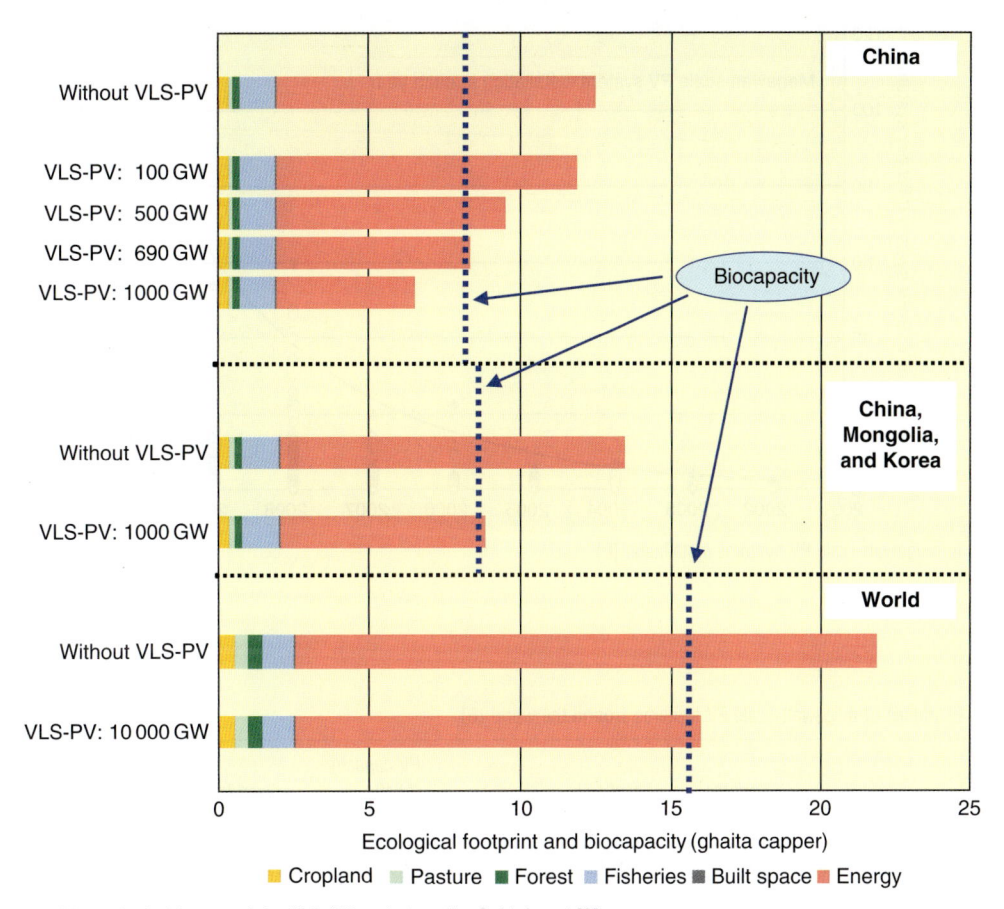

Figure 8 The possible ecological impact of the VLS-PV project on the Gobi desert [3].

1.35.3 Progress in VLS-PV

1.35.3.1 VLS-PV as a Dream

When the VLS-PV concept was presented in 1999, it was regarded as a 'dream' of scientists, although the concept attracted much public interest. The cost of PV was too high for massive applications compared with conventional power plants at that time. Additionally, there were no manufacturers that could produce such a large number of PV panels. Considering the fact that the cumulative PV capacity installed in the global market in 1999 was less than 500 MW in total, the reaction from the public may be reasonable.

1.35.3.2 Dream to Reality

As the PV market expands, the cost of PV system starts decreasing (**Figure 5**). The cost reduction curve is known as the 'experience curve' or 'learning curve'. As the cost of PV modules decreases, the concept of VLS-PV attains more reality.

Furthermore, introduction of renewable energy policies such as the 'feed-in-tariff' (FIT) enhances the competitiveness of VLS-PV considerably. FIT is a policy measure to foster grid-connected renewable energy power generations including PV by offering a relatively high tariff for electricity generated from greener energy sources.

As a result, a number of megawatt-scale PV systems were planned and constructed especially in Germany and Spain, where innovative FIT schemes were introduced. The number of megawatt-scale PV systems has increased drastically from around 10 at the beginning of the twenty-first century to more than 1000 today. The capacity of the plants also expands, with the maximum capacity becoming closer to 100 MW in 2010 (**Figure 9**). **Table 2** shows a list of examples of megawatt-scale PV systems currently installed or operated around the world.

1.35.3.3 Emerging New Initiatives in MENA Regions

In 2009, 10 years after the initial VLS-PV concepts, a new nonprofit foundation dedicated to renewable energy utilization in the EU-MENA regions (Europe, the Middle East, and North Africa) called 'DESERTEC' was founded. The DESERTEC initiative was founded by the German Association of the Club of Rome and other committed scientists or individuals [7]. The initial DESERTEC concept was designed during 2003–07 according to the DESERTEC foundation.

Figure 10 shows the conceptual image of the infrastructure development plan of DESERTEC. The red squares in the map represent 'concentrated solar thermal power (CSP)' plants. Although CSP and VLS-PV concepts assume different technologies, the

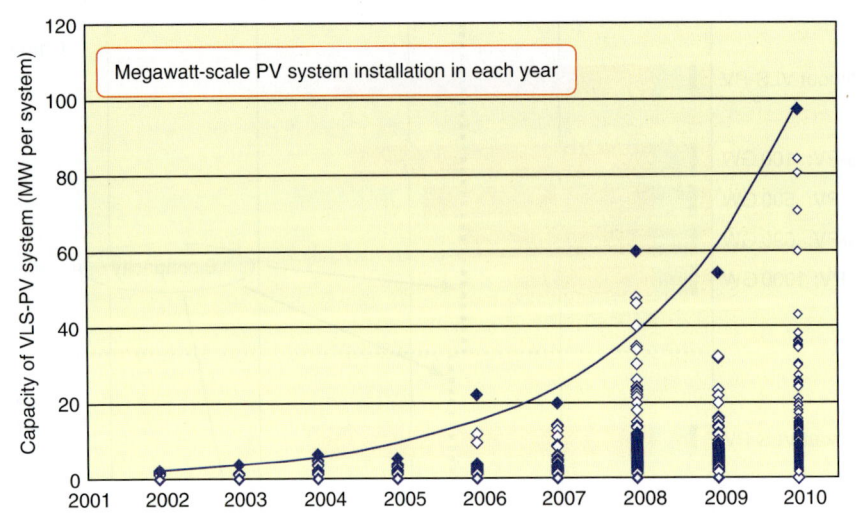

Figure 9 Trends in megawatt-scale PV systems installation [6].

Table 2 Examples of megawatt-scale PV systems around the world [6]

Name	Country	Location	PV capacity (MW)	Fixed/tracking	Installed operated
Sarnia PV power plant	Canada	Sarnia (Ontario)	97	Fixed	2010
Montalto di Castro PV power plant	Italy	Montalto di Castro (Lazio)	84.2	Fixed	2010
Solarpark Finsterwalde I, II, III	Germany	Finsterwalde	80.245	Fixed	2010
Solarpark Senftenberg II, III	Germany	Senftenberg	78	Fixed	2011
Lobpuri	Thailand	Lobpuri	73	Fixed	2011
Solarpark Lieberose	Germany	Turnow-Preilack	71	Fixed	2011
San Bellino PV power plant	Italy	San Bellino	70.556	Fixed	2010
Parque Fotovoltaico Olmedilla de Alarcón	Spain	Olmedilla (Castilla-La Mancha)	60	Fixed	2008
Copper Mountain Solar Facility	USA	Boulder City, NV	60	Fixed	2010
Avenal Solar Facility	USA	Kettleman Hills	57	Fixed	2011
Solarpark Straßkirchen	Germany	Straßkirchen	54	Fixed	2009
Solarpark Tutow I, II	Germany	Tutow (Mecklenburg-Vorpommern)	52	Fixed	2011
Parque Fotovoltaico Puertollano	Spain	Puertollano (Castilla-La Mancha)	47.6	Fixed	2008
Serenissima PV power plant	Italy	Canaro	48	Fixed	2011
Moura photovoltaic power plant	Portugal	Moura (Alentejo)	46	Tracking	2008
Solarpark Kothen	Germany	Kothen	45	Fixed	2011

overall missions and objectives are quite similar. Since CSP and VLS-PV have different technological features, those two technologies should be regarded as complementary rather than competitive.

Similarly, the French government proposed the Mediterranean Solar Plan (MSP) in 2008. MSP is one of the six flagship projects of the 'Union for the Mediterranean (UfM)'. The goal of the MSP was to achieve 20 GW of renewable energy projects by 2020, and the expected investment needed to achieve the goal was approximately €80 billion.

In response to those initiatives, northern African countries have developed their own strategies for renewable energy. For example, Morocco sets a renewable target of 4000 MW by 2020, with 2000 MW from solar energy (PV and CSP).

A number of companies, research institutes, and governments join these projects. The private companies involved in the framework include manufacturers, construction companies, trade companies, system integrators as well as banks. As such, the concept of solar energy in the desert is no longer a dream. It is now a commercially attractive option for business sectors.

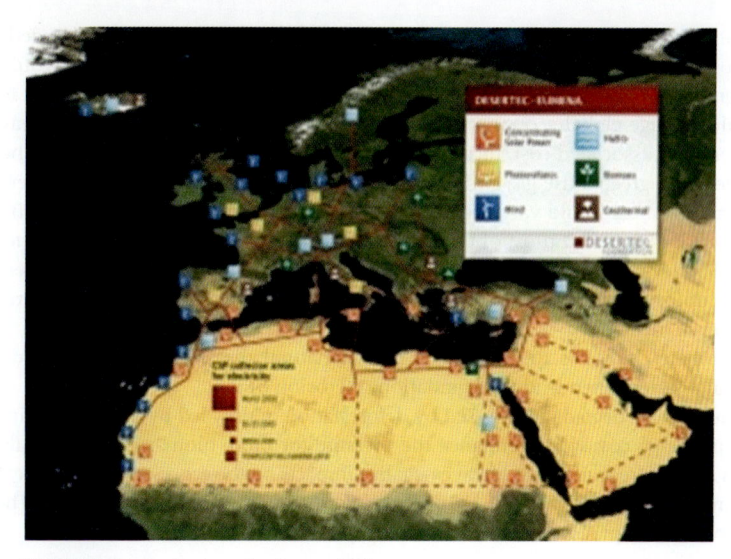

Figure 10 Conceptual image of DESERTEC infrastructure development [7].

1.35.4 Future for the VLS-PV

Although VLS-PV is now in the business process, the present share of renewable energies in the global energy mix is still marginal. Taking into account today's sustainability issues, the role of VLS-PV is far from its final goal. In other words, VLS PV has unlimited potential to contribute to the world's sustainability issues.

1.35.4.1 Sustainability Issues

Sustainability of our society has been threatened by various issues, namely, climate change, energy depletion, water resource shortage, food shortage, and ecosystems. These issues are not independent and closely influence each other in a very complicated manner. **Figure 11** is a simplified diagram of interrelations between various sustainability issues.

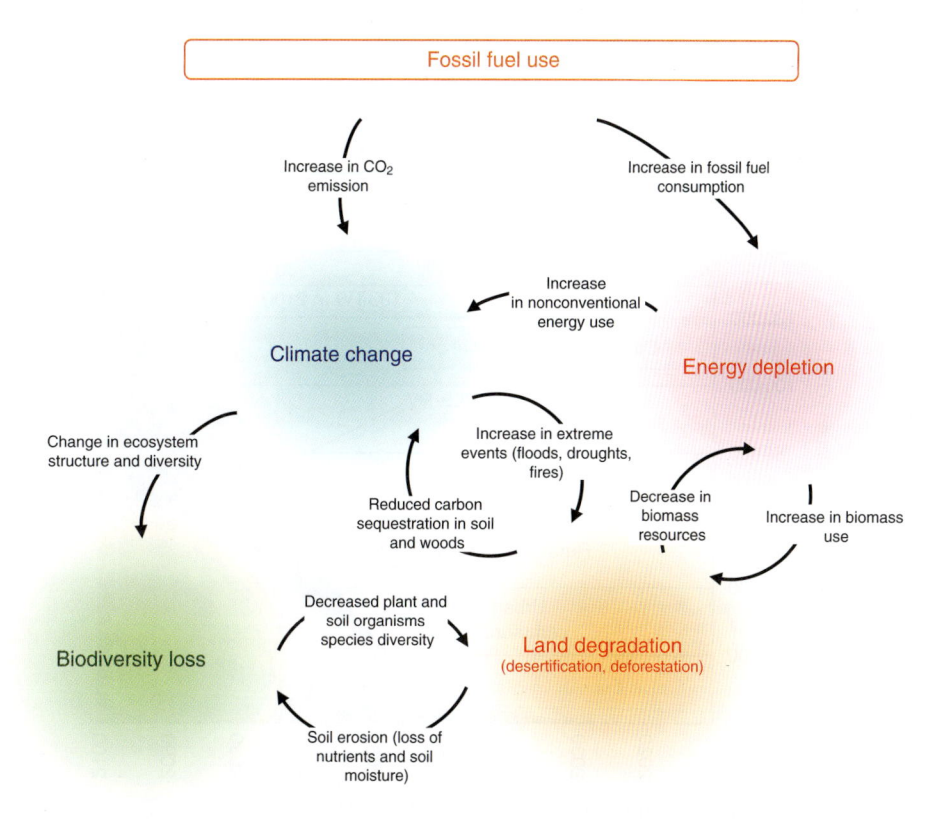

Figure 11 Vicious circle of environmental issues [3].

Increase in energy demand associated with economic expansion and population increase is regarded as one of the major issues for sustainability. Clearly, fossil fuels are finite energy resources and, sooner or later, these resources would be depleted. As fossil fuel use decreases, the costs of energy will increase because of the imbalance between demand and supply. It is needless to say that the increase in energy cost could damage global economy considerably. Since the current economy is heavily dependent on secured energy supply, energy depletion or associated cost, increase may damage most of the sectors all over the world.

Climate change associated with greenhouse gas emission from fossil fuel combustion is another serious issue to be overcome. The regional impacts of climate change would vary depending on the local conditions; however, the Intergovernmental Panel on Climate Change (IPCC) report indicates that most of the regions will experience economic losses if the global temperature rise is greater than 2–3 °C above 1990 levels [8]. To make matters worse, if energy depletion issues become serious and nonconventional fossil fuel energy sources are utilized, the greenhouse gas emissions per unit of energy consumption are expected to increase, thus accelerating climate change even further.

One of the threats of climate change is the increasing risk of natural disasters including flood, drought, forest fire, and desertification. Those natural disasters often lead to degradation or erosion of land.

There are also possibilities of land degradation caused by deforestation mainly led by the increase in biomass use for energy or material use. The increase in energy cost would enhance the pressure for more biomass use especially in developing countries. Naturally, land degradation and deforestation would have negative impacts on the ecosystems in the local and global communities. It is noteworthy that there are many regions where the economy relied mainly on rain-fed agricultures. The impacts on those regions could be significant if appropriate adaptation measures are not in place.

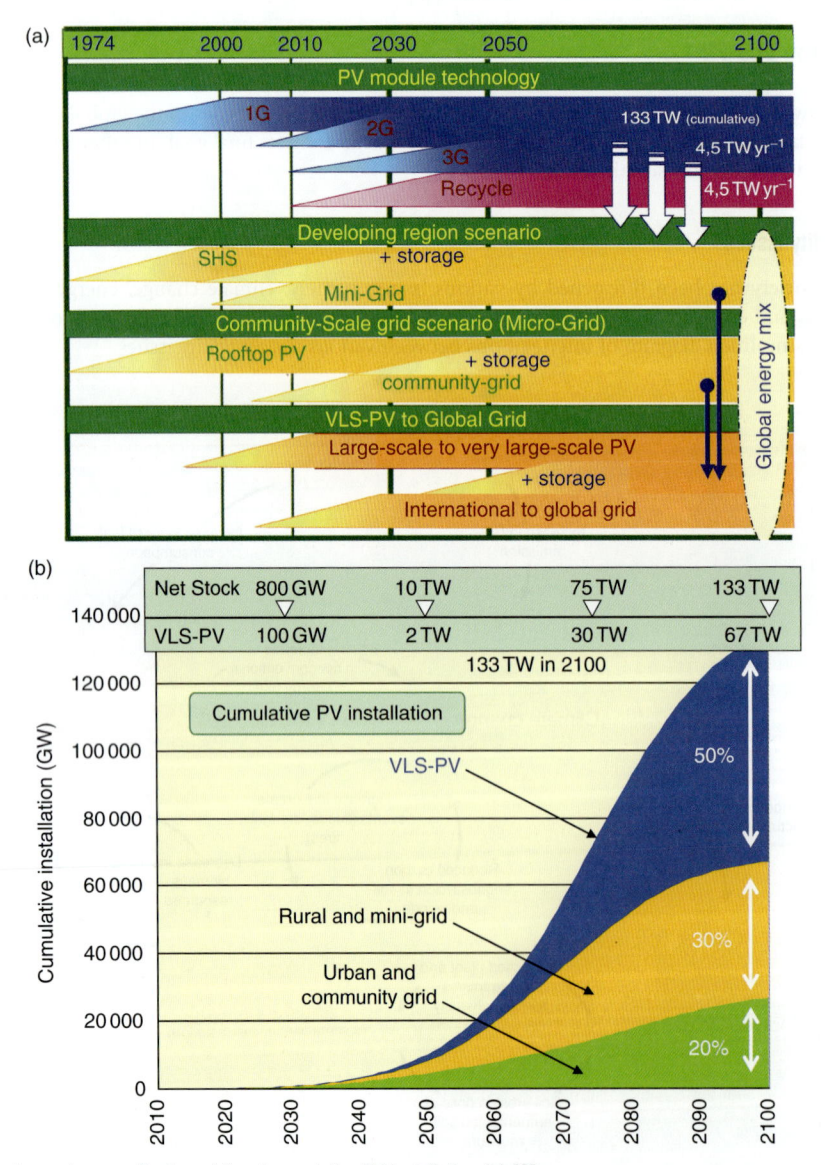

Figure 12 PV roadmap for various applications (a) and cumulative PV installation (b) [3].

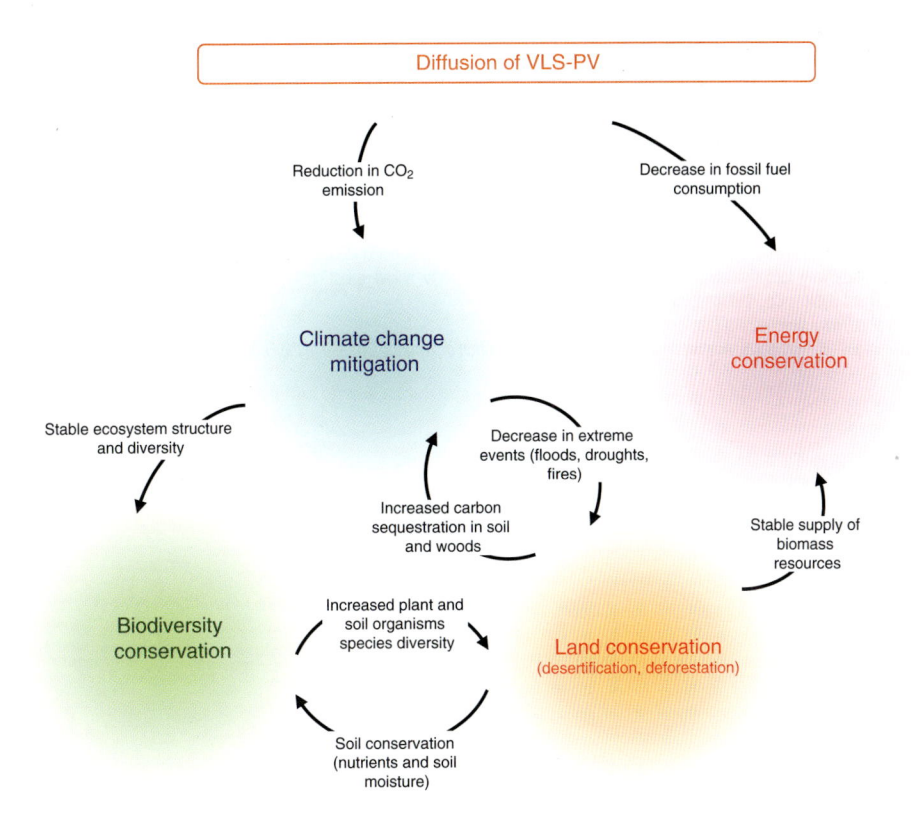

Figure 13 Virtuous circle of environmental issues [3].

1.35.4.2 VLS-PV Visions and Roadmap

In order to be a major source of energy in the global energy mix and contribute to sustainable energy development, VLS-PV should overcome a number of barriers. Such barriers include further system cost reduction, development of replacement or recycling scheme for decommissioned PV systems, and grid stability control.

In order to address those issues, a technological development and market penetration roadmap is developed as part of the IEA-PVPS Task 8 studies (**Figure 12**). The roadmap indicates that the replacement/waste issue would be an issue after 2015–20 and calls for development of recycling technologies.

As for VLS-PV, the market continues to grow with the development of global grid and storage technologies. The overall capacity of PV systems reaches 133 TW in 2100, and 50% of the capacity is from VLS-PV. Although the cost of PV systems continues to decrease, the PV market is expanded to US$5.1 billion yr^{-1}, US$214 billion yr^{-1}, and US$1.7 trillion yr^{-1} for 2020, 2050, and 2100, respectively.

If this vision is achieved in reality, PV is expected to supply approximately a third of global energy assumed in IPCC SRES A1 Scenario [8]. In such a world, various uses of VLS-PV output may become available such as solar hydrogen or solar methane production.

As already discussed above, VLS-PV has great potential to contribute to overcoming these global issues. Especially, after the nuclear accident in Fukushima, Japan, expectations for renewable energy including VLS-PV become higher.

The future dream for VLS-PV is to contribute to the global sustainable energy supply and to turn the vicious circle of the environmental issues into a virtuous circle as presented in **Figure 13**.

1.35.5 Conclusion

VLS-PV is a very unique idea originally presented in 1999 by the IEA-PVPS Task 8 group. The concept has been studied for more than 10 years and the feasibilities are widely evaluated. With the cost reduction of PV modules as well as favorable governmental support, such as the FIT, VLS-PV has become a commercially attractive option today. Currently, more than 1000 megawatt-scale plants are operating or constructed around the world. If the effort of technology and market development continues, VLS-PV would be a powerful solution for current sustainability issues. It is reasonably concluded that VLS-PV has a great potential to turn the vicious circle of environmental issues into a virtuous circle and to solve these problems at the same time.

References

[1] IEA-PVPS Task 8 http://www.iea-pvps.org/index.php?id=35 (accessed 27 October 2011).
[2] Kurokawa K (ed.) (2003) *Energy from the Desert – Feasibility of Very Large Scale Photovoltaic Power Generation (VLS-PV) Systems*. London, UK: James & James (Science Publishers).
[3] Kurokawa K, Komoto K, van der Vleuten P, and Faiman D (eds.) (2007) *Energy from the Desert – Practical Proposals for Very Large Scale Photovoltaic Systems*. London, UK: Earthscan.
[4] European Photovoltaic Industry Association (2011) Solar Photovoltaics Competing in the Energy Sector (available at: http://www.epia.org/index.php?eID=tx_nawsecuredl&u=0&file=fileadmin/EPIA_docs/publications/epia/Competing_Full_Report.pdf&t=1325939055&hash=964a868c9b3c7c432528399ef17ca57e).
[5] Global Footprint Network http://www.footprintnetwork.org/en/index.php/GFN/page/frequently_asked_questions/#gen1 (accessed 27 October 2011).
[6] Data Source: Resources Total System Co., Ltd. http://www.pvresources.com.
[7] DESERTEC Foundation http://www.desertec.org (accessed 27 October 2011).
[8] IPCC (2007) *Climate Change 2007 – Impacts, Adaptation and Vulnerability Contribution of Working Group II to the Fourth Assessment Report of the IPCC*. Cambridge: Cambridge University Press.

1.36 Concentration Photovoltaics

M Martinez, O de la Rubia, F Rubio, and P Banda, Instituto de Sistema Fotovoltaicos de Concentración (ISFOC), Puertollano, Spain

© 2012 Elsevier Ltd. All rights reserved.

1.36.1	**Introduction**	745
1.36.1.1	Cells	746
1.36.1.2	Thermal Management	747
1.36.1.3	Optics	747
1.36.1.4	Modules	748
1.36.1.5	Tracking Systems	748
1.36.2	**Historical Review**	749
1.36.3	**Standardization of CPV Systems and Components**	749
1.36.4	**ISFOC CPV Demonstration Power Plants**	750
1.36.4.1	Puertollano – La Nava	750
1.36.4.2	Concentrix – El Villar	751
1.36.4.3	SolFocus – Almoguera	751
1.36.4.4	Regulatory Framework	751
1.36.4.5	Engineering, Construction, and Commissioning of CPV Plants	753
1.36.5	**CPV Characterization and Rating**	754
1.36.5.1	Procedure	755
1.36.5.2	Standard Test Conditions	755
1.36.5.3	DC Rating Procedure	755
1.36.5.4	AC Rating Procedure	758
1.36.5.5	Status and Results	759
1.36.6	**Production Results**	760
1.36.6.1	Performance	760
1.36.6.2	Operation and Maintenance	762
1.36.7	**Outlook**	763
References		764
Further Reading		765
Relevant Websites		765

Glossary

Concentration Photovoltaics (CPV) Photovoltaic using concentrated sunlight into the cell using an optic.
Concentrator Assembly of CPV modules plus tracking system.
Direct Normal Irradiation (DNI) Component from the solar irradiation that comes directly from the sun.
Multijunction Solar Cells Solar cells based in Compound III-V Semiconductor with different junctions.
Tracking System Structure where the modules are mounted, that tracks the sun accurately and assures the proper performance of the Concentrator.
Optics Optical devices used to increase the luminous flux on the cells. Usually primary optic works as a light collector (fresnel lens, mirror) and secondary elements are in charged of homogenizing, filtering making the light reaching the cell.
Standard Test Conditions Set of ambient conditions in which the characterization is done to permit the comparison between devices. Usually the variables are DNI, wind and temperature.
Power Rating Characterization process for determining the power of a CPV element (cell, module, concentrator, or plant) in some fixed conditions (STC).
Balance of System (BOS) All components of a CPV installation other than the CPV modules and the tracker. It includes inverter, switches, wiring, etc.

1.36.1 Introduction

The key idea behind concentration photovoltaics (CPV) is to replace the area of active material, which currently is the most expensive, with optic elements that can be manufactured cheaper. At large concentrations, the cell size is reduced considerably (i.e., 500–1000 times as compared to one sun modules), allowing a cost distribution scheme different from traditional photovoltaics (PV). On the one hand, the challenges of this technology rely on future developments on the optic components, thermal

1.36.1.1 Cells

Cell technology has been greatly improved and the efficiency consequently increased. Si-based solar cells with back point contact [1] reached an efficiency record of 27.6%, and some manufacturers, like Amonix [2] or Guascor Foton [3], used this type of cells under more than 400 × concentration. However, the best improvement in cell technology lies in the use of compound III–V semiconductors. Ternary alloys of III–V elements, like GaAs together with In, Al, and P, allow a better temperature behavior of the cell. The GaAs thermal coefficient is $1.76 \times 10^{-3}\,°C^{-1}$, being about half that of Si, which is $3.21 \times 10^{-3}\,°C^{-1}$. Also, III–V technology brings the development of multijunction solar cells: two or more p–n junctions are monolithically integrated into a single device. The use of these cells allows a better use of the solar spectrum as each one of the junctions is optimized to capture the radiation of a different part of the spectrum. **Figure 1** shows the concept of spectrum exploitation by multijunction cells as compared to single-junction Silicon cell. Based on the spectral response, the theoretical limit efficiency of silicon cells is 31%, whereas multijunction cells could reach 86% [4]. Current records for laboratory multijunction cell are 43.5% from Solar Junction, 42.3% from Spire, 41.6% from Spectrolab [5], and 41.1% from Fraunhofer-Instituts für Solare Energiesysteme (ISE) (**Figure 2**). These four records were achieved with different technologies. Fraunhofer technology uses a metamorphic approach where the materials in the cells have different lattice constants resulting in more freedom for the selection of the composition of each junction. Spectrolab is using an advanced version of the traditional lattice-matched triple-junction technology with improved metal grid shadowing and serial resistance. The Spire record was reached with a new methodology that uses a bifacial approach, with a mismatched InGaAs cell that is epitaxially grown on the backside. Solar Junction has developed the new record cell using dilute nitride-based materials to optimize the performance through band gap tuning, maintaining a lattice-matched structure. Other new technology is used by QuantaSol who enhances the efficiency of cells using its quantum wells to tune sub-cell structures. In the near future, these manufacturers, together with Emcore, Azur Space, Cyrium, and others, will develop four-, five-, and six-junction cells aiming at efficiencies of up to 50%.

This very high efficiency allows the reduction of the cell size down to $1\,cm^2$ or even 1 or $2\,mm^2$, as in the Isofoton or Concentrix systems [6]. This decreasing area allows also the improvement of the thermal performance and decrease of the serial resistance [7]. Currently, almost all systems using multijunction cells have concentration ratios of more than 350 ×, mostly more than 450 × (such as Concentrix, SolFocus, Arima, etc.), and even 1000 × (such as Isofoton, Energy Innovations, etc.).

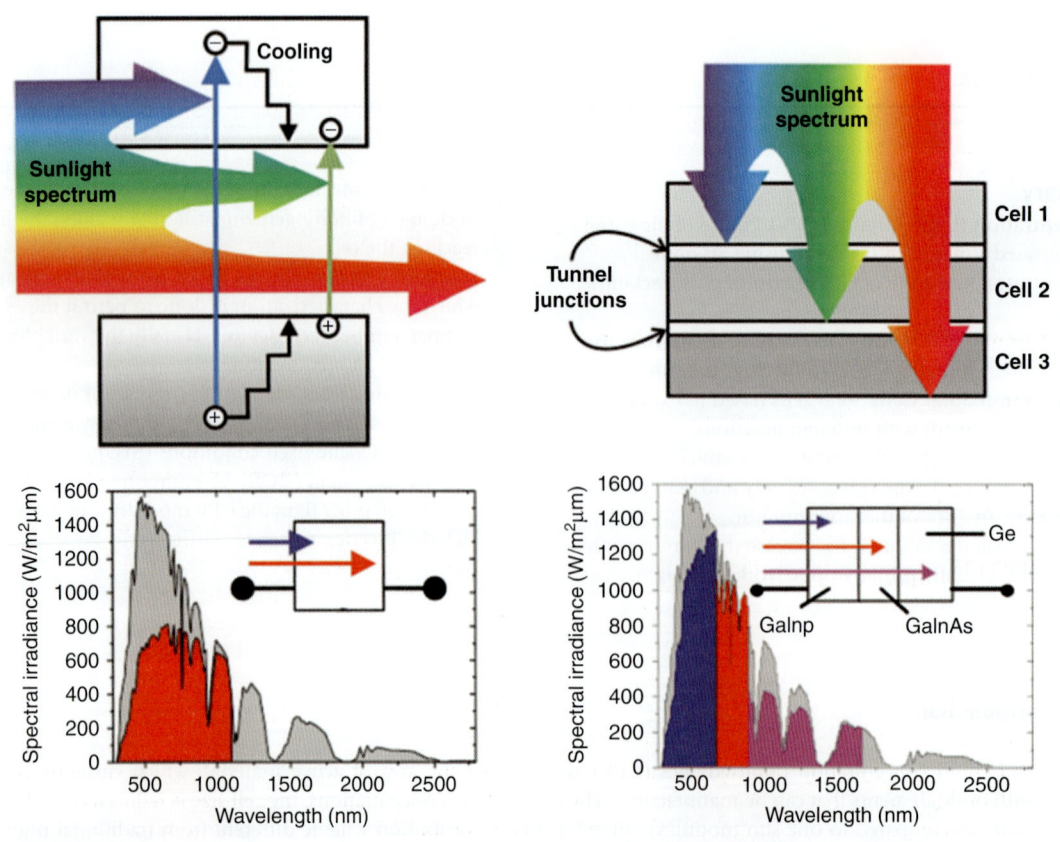

Figure 1 Solar spectrum in Si and multijunction cells. Courtesy of Antonio Luque from Institute of Solar Energy – UPM, Madrid.

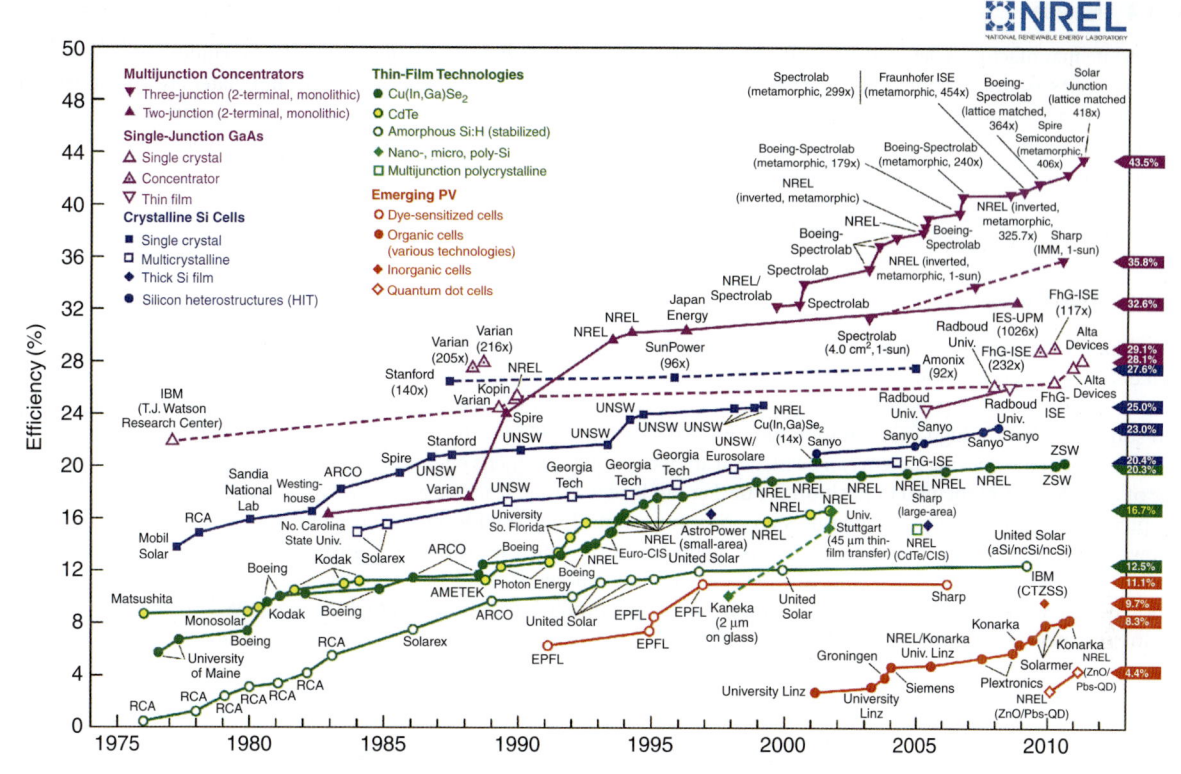

Figure 2 Best research cell efficiencies. Courtesy of National Renewable Energy Laboratory (NREL).

1.36.1.2 Thermal Management

Most of the manufacturers use some type of heat sink as passive cooling. In many designs, the solar cell is mounted on an alumina plate, which is a good electrical insulator and a good thermal conductor. To improve the thermal performance, there are designs that comprise a very simple and small copper or aluminum plate [8]. Some other designs consider the attachment of the cell mount directly to the metal housing of the module. Other options include the use of intermediate thermal systems. Higher concentrations will require the use of larger heat sinks in extruded aluminum with a very good thermal contact to the cells. In large parabolic mirror dish systems, such as those from Solar Systems (Australia) [9], due to the fact that all the cells are mounted side by side and the thermal dissipation area is lower, an active cooling system is needed.

1.36.1.3 Optics

Optical designs that meet the strict criteria for high-concentration systems are the key to new CPV concepts. Traditionally, flat Fresnel lens or mirrors have been used, as the ones in Sandia, Ramon Areces, and Euclides systems [10]. In current systems, Fresnel lens is still the preferred optical element (such as Concentrix, Amonix, Guascor, Emcore, Arima ECO, Renovalia CPV, Sol3G, Entech, etc.). Ease of design and simulation, as well as its reduced cost, are the reasons why this is the component of choice. Nevertheless, its manufacturing implies a number of challenges as required for high-concentration CPV. There are different technologies to manufacture a Fresnel lens, from injection or compression molding, with very difficult tuning, to silicone films. To improve the acceptance angle of the system, a secondary element may be used. This element is normally made of a solid glass or hollow metal prism, which allows a better light distribution on the cell and improves the collection of the light [11]. Nevertheless, optical systems without a secondary element can provide very high efficiency as well [12].

Alternatively, reflective optics is also being used. There are several approaches, such as a large parabolic mirror dish concentrating light onto a dense array of cells, as in the Solar Systems technology [13], or as compact mirror systems, with one parabolic mirror per cell, which can incorporate additional reflection steps as in the SolFocus system [14].

Additionally, other nonimaging optical concepts, like the total internal reflection (TIR) system [15], are being applied. In recent years, new optical concepts have been developed (i.e., combining reflective (X) and refractive (R) optical phases – XR [16] – or refractive, reflective, and internal reflection (I) phases – RXI [17]), to achieve very high concentration with a wide acceptance angle.

1.36.1.4 Modules

CPV module manufacturers define the specifications of the product along the whole value chain. This includes not only the design of cells, receivers, optics, and thermal management but also the housing of the module, its design, and materials. The housing must protect the components against the environment, considering that it also requires maintaining ventilation within the hollow modules. The electrical isolation of the module is also one of the requirements and challenges for this type of technology and it must be adapted to the environmental isolation constraints in the design.

Today, there are more than 60 CPV module manufacturers in the world, especially in the United States, Spain, Israel, Taiwan, Japan, Australia, Italy, Portugal, the United Kingdom, Germany, Canada, China, and Korea.

1.36.1.5 Tracking Systems

Depending on the acceptance angle of the optics and the module technology, the accuracy of the tracking system needs to be adapted. Up to a concentration ratio of 2.5 ×, there is no need for sun tracking. For a mid-concentration, up to 40 ×, the tracker can be linear, like the Euclides (**Figure 3**) or Skyline system, only with elevation movement in a polar axis or east-west movement in a north-south axis. But for high-concentration systems, two-axis sun tracking with a very high accuracy is mandatory (**Figure 4**) [18].

The control of the tracking system can be made in an open-loop (ephemeris equations) or closed-loop system (light sensor). The usage of a single control method to position the tracker can lead to errors. Tracking accuracy will be reduced if a system that has not been precisely installed and positioned uses an open-loop control. A closed-loop system will not work properly if the sensor is shadowed during operation. Current systems use hybrid control, which include both sun movement algorithms and radiation sensors [19]. Tracker manufacturers, like Abengoa, Sener, Titan Tracker, Payran, Feyna, and so on, or CPV systems manufacturers, like SolFocus, Emcore, Guascor, Renovalia CPV, and so on, are producing commercial high-accuracy systems.

Currently, new qualification and validation standards are being developed to assure the right operation and reliability of the trackers.

Figure 3 One-axis tracking in an Euclides system.

Figure 4 Two-axis trackers in an ISFOC CPV power plant.

1.36.2 Historical Review

CPV and its potential to reduce costs of solar electricity systems have been in the mind of the scientists since the 1970s [20]. At that time, the small volume of the PV market did not make the installations of CPV plants possible. It was not until 2005 that a few CPV plants were deployed. Only module prototypes or some demonstration systems of a few kilowatts were installed at research institutes (e.g., Instituto de Energía Solar, Universidad Politécnica de Madrid (IES-UPM) in Spain, Fraunhofer-ISE in Germany; APS, Sandia Laboratories, and NREL in the United States) and in the premises of very few R&D companies (e.g., Amonix, Entech, Solar System).

Since the early 1980s, IES-UPM has been developing CPV demonstration and R&D projects such as Ramon Areces, Miner, and Euclides. In 1998, after the success of the Euclides array, a demonstration plant of 480 kWp was installed in Tenerife (**Figure 5**). This was the largest CPV plant in the world until 2003. New versions and optimizations of the original Euclides design have been developed, and an American company, Skyline, is using a similar concept in its product.

Another pioneering installation has been the SOLERAS project in Saudi Arabia, installed by Sandia Laboratories in the 1980s. These systems showed degradation of up to 20% in 6 years, mainly due to delamination issues at high temperature. A further issue resulted from the use of outdated tracker technology, creating problems with the algorithms and control systems. Despite these hurdles, this project continued in operation for 18 years.

Apart from these projects, there were very few demonstration plants installed during those years until 2006. At that time, the PV market experienced an impressive growth in Europe, and CPV had an opportunity to show its potential.

The Institute of Concentration Photovoltaics Systems (ISFOC) was created in September 2006 with the objective of supporting the first steps of the emerging CPV industry moving from prototypes to commercial products [21]. ISFOC was originated from an R&D plan established in Castilla-La Mancha region, Spain, with the support of Regional and Spanish National governments and the UPM, and financial assistance of FEDER funds of the European Union. Since then, ISFOC has been thrusting the industrialization and commercialization of the most advanced CPV technologies through the installation of various CPV pilot power plants. The objective of these pilot plants is to assist the industries in the setting up of pilot fabrication lines and helping in the development of industry standards. Also, very valuable information is obtained in the process, such as reliability, suitability, and production from each of the technologies under test.

1.36.3 Standardization of CPV Systems and Components

In any emerging market and technology, standardization is needed to assure the quality of the design and to give credibility to the product through its reliability. All players in CPV technology are involved at different levels in the creation of new standards to accelerate the development of this industry. In this process, a reference for the comparison of various CPV products is being made available by ISFOC, providing a tool for the financing of the first power plants, which need to comply with performance and profitability requirements.

The first standard of the CPV technology was only approved officially in December 2007. This first standard is the IEC 62108 "Concentrator Photovoltaic (CPV) Modules and Assemblies – Design Qualification and Type Approval" [22]. The objective of this standard is to determine the electrical, mechanical, and thermal characteristics of the CPV modules and assemblies and to show, as far as possible within reasonable constraints of cost and time, that the CPV modules and assemblies are capable of withstanding prolonged exposure in open-air climates. This standard describes the qualification tests to be carried out on the CPV modules and assemblies consisting of climatic, electrical, weather, and mechanical outdoor tests.

The partner companies that deployed their systems at ISFOC plants were the first to perform the tests described in the standard. All of them had to make improvements in their design to pass the tests, proving the value of the standard. Nevertheless, reviews and improvements are being done in the standard to be adapted to new CPV modules, assemblies, and materials.

Figure 5 Euclides plant (480 kW) in Tenerife in 1999.

This standard was developed by the Working group 7 of the Technical Committee 82 of the International Electrotechnical Commission (IEC) (i.e., WG7 of the IEC TC82). This group work very actively on new standards to accelerate the development of the technology. The standards currently in preparation are as follows:

- *CPV power rating.* IEC 62670 'Module and Assembly Performance Testing and Energy Rating'. It defines a procedure for measuring the power of a CPV module under a standard set of conditions.
- *Energy performance ratio.* It provides a simple, but quantitative, method for determining an energy rating.
- *On-site plant acceptance.* It is a procedure to measure and evaluate the CPV power plant performance after its installation. It will allow the acceptance of a plant, once it is installed.
- *Cell's qualification and reliability.* It provides with a common set of product qualification tests and performance parameters for bare solar cells intended for CPV applications.
- *Tracker technical specifications.* It normalizes the terminology, allows meaningful comparison of specifications, and provides a foundation for design qualification, performance, safety and reliability standards
- *Tracker qualification.* This is a new standard that will specify the qualification tests that the tracker should pass to work in the CPV systems.

1.36.4 ISFOC CPV Demonstration Power Plants

The increase in the renewable energy market since 2005 meant a renewed interest in CPV, with its application to high-irradiation areas in the world. The ISFOC project proved to be instrumental for the development of the CPV industry in the period 2006–10. In this period, the first CPV demonstration power plants were deployed under ISFOC administration, and a considerable participation of systems manufacturers contributed to the success of the project.

The objective of these demonstration plants is contributing to the achievements set out in the White Paper for a Community Strategy and Action Plan [23] from the European Commission. It is intended that renewable energy will eventually represent 12% of the primary energy consumed in the European Union by 2010. The objective for PV solar energy is 3 GWp. To comply with this objective, the Plan for the Promotion of Renewable Energy in Spain was approved in 1999 [24]. This plan established a goal for PV of installing 144 MWp by 2010.

In August 2005, the Plan for Renewable Energy in Spain (Plan Nacional de Energías Renovables – PER), 2005–10 [25], was approved in which the 1999 plan was revised. The promise to cover 12% of the total consumption of energy from renewable sources by 2010 was kept and two other objectives were incorporated to achieve 29.4% of electric generation from renewable sources and 5.75% from biofuels for transport by the same year. For PV solar energy, the objective was raised from 144 MWp installed to 400 MWp by 2010. The very attractive market conditions and further modifications to the regulations led to a total accumulated PV installation of more than 3500 MW at the end of 2010 in Spain.

In 2006, the ISFOC launched an international call for tenders, looking for companies with a commercial product for CPV plants. The objective of this public bidding was to obtain both technical and financial proposals for the provision of CPV plants connected to the electrical network at a total of 2.7 MW. The PV plants were to be situated at different geographical locations within Castilla-La Mancha, Spain. As a result, three large CPV plants were built.

1.36.4.1 Puertollano – La Nava

The first installation has a nominal power of 800 kW adding up the inverter's rated power with ground coverage of 40 000 m^2. The layout of the installation is shown in **Figure 6**. **Table 1** summarizes its technical specifications.

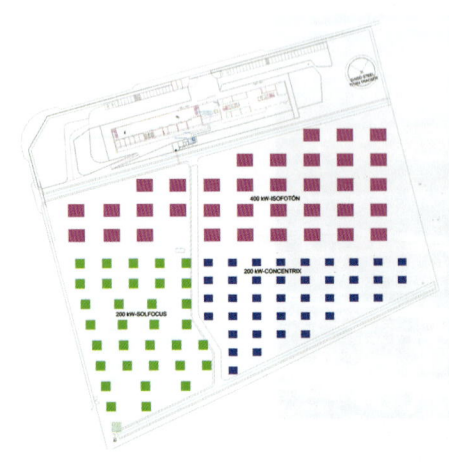

Figure 6 Layout and picture of the ISFOC La Nava power plant.

Table 1 Technical specifications of the La Nava installation

La Nava technology	SolFocus	Isofoton	Concentrix solar
Inverter nominal power (kW)	200	400	200
Number of trackers	33	36	36
Number of inverters	33	4	36
Nominal power of inverters (kW)	$31 \times 6; 2 \times 7$	4×100	36×5.5
CPV modules	CPV-16-205	HCP-30MM	CX150 and CX200
Optics and cells	Cassegrain reflector	TIR	Fresnel lens (silicon on glass)
Tracker	Inspira		Pairan trackers

1.36.4.2 Concentrix – El Villar

A second installation within the first call for tenders was built in the area where the second call for tenders would be later built. Taking a nominal power of 300 kW and covering a total of 18 000 m² it comprises only Concentrix systems (**Table 2**).

1.36.4.3 SolFocus – Almoguera

A third installation of the first call for tenders was built in Almoguera in the province of Guadalajara, comprising only SolFocus systems with the characteristics as shown in **Table 3** and **Figure 7**.

In the year 2008, ISFOC launched a second call for tender with the objective of bringing into the project new companies that were getting CPV products ready for the market.

More than 10 companies participated in the call and four of them were awarded an installation in the second phase of the project. With this second award, the project was setting the basis for CPV access to the market and opening new opportunities. This site was built in the El Villar area close to Puertollano. The grid connection for this installation is to be regulated under the RD 1565/2010, and as PV installations grew in Spain, the tariff was forced down to less than 55% of the tariff received by the first installation 2 years before. A nominal power of 1300 kW covers an area of 78 000 m² with four new technologies (see **Table 4** and **Figure 8**).

1.36.4.4 Regulatory Framework

PVs in Spain have been under government regulation since 1990s with the publishing, in 1998, of the Royal Decree RD 2818/1998. This decree was the first regulation for renewable power plants connected to the grid in Spain. At the beginning, tariffs of

Table 2 Technical specifications of the El Villar installation

Technology	Concentrix
Inverter nominal power (kW)	300
Number of trackers	38
Number of inverters	60
Nominal power of inverters (kW)	42×4.75 and 18×5.5
CPV modules	CX150 and CX200
Optics and cells	Fresnel lens
Tracker	27 Pairan trackers and 11 Abengoa trackers

Table 3 Technical specifications of the Almoguera installation

Technology	SolFocus
Inverter nominal power (kW)	300
Number of trackers	54
Number of inverters	27
Nominal power of inverters (kW)	27×11
CPV modules	CPV-16-205
Optics and cells	Cassegrain reflector
Tracker	Inspira

Figure 7 Layout and picture of the ISFOC Almoguera power plant.

Table 4 Technical specifications of the El Villar installation

Technology	Emcore	Renovalia CPV	Sol3G	Arima
Inverter nominal power (kW)	300	300	400	300
Number of trackers	15	99	12	99
Inverters	3 × 100 kW	TBD		99 × 3 kW
CPV modules	Emcore CPV array, 25 kW$_p$	Parabolic dish	Sol3g Gen1.2, Sol3g Gen2	HCPV-G1
Optics	Fresnel lens with reflective secondary, 500 ×	Parabolic dish	Fresnel lens and secondary	Fresnel lens with collimator, 476 ×
Cells	Multijunction, 1 cm^2	Close-packed multijunction cells	Multijunction	Multijunction, 0.3 cm^2
Tracker	Emcore CPV, 95 m^2	Renovalia	Abengoa Solar	HOUYI-1A

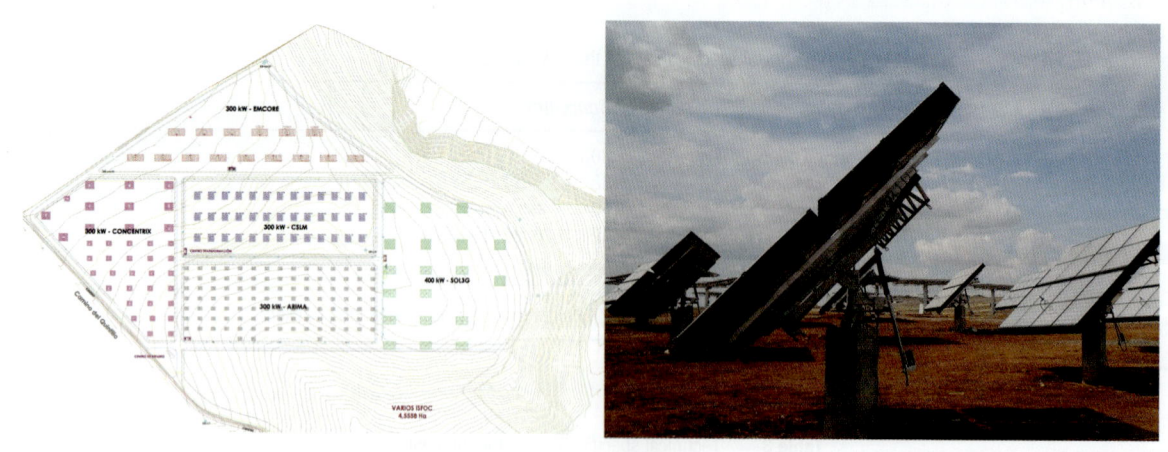

Figure 8 Layout and picture of the ISFOC El Villar power plant.

39.55 c€ kWh^{-1} for PV installations up to 5 kW and 21.64 c€ kWh^{-1} for PV installations with more than 5 kW were established. The tariffs were increased yearly, and in 2004, they were 40 and 22 c€ kWh^{-1}, respectively, for the two types of installations.

The PV Spanish market was growing fast in size and number of installations and a new regulation was needed. The Spanish Government published a second Royal Decree RD 436/2004. In this new regulation, a new tariff was established for PV installations up to 100 kW with a factor of 575% over a reference tariff (Tarifa Media de Referencia – TMR). The TMR was revised every year: 7.2072 c€ kWh^{-1} in 2004, 7.3304 c€ kWh^{-1} in 2005, and 7.6588 c€ kWh^{-1} in 2006.

A new RD Law 7/2006 modified the regulation in June 2006 when the bonus of 575% over the TMR was eliminated and a new Royal Decree was announced. In May 2007, the Royal Decree RD 661/2007 was announced and published and new tariffs were established: 44.0381 c€ kWh^{-1} for PV installations up to 100 kW and 41.75 c€ kWh^{-1} for PV installations between 100 kW and 10 MW.

One year later, on September 2008, a new regulation came in force, the RD 1578/2008. This new Royal Decree was for PV installations specifically. The PV installations were divided into two categories; rooftop applications and ground installations. The tariff was reduced – for rooftop installations, up to 20 kW, the tariff was 34 c€ kWh^{-1}; for rooftop installations over 20 kW, the tariff was 32 c€ kWh^{-1}; and for ground installations the tariff was 32 c€ kW^{-1}.

These tariffs were drastically reduced by the law RDL 14/2010 published in December 2010, which even limited the number of hours of operation of a PV power plant. It is worth noticing the key importance of the regulation on new technologies coming into a new market, as in a short period of time a highly beneficial environment can turn into a hostile framework for their deployment. **Figure 9** presents the evolution of tariffs along the last years in Spain and the influence of each change in the regulation on total power installed.

1.36.4.5 Engineering, Construction, and Commissioning of CPV Plants

The project lifecycle of any PV installation can be basically divided into three parts:

- Engineering or design.
- Construction or installation.
- Commissioning.

The objective of a CPV installation like any other generation power plant is to obtain economic benefits. As CPV technology only uses the direct normal irradiation (DNI) for conversion to electricity, availability of direct solar resource becomes the key parameter for the selection of a feasible location. Current estimations set a lower limit of about 1800 kWh m^{-2} yr^{-1} of DNI, although technology improvements in the future might reduce that limit.

A CPV project has to be engineered considering the best design to reduce energy losses during the plant operation. A shading study, energy losses in cables, and inverter selection are the most important aspects to be taken into account during the power plant design. The power plant design has to comply with local regulation for this purpose as well as with electrical and civil regulations. The equipment and elements of the installation have to be manufactured with the certificates established in these local regulations.

The construction and installation of a CPV power plant has the same problems as a conventional PV installation with trackers. The control of the tracker foundations, tracker installation, and CPV modules alignment are critical, as the tracker is one of the most important elements of a CPV installation. CPV technology is sensitive exclusively to direct radiation. So, the control of the tracker installation is critical to ensure the optimum performance of the systems.

Once the CPV power plant is ready for operation, it is necessary to check all the systems and elements installed. The aim of plant commissioning is to verify that the CPV plant operates properly and safely for operators. Proper alignment of modules and a precise performance of the trackers are the key points for good operation. Alarms and warnings offered by the control software together with the grounding system of the electrical installation are key for personal and equipment safety.

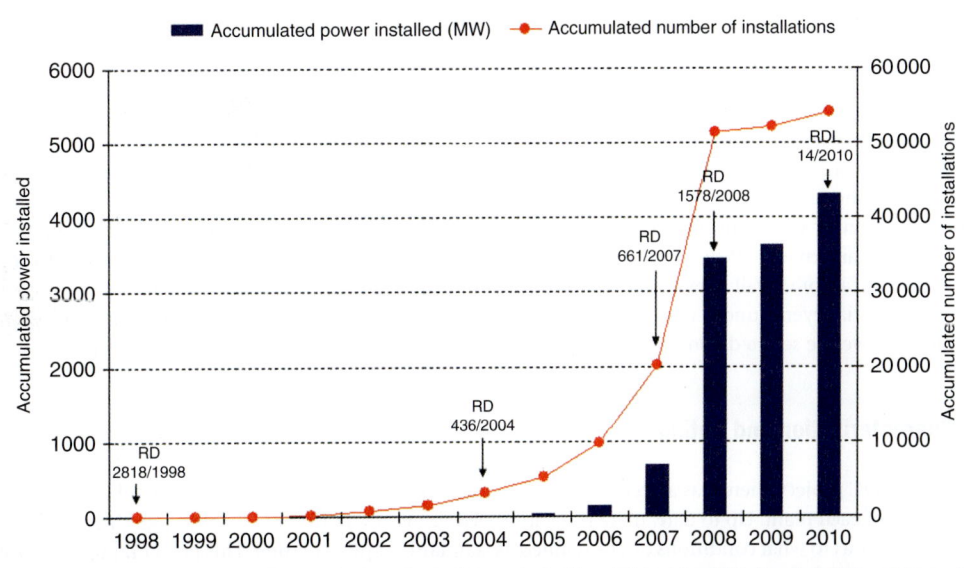

Figure 9 PV market in Spain and corresponding regulation. From data periodically published by CNE. Spanish National Commission of Energy (www.cne.es).

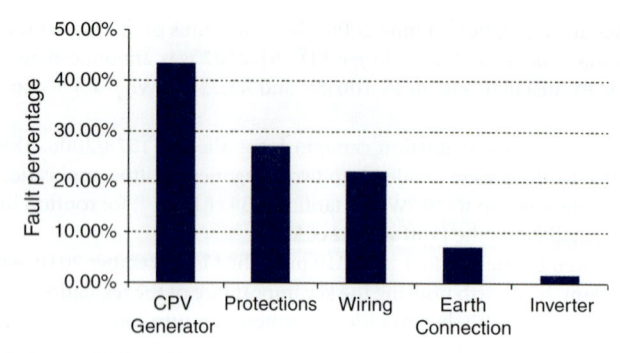

Figure 10 Breakdown of occurring faults in a CPV installation.

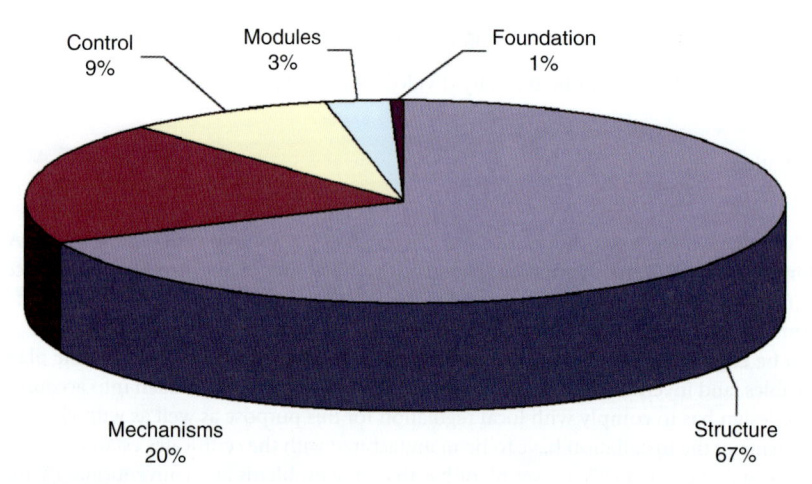

Figure 11 CPV generator fault distribution.

The first step in commissioning a CPV plant is the field technical inspection and the verification of the control software prior to starting up of the installation [26].

The field technical inspection consists of the verification and checking process performed on the installation prior to starting up to assure quality and reliability. Therefore, every installed component is evaluated to verify if they comply with health and safety requirements as well as with standards and technical specifications in Spain. For this verification, the installation is divided into two parts: DC side (i.e., CPV generator including tracker, modules, and DC wiring; protections, inverter; and DC grounding) and AC side (i.e., AC wiring, protections, grid connection, and AC grounding). All the elements or components on each side are checked individually.

The breakdown of the most common defects detected during a field technical inspection of CPV plants are depicted in **Figure 10** [27]. The defects are primarily located in the CPV generator with the distribution shown in **Figure 11**. CPV generator faults had their root cause in corrosion problems in the tracker (67%) and in the tracker mechanisms (20%).

However, although most of the faults do not affect the starting up of an installation, they may still affect the warranty periods and conditions in a maintenance contract.

The purpose of the control and monitoring software verification is to check the operation of the plant both in regular operation conditions and under maintenance. With this purpose, the software control should fulfil the requirements for controlling the complete installation to automatically track the sun and to implement all the warnings and alarms required to detect any malfunction. For the special events under maintenance, the control software must be able to manage each concentrator independently, being able to move the selected concentrators to special positions while the rest of the systems keep tracking the sun.

1.36.5 CPV Characterization and Rating

At the beginning of ISFOC project, there was a need to carry out rating and acceptance of power plants, which means the evaluation of the nominal power of each plant. Up to date, there is no approved rating standard for CPV, although there seems to be common agreement in the industry as to what conditions can be defined as standard for power rating. This power rating is key information for ISFOC as it is going to be used afterwards as an input to analyze the performance of the plants, which includes looking for the origin of the energy losses, the degradation of CPV modules, the effect of soiling, and so on. It is also very useful information for the manufacturers to evaluate their product and implement further improvements. With these tasks, ISFOC has also obtained very precious information to take active part in the process of developing rating standards, as it is so far the only organization that can test the procedures in different technologies.

1.36.5.1 Procedure

Nowadays, there is no official procedure for rating the electrical performance of a CPV system or for carrying out the acceptance of a CPV plant. The WG7 of the IEC TC82 is the group within the IEC committee that is working on these tasks.

The objective of the ISFOC rating procedure is to determine the CPV plant's nominal power, under standard test conditions (STC), at the point of connection to the grid. With this purpose, and guided by our R&D principle, first we determine the DC power of the plant, that is, the power generated by the concentrators, and then we make corrections to this number with the real losses of the plant to obtain the AC power [28–30].

The ISFOC procedure is based on power measurements in operating conditions and translation to STC with equations based on the Shockley model adapted to multijunction solar cells.

1.36.5.2 Standard Test Conditions

Currently, there is a lot of controversy around what are the suitable STC to be used in CPV [31, 32]; in fact, the IEC TC82 WG7 is now trying to define the best conditions, that is, what is the best value to use for DNI, and at which temperature. There is a need to define which temperature is to be used as standard. While an ambient temperature is suitable for predicting the performance of the systems at any location, equivalent cell temperature makes the measurements and characterization of the modules easier.

The STC used by ISFOC are based on the equivalent cell temperature parameter. The values are as follows:

- DNI of $850\,W\,m^{-2}$.
- Equivalent cell temperature of 60 °C.

ISFOC uses this temperature parameter instead of ambient conditions (i.e., ambient temperature and wind, speed, and direction) because it is very complex to accurately determine and formulate the influence of those variables on the electrical performance of a CPV system.

It is well known that there are more environmental conditions to be taken into account when rating a CPV plant [33–36], such as spectrum, wind, and circumsolar radiation. In the ISFOC rating procedure, some limitations to the ambient conditions are set upon taking the measurements in order to minimize the influence of those other variables.

1.36.5.3 DC Rating Procedure

The purpose of the DC power rating is to obtain the DC nominal power in STC of the installed plants. In this step of the procedure, the aim is to characterize the concentrators of the plant, to analyze the potential of the PV conversion of the systems. Furthermore, this number can be used as an input for examining the energy losses of the installation.

A set of concentrators is measured in operation conditions so as to obtain the DC nominal power under STC of those concentrators. Consequently, DC nominal power of the plant in STC will be the average obtained from those concentrators measured, following eqn [1]:

$$P_{DC,\,plant} = C \times \overline{P_{DC,\,conc}} \qquad [1]$$

where $P_{DC,plant}$ is the DC nominal power under STC for the CPV plant, C is the number of concentrators in the CPV plant, and $\overline{P_{DC,conc}}$ is the averaged DC nominal power under STC for the concentrator.

In most of the cases, we have obtained the DC nominal power of all the concentrators of the plant. In the future, these data can be used to analyze the degradation of the systems or to detect failures in the concentrators.

To calculate the DC nominal power, the measured maximum power of the concentrator in operation conditions is translated to STC. This procedure is replicated in all concentrators selected of the plant.

For each concentrator selected, the variables to be measured are as follows:

- The I–V curve or characteristic curve of the concentrator to obtain the maximum power in operation conditions.
- The DNI with two pyrheliometers in two independent trackers to assure an accurate value. This is a crucial parameter as it defines the energy input for a concentrator.
- For the calculation of the equivalent cell temperature under operation, the heat-sink temperature is registered. Several thermal sensors are installed on the back plate of the module behind the cells.
- Other ambient conditions are monitored using a meteorological station to complete the measurements with the ambient conditions (i.e., temperature and wind direction and speed).
- Finally, the DNI spectrum is measured with a spectroradiometer to compare the actual spectrum with the standard one.

Figure 12 DC power rating measuring equipments.

Figure 12 shows the equipments used for performing the measurements of the plant. At the left side of the figure, we can see the pyrheliometers on the tracker of the meteorological station for measuring the DNI, a spectroradiometer, and the second pyrheliometer on an independent tracker. In the center, the I–V curve tracer for measuring the power is shown. At the upper right side, there is a thermal probe measuring the heat-sink temperature of a module, and at the bottom, the equipment for measuring the ambient conditions, air temperature, and wind is shown.

To obtain a reliable value for the measured power, it is necessary to establish some limitations to the ambient conditions during the measurements. The DNI has to be higher than 700 W m^{-2}, assuring that the sky is clear with no clouds around the sun; this limitation tries to avoid, as much as possible, any spectral effect that is not taken into account and not corrected with the translation equations to STC. The wind speed has to be lower than 3.3 m s^{-1}, allowing the thermal stabilization of the concentrator, since wind speed is a factor that influences the heat dissipation of the system.

All of these variables are registered during a period of time to achieve a precise value for the power. First, the measurements are filtered to select a stable period where the concentrator is thermally stabilized with no relevant variations in the DNI. **Figure 13** shows the evolution of the temperature measured at the heat sink and the equivalent temperature calculated at the cell. It also shows the evolution of the open-circuit voltage (V_{OC}), which is a perfect thermometer, of the system. In the figure, the first measurements where the system is reaching the thermal stabilization are highlighted.

The selected measurements in operation conditions are translated to STC (**Figure 14**) using the equations presented in ISFOC call for tenders based on the Shockley model and defined for multijunction solar cells.

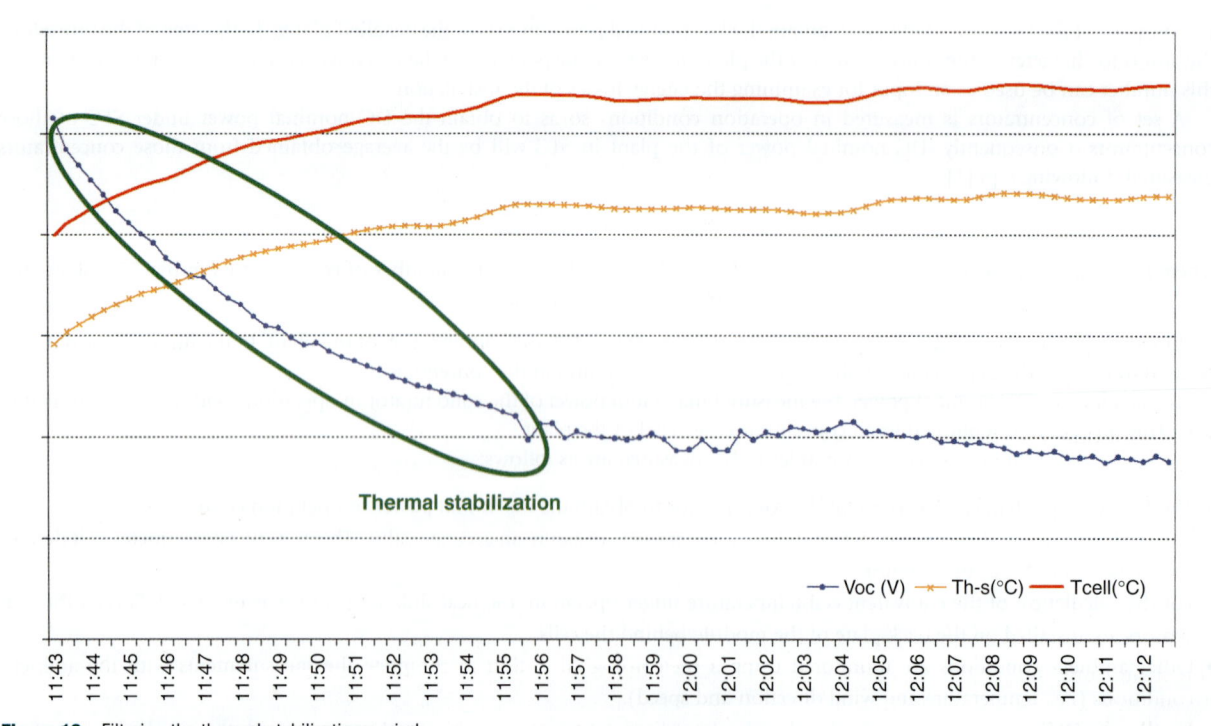

Figure 13 Filtering the thermal stabilization period.

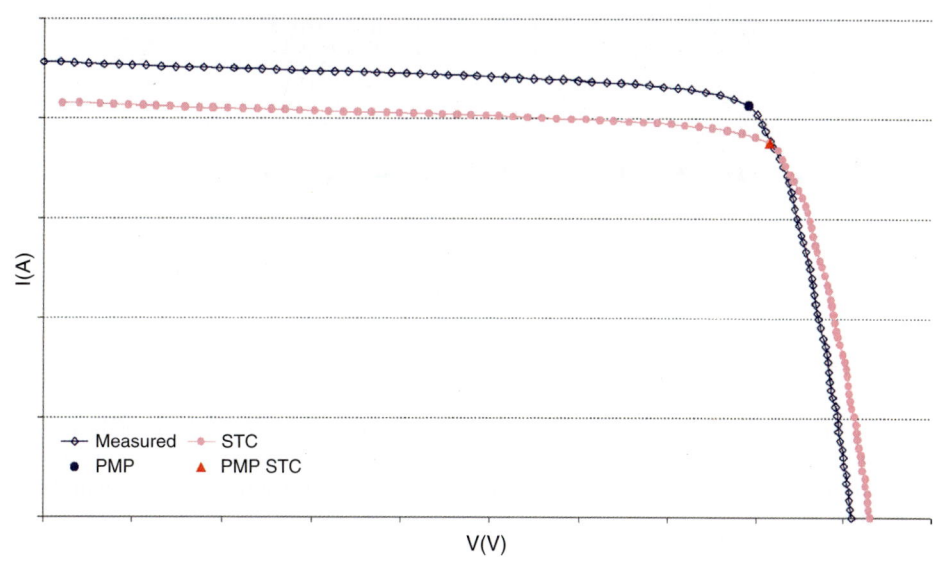

Figure 14 I–V curve measured and translated to STC.

By eqn [2], the equivalent operating cell temperature T_{cell} is calculated with the measured temperature in the heat sink $T_{\text{h-s}}$, using as input both the DNI and the equivalent thermal resistance R_{th} of the system. The thermal resistance is defined as the heat dissipation resistance between the cell and the back plate of the module for a determined value of DNI.

$$T_{\text{cell}} = T_{\text{h-s}} + (B \times R_{\text{th}}) \qquad [2]$$

where B is the DNI measured in operation conditions, T_{cell} is the equivalent cell temperature in operation conditions, $T_{\text{h-s}}$ is the heat-sink temperature measured in operation conditions at the back plate of the module behind the cell, and R_{th} is the equivalent thermal resistance for the concentrator.

Using eqns [3] and [4], current and voltage of the selected I–V curves, measured in operation conditions (B and T_{cell}), are translated to the STC ($B^{\text{STC}} = 850\,\text{W m}^{-2}$ and $T_{\text{cell}}^{\text{STC}} = 60\,°\text{C}$).

$$I^{\text{STC}} = I \frac{B^{\text{STC}}}{B} \qquad [3]$$

$$V^{\text{STC}} = V + N \frac{0.0257 \cdot (T_{\text{cell}}^{\text{STC}} - T_{\text{cell}})}{297} \times \ln\left(\frac{\prod_{j}^{J}(I_{Lj} - I)}{\prod_{j}^{J} I_{Lj}}\right) - I\left(\frac{B^{\text{STC}} - B}{B}\right) R_S$$

$$+ 3 \times N \frac{0.0257 \cdot T_{\text{cell}}^{\text{STC}}}{297}\left(\frac{B^{\text{STC}}}{B}\right) + \left(N\left(\sum_{j}^{J} E_{gj}\right) - V_{\text{OC}}\right)\left(1 - \frac{T_{\text{cell}}^{\text{STC}}}{T_{\text{cell}}}\right) \qquad [4]$$

where B, B^{STC} is the DNI measured in operation conditions and in STC, T_{cell}, $T_{\text{cell}}^{\text{STC}}$ is the equivalent cell temperature, in operation conditions and in STC, I, I^{STC} is the current measured in operation conditions and in STC; V, V^{STC} is the voltage measured in operation conditions and in STC, $T_{\text{h-s}}$ is the heat-sink temperature measured in operation conditions at the back plate of the module behind the cell, R_{th} is the equivalent thermal resistance for the concentrator, N is the total number of cells connected in series in the concentrator, R_S is the equivalent series resistance for the concentrator (cells + wires), V_{OC} is the open-circuit voltage measured in operation conditions for the concentrator, E_{gj} is the band gap energy for each junction of the cell (j), I_{Lj} is the equivalent short-circuit current in operation conditions for each junction of the cell (j), and J is the number of junctions of the cell.

In eqn [4], there is a term that represents the equivalent short-circuit current for each junction of the cell (I_{Lj}). It is calculated from the short-circuit current measured in operation conditions for the concentrator using eqn [5]. This equation assumes a constant factor of proportionality between the photogenerated current of the junctions.

$$I_{Lj} = I_{\text{SC}} \times k_{Lj} \text{ and } k_{Lj} = \frac{I_{Lj}(\text{ref})}{I_{L1}(\text{ref})} \qquad [5]$$

where I_{Lj} is the equivalent short-circuit current in operation conditions for each junction of the cell (j), I_{SC} is the short-circuit current measured in operation conditions for the concentrator, k_{Lj} is the proportionality factor between the photogenerated current of the junctions of the cell (j), and $I_{Lj}(\text{ref})$ is the reference value for the equivalent short-circuit current for each junction of the cell (j).

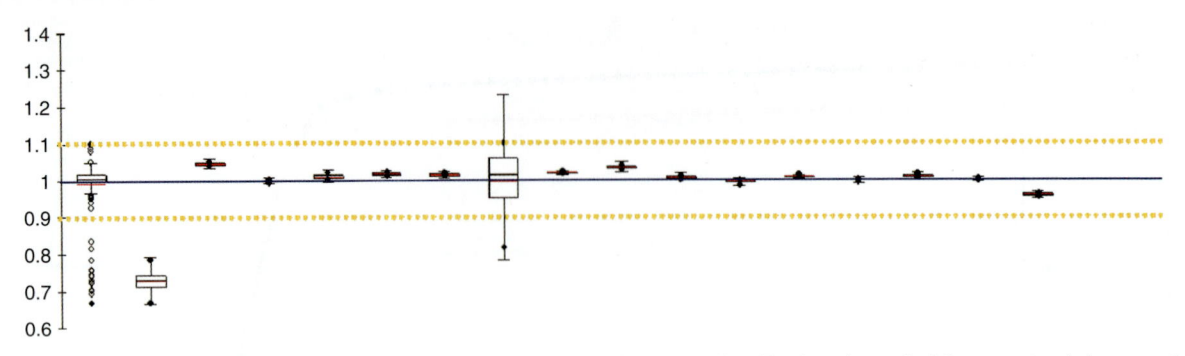

Figure 15 Box plots of the rating measurement results for each concentrator in a power plant. First box plot on the left represents whole power plant.

So, finally the DC nominal power of the concentrator is the average value of the maximum power of the *I–V* curves translated to STC. A value for the deviation is always calculated together with the value of DC nominal power of the concentrator. This deviation is used to control the precision of the rating procedure, including the measuring procedures, the works in the field, the equipment, the calculations, and so on.

Figure 15 is a box plot representation of the nominal power calculations for all the concentrators of one plant. The values represented have been normalized to the expected nominal value. This graph shows the value for the nominal power of each concentrator as well as the deviation from the calculations. A maximum deviation allowed of ±10% for the nominal power is referenced in the graph. This graph is a very useful representation to analyze if the rating process of the plant has been done in an adequate way comparing the data of one system with the rest of the installation.

In this particular case, we can see two anomalous points. One corresponds to a concentrator whose nominal power calculated is about 70% of the expected value and the second one which has a deviation of about 20%. The first one is due to bad tracking of the concentrator during the measurements, and the second is due to ambient conditions below the requirements.

Once the problems are solved, we can say that the acceptance of a plant has been done in an adequate way when the nominal power of all the concentrators is between the ±10% of the expected value with low dispersion.

1.36.5.4 AC Rating Procedure

The AC power rating assesses the energy generated by the plant during the acceptance period. The aim of this rating procedure is to evaluate the actual losses of the plant to obtain the AC nominal power in STC. It is calculated from the DC nominal power in STC corrected with the inverter efficiency and a correction factor (F) using eqn [6].

$$P_{AC,plant} = P_{DC,plant} \times \eta_{inv} \times F \quad [6]$$

where $P_{AC,plant}$ is the AC nominal power in STC of the CPV plant, $P_{DC,plant}$ is the DC nominal power in STC of the CPV plant, η_{inv} is the inverter efficiency, and F is the correction factor.

The correction factor (F) is the result of the assessment of the energy generated by the plant during the acceptance period. It compares the actual and the theoretical energy generated by the plant.

During the acceptance period, the energy generated by the plant is recorded at the same time as environmental parameters of operation conditions (i.e., DNI and temperature at the back plate of the module of several concentrators of the plant).

The initial data for this procedure are the DC nominal power of the plant calculated in the previous step. This DC nominal power in STC is translated to the operation conditions of the acceptance period with the same equations (eqns [3] and [4]); the result is the expected theoretical power of the plant under those conditions. The theoretical AC power of the plant is calculated after taking into account the inverter efficiency. If this value is integrated in all the acceptance period, it yields the theoretical energy expected for the plant. Equations [7] and [8] represent the procedure to calculate the expected energy.

$$P_{DC,plant} \xrightarrow{(3)\ (4)} P^{oc}_{DC,plant} \quad [7]$$

$$E_{th} = \int P^{oc}_{DC,plant} \times \eta_{inv} \quad [8]$$

where $P_{DC,plant}$ is the DC nominal power in STC of the CPV plant, $P^{oc}_{DC,plant}$ is the DC nominal power in operation conditions of the CPV plant, η_{inv} is the inverter efficiency, and E_{th} is the theoretical energy generated by the CPV plant during the acceptance period.

The correction factor (F) is the comparison between the actual and theoretical energy generation of the CPV plant and is calculated using eqn [9]:

$$F = \frac{E}{E_{th}} \quad [9]$$

where F is the correction factor, E is the energy generated by the CPV plant during the acceptance period, and E_{th} is the theoretical energy generated by the CPV plant during the acceptance period.

Therefore, the factor $(1-F)$, F being the correction factor, represents all the actual losses of the plant, consisting of:

- Shadowing.
- Wiring.
- Inverter actual performance.
- Mismatching between concentrators.
- Tracking losses during the day.
- Actual performance of the concentrators in different operation conditions.
- Malfunctions (such as inverter, tracker, or monitoring failure) or alarms (such as stow position due to high wind speed, etc.).

However, this factor does not differentiate the source of the losses, so it is impossible to identify the influence of each one of the factors.

The objective of the AC rating at ISFOC is to analyze the performance of the CPV plants when they are operating near the optimum conditions. So in order to apply this method, it is necessary to establish again some limits to the ambient conditions in the definition of the final acceptance period of analysis. The DNI has to be higher than $600\,\text{W}\,\text{m}^{-2}$, rejecting data collected during the periods of time when the concentrators are working with low DNI. Cloudy days and the hours near dawn and dusk should be avoided; furthermore, it is in these periods when the actual spectrum differs from the reference one (AM1.5). This largely influences the performance of the concentrators. The wind speed must be lower than $3.3\,\text{m}\,\text{s}^{-1}$. Periods of shadowing are also rejected, as the energy loss under those circumstances can be easily analyzed independently. Finally, the periods of time when any element of the plant is not operating or malfunctioning are also rejected, as it lays outside the objective of this study.

Considering the above limitations, the factor $(1-F)$ represents only the losses due to tracking, wiring, and mismatching between concentrators and actual performance of the inverter.

1.36.5.5 Status and Results

During the first years of operation at ISFOC, the rating of all the power plants has been carried out following this procedure. There are 10 plants (1 MW) completely accepted (DC and AC rating), 3 more plants (300 kW) have been rated only in DC prior to their connection to the grid, and 6 more plants (600 kW) are in the process of acceptance.

ISFOC is acquiring great experience in rating of the plants, gathering helpful results for every CPV manufacturer, thus helping in developing a reliable CPV technology.

The first results are related to the DC nominal power obtained for the concentrators. **Figure 16** represents in a 'Pareto diagram' the distribution of the nominal DC power normalized with the expected value stated by the manufacturer.

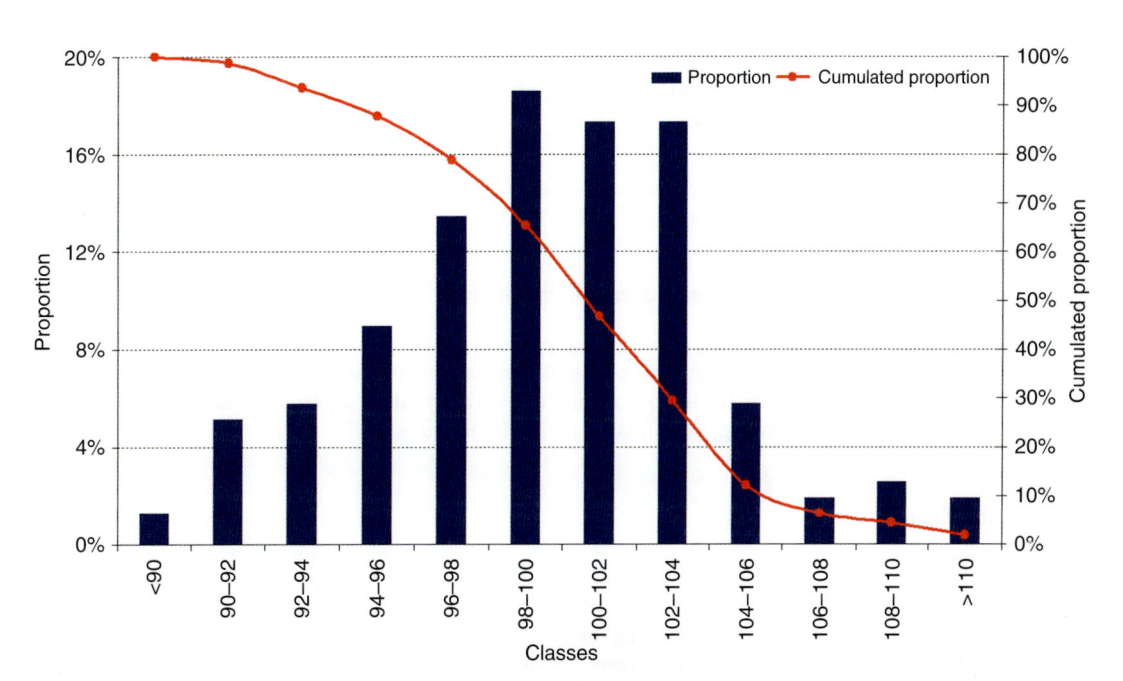

Figure 16 Statistical distribution of the DC power results centered in the estimated value.

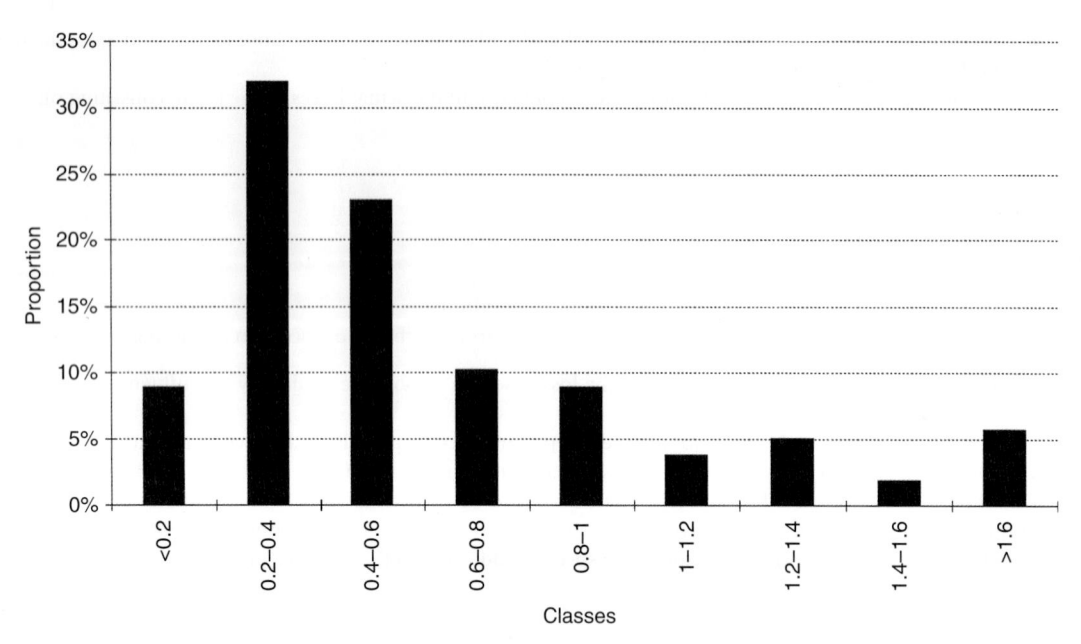

Figure 17 Distribution of the dispersion (calculated in percentage) obtained in the DC power calculations.

In the graph, we can observe that about 70% of the concentrators have values of power between ±5% of the expected value. From this result, we can conclude that the employed CPV technologies were practically ready for industrialization. These products were manufactured with low level of automation, and without an exhaustive manufacturing process control in the production line and reached the expected values. Only 1% of the systems yielded power values lower than 90% of the nominal value. The manufacturers, helped by the installation of these first demonstration plants, established the control needed in the production lines for future product generations.

Figure 17 represents the distribution of the deviation (in percentage) obtained from the calculation process of the nominal power for the concentrators.

As a conclusion, the rating method is producing optimum results, obtaining dispersion values lower than 1% in more than 80% of the cases. It is worth noticing that in some cases, close to 5%, there are dispersions larger than 1.5%, which must be analyzed in detail. It could be due to bad tracking of the concentrator, unstable ambient conditions during the measurements, and erroneous processing of data or variables that are not being taken into account in the process.

As it was explained in the AC rating procedure, the correction factor F is the main tool for calculating the AC power. The average value obtained for all the plants accepted is about 95.5% for F. Comparing the AC and DC power obtained, the yield of the installations is 93%, meaning that the energy losses from the concentrator to the connection to the grid in the complete installation are just 7%. The origins of the losses are as follows:

- Wiring.
- Inverter actual performance.
- Mismatching between concentrators.
- Tracking losses during the day.
- Actual performance of the concentrators in different operation conditions.

So, future work is oriented toward the study of the influence and proportion of each one of these sources.

As a final point, we have to say that the average value of the efficiency (calculated with the average AC power of the complete installation and the active area which collects the light) is about 20.5%. This result demonstrates that CPV technologies can be a competitive technology as it compares to average performance for flat PV modules.

1.36.6 Production Results

1.36.6.1 Performance

Typical production profile in kilowatt hour for a 100 kW-sized CPV power plant is presented in **Figure 18**. There is a close correlation between production and direct radiation during the day.

In **Figures 19** and **20**, the monthly production for the years 2009 and 2010 are shown. As expected, in Spain during the summer months, particularly in July, the production is much higher when the DNI radiation is higher. The cumulated yearly production for

Concentration Photovoltaics 761

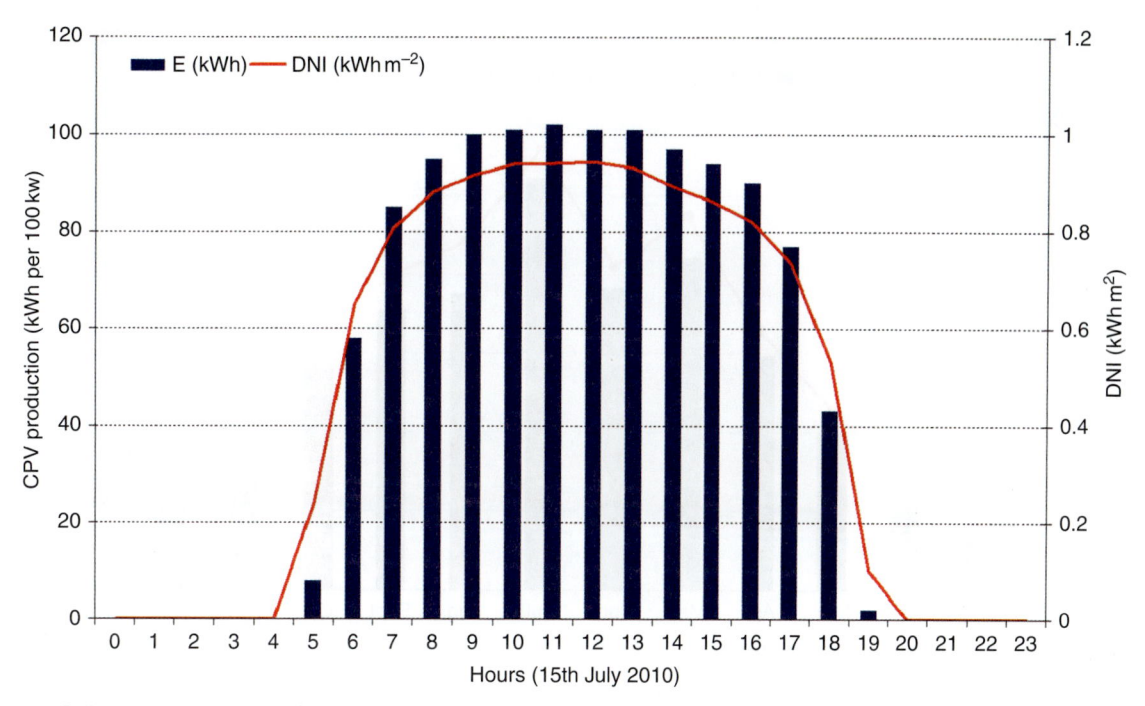

Figure 18 Daily production profile of a CPV power plant.

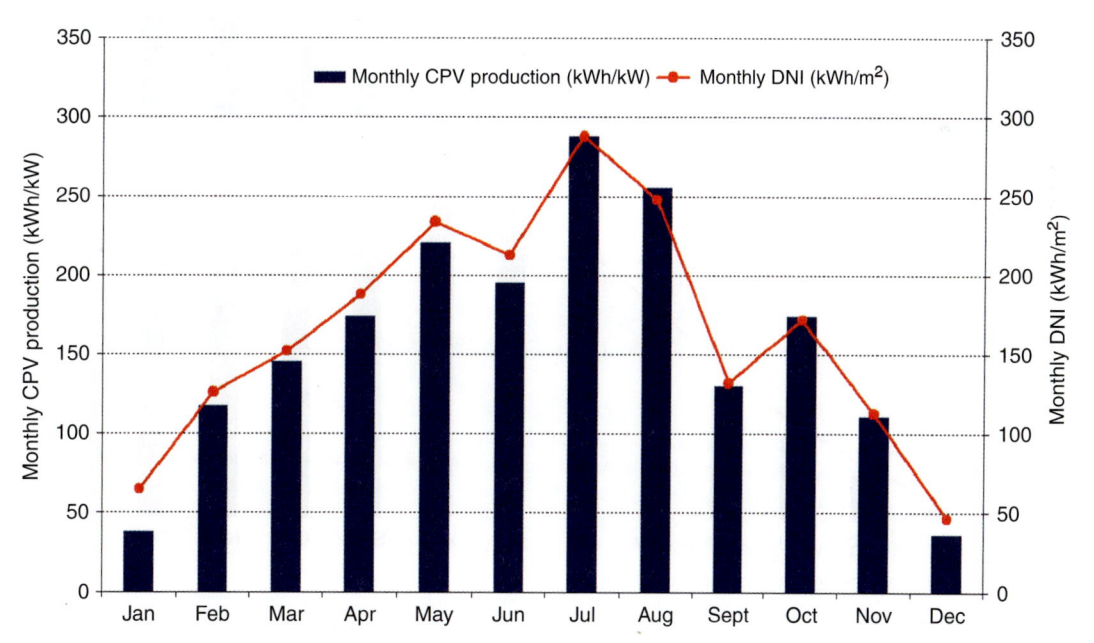

Figure 19 2009 CPV power plant production and DNI.

those two years is shown in **Figures 21** and **22**. The year 2010 was especially rainy in Spain; therefore, the cumulated production is much lower than in 2009 where the CPV production was almost 1.900 kWh kW^{-1} installed.

In **Figure 23**, the daily CPV production versus daily DNI is shown. As we can observe, the relation between the CPV production and the DNI has a linear trend. Even at high DNI, the trend is still linear and the production does not decrease, as expected for flat PV modules, due to thermal effects.

These results show that the CPV technology is capable of performing optimally in regions with very high radiation and temperatures, but it also performs reasonably well in medium radiation regions like Spain.

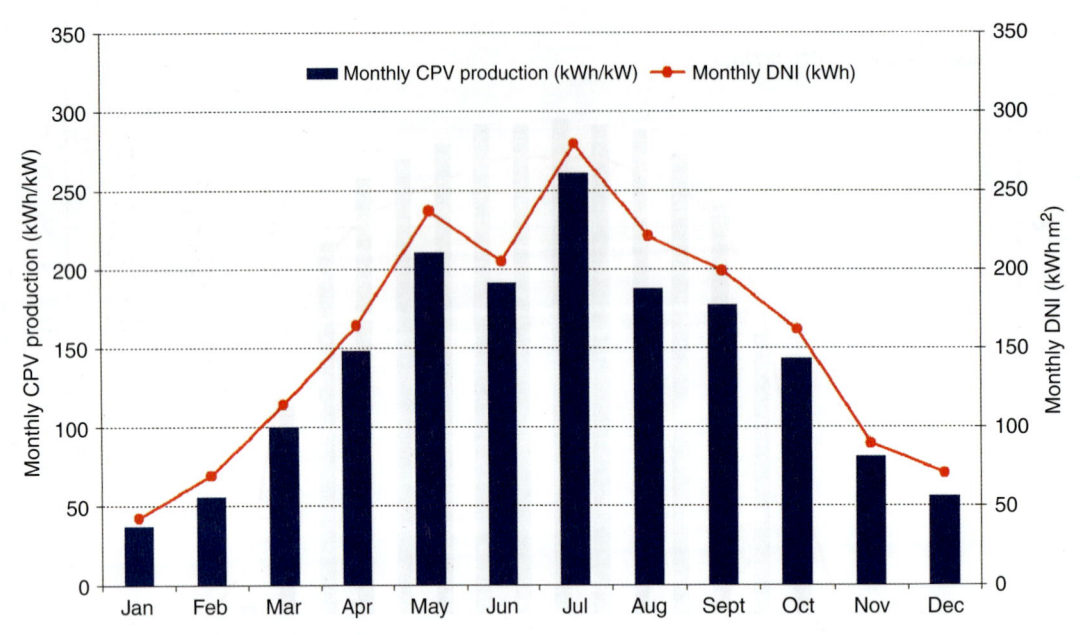

Figure 20 2010 CPV power plant production and DNI.

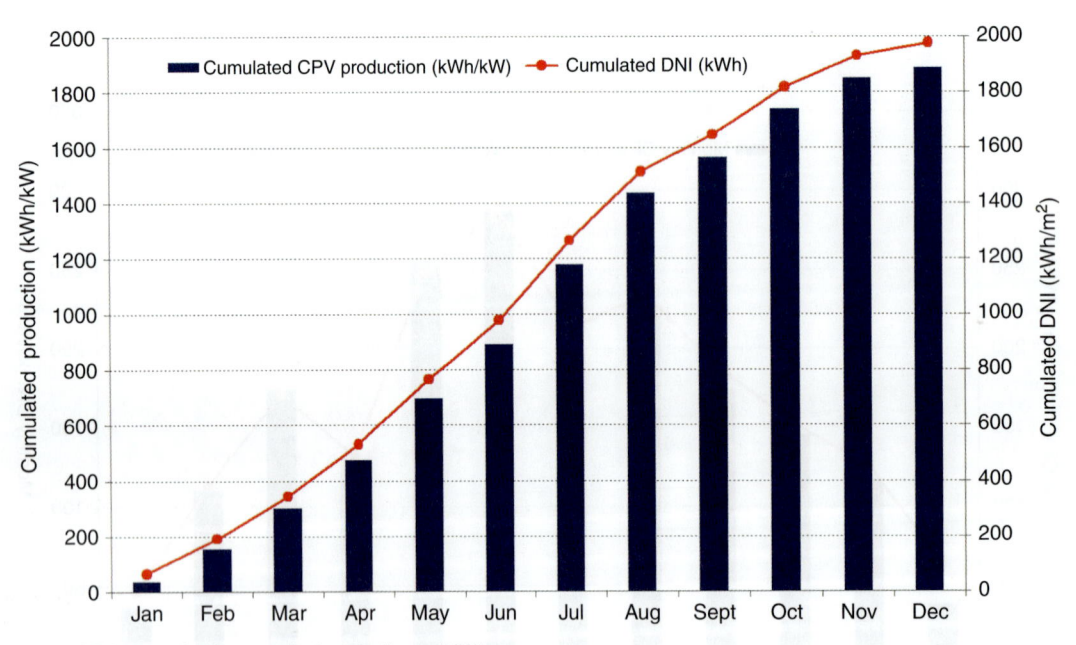

Figure 21 2009 CPV accumulated power plant production and DNI.

1.36.6.2 Operation and Maintenance

Once the power plant is connected to the grid, all acceptance tests passed, and generating energy, the need of an operation and maintenance (O&M) strategy becomes crucial. In general, works and costs of maintenance in a CPV power plant are similar to the ones in a conventional PV power plant with dual-axis trackers, although with stricter requirements. Module cleaning and tracker maintenance are the two key O&M tasks in a CPV plant. As CPV is sensitive to direct radiation, any dirt on the surface of the modules increases the loss of performance in a critical way. Trackers should be maintained at perfect condition at all times, as any slight deviation from the sun's position directly leads to loss of power. The tracker is an element that has to be monitored and perfectly adjusted for good results in energy production in CPV power plants. This is the most relevant difference between conventional PV power plants and CPV power plants: cleaning and strict requirements for trackers.

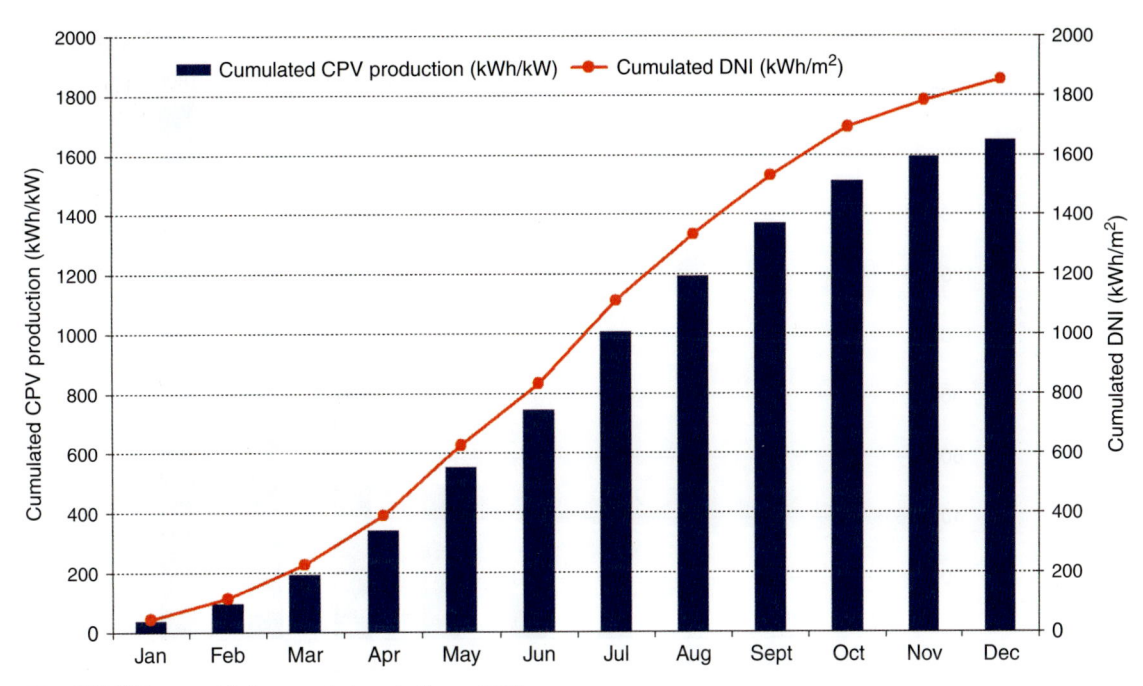

Figure 22 2010 CPV accumulated power plant production and DNI.

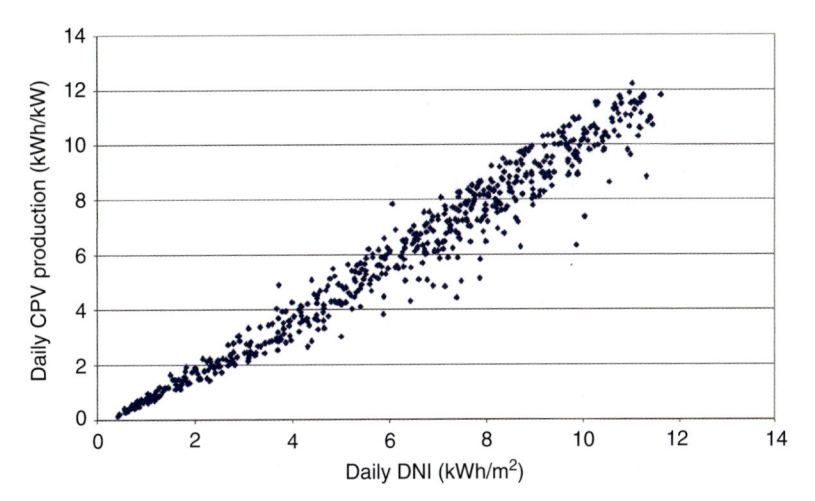

Figure 23 CPV production versus DNI.

1.36.7 Outlook

In the period from 2005 to 2010, there have been expectations for a sudden growth of CPV market. We must admit that the slow growth resulted in the development of a mature technology and identification of a niche market. ISFOC pilot installations have demonstrated that CPV is viable economically with an optimum yield in areas with a high direct solar resource. First commercial products are reaching 2000 equivalent hours with first generation of systems, keeping O&M costs within the range of other PV technologies.

Technology development for concentration applications has led to commercial products with significant improvements in cell efficiency, optics, module assembly, and Balance of Systems (BOS). These improvements were mainly the result of R&D projects for enhancement of performance, cost, reliability, manufacturing integration, logistics, deployment, and maintenance. Triple-junction cells reached efficiencies above 42% in the laboratory and could reach 45% for commercial products as early as 2015. The year 2010 saw CPV modules installed with efficiencies in the order of 30%. Technology development and market growth in high solar resource areas are building up the opportunities for CPV.

ISFOC has been instrumental in supporting this global growth during 2010, as it has become a reference project where standards are being developed, commercial products improved, and where performance at utility scale is being verified.

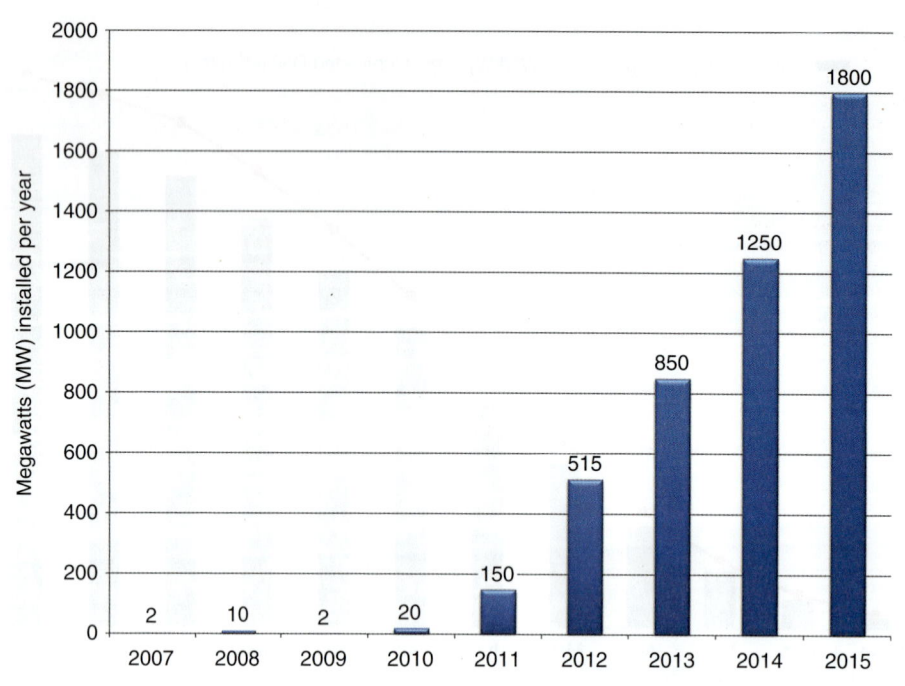

Figure 24 CPV market forecast. Source: 2007–09 EPRI, 2010–15 CPV Consortium Internal Report.

ISFOC work comprises all aspects of the CPV value chain, from laboratory tests of components to field demonstration. Spanish national projects are delivering initial results and envisaging future lines of work, with implication of universities, technology centers, and the industry. The European Union-funded project 'Nacir' is coming to an end in 2011, and its pilot installations in Egypt and Morocco are starting up. The ISFOC project in Masdar City in Abu Dhabi is in its construction phase and will soon become a center of collaboration with other institutes and companies.

All these results have favored the international market development. Countries like Italy and Portugal have established a regulatory framework specifically for CPV, which is attracting industrial activity in their territories. Large PV projects that include CPV installations are being defined in very attractive countries, like the United States, China, India, South Africa, and countries in North Africa and Middle East, in line with the future needs and economic development in some of these regions. It is in the Sunbelt regions where PV and most clearly CPV will show their potential [37].

Expected growth in coming years for CPV will bring a global market close to 2 GW in 2015, as concluded by the CPV Consortium (**Figure 24**). In order for these objectives to be met, innovation and industrialization support are key. Demonstration project at utility scale will still play a significant role in the deployment of new technologies and concepts, minimizing commercial risks. The ISFOC project will remain a model on how CPV technology can be evaluated and brought into commercial applications and at the same time participating in the development of the required industry standards. It is through increasing public R&D funding and its long-term assurance that the technology will meet industry needs and will get internationally deployed. An estimated PV capacity of 200 GW for the year 2020 with a market goal of 34 GW yr^{-1} [38] is opening the opportunity for CPV to take a share of this growth and develop super high-efficiency solutions (over 45%) beyond 2020.

References

[1] Swanson RM, Beckwith S, Crane R, et al. (1984) Point-contact silicon solar cells. *IEEE Transactions on Electron Devices* 31: 661.
[2] Slade A and Garboushian V (2005) 27.6% Efficient silicon concentrator cell for mass production. *15th International Photovoltaic Science and Engineering Conference, Technical Digest.* p. 701. Shanghai, China, 10–15 October.
[3] Castro M and Creixell J (2007) Contributions to the manufacturing of concentrator PV systems. *Proceedings of the 4th International Conference on Solar Concentrators for the Generation of Electricity or Hydrogen.* El Escorial, Spain, 12–16 March.
[4] Emery K, Meusel M, Beckert R, et al. (2000) Procedures for evaluating multijunction concentrators. *Proceedings of the 28th IEEE Photovoltaic Specialists Conference.* pp. 1126–1130. Anchorage, AK: IEE EDS.
[5] Green M, Emery D, Hishikawa Y, and Warta W (2011) Solar cell efficiency tables (version 37). *Progress in Photovoltaics* 19(1): 84.
[6] Bett AW, Siefer G, Baur C, et al. (2005) FLATCON® concentrator PV-technology ready for the market. *Proceedings of the 20th European Photovoltaic Solar Energy Conference.* pp. 114–117. Barcelona, Spain: WIP-Renewable Energies.
[7] Algora C and Díaz V (2000) Influence of the series resistance on the guidelines for the manufacture of concentrator p-on-n GaAs solar cells. *Progress in Photovoltaics* 8: 211–225.
[8] Jaus J, Fleischfresser U, Peharz G, et al. (2006) Heat sink substrates for automated assembly of concentrator modules. *Proceedings of the 21th European Photovoltaic Solar Energy Conference.* Dresden, Germany: WIP-Renewable Energies.
[9] Verlinden PJ, Lewandowski A, Bingham C, et al. (2006) Performance and reliability of multijunction III–V modules for concentrator dish and central receiver applications. *Proceedings of the 4th World Conference on Photovoltaic Energy Conversion.* pp. 592–597. Hawaii, USA, 7–12 May.

[10] Sala G and Luque A (2007) Past experiences and new challenges of PV concentrators. In: Luque, A and Andreev, V (eds.) *Concentrator Photovoltaics*, ch. 1, pp. 1–24. Berlin, Germany: Springer Series.
[11] Jaus J, Nitz P, Peharz G, et al. (2008) Second stage reflective and refractive optics for concentrator photovoltaics. *Proceedings of the 33rd IEEE Photovoltaic Specialists Conference*. San Diego, CA: IEE EDS.
[12] Bett AW and Lerchenmüller H (2007) The FLATCON system from concentrix solar. In: Luque, A and Andreev, V (eds.) *Concentrator Photovoltaics*, ch. 14, pp. 301–320. Berlin, Germany: Springer Series.
[13] Verlinden PJ, Lewandowski A, and Lasich JB (2006) Performance and reliability of a 30-kW triple-junction photovoltaic receiver for 500X concentrator dish or central receiver applications. *Proceedings of SPIE High and Low Concentrations for Solar Electric Applications*. vol. 6339, p. 633907. San Diego, CA, 13–14 August.
[14] Gordon JM (2007) Concentrator optics. In: Luque, A and Andreev, V (eds.) *Concentrator Photovoltaics*, ch. 6, pp. 113–132. Berlin, Germany: Springer Series.
[15] Alvarez JL, Hernández M, Benítez P, and Miñano JC (2001) TIR-R concentrator: A new compact high-gain SMS design. In: Roland, W (ed.) *Nonimaging Optics: Maximum Efficiency Light Transfer VI. Proceedings of SPIE*, vol. 4446, pp. 32–42. San Diego, CA: EE.UU.
[16] Benitez P, Miñano JC, Hernandez M, et al. (2007) A high-performance photovoltaic concentrator. *Proceedings of the 4th International Conference on Solar Concentrators for the Generation of Electricity or Hydrogen*. El Escorial, Spain, 12–16 March.
[17] Miñano JC, González JC, and Benítez P (1995) RXI: A high-gain, compact, nonimaging concentrator. *Applied Optics* 34: 7850–7856.
[18] Luque-Heredia I, Martín C, Mananes MT, et al. (2003) A subdegree precisión sun tracker for 1000X microconcentrator modules. *Proceedings of the 3rd World Conference on Photovoltaic Energy Conversion*, pp. 11–18. Osaka, Japan, 12–16 May.
[19] Luque-Heredia I, Gordillo F, and Rodríguez F (2004) A PI based hybrid sun tracking algorithm for photovoltaic concentration. *Proceedings of the 19th European Photovoltaic Solar Energy Conference*. Paris, France, 7–11 June.
[20] Burgess EL and Pritchard DA (1978) Performance of a one kilowatt concentrator photovoltaic array utilizing active cooling. *Proceedings of the 13th Photovoltaic Specialists Conference*, pp. 1121–1124. New York, 5–8 June.
[21] Rubio F, Banda P, Pachón JL, and Hofmann O (2007) Establishment of the Institute of Concentration Photovoltaics Systems – ISFOC. *Proceedings of the 22nd European Photovoltaic Solar Energy Conference*, pp. 803–804. Milan, Italy: WIP-Renewable Energies.
[22] International Electrotechnical Commission (IEC) 62108 (2007) Concentrator photovoltaic (CPV) modules and assemblies: Design qualification and type approval. Geneva, Switzerland: IEC.
[23] European Commission (1997) Energy for the future: Renewable sources of energy. White Paper for a Community Strategy and Action Plan. COM(97)599. Brussels, Belgium: European Commission.
[24] IDAE (1999) *Plan de Fomento de las Energías Renovables en España*. Madrid, Spain: IDAE.
[25] IDAE (2005) *Plan de Energías Renovables en España*. Madrid, Spain: IDAE.
[26] De la Rubia O, Sánchez D, García ML, et al. (2008) Acceptance procedure applied to ISFOC's CPV plants. *Proceedings of the 5th International Conference on Solar Concentrators*. Palm Desert, CA, 16–19 November.
[27] Gil E, Sánchez D, De la Rubia O, et al. (2010) Field technical inspection of CPV power plants. *Proceedings of the 25th European Photovoltaic Solar Energy Conference/5th World Conference on Photovoltaic Energy Conversion*, pp. 4483–4486. Valencia, Spain: WIP-Renewable Energies.
[28] Martínez M, De la Rubia O, García ML, et al. (2008) Concentrator photovoltaics connected to the grid and systems rating. *Proceedings of the 23rd European Photovoltaic Solar Energy Conference*, pp. 146–150. Valencia, Spain: WIP-Renewable Energies.
[29] Martínez M, Sánchez D, Rubio F, et al. (2008) CPV systems rating, results and lessons learned at ISFOC. *Proceedings of the 5th International Conference on Solar Concentrators*. Palm Desert, CA, 16–19 November.
[30] Martínez M, Sánchez D, Perea J, et al. (2009) ISFOC demonstration plants: Rating and production data analysis. *Proceedings of the 24th European Photovoltaic Solar Energy Conference*, pp. 159–164. Hamburg, Germany: WIP-Renewable Energies.
[31] Rubio F, Martínez M, Martin A, et al. (2010) Evaluation parameters for CPV production. In: Bett AW, Dimroth F, McConnell RD and Sala G (eds.) *Proceedings of the 6th International Conference on Concentrating Photovoltaic Systems*, pp. 252–255. Freiburg, Germany: American Institute of Physics.
[32] Kurtz S, Myers D, Townsend T, et al. (2000) Outdoor rating conditions for photovoltaic modules and systems. *Solar Energy Materials and Solar Cells* 62: 379–391.
[33] Muller M, Marion B, Kurtz S, and Rodriguez J (2010) An investigation into spectral parameters as they impact CPV module performance. In: Bett AW, Dimroth F, McConnell RD and Sala G (eds.) *Proceedings of the 6th International Conference on Concentrating Photovoltaic Systems*, pp. 252–255. Freiburg, Germany: American Institute of Physics.
[34] Domínguez C, Antón I, and Sala G (2010) Multijunction solar cell model for translating I–V characteristics as a function of irradiance, spectrum, and cell temperature. *Progress in Photovoltaics: Research and Applications* 18: 272–284.
[35] Sala G (1989) Cooling of solar cells. In: Luque A (ed.) *Solar Cells and Optics for Photovoltaic Concentration*, ch. 8, pp. 239–267. Bristol, UK: Adam Hilger.
[36] Martínez M, Antón I, and Sala G (2007) Effect of wind in the cooling of a PV concentrator and in its energy production. *Proceedings of the 22nd European Photovoltaic Solar Energy Conference*, pp. 790–793. Milan, Italy: WIP-Renewable Energies.
[37] El Gammal A, Llamas P, Masson G, et al. (2010) *Unlocking the Sunbelt Potential of Photovoltaics*. 1st edn. Brussels, Belgium: EPIA.
[38] International Energy Agency (2010) *Technology Roadmap: Solar Photovoltaic Energy*. Paris, France: IEA.

Further Reading

Luque, A and Andreev, V (2007) *Concentrator Photovoltaics*, 1st edn. Berlin, Germany: Springer.
Fraas, L and Partain, L (2010) *Solar Cells and Their Applications*, 2nd edn. New Jersey, NJ: Wiley.

Relevant Websites

www.cpvconsortium.org – Concentrator Photovoltaics Consortium.
www.epia.org – European Photovoltaic Industry Association.
www.ies.upm.es – Instituto de Energía Solar de la, Universidad Politécnica de Madrid.
www.isfoc.es – Instituto de Sistema Fotovoltaicos de Concentración.
www.idae.es – Instituto para la Diversificación y el Ahorro de la Energía.

1.37 Solar Power Satellites

GA Landis, NASA Glenn Research Center, Cleveland, OH, USA

Published by Elsevier Ltd.

1.37.1	Background and Historical Development	767
1.37.2	Power-Beaming Fundamentals	768
1.37.2.1	Efficiency of Microwave Transmission	768
1.37.2.2	Spot Diameter	768
1.37.2.3	Minimum Power Level for Microwave Beaming	769
1.37.2.4	Can a Large Aperture Be Synthesized from Many Small Transmitters?	770
1.37.2.5	Power Transmission by Laser Beaming	770
1.37.3	Why Put Solar in Space?	770
1.37.3.1	Continuous Sunlight	771
1.37.3.2	Sun Pointing	771
1.37.3.3	No Atmosphere	771
1.37.3.4	Summation: How Much More Power Do You Get by Putting the Cells in Space?	771
1.37.3.5	Future Evolution	771
1.37.4	Is Geosynchronous the Right Orbit?	772
1.37.5	The Economic Case	772
1.37.5.1	Quick and Dirty Economics	772
1.37.6	Beaming Power to Space: A First Step to SPS?	773
1.37.7	Summary Points to Ponder	774
References		774

1.37.1 Background and Historical Development

With the increases in energy cost and recent interest in finding ways to produce energy with reduced emission of greenhouse gasses, there has been renewed interest in the concept of producing power using solar panels in space and then beaming this power downward to provide electrical power for use on the Earth. This concept, called the 'Solar Power Satellite (SPS)', was first proposed by Peter Glaser in 1968 [1], in a conceptual design in which the SPS was placed in geosynchronous orbit and the energy beamed to a land site using a microwave beam. In revised and updated forms, the concept has been proposed many times since [2–5] as a possible solution to the energy crisis.

The Satellite Power System was studied in the late 1970s by NASA in collaboration with the Department of Energy, producing a conceptual 'reference' design [3] for a system. This design was analyzed and critiqued by an Office of Technology Assessment study [4]. The concept has gone by several different names and acronyms, starting as the 'SPS' or 'Satellite Solar Power System' (SSPS) and more recently studied under the name 'Space Solar Power' (SSP).

Figure 1 shows a summary of the 1980 'reference design' for such an SPS [3]. The baseline satellite concept produces about 10 GW of electrical power on the Earth, using a large (10 km by 15 km) solar array located in geosynchronous orbit. The power is transmitted to the Earth by a microwave beam at 2.45 GHz, and a large (approximately 100 km^2) rectifying antenna (or 'rectenna') array at Earth receives the beamed microwave power and converts it into DC electrical power. The early study also looked at several alternate technologies for both the energy conversion and the power transmission and made attempts to predict the possible future performance improvements in order to make cost estimates of a future large-scale system.

In 1995, NASA headquarters initiated a 'Fresh Look' study of SPSs, which did not revise the original concepts, but started with a clean sheet of paper to rethink the basic concepts and come up with a new design [5]. Some of the initial concepts examined included use of low Earth orbit instead of a geosynchronous orbit, gravity gradient-stabilized structures, sun-synchronous orbits, and use of large-area Fresnel lenses to focus light onto panels of concentrator cells. Later evolution of the Fresh Look study (which evolved into the Space Solar Power Exploratory Research and Technology (SERT) program [6–8] in the 1999–2000 time frame) returned to the geosynchronous orbit design, but continued to look at new options for satellite design, including alternative power transmission methods such as laser beaming.

In addition to these NASA studies, there have been several non-NASA studies of the concept [9], as well as a number of studies that have been proposed to use power-beaming technology for other applications, including defense applications [10] and in-space applications such as satellites, electric propulsion, and lunar bases [11].

It is worth noting that in 2004, the North American electrical energy generation was 4730 TWh, about 45% of which was generated by coal-fired plants. At a typical production cost of 5 ¢ (kWh)$^{-1}$, this represents a revenue of $230 billion yr^{-1} for the potential market in North America alone. Thus, although the concept requires mega-engineering on a scale that would dwarf all previous space projects, the potential revenue from it is extremely large.

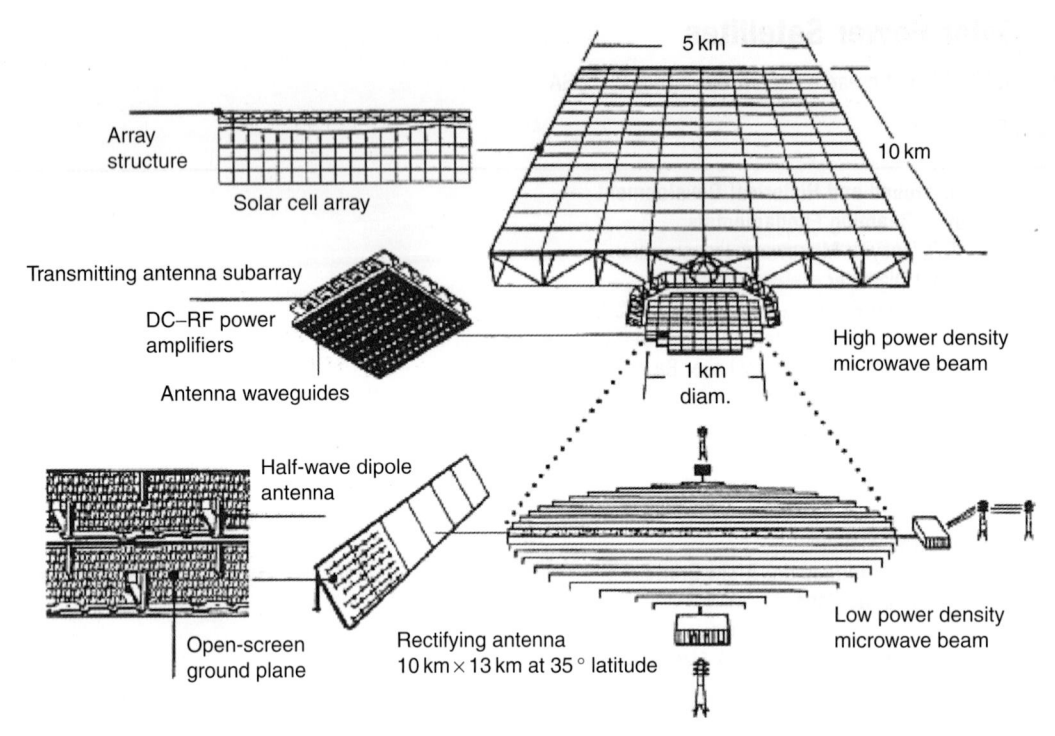

Figure 1 Conceptual diagram of 1980 SPS 'reference design' [3].

1.37.2 Power-Beaming Fundamentals

The ability to use solar power generated in space for terrestrial use requires beaming the power from the source, in space, to the user on the ground. This is done by converting the electrical power to electromagnetic radiation, beam the radiation across free space, and collecting it at a receiver that converts electromagnetic radiation to electrical power. In the 1980 study [3] (and most of the subsequent studies), it was proposed to do this using radio frequency (RF) beams at a frequency of 2.45 GHz (i.e., microwaves in the industrial, scientific, and medical band). This was chosen because of the high demonstrated conversion efficiency of electrical power to microwave energy and because of the transparency of the atmosphere to microwave radiation.

1.37.2.1 Efficiency of Microwave Transmission

In the 'ideal' case, RF power-beaming efficiency can be quite high. At these frequencies, magnetron tubes can convert DC to RF efficiency at transmitter efficiency of 90% or better, and a rectenna array (consisting of an array of GaAs Schottky diodes and quarter wave antennas) can convert RF power back to DC at receiver efficiency that has been demonstrated to be as high as 86%. The product of these two efficiencies yields an overall 'potential' transmission efficiency, DC in to DC out, of ~77%.

In the real world, however, it is very easy to produce much degraded efficiency. For example, Neville Marzwell estimated potential losses in a 'real world' estimated RF link efficiency [12], as listed in **Table 1**.

Multiplying each of these losses yields a much lower value of 37.5% for the overall DC-to-DC efficiency, and even this has not accounted for any losses of the transmitted beam not captured by receiver nor additional losses in power management and distribution either at the satellite or the user side of the system.

The reference design study assumed that the transmitter would be a phased array consisting of many millions of individual small transmitters operating in phase. The phase would be controlled by a 'beacon' at the ground site, and hence if the beacon is not present, the beam would fail to be in phase, and hence would not be focused. The requirement for a cooperative link at the ground station functions as an additional safety factor; in the event of an error, the transmitter is not capable of beaming high intensities to sites other than the ground station.

1.37.2.2 Spot Diameter

The minimum spot diameter of any transmitted electromagnetic beam is set by the diffraction limit. The Airy diffraction disk is the diffraction pattern produced from a uniformly illuminated circular aperture [13, 14]. This area contains 84% of the beam energy. The 'tails' of the diffraction pattern outside this have little power, with a fall-off in power of approximately $P \sim \exp[-r^2]$. The diameter of the Airy diffraction pattern is

Table 1 Estimated link efficiencies for a realistic microwave transmission [12]

Parameter	Loss factor
DC to RF efficiency	0.90
EMC and diplexing	0.794
Subarray aperture efficiency	0.95
Subarray failures	0.96
Amplitude errors and taper quantization	0.986
Phase errors	0.97
Electronic beam steering scan loss	0.977
Clear air absorption	0.9885
Propagation impairments (scattering)	0.933
Coupling efficiency (divergence)	0.918
Polarization mismatch	0.999
Rectenna aperture efficiency (reflections)	0.95
EMC filtering	0.891
Rectenna RF–DC conversion efficiency	0.86

$$d_{\text{spot}} = 2.44 \frac{\lambda x}{d_{\text{transmit}}} \qquad [1]$$

where d_{transmit} is the diameter of the transmitter aperture, x the source to receiver distance, and λ the wavelength. This is the fundamental physics of electromagnetic power transmission – a beam can do worse than this (i.e., a larger spot size) but cannot be focused into a smaller size.

We can use this equation to calculate the minimum spot size for a beam originating at geosynchronous orbit. For this case, the distance $x = 35\,786$ km. At a frequency of 2.45 GHz, the wavelength is 122 m (12.2 cm). The diffraction-limited spot size is

$$d_{\text{spot}} = \frac{10.7}{d_{\text{transmit}}} \text{ (for } d \text{ in km)} \qquad [2]$$

Thus, for a 1 km diameter transmitter, the minimum spot size on Earth is 10.7 km. This explains why the 1980 reference design (and most successive design concepts) is so large: it is necessarily large because of the beam spot size.

The transmitter or receiver diameter is reduced in size directly proportional to wavelength. Changing to other wavelengths has a direct effect on the size of the system. Assuming that both the transmitter and receiver diameters are reduced proportionately, the spot size, and hence the receiver diameter, for a beam transmitted from geosynchronous orbit is shown in **Table 2**.

1.37.2.3 Minimum Power Level for Microwave Beaming

These receiver sizes, in turn, mean that there is a minimum power level at which the system needs to operate. This is partly an economic issue. At lower power intensity the transmitter and receiver costs will be too expensive (i.e., it would not be economically feasible to build a 1 km diameter transmitting antenna in space to transmit a power of only 1 kW), but it is also an effect of the physics of the receiving antenna: rectennas are inefficient at low power intensities. A minimum intensity at the receiver is required in order for the diode rectifiers to convert power at high efficiency. Diffraction limits thus mean that SPS is inherently big: small scales are not feasible.

It is clear that the minimum feasible power scales directly with the wavelength, or 1/microwave frequency. Assuming minimum intensity of $100\,\text{W m}^{-2}$ ($100\,\text{MW km}^{-2}$), this minimum power is listed in **Table 3**. The data show that higher frequencies allow much smaller system sizes. However, the higher frequency microwaves have a higher absorption by water vapor, that is, 10 GHz microwaves will not penetrate rain, and 100 GHz microwaves need a receiver on mountaintops.

Table 2 Aperture size vs. frequency for a beam transmitting from geosynchronous orbit, for case of transmit aperture diameter = 10 × receiver aperture

Frequency (GHz)	$d_{transmit}$ (km)	$d_{receiver}$ (km)
2.45	1.07	10.7
5	0.73	7.3
10	0.51	5.1
100	0.16	1.6

Table 3 Minimum feasible power as a function of microwave frequency, assuming power density of 100 W m^{-2}

Frequency (GHz)	Power (GW)
2.45	9
5	5.3
10	1.6
100	0.5

1.37.2.4 Can a Large Aperture Be Synthesized from Many Small Transmitters?

Instead of making a single large aperture, the idea is sometimes suggested that a small spot size can be synthesized from a large array of small apertures. This is effectively a suggestion that a large aperture can be 'synthesized' using the interferometric aperture synthesis approach, which is done, for example, for radio telescopes such as the very large array (VLA).

The short answer to this question is no. While high observational 'resolution' can be achieved by aperture synthesis, this is not effective for transmission. A large transmitting array synthesized from many small arrays can beam to a smaller area, but the power density beamed into that area does not increase – in essence, the extra beam power is lost into the side lobes. This effect is known as the 'thinned array curse' [14].

1.37.2.5 Power Transmission by Laser Beaming

Power can also be beamed with a laser beam, using a photovoltaic (PV) array as a receiver [11, 15]. Laser power beaming still uses electromagnetic radiation and hence is still subject to the electromagnetic limitations on beam size due to diffraction. However, since laser radiation has much shorter wavelengths, smaller transmitter and receiver sizes can be used.

An example of 1 μm wavelength is chosen in the near IR, close to the response peak for a high-efficiency silicon PV receiver. Shorter wavelengths will reduce the size proportionately, but will require more expensive receiving arrays.

Assuming minimum intensity of 500 W m^{-2} for optical (producing an output equivalent to solar illumination, 1 sun intensity) and assuming a transmitting lens diameter of 2.3 m, a laser beaming system operating at 1 μm will produce a 23 m diameter minimum spot size on the ground, for an area of 0.0004 km^2. This results in a minimum power level of 208 kW.

Laser transmission removes the problem of inherently large sizes, but lasers have their own problems. First, laser efficiencies are considerably lower than microwave efficiencies, for lasers with good coherence. High-power semiconductor diode laser arrays are highly efficient (50% conversion efficiency or higher), but are not mutually coherent – the net result of a high-power laser diode array is that it will have the diffraction pattern characteristic of a flashlight, not the narrow diffraction-limited spot size of a laser. Existing technology lasers might have efficiency approaching ~40% (e.g., for a diode-pumped alkali laser).

A second problem is that PV converter efficiencies are also relatively low. The conversion efficiency is better than solar conversion efficiency, because the beam can be made monochromatic at a wavelength tuned to the optimum conversion wavelength of the cell, but is still lower than rectenna conversion efficiencies. A conversion efficiency of 50% is a reasonable efficiency.

For laser transmission, clouds are now a problem. In addition, eye safety is also a problem.

Overall, the use of a PV array for power receiving eliminates the signal advantage of an SSP, of putting the PV array in space, for cloud-free power. Laser-transmitted space power has less power per solar array area than ground solar.

Despite these disadvantages, laser transmission also has advantages.

The laser power converters are PV arrays and so can operate both on the beamed laser power and on solar power. Thus, laser power satellite could 'fill in' power to already existing solar arrays, either increasing the power level or allowing the array to continue to produce power when the sun is not available.

If a ground solar installation has already paid for the ground infrastructure, space PV power looks much more attractive! The ground infrastructure now gets double use for both solar and laser power. This may provide an evolutionary route to space power from ground power.

However, ground solar arrays typically do not cover 100% of the land area. This wastes laser power (unless ground arrays are redesigned). Both clouds and eye safety are still a problem.

1.37.3 Why Put Solar in Space?

The critical question is, why should the solar arrays be placed in space? Why not just put the same solar cells on the ground?

The proposed rationale for space solar is that, unlike the ground, space has solar power 24 h per day, 365 days per year. How much more power can be achieved by putting the cells in space? Three reasons are usually given for why more power is achieved for space solar:

1. space has continuous sunlight, 24 h per day;
2. space solar arrays are (or can be) directly sun pointing;
3. space has no atmosphere and no clouds.

1.37.3.1 Continuous Sunlight

The availability of 24 h sunlight inherently gives a factor of 2 advantage, somewhat more in winter, less in summer.

1.37.3.2 Sun Pointing

Space solar arrays are (or can be) directly sun pointing. The added benefit of tracking depends on pointing assumptions. For solar arrays located not too far from the equator, calculating the added power using the cosine approximation gives an added factor of $\pi/2$ in the average power on a solar array. This is exactly true only ignoring atmospheric effects (discussed in the next section), but is roughly true for a fixed solar array tilted south at the latitude angle.

It is also worthwhile to note that, in fact, ground solar arrays can be made sun pointing. This is slightly less efficient in the use of land area, but allows more effective utilization of the solar cell area.

1.37.3.3 No Atmosphere

This comprises two advantages: the sunlight is not filtered by atmosphere, and space has no clouds.

The solar intensity is $1.37\,W\,m^{-2}$ in space, compared with $1.0\,kW\,m^{-2}$ (AM1.5 standard). The AM1.5 standard only applies for high sun angles near noon; there is more atmosphere filtering at higher sun angles, earlier and later in the day. However, despite the higher intensity, solar cell efficiency in space is less than that achieved on ground by roughly a factor of 0.8. Accounting for both intensity and efficiency, solar cells produce about 10% more power at AM0 (space) than AM1.5 (ground spectrum).

Clouds also are an issue for ground solar. For a fair comparison of space and ground solar installations in the near term, however, we need to compare SSP with the best ground solar locations, not the average locations. From NREL data on average solar power, for the best locations in the southwest United States, the annual average solar radiation is $12\,kWh\,m^{-2}$, corresponding to $1\,kW\,m^{-2}$ for $12\,h\,day^{-1}$. This is, essentially, zero cloud loss.

1.37.3.4 Summation: How Much More Power Do You Get by Putting the Cells in Space?

A solar array in space produces a factor of $1.1\pi = 3.5$ times more energy per area than the solar arrays at the best ground locations, summarizing the above stated facts:

1. Space has solar power 24 h per day: added power = factor of 2.
2. Directly sun pointing: added power = factor $\pi/2$ (if ground arrays are not sun pointing).
3. Higher intensity in space: added power ~ factor 1.1.
4. Space has no clouds: no added power (over cloud-free ground locations).

The direct corollary to this is that, unless the DC-to-DC transmission efficiency of the power-beaming link is at least 29%, the net power output from the space system will be 'less' than the energy output from the same array placed (at the optimum location) on the ground. In the most optimistic case of transmitter efficiency–conversion efficiency of 90%, Airy disk capture of 84%, and rectenna conversion efficiency of 86%, the ground DC power is 65% of the power produced in space. This reduces the above numbers to an improvement of 2.25 for the space array compared with the ground array.

For the case that the ground array is tracking, the second factor reduces to 1, and a space array produces 2.2 times more power per unit area than a tracking array at the best site on the ground. Incorporating optimistic transmission factor of 65%, this reduces to 1.4 times more power.

1.37.3.5 Future Evolution

The discussion so far has compared space location of a solar array with the best locations on the ground. This is appropriate for the initial phases of solar power, since the first implementations of large-scale power production by PVs will, of course, be at the best locations, and not at the worst. However, looking into the longer term, not all sites on the ground are 'best' sites. Long-distance transmission lines can transmit power on the ground for some distance, but there will be large losses for transcontinental transmission – it is not feasible to produce power in the Mojave Desert and use it in New York. Ground solar is worse by a factor of 2 for areas of the United States outside of southwest and as much as a factor of 2.5 worse for New England, a significant electrical market.

It is worth noting, however, that the ground receivers for SSP also have significant location constraints, most notably a requirement for large areas of land in order to incorporate 'keep-out' zones near the beam, and thus may not be able to be located near large cities in the northeast in any case.

A caveat on this calculation is that it has implicitly been assumed that balance-of-systems cost of ground solar array (e.g., land cost) and space solar array (e.g., rectenna land area) are comparable.

In addition to the potentially higher total amount of power produced, SSP may have other virtues. Most notable of these is that the power is continuous, 24 h power, rather than power peaking at noon and dropping to zero at sunrise and sunset.

At the moment, however, 24 h power is not an asset, since during the nighttime hours, the power demand is very low, and power available at night sells at very low price. Ground solar produces power that is moderately well matched to the (early afternoon) peak demand.

Nevertheless, as solar capacity grows, this production curve will be increasingly mismatched to the demand and eventually solar will need to provide power outside peak solar hours. The transition of solar power from peak to a requirement for power outside of the midday peak is typically expected to occur when ground solar reaches ~10–15% of the energy market. (In the United States, this represents about $300 billion yr^{-1} total, although the price break occurs earlier in the areas where solar is most effectively used.) At this point, the continuous availability of power from space becomes an asset.

1.37.4 Is Geosynchronous the Right Orbit?

This analysis has assumed that a power satellite would be in geosynchronous Earth orbit (GEO). GEO is a location where the beaming station remains stationary (with respect to the Earth) over the equator at the longitude of the receiver. This maximizes the utility of the station at a given receiver site.

It is interesting to look at the possibility of other orbits, in particular, lower orbits that would allow a shorter distance to beam, and hence smaller spot sizes and a smaller system size.

Only GEO orbit puts satellite over ground station with 100% usage fraction, and hence any lower orbit will have an immediate disadvantage that it will be out of direct beaming line of sight of the ground station for much of the time. In addition to the nonstationary nature of lower orbits, another difficulty of low orbit is that these orbits will have to be nonequatorial if we want to get power to northern hemisphere users. Thus, low-orbit view factors are low; for example, for an orbital altitude of 1000 km, the time in view above 10° of elevation is only 12.6 min, twice a day. This results in a total use fraction of 25.2 min out of 24 h, which is too low a usage fraction to be economically feasible. One possible solution would be to make multiple ground stations for the power, receiving power at whatever location is in sight of the ground station, and likewise multiple power satellites, so that a satellite is available over each customer at any time. However, to make this work for low orbits would require a large number of ground stations dotted uniformly around the world, including in many locations where there are few customers for the power, such as the Pacific Ocean. The cost of such a system is several orders of magnitude higher than the baseline, since the number of satellites is much higher. It is difficult to make this an economic case.

An alternative would be to reconsider the proposal to send power directly to northern hemisphere ground sites and to put the power-beaming satellites into a low equatorial orbit and beam only to sites on, or near, the equator. Users at sites distant from the equator would then have to be served either by transmission lines or else by secondary beams passing through microwave relay satellites. This reduces the number of power satellites and receiver stations considerably; for example, approximately 24 satellites in 1000 km orbit could provide continuous power to service sites at or near the equator. Although this is a larger number of satellites than the single satellite required in geosynchronous orbit, the transmitting aperture of each satellite is 25 times smaller.

Another approach is to adapt the space power concept to the price structure of the electric power market, by redesigning SPS to maximize the amount of power available to service peak power markets, instead of base load. If this could be done, it would roughly double the revenue in terms of dollars per kWh. Analyses of this approach have been summarized in an earlier paper, 'Reinventing the Solar Power Satellite', NASA 2004-212743 [16, 17].

1.37.5 The Economic Case

The economic return for SSP requires return on investment. If an SPS is to be commercially viable, it must charge the utilities to which it is selling power (per kWh) less than the utility's cost of generating new power. Note that it is important to beat the utilities' cost, not the customer's electric cost. This cost may include the cost for externalities (e.g., possible penalties to be imposed for generating with coal), if any.

As a minimum, even if the operating cost is zero (i.e., small compared with the capital) and operating lifetime is infinite, the invested money must be returned.

1.37.5.1 Quick and Dirty Economics

It is instructive to calculate example numbers for return on investment case. The rate of return must be at least

$$\$ \, \text{yr}^{-1} > P \times \text{Capital cost} \times (1 + P)^T \qquad [3]$$

where P is the required rate of return on investment and T the time required for construction. This must be divided by the power produced per year to get the dollars per kWh. Power produced is

$$\text{kWh yr}^{-1} = 8700 \text{ h yr}^{-1} \times \frac{1\,000\,000 \text{ kW}}{\text{GW}} \times \text{Power (GW)} \qquad [4]$$

Thus

$$\$ \text{ kW}^{-1} \text{ h}^{-1} > P \times \text{Capital cost (million \$)} \times \frac{(1+P)^T}{8700} \times \text{Power (GW)} \qquad [5]$$

Let us assume an investment rate of return of 8.25% ($P = 0.0825$) and a construction time of 5 years ($T = 5$). Then the factor $(1+P)^T = 1.49$, which raises the effective interest rate to 12.3%. The equation then is

$$\$ \text{ kWh}^{-1} > 0.014 \times \frac{\text{Capital cost (billion \$)}}{\text{Power (GW)}} \qquad [6]$$

This can also be expressed as a limit on the capital cost, as a function of the selling cost of electricity:

$$\text{Capital cost (billion \$)} < 70.8(\$ \text{ kWh}^{-1}) \times \text{Power (GW)} \qquad [7]$$

Assuming a power level of 5 GW and a selling price of 5 ¢ $(\text{kWh})^{-1}$, this is

$$\text{Capital cost} < \$17.5 \text{ billion}$$

This analysis has assumed an infinite lifetime of the assets, and no associated operating costs. If, instead, the loan is to be paid off in a finite amount of time, a slightly higher rate of return is required. For 30-year payoff of 8.25% on the loan, the payment is 1.09 times higher rate; for a 25-year payoff, the yearly payment is 1.15 times higher.

If operating costs are not negligible, they need to be added directly to the cost per kilowatt-hour.

It is useful to divide the maximum allowable capital cost ($17.5 billion for the infinite lifetime/zero operations cost case) by the power produced, 5 GW. This shows that, to sell electricity at a price of $0.05 kWh^{-1}, the total cost of the system must not exceed $3.50 W^{-1}. This is an extremely challenging target, since it must include not only the solar arrays but also all of the in-space structure as well as the ground assets.

1.37.6 Beaming Power to Space: A First Step to SPS?

The economic calculation has so far assumed that the market for beamed power is in fact the terrestrial electric power market. The market on Earth, however, is currently served by relatively low-cost generating capacity. It is much more likely that the first steps to demonstrating and using beamed power would be for ground-to-space or space-to-space power beaming [18].

Probably the best market is to start with in-space power beaming. **Figure 2** shows a schematic. A ground-based power system, using a large aperture antenna, sends the energy beam (in the form of either a microwave or laser energy) to receivers in space, which could include satellites, orbital transfer vehicles using electric propulsion, or even (in the longer term) a lunar base [11]. Currently, electrical power in space has an effective price tag that is 10 000 times the price of power on the ground. It makes sense to beam power to the place where it is expensive from the place where it is cheap.

Figure 2 Earth to space power-beaming concept, showing possible receivers in satellites, electric propulsion transfer vehicles, and lunar bases [11]. Image Courtesy of NASA.

1.37.7 Summary Points to Ponder

Producing solar power in space to be sent to the surface of the Earth for use by consumers on the ground ('solar power satellite,' or SPS) has been proposed as a means of solving the problem of electrical supply on the surface of the Earth with a renewable, low-carbon-emission technology, see also [19]. The fundamental physics are feasible, but economical feasibility is as yet an open question. Although a space location for the solar panels gets more sun than a ground location, the bottom line numbers show that it is not that much more solar energy than the best ground locations. The added power mostly comes from 24 h sunlight, but much of the power may thus be produced when the need is low.

Electromagnetic beam diffraction limits mean that SPS is inherently big: 5 GW minimum for 5 GHz power beam; a higher frequency will not be able to penetrate rain. Switching to laser transmission allows very small satellites, but efficiency losses are large.

To a rough approximation, solar arrays in space produce 3.5 times more power than nontracking arrays on the ground array or 2.2 times more than tracking arrays on the ground. Accounting for transmission losses, this reduces to 1.63 times more power/solar cell area.

If the cost of solar arrays is less than 61% of the total SPS cost, a given solar array will produce energy at a lower cost on the ground, assuming that it can be placed in the optimum location, than if placed in space. While this is only applicable if ground locations are close in location to the highest selling price electric power markets, there may also be questions as to whether receiving rectenna arrays can be located close to the highest price markets. In general, SSP will be economically competitive only if ground solar is economically competitive in the best markets.

GEO seems to be the most reasonable choice for the orbital location. Other orbits are not over the receiver continuously; storage is not (yet) competitive.

A final question is, can solar cells that are qualified for use in space, and are of a suitable weight and efficiency for SPS use, be produced at a cost equal to the low production cost of terrestrial solar cells? This is yet to be demonstrated. Space solar cells have stringent requirements, and it is not yet clear whether the production cost can be reduced without compromising the quality.

References

[1] Glaser PE (1968) Power from the sun: Its future. *Science* 162: 957–961.
[2] Glaser PE, Davidson FP, and Csigi KI (eds.) (1994/1998) *Solar Power Satellites: The Emerging Energy Option*, 2nd edn. New York: Wiley.
[3] NASA (1980) *Satellite Power System Concept Development and Evaluation Program System Definition Technical Assessment Report*. U.S. Department of Energy, Office of Energy Research, Report DOE/ER/10035-03, December.
[4] U. S. Office of Technology Assessment (1981) *Solar Power Satellites*.
[5] Mankins J (1997) A Fresh Look At Space Solar Power: New Architecture, Concepts, and Technologies. *Paper IAF-97-R.2.03, 48th International Astronautical Congress*, pp. 347–359. Turin, Italy, 6–10 October. In: *Acta Astronautica*, vol. 41, pp. 4–10. August–November.
[6] Howell J and Mankins JC (2000) Preliminary results from NASA's space solar power exploratory research and technology program. *Proceedings of the 51st International Astronautical Congress*. Rio de Janeiro, Brazil.
[7] Dudenhoefer JE and George PJ (2000) Space solar power satellite technology: Development at the Glenn research center – An overview. *Paper NHTC2000–12067, 34th National Heat Transfer Conference*. Pittsburgh, PA, 20–22 August. NASA Technical Memorandum NASA/TM—2000-210210.
[8] Feingold H and Carrington C (2003) Evaluation and comparison of space solar power concepts. In: *Proceedings of the 53rd International Astronautical Federation Congress. Acta Astronautica*, vol. 53, pp.4–10, 547–559. August–November. doi: 10.1016/S0094–5765(03)80016–4.
[9] (1997) *Proceedings of the SPS '97 Conference, Space Power Systems: Energy and Space for Humanity*. Montréal, Canada, 24–28 August. Organized by the Canadian Aeronautics and Space Institute and the Sociéte des Électriciens et Électroniciens France.
[10] Johnson WN, Akins K, Armstrong J, et al. (2009) Space-based solar power: Possible defense applications and opportunities for NRL. *Naval Research Laboratory Report NRL/FR/7650-09-10,179*, 23 October.
[11] Landis GA (1991) Space power by ground-based laser illumination. *IEEE Aerospace and Electronics Systems* 6(6): 3–7. Presented at *26th Intersociety Energy Conversion Engineering Conference*, vol. 1, pp. 1–6. Boston, MA, USA, 4–9 August.
[12] Marzwell N (2007) The challenge of space solar power. *MIT Space Solar Power Workshop*. 15–17 May.
[13] Swinburne Centre for Astrophysics and Supercomputing COSMOS: The SAO Encyclopedia of Astronomy. http://cosmos.swin.edu.au/entries/airydisk/airydisk.html?e=1.
[14] Forward RL (1984) Roundtrip interstellar travel using laser pushed lightsails. *Journal of Spacecraft and Rockets* 21(2): 190. http://en.wikipedia.org/wiki/Thinned_array_curse
[15] Landis GA (1991) Photovoltaic receivers for laser beamed power. *Proceedings of the 22nd IEEE Photovoltaic Specialists Conference*, vol. II, pp. 1494–1502. Las Vegas, NV, USA, October. *NASA Report CR-189075*.
[16] Landis GA (2004) Reinventing the solar power satellite. *NASA Technical Memorandum TM-2004-212743*.
[17] Landis GA (2006) Re-evaluating satellite solar power systems for earth. *IEEE 4th World Conference on Photovoltaic Energy Conversion*. Waikoloa, HI, USA, 7–12 May.
[18] Landis GA (1990) An evolutionary path to SPS. *Space Power* 9(4): 365–371.
[19] Landis GA (2009) Solar power from space: Separating speculation from reality. *Presented at Space Photovoltaic Research and Technology XXI*. Brook Park, OH, USA, 6–8 October.

1.38 Performance Monitoring

N Pearsall, Northumbria University, Newcastle, UK
R Gottschalg, Loughborough University, Leicestershire, UK

© 2012 Elsevier Ltd.

1.38.1	Introduction	775
1.38.2	Defining Photovoltaic Performance	776
1.38.2.1	System Efficiency	776
1.38.2.2	System Yield	776
1.38.2.3	Performance Ratio	777
1.38.2.4	Performance of Stand-Alone Systems	777
1.38.3	Module Energy Prediction	778
1.38.4	PV Systems – Performance Prediction	781
1.38.5	PV Module Performance Monitoring in Practice	781
1.38.6	PV System Performance Monitoring in Practice	783
1.38.6.1	Measurements and Sensors	783
1.38.6.2	Monitoring in Practice	784
1.38.7	Summary	785
References		785

Glossary

Array yield The energy provided by the PV array over a defined period, expressed per kilowatt of array capacity.
Energy conversion efficiency The ratio of the energy provided by the PV system to the energy received as sunlight, usually expressed as a percentage.
Final yield The energy delivered to the load by the PV system over a defined period, expressed per kilowatt of array capacity.
Grid-connected system A system that is connected to the electricity distribution grid such that it can export electricity to the grid.
Peak power The power of a module or array measured at Standard Test Conditions, typically denoted as W_p or kW_p.
Performance ratio The ratio of the final yield to the reference yield for a PV system.
Reference yield The energy theoretically available from a PV system operating under reference conditions, expressed per kilowatt of array capacity.
Stand-alone system A system that is designed to be the sole power supply for a given load, independent of the electricity distribution grid.
Standard Test Conditions (STCs) A specific measurement condition at which the efficiency of the device is determined. This is defined as an irradiance of $1\,kW\,m^{-2}$, device temperature of $25\,°C$, an AM1.5G spectrum, and perpendicular incidence of the irradiance.

1.38.1 Introduction

The measurement of performance of any energy generation system allows quantification of its contribution to our energy needs, to determine whether it is operating in accordance with the design expectations and to make comparisons with other energy systems, whether of the same or different types. Establishing the performance level can address any operational problems that reduce energy output and improve system design and performance in the future. A photovoltaic (PV) system is inherently low maintenance and requires little user input for its operation in comparison with most other electricity generation technologies. Thus, it is particularly important to understand how to determine system performance without requiring a disproportionate effort from the user. There is also a wide range of system types, each one having its own performance characteristics and typical values.

Of course, simply determining the current performance cannot, in itself, tell us if the system is performing in line with expectation. We also need to consider how to predict the performance of the system in the location and for the application considered. Although much of that prediction is based on how the PV module performs under different conditions of solar irradiation and temperature, we also need to consider other system components, maintenance activities, and performance changes with time in order to measure and analyze system performance.

In this chapter, we will discuss the following:

- Methods of expressing performance at module and system level
- Prediction of performance as a function of location and operating conditions
- Measurement procedures for establishing performance and how these are implemented in practice

- Performance monitoring for different module and system types
- Challenges in long-term monitoring.

1.38.2 Defining Photovoltaic Performance

Before considering how performance is measured in practice, the term must be defined in the context of a PV system and what parameters can be used to express it.

PV performance is generally carried out for three distinct categories: modules, grid-connected systems, and stand-alone systems. The detailed design of the system is considered in other chapters in this volume, and thus this chapter will only deal with the evaluation of performance. Modules are evaluated largely to determine their energy yield and stability, with the output informing system design. The outcome is the specific behavior in different operating conditions. Grid-connected systems are operated in parallel with the conventional grid distribution system, and the overall energy output is the main parameter of interest. Stand-alone systems are designed to meet a specific load and, in general, to be the sole power supply for that load. Therefore, it is not the overall energy output that is of interest, but how well the system meets the load or provides the service that is required, for example, the provision of light or pumping of a particular volume of water. Therefore, different interpretations of performance are required, including what is measured, how the measurements are analyzed, and how the analyses are interpreted. Note that this chapter will only deal with the measurement and understanding of PV system performance for terrestrial systems and will also mainly consider flat-plate systems rather than those used under concentration, although many of the same principles apply.

The main parameters used to describe PV performance are efficiency (the ratio of the electrical output to the solar input, expressed in terms of power or energy), yield (the energy output over a defined period normalized to the module or system rating), performance ratio (PR) (which expresses the energy output of a system compared with the ideal system), and cost per generated unit of electricity. The last of these will not be considered in this chapter. Efficiency can be determined for individual components or for the whole system and yield can be defined at the module or system level. Over the past 20 years or so, the best way of expressing performance has been the subject of considerable discussion, since the output of any system is dependent on the specific operating conditions. In this chapter, generally accepted definitions of performance will be used, but with some comments on their limitations and usage. It should also be noted that different stakeholders will adopt different definitions as appropriate to their purposes.

1.38.2.1 System Efficiency

The efficiency of a PV component or system can be defined in terms of power or energy, where the latter is for a defined period. It is usual to define the power conversion efficiency of a PV module under Standard Test Conditions (STC, defined as a solar irradiance of $1000\,\text{W}\,\text{m}^{-2}$ at normal incidence, an operating temperature of $25\,°\text{C}$, and a defined AM1.5G spectrum [1]). However, as operating conditions change, so does the module efficiency, due to light intensity and temperature effects. The energy conversion efficiency, which averages the power conversion efficiency over the range of operating conditions experienced, can be more informative in terms of assessing the performance of a real system.

The energy conversion efficiency of any component or system is calculated by comparing the energy output of that component/system over a defined period with the energy input over the same period. In the case of a PV module or system, the energy input is given by the solar energy falling on the PV module or PV array surface, respectively. This is usually calculated from the solar irradiation level, expressed in $\text{kWh}\,\text{m}^{-2}$, multiplied by the module or array area, as required, in m^2.

$$\text{Energy conversion efficiency} = 100 \times \frac{\text{Energy output}}{\text{Area} \times \text{Irradiation}} \qquad [1]$$

where efficiency is expressed as percentage and the energy output is measured in kilowatt-hours. The irradiation is calculated for the same period as the energy output is determined (e.g., average daily irradiation multiplied by the number of days in the period). Thus, in order to determine the energy conversion efficiency for a real system, measurements of the energy output of the system and the irradiation falling on the array surface are required.

At the module and system level, the efficiency values derived will depend on the efficiency of the individual system components, particularly the PV module and the power conversion equipment (inverter) in the case of grid-connected systems. As for the PV module, the energy conversion efficiency over any given period is dependent on the range of operating conditions experienced. For a stand-alone system, it is a little more complicated, since the measured efficiency will depend on the detail of the load and the storage component. This is because the system does not always work at the maximum power point of the array, particularly when the battery is close to full charge (see Section 1.38.2.4 for further explanation).

1.38.2.2 System Yield

Yield figures describe the energy output over a defined period normalized to the power rating of the PV module or system. It is usually expressed in $\text{kWh}\,\text{kW}_\text{p}^{-1}$. This normalization allows yield values to be compared between modules or systems. They are often expressed as either average daily or annual values.

The following four yield values are generally considered:

- *Module yield*. The energy output of a single module (DC output)
- *Array yield*. The energy output from the PV array (DC output)
- *Final yield*. The final energy output of the system, the energy delivered to the load (or to the grid in the case of export from a grid-connected system)
- *Reference yield*. The energy output of the system if it operated at rated power levels at reference irradiance conditions for the number of hours that are equivalent to the irradiation received over the period.

In order to monitor the yield values, we require a measurement of the energy output and knowledge of the array rating. For the array yield, the DC energy output of the array should be measured, although this measurement is not always included in simple monitoring systems. The reference yield is more easily calculated by measuring the irradiation falling on the array. It can be shown that the reference yield is numerically equal to the irradiation measured in kWh m^{-2}.

The overall losses in the PV system can be estimated by comparing the final yield with the reference yield and this is the basis of the PR, which is discussed in the Section 1.38.2.3. Comparison of the array yield and the final yield gives information on the losses in the balance of systems components (inverter, wiring etc.). Comparison of the array yield and the reference yield determines the capture losses of the PV array, that is, the losses associated with the module operation itself. These losses include reduction of the absorption of light due to angle of incidence effects, reflection from the module surface, and dirt accumulation, together with an operating temperature higher than that for the standard measurement conditions.

Yield values are location-dependent, although typical values can be determined for a region. A final yield value based on the simulation of system operation under average climatic conditions is often used to define the predicted output of a PV system.

1.38.2.3 Performance Ratio

The PR of the system is calculated from the final and reference yields as follows:

$$\text{PR} = \frac{\text{Final yield}}{\text{Reference yield}} \qquad [2]$$

This expression can also be rewritten as

$$\text{PR} = \frac{\text{Final energy output}}{\text{Array rating} \times \text{Total irradiation}} \qquad [3]$$

where the final energy output is expressed in kWh, the array rating in kW$_p$, and the total irradiation in kWh m^{-2}. For measured data, the monitoring fraction, expressed as a number between 0 and 1, is introduced in the denominator to allow for missing data. The monitoring fraction expresses the proportion of actually measured values to planned measured values in the period. PR can be expressed as a fraction or as a percentage and is dimensionless.

In order to determine the PR value for a system, only the measurement of the final output and irradiation values in the plane of the array are required, together with the knowledge of the array rating. This makes it a fairly straightforward parameter to measure.

Essentially, the PR value gives a direct measure of the losses in the system by comparing the actual output of the system with that from an ideal system at the same location and under the same climatic conditions. Because it takes into account both the system rating and the irradiation conditions, it becomes possible to make direct comparisons of systems with different designs and in different locations and to provide guidance on acceptable PR values. A high-quality grid-connected system can be expected to have an annual PR value of 0.8–0.85. If lower values are obtained, the reason for the reduction should be understood and addressed if it is possible to do so.

Recently, there have been some discussions of whether PR values give an appropriate measure of performance, mainly since the calculations include the power rating of the array (see, e.g., King [2]). The array's power rating is determined by summing the STC ratings of all the modules connected into array and it is common to use the nameplate rating of the module for this purpose. Of course, there is a variation in the power rating arising from the manufacturing process and so there will be a level of uncertainty on that rating value. This can lead to a higher or lower PR value than would be expected as a result of the system losses, due to a higher or lower overall module rating than the nameplate value. The situation is complicated further if the module power is known to vary with time, for example, the seasonal variation in power output due to light exposure and annealing of amorphous silicon modules. In this case, it is usual for the nameplate rating to be the stabilized value of STC power, and so the system will appear to have a high PR value in early operation before the module output has stabilized. Nevertheless, as long as these limitations are understood, it is the authors' opinion that the PR value remains a valuable parameter for assessing and comparing the performance of grid-connected systems. In particular, it is very useful as an ongoing monitoring parameter, where the change in PR indicates changes in the loss levels in the system. Also, as yet, alternative assessment parameters appear to have other disadvantages in terms of direct identification of losses.

1.38.2.4 Performance of Stand-Alone Systems

The main judgment of performance for a stand-alone PV system is whether the load receives adequate power levels to allow it to operate for the required amount of time, consistent with the system design specifications. Assuming a stand-alone design with battery storage, the power to the load is assured if the PV array size is large enough to ensure that the battery is at a high state-of-charge (SOC) at most times and that the battery capacity is large enough to provide power to the load without charging for the number of days required by the climatic conditions. In general, the higher the reliability required for the system, the larger will be the array and the battery capacity in the design.

At times when the battery is close to or fully charged, the operating point of the array will be moved away from the maximum power point in order to reduce the charging current to an acceptable level and to match, but not exceed, the load. This is in contrast to a grid-connected system, where the usual mode of operation is to try and work at maximum power point at all times. Therefore, since the stand-alone system is working away from reference conditions, the PR will be reduced, even though the system is working exactly in line with design expectations and there are no unacceptable system losses.

In general, the lower the loss of load probability specified in the design, the more often the system will operate under conditions where the battery is at high SOC and therefore the lower will be the apparent PR. This means that systems designed for critical applications, where it is required to have a very low probability that the load will be lost, will have apparently low performance if the PR value is considered. Indeed, a high PR for a stand-alone system only indicates that the user is consuming nearly all the energy that can be produced under normal conditions, running the risk of loss of load under poor weather conditions. The situation is not improved if we use system efficiency or yield, since those parameters are also based on energy output rather than service provided.

Some measure of the availability of power to the load is required, although it is also possible to consider battery SOC as an indicative parameter. Several performance parameters have been proposed for stand-alone systems to be used alongside or instead of PR. Some of these take account of the length of time for which the battery is fully charged and/or propose consideration of charge parameters for the assessment in place of energy parameters. One of the issues to be addressed is that stand-alone system designs vary substantially, so all parameters tend to have a fairly large acceptable range which makes it more difficult to identify faults.

Vallvé (Trama Tecno Ambiental, private communication) has suggested the use of the battery index, which represents the number of days on which full charge is reached. Values over 30% are considered good, between 10% and 30% marginal and perhaps warranting investigation, and below 10% unsatisfactory. A low battery index suggests that loss of load is likely under poor weather conditions and that either the system design is unsuitable or that performance is not in line with expectation. The total time of disconnection is measured and it is also necessary to determine if that disconnection is due to overconsumption (rather than lower than expected generation) in order to determine whether the problem is one of design or usage patterns. The charge into and out of the battery is also derived from measurements of the current on both sides of the battery. As a bonus, these measurements also give some information in relation to battery aging and the requirements for maintenance.

1.38.3 Module Energy Prediction

Today, the prediction of the energy yield of PV modules is carried out in the initial stages of a system design in order to choose between different competing devices on offer. The basic building blocks of a yield prediction are illustrated in **Figure 1**. The ingredients are always a module description, the description of the environment and the mounting data. The latter is required as it influences the environment being seen by the device in terms of irradiance and device temperature.

There are two main uses of an energy yield prediction, which are distinguished by the environmental data sets being used. One is to predict for a specific site, which is then often called an energy certificate or a yield certificate. The second is to use a more generalized prediction that could, for example, be put into a module datasheet, where one would speak of an energy rating as currently being proposed by the International Electrotechnical Commission (IEC) [3]. A rating does, however, require a standard module description, a standard set of environmental data, and a standard methodology to calculate the output.

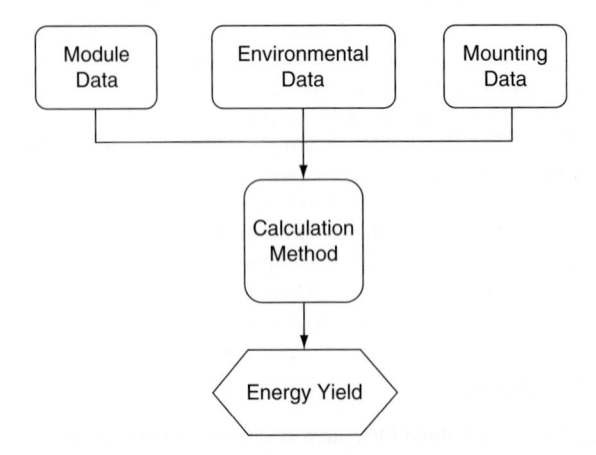

Figure 1 General modeling overview.

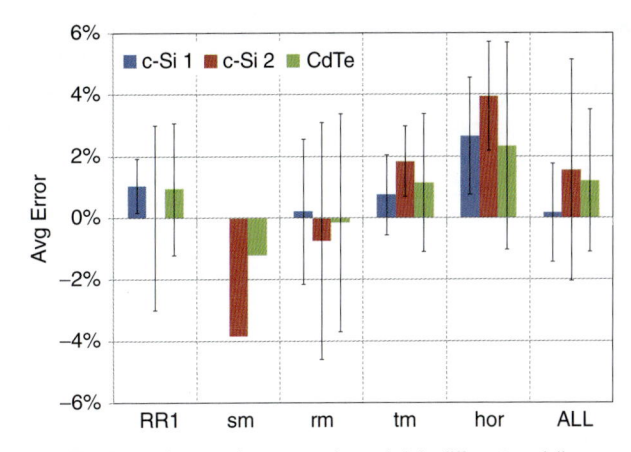

Figure 2 Evaluation of modeling accuracy. The figure shows an intercomparison of eight different modeling approaches, and the average deviation and the deviations in the modeling are shown. RR1 uses irradiance and temperature effects only; sm, spectral modeling; rm, reflection modeling; tm, modeling of module temperature; hor, translation of irradiance from the horizontal to the inclined and all the overall methods' accuracy. Adapted from Friesen G et al. (2009) Intercomparison of Different Energy Prediction Methods Within the European Project 'Performance' – Results of the 2nd Round Robin. In *Proceedings of the 24th European Photovoltaic Solar Energy Conference* [13].

The calculation method determines the structure of the input data. There are simplified empirical methods [4–6], methods simulating the current–voltage (I–V) characteristics [7–9], and statistical methods [10]. There are some differences between the required inputs, as some models model only irradiance and temperature effects, while others include effects of variable spectrum and angle of incidence. Recent intercomparisons have shown that even simple methods only modeling irradiance and temperature behavior can predict the yield to $\pm$ 3% in the case of crystalline silicon devices. This is shown in **Figure 2**, where the results of a recent evaluation of modeling approaches are shown. Overall, eight models were assessed. The starting point was modeling of irradiance and temperature effects only (indicated as RR1). The bars demonstrate the average agreement, while the error bars indicate the variations of the different modeling approaches. If the irradiance and the module temperature are known, then accuracies are expected to be in the range of $\pm$3%. However, normally one would start with the horizontal irradiance as given by relevant meteorological data sets and calculate the module temperature. The categories of hor and tm in **Figure 2** represent the addition of these factors. One can observe that most thermal models used in this group of participants tend to overestimate the temperature, resulting in an underestimation of power. This is due to the fact that hourly data sets, as used for this intercomparison, do not have any information on the variability of the irradiance during the time step. Paradoxically, the highest irradiances tend to occur on days with light clouds [11], which results in high irradiance conditions often being associated with variable operating conditions, which then results in the operating temperature being nonlinear with irradiance at higher irradiances [12]; in fact, they appear to be reduced compared with irradiances around, say, 900 W m^{-2}.

The calculation of the in-plane irradiance increased the uncertainty in the models significantly. It was also noted that when including spectral effects (sm) and reflection effects (rm) into the models, accuracy did not increase. The reasons for this are manifold, but, for example, in the case of the spectral modeling the apparent overestimation of energy was balanced with the reflection losses, so overall the model performed in the same way as without these effects. The issue is largely related to the available input data.

The differences introduced by the different calculation blocks (**Figure 1**) are thus not the drivers in the accuracy of a yield prediction. It was also noted during this intercomparison that models tended to perform well for one type of module, but less well for another. Thus, the differences observed in professional tools cannot be due to the different calculation and mounting structures. There are differences of some percentage points but not the values of >5% deviation that were reported for some commercial packages.

The module description is a major issue in any performance prediction as the required data are often not available. This is due to a number of issues, including that data provided by manufacturers are not consistent, there are uncertainties in the measurement of the different properties and finally the way modeling software parameterizes input data often results in very different device behavior.

The data available for modeling purposes are often taken from the datasheet. At the moment, this can be rather inconsistent. The temperature coefficient is measured for one module, the low light behavior for another (potentially by another laboratory altogether), and the STC power is a nominal value. As a result of manufacturing variations, modules are classified into different power categories, commonly known as power bins, depending on their measured output. This means that the power of a specific module will usually vary slightly from the nameplate power. The temperature coefficient is typically also larger for lower power bins than for higher ones, and if the temperature coefficient is not measured for a module of the specific bin, this can result in some deviations which will be visible in the prediction accuracy. The work of Friesen *et al.* [13] has shown that the difference of the specific module values for those given on the datasheet is by far the dominating factor in the modeling accuracy. One approach to get consistent data is the application of IEC 61853-1 [3] as this requires all measurements to be taken on one module. However, this is not a datasheet requirement [14] and thus is not available for all module types.

There are also significant deviations between laboratories in the way key parameters are measured. This depends on a great many parameters, including the equipment used and the traceability chain in the measurements. A European intercomparison [15] reported that after having carried out an optimization, an agreement between the European test and measurement laboratories of

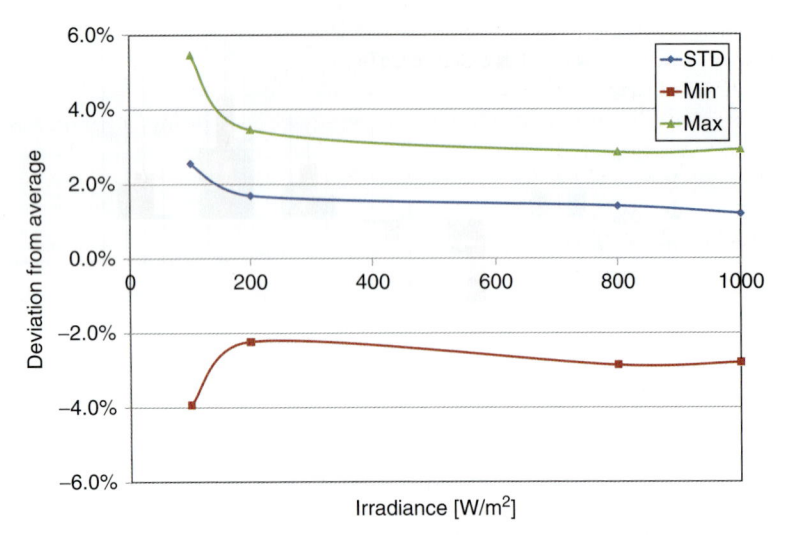

Figure 3 Agreement of power measurements in European test laboratories at varying irradiances. Data detailed in Herrmann W (2010) Results of the second round robin test of PV-performance. *Internal Deliverable D1.1.* 4: 25 [16].

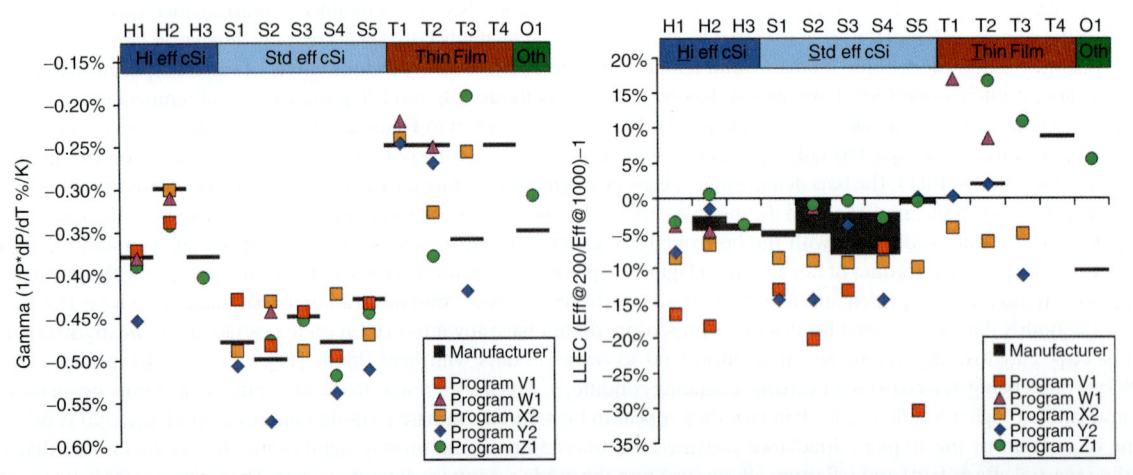

Figure 4 Comparison of manufacturer's data with values in simulation programs for the temperature coefficients (left) and low light behavior (right). Graphs taken from Ransome S, Sutterlueti J, and Kravets R (2011) How kWh/kW$_p$ modelling and measurement comparisons depend on uncertainty and variability. In: *Proceedings of the 37th IEEE Photovoltaic Specialists Conference.* Seattle, WA: IEEE [17].

±1.5% was achieved between the majority of test houses for crystalline silicon (counting all outliers, this would be closer to ±3%). Thin films showed a deviation of about ±5%. One should keep in mind that this is carried out after one optimization step and without this the agreement is significantly reduced. This rating is the uncertainty in the normalization. The measurement uncertainty in the parameters such as low light behavior and temperature coefficient are even more significant. The change in the agreement between the different laboratories in one round robin intercomparison is shown in **Figure 3**. It should be noted that two groups, the one with the maximum measurement and the one with the minimum measurement at STC, did not participate in the low light behavior measurements. Thus, it is surprising that the measurement at 100 W m^{-2} deviates by as much as −4% to +5% [15]. Clearly, this will affect the performance of any modeling routine, especially when modeling areas with high contributions of low light behavior. The difference in the temperature coefficients was even larger, about ±15%, which will have a significant effect on accuracy in high-temperature environments. Thus, the measurement uncertainty is a major factor in energy prediction.

The input data are then parameterized to make them useful for simulation codes. A major reason for the differences in the modeling results is in the way simulation codes translate the datasheet values into the module description for the module. Ransome *et al.* [17] compared the data used by a number of commercial software programs in terms of how well they match the manufacturer's datasheet. The findings are summarized in **Figure 4**. The temperature coefficient, shown in the left graph, varies by about 20% for standard silicon devices. This is actually within the measurement uncertainties, so could be justified by using different input data sets. In the case of thin-film devices, much more significant deviations can be seen. The low light behavior is defined here as the ratio of the efficiency at 200 W m^{-2} to the efficiency at 1000 W m^{-2}. The differences between the modeling programs and the datasheet values can be quite surprising. The relative differences are multiples rather than percentage values. Again thin-film devices fare worse in terms of agreement than crystalline devices. In areas such as the United Kingdom, where about 30% of incident irradiance is at levels below 300 W m^{-2}, this will easily cause >5% variation in the energy yield prediction.

The other main contribution to the uncertainty is the environmental data. It has been shown that even simulations using the same data source can result in rather different outcomes. An obvious reason is how horizontal input data are translated into in-plane irradiance. The time resolution can also influence the outcome of any simulation step. In addition, some devices show a rather significant spectral effect and/or idiosyncratic angle of incidence effects, which often will not be covered by simulation codes. One should also keep in mind that the modeling can only be as good as the input data. Modeling the spectral irradiance, for example, is either carried out using software codes or spectral irradiance measurements. The latter are few and far between, and thus there is a reliance on spectral models. In an intermediate step, one can use empirical correlations [18], but that requires longer-term measurements. Thus, one typically uses SMARTS [19] or similar codes, but these are not really designed for non-clear days, and thus, modeling the spectrum might actually introduce a bias into any simulation. On an annual basis, the angle of incidence and spectral shifts tend to balance. In shorter time periods, very significant modeling errors can be seen.

Module energy prediction can be summarized as being within 3% accuracy for crystalline silicon devices, if module characteristics, temperature, and in-plane irradiance are known. The key uncertainties are in the determination of these characteristics. Specific characteristics of unusual devices are more difficult to capture and need further research. In particular, if short-term prediction is required, for example, in the case of condition monitoring, the 'secondary' effects need to be evaluated in much more detail.

1.38.4 PV Systems – Performance Prediction

All the statements of the module energy prediction apply, as this tends to be the backbone of the system energy prediction. Most prediction methods will carry out the module energy prediction and then multiply the current and voltage results to account for parallel and series connections. The effects of the balance of system (BOS) components are then considered.

The measurement of system energy output and other related parameters, such as irradiation received and various voltage and current levels, can determine system performance, but the judgment of performance quality depends on whether this matches with expectation. Performance is a function of location, mainly relating to the climatic conditions and the detail of system design, including array orientation, component selection, component matching, and external factors such as shading. Therefore, it is important to have a reliable performance prediction against which to compare the measured values.

Performance prediction is usually carried out using specialist software tools, either proprietary to the company concerned, available for purchase, or in some cases, available without charge. In the latter category, it is possible to obtain a simple prediction of system output for a given location from the Photovoltaic Geographical Information System (PVGIS) web site developed by the Institute of Energy of the European Commission's (EC) Joint Research Centre [20, 21]. It is also possible to obtain performance predictions from a range of inverter manufacturers via their web sites. More complex design software, including the possibility to include external shading, select specific components, and modify embedded assumptions, can be purchased, with well-used examples being PVSyst [7] and PV*SOL [22]. There is a wide range of PV system simulation software available and the information given here should not be taken as a direct endorsement of the examples provided, although they are both popular and well-used programs. Such simulation programs will provide estimates of efficiency, yield, and PR that can then be compared with values achieved in practice.

Nevertheless, whatever simulation software is used, it needs to be recognized that the predictions relate to average conditions and use historical weather data. Therefore, when comparing with measured values, it is vital to consider how the irradiation level received relates to that used in the prediction process. It is also necessary to consider the accuracy with which both the measured and simulated values can be determined.

1.38.5 PV Module Performance Monitoring in Practice

The aim of module performance monitoring is, in the majority of cases today, for the differentiation between different modules, that is, demonstration of 'superior' energy yield of certain products. These lists can be produced 'independently' or openly by the manufacturer. A second common use is for long-term performance investigation, that is, durability and stability of products. Third, monitoring data are often used for the validation of energy prediction methods, or as input into these. All these uses have in common that high measurement accuracy is required. The section will review common arrangements in terms of measurement systems and the main issues encountered.

There are two different setups commonly in use for module monitoring, which are depicted in **Figure 5**. The left graph in **Figure 5** shows a typical system using a multiplexer-based system where $I-V$ traces are taken at fixed time intervals. An example of such a system is documented [23]. These systems use high-accuracy measurement components and normally four-quadrant power supplies using a Kelvin connection to minimize the influence of any transmission losses. The cost of measurements is very high, and thus, normally the measurements are multiplexed and measurements are taken in a serial fashion. The right graph in **Figure 5** depicts the other extreme, a system which tracks the maximum power point all of the time, as, for example, analyzed by Dittmann *et al.* [24]. The measurement components are typically of lower quality than the single measurement system approach, but measurements are taken in a parallel fashion. In reality, both system types have started to move towards the middle ground. Most measurement maximum power point trackers (MPPTs) now have features to trace the $I-V$ characteristic of the attached device. The multiplexer systems mostly have the feature

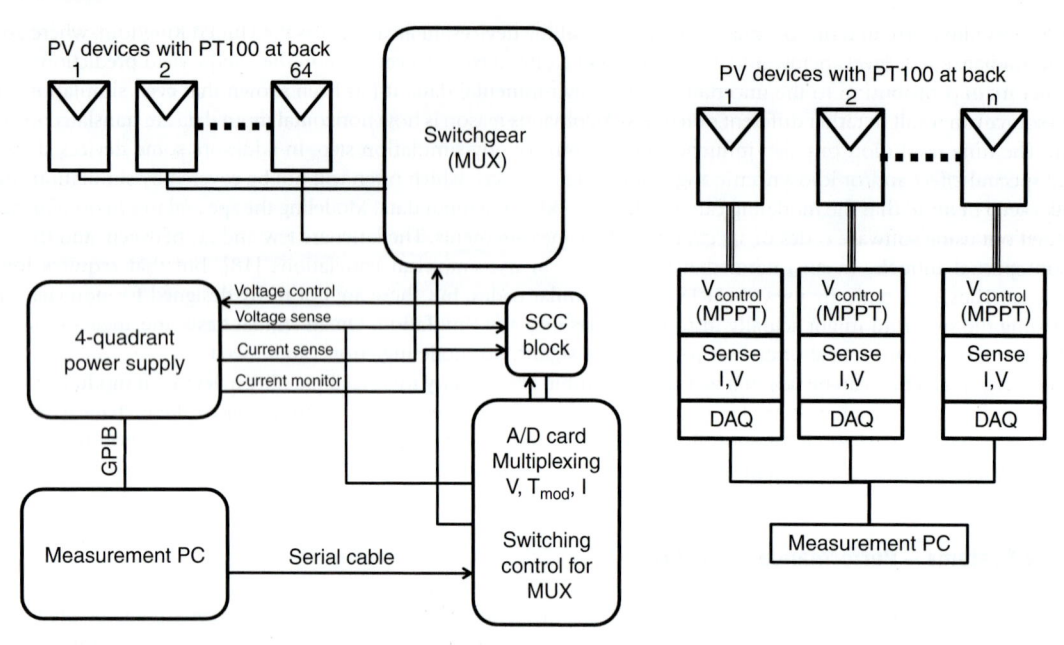

Figure 5 Typical module monitoring layouts. The left graph shows a typical multiplexed system, while the right graph shows one system with multiple maximum power point trackers (MPPTs).

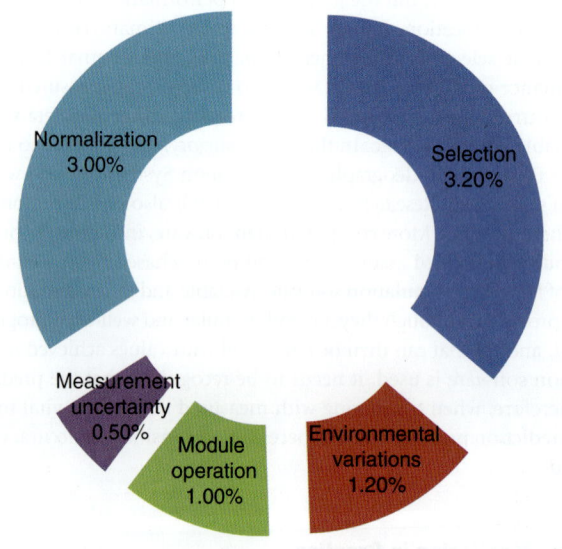

Figure 6 Contributions to the comparability of module measurements on a single site.

for a load to be present, as it has been shown that otherwise some devices might exhibit unrealistic aging [25]. Both approaches are used throughout the world and measurement accuracy depends as much on the circumstances around the measurement system as on the measurement system itself.

These monitoring campaigns tend to be mission-critical for manufacturers and thus tend to be frequently overinterpreted, by making rather small differences in energy yield seemingly significant. The uncertainty in the kilowatt-hour measurement tends to be rather low [23, 24], but that does not mean that the comparability of the devices is good enough. In many respects, the framework of the monitoring is much more important for a good intercomparison. Results are also typically compared on a kWh/kW$_p$ basis, which also has an influence on the comparability of devices. A typical intercomparison would have less than 5% comparability for the specific yield of a module (as illustrated in **Figure 6**).

The electrical measurements only account for 0.5% in the overall comparability. The two major sources of uncertainty are the normalization and the selection. The simulations used for **Figure 6** are based on a single-diode model. They allow all possible parameters of a PV module within the power bins, which clearly is an oversimplification. This would need to be simulated based on the analysis of a specific power production statistic to come to a more precise number. A contribution of maybe half of this would be expected (as quality assurance limits the parameter space significantly), but this would still result in a contribution of around 1.5% to the comparability.

The most significant uncertainty in outdoor monitoring is actually the calibration of the module power. It has been shown in **Figure 3** that the comparability of EU test houses is around 3%, and thus any power used for normalization will have such an uncertainty. It is now debatable what peak power value to use. Good practice would be to measure all devices in one location (i.e., one test house for all devices) as this reduces the uncertainty in the power calibration to the repeatability of the test house which typically is in the sub-1% range. Should one use the measurements supplied in the factory flash test, it should be kept in mind that the manufacturer's measurement uncertainty is at least 1% higher than that of the test house, as a transfer of the standard has to be carried out. If one uses the nameplate (or datasheet) value, the uncertainty to be used for the intercomparability is the manufacturer's measurement uncertainty (as the manufacturer is selecting the modules) plus the allowable bin width.

Environmental variations in **Figure 6** indicate that even in the same location, not all modules might see the same environment. Modules in the center of a test field will typically operate at slightly higher temperatures, as they will not experience as much windchill. Modules will receive slightly different amounts of light due to small variations in the viewing angles and/or ground reflection. These variations are extremely difficult to eliminate, and thus this represents a minimum value for comparability.

The final item is that different module operations can contribute to the absolute comparability. Different cabling lengths can be significant if no Kelvin connection is made. MPPTs do not always find the appropriate operating point as they are affected by instability of the environment and also are not 100% effective to find the MPP even in steady-state conditions.

Module measurements tend to be carried out on highly instrumented measurement systems, thus the choice of the sensor is not so much of an issue here as it is for PV systems monitoring. Typically, one would have a high-quality pyranometer and supplementary reference devices, preferably in a redundant setup. If the monitoring data are to be used for energy prediction as well, it is advisable to characterize the incident irradiance further, for example, beam/diffuse irradiance, incident spectrum, and angular distribution of the irradiance. A large number of extensions can be added, which all have in common that they are very costly.

1.38.6 PV System Performance Monitoring in Practice

It is straightforward to define what measurements can be made in order to assess PV system performance, but less obvious what measurement should be made in any specific case. The choice of parameters to measure, sensors and sensor positioning, frequency of data measurement and storage both the nature and frequency of the data analysis depend on the system type and the underlying purpose of undertaking performance monitoring.

The procedures for PV system monitoring were initially developed to determine the performance at installation and over a short period thereafter, typically up to 2 years. The main purposes of the monitoring were as follows: (1) the verification of the system quality especially where the installation was funded from public sources (e.g., national government, EC) and (2) the collection of information on the specific operating characteristics in order to allow lessons to be learned for the design of future systems. One of the first documents to address the requirements for system monitoring was produced by the EC Joint Research Centre at Ispra, Italy, for use in EC-funded PV demonstration projects [26] and included details on data format to allow collection of all performance data for comparison and system development. Subsequently, an international standard on PV system monitoring, IEC 61724, was adopted [27]. This document has a similar approach, being mainly concerned with the establishment of performance at the beginning of operation.

In the last 15 years, there has been a major shift to a situation where almost all PV installations are now commercial in nature and for the purpose of delivering electrical energy to the user. As a result, the purpose of monitoring has also changed from simply providing information on system performance issues to ensuring that the energy provision is as high as possible and in line with the expectations from the design stage. The monitoring process reflects the fact that the energy produced from the system now has a financial value. This means that the monitoring approach, in terms of what is measured, how rapidly any faults or problems can be identified, what magnitude of loss can be detected and the funds allocated for the monitoring process, depends on the value of the generated energy or the service for which it is used. As part of the EC Framework Programme 6 project PERFORMANCE, the European guidelines for PV system monitoring and assessment have been updated in an effort to reflect this change in focus and, especially, the need to consider monitoring and analysis over the full lifetime of the system [28].

In this section, we will first consider what can be measured and some principles of how faults or losses can be determined. We will then consider how the monitoring is implemented in practice.

1.38.6.1 Measurements and Sensors

The measurement of any quantity requires a sensor that will provide an output that varies as that quantity varies. Ideally, the sensor will have a linear response to the variation of the parameter being measured. Otherwise, some signal conditioning will be required to convert the sensor output to the correct value. Sensors vary in terms of accuracy, calibration requirements, mode of usage, and cost. The accuracy of the measurement has a direct impact on the ability to detect operational problems, since it is not possible to detect changes in performance that are smaller than the uncertainty in the measurement of the performance parameter itself. The output of the sensor can be displayed directly, but it is usual to record the outputs for later analysis. This also allows the use of historical data to determine performance trends.

The frequency with which a given parameter should be measured depends on how that parameter is expected to vary. In general, the more variable the parameter, the more often it needs to be measured to ensure that representative values across the required period are obtained. However, the more the measurements made, the greater are the storage capacity required and the analysis effort. However, given the advances in data storage in recent years, the issue of storage capacity is no longer a particular constraint and it is often useful to have additional values to consult when trying to understand the loss mechanisms.

The most commonly measured parameters for a grid-connected PV system are those given below (with the usual units):

- Global irradiance in the array plane (W m^{-2})
- Ambient temperature in the shade (°C)
- Module temperature (°C)
- Array output voltage (V)
- Array output current (total) (A)
- Inverter/rectifier AC power (kW) or cumulative energy output (kWh)
- Power to the utility grid (kW) or cumulative energy exported to the grid (kWh)
- Power from the utility grid (kW) or cumulative energy imported from the grid (kWh).

Where the PV system consists of several subsystems, it is useful to make AC measurements for all or a selection of the subsystems. Where the PV array consists of a number of subarrays, it is useful to make DC measurements for all or a selection of the subarrays. This allows the comparison of the performance of the subsystems or subarrays, which gives a powerful tool for the identification of losses when one subsystem or subarray has a lower output than the others.

In terms of defining system performance, the two most important parameters are the global irradiance in the array plane and the cumulative energy output from the inverter, with the other measurements providing information to aid the understanding of the values obtained for overall performance. All systems will have some measurement of energy output, although not all have irradiance measurements due to the expense of installing a local sensor. Solar measurements can also be obtained from nearby sites (e.g., meteorological stations) or from satellite data. Many of the monitoring services make use of satellite data for small systems where it is not economic to install a separate sensor. This gives a reduced accuracy in comparison with a local sensor and thus has an impact on the magnitude of problems and the losses that can be identified, but provides a service that could not be accessed otherwise.

1.38.6.2 Monitoring in Practice

The way in which performance monitoring is implemented in practice depends on the type and size of the PV system and the purpose of the monitoring itself. For most systems, the purpose is to establish the energy output and to determine if there are any problems or issues that need to be addressed. The way in which that is done depends on the value of the electricity being generated, the financial arrangements in regard to the installation, and the speed with which any problems need to be identified.

For some systems, where they are associated with research and development activities, more complex monitoring is justified since the purpose is to obtain detailed performance data under a range of operating conditions (see also the previous discussion on module performance comparisons). The information may be used for product development, product comparison, or system design improvement. Since these are specialist monitoring systems and therefore vary considerably in scope, the remainder of this section will concentrate on the monitoring of commercial systems.

For the majority of systems, especially those of small to medium size, the inverter performs the monitoring function and most major manufacturers provide options for measuring, storing, and displaying monitored data. This can include the ability to compare subarrays or subsystems and calculate most of the main performance parameters. Inverter-based monitoring systems do not usually incorporate solar irradiance sensors as standard, but some provide the opportunity to add a sensor. The electrical measurements are embedded in the inverter, which gives the advantage of not having to purchase and install separate sensors, but the user should consider if the range and accuracy of the measurements are sufficient. This is unlikely to be a problem for the small system user, but larger users might want to extend the range of measurements or use duplicate sensors to enhance reliability.

While the inverter-based systems will give some level of data interpretation, they usually need the user to interpret whether the PV system is operating according to expectation. In some countries, there are also options to purchase a monitoring service to give a higher level of diagnostic capability. These services take data directly from the system and compare the values and trends with other systems in the same area. This gives a more powerful diagnostic capability than for a single system, since it allows the identification of systems not operating in line with the majority of other systems.

For still larger systems, where most or all of the electricity generated is fed directly into the grid and for which any downtime would result in severe financial penalties, two other measures are often adopted. First, the system supplier will offer a combined maintenance and monitoring package, with a guarantee as to the speed with which operational problems will be identified and addressed. Second, the supplier is often required to provide a performance guarantee for the output of the system. These two measures are clearly linked, since it is advantageous both to the owner and the supplier to ensure that a robust performance monitoring system is in operation.

Performance guarantees must take account of the variability of the climatic conditions, which would affect the overall output of the system but are outside the control of the supplier and do not reflect on the quality of the system. The most common performance parameters used are a guaranteed minimum final yield or a guaranteed minimum PR. In terms of yield, the value needs to be corrected for the irradiation conditions in the period (usually 1 year) compared with the reference conditions used to set the minimum yield. Therefore, in both cases, it is necessary to have an accurate measurement of irradiation received as well as energy output. An accurate value for system rating is also required and it is common to make a direct measurement of some or all the modules to achieve this.

1.38.7 Summary

In this chapter, monitoring of PV module and system performance was considered. The purpose of monitoring has changed in recent years. In the module area it has changed from scientific performance evaluations for validating energy prediction methods to demonstrating product capabilities. In the system space, it has changed from the measurement of specific demonstration systems, to aid the development of components and improvement of system design, to the monitoring of a wide range of commercially installed systems, to determine the energy output and identify operational problems. This has resulted in the development of monitoring capability in or associated with the inverter in grid-connected systems and the provision of monitoring services.

For the stand-alone system, the performance measurement needs to determine whether the required service level has been met. This is best served by considering the period for which the battery remains at a high SOC and therefore capable of powering the load.

The module intercomparisons are nowadays often driven by product management, which results in frequent overinterpretation of data. Data campaigns are often scientifically instrumented, that is, nonstandard, but it is unfortunately not the measurement accuracy which drives the robustness of the measurements.

As the PV system market growth has changed the purpose of performance monitoring, advances in data storage, communication systems, and analysis methods have increased the possibilities of monitoring, even for small systems. As PV systems become part of an intelligent electricity grid, the requirements for and capabilities of performance monitoring will continue to develop rapidly.

References

[1] IEC (2005) *Crystalline Silicon Terrestrial Photovoltaic (PV) Modules – Design Qualification and Type Approval*, 2 edn., vol. IEC 61215. Geneva, Switzerland: IEC.
[2] King DL (2011) More "efficient" methods for specifying and monitoring PV system performance. *Proceedings of the 37th IEEE Photovoltaic Specialists Conference, Seattle, USA*. Piscataway, NJ: IEEE.
[3] IEC (2011) *Performance Testing and Energy Rating of Terrestrial PV Modules. Part 1: Irradiance and Temperature Performance Measurements and Power Rating*, IEC 60904-2011 edn., vol. IEC 61853. Geneva, Switzerland: IEC.
[4] Friesen G, Chianese D, Cereghetti N, and Bernasconi A (2004) Energy rating prediction method – Matrix method – Applied to CIS modules. In: Hoffmann W, Bal J-L, Ossenbrink H, *et al.* (eds.) *Proceedings of the 19th European Photovoltaic Solar Energy Conference, Paris*, pp. 1817–1819. Munich, Germany: WIP.
[5] Anderson D, Sample T, and Dunlop E (2001) Obtaining module energy rating from standard laboratory measurements. In: McNelis B, Palz W, Ossenbrink HA, and Helm P (eds.) *Proceedings of the 17th European Photovoltaic Solar Energy Conference, Munich*, pp. 832–835. Munich, Germany: WIP.
[6] Williams SR, Betts TR, Gottschalg R, and Infield DG (2005) Site-specific condition (SSC): A model for real PV modules performance. In: Gottschalg R, Pearsall N, Buckle C, and Hutchins MG (eds.) *Proceedings of the 2nd Photovoltaic Science, Application and Technology, Loughborough*, pp. 127–134. Oxford, UK: UK-ISES.
[7] van Dijk VAP (1996) Hybrid Photovoltaic Solar Energy Systems Design, Operation, Modelling, and Optimisation of the Utrecht PBB System. PhD Thesis, University of Utrecht.
[8] Anon (2010) www.pvsyst.com (accessed December 2011).
[9] Marion B (2002) A method for modeling the current-voltage curve of a PV module for outdoor conditions. *Progress in Photovoltaics: Research and Applications* 10(3): 205–214.
[10] Guerin de Montgareuil A (2007) Description of MOTHERPV, the new method developed at INES/CEA for the assessment of the energy production of photovoltaic modules. In: Willeke G, Ossenbrink H, and Helm P (eds.) *Proceedings of the 22nd European Photovoltaic Solar Energy Conference, Milan, Italy*, pp. 2608–2612. Munich, Germany: WIP.
[11] Zehner M, Weigl T, Hartmann M, *et al.* (2011) Energy loss due to irradiance enhancement. In: Ossenbrink H, Jäger-Waldau A, and Helm P (eds.) *Proceedings of the 26th Photovoltaic Solar Energy Conference, Hamburg*, pp. 3935–3938. Munich, Germany: WIP.
[12] Zhu J, Bründlinger R, Mühlberger T, *et al.* (2010) Optimised inverter sizing in high-latitude maritime climates. *IET Renewable Power Generation* 5(1): 58–66.
[13] Friesen G, Dittmann S, Williams SR, *et al.* (2009) Intercomparison of different energy prediction methods within the European project "performance" – Results of the 2nd round Robin. In: Ossenbrink H, Jäger-Waldau A, and Helm P (eds.) *Proceedings of the 24th European Photovoltaic Solar Energy Conference, Hamburg*, pp. 3189–3197. Munich, Germany: WIP.
[14] CENELEC (2003) *Datasheet and Nameplate Information for Photovoltaic Modules*, 2nd edn., vol. EN50380. Brussels, Belgium: CENELEC.
[15] Herrmann W, Zamini S, Fabero F, *et al.* (2010) PV module output power characterisation in test laboratories and in the PV industry – Results of the European performance project. In: de Santi GF, Ossenbrink HA, and Helm P (eds.) *Proceedings of the 25th European Photovoltaic Solar Energy Conference. Valencia*, pp. 3879–3883. Munich, Germany: WIP.
[16] Herrmann W (2010) Results of the second round Robin test of PV-performance. *Internal Deliverable* D1.1.4: 25.
[17] Ransome S, Sutterlueti J, and Kravets R (2011) How kWh/kWp modelling and measurement comparisons depend on uncertainty and variability. *Proceedings of the 37th IEEE Photovoltaic Specialists Conference, Seattle, USA*. Piscataway, NJ: IEEE.
[18] Betts TR, Gottschalg R, and Infield DG (2004) Spectral irradiance correction for PV system yield calculations. In: Hoffmann W, Bal J-L, Ossenbrink HA, *et al.* (eds.) *Proceedings of the 19th Photovoltaic Solar Energy Conference, Paris*, pp. 2533–2536. Munich, Germany: WIP.
[19] Gueymard CA (2001) Parameterized transmittance model for direct beam and circumsolar spectral irradiance. *Solar Energy* 71(5): 325–346.
[20] Suri M, Huld T, Dunlop ED, and Ossenbrink HA (2007) Potential of solar electricity generation in the European union member states and candidate countries. *Solar Energy* 81: 1295–1305.
[21] Anon (2011) PVGIS. http://re.jrc.ec.europa.eu/pvgis/index.htm (accessed October 2011).
[22] Anon (2010) http://www.solardesign.co.uk/pv.php (accessed October 2011).
[23] Betts TR, Bliss M, Gottschalg R, and Infield DG (2005) Analysis of a flexible measurement system for outdoor DC performance testing of photovoltaic modules. *Proceedings of the 15th Photovoltaic Science and Engineering Conference, Shanghai*. Shanghai, China: Shanghai Jiao Tong University.
[24] Dittmann S, Friesen G, Strepparava D, *et al.* (2011) Energy yield measurements at SUPSI – Importance of data quality control and its influence on kWh/Wp inter-comparison. In: Ossenbrink H, Jäger-Waldau A, and Helm P (eds.) *Proceedings of the 26th Photovoltaic Solar Energy Conference, Hamburg*, pp. 3629–3634. Munich, Germany: WIP.
[25] Astawa KS, Betts TR, and Gottschalg R (2009) The influence of exposure history on Amorphous Silicon properties under realistic operating conditions. In: Hutchins M and Pearsall N (eds.) *Proceedings of the 5th Photovoltaic Science, Application and Technology Conference, Wrexham*, pp. 209–213. Oxford, UK: UK-ISES.

[26] Blaesser G and Munro D (1995) *Guidelines for the Assessment of Photovoltaic Plants, Document A, Photovoltaic System Monitoring*. Luxembourg: Office for Official Publications of the European Communities.
[27] IEC (1998) *Photovoltaic System Performance Monitoring – Guidelines for Measurement, Data Exchange and Analysis*. vol. IEC 61724. Geneva, Switzerland: IEC.
[28] Pearsall NM, Atanasiu B, and Huld T (2010) European PV system monitoring guidelines. http://re.jrc.ec.europa.eu/monitoring/monitoring_main.php (accessed December 2011).

1.39 Standards in Photovoltaic Technology

H Ossenbrink, H Müllejans, R Kenny, and E Dunlop, European Commission DG Joint Research Centre, Ispra, Italy

© 2012 Elsevier Ltd. All rights reserved.

1.39.1	**History**	787
1.39.1.1	The Early PV Development in the United States	787
1.39.1.2	Establishment of IEC TC82	788
1.39.1.3	The European Commission's Joint Research Centre	788
1.39.1.4	The Early IEC Standards	788
1.39.1.5	The Working Groups	789
1.39.2	**Standards for Performance Determination of PV Devices**	789
1.39.2.1	Introduction	789
1.39.2.2	Performance Determination of PV Devices	789
1.39.2.2.1	Light sources	790
1.39.2.2.2	Measurement	790
1.39.2.2.3	Traceability	790
1.39.2.2.4	Preconditioning	790
1.39.2.3	Existing IEC Standards	790
1.39.2.3.1	Reference solar devices	791
1.39.2.3.2	Measurement conditions	791
1.39.2.3.3	Measurement practice	791
1.39.2.3.4	Data analysis	792
1.39.2.3.5	Device behavior	792
1.39.2.4	Discussion and Conclusion	792
1.39.3	**Reliability Testing of PV Modules**	793
1.39.3.1	Introduction	793
1.39.3.2	The Beginning of an International Standard for Type Approval Testing	793
1.39.3.3	Weathering Test or Dedicated Stress to Identify Failure Mechanisms	793
1.39.3.4	Type Approval Testing	793
1.39.3.5	Pass/Fail Criteria	793
1.39.3.6	Environmental Testing	794
1.39.3.7	Correlation of Reliability Testing with Lifetime	795
1.39.4	**Energy Performance and Energy Rating**	795
1.39.5	**Concentrating PV Standards**	797
1.39.5.1	CPV Design Qualification IEC 62108	797
1.39.5.2	Other Standards in Preparation	798
1.39.5.2.1	Power rating	798
1.39.5.2.2	Trackers	799
1.39.5.2.3	CPV system safety	799
1.39.6	**Outlook**	799
1.39.6.1	New Technologies	799
1.39.6.2	Major Markets	799
1.39.6.3	TC82 Priorities	799
1.39.7	**Conclusion**	799
Appendix		800
References		802

1.39.1 History

1.39.1.1 The Early PV Development in the United States

The use of photovoltaic (PV) solar cells on the ground actually started in the United States around 1978. At that time, the technology lead the United States had gained from power supply to spacecrafts, and consequently the governance of key knowledge, had spurred the first prototypes aiming to develop PV as a future electricity source also on the earth. Favored by the first oil crisis shock, the United States embarked on a range of demonstration projects aiming to develop cost-effective and reliable terrestrial applications. At the same time, companies that had never produced solar cells entered the field, comprised of not only US oil companies (Arco, Exxon, BP) but also semiconductor companies such as Motorola.

The demonstration program, sponsored by the US Department of Energy, assigned to the Jet Propulsion Laboratory (JPL; Pasadena, CA) the task of developing specifications that participants to the program must meet. The program as such was rolled out in 'blocks' along with the specifications. The final, and most influential in terms of standardization, specification was the 'Block V' specification (1980), describing a range of environmental and mechanical stress tests PV modules would need to pass before being admitted to the program.

1.39.1.2 Establishment of IEC TC82

The experience from this early demonstration program and the approach taken within the JPL specification had laid out one of the foundations for the international standardization process. In 1980 when the Commission of the European Union decided to finance a similar 'PV Pilot Program' with the European Member States as participants, there was enough dynamics and interest to launch a dedicated technical committee (TC) within the International Electrotechnical Commission (IEC), the partner organization of ISO, with headquarters in Geneva, Switzerland.

The countries represented at the first TC meeting, now named TC82, were the United States, Canada, Australia, United Kingdom, Germany, France, Spain, Italy, and Japan. Mr. Leclerque from France was elected as the first chairman, and the Secretariat rested with the United States. The scope for the TC82 'solar PV energy systems' was defined as

> To prepare international standards for systems of photovoltaic conversion of solar energy into electrical energy and for all the elements in the entire photovoltaic energy system.
> In this context, the concept 'photovoltaic energy system' includes the entire field from light input to a solar cell to and including the interface with the electrical system(s) to which energy is supplied.

In the beginning, phase work was organized along three working groups (WGs):

WG1 Glossary
WG2 Modules, nonconcentrating
WG3 Systems

Much of the work was concentrated in WG2, which had the task to collect existing standards and develop new ones in the two fields. One was regarding the measurements of electrical performance of solar cells and modules and included items like the definition of a reference spectral irradiance, the measurements of spectral response (SR) and current voltage characteristics, and requirements for solar simulators. The second focused on the test procedures to be harmonized and prescribed to establish an assessment of the expected reliability and minimum lifetime of terrestrial PV modules.

1.39.1.3 The European Commission's Joint Research Centre

In 1982, the European Communities launched a pilot program on PV system, comprising 15 installations in the range of 15–300 kWp, totaling just above 1 MWp. Around the same time (1981), the global annual production of terrestrial PV solar cells amounted to less than 5 MWp (in 2010, this quantity was produced every 3 h), and the pilot program intended to stimulate more manufacturing and deployment experience. To ensure the technical quality and performance of these installations, the European Commission's Joint Research Centre (JRC) was put in charge of experimentally verifying not only all the PV module types regarding their electrical performance and expected reliability but also the full installations after commissioning. For this purpose, the JRC had set up a specialized laboratory (European Solar Test Installation – ESTI) to perform these verifications according to their in-house specifications 101 ('Standard Procedures for Terrestrial Photovoltaic Performance Measurements') and 501 ('Qualification Test Procedures for Photovoltaic Modules').

It was of strategic importance for the JRC that their specifications were contributing to the TC82 program of work, anticipating that only worldwide standards would contribute to a reliable and performing PV technology. However, as the JRC as an international organization did not represent a national committee, a liaison was formed between IEC TC82 and the JRC, in order to allow the experts of ESTI to participate actively in the standards writing process from the end of 1982 onward. The JRC specification 501 evolved into the second edition (Spec. 502) during 1983, essentially dropping some less important test procedures. Its introduction stated

> This specification lays down the control tests of the Commission of the European Communities, applied by the Joint Research Centre for the qualification of modules for photovoltaic projects funded by the Commission, or upon special request from industry or other organizations. The general objective of these tests is to assess relative performances and to identify environmental factors and design features which could affect the attainment of a sufficiently long life-time. The results of these tests are an essential part of all the photovoltaic pilot and demonstration plant activities of the Commission, they are also used as reference values for JRC's monitoring programs.

1.39.1.4 The Early IEC Standards

The program of work of the IEC WG2 developed rapidly, and already in 1987, the first standard was published (IEC 891, today IEC 60891 ed. 2.0), and a range of others describing measurement procedures followed in a short sequence as a series IEC 904. WG3 developed work not only on components such as charge controllers and inverters but also on complete systems. The first publication was in 1992 (IEC 1194 – Characteristic parameters of stand-alone photovoltaic (PV) systems, today IEC 61194 – Ed. 2).

The work on standards regarding reliability test procedures took longer, as agreement about altogether 17 test procedures had to be found and the laboratory experience in particular at ESTI had to be taken into account. In order to allow the growing number of commercial clients a situation of stability, the JRC published in 1991 Specification 503, titled 'Qualification Test Procedures for Crystalline Silicon Photovoltaic Modules'.

This specification was essentially the content of the first committee draft (CD) of the new IEC 1215, which was still in the review process, anticipating that the publication would follow within 2 years. The consensus finding process took until 1993, and only after dropping the description of the UV exposure procedure and deciding upon a 1000 h damp heat test (as opposed to 2000 h) was this major standard which is in its 2nd edition still in use worldwide published as IEC 61215.

From today's view, this standard was and is certainly that which has influenced the development of PV module technology the most as it became mandatory in many public and private procurement programs. It represented a fair balance between rigid requirements to ensure at least 20 years of lifetime and sufficient room for development of lower cost PV modules.

1.39.1.5 The Working Groups

The work of WG2 on measurement procedures around the series IEC 60904 was almost completed; however, the standardization of calibration methods for reference cells (used as reference standards to calibrate PV modules and solar simulators) turned out to be difficult, as the few laboratories had different methods, which produced some discrepancies in a range of round-robin tests. It was only in 2009 that a document addressing the traceability of reference cells to SI standards could be published.

WG3 took on board the safety standards of both stand-alone and grid-connected systems, and in particular the consensus process on the latter was and still is lengthy, as existing national standards are often very different and difficult to harmonize.

For a short period in the late 1980s, WG4 existed with the scope to include electricity storage systems; however, it was dissolved in favor of a joint WG with TC82, named 'Accumulator Systems for Photovoltaic Solar Energy'.

In 1995, the markets evolved to the situation, which required improving the quality of PV production, deployment, and operation; an industry-developed approval system (PV GAP, photovoltaic Global Approval Program) was reason to establish WG5, titled 'Accreditation and Certification'. However, the Standard Management Board of the IEC pointed out that such quality assurance systems would be better placed within the IECQ (IEC's certification program for electronic components, processes, and related materials) organization, and the WG was discontinued. After some years, this activity was extended to a comprehensive quality assurance system under IECEE (Conformity Testing and Certification of Electrotechnical Equipment and Components).

During the following years, two new WGs have been established, WG6 for 'Balance of System Components' (1998) and WG7 for 'Concentrating modules and systems' (2003).

1.39.2 Standards for Performance Determination of PV Devices

1.39.2.1 Introduction

This section reviews the IEC standards relevant for the determination of the electrical performance of PV devices.

The electrical performance of a PV device is normally determined as the maximum power it can deliver under well-defined testing conditions. It is a key parameter for comparison with other PV devices, whether of the same type, of different type, or even of a different technology. The absolute value of maximum power is furthermore an important input for the evaluation of energy rating, that is, the total energy a PV device will produce during operation in the field.

A common application in industry is to sort the output of a production line according to the electrical power measured on each single device. This applies, for example, not only for single cells that are sorted to match them in the PV module into which they will be incorporated but also to finished modules. The latter are often sold in power classes, where the same product is sorted according to their real maximum power and priced differently.

In the field of research and development, the determination of the absolute maximum power (or device efficiency, which is the maximum power divided by the device area) is important to assess the progress of PV device and technology. The regularly published PV device efficiency tables [1] give an up-to-date picture of the state of the art and are based on maximum power measurements applying international standards at selected reference institutes.

The international standards relevant for PV devices and their measurement are developed within TC82 of the IEC. The way to new standards is normally paved by scientific research, first by single institutions and then applied by others of the international community. This might lead to some national standards. Eventually, however, once agreement in the international scientific community has been reached, an IEC standard is prepared. The standards relevant for this section are developed by WG2 of TC82.

1.39.2.2 Performance Determination of PV Devices

In this section, the main elements of the performance determination of PV devices are briefly described. The relevant standards will then be reviewed in the next section.

The determination of electrical performance of PV devices consists of exposing the device to irradiance from a light source and measuring its electrical behavior by a suitable load. The measured data are analyzed and the result reported together with the measurement conditions. The irradiance intensity is usually determined by a reference device that should provide traceability to the international irradiance scale. Care needs to be taken about the (meta-)stability of the device and its state.

1.39.2.2.1 Light sources

The PV devices are exposed either to natural or to simulated sunlight. The latter may be continuous or – especially for practical reasons for large area devices – of a pulsed nature.

The sun always provides a good quality irradiance to measure PV devices. However, a number of practical problems limit the measurements under natural sunlight. The main difficulties encountered are that natural sunlight is not reliably available due to weather conditions and the control of the measurement conditions is difficult.

Therefore, solar simulators are widely used to measure the electrical performance of PV devices. They can easily be integrated into a laboratory or production environment and allow measurements to be made at any time independent of weather conditions. For smaller devices such as single-crystalline silicon solar cells, continuous source simulators are used, whereas for larger areas, a pulsed light source is more common. However, there are also pulsed systems for single cells as well as large area steady-state simulators.

1.39.2.2.2 Measurement

1.39.2.2.2(i) IV characteristics

The maximum power is determined from a complete current voltage (IV) characteristic that is acquired using a suitable variable load while the PV device is illuminated by the natural or simulated sunlight. While the maximum power is defined in IEC 61836, there is actually no guidance given in any of the IEC standards on how to extract it from a measured IV characteristic.

1.39.2.2.2(ii) Standard test conditions

There are three main parameters that influence the performance of PV devices, namely the device temperature, the total irradiance, and its spectral distribution. For easy comparison, standard test conditions (STC) have been defined (see below). They foresee a device temperature of 25 °C and a total irradiance of 1000 W m^{-2} with a spectral irradiance as defined in IEC 60904-3 (for details see below).

The STC are an artificial set of conditions that combine an expected irradiance on a clear day around midday with a device temperature easily achievable in a laboratory environment. Under continuous exposure to an irradiance of 1000 W m^{-2}, the PV device would normally equilibrate at a much higher temperature, for example, 50–60 °C. Nevertheless, STC cannot be reached exactly and therefore data analysis and processing translate the measurement to STC, which is then reported. In the United States, the term standard reporting conditions (SRC) is more common and in effect somewhat more appropriate.

The STC are the reference conditions for PV device calibration. The calibration value of reference devices is quoted for STC. In updating IEC 60904-3 from first to second edition, the tabulated reference spectral irradiance distribution was recalculated. While maintaining the principal input parameters unchanged, the actual spectrum changed also because a newer version of software was used. This improved the resolution of the tabulated spectrum. However, it also changed the spectral irradiance distribution somewhat. The latter resulted in a shift of the calibration values of PV devices. The exact shift depends on the spectral response of the PV device. For crystalline silicon PV devices the change led typically to an increase of the short circuit current of +0.7% with a corresponding increase in maximum power. In conclusion the calibration values of all PV devices changed due to a redefinition of STC.

1.39.2.2.3 Traceability

Performing measurements of IV characteristics gives important information and in some cases the results need only be known on a relative scale. However, in most cases, absolute results are required. Therefore, all instruments used for a measurement have to be calibrated. Furthermore, each calibration has to have a traceability chain, which needs to connect to international standards. Only under these conditions are absolute performance measurements, or better calibration, achieved.

The most important instrument used for IV measurements is the reference device that is normally also a PV device, which is regulated by the IEC standards. Measurements of current and voltage are, however, not specific to PV and are therefore not included in the IEC series on PV.

1.39.2.2.4 Preconditioning

PV devices might not always be stable. Crystalline silicon remains stable for long time periods after a small initial degradation, whereas thin film devices are susceptible to stronger initial degradation, seasonal variations (during outdoor exposure), or metastable behavior depending on the storage conditions. This needs to be taken into account when measuring PV devices, as the result might depend on the history of the PV device as well as on the actual conditions immediately before and during measurement. This is a vast field that currently is only partly addressed by international standards, namely the stabilization through controlled light soaking in IEC 61646.

1.39.2.3 Existing IEC Standards

This section reviews the existing IEC standards applicable to determining the performance of PV devices as described in the previous section, concentrating on the standards regulating traceability, measurement execution, and data analysis. These are the IEC 60891 and the IEC 60904 series. The relevant standards are nominated, briefly described, and where relevant notes on their development are given as background information.

1.39.2.3.1 Reference solar devices

IEC 60904-2 sets the requirements for reference solar devices. The second edition of this standard unites the first editions of IEC 60904-2 (requirements for reference solar cells) and IEC 60904-6 (requirements for reference solar modules), the latter being discontinued.

IEC 60904-2 addresses the calibration of the reference solar devices together with the requirements for their classification, selection, packaging, marking, and care. The calibration traceability chain is mentioned and three levels of reference devices are defined, namely primary, secondary, and working reference devices. Furthermore, the calibration procedures for secondary references against a primary reference and working references against a secondary reference are described.

The crucial point of establishing calibration traceability to SI units (as required by IEC 60904-2) is addressed in IEC 60904-4 ed. 1. The calibration chain from primary standards over secondary standards to primary and secondary references is explained and the methods that are in use to transfer between these different levels are mentioned. The requirements for traceable calibration procedures are mainly that all instruments used must themselves have unbroken traceability chains, an inherent absolute precision, and documented measurement uncertainty and repeatability. Examples of calibration methods for the transfer from secondary standards to primary references are collected in an annex to IEC 60904-4. As far as solar reference devices are concerned, this is the most crucial step, as secondary standards are typically not PV devices but rather of a completely different technology with consequently different properties. An example is the absolute cavity radiometer, which has an extended spectral sensitivity and slower response time compared with a PV device. The other steps in the calibration and traceability chain have to satisfy the requirements of IEC 60904-4 but they are not described in the standard. The transfer between primary and secondary standards is outside its scope as they are normally of non-PV technologies, whereas the transfer between primary and secondary PV reference devices is already addressed in IEC 60904-2.

1.39.2.3.2 Measurement conditions

Measurement principles for PV devices are defined in IEC 60904-3 together with a definition of the reference spectral irradiance data. The description of the measurement principles in this standard is rather short, referring to the other standards. Interestingly, it mentions STC without actually defining them or providing a reference. In fact they are defined neither in the IEC 60904 series nor in IEC 60891, but in IEC 61836, and in IEC 61215.

The larger part of IEC 60904-3 is a table defining the reference spectral irradiance distribution. It was obtained from a solar spectral model SMARTS with a certain set of input parameters (CO_2 concentration, precipitable water, ozone content, turbidity, and pressure) for a surface tilted 37° to the horizontal and air mass AM1.5. The total integrated irradiance is 1000 W m^{-2} between 0 and ∞ wavelength. It is worth noticing that this defined reference spectrum is not actually observed in nature, although under suitable conditions the measured solar spectrum is very close to it. The spectrum is also often called AM1.5G referring to the air mass and that it represents global (direct and diffuse) irradiance.

IEC 60904-9 concerning the performance requirements of solar simulators is another important standard for measurements. In its second edition, each solar simulator can be assigned three different classes (labeled A, B, and C) for the following three criteria: spectral match (to AM1.5G defined in IEC 60904-3), spatial nonuniformity of irradiance in the test plane, and temporal instability of this irradiance. The latter is divided into short term (one data triplet of irradiance, current, and voltage) and long term (entire measurement of *IV* characteristics). The highest class (having best spectral match and lowest nonuniformity and instability) is class A, so a solar simulator best in each of the three criteria would be assigned class AAA. Such products are commercially available. Some manufacturers who claim that their specifications are significantly better than those required to achieve class A have labeled their products class A+, but this is not currently defined in any standard. IEC 60904-9 also mentions the measurement procedures for the three criteria.

It is worth realizing that a class AAA simulator is certainly of a high quality but depending on its application might nevertheless give significant deviations between actual measurement of a PV device and its true value. Therefore, even for such a simulator, data analysis and correction as well as a detailed measurement uncertainty analysis are required for quantitative results.

1.39.2.3.3 Measurement practice

The central measurement required for characterizing a PV device, namely the *IV* characteristics, is described in IEC 60904-1 ed. 2. This standard lays down basic requirements and defines different measurement procedures and guides toward minimizing measurement uncertainty. The general requirements are for the measurement of irradiance, temperature, current, and voltage. Furthermore, mounting and data correction (see below) are addressed. The section on apparatus and measurement procedures are separated for measurements in natural and simulated sunlight, the latter furthermore for steady state and pulsed. For data analysis and further measurement requirements, IEC 60904-1 refers to other standards within the series and IEC 60891.

For test devices different from the reference device, a spectral mismatch correction is required (see below) that requires the SR as input. The measurement of SR is described in IEC 60904-8 (currently under revision). The existing ed. 2 defines SR and how it can be determined for a test device with respect to a reference PV device. Essentially both devices are illuminated by (quasi-)monochromatic light and the induced short circuit current is measured. Three methods for obtaining suitable monochromatic light and measuring the SR are mentioned, namely using a monochromator or bandpass filter together with a steady-state light source and a chopper, or a pulsed solar simulator and bandpass filter.

1.39.2.3.4 Data analysis

A crucial step in data analysis is to correct from the actual measurement conditions to STC. In general, this requires procedures for temperature and irradiance corrections to measured *IV* characteristics described in IEC 60891. Three methods for *IV* curve translation are described. The first two procedures are mathematical translations of measured *IV* data pairs and require four correction parameters (the temperature coefficients of short circuit current and open circuit voltage, the internal series resistance, and the curve correction factor). These correction parameters have to be determined according to the methods given in the standard itself, if not know *a priori*. The third correction method is an interpolation method not requiring correction parameters but a minimum of three *IV* curves spanning the temperature and irradiance range for which correction is required.

A further important aspect in data analysis is the spectral mismatch between the test and reference device. IEC 60904-7 defines the spectral mismatch and its computation. It then proceeds to give two methods for correcting the spectral mismatch. In the first method, the irradiance is adjusted (normally only possible for simulated sunlight) before performing the *IV* measurement, which then does not need any further correction for spectral mismatch. In the second method, the measured *IV* curve is translated using IEC 60891, but with the nominal irradiance replaced by an effective irradiance taking into account the spectral mismatch.

An indispensable part of any data analysis is the evaluation of measurement uncertainties. Every component in the measurement and data analysis process has to be considered and the respective uncertainties and their influence on the final result calculated. The final results need to be stated together with their uncertainties, because any quantitative statement without its associated measurement uncertainty is worthless. Details and the state of the art are given in a comprehensive analysis of measurement uncertainty in PV device calibration [2].

1.39.2.3.5 Device behavior

For encapsulated PV devices such as modules, it can be difficult to measure the device temperature with temperature sensors. However, an equivalent cell temperature (ECT) can be determined by the open circuit voltage method as described in IEC 60904-5. The ECT is the average temperature of the electronic junctions in the PV device. The standard describes its determination based on the open circuit voltage at known temperature and irradiance conditions, the temperature coefficient of the open circuit voltage, and the thermal diode voltage.

For many methods described in the standards mentioned so far, the linearity of the PV device is required, which can be determined according to IEC 60904-10. Such a linearity check should be performed prior to any measurement or correction procedure, which requires linearity such as those in IEC 60891. The standard describes procedures for determining the degree of linearity and its calculation. Finally, it sets requirements for acceptable limits below which the device can be considered linear.

1.39.2.4 Discussion and Conclusion

The standards described above, IEC 60891 and IEC 60904 series, form a comprehensive set for the determination of the electrical performance of PV devices. All standards are applicable to PV devices in crystalline silicon technology. However, there are limits of their applicability to thin film technologies and more importantly to multi-junction technologies. These limitations are clearly listed in the scope of each single standard, giving hints on possible applications outside. An evolution can be observed comparing the current status with that of the original first edition of each standard, which was exclusively for crystalline silicon technology. Keeping in mind that these standards were developed in the late 1980s and early 1990s, this might not be surprising as crystalline silicon was the dominating technology at that time. However, as thin film technologies have developed, many measurement methods have been applied to them as well and the experience gained led to the inclusion of some of these in the scope of the standards.

Currently, there remain two areas which are not covered, namely multi-junction (nonconcentrating) PV devices and concentrating devices. Standards for the latter are under development (as described in another section), whereas for multi-junction flat-plate PV devices, there is a lack of any IEC standard while the industry is producing such devices in noticeable volumes.

The great benefit in international standards is that the community has agreed on the measurement methods and therefore the results become comparable on a global scale. This aids in the strive for transparency concerning the quality of products and fair markets.

The development of IEC standards is necessarily a slow process as it is based on international agreements. This becomes apparent when, as is the case for multi-junction technology, the development of industrial products progresses much faster than the development of suitable measurement methods. This is somewhat alleviated by a small number of international reference laboratories, which actively develop the measurement methods that will eventually be included in the IEC standards. Due to the experience and deep insight present in these laboratories, they offer a certain flexibility to apply standards beyond their scope or provide methods and procedures for which no standard yet exists. For the much larger number of laboratories providing routine measurements, this does not apply and the published IEC standards need to be strictly followed.

The near future will certainly see a further inclusion of thin film technologies in the scope of the IEC standards and should also see the development of suitable new standards covering the multi-junction technologies.

1.39.3 Reliability Testing of PV Modules

1.39.3.1 Introduction

PV modules purchased and installed in the present-day marketplace have as a minimum requisite type approval or qualification testing, as defined in the document IEC 61215 for crystalline silicon modules or IEC 61646 for thin-film-based modules. This type approval testing is often referred to as reliability testing or design qualification; it is not a lifetime test.

The early days of reliability testing and type approval for PV can be identified as the period in the early mid-1970s when in various parts of the world, and particularly in the United States and Europe, the first national and international programs were being launched to investigate alternatives to nonnuclear or conventional energy sources. Programs such as the then European Communities PV Demonstration projects began to offer co-funding of PV systems as demonstration projects. Since this co-funding was based on public finance, the funding bodies wished to obtain some form of assurance that these new PV materials could actually operate in an outdoor climate for extended periods. This heralded the request to testing bodies and research centers to develop methods to assure the soundness of public and private investments by certifying the reliability of PV modules.

1.39.3.2 The Beginning of an International Standard for Type Approval Testing

In 1975, the European Commission's Directorate-General XII and later the Directorate-General XIII (now DG Research and DG Energy, respectively) began promoting PV systems and installations and at the same time asked the JRC to support this promotion. In 1977, the European Solar Test Installation of the JRC formally began to study measurement, characterization, and reliability of PV systems. In this context, and together with similar activities around the world [3], the search for simple and cost-effective method for reliability testing of PV modules began in earnest.

1.39.3.3 Weathering Test or Dedicated Stress to Identify Failure Mechanisms

In the world of testing, different theories have been and still are applied. For material or components which are well established, it is often sufficient to develop a test which applies multiple stress/acceleration factors (e.g., temperature, humidity, thermal stress, thermal mechanical fatigue, and UV or IR stress) in a single test, a so-called weathering test. The benefit of this is that the test can be faster, since it is more extreme and potentially cheaper since it is a single test. However, with such a testing method, it is usually very difficult to correlate any resulting defects or failures during the test to a single stress and therefore to improve parts of the module or component design.

In the early days of module testing, the PV industry was also in its infancy so the approach of applying single or at most double stress factors was adopted. This approach brings the advantage that by analyzing the results of multiple stress tests of single or combined stress factors it is possible to establish where the design weakness is in a system. This analytical feedback to the module manufacturers allowed a timely correction and improvement of the products, while avoiding the necessity to over engineer (and therefore raise costs) associated with the solution of a problem resulting from a weathering test. From this decision, the concept to apply a series of combined tests developed into the first testing standards which were applied [3].

1.39.3.4 Type Approval Testing

The IEC type approval standard 61215 for crystalline silicon PV modules lays down IEC requirements for the design qualification and type approval of terrestrial photovoltaic modules suitable for long-term operation in general open-air climates. The objective of this test sequence is to determine the electrical and thermal characteristics of the module and to show, as far as is possible within reasonable constraints of cost and time, that the module is capable of withstanding prolonged exposure in climates described in the scope.

Eight PV modules are selected randomly from the production line to undergo type approval testing. One module is kept as a reference module to be used to verify that the measurement method to determine degradation is repeatable, one module is used on the electrical characterization leg, and two modules are used for each of the three environmental test legs.

The testing scheme is illustrated in **Figure 1**.

1.39.3.5 Pass/Fail Criteria

For crystalline silicon PV modules, in order to declare that if a given module type has been deemed to pass a qualification test sequence, it must meet six pass/fail criteria.

- First the total degradation of maximum power must be less than 8% after each test leg.
- There can be no open circuits detected during the test sequence.
- There must be no major visual defects (e.g., broken, cracked, or torn external surfaces, including superstrates, substrates, frames and junction boxes).
- The insulation requirements are met.

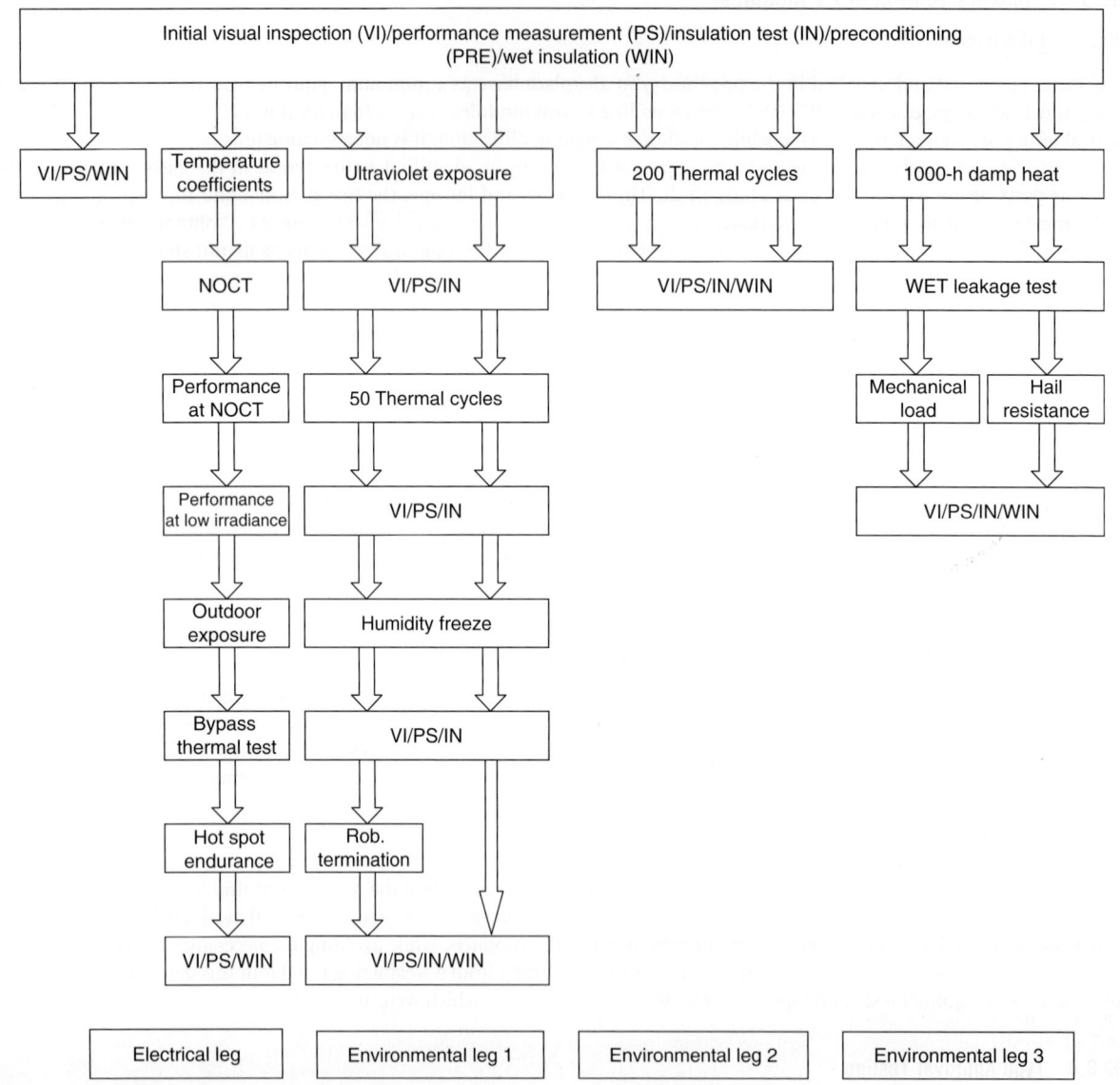

Figure 1 The IEC 61215 edition 2 schematic of the test sequence. NOCT, nominal operation cell temperature.

- The wet leakage tests are satisfied at the beginning and end of the test sequence.
- All specific requirements of the individual tests are met.

An extensive description is given in the IEC 61215 standard.

In the thin-film type approval standards IEC 61646, the test sequence is derived from IEC 61215 for the design qualification and type approval of terrestrial crystalline silicon PV modules. However, it no longer relies on meeting a plus/minus criterion before and after each test sequence, but rather on meeting a specified percentage of the rated minimum power after all of the tests have been completed and the modules have been light soaked. This eliminates the technology-specific preconditioning necessary to accurately measure the changes caused by the test. The testing criteria and stress levels are outlined in **Table 1** for crystalline silicon PV modules.

1.39.3.6 Environmental Testing

There are three main environmental test legs applied in the standards (see **Figure 1**) which are intended to separate the individual stress factors: the UV humidity freeze (leg 1), the thermal cycle (leg 2), and the damp heat (leg 3). An analysis of the various defects observed from each of these testing legs can be found in Reference 4. From this study comprising commercial PV module types conducted from 1990 to 2006, the classification of major defects in tested PV modules is related to either visual, loss of power, or

Table 1 The summary of test levels included in the IEC 61215 edition 2 test sequences

Acronym used in the text	Test title	Test conditions
OE	Outdoor exposure test	Exposure to solar irradiation of total of 60 kWh m^{-2}
UVE	UV test	Exposure to UV irradiation of total of 15 kWh m^{-2}. The UV wavelength range from 280 to 385 nm, with 5 kWh m^{-2} in the wavelength range from 280 to 320 nm
HSP	Hot spot test	5 h exposure to 1000 W m^{-2} irradiance in the worst-case hot-spot conditions
TC50 and TC200	Thermal cycling test	50 and 200 thermal cycles from −40 °C to +85 °C, with STC peak power current during 200 cycles
HUF	Humidity freeze test	10 cycles from +85 °C, 85% RH to −40 °C
DAH	Damp heat test	1000 h at +85 °C, 85% RH
ROB	Robustness of termination test	Determination of terminations' capability to withstand appropriate mechanical stress
MEL	Mechanical load test	2.4 kPa uniform load applied for 1 h to front and back surface in turn
HAR	Hail test	25 mm diameter ice ball at 23 m s^{-1}, directed at 11 impact locations
DT	Bypass diode thermal test	1 h at I_{sc} and 75 °C, 1 h at 1.25 times I_{sc} and 75 °C

insulation failures. The total number of module types tested was 174, out of those 130 module types (74.7%) passed certification procedure, 27 (15.5%) passed after successful retest, and 17 types (9.7%) were rejected.

The great majority of failures occur following the environmental tests. The reasons for failure can be broadly shared between power loss and major visual defect; the insulation failure occurred only once. The most stressful test provoking highest failure rate was the Thermal Cycle Test TC200, suggesting a cause from the high thermomechanical fatigue, which is not observed to the same extent in the case of the TC50. The DAH test still provokes many failures, although encapsulation systems appear to be quite mature in contemporary modules. The UVE test provoked much smaller number of failures than the DAH test. Mechanical tests provoked very few failures since the mechanical features of the modules are generally well understood; however, these tests can be fatal for nonstandard modules such as nonglass and pole-mounted types.

1.39.3.7 Correlation of Reliability Testing with Lifetime

The correlation between the results of reliability tests such as the IEC 61215 is often taken as indication of lifetime. This is not a correct assumption as the IEC testing does not directly determine degradation factors or estimate the lifetime; rather it sets a minimum level for the PV modules to be considered suitable for long-term outdoor exposure.

Exactly how long is 'long term' is the subject of continuing studies. In our paper 'The Results of Performance Measurements of Field-aged Crystalline Silicon Photovoltaic Modules' [5], we investigated this correlation. In this study, 204 crystalline silicon PV modules following long-term, continuous outdoor exposure were characterized before and after 20 years of outdoor exposure, in order to determine the relative degradation rates and the comparison to the assumption of 20 years lifetime of module certified to IEC type approval standard IEC 61215. We concluded from this study that the effective lifetime of PV modules is considerably greater than 20 years assumed from qualification testing. The definition of lifetime is a difficult task as there does not yet appear to be a fixed catastrophic failure point in module aging but more of a gradual degradation. Therefore, if a system continues to produce energy which satisfies the user needs, it has not yet reached its end of life. These studies and observations are continuing.

1.39.4 Energy Performance and Energy Rating

Manufacturers of PV modules currently provide a power rating (P_{max}) at STC. These conditions correspond to an irradiance level of 1000 W m^{-2} at a defined spectral irradiance distribution (AM1.5) and a module temperature of 25 °C. Other electrical information such as V_{oc} and I_{sc} are also typically provided. The performance of a PV module at STC is a useful indicator for comparing the peak performance of different module types, but on its own is not sufficient to accurately predict how much energy a module will deliver in the field when subjected to a wide range of real operating conditions. The reason for this is because the instantaneous power output of a PV module depends on the cell temperature and the intensity of the incident sunlight, which vary significantly as a function of location, climatic conditions, time of day, and season. These are the two principal factors, but others such as solar spectrum, angle of incidence, and soil also affect the performance [6–13].

Because the energy production over the module lifetime, or any shorter time period, is crucial in determining its economic viability, there has been much research interest in the performance of modules under real conditions in order to be able to provide a reliable rating for energy production. This would also enable differentiation of different modules on the basis of their expected output.

There exist several proposals for an energy rating for PV modules, which attempt to account for the varying operating conditions that one encounters in the field. A simple approach developed at ESTI has an emphasis on simplicity and practicality. It is based on the solar irradiance and temperature data that are readily obtainable for many locations. Furthermore, the proposed method incorporates existing internationally accepted standard measurements, discussed in other sections, to determine the module's 'performance surface' as a function of global in-plane irradiance and ambient temperature. Creating the performance surface using standard indoor tests is an advantage since no new test methods need be established. In order to predict energy production for a site of interest from the performance surface, a distribution surface of environmental conditions is required. The distribution surface provides an indication of the probability of occurrence of any given combination of irradiance and temperature for that location.

Other approaches to energy rating or prediction of real module performance are also under development and two approaches in particular are described here. A matrix-based energy rating method has been described by workers at The Institute for Applied Sustainability to the Built Environment (ISAAC), SUPSI, Switzerland. This method is also based on estimating P_{max} as a function of two parameters, irradiance and ambient temperature. However, in this case, a performance matrix is compiled from outdoor data measured over a long period of time, typically 1 year. Good results for energy prediction have been reported, but a disadvantage of this approach is clearly that a long outdoor measurement period is required in order to create the performance matrix. Furthermore, the performance matrix may be influenced by particular conditions of the site at which the measurements take place and may therefore be less suitable for prediction of energy production in other geographical locations.

Another approach involves the definition of 'standard days', which are intended to be representative of different climates types around the world. Complex modeling of module performance as a function of several parameters is performed in order to determine the energy rating for these standard locations. While certainly comprehensive, and quite possibly accurate, the disadvantage of this method is the complexity, which may prove impractical and of uncertain cost benefit.

Nonetheless, while each of the above approaches has its own advantages and disadvantages, it is largely this last approach that has been the subject of discussion in the IEC TC82 WG2. Due to the complexity and relative lack of data, the draft IEC international standard 61853, 'Performance Testing and Energy Rating of Terrestrial Photovoltaic (PV) Modules' was under development for a number of years before it was decided to break it into several parts so that as agreement on each aspect was reached, the relevant part could be published. The first part relating to the power rating was finally published in January 2011.

The current status of the IEC 61853 standard will be further discussed in the following. An extract from the scope for the 61853 series reads "this International Standard series establishes IEC requirements for evaluating PV module performance from both a power (watts) and energy (watt-hours) standpoint". It is further noted that "it is written to be applicable to all PV technologies, but the methodology does not take into account transient behavior such as light induced changes and/or thermal annealing". This means that it is expected to work well in the case of c-Si, but care must be taken with thin film technologies.

IEC 61853 Part 1 in particular describes requirements for evaluating PV module performance in terms of power (watts) rating over a range of irradiances and temperatures. The object is to define a testing and rating system, which provides the PV module power (watts) at maximum power operation for a set of defined conditions. A second purpose is to provide a full set of characterization parameters for the module under various values of irradiance and temperature.

Test methods (which employ the existing IEC standards, such as the 60904 series) are described to enable mapping of module performance over a wide range of temperature and irradiance conditions. The range of measurement conditions is then reported in a matrix format provided with the module. Even in the absence of the following parts of the series, these data will be valuable to end-users in the estimation of energy production.

Part 2, currently in draft version only, is expected to describe procedures for measuring the performance effect of the angle of incidence; the estimation of module temperature from irradiance, ambient temperature, and wind speed; and impact of SR on the module performance.

Part 3, currently in draft version only, is expected to describe the calculations of PV module energy (watt-hours) ratings based on the measurements taken according to the first two parts. It will define a rating methodology, which provides the PV module energy (watt-hours) and the performance ratio at maximum power operation for a set of defined ambient conditions. Potential applications are the comparison of various modules or module technologies, prediction of actual module output in a climatic zone, and optimization of module construction for a specific application.

The final Part 4, again currently in draft version only, describes the standard time periods and weather conditions that can be utilized for calculating energy ratings according to Part 3. It will describe standard time periods and contain the weather data that can be used to simulate the performance of a given module over these periods. The current draft defines six reference days with hourly datasets of ambient temperature, direct and diffuse irradiance, wind speed, angle of incidence, and spectral distribution. These are given the following acronyms and definitions:

HIHT: High Irradiance, High Temperature
HILT: High Irradiance, Low Temperature
MIMT: Medium Irradiance, Medium Temperature
MIHT: Medium Irradiance, High Temperature
LILT: Low Irradiance, Low Temperature
NICE: Normal Irradiance, Cool Environment

IEC 61853 Part 1 is already proving useful to manufacturers and end-users alike in the important task of predicting energy performance in a given installation location. This unfortunately still falls short of the ambition to provide an energy rating that would need to be a complete standardized method leading to the possibility of energy labeling of modules. Due to the complexity, progress has been slow, even limiting the scope to c-Si, but it is hoped that the remaining parts of IEC 61853 will be issued in the near future.

1.39.5 Concentrating PV Standards

Concentrating PV is the remit of WG7 of IEC TC82, which has already been described in Section 1.39.1. WG7 has approximately 40 members now and meets approximately two times per year. The longstanding convenor is Robert McConnell (United States).

WG7 (concentrator modules) has the following mission statement:

> To develop international standards for photovoltaic concentrators and receivers. These standards will be in the general areas of safety, photoelectric performance and environmental reliability tests. The standards ultimately produced should be universal and non-restrictive in their application, taking into account different environments and manufacturing technologies. In addition to the basic electrical and mechanical characteristics, standards will be written for other important factors such as thermal performance, high voltage performance, fault resistance and fault-tolerant design.

1.39.5.1 CPV Design Qualification IEC 62108

The first concentrator photovoltaic (CPV) standard published by the IEC is IEC 62108, which covers design qualification and type approval. It was published in 2008 and is in fact currently the IEC's only CPV-specific standard. This standard was identified from the beginning by WG7 as being of great importance, since failures in early CPV systems risked the market acceptance of new-generation systems then becoming available. It was believed that a strong qualification standard would boost confidence by demonstrating the potential for long term system reliability, a problem that has in the past damaged the reputation of the entire CPV sector. At the same time, it was necessary to ensure that the new CPV qualification standard would not be overly difficult to pass in comparison with existing flat-plate PV since this could prevent ground-breaking systems getting to the demonstration phase at all [14–17].

IEC 62108 has as its objective the determination of the electrical, mechanical, and thermal characteristics of CPV modules and assemblies and to show, within reasonable constraints of cost and time, that CPV modules and assemblies are capable of withstanding prolonged exposure in open air.

The standard is an evolution of two earlier standards. The first of these is the IEEE 1513 qualification standard, which was published in 2001. The second was IEC 61215, which was already in its second edition in 2005. This standard has been employed successfully to qualify literally hundreds of flat-plate module designs and has been a key part of the success of flat-plate PV to the present day. As an aside, we note that IEC 61646 deals specifically with the qualification of thin film modules, but this in turn is based on the earlier IEC 61215.

In the development of the standard, much time has been devoted to defining the terms to be used, complicated by the fact that many CPV system topologies are possible, operating over a range of concentration ratios involving different tracking requirements. For these reasons, reconciling the need for a 'universal and nonrestrictive' standard that can be applied 'within reasonable constraints of cost and time' was not an easy challenge.

It was decided to illustrate the wide range of possible configurations with five basic types. These types are the most widely used and should cover most implementations, but other types are not excluded:

point-focus dish PV concentrator
linear-focus trough PV concentrator
point-focus Fresnel lens PV concentrator
linear-focus Fresnel lens PV concentrator
heliostat PV concentrator

New terms, not needed in flat-plate PV, such as concentrator optics, receiver, module, and assembly were defined in order to be able to clearly identify these parts in the test specifications themselves. Several of these tests are applied to selected parts of the CPV system for reasons of practicality or cost.

Since the test sequence is partially based on that specified in IEC 61215, most of the test procedures are similar. However, the scope of the standard states "some changes have been made to account for the special features of CPV receivers and modules, particularly with regard to the separation of on-site and in-lab tests, effects of tracking alignment, high current density, and rapid temperature changes, which have resulted in the formulation of some new test procedures or new requirements". For example, the outdoor exposure test, the UV conditioning test, the damp heat and humidity freeze tests, and the maximum cell temperature and the thermal cycling tests have been modified significantly to be adapted to the requirements of CPV. Furthermore, the technical difficulties in measuring the performance of CPV modules on simulators, allied with the current lack of a CPV power rating standard, mean that side-by-side measurements using a reference module have to be used to determine module degradation. The potentially large size of some CPV systems meant that it was necessary to allow the option for the outdoor exposure test to be performed by an on-site witness.

The main differences between IEEE 1513 and IEC 62108 lie in the number and order of the tests applied to the modules and receivers in the qualification tests program and the CPV topologies included – IEEE 1513 takes into consideration only three types compared to the five in IEC 62108.

Although IEC 62108 has been recently introduced, discussion of a revision is ongoing due to some issues identified by test labs and manufacturers. One difficulty is that measuring the cell temperature during thermal cycling is not practical. The requirement to cycle the current (because it can cause too high cell temperatures and nonrepresentative cell failures due to reverse currents) may be dropped from the standard.

Retest guidelines are also being discussed, similar to those that exist for flat-plate modules to guide test labs in how to limit the test sequence to reduce costs when designs are modified.

1.39.5.2 Other Standards in Preparation

The current lack of other CPV standards is of concern to the CPV community. In their absence, reference has to be made to flat-plate standards that may not be strictly applicable or else manufacturers have to make their own *de facto* standards that can lead to confusion in the marketplace. Happily, several work items covering the most important areas are currently at an advanced draft stage, and they will be summarized here.

The most urgent of these are the following:

- Power and energy rating
- Tracker standard
- Safety standard

1.39.5.2.1 Power rating

Probably the most important standard currently missing relates to the performance rating. This means that there is no agreed definition of STC that should be used in CPV and furthermore there is no official procedure for rating the electrical performance. It is the difficulty in reaching an agreement on the test and operating conditions that has delayed the issue of this standard, together with technical difficulties in actually performing tests and performance measurement translations.

Although no IEC standard exists for power rating CPV, an ASTM standard E2527 [18]) has been available for several years. The standard under development in WG7 (IEC 62670 Power Rating Draft Standard) will allow both indoor and outdoor methods.

Outside the WG7, but of importance to CPV power rating, a new DNI spectrum (ASTM G173) has been defined to suit the requirements of present and future CPV systems [19]. As explained by Emery et al. [20], the previous direct reference spectrum was not representative of sunny conditions in regions with a high annual direct normal energy where concentrators might be deployed (in the United States, this is termed the 'the Sun Belt'). Historically, this issue did not matter because at a given total irradiance and cell temperature under direct, global, or clear-sky natural sunlight, single-junction concentrator PV cells produced a similar short circuit current. In contrast, the short circuit current of GaInP/GaAs/Ge triple-junction cells are much more sensitive to spectral variations. This sensitivity to spectrum becomes problematic if the indoor measurement spectrum differs significantly from the spectra that are typically observed outdoors. The new DNI spectrum improves this situation.

The choice of STC rating conditions for CPV is still causing serious debate. Options are 850, 900, and $1000\,W\,m^{-2}$ direct irradiance; $900\,W\,m^{-2}$ is a serious contender since the ASTM G173 direct spectrum integrates very close to this value. The latest consensus as of September 2011 is for the choice of $1000\,W\,m^{-2}$ for the pragmatic reason that it permits direct comparison with flat-plate ratings. Test temperature is also an issue, but a standard test temperature of 25 °C currently appears most likely [21].

A lot of effort has been directed toward defining specifications for indoor simulators that need to be collimated to measure STC and also how to measure outdoor standard operating conditions (exact conditions still undefined) and translation between these.

1.39.5.2.1(i) IEC 62670-2 Energy rating draft technical specification (energy rating by measurement)
A method of energy rating by measurement (closely related to the performance ratio concept) has been accepted as a new work item by TC82. The method employs outdoor monitoring over a minimum period of 6 months. The data are then analyzed in order to provide an energy rating for the tested system.

1.39.5.2.1(ii) CPV cell specification
The standard (or guideline) is basically designed to provide a blank specification for cell manufacturers to provide cell data in a consistent manner. The guidelines will not provide test methods for measuring cell electrical parameters.

1.39.5.2.2 Trackers

Trackers are used for traditional and CPV systems, but generally have more stringent tracking requirements for CPV applications due to their typically very small acceptance angle. A draft technical specification for tracker manufacturers has been assigned the number 62627. This will ensure that tracker performance parameters are clearly defined and so customers can compare specifications.

1.39.5.2.3 CPV system safety

A draft standard for the safety of CPV systems has been assigned the number 62688. Specific topics will be provided to assess the prevention of electrical shock, fire hazards, and personal injury due to mechanical and environmental stresses. This standard will be designed so that its test sequence can coordinate with those of IEC 62108, so that a single set of samples may be used to perform both the safety and performance evaluation of a CPV module and assembly.

1.39.6 Outlook

IEC TC82 has now 33 participating countries and 14 observer countries covering all continents. More than 150 experts contribute to the WGs, making TC82 well prepared to accelerate the pace of international standardization. The work program ahead requires continuously updating the already published standards in order to take into account progress in technology, measurement procedures, and feedbacks from both the PV manufacturing industry and the system operators. Since the establishment of TC82, the PV industry has grown by more than a factor of 1000, and forecasts anticipate a continued growth of at least 25% per year. Costs have decreased close to 100 US\$ m^{-2} or 1000 US\$ kWp^{-1}, making PV an attractive choice to cover peak supply by professional grid operators. The roof-top market will also continue to grow, as national incentive schemes around fixed feed-in-rates make PV very attractive for residential homeowners also. Furthermore, even if difficult to quantify, rural electrification systems seem to grow at the same rate as grid-connected systems, in particular due to the availability of mature mini-grid and hybrid systems for village electrification.

1.39.6.1 New Technologies

PV technology development is not at its end. Thin film technologies like a-Si-based tandems, CdTe, and CIS technologies are mature, exhibiting the same lifetime as standard crystalline silicon technology. Further, R&D on concentrator cells, modules, and systems has progressed continuously, making these technologies mature for utility markets. The early creation of WG7 that has meanwhile published a number of standards is an excellent example of how an anticipating standards policy actually accelerates innovation and allows a fast market take-up. To this end, IEC TC82 will soon embark on work on the latest organic cell technologies.

1.39.6.2 Major Markets

With the massive deployment of PV systems, safety is of an increasing concern, in particular regarding roof-top installations. The current situation that the fire risk in millions of roof-top systems is quite low is due to the continuous efforts on international standardization of safety tests and installation requirements. However, as many national regulations have to be met in this field, consensus on CDs is still difficult to achieve. A similar situation is observable in harmonizing standards for grid-feeding inverters, where many contradictions still exist in national, utility-based regulation.

1.39.6.3 TC82 Priorities

The principal mandate of the International Electrotechnical Commission is to contribute to the reduction or abolition of trade barriers between WTO (World Trade Organization) countries, as it allows innovation, competition, and lastly a reduction of costs. Therefore, the major priorities for work of TC82 are standards for these global markets on wafers, solar cells, modules, system components, and entire systems. More and swifter standards are required for inverters, safety, the grid interface, electromagnetic compatibility, recycling/disposal at the end of life, and the use of materials compatible with environmental standards.

1.39.7 Conclusion

TC82 is certainly a very successful committee of the IEC when measured against the impact on this relatively new energy technology. The standards established are today in use worldwide and have guided the whole value chain of PVs. The exactly 30 years of efforts of TC82 have contributed to millions of PV systems that today deliver reliable and continuous electricity, indifferent applications, sizes, and climates.

Appendix

Past Chairmen of TC82

1982: M. Leclerque, France
1992: Y. Sekine, Japan
1997: R. DeBlasio, USA

Since 2004, H. Ossenbrink, EU (as part of the German National Committee)

IEC Standards Published (2011)

IEC 60891	Edition 2.0 (14 December 2009)	Photovoltaic devices – Procedures for temperature and irradiance corrections to measured I-V characteristics
IEC 60904-1	Edition 2.0 (13 September 2006)	Photovoltaic devices – Part 1: Measurement of photovoltaic current-voltage characteristics
IEC 60904-2	Edition 2.0 (20 March 2007)	Photovoltaic devices – Part 2: Requirements for reference solar devices
IEC 60904-3	Edition 2.0 (9 April 2008)	Photovoltaic devices – Part 3: Measurement principles for terrestrial photovoltaic (PV) solar devices with reference spectral irradiance data
IEC 60904-4	Edition 1.0 (9 June 2009)	Photovoltaic devices – Part 4: Reference solar devices – Procedures for establishing calibration traceability
IEC 60904-5	Edition 2.0 (17 February 2011)	Photovoltaic devices – Part 5: Determination of the equivalent cell temperature (ECT) of photovoltaic (PV) devices by the open-circuit voltage method
IEC 60904-7	Edition 3.0 (26 November 2008)	Photovoltaic devices – Part 7: Computation of the spectral mismatch correction for measurements of photovoltaic devices
IEC 60904-8	Edition 2.0 (26 February 1998)	Photovoltaic devices – Part 8: Measurement of spectral response of a photovoltaic (PV) device
IEC 60904-9	Edition 2.0 (16 October 2007)	Photovoltaic devices – Part 9: Solar simulator performance requirements
IEC 60904-10	Edition 2.0 (17 December 2009)	Photovoltaic devices – Part 10: Methods of linearity measurement
IEC 61194	Edition 1.0 (15 December 1992)	Characteristic parameters of stand-alone photovoltaic (PV) systems
IEC 61215	Edition 2.0 (27 April 2005)	Crystalline silicon terrestrial photovoltaic (PV) modules – Design qualification and type approval
IEC 61345	Edition 1.0 (26 February 1998)	UV test for photovoltaic (PV) modules
IEC 61646	Edition 2.0 (14 May 2008)	Thin-film terrestrial photovoltaic (PV) modules – Design qualification and type approval
IEC 61683	Edition 1.0 (25 November 1999)	Photovoltaic systems – Power conditioners – Procedure for measuring efficiency
IEC 61701	Edition 1.0 (22 March 1995)	Salt mist corrosion testing of photovoltaic (PV) modules
IEC 61702	Edition 1.0 (22 March 1995)	Rating of direct coupled photovoltaic (PV) pumping systems
IEC 61724	Edition 1.0 (15 April 1998)	Photovoltaic system performance monitoring – Guidelines for measurement, data exchange and analysis
IEC 61725	Edition 1.0 (30 May 1997)	Analytical expression for daily solar profiles
IEC 61727	Edition 2.0 (14 December 2004)	Photovoltaic (PV) systems – Characteristics of the utility interface
IEC 61730-1	Edition 1.0 (14 October 2004)	Photovoltaic (PV) module safety qualification – Part 1: Requirements for construction
IEC 61730-2	Edition 1.0 (14 October 2004)	Photovoltaic (PV) module safety qualification – Part 2: Requirements for testing
IEC 61829	Edition 1.0 (31 March 1995)	Crystalline silicon photovoltaic (PV) array – On-site measurement of I-V characteristics
IEC/TS 61836	Edition 2.0 (13 December 2007)	Solar photovoltaic energy systems – Terms, definitions and symbols
IEC 61853-1	Edition 1.0 (26 January 2011)	Photovoltaic (PV) module performance testing and energy rating – Part 1: Irradiance and temperature performance measurements and power rating
IEC 62093	Edition 1.0 (29 March 2005)	Balance-of-system components for photovoltaic systems – Design qualification natural environments
IEC 62108	Edition 1.0 (7 December 2007)	Concentrator photovoltaic (CPV) modules and assemblies – Design qualification and type approval
IEC 62109-1	Edition 1.0 (28 April 2010)	Safety of power converters for use in photovoltaic power systems – Part 1: General requirements
IEC 62109-2	Edition 1.0 (23 June 2011)	Safety of power converters for use in photovoltaic power systems – Part 2: Particular requirements for inverters
IEC/PAS 62111	Edition 1.0 (29 July 1999)	Specifications for the use of renewable energies in rural decentralized electrification

(Continued)

(Continued)

IEC Standards Published (2011)

IEC 62116	Edition 1.0 (24 September 2008)	Test procedure of islanding prevention measures for utility-interconnected photovoltaic inverters
IEC 62124	Edition 1.0 (6 October 2004)	Photovoltaic (PV) stand alone systems – Design verification
IEC 62253	Edition 1.0 (15 July 2011)	Photovoltaic pumping systems – Design qualification and performance measurements
IEC 62446	Edition 1.0 (13 May 2009)	Grid connected photovoltaic systems – Minimum requirements for system documentation, commissioning tests and inspection
IEC 62509	Edition 1.0 (16 December 2010)	Battery charge controllers for photovoltaic systems – Performance and functioning

Recommendations for small renewable energy and hybrid systems for rural electrification

IEC/TS 62257-1	Edition 1.0 (11 August 2003)	Part 1: General introduction to rural electrification
IEC/TS 62257-2	Edition 1.0 (27 May 2004)	Part 2: From requirements to a range of electrification systems
IEC/TS 62257-3	Edition 1.0 (10 November 2004)	Part 3: Project development and management
IEC/TS 62257-4	Edition 1.0 (25 July 2005)	Part 4: System selection and design
IEC/TS 62257-5	Edition 1.0 (13 July 2005)	Part 5: Protection against electrical hazards
IEC/TS 62257-6	Edition 1.0 (22 June 2005)	Part 6: Acceptance, operation, maintenance and replacement
IEC/TS 62257-7	Edition 1.0 (9 April 2008)	Part 7: Generators
IEC/TS 62257-7-1	Edition 2.0 (29 September 2010)	Part 7-1: Generators – Photovoltaic generators
IEC/TS 62257-7-3	Edition 1.0 (9 April 2008)	Part 7-3: Generator set – Selection of generator sets for rural electrification systems
IEC/TS 62257-8-1	Edition 1.0 (21 June 2007)	Part 8-1: Selection of batteries and battery management systems for stand-alone electrification systems – Specific case of automotive flooded lead-acid batteries available in developing countries
IEC/TS 62257-9-1	Edition 1.0 (9 September 2008)	Part 9-1: Micropower systems
IEC/TS 62257-9-2	Edition 1.0 (9 October 2006)	Part 9-2: Microgrids
IEC/TS 62257-9-3	Edition 1.0 (9 October 2006)	Part 9-3: Integrated system – User interface
IEC/TS 62257-9-4	Edition 1.0 (9 October 2006)	Part 9-4: Integrated system – User installation
IEC/TS 62257-9-5	Edition 1.0 (21 June 2007)	Part 9-5: Integrated system – Selection of portable PV lanterns for rural electrification projects
IEC/TS 62257-9-6	Edition 1.0 (19 September 2008)	Part 9-6: Integrated system - Selection of Photovoltaic Individual Electrification Systems (PV-IES)
IEC/TS 62257-12-1	Edition 1.0 (21 June 2007)	Part 12-1: Selection of self-ballasted lamps (CFL) for rural electrification systems and recommendations for household lighting equipment

Standardization Work in Progress

IEC 61730-2 Ed. 2.0	Photovoltaic (PV) module safety qualification – Part 2: Requirements for testing
IEC 62670-1 Ed. 1.0	Concentrator photovoltaic (CPV) module and assembly performance testing and energy rating – Part 1: Performance measurements and power rating – Irradiance and temperature
IEC 62688 Ed. 1.0	Concentrator photovoltaic (CPV) module and assembly safety qualification
IEC 62716 Ed. 1.0	Ammonia corrosion testing of photovoltaic (PV) modules
IEC 61853-2 Ed. 1.0	Photovoltaic (PV) module performance testing and energy rating – Part 2: Spectral response, incidence angle and module operating temperature measurements
IEC 62548 Ed. 1.0	Design requirements for photovoltaic (PV) arrays
IEC 61701 Ed. 2.0	Salt mist corrosion testing of photovoltaic (PV) modules
IEC 61683 Ed. 2.0	Photovoltaic systems – Power conditioners – Procedure for measuring efficiency
IEC 62109-3 Ed. 1.0	Safety of power converters for use in photovoltaic power systems – Part 3: Controllers
IEC 62109-4 Ed. 1.0	Safety of power converters for use in photovoltaic power systems – Part 4: Particular requirements for combiner box
IEC 62670-2 Ed. 1.0	Concentrator photovoltaic (CPV) module and assembly performance testing and energy rating – Part 2: Energy rating by measurement
IEC 62759-1 Ed. 1.0	Transportation testing of photovoltaic (PV) modules – Part 1: Transportation and shipping of PV module stacks
IEC/TS 62738 Ed. 1.0	Design guidelines and recommendations for photovoltaic power plants
IEC/TS 62748 Ed. 1.0	PV systems on buildings
IEC/TS 62727 Ed. 1.0	Specification for solar trackers used for photovoltaic systems

(Continued)

(Continued)

Standardization Work in Progress

Proposed new work

PNW 82-654 Ed. 1.0	Photovoltaic devices – Part11: Measurement of initial light-induced degradation of crystalline silicon solar cells and photovoltaic modules
PNW 82-655 Ed. 1.0	Cross-linking degree test method for Ethylene-Vinyl Acetate applied in photovoltaic modules – Differential Scanning Calorimetry (DSC)
PNW 82-665 Ed. 1.0	Future IEC 6XXXX-1-2: Measurement procedures for materials used in photovoltaic modules – Part 1-2: Encapsulants – Measurement of volume resistivity of photovoltaic encapsulation and backsheet materials
PNW 82-666 Ed. 1.0	Future IEC 6XXXX-1-4: Measurement procedures for materials used in Photovoltaic Modules – Part 1-4: Encapsulants – Measurement of optical transmittance and calculation of the solar-weighted photon transmittance, yellowness index, and UV cut-off frequency
PNW 82-668 Ed. 1.0	Future IEC 6XXXX-1-3 Ed.1: Measurement procedures for materials used in photovoltaic modules – Part 1-3: Encapsulants – Measurement of dielectric strength
PNW 82-669 Ed. 1.0	Future IEC 6XXXX-1-5 Ed.1: Measurement procedures for materials used in photovoltaic modules – Part 1-5: Encapsulants – Measurement of change in linear dimensions of sheet encapsulation material under thermal conditions
PNW 82-673 Ed. 1.0	Concentrator photovoltaic (CPV) solar cells and cell-on-carrier (COC) assemblies – Reliability qualification
PNW 82-674 Ed. 1.0	Junction boxes for photovoltaic modules – Safety requirements and tests
PNW 82-675 Ed. 1.0	Connectors for DC-application in photovoltaic systems – Safety requirements and tests
PNW 82-676 Ed. 1.0	Dynamic mechanical load testing for photovoltaic (PV) modules
PNW/TS 82-652 Ed. 1.0	Specification for concentrator cell description

Member States of IEC TC82 (2011)

Austria (P)	Algeria (P)	Japan (P)	Serbia (O)
Australia (P)	Spain (P)	Kenya (P)	Russian Federation (P)
Belgium (P)	Finland (P)	Korea, Republic of (P)	Sweden (O)
Bulgaria (O)	France (P)	Malaysia (P)	Singapore (O)
Brazil (O)	UK (P)	Nigeria (P)	Slovenia (O)
Canada (P)	Hungary (O)	The Netherlands (P)	Thailand (P)
Switzerland (P)	Indonesia (P)	Norway (P)	Turkey (O)
China (P)	Ireland (P)	New Zealand (O)	Ukraine (O)
Cyprus (P)	Israel (P)	Oman (O)	USA (P)
Czech Rep.(P)	India (P)	Poland (O)	South Africa (P)
Germany (P)	Iran (O)	Portugal (P)	
Denmark (P)	Italy (P)	Romania (P)	

(P): Participating (O): Observer

References

[1] Green MA, Emery K, Hishikawa Y, *et al.* (2011) Solar cell efficiency tables (version 38). *Progress in Photovoltaics: Research and Applications* 19(5): 565–572.

[2] Müllejans H, Zaimann W, and Galleano R (2009) Analysis and mitigation of measurement uncertainties in the traceability chain for the calibration of photovoltaic devices. *Measurement Science and Technology* 20: 1–12.

[3] Osterwald CR and McMahon TJ (2009) History of accelerated and qualification testing of terrestrial photovoltaic modules: a literature review. *Progress in Photovoltaics: Research and Application* 17: 11–33.

[4] Skoczek A, Sample T, Dunlop ED, and Ossenbrink H (2008) Electrical performance results from physical stress testing of commercial PV modules to the IEC 61215 test sequence. *Solar Energy Materials & Solar Cells* 92: 1593–1604.

[5] Skoczek A, Sample T, and Dunlop ED (2009) The results of performance measurements of field-aged crystalline silicon photovoltaic modules. *Progress in Photovoltaics: Research and Application* 17: 227–240.

[6] Bucher K (1995) *13th European Photovoltaic Solar Energy Conference*, pp. 2097–2103.

[7] Kroposki B, Myres D, Emery K, *et al.* (1996) Photovoltaic module energy rating methodology development. In: *25th IEEE Photovoltaic Specialists Conference*.

[8] King DL, Kratochvil JA, Boyson WE, and Bower WI (1998) Field experience with a new performance characterization procedure for photovoltaic arrays. In: *2nd World Conference and Exhibition on Photovoltaic Solar Energy Conversion*. Vienna, Austria, 6–10 July.

[9] Anderson D, Sample T, and Dunlop E (2001) Obtaining module energy rating from standard laboratory measurements. In: *Proceedings of the 17th European PV Solar Energy Conference*. Munich, October 2001.

[10] Kenny RP, Dunlop ED, Sample T, *et al.* (2002) Energy rating of diverse PV module technologies through indoor and outdoor characterisation. In: *PV in Europe from PV Technology to Energy Solutions Conference*. Rome, 7–11 October.

[11] Friesen G, Chianese D, Rezzonico S, *et al.* (2002) Matrix method for energy rating calculations of PV modules. In: *Proceedings of the PV in Europe Conference*. Rome, September 2002.

[12] Kenny RP, Ioannides A, Müllejans H, and Dunlop ED (2004) Spectral effects on the energy rating of thin film modules. In: *19th EUPVSEC*. Paris, 7–11 June.

[13] Kenny RP, Dunlop ED, Ossenbrink H, and Müllejans H (2006) A practical method for the energy rating of c-Si PV modules based on standard tests. *Progress in Photovoltaics: Research and Applications* 14: 155–166.
[14] Ji L and McConnell R (2006) New qualification test procedures for concentrator photovoltaic modules and assemblies. In: *4th World Conference on Photovoltaic Energy Conversion*. Hawaii.
[15] Rubio F, *et al.* (2007) Establishment of the Institute of concentration photovoltaics systems – ISFOC. In: *Proceedings of the 4th International Conference on Solar Concentrators for the Generation of Electricity or Hydrogen*.
[16] Muñoz E, Vidal PG, Nofuentes G, *et al.* (2009) Standardization in concentrator photovoltaics. In: *24th European Photovoltaic Solar Energy Conference*. Hamburg, 21–25 September.
[17] McConnell R and Ji L (2007) Concentrator photovoltaic standards. In: *4th International Conference on Solar Concentrators for the Generation of Electricity or Hydrogen*. El Escorial, Madrid.
[18] ASTM International (2006) ASTM E 2527-06 Standard Test Method for Rating Electrical Performance of Concentrator Terrestrial Photovoltaic Modules and Systems under Natural *Sunlight*. ASTM International, USA.
[19] ASTM International (2008) *ASTM G173-03 Standard Tables for Reference Solar Spectral Irradiances: Direct Normal and Hemispherical on 37 Tilted Surfaces*.
[20] Emery K, Myers D, and Kurtz S (2002) What is the appropriate reference spectrum for characterizing concentrator cells? In: *Proceedings 29th IEEE PV Specialists Conference*. New Orleans, LA, USA, 20–24 May.
[21] Kurtz S, *et al.* (2010) Considerations for how to rate CPV. In: *6th International Conference on Concentrating Photovoltaic Systems (CPV-6)*. Freiburg, Germany, 7–9 April.